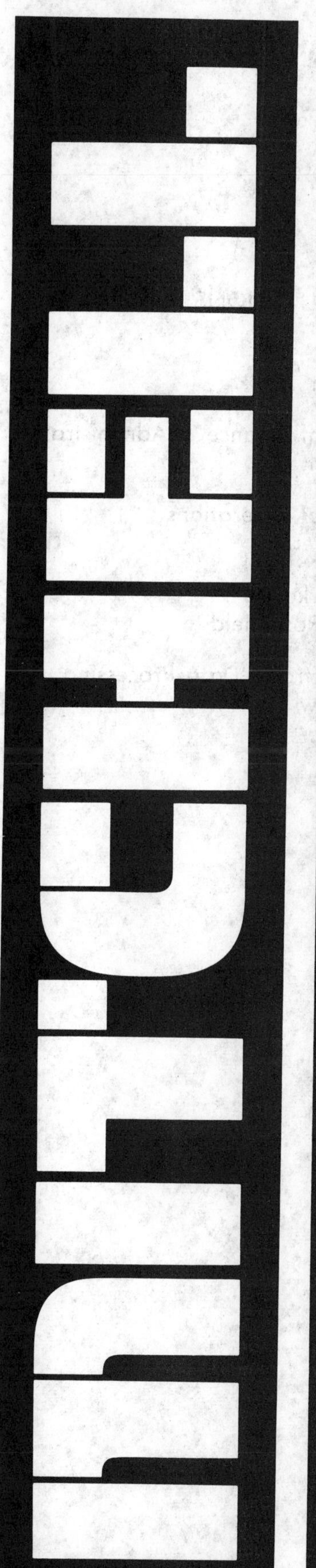

Over 50 Years of Service
National Service Data

1977 Imported Cars & Trucks

Tune-Up · Mechanical Service & Repair

Published By:
MITCHELL MANUALS, INC.
A Cordura Company
P.O. BOX 80427
SAN DIEGO, CALIFORNIA 92138

ISBN 0-8470-5777-1

ACKNOWLEDGEMENT

Mitchell Manuals thanks the automotive and equipment manufacturers, distributors, dealers and the entire automotive industry for their fine cooperation and assistance which makes the publication of this manual possible.

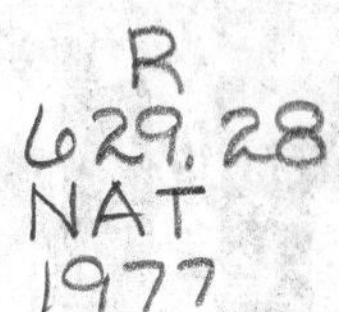

MITCHELL MANUALS, INC.

A Cordura Company

Vice President and Publisher
W. Gardner Barker, Jr.

Director of Publications
Paul W. Kelm

Managing Editor
Jerry H. Cole

Ass't. Managing Editor
David M. Rady

Graphics Supervisor
Larry Poindexter

Composition Manager
Doris J. Williams

Technical Editors
Kenneth R. Major
Kenneth A. Young
Dennis L. Bailey
Gary L. Haley
Daniel M. Kelley, Jr.
Don C. McComas
Daryl F. Visser
James B. Budvarson
Robert B. Johnson
Karl F. Broas
Steven L. Hansen
William E. McMahan

Graphics
Ervin R. Deis
Judie LaPierre
Pearl J. Hastings
Anna Freeby

Composition
Ann Klimetz - Coordinator
Grace F. Bryce
Margaret J. Jeneviez
Terri Zupp
Virginia Johnson
Randi S. Untiedt
Carol Tucker
Pam Dus
Marie C. Bennett
Kim Mumaw
Patricia A. Weiler
Lorinda Jones
Lori Bruno

CORDURA PUBLICATIONS, INC.

President
Cal Kobrin

Vice President of Finance & Administration
John Opelt

Vice President of Operations
Malcolm Ferrier

Director of Marketing
James R. Rosenfield

Director of Electronic Data Processing
Fred Lepow

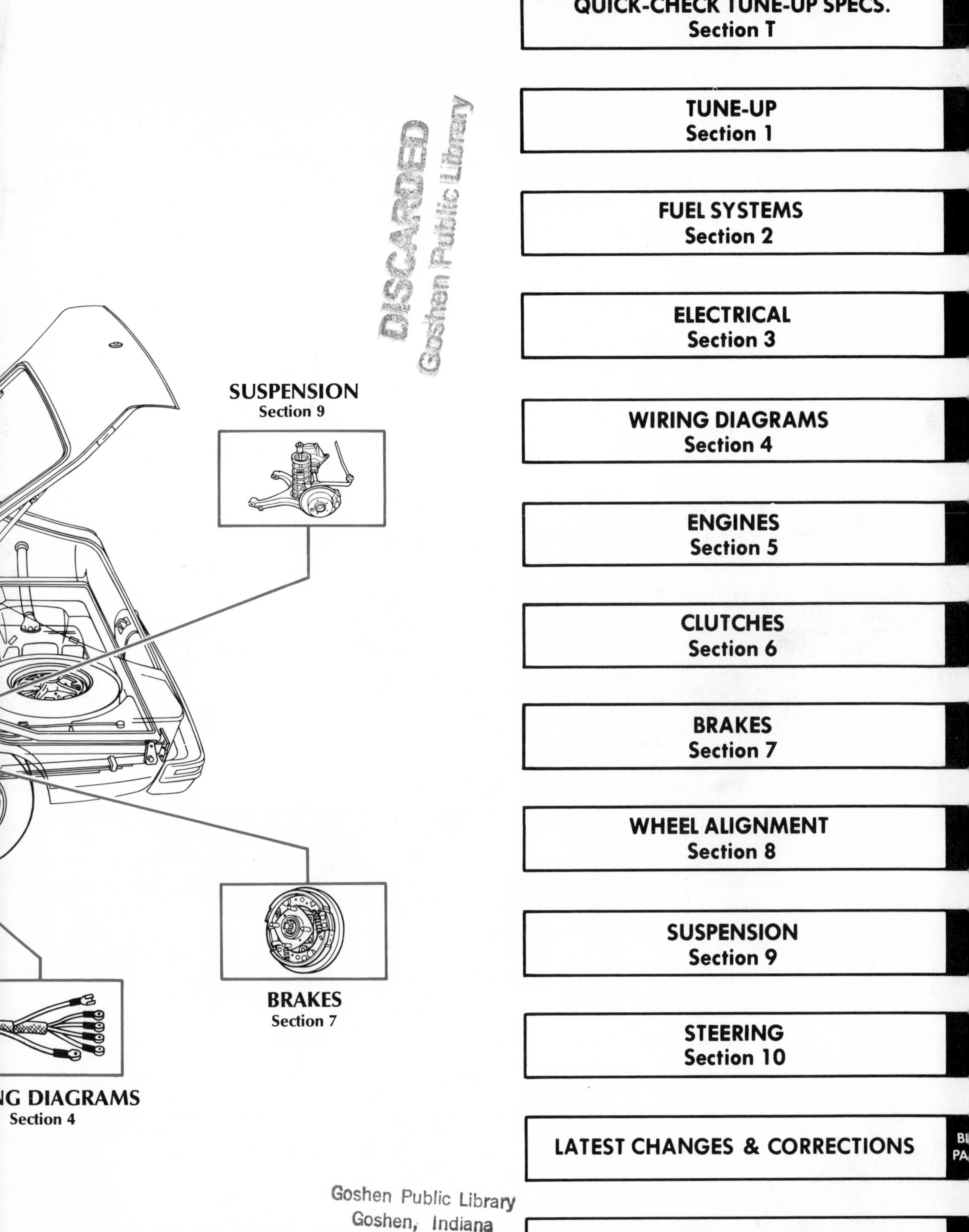

SUSPENSION
Section 9
BRAKES
Section 7
G DIAGRAMS
Section 4
QUICK-CHECK TUNE-UP SPECS.
Section T
TUNE-UP
Section 1
FUEL SYSTEMS
Section 2
ELECTRICAL
Section 3
WIRING DIAGRAMS
Section 4
ENGINES
Section 5
CLUTCHES
Section 6
BRAKES
Section 7
WHEEL ALIGNMENT
Section 8
SUSPENSION
Section 9
STEERING
Section 10
LATEST CHANGES & CORRECTIONS
GENERAL INDEX

PREFACE

This is the 1977 edition of Mitchell Manuals' Imported Car Tune-Up/Mechanical Service and Repair Manual. This book, like the many Mitchell publications which have preceded it, represents our commitment to professionalism in the automotive service market.

The automotive industry advances every year, and Mitchell Manuals pledges to advance and improve its products as we maintain the quality and usefulness of all Mitchell Manuals' publications.

We cordially acknowledge the good will and mutual goals that exist in the automotive business, and it is in this spirit that we thank the automotive manufacturers, distributors, dealers and the entire automotive industry for their fine cooperation and assistance which has made this publication possible.

TO THE PROFESSIONAL MECHANIC

Imported Car Tune-Up/Mechanical Service and Repair Manual

This all new 1977 Imported Car Service and Repair Manual is designed to provide you, the professional mechanic, with the most concise up-to-date Tune-Up and Mechanical information available anywhere. This one year manual is written to give you all the detailed material you should ever need to complete any repairs (major or minor) on the most popular of the imported cars and mini-pickups.

Editors have spent hundreds of hours compiling the information you need. Every available source has been drawn from to produce this manual for you. The range of coverage was developed with you in mind and should consequently allow you to perform your job more efficiently. Our aim, remember, is to keep you from spending your time fumbling through manuals.

There are over 400 individual articles written for you by automotive repair specialists. In each article the mechanic has been kept in mind as illustrated by the clear, easy-to-read formats. Each article has step-by-step procedures on testing and repair or overhaul. Hundreds of detailed schematics take away unnecessary guess work. Chassis wiring diagrams have been uniquely presented in an easy to understand format with individual wires being color coded for quick reference.

HOW TO USE THIS MANUAL

QUICK CHECK TUNE-UP SPECIFICATIONS
Section T

This year you will find 10 years of Quick Check Tune-Up Specifications for most Imported Cars and Trucks. For easy efficient use of these tables, locate make and model of vehicle, then scan across the two pages until you find the information you need. These pages are designed to provide you with quick tune-up reference when detailed information isn't necessary.

TUNE-UP
Section 1

The TUNE-UP Section in this manual is divided alphabetically by manufacturer and then by engine size. The first item in each article is Engine Identification. This provides you with the information to determine exactly what engine you are working on.

After the engine has been determined, use the remaining information to complete your tune-up. You will note that each article has illustrations showing engine firing orders and ignition timing marks to save you valuable time in locating timing marks and ensuring that the ignition wiring is correct. Throughout each article you will find *NOTES and CAUTIONS.* They should be read carefully and followed as they contain important information.

FUEL SYSTEMS
Section 2

On the FUEL SYSTEMS Section contents page you will find coverage by component manufacturer (Aisan, Ford, Hitachi, etc.). Directly under the component manufacturer's name will be the particular model designation number (1250 1-barrel, 5200 2-barrel, etc.). When dealing with Aisan carburetors you will find the sub-group designation done by Toyota engine types, this is the only exception.

Fuel Injection information along with Fuel Pump articles are located within the FUEL SYSTEMS Section. These Fuel Injection articles are placed near the end of the section and contain the same kind of overhaul and adjustment information that the carburetor articles cover. The last part of the section is devoted to Electric Fuel Pumps. Each separate article gives testing and key specifications.

ELECTRICAL
Section 3

Within the ELECTRICAL Section you will find Distributors and Ignition Systems such as conventional breaker point distributors and electronic ignition systems. You will find explanations of basic operating principles along with detailed testing procedures. Adjustments and overhaul procedures along with disassembled views give you information needed to service distributor assemblies and ignition systems.

Preceding the distributor articles you will note the distributor application and specification tables. Here you will find enough information to check out most imported cars and trucks. Advance and retard specifications are grouped by distributor manufacturer and listed in the specification tables by part number.

Information on alternators and starters contains test specifications and detailed test procedures. Overhaul of these components is presented in step-by-step procedures. Disassembled views of the components are given throughout the section.

The last part of the ELECTRICAL Section is devoted to Accessories and Equipment. Here you will find information on such items as speedometers, gauges, fuses and circuit breakers, and switches. Removal procedures are given along with component locations.

WIRING DIAGRAMS
Section 4

The WIRING DIAGRAM Section provides you with schematics of most all imported cars. The chassis wiring diagrams are listed by vehicle manufacturer and then by model name. This provides you with the greatest ease locating the diagram you need.

Each diagram spreads across two full pages to facilitate easy reading. All diagrams are standardized so that once you learn to read one diagram, you can quickly read any of the other chassis diagrams. The diagrams are designed so that wiring for front of the car and wiring for rear of the car flow together in an easy to read sequence. Each diagram is color coded to eliminate confusing abbreviations and number codes. Actual circuits are redrawn to show their circuitry and aid in identification as well as reinstallation.

Immediately following the chassis wiring diagrams are the sub-system diagrams. Here there are electrical schematics of various systems (Fuel Injection, Wiper/Washer Systems, etc.) We've take these components out of the chassis diagrams and provided an individual schematic so as not to overcrowd any one wiring diagram.

Also, at the end of section 4 you will find Fuses and Circuit Breakers covered. The information will help you quickly locate fuse blocks and indicate to you what amperage fuse to use for replacement.

ENGINES
Section 5

Located at the very front of the ENGINE Section you will find a table of contents. Here you will see that the section is arranged according to vehicle manufacturer and then by engine size. You will also find that Oil Pan Removal, Engine Removal and Engine Cooling are included in each individual article. Find the appropriate article on contents page and turn to the corresponding page number.

After turning to the engine article you need, you will find detailed step-by-step procedures to aid you in removing and installing major engine components. Illustrations, such as those showing the tightening sequence for cylinder heads and intake manifolds, will help you to install these components properly.

You will find repair procedures which give specific instructions for the inspection and checking of critical clearances within the engine. This information, along with the specification tables, will aid you in determining which components require attention. Illustrations showing correct piston ring gap location and timing gear or chain installation will allow you to assemble components without guess work.

Also, note that for the first time the Engine Specifications are all grouped together on the last page(s) of each individual article. This makes it easier to use the Specification Tables when procedural information isn't necessary.

CLUTCHES
Section 6

In the CLUTCH Section table of contents, you will find the articles arranged by vehicle manufacturer. Information at the beginning of each article will clarify clutch application. Within each article is the information necessary to complete adjustment and replacement work. Disassembled views of the clutch assembly will aid you in performing your repair work.

BRAKES
Section 7

In the BRAKE Section table of contents, you will find the articles listed by vehicle manufacturer. Each Brake System article includes all the information you need to service and repair imported cars and trucks. At the start of this section there is a Brake Trouble Shooting article that gives necessary information to diagnose potential problems.

For your convenience Master Cylinder and Power Brake Units have been included in each individual article. Detailed adjustment procedures are accompanied by illustrations, while exploded view illustrations clarify and complement the step-by-step procedures for overhaul. The large, easy to read tables give brake lining and brake system specifications for most all disc and drum brake assemblies. These tables will save you time when servicing brake systems.

Also, note that we are including for you as much Pressure Differential information as we have available. In addition, we are concentrating our efforts for you in the area of Power Brake Units.

WHEEL ALIGNMENT
Section 8

In the WHEEL ALIGNMENT Section, you will find specification tables at the very start of the section. Procedure information is ordered by vehicle manufacturer and listed in alphabetical order. Within each article you will find procedures for setting camber and caster, and illustrations to clarify things such as shim positioning and adjustment points.

Ball Joint Checking, Wheel Bearing Adjustment and Jacking and Hoisting Sections complete the information necessary to check and service components related to wheel alignment.

SUSPENSION
Section 9

In the SUSPENSION table of contents, you will find Front and Rear Suspension listed by vehicle manufacturer and models. This section has large and easy to understand illustrations that show proper position of bushings, shims and washers on the suspension assembly. Step-by-step removal and installation procedures allow you to service individual components within the system.

STEERING
Section 10

In the STEERING Section, you will find Steering Wheel and Column Switches, Steering Columns, and Steering Gears and Linkage articles that will give you all the procedures necessary for removal, overhaul, and installation. The many detailed illustrations will help make reassembly work faster and easier.

Detailed explanation and testing procedures for Power Steering Systems enable you to quickly determine problems. Precise, step-by-step procedures for removal, overhaul, and installation are made clear with complete illustrations. You should find repairs of steering components possible in the least amount of time.

LATEST CHANGES and CORRECTIONS
(BLUE PAGES)

LATEST CHANGES and CORRECTIONS are found in the next to last section. This section is printed on blue paper and contains information regarding current and previous models. This section, which is another Mitchell exclusive, has all the up-to-the-minute information which has arrived too late to be included in the regular manual.

LATEST CHANGES and CORRECTIONS (BLUE PAGES) Cont.

To make using this information easier, you will note each entry in the blue page section is preceded by a number enclosed in a box. To ensure that you do not overlook one of these important changes, simply write the boxed number down on the appropriate pages in the main manual. These items, which are NOT contained in other manuals, really give you an edge over your competitors.

We are also using the Blue Pages to make any significant corrections, as necessary, to information contained in earlier publications. We are trying to keep you up-to-date as best we can. Be sure that you check the Blue Pages to see if they reflect any changes to your early manuals.

GENERAL INDEX

The final section of the manual is designed to direct the mechanic to the exact location of the article, specification, or wiring diagram that he needs. This section is broken down into all of the vehicles major components and then divided into models under the component headings.

The first step in using these pages is to locate the listed component that you require information about. Next, go down the list under the component heading to the specific model or engine. Look in the right column to find corresponding page number for the article, specification, or wiring diagram you need.

Section T

QUICK-CHECK TUNE-UP SPECS.

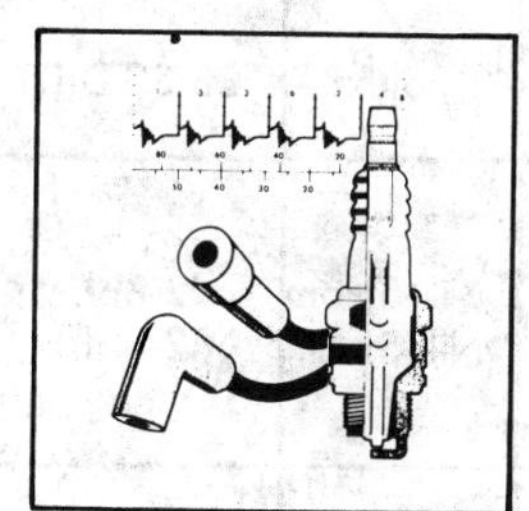

NOTE — ALSO SEE GENERAL INDEX.

1977 Tune-Up Specifications

CAR MODEL	SPARK PLUGS		CARBURETOR		VALVE CLEARANCE		DISTRIBUTOR		No.
	Type	Gap	Make	Model	Int.	Exh.	Point Gap	Cam Angle	
ARROW 1600 & 2000	NGK BPR-6ES	.030"	Solex	①28-32 DIDTA	.006"H	.010"H	.020"	49-55°	1
AUDI	Champion								
100 LS	N7Y	.035" ①	Bosch	Fuel Inj.	.006"H	.016" H	.016"	44-50°	2
Fox	N8Y	.028"	Bosch	Fuel Inj.	.008"C	.016"C	.016"	44-50°	3
BMW	Bosch								
320i	W145T30	.026"	Bosch	Fuel Inj.	.007"C	.007"C	.014"	59-65°	4
530i & 630CSi	W145T30	.026"	Bosch	Fuel Inj.	.010"C	.010"C	.015"	35-41°	5
CAPRI II	Autolite								
2300	AGRF52	.034" ③	Mtrcraft	2500	①	①	②	②	6
2800	AGR 42		Mtrcraft	2150 ④	.014"H	.016"H	②	②	7
COLT 1600 & 2000	NGK BPR-6ES	.030"	Solex	①28-32 DIDTA	.006"H	.010"H	.020"	49-55°	8
COURIER	NGK								
1800	BPR-6ES	.031"	Nik-Strom	2-Bbl.	.012"H ②	.012"H ②	.020" ③	49-55° ③	9
2300	AGRF52 ①	.031"	Nik-Strom	2-Bbl.					10
DATSUN	NGK								
F10 & B210	BP5ES-11	.041"	Hitachi	DCH-306	.010"C	.010"C	.020" ①	49-55°	11
200SX & 710	BPR6ES-11	.041"	Hitachi	DCH-340	.008"C	.010"C	.020" ①	49-55°	12
Pickup	BPR6ES-11	.041" ⑤	Hitachi	DCH-340	.008"C	.010"C	.020" ①	49-55°	13
810 & 280Z	B6ES-11	.041"	Bosch	Fuel Inj.	.008"C	.010"C	①	①	14
FIAT	Champion								
124 & 131	N9Y	.024"	Weber	32 ADFA	.018"C	.020"C	.016"	52-58°	15
128 & X1/9	N9Y	.024"	Weber	32 DATRA	.012"C	.016"C	.016"	52-58°	16
HONDA	NGK								
Civic	BP6-ES	.030"	Keihin	2-Bbl.	.005"C	.005"C	.020"	49-55°	17
Civic CVCC & Accord	B6EB	.030"	Keihin	2-Bbl.	.006"C	.006"C	.020"	49-55°	18
JAGUAR	Champion								
XJ6	N-11Y	.025"	Bosch/Luc	Fuel Inj	.013"C	.013"C	①	.....	19
XJ12 & XJS	N10Y	.035"	Bosch/Luc	Fuel Inj.	013"C	.013"C	②	.....	20
LANCIA All Models	Champion N9Y	.025"	Weber	32 DATRA	.018"C	.020"C	① .012-.019"	52-58°	21

1977 Tune-Up Specifications

No.	IGNITION TIMING	HOT IDLE RPM		FAST IDLE RPM	EXHAUST CO READING At Idle Speed	Remarks
		Man. Trans.	Auto. Trans.			
1	5°BTDC②	900-1000	800-900	2000	......	①2000cc, 30-32 DIDTA ②High Alt.,10°BTDC
2	6°ATDC	850-1000	850-1000	.....	.9% Max.②	①.028" Fed. Man. Trans. ②Calif.,.3% Max. ③Fed. A/T. Fed. M/T 1.5% Calif. .3% Max.
3	3°ATDC	850-1000	850-1000	.....	1.0%③	
4	25°BTDC①	850-1000	850-950	.....	2.0%	①Fed. At 2200 RPM. Calif. At 2400 RPM ②Fed. Calif. 2.5-3.5% ③Fed. At 1700 RPM Calif. At 2700 RPM.
5	22°BTDC③	850-1050	850-1050	.....	1.5-3.0%	
6	③	③	③	1800	③	①Hydraulic Lash Adjusters ②Electronic Ignition ③See Tune-Up Decal ④Calif., 2700 VV
7	③	③	③	1600	③	
8	5°BTDC②	900-1000	800-900	2000	.....	①2000cc, 30-32 DIDTA ②High Alt., 10°BTDC
9	5°BTDC	700	.....	④	1.5-2.5%	①Autolite ②Hydraulic Lash Adjusters ③Electronic Ignition ④See Tune-up Decal
10	6°BTDC	800	700	④	3.5-4.5%	
11	10°BTDC②	700	700③	2300④	1.0-3.0%	①Electronic Ign. .008-.016" ②Calif. B210 with A/T, 8°BTDC ③Calif. B210,650 RPM ④Auto. Trans.,2700 RPM ⑤ Fed. BPR6ES,.031-.035" ⑥Calif. with M/T 10°BTDC ⑦810 Models 700 M/T 650 A/T ⑧Calif. .5%
12	12°BTDC	600	600	2350④	3-2.0%	
13	12°BTDC⑥	750	650	2350④	1.0-3.0%	
14	10°BTDC	800⑦	700⑦	.....	1.0% ⑧	
15	TDC	800-900①	800-900①	1600②	1.5-2.5%	①Model131 (w/Cat. Conv.)- 700-750 RPM ②Model 131 A/T-1300 RPM
16	TDC	800-900	800-900	.....	1.5-2.5%	
17	TDC	700-800	700-800	1800	.35% Max.	①Calif. & High Alt. with M/T and Calif. Sedan with A/T 2°BTDC. Calif. exc Sedan with A/T, TDC ②Alt 2500 RPM
18	6°BTDC①	800	700	3000②	4% Max.	
19	8°BTDC	.....	750	.....	2.0-4.5%	①Pickup Air Gap .014-016" ②Pickup Air Gap .020-.022"
20	10°BTDC	.....	750	.....	1.0-2.0%	
21	TDC②	800-850	800-850	1550-1650	1.5-2.5%	①Calif models .015-.017" ②Calif 10°BTDC

1977 Tune-Up Specifications

CAR MODEL	SPARK PLUGS		CARBURETOR		VALVE CLEARANCE		DISTRIBUTOR		No.
	Type	Gap	Make	Model	Int.	Exh.	Point Gap	Cam Angle	
LUV	NGK								
Pickup	BPR6ES	.030″	Hitachi	DCP-340	.006″C	.010″C	.016-.022″	47-57°	22
MAZDA									
808 1300 & GLC	BP6ES	.029-.033″	Hitachi	DCG-360	.010″H	.012″H	① .018-.022″	49-55°	23
808 1600	BP6ES	.029-.033″	Nik-Strom	2-Bbl.	.012″H	.012″H	.018-.022″	49-55°	24
Rotary Engines	B7ET	.041″	Zen-Strom	4-Bbl.	.....	.....	.018″	55-61°	25
MERCEDES-BENZ	Bosch								
230	W145T30	.028″	Zen-Strom	175CDTU	.004″C	.008″C	.018	46-53°	26
280 Series	W145T30	.028″	Bosch	Fuel Inj.	.004″C	.010″C	①	.....	27
450 Series	W145T30	.028″	Bosch	Fuel Inj.	②	②	①	.....	28
6.9	W145T30	.028″	Bosch	Fuel Inj.	②	②	①	.....	29
MG									
Midget	N-12Y	.025″	Zen-Strom	150CD4T	.010″C	.010″C	.014-.016″	46-56°	30
MGB	N-9Y	.035″	Zen-Strom	175CD5T	.013″H	.013″H	.014-.016″ ②	46-56°	31
OPEL	NGK								
1.8	BPR6ES	.030″	Nikki	2-Bbl.	.006″C	.010″C	.018″	47-57°	32
PEUGEOT	Champion								
504	N-7Y	.024″	Solex	32BICSA①	②	.010″C	.016″	54-60°	33
604	BN-9Y	.024″	Solex	34TBIA PEU③	.004″C	.010″C	④	④	34
PORSCHE	Bosch								
911S	W235P21	.022″	Bosch	Fuel Inj.	.004″C	.004″C	.014″	35-41°①	35
Turbo Carrera	W280P21	.028″	Bosch	Fuel Inj.	.004″C	.004″C	④	④	36
924	W200T30	.030″	Bosch	Fuel Inj.	.009″H	.019″H	④	52-70°⑤	37
RENAULT	Champion								
R-5	L87Y①	.025-.028″	Weber	DIR32	.006″C	.008″C	.018″	55-59°	38
R-12	N9Y	.025-.028″	Weber	32 DARA	.008″C	.010″C	.018″	54-60°	39
R-17GTL	N9Y	.025-.028″	Weber	32 DARA	.008″C	.010″C	.018″	54-60°	40
R-17 Gordini	N3	.025-.028″	Bosch	Fuel Inj.	.010″C	.012″C	.018″	54-60°	41
SAAB	Bosch								
99	W175T30	.026″	Bosch	Fuel Inj.	.009″H	.017″H	.016″	47-53°	42

1977 Tune-Up Specifications

No.	IGNITION TIMING	HOT IDLE RPM Man. Trans.	HOT IDLE RPM Auto. Trans.	FAST IDLE RPM	EXHAUST CO READING At Idle Speed	Remarks
22	6°BTDC	900	900	3400 ①	②	①A/T 3200 RPM ②See Tune-Up Decal
23 24 25	10-12°BTDC ② 12-14°BTDC ③ 5°BTDC ⑤	700-750 800-850 ④ 725-775	600-650 800-850 ④ 725-775	.... 3250 ⑥	1.5-2.5% ..... Less .1%	①Electronic Ign. Air Gap .012-.014″ ②Fed. 808 1300,8.5-13.5° BTDC-GLC with M/T 6-8°BTDC ③Calif. 7-9°BTDC ④Calif. 650-700 RPM ⑤RX-3SP, TDC ⑥RX-3SP, 3600RPM
26 27 28 29	10°BTDC TDC TDC TDC	....	850 800 750 600	1800	.4-2.0% .4-2.0% .2-2.0% ③ .2-2.0% ③	①Electronic Ignition ②Hydraulic Lifters ③Hi Alt. - .2-.12%
30 31	10°BTDC ① 10°BTDC	800 850	800 850	....	3% 4.5-6.5%	①Calif., 2°ATDC ②.010-.017″ with CAT.
32	6°BTDC	875-925	.....	3200	.....	①±150 RPM. Auto. Trans. 3000 RPM
33 34	8°BTDC 10°BTDC	900	900 900	1560 1475	1.5-2.5% 3-4%	①Primary Carb. Sec. Carb. is 34BICSA ②#1 & #4 .008″C #2 & #3 .004″C ③Primary, Secondary 35 CEEI PEU (2-Bbl.) ④Breakerless Ignition
35 36 37	TDC ② 7°ATDC 10°ATDC ⑥	900-1000 ③ 950-1050 850-1000 ⑦	900-1000 ③ 850-1000	....	1.5-3.0% 2.0-4.0% 1.0-2.0% ⑧	①Marelli 34-40° ②Calif. 15° ATDC ③Calif. 950-1050 RPM ④Electronic Ignition ⑤At 1500 RPM ⑥1977½ Models, 3°ATDC ⑦1977½ Federal 900-1000 ⑧Federal. 1977 High Alt. .7-1.3%; Calif .7% Max. 1977½ Calif .5-1.0%
38 39 40 41	TDC 7°BTDC 7°BTDC TDC	800-900 800-900 750-950	..... 600-700 600-700	1900 ② 1500 1500	.5-3.0% .5-3.0% ③ .5-3.0% ③ 1.0-3.0%	①Calif. & High Alt. L92Y ②Calif. & High Alt. 1500 RPM ③Calif. 1.0-1.4%.
42	20°BTDC ①	825-925	825-925	.....	.75-2.75% ②	①At 2000 RPM ②Calif. .75%

1977 Tune-Up Specifications

CAR MODEL	SPARK PLUGS		CARBURETOR		VALVE CLEARANCE		DISTRIBUTOR		No.
	Type	Gap	Make	Model	Int.	Exh.	Point Gap	Cam Angle	
SUBARU	NGK								
1600	BP6ES	.032″	Hitachi	DCJ 306	.010″C	.014″C	.016″ [1]	49-55°	43
TOYOTA	NGK								
3K-C Engine	BP5ES-L	.030″	Aisan	2-Bbl.	.008″H	.012″H	.016″	50-54°	44
2T-C Engine	BP5ES-L	.030″	Aisan	2-Bbl.	.008″H	.013″H	.016″	50-54°	45
2 0R Engine	BP5ES-L	.030″	Aisan	2-Bbl.	.008″H	.012″H	.016″ [2]	50-54°	46
2F Engine	BP5EZ	.039″	Aisan	2-Bbl.	.008″H	.014″H	.018″	38-44°	47
TRIUMPH	Champion								
Spitfire	N12Y	.025″	Zen-Strom	150CD4T	.010″C	.010″C	.014-.016″ [1]	.....	48
TR7	N12Y	.025″	Zen-Strom	175CDFEVX	.008″C	.018″C	.014-.016″ [1]	.....	49
VOLKSWAGEN	Bosch								
Type 1	W145M1	.028″	Bosch	Fuel Inj.	.006″C	.006″C	.016″	44-50°	50
Type 2	W145M2	.028″	Bosch	Fuel Inj.	.006″C	.006″C	.016″	44-50°	51
Dasher	W175T30	.026″	Bosch	Fuel Inj.	.010″H	.018″H	.016″	44-50°	52
Rabbit/ Scirocco	W215T30	.026″	Bosch	Fuel Inj.	.010″H	.018″H	.016″	44-50°	53
VOLVO	Bosch								
240	W175T30	.030″	Bosch	Fuel Inj.	.015″C	.015″C	[1]	[1]	54
260	WA200T30	.030″	Bosch	Fuel Inj.	.005″C	.011″C	[1]	[1]	55

1977 Tune-Up Specifications

No.	IGNITION TIMING	HOT IDLE RPM Man. Trans.	HOT IDLE RPM Auto. Trans.	FAST IDLE RPM	EXHAUST CO READING At Idle Speed	Remarks
43	8°BTDC	800-900②	800-900②	.....	1.0-2.0%③	①Electronic Ign. Air Gap .008-.016" Nippondenso or .012-.016" Hitachi ②Calif. 850-950 RPM ③Calif. .1-.5%
44	8°BTDC	700-800	700-800	.....	.....	①Calif. & High Alt. 3000 RPM ②Calif. Celica GT Electronic Ignition Air Gap .008-.012"
45	10°BTDC	800-900	800-900	3400①	.....	
46	8°BTDC	750-850	800-900	2400	.....	
47	7°BTDC	600-700	.....	1800	.....	
48	10°BTDC②	700-900	.....	1800	3.0%	①Pickup Module Air Gap ②Calif. 2°ATDC
49	10°BTDC②	700-900	.....	1600	2.0-6.0%	
50	5°ATDC	850-950	.....	.....	2.0% Max.	①Calif. Fed. M/T 1.5% Fed. A/T 1.0%
51	7.5°BTDC	800-950	850-1000	.....	2.0% Max.	
52	3°ATDC	850-1000	850-1000	.....	.5%①	
53	3°ATDC	900-1000	900-1000	.....	.3%①	
54	12°BTDC	850-950	750-850②	.....	1.2-1.8%	①Electronic Ignition ②Calif. 850-950 RPM
55	10°BTDC	850-950	850-950	.....	1.4-2.0%	

Section 1
TUNE-UP

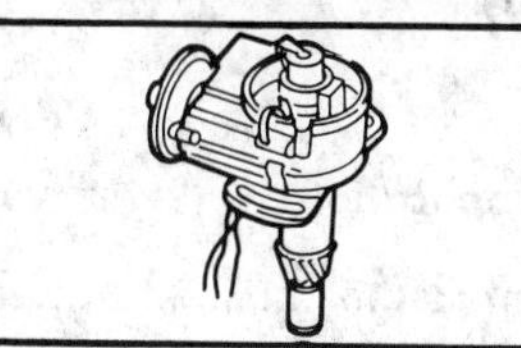

Contents

NOTE — ALSO SEE GENERAL INDEX IN BACK OF MANUAL.

TUNE-UP

Arrow
Colt

ENGINE IDENTIFICATION

Engine model number is located at lower left side of cylinder block below starter and serves to identify engine size. Engine serial number is stamped on boss on top side of cylinder block, below number one spark plug. This number can also serve to identify engine size as follows:

Displacement	Engine Model	Serial Number
1600 cc	4G32	2A00101 & Up
2000 cc	4G52	52A00101 & Up

MODEL IDENTIFICATION

VEHICLE IDENTIFICATION NUMBER

Model can be identified by first digit of Vehicle Identification Number. Number is stamped on a plate riveted to left front corner of instrument panel pad and visible through windshield. Number is also stamped on a label attached to left front door, above door lock. Code for Arrow is "7", and for Colt is "6".

COMPRESSION PRESSURE

Check compression pressure with engine at normal operating temperature, spark plugs removed, throttle valve wide open and engine at cranking speed. Compression pressure should not vary more than 10% between any two cylinders. Compression is as follows:

Application	Pressure psi (kg/cm²)
All Models	149 (10.5)

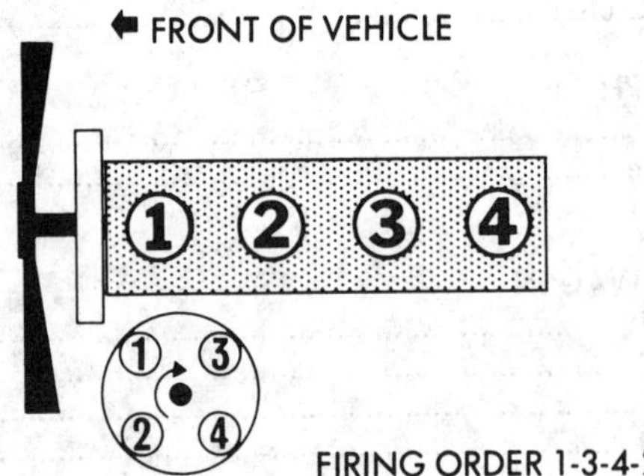

Fig. 1 Firing Order and Distributor Rotation (1600 cc & 2000 cc Engines)

VALVE TAPPET CLEARANCE

Adjust valves with engine off and at normal operating temperature.

Valve Clearances

Application	Clearance
Intake	.006" (.15 mm)
Exhaust	.010" (.25 mm)

VALVE ARRANGEMENT

Right Side — All Exhaust. Left Side — All Intake.

SPARK PLUGS

Gap	.028-.031" (.7-.8 mm)
Torque	14-21 ft. lbs. (1.9-2.9 mkg)

Spark Plug Type

Application	NGK	Champion
All Models	BPR-6ES	RN-9Y

HIGH TENSION WIRE RESISTANCE

Carefully remove high tension wires from spark plugs and distributor cap. Using an ohmmeter, check resistance of wire while gently twisting wire. If resistance is not to specification, or fluctuates from infinity to any value, replace wire.

Resistance (Ohms) Per Wire

Application	Resistance
All Models	Less Than 22,000

DISTRIBUTOR

Point Gap	.018-.020 (.46-.53 mm)
Cam Angle	49-55°
Breaker Arm Spring Tension	17-21 oz. (482-595 g)
Condenser Capacity	.22 mfd

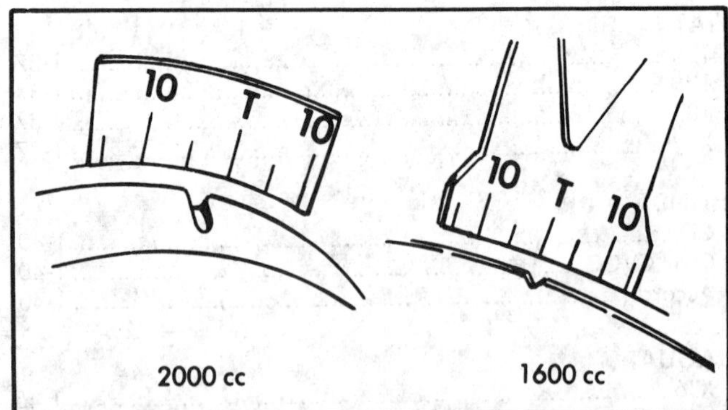

Fig. 2 Ignition Timing Mark Location

IGNITION TIMING

1) Adjust breaker point gap. Set piston in No. 1 cylinder at TDC on compression stroke. Crankshaft pulley notch should align with "T" mark on timing indicator. See *Fig. 2*.

2) Turn crankshaft pulley to set notch to basic ignition timing position. Loosen distributor mounting nut and turn distributor body until breaker points just begin to open. Tighten mounting nut.

TUNE-UP (Cont.)

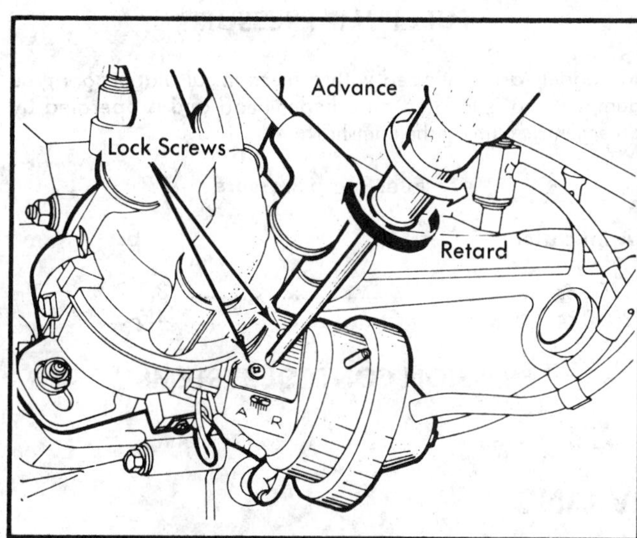

Fig. 3 Adjusting Distributor Timing Mechanism (1600 cc Standard Engine)

3) Remove rubber plug from retard side of distributor vacuum control chamber (only on cars equipped with dual diaphragm distributors — California and high altitude). No manifold vacuum then acts on retard side and timing is not retarded.

4) Start engine and check for proper idle speed. Prior to adjusting timing on 1600 cc standard engine, loosen two lock screws. *See Fig. 3.* Using Phillips screwdriver and timing light, adjust timing mechanism to specified setting. Then tighten lock screws.

5) In the 1600 cc Silent Shaft and 2000 cc engines, loosen distributor mounting nut. Rotate distributor body until specified timing is achieved. Tighten nut securely.

6) On engines with dual diaphragm type distributors, reinstall rubber plug and check actual ignition timing.

Ignition Timing Specifications

Application	①Basic Timing	②Actual Timing
1600 cc		
Federal	5°BTDC±1°	.....
Calif.	5°BTDC±1°	5°ATDC±3°
High Altitude	10°BTDC±1°	TDC±3°
2000 cc		
Federal	5°BTDC±1°	.....
Calif.	5°BTDC±1°	5°ATDC±3°

① — On dual diaphragm distributors, rubber plug removed from retard side of vacuum diaphragm.
② — On dual diaphragm distributors, rubber plug installed on retard side of vacuum diaphragm.

IDLE SPEED & MIXTURE

IDLE ADJUSTMENT

NOTE — *Before adjusting idle speed, check ignition timing, place shift lever in "N" position, and turn off air conditioning.*

1) With engine at normal operating temperature, disconnect air hose from air cleaner to reed valve (at valve). Plug air inlet at reed valve.

2) Adjust to specified idle speed, using both idle mixture and idle speed screws.

3) Now set CO level to leanest possible value within the range of 0.5-2.0% CO. With CO level set as specified, engine should not misfire. If misfiring occurs, change CO setting.

4) Replace air hose to reed valve and adjust idle to specified RPM with the idle speed screw.

5) Increase engine speed to 2500 RPM two or three times, engine should return to specified idle. If not, repeat adjustment procedure. Install an idle limiter to idle mixture screw.

Idle Speed (RPM) and CO Level (%)

Application	RPM	CO%
Man. Trans.	950±50	0.5-2.0
Auto. Trans.	850±50	0.5-2.0

DASH POT ADJUSTMENT

1) Dash pot is used on manual transmission models only. After idle speed and mixture adjustment, adjust dash pot as follows:

2) Push up on lower end of dash pot rod until rod stops. Check engine RPM, which should be 1900 to 2100 RPM.

3) Release dash pot rod quickly and note how many seconds it takes engine to return to normal idle speed. This time should be from 3.0 to 6.0 seconds.

4) If time range is not to specifications, turn adjusting screw until correct range is obtained. *See Fig. 4.*

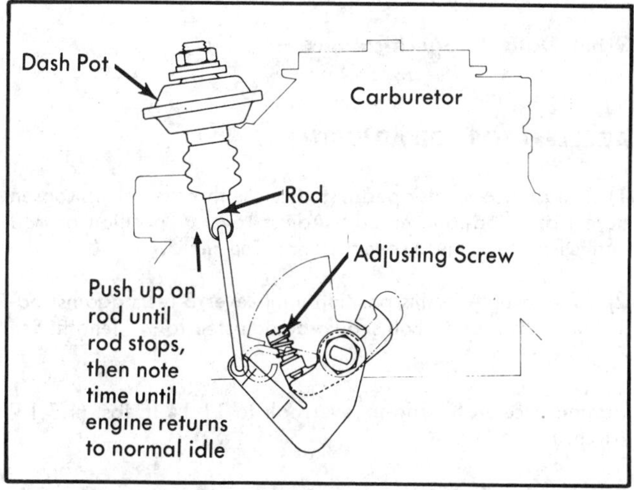

Fig. 4 Dash Pot Adjustment (All Models with Manual Transmissions)

TUNE-UP (Cont.)

COLD (FAST) IDLE RPM

With choke valve fully closed, adjust fast idle adjusting screw to obtain specified fast idle RPM.

Fast Idle Specification

Application	RPM
All Models	2000

AUTOMATIC CHOKE SETTING

Automatic choke is properly set when yellow punch mark on bimetal case is aligned with center projection on choke housing.

FUEL PUMP PRESSURE

All models are equipped with a mechanical diaphragm type pump. Pump is located on cylinder head and is operated by an eccentric cam on the camshaft.

Fuel Pump Pressure

Application	psi (kg/cm^2)
1600 cc	3.7-5.1 (.26-.36)
2000 cc	4.6-6.0 (.32-.42)

EMISSION CONTROL SYSTEMS

See Mitchell Manuals' Emission Control Manual.

GENERAL SERVICING

IGNITION

DISTRIBUTOR

All models for California and High Altitude use Mitsubishi dual diaphragm distributors. Federal models use single diaphragm distributors.

Other Data & Specifications — *See Tune-Up and Mitsubishi Distributors in ELECTRICAL Section.*

IGNITION COIL

Application	Resistance (Ohms)
Primary	1.26-1.54
Secondary	8,670-11,730

FUEL SYSTEMS

CARBURETORS

Application	Model
1600 cc & 2000 cc 2-Bbl.	Solex DIDTA

Other Data & Specifications — *See Tune-Up and Solex Carburetors in FUEL SYSTEMS Section.*

ACCELERATOR ROD ADJUSTMENT

1) Release accelerator pedal (fully close throttle valve). Loosen accelerator rod-to-lever bolt. Adjust Lever A position on rod until Distance "1" is to specifications. See *Fig. 5*.

2) Turn Lever A in this position until Lever B rests against adjusting bolt stopper. Bolt should be adjusted to ¾" length. See *Fig. 5*.

Tighten accelerator rod-to-lever bolt to 11-14 ft. lbs. (1.5-1.9 kg/cm^2)

CAUTION — *Be sure there is at least 0.4" clearance (coupe, sedan and hatchback) or 0.6" clearance (hardtop and station wagon) between Lever A and toe board insulator.*

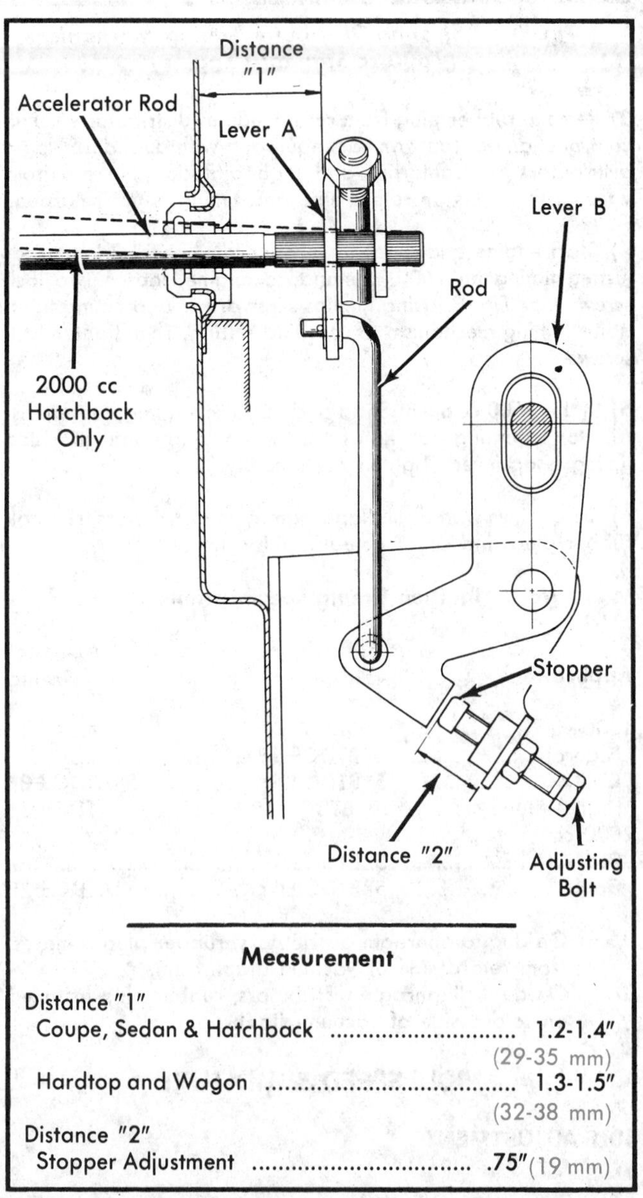

Measurement

Distance "1"	
Coupe, Sedan & Hatchback	1.2-1.4" (29-35 mm)
Hardtop and Wagon	1.3-1.5" (32-38 mm)
Distance "2"	
Stopper Adjustment	.75" (19 mm)

Fig. 5 Adjusting Accelerator Rod

GENERAL SERVICING (Cont.)

ELECTRICAL

BATTERY

12 Volt – Negative Ground.

Application	Amp. Hr. Rating
Colt	60

Battery Location – Front left side of engine compartment.

STARTER

All models use Mitsubishi overrunning clutch type starter.

Other Data & Specifications – *See Mitsubishi Starters in ELECTRICAL Section.*

ALTERNATOR

Application	Rated Amp. Output
All Models	45

Other Data & Specifications – *See Mitsubishi and Nippondenso Alternators and Regulators in ELECTRICAL Section.*

ALTERNATOR REGULATOR

The 1600 cc Silent Shaft engine uses a Nippondenso alternator regulator. The 1600 cc Standard and 2000 cc engines use Mitsubishi alternator regulators.

Other Data & Specifications – *See Mitsubishi and Nippondenso Alternators and Regulators in ELECTRICAL Section.*

ENGINE

INTAKE MANIFOLD TIGHTENING

Check manifold-to-cylinder head attaching bolts for 11-14 ft. lbs. (1.5-1.9 mkg) torque.

BELT ADJUSTMENT

Application	①Deflection
Fan Belt	.28-.38" (7-10 mm)
A/C Belt	②

① – Deflection is with 22 lbs. (10 kg) pressure applied midway on longest belt run.

② – Check A/C belt using Strand Tension Gauge; Tension should be 100-110 lbs. (45-50 kg).

FILTERS & CLEANERS

Filter or Cleaner	Service Interval (Miles)
Oil Filter	Replace every 10,000
Air Cleaner	①Replace every 30,000
Fuel Filter	Replace every 15,000
Canister Filter	Replace every 30,000
Auto. Trans. Filter	②Replace every 30,000

① – Clean every 15,000 miles.

② – Interval is for severe usage only; under normal usage, no service is required.

CAPACITIES

Application	Quantity
Crankcase (Includes Filter)	
1600 cc	4.2 qts.
2000 cc	4.5 qts.
Cooling System	
1600 cc	7.7 qts.
2000 cc	9.5 qts.
Man. Trans. (SAE 80 Gear Oil)	
4-Speed	1.8 qts.
5-Speed	
1600 cc	2.1 qts.
2000 cc	2.4 qts.
Auto. Trans. (Dexron)	6.8 qts.
Rear Axle (SAE 90 Gear Oil)	1.2 qts.
Fuel Tank	
Station Wagon	11.0 gals.
Sedan and Coupe	13.2 gals.
All Others	13.5 gals.

TUNE-UP

100 LS
Fox

ENGINE IDENTIFICATION

Serial number is stamped on left side of engine block (near clutch housing) on Audi 100 LS, and on left side of engine block near distributor on Audi Fox.

Engine Code Numbers

Application	Code
100LS	
Federal	
Man. Trans.	YG
Auto. Trans.	YH
California	YK
Fox	
Federal	
Man. Trans.	YR
Auto. Trans.	YD
California	
Man. Trans.	YC
Auto. Trans.	YD

MODEL IDENTIFICATION

VEHICLE IDENTIFICATION

Vehicle may be identified by the chassis number which is embossed on rear wall of engine compartment, on left windshield pillar (visible through windshield), and on safety sticker on left door jamb.

COMPRESSION PRESSURE

With engine at normal operating temperature, throttle wide open and engine at cranking speed, compression pressure should be as follows:

Application	Stand. Pressure psi (kg/cm²)	Min. Pressure psi (kg/cm²)
100LS	120-170 (8.4-12)	98 (6.89)
Fox	142-184 (10-13)	107 (7.5)

① – Maximum difference per cylinder is 42 psi (2.95 kg/cm²).

VALVE TAPPET CLEARANCE

Adjust valve clearance with engine at normal operating temperature and in firing order sequence. Remove air cleaner and rocker cover prior to adjustment. Place No. 1 cylinder at TDC position (both valves closed) and rocker arms of No. 4 cylinder in overlap position (both rocker arms move in opposite direction).

Valve Adjustment Sequence

Adjust Valves Of Cylinder	When Valves Overlap At Cylinder
No. 1	No. 4
No. 3	No. 2
No. 4	No. 1
No. 2	No. 3

100LS – Adjust valves by turning self-locking adjusting nuts on rocker arms.

Fox – Tappet clearance is obtained by adjusting or removing tappet clearance discs. Special tools 10-209 (VW 546) and 10-208 (US 4476) are required to remove tappet clearance discs.

NOTE – *Tappet clearance discs with thicknesses ranging from .118" (3.0 mm) to .167" (4.25 mm) in steps of .002" (.05 mm) are available .*

Valve Tappet Clearance

Application	Specification
100 LS	
Intake	.006" (.15 mm)
Exhaust	.016" (.41 mm)
Fox	
Warm	
Intake	.008-.012" (.2-.3 mm)
Exhaust	.016-.020" (.4-.5 mm)
Cold	
Intake	.006-.010" (.15-.25 mm)
Exhaust	.014-.018" (.35-.45 mm)

VALVE ARRANGEMENT

100 LS - I-E-I-E-I-E-I-E (front to rear).
Fox - E-I-E-I-I-E-I-E (front to rear).

SPARK PLUGS

Gap	
100 LS	
Auto. Trans.	.035" (.9 mm)
Man. Trans.	
Federal	.028" (.7 mm)
California	.035" (.9 mm)
Fox	.024-.032" (.6-.8 mm)
Torque	22 ft. lbs. (3 mkg)

Spark Plug Type

Application	Bosch	Beru	Champion
100LS			
Auto. Trans.	W225T2 W225T30	225/14/3A	N7Y
Man. Trans.			
Federal	W215T30	215/14/3A	N7Y
California	W225T2 W225T30	225/14/3A	N7Y
Fox	W175T30	175/14/3A	N8Y

TUNE-UP (Cont.)

HIGH TENSION WIRE RESISTANCE

Carefully remove ends of wire from spark plug and distributor. Using an ohmmeter, check resistance of wire while gently twisting wire. If resistance is not to specification, or fluctuates from infinity to any value, replace wire.

Resistance (Ohms) Per Wire

Application	Resistance
All Models	25,000-30,000

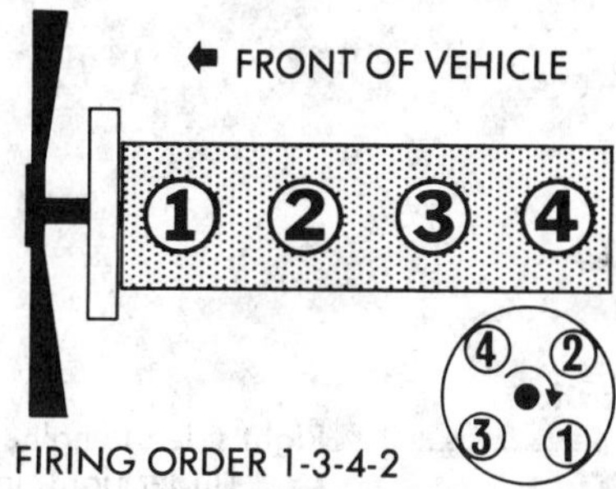

Fig. 1 Firing Order and Distributor Rotation (Audi 100LS)

DISTRIBUTOR

Point Gap (All Models)	.016″ (.4 mm)
Cam Angle (All Models)	47°±3°
Condenser Capacity (All Models)	.22 mfd.

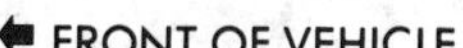

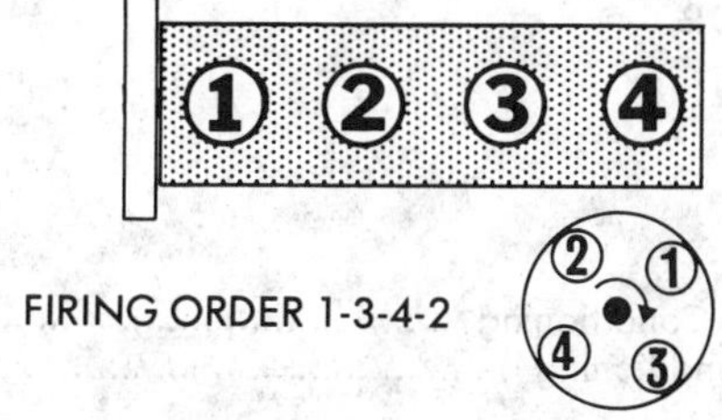

Fig. 2 Firing Order and Distributor Rotation (Audi Fox)

IGNITION TIMING

With timing light connected, engine speed set to specified RPM and vacuum hoses connected, rotate distributor until specified timing is obtained.

NOTE — For repair parts, flywheels have only the TDC reference mark "0". When installing, scribe a timing mark in correct location (14 mm to right of "0" mark on 100LS and 7 mm to right on Fox). These represent the 3° and 6° marks for ignition timing.

Ignition Timing Specifications

Application	RPM	Timing
Fox	925±75	①3°ATDC
100 LS	925±75	①6°ATDC

① — With vacuum hoses connected.

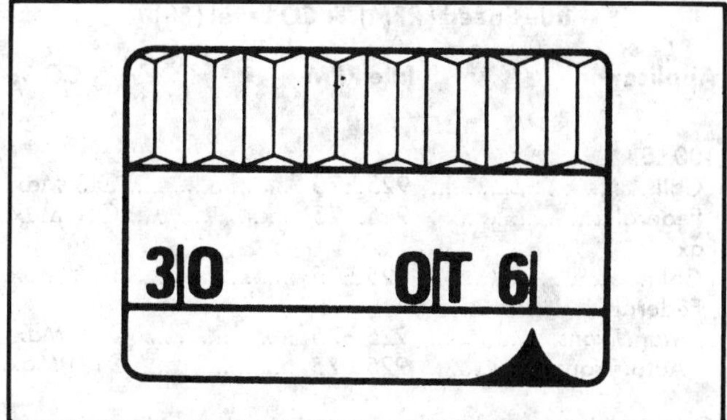

Fig. 3 Ignition Timing Mark Location (Audi 100LS)

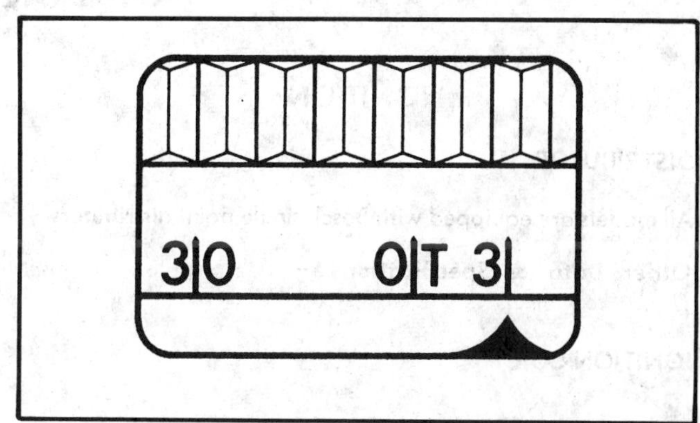

Fig. 4 Ignition Timing Mark Location (Audi Fox)

HOT (SLOW) IDLE RPM

1) With engine at normal operating temperature, check and make sure that ignition timing, valve clearance, spark plug gap and compression pressures are within specifications. Turn headlights on high beam and, if equipped, turn air conditioning off. Leave vacuum hoses connected.

2) Adjust idle speed to specifications by means of the idle control screw at the throttle plate housing.

3) To adjust CO level, remove plug from mixture control unit between fuel distributor and venturi. Insert suitable adjusting tool (P 377) and turn clockwise to raise CO% or counterclockwise to decrease CO% until the specified CO level is obtained.

NOTE — Engine will stall if pressure is exerted on adjusting tool. Use very small adjustments or CO level will be changed greatly.

4) Remove adjusting wrench and accelerate engine briefly. Wait until CO meter has stabilized for idle speed reading. Check idle speed and CO level and adjust if necessary.

TUNE-UP (Cont.)

Idle Speed (RPM) & CO Level (%)

Application	Idle RPM	CO %
100 LS		
Calif.	925±75	①.3 Max.
Federal	925±75	①.9 Max.
Fox		
Calif.	925±75	①.3 Max.
Federal		
Man. Trans.	925±75	①1.5 Max.
Auto. Trans.	925±75	①1.0 Max.

① — With vacuum hoses connected and air conditioning off.

FUEL PUMP PRESSURE

Pressure
All Models .... 64-74 psi (4.5-5.2 kg/cm²)
Delivery Rate .... Approx. 1 quart in 40 seconds

Other Data & Specifications — *See Tune-Up and Bosch CIS Fuel Injection in FUEL SYSTEMS Section.*

EMISSION CONTROL SYSTEMS

See Mitchell Manuals' Emission Control Manual.

GENERAL SERVICING

IGNITION

DISTRIBUTOR

All models are equipped with Bosch single point distributors.

Other Data & Specifications — *See Tune-Up & Bosch Distributors in ELECTRICAL Section.*

IGNITION COIL

Resistance Specifications①

Application	Primary (Ohms)	Secondary (Ohms)
100LS	1.8-1.9	.....
Fox	1.7-2.1	7,000-12,000

① — Ballast resistor — Fox has 0.9 ohm resistance.

FUEL SYSTEMS

FUEL INJECTION

All models are equipped with Bosch CIS Fuel Injection System.

Other Data & Specifications — *See Tune-Up and Bosch Fuel Injection in FUEL SYSTEMS Section.*

ELECTRICAL

BATTERY

12 Volt — Negative Ground

Application	Amp. Hr. Capacity
100 LS	54
Fox	
W/O Air Conditioning	45
W/Air Conditioning	54

Battery Location
100LS .... Right side of engine compartment.
Fox .... Under right side of rear seat.

STARTER

All models are equipped with Bosch Starters.

Other Data & Specifications — *See Bosch Starters in ELECTRICAL Section.*

ALTERNATOR

Application	Rated Amp. Output
100LS	
Without Air Conditioning	55
With Air Conditioning	75
Fox	
Without Air Conditioning	55
With Air Conditioning	65

Other Data & Specifications — *See Bosch and Motorola Alternators & Regulators in ELECTRICAL Section.*

ALTERNATOR REGULATOR

Motorola and Bosch — Non-adjustable, integral with alternator.

Operating Voltage .... 12.5-14.5 Volts

Other Data & Specifications — *See Bosch & Motorola Alternators & Regulators in ELECTRICAL Section.*

GENERAL SERVICING (Cont.)

BELT ADJUSTMENT

All Models – With a 20 lbs. (9.1 kg) pressure, belt should be able to be depressed .40" (9.8 mm).

FILTERS & CLEANERS

Filter or Cleaner	Service Interval (Miles)
Oil Filter	Replace every 7,500
Air Cleaner	Replace every 15,000
Fuel Filter	Replace every 15,000
EGR Filter	Replace every 30,000

CAPACITIES

Application	Quantity
Crankcase (Includes Filter)	
100LS	①4.3 qts.
Fox	②3.2 qts.
Cooling System	
100LS	8 qts.
Fox	③6.9 qts.
Manual Transmission	
100LS (SAE 80)	4.2 pts.
Fox (SAE 80W or 80W/90)	1.6 pts.
Automatic Transmission (Refill)	
100LS (Dexron)	6.3 pts.
Fox (Dexron)	④6.4 pts.
Final Drive of Auto. Trans.	
100LS (SAE 90)	2.2 pts.
Fox (SAE 90)	1.5 pts.
Fuel Tank	
100LS	⑤15.3 gals.
Fox	⑥11.9 gals.
Windshield Fluid Container	1.6 qts.

① – 3.8 qts. without filter.
② – 2.6 qts. without filter.
③ – Includes 0.6 qts. in expansion tank.
④ – Dry fill is 6.4 qts.
⑤ – Includes 1.3 gals. in reserve.
⑥ – Includes 2.4 gals. in reserve.

TUNE-UP

320i

ENGINE IDENTIFICATION

The engine number of the 1990 cc 4-cylinder, single overhead camshaft engine is located on the rear of the cylinder block above the starter near the left-hand side.

MODEL IDENTIFICATION

VEHICLE IDENTIFICATION NUMBER

The chassis number is located on a label attached to the upper steering column and on the support plate of the right-hand wheel arch in the engine compartment.

COMPRESSION PRESSURE

With battery fully charged, engine at normal operating temperature, throttle fully open and engine at cranking speed, compression pressure should be as follows:

Good	Above 149 psi (10.5 kg/cm²)
Normal	135-149 psi (9.5-10.5 kg/cm²)
Poor	Below 128 psi (9.0 kg/cm²)

VALVE TAPPET CLEARANCE

With engine either cold or at normal operating temperature, loosen nut on rocker arm and adjust position of eccentric cam to obtain proper clearance. Adjust valves in firing order sequence at TDC of compression stroke.

Adjust Cylinder at Top Dead Center	When Valves Of Cylinder Overlap
No. 1	No. 4
No. 3	No. 2
No. 4	No. 1
No. 2	No. 3

Application	Clearance In. (mm)
Cold, Intake & Exhaust	.006-.008 (.15-.20)
Warm, Intake & Exhaust	.008-.010 (.20-.25)

VALVE ARRANGEMENT
Left Side – All Intake.
Right Side – All Exhaust.

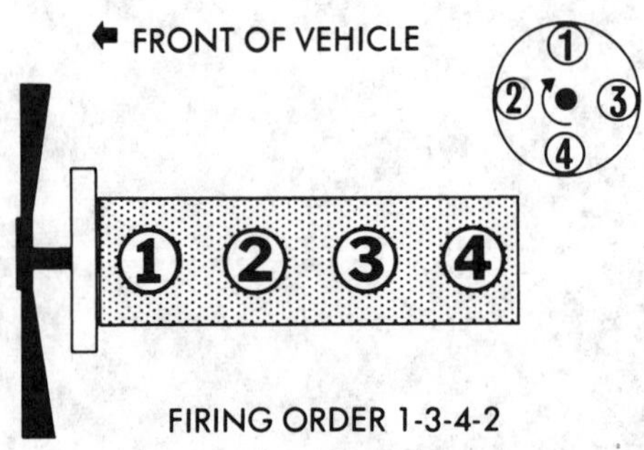

Fig. 1 Firing Order and Distributor Rotation

SPARK PLUGS

Gap	.024-.028" (.6-.7mm)
Torque	18-22 ft. lbs. (2.5-3 mkg)

Spark Plug Type

Application	Champion	Bosch
All Models	N-10Y	W 145 T30

HIGH TENSION WIRE RESISTANCE

Carefully remove ends of wire from spark plug and distributor. Using an ohmmeter, check resistance of wire while gently twisting wire. If resistance is not to specification, or fluctuates from infinity to any value, replace wire.

Resistance (Ohms) Per Wire

Application	Resistance
All Models	25,000-30,000

DISTRIBUTOR

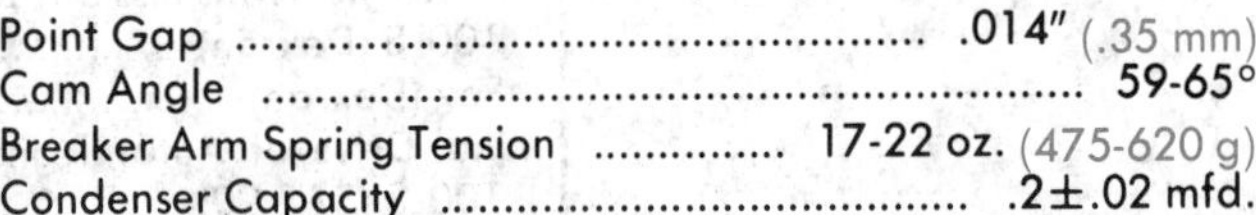

Point Gap	.014" (.35 mm)
Cam Angle	59-65°
Breaker Arm Spring Tension	17-22 oz. (475-620 g)
Condenser Capacity	.2±.02 mfd.

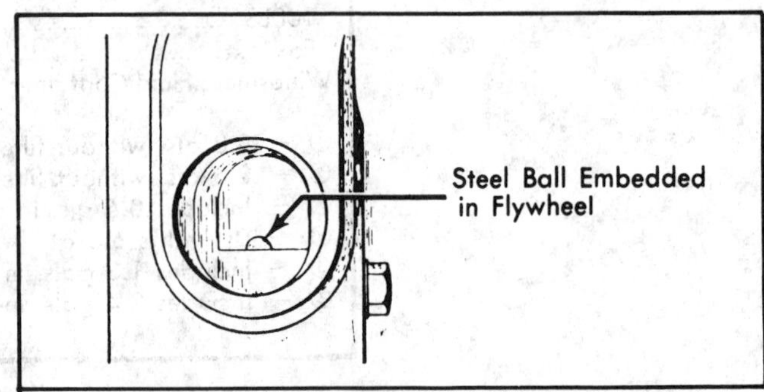

Fig. 2 Ignition Timing Mark Location

IGNITION TIMING

With engine at normal operating temperature, connect a timing light and tachometer to vehicle. Disconnect and plug distributor vacuum line. Start engine and adjust speed to specifications shown in following table. To adjust ignition timing, rotate distributor until center of ball embedded in flywheel is visible at edge of inspection hole. On models with automatic transmission, a long pin is used instead of the ball.

Ignition Timing Specifications

Application	RPM	Dynamic Timing
California	2400	25° BTDC
Federal	2200	25° BTDC

TUNE-UP (Cont.)

IDLE SPEED & MIXTURE

1) With air cleaner element in good condition, engine at normal operating temperature, ignition timing and valve clearance to specifications, disconnect air injection pump hose and plug check valve. Connect tachometer and exhaust gas analyzer to vehicle.

2) Adjust idle speed to specifications by adjusting idle air screw on throttle valve housing. Remove access plug, located next to fuel distributor. Insert a suitable Allen wrench (or special wrench 130 010) into plug hole and adjust to specified CO level.

CAUTION — *Do not accelerate engine while adjusting CO level.*

3) Reinstall plug and reconnect air hose.

Idle Speed (RPM) & CO Level (%)

Application	Idle RPM	CO%
California	900±50	2.5-3.5
Federal	900±50	2.0

FUEL PUMP PRESSURE

Application	psi (kg/cm²)
All Models	64-74 (4.5-5.2)

EMISSION CONTROL SYSTEMS

See Mitchell Manuals' Emission Control Manual.

GENERAL SERVICING

IGNITION

DISTRIBUTOR

All models are equipped with Bosch single point distributors.

Other Data & Specifications — *See Tune-Up & Bosch Distributors in ELECTRICAL Section.*

IGNITION COIL

Resistance	Ohms at 68°F (20°C)
Primary	1.7-2.1

FUEL SYSTEMS

FUEL INJECTION

All models are equipped with Bosch Continuous Injection System (CIS) fuel injection.

Other Data & Specifications — *See Bosch CIS Fuel Injection in FUEL SYSTEMS Section.*

ELECTRICAL

BATTERY

12 Volt — Negative Ground.

Application	Amp. Hr. Rating
All Models	55

Battery Location — In engine compartment.

STARTER

All models are equipped with Bosch Starters.

Other Data & Specifications — *See Bosch Starters in ELECTRICAL Section.*

ALTERNATOR

Application	Rated Amp. Output
All Models	55

Other Data & Specifications — *See Bosch Alternators & Regulators in ELECTRICAL Section.*

ALTERNATOR REGULATOR

All models are equipped with Bosch Alternator Regulators with an operating voltage of 13.9-14.2 volts at 68°F (20°C).

Other Data & Specifications — *See Bosch Alternators & Regulators in ELECTRICAL Section.*

GENERAL SERVICING (Cont.)

BELT ADJUSTMENT

Fan Belt – Adjust tension until it is possible to depress belt 3/16-3/8" (5-10 mm) midway between fan and alternator pulleys.

Air Pump – Adjust tension until it is possible to depress belt 3/16 - 3/8" (5-10 mm) midway between pulleys.

FILTERS & CLEANERS

Filter or Cleaner	Service Interval (Miles)
Oil Filter	Replace every 6,000
Air Cleaner	Clean every 6,000 Replace every 12,500
Fuel Filter	Replace every 12,500
Main Fuel Filter (Electric Pump)	Replace every 37,500

CAPACITIES

Application	Quantity
Crankcase (Includes Filter)	4.5 qts.
Cooling System (Includes Heater)	7.4 qts.
Man. Trans.	2.0 pts.
Auto. Trans. (Includes Oil Cooler)	6.4 qts.
Auto. Trans. (Refill)	2.1 qts.
Rear Axle	2.0 pts.
Fuel Tank	①16.0 gals.

① – Includes 2 gal. in reserve.

TUNE-UP

530i
630CSi

ENGINE IDENTIFICATION

The engine number for the 1986 cc 6-cylinder, single overhead camshaft engine is located at the rear of the cylinder block above the starter (near left side).

MODEL IDENTIFICATION

VEHICLE IDENTIFICATION NUMBER

Number is stamped on vehicle identification plate, which is located on the support plate of the right-hand wheel arch at the rear of the engine compartment.

COMPRESSION PRESSURE

With battery fully charged, engine at normal operating temperature, throttle fully open and engine at cranking speed, compression pressure should be as follows:

Good	Above 156 psi (11 kg/cm²)
Normal	142-156 psi (10-11 kg/cm²)
Poor	Below 142 psi (10 kg/cm²)

VALVE TAPPET CLEARANCE

With engine either cold or at normal operating temperature, loosen nut on rocker arm and adjust position of eccentric cam to obtain proper clearance. Adjust valves in firing order sequence at TDC of compression stroke. Measure clearance with feeler gauge between rocker arm eccentric and valve stem.

Adjust Cylinder at Top Dead Center	When Valves Of Cylinder Overlap
No. 1	No. 6
No. 5	No. 2
No. 3	No. 4
No. 6	No. 1
No. 2	No. 5
No. 4	No. 3

Valve Clearance Specifications

Application	Clearance In. (mm)
Cold	
Intake & Exhaust	.010-.012 (.25-.30)
Warm	
Intake & Exhaust	.012-.014 (.30-.35)

VALVE ARRANGEMENT

Left Side — All Intake.
Right Side — All Exhaust.

SPARK PLUGS

Gap	.024-.028" (.6-.7mm)
Torque	18-22 ft. lbs. (2.5-3.0 mkg)

Spark Plug Type

Application	Bosch	Champion
All Models	W 145 T30	N-10Y

HIGH TENSION WIRE RESISTANCE

Carefully remove ends of wire from spark plug and distributor. Using an ohmmeter, check resistance of wire while gently twisting wire. If resistance is not to specification, or fluctuates from infinity to any value, replace wire.

Resistance (Ohms) Per Wire

Application	Resistance
All Models	25,000-30,000

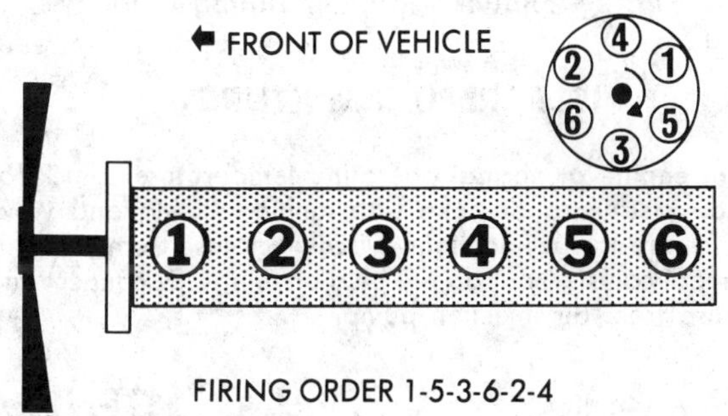

Fig. 1 Firing Order and Distributor Rotation

DISTRIBUTOR

Point Gap	.014-.016" (.35-.40 mm)
Cam Angle	35-41°
Breaker Arm Spring Tension	18-22 oz. (500-630 g)
Condenser Capacity	
530i	.15-.20 mfd.
630CSi	.18-.22 mfd.

IGNITION TIMING

1) With engine at normal operating temperature, disconnect vacuum hoses and increase engine RPM to specification. Steel ball embedded in flywheel (long pin on vehicles with automatic transmission) should line up with pointer attached to clutch housing.

2) Loosen distributor clamp, turn distributor until proper timing is achieved, and tighten clamp. Recheck timing and engine speed. Connect vacuum hoses and set idle speed to 950 RPM. Recheck timing with vacuum hose connected. "OT" mark on flywheel (short pin on vehicle with automatic transmission) should then be visible in sight hole in clutch housing.

Ignition Timing Specifications

Application	RPM	Dynamic Timing
California	2700±50	22° BTDC
Federal	1700±50	22° BTDC

TUNE-UP (Cont.)

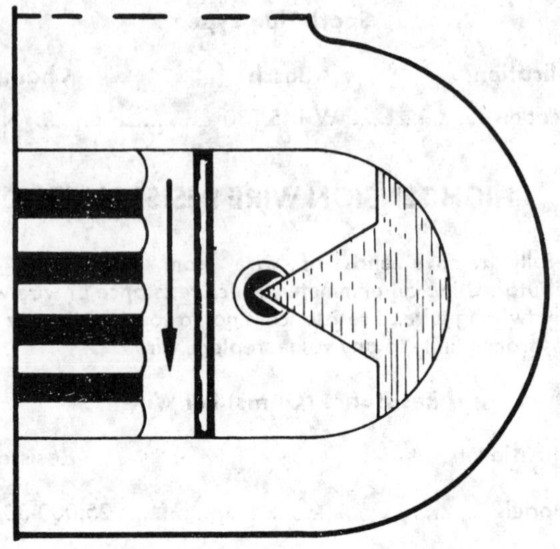

Fig. 2 Showing Ignition Timing Marks

IDLE SPEED & MIXTURE

1) With engine at normal operating temperature, check for clean air cleaner and make sure ignition timing and valve clearance are to specifications. Disconnect hose from collector to charcoal canister, but do not plug openings. Disconnect and plug hose from air injection pump.

2) Adjust engine idle speed to specified RPM by means of the adjusting screw located below throttle butterfly switch.

3) Remove plug from air flow sensor. Adjust idle air screw in air flow sensor until specified CO level is obtained. Reinstall air flow sensor plug. Check idle speed RPM and CO level and repeat adjustment procedures, if necessary. Reconnect all hoses when readings are to specifications.

Idle Speed (RPM) & CO Level (%)

Application	Idle RPM	CO %
All Models	950±100	1.5-3.0

FUEL PUMP PRESSURE & VOLUME

Pressure (At Idle)
- 530 i .... 32.3-38.3 psi (2.3-2.7 kg/cm²)
- 630CSi .... 43 psi (3.0 kg/cm²)

Volume
- 530i .... 29 gals. in 1 hr. (1.9 pts. in 30 sec.)
- 630CSi .... 105 qts. in 1 hr. (1.75 pts. in 30 sec.)

EMISSION CONTROL SYSTEMS

See Mitchell Manuals' Emission Control Manual.

GENERAL SERVICING

IGNITION

DISTRIBUTOR

All models are equipped with Bosch single point distributors.

Other Data & Specifications – *See Tune-Up & Bosch Distributors in ELECTRICAL Section.*

IGNITION COIL

Resistance	Ohms at 68°F (20°C)
Primary	1.7-2.1

FUEL SYSTEMS

FUEL INJECTION

All models are equipped with Bosch Electronic Fuel Injection System.

Other Data & Specifications – *See Tune-Up and Bosch Electronic Fuel Injection in FUEL SYSTEMS Section.*

ELECTRICAL

BATTERY

12 Volt – Negative Ground.

Application	Amp. Hr. Rating
All Models	55

STARTER

All models are equipped with Bosch Starters.

Other Data & Specifications – *See Bosch Starters in ELECTRICAL Section.*

ALTERNATOR

Application	Rated Amp. Output
530i	55
630CSi	65

Other Data & Specifications – *See Bosch Alternators & Regulators in ELECTRICAL Section.*

ALTERNATOR REGULATOR

All models are equipped with Bosch Alternator Regulators with an operating voltage of 13.5-14.2 volts at 68°F (20°C).

Other Data & Specifications – *See Bosch Alternators & Regulators in ELECTRICAL Section.*

GENERAL SERVICING (Cont.)

BELT ADJUSTMENT

Adjust tension until belt depresses .2-.4" (5-10 mm) midway between pulleys.

FILTERS & CLEANERS

Filter or Cleaner	Service Interval (Miles)
Oil Filter	Replace every 6,000
Air Cleaner	Clean every 6,000
	Replace every 12,500
Fuel Pump Filter	Clean every 12,500
Mesh Fuel Filter (In Tank)	Replace every 37,500

CAPACITIES

Application	Quantity
Crankcase (Includes Filter)	6.0 qts.
Cooling System (Includes Heater)	12.7 qts.
Man. Trans.	2.3 pts.
Auto. Trans. (Refill)	2.1 qts.
Rear Axle	3.1 pts.
Fuel Tank	
530i	16.4 gals.
630CSi	①17.0 gals.

① — 2 gals. in reserve.

1977 Capri 4 Tune-Up

TUNE-UP

Capri 2300 cc

ENGINE IDENTIFICATION

Engine code designation is located on bottom line of vehicle identification plate which is riveted to top of right fender apron. Engine code for 2300 cc engine is "YA".

MODEL IDENTIFICATION

VEHICLE IDENTIFICATION NUMBER

Vehicle Identification Number is located on vehicle identification plate which is riveted to top of right fender apron. Number is also stamped on driver's side windshield pillar and can be observed through windshield. Third and fourth digits of number identify model type. Code for Capri is "EC".

COMPRESSION PRESSURE

Check compression pressure with battery fully charged and engine at normal operating temperature. Remove all spark plugs and set carburetor throttle plates in wide open position. Crank engine at least five compression strokes and note highest reading cylinder. Lowest reading cylinder must be within 75% of highest reading cylinder.

HYDRAULIC LASH ADJUSTERS

NOTE — *Lash adjustment is not a part of regular maintenance, but should be performed after cylinder head overhaul.*

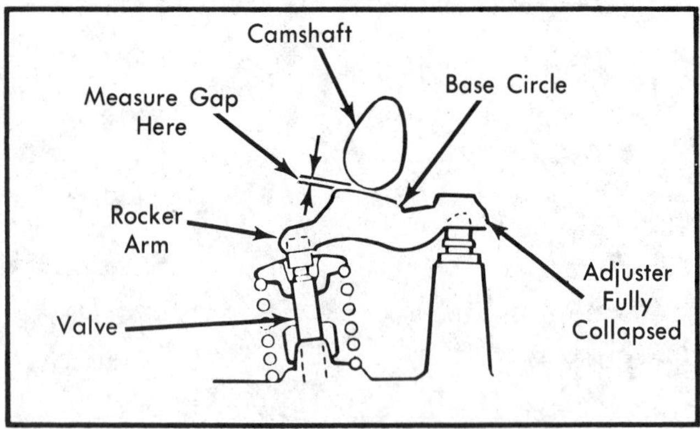

Fig. 1 Checking Hydraulic Lash Adjustment

To check valve clearance, rotate camshaft until cam lobe of valve to be checked is up. Position suitable valve spring compressor tool (T74P-6565-B) under camshaft and over rocker arm end of hydraulic lash adjuster. Compress lash adjuster to fully collapsed position and insert feeler gauge (from valve side) between cam lobe and rocker arm. If clearance is not within specifications, inspect rocker arm, valve spring, camshaft and lash adjuster for wear and replace worn part(s).

Application	Clearance
Base of Lobe-to-Rocker Arm	.035-.055" (0.9-1.4 mm)
Leak-down Rate	2-8 Seconds

VALVE ARRANGEMENT

E-I-E-I-E-I-E-I (front to rear).

SPARK PLUGS

Gap	.034" (.86 mm)
Torque	10-15 ft. lbs. (1.4-2.1 mkg)

Spark Plug Type

Application	Autolite No.
2300 cc	AGRF-52

HIGH TENSION WIRE RESISTANCE

Carefully remove high tension wires from spark plugs and distributor cap. Using an ohmmeter, check high tension wire resistance while gently twisting wires. If resistance is not to specifications, or fluctuates from infinity to any value, replace high tension wire(s).

Resistance (Ohms) Per Wire

Application	Ohms
All Models	25,000-30,000

DISTRIBUTOR

All models are equipped with Breakerless Ignition System and no adjustments are required.

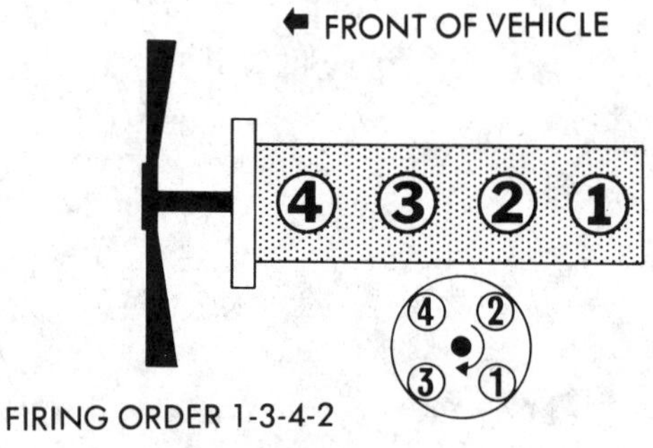

Fig. 2 Firing Order and Distributor Rotation

IGNITION TIMING

Check or adjust ignition timing using a timing light or suitable monolithic timing equipment. Set timing with engine at normal operating temperature, idle speed reduced to 600 RPM and distributor vacuum line disconnected and plugged.

Ignition Timing Specifications

Application	Timing
All	Refer To Tune-Up Decal

TUNE-UP (Cont.)

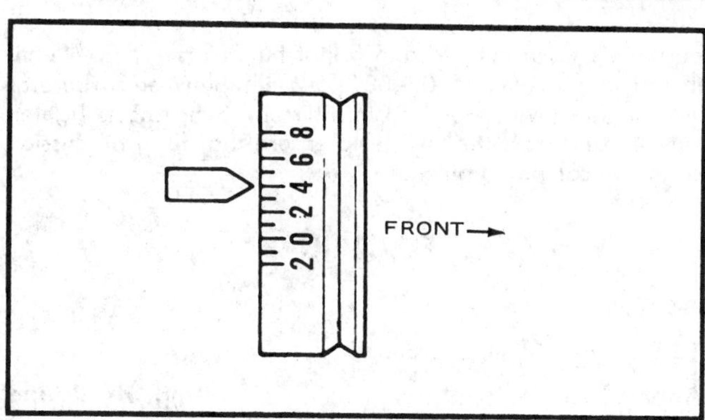

Fig. 3 Ignition Timing Mark Location

HOT (SLOW) IDLE RPM

Preparation – 1) With air cleaner removed and vacuum hoses plugged, check timing and adjust if required, then reconnect distributor vacuum advance hose.

2) Disconnect and plug EGR valve vacuum hose. Remove spark delay valve (if equipped) and route primary vacuum hose directly to distributor vacuum advance. Leave distributor retard connected (if equipped).

3) Place air conditioning in "OFF" position. Check and adjust fast idle RPM. Place manual transmission in neutral or automatic transmission in "D". Adjust idle as follows:

Models Without Throttle Stop Solenoid – Adjust curb idle speed screw in or out to obtain specified idle speed RPM. NOTE – *See engine compartment tune-up decal for specifications.*

Models With Throttle Stop Solenoid – With solenoid energized and plunger extended, adjust solenoid plunger contact screw to obtain higher specified RPM. Collapse and hold plunger into solenoid and adjust lower idle RPM (solenoid de-energized) using screw located on throttle body. Open throttle and allow plunger to extend.

NOTE – *See engine compartment tune-up decal for specifications.*

IDLE MIXTURE

ARTIFICIAL ENRICHMENT METHOD

Preparations – 1) With engine at normal operating temperature and idle speed correct, disconnect air cleaner-to-vapor canister hose. If applicable, disconnect PCV-to-air cleaner hose and cap air cleaner connection. Disconnect thermactor by-pass valve air hose at check valve.

NOTE – *When taking readings, air cleaner must be in place. Each time idle speed is adjusted, thermactor must be connected.*

2) Plug a suitable adjusting tool with bottled gas (Rotunda T75L-9600-A) into air cleaner at vapor canister hose nipple. Place manual transmission in neutral or automatic transmission in "D".

3) With engine at idle speed, richen mixture (using bottled gas) to obtain maximum RPM. Continue to richen mixture until RPM drops.

NOTE – *If speed does not drop with valve fully open, check bottle gas supply.*

Correct RPM Gain – If RPM gain is within specification given on engine compartment tune-up decal, remove tool and reconnect all hoses. Recheck idle speed and mixture settings.

Excessive RPM Gain – If RPM gain was higher than specified, richen mixture screw (without injecting gas) until RPM increase is equal to the excess increase. *EXAMPLE – If increase was 80 RPM and desired increase was 50 RPM, adjust mixture screw rich for 30 RPM increase.* Remove limiter cap if necessary to obtain excess RPM. Readjust idle speed after each mixture screw adjustment.

Insufficient RPM Gain – If speed increase was lower than specified, lean mixture screw (without injecting gas) until RPM decrease is equal to the RPM lag. *EXAMPLE – If increase was zero RPM and desired increase was 20 RPM, adjust mixture screw lean for a 20 RPM loss.* Readjust idle speed after each mixture screw adjustment.

COLD (FAST) IDLE RPM

Set fast idle with engine at normal operating temperature, ignition timing set to specifications and EGR vacuum hose disconnected and plugged. Remove spark delay valve (if equipped) and route primary vacuum hose directly to distributor vacuum advance. Place air conditioning in "OFF" position and transmission neutral. Set throttle so fast idle adjusting screw contacts kickdown step of choke cam, and adjust screw to obtain specified RPM.

Fast Idle Specification

Application	RPM
2300 cc	1800

AUTOMATIC CHOKE SETTING

Application	Setting
All	Refer To Tune-Up Decal

FUEL PUMP PRESSURE & VOLUME

Make all tests of the mechanical diaphragm type fuel pump at normal operating temperature and at idle speed with transmission in neutral. When making pressure test, pinch off pump-to-tank fuel return line.

Pressure	3.5-5.5 psi (.25-.39 kg/cm^2)
Volume (Minimum)	1 pt. in 25 sec.

EMISSION CONTROL SYSTEMS

See Mitchell Manuals' Emission Control Manual.

1977 Capri 4 Tune-Up

GENERAL SERVICING

IGNITION

DISTRIBUTOR

All models use Bosch Breakerless Ignition System.

Other Data & Specifications — *See Tune-Up and Bosch Distributors in ELECTRICAL Section.*

IGNITION COIL

Resistance

Primary at 68° F (20° C) .... 1.3-1.6 ohms
Secondary at 68° F (20° C) .... 7000-9300 ohms
Resistor Wire at 68° F (20° C) .... 1.3-1.6 ohms

FUEL SYSTEM

CARBURETOR

Application	Model
2300 cc 2-Bbl	Motorcraft 5200

Other Data & Specifications — *See Tune-Up and Motorcraft Carburetors in FUEL SYSTEMS Section.*

ACCELERATOR & KICKDOWN LINKAGE ADJUSTMENT

1) To adjust accelerator linkage, depress and hold accelerator pedal to full throttle position, then remove air cleaner. Turn throttle adjusting nut counterclockwise until carburetor is just in wide open throttle position. Operate accelerator pedal several times to ensure full throttle can be obtained. Install air cleaner.

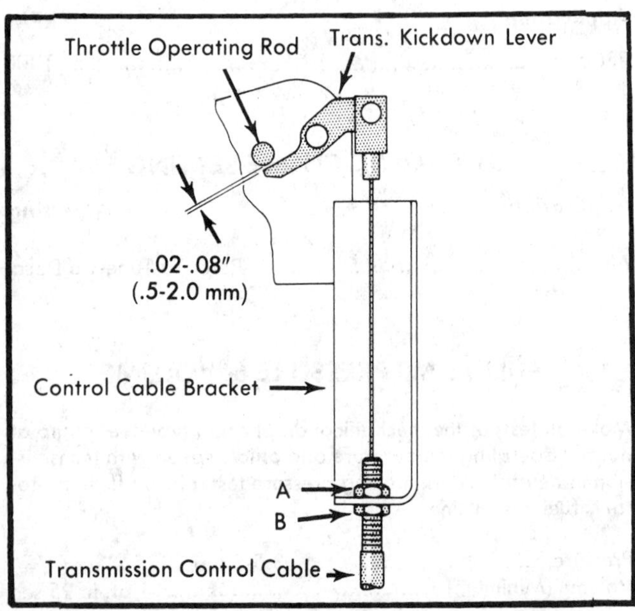

Fig. 4 Adjusting Accelerator Throttle Cable

2) To adjust kickdown cable on vehicles with automatic transmission, depress and hold accelerator pedal in wide open throttle position, then place transmission lever in full kickdown position. Loosen nut "A" and adjust nut "B" *(see Fig. 4)* until there is a clearance of .02-.08" (.5-2 mm) between carburetor linkage kickdown lever and throttle operating shaft. Tighten nut "A" and operate linkage to ensure that full transmission kickdown can be obtained.

ELECTRICAL

BATTERY

12 Volt — Negative Ground.

Application	Amp. Hr. Rating
Man. Trans.	55
Auto Trans.	66

Battery Location — Engine compartment.

STARTER

Bosch Pre-Engaged Type.

Engine Cranking Speed .... 180 RPM
Starter Current Draw.................................. 100-130 Amps.

Other Data & Specifications — *See Bosch Starters in ELECTRICAL Section.*

ALTERNATOR

Application	Rated Amp. Output
With A/C	35
Without A/C	55

Other Data & Specifications — *See Bosch Alternators & Regulators in ELECTRICAL Section.*

ALTERNATOR REGULATOR

Bosch — Non Adjustable; externally mounted.

Operating Voltage 13.7-14.4

Other Data & Specifications — *See Bosch Alternators & Regulators in ELECTRICAL Section.*

ENGINE

INTAKE MANIFOLD TIGHTENING

2300 cc — Check intake manifold bolts in two steps for 14-21 ft. lbs. (1.9-2.9 mkg) torque.

BELT ADJUSTMENT

Tension (Lbs.) Using Strand Tension Gauge

Application	New Belt	①Used Belt
¼" Belt	80	60
⅜, 15/32 & ½" Belt	140	110

① — Any belt operated for more than 10 minutes is considered used.

GENERAL SERVICING (Cont.)

FILTERS & CLEANERS

NOTE — *Refer to Vehicle Emission Control Information decal in engine compartment for maintenance schedule code.*

Filter or Cleaner	"A"	"B"
Oil Filter	10,000	10,000
Air Cleaner	20,000	30,000
Crankcase Filter	30,000	30,000
PCV Valve	20,000	30,000
Fuel Filter	①20,000	①15,000

① — Replace only one time.

CAPACITIES

Application	Quantity
Crankcase (Includes Filter)	4.5 qts.
Cooling System	8.5 qts.
Man. Trans. (SAE 80 E.P.)	2.8 pts.
Auto. Trans. (ESW-M2C33-F) Refill	8 qts.
Rear Axle (ESW-M2C105-A)	2.3 pts.
Fuel Tank	11.8 gals.

1977 Capri V6 Tune-Up

TUNE-UP

Capri 2800 cc

ENGINE IDENTIFICATION

Engine code designation is located on bottom line of vehicle identification plate which is riveted to top of right fender apron. Engine code for 2800cc engine is "PX".

MODEL IDENTIFICATION

VEHICLE IDENTIFICATION NUMBER

Identification number is located on vehicle identification plate which is riveted to top of right fender apron. Number is also stamped on drivers side windshield pillar. Third and fourth digits of number identify model type. Code for Capri is "EC".

COMPRESSION PRESSURE

Check compression pressure with battery fully charged and engine at normal operating temperature. Remove all spark plugs and set carburetor throttle plates in wide open position. Crank engine at least five compression strokes and note highest reading cylinder. Lowest reading cylinder must be within 75% of highest cylinder.

VALVE CLEARANCE

Adjust valve clearance with engine at normal operating temperature and idling. Set clearance using a step-type feeler gauge only (go and no go).

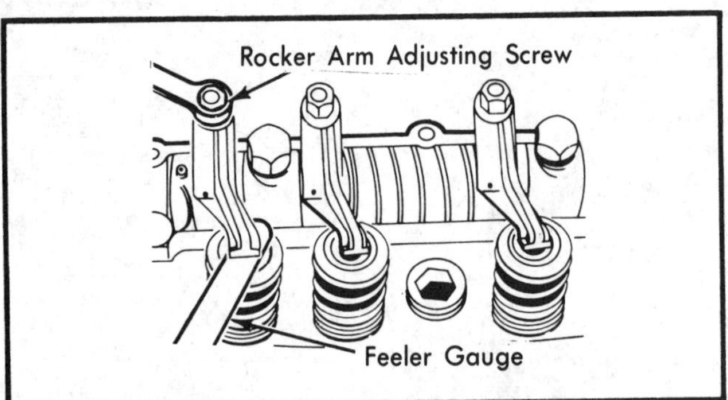

Fig. 1 Adjusting Valve Clearance

To adjust, turn adjusting screw until correct clearance is obtained. Adjusting screws are self-locking. Adjust valves in the following sequence, turning camshaft after adjusting each cylinder.

Valves Open	①Adjust Valves
No. 5 Cylinder	No. 1 Cylinder
No. 3 Cylinder	No. 4 Cylinder
No. 6 Cylinder	No. 2 Cylinder
No. 1 Cylinder	No. 5 Cylinder
No. 4 Cylinder	No. 3 Cylinder
No. 2 Cylinder	No. 6 Cylinder

① — If turned by hand from crankshaft.

Application	Clearance
Intake	.014" (.36mm)
Exhaust	.016" (.41mm)

VALVE ARRANGEMENT

I-E-E-I-E-I (Left bank, front to rear).
I-E-I-E-E-I (Right bank, front to rear).

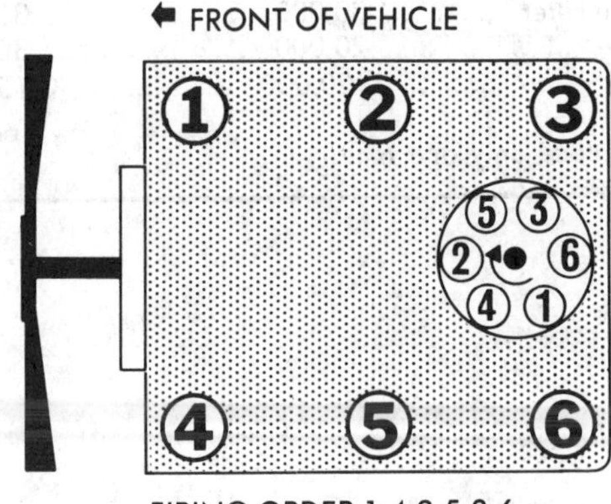

Fig. 2 Firing Order and Distributor Rotation

SPARK PLUGS

Gap	Refer To Tune-Up Decal
Torque	15-20 ft. lbs. (2.1-2.8 mkg)

Spark Plug Type

Application	Autolite No.
All	AGR-42

HIGH TENSION WIRE RESISTANCE

Carefully remove ends of wire from spark plug and distributor. Using an ohmmeter, check resistance of wire while gently twisting wire. If resistance is not to specification, or fluctuates from infinity to any value, replace wire.

Resistance (Ohms) Per Wire

Application	Resistance
All Models	25,000-30,000

DISTRIBUTOR

All models are equipped with Breakerless Ignition System and no adjustments are required.

TUNE-UP (Cont.)

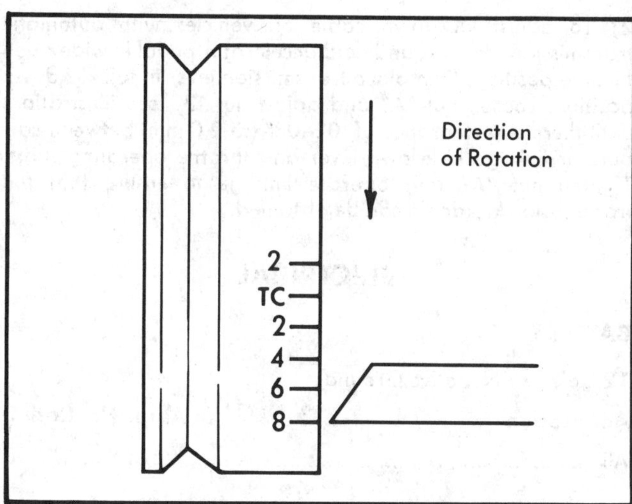

Fig. 3 Showing Ignition Timing Marks

IGNITION TIMING

Check or adjust ignition timing using a timing light or suitable monolithic timing equipment. Set timing with engine at normal operating temperature, idle speed reduced to 600 RPM and distributor vacuum lines disconnected and plugged.

Ignition Timing Specifications

Application	Timing
All	Refer To Tune-Up Decal

HOT (SLOW) IDLE RPM

1) Remove air cleaner, then disconnect and plug vacuum hoses. Check timing and adjust if necessary, then reconnect distributor vacuum advance hose.

2) Disconnect and plug EGR valve vacuum hose. Remove spark delay valve (if equipped) and route primary vacuum hose directly to distributor vacuum advance. Leave distributor retard hose connected.

3) Place air conditioning in "OFF" position. Check and adjust fast idle RPM, place transmission in neutral, then collapse and hold plunger in throttle stop solenoid. Adjust lower (solenoid de-energized) idle RPM using screw located on throttle body.

NOTE — *See engine compartment tune-up decal for specifications.*

4) Open throttle and allow plunger to extend. Place automatic transmission in "D", then adjust solenoid plunger contact screw to obtain higher (solenoid energized) idle RPM.

NOTE — *See engine compartment tune-up decal for specifications.*

IDLE MIXTURE

ARTIFICIAL ENRICHMENT METHOD

1) With engine at normal operating temperature and idle speed correct, disconnect air cleaner-to-vapor canister hose. If applicable, disconnect PCV-to-air cleaner hose, and cap air cleaner connection. Disconnect thermactor by-pass valve air hose at check valve.

2) Plug suitable idle adjusting tool with bottled gas (Rotunda T75L-9600-A) into air cleaner at vapor canister hose nipple. Place manual transmission in neutral or automatic transmission in "D".

NOTE — *When taking readings, air cleaner must be in place. Each time idle speed is adjusted, thermactor must be connected.*

3) With engine at idle speed, richen mixture (using bottled gas) to obtain maximum RPM. Continue to richen mixture until RPM drops.

NOTE — *If RPM does not drop, check bottle gas supply.*

Correct RPM Gain — If RPM gain is within specifications shown on engine compartment tune-up decal, remove tool and reconnect all hoses. Recheck idle speed and mixture settings.

Excessive RPM Gain — If RPM gain was higher than specified, richen mixture screw (without injecting gas) until RPM increase is equal to excess increase. *EXAMPLE — If increase was 80 RPM and desired increase was 50 RPM, adjust mixture screw rich for 30 RPM increase.* Remove limiter cap if necessary to obtain excess RPM. Readjust idle speed after each mixture screw adjustment.

Insufficient RPM Gain — If speed increase was lower than specified, lean mixture screw (without injecting gas) until RPM decrease is equal to RPM lag. *EXAMPLE — If increase was zero RPM and desired increase was 20 RPM, adjust mixture screw lean for a 20 RPM loss.* Readjust idle speed after each mixture screw adjustment.

COLD (FAST) IDLE RPM

Set fast idle with engine at normal operating temperature, ignition timing set to specifications and EGR vacuum hose disconnected and plugged. Remove spark delay valve (if equipped) and route primary vacuum hose directly to vacuum advance unit on distributor. Place air conditioning in "OFF" position and transmission in neutral. Set throttle so fast idle adjusting screw contacts kickdown step of choke cam, and adjust screw to obtain specified fast idle RPM.

Fast Idle RPM

Application	RPM
All	1600

AUTOMATIC CHOKE SETTING

Application	Setting
All	Refer To Tune-Up Decal

FUEL PUMP PRESSURE & VOLUME

Check the mechanical diaphragm type fuel pump at idle RPM with engine at normal operating temperature and transmission in neutral.

Pressure	3.5-5.5 psi (.25-.39 kg/cm^2)
Volume	1 pint in 25 seconds.

EMISSION CONTROL SYSTEMS

See Mitchell Manuals' Emission Control Manual.

1977 Capri V6 Tune-Up

GENERAL SERVICING

IGNITION

DISTRIBUTOR

All models use Bosch Breakerless Ignition System.

Other Data & Specifications – *See Tune-Up and Bosch Distributors in ELECTRICAL Section.*

IGNITION COIL

Resistance

Primary at 68° F (20° C) .... 1.3-1.6 ohms
Secondary at 68° F (20° C) .... 7000-9300 ohms
Resistor Wire at 68° F (20° C) .... 1.3-1.6 ohms

FUEL SYSTEMS

CARBURETOR

Application	Model
2800 cc	Motorcraft 2150

Other Data & Specifications – *See Tune-Up and Motorcraft Carburetors in FUEL SYSTEMS Section.*

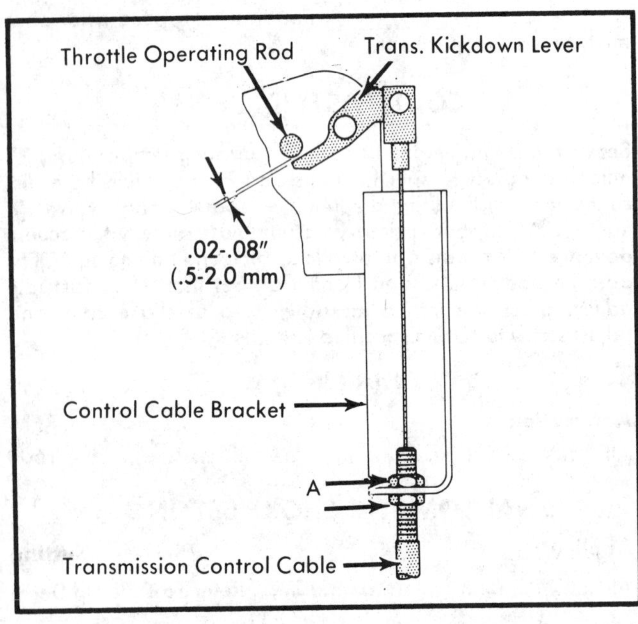

Fig. 4 Adjusting Accelerator Cable

ACCELERATOR & KICKDOWN LINKAGE ADJUSTMENT

1) To adjust accelerator linkage, depress and hold accelerator pedal to full throttle position, then remove air cleaner. Turn throttle adjusting nut counterclockwise until carburetor is just in wide open throttle position. Operate accelerator pedal several times to ensure full throttle can be obtained. Install air cleaner.

2) To adjust kickdown cable on vehicles with automatic transmission, depress and hold accelerator pedal in wide open throttle position, then place transmission lever in full kickdown position. Loosen nut "A" and adjust nut "B" (see illustration) until there is a clearance of .02-.08" (.5-2.0 mm) between carburetor linkage kickdown lever and throttle operating shaft. Tighten nut "A" and operate linkage to ensure that full transmission kickdown can be obtained.

ELECTRICAL

BATTERY

12 Volt – Negative Ground.

Application	Amp. Hr. Rating
All	66

Battery Location – In engine compartment.

STARTER

Bosch Pre-Engaged Type.

Engine Cranking Speed .... 180 RPM
Starter Current Draw .... 100-130 Amps.

Other Data & Specifications – *See Bosch Starters in ELECTRICAL Section.*

ALTERNATOR

Application	Rated Amp. Output
With A/C	35
Without A/C	55

Other Data & Specifications – *See Bosch Alternators & Regulators in ELECTRICAL Section.*

ALTERNATOR REGULATOR

Bosch – Non-Adjustable; externally mounted.

Operating Voltage 13.7-14.4

Other Data & Specifications – *See Bosch Alternators & Regulators in ELECTRICAL Section.*

ENGINE

INTAKE MANIFOLD TIGHTENING

Tighten intake manifold-to-cylinder head bolts in four steps to a final torque of 15-18 ft. lbs. (2.1-2.5 mkg). Tighten intake manifold-to-cylinder head stud nuts to 10-12 ft. lbs. (1.4-1.7 mkg).

GENERAL SERVICING (Cont.)

CAPACITIES

Application	Quantity
Crankcase (Includes Filter)	5.0 qts.
Cooling System	8.5 qts.
Man. Trans. (SAE 80 E.P.)	2.8 pts.
Auto. Trans. (Refill - ESW-M2C33-F)	8.0 qts.
Rear Axle (ESW-M2C105-A)	2.3 pts.
Fuel Tank	11.8 gals.

BELT ADJUSTMENT

Tension (Lbs.) Using Strand Tension Gauge

Application	New Belt	① Used Belt
¼" Belt	80	60
⅜, 5/32, & ½" Belt	140	110

① — Any belt operated for more than 10 minutes is considered used.

FILTERS & CLEANERS

NOTE — *Refer to Vehicle Emission Control Information decal in engine compartment for maintenance schedule code.*

Filter or Cleaner	Replacement Interval (Miles) Per Maintenance Schedule "A"	"B"
Oil Filter	10,000	10,000
Air Cleaner	20,000	30,000
Crankcase Filter	30,000	30,000
PCV Valve	20,000	30,000
Fuel Filter	①20,000	①15,000

① — Replace only one time.

TUNE-UP

Courier

ENGINE IDENTIFICATION

The engine identification number is stamped on model identification plate which is attached to body at right rear corner of engine compartment.

MODEL IDENTIFICATION

VEHICLE IDENTIFICATION NUMBER

Vehicle identification number is stamped on model identification plate which is attached to body at right rear corner of engine compartment.

COMPRESSION PRESSURE

Check compression pressure with engine at normal operating temperature, all spark plugs removed, throttle valve wide open and engine at cranking speed. Compression pressure is within specifications if lowest reading cylinder is within 75% of highest.

VALVE TAPPET CLEARANCE

1800 cc	Clearance
Intake and Exhaust (Hot)	.012"(.30 mm)

HYDRAULIC LASH ADJUSTERS

2300 cc	Clearance
Desired Clearance	①.040-.050"(1.0-1.3 mm)
Allowable Clearance	①.035-.055"(0.9-1.4 mm)

① — Measured between base circle of cam lobe and cam follower, with adjuster collapsed. Leakdown rate is 2-8 seconds.

VALVE ARRANGEMENT

1800 cc
Right Side — All Exhaust
Left Side — All Intake
2300 cc — E-I-E-I-E-I-E-I

SPARK PLUGS

Gap .029-.033" (.7-.8mm)
Torque 10-16 ft. lbs.(1.4-2.2 mkg)

Spark Plug Type

Application	Autolite	NGK
1800 cc	.....	BPR-6ES
2300 cc	AGRF 52	.....

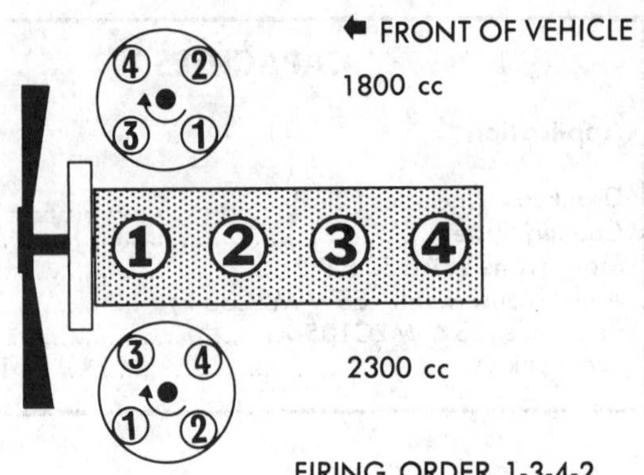

Fig. 1 Distributor Rotation and Firing Order

DISTRIBUTOR ①

1800 cc
Point Gap .018-.022"(.45-.55 mm)
Cam Angle 49-55°
Breaker Arm Spring Tension 17-23 ozs.(525-652 g)
Condenser Capacity .20-.24 mfd
2300 cc
Armature Tooth-to-Magnetic Pickup Gap .008-.024"(0.2-0.6 mm)

① — 1800 cc engine has breaker point type distributor; 2300 cc engine has magnetic pulse type.

HIGH TENSION WIRE RESISTANCE

Carefully remove ends of wire from spark plug and distributor. Using an ohmmeter, check resistance of wire while gently twisting wire. If resistance is not to specification, or fluctuates from infinity to any value, replace wire.

Resistance (Ohms) Per Wire

Application	Resistance
All Models	①25,000-30,000

① — Resistance should not exceed 1000 ohms per inch of wire.

IGNITION TIMING

Check or adjust ignition timing with engine at normal operating temperature, at correct idle speed, and with distributor vacuum advance line disconnected and plugged.

Ignition Timing Specifications

Application	Timing
1800 cc	①5° BTDC
2300 cc	①6° BTDC

① — ±1°

TUNE-UP (Cont.)

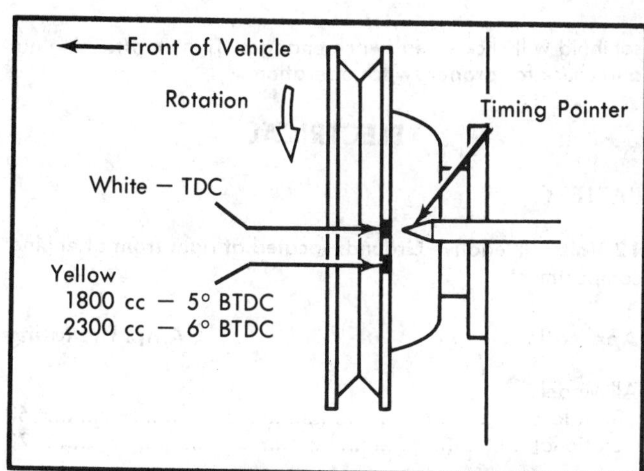

Fig. 2 Ignition Timing Mark Locations

HOT (SLOW) IDLE RPM

Adjust idle speed and CO level with engine at normal operating temperature. Connect tachometer and exhaust gas analyzer to vehicle. Set curb idle speed to specifications by turning curb idle adjusting screw. Adjust idle CO level to specifications by turning idle mixture adjusting screw in or out until correct CO level is obtained at specified idle speed RPM.

See Vehicle Emission Control Label on right hand underside of hood for exact specifications.

Idle Speed (RPM) & CO Level (%)

Application	RPM	CO%
1800 cc	650-750	1.5-2.5
2300 cc		
Man.Trans.	750-850	3.5-4.5
Auto. Trans.	650-750	3.5-4.5

COLD (FAST) IDLE RPM

With choke plate fully closed, measure clearance between primary throttle plate and wall of throttle bore. If clearance is not within specifications, bend fast idle lever where it contacts throttle lever tang until proper clearance is obtained.

Fast Idle Specifications

Application	Clearance
Federal	.071″ (1.8 mm)
Calif.	.067″ (1.7 mm)

DASH POT ADJUSTMENT

Check engine idle speed and carburetor air-fuel mixture. With engine at operating temperature and air cleaner removed, attach tachometer to engine.

Loosen dash pot lock nut. See *Fig. 3.* Move throttle lever and hold in place to maintain specified engine speed. Turn dash pot until dash pot rod contacts throttle lever. Release throttle lever and tighten lock nut. Move throttle lever until it contacts dash pot rod and check engine speed again. Repeat adjustment if necessary.

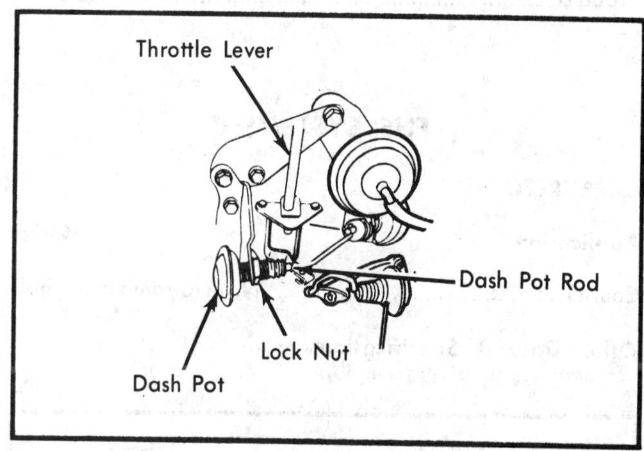

Fig. 3 Adjusting Dash Pot

Engine Speed for Dash Pot Adjustment

Application	RPM
Federal	2500±100
Calif.	2200±100

FUEL PUMP PRESSURE & VOLUME

Pressure (At Idle) .... 2.8-3.6 psi (.20-.25 kg/cm²)
Volume (At Idle) .... 2 pts. (950 cc)/min.

EMISSION CONTROL SYSTEMS

See Mitchell Manuals' Emission Control Manual.

GENERAL SERVICING

IGNITION

DISTRIBUTOR

All models have Mitsubishi distributors. The 1800 cc uses a single point distributor; the 2300 cc a magnetic pulse distributor.

Other Data & Specifications — *See Mitsubishi Distributors in ELECTRICAL Section.*

GENERAL SERVICING (Cont.)

IGNITION COIL

Resistance

Primary	
1800 cc	1.42 ohms
2300 cc	.81-.99 ohms
Secondary	
1800 cc	8610 ohms
2300 cc	6800-9200 ohms
Magnetic Pickup Coil	
2300 cc	760-840 ohms
Ballast Resistor	
1800 cc	1.6 ohms

FUEL SYSTEMS

CARBURETORS

Application	Model
Courier	Nikki (Stromberg) 2-Bbl.

Other Data & Specifications – *See Tune-Up and Nikki (Stromberg) carburetors in FUEL SYSTEMS section.*

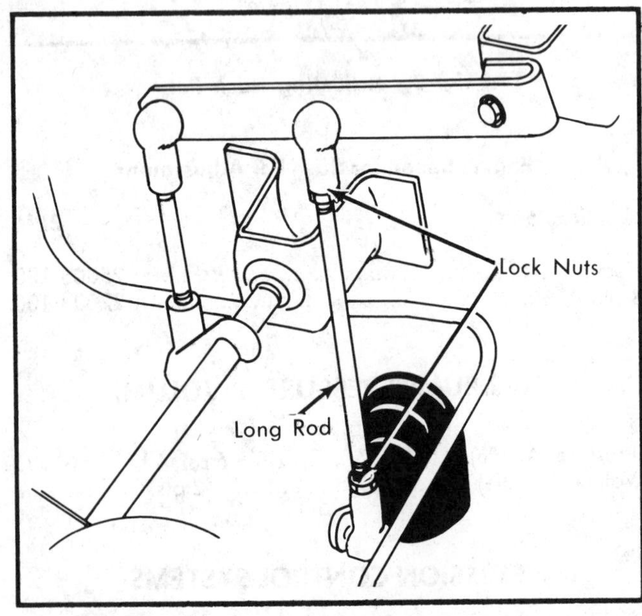

Fig. 4 Throttle Linkage Adjustment Points

THROTTLE LINKAGE ADJUSTMENT

To adjust throttle linkage, loosen lock nuts on longer linkage rod (*see Fig. 4*) and rotate both rods in their sockets until proper accelerator travel, from idle to wide open throttle, is achieved. Tighten lock nuts.

KICK-DOWN SWITCH ADJUSTMENT

Turn ignition switch to "ON" position. Loosen kick-down switch attaching nut and adjust switch to engage when accelerator pedal is between ⅞ and 15/16 of full pedal travel. Down-shift solenoid will click when switch engages. Tighten attaching nut and check for proper switch operation.

ELECTRICAL

BATTERY

12 Volt – Negative Ground. Located at right front of engine compartment.

Application	Amp. Hr. Rating
All Models	
Standard	60
Optional	70

STARTER

Nippondenso solenoid-actuated with overrunning clutch. The starter on 2300 cc engine rotates in opposite direction of starter for 1800 cc engine.

Free Speed Voltage	11 at 5000 RPM
Free Speed Amperage	50 at 5000 RPM

Other Data & Specifications – *See Nippondenso Starters in ELECTRICAL Section.*

ALTERNATOR

Application	Rated Amp. Output
Courier	35

Other Data & Specifications – *See Mitsubishi Alternators and Regulators in ELECTRICAL Section.*

ALTERNATOR REGULATOR

Mitsubishi – Non-adjustable, externally mounted.

Other Data & Specifications – *See Mitsubishi Alternators and Regulators in ELECTRICAL Section.*

ENGINE

INTAKE MANIFOLD TIGHTENING

Tighten intake and exhaust manifold-to-cylinder head bolts, starting at center and working out.

Manifold Torque Specifications

Application	Ft. Lbs. (mkg)
1800 cc	
Intake	13.5-19 (1.9-2.6)
Exhaust	16-21 (2.2-2.9)
2300 cc	
Intake	14-21 (1.9-2.9)
Exhaust	16-23 (2.2-3.2)

GENERAL SERVICING (Cont.)

FILTERS & CLEANERS

Filter or Cleaner	Service Interval (Miles)
Oil Filter	Replace every 6,250
Air Cleaner	①Replace every 25,000
Fuel Filter	Replace every 12,500
PCV Valve	②Replace every 25,000
Canister Filter	②Inspect every 25,000

① — Inspect and clean air filter every 12,500 miles.
② — Inspect every 12,500 miles.

BELT ADJUSTMENT

Application	①Deflection New Belt	①Deflection Used Belt
1800 cc	0.4-0.5" (10.2-12.7 mm)	0.5-0.6" (12.7-15.2 mm)
2300 cc	0.6-0.7" (15.2-17.8 mm)	0.8-0.9" (20.3-22.9 mm)

① — Deflection is with 22 lbs. (10 kg) pressure applied midway on longest belt run.

CAPACITIES

Application	Quantity
Crankcase (Includes Filter)	4.5 qts.
Cooling System	
1800 cc	7.6 qts.
2300 cc	9.0 qts.
Man. Trans.(SAE 90 with EP)	
4-Speed	1.5 qts.
5-Speed	1.8 qts.
Auto. Trans. (Type F Trans. Fluid)	6.6 qts.
Rear Axle (Hypoid Gear Lubricant)	3.2 pts.
Fuel Tank	
Standard	15 gals.
Optional	17.5 gals.

TUNE-UP

F10
B210
200SX
710
Pickup

ENGINE IDENTIFICATION

Engine model number followed by engine serial number is stamped on right side of cylinder block, just below the No. 4 spark plug. Model numbers are as follows:

Application	Engine Model Number
F10	A14
B210	A14
200SX	L20B
710	L20B
Pickup	L20B

MODEL IDENTIFICATION

VEHICLE IDENTIFICATION NUMBER

Vehicle identification number is stamped on a plate attached to instrument panel and is visible through windshield from outside of vehicle. Number on Pickup is on upper face of right side member. An identification plate also is found inside the engine compartment.

COMPRESSION PRESSURE

Check compression pressure with engine at normal operating temperature, all spark plugs disconnected, electrical lead to anti-dieseling solenoid disconnected, choke and throttle valves wide open and engine at cranking speed.

Lowest cylinder pressure should be at least 80% that of the highest cylinder pressure. Compression pressure should be as follows:

Compression Pressure @350 RPM

Application	psi (kg/cm²)
F10 & B210	178-206 (12.5-14.5)
All Others	128-171 (9-12)

VALVE TAPPET CLEARANCE

A14 ENGINE

Adjust valve clearance to specifications with engine off and at normal operating temperature. Rotate crankshaft to bring No. 1 cylinder to TDC on compression stroke. Adjust the following valves while engine is still hot.

Location in Fig. 1	Valves to Adjust
Location ①	Exhaust Valve No. 1
Location ②	Intake Valve No. 1
Location ③	Intake Valve No. 2
Location ⑤	Exhaust Valve No. 3

Rotate crankshaft until No. 4 cylinder is at TDC on compression stroke. Adjust the following valves:

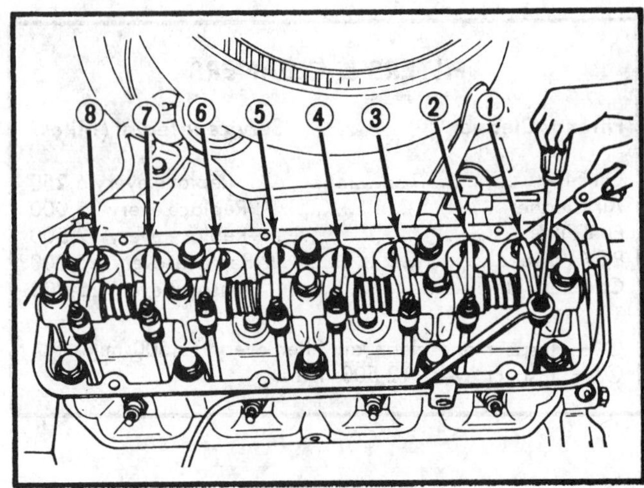

Fig. 1 Adjusting Valve Clearance (F10 and B210)

Location in Fig. 1	Valves to Adjust
Location ④	Exhaust Valve No. 2
Location ⑥	Intake Valve No. 3
Location ⑦	Intake Valve No. 4
Location ⑧	Exhaust Valve No. 4

After adjustment, tighten lock nuts firmly.

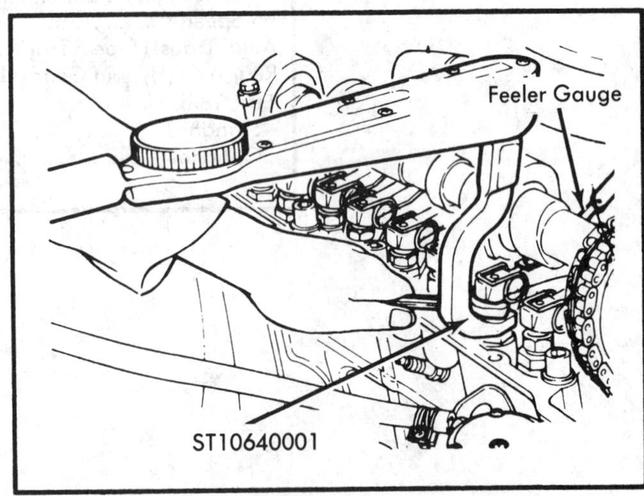

Fig. 2 Adjusting Valve Clearance (200SX, 710 and Pickup)

L20B ENGINE

With engine off, adjust valves first with engine cold. Then check clearance again with engine at normal operating temperature. Readjust if necessary. Adjust as follows:

1) Loosen pivot locking nut and turn pivot screw until specified clearance is obtained with engine cold for each valve. Insert feeler gauge from valve side. Adjust clearance, tighten lock nut, and recheck clearance.

2) Operate engine until warm, then turn it off and measure clearance according to hot specified setting. If clearance deviates from specified hot-engine setting, make adjustments as necessary.

TUNE-UP (Cont.)

Application	Intake	Exhaust
A14 Engine		
Cold	.010" (.25 mm)	.010" (.25 mm)
Hot	.014" (.35 mm)	.014" (.35 mm)
L20B Engine		
Cold	.008" (.20 mm)	.010" (.25 mm)
Hot	.010" (.25 mm)	.012" (.30 mm)

VALVE ARRANGEMENT

All Models — E-I-I-E-E-I-I-E (front to rear).

SPARK PLUGS

Gap	
Pickup (Federal)	.031-.035" (.8-.9 mm)
All Others	.039-.043" (1.0-1.1 mm)
Torque	
F10, B210, Pickup	11-14 ft. lbs. (1.5-2.0 mkg)
All Others	11-18 ft. lbs. (1.5-2.5 mkg)

Standard Spark Plug Type

Application	Hitachi No.	NGK No.
F10 & B210	L46PW-11	BP5ES-11
Pickup (Federal)	L45PW	BPR6ES
All Others	L45PW-11	BPR6ES-11

HIGH TENSION WIRE RESISTANCE

Remove distributor cap from distributor but do not disconnect high tension wires from cap. Disconnect high tension wires from spark plugs. Using an ohmmeter, check resistance from contact at spark plug end of wires to contact inside of distributor cap. Resistance should be 30,000 ohms. If resistance is more, disconnect wire from cap and check resistance of wire again. Replace wire if resistance is more than specifications.

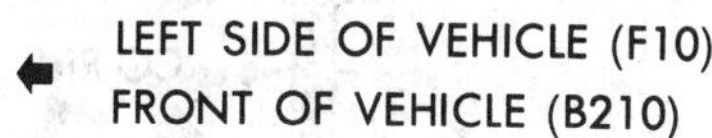

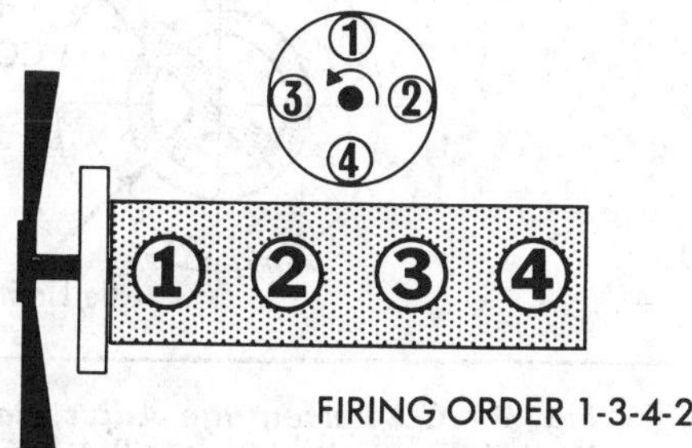

Fig. 3 Firing Order and Distributor Rotation (F10 and B210 Models)

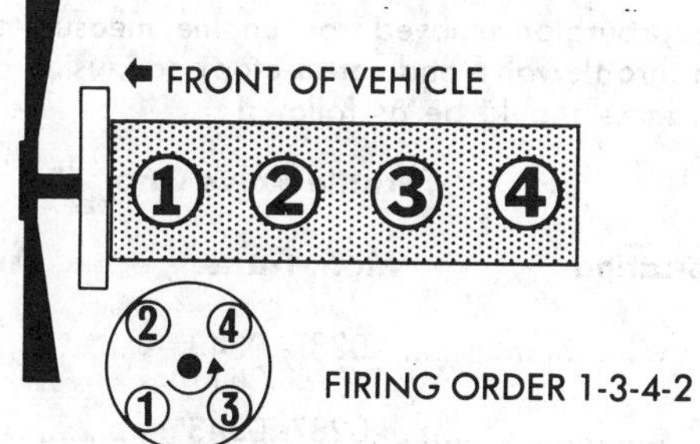

Fig. 4 Firing Order and Distributor Rotation (200SX, 710 and Pickup Models)

DISTRIBUTOR

NOTE — All vehicles sold in California are equipped with a Transistor Ignition system which uses no breaker points. The only adjustment provided is for air gap between the reluctor and pickup coil. Measure air gap using a non-magnetic feeler gauge. If gap is not to specifications, loosen pickup coil screws and adjust gap.

Air Gap	①.008-.016" (.2-.4 mm)
Point Gap	.018-.022" (.45-.55 mm)
Cam Angle	49-55°
Breaker Arm Spring Tension	.9-1.2 lbs. (.40-.55 kg)
Condenser Capacity	.20-.24 mfd.

① — Vehicles with Transistor Ignition systems only.

IGNITION TIMING

Check or adjust ignition timing with engine at normal operating temperature, cam angle or air gap set within specifications and engine idle speed correct for vehicle.

To adjust, loosen distributor set screw and rotate distributor until correct timing is achieved. Lock set screw and recheck timing setting.

Ignition Timing Specifications

Application	Man. Trans.	Auto. Trans.
F10	10° BTDC	.....
B210		
Federal	10° BTDC	10° BTDC
Calif.	10° BTDC	8° BTDC
200SX & 710	①12° BTDC	①12° BTDC
Pickup		
Federal	12° BTDC	12° BTDC
Calif.	10° BTDC	12° BDTC

① — Set timing for California 200SX & 710 Models @600 RPM.

Fig. 5 Ignition Timing Mark Location (F10 and B210 Models)

Fig. 6 Ignition Timing Mark Location (200SX, 710, and Pickup Models)

TUNE-UP (Cont.)

IDLE SPEED & MIXTURE

1) With engine warmed up to normal operating temperature, disconnect and plug air hose from air check valve. *See Figures 7 and 8.* Connect tachometer and exhaust gas analyzer.

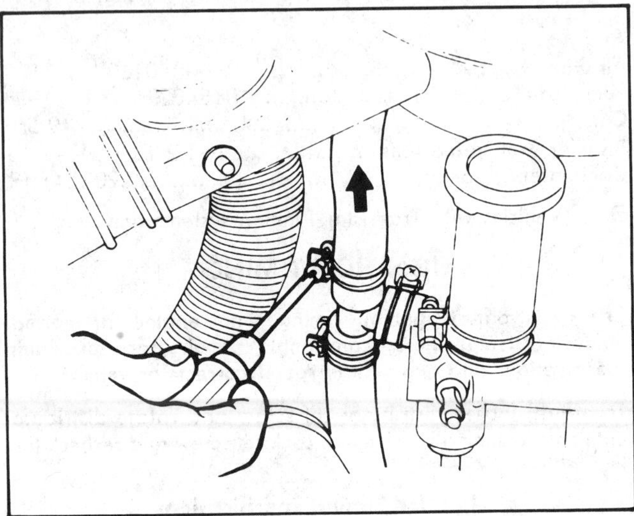

Fig. 7 Disconnecting Air Hose at Check Valve (Pickup, 200SX, & 710 Shown)

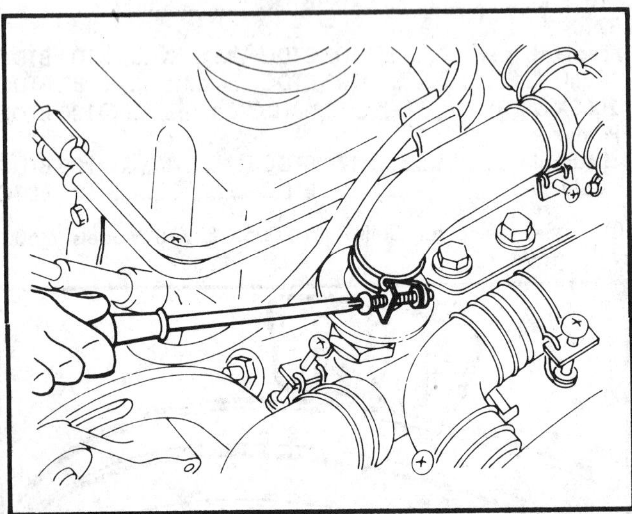

Fig. 8 Disconnecting Air Hose at Check Valve (F10 and B210 Shown)

2) Adjust idle speed screw until specified RPM is reached:

Model	RPM(M/T)	RPM(A/T)①
F10	700	700
200SX, 710	600	600
B210	700	650
Pickup	750	650

① — Transmission in "D"

3) Adjust air/fuel mixture screw until specified CO%, at specified idle RPM, is obtained:

F10, B210 & Pickup	2%±1%
200SX & 710	1% +1% or −.7%

4) If exhaust gas analyzer is not available, adjust idle speed screw and air/fuel mixture screw until best idle is obtained at the following RPM:

Model	RPM Man. Trans.	RPM Auto. Trans.①
F10	740	740
200SX & 710	650	650
B210	740	665
Pickup	815	670

① — Transmission in "D"

5) Now turn idle adjusting screw clockwise until engine speed DROPS down below best idle RPM by following amounts:

Model	Man. Trans.	Auto. Trans.①
F10	35-45 RPM	35-45 RPM
200SX & 710	45-55 RPM	45-55 RPM
B210	35-45 RPM	10-20 RPM
Pickup	60-70 RPM	15-25 RPM

① — Transmission in "D"

NOTE — *Do not remove idle limiter cap unless it is necessary to obtain proper CO% or best idle speed and drop.*

6) Reconnect air hose to air check valve. If engine RPM rises, reset RPM to correct "dropped" speed.

7) If idler limiter cap was removed, install so that idle screw can be turned ⅛ turn in rich direction. *See Figure 9.*

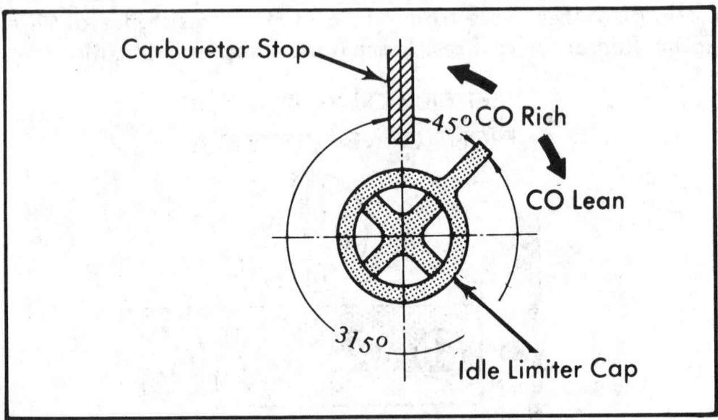

Fig. 9 CO Percentage Adjustment With Idler Limiter Cap (All Models)

COLD (FAST) IDLE RPM

With carburetor removed from engine, measure clearance between throttle valve and carburetor body, using a wire gauge. Clearances should be as follows:

Throttle Valve Gap

Application	Man. Trans.	Auto. Trans.
F10	.0287-.0343" (.73-.87 mm)	.....
B210	.0287-.0343" (.73-.87 mm)	.0394-.0449" (1.0-1.14 mm)
All Others	.052-.058" (1.33-1.47 mm)	.062-.068" (1.58-1.72 mm)

TUNE-UP (Cont.)

If gap is not within specifications, adjust by turning fast idle screw.

To check fast idling cam setting by engine speed, warm engine and set fast idling cam on second step. Engine speed should be within the following specifications:

Fast Idle RPM

Application	Man. Trans.	Auto. Trans.
F10	1900-2700	.....
B210	1900-2700	2400-3200
All Others	1900-2800	2200-3200

DASHPOT ADJUSTMENT

With engine at normal operating temperature and idle speed and mixture correctly set, turn throttle valve by hand and read engine speed when dashpot just contacts stop lever. Adjust position of dashpot by turning nut until engine speed is in specified range. Tighten locknut and make sure that engine decelerates smoothly from 2000 RPM to 1000 RPM in about three seconds.

Dashpot Adjusting Specifications

Application	Man. Trans.	Auto. Trans.
F10	①1900-2000	.....
B210	①1900-2000	1900-2000
All Others	1900-2100	1650-1850

① – On Federal Models, adjust speed to 2300-2400 RPM.

FUEL PUMP PRESSURE & VOLUME

Pressure .... 3.0-3.8 psi (.21-.27 kg/cm^2)
Volume at 1000 RPM
F10 & B210 .... 1.25 pts. (600 cc)/ min.
200SX .... 3.48 pts. (1700 cc)/ min.
All Others .... 2.12 pts. (1000 cc)/ min.

EMISSION CONTROL SYSTEMS

See Mitchell Manuals' Emission Control Manual.

GENERAL SERVICING

IGNITION

DISTRIBUTOR

All vehicles sold in California are equipped with Hitachi electronic ignition distributor. All other vehicles are equipped with Hitachi conventional distributor.

Other Data & Specifications – *See Tune-Up & Hitachi Distributors in ELECTRICAL Section.*

IGNITION COIL

Resistance	Ohms at 68°F (20°C)
Primary	
Calif.①	.45-.55
Federal	1.08-1.32
Secondary	
Calif.①	8500-12,700
Federal	
200SX & 710	8300-12,300
All Others	8200-12,400
External Resistor	
Calif.①	
200SX & 710	1.15-1.45
All Others	1.3
Federal	
200SX & 710	1.5-1.72
All Others	1.5

① – California models have Transistor Ignition System.

FUEL SYSTEMS

CARBURETORS

Application	Model
F10 & B210 2-Bbl.	DCH 306
All Others	DCH 340

Other Data & Specifications – *See Tune-Up & Hitachi Carburetors in FUEL SYSTEMS Section.*

ELECTRICAL

BATTERY

12 Volt – Negative Ground.

Application	Amp. Hr. Rating
All Models (Except Canada)	60
Canada	65

Battery Location – Engine Compartment.

GENERAL SERVICING (Cont.)

STARTER

Hitachi solenoid actuated with overrunning clutch.

Free Speed Voltage (All Models)
- Man. Trans. .... 12 @7000 RPM
- Auto. Trans. .... ①12 @6000 RPM

Free Speed Amperage (All Models)
- Man. Trans. .... 60 @7000 RPM
- Auto. Trans. .... ①60 @6000 RPM

① — B210 with Auto. Trans. is 60 Amps. and 12 V. at 7000 RPM.

Other Data & Specifications — *See Hitachi Starters in ELECTRICAL Section.*

ALTERNATOR

Application	Rated Amp. Output
F10 & B210	50
200SX & 710	
All (Except Canada)	50
Canada	60
Pickup	35
Standard	35
With Air Conditioning	38

Other Data & Specifications — *See Hitachi Alternators & Regulators in ELECTRICAL Section.*

ALTERNATOR REGULATOR

All models use a Hitachi alternator regulator with an operating voltage of 14.3-15.3 volts at 68°F (20°C).

Other Data & Specifications — *See Hitachi Alternators & Regulators in ELECTRICAL Section.*

ENGINE

INTAKE MANIFOLD TIGHTENING

Check manifold attaching nuts for 11-14.5 ft. lbs. (1.5-2.0 mkg) torque on F10 and B210 models or 9-12 ft. lbs. (1.2-1.6 mkg) on all other models.

FILTERS & CLEANERS

Filter or Cleaner	Service Interval (Miles)
Oil Filter	①Replace every 6,250
Air Cleaner	②Replace every 25,000
Fuel Filter	②Replace every 25,000
PCV Valve & Filter	②Replace every 25,000
Canister Filter	②Replace every 25,000

① — Replace every 7,500 miles on 200SX.
② — Replace every 30,000 miles on 200SX.

BELT ADJUSTMENT

Application	①Deflection
Fan Belt	
F10 & B210	.47-.63" (12-16 mm)
All Others	.32-.47" (8-12 mm)
Air Pump Belt	
F10 & B210	.39-.55" (10-14 mm)
710	.43-.59" (11-15 mm)
200SX & Pickup	.32-.47" (8-12 mm)
A/C Belt	
710	.24-.39" (6-10 mm)
All Others	.32-.47" (8-12 mm)

① — Deflection is with 22 lbs. (10 kg) pressure applied midway on longest belt run.

CAPACITIES

Application	Quantity
Crankcase (Includes Filter)	
F10	3.6 qts.
B210	3.9 qts.
All Others	4.5 qts.
Cooling System (Includes Heater)	
F10	7 qts.
B210	①6 qts.
200SX	7.9 qts.
710	7.25 qts.
Pickup	①8.25 qts.
Manual Transmission (API GL-4)	
F10	4.9 pts.
B210	
4-speed	2.75 pts.
5-speed	3.6 pts.
200SX & 710	3.6 pts.
Pickup	
4-speed	3.6 pts.
5-speed	4.25 pts.
Automatic Transmission (Dexron)	
B210	5.6 qts.
All Others (Except F10)	5.9 qts.
Rear Axle (API GL-5)	
B210	1.9 pts.
200SX & 710	2.75 pts.
Pickup	2.13 pts.
Fuel Tank	
F10	10.6 gals.
B210	
Sedan	11.6 gals.
Coupe	11.4 gals.
200SX	15.9 gals.
710	
Sedan & Hardtop	13.25 gals.
Station Wagon	
Federal	11.9 gals.
Calif.	13.25 gals.
Pickup	11.9 gals.

① — Add .25 qts. for models with Man. Trans.

TUNE-UP

280Z
810

ENGINE IDENTIFICATION

Engine serial number is stamped on right rear side of cylinder block at cylinder head contact surface. Serial number is preceded by engine model number:

Engine Model Number

Application	Model No.
280Z	L28
810	L24

MODEL IDENTIFICATION

VEHICLE IDENTIFICATION NUMBER

Vehicle identification number is stamped on a plate attached to instrument panel and is visible through windshield from outside of vehicle.

COMPRESSION PRESSURE

Test compression with engine at normal operating temperature, spark plugs removed, throttle and choke open, and engine at cranking speed. Lowest reading cylinder must be at least 80% of highest reading cylinder. Compression pressure should be as follows at 300-400 RPM:

Application	Min. Pressure psi (kg/cm²)	Max. Pressure psi (kg/cm²)
280Z	164 (11.5)	178 (12.5)
810	164 (11.5)	185 (13)

VALVE TAPPET CLEARANCE

Valve adjustment cannot be made with engine running. With engine cold, loosen pivot locking nut and turn pivot screw until cold adjustment clearance is obtained, tighten lock nut and check clearance. Warm-up engine and turn off. Measure hot engine valve clearance in same manner as for cold adjustment. If clearance deviates from hot engine setting value, readjust valves as necessary.

Application	Intake	Exhaust
Cold Engine	.008" (.20 mm)	.010" (.25 mm)
Hot Engine	.010" (.25 mm)	.012" (.30 mm)

VALVE ARRANGEMENT

E-I-I-E-I-E-E-I-E-I-I-E (front to rear).

SPARK PLUGS

Gap	.039-.043" (1.0-1.1 mm)
Torque	11-14 ft. lbs. (1.5-2.0 mkg)

Spark Plug Type

Application	Hitachi No.	NGK No.
280Z & 810	L45W-11	B6ES-11

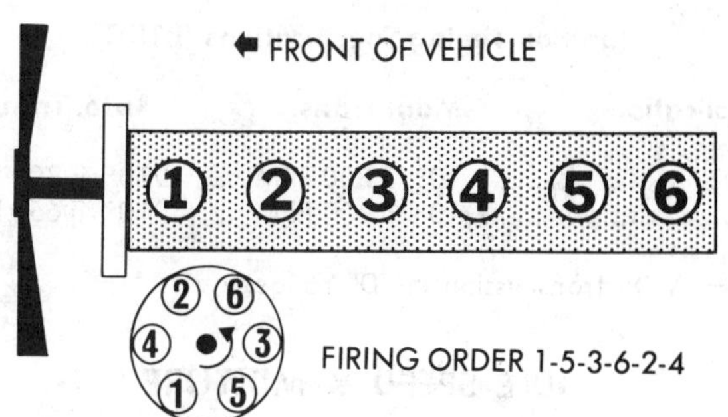

Fig. 1 Firing Order and Distributor Rotation

HIGH TENSION WIRE RESISTANCE

Remove distributor cap from distributor but do not disconnect high tension wires from cap. Disconnect high tension wires from spark plugs. Using an ohmmeter, check resistance from contact at spark plug end of wires to contact inside of distributor cap. Resistance should be 30,000 ohms. If resistance is more, disconnect wire from cap and check resistance of wire again. Replace wire if resistance is more than specifications.

DISTRIBUTOR

All models use a single pickup transistor ignition system, which uses no breaker points. The only adjustment provided is for air gap between the reluctor and pickup coil.

Measure air gap using a non-magnetic feeler gauge. If gap is not to specifications, loosen pickup coil screws and adjust gap.

Air Gap	.008-.016" (.2-.4 mm)

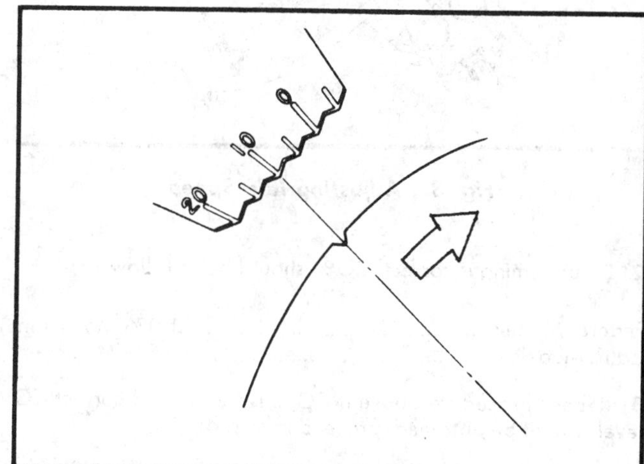

Fig. 2 Ignition Timing Mark Location

IGNITION TIMING

With engine at normal operating temperature, connect a timing light and tachometer to engine. Check air gap and idle speed and adjust to specifications if necessary. To adjust timing, loosen set screw and rotate distributor until timing is set to specifications, then tighten set screw and recheck timing.

TUNE-UP (Cont.)

Ignition Timing Specifications (BTDC)

Application	Man. Trans.	Auto. Trans.
280Z	10° @800 RPM	①10° @700 RPM
810	10° @700 RPM	①10° @650 RPM

① – With transmission in "D" range.

IDLE SPEED & MIXTURE

1) With engine warmed up to operating temperature, connect tachometer and exhaust gas analyzer. Adjust idle speed to following RPM:

Application	Man. Trans.	Auto. Trans.
280Z	800	①700
810	700	①650

① – With transmission in "D" range.

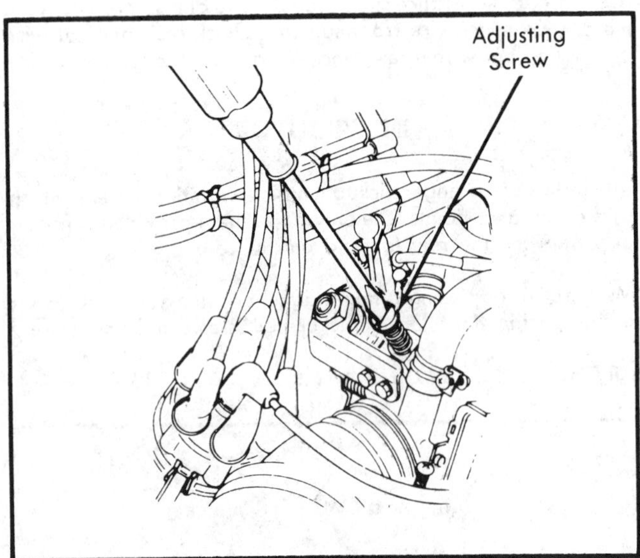

Fig. 3 Adjusting Idle Speed

2) Ensure timing is correct. CO% should be as follows:

Federal Models	1.0% Maximum
Calif. Models	.5% Maximum

3) Repeat procedure above if CO% is too high. If correct CO level cannot be obtained, proceed to step **4**.

4) Remove throttle valve switch harness connector. See *Fig. 4*.

NOTE – *If adjusting idle CO% at altitude of 2,500 ft. (750 m) or higher, or if vehicle is a California model, unhook altitude switch connector.*

5) With a piece of electrical wire, connect No. 3 and No. 18 terminals of throttle valve switch connector.

NOTE – *This procedure short circuits the enrichment system and allows the idle mixture to run at full load enrichment. This step is necessary to enrichen the CO% at idle enough to be read by an exhaust gas analyzer.*

6) Remove plastic plug to gain access, and turn air by-pass screw to adjust idle CO%. Turn clockwise to obtain richer mixture and counterclockwise for leaner mixture. CO% values should be as follows:

Altitude	Idle CO%
0-2000 ft. (0-600 m)	3.3%
2000-4000 ft. (600-1200 m)	4.7%
4000-6000 ft. (1200-1800 m)	5.7%
Above 6000 ft.	6.7%

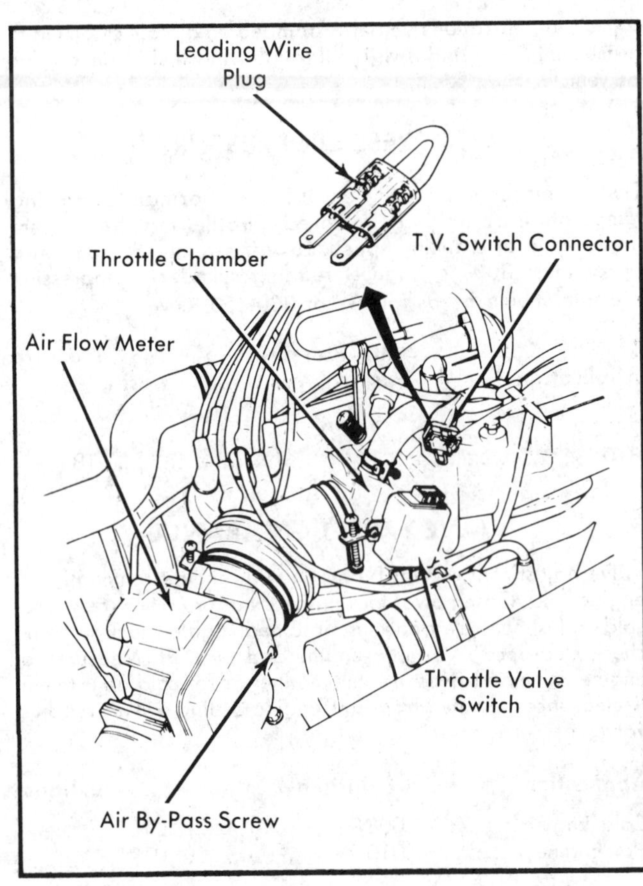

Fig. 4 Idle Mixture Ratio Adjustment (280Z Shown – 810 Similar)

7) Once correct CO values are obtained, remove wire from throttle valve switch connector. Reinstall connector to proper location. Plug altitude switch connector back into original position (if removed on Calif. models only).

8) Install new rubber plug over air by-pass screw opening in air flow meter. Recheck CO%.

TUNE-UP (Cont.)

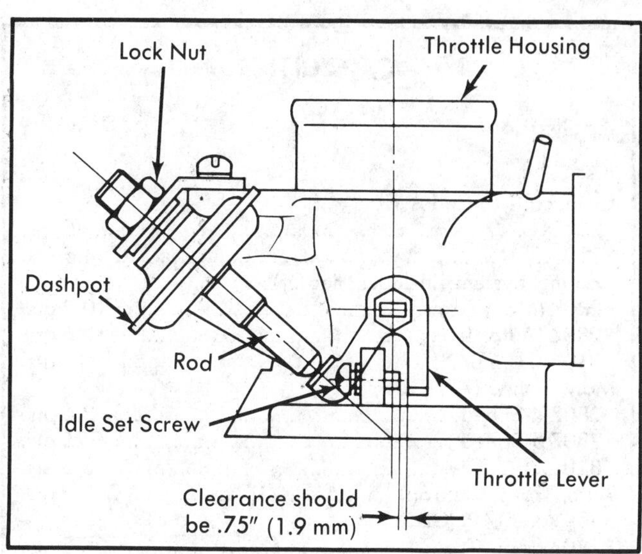

Fig. 5 Dashpot Adjustment

DASHPOT ADJUSTMENT

Check clearance between idle set screw and throttle lever. Clearance should be .075" (1.9 mm). Check that dashpot rod end touches throttle lever when rod is fully extended (or when no back pressure is present at diaphragm). If necessary, loosen lock nut and turn dashpot until rod just touches throttle lever, then tighten lock nut *(refer to Fig. 5)*.

FUEL PUMP PRESSURE

Pressure .... 43-64 psi (3.0-4.5 kg/cm²)

EMISSION CONTROL SYSTEMS

See Mitchell Manuals' Emission Control Manual.

GENERAL SERVICING

IGNITION

DISTRIBUTOR

All models are equipped with Hitachi Transistor Ignition System.

Other Data & Specifications – *See Tune-Up & Hitachi Distributors in ELECTRICAL Section.*

IGNITION COIL

Resistance	Ohms at 68°F (20°C)
Primary	.45-.55
Secondary	8500-12,7000
External Resistor	1.15-1.45

FUEL SYSTEMS

FUEL INJECTION

All models are equipped with Bosch Electronic Fuel Injection System.

Other Data & Specifications – *See Tune-Up and Bosch Electronic Fuel Injection in FUEL SYSTEMS Section.*

ELECTRICAL

BATTERY

12 Volt – Negative Ground.

All (Except Canada)	60
Canada	65

Battery Location – Right side of engine compartment.

STARTER

Hitachi .... Overrunning Clutch

Free Speed Voltage
- Man. Trans. .... 12 at 5000 RPM
- Auto. Trans. .... 12 at 6000 RPM

Free Speed Amperage
- Man. Trans. .... 60 (Max.) at 5000 RPM
- Auto. Trans. .... 60 (Max.) at 6000 RPM

Other Data & Specifications – *See Hitachi Starters in ELECTRICAL Section.*

ALTERNATOR

Application	Rated Amp. Output
All Models	60

Other Data & Specifications – *See Hitachi Alternators & Regulators in ELECTRICAL Section.*

ALTERNATOR REGULATOR

All models use a Hitachi alternator regulator with an operating voltage of 14.3-15.3 volts at 68°F (20°C).

Other Data & Specifications – *See Hitachi Alternators & Regulators in ELECTRICAL Section.*

ENGINE

INTAKE MANIFOLD TIGHTENING

Check manifold attaching bolts for the following torque:

GENERAL SERVICING (Cont.)

Intake Manifold Tightening

Application	Ft. Lbs. (mkg)
8 mm Bolts	10-13 (1.4-1.8)
10 mm Bolts	25-36 (3.5-5.0)

BELT ADJUSTMENT

Application	①Deflection
Fan Belt	.32-.47" (8-12 mm)
Air Cond. Belt	.32-.47" (8-12 mm)

① — Deflection is with 22 lbs. (10 kg) pressure applied midway on belt run.

FILTERS & CLEANERS

Filter or Cleaner	Service Interval (Miles)
Oil Filter	Replace every 6,250
Air Cleaner	Replace every 25,000
Fuel Filter	Replace every 25,000
PCV Valve	Replace every 25,000
Canister Filter	Replace every 25,000

CAPACITIES

Application	Quantity
Crankcase (Includes Filter)	
280Z	5 qts.
810	4.5 qts.
Cooling System (Includes Heater)	
280Z (Man. Trans.)	10.9 qts.
280Z (Auto. Trans.)	10.6 qts.
810	11 qts.
Man. Trans. (API GL-4)	
280Z 4-Speed	3.6 pts.
280Z 5-Speed	4.25 pts.
810	3.6 pts.
Auto. Trans. (Dexron)	5.9 qts.
Rear Axle (API GL-5)	
280Z (Man. Trans.)	2.75 pts.
280Z (Auto. Trans.)	2.13 pts.
810 Sedan	2.75 pts.
810 Station Wagon	2.13 pts.
Fuel Tank	
280Z	17.13 gals.
810 Sedan	15.9 gals.
810 Station Wagon	14.5 gals.

TUNE-UP

124 Models
128 Models
131 Models
X1/9

ENGINE IDENTIFICATION

124 & 131 Models – Engine identification number is stamped on crankcase near oil filter mount.

128 & X 1/9 Models – Engine identification number is stamped on crankcase (flywheel end).

Application	Engine No. Without Cat. Conv.	Engine No. With Cat. Conv.
124	132 A1.040.6	132 A1.031.6
131	132 A1.040.6	132 A1.031.6
128	128 A1.040.6	128 A1.031.6
128 3P	128 A1.040.6	128 A1.031.6
X1/9	128 A5.031.5	128 A5.031.6

MODEL IDENTIFICATION

VEHICLE IDENTIFICATION NUMBER

Model can be identified by prefix of vehicle identification number, which is stamped on a plate attached to top of instrument panel between instrument cluster and windshield. Number also is found on engine compartment bulkhead of 124 and 131 models, on right-hand front wheel suspension mounting on 128 and 128 3P models, and in front trunk compartment, right-hand rear wall of X1/9 models. Model codes are as follows:

Application	Code
124 Models	
Sport Spider	124 CS1
128 Models	
Sedan	128 A1
Station Wagon	128 AF1
128 3P Models	128 AC
131 Models	
Sedan	131 A3
Station Wagon	131 AF2
X 1/9	128 AS

VALVE TAPPET CLEARANCE

Application①	Intake	Exhaust
124 & 131 Models	.018" (.45 mm)	.020" (.50 mm)
128 & X 1/9 Models	.012" (.30 mm)	.016" (.40 mm)

① – Set valves with engine cold.

VALVE ARRANGEMENT

124 & 131 Models

Right Side – All Exhaust.
Left Side – All Intake.
128 & X1/9 Models – E-I-I-E-E-I-I-E

SPARK PLUGS

Gap	.020-.027" (.5-.7 mm)
Torque	
131 Models	29 ft. lbs. (4.0 mkg)
All Others	25 ft. lbs. (3.5 mkg)

Spark Plug Type

Application	Champion No.	AC No.
All Models	N-9Y	42 XLS

HIGH TENSION WIRE RESISTANCE

Carefully remove ends of high tension wire from spark plug and distributor cap. Using an ohmmeter, check resistance of wire while gently twisting wire. If resistance is not to specification, or if resistance fluctuates from infinity to any value, replace high tension wire(s).

Resistance (Ohms) Per Wire

Application	Resistance
All Models	25,000-30,000

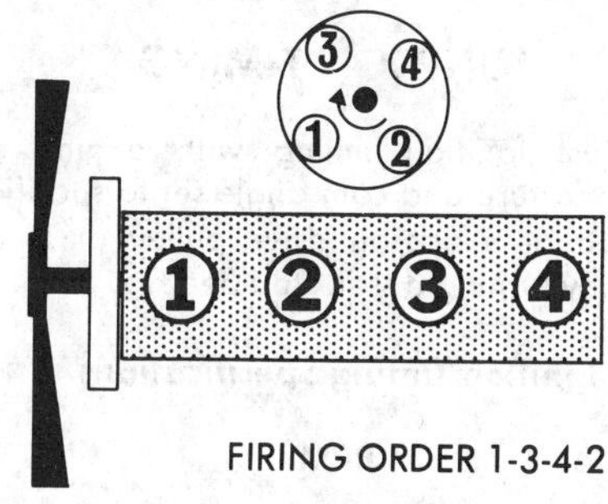

Fig. 1 Firing Order and Distributor Rotation (124 & 131 Models)

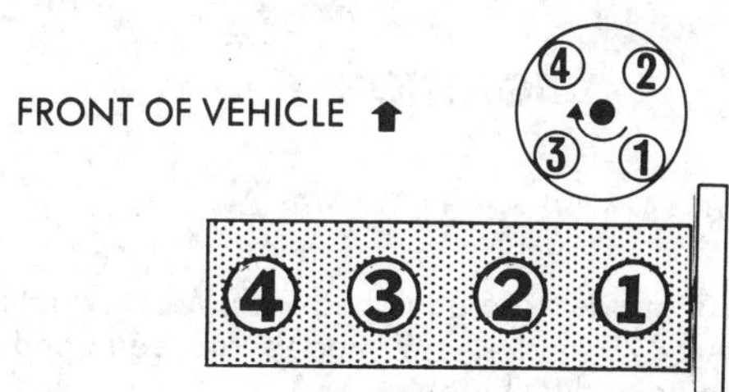

Fig. 2 Firing Order and Distributor Rotation (128, 128 3P, & X1/9 Models)

TUNE-UP (Cont.)

DISTRIBUTOR

Point Gap .... ①.015-.017" (.37-.43 mm)
Cam Angle .... 55±3°
Breaker Arm Spring Tension
124 & 131 Models .... ②19.4±1.8 ozs. (550±50 g)
128 & X 1/9 Models.................. 15.9±1.8 ozs. (450±50 g)
Condenser Capacity
124 & 131 Models .... .20-.25 mfd.
128 & X 1/9 Models....................................... .22-.23 mfd.

① – On models with dual point distributors, set secondary point gap to .012-.019" (.31-.49 mm).

② – Tension on secondary points should be 14.1±1.8 ozs. (400±50 g).

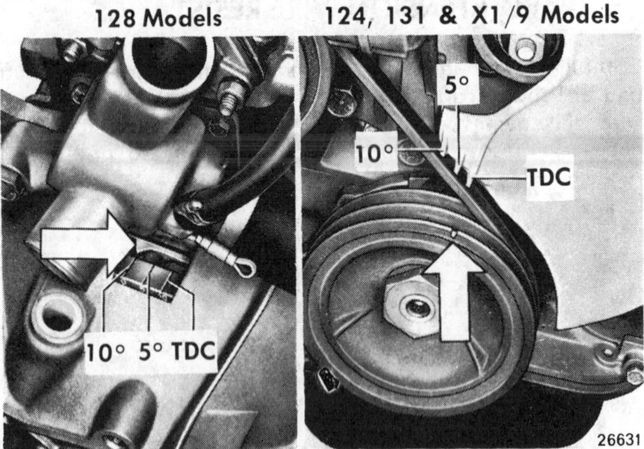

Fig. 3 Ignition Timing Mark Location

IGNITION TIMING

Check or adjust ignition timing with engine at normal operating temperature and cam angle set to specifications. To adjust timing, align mark on drive pulley or flywheel with specified mark by turning distributor. *See Fig. 3.*

Ignition Timing Specifications

Application	RPM	Timing
All Models	850±50	TDC

HOT (SLOW) IDLE RPM

With engine at normal operating temperature, connect a tachometer and exhaust gas analyzer to vehicle. On vehicles with a catalytic converter, disconnect or pinch air injection hose. Place automatic transmission in Drive and manual transmission in neutral. Adjust idle speed to specified RPM by turning idle adjusting screw. Set CO level to specifications by turning mixture adjusting screw; turn mixture screw clockwise to decrease CO % and counterclockwise to increase CO %. Repeat procedure until specified CO level is obtained at specified idle speed RPM. If disconnected, reconnect air injection hose. Idle speed should increase 50 RPM.

Idle Speed (RPM) & CO Level (%)

Application	Idle RPM	CO%
All Models①	800-850	1.5-2.5

① – When checking CO% set idle speed to 800-850 RPM with air injection hose pinched off. When hose is reconnected engine speed should increase 50 RPM. Automatic transmission vehicles should be set in "D" position.

COLD (FAST) IDLE RPM

124 & 131 MODELS ONLY

To adjust fast idle RPM, depress button on firewall in engine compartment, which energizes control electrovalve, and turn fast idle adjusting screw until engine RPM is within specifications.

Fast Idle RPM

Application	RPM
124 & 131 Man. Trans.	1600±50
131 Auto. Trans. (In "N")	1300±50

EMISSION CONTROL SYSTEMS

See Mitchell Manuals' Emission Control Manual.

GENERAL SERVICING

IGNITION

DISTRIBUTOR

All 124 and 131 models are equipped with Marelli dual point distributors. All 128 and X 1/9 models are equipped with Ducellier single point distributors.

Other Data & Specifications – *See Tune-Up, Marelli & Ducellier Distributors in ELECTRICAL Section.*

IGNITION COIL

Resistance	Ohms at 68° F (20° C) 128 Models	124 & 131
Primary		
W/Marelli Coil	3.2-3.4	2.6-2.8
W/MMartinetti Coil	①3.0-3.3	②2.6-2.95
Secondary		
W/Marelli Coil	9,000-11,000	6,750-8,250
W/Martinetti Coil	①6,500-8,000	②7,000-8,500

① – 128 3P (Martinetti Coil) primary resistance is 2.6-3.1 ohms; secondary is 8,500-12,000 ohms.

② – Applies also to X1/9 Models.

GENERAL SERVICING (Cont.)

FUEL SYSTEMS

CARBURETORS

Application	Model
124 Model	
Without Cat. Conv.	Weber 32 ADFA 12/100
With Cat. Conv.	Weber 32 ADFA 15/100
128 Models	
Without Cat. Conv.	Weber 32 DATRA 11/100
With Cat. Conv.	Weber 32 DATRA 14/100
131 Models	
Man. Trans.	
Without Cat. Conv.	Weber 32 ADFA 1/100
With Cat. Conv.	Weber 32 ADFA 3/100
Auto. Trans.	
Without Cat. Conv.	Weber 32 DATRA 4/100
With Cat. Conv.	Weber 32 DATRA 6/100
X1/9 Models	
Without Air Conditioning	
Without Cat. Conv.	Weber 32 DATRA/201
With Cat. Conv.	Weber 32 DATRA 10/200
With Air Conditioning	
Without Cat. Conv.	Weber 32 DATRA/101
With Cat. Conv.	Weber 32 DATRA/10/100

Other Data & Specifications – *See Tune-Up & Weber Carburetors in FUEL SYSTEMS Section.*

ELECTRICAL

BATTERY

12 Volt – Negative Ground.

Application	Amp Hr. Rating
All Models	60

Battery Location – Battery is located in engine compartment on all except 124 sports models. On these models, battery is located in trunk.

STARTER

All models are equipped with a Fiat Starter.

Free Speed Voltage	
124 & 131 Models	12 at 5200±500 RPM
128 & X 1/9 Models	11.7 at 7000±500RPM
Free Speed Amperage	
124 & 131 Models	28 at 5200±500 RPM
128 & X 1/9 Models	35 at 7000±500 RPM

Other Data & Specifications – *See Fiat Starters in ELECTRICAL Section.*

BELT ADJUSTMENT

Belt tension is correct when under a pressure of about 22 lbs. (10 kg) belt can be depressed .4-.6" (10-15 mm).

ALTERNATOR

Application	Rated Amp. Output
124 Models	44
128 Models	60
131 & X 1/9 Models	
Standard	44
With A/C	60

Other Data & Specifications – *See Marelli Alternators & Regulators in ELECTRICAL Section.*

ALTERNATOR REGULATOR

All models are equipped with a Marelli Alternator Regulator with an operating voltage of 14.2±.3 volts.

Other Data & Specifications – *See Marelli Alternators & Regulators in ELECTRICAL Section.*

FILTERS & CLEANERS

Filter or Cleaner	Service Interval (Miles)
Oil Filter	Replace every 6000
Air Cleaner	Replace every 12,500
Fuel Filter	Replace every 12,500
Charcoal Canister	Replace every 25,000

CAPACITIES

Application	Quantity
Crankcase (Includes Filter)	
124 & 131 Models	4.0 qts.
128, 128 3P, & X1/9 Models	4.5 qts.
Cooling System	
124 Models	8.5 qts.
128 Models	6.8 qts.
128 3P Models	7.4 qts.
131 Models	8.0 qts.
X1/9	11.4 qts.
Man. Trans. (SAE 90)	
124 Models	3.5 pts.
131 Models	3.8 pts.
Auto. Trans. (Dexron)	
131 Models Only (Refill)	6.0 pts.
Rear Axle (SAE 90)	
124 Models	2.8 pts.
131 Models	2.1 pts.
Transaxle (SAE 90)	
128 & X1/9 Models	6.6 pts.
Fuel Tank	
124 Models	11.4 gals.
128 Sedan & Wagon	9.5 gals.
128 3P Models	12.5 gals.
131 Models	12.2 gals.
X1/9 Models	12.2 gals.

TUNE-UP

Accord
Civic
Civic CVCC

ENGINE IDENTIFICATION

Engine serial number is stamped on a machined surface at rear of engine, near starter. Engine serial number is preceded by engine model number. Model numbers are as follows:

Application	Model Code
Accord	EFI
Civic	EB2
Civic CVCC	
Sedan	ED3
Station Wagon	ED4

MODEL IDENTIFICATION

Model identification number is stamped on a metal tag and riveted to dash. Tag is visible through windshield. Number also appears on left door post, and on body under hood behind air cleaner.

COMPRESSION PRESSURE

Check compression with engine at normal operating temperature, air cleaner and spark plugs removed, throttle and choke valve wide open.

Compression Pressure @ 400 RPM

Application	Pressure
Accord	136-192 psi (10-14 kg/cm²)
Civic	155 psi (11 kg/cm²)
Civic CVCC	136-192 psi (10-14 kg/cm²)

VALVE TAPPET CLEARANCE

1) Adjust valve clearance to specifications with engine cold.

2) With piston of No. 1 cylinder at TDC (camshaft keyway pointing up), adjust intake valves 1 and 2; exhaust valves 1 and 3; and auxiliary valves 1 and 2.

3) Rotate crankshaft one full turn until piston of No. 4 cylinder is at TDC (camshaft keyway pointing down). Adjust intake valves 3 and 4; exhaust valves 2 and 4; and auxiliary valves 3 and 4.

4) To adjust, loosen lock nut and turn adjusting screw until feeler gauge slides back and forth with slight drag. Tighten intake and exhaust valve lock nuts to 12-16 ft. lbs. (1.8-2.2 mkg) and auxiliary valve lock nuts to 9-12 ft. lbs. (1.2-1.6 mkg). Recheck clearance.

Valve Clearance Specifications

Application	Clearance
Accord and Civic CVCC	
All valves	.005-.007" (.12-.18 mm)
Civic	
Intake and Exhaust	.004-.006" (.10-.16 mm)

VALVE ARRANGEMENT

Accord
Left Side — I-E-E-I-I-E-E-I
Right Side — All Auxiliary.
Civic
Left Side — All Intake.
Right Side — All Exhaust.
Civic CVCC
Left Side — I-E-E-I-I-E-E-I
Right Side — All Auxiliary.

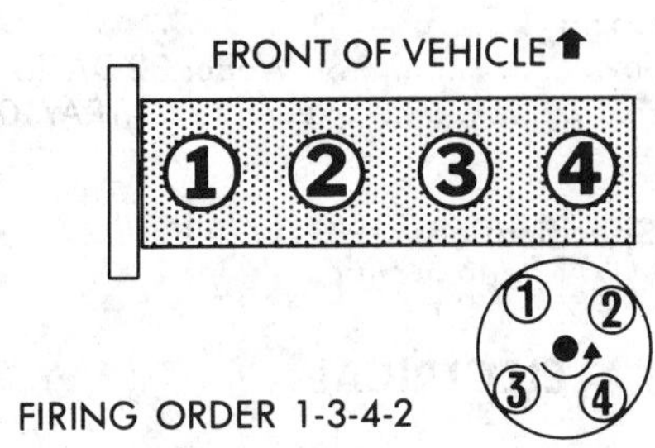

Fig. 1 Firing Order and Distributor Rotation (Accord and Civic CVCC)

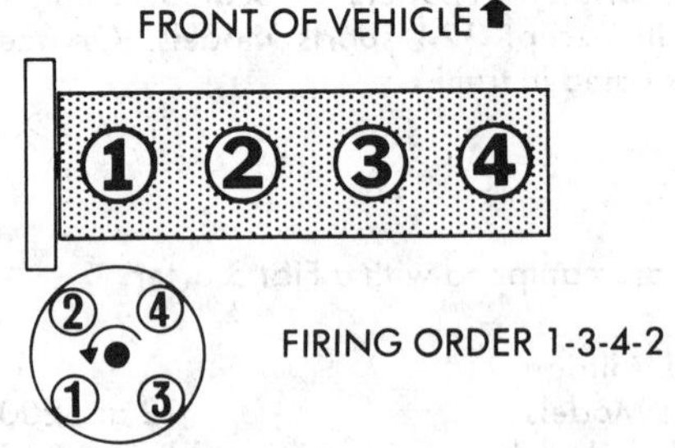

Fig. 2 Firing Order and Distributor Rotation (Civic)

SPARK PLUGS

Gap	.028-.032" (.7-.8 mm)
Torque	
Accord	11-18 ft. lbs. (1.5-2.5 mkg)
Civic	9-12 ft. lbs. (1.3-1.7 mkg)
Civic CVCC	11-18 ft. lbs. (1.5-2.5 mkg)

TUNE-UP (Cont.)

Spark Plug Type

Application	Nippondenso	NGK
Accord	①W-20ES-L	②B-6EB
Civic	W-20EP	BP-6ES
Civic CVCC	①W-20ES-L	②B-6EB

① — Cold Climates — W-1635-L
② — Cold Climates — B-5EB

HIGH TENSION WIRE RESISTANCE

Carefully remove ends of wire from spark plug and distributor. Using an ohmmeter, check resistance of wire while gently twisting wire. If resistance is not to specification, or fluctuates from infinity to any value, replace wire.

Resistance (Ohms) Per Wire

Application	Resistance
All Models (2 ft. length)	25,000 Max.

DISTRIBUTOR

Point Gap	.018-.022" (.45-.55 mm)
Cam Angle	49-55°
Breaker Arm Spring Tension	18-23 ozs. (500-650 g)
Condenser Capacity	.20-.24 mfd.

IGNITION TIMING

Accord & Civic CVCC — 1) With engine at normal operating temperature, connect a timing light and tachometer to engine, then remove rubber cup from inspection window on cylinder block (at flywheel housing).

2) To adjust timing, loosen adjusting bolt and rotate distributor until specified mark on flywheel (red mark) is aligned with index pointer. Tighten adjusting bolt and recheck timing.

Civic — 1) With engine at normal operating temperature, connect a timing light and tachometer to engine. Check idle speed and adjust to specifications if necessary.

2) To adjust timing, loosen distributor retaining bolt and rotate distributor until timing mark aligns with reference mark. Tighten retaining bolt and recheck timing.

Ignition Timing Specifications

Application	Federal	Calif. & High Alt.
Accord and Civic CVCC		
Man. Trans.	6° BTDC	2° BTDC
Auto. Trans.①	6° BTDC	②0° TDC
Civic		
All Models	0° TDC	0° TDC

① — Set timing with transmission selector lever in "2" range.
② — Automatic sedan for California, 2° BTDC.

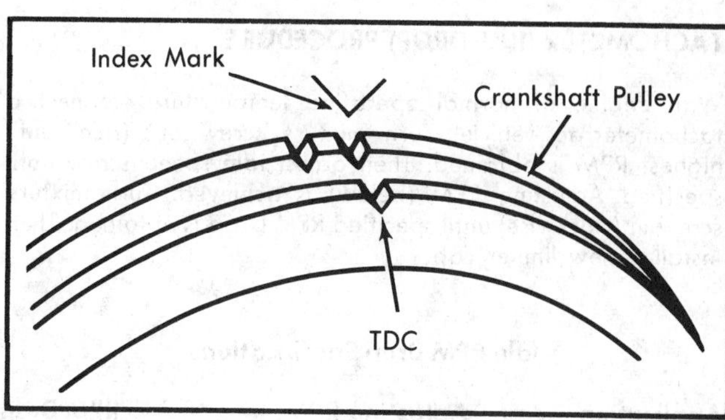

Fig. 3 Ignition Timing Mark Location (Civic)

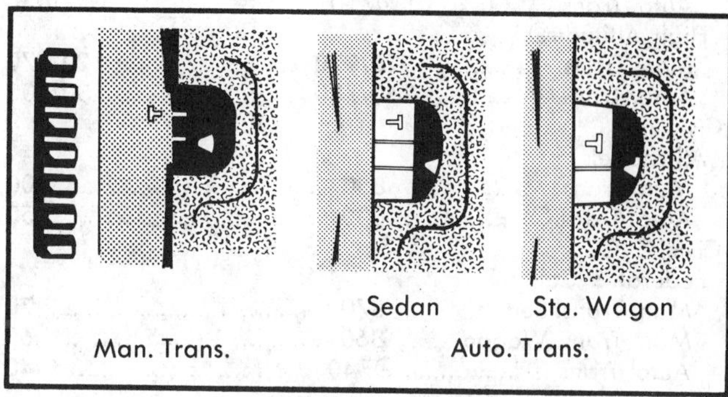

Fig. 4 Ignition Timing Mark Location (Accord & Civic CVCC)

IDLE SPEED & MIXTURE

EXHAUST GAS ANALYZER PROCEDURE

1) With engine at normal operating temperature, connect an exhaust gas analyzer and tachometer to vehicle. Turn headlights and cooling fan on. Disconnect crankcase breather hose from valve cover.

2) Place manual transmission in neutral or automatic transmission in drive ("2" range).

3) Adjust idle speed screw until idle speed is set to specifications. Remove mixture screw limiter cap and adjust mixture screw until CO level is within specifications.

4) Recheck idle speed and CO level and adjust as necessary to obtain best balance between idle speed and CO level. Install new limiter cap on mixture screw.

Idle Speed (RPM) and CO Level (%)

Application	Idle RPM	CO%
Accord and Civic CVCC		
Man. Trans.	750-850	.4
Auto. Trans.①	②650-750	.4
Civic		
Man. Trans.	700-800	.35
Auto. Trans.①	700-800	.35

① — With transmission selector lever in "2" range.
② — Accord Auto. Trans. should be 630-730 RPM.

TUNE-UP (Cont.)

TACHOMETER (IDLE DROP) PROCEDURE

With engine at normal operating temperature, connect a tachometer to vehicle. Turn mixture screw out (rich) until highest RPM is obtained. Then adjust idle speed screw until specified Adjusting RPM (below) is achieved. Turn mixture screw in (clockwise) until specified RPM Drop is obtained. Then install a new limiter cap.

Idle RPM Drop Specifications

Application	Adjusting RPM	RPM Drop
Accord		
Federal & Calif.		
Man. Trans.	850	50
Auto. Trans.①	②710	②30
High Altitude③		
Man. Trans.	920/970	120/170
Auto. Trans.①	760/780	80/100
Civic		
All Models		
Man. Trans.	850	100
Auto. Trans.①	800	50
Civic CVCC		
Federal & Calif.		
Man. Trans. Sedan	870	70
Man. Trans. Wagon	860	60
Auto. Trans ①	④740	④40
High Altitude③		
Man. Trans.	920/970	120/170
Auto. Trans①	780/800	80/100

① — With transmission selector lever in "2" range.
② — Adjust Calif. Auto. Trans. to 720 RPM with 40 RPM drop.
③ — First RPM reading (before slash) is at altitude; second RPM reading is at sea level.
④ — Adjust Calif. Auto. Trans. to 760 RPM with 60 RPM drop.

COLD (FAST) IDLE RPM

Accord & Civic CVCC — With engine at normal operating temperature, choke pulled out to second detent, A/C off, and cooling fan and headlights on, fast idle speed should be within specifications. If not, adjust by altering size of slot in fast idle link. To lower RPM, narrow the slot; to increase RPM, widen slot.

Civic — With engine at normal operating temperature, choke knob should return to off position when pulled out. Position reference arm of choke lever to reference boss on air horn. Engine speed should be within specifications.

Fast Idle RPM

Application	RPM
Accord & Civic CVCC	
Man. Trans.	2500-3500
Auto. Trans.	2000-3000
Civic	1400-2200

THROTTLE CONTROLLER

DIAPHRAGM SET SPEED

Connect a vacuum pump directly to the vacuum port of throttle controller diaphragm. Draw a vacuum in excess of 16 in. Hg (400 mm Hg). Engine speed should be as follows:

Diaphragm Set Speed

Application	RPM
Accord & Civic CVCC	
Man. Trans.	2200-3200
Auto. Trans.	1700-2700
Civic	1300-1900

DASH POT CHECK

Reconnect vacuum line. Raise engine speed to 3500 RPM for 2 to 3 seconds. Release throttle and check time required for throttle to close:

Throttle Closing Time

Application	Time Required
Accord & Civic CVCC	1-4 Seconds
Civic	2-8 Seconds

THROTTLE OPENER (CALIF. & HIGH ALT.)

Accord & Civic CVCC

1) Apply battery voltage to yellow/black wire at control box connector block (connect jumper wire from battery to yellow/black wire).

2) Squeeze the vacuum hose shut between dash pot check valve and carburetor (hose No. 3).

3) Raise engine speed slowly to 3500 RPM and release throttle. It should close within 2 to 8 seconds.

SPEED SENSOR (CALIF. & HIGH ALT.)

Accord & Civic CVCC

Connect voltmeter positive probe to the yellow/black wire at control box connector block. Connect negative probe to any convenient ground. Raise both wheels off ground and place vehicle on safety stands.

TUNE-UP (Cont.)

Speed Sensor Test Conditions

Application	No Voltage Below	Voltage Present Above
Accord	10 mph	20 mph
Civic CVCC	5 mph	15 mph

FUEL PUMP PRESSURE & VOLUME

Pressure (At Cranking Speed)
All Models .... 2-3 psi (.13-.18 kg/cm²)
Volume (At Cranking Speed)
All Models .... .4 pts. in 30 sec.

EMISSION CONTROL SYSTEMS

See Mitchell Manuals' Emission Control Manual.

GENERAL SERVICING

IGNITION

DISTRIBUTOR

All models are equipped with Hitachi single point distributors.

Other Data & Specifications – *See Tune-Up and Hitachi Distributors in ELECTRICAL Section.*

IGNITION COIL

Resistance	Ohms at 68°F (20°C)
Primary	
Accord & Civic CVCC	1.35-1.65
Civic	3.42-4.12
Secondary	
Accord & Civic CVCC	8,000-12,000
Civic	6,400-9,600
Ballast Resistor	1.44-1.76

FUEL SYSTEMS

CARBURETORS

Application	Model
Accord	Keihin 15A, 15B, 15BA, 16A, 16B
Civic	Keihin 06, 07A
Civic CVCC	Keihin 12A, 12B, 13A, 13B

Other Data & Specifications – *See Tune-Up and Keihin Carburetors in FUEL SYSTEMS Section.*

ELECTRICAL

BATTERY

12 Volt – Negative Ground.

Application	Amp. Hour
All Models	47

Battery Location – Under hood on right front side.

STARTER

Application	Type
Accord	Nippondenso Overrunning Clutch
Civic	Hitachi Overrunning Clutch
Civic CVCC	Nippondenso Overrunning Clutch

Free Speed Voltage
Accord .... 11.5 at 5000 RPM (Min.)
Civic .... 12 at 7000 RPM
Civic CVCC .... 11.5 at 7000 RPM
Free Speed Amperage
Accord .... 90 Amps. (Max.) at 5000 RPM (Min.)
Civic .... 70 Amps. (Max.) at 7000 RPM
Civic CVCC .... 80 Amps. (Max.) at 7000 RPM

Other Data & Specifications – *See Hitachi or Nippondenso Starters in ELECTRICAL Section.*

ALTERNATOR

Application	Rated Amp. Output (2000 RPM)
Accord	50
Civic	40
Civic CVCC	
Without A/C	35
With A/C	45

Other Data & Specifications – *See Nippondenso Alternators and Regulators in ELECTRICAL Section.*

ALTERNATOR REGULATOR

All models are equipped with Nippondenso alternator regulators with an operating voltage of 13.5-14.5 volts.

Other Data & Specifications – *See Nippondenso Alternators and Regulators in ELECTRICAL Section.*

ENGINE

INTAKE MANIFOLD TIGHTENING

Tighten intake manifold attaching bolts to the following specifications.

GENERAL SERVICING (Cont.)

Intake Manifold Tightening Specifications

Application	Ft. Lbs. (mkg)
Accord	14-17 (2.0-2.4)
Civic	13-17 (1.8-2.4)
Civic CVCC	16 (2.2)

FILTERS & CLEANERS

Filter or Cleaner	Service Interval (Miles)
Oil Filter	Replace every 5000
Air Cleaner	Replace every 15,000
Fuel Filter	①
Charcoal Canister	Replace every 30,000

① – Replace at first 15,000 miles and then every 30,000 miles thereafter.

BELT ADJUSTMENT

All Models – Deflection of belt should be .47-.67" (12-17 mm) when 19.8-24.3 lbs. (9-11 kg) pressure is applied midway between alternator and fan pulleys.

CAPACITIES

Application	Quantity
Crankcase (Includes Filter)	
All Models	3.2 qts.
Cooling System (Includes Heater)	
Accord	5.3 qts.
All Other Models	4.2 qts.
Man. Trans. (SAE 10W-40)	
4-Speed	2.6 qts.
5-Speed	2.8 qts.
Auto. Trans. (Dexron)	2.6 qts.
Fuel Tank	
Accord	13.2 gals.
Civic	10.0 gals.
Civic CVCC Station Wagon	11.1 gals
All Other Models	10.6 gals

TUNE-UP

XJ6

ENGINE IDENTIFICATION

Engine number is stamped on top of cylinder block at rear of engine. Number is also stamped on Commission Plate, which is located in the engine compartment. Suffix following engine number indicates compression ratio, "L" — Low.

MODEL IDENTIFICATION

VEHICLE IDENTIFICATION NUMBER

Number is stamped on a metal tag and attached to the left side rear pillar. Information on tag identifies production date and chassis number.

COMPRESSION PRESSURE

Check compression pressure with engine at normal operating temperature, throttle valve wide open, all spark plugs removed and coil wire disconnected. Compression pressure is normal if all cylinders are within 5 psi (.35 kg/cm²) of each other.

VALVE TAPPET CLEARANCE

Application	Clearance (Cold)
Intake	.012-.014" (.30-.35 mm)
Exhaust	.012-.014" (.30-.35 mm)

VALVE TAPPET ADJUSTMENT

1) With camshaft covers removed, rotate camshafts and record clearance between heel of each cam lobe and its respective tappet. If adjustment is necessary, rotate camshaft and install valve timing gauge (C.3993) before removing final camshaft retaining nut. If required, disconnect sprockets from camshafts.

NOTE — *DO NOT rotate engine while camshaft sprockets are disconnected.*

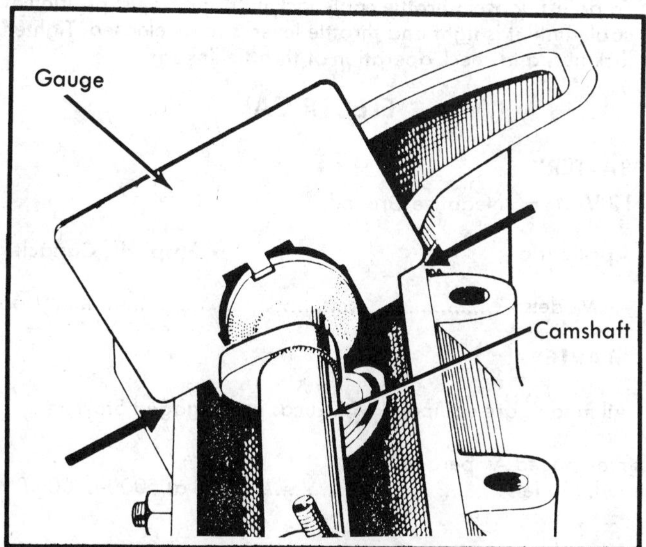

Fig. 1 Position of Valve Timing Gauge

2) Remove camshaft bearing caps and lift off camshaft. Remove each tappet that requires adjustment and note its location for reassembly in its original position. Remove adjusting pad. Subtract specified valve clearance from initial clearance measured. Select appropriate adjusting shim which will equal this measurement. Adjusting pads are available in increments of .001" (.03 mm) from .085" (2.16 mm) to .110" (2.79 mm) and are marked with letters from "A" to "Z" respectively.

3) Insert correct adjusting pads and install tappets. Attach camshafts (using timing gauge). Torque camshaft bearing cap nuts to 9 ft. lbs. (1.2 mkg), connect camshaft sprockets, and install camshaft covers.

VALVE ARRANGEMENT

Left Side — All Exhaust
Right Side — All Intake

SPARK PLUGS

Gap .... .025" (.64 mm)
Torque .... 27 ft. lbs (3.7 mkg)

Spark Plug Type

Application	Champion No.
All Models	N-11Y

HIGH TENSION WIRE RESISTANCE

Carefully remove high tension wires from spark plugs and distributor cap. Using an ohmmeter, check resistance of each wire while gently twisting wire. If resistance is not to specifications, or fluctuates from infinity to any value, replace wire.

Resistance (Ohms) Per Wire

Application	Resistance
All Models	25,000-30,000

DISTRIBUTOR

NOTE — *All models are equipped with Opus Electronic System.*

Pick-Up Module Air Gap .... ①.014-.016" (.36-.41 mm)

① — Measured between rotor and pick-up module.

IGNITION TIMING

Check or adjust ignition timing with engine at normal operating temperature, idle speed set to specification and distributor vacuum line connected. If timing is not correct, loosen distributor clamp bolt and rotate distributor to achieve specified timing. Then tighten clamp bolt.

Ignition Timing Specifications

Application	Timing
All Models At 750 RPM	8°BTDC

TUNE-UP (Cont.)

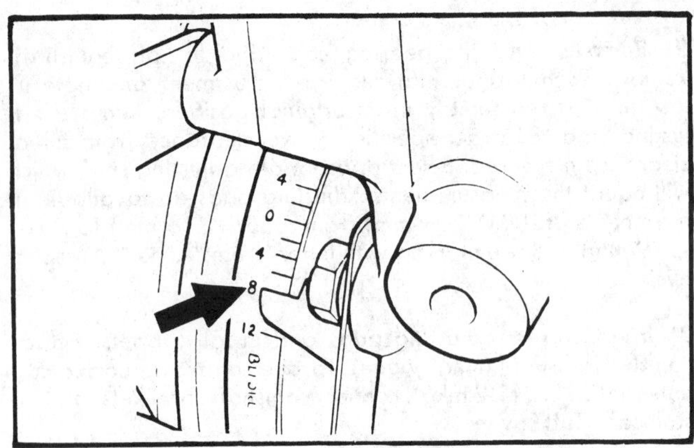

Fig. 2 Ignition Timing Mark Location

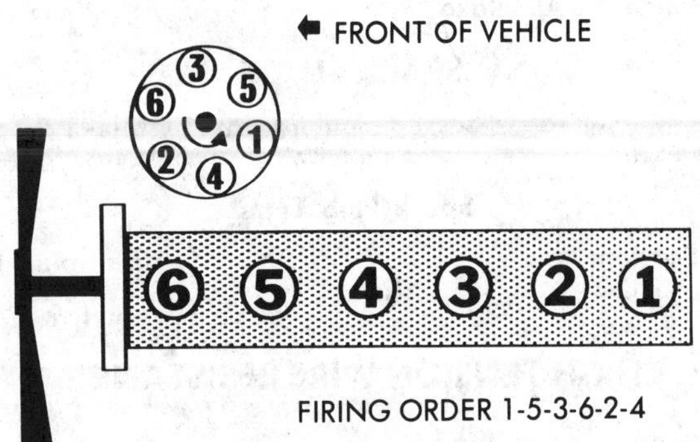

Fig. 3 Firing Order and Distributor Rotation

HOT (SLOW) IDLE RPM

1) With engine at normal operating temperature, connect a tachometer and exhaust gas analyzer to vehicle. Ensure that oil level in carburetor dampers is ¼" below top of piston guide rod.

2) Loosen idle screw of each carburetor until it no longer contacts throttle lever. Make sure choke is fully open. Loosen clamp bolts on throttle interconnecting shaft and make sure both throttles are fully closed, then tighten clamping bolts.

3) Screw in rear idle screw until contact is made with throttle lever. Start engine and adjust rear idle screw until specified idle speed RPM is obtained. Screw in front idle screw until contact is made with throttle lever, then synchronize carburetors using air flow balance meter.

4) Disconnect air injection system and check CO level. If CO level is not within specifications, adjust mixture needles using special tool (BLT2010), move each needle an equal amount. Move needles ⅛ turn at a time. Clockwise rotation richens mixture and counterclockwise rotation leans mixture.

Idle Speed (RPM) & CO Level (%)

Application	Idle RPM	CO %
All Models	750	2.0-4.5

COLD (FAST) IDLE RPM

With engine at normal operating temperature and idle speed set to specifications, loosen lock nut on rear carburetor fast idle screw. Adjust fast idle screw until gap between head of screw and fast idle cam is .045-.055" (1.1-1.4 mm). Tighten lock nut.

FUEL PUMP PRESSURE

Pressure .... 2.5-3.0 psi (.18-.21 kg/cm²)

EMISSION CONTROL SYSTEMS

See Mitchell Manuals' Emission Control Manual.

GENERAL SERVICING

IGNITION

DISTRIBUTOR

All models are equipped with Lucas Opus Electronic Ignition System.

Other Data & Specifications – *See Tune-up & Lucas Distributors in ELECTRICAL Section.*

FUEL SYSTEMS

CARBURETORS

Application	Model
All Models	①Zenith-Stromberg 175 CD2SET

① – All models are equipped with two carburetors.

Other Data & Specifications – *See Tune-Up and Zenith-Stromberg Carburetors in FUEL SYSTEMS Section.*

THROTTLE LINKAGE ADJUSTMENT

To adjust, loosen throttle cable lock nuts and adjust position of cable until it is tight and throttle lever is fully released. Tighten lock nuts and check operation of throttle linkage.

ELECTRICAL

BATTERY

12 Volt – Negative Ground.

Application	Amp. Hr. Capacity
All Models	66

STARTER

All models are equipped with Lucas pre-engaged Starters.

Free Speed Amperage
All Models .... 100 at 5000-6000 RPM

Other Data & Specifications – *See Lucas Starters in ELECTRICAL Section.*

GENERAL SERVICING (Cont.)

ALTERNATOR REGULATOR

Lucas — Non-Adjustable; Integral with Alternator.

Other Data & Specifications — *See Lucas Alternators & Regulators in ELECTRICAL Section.*

ALTERNATOR

Application	Rated Amp. Output
All Models	
With A/C	66
Without A/C	45

Other Data & Specifications — *See Lucas Alternators & Regulators in ELECTRICAL Section.*

BELT ADJUSTMENT

Belt	① Deflection
Fan/Steering Pump	Self Adjusting
Alternator	.15"(3.8 mm)
Air Conditioning	.17"(4.3 mm)

① — Deflection is with pressure applied midway on longest belt run.

CAPACITIES

Application	Quantity
Crankcase (Includes Filter)	8.7 qts.
Cooling System	19.5 qts.
Auto. Trans. (Type F)	8.6 qts.
Rear Axle (SAE 90 E.P.)	3.25 pts.
Fuel Tank	
Right Side	12.6 gals.
Left Side	12.6 gals.

FILTERS & CLEANERS

Filter or Cleaner	Service Intervals (Miles)
Oil Filter	Replace every 6000
Air Cleaner	Replace every 12,000
Engine Breather Filter	Replace every 12,000
Fuel Filter	①
Charcoal Canister	Replace every 50,000

① — Replace at 1000 miles and then every 6,000 miles.

TUNE-UP

XJ12
XJS

ENGINE IDENTIFICATION

Engine identification number is stamped on rear of crankcase between cylinder heads.

MODEL IDENTIFICATION

VEHICLE IDENTIFICATION NUMBER

Vehicle identification number is stamped on a plate which is located on right side of firewall adjacent to the heater.

COMPRESSION PRESSURE

Check compression pressure with engine at normal operating temperature, spark plugs removed, throttle wide open and engine at cranking speed. Pressure should be 120-140 psi (8.4-9.8 kg/cm²) with a maximum variation between cylinders of 5 psi (.35 kg/cm²).

VALVE TAPPET CLEARANCE

Application	Clearance (Cold)
All Models	
Intake	.012-.014" (.30-.35mm)
Exhaust	.012-.014" (.30-.35mm)

1) With intake manifolds and camshaft covers removed, check clearance between each tappet and heel of each cam. Record clearance for each valve and then subtract appropriate valve clearance from clearance obtained. Select suitable adjusting pads which equal this new measurement.

2) To install new adjusting pads, proceed as follows to remove camshaft and tappets: Bend back locking tabs and remove two camshaft sprocket retaining bolts. Rotate engine until access to remaining bolts is obtained. Bend back locking tabs, mark position of camshaft to sprocket, and remove bolts.

3) Using suitable tool (Jaguar Sprocket Retaining Tool JD.40) hold sprocket in place. Lift camshaft out of tappet block. Remove tappets and install adjusting pads.

NOTE — *Do not rotate engine with camshaft disconnected.*

4) Reinstall tappets, camshaft, bearing caps, washers and nuts. Tighten bearing cap nuts evenly to 9 ft. lbs. (1.2 mkg). Recheck valve clearance, reassemble, replace camshaft cover and manifolds.

NOTE — *Adjusting pads are available in .001" (.03 mm) increment sizes from .085-.110" (2.16-2.79 mm). Pads have a letter stamped on surface which indicates size ("A" through "Z" respectively).*

VALVE ARRANGEMENT

E-I-E-I-E-I-I-E-I-E-I-E (both banks, front-to-rear)

SPARK PLUGS

Gap	.035" (.9 mm)
Torque	25 ft. lbs. (3.5 mkg)

Spark Plug Type

Application	Champion No.
All Models	N-10Y

HIGH TENSION WIRE RESISTANCE

Carefully remove high tension wires from spark plugs and distributor cap. Using an ohmmeter, check high tension wire resistance while gently twisting wires. If resistance is not to specifications, or fluctuates from infinity to any value, replace high tension wire(s).

Resistance (Ohms) Per Wire

Application	Ohms
All Models	25,000-30,000

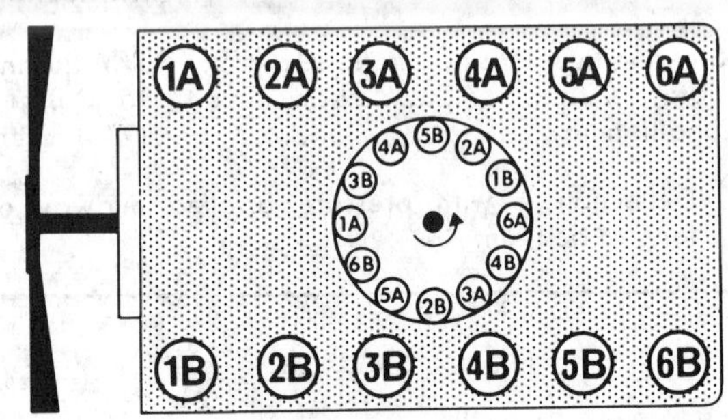

Fig. 1 Firing Order and Distributor Rotation

DISTRIBUTOR

NOTE — *All models equipped with Lucas Opus Electronic Ignition System.*

Pick-Up Module Air Gap	①.020-.022" (.50-.55mm)
Resistance	
Center Terminal to Outer Terminal with Red Cable	2.25-2.75 ohms
Center Terminal to Outer Terminal with Black Cable	.81-.99 ohms

① — Measured between rotor and pick-up module.

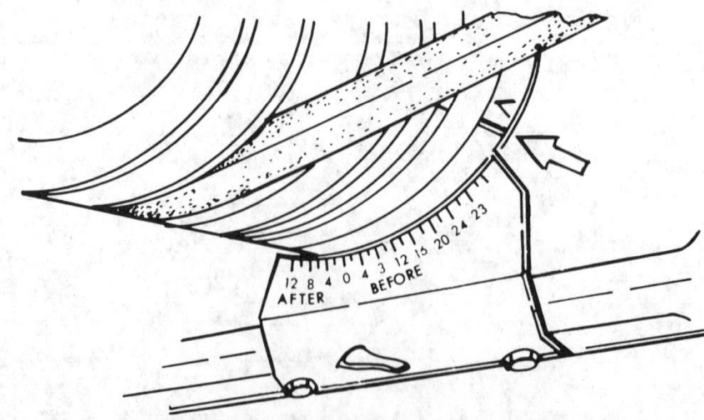

Fig. 2 Ignition Timing Mark Location

TUNE-UP (Cont.)

IGNITION TIMING

Set ignition timing with engine at specified idle RPM and distributor vacuum hose connected. If timing is not 10° BTDC, adjust distributor to achieve specified timing. *See Fig. 2.*

Ignition Timing Specifications

Application	Timing
All Models	10°BTDC

HOT (SLOW) IDLE RPM

1) Idle speed is controlled by Auxiliary Air Valve which is located on left cylinder bank rear water pipe. With engine at normal operating temperature, throttle linkage correctly set, and transmission in neutral, adjust idle screw to obtain specified idle speed RPM.

NOTE — *Idle CO should be checked with air injection system inoperative. Remove blanking plug from diverter valve diaphragm housing.*

2) Use an exhaust gas analyzer to check CO level. Electronic Control Unit (ECU), located in trunk of vehicle, is used to control CO level. Adjust ECU control knob one "click" at a time until specified level is reached.

3) With engine running at idle, check CO levels at sample points located in air injection distribution rails.

4) Check both banks for correct CO level. A high reading on one bank could indicate a leaking injector or cold start injector.

NOTE — *If adjusting procedures take over two minutes, engine must be run at 2500 RPM for 30 seconds. A hot engine may operate thermostatic vacuum switch and advance ignition timing.*

Idle Speed (RPM) & CO Level (%)

Application	Idle RPM	Idle CO %
All Models	750	1-2

FUEL PUMP PRESSURE

Pressure .... 28.5-30 psi (2.0-2.1 kg/cm^2)

EMISSION CONTROL SYSTEMS

See Mitchell Manuals' Emission Control Manual.

GENERAL SERVICING

IGNITION

DISTRIBUTOR

All models are equipped with Lucas Opus Electronic Ignition System.

Other Data & Specifications — *See Tune-Up and Lucas Distributors in ELECTRICAL Section.*

IGNITION COIL

Resistance	Ohms at 68° F (20° C)
Primary	
XJ12	0.8-1.0
XJS	0.9-1.1

FUEL SYSTEMS

FUEL INJECTION

All models are equipped with Lucas-Jaguar Electronic Fuel Injection System.

Other Data & Specifications — *See Tune-Up and Lucas-Jaguar Electronic Fuel Injection in FUEL SYSTEMS Section.*

THROTTLE LINKAGE ADJUSTMENT

1) Release throttle cross-rods from throttle pulley. Loosen clamps securing levers to rear of throttle shafts. With butterfly valves closed against their stops, relay arm against its stop and play in coupling taken up in opening direction, tighten clamp-to-lever on rear of throttle shaft. Repeat procedure for the other side of engine.

2) Now try to refit cross-rods to ball connectors on pulley; rods must fit without moving pulley or linkage. If rods will not fit without moving pulley or linkage, loosen lock nut on cross-rods and adjust length until attachment can be accomplished without moving any part of linkage. Tighten lock nuts and ensure ball joints remain free.

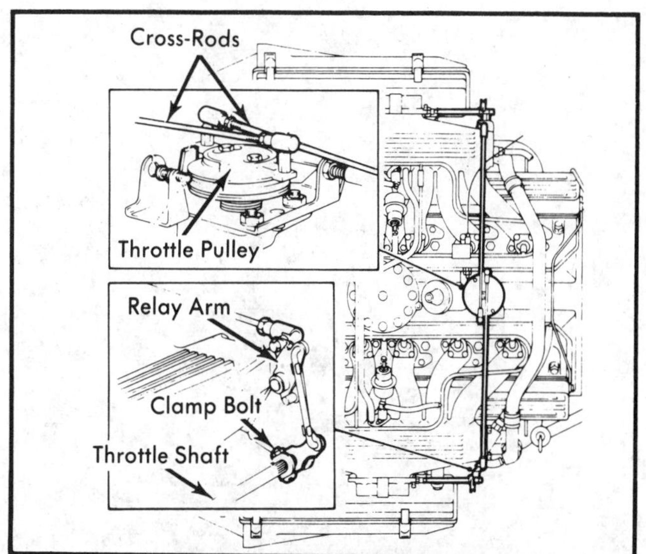

Fig. 3 Throttle Linkage Adjustment Points

GENERAL SERVICING (Cont.)

3) Loosen lock nut on throttle pulley and back out stop screw to full extent of travel. Hold throttle relay arm pulley fully open and check that butterfly stop arms are against throttle housing. Adjust stop to just touch throttle pulley and tighten lock nut.

ELECTRICAL

BATTERY

12 Volt – Negative ground.

Application	Amp. Hr. Rating
All Models	68

Battery Location – Under hood on right side.

STARTER

All models are equipped with a Lucas pre-engaged Starter.

Free Speed Amperage

XJS	100 at 5000-7000 RPM
XJ12	100 at 5000-6000 RPM

Other Data & Specifications – *See Lucas Starters in ELECTRICAL Section.*

ALTERNATOR

Application	Rated Amp. Output
All Models	66

Other Data & Specifications – *See Lucas Alternators & Regulators in ELECTRICAL Section.*

ALTERNATOR REGULATOR

Lucas – Non-Adjustable; integral with alternator.

Other Data & Specifications – *See Lucas Alternators & Regulators in ELECTRICAL Section.*

BELT ADJUSTMENT

Alternator Belt – With a pressure of 3.2 lbs. (1.5 kg) applied midway on longest belt run, belt deflection should be .16" (4.3 mm).

All Other Belts – With a pressure of 6.4 lbs. (2.9 kg) applied midway on longest belt run, belt deflection should be .16-.22" (4.3-5.6 mm).

FILTERS & CLEANERS

Filter or Cleaner	Service Interval (Miles)
Oil Filter	Replace every 6,000
Air Filter	Replace every 12,500
Fuel Line Filter	Replace every 6,000
Crankcase Breather	Clean every 12,500
Charcoal Canister	Replace every 25,000

CAPACITIES

Application	XJS Quantity	XJ12 Quantity
Crankcase (Inc. Filter)	12 qts.	11.4 qts.
Cooling System	22.2 qts.	21.5 qts.
Auto. Trans. (Type F)	9.6 qts.	9.9 qts.
Rear Axle (SAE 90 EP)	3.3 pts.	3.25 pts.
Fuel Tank		
XJS	24 gals.	.....
XJ12 R.H.	.....	12.6 gals.
XJ12 L.H.	.....	12.6 gals.

TUNE-UP

Lancia Beta, All Models

ENGINE IDENTIFICATION

Engine identification number is found on top edge of firewall in engine compartment.

Application	Code
1800 cc	
Federal	828 A1.040.6
California	828 A1.031.6

MODEL IDENTIFICATION

Vehicle identification number appears on left side of instrument panel, visible through windshield. Chassis number also appears on trailing edge of left door.

Application	Code
Coupe	828 AC.1
Sedan	828 CB.6
HPE	828 AF.1

COMPRESSION PRESSURE

With engine at normal operating temperature and NOT running, remove spark plugs and disconnect lead from ignition coil. Starting with cylinder No. 1 (front of engine), check compression by cranking with accelerator fully depressed.

Compression Pressure

Application	psi (kg/cm²)
All Models	①114 (8)

① — Maximum allowable variation between cylinders not to exceed 10%.

VALVE TAPPET CLEARANCE

1) Remove air cleaner, choke control valve, spark plug wires, intermediate tubing and EGR valve. Remove both valve tappet covers.

NOTE — *Perform check with engine cold.*

2) Turn crankshaft to bring cylinder No. 1 to TDC of ignition stroke (noted by camshaft lobes of appropriate tappets pointing upward).

3) Use feeler gauge to check and note clearance at intake and exhaust valves. Adjustment may be made by use of shims. Recheck clearance after adjustment. Repeat procedure for each cylinder.

Valve Clearance Specifications

Application	Intake In. (mm)	Exhaust In. (mm)
All Models	.016-.019 (.41-.48)	.018-.021 (.45-.51)

VALVE ARRANGEMENT

Left Side — All Intake. (Viewed from flywheel end).

Right Side — All Exhaust. (Viewed from flywheel end).

SPARK PLUGS

Gap (All Models) .023-.027" (.58-.68 mm)

Spark Plug Type

Application	Champion No.
All Models	N9Y

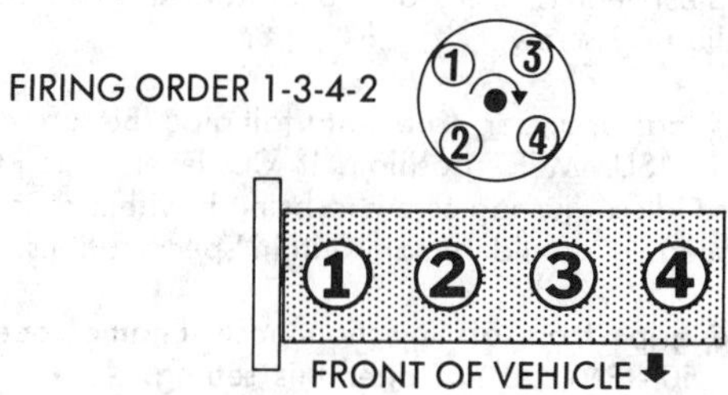

Fig. 1 Firing Order and Distributor Rotation

DISTRIBUTOR

Point Gap	
Exc. Calif.	.012-.019" (.30-.48 mm)
Calif.	.015-.017" (.38-.43 mm)
Cam Angle	55°±3°

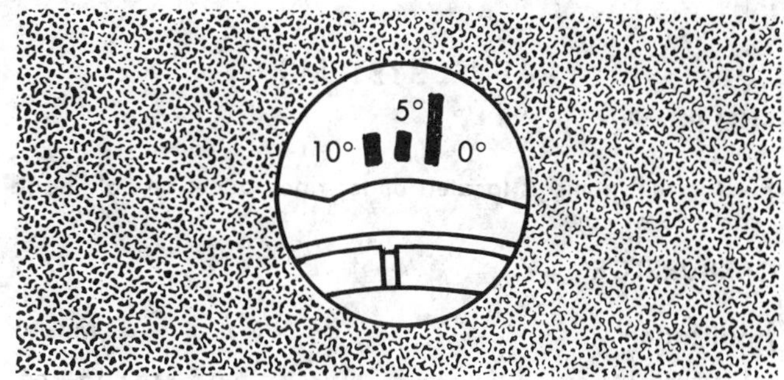

Fig. 2 Ignition Timing Mark Location (Viewed From Right Front Wheel Well)

IGNITION TIMING

1) Turn front wheels fully to right to gain access to right wheel well. Remove rubber plug from inner fender panel.

2) Connect timing light and run engine until normal operating temperatures are reached. Set engine at normal curb idle. Check "fixed advance" setting.

3) Increase engine RPM to 3600 and check "automatic advance" setting. Adjust distributor position as necessary to attain settings. Recheck timing after adjustment.

Ignition Timing Specifications

Application	Fixed Advance @850±50 RPM	Auto. Advance @3600 RPM
All Models		
Exc. Calif.	0°	36°
Calif.	10°	28°

TUNE-UP (Cont.)

IDLE SPEED & MIXTURE

1) Run engine until normal operating temperatures are reached (cooling fan cuts in). With air cleaner and cover installed, set air cleaner to "SUMMER" position (reset to appropriate season after adjustment).

2) Using vise grip pliers, pinch off air injection hose to exhaust manifold (between diverter valve and non-return valves). After cooling fan cuts out, turn idle speed adjusting screw to obtain smoothest engine operation at specified RPM setting.

3) If further adjustment is necessary to obtain RPM setting, turn throttle adjusting screw.

4) Insert exhaust gas analyzer probe into tail pipe. Be sure air cleaner is still in "SUMMER" position. If CO level is not to specification, use idle adjusting screw to bring it within range. Recheck idle speed. It should remain within specifications.

5) Remove vise grips from air injection hose. Engine speed should increase 50 RPM. Do not alter this setting.

Idle Speed (RPM) & CO Level (%)

Application	RPM	CO%
All Models	800-850	2±.5

COLD (FAST) IDLE

After setting curb idle, depress fast idle checking button (located near right front suspension mounting in engine compartment). Hold button down while opening and closing throttle. Fast idle should register within specification. Adjust with fast idle screw, if necessary.

Cold (Fast) Idle Specification

Application	RPM
All Models	1550-1650

EMISSION CONTROL SYSTEMS

See Mitchell Manuals' Emission Control Manual.

GENERAL SERVICING

IGNITION

DISTRIBUTOR

Federal models use a Marelli 401 P1 distributor; California models a Marelli 401 P3 distributor.

Other Data & Specifications – *See Tune-Up and Marelli distributors in ELECTRICAL section.*

FUEL SYSTEMS

FUEL PUMP

Electric fuel pump is located under floor panel on right-hand rear side of car.

CARBURETOR

Application	Model
Federal Models	Weber 32 DATRA 13/100
California Models	Weber 32 DATRA 12/101

Other Data & Specifications – *See Tune-Up and Weber carburetors in FUEL SYSTEMS section.*

ELECTRICAL

BATTERY

12-Volt – Negative Ground.

Application	Amp. Hr. Rating
Sedan	60
All Other Models	45

Battery Location – In engine compartment on left side.

STARTER

Bosch	Overrunning Clutch
Free Speed Voltage	11-11.5 at 4800 RPM
Free Speed Amperage	27-40 at 4800 RPM

Other Data & Specifications – *See Bosch starters in ELECTRICAL section.*

ALTERNATOR

All models use a Bosch K1 14-volt alternator with built-in electronic regulator.

Application	Rated Amp. Output
All Models	55

Other Data & Specifications – *See Bosch alternators in ELECTRICAL section.*

BELT ADJUSTMENT

Application	①Deflection
All Models	.39-.49" (9.9-12.5 mm)

① – Deflection is with 11 pounds (4.99 kg) pressure applied midway between water pump and alternator.

FILTERS & CLEANERS

Filter or Cleaner	Service Interval (Miles)
Oil Filter	Replace Every 6,000
Air Cleaner	Replace Every 12,500
Fuel Filter	Replace Every 12,500
EGR Valve & Cat. Converter	①Inspect Every 25,000
Evap. Canister Filter	Replace Every 25,000

① – Clean, inspect and reset warning light.

CAPACITIES

Application	Quantity
Crankcase (Includes Filter)	①5.2 qts.
Cooling System (Includes Heater)	8.8 qts.
Transaxle (SAE 40/50)	2.56 qts.
Fuel Tank	②12.5 gals.

① – 4.25 qts. without filter change.
② – Includes 2.1 gals. in reserve.

TUNE-UP

LUV

ENGINE IDENTIFICATION

Engine serial number is stamped on pad between distributor and cylinder head.

MODEL IDENTIFICATION

VEHICLE IDENTIFICATION NUMBER

Vehicle identification number is stamped on a plate attached to rear face of drivers door.

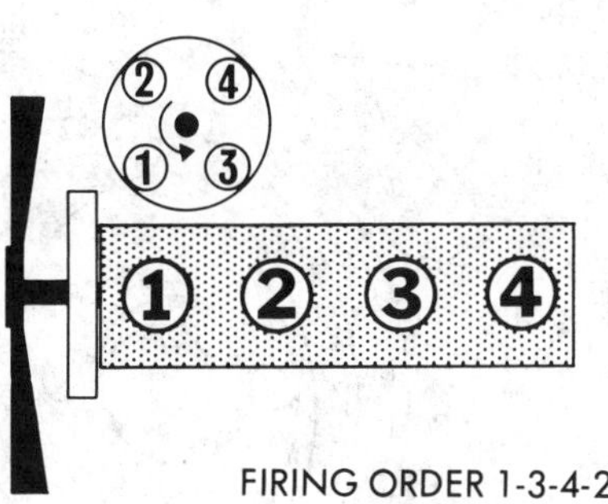

Fig. 1 Firing Order and Distributor Rotation

COMPRESSION PRESSURE

Test compression with engine at normal operating temperature, spark plugs removed, throttle valve wide open and engine at cranking speed. Maximum variation between cylinders should not exceed 8.5 psi (.6 kg/cm²).

Compression Pressure @ 300 RPM

Application	Min. Pressure psi (kg/cm²)	Std. Pressure psi (kg/cm²)
All Models	119 (8.4)	171 (12)

VALVE TAPPET CLEARANCE

NOTE — *Before adjusting valve tappet clearance, check torque of cylinder head and camshaft bolts. Valves should be adjusted every 15,000 miles.*

1) Measure valve clearance between rocker arm and valve stem. Position piston number one on compression stroke at TDC. Adjust intake valves 1 and 2 and exhaust valves 1 and 3.

2) Turn crankshaft one full turn until number four cylinder is at TDC. Adjust intake valves 3 and 4 and exhaust valves 2 and 4.

Valve Tappet Clearance

Application	Clearance (Cold)
Intake	.006" (.15 mm)
Exhaust	.010" (.25 mm)

VALVE ARRANGEMENT

All Models
Right Side — All Intake
Left Side — All Exhaust

SPARK PLUGS

Gap .... .030" (.8 mm)
Torque .... 18-25 ft. lbs. (2.5-3.5 mkg)

Spark Plug Type

Application	AC	NGK
All Models	R44XLS	BPR6ES

HIGH TENSION WIRE RESISTANCE

Carefully remove high tension wires from spark plugs and from distributor cap. Using an ohmmeter, check resistance of wire while gently twisting wire. If resistance is not to specification, or fluctuates from infinity to any value, replace wire.

Resistance (Ohms)

Application	Resistance
All Models	25,000-30,000

DISTRIBUTOR

Point Gap .... .016-.022" (.41-.51 mm)
Cam Angle .... 47-57°
Breaker Arm Spring Tension .... 17-22 ozs. (500-635 g)
Condenser Capacity .... .20-.24 mfd.

IGNITION TIMING

1) With engine at normal operating temperature, connect a timing light to either number one or number four cylinder. Disconnect distributor vacuum line and plug end. Check timing with marks on crankshaft pulley and rotate distributor to adjust timing.

TUNE-UP (Cont.)

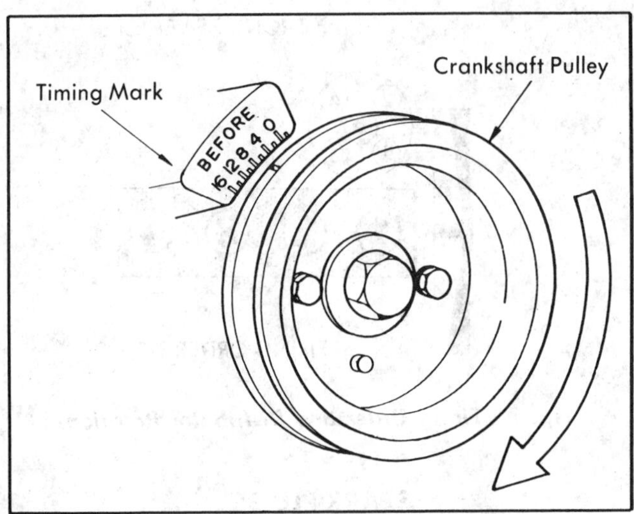

Fig. 2 Ignition Timing Mark Location

Ignition Timing Specifications

Application	Timing
All Models	①6° BTDC

① — With engine running at 900 RPM.

HOT (SLOW) IDLE RPM

Set idle with engine at normal operating temperature, valve clearance correctly set and ignition timing to specifications. Choke should be open, air conditioning off and air cleaner installed. Disconnect distributor vacuum line and hot idle compensator vacuum line and plug both. Then proceed as follows:

1) Turn mixture adjusting screw all the way in, then back out three complete turns. Adjust idle speed screw until 900 RPM is reached. Adjust idle mixture screw for maximum RPM.

2) Readjust idle speed screw for 900 RPM. Turn mixture adjusting screw clockwise (lean) until 850 RPM is reached. Then turn idle mixture screw ½ turn counterclockwise (rich).

3) Adjust idle speed screw for a final idle speed of 900 RPM.

4) On vehicles with air conditioning, turn air conditioning on max cold and high blower. Open throttle enough to allow speed up solenoid to reach full travel. Then adjust speed up controller adjusting screw for an idle speed of 900 RPM.

Idle Speed (RPM) & CO Level (%)

Application	Idle RPM	C0 %
All Models	900	①

① — See Emission Control Decal.

COLD (FAST) IDLE RPM

Automatic choke fast idle is adjusted by opening angle of throttle valve on carburetor, rather than by engine speed. Adjust valve opening at 1st step of fast idle cam to 16-18°.

Disconnect and plug distributor, hot idle compensator and EGR valve vacuum lines after engine warm up. Adjust idle speed as follows:

Fast Idle Specifications

Application	Engine Speed
Man. Trans.	3400 RPM
Auto. Trans.	3200 RPM

AUTOMATIC CHOKE

Automatic choke is correctly set when thickest line on the thermostat housing is aligned with index mark on thermostat cover.

FUEL PUMP PRESSURE

Pressure	3.6 psi (.25 kg/cm^2)

EMISSION CONTROL SYSTEMS

See Mitchell Manuals' Emission Control Manual.

GENERAL SERVICING

IGNITION

DISTRIBUTOR

All Models are equipped with a Nippondenso single point distributor.

Other Data & Specifications — *See Tune-Up & Nippondenso Distributors in ELECTRICAL Section.*

IGNITION COIL

Resistance	Ohms
Primary	1.3-1.4
Secondary	7,650-9,350

FUEL SYSTEMS

CARBURETORS

Application	Model
LUV 2-Bbl	Hitachi DCP-340-1

Other Data & Specifications — *See Tune-Up & Hitachi Carburetors in FUEL SYSTEMS Section.*

ELECTRICAL

BATTERY

12 Volt — Negative Ground.

GENERAL SERVICING (Cont.)

Application	Amp. Hr. Rating
LUV	50

Battery Location – Engine compartment, left side of engine.

STARTER

Hitachi	Overrunning Clutch
Free Speed Voltage	12 at 6000 RPM
Free Speed Amperage	60 at 6000 RPM

Other Data & Specifications – *See Hitachi Starters in ELECTRICAL Section.*

ALTERNATOR

Application	Rated Amp. Output
LUV	35

Other Data & Specifications – *See Hitachi Alternators & Regulators in ELECTRICAL Section.*

ALTERNATOR REGULATOR

All models utilize a Hitachi adjustable alternator regulator with an operating voltage of 13.8-14.8 volts.

Other Data & Specifications – *See Hitachi Alternators & Regulators in ELECTRICAL Section.*

BELT ADJUSTMENT

Belt deflection for both drive belts should be .4" (10mm) with pressure applied midway on belt run.

FILTERS & CLEANERS

Filter or Cleaner	Service Interval (Miles)
Oil Filter	①Replace every 15,000
Air Cleaner	Replace every 30,000
Fuel Filters	Replace every 15,000
PCV Valve	Replace every 15,000

① – Replace at 7500 miles and then every 15,000 miles.

CAPACITIES

Application	Quantity
Crankcase (Includes Filter)	5.7 qts.
Cooling System	6.4 qts.
Auto. Trans. (Dexron II)	6.5 qts.
Man. Trans. (SAE 30)	2.7 pts.
Rear Axle (SAE 90)	2.7 pts.
Steering Gear (SAE 90)	.63 pts.
Fuel Tank	13.2 gals.

TUNE-UP

808 1300 cc (Mizer)
GLC 1300 cc
808 1600 cc

ENGINE IDENTIFICATION

Engine number is stamped on machined surface of cylinder block.

MODEL IDENTIFICATION

VEHICLE IDENTIFICATION NUMBER

Number is stamped on identification plate which is located at left lower inner corner of windshield and visible from outside of vehicle.

COMPRESSION PRESSURE

Check compression pressure with engine at normal operating temperature, spark plugs removed, throttle valve wide open and engine at cranking speed. Crank engine until maximum pressure is reached at each cylinder. Compression is normal if maximum cylinder pressures are within 75% of each other.

Compression at 300 RPM

Application	Pressure psi (kg/cm^2)
808 1600 cc	169 (11.9)
All Others	164 (11.5)

VALVE TAPPET CLEARANCE ①

Application	Intake	Exhaust
GLC & 808 1300 cc	.010" (.25 mm)	.012" (.30 mm)
808 1600 cc	.012" (.30 mm)	.012" (.30 mm)

① – Adjust valves with engine hot.

VALVE ARRANGEMENT

All Models
Right Side – All Exhaust.
Left Side – All Intake.

SPARK PLUGS

Gap	
All Models	.029-.033" (.75-.85 mm)
Torque	11-15 ft. lbs. (1.5-2.1 mkg)

Spark Plug Type

Application	Nippondenso	NGK
All Models	W-20EP	①BP6ES

① – Use BPR6ES where required for radio interference suppression.

HIGH TENSION WIRE RESISTANCE

Carefully remove high tension wires from spark plugs and distributor cap. Using an ohmeter, check resistance of wires while gently twisting wire. If resistance is not to specification, or fluctuates from infinity to any value, replace wire.

Resistance (Ohms) of Wire

Application	Resistance
All Models	4875 Ohms per Foot

FRONT OF VEHICLE

FIRING ORDER 1-3-4-2

Fig. 1 Firing Order and Distributor Rotation (GLC & 808 1300 cc)

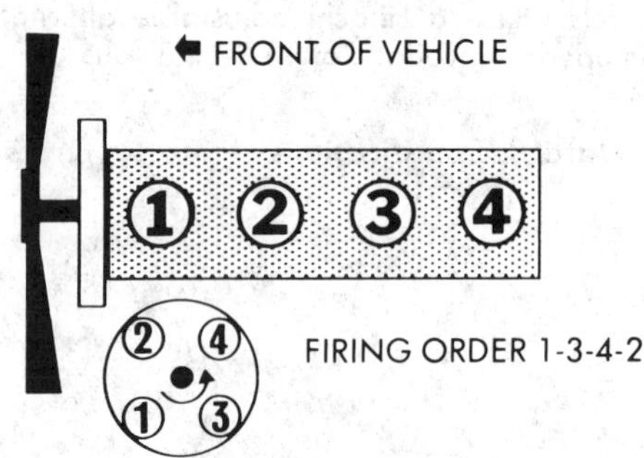

Fig. 2 Firing Order and Distributor Rotation (808 1600 cc)

DISTRIBUTOR

Point Gap	.018-.022" (.45-.55 mm)
Air Gap①	.012-.014" (.3-.35 mm)
Cam Angle	49-55°
Breaker Arm Spring Tension	17.6-22.4 oz. (500-650 g)
Condenser Capacity	.20-.24 mfd.

① – On Federal and Altitude 808 1300 cc models only.

IGNITION TIMING

808 1300 cc FEDERAL

1) Check air gap between reluctor and pickup coil. Check or adjust ignition timing with engine at normal operating temperature and idle speed to specifications.

2) Connect tachometer and timing light (to No. 1 cylinder). Check retard timing and adjust if necessary by loosening lock bolt and rotating distributor.

TUNE-UP (Cont.)

3) When timing is correct, tighten lock bolt and recheck timing.

4) Disconnect coupler from accelerator switch to operate advance (normal) timing. Check advance timing.

808 1300 cc CALIFORNIA AND GLC 1300 cc

1) Check distributor point gap. Check or adjust ignition timing with engine at normal operating temperature and idle speed to specifications. Check with automatic transmission in Drive position.

2) Connect tachometer and timing light (to No. 1 cylinder). Loosen lock bolt and rotate distributor until proper timing is obtained. Then, tighten lock bolt and recheck timing.

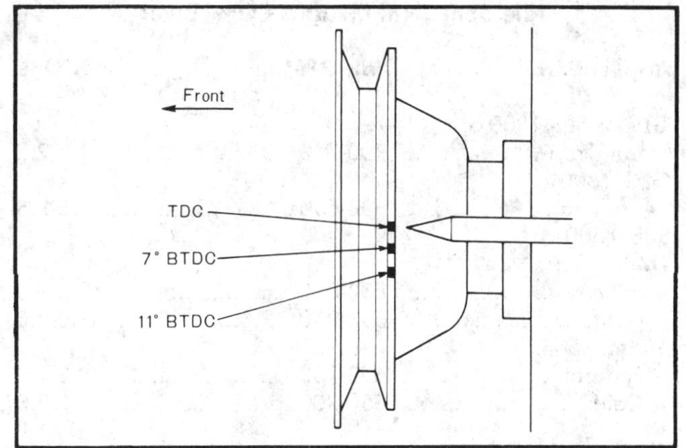

Fig. 3 Ignition Timing Mark Location (GLC and 808 1300 cc)

808 1600 cc

1) Check distributor point gap. Check or adjust ignition timing with engine at normal operating temperature and idle speed to specifications.

2) Connect tachometer and timing light (to No. 1 cylinder).

3) On Federal vehicles, disconnect coupler connecting to breaker points. Attach a jumper wire between advance terminals of coupler halves to operate advance (normal) point.

4) On all vehicles, place manual transmission in Neutral or automatic transmission in Drive position. Check advance timing.

5) If timing is incorrect, loosen lock bolt and rotate distributor housing until correct. Then, tighten lock nut and recheck timing.

6) On Federal vehicles, remove jumper wire and reconnect coupler to distributor. Check retard timing.

7) If retard timing is incorrect, loosen retard breaker plate set screws, and adjust by moving breaker plate. Do not, however, rotate distributor housing when correcting retard timing.

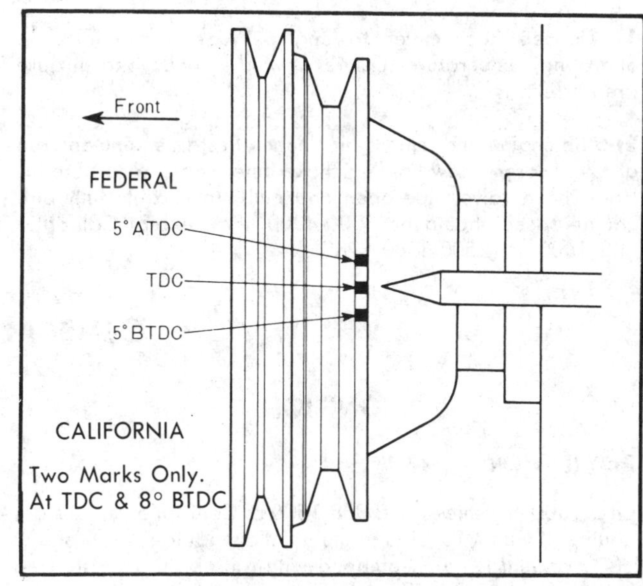

Fig. 4 Ignition Timing Mark Location (808 1600 cc)

Ignition Timing Specifications

Application	Point Gap	Timing (BTDC)
808 1300 cc		
Federal	①.012-.014" (.30-.35 mm)	②8.5-13.5°
Altitude	①.012-.014" (.30-.35 mm)	10-12°
Calif.	.018-.022" (.45-.55 mm)	10-12°
GLC 1300 cc		
Man. Trans.	.018-.022" (.45-.55 mm)	③6-8°
Auto. Trans.	.018-.022" (.45-.55 mm)	10-12°
808 1600 cc		
Federal	.018-.022" (.45-.55 mm)	④12-14°
Calif.	.018-.022" (.45-.55 mm)	7-9°

① — Air gap on transistorized ignition.
② — Retard Timing is 6-8°.
③ — California Vehicles are at 10-12°.
④ — Retard Timing is 4-6°.

IDLE SPEED AND MIXTURE

1) Set parking brake and block wheels. Turn accessories off. Connect tachometer to engine. Warm up engine and ensure choke valve is fully open.

2) Using throttle adjusting screw, adjust to proper idle speed.

3) Connect exhaust gas analyzer and follow manufacturer's instructions to check CO% level.

4) On California vehicles, disconnect hose between air pump and check valve and plug check valve port. On Federal vehicles, unhook hose between air silencer and reed valve and plug reed valve port.

5) Adjust CO% level using mixture adjusting screw. Reinstall all hoses and recheck hot idle speed. Reset if necessary.

TUNE-UP (Cont.)

Idle Speed (RPM) and CO% Level

Application	①Idle RPM	②CO%
GLC or 808 1300 cc		
Man. Trans.	700-750	1.5-2.5
GLC 1300 cc		
Auto. Trans.	600-650	1.5-2.5
808 1600 cc		
Man. Trans.		
Federal	800-850	③.3-1.0
Calif.	800-850	1.0-2.0
Auto. Trans.		
Federal	650-700	③.3-1.0
Calif.	650-700	1.0-2.0

① — With air injection.
② — Without air injection.
③ — As close to .3% as possible, but less than 1.0%.

COLD (FAST) IDLE RPM

1) Connect tachometer to engine. Warm up engine to operating temperature. Ensure slow idle speed and mixture are correct.

2) Stop engine and remove air cleaner. Restart engine and run at idle. Loosen screw holding choke outer cable to carburetor. Hold choke valve wide open and pull choke cable fully out. Engine speed should be 3000-4000 RPM, except California 808 1600 cc (2500-3500 RPM).

3) If adjustment is needed, bend choke connecting rod on GLC models. On other models, remove carburetor from engine. Invert carburetor and measure between PRIMARY throttle valve and wall of bore with choke fully closed.

4) Measurement should be as follows. If not within specifications on 808 1300 cc and 1600 cc vehicles, bend fast idle rod until clearance is correct:

Fast Idle Specifications

Application	Clearance
GLC and 808 1300 cc	.048-.060" (1.22-1.52 mm)
808 1600 cc	
Federal	.066-.076" (1.69-1.93 mm)
Calif.	.062-.072" (1.58-1.82 mm)

FUEL PUMP PRESSURE & VOLUME

Pressure	
GLC & 808 1300 cc (Mechanical)	2.84-3.84 psi (.20-.27 kg/cm²)
808 1600 cc (Electric)	2.8-3.6 psi (.20-.25 kg/cm²)
Volume at Idle Speed	
GLC and 808 1300 cc (Mechanical)	1.05 qts. in 1 min.
808 1600 cc (Electric)	.8 qts. in 1 min.

EMISSION CONTROL SYSTEMS

See Mitchell Manuals' Emission Control Manual.

GENERAL SERVICING

IGNITION

DISTRIBUTOR

GLC 1300 cc vehicles and 808 1600 cc California vehicles are equipped with Mitsubishi single point distributors. Federal 808 1300 cc vehicles are equipped with Mitsubishi transistorized ignition. Federal 1600 cc vehicles have dual point distributors.

Other Data & Specifications — *See Tune-Up & Mitsubishi Distributors in ELECTRICAL Section.*

IGNITION COIL

Primary Resistance	1.5 Ohms
Secondary Resistance	9,000 Ohms

FUEL SYSTEMS

CARBURETORS

Application	Model
808 1600 cc	Nikki (Stromberg) 2-Bbl.
All Other Models	Hitachi 2-Bbl.

Other Data & Specifications — *See Tune-Up & Hitachi & Nikki (Stromberg) Carburetors in FUEL SYSTEMS Section.*

ELECTRICAL

BATTERY

12 Volt — Negative Ground.

Application	Amp. Hr. Rating
Federal	50
Calif.	35

STARTER

Mitsubishi	Overrunning Clutch
Free Speed Voltage	10.5 at 5000 RPM
Free Speed Amperage	53 at 5000 RPM

Other Data & Specifications — *See Mitsubishi Starters in ELECTRICAL Section.*

ALTERNATOR

Application	Rated Amp. Output
GLC and 808 1300 cc	40
808 1600 cc	50

GENERAL SERVICING (Cont.)

ALTERNATOR REGULATOR

All models are equipped with a Mitsubishi adjustable alternator regulator with an operating voltage of 14-15 volts.

Other Data & Specifications – *See Mitsubishi Alternators & Regulators in ELECTRICAL Section.*

FILTERS & CLEANERS

Filter or Cleaner	Service Interval (Miles)
Oil Filter	Replace every 6000
Air Cleaner	Clean every 12,500
	Replace every 25,000
Fuel Filter	Replace every 12,500
Charcoal Canister	Replace every 25,000

ENGINE

INTAKE MANIFOLD TIGHTENING

Tighten intake manifold attaching bolts to 14-19 ft. lbs. (1.9-2.6 mkg).

BELT ADJUSTMENT

Application	New ①Deflection	Used ①Deflection
Alternator Belt	.3-.4" (8-11 mm)	.4-.5" (11-12 mm)
Air Pump Belt	.3-.4" (8-11 mm)	.4-.5" (11-12 mm)

① – Deflection is with 22 lbs. (10 kg) pressure applied midway on longest belt run.

CAPACITIES

Application	Quantity
Crankcase	
GLC & 808 1300 cc	3.2 qts.
808 1600 cc	3.8 qts.
Cooling System (Includes Heater)	
GLC & 808 1300 cc	5.8 qts.
808 1600 cc	7.9 qts.
Man. Trans.(4-Speed)	
GLC & 808 1300 cc	2.8 pts.
808 1600 cc	3.2 pts.
Man. Trans. (5-Speed)	
GLC & 808 1600 cc	3.6 pts.
Auto. Trans.	
GLC 1300 cc	6.0 qts.
808 1600 cc	6.6 qts.
Rear Axle	
GLC & 808 1300 cc	1.6 pts.
808 1600 cc	3 pts.
Fuel Tank	
GLC 1300 cc	10.6 gals.
808 1300 cc Wagon	10.6 gals.
808 1600 cc Wagon	10.6 gals.
All Other Models	11.1 gals.

TUNE-UP

RX-3SP
RX-4
Cosmo
Rotary Pickup

ENGINE IDENTIFICATION

Engine type code is stamped on rear rotor housing, to the rear of oil filter. Engine serial number is stamped on front rotor housing behind distributor. Engine type codes are as follows:

Engine Type Codes

Application	Code
RX-3SP	12A
RX-4, Cosmo & Rotary Pickup	13B

MODEL IDENTIFICATION

VEHICLE IDENTIFICATION NUMBER

Number is stamped on identification plate, located at left, lower inner corner of windshield, and is visible from outside of vehicle. On Rotary Pickup, number is on front of left frame member, visible from engine compartment.

COMPRESSION PRESSURE

Application	Pressure
All Models	① 85 psi (6 kg/cm²)

① — At 250 RPM.

SPARK PLUGS

Gap	.039-.043" (1-1.1 mm)
Torque	9-13 ft. lbs. (1.3-1.8 mkg)

Spark Plug Type①

Make	Standard	Cold Type
NGK	B-7ET, BR-7ET	B-8ET, BR-8ET
Nippondenso	W22EB, W22EBR	W25EB, W25EBR
Champion	N280B, RN280B	N278B, RN278B

① — Second plug listed in each application is for use in areas requiring suppression of radio interference.

HIGH TENSION WIRE RESISTANCE

Carefully remove high tension wires from spark plugs and distributor cap. Using an ohmmeter, measure resistance of wires while gently twisting wires. If resistance is not to specifications, or fluctuates from infinity to any value, replace high tension wire(s).

Resistance (Ohms) Per Wire

Application	Ohms
All Models	4877 per foot

DISTRIBUTOR

Point Gap	.018±.002 (.45±.05 mm)
Cam Angle Leading & Trailing	58±3°
Breaker Arm Spring Tension	17.6-22.4 ozs. (500-650 g)
Condenser Capacity	.24-.30 mfd.

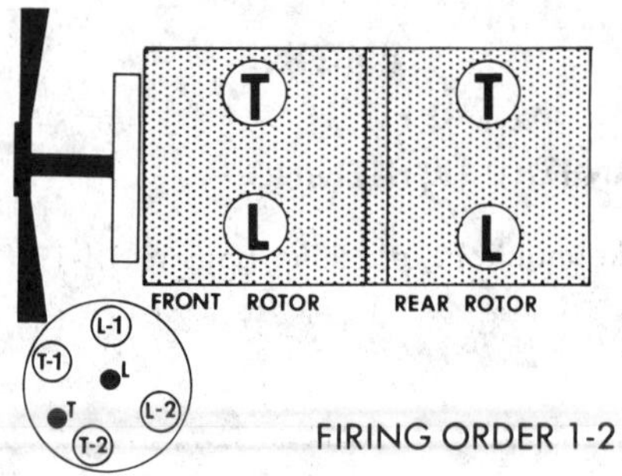

Fig. 1 Firing Order and Distributor Rotation

IGNITION TIMING

NOTE — *On vehicles equipped with automatic transmission, place selector lever in "D" position and block the wheels.*

ALL MODELS

1) Ensure all point gaps are properly set. Warm up engine to operating temperature and connect tachometer to engine.

2) Connect timing light to leading spark plug on front rotor housing. *See Fig. 2.* Start engine and run at idle speed.

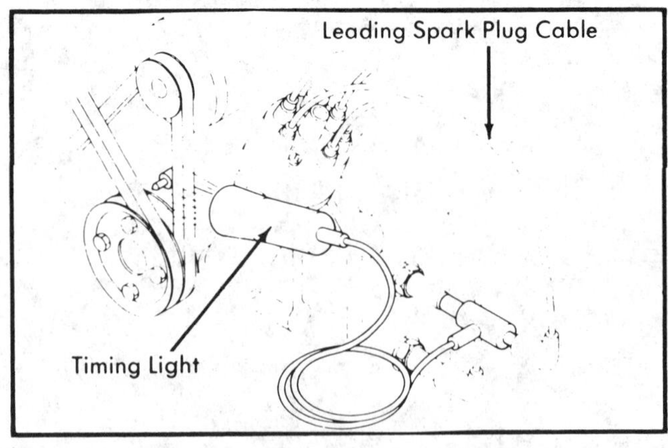

Fig. 2 Connecting Timing Light

3) Check leading timing. If not to specifications, adjust timing by rotating distributor housing until correct. Tighten lock nut.

NOTE — *Turning distributor housing clockwise advances both leading and trailing timing.*

TUNE-UP (Cont.)

4) Recheck leading timing. Then, connect timing light to trailing spark plug cable on front housing. Start engine and check trailing timing. If not to specifications, proceed by following instructions for specific model vehicle.

RX-3SP (AUTO. TRANS.) & ROTARY PICKUP

NOTE — *Manual transmission is same as RX-4 and Cosmo. On California models, leading RETARD ignition is performed by using trailing point.*

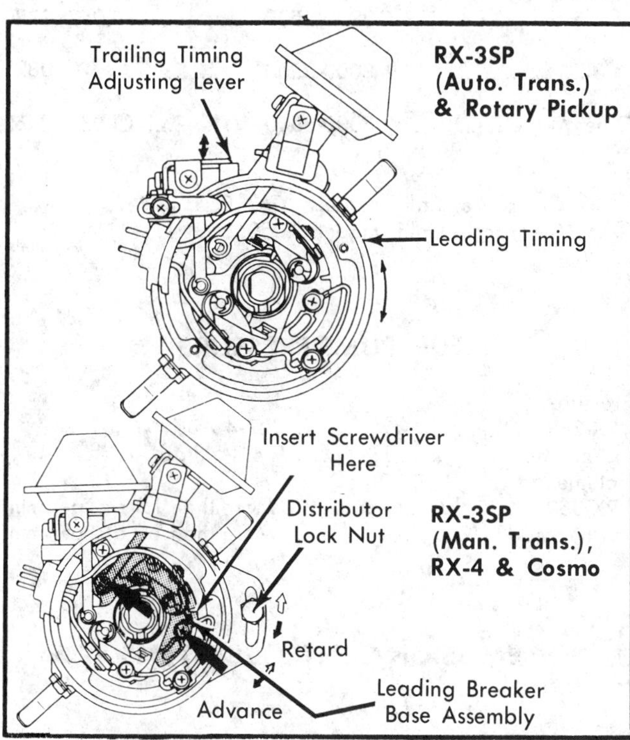

Fig. 3 Locations for Adjusting Ignition Timing

Adjust trailing timing by using external adjusting lever. See *Fig. 3.*

NOTE — *Rotary Pickup Federal models have a vacuum control valve which controls leading vacuum advance.*

RX-3SP (MAN. TRANS.), RX-4, & COSMO

1) Loosen distributor lock nut and adjust trailing timing by rotating distributor housing.

NOTE — *Turning distributor housing clockwise advances both leading and trailing timing.*

2) Stop engine and remove distributor cap and rotor. Slightly loosen breaker base set screws of leading side, and using screwdriver in slot, turn base plate as required. Tighten set screws. See *Fig. 3.* Install distributor rotor and cap.

3) Recheck and more accurately adjust leading timing by rotating distributor housing. Tighten lock nut.

4) Recheck trailing timing. If timing is not within specifications, repeat steps 1) through 3).

NOTE — *Turning breaker base clockwise advances leading timing.*

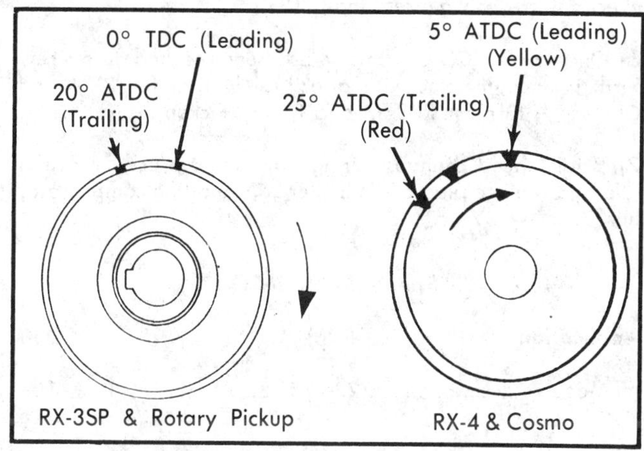

Fig. 4 Rotary Engine Timing Marks

Ignition Timing Specifications

Application	Timing
Leading Side	
RX-3SP	①TDC
RX-4, Cosmo & Rotary Pickup	①5° ATDC
Trailing Side	
RX-3SP	②20° ATDC
RX-4 & Cosmo	②25° ATDC
Rotary Pickup	①20° ATDC
Leading Retard Side	
RX-3SP Calif.	②20° ATDC
Rotary Pickup, Calif.	①20° ATDC

① — ±1°
② — ±4°

NOTE — *Be sure parking brake is engaged and wheels are blocked. Do not use vehicle's tachometer for testing and adjustment.*

HOT (SLOW) IDLE RPM

All Models — Place manual transmission shift lever in Neutral or automatic transmission in Drive position.

1) Ensure engine is warmed up to normal operating temperature. Run engine at 2000 RPM for about 3 minutes.

2) Turn OFF all accessories. Unhook and plug idle compensator hose. Remove fuel filler cap. Connect exhaust gas analyzer to exhaust pipe and tachometer to engine.

TUNE-UP (Cont.)

3) Check or adjust idle speed to 725-775 RPM by turning air adjustment screw. If CO percentage is less than .1% and engine is stable, idle mixture adjustment is not required.

4) If CO level is not within specifications, remove plastic idle limiter cap from mixture adjusting screw. Turn screw clockwise until engine "hunts" severely.

5) Slowly turn mixture adjusting screw counterclockwise (in small steps) until CO percentage decreases to .1%. Do not overturn screw to get less than .1%.

6) Once correct CO percentage has been reached, turn screw further in counterclockwise direction (¼ turn for RX-4 and Cosmo; ½ turn for RX3-SP and Rotary Pickup).

7) If idle speed changes during adjustment procedure, reset idle and replace plastic idle limiter cap and idle compensator hose.

Idle Speed (RPM) & CO (%)

Application	RPM	CO%
All Models	725-775	Less than .1%

COLD (FAST) IDLE RPM

All Models – 1) Connect tachometer to engine and run engine until normal operating temperature is reached. Stop engine.

2) Pull choke knob out fully. Restart engine. Engine speed should reach RPM shown in chart within 10 seconds of starting.

3) If fast idle speed is not within specifications, remove carburetor from engine. With carburetor removed, be sure choke valve is held fully closed.

4) Measure clearance between PRIMARY throttle valve and wall of throttle bore. Clearance should be as shown in chart. If not, bend fast idle rod until correct clearance is reached.

Fast Idle Specifications

Application	RPM	Bore Clearance
RX-3SP	3200-4000	①.035-.043" (.9-1.1 mm)
Rotary Pickup		
Federal	2800-3500	.057-.073" (1.45-1.85 mm)
Calif.	3000-3500	.070-.082" (1.79-2.08 mm)
Other Models	3000-3500	②.037-.045" (.94-1.14 mm)

① – Clearance, Calif. models, .043-.055" (1.1-1.4 mm).
② – Clearance, Calif. models, .050-.058" (1.27-1.47 mm).

FUEL PUMP PRESSURE

Pressure	
RX-3SP	3.7-4.7 psi (.26-.33 kg/cm²)
Other Models	4.3-5.3 psi (.3-.38 kg/cm²)
Volume	
RX-3SP	More than 1.1 qts. per min.
Other Models	More than 1.2 qts. per min.

EMISSION CONTROL SYSTEMS

See Mitchell Manuals' Emission Control Manual.

GENERAL SERVICING

IGNITION

IGNITION COIL

Resistance	Ohms @ 68°F (20°C)
Primary	
Leading	1.35
Trailing	1.5
Secondary	
Leading	8,700
Secondary	9,500

DISTRIBUTOR

All models are equipped with Mitsubishi distributors with two sets of ignition points.

Other Data & Specifications – *See Tune-Up & Mitsubishi Distributors in ELECTRICAL Section.*

FUEL SYSTEMS

CARBURETOR

Application	Model
All Models 4-Bbl.	Zenith-Stromberg

Other Data & Specifications – *See Tune-Up & Zenith-Stromberg Carburetor in FUEL SYSTEMS Section.*

GENERAL SERVICING (Cont.)

ELECTRICAL

BATTERY

12 Volt – Negative Ground.

Application	Amp. Hr. Capacity
RX-3SP	
Federal (Man. Trans.)	45
Federal (Auto. Trans.)	60
Calif.	45
RX-4	
Federal (Man. Trans.)	45
Federal (Auto. Trans.)	70
Calif.	45
Cosmo & Rotary Pickup	
Federal (Man. Trans.)	60
Federal (Auto. Trans.)	70
Calif.	60

Battery Location – In engine compartment

STARTER

Mitsubishi .... Overrunning Clutch

Free Speed Voltage
All Models .... 11.5 @ 5600 RPM

Free Speed Amperage
Man. Trans. .... ①Less than 50@5600 RPM
Auto. Trans. .... Less than 100@6600 RPM

① – Less than 75@5600 RPM for Rotary Pickup.

Other Data & Specifications – *See Mitsubishi Starters in ELECTRICAL Section*

ALTERNATOR

Application	Rated Amp. Output
RX-3	40
RX-4 & Cosmo	56
Rotary Pickup	50

Other Data & Specifications – *See Mitsubishi Alternators in ELECTRICAL Section.*

ALTERNATOR REGULATOR

All models are equipped with Mitsubishi adjustable alternator regulators with an operating voltage of 14.5±.5 volts.

Other Data & Specifications – *See Mitsubishi Alternator Regulators in ELECTRICAL Section.*

ENGINE

INTAKE MANIFOLD TIGHTENING

Tighten all intake manifold attaching bolts to 12-17 ft. lbs. (1.6-2.3 mkg) of torque.

FILTER & CLEANERS

Filter or Cleaner	Service Interval (Miles)
Oil Filter	Replace every 12,500
Air Cleaner	Replace every 25,000
Fuel Filter	Replace every 12,500

BELT ADJUSTMENT

Application	①Deflection
Alternator Belt	.51-.67" (13-17 mm)
Air Pump Belt	.43-.51" (11-13 mm)
A/C Belt	.31-.39" (8-10 mm)
Pow. Steering Belt	.31-.39" (8-10 mm)

① – Deflection is with 22 lbs. (10 kg) pressure applied midway on longest belt run.

CAPACITIES

Crankcase①	
RX-3SP	4.4 qts.
RX-4, Cosmo & Rotary Pickup	5.3 qts.
Cooling System	
RX-3SP	9.8 qts.
RX-4	10 qts.
Cosmo	10.6 qts.
Rotary Pickup	10.8 qts.
Manual Transmission (SAE 90)	
4-Speed	3 pts.
5-Speed	3.6 pts.
Automatic Transmission (Type F)	6.6 qts.
Rear Axle (SAE 90)	
RX-3SP	2.6 pts.
RX-4, Cosmo & Rotary Pickup	2.8 pts.
Fuel Tank	
RX-3SP	15.1 gals.
RX-4 Sedan & Coupe	17.2 gals.
RX-4 Wagon	17.7 gals.
Cosmo	17.2 gals.
Rotary Pickup	21.2 gals.

① – Refill capacity does not include oil remaining in oil filter, pump or cooler.

TUNE-UP

230

ENGINE IDENTIFICATION

Engine Code Designation – First six digits of engine identification number, located on tag at rear left side of engine crankcase, identify engine as follows:

Application	Code
230	115.954

MODEL IDENTIFICATION

VEHICLE IDENTIFICATION NUMBER

First six digits of identification number, located above instrument panel and visible through windshield, identify model as follows:

Application	Code
230	123.023

COMPRESSION PRESSURE

Check pressure with engine at normal operating temperature and throttle valve wide open, crank engine a minimum of eight revolutions to obtain following specifications:

Application	Pressure
Normal	128-142 psi (9-10 kg/cm²)
Min. Pressure	107 psi (7.5 kg/cm²)

VALVE TAPPET CLEARANCE

Engine Temp.	Intake	Exhaust
Cold	.004″ (.10 mm)	.008 (.20 mm)
Hot	.006″ (.15 mm)	.010″ (.25 mm)

VALVE ARRANGEMENT

All Models – E-I-I-E-E-I-I-E (front to rear).

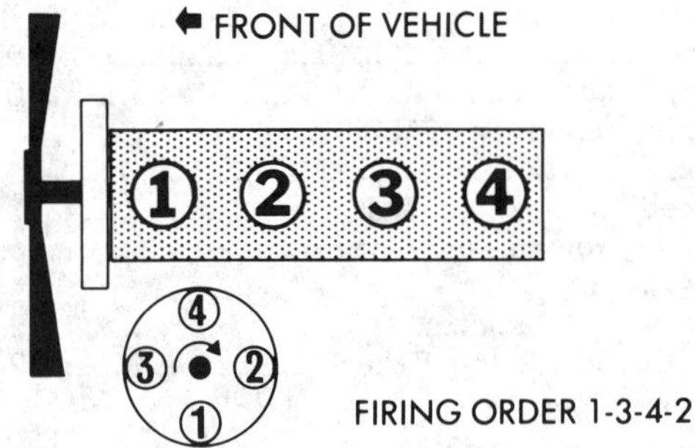

Fig. 1 Firing Order and Distributor Rotation

SPARK PLUGS

Gap	.028″ (.7 mm)
Torque	18-22 ft. lbs. (2.5-3.0 mkg)

Spark Plug Type①

Application	Bosch No.	Champion No.
230	W145 T 30	N-10Y

① – Beru No. is 145/14/3A.

HIGH TENSION WIRE RESISTANCE

Carefully remove high tension wires from spark plugs and distributor cap. Using an ohmmeter, check resistance of wires while gently twisting wires. If resistance is not to specification, or fluctuates from infinity to any value, replace wire.

Resistance (Ohms) Per Wire

Application	Resistance
All Models	25,000-30,000

DISTRIBUTOR

Point Gap	.016-.020″ (.4-.5 mm)
Cam Angle	46-53°
Breaker Arm Spring Tension	17.6-22.2 oz. (500-630 g)

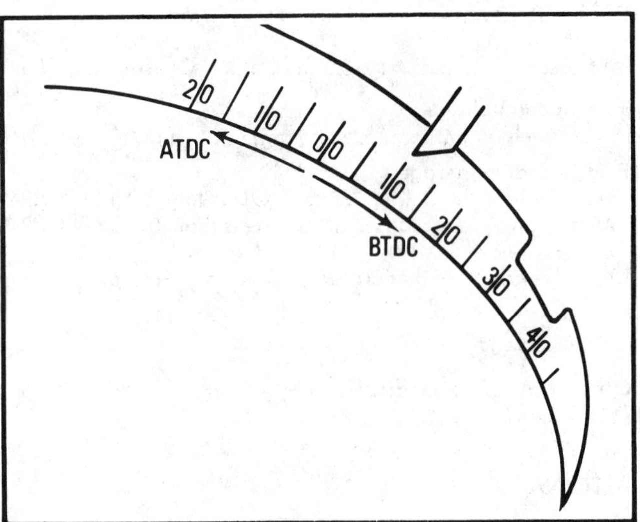

Fig. 2 Illustration of Timing Marks

IGNITION TIMING

Check or adjust ignition timing with engine at normal operating temperature, idle speed set to specifications and vacuum lines connected.

Ignition Timing Specifications

Application	RPM	Timing
230	850	10°BTDC

HOT (SLOW) IDLE RPM

1) Check spark plug gap, dwell angle, ignition timing, and check for leaks in intake system. Turn off air conditioning.

TUNE-UP (Cont.)

2) Run engine until normal operating temperature is reached, preferably 140-176° F (60-80° C) oil temperature. Do not disconnect air injection hose.

3) Cruise control cable should rest tension-free against throttle lever. Adjust if necessary. Adjust idle speed using idle mixture adjusting screw. Connect a CO tester to the exhaust pickup tube (must be in front of catalyst), using a hose with adapter No. 700 589 07 07 00.

4) Adjust idle speed CO level with idle air adjusting screw. Accelerate engine briefly and recheck CO value and idle speed. Readjust as necessary.

5) Adjust linkage at idle speed so that it is free of play at its completely extended position. With engine running at idle speed, remove hose from vacuum governor and adjust screw at throttle valve lever to achieve 1200-1400 RPM. *See Fig. 3.* Replace vacuum hose. Check clearance between lever and screw for .020" (.5 mm). If necessary, adjust at large adjusting nut.

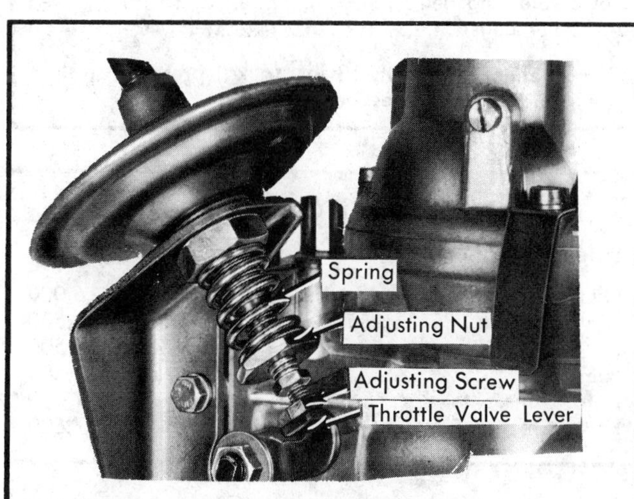

Fig. 3 Adjusting Vacuum Governor

6) Place gear selector lever in "D" position. Turn steering to full lock position and turn on air conditioning. Engine should run smoothly. If not, readjust idle speed with adjusting nut on vacuum governor.

Idle Speed (RPM) & CO Level (%) ①

Application	Idle RPM	CO%
All Models	850	.4-2.0

① – Air injection system connected.

BASIC IDLE SPEED ADJUSTMENT

NOTE – *Do not attempt to make this adjustment unless idle speed adjustment values cannot be achieved with hot (slow) idle adjustment.*

1) Run engine until oil temperature reaches 176° F (80° C). Turn idle mixture adjusting screw counterclockwise until highest speed is obtained.

2) Remove plastic cap from throttle valve adjusting screw and adjust to 1000 RPM level. Replace plastic cap and adjust idle speed with idle mixture adjusting screw to 800-900 RPM. Then turn idle AIR adjusting screw clockwise to stop.

3) On Federal models, remove altitude compensation handwheel and adjust fuel adjusting screw until an idle CO level of 3.5% is obtained. Reinstall handwheel and set to proper stop (NORMAL or 4000 ft.).

4) On California models, remove safety cap by breaking it. Adjust fuel adjusting screw until 3.5% CO level is achieved. Press on new safety cap, 000 988 51 35, using special tool 115 589 00 15 00. Adjust idle CO value with idle air adjusting screw to .4-2.0% level.

COLD (FAST) IDLE & MIXTURE

1) With engine at operating temperature and engaging lever on second step of fast idle cam, check fast idle speed is to specifications. If not, adjust idle mixture adjusting screw.

2) Attach exhaust gas analyzer and check CO level. If necessary to adjust, use auxiliary air adjusting screw on automatic choke housing.

Fast Idle Speed (RPM) & CO Level (%)

Application	Fast Idle RPM	CO%
All Models	1800	6.0-8.0

AUTOMATIC CHOKE

Choke is pretensioned at factory and should be reset at mark at second service period (6000 miles). Do not attempt to adjust set screw in diaphragm cover. Only use the auxiliary air adjusting screw in choke housing, when adjusting CO levels.

FUEL PUMP PRESSURE

Pressure	
At Cranking Speed	3.6-5.4 psi (.25-.38 kg/cm²)

EMISSION CONTROL SYSTEMS

See Mitchell Manuals' Emission Control Manual.

GENERAL SERVICING

IGNITION

DISTRIBUTOR

All models are equipped with Bosch single point distributors.

Other Data & Specifications – *See Tune-Up & Bosch Distributors in ELECTRICAL Section.*

IGNITION COIL

Resistance	Ohms At 68°F (20°C)
Primary	.38-.45
Secondary	8,000-11,000

FUEL SYSTEMS

CARBURETORS

Application	Model
All Models	Zenith-Stromberg 175 CDTU

Other Data & Specifications – *See Tune-Up & Zenith-Stromberg Carburetors in FUEL SYSTEMS Section.*

ELECTRICAL

BATTERY

12 Volt – Negative Ground.

Application	Amp. Hr. Rating
230	66

Battery Location – In engine compartment.

STARTER

All models are equipped with Bosch starters.

Free Speed Voltage	
All Models	11.5 at 8000-10,000 RPM
Free Speed Amperage	
All Models	50-80 at 8000-10,000 RPM

Other Data & Specifications – *See Bosch Starters in ELECTRICAL Section.*

ALTERNATOR REGULATOR

Bosch – Non-Adjustable; integral with Alternator.

Other Data & Specifications – *See Bosch Alternators & Regulators in ELECTRICAL Section.*

ALTERNATOR

Application	Rated Amp. Output
All Models	55

Other Data & Specifications – *See Bosch Alternators & Regulators in ELECTRICAL Section.*

BELT ADJUSTMENT

Application	①Deflection
Power Steering Belt	.20" (5 mm)
All Other Belts	.40" (10 mm)

① – Deflection is with 13 lbs. (6 kg) pressure applied midway on longest belt run.

FILTERS & CLEANERS

Filter or Cleaner	Service Interval (Miles)
Oil Filter	Replace every 6,000
Air Cleaner	Clean every 12,500
	Replace every 37,500
Fuel Filter	Replace every 37,500
Auto. Trans. Filter	Replace every 37,500
Power Steering Filter	Replace every 37,500

CAPACITIES

Application	Quantity
Crankcase (Includes Filter)	①5.8 qts.
Cooling System (Includes Heater)	10.6 qts.
Auto. Trans. (ATF)	②5.1 qts.
Rear Axle (SAE 90)	2.1 pts.
Fuel Tank	③21.1 gals.

① – 5.3 qts. without filter change.
② – 6.45 qts. at initial fill.
③ – Includes 3 gals. in reserve.

TUNE-UP

240 D

ENGINE IDENTIFICATION

First six digits of engine identification number, located on a tag at the rear, left side of engine crankcase, identify engines as follows:

Model	Code
240D	616.912

MODEL IDENTIFICATION

VEHICLE IDENTIFICATION NUMBER

First six digits of vehicle identification number, located on a tag on left, front window post (visible through windshield) and on rear firewall in engine compartment, identify model as follows:

Model	Code
240D	123.123

COMPRESSION PRESSURE

Check compression pressure with engine at normal operating temperature and throttle valve fully open. Crank engine through at least 8 revolutions.

Application	Pressure
Normal	313-341 psi (22-24 kg/cm²)
Min. Pressure	213 psi (15 kg/cm²)

VALVE TAPPET CLEARANCE

Valves must be adjusted at ignition TDC and in firing order of individual cylinders. With engine cold, measure clearance between rocker arm and base circle of cam. Adjust valves to following specifications:

Valve Clearance Specifications

Application	Intake	Exhaust
Cold	.004" (.10 mm)	.012" (.30 mm)
Warm	.006" (.15 mm)	.014" (.35 mm)

VALVE ARRANGEMENT

All Models – E-I-I-E-E-I-I-E (front to rear).

FIRING ORDER

All Models – 1-3-4-2

GLOW PLUGS

Torque .... 36 Ft. Lbs. (5mkg.)

Glow Plug Type

Application	Bosch Part No.	Beru Part No.
240D	0 250 001 016	382 GK

DIESEL FUEL INJECTION SYSTEM

240D – *For complete information on the Diesel fuel injection system, see Bosch Diesel Fuel Injection (Mercedes-Benz) in the FUEL SYSTEMS Section. Information includes description, system components, service procedures, removal and installation, as well as idle speed adjustment and start of delivery timing.*

IDLE SPEED ADJUSTMENT

NOTE – *For adjustment procedure, see Bosch Diesel Fuel Injection (Mercedes-Benz) in FUEL SYSTEMS Section.*

Application	Idle RPM
240D	650-750

GENERAL SERVICING

FUEL SYSTEMS

FUEL INJECTION

All Models use Bosch Diesel Fuel Injection.

Other Data & Specifications – *See Tune-Up and Bosch Diesel Fuel Injection in FUEL SYSTEMS Section.*

ELECTRICAL

BATTERY

12 Volt – Negative Ground.

Application	Amp. Hr. Rating
240 D	88

STARTER

All models are equipped with Bosch Starters.

Free Speed Voltage .... 11.5 at 6500-8500 RPM
Free Speed Amperage .... 65-95 at 6500-8500 RPM

Other Data & Specifications – *See Bosch Starters in ELECTRICAL Section.*

ALTERNATOR

Application	Rated Amp. Output
All Models	55

Other Data & Specifications – *See Bosch Alternators & Regulators in ELECTRICAL Section.*

GENERAL SERVICING (Cont.)

ALTERNATOR REGULATOR

Bosch — Non-Adjustable; integral with alternator.

Other Data & Specifications — *See Bosch Alternators & Regulators in ELECTRICAL Section.*

CAPACITIES

Application	Quantity
Crankcase (Includes Filter)	①6.8 qts.
Cooling System	10.5 qts.
Man. Trans. (ATF)	3.4 pts.
Auto. Trans. (ATF)	②5.1 qts.
Rear Axle (SAE 90)	2.1 pts.
Fuel Tank	③21.5 gals.

① — Without filter, 5.3 qts.
② — Refill shown. Initial fill, 6.5 qts.
③ — Includes 3.0 gals. in reserve.

FILTERS & CLEANERS

Filter or Cleaner	Service Interval (Miles)
Oil Filter	Replace every 3,000
Air Cleaner	Replace every 12,500
Fuel Filter	Replace every 37,500

BELT ADJUSTMENT

Application	①Deflection
Power Steering Belt	.20″ (5 mm)
All Other Belts	.40″ (10 mm)

① — Deflection is with a pressure of 13 lbs. (6 kg) applied midway on longest belt run.

TUNE-UP

300 D

ENGINE IDENTIFICATION

First six digits of engine identification number, located on a tag on the rear, left side of engine crankcase, identify engine as follows:

Model	Engine Code
300D	617.912

MODEL IDENTIFICATION

VEHICLE IDENTIFICATION NUMBER

First six digits of vehicle identification number, located on a tag on left, front window post and on rear firewall in engine compartment, identify model as follows:

Model	Model Code
300D	123.130

COMPRESSION PRESSURE

Check compression pressure with engine at normal operating temperature and throttle valve wide open, crank engine a minimum of eight compression strokes to obtain following specifications:

Application	Pressure
300 D	
Normal	313-341 psi (22-24 kg/cm²)
Minimum	213 psi (15 kg/cm²)

VALVE TAPPET CLEARANCE

Valves must be adjusted at ignition TDC and in firing order of individual cylinders. With engine cold, measure clearance between rocker arm and base circle of cam.

Valve Clearance Specifications

Application	Intake	Exhaust
Engine Cold	.004" (.10 mm)	.012" (.30 mm)
Engine Warm	.006" (.15 mm)	.014" (.35 mm)

VALVE ARRANGEMENT

E-I-I-E-E-I-I-E-E-I (front-to-rear)

FIRING ORDER

1-2-4-5-3

GLOW PLUGS

Torque .... 36 ft. lbs. (5 mkg)

Glow Plug Type

Application	Bosch Part No.	Beru Part No.
300D	0 250 001 016	382 GK

DIESEL FUEL INJECTION SYSTEM

300D — *For complete information on the Diesel fuel injection system, see Bosch Diesel Fuel Injection (Mercedes-Benz) in the FUEL SYSTEMS Section. Information includes description, system components, service procedures, removal and installation, as well as idle speed adjustment and start of delivery timing.*

IDLE SPEED ADJUSTMENT

NOTE — *For adjustment procedure, see Bosch Diesel Fuel Injection (Mercedes-Benz) in FUEL SYSTEMS Section.*

Application	Idle RPM
300D	650-750

GENERAL SERVICING

ELECTRICAL

BATTERY

12 Volt — Negative Ground.

Application	Amp. Hr. Rating
300 D	88

STARTER

All models are equipped with Bosch starters.

Free Speed Voltage .... 11.5 at 6500-8500 RPM
Free Speed Amperage .... 65-95 at 6500-8500 RPM

Other Data & Specifications — *See Bosch Starters in ELECTRICAL Section.*

ALTERNATOR

Application	Rated Amp. Output
300 D	55

Other Data & Specifications — *See Bosch Alternators & Regulators in ELECTRICAL Section.*

ALTERNATOR REGULATOR

Bosch — Non-Adjustable; integral with alternator.

Other Data & Specifications — *See Bosch Alternators & Regulators in ELECTRICAL Section.*

GENERAL SERVICING (Cont.)

BELT ADJUSTMENT

Application	①Deflection
Power Steering Belt	.20"(5 mm)
All Other Belts	.40"(10 mm)

① – Deflection is with a pressure of 13 lbs. (6 kg) applied midway on longest belt run.

FILTERS & CLEANERS

Filter or Cleaner	Service Interval (Miles)
Oil Filter	Replace every 3,000
Air Cleaner	Replace every 12,500
Fuel Filter	Replace every 37,500

CAPACITIES

Application	Quantity
Crankcase (Includes Filter)	①6.8 qts.
Cooling System	11.6 qts.
Auto. Trans. (ATF)	②5.1 qts.
Rear Axle (SAE 90)	2.1 pts.
Fuel Tank	③21.1 gals.

① – 5.3 qts. without oil filter change.
② – Refill shown. Initial fill is 6.5 qts.
③ – Includes 3.0 gals. in reserve.

TUNE-UP

280 E
280 SE

ENGINE IDENTIFICATION

First six digits of engine identification number, located on tag on front left side of engine crankcase, identify engine as follows:

Application	Code
280 E	110.984
280 SE	110.985

MODEL IDENTIFICATION

VEHICLE IDENTIFICATION NUMBER

First six digits of identification number, located above instrument panel and visible through windshield and on a tag on rear firewall of engine compartment, identify models as follows:

Application	Code
280 E	123.033
280 SE	116.024

COMPRESSION PRESSURE

Check compression pressure with engine at normal operating temperature and throttle valve fully open. Crank engine a minimum of eight revolutions to obtain following specifications:

Application	Pressure
All Models	
Normal Pressure	130-144 psi (9-10 kg/cm²)
Minimum Pressure	108 psi (7.5 kg/cm²)

NOTE — *Maximum variation between cylinders should not exceed 21 psi (1.5 kg/cm²).*

VALVE TAPPET CLEARANCE

Engine Temp.	Intake	Exhaust
Cold	.004" (.10 mm)	.010" (.25 mm)
Hot	.006" (.15 mm)	.012" (.30 mm)

VALVE ARRANGEMENT

All Models
Right Side — All Exhaust.
Left Side — All Intake.

SPARK PLUGS

Gap	.028" (.7 mm)
Torque	18-22 ft. lbs. (2.5-3.0 mkg)

Spark Plug Type①

Application	Bosch No.	Champion No.
All Models	W 145 T 30	N-10Y

① — Beru Spark Plug No. 145/14/3A.

HIGH TENSION WIRE RESISTANCE

Carefully remove high tension wires from spark plugs and distributor cap. Using an ohmmeter, measure resistance while gently twisting wire. If resistance is not to specifications or fluctuates from infinity to any value, replace wire(s).

Resistance (Ohms) Per Wire

Application	Ohms
All Models	25,000-30,000

FRONT OF VEHICLE

FIRING ORDER 1-5-3-6-2-4

Fig. 1 Firing Order and Distributor Rotation

DISTRIBUTOR

Mercedes-Benz 6-cylinder vehicles are now equipped with breakerless, transistorized ignition systems.

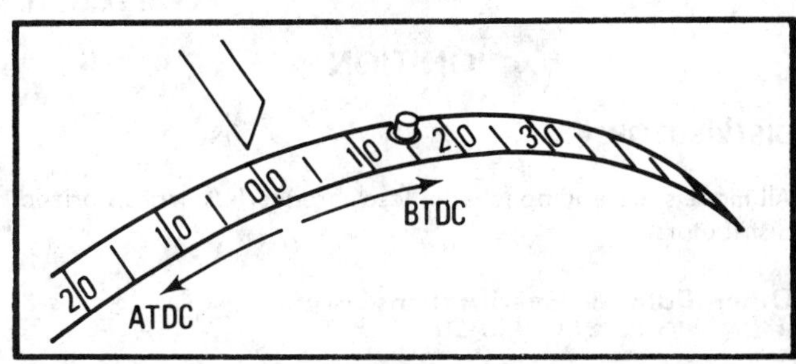

Fig. 2 Timing Marks for 6-Cylinder Engines

IGNITION TIMING

Check or adjust ignition timing with engine at normal operating temperature, idle speed set to specifications and distributor vacuum lines connected.

Ignition Timing Specifications

Application	RPM	Timing
All Models	800	TDC

HOT (SLOW) IDLE RPM

NOTE — *Be sure spark plug gap and ignition timing are to specifications, and check air intake system for leaks. Turn off air conditioning system when making adjustment.*

TUNE-UP (Cont.)

1) Run engine until it reaches normal operating temperature, about 140-176° F (60-80° C) oil temperature. Remove air cleaner and be sure cruise control cable rests tension-free against throttle lever.

2) Disconnect the control rod at the bell crank and be sure throttle valve is at the idle speed stop. Then, reconnect control rod tension-free. Cam roller should be resting free of play in the gate lever.

3) Adjust idle to correct RPM, using idle air adjusting screw. Connect a CO gas analyzer at the exhaust pick-up tube (exhaust back pressure line), using adapter 700 589 07 07 00.

4) Check CO value without air injection. To do so, remove blue vacuum line on blue thermo-vacuum valve and plug the line. To adjust for proper CO value, remove plug from mixture control regulator, insert Allen wrench and turn idle mixture adjusting screw clockwise to richen, or counterclockwise to lean the mixture.

5) Close bore for idle mixture adjusting screw, accelerate engine briefly, and check CO value at idle speed. Readjust if necessary. Install air cleaner and recheck both idle speed and CO value. Connect vacuum line to thermo-vacuum valve. Place automatic transmission lever in "D" position, switch on air conditioning and turn steering to full lock position. Engine should continue to run smoothly. If not, readjust.

Idle Speed (RPM) and CO Level (%)①

Application	Idle RPM	CO%
All Models	850	.4-2.0

① — Without air injection.

COLD (FAST) IDLE RPM

There is no fast idle speed adjustment, as fast idle is controlled by the cold start valve.

FUEL PUMP DELIVERY RATE

1) Remove fuel return hose from fuel distributor. Connect short length of hose at point of removal. Hold end of hose in 1 liter measuring vessel.

2) Turn on ignition. Disconnect plug on safety switch for 30 seconds and reinstall plug. If delivery rate is below specifications, check for 11.5 volts at fuel pump, kinks in lines, faulty fuel filter or accumulator. If all check out, then replace fuel pump and reconnect return line.

Fuel Pump Delivery Rate

Delivery Rate	1.06 qts. (1 liter) in 30 seconds

EMISSION CONTROL SYSTEMS

See Mitchell Manuals' Emission Control Manual.

GENERAL SERVICING

IGNITION

DISTRIBUTOR

All models are equipped with Bosch breakerless, transistorized distributors.

Other Data & Specifications — *See Tune-Up & Bosch Distributors in ELECTRICAL Section.*

IGNITION COIL

Resistance	Ohms at 68°F
Primary	.38-.43
Series	①

① — Ignition system is equipped with two resistors. Resistance at first resistor (identified by blue fastening clip) should be .4±.05 ohms. Resistance at second resistor (metallic fastening clip) should be .6±.05 ohms.

FUEL SYSTEM

FUEL INJECTION

Application	Model
All Models	Bosch CIS Fuel Injection

Other Data & Specifications — *See Tune-Up & Bosch CIS Fuel Injection in FUEL SYSTEMS Section.*

THROTTLE CONTROL LINKAGE

1) Check control linkage for easy operation and straightness. Disconnect throttle control rod and check whether throttle valve rests against idle stop. Reconnect control rod. Adjust control rod so that the roller rests tension-free in slot of gate lever. *See Fig. 3.*

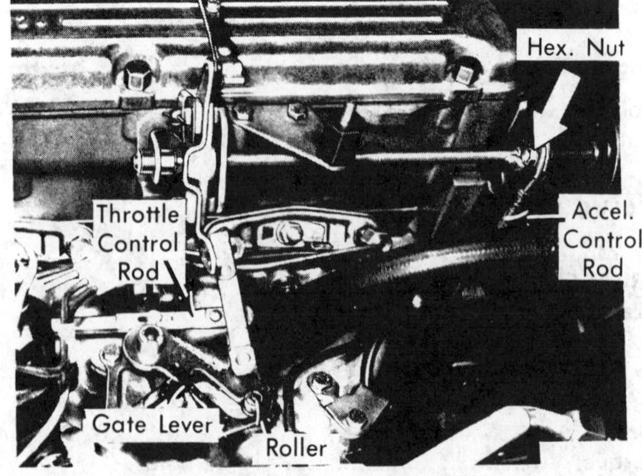

Fig. 3. Adjusting Accelerator Linkage

2) With engine stopped, press down accelerator pedal inside vehicle until it rests on kickdown switch. Throttle valve lever should rest against full throttle stop. If necessary, adjust con-

GENERAL SERVICING (Cont.)

trol linkage at hex. nut (arrow in *Fig. 3*) until throttle valve lever rests against full throttle stop.

3) If full throttle stop or the idle stop is not reached with this adjustment, adjust control rod connecting the horizontal shaft to the accelerator pedal.

4) Adjust automatic transmission control pressure rod at idle position. Disconnect rod and push toward rear against the stop. Reconnect rod tension-free, adjusting ball socket if necessary. *See Fig. 4.*

Control Rod Length Adjustments

Application	Length In. (mm)
Throttle Control Rod	13.50 (343)
Control Rod (Over Top of Engine)	12.05 (306)
Accelerator Pedal Control Rod	7.32 (186)

Fig. 4 Adjusting Automatic Transmission Linkage

ELECTRICAL

BATTERY

12 Volt — Negative Ground.

Application	Amp. Hour Rating
All Models	55

Battery Location — In engine compartment.

STARTER

All models are equipped with Bosch starters.

Free Speed Voltage
All Models .... 11.5 at 8000-10,000 RPM
Free Speed Amperage
All Models .... 50-80 at 8000-10,000 RPM

Other Data & Specifications — *See Bosch Starters in ELECTRICAL Section.*

ALTERNATOR

Application	Rated Amp. Output
All Models	55

Other Data & Specifications — *See Bosch Alternators & Regulators in ELECTRICAL Section.*

ALTERNATOR REGULATOR

Bosch — Regulating voltage of 13.7-14.5 volts; integral with alternator; transistorized.

Other Data & Specifications — *See Bosch Alternators & Regulators in ELECTRICAL Section.*

FILTERS & CLEANERS

Filter or Cleaner	Service Interval (Miles)
Oil Filter	Replace every 6,000
Air Cleaner	Clean every 12,000
	Replace every 37,500
Fuel Filter	Replace every 37,500
Auto. Trans. Filter	Replace every 37,500
Power Steering Filter	Replace every 37,500

BELT ADJUSTMENT

Application	①Deflection
Power Steering Belt	.20" (5 mm)
All Other Belts	.40" (10 mm)

① — Deflection with 12 lbs. pressure applied midway on belt run.

CAPACITIES

Application	Quantity 280 E	Quantity 280 SE
Crankcase & Filter	①6.9 qts.	①6.9 qts.
Cooling System	11.1 qts.	11.6 qts.
Auto. Trans. Refill②	5.6 qts.	5.6 qts.
Rear Axle (SAE 90)	2.1 pts.	2.1 pts.
Fuel Tank	③21.1gals.	④25.4 gals.

① — Without filter change, subtract 0.6 qts.
② — Initial fill is 7.0 qts.
③ — Includes 3.0 gals. in reserve.
④ — Includes 3.4 gals. in reserve.

TUNE-UP

450 SEL
450 SL
450 SLC
6.9

ENGINE IDENTIFICATION

First six digits of engine identification number, located on tag attached to engine crankcase (6.9, at front; 450 Series, at rear left side of block), identify engines as follows:

Application	Code
450 SEL	117.986
450 SL	117.985
450 SLC	117.985
6.9	100.985

MODEL IDENTIFICATION

VEHICLE IDENTIFICATION NUMBER

First six digits of identification number, located on a tag at left side of instrument panel (visible through windshield) and in engine compartment (6.9 on rear firewall; 450 Series to left of hood latch), identify models as follows:

450 SEL	116.033
450 SL	107.044
450 SLC	107.024
6.9	116.036

COMPRESSION PRESSURE

Check compression pressure with engine at normal operating temperature and throttle valve fully open. Crank engine a minimum of eight revolutions to obtain following specifications:

Application	Pressure
All Models	
Normal Pressure	130-144 psi (9-10 kg/cm²)
Minimum Pressure	108 psi (7.5 kg/cm²)

NOTE — *Maximum variation between cylinders should not exceed 21 psi (1.5 kg/cm²).*

VALVE TAPPET CLEARANCE

Hydraulic Valve Lifters — *For adjustment see Mercedes-Benz V8 Engines in ENGINE Section.*

VALVE ARRANGEMENT

450 Series
Right Bank — E-I-E-I-E-I-I-E (front to rear).
Left Bank — E-I-I-E-I-E-I-E (front to rear).
6.9 Models
Right Bank — I-E-I-E-I-E-I-E (front to rear).
Left Bank — E-I-E-I-E-I-E-I (front to rear).

SPARK PLUGS

Gap	.028" (7 mm)
Torque	18-22 ft. lbs. (2.5-3.0 mkg)

Spark Plug Type①

Application	Bosch No.	Champion No.
All Models	W 145 T 30	N-10Y

① — Beru Spark Plug No. is 145/14/3A.

HIGH TENSION WIRE RESISTANCE

Carefully remove high tension wires from spark plugs and distributor cap. Using an Ohmmeter, check resistance of wires while gently twisting wire. If resistance is not to specifications, or fluctuates from infinity to any value, replace wire(s).

Resistance (Ohms) Per Wire

Application	Ohms
All Models	25,000-30,000

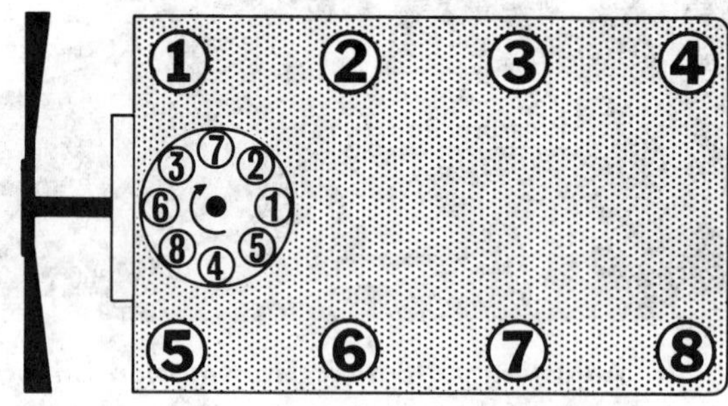

Fig. 1 Firing Order and Distributor Rotation

DISTRIBUTOR

All models feature a breakerless, transistorized ignition system.

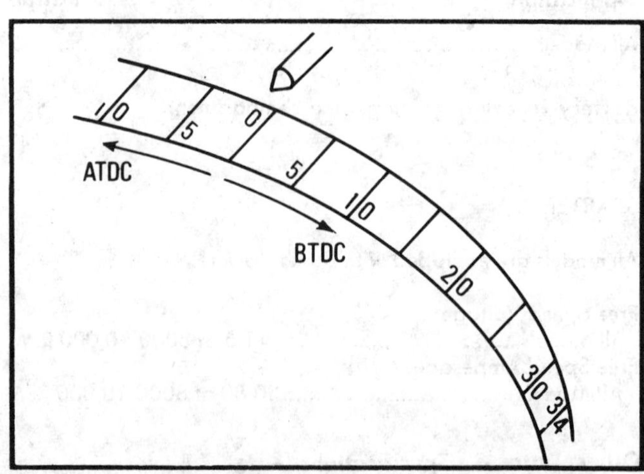

Fig. 2 Timing Marks Illustrated (All Models)

TUNE-UP (Cont.)

IGNITION TIMING

Check or adjust ignition timing with engine at normal operating temperature, idle speed set to specifications and distributor vacuum lines connected. *See Fig. 2.*

Ignition Timing Specifications

Application	Timing
All Models	TDC at 800 RPM

HOT (SLOW) IDLE RPM

NOTE — *Before adjusting idle speed, be sure spark plug gap and ignition timing are correct. Check air intake system for leaks and turn off air conditioning.*

1) Run engine until oil reaches 140-176° F (60-80° C). Remove air cleaner. Be sure cruise control cable rests tension-free against throttle lever. If necessary, adjust screw.

2) Disconnect control rod at bell crank. Check that throttle valve is at idle speed stop. Reconnect control rod so that it is tension-free. Use idle speed air adjusting screw to set correct idle speed.

3) Connect a CO gas analyzer at the exhaust pick-up tube (exhaust back pressure line). Connection must be in front of catalyst. Use a 700 589 07 07 00 Adapter. Check CO value WITH air injection on Federal and High Altitude models of the 450 Series. Check WITHOUT air injection on 6.9 Models and on California 450 Series vehicles.

NOTE — *To disconnect air injection, remove the blue/purple vacuum line on the straight connection of the blue thermo-vacuum valve. Plug the valve connection.*

4) To adjust the CO level, remove plug from center of mixture control unit, and insert Allen wrench into idle mixture adjusting screw. Turn counterclockwise to make mixture more lean; clockwise to enrichen. Then, plug adjusting screw bore, accelerate engine briefly, and check CO value at idle speed. Readjust as necessary.

5) Install air cleaner. Recheck idle RPM and CO value. Again, readjust if necessary. Remove the air cleaner and reconnect vacuum line to thermo-vacuum valve. Place automatic transmission lever in "D" position, switch on the air conditioning, and turn the steering to full lock position. The engine should continue to run smoothly. Readjust idle RPM if necessary. Install air cleaner.

Idle Speed (RPM) and CO Level (%)

Application	Idle RPM	CO%
450 Series		
Federal	750	①.2-2.0
High Altitude	750	①.2-1.2
California	750	②.2-2.0
6.9 Models		
Federal	600	②.2-2.0
High Altitude	600	②.2-1.2
California	600	②.2-2.0

① — With air injection.
② — Without air injection.

COLD (FAST) IDLE RPM

There is no fast idle speed adjustment, as fast idle is controlled by the cold start valve.

FUEL PUMP PRESSURE & VOLUME

Rate of Delivery .... 1.06 qts. (1 liter) each 30 seconds.

NOTE — *For rest, system, and warm and cold control pressures, see Bosch CIS Fuel Injection in FUEL SYSTEMS Section.*

EMISSION CONTROL SYSTEMS

See Mitchell Manuals' Emission Control Manual.

GENERAL SERVICING

IGNITION

DISTRIBUTOR

All models are equipped with Bosch breakerless ignition system.

Other Data & Specifications — *See Tune-Up & Bosch Distributors in ELECTRICAL Section.*

IGNITION COIL

Application	Ohms At 68° F (20° C)
Primary	.33-.46
Secondary	7,000-12,000

FUEL SYSTEMS

FUEL INJECTION

All models use Bosch Continuous Injection System fuel injection.

Other Data & Specifications — *See Tune-Up & Bosch CIS Fuel Injection in FUEL SYSTEMS Section.*

ELECTRICAL

BATTERY

12 Volt — Negative Ground.

Application	Amp. Hr. Rating
450 Series	88
6.9 Models	66

GENERAL SERVICING (Cont.)

Battery Location – Battery is located in engine compartment on 6.9 and 450 SEL models and in right side of trunk on 450 SL and 450 SLC models.

STARTER

All models are equipped with Bosch starters.

Free Speed Voltage
- 450 Series .... 11.5 at 8,000-10,000 RPM
- 6.9 Models .... 11 at 8,500-10,000 RPM

Free Speed Amperage
- 450 Series .... 50-80 at 8,000-10,000 RPM
- 6.9 Models .... 55-85 at 8,500-10,000 RPM

Other Data & Specifications – *See Bosch Starters in ELECTRICAL Section.*

ALTERNATOR

Application	Rated Amp. Output
450 Series	55
6.9 Models	75

Other Data & Specifications – *See Bosch Alternators & Regulators in ELECTRICAL Section.*

ALTERNATOR REGULATOR

Bosch – Integral with alternator; regulating voltage of 13.7-14.5 volts.

Other Data & Specifications – *See Bosch Alternators & Regulators in ELECTRICAL Section.*

BELT ADJUSTMENT

Application	① Deflection
A/C Compressor Belt	.20" (5 mm)
All Other Belts	.40" (10 mm)

① – Deflection with 12 lbs. pressure applied midway on belt run.

FILTERS & CLEANERS

Filter or Cleaner	Service Intervals (Miles)
Oil Filter	
450 Series	Replace every 6,000
6.9 Models	Replace every 12,500
Air Cleaner	Clean every 12,500
	Replace every 37,500
Fuel Line Filter	Replace every 37,500
Fuel Tank Filter	Replace every 37,500
Auto. Trans. Filter	Replace every 37,500

CAPACITIES

Application	Quantity
Crankcase (Including Filter)	
450 SL, SLC	①8.5 qts.
450 SEL	①8.9 qts.
6.9	①11.7 qts.
Cooling System	
450 Series	15.8 qts.
6.9 Models	16.9 qts.
Auto. Trans. Refill (ATF)	②8.3 qts.
Rear Axle (SAE 90)	2.7 qts.
Fuel Tank	
450 SEL & 6.9	③25.4 gals.
450 SL & SLC	③28.3 gals.

① – Without filter change, subtract 1 qt. for 6.9 Models or .8 qt. for 450 Series vehicles.
② – Initial fill is 9.4 qts.
③ – Includes 3.4 gals. in reserve.

TUNE-UP

Midget
MGB

ENGINE IDENTIFICATION

Engine number on the Midget is stamped either on a plate or directly onto cylinder block on the left side of engine. On the MGB number is stamped on a plate attached to right side of cylinder block. Engine may be identified by prefix of engine number as follows:

Application	Engine Code
Midget	9E 94J
MGB	
With Overdrive	
Federal	18V833
Calif.	18V890
Without Overdrive	
Federal	18V884
Calif.	18V891

MODEL IDENTIFICATION

VEHICLE IDENTIFICATION NUMBER

Vehicle identification number is stamped on a plate attached to left hand door post and to rear underside of hood.

COMPRESSION PRESSURE

Application	Pressure
Midget	①
MGB	130 psi (9.14 kg/cm²)

① — Not available at time of publication.

VALVE TAPPET CLEARANCE

Remove valve cover and observe opening and closing of valves. Measure clearance between rocker arms and valve stems for a "sliding" fit. To check clearance, turn crankshaft until valves in first column are fully open, then check or adjust valves in second column. Adjust in following order:

NOTE — *Count valves from front to rear.*

Valve Open	Valve to Adjust
8	1
6	3
4	5
7	2
1	8
3	6
5	4
2	7

Application	①Clearance
Midget (Cold)	.010" (.25 mm)
MGB (Hot)	.013" (.33 mm)

① — Intake and exhaust valves set to same clearance.

VALVE ARRANGEMENT

E-I-I-E-E-I-I-E (front to rear).

SPARK PLUGS

Gap
- Midget .... .025" (.64 mm)
- MGB .... .035" (.90 mm)

Torque
- Midget .... 20 ft. lbs. (2.8 mkg)
- MGB .... 18 ft. lbs. (2.5 mkg)

Spark Plug Type

Application	Champion No.
Midget	N-12Y
MGB	N-9Y

HIGH TENSION WIRE RESISTANCE

Remove high tension wires from spark plugs and distributor cap. Using an ohmmeter, check high tension wire resistance while gently twisting wire. If resistance is not to specifications, or fluctuates from infinity to any value, replace wire(s).

Resistance (Ohms) Per Wire

Application	Ohms
All Models	25,000-30,000

DISTRIBUTOR

Air Gap
- Midget .... .014-.016" (.35-.40 mm)
- MGB (W/CAT. Only) .... .010-.017" (.25-.43 mm)

Point Gap (MGB W/O CAT.) .... .014-.016" (.35-.40 mm)
Cam Angle .... 46-56°
Breaker Arm Spring Tension .... 18-24 ozs. (510-680 g)
Condenser Capacity .... .18-.25 mfd.

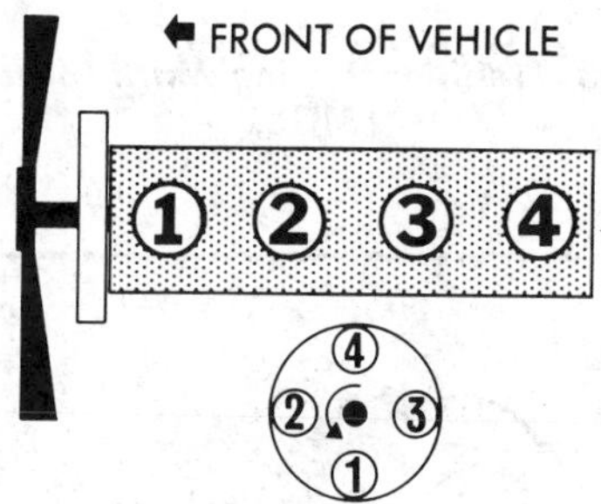

Fig. 1 Firing Order and Distributor Rotation (Midget)

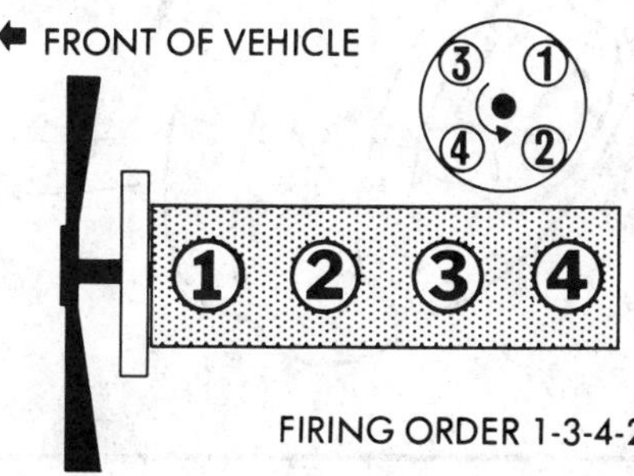

Fig. 2 Firing Order and Distributor Rotation (MGB)

TUNE-UP (Cont.)

IGNITION TIMING

Check or adjust ignition timing with engine at normal operating temperature and point or air gap set to specifications. Rotate distributor housing to achieve correct timing. Tighten lock nut.

Ignition Timing Specifications

Midget (At 800 RPM)	
Federal	10° BTDC
Calif.	2° ATDC
MGB (At 1500 RPM)	
Federal	10° BTDC
Calif.	10° BTDC
Canada (No Cat. Converter)	13° BTDC

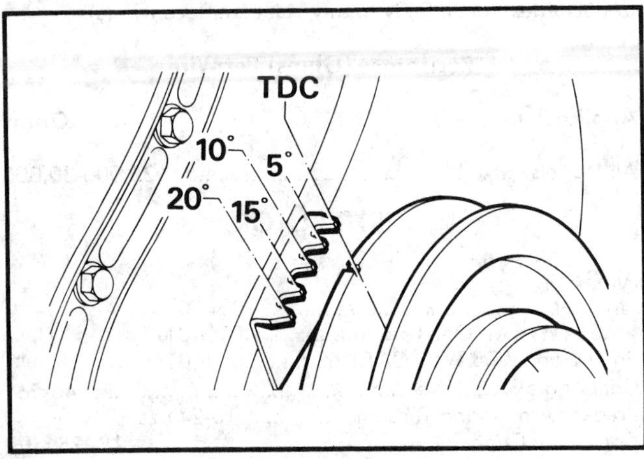

Fig. 3 Ignition Timing Mark Location (MGB)

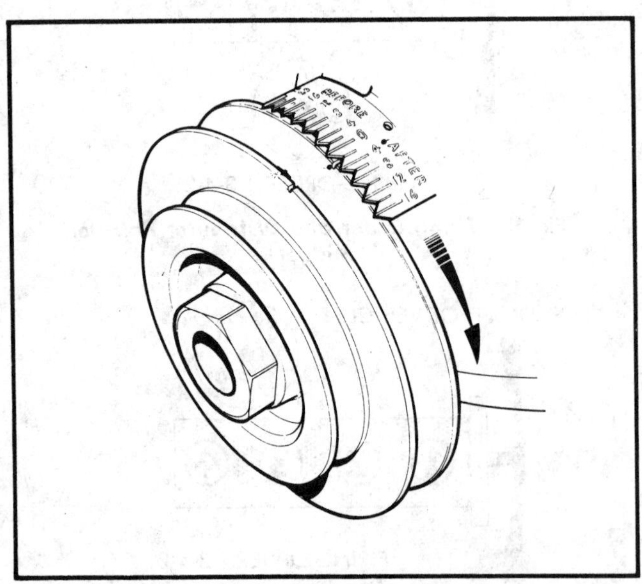

Fig. 4 Ignition Timing Mark Location (Midget)

HOT (SLOW) IDLE RPM

NOTE — *Before checking idle speed and CO% level, be sure valve clearance, spark plug gap and ignition timing are to specifications. Install tachometer on engine.*

1) Run engine until it reaches normal operating temperature. Remove air cleaner. Ensure choke is off and fast idle screw is not in contact with fast idle cam. Make sure oil in carburetor damper is ¼" below top of piston guide rod.

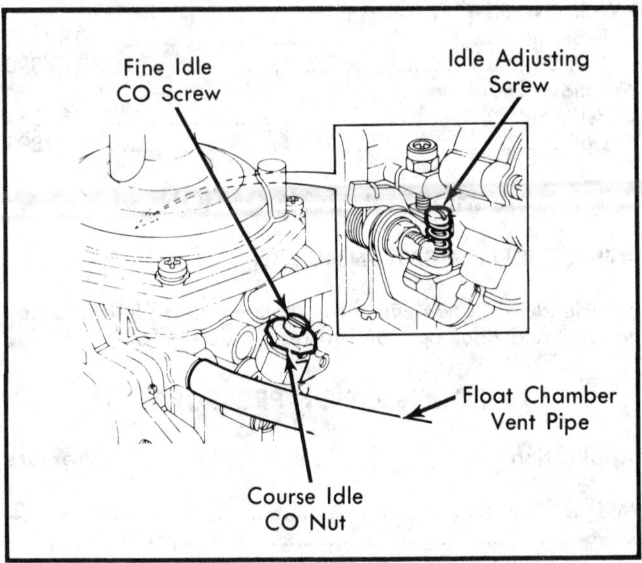

Fig. 5 Adjusting Idle Speed and CO% Level

2) Disconnect air injection pump outlet hose and plug the hose. Do not plug air pump outlet, or damage to pump may occur. Disconnect float chamber vent pipe from carburetor. See *Fig. 5.*

3) Run engine at 2500 RPM for 30 seconds and check idle speed. Adjust idle speed to specifications, using idle adjusting screw.

4) Connect an exhaust gas analyzer to vehicle. If CO% level is not within specifications, turn FINE idle CO screw clockwise to enrich and counterclockwise to weaken mixture. If correct CO% level cannot be achieved, proceed to specific instructions for vehicle.

MGB VEHICLES ONLY

1) Turn FINE idle CO screw clockwise as far as possible, and then counterclockwise 2½ turns. This places screw in mid-point of adjustment range.

2) Remove suction chamber cover, spring and air valve from carburetor. Check that initial needle adjustment is correct (shoulder of needle should be flush with air valve underside).

TUNE-UP (Cont.)

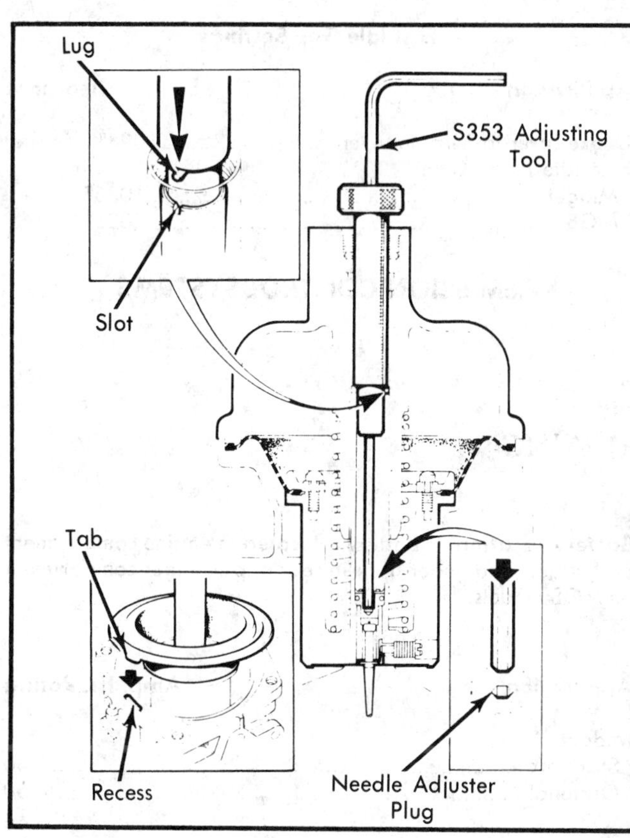

Fig. 6 Setting Initial Needle Adjustment

3) If needle requires adjustment, remove air valve damper from suction chamber. Carefully insert inner part of adjusting tool (S353) into hexagon hole in needle adjuster plug. *See Fig. 6.* Turn tool to properly adjust needle position.

4) Install air valve with diaphragm tab in housing recess. Align and install suction chamber cover and damper. Recheck idle speed and CO% level as previously instructed.

5) If it is still impossible to obtain correct CO% level, adjust FINE idle CO screw to mid-point of adjustment range (step **1**). Then, adjust COURSE idle CO NUT clockwise to enrich and counterclockwise to weaken mixture.

6) If CO% level is still not within specifications, turn NUT clockwise as far as possible without forcing, and then counterclockwise 2 turns to mid-point of its adjustment range.

ALL MODELS

1) If CO% level is still not achieved, remove air valve damper and insert adjusting tool (S353) into dashpot until outer tool engages the air valve and inner tool engages hexagon hole in needle adjuster plug.

NOTE — *Lug of outer tool must engage slot in air valve or diaphragm may be torn. See Fig. 6.*

2) Hold outer tool firmly and turn inner tool clockwise to enrich or counterclockwise to weaken mixture. Remove tool. Top up hollow piston rod with oil (¼" below top of piston guide rod) and install damper.

3) Recheck CO% level and if necessary repeat this final adjusting procedure (steps **1**) and **2**) above) until correct level is achieved.

4) Remove plug from air manifold hose and install hose to air pump and float chamber vent pipe to carburetor. Increase engine speed to 2500 RPM for 30 seconds and readjust idle screw to achieve required idle speed.

Idle Speed (RPM) and CO Level (%)

Application	Idle RPM	CO %
Midget	800±100	①3
MGB	850±100	5½±1

① — Nominal setting. Federal, ½ to 6½ % acceptable; Calif., ½ to 6% acceptable.

COLD (FAST) IDLE RPM

1) All models are equipped with automatic chokes for fuel enrichment. To check and adjust, remove carburetor. Open throttle butterfly and wedge open. Remove bolt and washer holding water jacket and three screws retaining heat mass.

2) Rotate the operating arm and check vacuum kick piston and rod for full, free movement; fast idle cam and thermostat lever freeness to pivot; and spring operation on cam and lever.

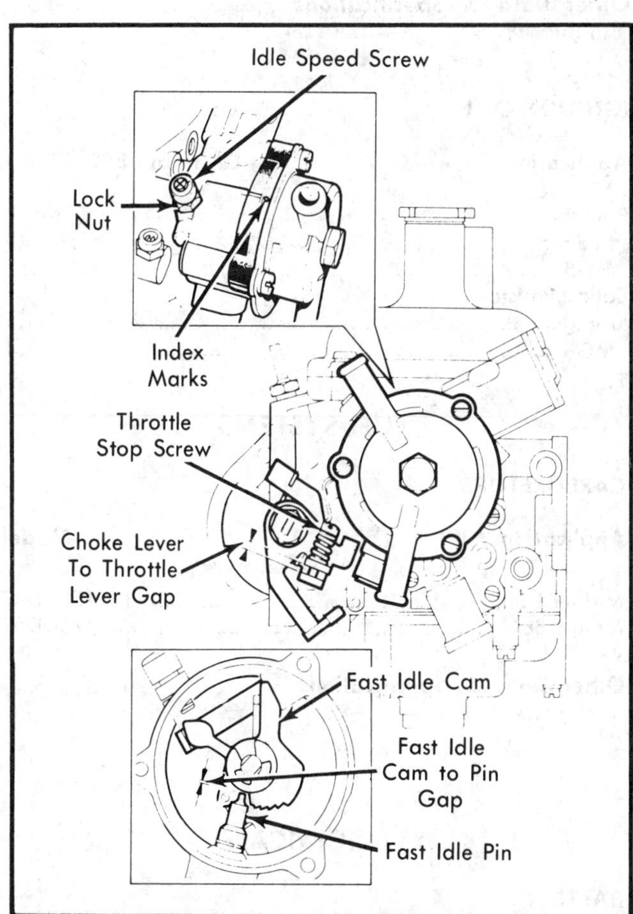

Fig. 7 Setting Fast Idle Clearances

TUNE-UP (Cont.)

3) Remove wedge from throttle opening.

4) Set gap between choke and throttle levers to proper clearance. Adjust by turning idle speed screw.

5) Adjust throttle stop screw to obtain proper clearance between end of fast idle pin and cam. Lock adjusting screw with lock nut.

6) Install parts previously removed, being sure to align index marks on heat mass and automatic choke body. Reinstall carburetor and check or adjust idle speed and CO% level.

Fast Idle Gap Settings

Application	Clearance
Choke Lever-to-Throttle Lever	.094" (2.4 mm)
Fast Idle Pin-to-Cam	
Midget	.035" (.9 mm)
MGB	.025" (.6 mm)

EMISSION CONTROL SYSTEMS

See Mitchell Manuals' Emission Control Manual.

GENERAL SERVICING

IGNITION

DISTRIBUTOR

All Midgets are equipped with Lucas Opus Electronic Ignition System. MGB models with catalytic converters are equipped with Lucas Opus Electronic Ignition System. MGB models without catalytic converters are equipped with conventional Lucas single point distributors.

Other Data & Specifications — *See Tune-Up & Lucas Distributors in ELECTRICAL Section.*

IGNITION COIL

Application	Ohms at 68°F (20°C)
Primary	
Midget	1.3-1.45
MGB	1.43-1.58
Ballast Resistor	
Midget	1.3-1.5
MGB	1.3-1.4

FUEL SYSTEMS

CARBURETORS

Application	Model
Midget 1-Bbl.	150CD4T
MGB 1-Bbl.	175CD5T

Other Data & Specifications — *See Tune-Up & Zenith-Stromberg Carburetors in FUEL SYSTEMS Section.*

ELECTRICAL

BATTERY

12 Volt — Negative Ground.

Battery Location — Battery is located in engine compartment on Midgets and under floor in rear of passenger compartment on MGB models.

Application	Amp. Hr. Rating
Midget	
Standard	40
Optional	50
MGB	66

STARTER

All models are equipped with Lucas Starters.

Free Speed Amperage	
Midget	65 at 8000-10,000 RPM
MGB	40 at 6000 RPM

Other Data & Specifications — *See Lucas Starters in ELECTRICAL Section.*

ALTERNATOR

Application	Rated Amp. Output
Midget	34
MGB	43

Other Data & Specifications — *See Lucas Alternators & Regulators in ELECTRICAL SECTION.*

ALTERNATOR REGULATOR

Lucas — Non-Adjustable; Integral with Alternator.

Other Data & Specifications — *See Lucas Alternators & Regulators in ELECTRICAL Section.*

GENERAL SERVICING (Cont.)

BELT ADJUSTMENT

Application	①Deflection
Alternator Belt	
Midget	.75" (19 mm)
MGB	.50" (13 mm)
Air Pump Belt	.50" (13 mm)

① — Deflection is with moderate hand pressure applied midway on longest belt run.

FILTERS & CLEANERS

Filter or Cleaner	Service Interval (Miles)
Oil Filter	Replace every 6,500
Air Cleaner	Replace every 12,500
Fuel Filter	Replace every 12,500
Charcoal Canister①	Replace every 25,000
Catalytic Converter	Replace every 15,000

① — Replace every 50,000 miles in Midget.

CAPACITIES

Application	Quantity
Crankcase (Includes Filter)	
Midget	4.8 qts.
MGB	3.6 qts.
Cooling System (Includes Heater)	
Midget	5.7 qts.
MGB	7.2 qts.
Man. Trans.	
Midget (H.D. 90)	1.75 pts.
MGB (SAE 20W-50)	①6.0 pts.
Rear Axle	
Midget (H.D. 90)	2.1 pts.
MGB (H.D. 90)	2.0 pts.
Fuel Tank	
Midget	7.7 gals.
MGB	12.0 gals.

① — With overdrive add 1.25 pts.

TUNE-UP

Opel

ENGINE IDENTIFICATION

Engine code is stamped on a machined pad at the top right front corner of engine block.

MODEL IDENTIFICATION

VEHICLE IDENTIFICATION NUMBER

Number is stamped on a plate which is attached to left side of dash (driver's side) and visible through windshield.

COMPRESSION PRESSURE

Check compression pressure with engine at normal operating temperature, all spark plugs and air cleaner element removed, and throttle valve fully open. Compression should be within specifications with a maximum variation between cylinders of 9 psi (.63 kg/cm²).

Compression Pressure @ 300 RPM

Application	Standard psi (kg/cm²)	Limit for Use psi (kg/cm²)
All Models	170 (11.95)	120 (8.44)

VALVE TAPPET CLEARANCE

Check valve clearance with engine cold. Make sure rocker arm shaft nuts are torqued to 16 ft. lbs. (2.2 mkg). Bring piston number one to top dead center on compression stroke by aligning notch on crankshaft pulley with "O" on front cover. Adjust valves as listed in table. Then rotate crankshaft 360° until number four cylinder is at TDC and adjust remaining valves.

Piston No. 1 at TDC

Adjust Valves
- Intake 1, 2
- Exhaust 1, 3

Piston No. 4 at TDC

Adjust Valves
- Intake 3, 4
- Exhaust 2, 4

Valve Tappet Clearance

Application	Clearance (Cold)
All Models	
Intake	.006" (.15 mm)
Exhaust	.010" (.25 mm)

VALVE ARRANGEMENT

All Models

Right Side — All Intake
Left Side — All Exhaust

SPARK PLUGS

Gap .... .030" (.8 mm)
Torque .... 15-22 ft. lbs. (2-3 mkg)

Spark Plug Type

Application	AC	NGK
All Models	R44XLS	BPR6ES

HIGH TENSION WIRE RESISTANCE

Carefully remove high tension wires from spark plugs and distributor cap. Using an ohmmeter, check resistance of wires while gently twisting wires. If resistance is not to specifications or fluctuates from infinity to any valve, replace wire(s).

Resistance (Ohms) Per Wire

Application	Ohms
All Models	25,000-30,000

DISTRIBUTOR

Point Gap .... .016-.020" (.4-.5 mm)
Cam Angle .... 47-57°
Breaker Arm Spring Tension .... 14-19 ozs. (397-540 g)
Condenser Capacity .... .25 mfd.

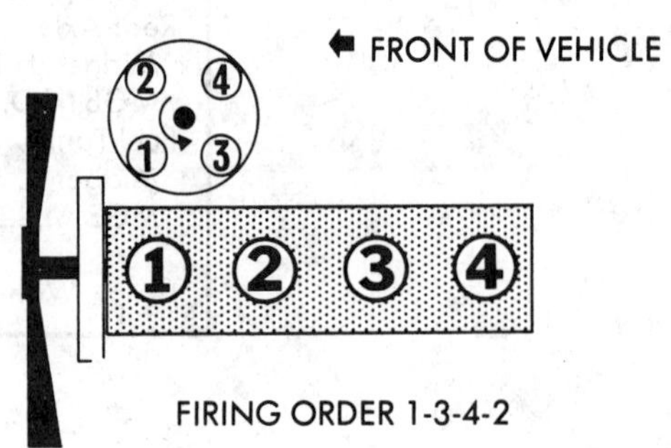

Fig. 1 Firing Order and Distributor Rotation

IGNITION TIMING

Make sure distributor point gap is set correctly and engine is idling smoothly and at correct RPM. Adjust timing as follows:

1) Start engine and run until engine is at normal operating temperature. Stop engine and connect tachometer and a timing light to No. 1 cylinder.

2) Adjust timing by rotating distributor clockwise or counterclockwise until notch on pulley aligns with 6° BTDC mark on machined pad on front cover ("0" mark is TDC). Turning distributor clockwise advances timing, while counterclockwise retards timing.

Ignition Timing Specifications

Application	RPM	Timing
All models	875-925	6° BTDC

TUNE-UP (Cont.)

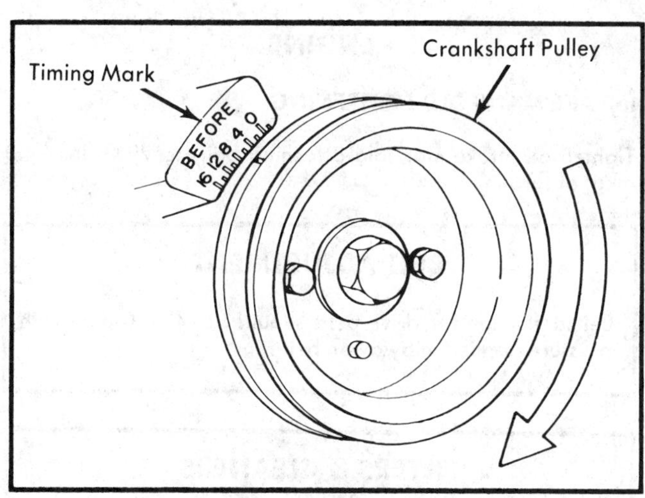

Fig. 2 Ignition Timing Mark Location

HOT (SLOW) IDLE RPM

Make sure spark plug gap, distributor point gap, and accelerator control are adjusted properly. Ignition timing and valve clearance should be properly adjusted. Carburetor float level should be set to specifications. With transmission in neutral, air conditioning off (if equipped), air cleaner installed, vacuum lines to distributor and idle compensator disconnected and plugged, adjust idle speed as follows:

NOTE — *Information (RPM and number of turns) enclosed in parenthesis applies to California and High Altitude vehicles only.*

1) Turn mixture adjusting screw all the way in, then back out 4½ (3) turns. Adjust idle speed screw until 950 (900) RPM is reached. Adjust idle mixture screw for maximum RPM.

2) Readjust idle speed screw for 950 (900) RPM. Turn mixture adjusting screw clockwise (lean) until 900 (850) RPM is reached. Then turn idle mixture screw ½ turn counterclockwise (rich).

3) Adjust idle speed screw for a final speed of 900±25 RPM.

4) On vehicles with air conditioning, after making these adjustments, turn air conditioning on maximum cold and high blower. Open throttle enough to allow speed up solenoid to reach full travel. Then adjust speed up controller adjusting screw for an idle speed of 900±25 RPM.

Idle Speed (RPM) & CO Level (%)

Application	RPM	CO%
All Models	875-925	①

① — See Emission Control Decal.

DASHPOT ADJUSTMENT

1) Check that the engine speed at which the dashpot shaft contacts the throttle lever is within 2600-3000 RPM for Federal vehicles and 2400-2800 RPM for California vehicles.

2) If not within specifications, hold engine speed to specification by using throttle lever. Loosen lock nut and turn dashpot until end of shaft contacts throttle lever. Tighten lock nut.

3) Repeat step **1)** and check that idle speed is 875-925 RPM.

COLD (FAST) IDLE RPM

1) Disconnect and plug vacuum advance and EGR vacuum hoses. Remove air cleaner cover. With engine off, open throttle halfway and close choke valve. Release throttle, then release choke.

2) Start engine without moving throttle. Using fast idle screw, set fast idle to specifications.

Cold (Fast) Idle Specifications

Application	Man. Trans. RPM	Auto. Trans. RPM
All Models	3200±150	3000±150

FUEL PUMP PRESSURE

Pressure (At 900-4800 RPM)
All Models .... 2.4-3.3 psi (.17-.23 kg/cm²)
Delivery Volume (At 1.4 psi or .1 kg/cm²)
All Models .... .85 qts. per minute minimum

GENERAL SERVICING

IGNITION

DISTRIBUTOR

All models are equipped with Nippondenso single point distributors.

Other Data & Specifications — *See Tune-Up & Nippondenso Distributors in ELECTRICAL Section.*

IGNITION COIL

Primary Resistance .... 1.33-1.47 Ohms
Secondary Resistance .... 7,650-9350 Ohms

FUEL SYSTEMS

CARBURETOR

Application	Type
All Models	Nikki 2-Bbl.

Other Data & Specifications — *See Tune-Up and Nikki Carburetors in FUEL SYSTEMS Section.*

GENERAL SERVICING (Cont.)

ELECTRICAL

BATTERY

12 Volt – Negative Ground.

Application	Amp. Hr. Rating
All Models	50

Battery Location – Under hood in right front corner of engine compartment.

STARTER

Hitachi	Overrunning Clutch

Other Data & Specifications – *See Hitachi Starters in ELECTRICAL Section.*

ALTERNATOR

Application	Rated Amp. Output
All Models	40

Other Data & Specifications – *See Nippondenso Alternators & Regulators in ELECTRICAL Section.*

ALTERNATOR REGULATOR

All models are equipped with Nippondenso alternator regulators with an operating voltage of 13.8-14.8 volts at an engine speed of 1400-1850 RPM.

Other Data & Specifications – *See Nippondenso Alternators & Regulators in ELECTRICAL Section.*

ENGINE

INTAKE MANIFOLD TIGHTENING

Tighten all intake manifold attaching bolts to 29 ft. lbs. (4.0 mkg) of torque.

BELT ADJUSTMENT

Belt deflection for drive belts should be .4" (10 mm) with pressure applied midway on belt run.

FILTERS & CLEANERS

Filter or Cleaner	Service Interval (Miles)
Oil Filter	①Replace every 7,500
Air Cleaner	Replace every 30,000
Fuel Filter	Replace every 15,000
Vapor Canister Filter	Replace every 15,000
Auto. Trans. Strainer	②Replace every 30,000

① – At first oil change and then every second change.
② – Under severe conditions, replace every 15,000 miles.

CAPACITIES

Application	Capacity
Crankcase	5 qts.
Cooling System	6.8 qts.
Man. Trans. (SAE 30)	
4-Speed	2.65 qts.
5-Speed	3.25 qts.
Auto. Trans. (Dexron II)	6.5 qts.
Rear Axle (SAE 90)	2.5 pts.
Fuel Tank	13.7 gals.

TUNE-UP

504 SL Gasoline
504 Gasoline

ENGINE IDENTIFICATION

Engine number is stamped on camshaft tunnel, near starter. Engine codes include:

Man. Trans.	XNAC. CAL. M
Auto. Trans.	XNAC. CAL. A

MODEL IDENTIFICATION

VEHICLE IDENTIFICATION NUMBER

Identification plate is located in engine compartment on top of right-hand side of fender panel. Serial number is stamped on fender panel next to identification plate. Plate includes:

Space A – Indicates Model (504 SL or 504)

Space B – Indicates Body Type:

Sedan	
Man. Trans.	A91
Auto Trans.	A93
Station Wagon	
Man. Trans.	D91
Auto. Trans.	D93

Space C – Indicates Gross Vehicle Load

Fig. 1 Typical Peugeot Identification Plate

COMPRESSION PRESSURE

With engine at normal operating temperature, disconnect and plug fuel line to carburetor, then remove float bowl plug and drain fuel from carburetor. Disconnect primary lead from coil, lock throttle plate fully open and remove all spark plugs. Crank engine for four seconds on each cylinder to obtain an accurate compression reading. Compression pressure should check approximately as shown in following table with a maximum variation between cylinders of 14.5 psi (1.0 kg/cm²).

Application	Psi(kg/cm²)
All Models	160(11.2)

VALVE TAPPET CLEARANCE

Valves must be set with engine cold. To adjust valves, turn engine until valve listed in second column is fully open, then adjust valves in first column to specifications. Valves are numbered from REAR to FRONT.

Valve Clearance

Valve	①Clearance
Intake	
No. 2 & 3	.004"(.10 mm)
No. 1 & 4	.008"(.20 mm)
Exhaust	.010"(.25 mm)

① – +.002" (5 mm)

VALVE ARRANGEMENT

All Models
Right Side – All Exhaust.
Left Side – All Intake.

SPARK PLUGS

Gap	.024"(.6 mm)

Spark Plug Type

Application	Number
Champion	N-7Y or N-288
AC	44 XL
Marchal	35 HS

HIGH TENSION WIRE RESISTANCE

Carefully remove high tension wires from spark plugs and distributor cap. Using an ohmmeter, check high tension wire resistance while gently twisting wire. If resistance is not to specification, or fluctuates from infinity to any value, replace wire(s).

Resistance (Ohms) Per Wire

Application	Ohms
All Models	25,000-30,000

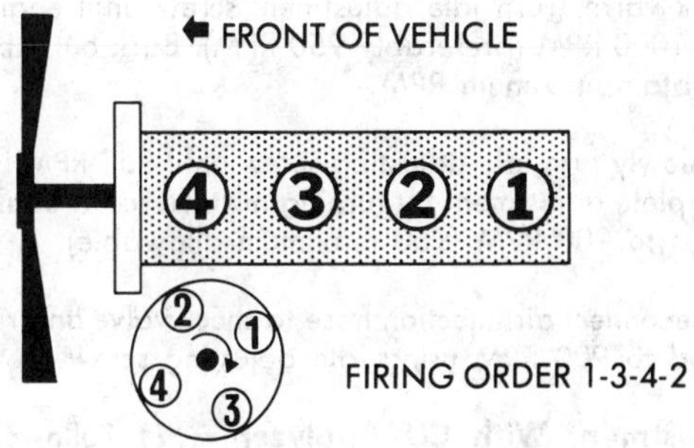

Fig. 2 Firing Order and Distributor Rotation

DISTRIBUTOR

Point Gap	.014-.018"(.35-.45 mm)
Dwell Angle	54-60°
Dwell Ratio	60-66%

TUNE-UP (Cont.)

IGNITION TIMING

1) Disconnect vacuum advance hose and plug it. Connect timing light, dwell meter and tachometer. Start engine and check dwell angle.

2) With engine idling at 900 RPM, check ignition timing. The 8° reference mark should align with notch on pulley. To adjust timing, loosen distributor flange and turn distributor until timing is to specifications. Tighten flange. Reconnect vacuum hose to distributor.

Ignition Timing Specifications

Application	RPM	Timing
All Models	900 +50	8±2° BTDC

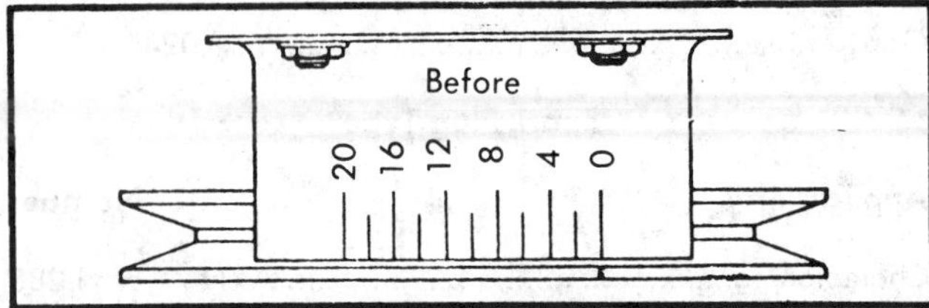

Fig. 3 Timing Marks Illustrated

IDLE SPEED & MIXTURE

Adjustment Without CO Analyzer – **1)** Check and set dwell angle and ignition timing. Be sure engine is at normal operating temperature. Place transmission selector lever in "P" or "N" and turn off the air conditioning and all electrical accessories.

NOTE – *The idle adjustment must always be made ONLY on the screws of the primary carburetor (32 BICSA). NEVER change adjustment of screws on secondary carburetor (34 BICSA).*

2) Disconnect air injection system by detaching air hose from check valve. Turn idle adjustment screw until engine idles at 950-1000 RPM (preferably 950 RPM). Back out mixture screw to obtain maximum RPM.

3) Slowly turn idle adjusting screw until 950 RPM is obtained. Complete adjustment by turning mixture screw until idle speed drops to 900 RPM (950 maximum allowable).

4) Reconnect air injection hose to check valve and readjust idle speed to 900 RPM using idle adjusting screw.

Adjustment With CO Analyzer – **1)** Follow procedures described in steps **1)** and **2)** above through disconnecting air injection system.

2) Then adjust mixture screw to obtain CO level of 1.5-2.5%. Turn idle adjusting screw to reach 900 RPM (950 RPM maximum allowable).

3) Recheck that CO% has remained at proper level (1.5-2.5%). If not, repeat mixture screw and idle adjusting screw adjustment until proper CO% and 900 RPM are obtained.

4) Reattach hose to air injection check valve and adjust idle speed to 900 RPM (950 RPM maximum allowable) by using idle adjusting screw.

Idle Speed (RPM) & CO Level (%)

Application	RPM	CO%
All Models	①900	1.5-2.5

① – 950 RPM maximum allowable.

COLD (FAST) IDLE RPM

1) With engine at operating temperature and idle adjusted to 900 (+50) RPM, place gear selector lever in "N" and turn all electrical accessories to "OFF" position.

2) Disconnect hose (with red ring) from deceleration vacuum unit. Disconnect hose (with green ring) from "T" connector at deceleration valve and attach it where previous hose was removed from vacuum unit.

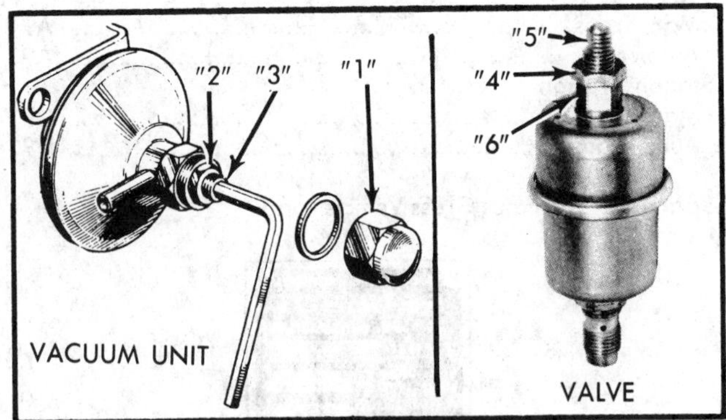

Fig. 4 Adjusting Fast Idle at Deceleration Vacuum Unit and Valve

3) Remove domed nut "1" in *Fig. 4*. Loosen locknut "2" and start engine. Engine speed should be 1500 (+50) RPM.

4) If engine speed is not correct, adjust screw "3" to specification, using a 3 mm Allen wrench. Tighten lock nut "2" and install domed nut "1", making sure gasket is in place.

5) Replace vacuum hoses, previously removed, to their original locations. Loosen lock nut "4" on deceleration valve (not on vacuum unit).

NOTE – Do not use mixture control screw in threaded rod "5" of deceleration valve to obtain proper fast idle speed.

6) Increase engine speed to 3000 RPM without load, and allow engine speed to decrease. Unscrew threaded rod "5" one-half a turn at a time until normal idle (900 RPM) is obtained.

7) Then unscrew threaded rod one additional half turn and tighten lock nut.

NOTE – *Always hold part "6" with wrench when loosening or tightening lock nut on deceleration valve, so as not to exert force on diaphragm.*

TUNE-UP (Cont.)

Fast Idle RPM

Application	RPM
All Models	1500 (+50) RPM

EMISSION CONTROL SYSTEMS

See Mitchell Manuals' Emission Control Manual.

GENERAL SERVICING

IGNITION

DISTRIBUTOR

All models are equipped with Ducellier single point distributors.

Other Data & Specifications — *See Tune-Up & Ducellier Distributors in ELECTRICAL Section.*

FUEL SYSTEMS

CARBURETORS

Application	Model
Federal & California	
No. 1 Carburetor	Solex 32 BICSA PEU 190
No. 2 Carburetor	Solex 34 BICSA PEU 191
High Altitude	
No. 1 Carburetor	Solex 32 BICSA PEU 187
No. 2 Carburetor	Solex 34 BICSA PEU 194

NOTE — *To change for high altitude use, convert No. 1 Carburetor (32 BICSA) by substituting a 115 Main Jet for the original 120 Main Jet and a 180 Air Correction Jet for the original 170 Air Correction Jet. To convert No. 2 Carburetor (34 BICSA), replace original 110 Main Jet with a 105 Main Jet, and the original 50 Idle Jet with a 47 Idle Jet.*

Other Data & Specifications — *See Tune-Up & Solex Carburetors in FUEL SYSTEMS Section.*

ELECTRICAL

BATTERY

12 Volt — Negative Ground.

Application	Amp. Hour Capacity
All Models	60

Battery Location — Left side of engine compartment.

STARTER

Ducellier or Paris-Rhone	Overrunning Clutch

Other Data & Specifications — *See Ducellier & Paris-Rhone Starters in ELECTRICAL Section.*

ALTERNATOR

Application	Rated Amp. Output
All Models	55

ALTERNATOR REGULATOR

A single-stage Paris Rhone alternator regulator is mounted on the fender well of engine compartment.

FILTER & CLEANERS

Filter or Cleaner	Service Interval (Miles)
Oil Filter	Replace every 6,000
Air Cleaner	Replace every 12,500

BELT ADJUSTMENT

Make two marks on fan or air pump belt 100 mm apart. When placing a used belt on cold engine, stretch belt until marks are 101.5 mm part. When installing new belt, marks should be 102-102.5 mm apart.

CAPACITIES

Application	Quantity
Crankcase (Includes Filter)	4.22 qts.
Cooling System	8.50 qts.
Man. Trans. (SAE 20W-40)	2.24 pts.
Auto. Trans. (Dexron)	5.5 qts.
Auto. Trans., Refill (Dexron)	2.7-3.3 pts.
Rear Axle	
Sedan (Esso Gear Oil 90)	2.5 pts.
Station Wagon (Esso Gear Oil 90)	3.4 pts.
Fuel Tank	
Sedan	18.5 gals.
Station Wagon	15.8 gals.

TUNE-UP

504 Diesel

ENGINE IDENTIFICATION

Engine number is stamped on left side of engine block just below cylinder head. XD 90 engine numbers are 900001 and up.

Engine Codes

Application	Code
Without Air Conditioning	XD 4.90 USA
With Air Conditioning	XD 4.90 USA/AC

MODEL IDENTIFICATION

VEHICLE IDENTIFICATION

Identification plate is located in engine compartment on top of right side fender panel. Serial number is stamped on fender panel next to identification plate. Plate includes:

Space A — Indicates Model (504 Diesel)

Space B — Indicates Body Type:

Sedan	
Man. Trans.	AC0
Auto. Trans.	AC5
Station Wagon	
Man. Trans.	DC0
Auto. Trans.	DC5

Fig. 1 Typical Peugeot Identification Plate

COMPRESSION PRESSURE

With engine at normal operating temperature, remove injectors. Block injection pump stop control in the "cut-off" position. Install suitable pressure gauge on No. 1 cylinder and crank for about 4 seconds. Compression should be to specifications.

Application	Pressure
All	580-650 psi (40-45 kg/cm²)

VALVE TAPPET CLEARANCE

Valves must be set with engine cold. To adjust valves, turn engine until valve listed in second column is fully open, then adjust valves in first column to specifications. Valves are numbered from REAR to FRONT.

Valves To Adjust	Valve Open
No. 3 Int. & No. 4 Exh.	No. 1 Exh.
No. 4 Int. & No. 2 Exh.	No. 3 Exh.
No. 2 Int. & No. 1 Exh.	No. 4 Exh.
No. 1 Int. & No. 3 Exh.	No. 2 Exh.

Valve Clearance

Valve	①Clearance
Intake................................	.006" (.15 mm)
Exhaust................................	.010" (.25 mm)

① — Set cold.

VALVE ARRANGEMENT

All Models — I-E-E-I-I-E-E-I (front to rear).

GLOW PLUGS

Torque................................ 33 ft. lbs. (4.5 mkg)

Glow Plug Type

Application	Bosch Type No.
All Models	KE/GSA 9/1

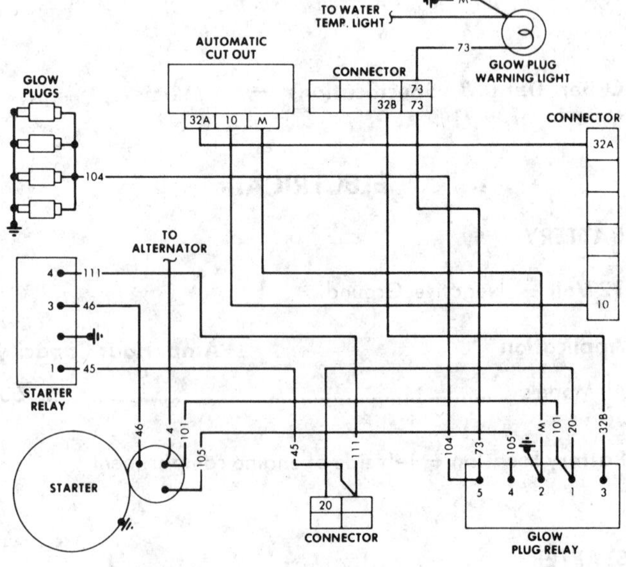

Fig. 2 Schematic of Glow Starting Circuit

DIESEL INJECTION SYSTEM

FIRING ORDER

All Models — 1-3-4-2 (rear to front)

TUNE-UP (Cont.)

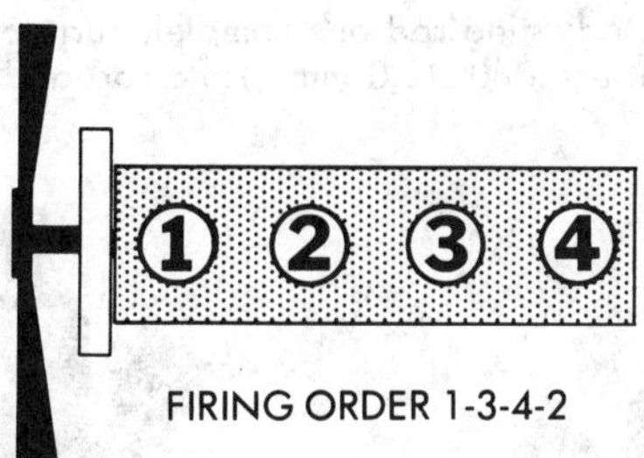

Fig. 3 Firing Order for 504 Diesel

INJECTION TIMING

Timing is 8° BTDC. Fuel pump piston lift is .026" (.65 mm).

FAST IDLE ADJUSTMENT

Fast idle is properly adjusted when there is .080" (2 mm) play between cable pulley and plunger support.

IDLE SPEED ADJUSTMENT

NOTE – *It is necessary to use a friction drive tachometer, such as Jaegar No. 42.839 with friction disc No. 87.645. To read corrected idle RPM, it is necessary to divide tachometer reading by two.*

Idle Speed RPM

Application	Equipment	RPM
XD 4.90 USA	Without A/C	700 (+50)
XD 4.90 USA/AC	With A/C	770 (+50)

EP/VM Pumps – 1) With engine at normal operating temperature, release accelerator cable. Loosen lock nut on fast idle RPM adjustment "1" and loosen adjusting screw several turns. On idle speed adjustment rod, loosen lock nut "2" on front of pump. Using suitable friction tachometer, apply friction disc to fan drive belt.

Fig. 4 Showing Location of Components for Making Idle Adjustment on EP/VM Pump

2) Adjust to proper idle speed by turning idle adjustment rod "3". Unscrew fast idle speed adjusting screw until engine speed increases. Tighten fast idle stop screw one full turn and tighten lock nut. Secure accelerator cable, ensuring that pedal travel corresponds to full depression of lever "4".

3) On instrument panel, turn fast idle control cable to minimum position and connect fast idling control cable by bottoming cable clamp against slide link.

NOTE – *Never use fast idle stop screw to adjust idle speed.*

EP/VAC Pumps – NOTE – *Idle speed adjustment is accomplished by adjusting Deferred Injection Device on these pumps.*

DEFERRED INJECTION DEVICE ADJUSTMENT

EP/VM Pumps – 1) With engine at normal operating temperature, turn idle control on instrument panel to minimum position. Disconnect link rod where it connects to deferred injection accumulator lever. Push accumulator lever to fully open position (minimum engine speed). Adjust idle speed through .080" (2.0 mm) throttle lever free travel.

Fig. 5 Adjusting Throttle Stop on EP/VM Pump

2) Push accumulator lever back toward accumulator until engine speed just begins to increase. This point is easily ascertained by an appreciable increase in engine noise. Adjust length of link rod so that it just attaches to accumulator lever at point where engine speed begins to increase.

NOTE – *Correct adjustment will be evident by existence of .039" (1.0 mm) clearance between throttle stop and throttle lever.*

3) Correct position can also be determined by running characteristics of engine. If link is too long, accumulator is out of circuit and advantages of accumulator are lost. If link is too short, engine speed is increased at idle, vehicle will have poor acceleration and exhaust will smoke.

TUNE-UP (Cont.)

Fig. 6 Making Accumulator Initial Operation Adjustment on EP/VM Pump

EP/VAC Pumps – 1) With engine at normal operating temperature, place idle control on instrument panel in minimum position. Loosen lock nuts on accumulator rod and disconnect accumulator rod at accumulator actuating lever.

2) Push accumulator lever to full open position which is evident by minimum engine speed. Adjust idle stop screw to obtain proper idle speed.

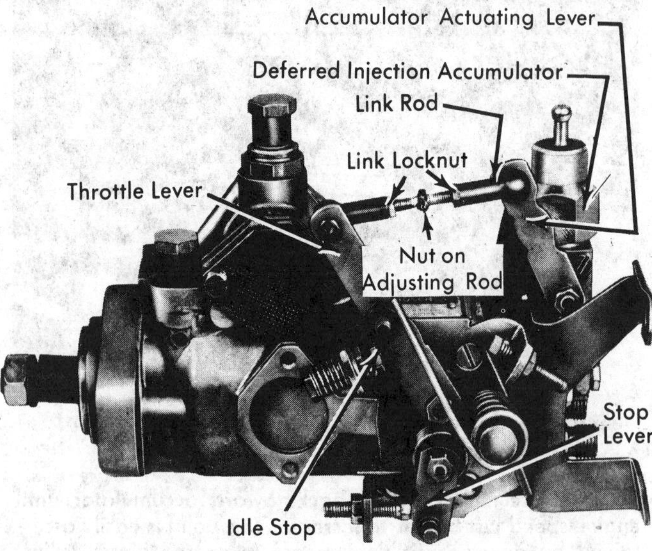

Fig. 7 Adjusting Points on EP/VAC Pump

3) Move accumulator actuating lever toward accumulator until engine speed just begins to increase. This position is also evident by an increase in engine noise. Mark one side of center nut on adjusting rod. See *Fig. 7*.

4) Adjust length of rod to allow installation of rod end on accumulator lever without changing position of accumulator actuating lever.

5) Rotate the adjusting rod one complete turn to shorten link by approximately .080" (2.0 mm). Hold rod and tighten lock nuts.

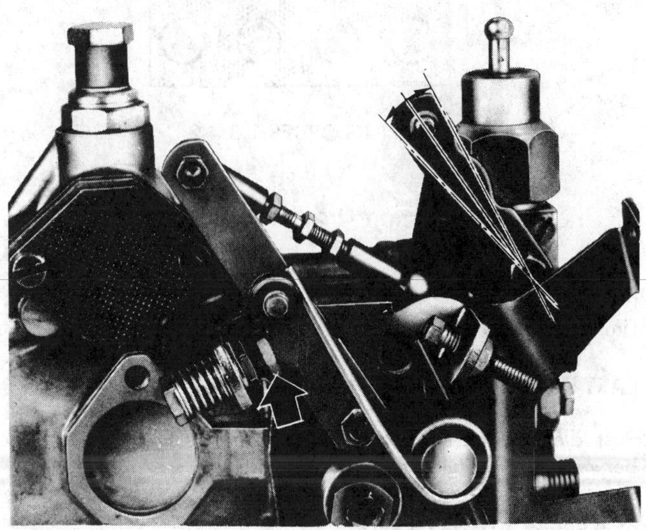

Fig. 8 Adjusting EP/VAC Pump

BLEEDING FUEL SYSTEM

On top of fuel filter, loosen needle valve and actuate primer lever. Tighten needle valve when water has drained through drain tube. Loosen air bleed screw and actuate lever. When resistance is felt, tighten air bleed screw.

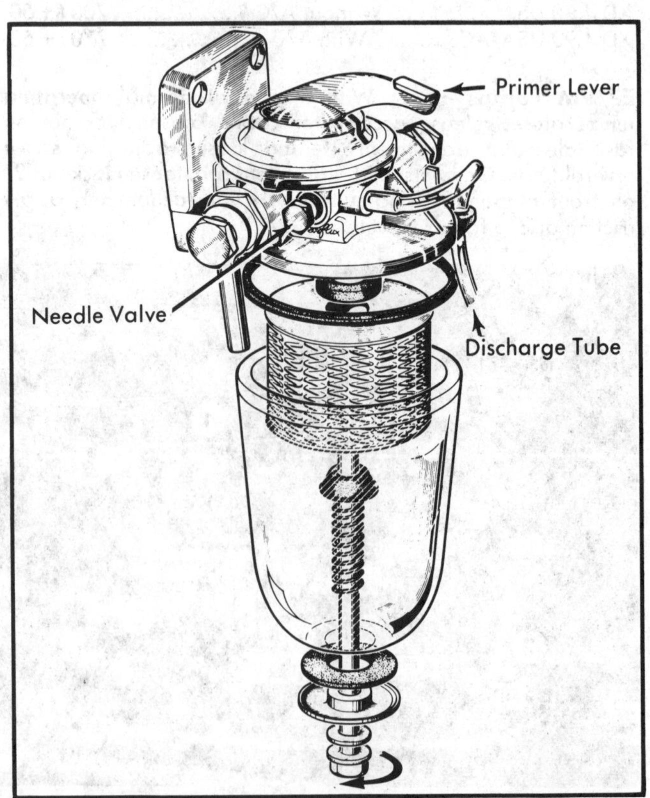

Fig. 9 Cutaway View of Fuel Filter Assembly

TUNE-UP (Cont.)

PRIMING FUEL SYSTEM

1) First, bleed the fuel system as described above. On systems equipped with EP/VM pumps, loosen injection pump bleed screw and actuate pump lever until fuel flows bubble free. Tighten bleed screw.

Fig. 10 Tightening Bleed Screw on EP/VM Pump

2) On systems using EP/VAC pump, place stop lever (on instrument panel) in "STOP" position. Actuate primer lever on fuel filter 30-40 times. With stop lever released, switch ignition switch "ON". Turn idle control (on instrument panel) clockwise to maximum position. Press starter button for 10-15 seconds, then preheat glow plugs until signal light comes on. Press starter button again.

FUEL PUMP TESTING

In the event of poor idle, stalling or lack of engine power, fuel pump should be checked as follows:

1) Disconnect fuel feed hose from inlet of injection pump. Connect a 4" (100 mm) length of 5/16" (8 mm) inside diameter clear nylon hose to injection pump inlet. Insert a 1.5" (40 mm) length of 5/16" (8 mm) outside diameter copper tube into fuel delivery line. Insert clear tubing over copper tube and secure all joints with hose clamps.

2) Start engine and observe flow of fuel through clear hose. At speeds less than 3000 RPM, no air bubbles should be seen. Bubble formation is normal at higher engine speeds. If air bubbles are seen, check filter and pump seals, connections, hoses and clamps.

GENERAL SERVICING

FUEL SYSTEMS

FUEL INJECTION

Application	Bosch Type No.
Injection Pump	EP/VM or EP/VAC
Injector Holders	KB.35.SD 593/4
Injectors	DN OSD 203

Other Data & Specifications — *See Tune-Up and Bosch (Peugeot) Diesel Fuel Injection in FUEL SYSTEMS Section.*

ELECTRICAL

BATTERY

12 Volt — Negative Ground.

Application	Amp. Hour Capacity
All Models	90

Battery Location — In engine compartment.

STARTER

Paris-Rhone .... Overrunning Clutch

Other Data & Specifications — *See Paris-Rhone Starters in ELECTRICAL Section.*

ALTERNATOR

Application	Rated Amp. Output
All Models	55

ALTERNATOR REGULATOR

Alternator regulator is mounted on the fender well of engine compartment.

FILTERS & CLEANERS

Filter or Cleaner	Service Interval (Miles)
Oil Filter	Replace 3,000
Air Filter	Replace 3,000
Fuel Filter	Replace 12,000

BELT ADJUSTMENT

When installing or replacing belt, make two marks 100 mm apart. Install belt, tightening it until the marks are approximately 102 mm apart.

CAPACITIES

Application	Quantity
Crankcase	5.3 qts.
Cooling System (Includes Heater)	10.55 qts.
Transmission (SAE 20W-40)	2.4 pts.
Rear Axle	
Sedan (SAE 90)	2.5 pts.
Station Wagon (SAE 90)	2.4 pts.
Fuel Tank	
Sedan	18.5 gals.
Station Wagon	15.8 gals.

1977 Peugeot V6 Tune-Up

TUNE-UP

604 SL

ENGINE IDENTIFICATION

Engine number is stamped on camshaft tunnel, near starter. Engine codes are:

Engine Code Numbers

Application	Code Number
Federal	
Man. Trans.	112.9.D.M.
Auto. Trans.	112.9.D.A.
California	
Man. Trans.	112.9.E.M.
Auto. Trans.	112.9.E.A.

MODEL IDENTIFICATION

VEHICLE IDENTIFICATION NUMBER

The identification plate is located in engine compartment on top of right-hand fender panel. Serial number is stamped on fender panel near identification plate. Information includes:

Space A – Indicates Model (604 SL)

Space B – Indicates Body Type:

Sedan	
Man. Trans.	AA1S
Auto. Trans.	AA3S

Space C – Indicates Gross Vehicle Load

Fig. 1 Typical Peugeot Identification Label

COMPRESSION PRESSURE

With engine at normal operating temperature, disconnect and plug fuel line to carburetor. Lock throttle plate fully open and remove all spark plugs. Crank engine for four seconds on each cylinder to obtain an accurate compression reading. Compression pressure should check approximately as shown in table, with a maximum variation between cylinders of 14.5 psi (1.0 kg/cm²).

Application	psi (kg/cm²)
All Models	160 (11.2)

VALVE TAPPET CLEARANCE

1) Valves must be set with engine cold. Bring piston of No. 1 cylinder to TDC on ignition stroke. Align distributor rotor with timing mark on distributor housing. Check that slot in crankshaft pulley aligns with "0" mark on timing plate. Adjust the following valves:

Exhaust Valves	Intake Valves
No. 1, No. 3, & No. 6	No. 1, No. 2, & No. 4

2) Bring piston of No. 1 cylinder to TDC at end of exhaust stroke. Rotate crankshaft one full turn. Distributor rotor should now point 180° away from housing timing mark. Slot of crankshaft pulley should again align with "O" mark on timing plate. Adjust valves:

Exhaust Valves	Intake Valves
No. 2, No. 4, & No. 5	No. 3, No. 5 & No. 6

Valve Clearance Specifications

Valves	Clearance
Intake	.004" (.10 mm)
Exhaust	.010" (.25 mm)

VALVE ARRANGEMENT

Intake Valves – Center of "V" (Inner Row of Valves in Each Head)

Exhaust Valves – Outer Row of Valves in Each Head

SPARK PLUGS

Gap	.024" (.6 mm)
Torque	13 ft. lbs. (1.8 mkg)

Spark Plug Type

Application	Champion No.
604 SL	BN-9Y

HIGH TENSION WIRE RESISTANCE

Carefully remove high tension wires from spark plugs and distributor cap. Using an ohmmeter, check high tension wire resistance while gently twisting wire. If resistance is not to specification, or fluctuates from infinity to any value, replace wire(s).

Resistance (Ohms) Per Wire

Application	Ohms
604 SL	25,000-30,000

TUNE-UP (Cont.)

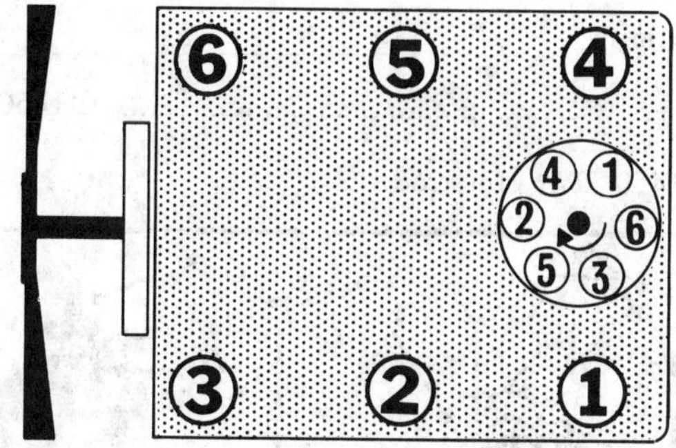

Fig. 2 Firing Order and Distributor Rotation

DISTRIBUTOR

All models are equipped with breakerless ignition system.

IGNITION TIMING

1) With engine at normal operating temperature, but not running, connect the non-positive leads of the air injection system electro valve terminals (on left front fender well) to vehicle ground by means of a jumper wire.

NOTE — *These electro valve terminals are connected to the thermoswitch, not to the in-line fuse.*

2) Be sure idle at this time is within 800-850 RPM. Disconnect and plug advance unit vacuum line. Connect high-voltage sensor of timing light to No. 1 cylinder or No. 6 cylinder.

3) Start engine and adjust timing mark (if necessary) on crankshaft pulley with 10° BTDC mark on timing plate. To adjust, move distributor until marks align. Tighten distributor flange after adjustment.

4) Reconnect line for vacuum advance and remove jumper wire from electro valve leads. Idle speed should now be 900-950 RPM.

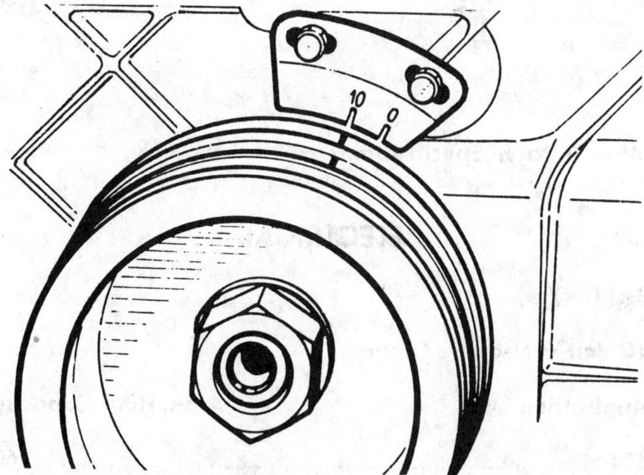

Fig. 3 Timing Mark Location for 604 SL

Ignition Timing Specifications

Application	Timing
604 SL	10±2° BTDC

IDLE SPEED & MIXTURE

1) With engine at normal operating temperature, ignition timing set to specifications, and transmission shift lever in "N", turn off air conditioning and all electrical accessories. Be sure all control lines for emission system are properly connected.

NOTE — *Adjustments are to be made using only idle speed screw and idle mixture screw on primary carburetor (34 TBIA) ONLY. DO NOT TOUCH setting of screws on secondary carburetor (35 CEEI).*

2) Disconnect the air injection system by connecting the non-positive terminals of the air injection system electro valves (located on left front fender well) to vehicle ground, using a jumper wire.

NOTE — *These electro valve terminals are connected to the thermoswitch, not to the in-line fuse.*

3) Remove air filter. Turn idle mixture screw to obtain a CO level of 3-4% (preferably 3.5%). Then turn idle speed screw to obtain 800 RPM (850 RPM allowable).

4) Check CO level to ensure it is within 3-4% range. If not, repeat step **3)** until proper CO% and idle speed are reached.

5) Remove jumper wire from electro valves. If necessary, readjust idle speed, which should now be 900 RPM (950 RPM allowable). Replace air filter.

Idle Speed (RPM) and CO Level (%)

Application	RPM	CO%
604 SL	①900	3-4

① — 950 RPM maximum allowable.

COLD (FAST) IDLE RPM

1) Check engine for idle speed of 900-950 RPM with engine at normal operating temperature. Disconnect the vacuum line (with red ring) from the deceleration vacuum unit. Check for 1 mm play between throttle lever and screw.

2) If there is no play present, loosen lock nut and adjust screw. Then loosen domed nut "1" (See *Fig. 4*), saving gasket.

3) Disconnect vacuum line (with green ring) from "T" connector leading to deceleration valve. Connect this line to the deceleration vacuum unit where line with red ring was previously removed.

4) Start the engine. Fast idle speed should be within a range of 1450-1500 RPM (1450 RPM preferred). If not within this

TUNE-UP (Cont.)

range, loosen lock nut "2", and adjust screw "3" using a 3 mm Allen wrench.

5) When to specification, tighten lock nut "2". Install gasket and domed nut "1". Then remove and reinstall vacuum lines to previous locations (green line to "T" connector of deceleration valve and red line to deceleration vacuum unit).

6) Then loosen lock nut "4" (*See Fig. 4*) on deceleration valve.

NOTE — *Do not use throttle cable screw in threaded rod "5" of deceleration valve to obtain proper fast idle speed.*

7) Increase engine speed to 3000 RPM and allow it to decrease. Unscrew threaded rod "5" one-half turn at a time until idle speed returns to 900-950 RPM (900 preferred). Then, turn threaded rod one additional half turn. Tighten lock nut "4".

NOTE — *Always hold part "6" on deceleration valve when loosening or tightening lock nut "4". This will prevent damage to diaphragm.*

Fast Idle RPM

Application	RPM
604 SL	①1450-1500

① — 1450 RPM preferred.

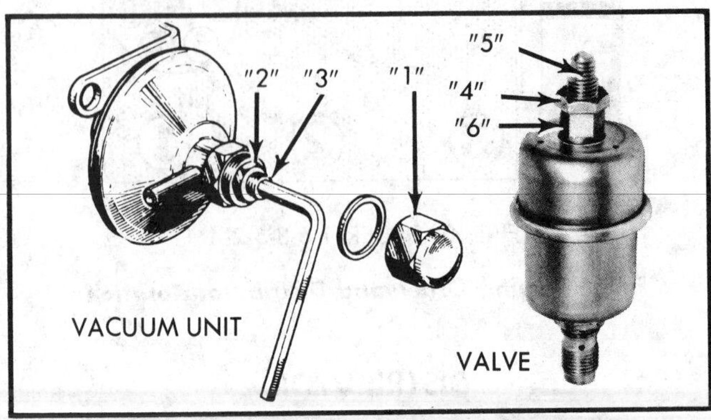

Fig. 4 Adjusting Fast Idle at Deceleration Vacuum Unit and Valve

EMISSION CONTROL SYSTEMS

See Mitchell Manuals' Emission Control Manual.

GENERAL SERVICING

IGNITION

DISTRIBUTOR

The 604 SL is equipped with a Bosch breakerless distributor, electronic module and coil.

Other Data & Specifications — *See Tune-Up & Bosch Breakerless Distributors in ELECTRICAL Section.*

IGNITION COIL

Resistance in Ohms

Application	Ohms
Primary Resistance	.33-.46
Secondary Resistance	7,000-12,000

FUEL SYSTEMS

CARBURETORS

Application	Model
Federal	
No. 1 Carburetor	Solex 34 TBIA PEU 182 (1-Bbl.)
No. 2 Carburetor	Solex 35 CEEI PEU 186 (2-Bbl.)
California	
Man. Trans	
No. 1 Carburetor	Solex 34 TBIA PEU 182 (1-Bbl.)
No. 2 Carburetor	Solex 35 CEEI PEU 186 (2-Bbl.)
Auto. Trans.	
No. 1 Carburetor	Solex 34 TBIA PEU 183 (1-Bbl.)
No. 2 Carburetor	Solex 35 CEEI PEU 186 (2-Bbl.)

CARBURETORS (Cont.)

Application	Model
High Altitude①	
All Man. Trans. & Federal Auto. Trans.	
No. 1 Carburetor	Solex 34 TBIA PEU 195 (1-Bbl.)
No. 2 Carburetor	Solex 35 CEEI PEU 196 (2-Bbl.)
California Auto. Trans.	
No. 1 Carburetor	Solex 34 TBIA PEU 214 (1-Bbl.)
No. 2 Carburetor	Solex 35 CEEI PEU 196 (2-Bbl.)

① — Converted from Federal and California models by changing jets. If carburetor is modified, change vehicle emission control information label.

NOTE — *To convert low-altitude carburetors for high altitude use requires replacement of main and idle jets. To change 34 TBIA carburetors for high altitude, replace 140 Main Jet with 137.5 Main Jet and 50 Idle Jet with 48 Idle Jet. To convert 35 CEEI carburetors for high altitude, replace 145 Main Jet with 142.5 Main Jet and 47 Idle Jet with 45 Idle Jet.*

Other Data & Specifications — *See Tune-Up & Solex Carburetors in FUEL SYSTEMS Section.*

ELECTRICAL

BATTERY

12 Volt — Negative Ground.

Application	Amp. Hour Capacity
604 SL	60

Battery Location — Left side of engine compartment.

GENERAL SERVICING (Cont.)

STARTER

Bosch GF .... Overrunning Clutch

Other Data & Specifications – *See Bosch Starters in ELECTRICAL Section.*

ALTERNATOR

Application	Rated Amp. Output
604 SL	40

ALTERNATOR REGULATOR

Alternator regulator, manufactured by Paris-Rhone, Ducellier, or SEV Frida, is mounted on fender well of engine compartment.

FILTER & CLEANERS

Filter or Cleaner	Service Interval (Miles)
Oil Filter	①Replace every 6,500
Air Cleaner	Replace every 12,500
Fuel Filter	Replace every 12,500

① – Replace at 600 miles, 3500 miles and then every 6,500 miles.

BELT ADJUSTMENT

When installing or replacing belt, make two marks on belt 100 mm apart. Then tighten belt until marks are 101.5 mm apart for used belt or 102-102.5 mm apart for new belts.

CAPACITIES

Application	Quantity
Crankcase (Includes Filter)	6.3 qts.
Cooling System	11.0 qts.
Man. Trans. (SAE 10W-50)	2.8 pts.
Auto. Trans. (Dexron)	6.1 qts.
Auto. Trans. Refill (Dexron)	1.6-1.9 qts.
Rear Axle (SAE 80 API GL-5①)	3.3 pts.
Fuel Tank	②18.5 gals.
Windshield Washer Tank	1.5 qts.

① – SAE 80 Mil L 2105B also acceptable.
② – Includes 2.5 gals. in reserve.

TUNE-UP

924

ENGINE IDENTIFICATION

The 924 in 1977 features a 2.0 liter (1984 cc) engine, and is available as both 1977 and 1977½ models. The engine number is located on the left side of crankcase next to the clutch housing. Engine code numbers are as follows:

Engine Code Numbers

Application	1977 Codes	1977½ Codes
924 Federal	XH	XG
924 Calif.	XF	XE

MODEL IDENTIFICATION

VEHICLE IDENTIFICATION NUMBER

The vehicle identification number is stamped on a plate located near the battery in the engine compartment. Number also appears on plate attached to left windshield pillar, visible from outside vehicle.

COMPRESSION PRESSURE

Test compression pressure with fully open throttle, oil temperature above 140° F (60° C), all spark plugs removed and engine at cranking speed. Each cylinder should be allowed about 12 compression strokes. Differences between cylinders should not exceed 43 psi (3 kg/cm²).

Application	Standard Pressure psi (kg/cm²)	Minimum Pressure psi (kg/cm²)
All Models	114-156 (8-11)	85 (6)

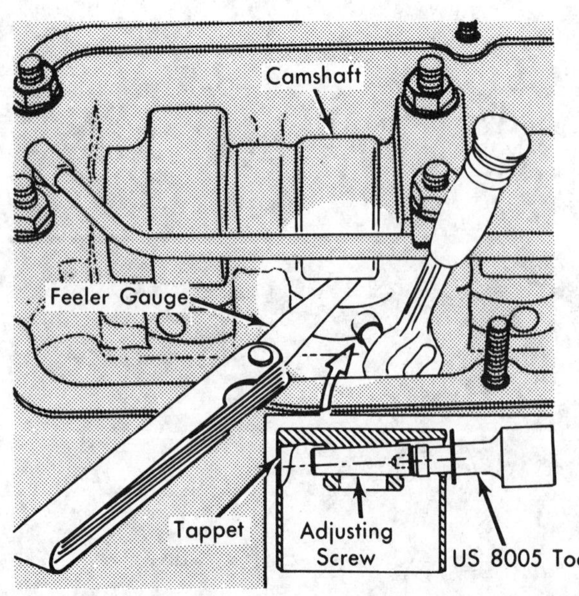

Fig. 1 Adjusting Valve Clearance

VALVE TAPPET CLEARANCE

It is recommended that valve clearances be checked and adjusted with engine oil temperature at 176° F (80° C). To adjust, remove cylinder head cover and turn crankshaft until cam lobes of cylinder to be adjusted point upward.

Check valve clearance. Correct by making complete turns of adjusting screw, using US 8005 adjusting tool. See *Fig. 1*. One turn changes clearance by .002" (.05 mm). Various adjusting screws are available. Camshaft must be removed to replace screws.

Valve Clearance Specifications

Application	Clearance
1977 Models	
Warm	
Intake	.008-.010" (.20-.25 mm)
Exhaust	.018-.020" (.45-.50 mm)
Cold	
Intake	.004-.006" (.10-.15 mm)
Exhaust	.016-.018" (.40-.45 mm)
1977½ Models	
Warm	
Intake	.008-.010" (.20-.25 mm)
Exhaust	.018-.020" (.45-.50 mm)
Cold	
Intake	.006-.008" (.15-.20 mm)
Exhaust	.016-.018" (.40-.45 mm)

VALVE ARRANGEMENT

Both Banks — I-E-I-E-I-E-I-E

SPARK PLUGS

Gap	.028-.032" (.6-.8 mm)
Torque	21 ft. lbs. (3 mkg)

Spark Plug Type①

Application	Bosch	Beru
All Models	W200T30	200/14/3A

① — Champion Plug N-8Y.

HIGH TENSION WIRE RESISTANCE

Carefully remove high tension wires from spark plugs and distributor cap. Using an ohmmeter, check resistance of high tension wires while gently twisting wire. If resistance is not to specification, or fluctuates from infinity to any value, replace high tension wire(s).

Resistance (Ohms) Per Wire

Application	Ohms
All Models	6,000

TUNE-UP (Cont.)

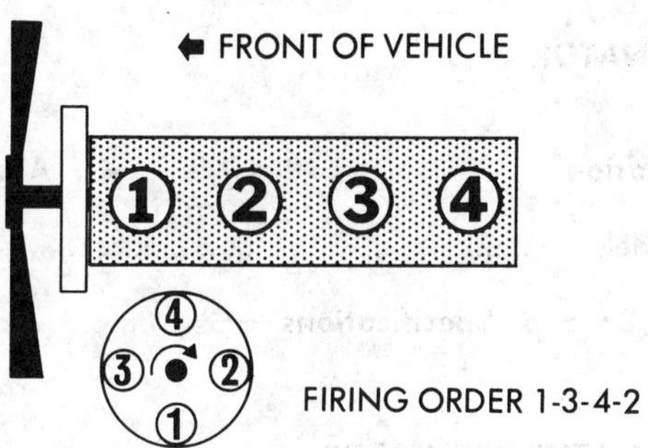

Fig. 2 Firing Order and Distributor Rotation

DISTRIBUTOR

Air Gap (Rotor-to-Stator) .... ①
Dwell Angle
At 1500 RPM .... 52-70°
At 5000 RPM .... 42-68°

① – Information not available at time of publication.

IGNITION TIMING

Check or adjust ignition timing with engine at specified RPM and both distributor vacuum advance hoses connected. Adjust timing by turning distributor until mark on flywheel aligns with reference edge on clutch housing.

Ignition Timing Specifications

Application	RPM	Timing
1977 Models	850-1000	10°±1° ATDC
1977½ Models	900-1000	3° ATDC

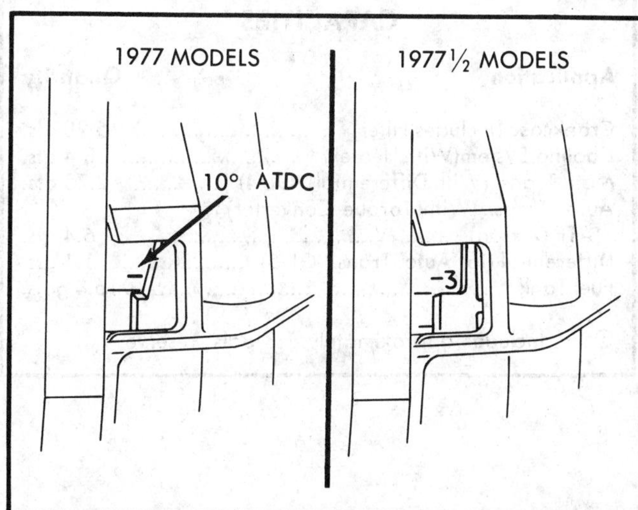

Fig. 3 Flywheel Ignition Timing Marks

HOT (SLOW) IDLE RPM

NOTE – *Ignition timing and valve clearance should be to specifications prior to setting idle RPM.*

1) With engine at normal operating temperature, connect tachometer and exhaust gas analyzer following manufacturer's instructions.

NOTE – *On models equipped with catalytic converter, connect suitable exhaust probe (VW 1311) in front of converter.*

2) Disconnect and plug air injection hose at air pump. Clamp hose to charcoal canister and air cleaner. On California 1977½ vehicles, detach air hose at diverter valve and plug.

3) Adjust idle speed to specifications by turning idle air bypass screw on throttle valve housing. Remove plug in mixture control unit between fuel distributor and venturi or puncture plastic cap with small screwdriver.

4) Insert adjusting wrench (P377) and adjust CO% level.

NOTE – *Always adjust CO% from lean to rich. (Example: If setting is too rich, turn idle adjusting screw all the way counterclockwise, and adjust back toward richer setting.) Never apply pressure to wrench during adjustment.*

5) Remove wrench and accelerate engine. Check CO% level and repeat procedure, if necessary. Recheck idle speed, adjusting as necessary.

6) Insert plug or secure adjusting screw with new blue plastic cap.

Idle Speed (RPM) & CO Level (%) ①

Application	Idle RPM	CO%
1977 Models		
Federal	850-1000	② 1.0-2.0
High Altitude	850-1000	② .7-1.3
Calif.	850-1000	③ .7 (Max.)
1977½ Models		
Federal	900-1000	1.0-2.0
Calif.		④ .5-1.0

① – Always check engine compartment decal.
② – With air pump & carbon canister disconnected.
③ – With carbon canister (only) disconnected. Measure in front of catalytic converter.
④ – Measure in front of catalytic converter.

FUEL PUMP PRESSURE

Pressure at 104°F (40°C)
All Models .... 36 psi (2.5 kg/cm²)
Delivery Rate .... 1 qt. in 40 seconds

1977 Porsche 4 Tune-Up

GENERAL SERVICING

IGNITION

DISTRIBUTOR

All models are equipped with Bosch transistorized ignition system.

Other Data & Specifications – *See Tune-Up & Bosch Distributors in ELECTRICAL Section.*

IGNITION COIL

Primary Resistance	1.0-1.35 Ohms
Secondary Resistance	5,500-8,000 Ohms

FUEL SYSTEMS

FUEL INJECTION

All models are equipped with Bosch CIS Fuel Injection.

Other Data & Specifications – *See Tune-Up & Bosch CIS Fuel Injection in FUEL SYSTEMS Section.*

ELECTRICAL

BATTERY

CAUTION – *Battery should be disconnected before charging. Precaution will prevent damage to fuel injection control unit.*

12 Volt – Negative Ground.

Application	Amp. Hr. Rating
All Models	63

Battery Location – Battery is located at right rear corner of engine compartment.

STARTER

Bosch	Overrunning Clutch
Free Speed Voltage	
All Models	①
Free Speed Amperage	
All Models	①

① – Information not available at time of publication.

Other Data & Specifications – *See Bosch Starters in ELECTRICAL Section.*

ALTERNATOR

Application	Rated Amp. Output
All Models	75

Other Data & Specifications – *See Bosch Alternators in ELECTRICAL Section.*

ALTERNATOR REGULATOR

All models are equipped with Bosch alternator regulators. With rear window defogger and headlights turned on, operating voltage should be 13.5-14.5 volts at 2000 RPM.

Other Data & Specifications – *See Bosch Alternator Regulators in ELECTRICAL SECTION.*

BELT ADJUSTMENT

Tension is correct when center portion of belt can be depressed approximately 3/16 to 3/8" (5-10 mm) by firm thumb pressure. Adjustment is made by shifting position of alternator. Remove small plate from alternator cover for access to adjustment lock screw.

FILTERS & CLEANERS

Filter or Cleaner	Service Interval (Miles)
Oil Filter	Replace every 15,000
Air Cleaner	Replace every 15,000
Fuel Filter	Replace every 15,000
Air Pump Filter	Replace every 15,000

CAPACITIES

Application	Quantity
Crankcase (Includes Filter)	5.28 qts.
Cooling System(With Heater)	8.4 qts.
Man. Trans. (With Differential) (GL-4)	2.75 qts.
Auto. Trans. (With Torque Converter) (ATF Dexron)	6.4 qts.
Differential (for Auto. Trans.)(GL-5)	1.1 qts.
Fuel Tank	①16.4 gals.

① – Includes approximately 1.3 gals. reserve.

TUNE-UP

911 S
Turbo Carrera

ENGINE IDENTIFICATION

Engine identification number is stamped on engine crankcase near oil temperature sensor.

Application	Code
911S	
Man. Trans.	911/85
Sportmatic Trans.	911/90
Turbo Carrera	930/53

MODEL IDENTIFICATION

VEHICLE IDENTIFICATION NUMBER

Number is located on left windshield post and can be seen from outside of vehicle. Number is also located on rear door post on the drivers side on the Safety Compliance Sticker and on the identification plate. The identification plate is located on right side of luggage compartment.

COMPRESSION PRESSURE

Perform compression test with wide open throttle and oil temperature not less than 140°F (60°C). Remove all spark plugs and allow about 12 piston strokes per cylinder test. Pressure difference between cylinders should not exceed 22 psi (1.5 kg/cm²).

VALVE TAPPET CLEARANCE

Adjust valve clearance to specifications with engine cold.

Application	Clearance
All Models (Intake & Exhaust)	.004"(.1 mm)

VALVE ARRANGEMENT

Engine cylinders have individual heads and contain one intake and one exhaust valve per head. Upper valves are intake and lower valves are exhaust.

SPARK PLUGS

Gap	
911S	.022"(.55 mm)
Turbo Carrera	.028"(.70 mm)
Torque	18-22 ft. lbs.(2.5-3.0 mkg)

Spark Plug Type

Application	Bosch	Beru
911S	W 235 P21	235/14/3P
Turbo Carrera	W 280 P21	.....

HIGH TENSION WIRE RESISTANCE

Carefully remove high tension wires from spark plugs and distributor cap. Using an ohmmeter, check high tension wire resistance while gently twisting wires. If resistance is not to specifications, or fluctuates from infinity to any value, replace high tension wire(s).

Resistance (Ohms) Per Wire

Application	Ohms
All Models	25,000-30,000

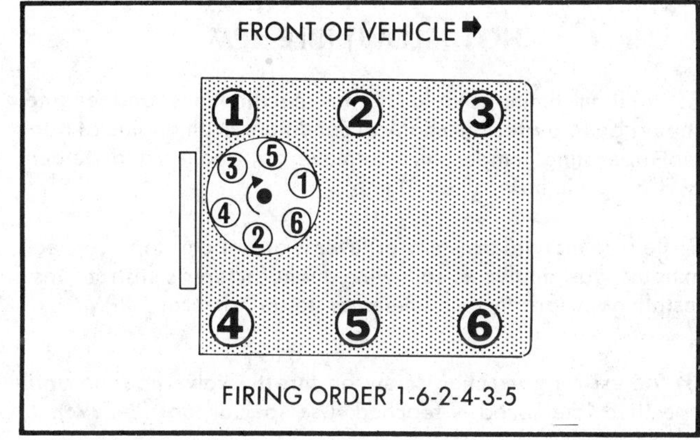

Fig. 1 Firing Order and Distributor Rotation

DISTRIBUTOR

911S	
Point Gap	.014"(.35 mm)
Cam Angle	
Bosch Distributor	38±3°
Marelli Distributor	37±3°
Breaker Arm Spring Tension	22-28 ozs.(624-794 g)

IGNITION TIMING

With engine idling at normal operating temperature, adjust ignition timing to specifications. Vacuum hose should be connected to distributor. Appropriate mark on pulley should be aligned with mark on blower housing.

NOTE — *Each millimeter on pulley circumference corresponds to 1° on crankshaft.*

CAUTION — *On 1977 Turbo Carrera, a standard tachometer cannot be used. Use a tester which records engine speed by inductive pickup when placed around an ignition cable.*

Ignition Timing Specifications

Application	RPM	Timing
911S		
Federal	950-1000	TDC±2°
Calif.	1000	15±2° ATDC
Turbo Carrera	950-1050	7±2° ATDC

TUNE-UP (Cont.)

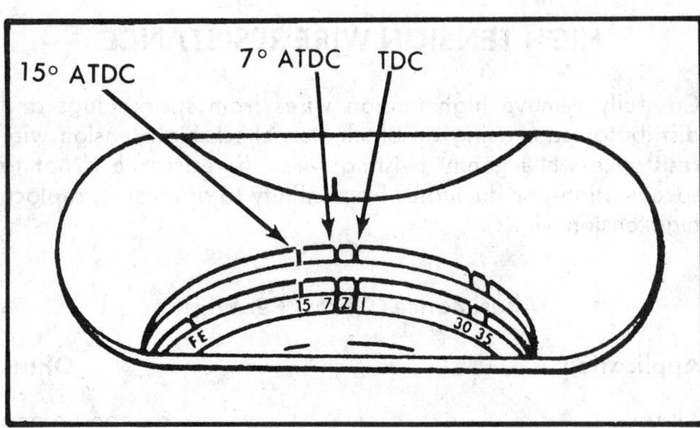

Fig. 2 Ignition Timing Marks

HOT (SLOW) IDLE RPM

1) Ignition timing should be to specifications and engine should be in perfect mechanical condition. With engine at normal operating temperature, remove air cleaner and detach and plug air hose at air pump.

2) Be sure manual accelerator lever is at bottom stop. Connect exhaust gas analyzer, following manufacturer's instructions. Install appropriate tachometer or tester to record RPM. See CAUTION *under Ignition Timing.*

3) Adjust air correction screw on throttle valve housing until specified idle speed is reached. Use special tool (P 229c).

4) Adjust CO% level. Remove plug with seal in top of mixture control unit. Guide adjusting wrench (P 377) in and turn clockwise to enrichen mixture, counterclockwise to weaken mixture.

NOTE — *Always make adjustment from lean to rich. EXAMPLE: If idle screw setting is too rich, turn counterclockwise until too lean and then adjust clockwise toward richer setting. Never apply pressure to wrench while adjusting.*

5) Turn control screw very slightly, as even smallest turn changes CO% considerably. When checking or adjusting CO% level, plug adjusting hole before taking CO reading.

6) Remove wrench. Accelerate engine briefly. When CO is to specification, install air cleaner and recheck idle and CO% level.

Idle Speed (RPM) and CO Level (%)①

Application	Idle RPM	CO%
911S		
Federal	900-1000	1.5-3.0
Calif.	950-1050	1.5-3.0
Turbo Carrera	950-1050	2.0-4.0

① — Hose at air pump detached and plugged.

FUEL PUMP PRESSURE & VOLUME

Pressure	
911S (One Pump①)	64-74 psi (4.5-5.2 kg/cm²)
Turbo Carrera (Two Pumps①)	87-97 psi (6-6.7 kg/cm²)
Volume	
911S	Min. 1.6 pts. in 30 sec.
Turbo Carrera	2.5 pts. in 30 sec.

① — Electric roller cell pumps.

EMISSION CONTROL SYSTEMS

See Mitchell Manuals' Emission Control Manual.

GENERAL SERVICING

IGNITION

DISTRIBUTOR

911S models are equipped with Capacitor Discharge Ignition system with Bosch or Marelli single point distributors. Turbo Carrera models are equipped with Capacitor Discharge Ignition system with Bosch breakerless distributors.

Other Data & Specifications — *See Tune-Up and Bosch or Marelli Distributors in ELECTRICAL Section.*

FUEL SYSTEMS

FUEL INJECTION

All models are equipped with Bosch Continuous Injection System (CIS). Turbo Carrera is equipped with exhaust gas turbocharger.

Other Data & Specifications — *See Tune-Up and Bosch Continuous Injection System (CIS) in FUEL SYSTEMS Section.*

ELECTRICAL

BATTERY

12 Volt — Negative Ground.

Application	Amp. Hr. Rating
All Models	66

Battery Location — Battery is located on left in front luggage compartment, under the floor mat.

GENERAL SERVICING (Cont.)

STARTER

Bosch .... Overrunning Clutch

Free Speed Voltage .... 11.5 at 7300-9300 RPM
Free Speed Amperage .... 50-80 at 7300-9300 RPM

Other Data & Specifications – *See Bosch Starters in ELECTRICAL Section.*

ALTERNATOR

Application	Rated Amp. Output
All Models	70

Other Data & Specifications – *See Bosch or Motorola Alternators & Regulators in ELECTRICAL Section.*

BELT ADJUSTMENT

Application	①Deflection
Fan Belt	.5-.75" (13-19 mm)
Air Pump Belt	.6" (15 mm)

① – Deflection is with thumb pressure applied midway on longest belt run. To adjust add or delete spacers between pulley halves.

FILTERS & CLEANERS

Filter or Cleaner	Service Interval (Miles)
Oil Filter	Replace every 15,000
Air Cleaner	Replace every 15,000
Fuel Filter	Replace every 15,000
Air Pump Filter	Replace every 15,000
EGR Filter	Replace every 15,000

ALTERNATOR REGULATOR

All models are equipped with Bosch or Motorola alternator regulators with an operating voltage of 14.2 volts at 2500 RPM.

Other Data & Specifications – *See Bosch or Motorola Alternators & Regulators in ELECTRICAL Section.*

CAPACITIES

Application	Quantity
Crankcase	
911 S①	
Total Capacity	11.6 qts.
Oil Change	10.6 qts.
Turbo Carrera	
Total Capacity	13.8 qts.
Oil Change	10.6 qts.
Transaxle (SAE 90)	
911 S	3.2 qts.
Turbo Carrera	3.9 qts.
Fuel Tank	②21 gals.

① – If equipped with Sportmatic trans. add 2.6 qts.
② – Includes 2.1 gals. reserve.

TUNE-UP

R-5
R-12
R-17GTL
R-17 Gordini

ENGINE IDENTIFICATION

Type of vehicle and engine number is marked on a number plate riveted to the left rear side of the engine block. Plate is located just below cylinder head mating surface. First five digits indicate engine type.

Engine Codes

Application	Code
R-5	810-28
R-12	
Man. Trans.	843-10
Auto. Trans.	843-11
R-17GTL	843-16
R-17 Gordini	843-13

MODEL IDENTIFICATION

VEHICLE IDENTIFICATION NUMBER

In addition to the identification on the engine, an oval plate and a diamond shaped plate are located in the engine compartment. The vehicle identification number is composed of the type number (A, *Fig. 1*) and chassis number (B), appearing on the diamond shaped plate.

The oval plate contains the vehicle identification code or type number (1), the equipment number — 141 for Federal or 143 for California and High Altitude models (3), and the fabrication number for parts ordering purposes (5). Shaded numbers 2, 4, and 6 do not normally appear on models marketed in the United States.

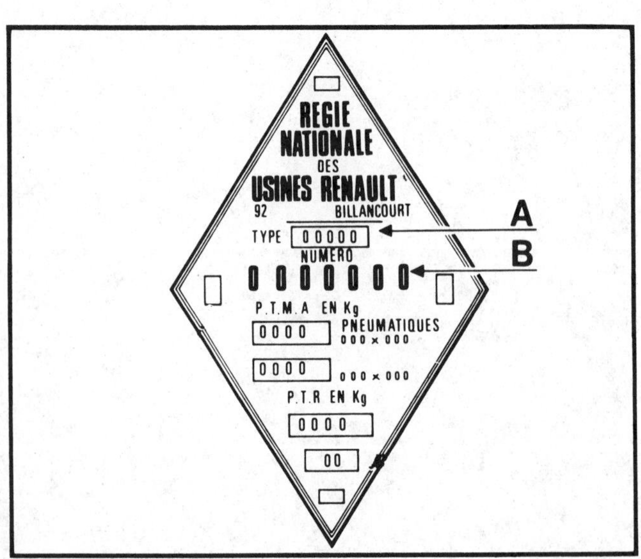

Fig. 1 Typical Diamond Shaped Chassis Plate

Vehicle Identification Codes

Application	Codes
R-5	R-1228
R-12	
Sedan	R-1174
Station Wagon	R-1334
R-17GTL	R-1328
R-17 Gordini	R-1326

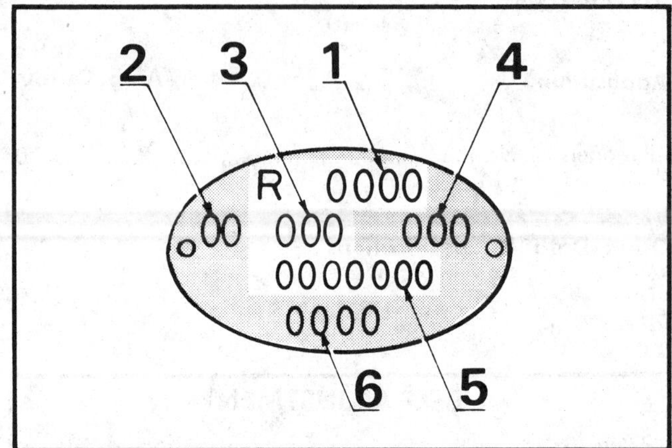

Fig. 2 Typical Oval Identification Plate

VALVE TAPPET CLEARANCE

Application	Intake	Exhaust
R-5①	.006" (.15 mm)	.008" (.2 mm)
R-12 & R-17GTL②	.008" (.2 mm)	.010" (.25 mm)
R-17 Gordini②	.010" (.25 mm)	.012" (.3 mm)

① — Set valves with engine cold. After 50 minutes cooling, setting would be .007" (.18 mm) for intake and .010" (.25 mm) for exhaust.
② — Set valves with engine cold.

VALVE ARRANGEMENT

All Models (Exc. R-17 Gordini) — E-I-I-E-E-I-I-E (Front to Rear).
R-17 Gordini
Right Side — All Exhaust.
Left Side — All Intake.

SPARK PLUGS

Gap	.025-.028" (.6-.7 mm)
Torque	Maximum of 20 ft. lbs (2.77 mkg)

TUNE-UP (Cont.)

Spark Plug Type

Application	AC	Champion
R-5		
Federal	42FS	L87Y
Calif. & High Alt.	43FS	L92Y
R-12 & R-17GTL	42XLS	N9Y
R-17 Gordini	....	N3

HIGH TENSION WIRE RESISTANCE

Carefully remove high tension wires from spark plugs and distributor cap. Using an ohmmeter, check resistance of high tension wires while gently twisting wires. If resistance is not to specification, or fluctuates from infinity to any value, replace high tension wire(s).

Resistance (Ohms) Per Wire

Application	Ohms
All Models	25,000-30,000

DISTRIBUTOR

Point Gap	.016-.020" (.4-.5 mm)
Cam Angle	
R-5	57±2°
All Other Models	57±3°
Breaker Arm Spring Tension	16 ozs. (454 g)

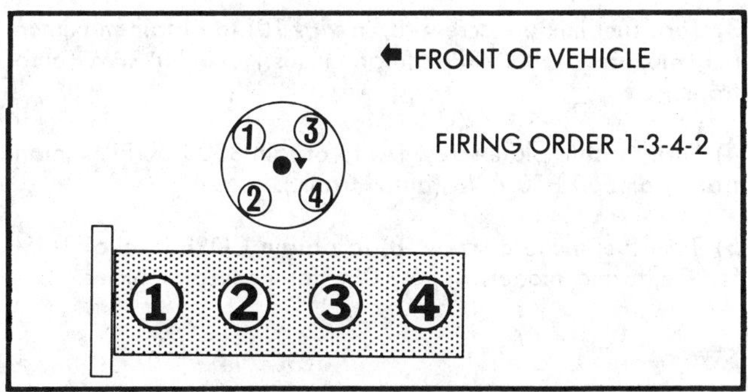

Fig. 3 Firing Order and Distributor Rotation (R-5 Model)

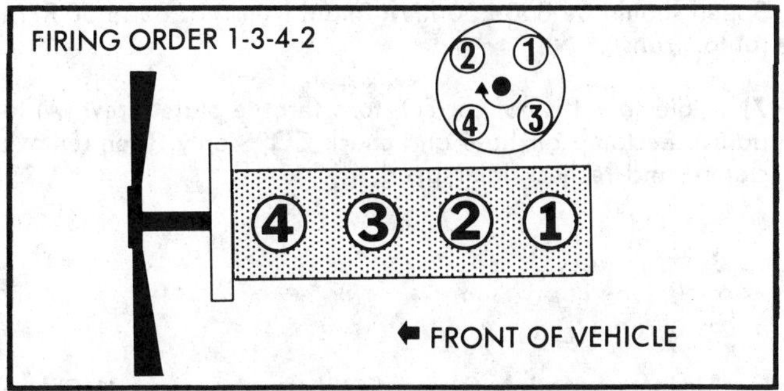

Fig. 4 Firing Order and Distributor Rotation (R-12 Models)

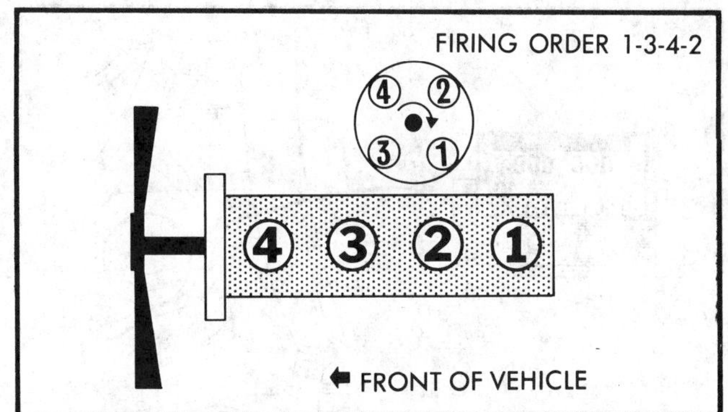

Fig. 5 Firing Order and Distributor Rotation (R-17GTL & R-17 Gordini)

IGNITION TIMING

Check or adjust ignition timing with vacuum line disconnected and plugged and engine running at idle speed. To adjust, turn distributor until specified mark on flywheel is aligned with specified graduation mark on clutch housing. Reconnect distributor vacuum hose.

Ignition Timing Specifications

Application	RPM	Timing (±1°)
R-5		
Federal & Calif.	850	TDC
High Alt.	800	TDC
R-12		
Man. Trans.	850	7° BTDC
Auto. Trans.	650	7° BTDC
R-17GTL	850	7° BTDC
R-17 Gordini	850	①TDC

① — 12° BTDC with both retard and advance capsules disconnected.

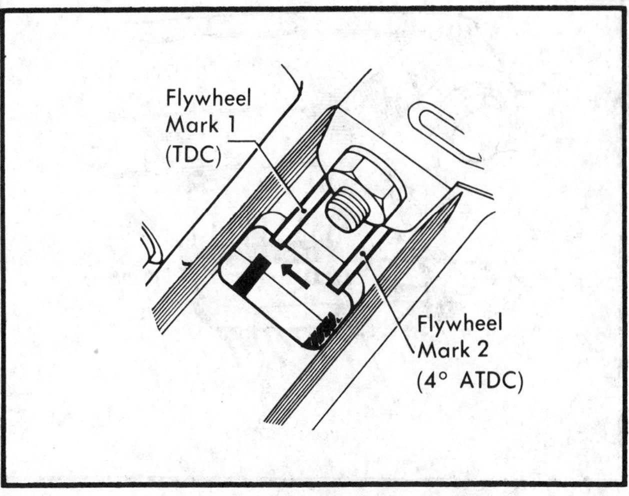

Fig. 6 Location of Timing Mark (R-5 Models)

TUNE-UP (Cont.)

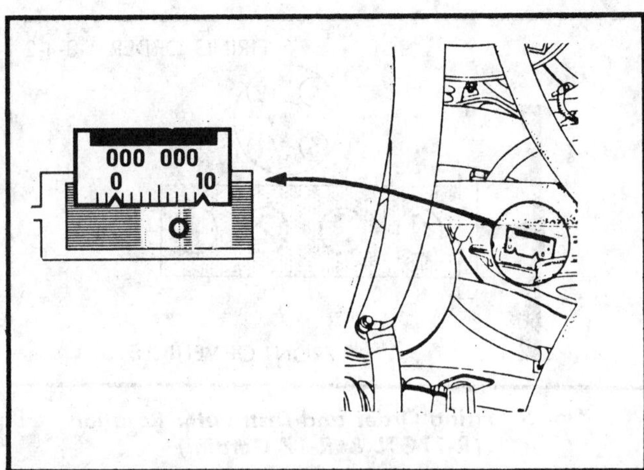

Fig. 7 Location of Timing Mark (R-12 with Auto. Trans. & R-17GTL)

Fig. 8 Location of Timing Mark (R-12 with Man. Trans.)

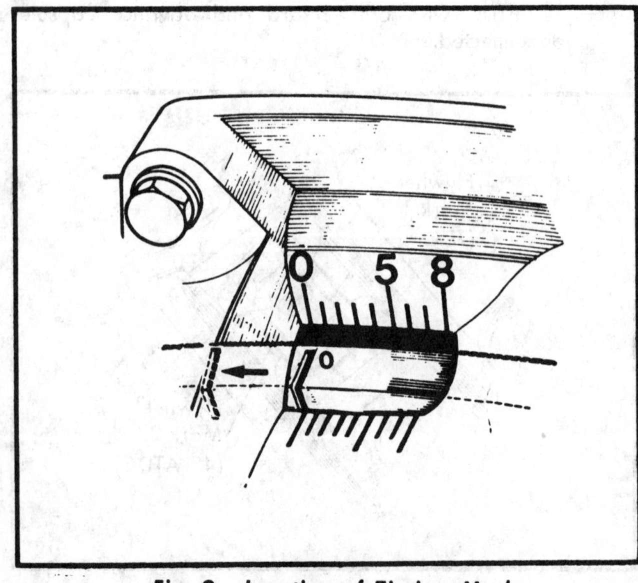

Fig. 9 Location of Timing Mark (R-17 Gordini)

HOT (SLOW) IDLE RPM

Carburetor Models – 1) Cut off air injection system by clamping hose from diverter valve. Warm up engine to operating temperature.

2) Place manual transmission in NEUTRAL or automatic transmission in DRIVE. Be sure parking brake is engaged and wheels are blocked.

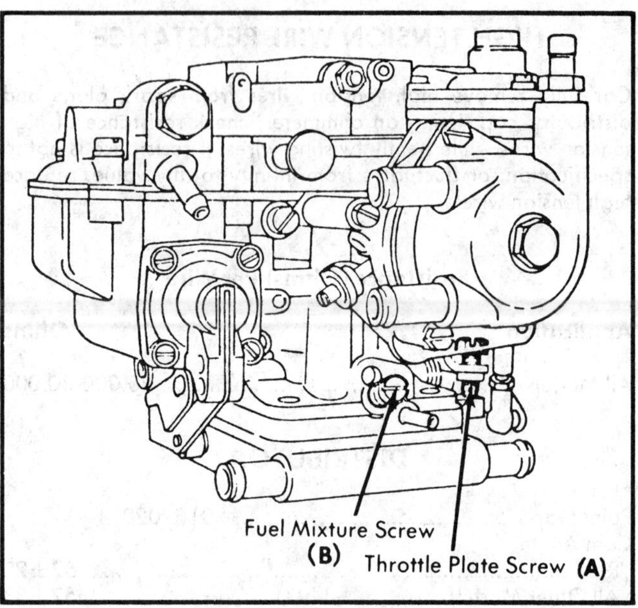

Fig. 10 Idle and CO% Adjusting Screws (All Models Except R-17 Gordini)

3) Turn fuel mixture screw (B, in *Fig. 10*) to obtain maximum rich mixture at 800 RPM (man. trans.) or 650 RPM (auto. trans.).

4) Turn throttle plate screw (A) to obtain 850±50 RPM (man. trans.) or 650±50 RPM (auto. trans.).

5) Turn fuel mixture screw (B) to obtain CO% level of 1-4% for California models or .5-3.0% for Federal vehicles.

NOTE – *If CO% analyzer is not available, turn fuel mixture screw (B) clockwise to lean mixture. Obtain speed drop of 50 RPM without affecting engine smoothness.*

6) Remove clamp on air injection hose and check idle speed. Speed should be 850±50 RPM (man. trans.) or 650±50 RPM (auto. trans.).

7) If idle speed is not correct, turn throttle plate screw (A) to adjust. Reclamp air hose and check CO% only. Then remove clamp, and recheck idle speed.

NOTE – *If no CO% analyzer is available and speed is not correct, repeat procedure keeping in mind different engine speed obtained on first adjustment.*

Fuel-Injected Models (Using CO% Analyzer) – 1) Clamp air injection hose below relief valve to deactivate air injection system. Warm engine to normal operating temperature.

TUNE-UP (Cont.)

2) Turn throttle plate screw (A, in *Fig. 11*) to obtain 850 RPM.

3) Adjust flowmeter bypass screw (B) to obtain CO% of 1-3%. Turn screw (A) again to adjust RPM if necessary.

4) Remove air injection hose clamp. Idle speed should be 850-950 RPM. Adjust by turning screw (A).

Fuel-Injected Models (Without CO% Analyzer) – 1) With engine fully warmed up, clamp off air injection hose from diverter valve.

2) Turn flowmeter bypass screw (B, in *Fig. 11*) in fully. Adjust throttle screw (A) to obtain 900 RPM.

3) Turn bypass screw (B) to decrease engine speed by 50 RPM. Remove air injection hose clamp. Idle speed should be 850-950 RPM. If not, adjust with throttle screw (A).

Idle Speed (RPM) & CO Level (%)

Application	Idle RPM	CO%
R-5	800-900	.5-3
R-12		
Man. Trans.	800-900	①.5-3
Auto. Trans.	②600-700	①.5-3
R-17GTL	②600-700	①.5-3
R-17 Gordini	750-950	1-3

① – Federal Level; Calif. Level is 1-4% CO.
② – With transmission lever in DRIVE.

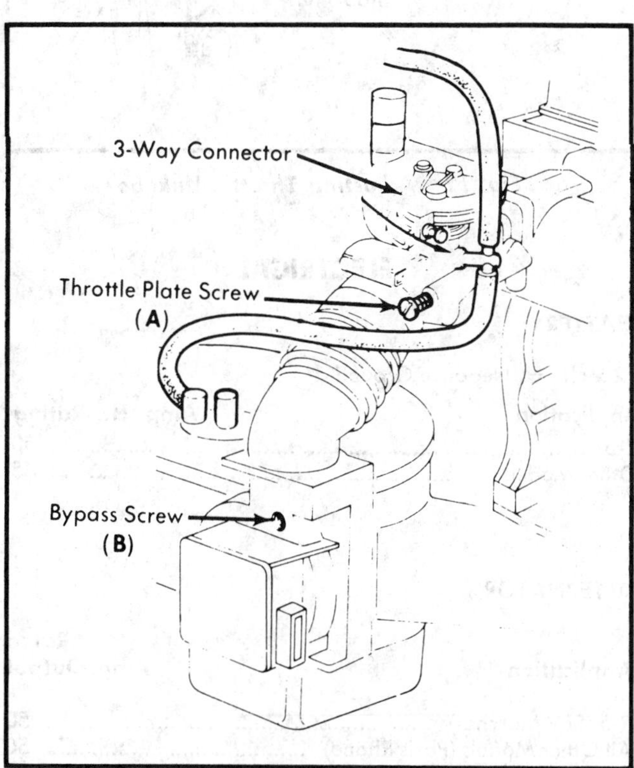

Fig. 11 Idle and CO% Adjusting Screws (R-17 Gordini)

COLD (FAST) IDLE RPM

NOTE – *Fast idle adjustments apply only to R-5, R-12 and R-17GTL models. R-17 Gordini uses an electronic fuel injection system which does not use a fast idle setting (cold engine running is taken care of by cold start valve).*

R-5 (Calif.) – 1) With idle speed to specifications and ignition OFF, disconnect negative lead on solenoid flap valve. Activate solenoid flap valve by connecting a lead from the negative (-) battery cable to free terminal.

2) Turn screw in end of throttle plate valve to obtain engine speed of 1500±100 RPM. Remove temporary lead between battery and solenoid flap valve and reconnect negative lead.

Other Models Except R-17 Gordini – 1) With idle speed to specifications and engine at normal operating temperature, disconnect throttle plate opener capsule from solenoid valve.

2) Connect a length of hose between throttle plate opener capsule and intake manifold at white vacuum pipe.

3) Increase engine speed to 2500 RPM and let it decrease gradually. Check fast idle speed imposed by throttle plate opener.

4) Adjust fast idle speed to specification, turning screw in end of throttle plate opener capsule. Unscrew to increase fast idle speed.

5) If fast idle speed is still incorrect, loosen lock nut below throttle plate opener capsule and adjust linkage length. Tighten lock nut and recheck fast idle setting.

Fast Idle Specifications

Application	RPM
R-5	
Federal	1900±100
Calif. & High Alt.	1500±100
R-12 and R-17GTL	1500±100

FUEL PUMP PRESSURE

R-5 (Mechanical)	2.5-4 psi (.18-.28 kg/cm²)
R-12 & R-17GTL (Electric)	2.5-4 psi (.18-.28 kg/cm²)
R-17 Gordini (Electric)	35 psi (2.5 kg/cm²)

EMISSION CONTROL SYSTEMS

See Mitchell Manuals' Emission Control Manual.

GENERAL SERVICING

IGNITION

DISTRIBUTOR

All models are equipped with Ducellier single point distributors.

Other Data & Specifications – *See Tune-Up and Ducellier Distributors in ELECTRICAL Section.*

IGNITION COIL

All models (Exc. R-5) use either a Ducellier or SEV 12 volt coil. R-5 models use a Mallory 12 volt coil.

FUEL SYSTEMS

CARBURETORS

Application	Model
R-5	
Federal	Weber 32 DIR 56
Calif.	Weber 32 DIR 55
High Alt.	Weber 32 DIR 53
R-12	
Federal (Man. Trans.)	Weber 32 DARA 12
Federal (Auto. Trans.)	Weber 32 DARA 13
Calif. (Man. Trans.)	Weber 32 DARA
Calif. (Auto. Trans.)	Weber 32 DARA 1
R-17GTL	
Federal	Weber 32 DARA 13
Calif.	Weber 32 DARA 1

Other Data & Specifications – *See Tune-Up & Weber Carburetors in FUEL SYSTEMS Section.*

FUEL INJECTION

Application	Type
R-17 Gordini	Bosch CIS Electronic

Other Data & Specifications – *See Tune-Up & Bosch CIS Electronic Fuel Injection in FUEL SYSTEMS Section.*

AUTOMATIC TRANSMISSION THROTTLE LINKAGE ADJUSTMENT

NOTE – *Accelerator pedal travel, kickdown switch adjustment and governor control cable are all closely related. It is recommended that they be checked and adjusted together.*

Accelerator Pedal Travel & Governor Control – Turn outer cable stop nut to allow about .012-.020" (.3-.5 mm) free play between sector and pointer (*See Fig. 12*). Tighten lock nut.

Kickdown Switch Adjustment – Connect test lamp between kickdown switch and battery positive terminal. Press accelerator pedal down all the way. If switch is working, lamp will light. With choke fully off, make sure that accelerator cable has enough play to provide movement of .012-.020" (.3-.5 mm) of compensating spring pad on kickdown switch.

Accelerator Pedal Switch Adjustment (R-17) – Adjust throttle pedal stop so that pedal rod does not contact pedal support. Insert a .020" (.5 mm) spacer between pedal rod and stop and insure that throttle is in idle position. Remove spacer and release pedal. Turn adjusting screw of switch until contacts are open, then turn in another ½ turn to insure positive cut off. Lock adjusting screw.

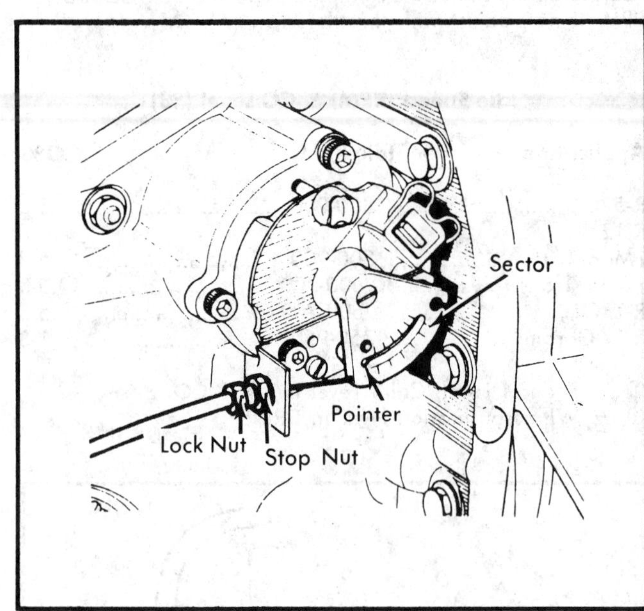

Fig. 12 Adjusting Throttle Linkage

ELECTRICAL

BATTERY

12 Volt – Negative Ground.

Application	Amp. Hr. Rating
R-5	50
Other Models	45

ALTERNATOR

Application	Rated Amp. Output
R-5 (SEV Marchal)	50
All Other Models (Paris Rhone)	50

Other Data & Specifications – *See SEV Marchal or Paris Rhone Alternators & Regulators in ELECTRICAL Section.*

GENERAL SERVICING (Cont.)

STARTER

All models are equipped with a Paris Rhone starter.

Other Data & Specification – *See Paris Rhone Starters in ELECTRICAL Section.*

ALTERNATOR REGULATOR

All models are equipped with a Ducellier regulator with an operating voltage of 13.8-14.8.

Other Data & Specifications – *See Ducellier Alternators & Regulators in ELECTRICAL Section.*

CAPACITIES

Application	Quantity
Crankcase (Includes Filter)	
R-5	3.5 qts.
All Other Models	4.5 qts.
Cooling System (Includes Heater)	
R-5	6.5 qts.
R-12	9.5 qts.
R-17GTL	7 qts.
R-17 Gordini	8 qts.
Manual Transmission (SAE 90)	2 qts.
Auto. Transmission (Dexron)①	3.3 qts
Fuel Tank	
R-5	10 gals.
R-17 Gordini	12.5 gals.
All Other Models	13.7 gals.

① – 6.5 qts. for R-12 auto. transmission with torque converter.

BELT ADJUSTMENT

Application	①Deflection
Alternator Belt	.22-.26" (5.5-6.5 mm)
Water Pump Belt	.10-.14" (2.5-3.5 mm)
Air Pump Belt	.31-.39" (8-10 mm)

① – Deflection is with pressure applied midway on longest belt run.

FILTERS & CLEANERS

Filter or Cleaner	Service Interval (Miles),
Oil Filter	①Replace every 13,000
Air Cleaner	Replace every 12,500
Air Pump Filter	Replace every 12,500

① – Replace filter after first 6,000 miles, then every 13,000 miles after that.

TUNE-UP

99

ENGINE IDENTIFICATION

Engine number is stamped on a machined pad on engine block below CIS throttle housing.

Application	Code
Federal Models	
Man. Trans.	BI P06
Auto. Trans.	BI P03
Calif. Models	
Man. Trans.	BI P04
Auto. Trans.	BI P05

MODEL IDENTIFICATION

VEHICLE IDENTIFICATION NUMBER

Chassis number is stamped on body under left side of rear seat. Number is also stamped on a plate attached to upper left hand corner of instrument panel and is visible through windshield.

VALVE TAPPET CLEARANCE

Bring camshaft into correct position for checking valves. Using a suitable go and no-go feeler gauge, check that clearance between valve tappet and heel of cam is to specifications given under "Preliminary Check." If within specifications, no further adjustment is necessary. If not, proceed as follows:

1) Using special tool (8391450) and a dial indicator, measure clearance of each valve. With measuring point of dial indicator resting on tip of cam, zero dial indicator.

2) Lift valve depressor with special tool and note movement of dial indicator, indicating present valve clearance. Any valve not within "Adjustment Limit" specifications should be adjusted as follows:

3) Remove camshaft, valve depressors and adjusting pads of valves needing adjustment. Measure thickness of adjusting pad with special tool (8391633) and calculate thickness of new pad required to bring valve clearance within "Adjustment Limit" specifications.

4) Measured valve clearance plus adjusting pad thickness equals total distance between valve and cam. This total distance less the specified valve clearance, determines thickness of new adjusting pad to be installed.

5) Install new adjusting pad, valve depressors, and camshaft and recheck that clearances are correct.

Valve Clearances①

Application	Clearance
Preliminary Check	
Intake	.006-.012" (.15-.30 mm)
Exhaust	.014-.020" (.35-.50 mm)
Adjustment Limit	
Intake	.008-.010" (.20-.25 mm)
Exhaust	.016-.018" (.40-.45 mm)

① – When checked 30 minutes after driving vehicle at normal operating temperature.

VALVE ARRANGEMENT

E-I-I-E-E-I-I-E (front to rear).

SPARK PLUGS

Gap .024-.028" (.6-.7 mm)
Torque 18- 22 ft. lbs. (2.5-3.0 mkg)

Spark Plug Type

Application	Bosch No.	NGK No.
All	W 175 T 30	BP-6ES

HIGH TENSION WIRE RESISTANCE

Carefully remove high tension wires from spark plugs and distributor cap. Using an ohmmeter, check high tension wire resistance while gently twisting wires. If resistance is not to specifications, or fluctuates from infinity to any value, replace high tension wire(s).

Resistance (Ohms) Per Wire

Application	Ohms
All Models	
Wires to Cylinder 1 & 2	3200±640
Wires to Cylinder 3 & 4	3000±600
Wire from Coil to Distributor	1000±200

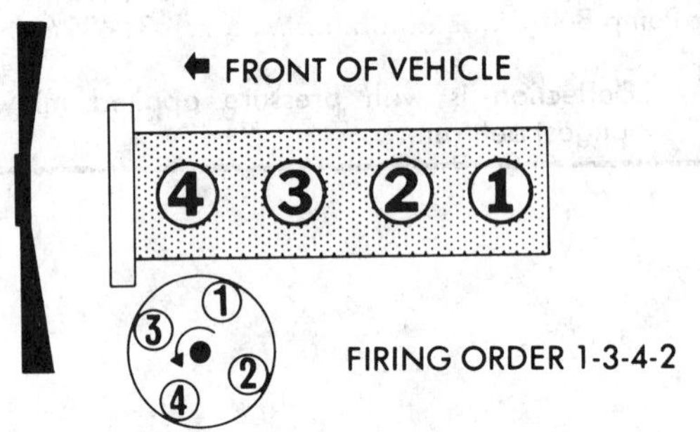

Fig. 1 Firing Order and Distributor Rotation

DISTRIBUTOR

Point Gap .016" (.4 mm)
Cam Angle 50±3°
Breaker Arm Spring Tension 18-23 ozs. (510-652 g)
Condenser Capacity .18-.23 mfd.

IGNITION TIMING

Connect cam angle meter, tachometer and timing light. Disconnect vacuum hose and place transmission in neutral position. Adjust as follows:

1) Check cam angle at starter speed and idling speed. Adjust as necessary. Check timing at 2000 RPM.

2) If not within specifications, loosen distributor retaining screw and rotate distributor housing. Turn clockwise for earlier ignition; counterclockwise for later.

TUNE-UP (Cont.)

3) Reconnect vacuum hose and adjust engine idle speed.

Ignition Timing Specifications

Application	RPM	Timing
All Models		
Federal	2000	20° BTDC
Calif.	2000	20° BTDC

Fig. 2 Location of Saab 99 Timing Marks

HOT (SLOW) IDLE RPM

1) Remove thick hose at charcoal canister. On vehicles with air injection, remove and plug hose from air pump.

2) With engine at normal operating temperature, adjust idle speed to specifications by turning adjusting screw on throttle valve by-pass duct. See *Fig. 3*.

Fig. 3 Adjusting Idle Speed

3) Check CO level and, if necessary, adjust using Allen "T" wrench (8392482) to turn adjustment screw in air flow sensor. Turn clockwise to richen mixture.

4) Repeat idle speed and mixture adjustments until specified idle speed and CO% is obtained.

CAUTION — *Remove Allen "T" wrench from adjustment screw after each adjustment. If key is left in screw and engine is accelerated, lever could be damaged.*

5) If equipped with air injection, remove plug and reconnect hose to air pump. Then, recheck idle speed and adjust if necessary.

Idle Speed (RPM) & CO Level (%)

Application	RPM	CO%
All Models		
Federal	825-925	1.25±.75
Calif.	825-925	①.75

① — With sensor disconnected. With sensor connected, a maximum of .4% is permissible. Permissible deviation while checking is .25-1%.

DECEL VALVE ADJUSTMENT

1) To adjust the decel valve, located in the inlet manifold and connected by means of a hose to the throttle housing, connect a tachometer and run engine until warm.

2) Unscrew the adjusting screw until valve closes completely. Set specified idle speed by adjusting idling adjusting screw. Turn down adjusting screw until engine speed is 1600 RPM.

3) Then back off adjusting screw two turns. Set specified idling speed with the idling adjusting screw. Check deceleration time and make any necessary fine adjustments.

CAUTION — *To prevent faulty deceleration readings, disconnect cooling fan cable from thermal switch during check.*

4) To check decleration valve, increase engine speed to 3000 RPM. Release throttle and note how long it takes for engine to return to idle speed. Be sure engine is warm.

Deceleration Time Requirements

Application	Time Required
Federal & Calif.	4-6 seconds
High Alt.	3-4 seconds

FUEL PUMP PRESSURE

Pressure	64-72 psi (4.5-5.1 kg/cm²)
Volume	①45.7 cu. in. (750 cc)/30 seconds

① — Measured in return fuel line.

EMISSION CONTROL SYSTEMS

See Mitchell Manuals Emission Control Manual.

1977 Saab 4 Tune-Up

GENERAL SERVICING

IGNITION

DISTRIBUTOR

All models are equipped with Bosch single point distributors.

Other Data & Specifications – *See Tune-Up and Bosch Distributors in ELECTRICAL Section.*

IGNITION COIL

Resistance	At 80°F (20°C)
Primary	1.7-2.1 Ohms

FUEL SYSTEMS

FUEL INJECTION

All models are equipped with Bosch Continuous Injection System (CIS). However, on California vehicles, the CIS is supplemented with a Lambda oxygen sensor in the exhaust manifold, a modulating valve, throttle valve switch, relay switch, catalytic converter and Electronic Control Unit.

Other Data & Specifications – *For Federal Models, see Tune-Up and Bosch Continuous Injection System (CIS) in FUEL SYSTEMS Section. For California Models, see Tune-Up and Bosch Lambda Continuous Injection System in FUEL SYSTEMS Section.*

ELECTRICAL

BATTERY

12 Volt – Negative Ground.

Application	Amp. Hr. Rating
All Models	60

Battery Location – In engine compartment on right side.

STARTER

Bosch	Overrunning Clutch
Free Speed Voltage	11.5 at 6500-8500 RPM
Free Speed Amperage	35-55 at 6500-8500 RPM

Other Data & Specifications – *See Bosch Starters in ELECTRICAL Section.*

ALTERNATOR

Application	Rated Amp. Output
All Models	55

Other Data & Specifications – *See S.E.V. Marchal and Bosch Alternators and Regulators in ELECTRICAL Section.*

ALTERNATOR REGULATOR

All models are equipped with S.E.V. Marchal or Bosch alternator regulators.

Other Data & Specifications – *See S.E.V. Marchal and Bosch Alternators and Regulators in ELECTRICAL Section.*

FILTERS & CLEANERS

Filter or Cleaner	Service Interval (Miles)
Oil Filter	Replace every 5000
Air Cleaner	Replace every 15,000
Fuel Filter	Replace every 15,000
Charcoal Canister	①Replace every 30,000

① – First change at 15,000 miles.

BELT ADJUSTMENT

Application	①Deflection
Alternator Belt	.4" (10 mm)

① – Deflection is with 3.3 lbs (1.5 kg) pressure applied midway on longest belt run.

CAPACITIES

Application	Quantity
Crankcase (Includes Filter)	4 qts.
Cooling System (Includes Heater)	8.5 qts.
Man. Trans. (SAE 75 EP) Includes Rear Axle	3 qts.
Auto. Trans. (Dexron)	8.5 qts.
Rear Axle (SAE 75 EP)	2.6 pts.
Fuel Tank	14.5 gals.

TUNE-UP

1600

ENGINE IDENTIFICATION

Engine can be identified by a letter-number combination stamped on machined pad on side of engine, near distributor (below carburetor). Engine codes are as follows:

4-Speed Transmission
- Federal EA71AF
- California EA71AF2
- High Altitude EA71AF3

4-Speed Transmission (4-Wheel Drive)
- Federal EA71EF
- California EA71EF2
- High Altitude EA71EF3

5-Speed Transmission
- Federal EA71AP
- California EA71AP2
- High Altitude EA71AP3

Automatic Transmission
- Federal EA71AT4
- California EA71AT5
- High Altitude EA71AT6

MODEL IDENTIFICATION

The vehicle identification number is located on the left side of the instrument panel and is visible through the windshield. The chassis number may be found on firewall in engine compartment.

COMPRESSION PRESSURE

Check pressure with engine warm, plugs removed, throttle valve wide open and engine at cranking speed. Pressure should be as specified with a variation of 7 psi (.5 kg/cm²) maximum between cylinders.

Application	Pressure psi (kg/cm²)
1600 @250 RPM	149 (10.5)
1600 @350 RPM	156 (10.97)

VALVE TAPPET CLEARANCE

With engine cold, bring piston to be checked to top dead center of compression stroke. Loosen lock nuts and turn adjusting screws to proper clearance. Adjust valves in firing order sequence (1-3-2-4) using valve clearance adjusting tool 398760100 (or equivalent).

Valve Clearance Specifications

Application	Clearance
Intake	.009-.011" (.23-.27 mm)
Exhaust	.013-.015" (.33-.37 mm)

VALVE ARRANGEMENT

I-E-E-I (both banks, front to rear).

SPARK PLUGS

Gap .... .032" (.8 mm)
Torque .... 13-17 ft. lbs. (1.8-2.4 mkg)

Spark Plug Type

Manufacturer	Spark Plug No.
NGK	BP6ES
Nippondenso	W20EP
Hitachi	L45PW

HIGH TENSION WIRE RESISTANCE

Carefully remove high tension wires from spark plugs and ignition coil. Remove distributor cap with wires still in place. Using an ohmmeter, check high tension wire resistance between free end of wire and distributor cap electrode. If resistance is not to specifications, or fluctuates from infinity to any value, replace high tension wire(s).

Resistance (Ohms) Per Wire

Application	Ohms
All Models	15,000 (Max.)

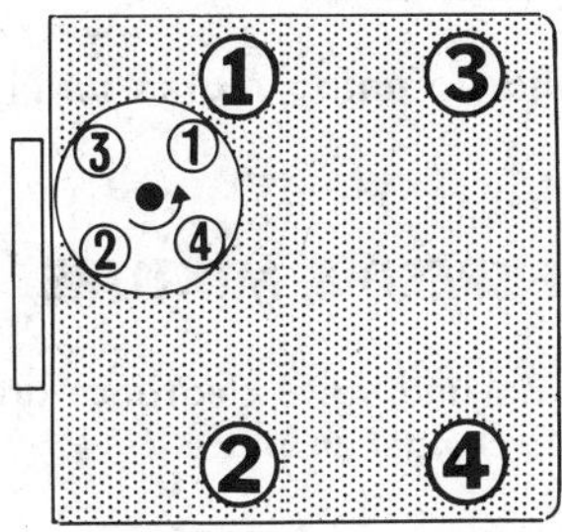

Fig. 1 Firing Order and Distributor Rotation

DISTRIBUTOR

Point Gap (Federal) .... .016-.020" (.40-.50 mm)
Air Gap (California)
- Nippondenso .... .008-.016" (.20-.40 mm)
- Hitachi .... .012-.016" (.30-.40 mm)

Cam Angle .... 49-55°
Breaker Arm Spring Tension .... 1.1-1.5 lbs. (.50-.70 kg)
Condenser Capacity .... .22 mfd

IGNITION TIMING

1) Adjust timing with shift lever in "N" or "P" position. Disconnect and plug vacuum hoses from distributor retard and advance mechanism. Connect timing light to No. 1 cylinder ignition wire.

TUNE-UP (Cont.)

2) Adjust engine idle speed to 850 RPM for Federal and 900 RPM for California models. To set timing, loosen distributor lock down bolt and turn distributor to specified setting. Tighten lock down bolt.

Timing Specifications

Application	RPM	Timing
Federal	850	8±2° BTDC
California	900	8±2° BTDC

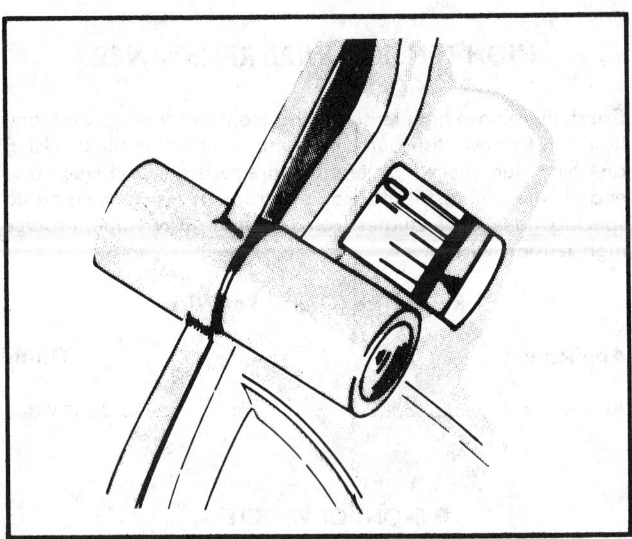

Fig. 2 Subaru Timing Marks on Flywheel

IDLE SPEED & MIXTURE

Be sure ignition timing and valve clearance are to specifications. Adjust with air cleaner in place.

USING CO METER

With AIR Disconnected – 1) Warm engine to normal operating temperature. Disconnect air suction hose from silencer. Cap open end of silencer with tape.

2) Adjust both throttle adjusting screw and idle mixture adjusting screw to obtain the specified idle speed and CO percentage.

Idle Speed (RPM) & CO Level (%) Without AIR①

Application	Idle RPM	CO%
Federal	850±50	1.0-2.0
California	900±50	0.5-1.0

① – Shift lever in "N" or "P".

With AIR Connected – 1) Remove tape from end of silencer. Connect the air suction hose from the air cleaner to the silencer.

2) Check that idle and CO level are to following specifications without further adjustment:

Idle Speed (RPM) & CO Level (%) With AIR①

Application	Idle RPM	CO%
Federal	850±50	0.5-1.5
California	900±50	0.1-0.5

① – Shift lever in "N" or "P".

WITHOUT CO METER

1) Check that engine is at normal operating temperature and ignition timing and valve clearance are to specifications.

2) Using the throttle adjusting screw and idle mixture adjusting screw, set engine idle speed of Federal and High Altitude models to 930 RPM and California models to 990 RPM.

3) Then turn idle mixture adjusting screw clockwise until idle speed for Federal and High Altitude models drops to 850 RPM and California models to 900 RPM.

4) After adjustment, CO emission should be as specified in previous two charts. *See USING CO METER.*

COLD (FAST) IDLE RPM

With cam adjusting lever on fourth step of fast idle cam, primary throttle valve opening angle and clearance should be as follows. If not, adjust fast idle screw.

Fast Idle Specifications

Application	Throttle Valve Opening Angle	Clearance Valve-to-Body
Federal	15°	.043"(1.09 mm)
Calif. & High Alt.	19°	.060"(1.53 mm)

NOTE – *Repair carburetors (DCJ306-8) are adjusted to Federal Low Altitude specifications. For use on California models, readjust primary throttle valve opening angle from 15° to 19° by turning fast idle adjusting screw 3 turns clockwise.*

FUEL ENRICHMENT ADJUSTMENT

On Hitachi DCJ306-9 Carburetors used on High Altitude vehicles, an adjusting screw is provided on the choke chamber to tune carburetor to proper altitude. Stop engine before adjusting screw. For altitudes higher than 4000 feet, turn screw in until it bottoms and back off 6 turns. For altitudes less than 4000 feet, turn screw in until it stops.

EMISSION CONTROL SYSTEMS

See Mitchell Manuals' Emission Control Manual.

GENERAL SERVICING

IGNITION

DISTRIBUTORS

Hitachi single point distributors are used on all Federal and High Altitude vehicles. Nippondenso breakerless distributors are used on California vehicles with manual transmission and Hitachi breakerless distributors on California vehicles with automatic transmissions.

Other Data & Specifications – *See Tune-Up and Hitachi and Nippondenso Distributors in ELECTRICAL section.*

IGNITION COIL

Resistance	Ohms
Primary	
Hitachi	
Federal & High Altitude	1.35-1.65
California (Auto. Trans.)	.81-.99
Nippondenso	
California (Man. Trans.)	1.33-1.63
Secondary	
Hitachi	
Federal & High Altitude	6,800-10,200
California (Auto. Trans.)	8,500-12,900
Nippondenso	
California (Man. Trans.)	11,100-13,700

FUEL SYSTEMS

FUEL PUMP

12 Volt Electromagnetic Fuel Pump.

CARBURETORS

Application	Model
High Altitude	Hitachi DCJ306-9
All Other Models	Hitachi DCJ306-8

Other Data & Specifications – *See Tune-Up and Hitachi Carburetors in FUEL SYSTEMS section.*

ELECTRICAL

BATTERY

12 Volt – Negative Ground.

Application	Amp. Hr. Capacity
All	60

Battery Location – Engine compartment; front.

STARTER

Nippondenso .... Magnetic Switch Type

Free Speed Voltage
All Models .... 11 at 5000 RPM
Free Speed Amperage
All Models .... 50 (Max.) at 5000 RPM

Other Data & Specifications – *See Nippondenso Starters in ELECTRICAL Section.*

ALTERNATOR

Application	Rated Amp. Output
All Models	50

Other Data & Specifications – *See Hitachi Alternators and Regulators in ELECTRICAL Section.*

ALTERNATOR REGULATOR

All models are equipped with Hitachi alternator regulators with an operating voltage of 14.0-14.5 volts.

Other Data & Specifications – *See Hitachi Alternators and Regulators in ELECTRICAL Section.*

ENGINE

INTAKE MANIFOLD TIGHTENING

Tighten intake manifold attaching bolts to 13-16 ft. lbs. (1.8-2.2 mkg).

BELT ADJUSTMENT

Application	①Deflection
4-Wheel Drive Models	.35-.43" (9-11 mm)
All Other Models	.51-.55" (13-14 mm)

① – Deflection is with 22 lbs. (10 kg) pressure applied midway on longest belt run.

FILTERS & CLEANERS

Filter or Cleaner	Service Interval (Miles)
Oil Filter	Replace every 6250
Air Cleaner	Replace every 12,500
Fuel Filter	Replace every 12,500
Charcoal Canister Filter	Replace every 25,000

GENERAL SERVICING (Cont.)

CAPACITIES

Application	Quantity
Crankcase (Includes Filter)	①3.8 qts.
Cooling System	6.3 qts.
Transmission	
Manual	
4-Speed (SAE 85-90W)	2.64 qts.
5-Speed (SAE 85-90W)	2.85 qts.
4-Speed w/4WD (SAE 80-85W)	3.17 qts.
Automatic (Dexron)	5.9-6.3 qts.
Differential	
4-Wheel Drive	0.85 qts.
Automatic Transmission	0.9-1.3 qts.
Fuel Tank	
Sedan, Coupe & Hardtop	13.2 gals.
Station Wagon & 4-Wheel Drive	11.9 gals.

① – 3.5 qts. without filter.

TUNE-UP

Celica
Corolla
Corona
Pickup

ENGINE IDENTIFICATION

Each engine serial number contains an identifying engine code number. Engine codes are the first group of numbers and letters on Corolla models and the last group on other models.

On Corolla 1166 cc engines (3K-C), the serial number appears on the right side of the cylinder block below the spark plugs. On Corolla 1588 cc engines (2T-C), the serial number appears on the left side behind dipstick.

Engine serial numbers of Celica, Corona and Pickup models, featuring the 2189 cc engine (20R), are on right side of cylinder block. Engine codes are as follows:

Engine Codes

Application	Displacement	Code
Corolla	1166 cc	3K-C
Corolla	1588 cc	2T-C
Corona, Celica & Pickup	2189 cc	20R

MODEL IDENTIFICATION

VEHICLE IDENTIFICATION NUMBER

Vehicle identification number is located on top of instrument panel on all models, and on firewall of engine compartment on all but Pickup models. On Pickups, number appears on front left fender apron, near windshield fluid tank. First two digits of number identify engine and model series.

Application	Engine	Model Code
Corolla		
1166 cc	3K-C	KE
1588 cc	2T-C	TE
Corona	20R	RT
Celica	20R	RA
Pickup	20R	RN

COMPRESSION PRESSURE

With engine at normal operating temperature, spark plugs removed, throttle valve wide open and engine at cranking speed, compression pressures should be as follows with a maximum variation between cylinders of 14 psi (1 kg/cm²):

Application	Stand. Pressure psi (kg/cm²)	Min. Pressure psi (kg/cm²)
Corolla (2T-C)	171 (12)	142 (10)
All Other Models	156 (11)	128 (9)

VALVE TAPPET CLEARANCE

Check or adjust valve clearance with engine at normal operating temperature.

Valve Clearance Specifications

Application	Intake	Exhaust
Corolla (2T-C)	.008" (.20 mm)	.013" (.33 mm)
All Other Models	.008" (.20 mm)	.012" (.30 mm)

VALVE ARRANGEMENTS

Corolla (3K-C) — E-I-I-E-E-I-I-E (front to rear)
All Other Models
Right Side — All Intake
Left Side — All Exhaust

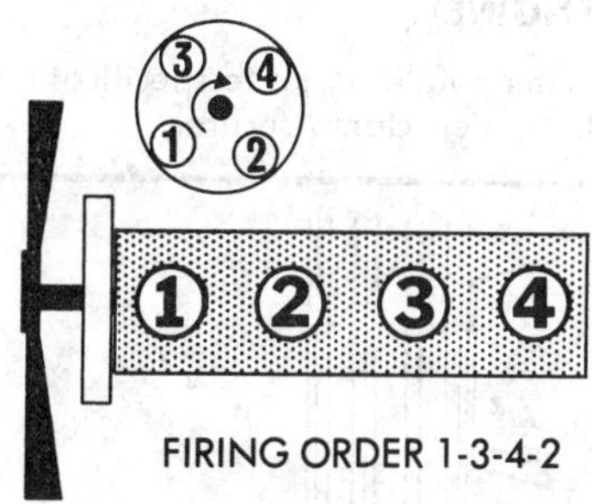

Fig. 1 Firing Order and Distributor Rotation (Corolla — 3K-C & 2T-C Engines)

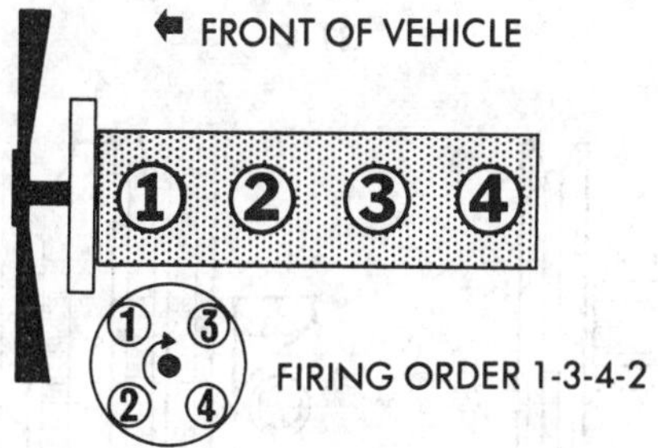

Fig. 2 Firing Order and Distributor Rotation (Corona, Celica & Pickup — 20R Engine)

SPARK PLUGS

Gap	.028-.032" (.7-.8 mm)
Torque	11-15 ft. lbs. (1.5-2.1 mkg)

Spark Plug Type

Application	NGK No.	Nippondenso No.
All Models	BP5ES-L	W16EP

HIGH TENSION WIRE RESISTANCE

Carefully remove high tension wires from spark plugs and distributor cap. Using an ohmmeter, check high tension wire resistance while gently twisting wires. If resistance is not to specifications, or fluctuates from infinity to any value, replace high tension wire(s).

Resistance (Ohms) Per Wire

Application	Ohms
All Models	16,000-25,000

TUNE-UP (Cont.)

DISTRIBUTOR

Air Gap (Celica GT, Calif. only) .... .008-.012" (.2-.3 mm)
Point Gap .... .016-.020" (.4-.5 mm)
Cam Angle .... 50-54°
Breaker Arm Spring Tension .... 18-25 oz. (500-700 g)
Condenser Capacity .... .20-.24 mfd.

IGNITION TIMING

With engine at normal operating temperature, connect a tachometer and dwell meter to engine. Set for correct idle speed. Check dwell angle and point gap (air gap on Calif. Celica GT). Adjust timing as follows with transmission in "N" position:

COROLLA (3K-C ENGINE)

Check timing with timing light. If not to specification, turn distributor to correct. Tighten clamp securely.

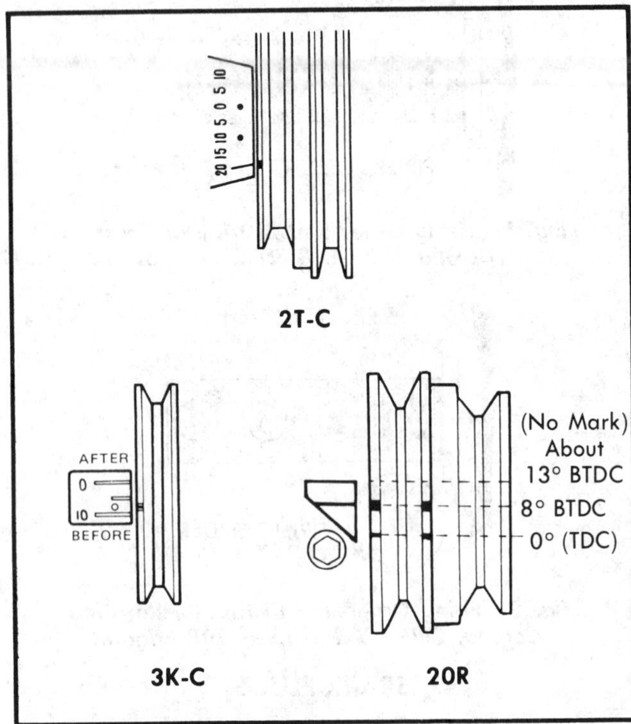

Fig. 3 Ignition Timing Mark Locations

COROLLA (2T-C ENGINE)

Engines Without High Altitude Compensation (HAC) – 1) Check timing with timing light. If not to specifications, turn distributor to correct. If only slightly out of adjustment turn octane selector on distributor.

2) If engine has cold weather distributor, pinch hose between Bimetal Vacuum Switching Valve (BVSV) and carburetor. Timing should read 20° BTDC. Tighten clamp securely.

Engines With High Altitude Compensation (HAC) – 1) Disconnect hose between HAC valve and distributor. Plug end of hose removed from distributor sub-diaphragm. Timing should be 10° BTDC at 700-900 RPM.

2) If not within specifications, turn distributor or for minor adjustment, adjust octane selector on distributor. Reconnect hose to sub-diaphragm and recheck timing for about 20° BTDC. If still not to specification, pinch hose between HAC valve and three-way connector. Timing should be 20° BTDC.

ALL OTHER MODELS (20R ENGINE)

Engines Without High Altitude Compensation (HAC) – Timing should be 8° BTDC at 800 RPM (man. trans.) or 850 RPM (auto. trans.). Correct timing by adjusting octane selector or by turning distributor.

Engines With High Altitude Compensation (HAC) – 1) Disconnect hose between HAC valve and plug end removed from distributor sub-diaphragm. Timing should be 8° BTDC at 700-900 RPM.

2) If out of specification, adjust octane selector or turn distributor. Reconnect hose to sub-diaphragm. Timing should now be about 13° BTDC.

3) If still about 8° BTDC, pinch vacuum hose between HAC valve and three-way connector. Timing should then be 13° BTDC.

Ignition Timing Specifications

Application	RPM	Timing
Corolla (3K-C)	750	8° BTDC
Corolla (2T-C)①	850	10° BTDC
All Other Models②		
Man. Trans.	800	8° BTDC
Auto. Trans.	850	8° BTDC

① – With HAC, hose disconnected, 10° BTDC@700-900 RPM. After reconnecting hose, 20° BTDC.
② – With HAC, hose disconnected, 8° BTDC@700-900 RPM. After reconnecting hose, 13° BTDC.

HOT (SLOW) IDLE RPM

1) With engine at normal operating temperature, and dwell angle, point gap and ignition timing to specifications, be sure choke valve is fully open and all accessories are in "OFF" position. Place transmission in neutral and see that air cleaner is installed, vacuum lines connected and carburetor fuel level is correct.

2) Adjust idle speed to maximum by means of idle mixture screw. Adjust idle speed to specified mixture adjustment speed by means of idle speed adjusting screw. Continue adjusting screws until maximum speed obtainable by idle mixture screw is same as mixture adjustment speed. Then screw in idle mixture screw to obtain specified initial idle speed.

Idle Speed and Mixture

Application	Mixture Adjust. RPM	Initial Idle RPM
Corolla (3K-C)	830	750±50
Corolla (2T-C)		
Federal	930	850±50
Calif. & High Alt.	910	850±50
All Other Models (20R)		
Man. Trans.	870	800±50
Auto. Trans.	920	850±50

TUNE-UP (Cont.)

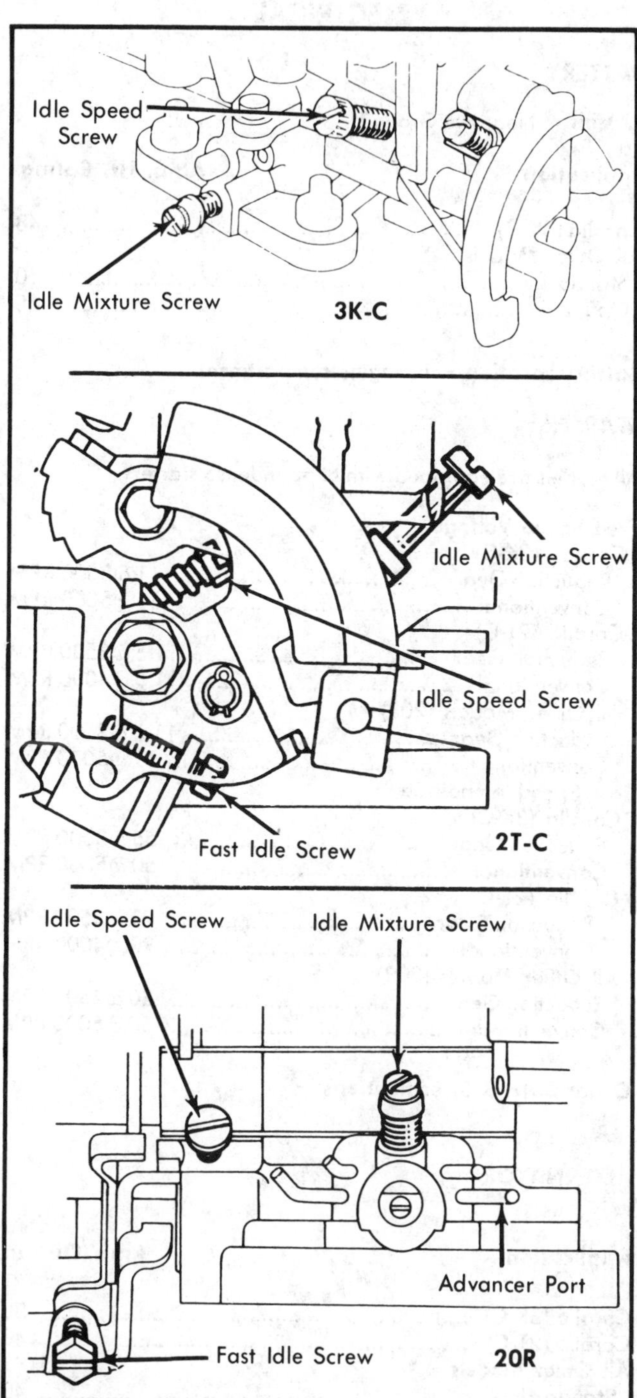

Fig. 4 Carburetor Adjusting Screws

COLD (FAST) IDLE RPM

1) With engine at normal operating temperature, close choke and throttle valves. On models equipped with 20R engine, disconnect EGR vacuum hose from valve and pinch the vacuum hose between the advancer port and the TVSV or VTV valves.

NOTE — *This is the Thermostatic Vacuum Switching Valve on Corona and Celica models; the Vacuum Transmitting Valve on Pickups.*

2) Start engine without stepping on accelerator pedal. Check engine speed against fast idle specifications. Adjust by turning fast idle adjusting screw.

3) On vehicles with 20R engine, release hose and reconnect EGR valve.

Fast Idle Specifications

Application	RPM
Corolla (3K-C)	①
Corolla (2T-C)	
Federal	3400±200
Calif. & High Alt.	3000±200
All Other Models (20R)②	2400±200

① — Not available at time of publication.
② — With EGR hose disconnected and main vacuum hose pinched off.

AUTOMATIC CHOKE

On 2T-C engines, an electric assist choke is used. The system consists of a choke breaker diaphragm, an electrically-heated bimetal choke cap, and a choke control relay. On 20R engines, the system consists of a choke breaker diaphragm and a coolant water-heated bimetal choke cap.

FUEL PUMP PRESSURE & VOLUME

Pressure	
Corolla	2.8-4.3 psi (.2-.3 kg/cm²)
All Other Models	2.1-4.3 psi (.15-.3 kg/cm²)
Volume	
Corolla	①.9 pts. in 30 sec.
All Other Models	1.3 pts. in 30 sec.

① — Models with electric fuel pumps — 1.3 pts. in 30 sec.

EMISSION CONTROL SYSTEMS

See Mitchell Manuals' Emission Control Manual.

GENERAL SERVICING

IGNITION

DISTRIBUTOR

All models are equipped with conventional Nippondenso single point distributors, except the Calif. Celica GT which has a fully transistorized ignition system.

Other Data & Specifications — *See Tune-Up and Nippondenso Distributors in ELECTRICAL Section.*

GENERAL SERVICING (Cont.)

IGNITION COIL

Resistance	Ohms
Primary	
Corolla (3K-C)	3.6
All Other Models	1.3-1.65
Secondary	
All Models	12,800-15,200

FUEL SYSTEMS

CARBURETORS

Application	Make
All Models	Aisan 2-Bbl.

Other Data & Specifications – *See Tune-Up and Aisan Carburetors in FUEL SYSTEMS Section.*

THROTTLE POSITIONER ADJUSTMENT

With engine at normal operating temperature and idling at specified idle speed, disconnect positioner diaphragm vacuum hose. Accelerate engine and release throttle. Engine should idle at specified throttle positioner speed, if not, adjust throttle positioner adjusting screw. Then, reconnect the positioner vacuum hose. The throttle positioner adjusting screw should release from throttle valve lever, returning engine to normal idle RPM.

Throttle Positioner Setting RPM

Application	Man. Trans.	Auto. Trans.
Corolla (2T-C)	1400±100	1200±100
Other Models (20R Only)	1400±100	1050±100

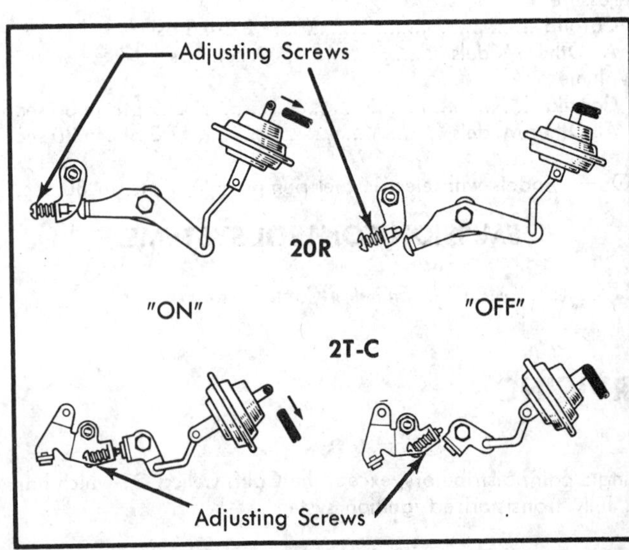

Fig. 5 Throttle Positioner Adjustment Points

ELECTRICAL

BATTERY

12 Volt – Negative Ground.

Application	Amp. Hr. Rating
Corolla (3K-C)	48
All Other Models	
Standard	50
Optional	60

Battery Location – In engine compartment.

STARTER

All models are equipped with Nippondenso starters.

Free Speed Voltage	
Corolla (3K-C)	
Reduction Gear	11@3500 RPM
Conventional	11@5000 RPM
Corolla (2T-C)	
Reduction Gear	11.5@3500 RPM
Conventional	11.5@4000 RPM
All Other Models (20R)	
Reduction Gear	11.5@3500 RPM
Conventional	11@5000 RPM
Free Speed Amperage	
Corolla (3K-C)	
Reduction Gear	55@3500 RPM
Conventional	50@5000 RPM
Corolla (2T-C)	
Reduction Gear	90@3500 RPM
Conventional	90@4000 RPM
All Other Models (20R)	
Reduction Gear	80@3500 RPM
Conventional	50@5000 RPM

Other Data & Specifications – *See Nippondenso Starters in ELECTRICAL Section.*

ALTERNATOR

Application	Rated Amp. Output
Corolla (3K-C)	30
Corolla (2T-C)	40
All Other Models	
Standard	40
Optional	45

Other Data & Specifications – *See Nippondenso Alternators and Regulators in ELECTRICAL Section.*

ALTERNATOR REGULATOR

All models are equipped with Nippondenso alternator regulators with an operating voltage of 13.8-14.8 volts.

Other Data & Specifications – *See Nippondenso Alternators and Regulators in ELECTRICAL Section.*

GENERAL SERVICING (Cont.)

ENGINE

INTAKE MANIFOLD TIGHTENING

Tighten intake manifold attaching bolts to 7-11 ft. lbs. (1.0-1.5 mkg) on Corolla models and 11-15 ft. lbs. (1.5-2.1 mkg) on all other models.

FILTERS & CLEANERS

Filter or Cleaner	Service Interval (Miles)
Oil Filter	Replace every 6,000
Air Filter	Replace every 25,000
Fuel Filter	Replace every 25,000
PCV Valve	Replace every 25,000
Charcoal Canister	Replace every 50,000

BELT ADJUSTMENT

Application	①Deflection
Fan Belt	
Corolla (2T-C)	.31-.47" (8-12 mm)
All Other Models	.31-.51" (8-13 mm)
Air Pump Belt	
Corolla	.51-.71" (8-18 mm)
All Other Models	.31-.51" (8-13 mm)
A/C Belt	.43-.55" (11-14 mm)

① — Deflection is with 22 lbs. (10 kg) pressure applied midway on longest belt run.

CAPACITIES

Application	Quantity
Crankcase (Includes Filter)	
Corolla (3K-C)	3.7 qts.
Corolla (2T-C)	4.6 qts.
Corona & Celica	5.3 qts.
Pickup	4.8 qts.
Cooling System	
Corolla (3K-C)	5.8 qts.
Corolla (2T-C)	
Man. Trans.	8.2 qts.
Auto. Trans.	8.1 qts.
All Other Models	8.5 qts.
Man. Trans.	
Corolla (3K-C)	
4-Speed	3.6 pts.
5-Speed	5.2 pts.
Corolla (2T-C)	3.2 pts.
Corona & Celica	
4-Speed	5.8 pts.
5-Speed	5.4 pts.
Pickup	
4-Speed	4 pts.
5-Speed	5.6 pts.
Auto. Trans.	
Corolla (3K-C)	4.9 qts.
Pickup	7 qts.
All Other Models	6.7 qts.
Rear Axle	
Corolla (3K-C)	2.2 pts.
Corolla (2T-C)	
6.38" Differential	2.2 pts.
6.7" Differential	2.6 pts.
Pickup	3.4 pts.
All Other Models	2.6 pts.
Fuel Tank	
Corolla	
Sedan and Hardtop	13.2 gals.
Station Wagon	12.4 gals.
Corona & Celica	15.3 gals.
Pickup	
Short Bed	12.2 gals.
Long Bed	16.1 gals.

TUNE-UP

Land Cruiser

ENGINE IDENTIFICATION

Engine can be identified by prefix of engine serial number. Serial number is stamped on right side of cylinder block near dipstick. Engine code for Land Cruiser is 2F.

MODEL IDENTIFICATION

VEHICLE IDENTIFICATION NUMBER

Vehicle identification number is located on the left hand front fender apron on station wagon and right hand front fender apron on other models. First two letters designate engine and model series. Land Cruiser is FJ model.

COMPRESSION PRESSURE

Check compression pressure with engine at normal operating temperature, all spark plugs removed, throttle valve wide open and engine at cranking speed. Maximum variation between cylinders should not exceed 14 psi (1.0 kg/cm²). Standard and minimum pressures are as follows:

Application	Standard psi (kg/cm²)	Minimum psi (kg/cm²)
Land Cruiser	149 (10.5)	114 (8)

VALVE TAPPET CLEARANCE

NOTE — *Check or adjust valve clearance with engine at normal operating temperature.*

Application	Intake	Exhaust
Land Cruiser	.008" (.21 mm)	.014" (.36 mm)

VALVE ARRANGEMENT

Land Cruiser — E-I-I-E-E-I-I-E-E-I-I-E (front-to-rear).

SPARK PLUGS

Gap .... .039" (1.0 mm)
Torque .... 10-15 ft. lbs. (1.4-2.1 mkg)

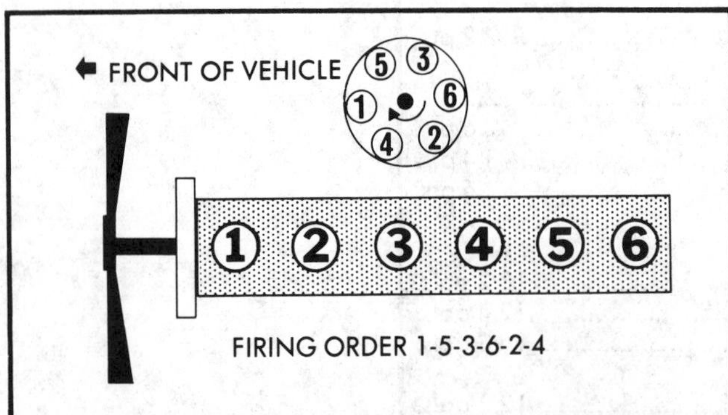

Fig. 1 Firing Order and Distributor Rotation

Spark Plug Type

Application	NGK	Nippondenso
Land Cruiser	BP5EZ	W14EX

HIGH TENSION WIRE RESISTANCE

Carefully remove high tension wires from spark plugs and distributor cap. Using an ohmmeter, check high tension wire resistance while gently twisting wires. If resistance is not to specifications, or fluctuates from infinity to any value, replace high tension wire(s).

Resistance (Ohms) Per Wire

Application	Ohms
All Models	16,000-25,000

DISTRIBUTOR

Point Gap .... .016-.020" (.4-.5mm)
Cam Angle .... 38-44°
Breaker Arm Spring Tension .... 18-25 ozs. (500-700 g)
Condenser Capacity .... .20-.24 mfd.

IGNITION TIMING

1) Check or adjust ignition timing with engine at normal operating temperature and choke valve fully open. Connect tachometer and dwell meter to engine. See that idle speed and cam angle are set to specifications and distributor vacuum line is connected.

2) To adjust timing, loosen distributor clamp and rotate distributor until timing is to specification.

Ignition Timing Specifications

Application	RPM	Timing
Land Cruiser	650	7° BTDC

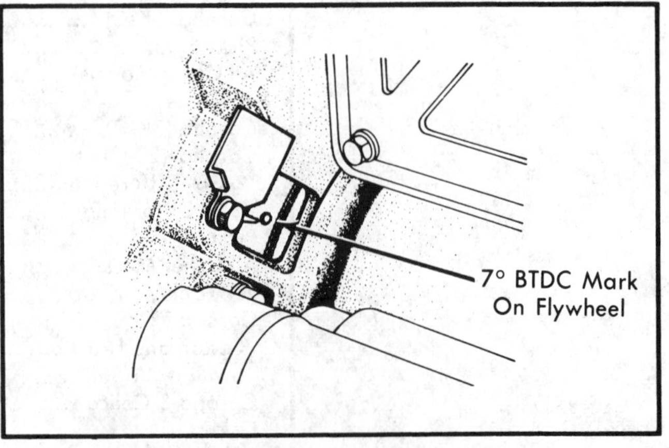

Fig. 2 Land Cruiser Timing Marks (Ball and Pointer)

TUNE-UP (Cont.)

HOT (SLOW) IDLE RPM

1) With engine at normal operating temperature, choke valve fully open, all accessories off, all vacuum lines connected, ignition timing set to specifications and transmission in neutral, check that fuel level is aligned with dot on sight glass of carburetor float bowl. Adjust float level if necessary.

2) With air cleaner installed, adjust idle mixture screw until fastest idle RPM is obtained. Then, adjust idle speed screw until specified mixture adjustment RPM is achieved.

3) Repeat procedure until RPM cannot be increased by adjusting mixture screw. Set idle to specified initial idle RPM by adjusting idle speed screw in a clockwise direction.

Idle Speed Specifications

Application	Mixture Adjust. RPM	Initial Idle RPM
Land Cruiser	690	650±50

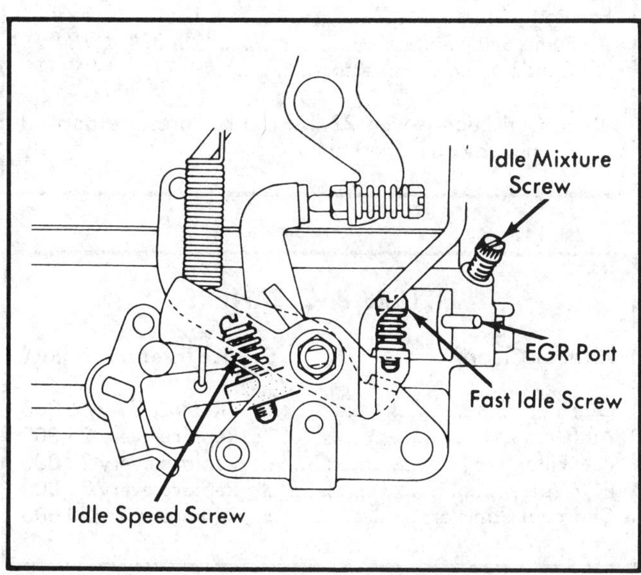

Fig. 3 Carburetor Adjusting Screw Locations

COLD (FAST) IDLE RPM

1) With engine at normal operating temperature, pull out choke knob as far as it will go. On California models pinch hose between EGR port and BVSV; on High Altitude models pinch hose between EGR port and three-way connector.

NOTE — *EGR refers to Exhaust Gas Recirculation; BVSV to Bimetal Vacuum Switching Valve.*

2) Open choke valve with a screwdriver and start engine. Set fast idle to specifications by turning fast idle screw.

3) Push choke knob all the way in. Engine should return to normal idle RPM.

Fast Idle Specifications

Application	RPM
Land Cruiser	
Federal	①1800±200
Calif. & High Alt.	②1800±200

① — With spark control and exhaust gas recirculation normal.
② — With exhaust gas recirculation system off and vacuum advance and retard disconnected.

THROTTLE POSITIONER ADJUSTMENT

1) With engine at normal operating temperature, disconnect vacuum hose from throttle positioner diaphragm. Idle RPM should increase to specifications. If not, adjust by turning throttle positioner adjusting screw.

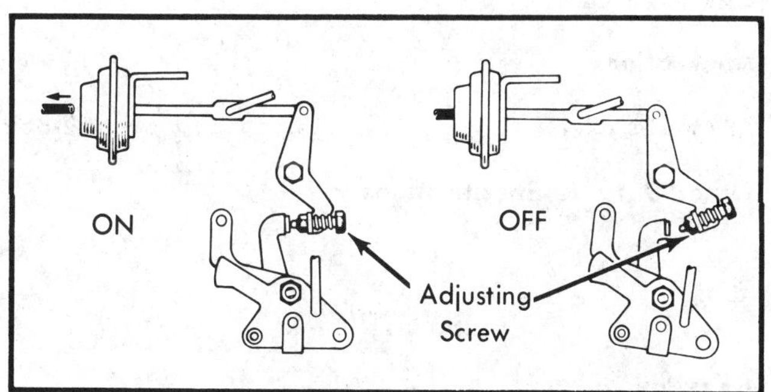

Fig. 4 Throttle Positioner Adjusting Screw

2) Reconnect vacuum hose. Screw should move from throttle valve lever and engine speed should return to normal idle. If not check for a defective diaphragm, vacuum transmitting valve (VTV) and linkage, or plugged or leaking vacuum hose.

Throttle Positioner RPM

Application	RPM
Land Cruiser	
Federal	1200±100
Calif. & High Alt.	1400±100

FUEL PUMP PRESSURE & VOLUME

Pressure	3.4-4.8 psi(.24-.34 kg/cm²)
Volume	①2.5 pts. in 30 sec.

① — At 2000 RPM.

EMISSION CONTROL SYSTEMS

See Mitchell Manuals' Emission Control Manual.

GENERAL SERVICING

IGNITION

DISTRIBUTOR

All models are equipped with Nippondenso single point distributors.

Other Data & Specifications – *See Tune-Up and Nippondenso Distributors in ELECTRICAL Section.*

IGNITION COIL

Resistance	Ohms
Primary	1.3-1.6
Secondary	9500-14,500
Ballast Resistor	1.3-1.7

FUEL SYSTEMS

CARBURETORS

Application	Model
All Models	Aisan 2-Bbl.

Other Data & Specifications – *See Tune-Up and Aisan Carburetors in FUEL SYSTEMS Section.*

ELECTRICAL

BATTERY

12 Volt – Negative Ground.

Application	Amp. Hr. Rating
All	70

Battery Location – In engine compartment.

STARTER

All models are equipped with Nippondenso Starters.

Free Speed Voltage	11 at 5000 RPM
Free Speed Amperage	50 (Max.) at 5000 RPM

Other Data & Specifications – *See Nippondenso Starters in ELECTRICAL Section.*

ALTERNATOR

Application	Rated Amp. Output
Land Cruiser	
Standard	40 or 50
Optional	50 or 55

Other Data & Specification – *See Nippondenso Alternators and Regulators in ELECTRICAL Section.*

ALTERNATOR REGULATOR

All models are equipped with Nippondenso alternator regulator with an operating voltage of 13.8-14.8 volts.

Other Data & Specifications – *See Nippondenso Alternators and Regulators in ELECTRICAL Section.*

ENGINE

INTAKE MANIFOLD TIGHTENING

Tighten intake manifold attaching bolts to 28-37 ft. lbs. (3.9-5.1 mkg).

BELT ADJUSTMENT

Application	①Deflection
Fan Belt	.51-.59" (13-15 mm)
Air Pump Belt	.28-.39" (7-10 mm)
Air Conditioning Compressor	.59-.71" (15-18 mm)

① – Deflection is with 22 lbs. (10 kg) pressure applied midway on longest belt run.

FILTERS & CLEANERS

Filter or Cleaner	Service Interval (Miles)
Oil Filter	Replace every 6,000
Air Filter	Replace every 25,000
Fuel Filter	Replace every 25,000
PCV Valve	Replace every 25,000
Charcoal Canister	Replace every 50,000

CAPACITIES

Application	Quantity
Crankcase (Includes Filter)	8.5 qts.
Cooling System	
Station Wagon	17.6 qts.
All Others	16.8 qts.
Man. Trans.	
4-Speed	6.6 pts.
3-Speed	3.6 pts.
Differential (Front and Rear)	5.2 pts.
Transfer Case	3.6 pts.
Fuel Tank	
Station Wagon	21.7 gals.
All Others	16.4 gals.

TUNE-UP

Spitfire 1500
TR7

ENGINE IDENTIFICATION

Engine number is stamped on engine boss on left side of block below number four spark plug on Spitfire models and is stamped on the cylinder head between carburetors on TR7 models. The following engine codes (prefix letters) denote engines designed specifically for the USA market.

Application	Code
Spitfire	
Federal	FM XXXX U
Calif.	FM XXXX C
TR7	
Federal	CL XXXX U
Calif.	CL XXXX C

MODEL IDENTIFICATION

VEHICLE IDENTIFICATION NUMBER

Number is stamped on a metal plate attached to the driver's door on TR7 models and to door post on Spitfire models. Number is also stamped on a small plate and mounted on left corner of instrument panel, visible through the windshield.

COMPRESSION PRESSURE

Check compression with engine at normal operating temperature, spark plugs removed and throttle wide open. Crank engine through four compression strokes before taking reading. On Spitfire models, minimum pressure is 145 psi (10.2 kg/cm²). On both Spitfire and TR7 models, lowest pressure should be at least 85% that of highest cylinder.

VALVE TAPPET CLEARANCE

Spitfire – 1) Disconnect battery, then remove valve cover and spark plugs. Check valve clearance with engine cold. Adjust valves in outlined sequence (numbered front to rear):

Valves Open	Adjust Valves
No. 8 & No. 6	No. 1 & No. 3
No. 4 & No. 7	No. 5 & No. 2
No. 1 & No. 3	No. 8 & No. 6
No. 5 & No. 2	No. 4 & No. 7

2) Turn crankshaft until appropriate valves in first column open. Then check and adjust valves listed in second column.

3) To adjust, loosen lock nut and turn slotted adjusting pin clockwise to decrease clearance and counterclockwise to increase clearance. Tighten lock nut when correct.

TR7 – 1) Disconnect battery and remove camshaft cover. Loosen camshaft bearing cap nuts and retighten to 10-14 ft. lbs. (1.4-1.9 mkg). Rotate engine. Check and record clearance between cam heel and tappet. Maximum clearance is present when cam is in vertical position.

2) If clearance is not within specifications, remove camshaft and individually lift out each tappet and adjusting shim.

3) Using a micrometer, measure thickness of adjusting shim removed. Add to this the measured valve clearance and subtract the specified clearance from the total. This will offer you the thickness of adjusting shim necessary to bring the clearance within specifications.

4) Install shims and tappets (as needed). Install camshaft and tighten bearing caps. Recheck valve clearance, and when correct, install camshaft cover.

Valve Clearance Specifications

Application	Clearance (Cold)
Spitfire	
Intake & Exhaust	.010" (.25 mm)
TR7	
Intake	.008" (.20 mm)
Exhaust	.018" (.50 mm)

VALVE ARRANGEMENT

E-I-I-E-E-I-I-E (front to rear).

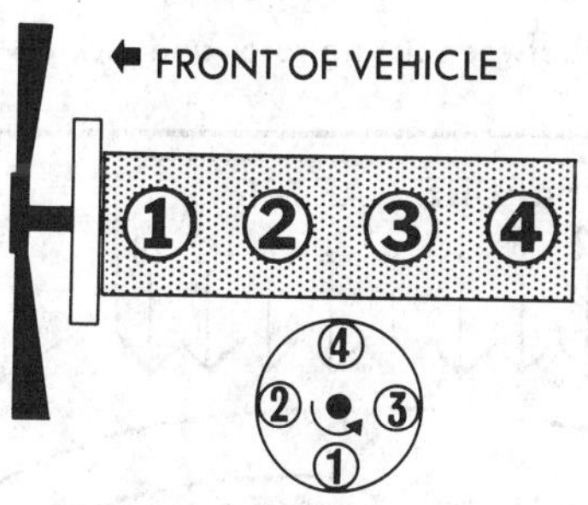

Fig. 1 Firing Order and Distributor Rotation (Spitfire)

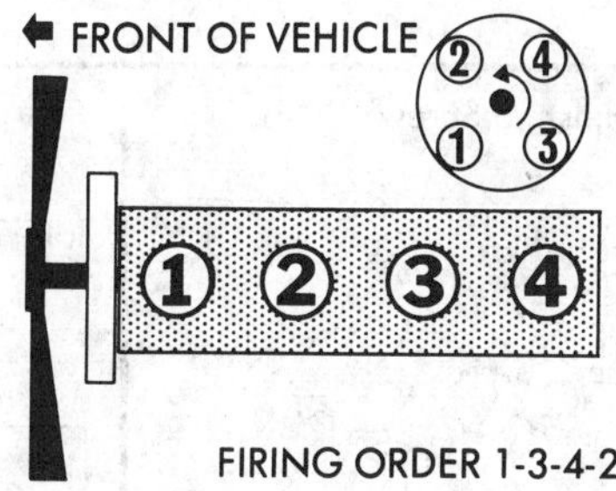

Fig. 2 Firing Order and Distributor Rotation (TR7)

SPARK PLUGS

Gap	.024-.026" (.61-.66 mm)
Torque	20 ft. lbs. (2.8 mkg)

Spark Plug Type

Application	Champion No.
Spitfire & TR7	N-12Y

TUNE-UP (Cont.)

HIGH TENSION WIRE RESISTANCE

Carefully remove high tension wires from spark plugs and distributor cap. Using an ohmmeter, check high tension wire resistance while gently twisting wires. If resistance is not to specifications, or fluctuates from infinity to any value, replace high tension wire(s).

Resistance (Ohms) Per Wire

Application	Ohms
All Models	25,000-30,000

DISTRIBUTOR

All models are equipped with Opus Electronic Ignition System and the only adjustment required is adjusting the Pick-Up Module air gap.

CAUTION — *DO NOT insert feeler gauge into pick-up air gap when the ignition circuit is energized.*

Pick-Up Module Air Gap .... ①.014-.016″ (.35-.40 mm)

① — Measured between timing rotor and pick-up module.

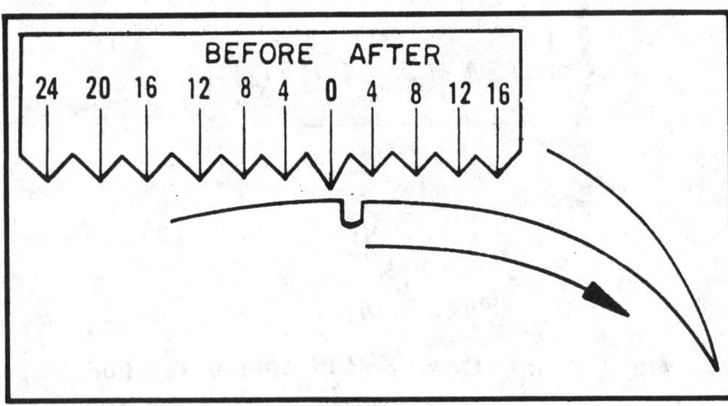

Fig. 3 Ignition Timing Mark Location

IGNITION TIMING

Check or adjust ignition timing with engine at normal operating temperature, idle speed at specification and distributor vacuum retard hose connected. If correction is necessary, rotate distributor.

Ignition Timing Specifications

Application	RPM	Timing
Spitfire & TR7①		
Federal	700-900	10° BTDC
Calif.	700-900	2° ATDC

① — Static timing on all models is 10° BTDC.

IDLE SPEED & MIXTURE

NOTE — *See Fig. 4.*

1) Remove air cleaner and fresh air duct (dual carburetor models only), then ensure oil in carburetor damper is ¼″ below top of damper tube. With engine at normal operating temperature, connect a tachometer and exhaust gas analyzer to vehicle. Back off on fast idle adjusting screw until it no longer contacts fast idle cam.

2) On models with a single carburetor, adjust idle speed to specifications by adjusting throttle adjusting screw. On models with dual carburetors, use an air flow balance meter and synchronize carburetors, then adjust idle speed to specifications by adjusting throttle adjusting screw on each carburetor an equal amount.

3) On all models, stop engine and disconnect and plug air pump outlet hose. Start engine and check CO level. If CO level is not within specifications, adjust idle trim screw(s) clockwise to richen mixture or counterclockwise to lean mixture until CO level is within specified limit. If CO level cannot be adjusted within limits by adjusting the idle trim screw(s), proceed to step 4).

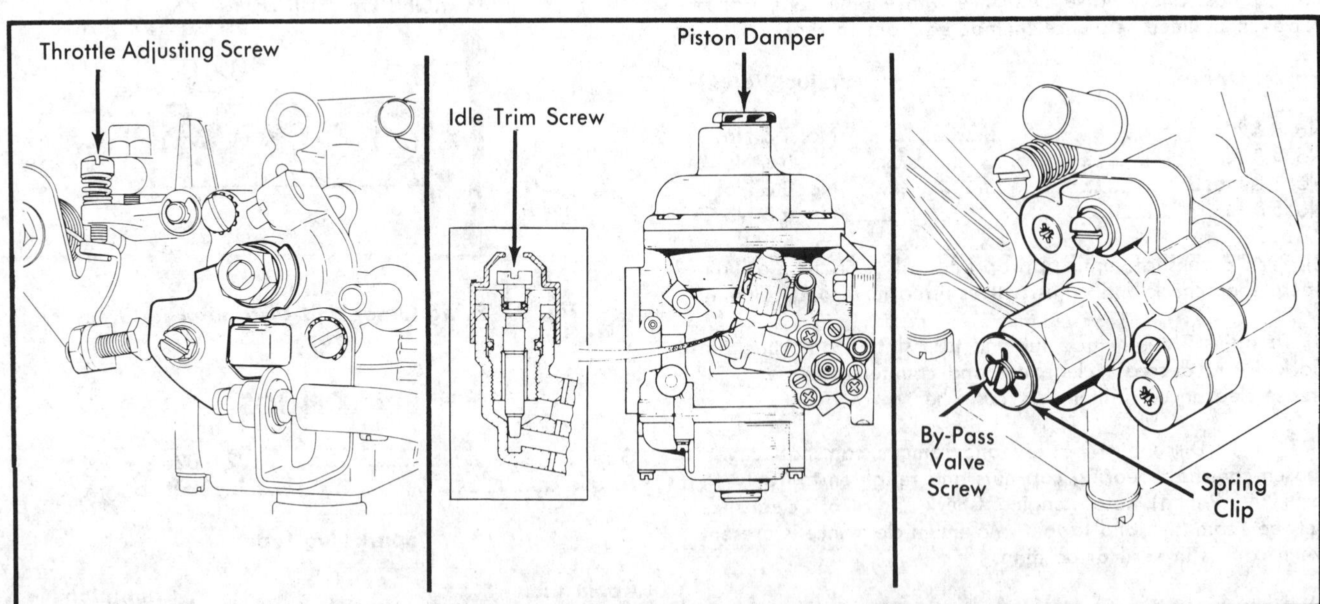

Fig. 4 Screws for Adjusting Idle Speed, Mixture, & Decel Valve

TUNE-UP (Cont.)

4) Remove piston damper from carburetor(s). Then carefully insert needle adjusting tool (S 353) into dashpot until outer tool engages air valve and inner tool engages hexagon in needle adjuster. Hold outer tool stationary and turn inner tool clockwise to richen mixture or counterclockwise to lean mixture until CO level is within specified limit. Remove tool and reinstall piston, then recheck CO level and idle RPM and adjust as necessary.

Idle Speed (RPM) & CO Level (%)

Application	Idle RPM	CO%
Spitfire	800±100	①.5-6
TR7	800±100	2-6

① – 3% is nominal.

COLD (FAST) IDLE RPM

MANUAL CHOKE

1) With engine at normal operating temperature, ensure that choke cam lever on carburetor(s) returns fully to its stop. Adjust choke cable, if necessary. Then pull choke knob out approximately ¼" until fast idle cam(s) engage spring-loaded detent ball(s).

2) Loosen lock nut on carburetor(s) and turn fast idle screw against cam until engine reaches fast idle speed. Be sure carburetors are in balance. Tighten lock nut and push in choke knob fully.

AUTOMATIC CHOKE

On models with automatic chokes, remove cover and turn fast idle screw until the gap between base circle of cam and fast idle pin is within .035" (.89 mm) on TR7 and .020" (.5 mm) on Spitfire.

Fast Idle Specifications

Application	RPM
Spitfire	①1700-1900
TR7	②1600

① – Corresponds to 1100-1300 cold setting.
② – Corresponds to 1300 RPM cold setting.

DECEL VALVE ADJUSTMENT

With engine at normal operating temperature, disconnect and plug distributor vacuum retard line. Engine speed should increase to approximately 1300 RPM. If engine speed increases to 2000-2500 RPM, decel valve will need to be adjusted. To adjust, turn by-pass valve adjusting screw until speed drops to 1300 RPM, then turn screw an additional ½ turn to fully seat valve.

NOTE – *See Fig. 4.*

FUEL PUMP PRESSURE

Pressure (At Idle)

Spitfire	2.5-3.8 psi (.17-.26 kg/cm²)
TR7	2.5-3.5 psi (.17-.24 kg/cm²)

EMISSION CONTROL SYSTEMS

See Mitchell Manuals' Emission Control Manual.

GENERAL SERVICING

IGNITION

DISTRIBUTOR

All models are equipped with Lucas Opus Electronic Ignition System.

Other Data & Specifications – *See Tune-Up & Lucas Distributors in ELECTRICAL Section.*

IGNITION COIL

Resistance	Ohms at 68°F (20°C)
Primary	
Spitfire	1.30-1.45
TR7	1.20-1.50
Ballast Resistor	
All Models	1.30-1.50

FUEL SYSTEMS

CARBURETORS

Application	Model
Spitfire	1 Zenith-Stromberg 150 CD4T
TR7	2 Zenith-Stromberg 175 CDFEVX

Other Data & Specifications – *See Tune-Up and Zenith-Stromberg Carburetors in FUEL SYSTEMS Section.*

ELECTRICAL

BATTERY

12 Volt – Negative Ground.

Application	Amp. Hr. Capacity
Spitfire	40
TR7	50

Battery Location – In engine compartment, on firewall.

GENERAL SERVICING (Cont.)

STARTER

Lucas .... Overrunning Clutch

Free Speed Amperage
- Spitfire .... 65 at 8000-10,000 RPM
- TR7 .... 40 at 6000 RPM

Other Data & Specifications – *See Lucas Starters in ELECTRICAL Section.*

ALTERNATOR

Application	Rated Amp. Output
Spitfire	36 at 6000 RPM
TR7	①36 at 6000 RPM

① – With Air Conditioning – Optional, 66 at 6000 RPM.

Other Data & Specifications – *See Lucas Alternators & Regulators in ELECTRICAL Section.*

ALTERNATOR REGULATOR

Lucas – Non-Adjustable, integral with alternator, with an operating voltage of 13.6-14.4 volts.

Other Data & Specifications – *See Lucas Alternators & Regulators in ELECTRICAL Section.*

ENGINE

INTAKE MANIFOLD TIGHTENING

Tighten intake manifold attaching bolts to 25 ft. lbs. (3.5 mkg) on Spitfire models and to 15-20 ft. lbs. (2.1-2.7 mkg) on TR7 models.

BELT ADJUSTMENT

Application	①Deflection
All Models	
Fan Belt	.75-1" (19-25 mm)
Air Pump Belt	.25" (6.4 mm)

① – Deflection is with pressure applied midway on longest belt run.

FILTERS & CLEANERS

Application	Service Interval (Miles)
Oil Filter	①Replace every 12,000
Air Cleaner	②Replace every 25,000
Fuel Filter	②Replace every 25,000
Carbon Canister Assy.	Replace every 50,000

① – Replace after first 6,000 miles and then at 12,000 mile intervals.

② – Replace after first 12,500 miles and then at 25,000 mile intervals.

CAPACITIES

Application	Quantity
Crankcase (Includes Filter)	4.8 qts.
Cooling System (Includes Heater & Reservoir)	
Spitfire	4.75 qts.
TR7	7.8 qts.
Man. Trans. (SAE 90 EP)	
Spitfire	
Without Overdrive	1.8 pts.
With Overdrive	3.17 pts.
TR7	
4-Speed	2.4 pts.
5-Speed	3.3 pts.
Auto. Trans., TR7	5.7 qts.
Rear Axle (SAE 90 EP)	
Spitfire	1.2 pts.
TR7	
4-Speed	2.7 pts.
5-Speed	2.4 pts.
Fuel Tank	
Spitfire	8.7 gals.
TR7	14.4 gals.

TUNE-UP

Type 1
Type 2
Dasher
Rabbit
Scirocco

ENGINE IDENTIFICATION

Engine code prefixes are placed in the following locations:

Type 1 – Engine serial number is stamped on alternator support flange.

Type 2 – Engine serial number is stamped on crankcase below breather and also near ignition coil.

All Other Models – Engine serial number is stamped on left side of engine near ignition distributor.

Engine Codes

Application	Code
Type 1	
Fuel Injected	AJ
Type 2	GD
Dasher	
Federal	
Man. Trans.	YG
Auto Trans.	YH
California	YK
Rabbit & Scirocco	
Man. Trans.	EE
Auto. Trans.	EF

MODEL IDENTIFICATION

VEHICLE IDENTIFICATION NUMBER

The Vehicle Identification Number is stamped on a plate attached to left windshield pillar on Dasher and Scirocco models. Number also appears on Dasher models at rear of engine compartment above windshield washer reservoir and on Rabbit and Scirocco models atop the suspension strut mounting of the right-hand front wheel housing. Type 1 & 2 and Rabbit vehicles have number stamped on instrument panel. All models feature numbers visible through the windshield.

COMPRESSION PRESSURE

Application	Stan. Pressure psi (kg/cm²)	①Min. Pressure psi (kg/cm²)
Type 1	107-135 (7.5-9.5)	85 (6.0)
Type 2	85-135 (6.0-9.5)	71 (5.0)
All Other Models	142-185 (10.0-13.0)	107 (7.5)

① – Maximum variation between cylinders should not exceed 28 psi (2 kg/cm²) on Type 1 and 2 vehicles or 42 psi (3 kg/cm²) on all other vehicles.

VALVE TAPPET CLEARANCE

Type 1 & 2 – Perform adjustment with engine cold. Turn crankshaft until No. 1 cylinder is at TDC position and distributor rotor points to No. 1 cylinder position. Loosen lock nut and adjust rocker arm adjusting screw until valve clearance is to specification. Check clearance between adjusting screw and valve stem of both valves. Tighten lock nut. Turn crankshaft 90 degrees, while observing distributor rotor travel. Adjust valves of No. 2, 3, and 4 cylinders in turn.

All Other Models – Remove distributor cap and set engine at TDC. Align distributor rotor with No. 1 cylinder mark on distributor body. Adjust by replacing tappet discs. Discs are available in 26 thicknesses from .119-.166" (3.0-4.25 mm). Adjust valves in firing order, 1-3-4-2, according to following procedure:

Valve Adjusting Sequence①

Check or Adjust	When Valves Overlap
No. 1	No. 4
No. 3	No. 2
No. 4	No. 1
No. 2	No. 3

① – Turn crankshaft 180° in normal direction of rotation after adjusting valves of each cylinder.

NOTE – *Use special tool VW546 to press down cam follower, so that adjusting disc can be readily removed with tool 10-208. When depressing cam followers, turn so that openings are at 90° angle to camshaft.*

Valve Clearance Specifications

Application	Clearance Cold	Clearance Hot
Type 1 & 2		
Intake & Exhaust		.006" (.15 mm)
All Other Models		
Intake	.006-.010" (.15-.25 mm)	.008-.012" (.20-.30 mm)
Exhaust	.014-.018" (.36-.46 mm)	.016-.020" (.40-.50 mm)

VALVE ARRANGEMENT

Type 1 & 2 – E-I-I-E (both banks, front-to-rear).
All Others – E-I-E-I-I-E-I-E (front-to-rear).

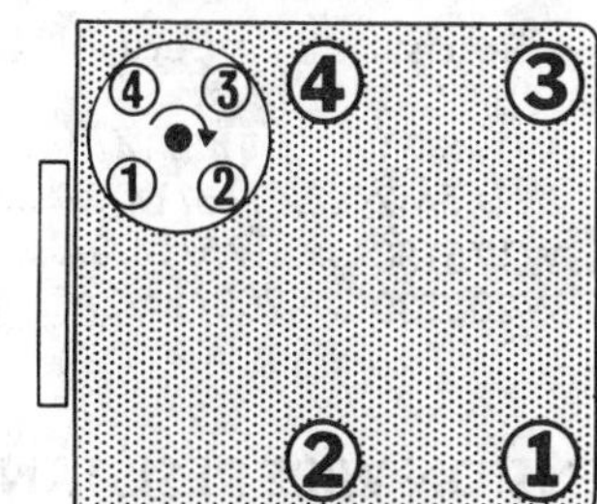

Fig. 1 Firing Order and Distributor Rotation (Type 1 & 2)

TUNE-UP (Cont.)

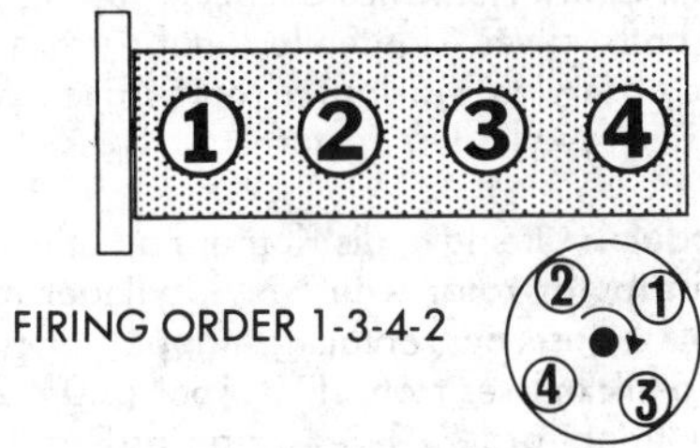

Fig. 2 Firing Order and Distributor Rotation (Dasher)

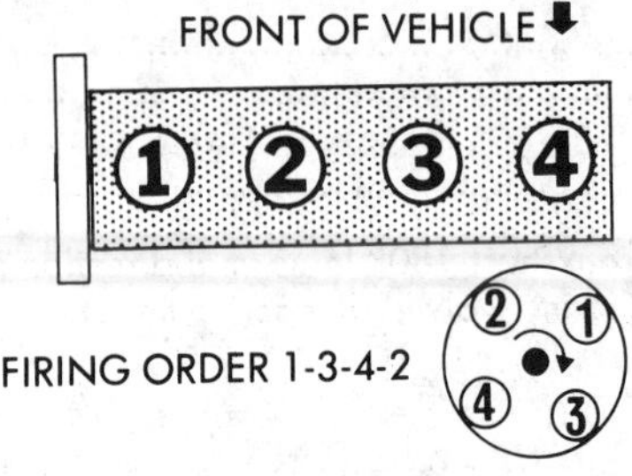

Fig. 3 Firing Order and Distributor Rotation (Rabbit & Scirocco)

DISTRIBUTOR

Point Gap .016" (.4 mm)
Dwell Angle 44-50°
Breaker Arm Spring Tension 14-21 ozs. (450-600 g)
Condenser Capacity .20 mfd.

SPARK PLUGS

Gap
Type 1 & 2 .028" (.7 mm)
All Other Models .024-.028" (.6-.7 mm)
Torque 22 ft. lbs. (3 mkg)

Spark Plug Type

Application	Bosch	Beru	Champion
Type 1	W145M1	145/14/L	L-288
Type 2	W145M2	145/14/3L	N-288
Dasher	W175T30	175/14/3A	N-8Y
Rabbit & Scirocco	W200T30	200/14/3A1	N-8Y

HIGH TENSION WIRE RESISTANCE

Carefully remove high tension wires from spark plugs and distributor cap. Using an ohmmeter, check high tension wire resistance while gently twisting wires. If resistance is not to specifications, or fluctuates from infinity to any value, replace high tension wire(s).

Resistance (Ohms) Per Wire

Application	Ohms
All Models	25,000-30,000

IGNITION TIMING

Connect timing light and tachometer to vehicle. On all models check or adjust ignition timing with engine at normal operating temperature and distributor vacuum lines connected. Adjust timing with engine at specified RPM. To correct timing, loosen distributor holddown bolt, turn distributor, and retighten bolt to 14 ft. lbs. (1.94 mkg).

Ignition Timing Specifications

Application	RPM	Timing
Type 1 (Man. Trans.)	800-950	5° ATDC
Type 2		
Man. Trans.	800-950	7.5° BTDC
Auto. Trans.	850-1000	7.5° BTDC
Dasher	850-1000	3° ATDC
Rabbit & Scirocco	900-1000	3° ATDC

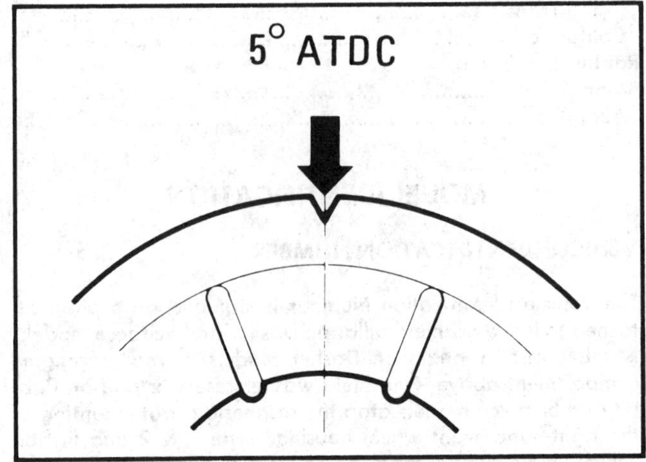

Fig. 4 Ignition Timing Mark Location (Type 1)

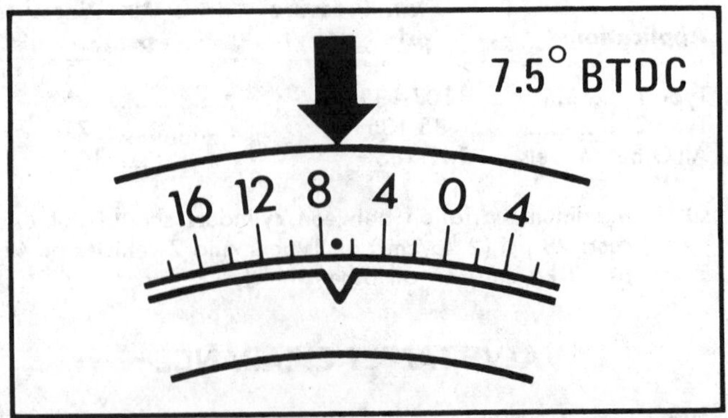

Fig. 5 Ignition Timing Mark Location (Type 2)

TUNE-UP (Cont.)

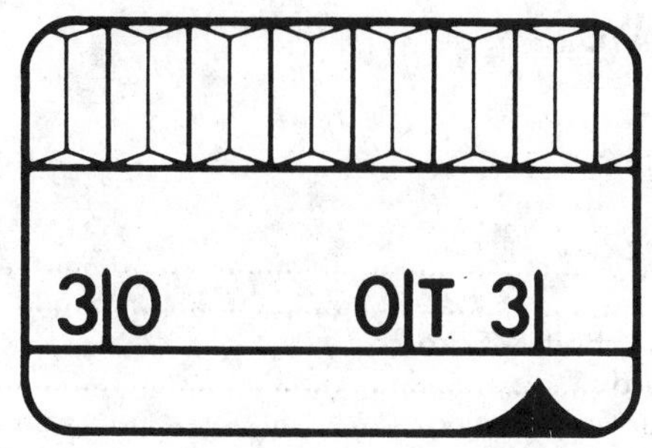

Fig. 6 Ignition Timing Mark Location (Dasher)

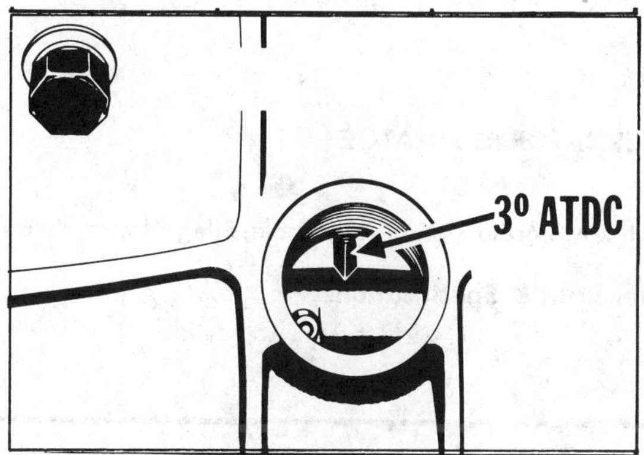

Fig. 7 Ignition Timing Mark Location (Rabbit & Scirocco)

IDLE SPEED & MIXTURE

Type 1 & 2 – 1) With engine at normal operating temperature, remove hose between charcoal filter and air cleaner. Turn idle speed adjusting screw (by-pass screw) on throttle valve housing until speed is to specification. Turn clockwise to decrease speed, counterclockwise to increase speed.

2) With idle properly adjusted, adjust mixture (CO%). Connect an exhaust gas analyzer as instructed by manufacturer, but ahead of catalytic converter, if so equipped.

3) If adjustment is required, remove rubber plug from air flow sensor housing and turn mixture adjusting screw until CO% is to specification. Turn screw clockwise to increase CO% level, counterclockwise to decrease CO%. Recheck idle speed and adjust if necessary.

Dasher, Rabbit, & Scirocco – 1) With engine at normal operating temperature, brake set, A/C and headlights on (high beam), connect dwell meter tachometer. Turn idle speed adjusting screw (by-pass screw) on throttle valve housing until speed is to specifications. Turn screw clockwise to decrease speed; counterclockwise to increase speed.

2) Disconnect evaporative emission control purge hose from charcoal filter to air cleaner. Connect exhaust gas analyzer according to manufacturer's instructions. Insert probe into tailpipe (even if equipped with catalytic converter).

3) If CO% is not correct at specified idle speed, remove rubber plug from top of mixture control unit. Use P377 adjusting tool (or equivalent) to turn idle mixture screw to correct CO% setting. Turn screw clockwise to increase CO% or counterclockwise to reduce CO% level. Recheck idle and adjust if necessary. Disconnect all test equipment and reconnect hose.

Idle Speed (RPM) and CO Level (%)

Application	Idle RPM	Maximum CO%
Type 1①		
Man. Trans.	800-950	2.0
Type 2①		
Man. Trans.	800-950	2.0
Auto. Trans.	850-1000	2.0
Rabbit & Scirocco②		
California	900-1000	0.3
Federal		
Man. Trans.	900-1000	1.5
Auto. Trans.	900-1000	1.0
Dasher②		
California	850-1000	0.5
Federal		
Man. Trans.	850-1000	1.5
Auto. Trans.	850-1000	1.0

① – Probe inserted in front of catalytic converter.
② – Probe inserted in tailpipe.

EMISSION CONTROL SYSTEMS

See Mitchell Manuals' Emission Control Manual.

GENERAL SERVICING

IGNITION

DISTRIBUTOR

All models are equipped with Bosch single point distributors.

Other Data & Specifications – *See Tune-Up and Bosch Distributors in ELECTRICAL Section.*

FUEL SYSTEMS

FUEL INJECTION

Type 1 & 2 – All models use Bosch AFC Electronic Fuel Injection.

Dasher, Rabbit & Scirocco – All models use Bosch Continuous Injection System (CIS).

Other Data & Specifications – *See Tune-Up and Bosch AFC Electronic or Bosch CIS Fuel Injection Systems in FUEL SYSTEMS Section.*

GENERAL SERVICING (Cont.)

ELECTRICAL

BATTERY

12 Volt – Negative Ground.

Application	Amp Hr. Capacity
Type 1	45
Type 2	54
Dasher, Rabbit & Scirocco	
Standard	45
With Air Conditioning	54

Battery Location – Battery is located under the rear seat, on right side (Type 1 models) or in engine compartment (all other models).

STARTER

All models are equipped with Bosch starters.

Other Data & Specifications – *See Bosch Starters in ELECTRICAL Section.*

ALTERNATOR

Application	Rated Amp. Output
Type 1	50
Type 2	55
Dasher, Rabbit & Scirocco	
Standard	55
With Air Conditioning	65

Other Data & Specifications – *See Bosch & Motorola Alternators & Regulator in ELECTRICAL Section.*

ALTERNATOR REGULATOR

Bosch & Motorola – Non-Adjustable; integral with alternator.

Other Data & Specifications – *See Bosch & Motorola Alternators & Regulators in ELECTRICAL Section.*

BELT ADJUSTMENT

Application	① Deflections
All Models	.4-.6" (10-15 mm)

① – Deflection is with thumb pressure, about 16.5 lbs. (7.5 kg), applied midway on longest belt run.

FILTERS & CLEANERS

Filter or Cleaner	Service Interval (Miles)
Oil Strainer (Type 1)	Clean every 5,000
Oil Filter (All Other Models	Replace every 15,000
Air Cleaner	
Dasher Only	Clean every 15,000
All Other Models	Replace every 30,000
Fuel Filter	
Rabbit & Scirocco	Replace every 30,000
All Other Models	Replace every 15,000
EGR Filter	Replace every 15,000

CAPACITIES

Application	Quantity
Crankcase	
Type 1	2.6 qts.
Dasher	①3.2 qts.
All Other Models	②3.7 qts.
Cooling System	
Dasher	③6.3 qts.
Rabbit & Scirocco	4.9 qts.
Man. Trans. & Final Drive (SAE 80 – API GL 4)	
Type 1	2.6 pts.
Type 2	7.4 pts.
Dasher	3.4 pts.
Rabbit & Scirocco	2.6 pts.
Auto. Trans. Refill (Dexron B)	④6.4 pts.
Auto. Trans. Final Drive (SAE 90 – API GL 5)	
Type 2	2.6 pts.
Dasher, Rabbit & Scirocco	1.6 pts.
Fuel Tank	
Type 1	
Beetle	10.6 gals.
Convertible	11.5 gals.
Type 2	14.6 gals.
Dasher	12.1 gals.
Rabbit & Scirocco	11.0 gals.

① – Includes oil filter (w/o filter, 2.6 qts.).
② – Includes oil filter (w/o filter, 3.2 qts.).
③ – 6.9 qts. with expansion tank.
④ – Dry fill is 6.4 qts.

TUNE-UP

Rabbit Diesel

ENGINE IDENTIFICATION

The first two letters of the engine identification number, stamped on the cylinder block just below the glow plug of cylinder number 3, identifies the engine as:

Model	Code
Rabbit	CK

MODEL IDENTIFICATION

VEHICLE IDENTIFICATION NUMBER

The vehicle identification number is located on the left side of the instrument panel and is visible through the windshield.

COMPRESSION PRESSURE

Remove electrical wire from stop control on injection pump. Insulate wire end and remove injector pipes and injector. Use special adapter (VW 1323/2) or its equivalent and compression tester (VW 1323).Be sure old heat shield is between adapter and head. Operate starter and read compression.

Application	①Pressure	
New	483 psi	(34 kg/cm²)
Wear Limit	398 psi	(28 kg/cm²)

① – 71 psi (5 kg/cm²) maximum difference between cylinders.

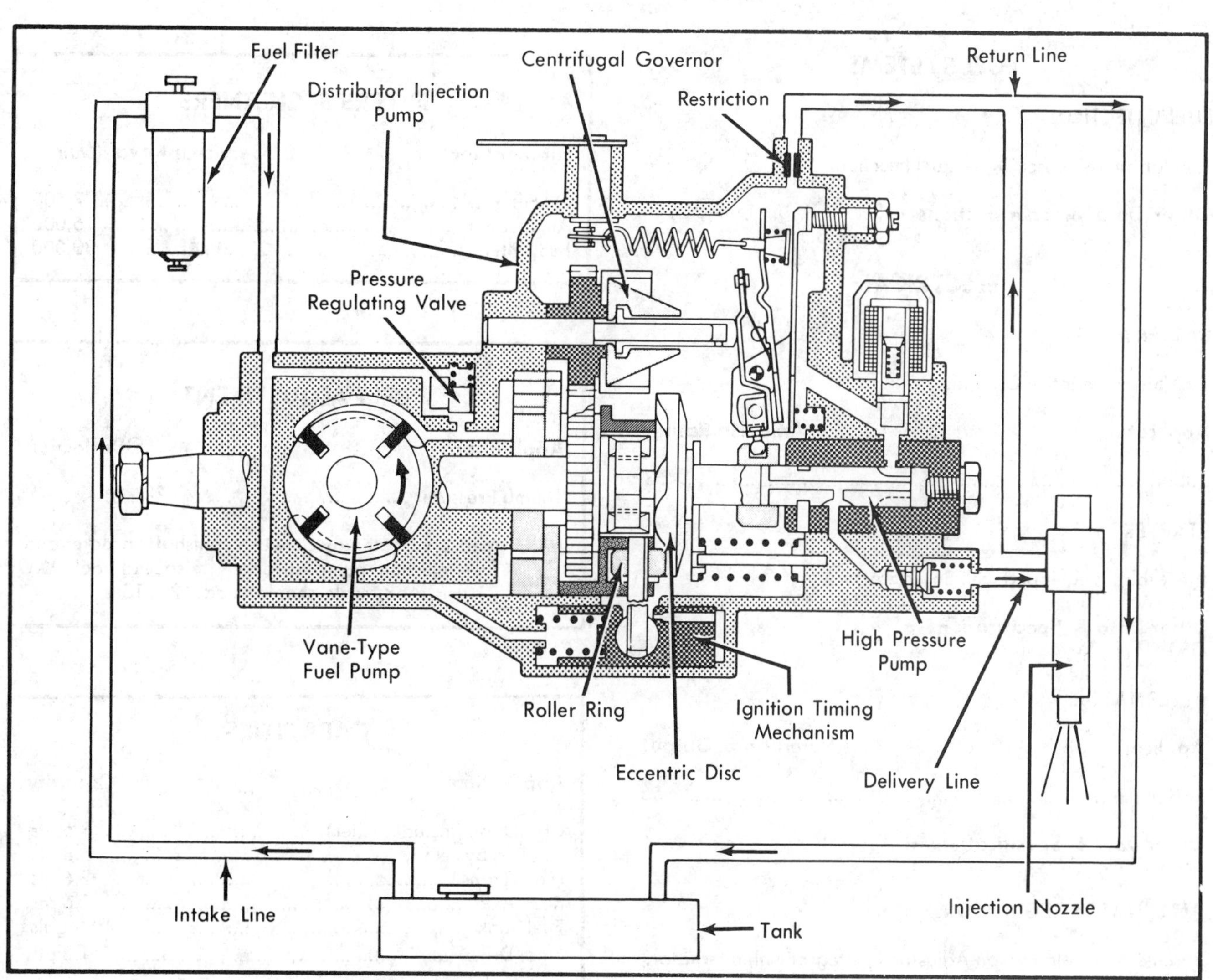

Fig. 1 Fuel Supply System for Volkswagen Diesel

TUNE-UP (Cont.)

VALVE CLEARANCE

CAUTION — *When adjusting valves, pistons MUST NOT be at TDC. Turn crankshaft ¼ turn past TDC so valves do not hit pistons when tappets are depressed.*

CAUTION — *When adjusting valves, do not turn engine by turning camshaft pulley. This will stretch the drive belt. Place vehicle in 4th gear and push to turn engine.*

1) Valves may be checked when engine is either warm or cold. If warm, coolant should be 95°F (35°C). Check valve clearance in firing order, 1-3-4-2.

2) Measure between cam lobes and adjusting disc, when both lobes to be checked point upward. Adjust clearance to specifications by changing disc thickness. Twenty six discs are available in thicknesses from .118-.167" (3.00-4.25 mm).

3) To remove adjusting discs, use a 10-208 removal tool, while holding cam follower down with special tool VW 546 (10-209).

Valve Clearance Specifications

Application	Intake	Exhaust
Engine Warm	.008-.012" (.2-.3 mm)	.016-.020" (.4-.5 mm)
Engine Cold	.006-.010" (.15-.25 mm)	.014-.018" (.35-.45 mm)

VALVE ARRANGEMENT

All Models — E-I-E-I-I-E-I-E (right of vehicle to left)

FIRING ORDER

All Models — 1-3-4-2

GENERAL SERVICING

FUEL SYSTEMS

FUEL INJECTION

The Rabbit uses Bosch Diesel Fuel Injection.

Other Data & Specifications — *See Tune-Up and Bosch Diesel Fuel Injection in FUEL SYSTEMS Section.*

ELECTRICAL

BATTERY

12 Volt — Negative Ground.

Application	Amp. Hr. Rating
Rabbit	63

STARTER

The Rabbit is equipped with Bosch Starter.

Other Data & Specifications — *See Bosch Starters in ELECTRICAL Section.*

ALTERNATOR

Application	Rated Amp. Output
Rabbit	55

Other Data & Specifications — *See Bosch & Motorola Alternators in ELECTRICAL Section.*

ALTERNATOR REGULATOR

Bosch & Motorola — Non-Adjustable; integral with alternator.

Other Data & Specifications — *See Bosch Alternators & Regulators in ELECTRICAL Section.*

FILTERS & CLEANERS

Filter or Cleaner	Service Interval (Miles)
Oil Filter	7,500
Air Cleaner	15,000
Fuel Filter	30,000

BELT ADJUSTMENT

Application	①Deflection
Thumb Pressure	⅜-⅝"(10-15 mm)

① — Measured half way between camshaft sprocket and fuel injection pump sprocket. If special tool (VW 210) is used, scale should read 12 - 13.

CAPACITIES

Application	Quantity
Crankcase (Includes Filter)	①3.5 qts.
Cooling System	6.8 qts.
Man. Trans.	2.6 qts.
Rear Axle	1.6 pts.
Fuel Tank	10.9 gals.
Final Drive	1.3 pts.

① — 3.2 without filter change.

TUNE-UP

240 Series

ENGINE IDENTIFICATION

Engine identification code is stamped on left side of engine block. Code numbers for the B21F engine are also found on the model plate on the front right-hand suspension strut mounting in the engine compartment (digits 4, 5 and 6 of code number).

Application	Code
Federal	453
California	459
Canada	452 & 455

MODEL IDENTIFICATION

VEHICLE IDENTIFICATION NUMBER

The vehicle identification plate is attached to the left windshield pillar and is visible from outside the vehicle. Number also appears on model plate on front right-hand suspension strut mounting and stamped on right-hand door pillar.

COMPRESSION PRESSURE

With engine at normal operating temperature, spark plugs removed, throttle valve wide open and cranking speed at 250-300 RPM, compression should be as follows:

Application	psi (kg/cm²)
All Models	128-156 (9-11)

VALVE TAPPET CLEARANCE

1) Valve clearance is adjusted with engine shut off and either warm or cold. Remove valve cover. Turn crankshaft center bolt until camshaft is in position for firing No. 1 cylinder. Both cam lobes should point up at equally large angles. Pulley timing mark should be at 0°.

2) Check valve clearance of No. 1 cylinder, using a feeler gauge between camshaft lobe and adjusting discs. Intake and exhaust valves have same clearances.

3) If clearances are incorrect adjust by changing thickness of discs, which are available in .05 mm increments from 3.30 to 4.50 mm.

4) After valves for No. 1 cylinder are properly adjusted, rotate crankshaft to firing position for No. 3, No. 4, and No. 2 cylinders in sequence and complete adjustment.

Valve Clearances

Application	Cold In. (mm)	Hot In. (mm)
Checking	.010-.018 (.25-.45)	.012-.020 (.30-.50)
Setting	.014-.016 (.35-.40)	.016-.018 (.40-.45)

VALVE ARRANGEMENT

E-I-E-I-E-I-E-I (front to rear).

SPARK PLUGS

Gap	.028-.032"	(.7-.8 mm)
Torque	25-29 ft. lbs.	(3.5-4.0 mkg)

Spark Plug Type

Application	Volvo No.	Bosch No.
All Models	27 35 45	W175T30

DISTRIBUTOR

All models are equipped with Breakerless Electronic Ignition System and no adjustments are required.

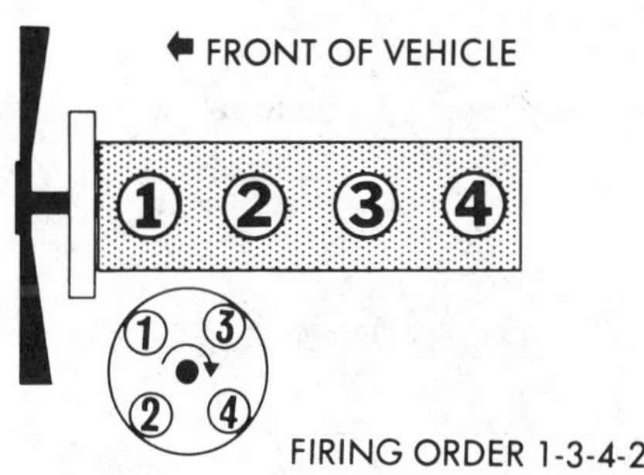

Fig. 1 Firing Order and Distributor Rotation

IGNITION TIMING

NOTE — *Preliminary to setting ignition timing, it is necessary to adjust throttle linkage and micro switch (on California vehicles) first. Procedures are given below.*

1) Install CO meter and timing light. Disconnect A.I.R. hose at air pump and plug hose. Disconnect and plug EGR vacuum hose at EGR valve.

2) Disconnect throttle link and cable at throttle control pulley. Loosen lock nut and screw out throttle shaft adjusting screw. Turn screw in until it just touches boss, then in one additional turn. Lock with lock nut. Check that throttle valve does not bind.

3) Ensure that throttle control link (from pulley to lever ball), can be attached to lever ball without changing the pulley position.

4) Attach throttle cable to pulley. Adjust cable sheath so that cable is snug but does not change pulley position. Depress throttle completely; pulley should touch the full throttle boss.

5) Adjust throttle cable to automatic transmission so that cable clip will travel 2" (51 mm) from idle position to full throttle position. At idle there should be .040" (1 mm) clearance between clip and adjusting sheath.

TUNE-UP (Cont.)

6) On California vehicles, micro switch must be adjusted: Connect test lamp to micro switch and turn ignition to "ON". Place a .060" (1.5 mm) feeler gauge between throttle screw and boss. Light should stay on. Insert a .080" (2 mm) feeler gauge; light should go out.

7) To adjust micro switch, place original feeler gauge between throttle screw and boss. Loosen lock nut and screw out micro switch adjusting screw (test lamp should go off). Turn in screw until a click is heard from the micro switch and test lamp comes on. Tighten lock nut, remove feeler gauge and lamp.

8) On all models, disconnect and plug vacuum hose at distributor. Use air adjusting screw to set idle speed to 700-800 RPM, then set ignition timing to specification. Reconnect distributor hose.

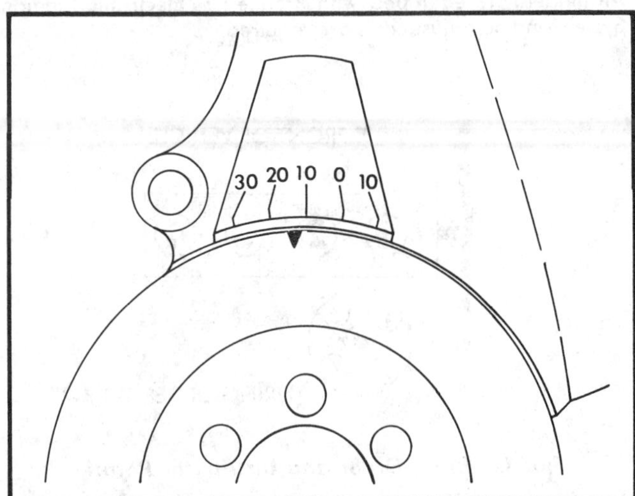

Fig. 2 240 Series Timing Mark Location

Ignition Timing Specifications

Application	RPM	Timing
All Models	700-800	12±2° BTDC

IDLE SPEED & MIXTURE

After making all preliminary adjustments and ignition timing adjustment as described above, turn out idle air adjusting screw until idle speed is to specifications. On California and High Altitude models disconnect oxygen sensor. Make final CO adjustment with engine still at idle. Turn clockwise to increase and counterclockwise to decrease CO% level. After adjustment, reconnect EGR valve, air pump and oxygen sensor, if so equipped.

Idle Speed (RPM) & CO Level (%)

Application	RPM	CO%
Federal		
Man. Trans.	900±50	1.2-1.8
Auto. Trans.	800±50	1.2-1.8
California	900±50	①1.2-1.8

① — When oxygen sensor is reconnected, CO% should drop below 1% level.

FUEL PUMP PRESSURE

Pressure .... 64-74 psi (4.5-5.2 kg/cm²)

EMISSION CONTROL SYSTEMS

See Mitchell Manuals' Emission Control Manual.

GENERAL SERVICING

DISTRIBUTOR

All models are equipped with Bosch Electronic Ignition System.

Other Data & Specifications — *See Tune-Up & Bosch Distributors in ELECTRICAL Section.*

IGNITION COIL

Starting Voltage	20,000 Volts
Maximum Voltage	25,000 Volts

FUEL SYSTEM

FUEL INJECTION

Federal models are equipped with Bosch Continuous Injection System (CIS). California models use oxygen sensor feedback system (Lambda).

Other Data & Specifications — *See Tune-Up and Bosch Continuous Injection System (CIS) and Lambda System in FUEL SYSTEMS Section.*

ELECTRICAL

BATTERY

12 Volt — Negative Ground.

Application	Amp. Hour Rating
All	60

NOTE — *On models equipped with electronic fuel injection it is important to disconnect battery cables before charging battery. Damage may result to the electronic components if battery is not disconnected.*

STARTER

Bosch .... Overrunning Clutch

Free Speed Voltage
All Models .... 11.5 at 5800-7800 RPM

Free Speed Amperage
All Models .... 30-50 at 5800-7800 RPM

Other Data & Specifications — *See Bosch Starters in ELECTRICAL Section.*

GENERAL SERVICING (Cont.)

ALTERNATOR

Application	Rated Amp. Output
All Models	55

Other Data & Specifications – *See Bosch Alternators & Regulators in ELECTRICAL Section.*

ALTERNATOR REGULATOR

All models are equipped with Bosch Alternator Regulators with an operating voltage of 13.9-14.8 volts at 4000 RPM.

Other Data & Specifications – *See Bosch Alternators & Regulators in ELECTRICAL Section.*

CAPACITIES

Application	Quantity
Crankcase (Includes Filter)	①4.0 qts.
Cooling System	②10.0 qts.
Transmissions	
Auto. Trans. (Type F)	7.0 qts.
Man. Trans. (Type F)	0.8 qts.
Man. Trans. with Overdrive (Type F)	2.4 qts.
Rear Axle (SAE 90)(API GL-5)	1.7 qts.
Fuel Tank	15.8 gals.

① – 3.5 qts. without filter.

② – Includes 1 qt. in expansion tank.

BELT ADJUSTMENT

Application	①Deflection
All Belts	$\frac{1}{4}$ - $\frac{3}{8}$" (6-10 mm)

① – Deflection is with thumb pressure applied midway on longest belt run.

FILTERS & CLEANERS

Filter or Cleaner	Service Interval (Miles)
Oil Filter	Replace every 7,500
Air Cleaner	Replace every 30,000
Fuel Filter	Replace every 30,000
Fuel Tank Filter	Clean every 15,000
EGR Valve	Replace every 30,000
Evap. Canister Filter	Replace every 45,000

TUNE-UP

260 Series

ENGINE IDENTIFICATION

The B27F Engine may be identified by the number stamped on left side of engine block just forward of distributor. Number also is found on model plate, located on front, right-hand suspension strut mounting in engine compartment (digits 4, 5 and 6).

Application	Code
Federal	653
California	651
Canada	652 and 655

MODEL IDENTIFICATION

VEHICLE IDENTIFICATION

Number is stamped on the right front door pillar. Also a chassis number plate is located on a metal tag attached to the left windshield pillar.

COMPRESSION PRESSURE

With engine at normal operating temperature, spark plugs removed, throttle valve wide open and cranking speed at 250-300 RPM, compression should be as follows:

Compression Pressure

Application	psi (kg/cm^2)
All Models	114-156 (8-11)

NOTE — *When checking compression pressure disconnect triggering contact cable on distributor to shut off fuel flow to injector while engine is being cranked.*

VALVE TAPPET CLEARANCE

1) Adjust valves with engine shut off. Valve clearance may be checked with engine hot or cold. Rotate crankshaft so that No. 1 cylinder is at TDC of ignition stroke (both rocker arms for No. 1 cylinder have clearance).

NOTE — *Crank pulley has two notches. When No. 1 cylinder is at TDC, upper notch will align with "0" notch on timing marker and lower crank pulley notch will be 150° counterclockwise from upper notch. (Second notch is TDC for No. 6 cylinder when aligned with "0" on timing marker.*

2) Adjust valves in sequence as follows:

Intake	Exhaust
Cyl. 1	Cyl. 1
Cyl. 2	Cyl. 3
Cyl. 4	Cyl. 6

3) Now, rotate crankshaft one complete turn, so that crank pulley notches line up as indicated in previous step. This will set No. 1 cylinder at TDC of exhaust stroke (rocker arms for No. 1 cylinder rock, indicating no clearance). Adjust valves in following sequence:

Intake	Exhaust
Cyl. 3	Cyl. 2
Cyl. 5	Cyl. 4
Cyl. 6	Cyl. 5

Valve Clearance Specifications

Application	Cold In. (mm)	Hot In. (mm)
Intake	.004-.006 (.10-.15)	.006-.008 (.15-.20)
Exhaust	.010-.012 (.25-.30)	.012-.014 (.30-.35)

VALVE ARRANGEMENT ①

Right Bank: E-I-E-I-E-I (front to rear).
Left Bank: I-E-I-E-I-E (front to rear).

① — Intake valves are inside the engine's "V"; exhaust valves are on outer sides of heads.

SPARK PLUGS

Gap	.028-.032" (.6-.7 mm)
Torque	13-14.5 ft. lbs. (1.8-2.0 mkg)

Spark Plug Type

Application	Champion No.	Bosch No.
All Models	BN9Y	WA200T30

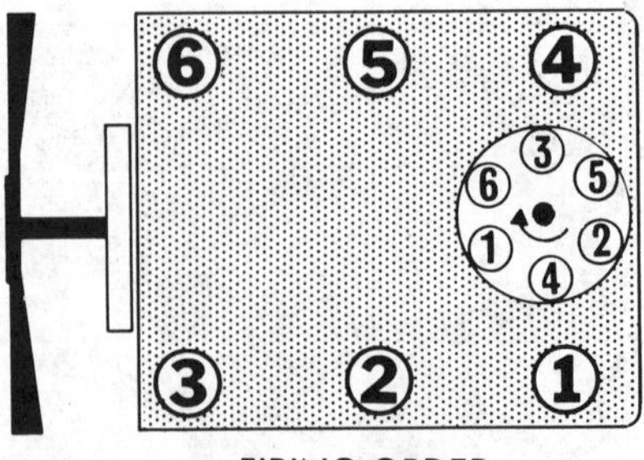

Fig. 1 Firing Order and Distributor Rotation

TUNE-UP (Cont.)

DISTRIBUTOR

All models are equipped with Breakerless Solid State Ignition System and no adjustments are required.

IGNITION TIMING

NOTE – *Preliminary to setting ignition timing, it is necessary to adjust throttle linkage, set balance screws, and micro switch (on California vehicles) first. Procedures are included below.*

1) Install CO meter and timing light. Disconnect A.I.R. hose at air pump and plug hose. Disconnect and plug EGR vacuum hose at EGR valve. Turn A/C off.

2) Disconnect throttle link and cable at throttle control pulley. Loosen lock nut and screw out throttle shaft adjusting screw. Now,turn screw in until it just touches boss, then in one additional turn. Lock with lock nut. Check that throttle valve does not bind.

3) Ensure that throttle control link (from pulley to lever ball) can be attached to lever ball without changing the pulley position.

4) Attach throttle cable to pulley. Adjust cable sheath so that cable is snug but does not change pulley position. Depress throttle completely; pulley should touch the full throttle boss.

5) Adjust throttle cable to automatic transmission so that cable clip will travel 2" (51 mm) from idle position to full throttle position. At idle there should be .040" (1 mm) clearance between clip and adjusting sheath.

6) Locate the set balance screws; there are three in a row just ahead of the carburetor. Turn in the front two screws until they bottom, then back each one out 4 turns.

7) On California vehicles, micro switch must be adjusted: Connect test lamp to micro switch and turn ignition to "ON". Place a .060" (1.5 mm) feeler gauge between throttle screw and boss. Light should stay on. Insert a .080" (2 mm) feeler gauge; light should go out.

8) To adjust micro switch, place original feeler gauge between throttle screw and boss. Loosen lock nut and screw out micro switch adjusting screw (test lamp should go off). Turn in screw until a click is heard from the micro switch and test lamp comes on. Tighten lock nut; remove feeler gauge and lamp.

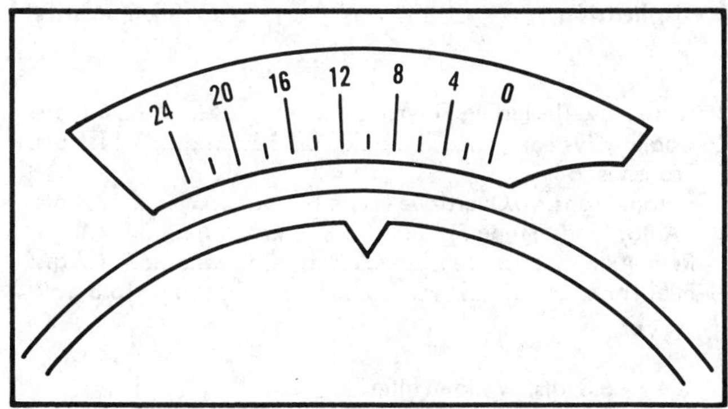

Fig. 2 Ignition Timing Mark Location

9) On all models, disconnect and plug vacuum hose at distributor. Use air adjusting screw (set balance screw No. 3) to set idle speed to 700-800 RPM. Now set timing to specification by adjusting position of distributor. Reconnect vacuum hose.

Ignition Timing Specifications

Application	RPM	Timing
All Models	700-800	10±2° BTDC

IDLE SPEED & MIXTURE

1) After making preliminary adjustments and ignition timing adjustment, make sure engine is at normal operating temperature.

2) Using air adjustment screw (third screw back), turn screw in until it bottoms. Engine speed should drop to 500-600 RPM. Turn air adjusting screw out until 900 RPM is reached.

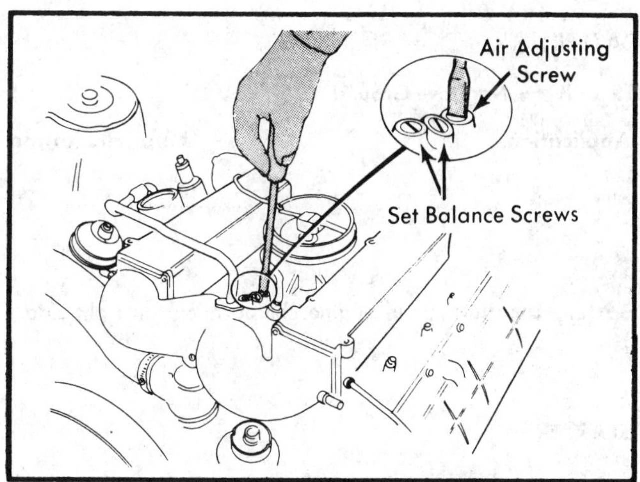

Fig. 3 Setting Idle Speed With Air Adjusting Screw

3) Using CO meter, adjusting screws on raised boss just behind air sensor (Allen wrench required after removing plug), and front two balance screws, adjust idle CO level to specifications. Turning counterclockwise reduces CO%; turning clockwise increases it.

Idle Speed (RPM) & CO Level (%)

Application	RPM	CO%
All Models	900±50	1.4-2.0

FUEL PUMP PRESSURE

Pressure .... 64-74 psi (4.5-5.2 kg/cm²)

EMISSION CONTROL SYSTEMS

See Mitchell Manuals' Emission Control Manual.

1977 Volvo V6 Tune-Up

GENERAL SERVICING

IGNITION

DISTRIBUTOR

All models are equipped with Bosch Breakerless Solid State Ignition System.

Other Data & Specifications – *See Tune-Up & Bosch Distributors in ELECTRICAL Section.*

FUEL SYSTEM

FUEL INJECTION

All models are equipped with Bosch CIS Fuel Injection.

Other Data & Specifications – *See Tune-Up and Bosch CIS Fuel Injection in FUEL SYSTEMS section.*

ELECTRICAL

BATTERY

12 Volt – Negative Ground.

Application	Amp. Hr. Rating
All Models	70

NOTE – *Battery must be disconnected before charging.*

Battery Location – In engine compartment on right side.

STARTER

Bosch .... Overrunning Clutch

Free Speed Voltage
All Models .... 11.5 at 5800-7800 RPM
Free Speed Amperage
All Models .... 30-50 at 5800-7800 RPM

Other Data & Specifications – *See Bosch Starters in ELECTRICAL Section.*

ALTERNATOR

All models are equipped with SEV Marchal alternators.

Application	Rated Amp. Output
All Models	55

Other Data & Specifications – *See SEV Marchal Alternators in ELECTRICAL section.*

ALTERNATOR REGULATOR

Some early models had SEV Marchal alternator regulators. Later models were equipped with Bosch, non-integral, non-adjustable regulators.

Operating Voltage .... 13.5-14.1 Volts

Other Data & Specifications – *See Bosch Alternator Regulators in ELECTRICAL section.*

FILTERS & CLEANERS

Filter or Cleaner	Service Interval (Miles)
Oil Filter	Replace every 7500
Air Cleaner	Replace every 30,000
Fuel Filter	Replace every 30,000
Fuel Tank Filter	Clean every 15,000
EGR Valve	Clean every 15,000
Evap. Canister Filter	Replace every 45,000

BELT ADJUSTMENT

Application	① Deflection
All Belts	5/16" (7.9 mm)

① – Deflection is measured with thumb pressure applied at midpoint of longest belt run.

CAPACITIES

Application	Quantity
Crankcase (Including Filter)	① 6.8 qts.
Cooling System	11.5 qts.
Transmissions	
Man. Trans. w/Overdrive (Type F)	2.4 qts.
Auto. Trans. (Type F)	7.0 qts.
Rear Axle	1.7 qts.
Fuel Tank	15.8 gals.

① – 6.3 qts. without filter.

Section 2
FUEL SYSTEMS

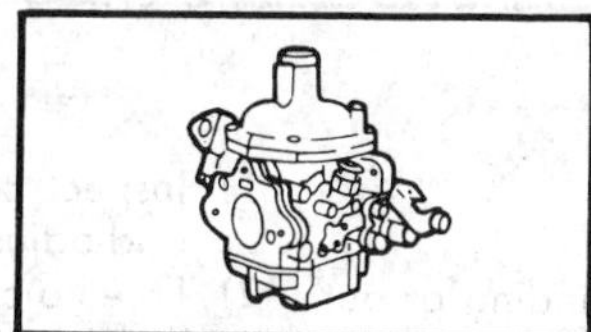

Contents

CARBURETORS

GASOLINE FUEL INJECTION

DIESEL FUEL INJECTION

ELECTRIC FUEL PUMPS

1977 Fuel Systems Trouble Shooting

CARBURETION TROUBLE SHOOTING

NOTE — *This is a general troubleshooting guide. Not all steps will apply to all carburetors. When using this guide, locate the symptom in column one that corresponds to your problem and determine the possible causes in column two. Match the number of the possible cause with the same number in column three, and you will have the correction required.*

CONDITION	POSSIBLE CAUSE	CORRECTION
COLD STARTING SYMPTOM		
▶ Engine cranks but will not start	1) Choke not closing (frozen)	1) Inspect choke plate and coil; free up and adjust
	2) Choke cable or linkage binding or out of adjustment	2) Free up and adjust
	3) Faulty cold start or thermo-start valve	3) Test, replace if needed
	4) No fuel to carburetor	4) Add fuel if needed, check for pinched or blocked fuel line or filter
	5) Faulty fuel pump	5) Test and/or replace
▶ Flooding	1) Faulty fuel inlet needle and/or seat	1) Replace
	2) Dirt holding needle off seat	2) Clean and reinstall
	3) Excessive fuel pump pressure	3) Test, replace if needed
	4) Improper fuel/float level (too high)	4) Adjust float level and drop
	5) Restricted (dirty) air cleaner	5) Clean and/or replace
	6) Ruptured, split internal carburetor seals or gaskets	6) Replace as needed
	7) Choke plate setting (vacuum kick) too narrow	7) Adjust, check linkage
	8) Wrong fast idle cam index	8) Check linkage, adjust fast idle cam setting
	9) Fast idle RPM too low	9) Adjust RPM
▶ Engine stalls after starting	1) Choke plate setting (vacuum kick) too wide	1) Adjust, check linkage
	2) Fast idle RPM too low	2) Adjust RPM
	3) Wrong fast idle cam index	3) Check choke control lever; set cam index correctly
	4) Vacuum leak	4) Locate and repair
	5) Low fuel pump output	5) Test and/or replace
	6) Fuel/float level too low	6) Adjust float level and float drop
	7) Faulty intake manifold gasket	7) Replace gasket
	8) Incorrect fuel/air mixture setting	8) Adjust fuel/air mixture
	9) Faulty idle fuel shut off valve	9) Replace shut off valve
	10) Idler jet blocked	10) Clean
	11) Damaged idle adjust screw	11) Replace screw
▶ Engine starts; idles rough and erratic	1) Flooding in carburetor	1) *See Flooding in this table*
	2) Vacuum leak	2) Locate and correct
	3) Incorrect idle RPM	3) Adjust fast idle RPM
	4) Damaged idle adjust screw	4) Replace screw
	5) Clogged slow jet	5) Clean
	6) Incorrect fast idle cam index setting	6) Adjust fast idle cam setting
	7) Carburetor seals leaking	7) Locate and replace
	8) Carburetors not synchronized; dual carburetor models only	8) Synchronize carburetors
	9) Incorrect fuel/float level	9) Adjust float drop and float setting
	10) Idling air and/or bypass holes blocked	10) Clean
	11) Faulty anti-dieseling solenoid valve	11) Replace solenoid
	12) Worn throttle shafts	12) Replace
	13) Stuck anti-stall dashpot	13) Replace dashpot

CARBURETION TROUBLE SHOOTING (Cont.)

CONDITION	POSSIBLE CAUSE	CORRECTION
HOT STARTING SYMPTOM		
▸ Engine cranks but will not start	1) Engine flooded, fuel level too high	1) Adjust float drop and setting; inspect needle and seat for proper seating; check for dirt
	2) Fuel vapors in carburetor bowl	2) Inspect bowl vent operation and correct
	3) Fuel line hot, touching engine block or exhaust	3) Inspect and reroute fuel line
COLD ENGINE DRIVEABILITY SYMPTOM		
▸ Engine stalls when put in gear	1) Incorrect choke vacuum kick setting	1) Inspect and correct
	2) Fast idle RPM too low	2) Adjust fast idle RPM
	3) Incorrect fast idle cam setting	3) Correct cam positioning
	4) Improper choke adjustment	4) Adjust choke
▸ Hesitation, stalling during acceleration	1) Defective choke control switch	1) Test, replace if needed
	2) Incorrect choke vacuum kick setting	2) Adjust vacuum kick
Backfire	3) Low fuel/float level	3) Adjust float drop and setting; check fuel level
Stumble	4) Faulty accelerator pump or blocked pump discharge	4) Inspect, adjust pump stroke, plunger; test fuel discharge quantity; check pump spray direction
	5) Secondary throttle not closed, wrong lockout adjustment	5) Adjust secondary throttles
	6) Bypass holes and ducts blocked	6) Clean preheater assembly
	7) Incorrect intake air preheater setting	7) Set to proper season
	8) Incorrect carburetor synchronization; on dual carburetor models	8) Synchronize carburetors
	9) Main and/or air corrector jets blocked	9) Inspect and clean
	10) Faulty power valve	10) Replace
	11) Plugged heat crossover system	11) Clean and test heat crossover valve; clean passages
WARM ENGINE DRIVEABILITY SYMPTOM		
▸ Low power, Surging high speed operation	1) Main jets clogged	1) Clean
	2) Fuel filter dirty (restricted)	2) Replace filter
	3) Pinched, blocked fuel line	3) Inspect and repair
	4) Air cleaner dirty (restricted)	4) Replace air cleaner
	5) Faulty power valve	5) Adjust or replace
	6) Throttle linkage out of adjustment; not opening fully	6) Inspect and adjust linkage
	7) Low fuel pump output	7) Replace after testing
	8) Improper fuel level	8) Adjust float/fuel level
	9) Carburetor seals leaking	9) Replace seals, gaskets
▸ Carburetors cannot be synchronized	1) Weak return springs	1) Replace springs
	2) Linkage binding, needs adjusting	2) Inspect, clean and adjust
	3) Blocked idler jets	3) Clean jets
(Dual Carburetor models)	4) Faulty mixture control screw(s)	4) Replace screw(s)
	5) Faulty carburetor seals	5) Replace seals as needed
	6) Vacuum leak(s); Check for leak at brake unit	6) Locate and correct leak
	7) Carburetors not tightened to intake manifold properly	7) Evenly tighten carburetor screws; check torque

1977 Fuel Systems Trouble Shooting

CARBURETION TROUBLE SHOOTING (Cont.)

CONDITION	POSSIBLE CAUSE	CORRECTION
▸ High fuel consumption	1) Fuel system leak	1) Locate and repair leak
	2) Wrong size jets	2) Install correct jets
	3) Faulty fuel inlet needle and/or seat	3) Replace needle and seat
	4) Fuel mixture setting incorrect	4) Adjust idle RPM and mixture
	5) Dirty air cleaner	5) Clean or replace
	6) Excessive accelerator pump discharge	6) Test and adjust fuel discharge quantity
	7) Intake air preheater not ON or OFF according to season	7) Temperature above 50°F (10°C), preheater should be OFF
	8) Enrichment system does not switch off	8) Free up vacuum plunger
	9) Choke valve not opening all the way	9) Adjust choke valve
	10) Secondary throttle opens too early	10) Inspect secondary throttle linkage, adjust or repair as needed

GASOLINE FUEL INJECTION TROUBLE SHOOTING

CONDITION	POSSIBLE CAUSE	CORRECTION
COLD START SYMPTOM		
▸ Engine cranks, will not start	1) Fuel pump not working	1) Check fuel pump and double fuse relay, replace as necessary
	2) "Cold" control pressure incorrect (CIS)	2) Replace warm-up regulator if pressure not to specification
	3) Auxiliary air valve does not open	3) Replace valve
	4) Cold start valve does not operate	4) Check electrical power to valve, replace valve if necessary
	5) Cold start valve leaking	5) Replace valve
	6) Sensor plate stop set incorrectly (CIS)	6) Adjust to specifications
	7) Sensor plate and/or plunger sticking	7) Free up or replace as needed
	8) Vacuum leak	8) Repair vacuum leaks
	9) Fuel system leak	9) Repair fuel leaks
	10) Faulty Thermo Time switch	10) Replace switch
	11) Distributor triggering contacts (AFC & EFI)	11) Repair or replace as needed
	12) Temperature sensors 1 & 2 (AFC & EFI)	12) Replace as necessary
▸ Engine hard starting	1) "Cold" control pressure incorrect (CIS)	1) Replace warm-up regulator
	2) Auxiliary air valve does not open	2) Replace valve
	3) Cold start valve does not open	3) Check for electrical power to valve, replace valve if necessary
	4) Cold start valve leaking	4) Replace cold start valve
	5) Sensor plate stop set incorrectly (CIS)	5) Adjust sensor plate stop to specifications
	6) Sensor plate and/or plunger stuck (CIS)	6) Free up or replace as necessary
	7) Vacuum leak(s)	7) Repair vacuum leak(s)
	8) Fuel leak(s)	8) Repair fuel leak(s)
	9) Thermo Time switch does not close	9) Replace Thermo Time switch

GASOLINE FUEL INJECTION TROUBLE SHOOTING (Cont.)

CONDITION	POSSIBLE CAUSE	CORRECTION
HOT STARTING SYMPTOM		
▸ Engine cranks, will not start	1) Electric fuel pump not operating	1) Check fuel pump and relay fuse, replace as needed
	2) "Warm" control pressure incorrect (CIS)	2) Replace warm-up regulator
	3) Sensor plate stop adjustment incorrect (CIS)	3) Adjust sensor plate stop
	4) Sensor plate and/or plunger stuck (CIS)	4) Free up or replace
	5) Vacuum leak(s)	5) Repair vacuum leak(s)
	6) Fuel system leak(s)	6) Repair fuel leak(s)
	7) Injectors leaking	7) Clean or replace as necessary
	8) Idle mixture out of adjustment	8) Adjust mixture to specifications
▸ Engine Hard Starting (Long Cranking Time)	1) "Warm" control pressure incorrect (CIS)	1) Replace warm-up regulator
	2) Auxiliary air valve does not close	2) Replace valve
	3) Sensor plate stop adjustment incorrect (CIS)	3) Adjust to specification
	4) Sensor plate and/or plunger stuck (CIS)	4) Free up or replace as necessary
	5) Vacuum leak(s)	5) Repair vacuum leak(s)
	6) Fuel system leaks	6) Repair fuel leak(s)
	7) Injectors leaking	7) Clean or replace as necessary
	8) Idle mixture out of adjustment	8) Adjust mixture to specifications
COLD ENGINE DRIVEABILITY SYMPTOM		
▸ Rough Idle During Warm-Up	1) "Cold" control pressure incorrect (CIS)	1) Replace warm-up regulator
	2) Auxiliary air valve does not close	2) Replace valve
	3) Auxiliary air valve does not open	3) Replace valve
	4) Cold start valve leaking	4) Clean or replace valve
	5) Vacuum leak	5) Repair vacuum leaks
	6) Fuel system leak(s)	6) Repair fuel leaks
	7) Injectors leaking	7) Clean or replace as necessary

1977 Fuel Systems Trouble Shooting

GASOLINE FUEL INJECTION TROUBLE SHOOTING (Cont.)

CONDITION	POSSIBLE CAUSE	CORRECTION
HOT ENGINE DRIVEABILITY SYMPTOM		
► Rough idle with warm engine	1) "Warm" control pressure incorrect (CIS) 2) Auxiliary air valve does not close 3) Faulty cold start valve 4) Sensor plate and/or plunger stuck (CIS) 5) Vacuum leak(s) 6) Fuel system leak(s) 7) Injectors leaking 8) Idle mixture out of adjustment	1) Replace warm-up regulator 2) Replace air valve 3) Clean or replace as necessary 4) Free up or replace as necessary 5) Repair vacuum leak(s) 6) Repair fuel leak(s) 7) Clean or replace injectors 8) Adjust mixture to specifications
► CO level too high at idle	1) "Warm" control pressure incorrect (CIS) 2) Cold start valve leaking 3) Sensor plate and/or plunger stuck (CIS) 4) Fuel system leaking 5) Idle mixture out of adjustment	1) Replace warm-up regulator 2) Replace valve 3) Free up or replace as necessary 4) Repair fuel leak(s) 5) Adjust mixture to specifications
► CO level too low at idle	1) "Warm" control pressure incorrect (CIS) 2) Vacuum leak 3) Idle mixture out of adjustment	1) Replace warm-up regulator 2) Repair vacuum leak(s) 3) Adjust mixture to specifications
► Poor engine performance	1) "Warm" control pressure incorrect (CIS) 2) Cold start valve leaking 3) Sensor plate and/or plunger stuck (CIS) 4) Idle mixture out of adjustment 5) Throttle valve does not open completely	1) Replace warm-up regulator 2) Clean or replace valve 3) Free up or replace as necessary 4) Adjust mixture to specifications 5) Check and adjust as necessary
► Excessive fuel consumption	1) "Warm" control pressure incorrect (CIS) 2) Cold start valve leaks 3) Fuel system leaking 4) Idle mixture out of adjustment	1) Replace warm-up regulator 2) Clean or replace as necessary 3) Repair fuel leak(s) 4) Adjust mixture to specifications
► Engine misfire at high speed	1) Loose electrical contact at fuel pump 2) Primary pressure too low or too high 3) Fuel system leaking	1) Check and repair as necessary 2) Check pressure and adjust if not within specifications 3) Repair fuel leak(s)
► Engine "Diesels"	1) Sensor plate and/or plunger stuck (CIS) 2) Injectors leaking 3) Faulty cold start valve	1) Free up or replace as necessary 2) Clean or replace as necessary 3) Clean or replace as necessary

GASOLINE FUEL INJECTION TROUBLE SHOOTING (Cont.)

CONDITION	POSSIBLE CAUSE	CORRECTION
▸ Idle Speed Too High and Cannot Be Adjusted Lower	1) Auxiliary air valve does not close	1) Replace valve
▸ Engine Backfires into Intake Manifold	1) "Warm" control pressure incorrect (CIS) 2) Vacuum leak(s) 3) Idle mixture out of adjustment	1) Replace warm-up regulator 2) Repair vacuum leaks 3) Adjust mixture to specifications
▸ Engine Backfires into Exhaust Manifold	1) "Warm" control pressure incorrect (CIS) 2) Cold start valve leaks 3) Fuel system leaking 4) Idle mixture out of adjustment	1) Replace warm-up regulator 2) Clean or replace as necessary 3) Repair fuel leaks 4) Adjust mixture to specifications

DIESEL FUEL INJECTION TROUBLE SHOOTING

CONDITION	POSSIBLE CAUSE	CORRECTION
HARD STARTING SYMPTOMS ▸ Engine cranks but will not start:	1) Incorrect fuel or no fuel 2) Glow plug not working properly 3) Air in fuel system 4) Faulty injector(s) 5) Injection pump faulty	1) Fill or replace fuel as necessary 2) Repair or replace as necessary 3) Bleed fuel system 4) Repair or replace 5) Repair as necessary
▸ Engine starts but will not run:	1) Air in fuel system 2) Modulator valve out of adjustment 3) Fuel lines, filter or tank plugged 4) Idle speed adjustment incorrect	1) Bleed fuel system 2) Adjust modulator valve 3) Clear fuel system 4) Adjust as necessary
LOW SPEED DRIVEABILITY SYMPTOM ▸ Engine runs rough:	1) Air or dirt in fuel system 2) Fuel system leak 3) Fuel flow uneven 4) Incorrect fuel 5) Governor or timing incorrect	1) Clean or Bleed fuel system 2) Repair fuel leaks 3) Repair as necessary 4) Change to correct fuel 5) Adjust to specifications
▸ Engine idle speed too high:	1) Idle speed set incorrectly 2) Modulator valve jammed 3) Governor improperly adjusted 4) Vacuum leaks in manifold	1) Adjust to specifications 2) Repair as necessary 3) Adjust to specifications 4) Repair vacuum leaks
▸ Poor acceleration:	1) Incorrect fuel 2) Timing device stuck in idle position 3) Fuel pump not operating correctly	1) Change to correct fuel 2) Repair as necessary 3) Repair or replace
▸ Engine knocks:	1) Incorrect fuel 2) Air in fuel system 3) Incorrect injection timing 4) Dirt in pump or injectors	1) Change to correct fuel 2) Bleed fuel system 3) Adjust timing 4) Clean and replace filter

1977 Fuel Systems Trouble Shooting

DIESEL FUEL INJECTION TROUBLE SHOOTING (Cont.)

CONDITION	POSSIBLE CAUSE	CORRECTION
HIGH SPEED DRIVEABILITY SYMPTOM ► Engine smokes:	1) Incorrect fuel 2) Air leak in fuel system 3) Injection pump misadjusted	1) Change to correct fuel 2) Repair air leak 3) Adjust to specifications
► Engine has power loss:	1) Throttle valve not fully open 2) Clogged air filter 3) Badly worn pump plungers 4) Low fuel pressure 5) Timing device stuck in idling position 6) Control rod stuck 7) Incorrect fuel	1) Adjust as necessary 2) Replace filter 3) Replace injection pump 4) Repair or replace fuel pump or injector pump 5) Repair 6) Repair 7) Change to correct fuel
► Engine exceeds maximum permissible speed	1) Maximum speed stop misadjusted 2) Faulty governor 3) Control rod sticks open 4) Vacuum leaks	1) Adjust to specifications 2) Repair or replace 3) Repair or replace 4) Repair vacuum leaks
► Engine will not stop:	1) Stop cable broken or misadjusted 2) Idle speed misadjusted 3) Governor malfunction	1) Replace or Repair 2) Adjust to specifications 3) Repair or replace

ELECTRIC FUEL PUMP TROUBLE SHOOTING

NOTE — *This is a general trouble shooting guide. Not all steps will apply to all fuel pumps. Most electrical fuel pumps are sealed units and must be replaced if found defective.*

CAUTION — *Be sure to relieve fuel pressure on systems which maintain fuel pressure at all times. Do not allow smoking, open flames or sparks in area while performing work on any fuel system components. Fuel vapors may be present and danger of fire or explosion exists. Disconnect battery while working on fuel system.*

CONDITION	POSSIBLE CAUSE	CORRECTION
► Pump motor not operating; no fuel output	1) Check wiring to pump, check for blown pump fuse 2) Check for damaged pump body	1) Repair wiring, ensure proper electrical current to pump 2) Replace if damaged
► Pump operating; low fuel output	1) Check for restricted fuel line, filter or accumulator 2) Check fuel tank venting (may cause vacuum in tank if blocked) 3) Check for air leak on inlet side of pump	1) Repair or replace 2) Repair tank venting system. Test pump output with gas cap removed to check venting. 3) Repair air leak

ELECTRIC FUEL PUMP TROUBLE SHOOTING (Cont.)

CONDITION	POSSIBLE CAUSE	CORRECTION
► Pump operating; no fuel output	1) Check fuel supply 2) Check for pinched or blocked fuel line from pump to carburetor 3) Check for blocked fuel filter 4) Check fuel cut-off valve 5) Check contact points in pump	1) Add fuel 2) Locate and repair 3) Replace 4) If blocked, disconnect outlet hose at valve and apply low air pressure to valve to reseat check ball. Recheck pump output. 5) Clean or replace points
► Pump noisy	1) Check for air leak on inlet (suction) side of pump 2) Pump loose, vibrating against other parts 3) Pump lines (metal) touching body parts 4) Check foam rubber insulation at pump mounting	1) Locate and repair leak 2) Tighten pump evenly 3) Reroute lines for clearance 4) Position insulation correctly or replace
► Excessive pump pressure	1) Defective pressure relief valve	1) Replace pump assembly

AISAN 2-BARREL — TOYOTA 2F ENGINE

Land Cruiser

DESCRIPTION

Carburetor is a 2-barrel, downdraft type and is equipped with a vacuum operated choke opener. Choke design improves cold engine operation. A secondary slow port helps fuel mixing at start of secondary valve opening. Improvement of operation is noticed during low speed load. A carburetor throttle positioner prevents throttle from completely closing during deceleration. A throttle stop solenoid is also used to prevent dieseling during engine shut down.

CARBURETOR IDENTIFICATION

Application	Carburetor No.
Federal	21100-61022
California	21100-61063
	21100-61073
High Altitude	21100-61090
Canada	21100-61100

ADJUSTMENT

HOT (SLOW) IDLE RPM

See appropriate article in TUNE-UP Section.

IDLE MIXTURE

See appropriate article in TUNE-UP Section.

COLD (FAST) IDLE RPM

See appropriate article in TUNE-UP Section.

NOTE — *For performing the outlined adjustment procedures, kit No. 09240 00011 is recommended.*

FAST IDLE (OFF VEHICLE)

1) With choke valve fully closed, check clearance between throttle bore and primary throttle valve.

2) Adjust fast idle by turning fast idle adjusting screw until a clearance of .051" (1.3 mm) is obtained between bore and throttle blade. See *Fig. 1.*

Fig. 1 Making Fast Idle Measurement and Adjustment

THROTTLE POSITIONER ADJUSTMENT

1) Remove carburetor. Turn carburetor upside-down.

2) Place throttle positioner adjustment screw against tab on throttle lever.

3) Check clearance between throttle bore and primary valve. Turn throttle positioner adjustment screw until correct clearance is obtained. *See Fig. 2.*

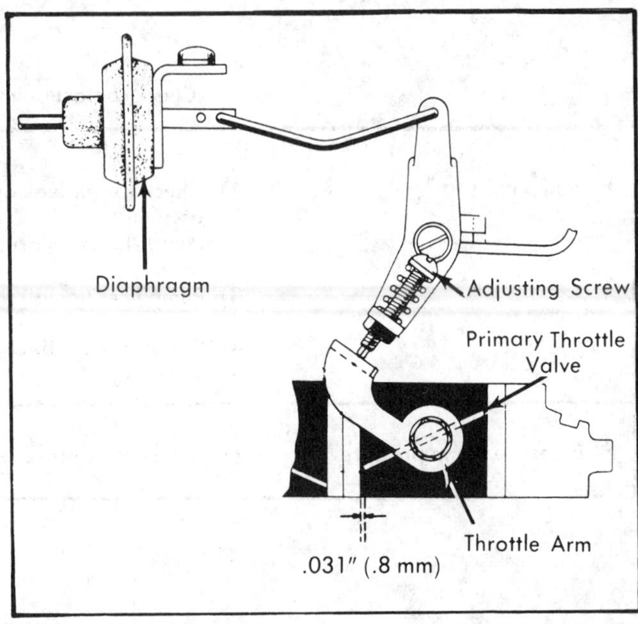

Fig. 2 Aisan 2-Barrel Throttle Positioner Adjustment

FLOAT LEVEL ADJUSTMENT

Turn air horn assembly upside-down. Measure clearance between upper surface of float and gasket surface of air horn. Bend center float tab until float level is correct. *See Fig 3.*

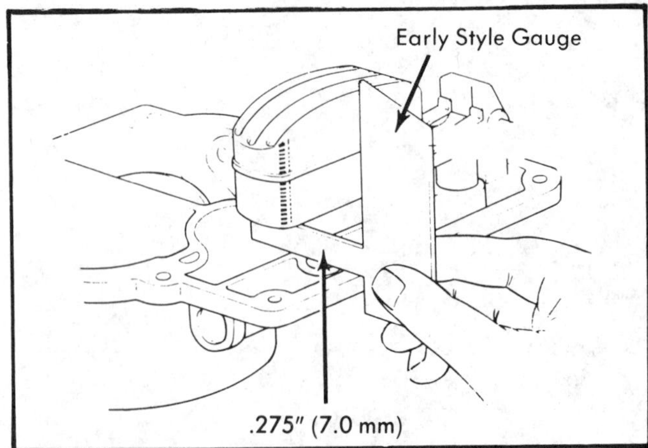

Fig. 3 Measuring Carburetor Float Level

FLOAT DROP ADJUSTMENT

1) Turn air horn assembly upside-down. Measure clearance between needle push pin and float tab. Clearance should be as shown in *Fig. 4.*

AISAN 2-BARREL – TOYOTA 2F ENGINE (Cont.)

2) Bend both outside float tabs until correct clearance is obtained.

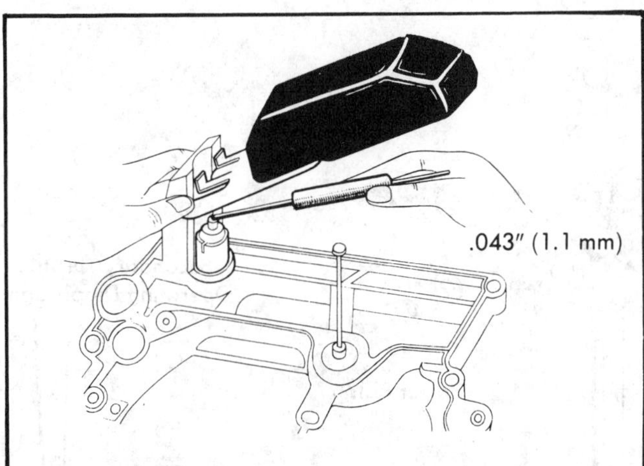

Fig. 4 Measuring Carburetor Float Drop with Gauge

PRIMARY & SECONDARY THROTTLE VALVE ADJUSTMENT

1) Open primary throttle valve. Then, open secondary throttle valve. Make sure valves are perpendicular to flange surface when fully opened.

2) Bend throttle lever stopper(s) until proper opening is obtained.

ACCELERATOR PUMP ADJUSTMENT

1) Accelerator pump stroke should be .374" (9.5 mm).

2) Bend accelerator pump link to obtain right setting.

NOTE – *Measurement should be taken at boot end of accelerator pump lever.*

VACUUM BREAK ADJUSTMENT

1) Push choke vacuum break diaphragm rod to open choke valve. Measure choke valve angle.

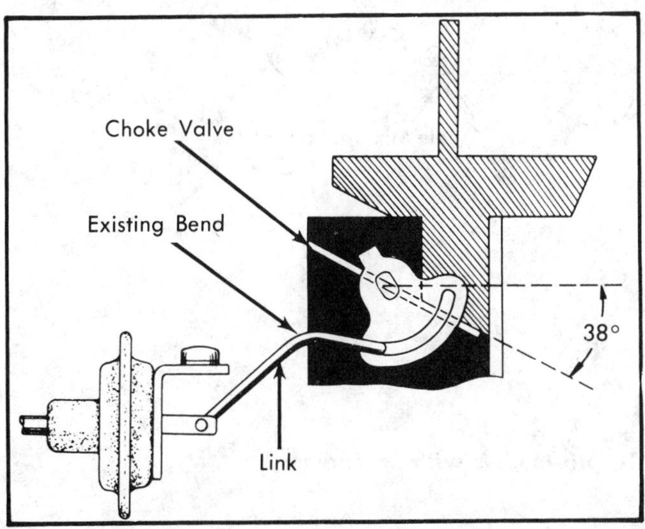

Fig. 5 Vacuum Break Adjustment

2) Bend choke-to-vacuum break diaphragm rod at existing bend. Release diaphragm rod and check operation. Movement of choke valve should be easy.

SECONDARY THROTTLE OPENING ANGLE (KICK-UP)

1) Remove carburetor. Turn carburetor upside-down. Open primary throttle valve all the way.

2) Check angle between secondary throttle bore wall and secondary throttle valve with angle gauge. *(See Fig. 6).*

3) Bend secondary throttle lever to obtain right clearance.

4) Clearance is correct when opening angle is 28° (from bore) for Federal models or 25° (from bore for California models).

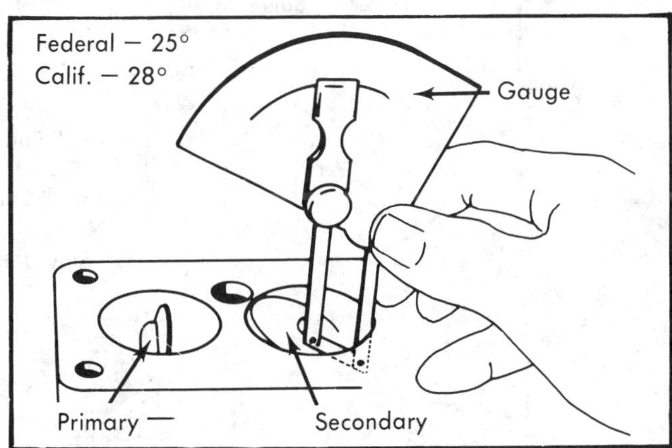

Fig. 6 Adjusting Secondary Throttle Opening Angle (Kick-Up)

OVERHAUL

1) Remove pump arm, pump connecting link, choke connecting link, fast idle connecting link, and throttle positioner assembly. Remove screws securing air horn to main body and carefully lift off air horn assembly. Disassemble air horn by removing float and needle assembly, fuel shut-off solenoid, power piston assembly, accelerator pump piston assembly and fuel inlet fittings.

2) From main body assembly, remove the following parts: both venturis, pump outlet check ball and spring, pump dampening spring, inlet check ball, slow metering jet, AAP assembly and check ball, power valve, main jet and secondary operating diaphragm.

3) Remove the throttle body from main body. Remove only those parts from throttle body which are necessary to proper cleaning and inspection.

CLEANING & INSPECTION

Clean all parts in suitable carburetor solvent and blow dry with compressed air. Inspect all parts for wear or damage and replace necessary components.

AISAN 2-BARREL – TOYOTA 2F ENGINE (Cont.)

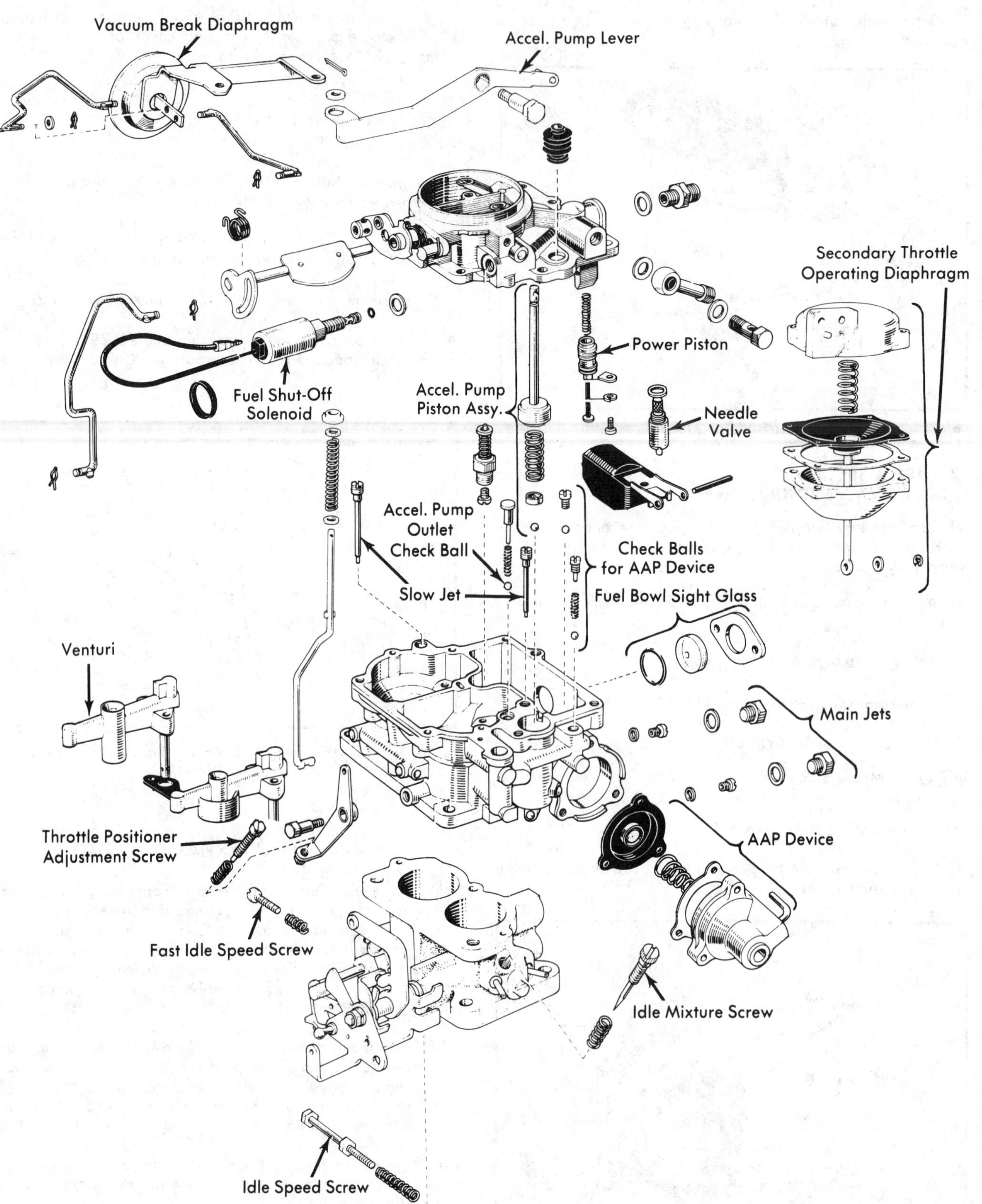

Fig. 7 Carburetor Assembly for Toyota Models with 2F Engines

AISAN 2-BARREL – TOYOTA 2F ENGINE (Cont.)

REASSEMBLY

Put carburetor together in reverse of disassembly procedure. Make note of the following cautions:

1) Peen over choke valve retaining screws.

2) Make sure power piston operates smoothly after installing retaining screw.

3) Make sure that needle valve, spring and plunger are properly installed in correct order. Float must be correctly adjusted.

4) Make sure that longer (larger) jet is installed on secondary side. Make sure brass colored main jet is installed in primary side.

5) When installing AAP check balls, smaller ball should be placed in pump inlet (outside of fuel bowl) and larger should be placed inside fuel bowl in pump outlet. AAP spring should be placed with its small end away from diaphram or toward the cover.

6) When installing air horn to main body, take care not to damage pump plunger leather.

CARBURETOR ADJUSTMENT SPECIFICATIONS

Application	Idle Speed (Engine RPM)		Float Level Setting In. (mm)	Float Drop In. (mm)	Fast Idle Opening In. (mm)	Choke Pulling Angle	Accel. Pump Stroke In. (mm)	Throttle Positioner In. (mm)
	Hot	Fast						
Land Cruiser	600-700	1600-2000	.275" (7.0)	.043" (1.1)	.051" (1.3)	38°	.374" (9.5)	.031" (.8)

1977 Aisan Carburetors

AISAN 2-BARREL – TOYOTA 2T-C ENGINE

Corolla

DESCRIPTION

Carburetor is of 2-barrel, downdraft design and is equipped with automatic choke which is heated by an electrically operated bimetal heating coil. A piston type accelerator pump is incorporated into the primary barrel and an auxiliary accelerator pump system is added in 1977 to aid in cold engine acceleration. Unit also has a throttle positioner and is equipped with a diaphragm which opens secondaries at high speed and full throttle operation. In addition to systems already mentioned, this carburetor now has a mixture control system (M/T only), EGR vacuum port below throttle plate, choke opener and high altitude compensating device.
For additional information on emission related systems, see TOYOTA SYSTEMS & SERVICE PROCEDURES in Exhaust Emission Systems Section.

Application	Carburetor Part No. Man. Trans.	Carburetor Part No. Auto. Trans.
Corolla		
2T-C Engine		
Federal	21100-26510	21100-26520
Calif.	21100-26393	21100-26393
High Alt.	21100-26600	21100-26600

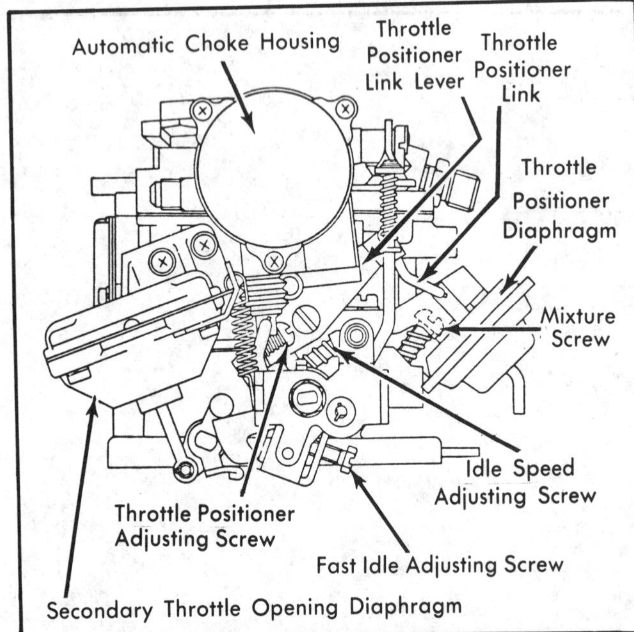

Fig. 1 Assembled View of Aisan 2-Barrel Carburetor

ADJUSTMENT

HOT (SLOW) IDLE RPM

See appropriate article in TUNE-UP Section.

IDLE MIXTURE

See appropriate article in TUNE-UP Section.

COLD (FAST) IDLE RPM

See appropriate article in TUNE-UP Section.

FLOAT LEVEL

NOTE – *When top and bottom lever positions are properly adjusted, float will maintain specified fuel level (glass level mark) when engine is running.*

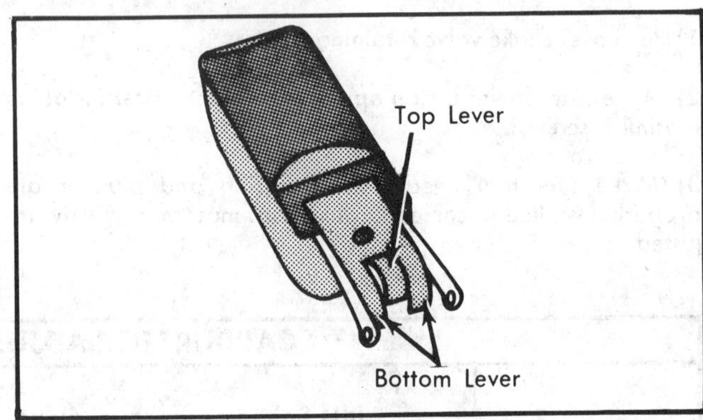

Fig. 2 Carburetor Float with Float Lever Points Called Out

Hold air horn upside-down. Allow float to hang by its own weight. Measure gap between float lip and air horn gasket surface. Bend float lip (top lever) until gap is correct. *See Fig. 3.*

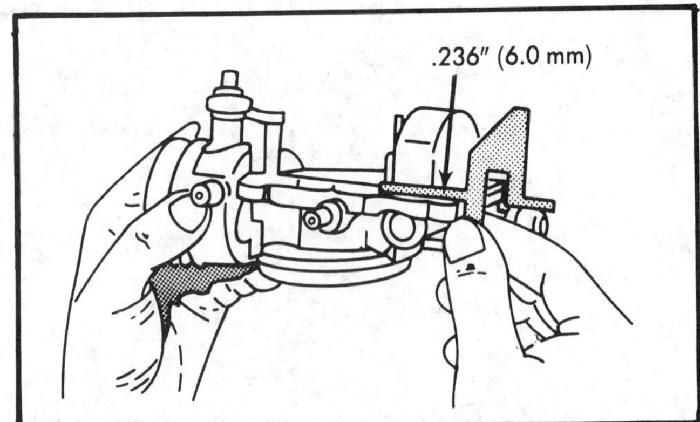

Fig. 3 Float Level Measurement Points and Gauge

FLOAT DROP

Lift up float. Measure gap between needle valve and float lip. Gap should be .047" (1.2 mm). Bend float tang (bottom lever) until gap is correct. *See Fig. 4.*

Fig. 4 Measuring Carburetor Float Drop for Adjustment

AISAN 2-BARREL — TOYOTA 2T-C ENGINE (Cont.)

THROTTLE VALVE ADJUSTMENT

1) Open primary throttle valve. Then, open secondary throttle valve. Make sure valves are perpendicular to flange surface when fully opened.

2) Bend throttle lever stopper(s) until proper opening is obtained.

NOTE — *After adjusting, check links to see that they move lightly and do not bind.*

CHOKE UNLOADER ADJUSTMENT

Insert angle gauge. Adjust angle of choke valve so it will be 47° from fully closed position when primary throttle valve is fully open. Bend fast idle cam follower or choke shaft lip to obtain correct angle. See *Fig. 5*.

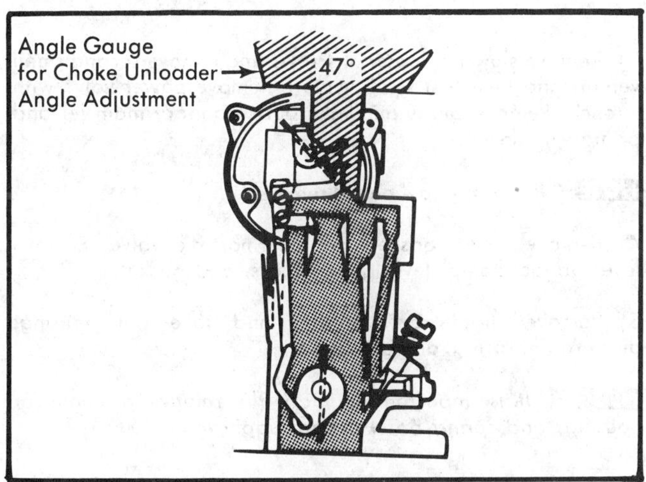

***Fig. 5** Choke Unloader Adjustment with Gauge Inserted*

SECONDARY THROTTLE OPENING ANGLE (KICK-UP)

Bend secondary throttle lever to obtain .008" (.2 mm) clearance between secondary throttle valve and body when primary throttle valve opening is between 57° (from bore) and full open.

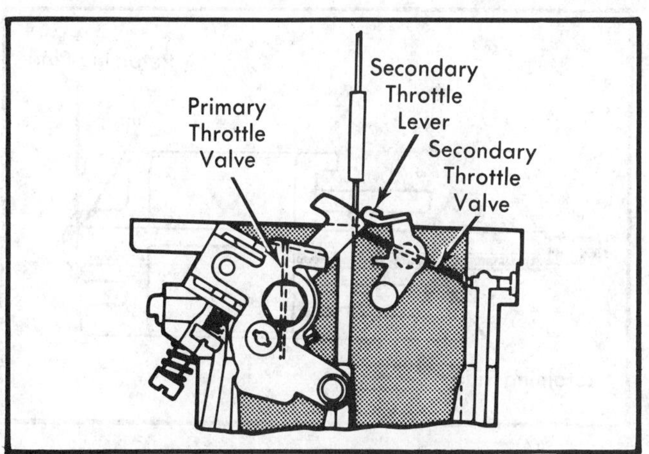

***Fig. 6** Carburetor Kick-Up Adjustment*

THROTTLE POSITIONER

1) Hold choke valve open, open and release throttle lever. This will trap throttle lever on fast idle position.

2) Check that adjusting screw "A" *(Fig. 7)* is within .08" (.2mm) of outside edge of stop.

3) Bend throttle positioner link. Depress diaphragm (by hand) and check that clearance "B" *(Fig. 7)* is .02" (.5 mm).

4) Run engine. Disconnect vacuum hose to throttle positioner diaphragm. Turn throttle positioner adjusting screw until idle is 1400 RPM. Check operation by reconnecting diaphragm and noting if engine returns to normal idle RPM.

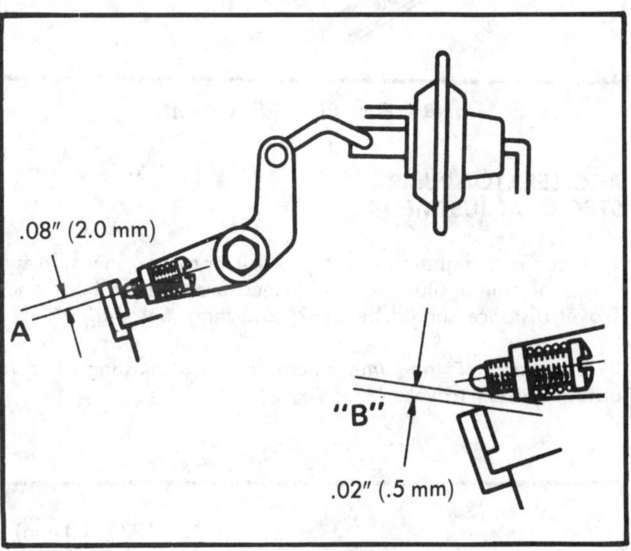

***Fig. 7** Showing Clearance for Throttle Positioner Adjustment*

AUTOMATIC CHOKE ADJUSTMENT

1) With choke valve fully opened, turn coil housing counterclockwise. Check if choke valve closes. Set coil housing scale to center line of thermostat case.

NOTE — *Choke valve closes fully at atmospheric temperature of 77°F (25°C).*

2) Turn coil housing and adjust engine starting mixture to conform with vehicle operating conditions. When mixture for starting is too rich, turn clockwise, when too lean, turn counterclockwise. One graduation of scale on thermostat case is equal to 9°F (5°C) change.

FAST IDLE ADJUSTMENT (OFF CAR)

Close choke valve. Check clearance between throttle valve and throttle bore with a wire gauge. This clearance should be as shown in *Fig. 8*. Turn fast idle screw until correct clearance is obtained.

AISAN 2-BARREL – TOYOTA 2T-C ENGINE (Cont.)

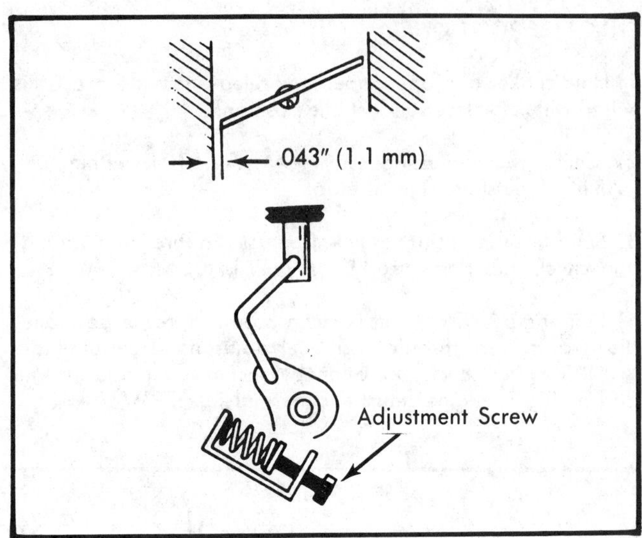

Fig. 8 Fast Idle Adjustment

ACCELERATOR PUMP STROKE ADJUSTMENT

1) Place a straightedge on top of air horn and measure full travel of pump plunger. Make measurement at boot end. Travel distance should be .197" (5.0 mm). See *Fig. 9*.

2) Bend accelerator pump actuating rod at existing bend to obtain correct travel.

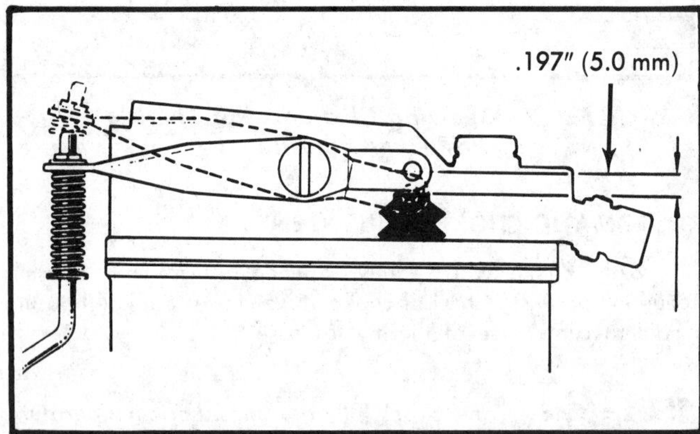

Fig. 9 Carburetor Accelerator Pump Stroke Adjustment

OVERHAUL

DISASSEMBLY

Air Horn – 1) Loosen horn arm set screw, and remove pump lever together with connecting rod. Remove link and loosen six bolts. Remove air horn from body of carburetor.

2) Remove float lever pin and float. Remove needle valve, spring, push pin, and seat. Remove power piston, spring, and pump plunger. Remove plug, gasket and strainer.

Automatic Choke – 1) Remove coil housing, gasket, and housing plate. Remove cam float and sliding rod.

NOTE – *Perform step 2 only if required.*

2) File off peened part of valve set screw and remove choke valve. Remove connector set screw and take out choke shaft and vacuum piston.

3) Remove thermostat case.

Body Parts – 1) Remove gasket, stopper, discharge weight, and ball. Remove back spring and diaphragm from diaphragm lever.

2) Remove 4 flange set screws and separate flange from body. Remove check ball retainer and steel ball.

3) Remove slow jet, loosen 4 screws and remove second small venturi and then first small venturi. Remove power valve with wrench. Remove plugs and take out secondary main jet and primary main jet.

NOTE – *Perform step 4 only if required.*

4) Remove cover, gasket, and thermostatic valve. Remove level gauge clamp, level gauge glass, and gasket.

5) Remove diaphragm housing and take out housing, diaphragm, spring, and gasket.

NOTE – *It is important to mark the relative positions of housing, and spring bracket and diaphragm.*

Flange Parts – 1) Remove idle adjustment screw.

NOTE – *Perform steps 2 and 3 only when required.*

2) File off peened part of valve set screws and take off the throttle valves. Remove secondary throttle shaft and remove throttle lever.

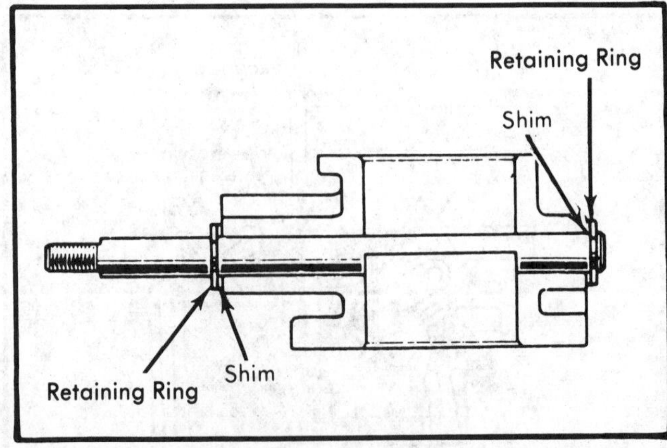

Fig. 10 Primary Throttle Valve Adjustment Points

AISAN 2-BARREL — TOYOTA 2T-C ENGINE (Cont.)

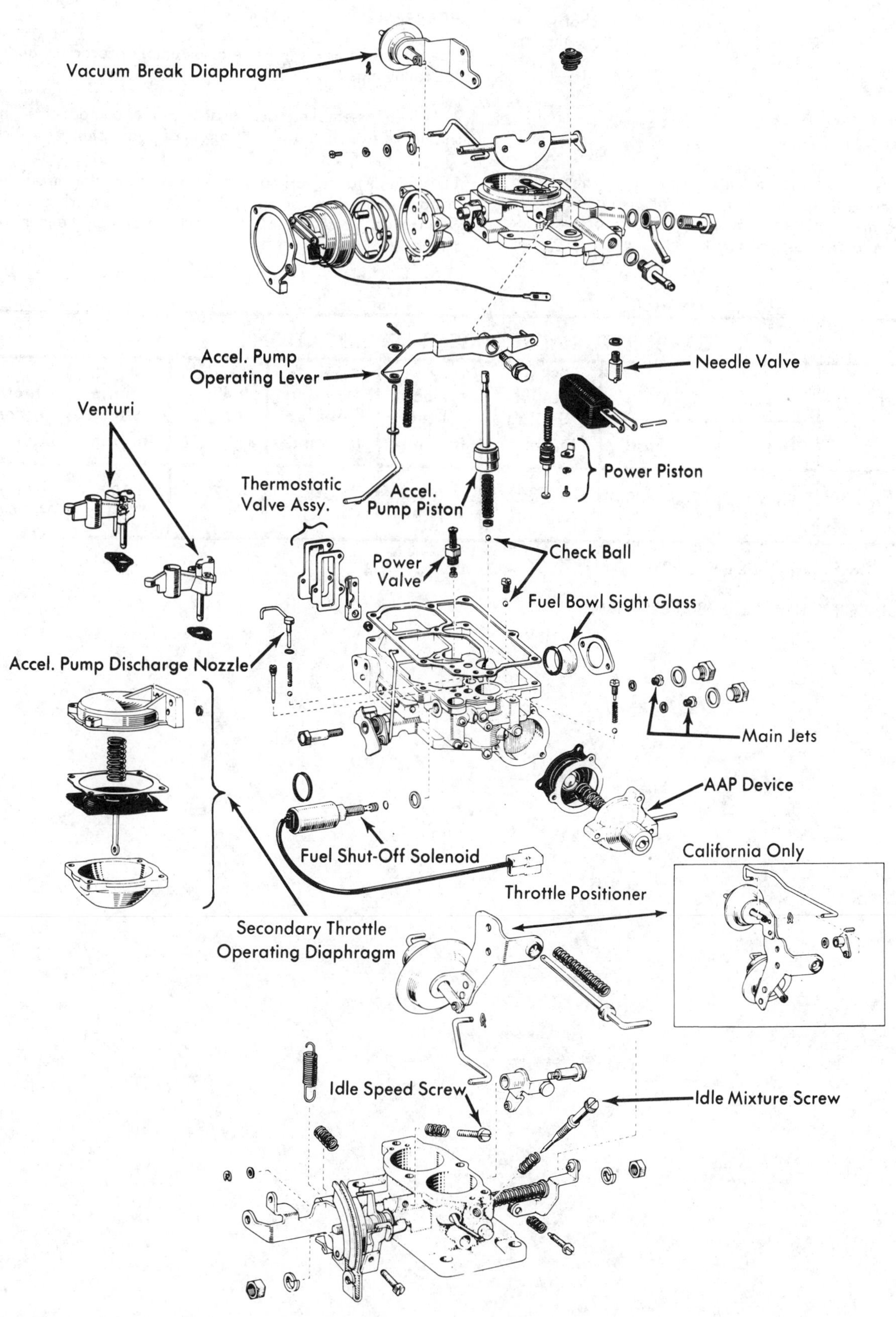

Fig. 11 Carburetor Assembly for Toyota 2T-C Engine

AISAN 2-BARREL – TOYOTA 2T-C ENGINE (Cont.)

3) Remove idle adjusting lever with throttle shaft arm attached. Remove retainer ring and take out primary throttle shaft.

CLEANING & INSPECTION

Clean all parts in suitable solvent (carburetor cleaner) and blow dry. Do not attempt to clean jets or other passages with wire or other metal objects. Inspect all parts for wear or damage and replace necessary parts.

REASSEMBLY

Use all new gaskets, reverse disassembly procedure and note the following:

1) When assembling accelerator pump components, install smaller of two steel balls at bottom of pump plunger orifice.

2) When installing primary throttle valve, center throttle shaft in bore using shims on shaft. *See Fig. 11*. Centering is correct when shaft notch is adjusted to bore center. Peen new set screw.

CARBURETOR ADJUSTMENT SPECIFICATIONS

Application	Idle Speed (Engine RPM)		Float Level Setting In. (mm)	Float Drop In. (mm)	Fast Idle Opening Angle In. (mm)	Choke Pulling Angle	Accel. Pump Stroke In. (mm)	Throttle Positioner In. (mm)
	Hot	Fast						
Corolla	930①	2200-2600②	.236 (6.0)	.047 (1.2)	.043 (1.1)	47°	.197 (5)	16° M/T 15° A/T

① – Federal; Calif. & High Alt. is 910 RPM

② – Federal; Calif. & High Alt. is 2800-3200 RPM

AISAN 2-BARREL – TOYOTA 3K-C ENGINES

Corolla

DESCRIPTION

Two barrel downdraft type carburetor, similarly constructed as two single barrel carburetors, but built into one unit. Both primary and secondary systems are provided with double venturi. Each system consists of an air horn, main nozzle, and throttle valve, with one set forming the primary side and the other the secondary side. Primary system is comprised of low speed, high speed, power, acceleration, and choke systems, and is able to supply air-fuel mixture for normal operation. With primary throttle valve fully open, secondary system also operates to supply air-fuel mixture, along with the primary system. The throttle valves of both primary and secondary sides are operated by linkage and are inter-locked, thus making it possible for both throttle valves to be fully opened at the same time.

Auxiliary Slow System – On deceleration, manifold vacuum pressure passes through a sensing line and displaces a diaphragm, opening a valve, and allowing maximum air-fuel mixture into intake manifold.

ADJUSTMENT

HOT (SLOW) IDLE RPM

See appropriate article in TUNE-UP Section.

IDLE MIXTURE

See appropriate article in TUNE-UP Section.

COLD (FAST) IDLE RPM

See appropriate article in TUNE-UP Section.

NOTE – *To conform with International Organization of Standardization (ISO) standards, the pitch (distance between threads) of many bolts, nuts and screws has been changed. DO NOT install other than ISO standard parts to avoid stripping or breaking carburetor parts.*

FLOAT LEVEL ADJUSTMENT

With air horn inverted and using suitable measuring gauge, check clearance between end of float and air horn surface. If gap is not as shown in illustration, adjust by bending center float tab.

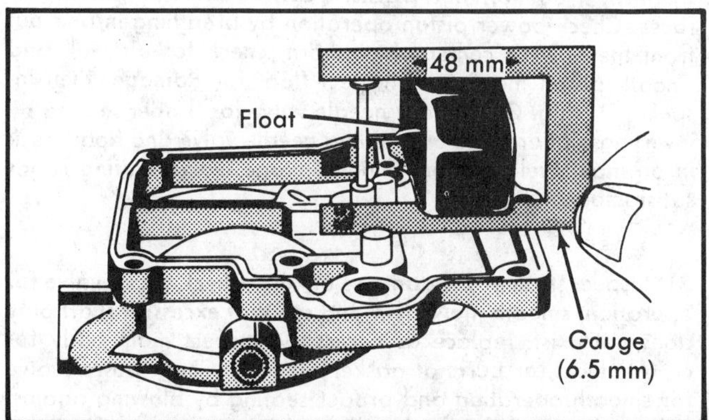

Fig. 1 Measuring Float Level

FLOAT DROP ADJUSTMENT

Using suitable gauge, measure distance from bottom of air horn surface to bottom of float. If distance is not as shown in illustration, adjust by bending outside float tabs.

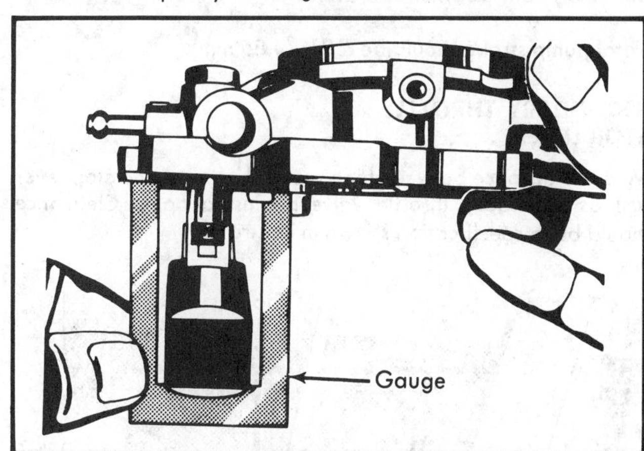

Fig. 2 Measuring Float Drop

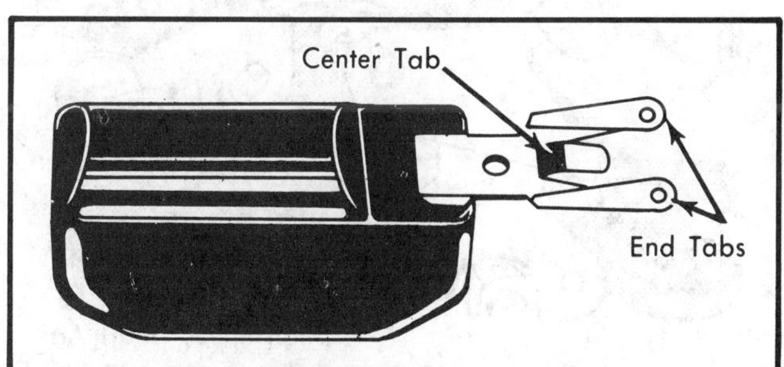

Fig. 3 Float Tab Location

PRIMARY & SECONDARY THROTTLE VALVES

When primary throttle valve is fully opened, secondary throttle valve should also be completely opened. If adjustment is necessary, bend at throttle shaft link. **NOTE** – *Secondary throttle valve should begin to open when primary throttle valve is 30° opened.*

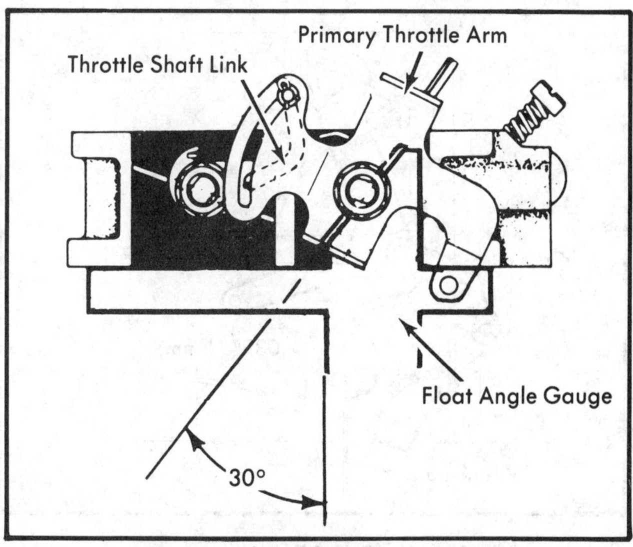

Fig. 4 Throttle Valve Opening

AISAN 2-BARREL – TOYOTA 3K-C ENGINES (Cont.)

ACCELERATOR PUMP

Upper (left) hole in accelerator pump connecting rod link is the setting for normal weather operation. Other hole is used for extremely cold weather operation.

Total pump stroke should be .191" (4.85 mm).

SECONDARY THROTTLE STOP LEVER

Measure distance between high speed shaft arm and stop lever just as secondary throttle valve begins to open. Clearance should be to specification shown in illustration.

Fig. 5 Stop Lever Measurement

FAST IDLE ADJUSTMENT (OFF CAR)

Using suitable wire gauge, measure, and if necessary, adjust clearance between throttle valve end and body with choke fully closed. Adjust fast idle screw to obtain clearance shown in illustration.

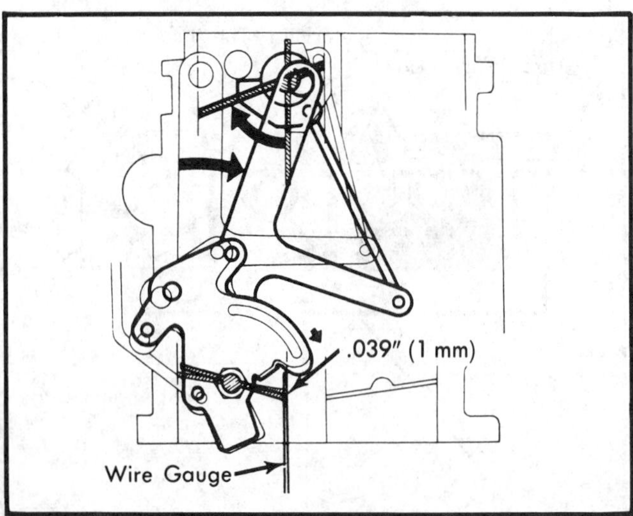

Fig. 6 Fast Idle Adjustment

OVERHAUL

DISASSEMBLY

1) Disconnect fast idle connector and pump lever connecting link. Remove pump lever retaining screw, pump lever, and disconnect pump connecting link.

2) Unscrew Air Suction System valve fuel line banjo fitting bolt and (2) washers. Remove fuel line. Loosen AS diaphragm housing from its base but do not unscrew completely. Remove (2) AS valve mounting screws and remove valve. Remove adaptor and gasket. Remove (4) air horn retaining screws and carefully lift off air horn assembly straight up.

3) Remove pump plunger and dampening spring. Invert carburetor and remove pump discharge weight and check ball, using extreme caution not to lose check ball. Remove flange retaining screws, separate flange from main body.

4) Remove float lever pin, float, needle valve with push pin and spring, then remove seat with gasket. Remove power piston stopper retaining screw, and remove power piston and spring. Loosen and remove main passage plug, take out strainer.

5) Remove small primary venturi retaining screws, then remove venturi with gasket. Also remove small secondary venturi. From bottom of pump cylinder, remove check ball retainer, invert carburetor and remove check ball. Carefully unscrew and remove slow jet, being careful not to damage threads. Remove primary and secondary main jets along with gaskets.

6) Remove drain plug with gasket, then remove power valve, using a suitable tool. Remove power jet from power valve. Remove idle adjusting screw along with spring.

CLEANING & INSPECTION

1) Wash all parts in clean gasoline and blow all fuel passages dry with compressed air. Clean exterior parts with gasoline and a soft wire brush, remove carbon deposits from around throttle valve. Never use wire for cleaning jets.

2) Inspect air horn for cracks, nicks, or burrs at gasket surfaces. Check power piston operation by breathing in and out from the hole at center of air horn, check for air leak and smooth piston movement. Inspect float for damage, then inspect "O" ring. Check float needle valve for proper seating by inverting air horn and assembling needle valve and float. Suck in on main fuel passage; if any linkage, valve seating is not satisfactory.

3) Inspect strainer for damage or rust. Check choke valve for operation, smooth movement and see that excessive shaft play does not exist, replace as necessary. Inspect main body for cracks, nicks, or burrs at gasket surfaces. Check power valve for smooth operation and proper seating by blowing against valve. Inspect jets for damaged threads or passages. Check for pump plunger wear, then check spring for rust or weakness.

AISAN 2-BARREL – TOYOTA 3K-C ENGINES (Cont.)

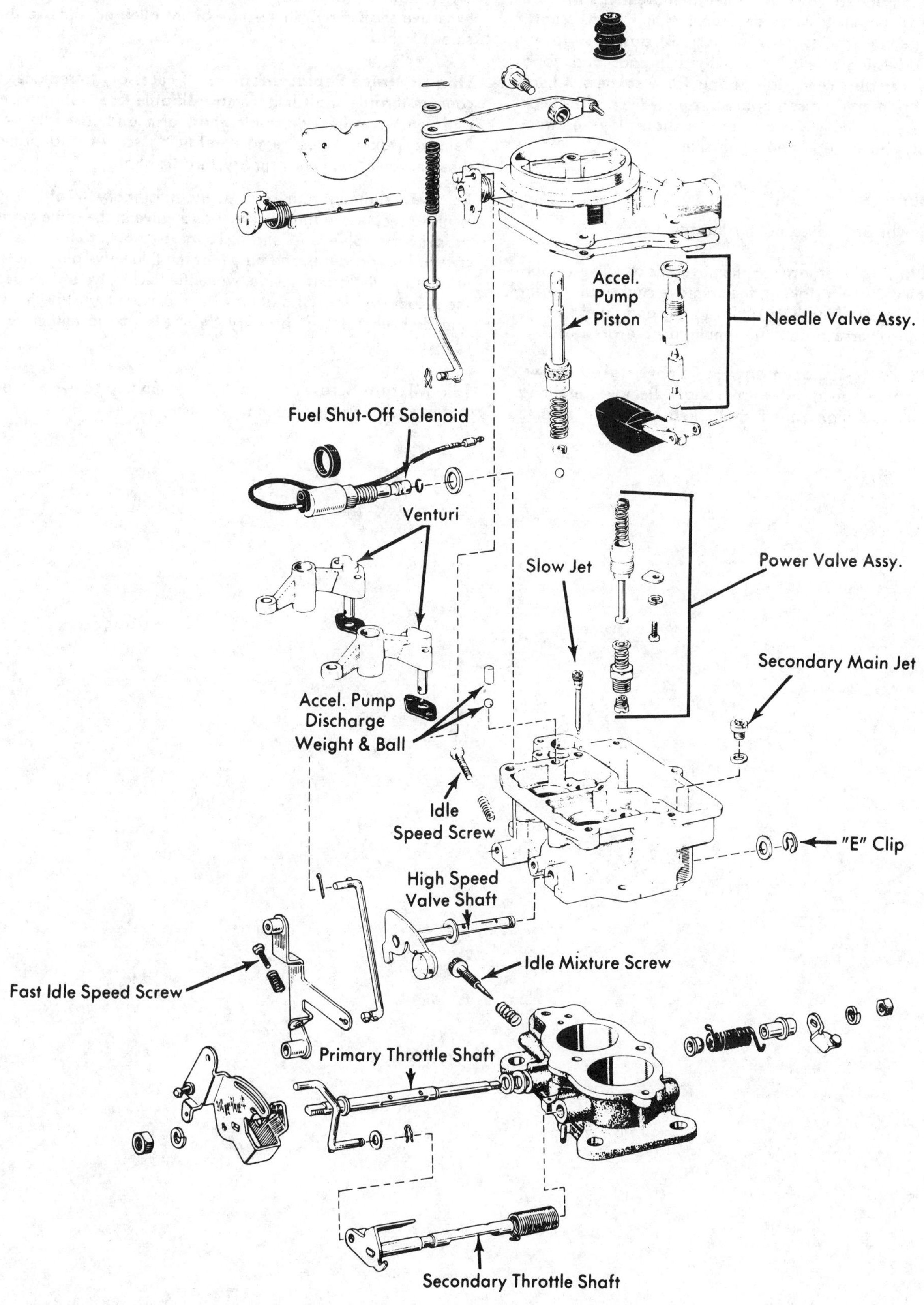

Fig. 7 Aisan 2-Barrel – 3K-C Engine (Typical)

AISAN 2-BARREL – TOYOTA 3K-C ENGINES (Cont.)

4) Check high speed valve for smooth movement; be sure shaft play is minimal. If necessary, replace high speed shaft. Inspect flange for cracks, nicks, or burrs at gasket surfaces. Check idle adjusting screw for damaged threads and good seating surface, also check idle spring for weakness. Check operation of primary and secondary throttle valves, also check for excessive shaft play. Primary throttle shaft play (in direction of shaft) can be adjusted using shims.

REASSEMBLY

Reverse removal procedure noting the following:

Choke Valve Replacement – Remove choke valve retaining screws by removing staking, then remove choke valve from shaft; remove shaft along with return spring and relief spring. Reassemble in reverse order using multipurpose grease.

High Speed Shaft Replacement – Remove staked screws, then remove high speed valve from shaft. Remove retaining ring and pull out high speed shaft. Reassemble in reverse order, noting that it may be necessary to use shims to remove excessive shaft play. Shims may be installed on either or both sides of shaft.

Throttle Valve Replacement – If necessary to replace, disconnect throttle shaft link, remove throttle lever retaining nut, and remove primary throttle shaft arm and fast idle lever. Remove staking, then remove retaining screws and primary throttle valve, remove primary throttle shaft.

Remove retaining ring and pull out primary throttle shaft. Remove secondary throttle shaft and valve in the same manner as primary valve and shaft. To reassemble, follow the disassembly procedures and note that the thin valve plate must be installed to the primary side, while the thick valve plate goes to the secondary side. Also, it may be necessary to install shims on one or both sides of primary throttle shaft, to eliminate excessive shaft play.

Idle Mixture Screw – Lightly seat mixture screw and back out two turns as a preliminary adjustment.

AISAN 2-BARREL – TOYOTA 20R ENGINE

Celica
Corona
Pickup

DESCRIPTION

Carburetor is a two barrel downdraft design with primary and secondary venturis. Automatic choke contains a bimetal spring heated by exhaust gases for air/fuel mixture control during engine warm-up. Secondary throttle valve is actuated by a vacuum diaphragm unit with a kick-up (open) lever. Secondary valve begins to open when primary throttle valve opening angle exceeds 55°. During deceleration, a throttle positioner slightly opens primary throttle valve to maintain proper combustion of air/fuel mixture. A thermostatic valve is used to provide air flow under secondary throttle valve when ambient air temperature is high. System helps maintain proper combustion.

ADJUSTMENT

HOT (SLOW) IDLE RPM

See appropriate article in TUNE-UP Section.

IDLE MIXTURE

See appropriate article in TUNE-UP Section.

COLD (FAST) IDLE RPM

See appropriate article in TUNE-UP Section.

NOTE – *It is recommended that Toyota carburetor adjustment kit 09240-00011 be used to make the following adjustments.*

ACCELERATOR PUMP STROKE ADJUSTMENT

Measure distance from top of accelerator pump operating lever to top of air horn. Make measurement with throttle valves in idle position. Make measurement again, but with throttle valves in wide open position. Difference between the two measurements is total stroke travel. Travel should be .180" (4.5 mm).

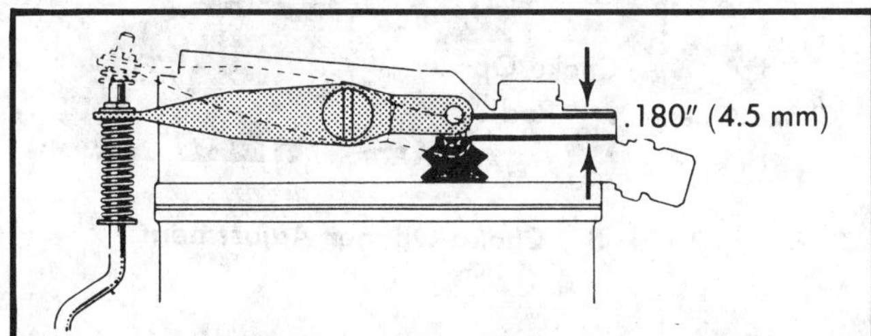

Fig. 1 Accelerator Pump Adjustment and Measurement

FLOAT LEVEL ADJUSTMENT

1) Allow float to hang down by its own weight. Check clearance between float tip and air horn. *See Fig. 2.*

2) Adjust by bending float lip (A).

NOTE – *Measurement must be made without gasket on air horn.*

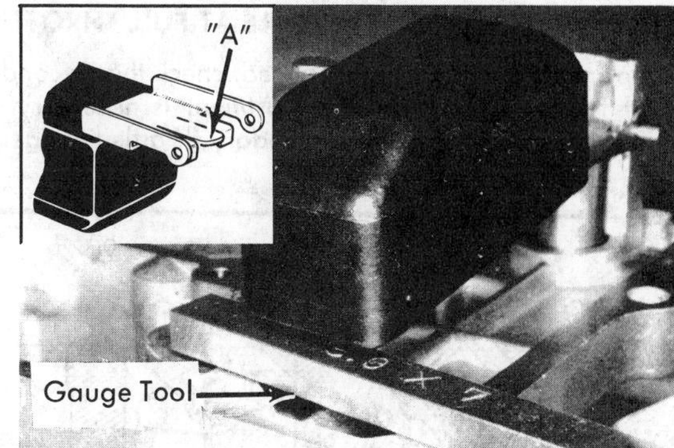

Fig. 2 Adjustment Points for Float Level

FLOAT DROP ADJUSTMENT

1) Lift up float. Check clearance between needle valve plunger and float lip.

2) Clearance should be .04" (1 mm). Adjust by bending float tab (B).

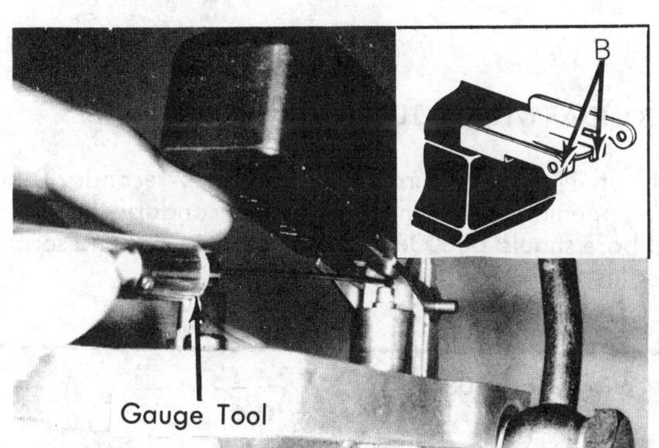

Fig. 3 Float Drop Adjustment Using Angle Gauge

UNLOADER ADJUSTMENT

1) Open primary throttle valve. Check choke valve angle with 50° gauge.

2) If angle is not correct, bend fast idle cam follower lip.

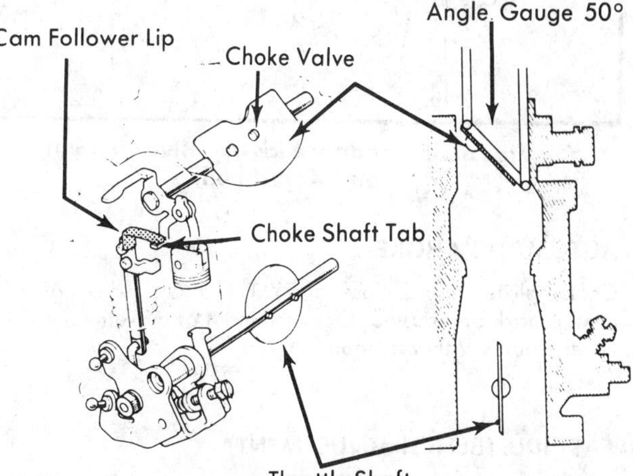

Fig. 4 Choke Unloader Adjustment Points and Measurements

AISAN 2-BARREL – TOYOTA 20R ENGINE (Cont.)

PRIMARY-TO-SECONDARY ANGLE AT FULL THROTTLE

When primary throttle is fully opened, check that secondary is also at full open position. If adjustment is necessary, bend linkage between primary and secondary throttle linkage.

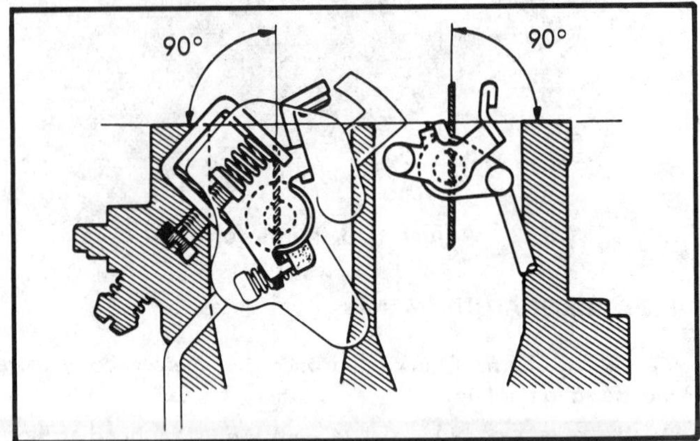

Fig. 5 Adjusting Secondary Touch Angle

SECONDARY THROTTLE KICK-UP

Fully open primary throttle valve. Check secondary throttle valve opening. Clearance between secondary throttle valve and bore should be .008" (.2 mm). See *Fig. 6*. Bend secondary throttle lever.

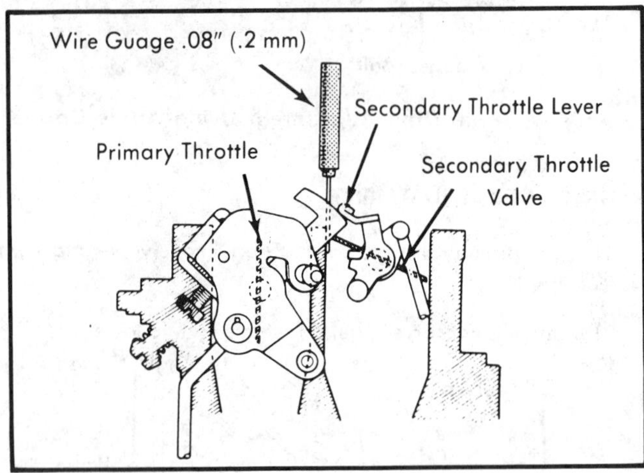

Fig. 6 Secondary Kick-Up Measurement and Adjustment

AUTOMATIC CHOKE

Choke plate should close at 77°F (25°C). Index cover with center mark on housing. One increment of movement on choke cover equals 9°F variation.

FAST IDLE (BENCH ADJUSTMENT)

With choke valve fully open, check clearance between primary throttle valve and throttle bore. If clearance is not as illustrated, adjust by turning fast idle screw.

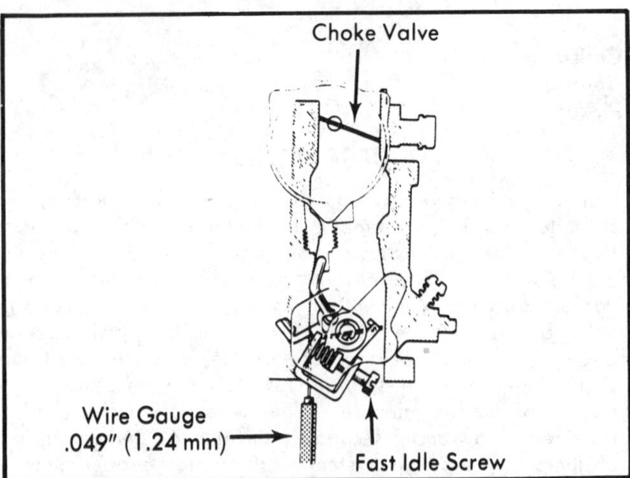

Fig. 7 Bench Adjustment of Carburetor Fast Idle

VACUUM BREAK ADJUSTMENT

Push (depress) choke breaker rod to open choke valve. Check choke valve angle (35° from bore). Bend relief lever until correct measurement is obtained.

CHOKE OPENER ADJUSTMENT

Push in choke opener rod. Check choke valve angle (50° from bore). Bend choke opener link until correct measurement is obtained. See *Fig. 8*.

Fig. 8 Choke Opener Adjustment

OVERHAUL

DISASSEMBLY

1) Remove the following parts from air horn assembly:
   - Pump arm with connecting rod
   - Connecting links and 7 air horn screws
   - Choke opener, lift off air horn
   - Float pivot pin and float
   - Needle valve assembly
   - Pump plunger and power piston

AISAN 2-BARREL – TOYOTA 20R ENGINE (Cont.)

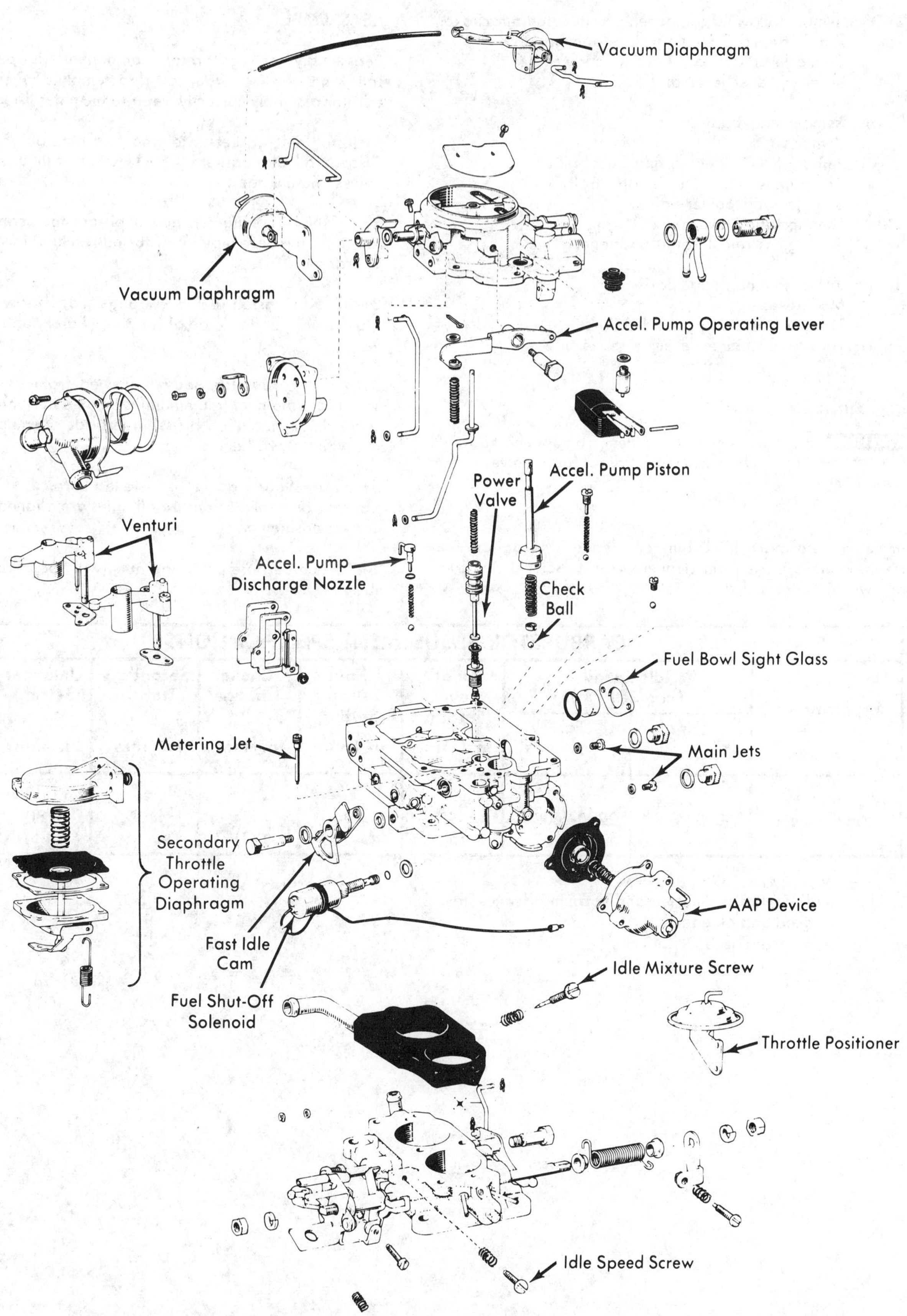

Fig. 9 Exploded View of Toyota 20R Engine Carburetor

AISAN 2-BARREL – TOYOTA 20R ENGINE (Cont.)

2) Disassemble following components from automatic choke:
Water and coil housing/plate and gasket
Choke lever and coil housing body
Breaker, relief lever and link

3) Disassemble main body parts:
Venturis
Pump jet, "O" ring, spring and ball
Damping spring, retainer and ball
Slow jet and power valve
Thermostatic valve and "O" ring
Sight glass and throttle positioner

4) Take off remaining flange parts:
Mixture screws
Throttle lever, spring and collars
Throttle positioner lever

CLEANING

CAUTION – *Do not immerse synthetic components (gaskets, plastics, rubber) or thermostat and diaphragm valves in carburetor cleaner.*

Immerse metal parts in carburetor cleaner and agitate until clean. Remove parts from cleaner, wash in solvent and blow dry with compressed air.

REASSEMBLY

Reassembly of carburetor components is performed by following reverse order of disassembly. To complete carburetor assembly correctly, refer to the notes listed below.

1) Install new gaskets throughout carburetor where required. Discard all old gaskets. Check for smooth operation of all valves and linkage.

2) DO NOT overtighten power piston stop screw. If screw is too tight, the bore may be distorted resulting in sticking piston operation.

3) DO NOT install fuel level gauge glass backwards. Dot on glass should be to inside of float bowl and bubble facing outward.

4) When carburetor body is viewed from sight glass end, secondary main jet (aluminum) is located in right side opening and primary main jet (brass) in left side opening. Install both jets with flat washers.

5) Ensure flange gasket is installed correctly. Gasket will fit backwards easily, so ensure all holes are aligned properly for correct positioning.

6) Torque carburetor flange nuts (with lock washers) to 5 ft. lbs.

CARBURETOR ADJUSTMENT SPECIFICATIONS

Application	Idle Speed (Engine RPM)		Float Level Setting	Float Drop Setting	Choke Linkage	Secondary Throttle	Unloader Setting	Vacuum Break
	Hot	Fast	In. (mm)	In. (mm)	In. (mm)	In. (mm)	In. (mm)	In. (mm)
All Models W/ 20R Engine	800-900①	2200-2600②	.197 (5)	.04 (1)	.04 (1)	40°	.180 (4.5)	.22"③ (1.55)

① – Man. Trans. is 750-850 RPM.
② – With EGR disconnected and vacuum advance hose unhooked and plugged
③ – Auto. Trans. is .017" (.43 mm)

MOTORCRAFT 2150 2-BARREL

Capri
2800 cc (Federal & High Alt.)

DESCRIPTION

Motorcraft 2150 carburetors have two main assemblies, air horn and main body. Air horn serves as main body cover and contains choke plate and choke diaphragm. Throttle plate, accelerating pump, power valve and fuel bowl are in main body. Each bore contains main and boost venturis, main fuel discharge, accelerator pump discharge and throttle plate. The boost venturis contain high speed bleed orifices and mechanical high speed bleed control system. This system consists of mechanical lift rod that actuates reverse tapered metering rods in high speed bleed jets. This system allows control of air/fuel mixture (to boost venturis) for more precise high speed operation and improved low speed response.

CARBURETOR IDENTIFICATION

Carburetor number prefix and suffix (example D3ZF-EA) is stamped on tag attached to carburetor. First letter of second line on tag ("A" etc.) indicates design changes. Changes may effect parts replacement. Other letters indicate assembly code, designating time of manufacture.

Application	Ford Carburetor No. Man. Trans.	Auto. Trans.
2800 cc		
Federal	77TF-KA	77TF-LA
High Altitude	77TF-KA	77TF-LA

ADJUSTMENTS

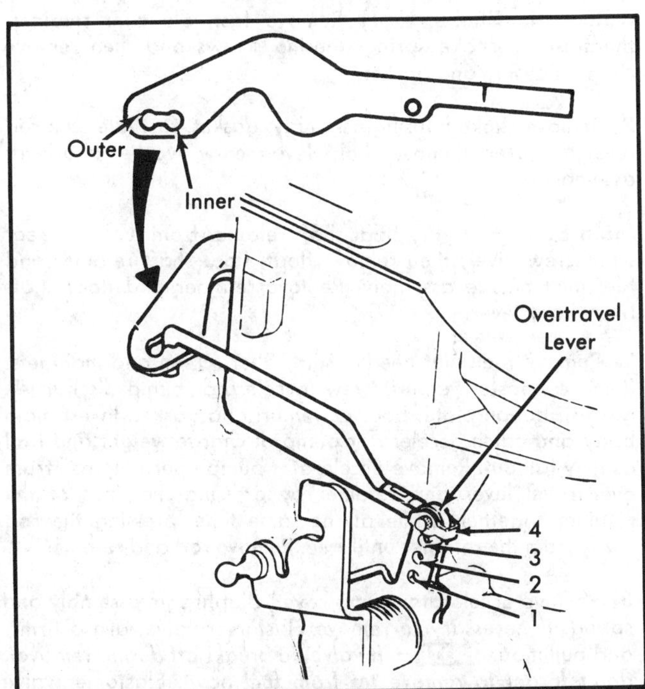

Fig. 1 Accelerator Pump Stroke Adjustment Holes with Rod

ACCELERATOR PUMP STROKE

NOTE – *Accelerator pump stroke has been preset at factory for each particular engine application. Additional holes are only provided for different engine applications.*

Check to be sure pump connecting rod is in inner hole (hole nearest carburetor body) of pump lever. Connecting rod should be in specified hole on lever. See *Fig. 1.*

FLOAT LEVEL (WET SETTING)

With air horn and gasket installed temporarily on carburetor, idle engine for at least three minutes to stabilize fuel level in bowl, then remove air horn and gasket. With engine idling, use "T" scale to measure from top machined surface of bowl to surface of fuel at a point at least 1/4" away from any vertical surface. If fuel level not correct, stop engine and adjust by bending float tab toward or away from inlet needle as required **CAUTION** – *Do not allow float tab to contact needle while making adjustment).* Repeat entire procedure to recheck fuel level. After adjustment completed, install air horn and gasket and make necessary carburetor adjustments.

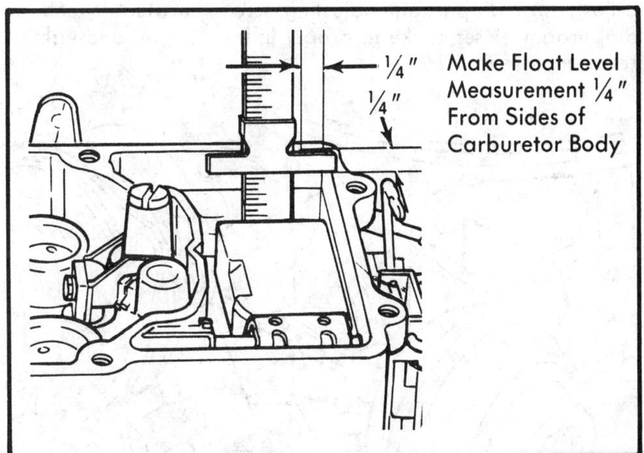

Fig. 2 Fuel Level Measurement with Appropriate Gauge

FLOAT LEVEL (DRY SETTING)

NOTE – *Dry float setting is preliminary adjustment only. Final adjustment (wet setting) must be made after carburetor is mounted on vehicle.*

With air horn removed, depress float tab to seat fuel inlet needle. Measure distance from top of main body (gasket removed) to float, at point ⅛" from free end of toe. If adjustment is necessary, bend float tab. **NOTE** – *Do not allow float tab to contact needle while making adjustment as Viton needle tip may be damaged.*

MOTORCRAFT 2150 2-BARREL (Cont.)

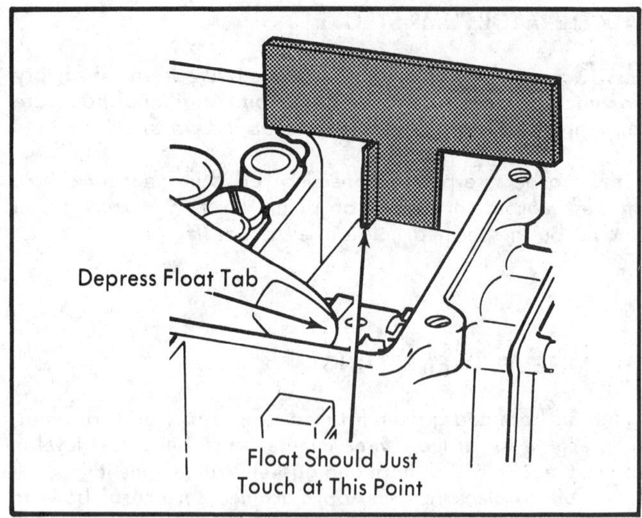

Fig. 3 Making Dry Float Level Measurement and Adjustment

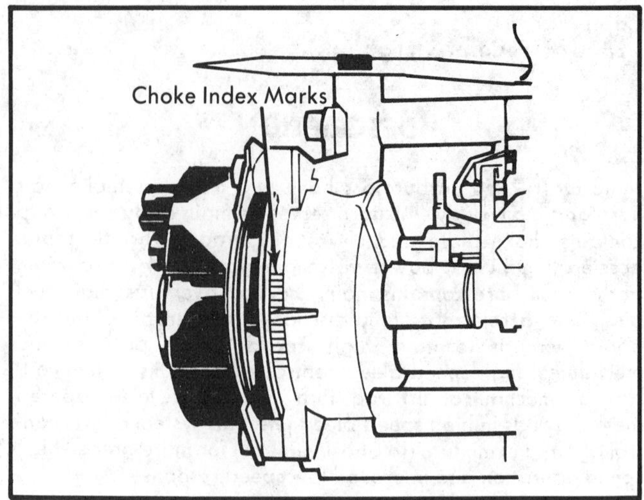

Fig. 5 Automatic Choke Adjustment

INITIAL CHOKE VALVE CLEARANCE (CHOKE VALVE PULL-DOWN)

With fast idle screw set on high step of fast idle cam, note index position of choke cover and loosen retaining screws. With retaining screws loose, rotate cover 90° in rich direction and tighten screws. Use outside vacuum source (or seat by hand) to seat diaphragm. Insert specified gauge between lower edge of choke valve and air horn wall. If necessary to adjust, turn diaphragm adjusting screw, located in end of diaphragm. Reset choke to proper index position and tighten retaining screws.

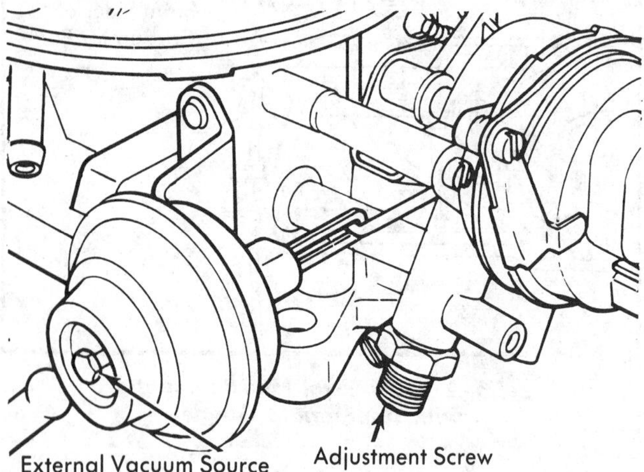

Fig. 4 Choke Pull-Down Diaphragm Adjustment Screw Location

AUTOMATIC CHOKE

Loosen choke cover retaining screws and rotate cover and thermostatic coil assembly in "Rich" or "Lean" direction to align reference mark on cover with correct scale graduation on housing.

NOTE – *"Index" setting is with reference mark on cover aligned with longer center mark on housing.*

OVERHAUL

DISASSEMBLY

Air Horn – 1) Remove air cleaner anchor screw and automatic choke control rod retainer. Remove air horn attaching screws, lockwashers, carburetor I.D. tag, then remove air horn and gasket. Remove choke control rod by loosening screw attaching choke shaft lever to choke shaft. Remove rod from air horn and slide plastic dust seal out of air horn.

2) Remove choke diaphragm assembly, then if necessary to remove choke plate, remove staking marks on attaching screws and remove screws. Remove choke plate by sliding it out of shaft from top of air horn, then remove shaft from air horn.

Automatic Choke – 1) Remove fast idle cam retainer, thermostatic choke spring housing screws and then remove clamp, housing and gasket.

2) Remove choke housing assembly, gasket, fast idle cam rod and cam lever. Remove choke lever screw, washer and lever assembly.

Main Body – 1) Pry float shaft retainer from fuel inlet seat with screwdriver, then remove float, float shaft retainer and fuel inlet needle assembly. Remove retainer and float shaft from float lever.

2) Remove fuel inlet needle, seat, filter screen and main jets. Remove booster venturi screw (accelerator pump discharge), air distribution plate, booster venturi and gasket. Invert main body and catch accelerator pump discharge weight and ball as they fall out. Remove accelerator pump operating rod from over-travel lever and retainer by pressing the ends of the retainer together, while at the same time, pressing the rod away from the retainer until free. Remove rod and retainer.

3) Remove accelerator pump cover, diaphragm assembly and spring. If necessary to remove Elastomer valve, grasp firmly and pull it out. **NOTE** – *If valve tip breaks off during removal, don't forget to remove tip from fuel bowl.* Elastomer valve must always be replaced whenever it has been removed from carburetor.

MOTORCRAFT 2150 2-BARREL (Cont.)

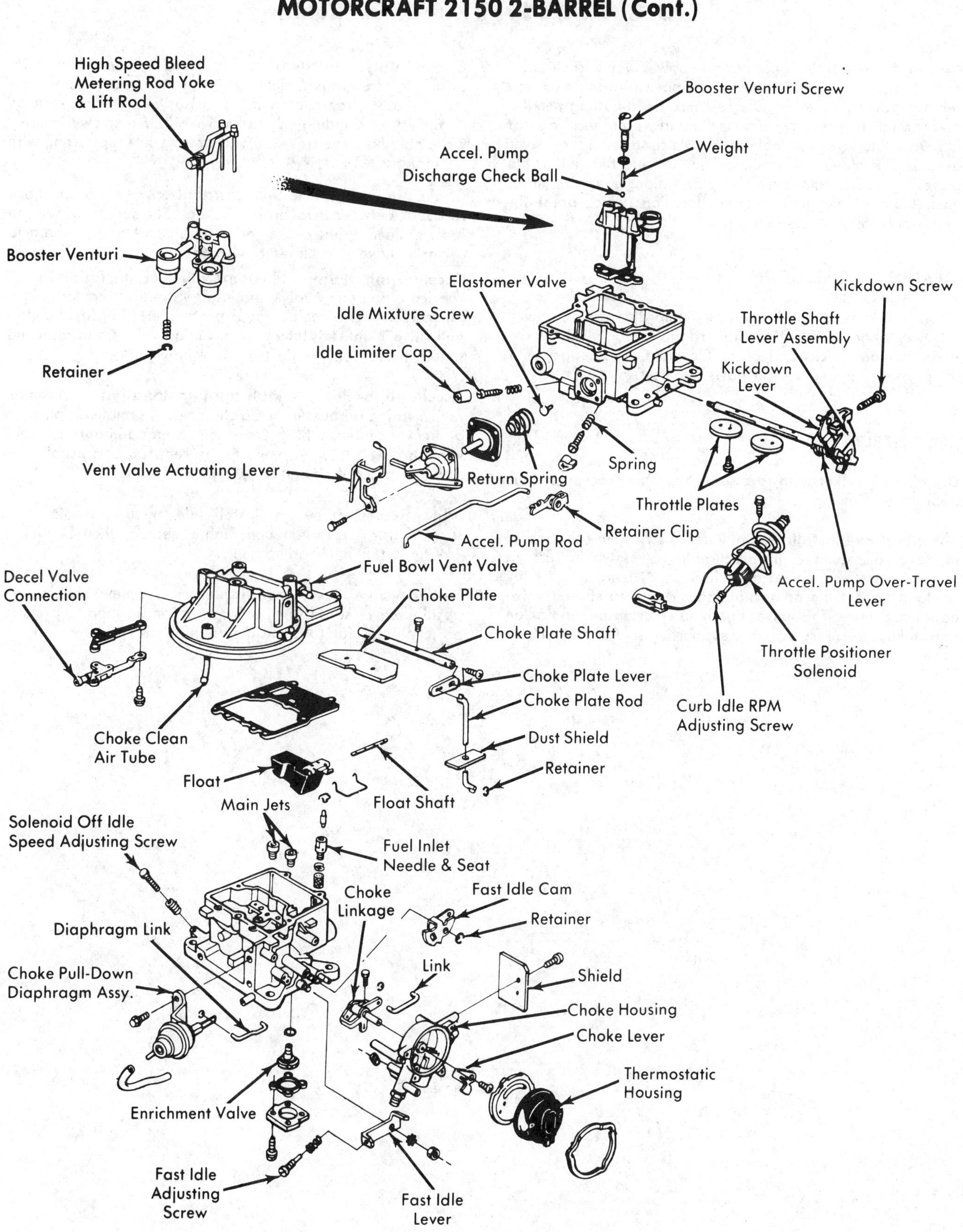

Fig. 6 Exploded View of Motorcraft 2150 Carburetor Assembly

MOTORCRAFT 2150 2-BARREL (Cont.)

4) Invert main body and remove power valve cover and gasket. Using a suitable wrench, remove power valve and remove gasket. Take out idle fuel mixture adjusting needles and springs. If necessary, remove nut and washer securing fast idle adjusting lever assembly to throttle shaft and lift off lever assembly. Remove anti-stall dashpot or solenoid. If throttle plates are to be removed, scribe plates along shaft and mark each plate to match its original location (which bore) for reassembly. Slide throttle shaft from main body.

CLEANING & INSPECTION

Clean all parts, except accelerator pump diaphragm, power valve, secondary operating diaphragm. Check all parts for wear, damage, nicks and burrs. Blow out all passages with compressed air. Replace all parts as necessary.

REASSEMBLY

Use all new gaskets and reverse disassembly procedure while noting the following:

Throttle Valve Installation – Refer to scribe lines and marks made at disassembly. Install throttle valves with attaching screws snug. Close valves and check fit by holding assembly up to a light. Little or no light should show between valve edges and bore. Tap valves lightly to centralize, then tighten and stake screws securely while supporting shaft on metal bar.

Choke Valve Installation – Install choke valve with attaching screws snug. Check valve fit and free movement by moving valve from closed to open position. Binding can be corrected by grinding edge of valve. Tighten screws securely while holding valve closed. Stake screws while supporting with a metal bar.

Choke Valve Rod and Seal Installation – Assemble choke rod seal between two brass washers. Slide into position on seal retainer. Insert choke rod through seal and air horn to engage choke shaft lever clevis nut.

Accelerating Pump Elastomer Valve Installation – Lubricate tip of new valve and insert valve tip in center hole in pump cavity. Use needle nosed pliers inserted in fuel bowl to pull valve in until it is fully seated. Cut off valve tip at retaining shoulder and remove tip from fuel bowl.

Accelerating Pump Diaphragm Installation – Position return spring on boss in pump chamber. Assemble diaphragm and cover and install two cover screws that do not retain vent valve bracket. Insert a new plug in vent rod and install vent rod and bracket assembly on pump.

Idle Mixture Screw – Install idle mixture needles and springs. Turn screws in until lightly seated, then back out 1½ turns for initial adjustment.

Power Valve Cover Installation – Use new gasket and position cover so that limiter stops are in position to provide positive stops for tabs on idle mixture screw limiter caps.

MOTORCRAFT MODEL 2700 VV 2-BARREL

Capri
2800 cc (Calif. only)

DESCRIPTION

Motorcraft 2700 VV (Variable Venturi) carburetor is different than all other Motorcraft units in that it has the ability to change the area of its venturi for varying demands of the engine. This assembly uses a dual-element venturi valve that moves in and out of air stream flowing into two carburetor throats. Valve is controlled by throttle position and engine vacuum. 2700 VV unit has fuel inlet, main metering, control vacuum, cranking and cold enrichment, idle trim and accelerator pump systems and is externally vented to a carbon canister. Auxiliary systems such as idle, pullover and power systems are not needed or used.

CARBURETOR IDENTIFICATION

Model identification is stamped on top of carburetor on flat surface of venturi valve cover plate.

Application	Carburetor No. Man. Trans.	Carburetor No. Auto. Trans.
Capri		
California	77TF-NA	77TF-MA

ADJUSTMENT

ACCELERATOR PUMP (INTERNAL VENT)

With curb idle speed properly adjusted, insert .010" feeler gauge between pump operating link and pump stem. Slight drag should be felt when gauge is removed. If adjustment is necessary, turn nylon adjusting nut until correct clearance is obtained. NOTE — *Check this adjustment whenever curb idle speed is adjusted.*

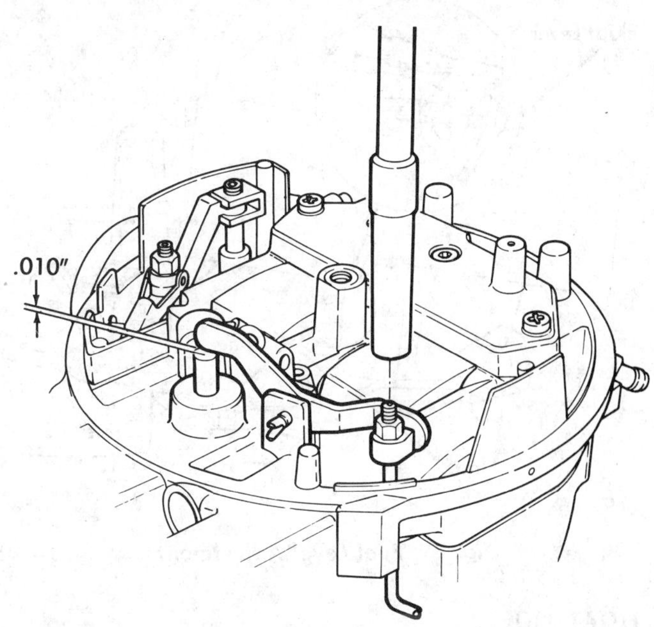

Fig. 2 Accelerator Pump (Internal Vent) Adjustment

FUEL LEVEL (DRY SETTING)

Remove upper carburetor body assembly and old gasket. Install new gasket prior to making adjustment. Invert upper body assembly and, using suitable gauging tool, place gauge on CAST surface of upper body. NOTE — *Do not rest gauge on gasket.* Measure distance from cast surface to float bottom.

Fig. 1 Motorcraft Model 2700 VV Carburetor

MOTORCRAFT MODEL 2700 VV 2-BARREL (Cont.)

Bend float lever away from fuel inlet needle to decrease setting and toward to increase. Float pontoon should be parallel with gasket. Check float drop adjustment.

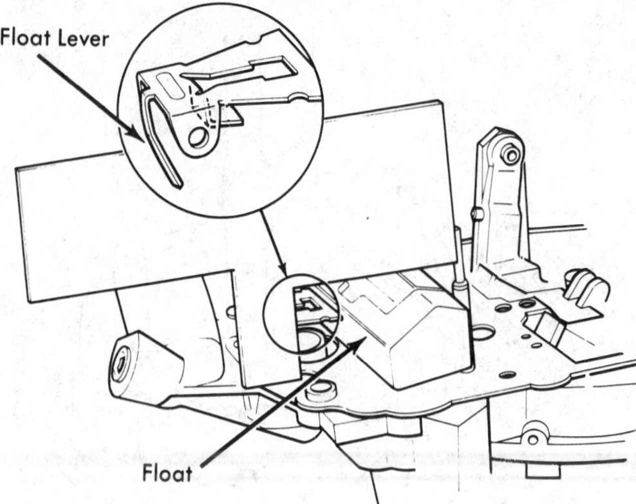

Fig. 3 Fuel Level Adjustment

FLOAT DROP

With upper body assembly removed, hold in upright position and place gauge against cast surface of upper body (not on gasket). Measure distance between cast surface and float bottom. To adjust, bend stop tab on float lever toward hinge pin to decrease setting and away to increase.

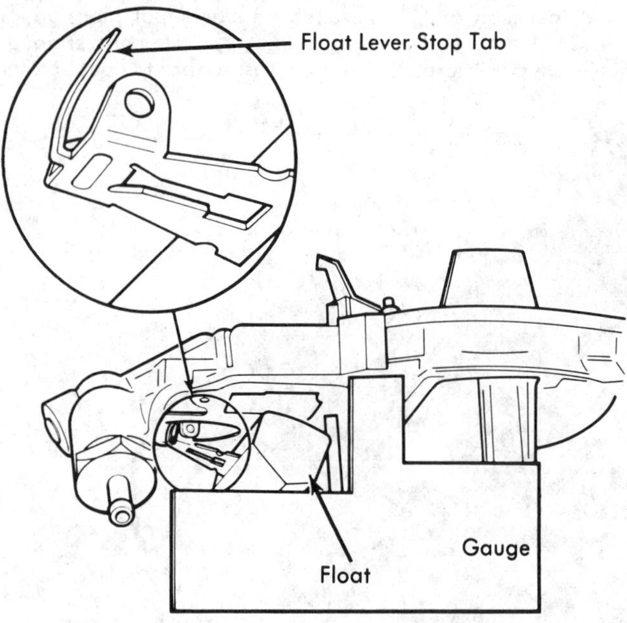

Fig. 4 Float Drop Adjustment

HIGH CAM SPEED POSITIONER

With high cam speed positioner in corner of correct cam step, place fast idle lever in corner of high cam speed positioner. Firmly hold throttle in closed position. With diaphragm cover removed, turn diaphragm assembly clockwise until bottomed on casting. Now rotate counterclockwise ½ turn to 1½ turns until vacuum port is aligned with diaphragm hole. Install diaphragm cover.

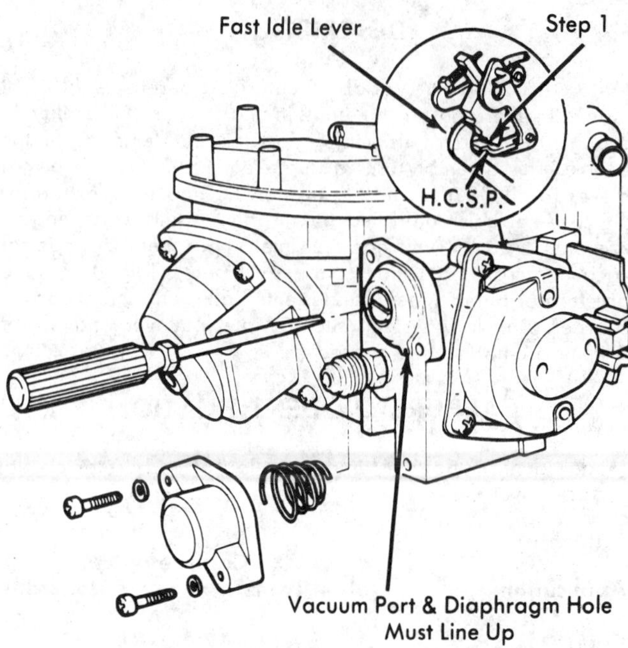

Fig. 5 High Cam Speed Positioner Adjustment

COLD ENRICHMENT ROD

Remove choke cap. With stator cap tool (T77L-9848-A or equivalent) installed, ensure cold enrichment rod is seated. Mount dial indicator with tip on top surface of enrichment rod and zero indicator. Remove stator cap and reinstall to index position. Dial indicator should read .125″ ± .005″. To adjust, turn nut clockwise to increase height or counterclockwise to decrease. Put on choke cap and set to proper position.

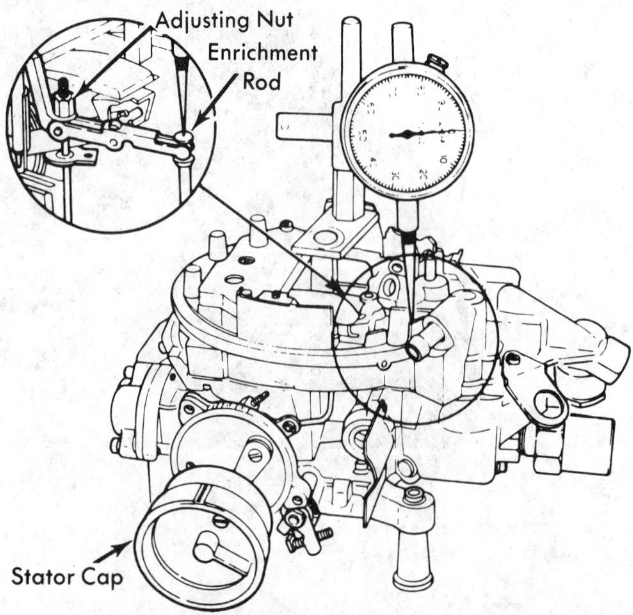

Fig. 6 Adjusting Cold Enrichment Rod

MOTORCRAFT MODEL 2700 VV 2-BARREL (Cont.)

CONTROL VACUUM

With tachometer installed, start engine and ensure idle is set to specification. Use an allen wrench to turn venturi valve adjusting screw clockwise to close valve. Connect vacuum gauge to vacuum tap on venturi valve cover. With engine at operating temperature, at curb idle, turn venturi bypass adjusting screw (allen screw) to reach specified vacuum setting. **NOTE** — *Throttle must be cycled while adjusting to obtain proper vacuum drop.* Check and/or reset curb idle.

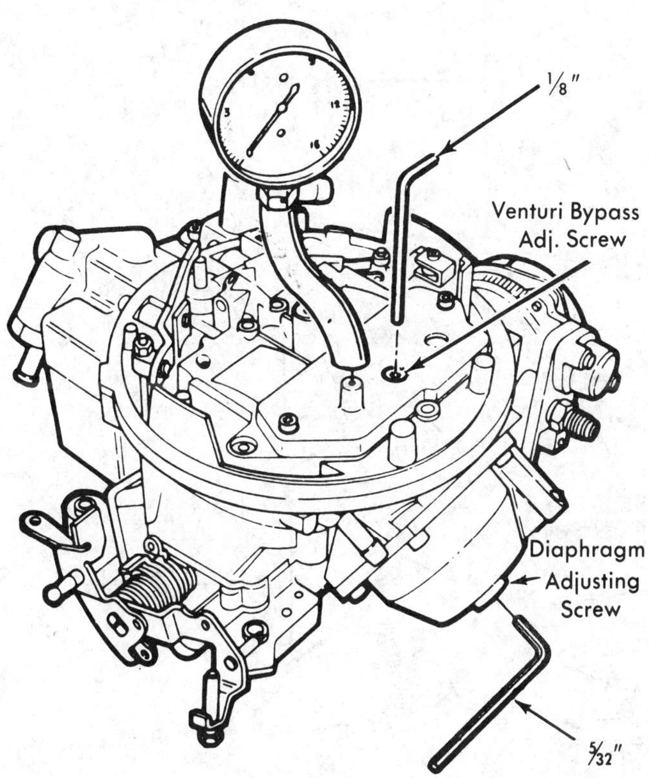

Fig. 7 Control Vacuum Adjustment

CONTROL VACUUM REGULATOR (CVR)

NOTE — *Cold enrichment rod adjustment must be properly set prior to making this adjustment.*

Turn choke cap $\frac{1}{2}$ turn in rich direction (clockwise) from index and cycle throttle to set fast idle speed cam. Press lightly on CVR rod and note any down travel. If present, rod is not correctly seated and requires adjustment. Turn screw counterclockwise until some down travel is felt and proceed with adjustment. Rotate CVR rod clockwise until adjusting nut just begins to rise. Recheck down travel on rod. If any spring-back is evident, rod is not fully seated. Turn adjusting screw clockwise in $\frac{1}{4}$ turn increments until spring-back is cancelled. Reset choke cap.

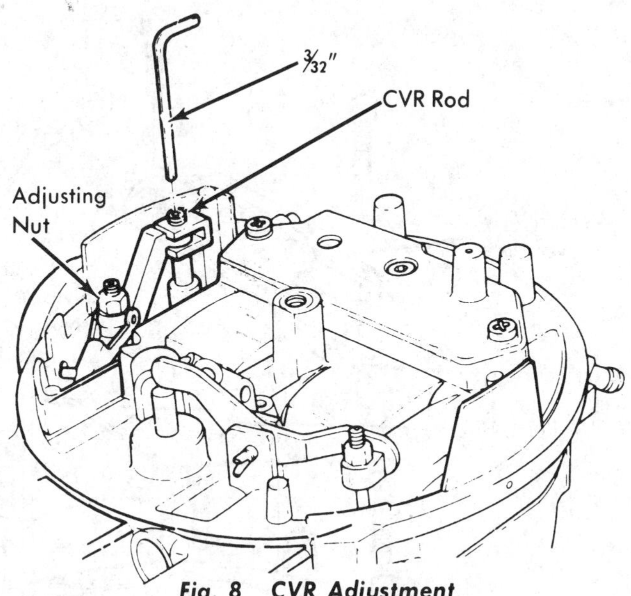

Fig. 8 CVR Adjustment

VENTURI VALVE LIMITER

Remove carburetor, remove venturi valve cover and roller bearings. Take out expansion plug at rear of main body on throttle side of carburetor. **NOTE** — *Center punch until loose.* With allen wrench, remove venturi valve W.O.T. stop screw. Block throttle plates wide open. While applying light closing pressure on venturi valve, measure gap between valve and air horn wall. Move valve to wide open position and insert allen wrench in hole from which stop screw was removed. Turn limiter adjusting screw clockwise to increase gap and counterclockwise to decrease. With allen wrench removed, apply closing pressure to valve and recheck gap. Install venturi valve W.O.T. stop screw and turn clockwise until it touches valve. Press valve to wide open position and check gap between air horn wall and valve. Turn stop screw until gap is correct. Install new expansion plug in access hole. Install venturi valve cover and roller bearings. Replace carburetor on vehicle.

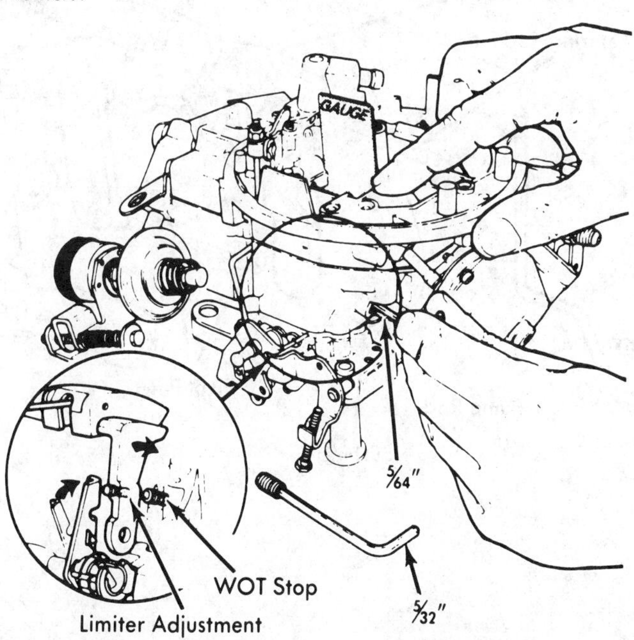

Fig. 9 Venturi Valve Limiter Adjustment

MOTORCRAFT MODEL 2700 VV 2-BARREL (Cont.)

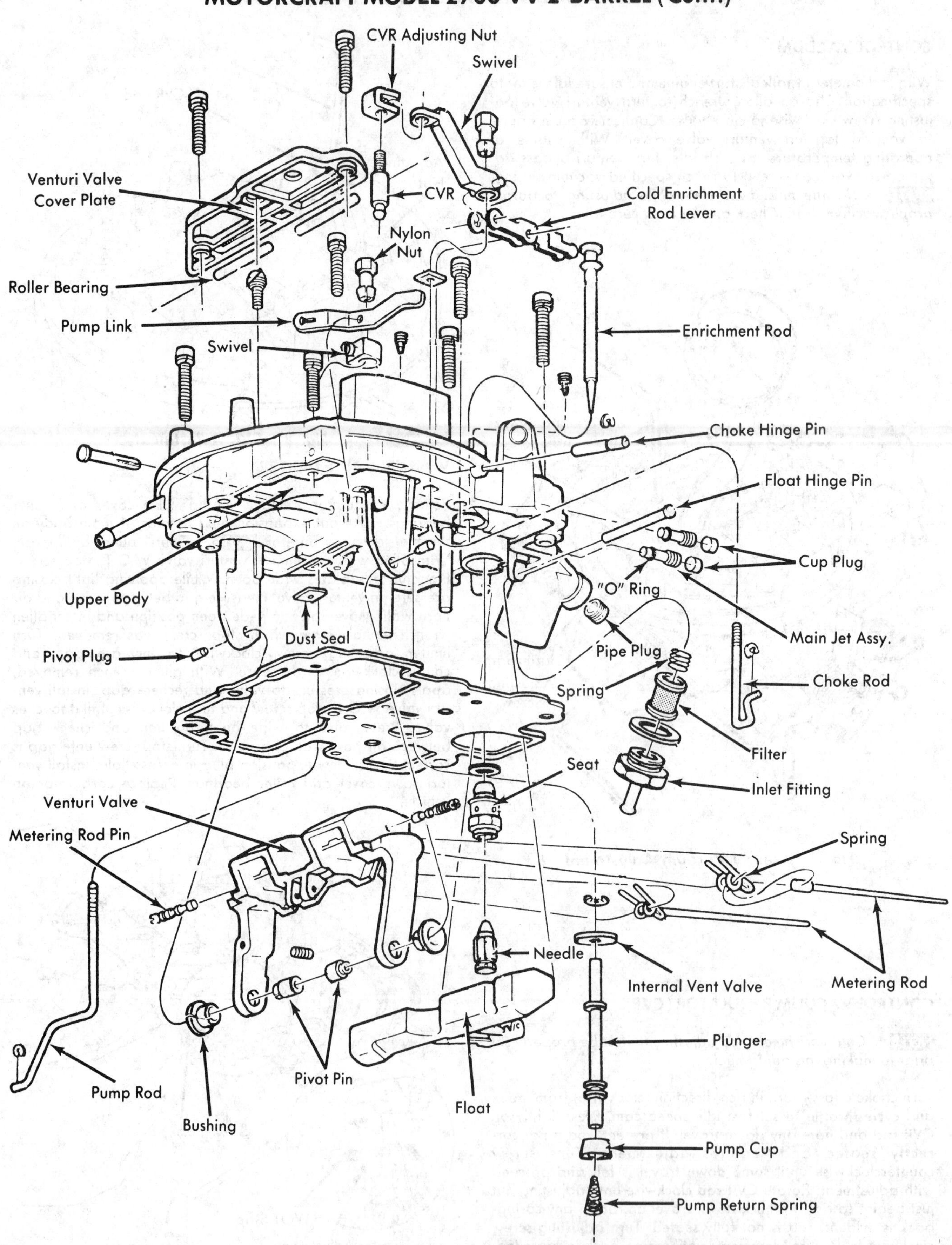

Fig. 10 Exploded View of Upper Carburetor Body

MOTORCRAFT MODEL 2700 VV 2-BARREL (Cont.)

OVERHAUL

DISASSEMBLY

Upper Body – 1) With carburetor mounted on a suitable stand, remove fuel inlet fitting, filter, gasket and spring. Remove "E" rings on accelerator pump and choke control rods and unhook rods. Take off air cleaner stud. Remove seven attaching screws and lift off upper body, noting position of two longer screws. Remove float hinge pin and float assembly.

2) Lift off float bowl gasket and take out fuel inlet valve, seat and gasket. Remove accelerator pump rod, dust seal, pump link retaining pin and link. Remove pump swivel and adjusting nut. Unhook choke control rod. Carefully lift retainer and slide out dust seal. Remove choke hinge pin. Remove cold enrichment rod nut, lever, swivel, control vacuum regulator and adjusting nut as an assembly. Only disassemble if required for parts replacement.

3) Slide cold enrichment rod from casting, and remove venturi valve cover plate and roller bearings. Take off venturi air bypass screw. Using tool (T77P-9928-A or equivalent), press tapered plugs from venturi valve pivot pins. Push out pivot pins and slide venturi valve rearward until free of casting. Remove pivot pin bushings and metering rod pivot pins (on outboard sides of venturi valves). Lift out metering rods and springs. **NOTE** – *Note position of rods (throttle or choke side) for assembly.*

4) **CAUTION** – *Block venturi valve wide open while working on jets.* Remove cup plugs recessed in upper body casting, with jet plug removal tool (T77L-9533-B). **NOTE** – *Due to importance of main metering jet setting, following steps must be carefully adhered to.*

5) With jet wrench (T77L-9553-A or equivalent), turn each main jet clockwise, noting number of turns, until bottomed in casting. Record to nearest ¼ turn. Rotate jet assembly counterclockwise to remove. Take off "O" rings and identify throttle or choke side jets for assembly. Remove accelerator pump assembly and idle trim (mixture) screws. Remove venturi valve limiter adjusting screw from venturi valve (throttle side). If required for cleaning, remove ⅛" plug from fuel inlet boss.

Main Body – 1) Remove starting enrichment solenoid and "O" ring seal. Remove valve diaphragm cover assembly, spring guide and spring. Loosen diaphragm and slide from main body. Remove diaphragm adjusting screw and valve wide open stop screw. **NOTE** – *Center punch access hole plug until loose.* Remove starting fuel control assembly. **CAUTION** – *Do not remove unless there is evidence of damage.* If necessary to remove, bend bimetal to expose discharge port. Using jet plug removal tool (T77L-9533-B), extract control assembly.

2) Invert carburetor on clean surface (catch check ball and weight), and remove five throttle body retaining screws. Remove throttle body and gasket. Remove choke heat shield.

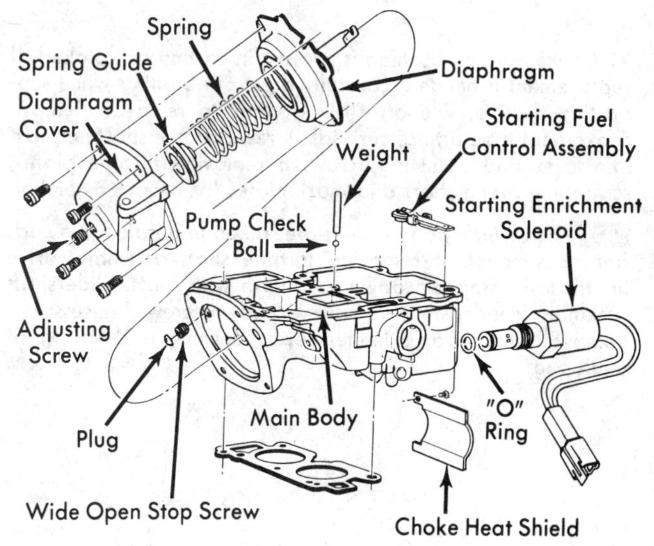

Fig. 11 Exploded View of Main Body

Throttle Body – 1) Take off throttle return control (sol-a-dash), solenoid, dashpot and bracket. Remove choke housing. Remove choke thermostatic lever; slide choke shaft and lever assembly from casting and remove fast idle cam. Remove high cam speed positioner assembly, cover screws, cover, spring, diaphragm and rod.

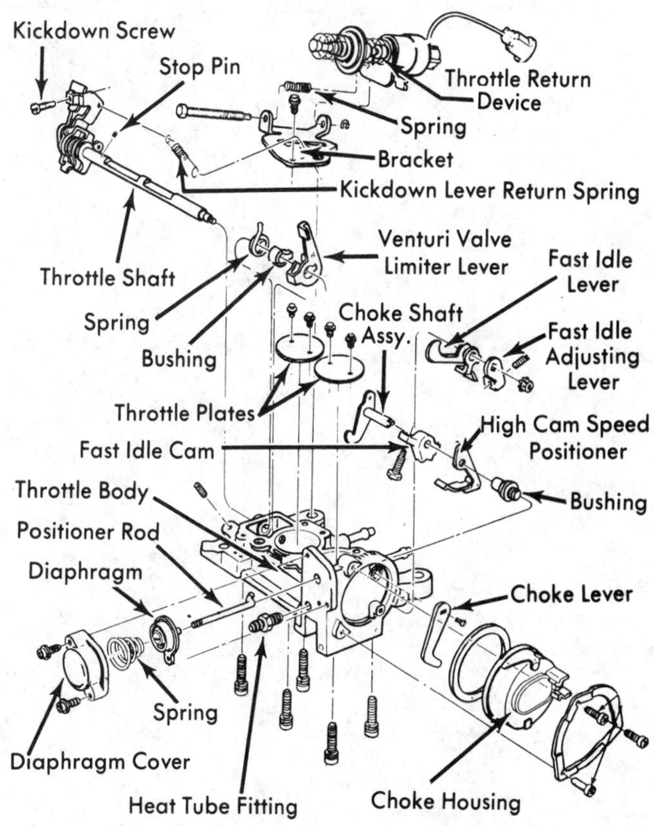

Fig. 12 Exploded View of Throttle Body

MOTORCRAFT MODEL 2700 VV 2-BARREL (Cont.)

2) Choke housing bushing is pressed in casting and staked. If replacement is needed, carefully press out bushing while supporting casting. File off staking prior to removal. Remove choke heat tube fitting, curb idle screw, throttle shaft nut, fast idle lever and adjusting screw. If removing throttle plates, scribe line along shaft and mark plates for proper assembly.

NOTE – *Throttle plate screws are staked in position; file ends before removal.* If removing throttle shaft assembly, drive limiter lever stop pin down until flush with shaft. Slide shaft assembly from casting (remove kickdown screw if necessary). Remove venturi valve limiter lever, bushing and spring (if equipped).

ASSEMBLY

NOTE – *Prior to installation, support throttle assembly and drive limiter stop pin out. Install new pin after throttle plates are installed and staked, leaving about 1/8" exposed.*

To assemble, reverse removal procedures noting the following steps.

Adjust high cam speed positioner diaphragm before installing cover. Lubricate all "O" rings with mild solution of soapy water before installing. Ensure venturi valve diaphragm stem engages venturi valve when assembling upper body to main body.

MOTORCRAFT 5200 2-BARREL

Capri
2300 cc

DESCRIPTION

Carburetor is two stage, two venturi type with primary venturi smaller than secondary. Secondary stage is operated by mechanical linkage. Primary stage includes curb idle, accelerator pump, idle transfer, main metering jet, and power enrichment systems. Secondary stage includes transfer, main metering jet, and power enrichment systems. A single fuel bowl supplies fuel for both stages.

CARBURETOR IDENTIFICATION

Carburetor identification number may be found stamped on side of float bowl or on a metal tag attached to carburetor.

Capri 2300 cc		
Federal	777F-AA①	777F-BA①
	777F-EA②	777F-GA②
California	777F-CA①	777F-DA①
	777F-HA②	777F-JA②
High Altitude	D7RE-EA①	777F-BA①
	D7RE-LA②	777F-GA②

① — Without Air Conditioning
② — With Air Conditioning

ADJUSTMENT

FLOAT LEVEL

Hold carburetor bowl cover in an inverted position with float tang resting on needle valve. Measure clearance between edge of float and bowl cover. Adjust to specifications by bending float tang.

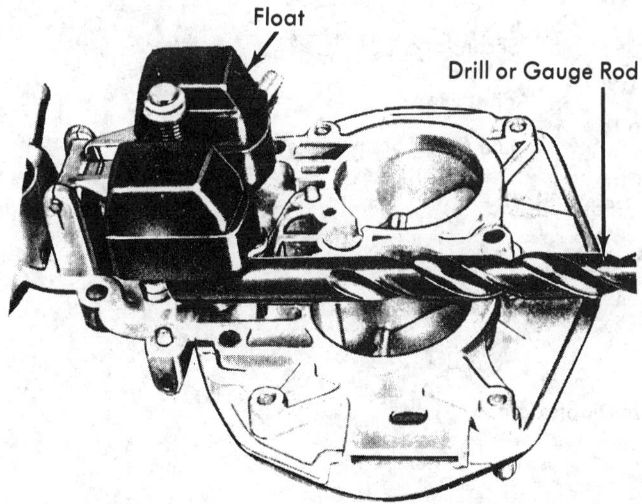

Fig. 1 Float Level Measurement with Drill for Gauge

SECONDARY THROTTLE STOP SCREW

Back off secondary throttle stop screw until secondary throttle plate seats in its bore. Now turn screw inward until it touches tab on secondary throttle lever; turn screw in an additional ¼ turn.

CHOKE PLATE PULL-DOWN

1) Remove choke thermostatic spring cover.

2) Set fast idle cam on top step. Push diaphragm stem back against stop. Insert gauge *(Fig. 2)* between lower edge of choke plate and air horn wall.

3) Take up slack in linkage by pressing down on top edge of choke plate. Remove plug from diaphragm. Turn adjusting screw until clearance is right.

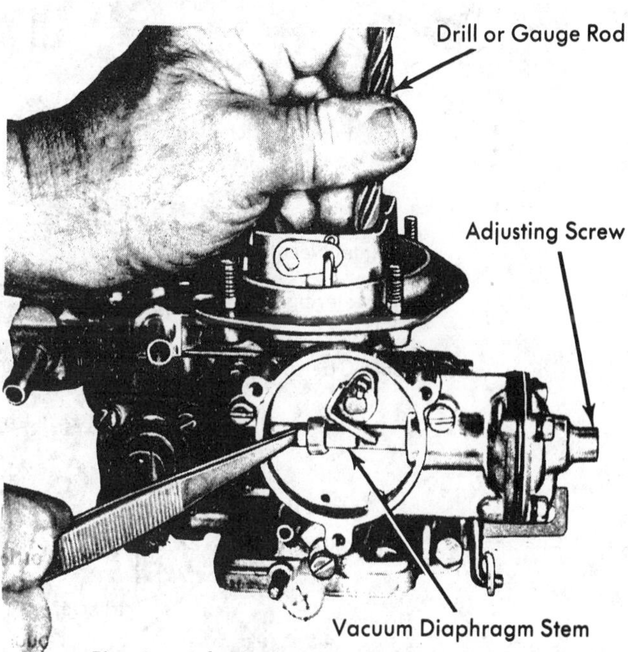

Fig. 2 Adjustment of Choke Pull Down with Related Tools

CHOKE UNLOADER

Put throttle lever in wide open position. Insert a drill or gauge between lower edge of choke valve and air horn wall. If a slight drag is not felt on gauge, bend tang on fast idle lever.

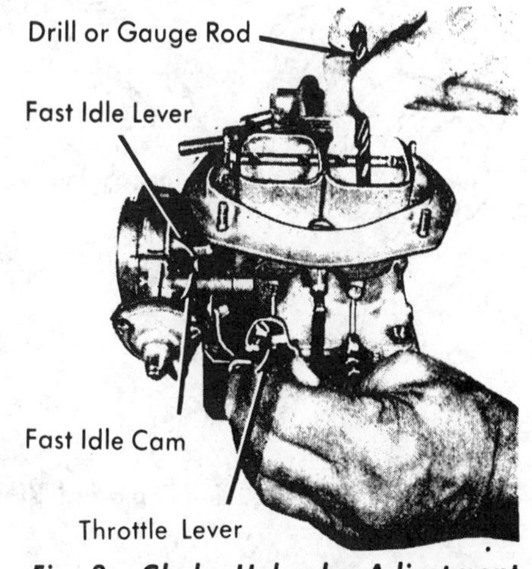

Fig. 3 Choke Unloader Adjustment

MOTORCRAFT 5200 2-BARREL (Cont.)

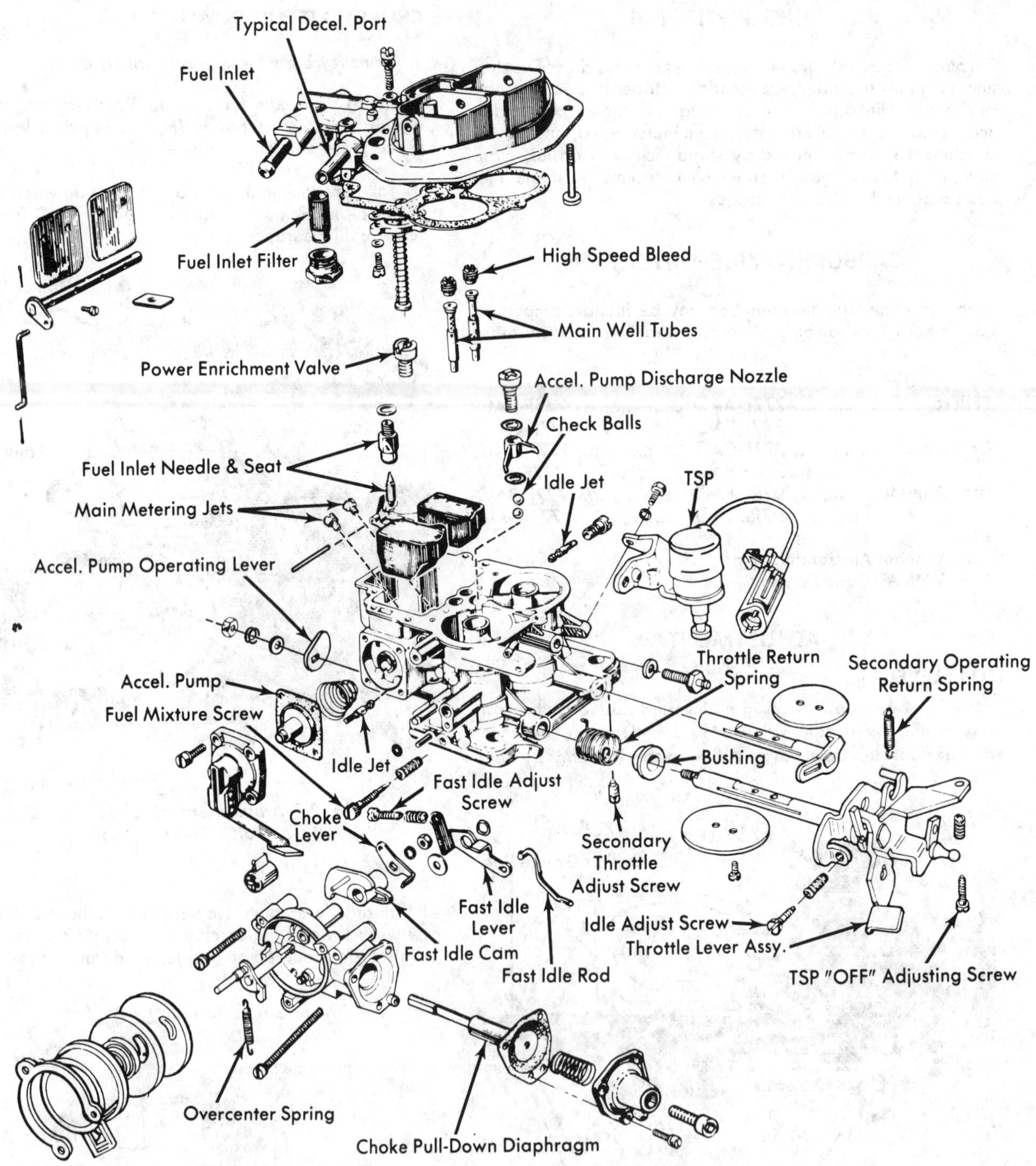

Fig. 4 Exploded View of Motorcraft 5200 Carburetor Assembly

MOTORCRAFT 5200 2-BARREL (Cont.)

FAST IDLE CAM CLEARANCE

Position fast idle speed screw on bottom step of fast idle cam. Insert specified gauge between lower edge of choke valve and air horn wall. Measure distance between tang on choke arm and fast idle cam. If clearance is not correct, bend tang on choke lever.

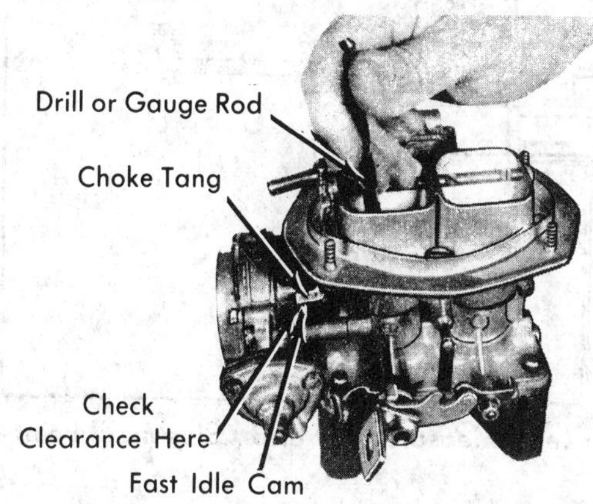

Fig. 5 Using Drill to Measure Fast Idle Cam Clearance

FAST IDLE SPEED (ON CAR)

Run engine to reach normal operating temperature. Position fast idle screw on second step of fast idle cam, against shoulder of first stop. Fast idle speed can now be properly adjusted. Refer to *Fig. 5* for screw location.

AUTOMATIC CHOKE

Choke cover can be rotated slightly after loosening three screws. It is not necessary to loosen or remove water cover. Adjust choke cover to make setting correct.

OVERHAUL

DISASSEMBLY

1) Remove fuel inlet filter and screen assembly. Remove bowl cover screws, retaining clips from choke rod, and bowl cover. Remove choke shaft, float, inlet needle, then remove vacuum diaphragm screws, washers, and diaphragm.

2) Remove choke housing and gasket. Slip housing away from main body and disengage fast idle rod (noting location of long screws). Remove "O" ring from vacuum passage, then remove choke shaft nut and lock washer. Note position of fast idle cam and spring.

3) Remove pump cover, diaphragm, and return spring. Remove pump discharge valve assembly and discharge nozzle. Then remove two pump discharge check balls.

4) Remove primary and secondary high speed bleed and main wells, noting sizes for reinstallation. Remove primary and secondary main metering jets, noting sizes for reinstallation. Remove power valve and primary and secondary idle jets.

5) Turn idle limiter caps to stop, remove caps, and lightly seat screws. After noting number of turns to seat, remove screws. Remove secondary operating lever return spring, then remove primary throttle lever. Remove idle adjusting lever spring, noting how primary throttle return spring is hooked. Remove secondary throttle lever and adjusting screw.

CLEANING & INSPECTION

Clean all parts in suitable solvent and blow dry. Inspect all parts for excessive wear and replace if necessary. **NOTE** – *Do not place any diaphragm or plastic parts in solvent, these should be cleaned with a soft brush or cloth.*

REASSEMBLY

To reassemble, reverse disassembly procedure, refer to *Fig. 5*, and also make the following notes:

1) Use all new gaskets. Install idle mixture screw and spring until screw lightly bottoms. Back out same number of turns recorded on disassembly.

2) Make sure primary and secondary main jets are installed in correct positions. Make sure primary and secondary main well tubes and high speed bleeds are installed in correct positions. Adjust float position before installing bowl cover.

HITACHI DCG 306, DCH 306 & DCJ 306 2-BARREL

Datsun F10 & B210
Mazda 808 (1300)
Mazda GLC
Subaru

DESCRIPTION

Carburetor is a two barrel downdraft design with primary and secondary throttle systems. A choke valve and idle circuit are used in primary system only. Both primary and secondary venturis have main fuel nozzles. When the primary throttle valve is nearly wide open, secondary throttle valve begins to open. An auxiliary throttle valve, located above secondary throttle valve, provides smooth operation as secondary begins to open. A mechanical accelerator pump and vacuum operated power valve are used for increased fuel requirements. An anti-dieseling solenoid valve is used to stop fuel flow in idle circuit (on some models) when the ignition switch is turned off. Datsun vehicles use a throttle positioner for controlling exhaust emissions during engine deceleration and a dashpot is installed to prevent throttle from closing too quickly. Subaru and Datsun models have an electric choke system, while Mazda uses a manual choke with an automatic return feature.

CARBURETOR IDENTIFICATION

Application	Hitachi Carb. No. Man. Trans.	Auto. Trans.
Datsun		
B210		
Federal	DCH 306-10B	DCH 306-14B
California	DCH 306-11B	DCH 306-15B
F10		
Federal	DCH 306-16A	.....
California	DCH 306-17A	.....
Mazda	DCG 306	DCG 306
Mazda GLC	DCG 306	DCG 306
Subaru		
Fed. & High Alt.	DCJ 306-9	DCJ 306-9
California	DCJ 306-8	DCJ 306-8

ADJUSTMENT

HOT (SLOW) IDLE RPM

See appropriate article in TUNE-UP Section.

IDLE MIXTURE

See appropriate article in TUNE-UP Section.

COLD (FAST) IDLE RPM

See appropriate article in TUNE-UP Section.

FLOAT LEVEL

With air horn removed and inverted, raise float and lower it slowly. Measure distance from air horn gasket surface to float. Bend tang to adjust to specifications. See *Carburetor Adjustment Specifications table for correct specifications.*

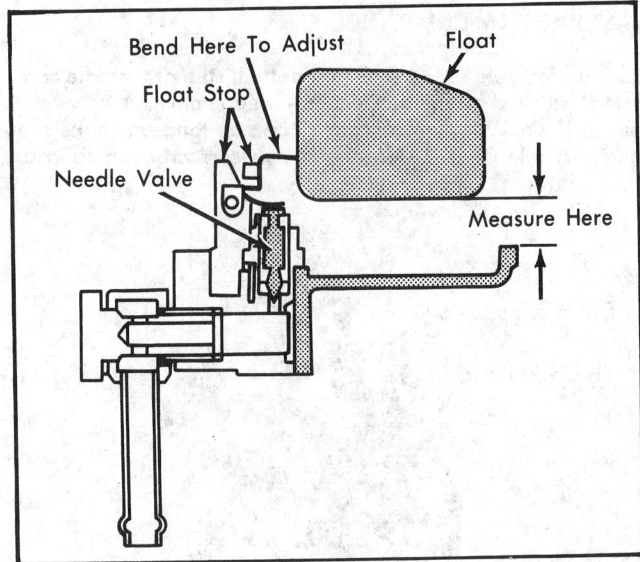

Fig. 1 Float Level Measurement and Adjustment Points

FLOAT DROP

After checking float level, raise float until float stop contacts air horn projection. With float held up in this position, measure clearance between float tang and needle valve seat. If clearance is not to specifications, adjust by bending float stop. *See Carburetor Adjustment Specifications table for correct specifications.*

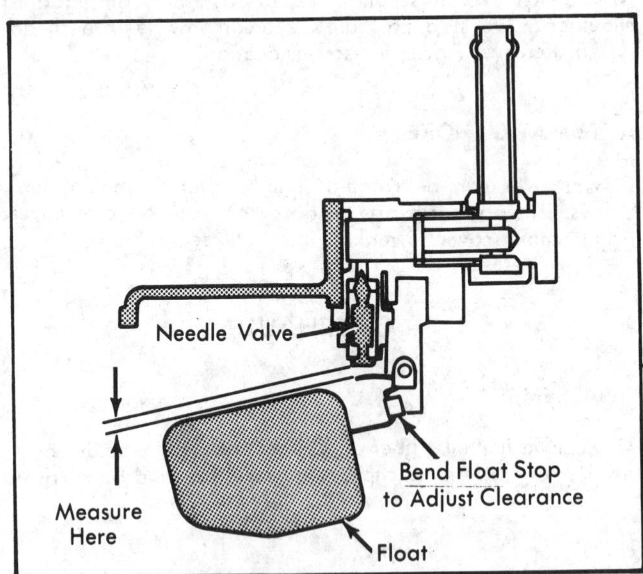

Fig. 2 Float Drop Measurement and Adjustment Points

FAST IDLE (OFF CAR)

Datsun – With choke cover removed, place fast idle adjusting screw on second step of fast idle cam and measure clearance between primary throttle plate and throttle bore. To adjust, turn fast idle adjusting screw until a clearance of .039-.045" (1-1.14 mm) for automatic transmission vehicles or .029-.034" (.73-.87 mm) for manual transmission vehicles is obtained.

HITACHI DCG 306, DCH 306 & DCJ 306 2-BARREL (Cont.)

Mazda – With choke plate fully closed, measure clearance between primary throttle plate and bore wall. Clearance should be .054" (1.37 mm). If not, bend fast idle rod until correct clearance is obtained.

Subaru – Place fast idle lever on 4th step of fast idle cam. Adjust throttle plate-to-throttle bore clearance to .060" (1.53 mm) on California and High Altitude vehicles and .043" (1.09 mm) on Federal vehicles.

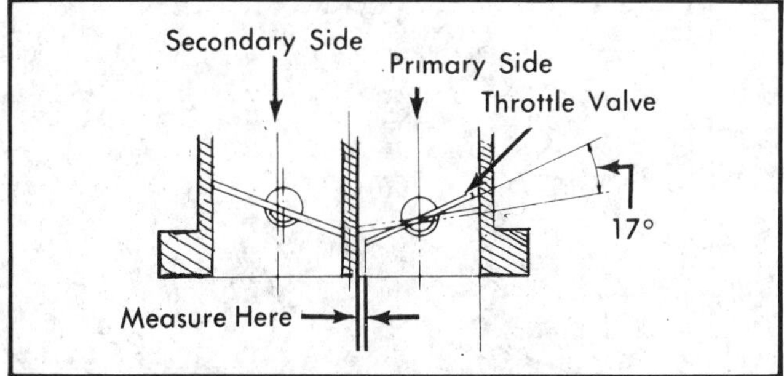

Fig. 3 Fast Idle Bench Adjustment

SECONDARY THROTTLE INITIAL OPENING

All Models – With primary-to-secondary throttle connecting rod contacting end of slot in primary throttle lever, measure clearance between primary throttle plate and bore. If adjustment is necessary, bend connecting rod to obtain specified clearance. *See Carburetor Adjustment Specifications table for correct specifications.*

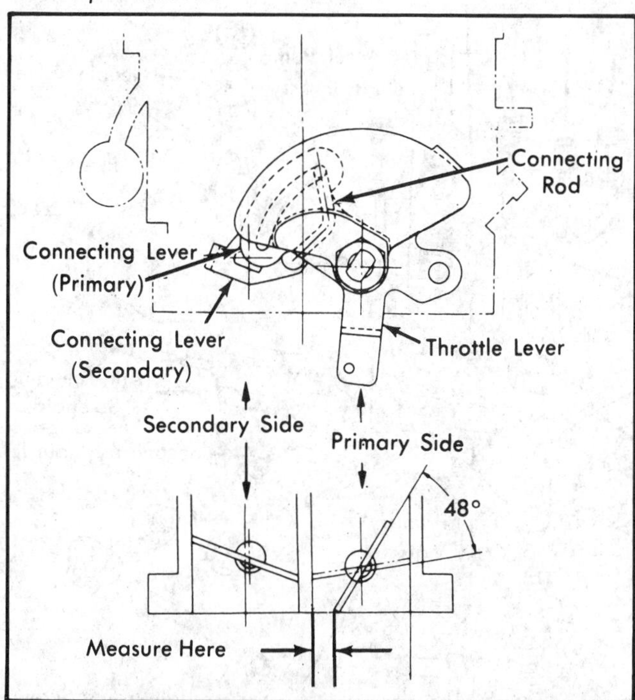

Fig. 4 Secondary Throttle Initial Opening Adjustment

VACUUM BREAK

All Models – Open throttle and close choke. Release throttle lever first, to trap choke closed. Remove choke cover, and using rubber band, hold choke valve closed. Manually pull vacuum break diaphragm stem out fully (keep straight) in order to compress diaphragm. Measure clearance between choke valve and air horn wall. If adjustment is necessary, bend vacuum break connecting rod.

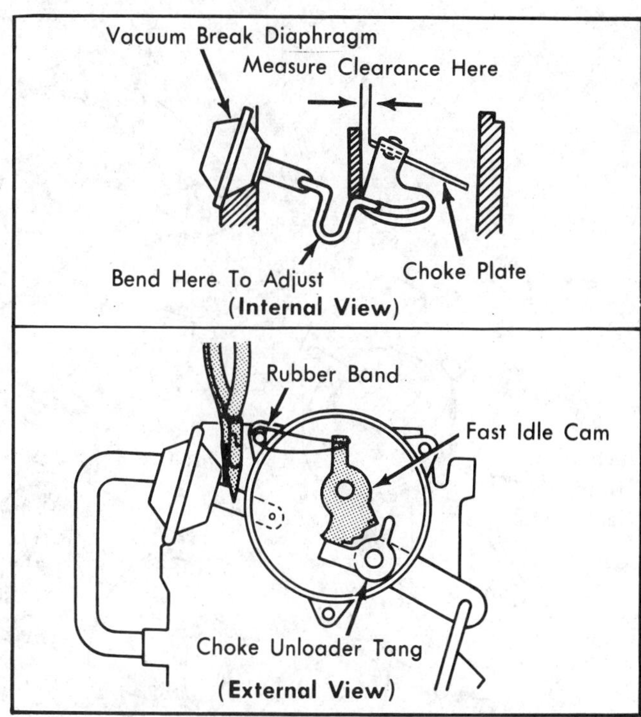

Fig. 5 Vacuum Break Adjustment

CHOKE UNLOADER

Datsun & Subaru – Open throttle valve to wide open position. Hold choke valve closed with rubber band (as illustrated). With throttle wide open and choke closed by rubber band, measure clearance between choke valve and air horn wall. If adjustment is necessary, bend choke unloader tang. *See Carburetor Adjustment Specifications table for correct specifications.*

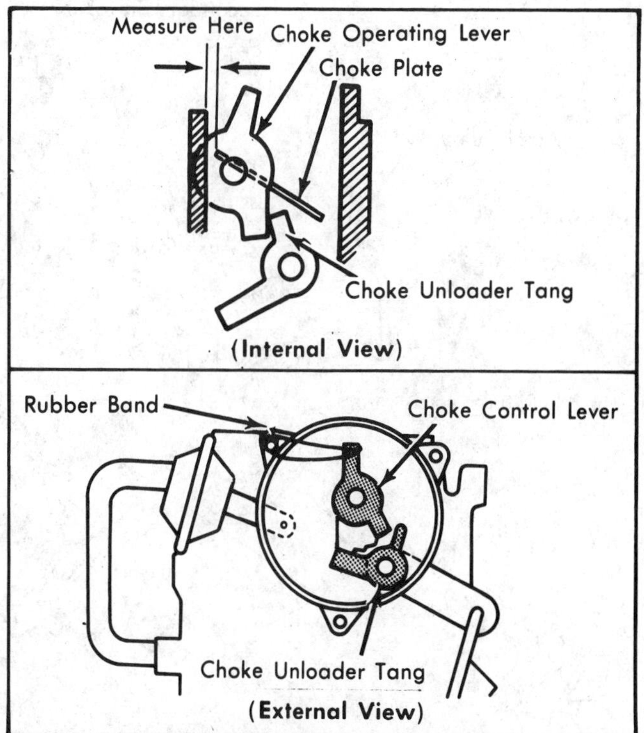

Fig. 6 Choke Unloader Adjustment

HITACHI DCG 306, DCH 306 & DCJ 306 2-BARREL (Cont.)

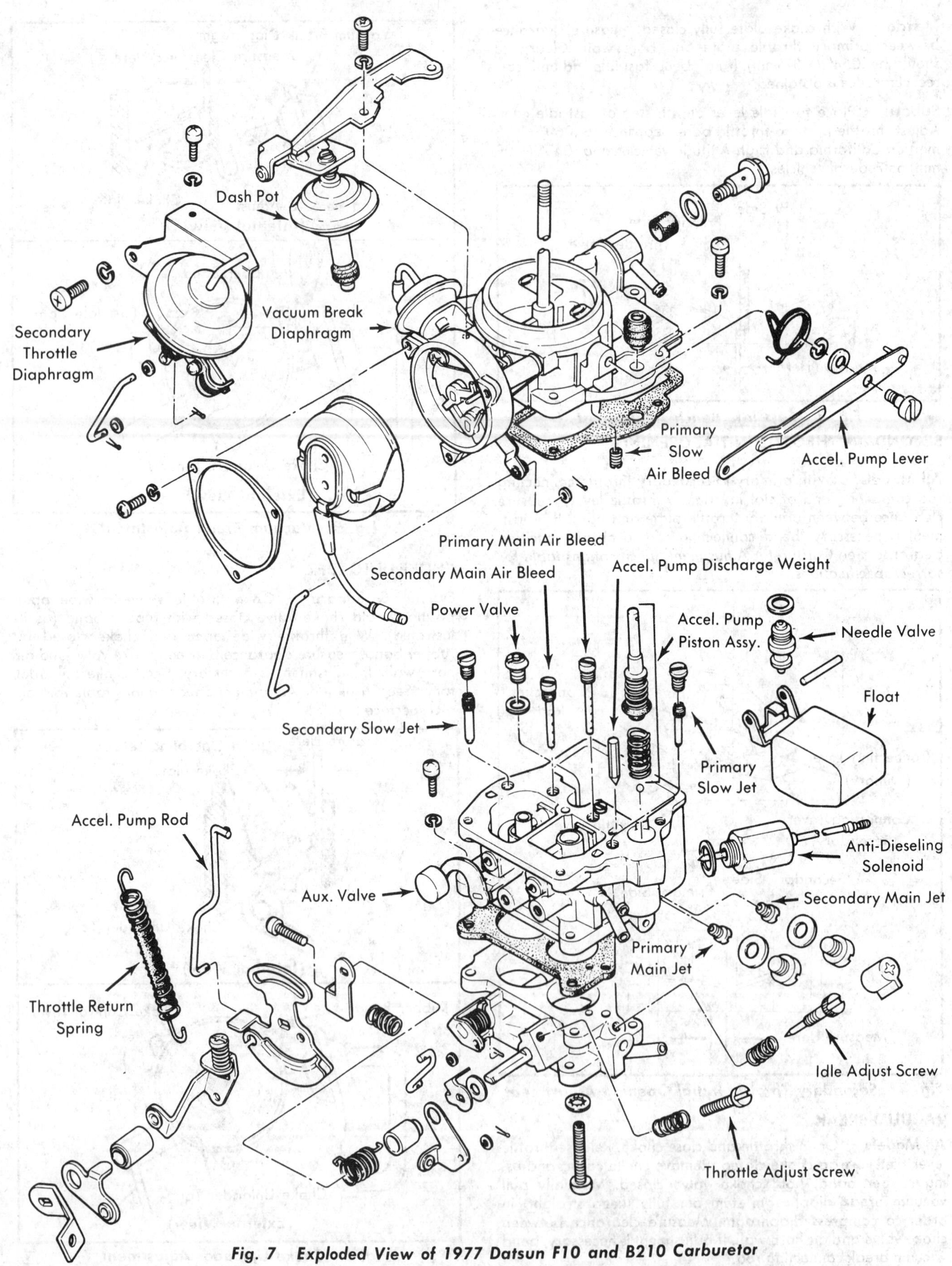

Fig. 7 Exploded View of 1977 Datsun F10 and B210 Carburetor

HITACHI DCG 306, DCH 306 & DCJ 306 2-BARREL (Cont.)

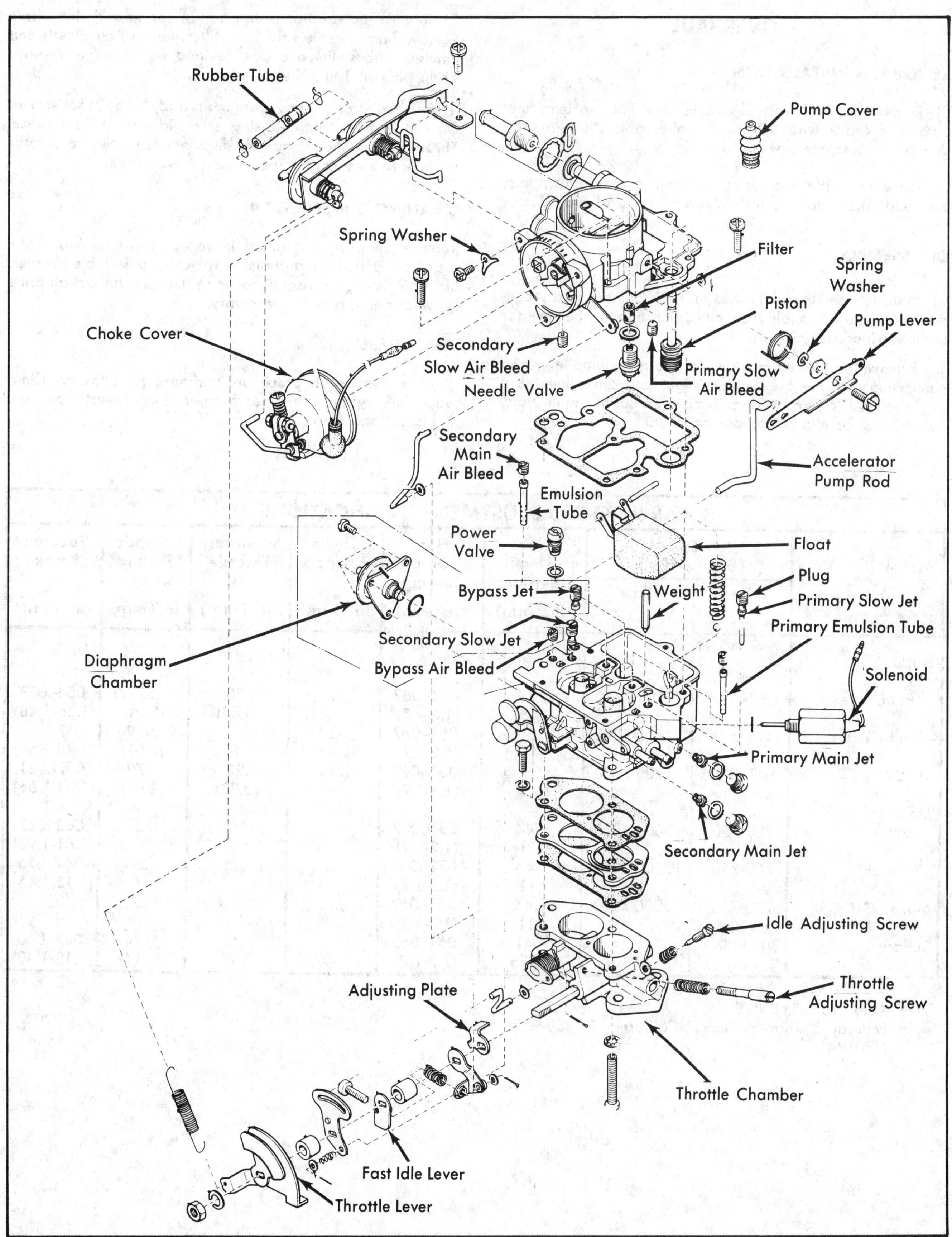

Fig. 8 Exploded View of 1977 Subaru Carburetor

1977 Hitachi Carburetors

HITACHI DCG 306, DCH 306 & DCJ 306 2-BARREL (Cont.)

OVERHAUL

REMOVAL & INSTALLATION

1) Remove air filter unit, disconnect fuel line, vacuum line, automatic choke wires (Datsun), choke cable (Subaru) and anti-dieseling solenoid wires (if equipped).

2) Remove throttle lever or cable. Remove carburetor flange nuts and carburetor. To install, reverse removal procedure.

DISASSEMBLY

1) Main jets and needle valves on both primary and secondary sides are accessible from outside carburetor. Remove for service as necessary.

2) Remove throttle return spring, accelerator pump lever and connecting rod. Remove spring hanger and choke linkage if equipped and choke housing. Remove carburetor main body cover being careful not to damage float.

3) Remove accelerator piston, return spring and check ball. Remove float, needle valve and filter. Remove air bleeds and emulsion tubes. Remove slow jet and power valve. Remove drain plug and main jet.

4) Remove throttle body from main body with (3) set screws. Do not remove anti-dieseling solenoid except to replace. Throttle body should not be disassembled unless a throttle valve or rod is being replaced.

CLEANING & INSPECTION

Replace all parts contained in service overhaul kits. Soak metal parts (except anti-diesel valve) in a suitable cleaner. Blow air through passages to clean and dry. Inspect all parts for wear and replace as necessary.

REASSEMBLY

Reverse disassembly procedure and note the following: Check each link system for smooth operation. Adjust float and linkage as required.

CARBURETOR ADJUSTMENT SPECIFICATIONS

Model	Idle Speed (Engine RPM)		Float Level Setting In. (mm)	Float Drop Setting In. (mm)	Choke Linkage In. (mm)	Secondary Throttle In. (mm)	Unloader Setting In. (mm)	Vacuum Break In. (mm)
	Hot①	Fast						
Datsun								
B210								
Man. Trans.	740	1900-2700	.59 (15)	.051-.067 (1.3-1.7)	.....	.23 (5.83)	.079 (2.01)	.054-.058 (1.36-1.48)
Auto. Trans.	665	2400-3200	.59 (15)	.051-.067 (1.3-1.7)	.....	.23 (5.83)	.079 (2.01)	.057-.061 (1.44-1.56)
F10	700	1900-2700	.59 (15)	.051-.067 (1.3-1.7)	.....	.23 (5.83)	.079 (2.01)	.057-.061 (1.44-1.56)
Mazda								
Calif.	700-750	3000-4000	.44 (11)	.051-.067 (1.3-1.7)	.....	.....	.....	.063-.077 (1.61-1.95)
Federal	700-750	3000-4000	.44 (11)	.051-.067 (1.3-1.7)	.....	.....	.....	.044-.056 (1.15-1.45)
Mazda GLC	700-750	3000-4000	.44 (11)	.051-.067 (1.3-1.7)	.....	.....	.....	.....
Subaru	800-900②	.....	.41 (10.5)	.051-.067 (1.3-1.7)	.....	.24 (6)	.124 (3.14)	.047-.060 (1.18-1.42)

① — Auto. Trans. in DRIVE
② — Federal & High Altitude.; California is 850-950 in NEUTRAL

HITACHI DCH 340 & DCP 340 2-BARREL

Datsun 200SX
Datsun 620 Pickup
Datsun 710
Chevrolet LUV Pickup

DESCRIPTION

Carburetor is a 2-barrel downdraft type equipped with piston type accelerator pump. Carburetor consists of low speed (primary) barrel and high speed (secondary) barrel integrated into a single unit with common fuel bowl. Secondary throttle is actuated by vacuum diaphragm when primary throttle is opened a predetermined amount. Additional equipment includes an anti-dieseling solenoid, electric choke, altitude compensator and dash pot.

CARBURETOR IDENTIFICATION

Application	Carburetor No. Man. Trans.	Carburetor No. Auto. Trans.
Datsun 200SX		
Federal	DCH 340-53B	DCH 340-54B
Calif.	DCH 340-49A	DCH 340-50A
Datsun 620 Pickup		
Federal	DCH 340-47A	DCH 340-48A
Calif.	DCH 340-45B	DCH 340-46A
Datsun 710		
Federal	DCH 340-51A	DCH 340-52A
Calif.	DCH 340-41B	DCH 340-42C
Chevrolet LUV Pickup		
All Models	DCP 340	DCP 340

ADJUSTMENT

HOT (SLOW) IDLE RPM

See appropriate article in TUNE-UP Section.

COLD (FAST) IDLE RPM

See appropriate article in TUNE-UP Section.

IDLE MIXTURE

See appropriate article in TUNE-UP Section.

FLOAT LEVEL

NOTE – *Fuel bowl is equipped with a sight glass. Line on sight glass indicates proper fuel level. If adjustment must be made to correct improper level, use following procedure.*

Datsun – With sight glass removed and carburetor main body inverted, measure distance from top of float to top of float bowl. If distance is not to specifications, bend float tang.

LUV – With sight glass removed and carburetor main body inverted, bend float tang until float is parallel with top of float bowl.

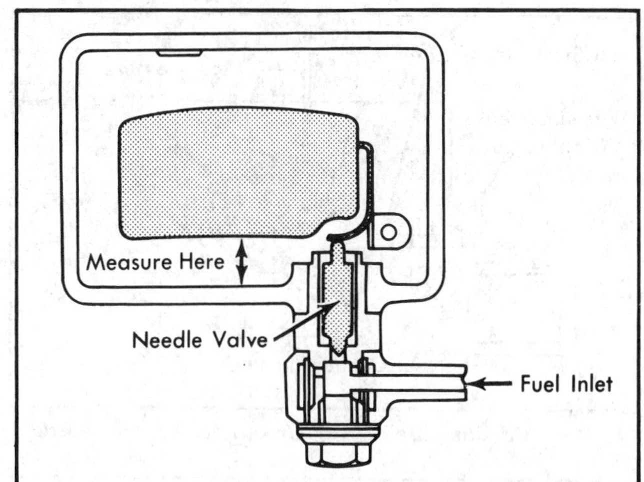

Fig. 1 Float Level Measurement Point

FLOAT DROP

With float bowl removed and held upright, measure clearance between needle valve and float tang. If clearance is not .059" (1.5 mm), adjustment will be necessary. Adjust by bending float tang which contacts needle valve.

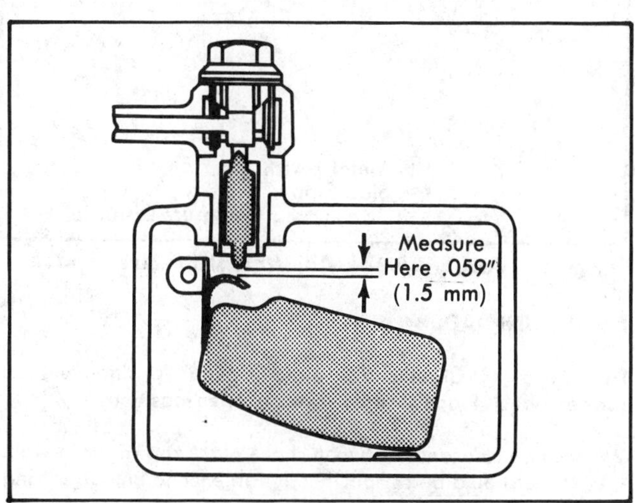

Fig. 2 Float Drop Measurement Point

VACUUM BREAK

Datsun – Close choke and hold closed with rubber band stretched between choke piston and stationary part of carburetor. Grip stem of vacuum break diaphragm and pull straight outward (stem extended). Adjust gap between choke plate and air horn wall, by bending vacuum break rod.

LUV – Fully depress vacuum break diaphragm stem and measure distance between bi-metal lever side stopper and stop on choke thermostatic cover. If distance is not as specified, turn adjusting screw.

HITACHI DCH 340 & DCP 340 2-BARREL (Cont.)

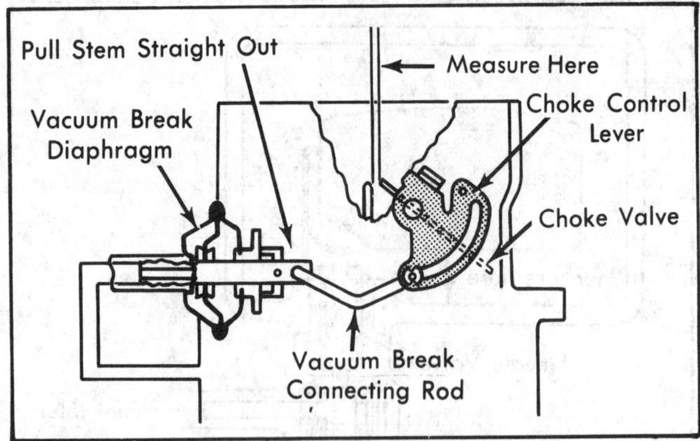

Fig. 3 Vacuum Break Adjustment for Datsun Models

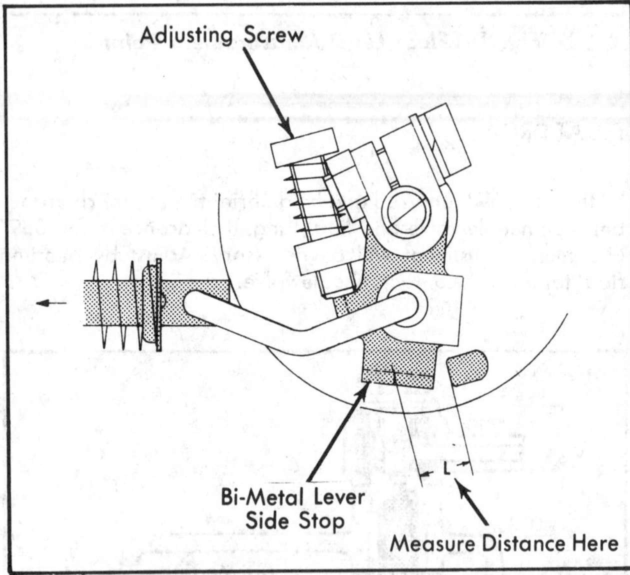

Fig. 4 Vacuum Break Adjustment for LUV Models

CHOKE UNLOADER

Datsun – 1) Close choke plate. Hold in position with a rubber band. Place throttle in wide open position.

2) Measure clearance between choke plate and air horn wall. Clearance should be as specified in table. Bend unloader tang to adjust.

NOTE – *It is important to check that throttle valve opens fully when carburetor is mounted on vehicle. If throttle does fail to open, unloader becomes inoperative.*

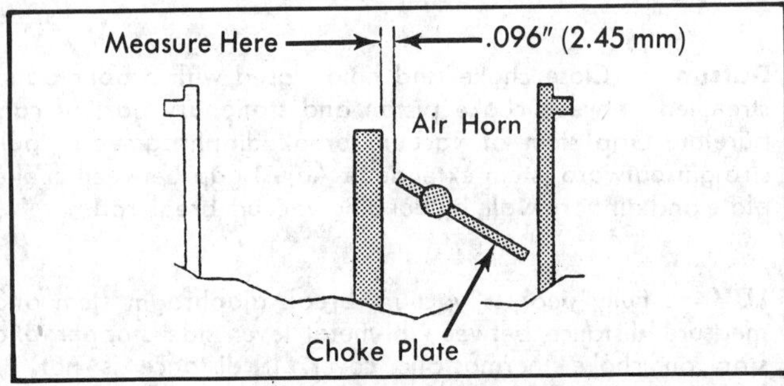

Fig. 5 Datsun Choke Unloader Adjustment

SECONDARY THROTTLE INITIAL OPENING

When primary throttle valve opens 50° (47° on LUV), primary throttle lever tang contacts secondary throttle lock-out. Any further opening of throttle valve will force secondary throttle lock-out lever to actuate secondary throttle lever and secondary throttle valve will begin to open. Check and adjust as follows:

Open primary throttle valve until it is observed that secondary is just begining to open. Hold throttle in this position and measure clearance between primary throttle valve and throttle bore. If clearance is not to specifications, adjust by bending primary throttle tang.

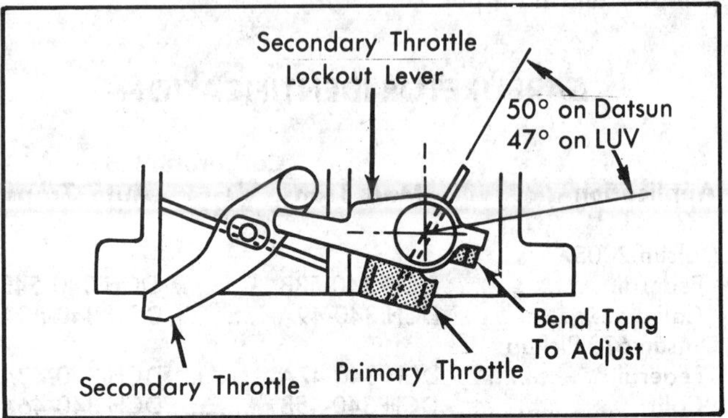

Fig. 6 Secondary Throttle Initial Opening Adjustment

CHOKE LINKAGE (FAST IDLE BENCH)

With fast idle speed screw on second step of fast idle cam, invert carburetor and close choke valve. Measure clearance between throttle plate and throttle bore. If adjustment is necessary, turn fast idle speed screw.

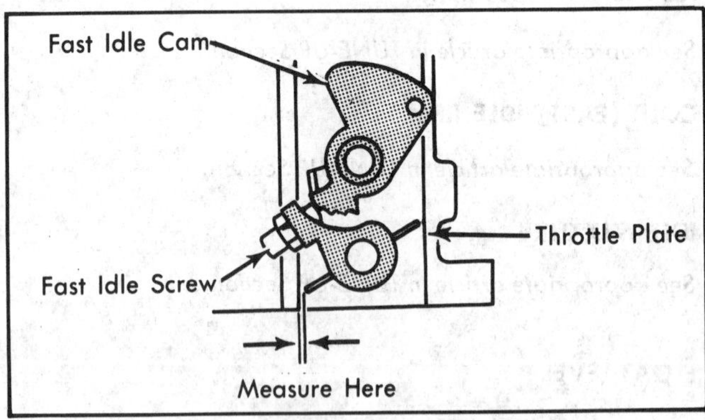

Fig. 7 Choke Linkage Adjustment

OVERHAUL

DISASSEMBLY

1) With carburetor removed, disconnect accelerator pump lever and remove throttle switch with bracket assembly. Remove throttle return spring, return spring of diaphragm, choke chamber assembly with choke wire bracket.

HITACHI DCH 340 & DCP 340 2-BARREL (Cont.)

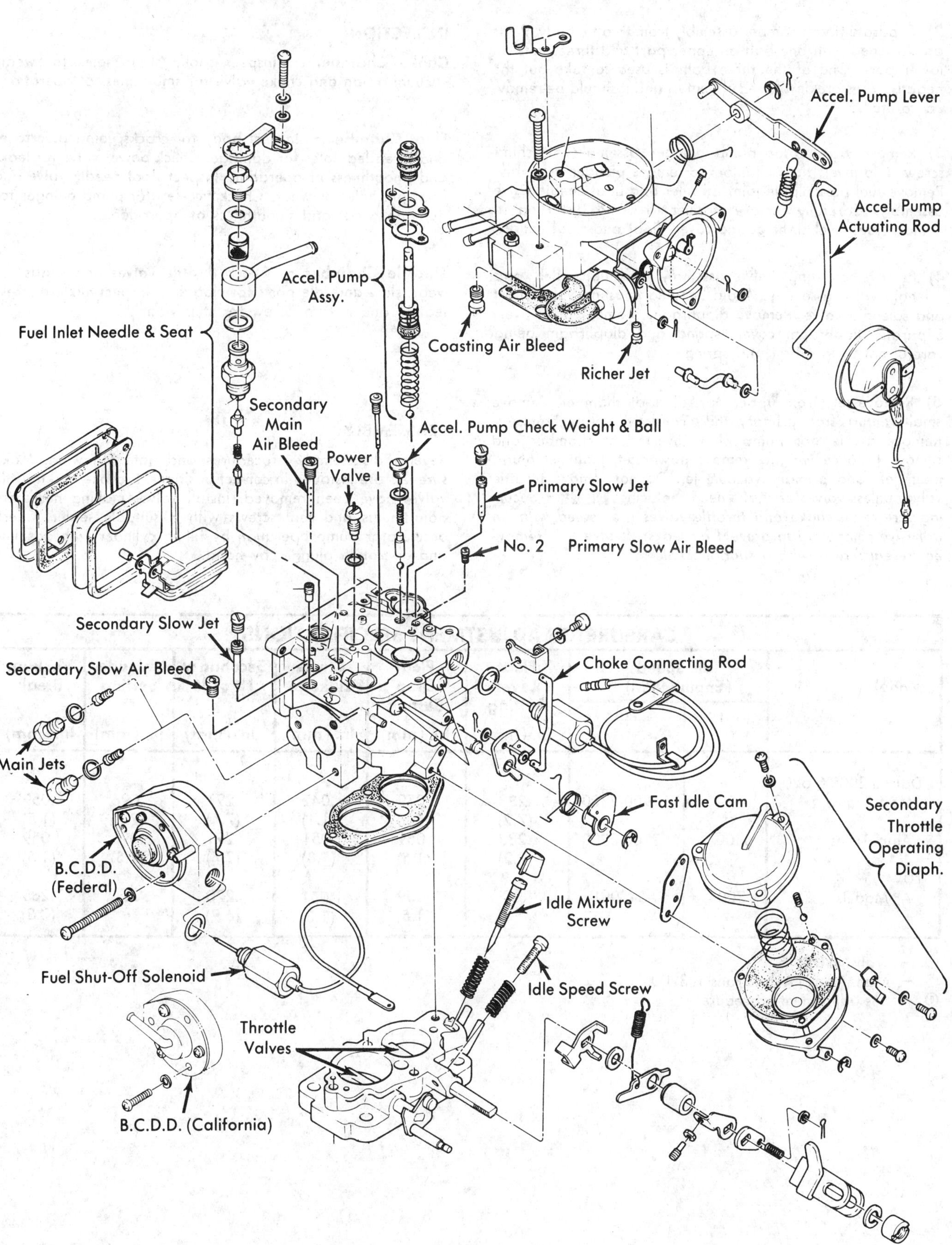

Fig. 8 Exploded View of Hitachi DCH Carburetor Assembly

HITACHI DCH 340 & DCP 340 2BARREL (Cont.)

2) Separate float chamber assembly from throttle body. Parts are fastened with one bolt on upper part and three bolts on lower part. One of the three bolts is used to take out the negative pressure developed in Venturi and it should be removed carefully.

3) Remove accelerator pump plunger assembly attaching screws and invert float chamber to remove plunger assembly. Remove fuel pipe nipple joint, strainer and float needle valve assembly. Carefully remove strainer to avoid distorting it. Remove fuel level sight gauge cover, float and float collar.

4) Remove coasting valve assembly, throttle switch and solenoid valve assembly. Avoid bending coasting valve shaft and solenoid valve. Remove diaphragm chamber and cover. Separate diaphragm cover, spring and diaphragm being careful not to lose ball and spring.

5) Remove jets from upper part of float chamber. Remove small Venturis from primary and secondary Venturi chambers. Remove accelerator pump plug, invert float chamber and remove balance weight. Remove power jet, main jet plugs, main jets and primary vacuum jet. Do not remove throttle valves unless valves or shafts need replacing. **NOTE** – *Securing screws on choke and throttle valves are sealed with an adhesive compound to prevent air leaks. If valves are removed, reseal screws with a suitable sealer.*

INSPECTION

Choke Chamber – Inspect choke shaft holes for wear, vacuum piston and choke valve for smoothness of operation.

Float Chamber – Inspect body for cracks, jointing surfaces and threaded holes for damage. Check power valve for leaks and smoothness of operation. Inspect float needle valve and float pin hole for wear. Check accelerator pump plunger for damage, wear and smoothness of operation.

Throttle Chamber – Check throttle valves and shafts for wear, slow and idle ports for clogging. Inspect mixture screw seating and mixture screw for step wear.

REASSEMBLY

Reverse disassembly procedures and note following: Make sure jets are installed in correct positions. If choke and throttle valves have been removed, install valves making necessary adjustments and seal screws with a suitable sealer. Check accelerator pump operation by filling cylinder with gasoline and operating plunger by hand.

CARBURETOR ADJUSTMENT SPECIFICATIONS

Model	Idle Speed (Engine RPM) Hot	Idle Speed (Engine RPM) Fast	Float Level Setting In. (mm)	Float Drop Setting In. (mm)	Choke Linkage In. (mm)	Secondary Throttle In. (mm)	Unloader Setting In. (mm)	Vacuum Break In. (mm)
Datsun 200SX, 620, Man. Trans.	650	1900-2800	.283 (7.2)	.059 (1.5)	.042 (1.1)	.291 (7.4)	.096 (2.5)	.059 (1.5)
Auto. Trans.	650①	2200-3200	.283 (7.2)	.059 (1.5)	.051 (1.3)	.291 (7.4)	.096 (2.5)	.059 (1.5)
LUV All Models	700	3400②	③	.059 (1.5)	.051 (1.3)	.270 (6.9)	.....	.285 (7.3)

① – Trans. in DRIVE
② – Man. Trans.; Auto. Trans. is 3200
③ – See adjustment procedure

KEIHIN 2-BARREL – EXCEPT CVCC ENGINE

Honda Civic

DESCRIPTION

Honda Civic models, except for those with CVCC engines, are equipped with a new Keihin 2-bbl. carburetor for 1977. Carburetor is a downdraft design with a primary and secondary throttle system. Unit is equipped with an internal choke valve which is manually operated by a knob and cable assembly. Both primary and secondary bores have main jets which draw fuel from a common float bowl. Accelerator is a lever and diaphragm type. Manual transmission equipped vehicles utilize a vacuum operated throttle opener system which acts similar to a dashpot.

ADJUSTMENT

HOT (SLOW) IDLE ADJUSTMENT

See appropriate article in TUNE-UP Section.

IDLE MIXTURE ADJUSTMENT

See appropriate article in TUNE-UP Section.

COLD (FAST) IDLE ADJUSTMENT

See appropriate article in TUNE-UP Section.

FLOAT LEVEL

1) Remove carburetor air horn and hold it upside down. Float arm should touch needle valve gently.

2) Measure distance from air horn gasket to center of float *(See Fig. 1).*

3) Adjust by turning needle valve seat. **NOTE** – *Do not allow valve seat to stick out above its threaded housing to prevent needle valve from falling out.*

4) After adjustment, be sure needle valve seat is clean and that float moves freely.

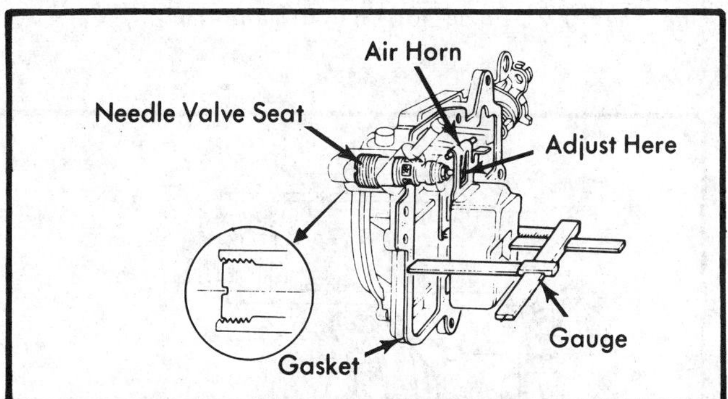

Fig. 1 Float Level Adjustment

ACCELERATOR PUMP

1) Measure total travel of accelerator pump arm.

2) Adjust to .445" (11.3 mm) by bending the arm as shown in *Fig. 2.*

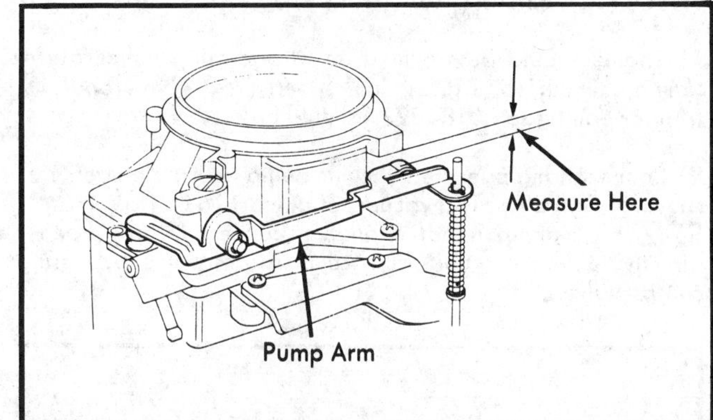

Fig. 2 Accelerator Pump Arm Travel

IDLE ADJUSTING SCREW

1) If idle adjusting screw has been removed or is out of adjustment, install screw and turn it until it bottoms gently.

2) Back out screw $2\frac{5}{8} \pm \frac{1}{2}$ turns. Install limiter cap so tab on cap is facing 180° away from stop on carburetor.

THROTTLE & CHOKE CABLE TENSION

Throttle Cable Tension – 1) Turn adjusting nut on carburetor bracket until inner cable play is zero with throttle valve fully closed.

2) Back out adjusting nut .079" (2 mm). Inner cable play should be about .157-.394" (4-10 mm) between throttle link and bracket *(See Fig. 3).*

3) Be sure carburetor throttle valve opens fully when accelerator pedal is pushed all the way down. Check to see linkage returns freely and smoothly to idle position.

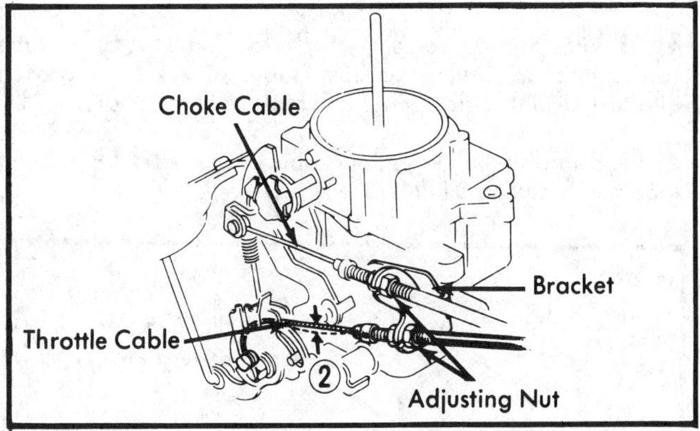

Fig. 3 Adjusting Throttle Cable Tension

Choke Cable Tension – 1) Turn adjusting nut until there is no clearance between choke lever and bracket. *(See Fig. 3).*

2) Pull choke knob OUT all the way. Choke valve should close completely.

3) Push choke knob all the way IN. Choke valve should be fully open.

KEIHIN 2-BARREL – EXCEPT CVCC ENGINE (Cont.)

THROTTLE OPENER (Man. Trans.)

1) Engine should be warmed up to operating temperature. Ignition timing (5° BTDC), idle speed (750 RPM), and distributor point gap (.018-.022") should be correct.

2) Connect hand operated vacuum pump to throttle opener as shown in *Fig. 4*. Apply a vacuum of at least 16 in. Hg.
NOTE – *If pump is not available, connect throttle opener directly to intake manifold vacuum source while bypassing control valve.*

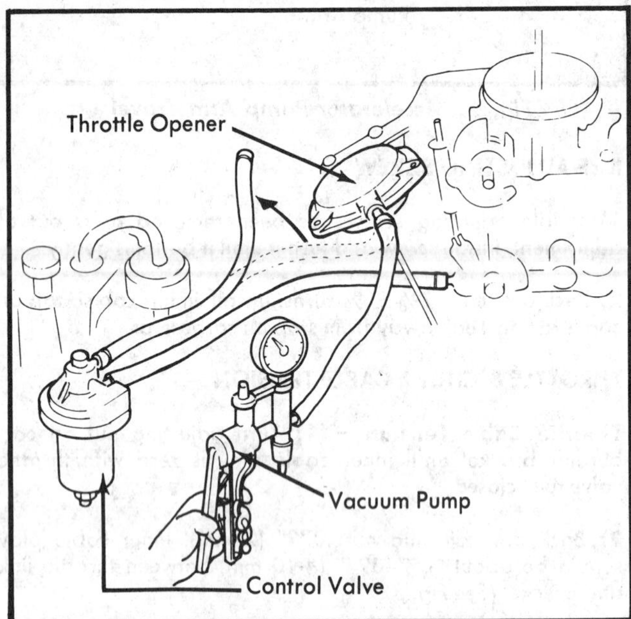

Fig. 4 Vacuum Pump Connection to Throttle Opener

3) Engine speed should increase to 1600 ± 300 RPM. Cycle accelerator a few times to stabilize engine speed.

4) If RPM is not correct, check for loose vacuum tube connection or faulty vacuum tube. Check for broken diaphragm in throttle opener and replace as necessary.

5) Bend throttle link lever forks apart to increase RPM; bend together to decrease RPM. *(See Fig. 5).*

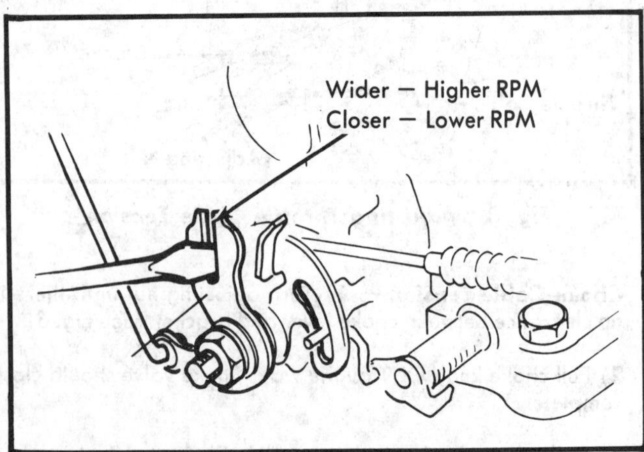

Fig. 5 Throttle Link RPM Adjustment

6) Increase engine speed to 3500 RPM. Release throttle suddenly. Throttle should close in 2-8 seconds.

7) If adjustment is required, loosen control valve lock nut. Turn adjusting nut clockwise to decrease time; counterclockwise to increase time. *(See Fig. 6).*

8) Tighten lock nut. Repeat step **6)**. If correct time cannot be obtained within full range of adjustment, replace control valve and repeat testing procedure.

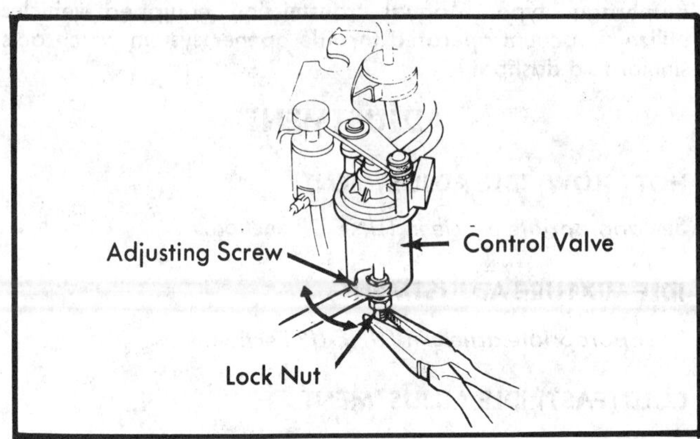

Fig. 6 Adjusting Control Valve

OVERHAUL

DISASSEMBLY

1) Remove accelerator pump rod cup. Remove (5) air horn-to-throttle body screws. Lift off air horn carefully.

2) Pull out cotter pin retaining rocker arm and remove rocker arm. Remove accelerator pump rod and rubber cap.
NOTE – *Do not take choke valve out of air horn unless it is to be replaced.*

3) Gently remove float arm pin with pin punch.
NOTE – *Tap pin out from long leg side; install from short leg side (See Fig. 7).* Do not tap on float support leg.

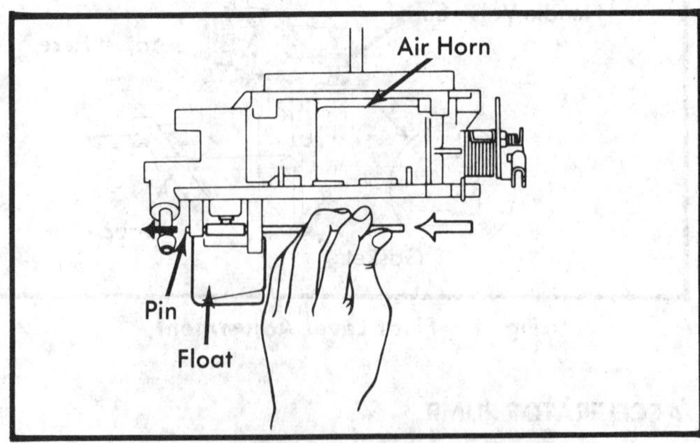

Fig. 7 Removing Float Pivot Pin

4) Remove needle valve seat assembly. Use care not to damage "O" ring.

KEIHIN 2-BARREL – EXCEPT CVCC ENGINE (Cont.)

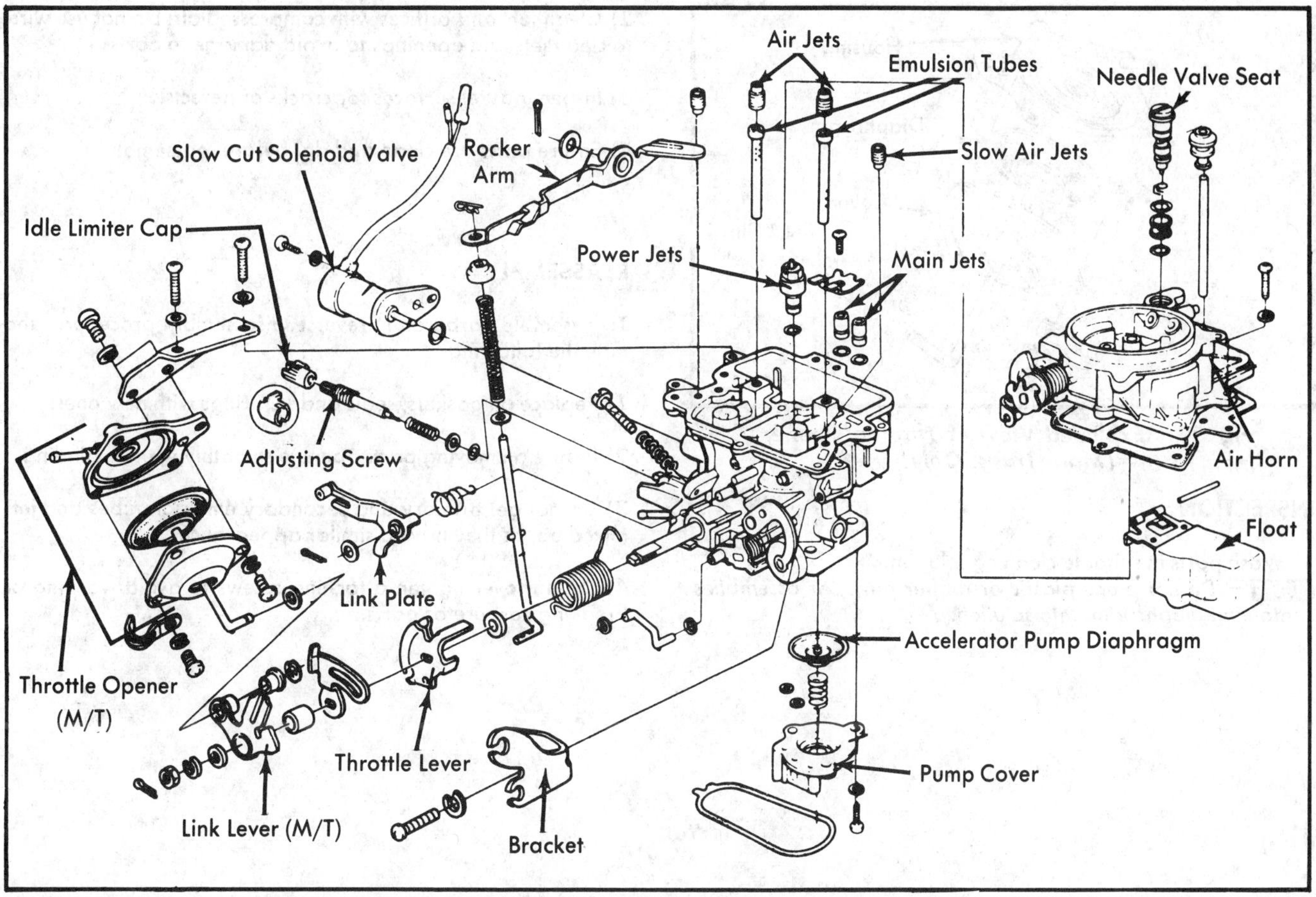

Fig. 8 Exploded View of Keihin 2-Barrel Carburetor (Honda Civic Application Shown)

5) Remove primary and secondary air jets. Disconnect emulsion tubes. Remove primary and secondary slow air jets.

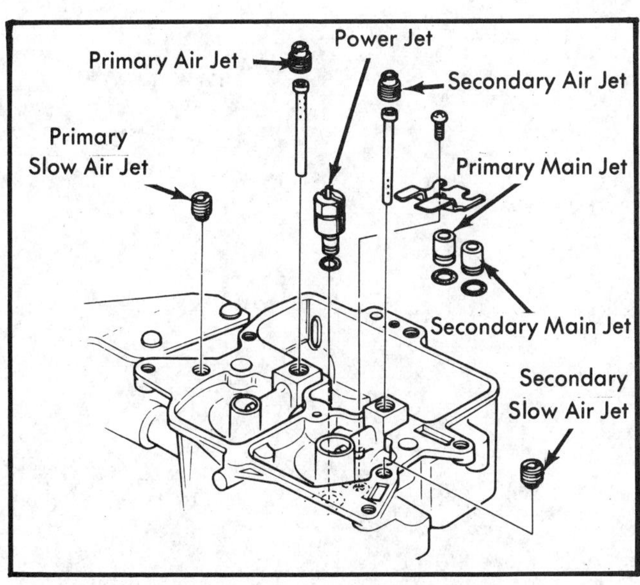

Fig. 9 Location of Various Jets

6) Take off clip plate. Remove main jets and valve seat.

7) Remove throttle opener by pulling out link plate cotter pin. Remove bracket retaining screw and remove assembly.

8) Remove fast idle ring. Remove throttle cable bracket, throttle lever and spring. **NOTE** – *Do not disassemble auxiliary and throttle valves.*

9) To disassemble accelerator pump, refer to *Fig. 10*.

10) To disassemble throttle opener, refer to *Fig. 11*.

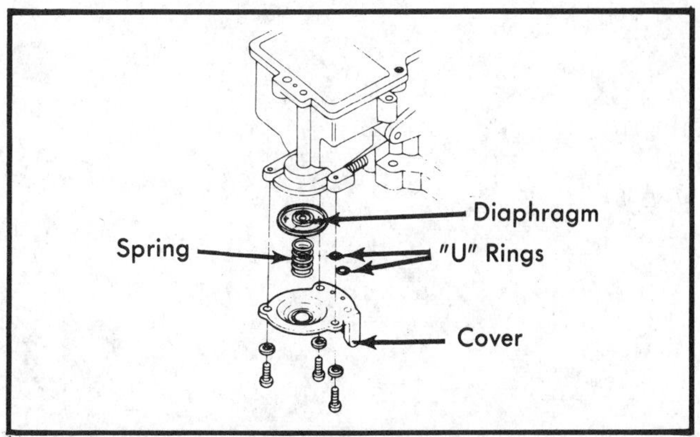

Fig. 10 Exploded View of Accelerator Pump

KEIHIN 2-BARREL – EXCEPT CVCC ENGINE (Cont.)

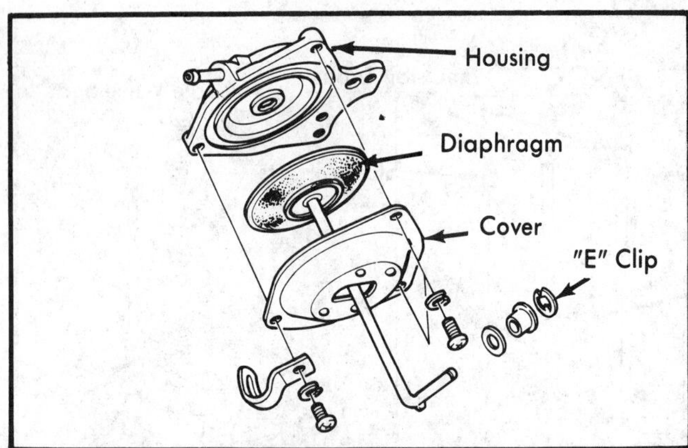

Fig. 11 Exploded View of Throttle Opener (Man. Trans. Only)

INSPECTION

1) Wash parts in suitable cleaning solution.
NOTE – *Do not place plastic or rubber parts, or assemblies containing diaphragms into solution.*

2) Clean jets and orifices with compressed air. Do not use wire to clean jets and openings to avoid damage to parts.

3) Inspect gasket surfaces for cracks or defects.

4) Ensure parts are clean and dry before reassembly.

REASSEMBLY

To assemble carburetor, reverse disassembly procedure and note the following:

1) Replace all gaskets, seals and "O" rings with new ones.

2) Ensure all moving parts operate smoothly with no binding.

3) Do not get primary and secondary emulsion tubes and jets mixed up, as they have a similar appearance.

4) Do not over tighten attaching screws to avoid warping or breaking carburetor parts.

KEIHIN 2-BARREL – HONDA CVCC ENGINE

Civic (CVCC)
Accord

DESCRIPTION

Carburetor is a two barrel, three venturi downdraft design. Carburetor contains two systems, primary and auxiliary. Primary system utilizes primary and secondary venturis, float system, accelerator pump system, and on idle system. Auxiliary system utilizes an auxiliary venturi with a float and idle system. Auxiliary system provides fuel to the pre-combustion chamber.

Carburetor components include: manually operated choke, choke opener diaphragm, secondary throttle operating diaphragm, primary throttle opener diaphragm, fuel shut-off solenoid and a primary/main fuel shut-off solenoid.

ADJUSTMENTS

HOT (SLOW) IDLE RPM

See appropriate article in TUNE-UP Section.

COLD (FAST) IDLE RPM

See appropriate article in TUNE-UP Section.

IDLE MIXTURE

See appropriate article in TUNE-UP Section.

CHOKE OPENER

Testing – 1) Pull choke knob to second detent position. While cranking engine observe that choke butterfly valve moves between partially open and fully closed.

2) Now start engine and check to see if butterfly is partially open. If butterfly valve is not operating properly, remove screws securing choke opener diaphragm and proceed with testing.

3) Swing choke opener assembly upward until it is straight up and down above carburetor *See Fig. 1*. Holding opener assembly in this position, press downward.

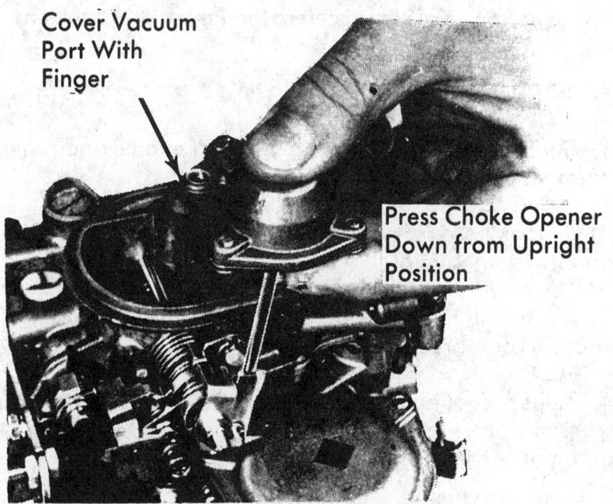

Fig. 1 Testing Choke Opener Diaphragm

4) Choke opener diaphragm is now actuated. Place finger over vacuum port and hold for about five seconds. Check that diaphragm does not leak off during this time. If it does leak down, replace diaphragm unit.

5) If diaphragm assembly does not leak down, check carburetor vacuum port for vacuum and repair as necessary.

Adjustment – 1) Pull choke cable out to 2nd detent (half way out). Depress choke opener diaphragm by hand.

2) Insert drill bit or gauge rod of 7/64" (.278 mm) between upper edge of choke valve and air horn wall.

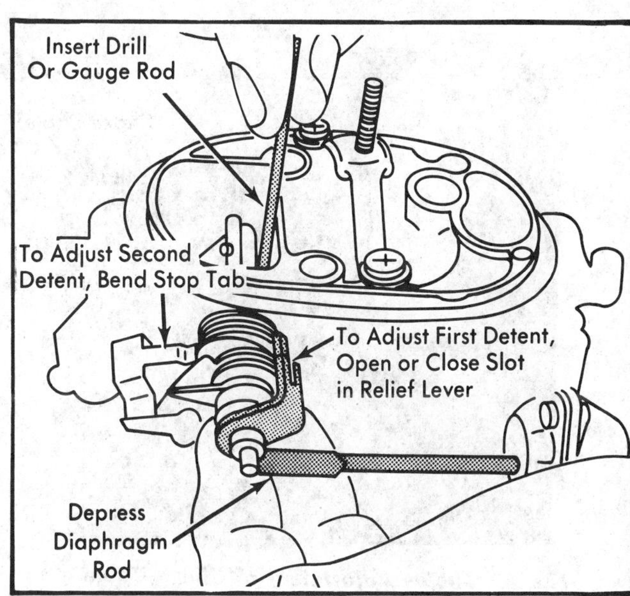

Fig. 2 Choke Opener Adjustment

3) If adjustment is needed, open or close slot in relief lever. To increase clearance, use screwdriver to widen slot; to decrease clearance, use pliers to press legs of lever together gently until correct measurement is obtained. *(See Fig. 2).*

CHOKE CABLE

1) Check that throttle cable operates smoothly with no binding or sticking. Push choke knob all the way in and remove carburetor air cleaner. Be sure that choke plate is fully open against stop tab in air horn *(See Fig. 3).*

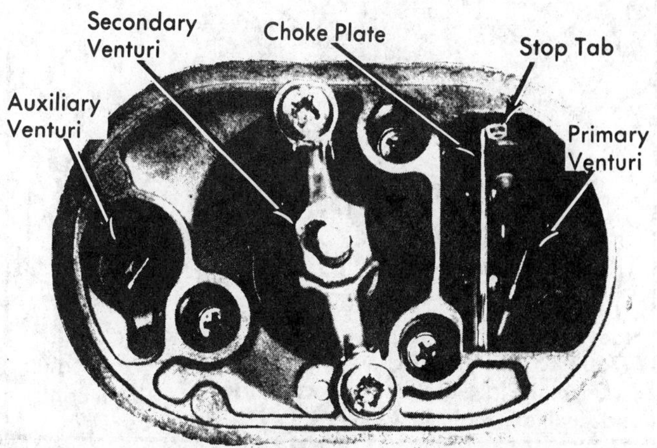

Fig. 3 Checking the Position of Choke Butterfly

KEIHIN 2-BARREL – HONDA CVCC ENGINE (Cont.)

2) Loosen lock nut of choke cable and tighten adjusting nut to move choke plate away from stop tab. Now turn adjusting nut until choke plate returns to stop tab. Tighten lock nut.

3) Have assistant pull out choke knob to second detent position, while observing action in carburetor air horn. As choke knob is pulled to second detent position, choke plate should just close. If it does not close, inspect choke plate and return spring for signs of binding.

4) Have assistant pull choke knob all the way out and observe that choke plate remains in the closed position. Replace air cleaner.

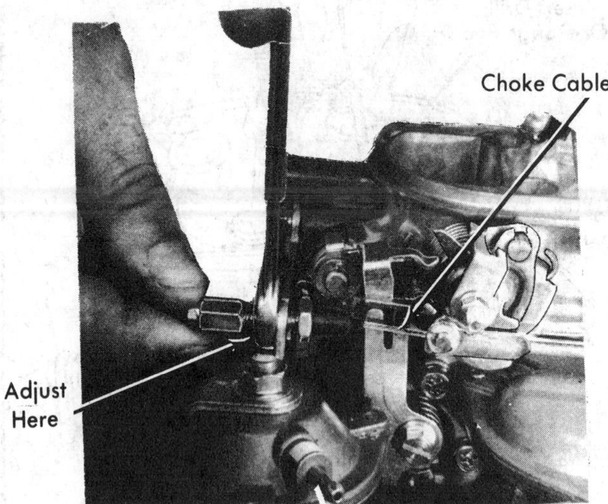

Fig. 4 Shows Adjustment of Choke Cable

FLOAT LEVEL

NOTE – *Float level gauge set, part number 07501-7570001, must be used to check and adjust float level. Gauge set contains a see thru adapter, with a red line as a fuel level indicator. Gauge set is bolted to the primary/secondary and auxiliary main jet covers.*

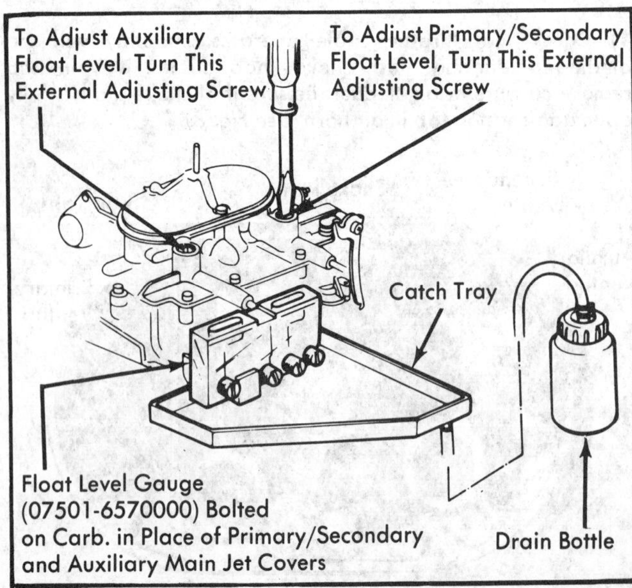

Fig. 5 Keihin Float Level Adjustment – External

1) With air cleaner removed and carburetor installed on vehicle, remove primary/secondary and auxiliary main jet covers. Attach special float level gauge, catch tray and drain bottle to carburetor.

2) Start engine and allow it to stabilize. Float level should remain at red line on gauge. If not, adjustment is made by turning external float level adjusting screws *(See Fig. 5)*.

3) Allow time for fuel level to stabilize and check again. When correct float level is achieved, paint adjusting screws to keep adjustment from changing.

ACCELERATOR PUMP

Accelerator pump stroke is adjusted by bending accelerator pump lever tang. Bend tang to get a clearance of .46-.48" (11.7-12.3 mm) between tang and throttle body stop tab *(See Fig. 6)*.

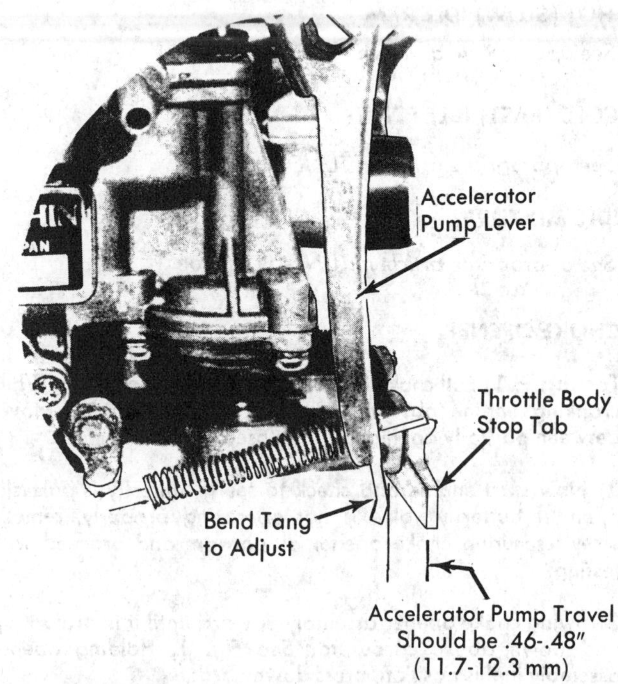

Fig. 6 Keihin Accelerator Pump Adjustment

THROTTLE CONTROLLER

1) Connect tachometer to engine. Start engine and run until at normal operating temperature.

2) Unhook hose from throttle controller diaphragm. Connect a hand vacuum pump.

3) With engine running, apply at least 15.75 in. Hg. of vacuum for more than one minute.

4) Speed should increase to 2700± 500 RPM for manual transmission equipped vehicles, or 2200± 500 RPM on automatic transmission vehicles.

5) Reconnect vacuum hose. Increase engine speed to 3500 RPM and hold for 2 or 3 seconds. Release throttle suddenly.

KEIHIN 2-BARREL – HONDA CVCC ENGINE (Cont.)

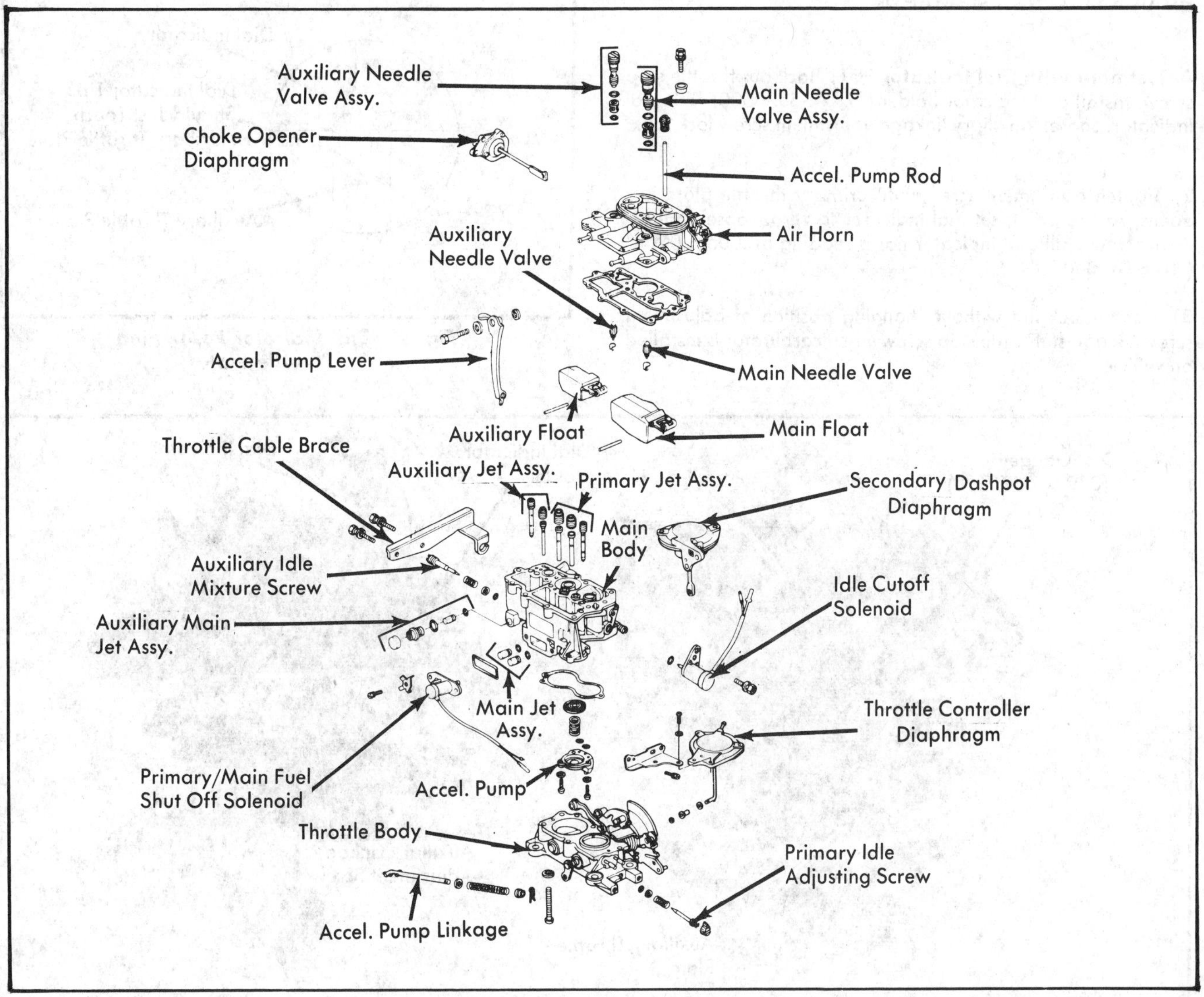

Auxiliary Needle Valve Assy.
Main Needle Valve Assy.
Choke Opener Diaphragm
Accel. Pump Rod
Air Horn
Auxiliary Needle Valve
Accel. Pump Lever
Main Needle Valve
Auxiliary Float
Main Float
Throttle Cable Brace
Auxiliary Jet Assy.
Primary Jet Assy.
Secondary Dashpot Diaphragm
Main Body
Auxiliary Idle Mixture Screw
Idle Cutoff Solenoid
Auxiliary Main Jet Assy.
Main Jet Assy.
Throttle Controller Diaphragm
Primary/Main Fuel Shut Off Solenoid
Accel. Pump
Throttle Body
Primary Idle Adjusting Screw
Accel. Pump Linkage

Fig. 7 Exploded View of Keihin Carburetor

6) RPM should drop to about 2400 and return to idle in 1 to 4 seconds. Unit acts as dashpot in this application.

7) If RPM is too high, use pliers to press adjustment slot in dashpot speed adjustment lever narrower. If RPM is too low, widen slot with screwdriver.

8) If adjustment cannot be made correctly or diaphragm will not maintain a vacuum, replace diaphragm assembly.

AUXILIARY IDLE MIXTURE

Auxiliary idle mixture screw position should be marked before removal. If screw is removed and not marked, lightly seat screw then back out 1¾ turns.

Throttle Controller Diaphragm
Vacuum Pump

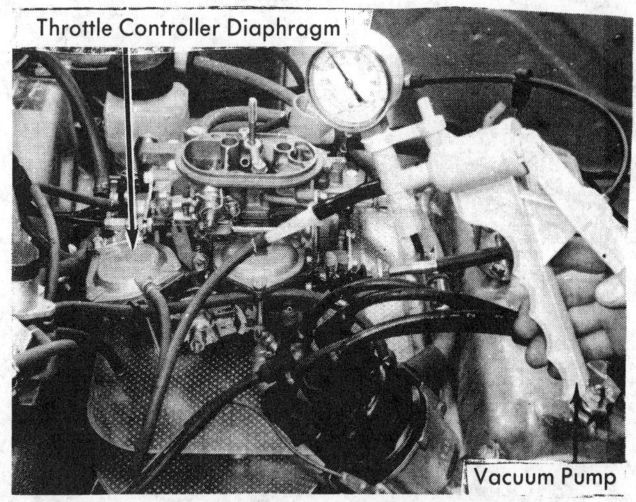

Fig. 8 Keihin Throttle Controller Adjustment

KEIHIN 2-BARREL – HONDA CVCC ENGINE (Cont.)

AUXILIARY (LAMBDA) LINKAGE

Adjustment with Dial Indicator – 1) Back out throttle stop screw. Install dial indicator holder (07974-6570600) with dial indicator. Loosen auxiliary linkage adjustment screw lock nut.

2) Tighten adjustment screw until primary throttle plate just opens. At this point, set dial indicator to zero. Loosen adjustment screw until dial indicator has a reading of .006±.0004" (.14±.01 mm).

3) Tighten lock nut without changing position of adjustment screw. Readjust throttle stop screw when carburetor is installed on vehicle.

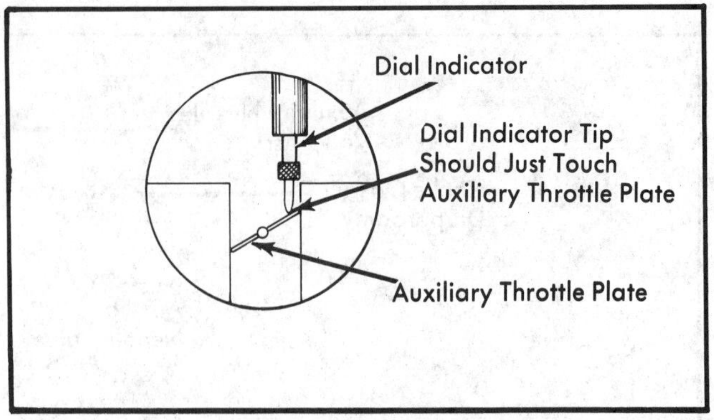

Fig. 9 Dial Indicator Positioning On Throttle Plate

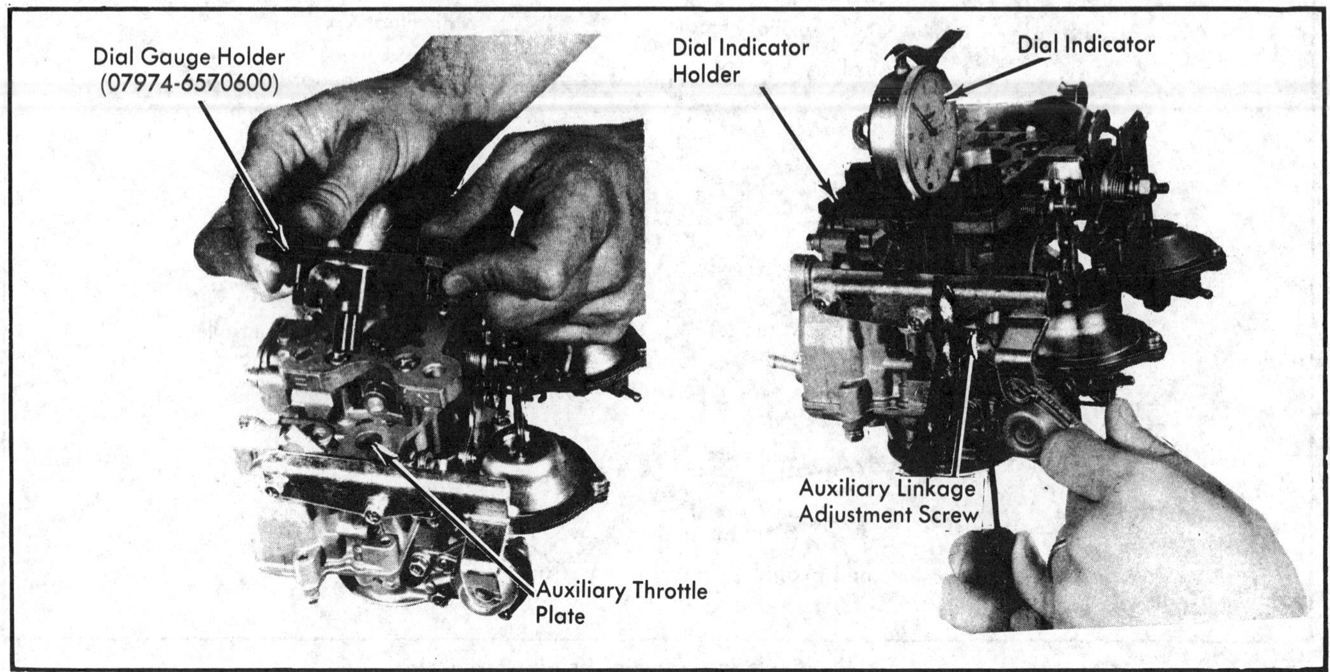

Fig. 10 Auxiliary (Lambda) Linkage Adjustment With Dial Indicator

NIKKI 2-BARREL

Opel

DESCRIPTION

Carburetor is a Nikki 2-barrel, downdraft type. It is equipped with an electric automatic choke, an anti-dieseling solenoid, a coasting richer system (fuel enrichment) solenoid, and on manual transmission models, a throttle closing dashpot. A double venturi provides for high air flow velocity at the venturi under all operating conditions, resulting in more efficient atomization of fuel for smooth combustion.

ADJUSTMENTS

HOT (SLOW) IDLE RPM

See appropriate article in TUNE-UP Section.

COLD (FAST) IDLE RPM

See appropriate article in TUNE-UP Section.

IDLE MIXTURE

See appropriate article in TUNE-UP Section.

AUTOMATIC CHOKE SETTING

Align the setting mark on the thermostat case with the setting mark on the thermostat housing and then install and tighten the set screws securely.

CHOKE PISTON STROKE

Hold the bimetal lever against the stopper then move choke piston link and check that stroke, as measured at clip end, is 3/16-7/32". If stroke is not within specifications, bend piston link at point shown in *Fig. 1*.

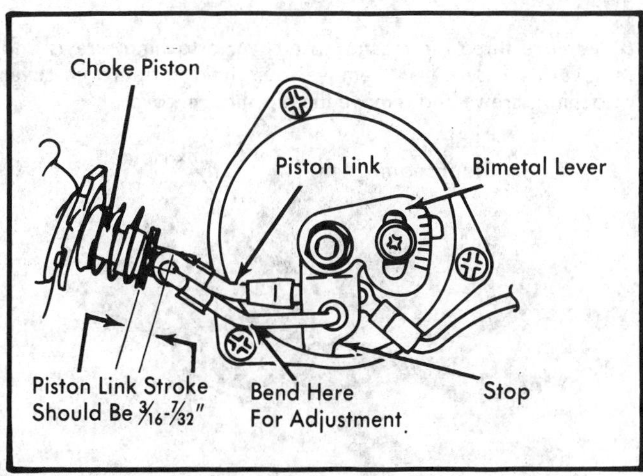

Fig. 1 Checking Choke Piston Stroke

PRIMARY & SECONDARY THROTTLE VALVE ANGLES

NOTE – *Relative angles between primary and secondary throttle valves should be adjusted during carburetor overhaul or replacement only.*

1) Slowly open primary throttle valve until secondary throttle arm starts to move. Using set gauge (J-26618 or equivalent), check angle of primary valve. *(See Fig. 2).*

2) If adjustment is needed, bend throttle link. *(See Fig. 9 for location).*

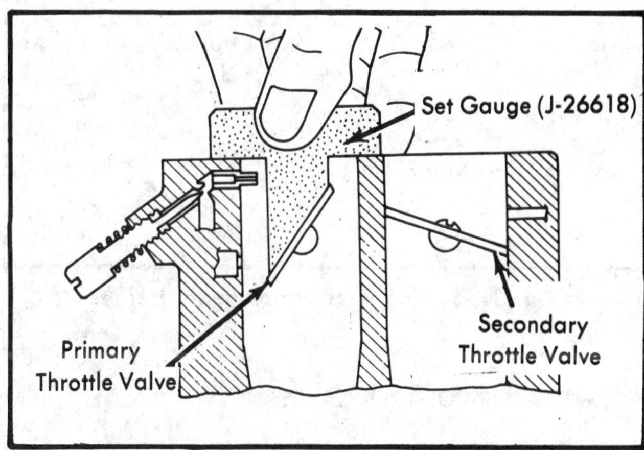

Fig. 2 Checking Relative Angles Between Primary & Secondary Throttle Valves

FLOAT LEVEL ADJUSTMENT

Adjust float level by adding or removing copper gaskets to or from the float valve seat. The float level increases with additional gaskets. The fuel level is normal when it is even with the mark on the float bowl glass window when engine is running or stopped.

CHOKE UNLOADER ADJUSTMENT

1) Apply light pressure on choke valve in closing direction.

2) Open throttle valve to wide open position. This will force choke valve open part way.

3) Measure distance from lower edge of choke valve to air horn wall. Measurement should be .215".

4) To adjust, remove choke heater coil cover. Bend choke unloader tang to obtain correct clearance.

ACCELERATOR PEDAL HEIGHT

Adjust accelerator pedal height by changing the setting of the accelerator switch. The distance between the accelerator pedal and brake pedal should be held to 2.4" (61 mm), as shown in *Fig. 3*.

NIKKI 2-BARREL (Cont.)

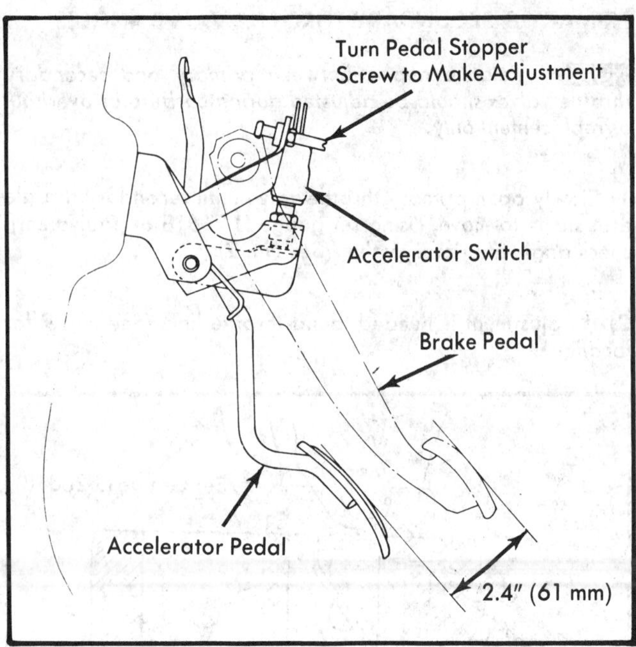

Fig. 3 Setting Accelerator Pedal Height

ACCELERATOR CONTROL CABLE

1) After completing adjustment of accelerator pedal height, as described above, adjust the control cable setting. Turn the adjusting nut until throttle valve begins to open.

2) Move control cable about .35" (8.9 mm), or the equivalent of 7-7½ turns of adjusting nut, inward toward the carburetor. Lock control cable in this position with the lock nut.

3) Depress the accelerator pedal slowly and check that carburetor throttle valve does not open while accelerator switch plunger is in contact with the accelerator pedal. Readjust control cable setting if required.

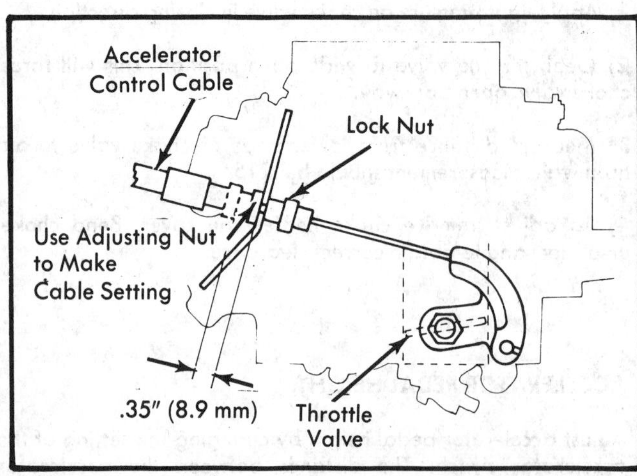

Fig. 4 Setting Accelerator Control Cable

OVERHAUL

DISASSEMBLY

NOTE – *During disassembly, be sure to keep components in groups as removed; particularly be sure not to interchange primary and secondary components.*

Air Horn – 1) Remove pump arm return spring, then take out snap ring and remove pump arm and pump link.

2) Remove fuel pipe union cap nut, then remove union and strainer. Disconnect automatic choke lead wire from its connector.

3) Remove snap ring from select lever rod, disconnect select rod from select lever, then detach rod at choke piston assembly.

Fig. 5 Parts Removal for Air Horn Disassembly

4) Disconnect automatic choke vacuum hose from choke diaphragm cover. Raise the automatic choke lead wire clip and remove lead wire from clip.

5) Remove six air horn mounting screws and detach air horn assembly.

6) Remove three thermostat case cover attaching screws and remove the case cover. Remove four choke diaphragm cover attaching screws and remove the diaphragm cover.

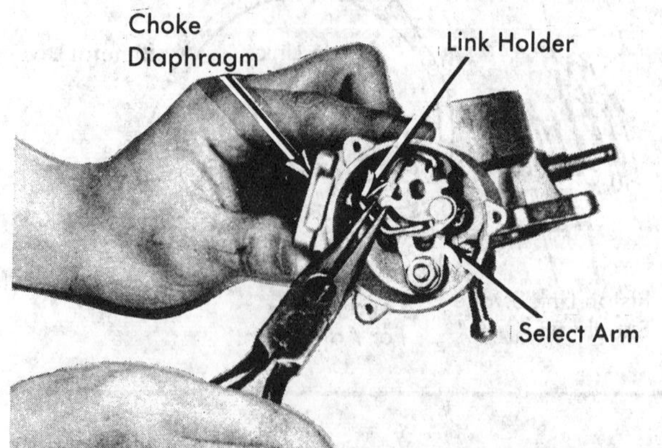

Fig. 6 Link Holder & Select Arm Removal

NIKKI 2-BARREL (Cont.)

7) Remove the link holder on the choke diaphragm rod and remove the choke diaphragm.

8) Remove nut retaining select lever and disconnect the select lever and select arm.

Float Bowl & Throttle Body – 1) Remove nut retaining primary throttle lever; then, remove the throttle lever, rods, and link levers (keeping these in proper order for reassembly).

2) Remove two screws attaching the second throttle link and remove the link. Raise the solenoid valve lead wire clip and remove the lead wire from the clip. Remove the clip from the secondary throttle arm and remove the secondary diaphragm rod from the secondary throttle arm. Remove the secondary throttle arm.

3) Remove three diaphragm chamber attaching screws and remove the secondary diaphragm chamber. Remove three bolts connecting float bowl to throttle body and separate the two.

NOTE – *One of the three bolts is installed from the lower side of the throttle body. Remove this bolt carefully, as it also serves as the power circuit ground.*

4) Remove three float chamber cover attaching screws and then remove the glass, float pin collar, float, and float valve. Remove the float valve body, accelerator pump plunger, and solenoid valves.

5) Carefully remove the following jets (match number given to number shown in *Fig. 7*):

1. Primary Second Slow Air Bleed
2. Primary Slow Jet
3. Accelerating Pump Discharge Valve
4. Primary Main Air Bleed
5. Power Valve Jet
6. Secondary Main Air Bleed
7. Secondary Step Jet
8. Secondary Step Air Bleed
9. Coasting Jet

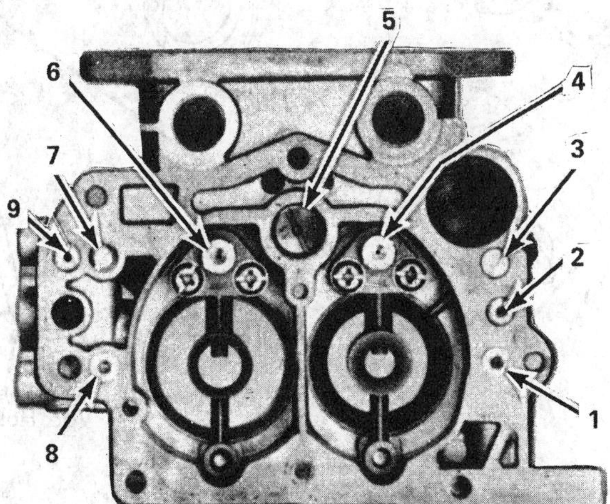

Fig. 7 Carburetor Jet Identification

6) Remove plugs and then primary and secondary main jets (the jet with the smallest hole is the primary side).

7) Remove screws attaching the small venturi and remove the primary and secondary small venturis. Remove the secondary diaphragm cover attaching screws, then remove the cover, spring and diaphragm.

INSPECTION

1) Thoroughly clean all parts and use compressed air to clean jet and fuel ports (DO NOT use a wire brush).

2) Check the following for wear, distortion, or damage: fitting face of air horn; choke valve; choke shaft; fast idle cam; select lever; select arm; tape bushing; and bimetal choke coil.

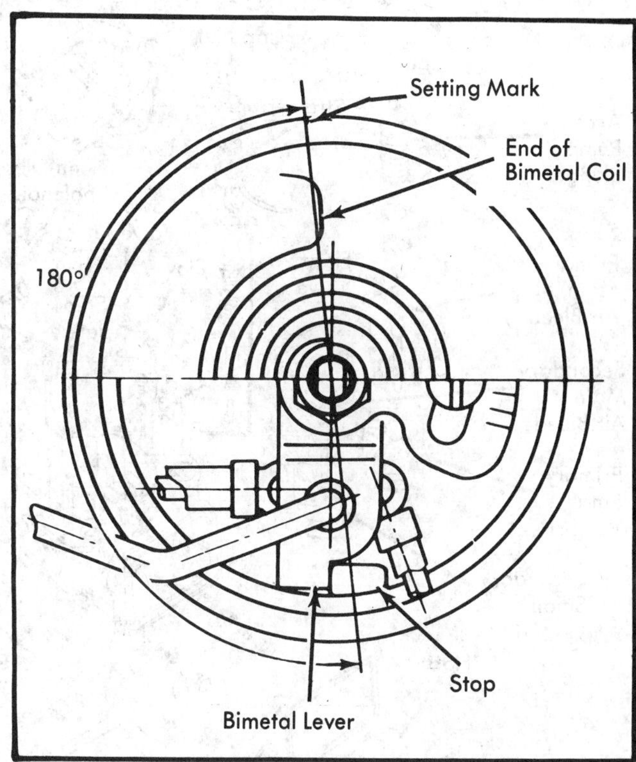

Fig. 8 Alignment of Choke Bi-Metal

3) Heat bimetal to 93°F (20°C) for six minutes, then move bimetal lever until it contacts the stop. Check that end of bimetal coil is about 180° from the stop.

4) Check heater coil for an opening or oxidation. Check insulator for cracking or damage. Measure heater coil resistance. The standard resistance should be 10.5-11.5 ohms. Check choke diaphragm for breakage or deterioration.

5) Check the following portions of the float bowl assembly for any wear or damage: float bowl and threaded portions and jet fitting face; jet orifices, threaded portions, fitting face and slit; accelerator pump; springs; and boots.

NIKKI 2-BARREL (Cont.)

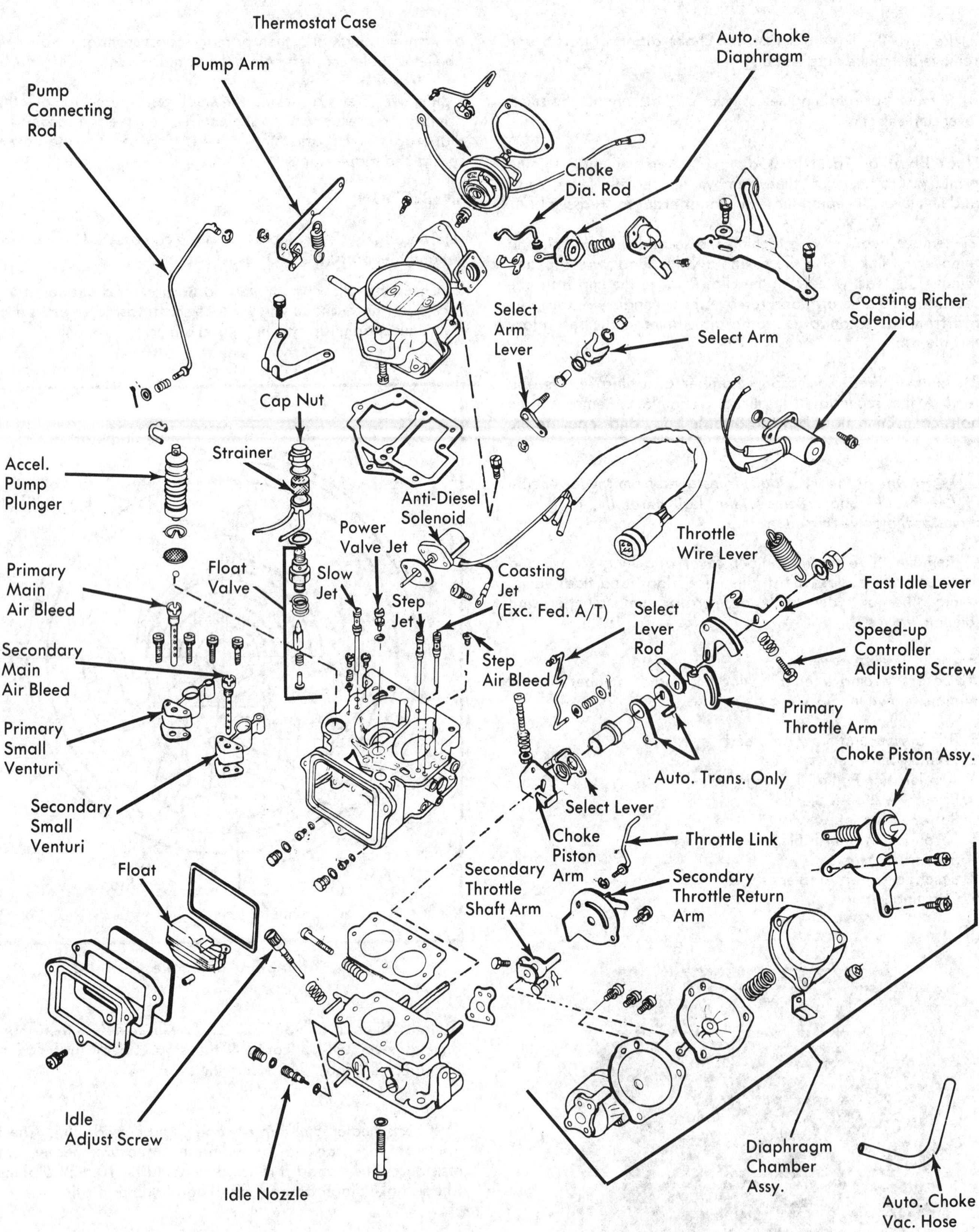
Thermostat Case
Auto. Choke Diaphragm
Pump Arm
Pump Connecting Rod
Choke Dia. Rod
Select Arm Lever
Coasting Richer Solenoid
Select Arm
Cap Nut
Strainer
Accel. Pump Plunger
Anti-Diesel Solenoid
Power Valve Jet
Throttle Wire Lever
Primary Main Air Bleed
Float Valve
Slow Jet
Coasting Jet (Exc. Fed. A/T)
Fast Idle Lever
Step Jet
Select Lever Rod
Speed-up Controller Adjusting Screw
Secondary Main Air Bleed
Step Air Bleed
Primary Small Venturi
Primary Throttle Arm
Choke Piston Assy.
Auto. Trans. Only
Secondary Small Venturi
Select Lever
Choke Piston Arm
Throttle Link
Float
Secondary Throttle Shaft Arm
Secondary Throttle Return Arm
Idle Adjust Screw
Diaphragm Chamber Assy.
Idle Nozzle
Auto. Choke Vac. Hose

Fig. 9 Exploded View of Nikki 2-Barrel Carburetor

NIKKI 2-BARREL (Cont.)

6) Check movement of parts within pump housing. Check for seepage of fuel into the float. Again, check the following for wear or damage: float lever pin; float needle and seat; float needle spring; anti-dieseling solenoid valve (also check its operation); coasting richer valve; springs; and "O" rings.

7) Check the following portions of the throttle body for wear or damage: throttle body; throttle valves and shafts; idle adjusting screw fitting face, threaded portion, and end of screw; and secondary throttle valve diaphragm.

REASSEMBLY

To reassemble, reverse disassembly procedures, noting the following: Make sure jets are installed in correct positions (all jets in the secondary side are plated with the exception of the coasting richer jet). Securely tighten the jets.

CARBURETOR ADJUSTMENT SPECIFICATIONS

Application	Idle Speed (Engine RPM)		Float Level Setting	Unloader Setting	Throttle Valve Closing Angle		Choke Valve Closing Angle	Sec. Throttle Valve Opening Angle
	Hot	Fast			Primary	Secondary		
Opel	900	2850-3150①	②	.215"	7°	20°	20°	51°

① — Auto. Trans.; Man. Trans. is 3050-3350 RPM
② — Fuel level must be even with sight bowl line

NIKKI (STROMBERG) 2-BARREL

Courier
Mazda 808 (1600)

DESCRIPTION

Carburetor is a 2-barrel downdraft type. The primary barrel includes an idle system, a piston type accelerator pump system, an idle transfer system, main metering and power enrichment systems. The secondary stage includes an idle transfer system, main metering and power enrichment systems also. Carburetor is equipped with a cable operated, manual, butterfly valve type choke which operates on the primary barrel of the carburetor. In addition, a throttle solenoid valve is provided to cut off fuel from the carburetor when the ignition is shut off.

ADJUSTMENTS

NOTE – *All carburetor adjustments are similar, however there are some physical differences between the various carburetors.*

HOT (SLOW) IDLE RPM

See appropriate article in TUNE-UP Section

IDLE MIXTURE

See appropriate article in TUNE-UP Section.

COLD (FAST) IDLE RPM

See appropriate article in TUNE-UP Section.

FLOAT LEVEL

With engine running, check fuel level in bowl sight glass. If fuel level is not within specified range, remove carburetor from engine. Remove fuel bowl cover and invert carburetor. Lower float until tang on float just contacts needle valve. Measure clearance between float and edge of bowl. If clearance is not to specifications, bend float tang to achieve proper clearance.

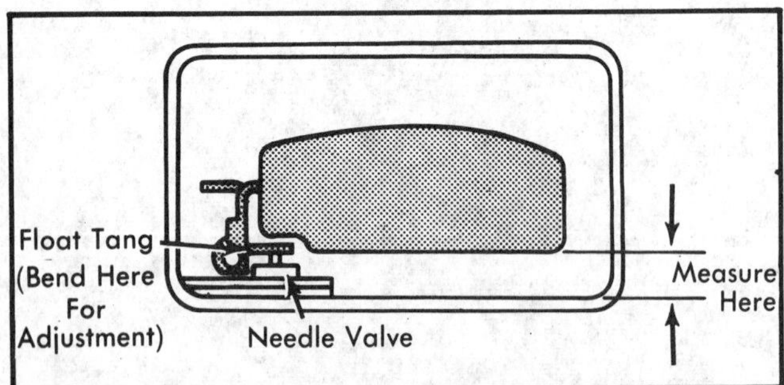

Fig. 1 Measurement for Float Level Adjustment (Carburetor Upside-Down)

FLOAT DROP

Mazda 808(1600) Only – With carburetor upright, measure clearance between lowest tip of float and fuel bowl bottom *See Fig. 2*. If clearance is not within specifications, bend float stopper until correct clearance is obtained.

NOTE – *Float drop adjustment procedures similar for other models equipped with this carburetor.*

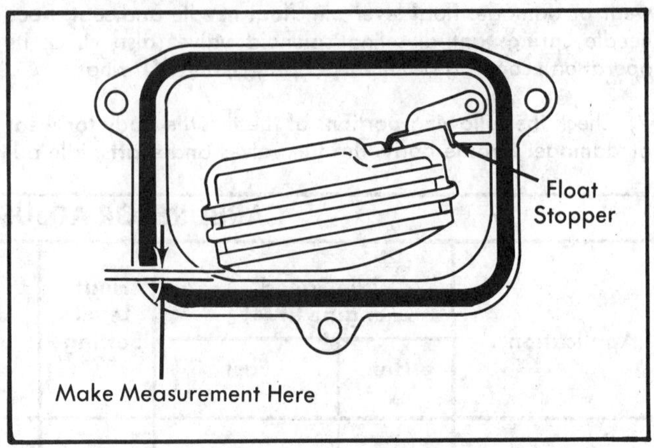

Fig. 2 Float Drop Measurement Location Mazda 808 (1600) Shown

VACUUM BREAK DIAPHRAGM

1) On California models, unhook electrical connectors from water thermo switch and connect jumper wire to both connectors. On all models, pull out choke knob to fully close choke valve. Disconnect vacuum tube to vacuum break diaphragm. Use a variable outside vacuum source connected to vacuum break diaphragm to apply specified vacuum. With 5.9-7.5 in. Hg. applied to vacuum diaphragm, choke valve should just begin to open.

2) Now apply 9.8-12.0 in. Hg. of vacuum to diaphragm and measure clearance between top of choke valve and air horn wall. Clearance should be .06-.08" (1.52-2.03 mm). If clearance is not to specifications, adjust by bending choke-to-vacuum break diaphragm connecting rod.

CHOKE ADJUSTMENT

Courier – Push choke knob all the way in. Loosen choke cable screws at the choke cable bracket and at the choke lever. **NOTE** – *Ensure choke plate is fully open.* With choke cable inserted into choke lever, tighten attaching screw *See Fig. 5.* Remove all slack between choke lever and choke cable bracket by pulling outward, and tighten attaching screws at bracket. Operate choke to make sure of smooth movement without binding of cable or choke plate.

Mazda 808 (1600) – These models are equipped with an Automatic Choke Release System. Choke can be manually operated by knob and cable from instrument panel. To prevent excessively high exhaust manifold temperatures if choke is left in cold start position too long, choke is connected to a series of switches. When engine warms and coolant temperature reaches 131° ± 9° F (55° ± 5° C), thermal and electromagnetic switches allow force of choke return spring to pull choke to OFF position.

NIKKI (STROMBERG) 2-BARREL (Cont.)

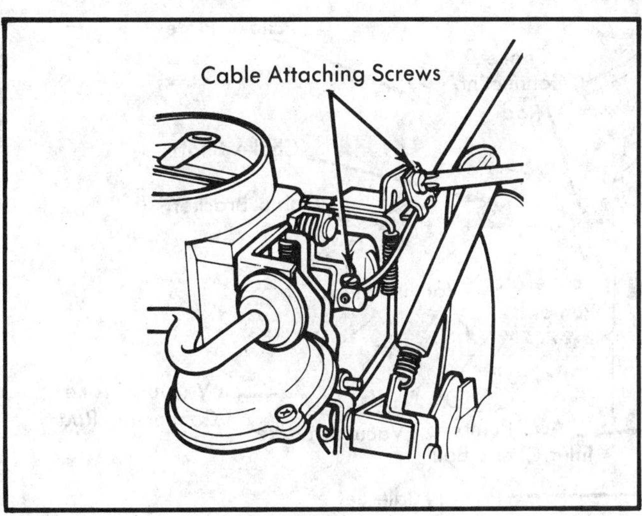

Fig. 3 Choke Cable Attachment Points (Courier Shown)

OVERHAUL

DISASSEMBLY

1) After removing carburetor from engine, remove throttle spring. Remove split pin and washer from pump connecting rod, and separate rod from connecting lever. Remove spring and washer from rod.

2) Remove pump lever retainer, pump lever and pump piston rod from air horn. Disconnect choke rod (fast idle rod) from lever. On Courier models, remove coasting richer valve assembly (deceleration valve), and disconnect wire at junction. Disconnect secondary throttle rod from shaft, remove secondary throttle actuator-to-main body screws, remove slow fuel cut valve lead and remove assembly from carburetor body. Remove slow fuel cut valve (throttle solenoid). Remove the screw retaining fuel inlet assembly bolt lock, remove lock and spacer. On all models, remove air horn attaching screws and lift air horn away from main body.

3) Remove pump plunger and pump strainer retaining clip. Invert carburetor and catch strainer and inlet check ball as they fall out. Remove screw and washer retaining pump discharge weight, invert carburetor and catch weight and outlet check ball. Remove bolts that attach throttle body to main body. **NOTE** — *One of these bolts is on underside of carburetor.* Separate throttle body from main body.

4) Remove bowl cover attaching screws and remove bowl cover and rubber gasket. Invert main body and remove collar and float from float pin. Remove needle valve assembly.

5) Remove fuel inlet fitting and note number of copper seat gaskets. Remove solenoid assembly, main air bleeds, slow air bleeds, and slow jets.

6) Remove plugs from main body and remove main jets. Remove power valve with screwdriver (Special Tool 490118 870A). Remove idle adjusting needle and spring from throttle body.

7) Remove split pin and washer from throttle lever connecting link, and separate link from primary throttle shaft arm. Remove diaphragm cover attaching screws and remove cover and return spring.

8) Remove throttle return lever and dust cover from diaphragm body. Remove clip, disconnect diaphragm rod, and remove diaphragm and rod assembly.

INSPECTION & CLEANING

Clean all parts thoroughly in solvent and check all passages and parts for wear or damage. Make sure that all jets are clear and clean. Do not attempt to clean jets by using wire or other objects which might damage calibrated orifices. Discard old gaskets and use new gaskets for assembly.

REASSEMBLY

Reassemble carburetor in reverse order of disassembly. Make sure that primary and secondary components are installed in their correct locations. When installing throttle valve or choke valve, make sure to eliminate gap between valve and wall of carburetor.

CARBURETOR ADJUSTMENT SPECIFICATIONS

Application	Idle Speed (Engine RPM)		Float Level Setting	Float Drop Setting	Choke Linkage	Secondary Throttle	Unloader Setting	Vacuum Break
	Hot	Fast	In. (mm)	In. (mm)	In. (mm)	In. (mm)	In. (mm)	In. (mm)
Courier	①	①	.256 (6.5)	.....	.063-.067 (1.6-1.7)	.....	.....	.06-.08 (1.52-2.03)
Mazda 808 (1600)	800-850	3000-4000②	.256③ (6.5)	.047 (1.2)	.....	.....	.....	.06-.08④ (1.52-2.03)

① — See Emission Control Tune-Up Decal
② — Calif. is 2500-3500 RPM
③ — Calif. is .236" (6 mm)
④ — Calif. is .06-.07" (1.6-1.9 mm)

NIKKI (STROMBERG) 2-BARREL (Cont.)

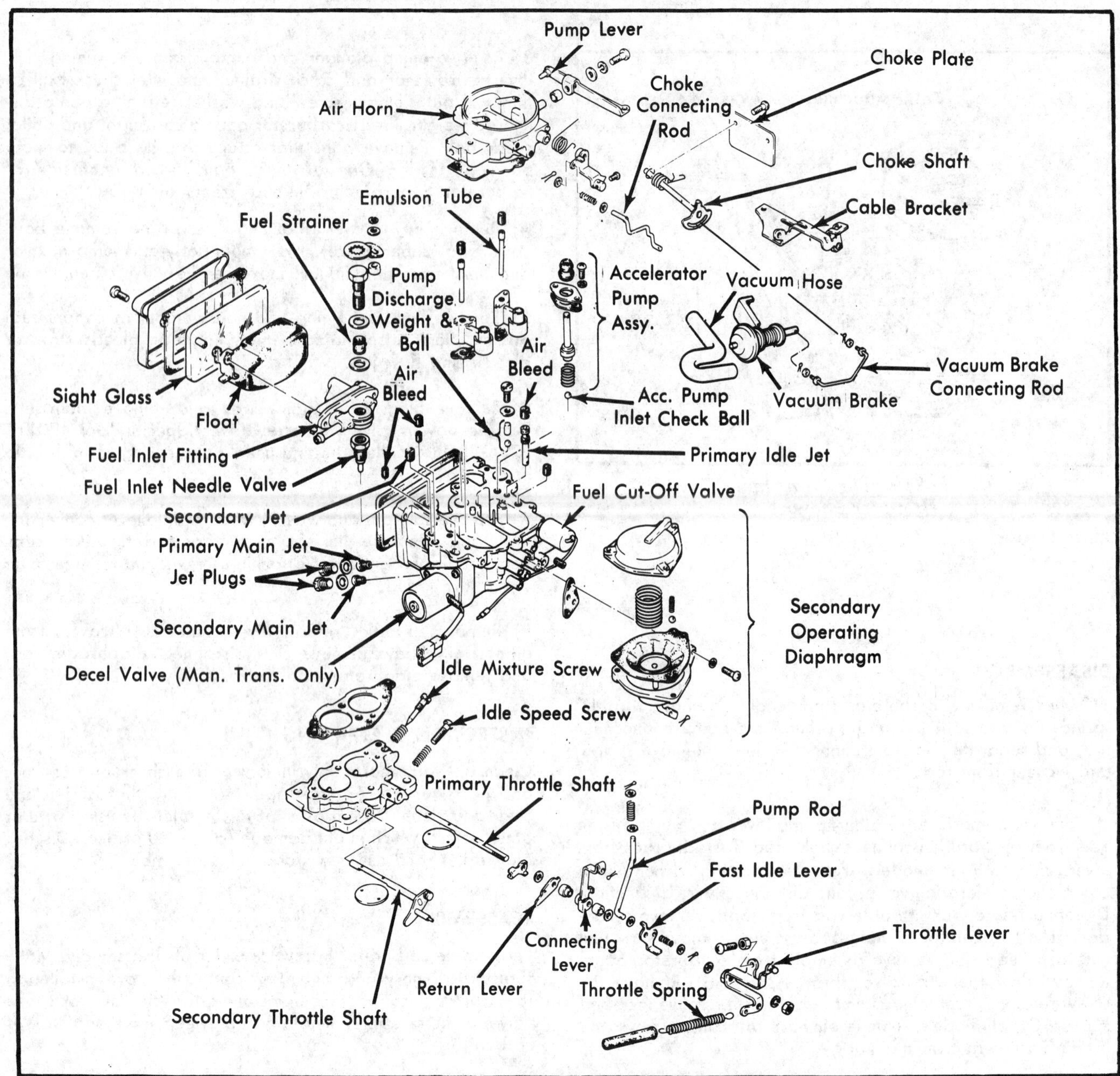

Fig. 4 Exploded View of Nikki (Stromberg) Carburetor (Courier Shown)

SOLEX 32 BICSA & 34 BICSA 1-BARREL

Peugeot 504

DESCRIPTION

Two 1-barrel carburetors are used together to form a compound carburetion system. Only the primary carburetor (32 BICSA2) is equipped with a butterfly type choke valve. Both carburetors are equipped with a diaphragm type accelerator pump. Both carburetors also have a fuel cut-off solenoid switch which prevents engine dieseling by shutting off fuel supply when ignition is turned off. Linkage between the carburetors allows throttle valve of secondary unit (34 BICSA6) to begin opening at ⅓ throttle of primary carburetor. System is equipped with a fast idling control for exhaust emission reduction purposes.

Application	Carburetor No. Primary	Secondary
Federal & Calif.	32 BICSA PEU 190	34 BICSA PEU 191
High Altitude	32 BICSA PEU 187	34 BICSA PEU 194

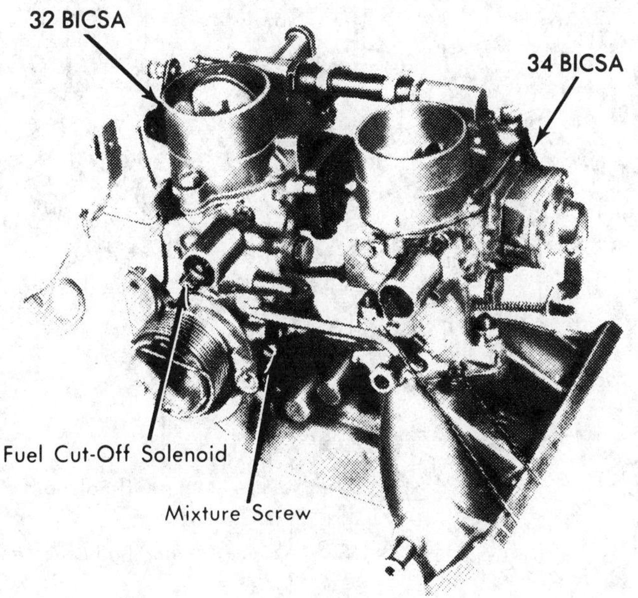

Fig. 1 Assembled View of Solex 32 BICSA & 34 BICSA

ADJUSTMENT

IDLE ADJUSTMENT

NOTE – *Idle adjustment should be accomplished by setting adjustment screws on primary carburetor only. Setting of secondary carburetor should not be altered.*

Ensure that dwell and timing are properly set and that engine is at operating temperature. Transmission should be in NEUTRAL and all accessories OFF. Adjust idle speed RPM using following steps:

1) Adjust idle screw to obtain 900 RPM.

2) Turn mixture screw in until a definite drop in RPM is apparent.

3) Back out mixture screw to obtain maximum possible RPM.

4) Now adjust idle speed screw to obtain 900 RPM.

5) Idle speed should return to 900 RPM after each movement of accelerator linkage.

ACCELERATOR PUMP

1) Remove carburetor from intake manifold.

2) Invert carburetor and insert a drill bit or pin gauge between lower edge of throttle plate and bore wall while holding throttle plate open.

3) Release throttle until plate touches drill bit. Use 9/64" (3.5 mm) drill bit on 32 BICSA and 5/64" (2.0 mm) for 34 BICSA carburetor.

4) Adjust accelerator pump by loosening nut on pump lever spring rod and slowly retightening until contact is made with tab on pump lever.

5) Install carburetors on manifold.

CARBURETOR SPECIFICATIONS①

Application	32 BICSA	34 BICSA
Venturi	24± .05	26± .05
Main Jet	120± 5②	110± 5②
Air Correction Jet	170± 20②	185± 20②
Idle Jet	62± 10②	50± 10②
Pump Injector	40± 10	40± 10
Economizer	.....	120± 20
Float (weight)	5.7± gram	5.7± gram
Needle Valve	1.2± .20	1.5± .20

① – Measurements in micromillimeters unless noted otherwise
② – Replacement jets must be same size

1977 Solex Carburetors

SOLEX 32 BICSA & 34 BICSA 1-BARREL (Cont.)

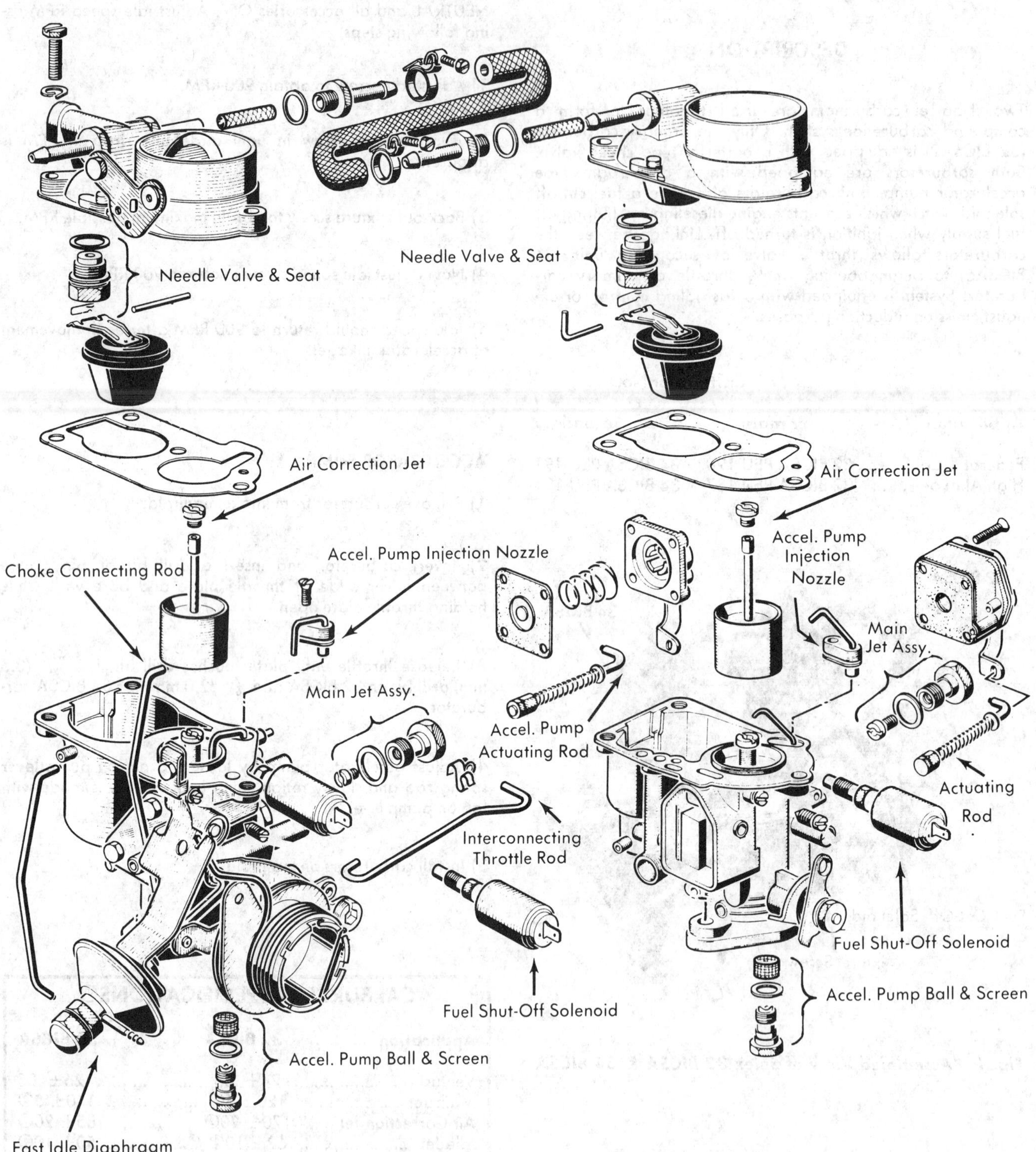

Fig. 2 Exploded View of 32 BICSA & 34 BICSA Carburetors

SOLEX 34 TBIA 1-BARREL & SOLEX 35 CEEI 2-BARREL

Peugeot 604

DESCRIPTION

The carburetion for the 1977 Peugeot 604 is made up of a primary one barrel carburetor and a secondary two barrel unit. These carburetors are mounted inline and are both downdraft designs. The secondary two barrel is vacuum controlled, while the primary carburetor operates directly from the throttle linkage. Opening of the secondary carburetor is progressive. With only slight accelerator pedal depression, a mechanical stop prevents secondary unit from opening. As pedal depression increases, stop moves and allows the rear carburetor to begin operation. Vacuum pickup for secondary carburetor operation is located at the main venturis of both the carburetors.

Idle system on both carburetors operate continually to ensure smooth transfer of operation when secondary unit begins to open. Primary uses an anti-dieseling solenoid cut-off valve. High Altitude models are different in that internal jetting sizes are reduced to compensate for difference in air density.

CARBURETOR IDENTIFICATION

Carburetor is identified by a metal tag attached to front part of unit on driver's side and is held on by one of the air horn screws.

	Carburetor No.	
Application	**Solex 34 TBIA**	**Solex 35 CEEI**
Peugeot 604		
Federal	PEU 182	PEU 186
California (M/T)	PEU 182	PEU 186
California (A/T)	PEU 183	PEU 186
High Altitude	PEU 195	PEU 196
		PEU 214

ADJUSTMENT

HOT (SLOW) IDLE ADJUSTMENT

NOTE — *Do not attempt to adjust secondary carburetor. All adjustments are made to primary unit only.*

1) Ensure engine is at operating temperature and that ignition system has been correctly adjusted.

2) Connect tachometer to engine.

3) With air filter in place, turn sweep air adjusting screw to set idle speed to 900-950 RPM.

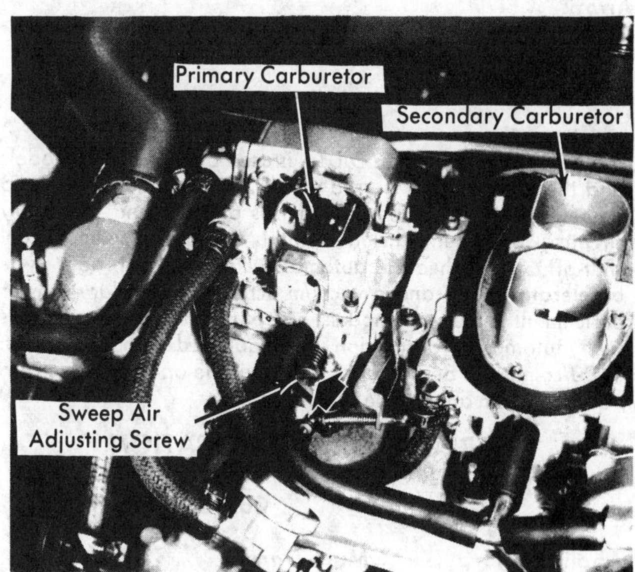

Fig. 1 Adjusting Screw Location for Idle Adjustment

THROTTLE CONTROL

1) Rotate throttle drum to full open position. Stop should be against washer to opposite side of flat area.

2) Loosen lock nuts and turn throttle link to adjust. Clearance of .067" (1.7 mm) should exist between fixed stop and movable stop.

3) With engine warmed up, bring release lever against its stop in clockwise direction. Do not allow carburetor throttle plate to open.

4) Clearance of .157" (4 mm) should exist between control quadrant stop and return link. *(See Fig. 2).*

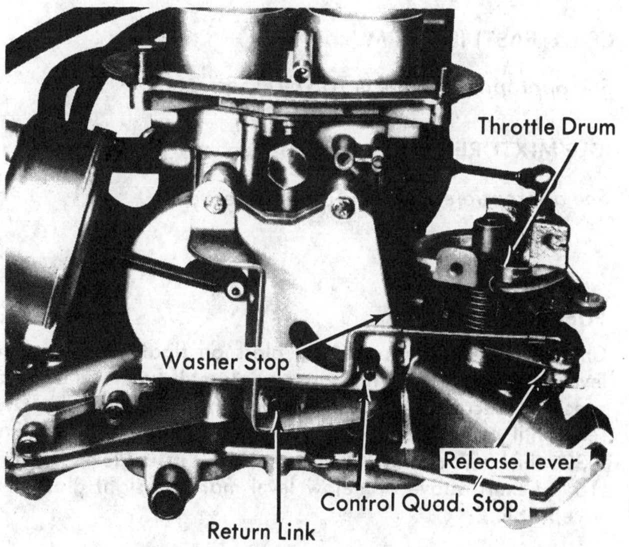

Fig. 2 Adjusting Throttle Control (Primary Carburetor Only)

SOLEX (MIKUNI) DIDTA 2-BARREL

Arrow
Colt

DESCRIPTION

The Solex (Mikuni) 28-32 DIDTA is used on all 1600 cc models and the 30-32 DIDTA is used on all 2000 cc models. This two barrel, two stage carburetor utilizes primary and secondary circuits. Components included in this unit are: a solenoid fuel shut-off, water heated automatic choke, diaphragm type accelerator pump and a vacuum actuated secondary (power enrichment) circuit. All models, except Federal 1600 cc models with automatic transmission, are equipped with a dashpot. 1600 cc models destined for High Altitude operation are also equipped with an altitude compensator.

CARBURETOR IDENTIFICATION

	Carburetor No.	
Application	Man. Trans.	Auto. Trans.
1600 cc		
Federal	28-32 DIDTA-64	28-32 DIDTA-65
California	28-32 DIDTA-60	28-32 DIDTA-60
High Alt.	28-32 DIDTA-66	.....
2000 cc		
Federal	30-32 DIDTA-64	30-32 DIDTA-65
California	30-32 DIDTA-60	30-32 DIDTA 62
1600 cc (Canada)		
All Models	28-32 DIDTA-61	28-32 DIDTA-63
2000 cc (Canada)		
All Models	30-32 DIDTA-61	30-32 DIDTA-63

ADJUSTMENTS

HOT (SLOW) IDLE RPM

See appropriate article in TUNE-UP Section.

COLD (FAST) IDLE RPM

See appropriate article in TUNE-UP Section.

IDLE MIXTURE

See appropriate article in TUNE-UP Section.

FUEL LEVEL

Check fuel level through sight glass on float chamber. Fuel level should be even with center of glass. If fuel level is not as specified, increase or decrease packing under needle valve seat until correct fuel level is obtained. A sheet of packing .039" thick will change float level .118". If fuel level is within .16" (4 mm) above or below level mark on sight glass, it is acceptable.

DASHPOT

1) Ensure idle RPM is set correctly. Gently push dashpot connecting rod up until it stops.

2) Engine idle should now be within following specifications:

1600 cc	
Federal	2000± 100 RPM
California	1900± 100 RPM
High Altitude	1900± 100 RPM
2000 cc	
Federal	2000± 100 RPM
California	1500± 100 RPM

3) Quickly release dashpot rod when correct idle is obtained. Idle speed should drop to following RPM in 3 to 6 seconds:

1600 cc	
Federal	900 RPM (M/T)
Calif. & High Alt.	1000 RPM (M/T)
	900 RPM (A/T)
2000 cc	
Federal	1000 RPM (M/T)
	900 RPM (A/T)
Calif. & High Alt.	1000 RPM (All)

4) Engine RPM level can be set by dashpot adjusting screw.

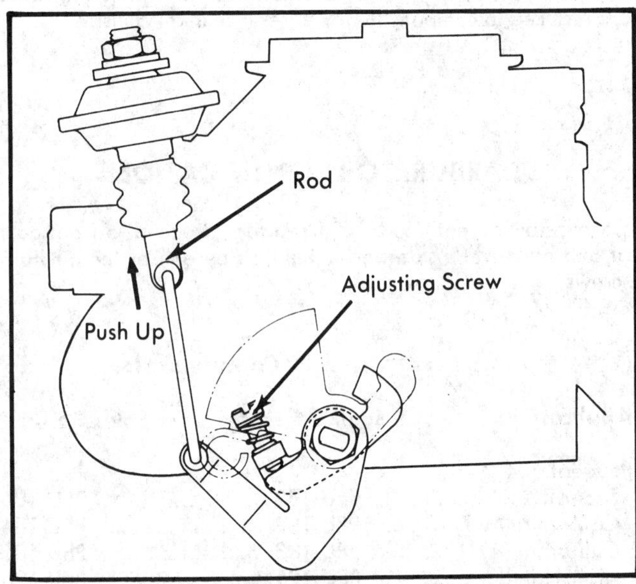

Fig. 1 Dashpot Adjustment

OVERHAUL

DISASSEMBLY

NOTE — *Do not remove inner venturi, by-pass screw (sealed with white paint), throttle shaft or valve. Do not disassemble parts of the automatic choke body.*

1) Disconnect carburetor linkage, water hose to choke body and choke rod. Remove float chamber cover, float, and related parts. Disassemble and remove depression chamber.

2) Remove accelerator pump, cover, spring, and membrane from main body. Take out accelerator pump weight and ball. Remove enrichment cover, spring, and valve body, but do not disassemble valve body. Remove both main jet and pilot jet.

3) Disassemble throttle body by removing throttle lever nut, throttle lever, collar, abatement plate, collar, and intermediate lever.

SOLEX (MIKUNI) DIDTA 2-BARREL

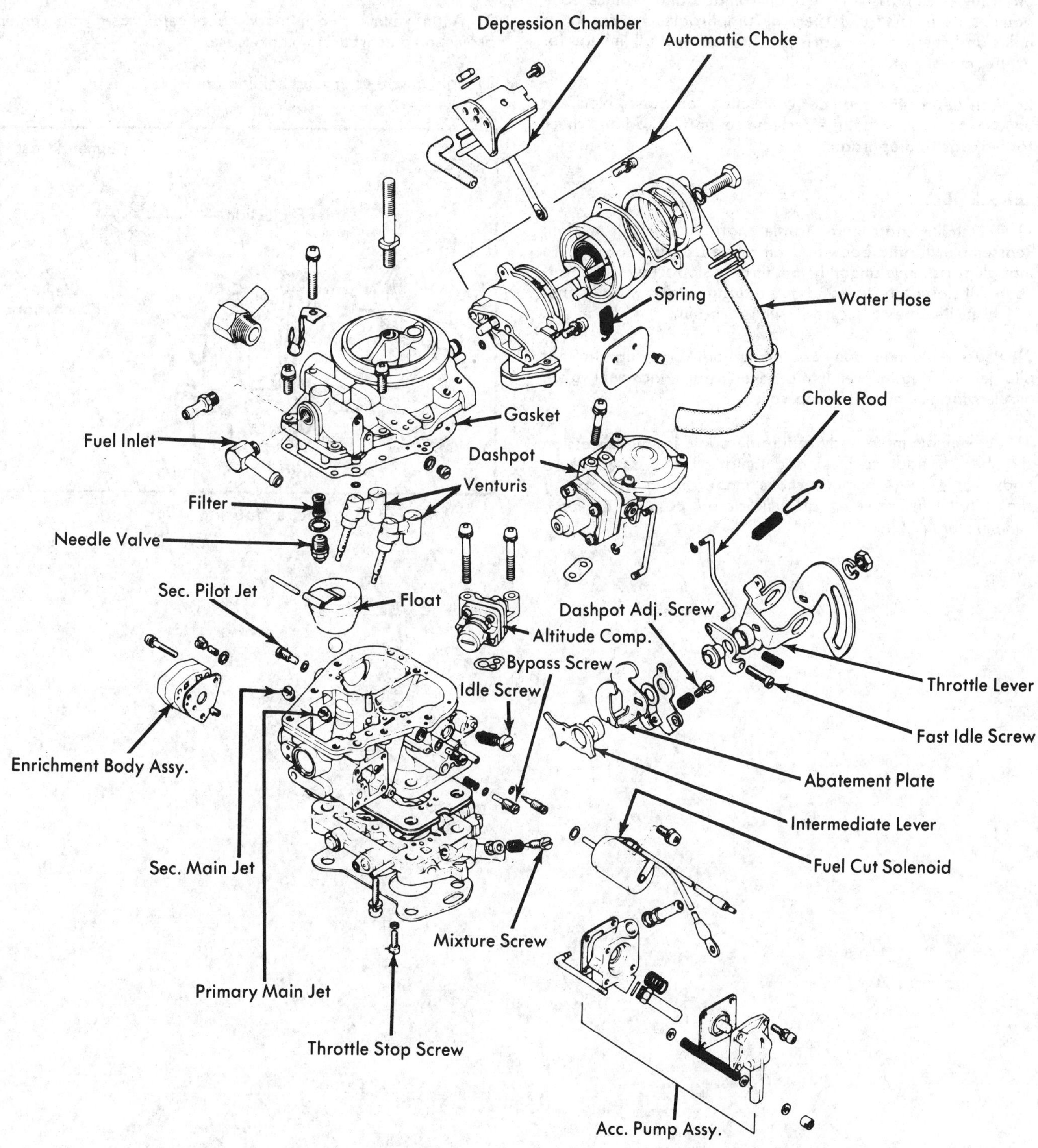

Fig. 2 Exploded View of Solex (Mikuni) DIDTA 2-Barrel Carburetor

SOLEX (MIKUNI) DIDTA 2-BARREL (Cont.)

INSPECTION

1) Clean all parts in suitable solvent and dry with compressed air. Check all parts for wear or damage and replace components as necessary. Inspect all diaphragms for cracks or holes and check rubber parts for leakage. Test all linkage for proper movement.

2) Push depression chamber connecting rod down, block off vacuum passage with finger, release connecting rod and check for leakage at diaphragm.

REASSEMBLY

1) Oil choke shaft and throttle shaft interlocking section. Reassemble throttle body and all related parts, making sure that all parts move smoothly. Set throttle stop screw with throttle in full closed position and give adjustment screw additional 1/4 turn. Be sure to secure it. with lock nut.

2) Reassemble main body and related parts, making sure that pilot jet "O" ring fits well into groove. Install enrichment valve, accelerator pump, and pump cover.

3) Reassemble main body to throttle body. Install depression chamber to float cover and automatic choke assembly to body. **NOTE** – *Automatic choke index setting is proper if choke butterfly valve is at fully closed position at room temperature (77°F).*

AUTOMATIC CHOKE

1) Loosen screws holding metal ring around choke housing. This allows housing to be turned but not removed.

2) Align yellow punch mark on bimetal case with center projection on carburetor choke case.

3) Tighten screws around holding ring.

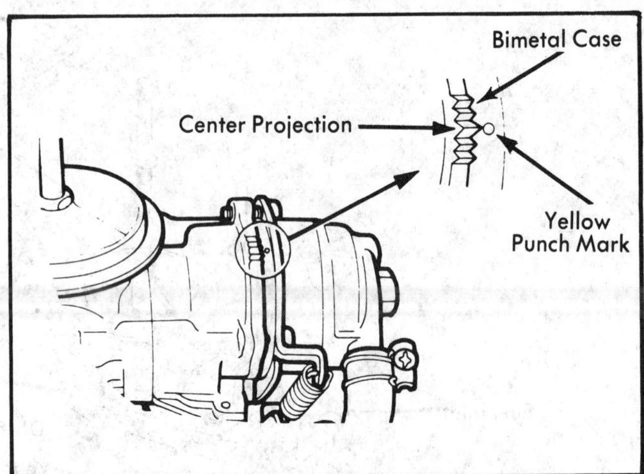

Fig. 3 Choke Housing Alignment

WEBER 32 ADFA 2-BARREL

Fiat 124
Fiat 131

DESCRIPTION

Carburetor is a two stage, two barrel downdraft type unit. Primary stage is mechanically operated by accelerator linkage. Secondary stage is operated by mechanical linkage and a vacuum diaphragm. Primary stage includes idle and transition, main metering system and acceleration system. Secondary stage includes power enrichment, secondary main metering and transfer circuits. A single fuel bowl supplies fuel for both stages. A coolant heated choke bi-metal spring operates the choke plate through linkage and is completely automatic.

CARBURETOR IDENTIFICATION

Carburetor number is located on lower edge of main body base on the side facing the engine. It can be quickly found by looking just above the gasket between main body and throttle plate housing.

Application	Carburetor
Fiat 124 (All)	32 ADFA 12/100
Fiat 131	
Without Catalytic Converter	
Man. Trans.	32 ADFA 1/100
Auto. Trans.	32 ADFA 3/100
With Catalytic Converter	
Man. Trans.	32 ADFA 4/100
Auto. Trans.	32 ADFA 6/100

ADJUSTMENT

HOT (SLOW) IDLE RPM

See appropriate article in TUNE-UP Section.

IDLE MIXTURE

See appropriate article in TUNE-UP Section.

COLD (FAST) IDLE RPM

See appropriate article in TUNE-UP Section.

FLOAT LEVEL & FLOAT DROP

1) Remove air horn from carburetor. Hold vertical and ensure gasket is in place. Weight of float should gently depress needle valve. Measure distance between top of float and gasket surface. Distance should be .217-.295" (5.5 - 7.5 mm). If adjustment to float level is needed, bend float arm where it joins float. *(See Fig. 1).*

2) To measure float drop, hold air horn in upright position and allow float to hang down fully. Measure distance from gasket surface to float top at leading edge. Distance should be .551" (14.0 mm). If necessary to adjust, bend float drop tang.

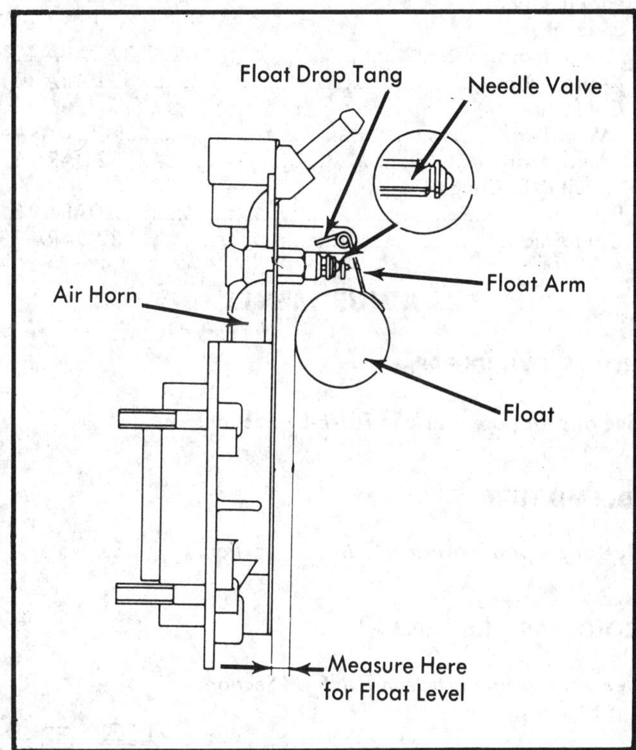

Fig. 1 Float Level & Float Drop Adjustment (Fiat 124 & 131)

WEBER 32 DARA 2-BARREL

Renault
R-12
R-17 Coupe

DESCRIPTION

Carburetor is a downdraft 2-barrel with semi-automatic choke. Both semi-automatic choke and carburetor base are warmed by engine coolant. Automatic transmission models of R-12 are also equipped with electric heating coil assist for choke mechanism.

CARBURETOR IDENTIFICATION

Application	Model No.
Renault R-12	
Federal	
Man. Trans.	32 DARA 12
Auto. Trans.	32 DARA 13
California	
Man. Trans.	32 DARA
Auto. Trans.	32 DARA 1
Renault R-17 Coupe	
Federal	32 DARA 13
California	32 DARA 1

ADJUSTMENTS

HOT (SLOW) IDLE RPM

See appropriate article in TUNE-UP Section.

IDLE MIXTURE

See appropriate article in TUNE-UP Section.

COLD (FAST) IDLE RPM

See appropriate article in TUNE-UP Section.

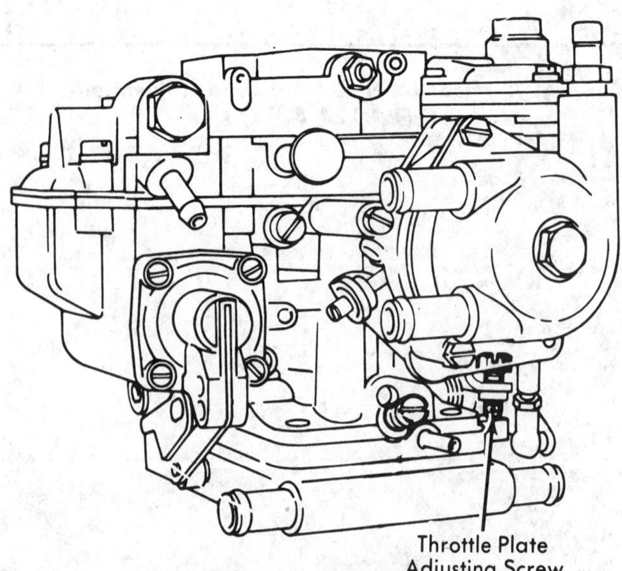

Fig. 1 Initial Throttle Plate Opening (Off Car) Adjustment

INITIAL THROTTLE PLATE OPENING

With carburetor removed from vehicle, hold throttle closed and measure clearance between throttle and bore. On manual transmission models, this measurement should be .047-.051" (1.2-1.3 mm) and on automatic transmission models it should be .059" (1.5 mm). If necessary, adjust by turning idle adjusting screw located on throttle linkage (see illustration).

FLOAT LEVEL & FLOAT DROP (TRAVEL)

1) With air horn removed, hold carburetor vertical so that float hangs down and closes needle valve. Measure distance between float and gasket surface. Distance should be .281" (7 mm).

2) If adjustment is necessary, bend float level tang to obtain correct clearance.

3) Now move float outward as far as it will go and measure distance between float and gasket surface. This is the float drop measurement and it should be .313" (11 mm). If adjustment is needed, bend float drop tang.

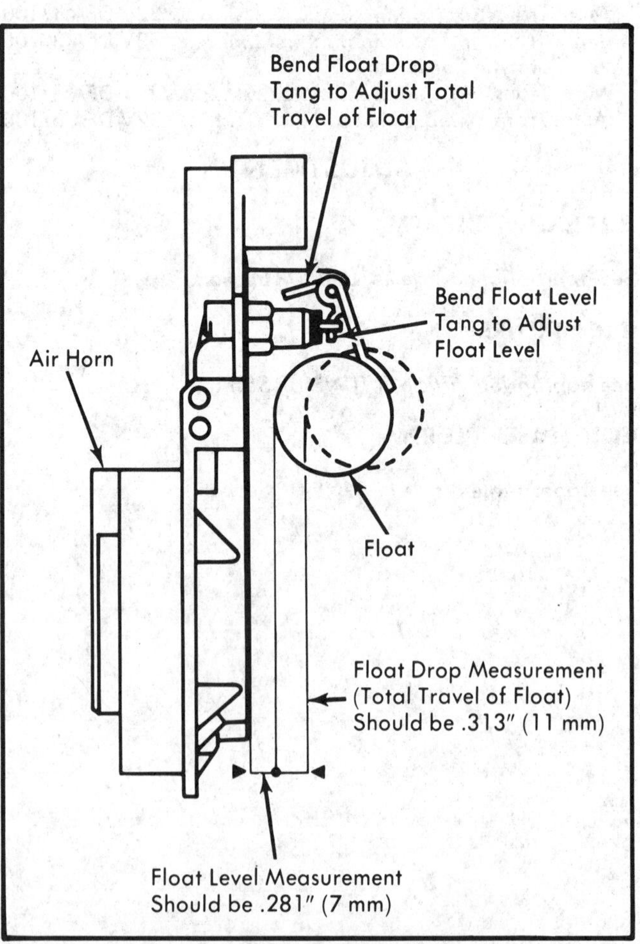

Fig. 2 Float Level & Float Drop (Travel) Adjustment

WEBER 32 DARA 2-BARREL (Cont.)

INITIAL CHOKE PLATE OPENING

Vacuum – 1) Remove choke housing cover. Push activating lever to close choke plates. Gently force rod up into diaphragm as far as it will go.

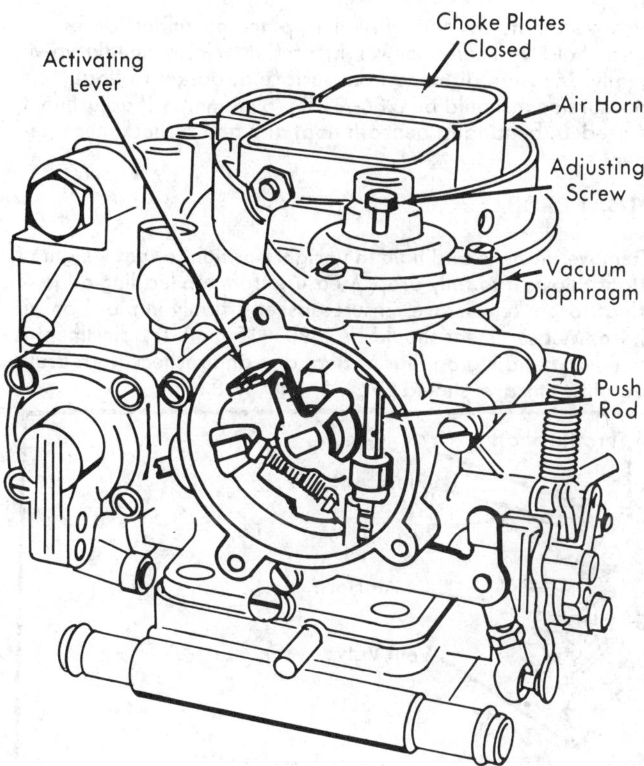

Fig. 3 Initial Choke Plate Opening (Vacuum) Adjustment

2) Hold activating lever against push rod. Measure gap between choke plates and air horn wall.

3) Measurement should be .203-.281" (5-7 mm). If adjustment is needed, turn adjusting screw to obtain correct clearance. *See Fig. 3.*

Mechanical – 1) Close choke plates. Open throttle plates to Wide Open Throttle (WOT) position. This will open choke plates slightly.

2) Now measure gap between choke plates and air horn wall. Clearance should be .281" (7 mm). If adjustment is needed, turn adjusting screw until proper gap is obtained. *See Fig. 4.*

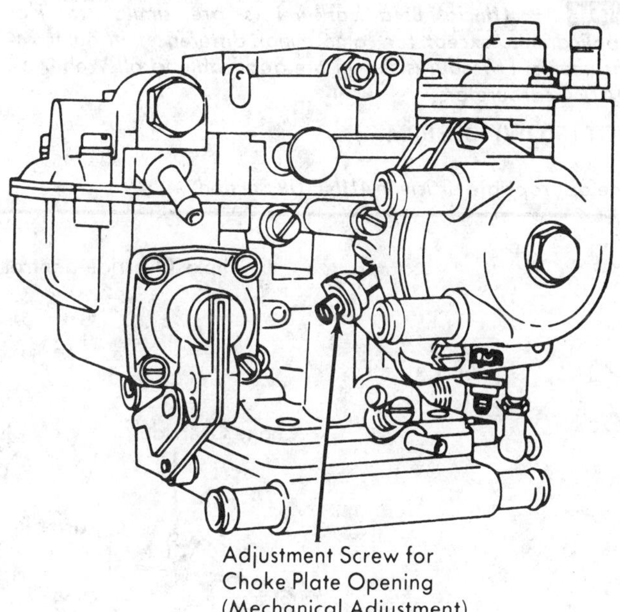

Fig. 4 Initial Choke Plate Opening (Mechanical) Adjustment

CARBURETOR ADJUSTMENT SPECIFICATIONS

Carb. No.	Idle Speed (Engine RPM)		Float Level Setting	Float Drop Setting	Choke Linkage	Secondary Throttle	Unloader Setting	Vacuum Break
	Hot	Fast	In. (mm)	In. (mm)	In. (mm)	In. (mm)	In. (mm)	In. (mm)
Weber								
M/T Models	800-900	1500	.281 (7)	.313 (8)	.281 (7)	.203-.281 (5-7)	.....	.....
A/T Models	625-675	1500	.281 (7)	.313 (8)	.281 (7)	.203-.281 (5-7)	.....	.....

WEBER 32 DATRA 2-BARREL

Fiat 128
Fiat X 1/9
Lancia Beta

DESCRIPTION

Carburetor is two barrel downdraft design. This unit uses a diaphragm type accelerator pump, a crankcase ventilation device, carbon monoxide idling control device, excess fuel recycling device (from carburetor to fuel tank), anti-dieseling solenoid and a dashpot. A choke unloader is used to prevent excessively rich mixtures when cold starting. This system operates both by vacuum and mechanical lever and spring action. A coolant heated automatic choke system has been added for 1977.

ADJUSTMENTS

NOTE – *Lancia Beta carburetors are similar to Fiat applications, except for some minor differences in outer attachments. Procedures shown are applicable to all Weber 32 DATRA carburetors.*

HOT (SLOW) IDLE RPM

See appropriate article in TUNE-UP Section.

IDLE MIXTURE

See appropriate article in TUNE-UP Section.

COLD (FAST) IDLE RPM

See appropriate article in TUNE-UP Section.

FLOAT LEVEL

Remove air horn. With gasket in place on underside of air horn, hold vertically so weight of float closes needle valve gently. Measure distance from surface of gasket to float. This measurement should be .236-.315" (6 - 8 mm). If adjustment is needed, bend tang beneath float arm and recheck measurement.

FLOAT DROP

Remove air horn and hold in upright position so that weight of float allows it to fully drop. Measure from top leading edge of float to gasket surface. Ensure gasket is firmly in place on air horn. Measurement should be .590" (15 mm). If adjustment is needed, bend lug on rear of float arm and recheck float drop. Total float travel should be .275-.354" (7-8 mm).

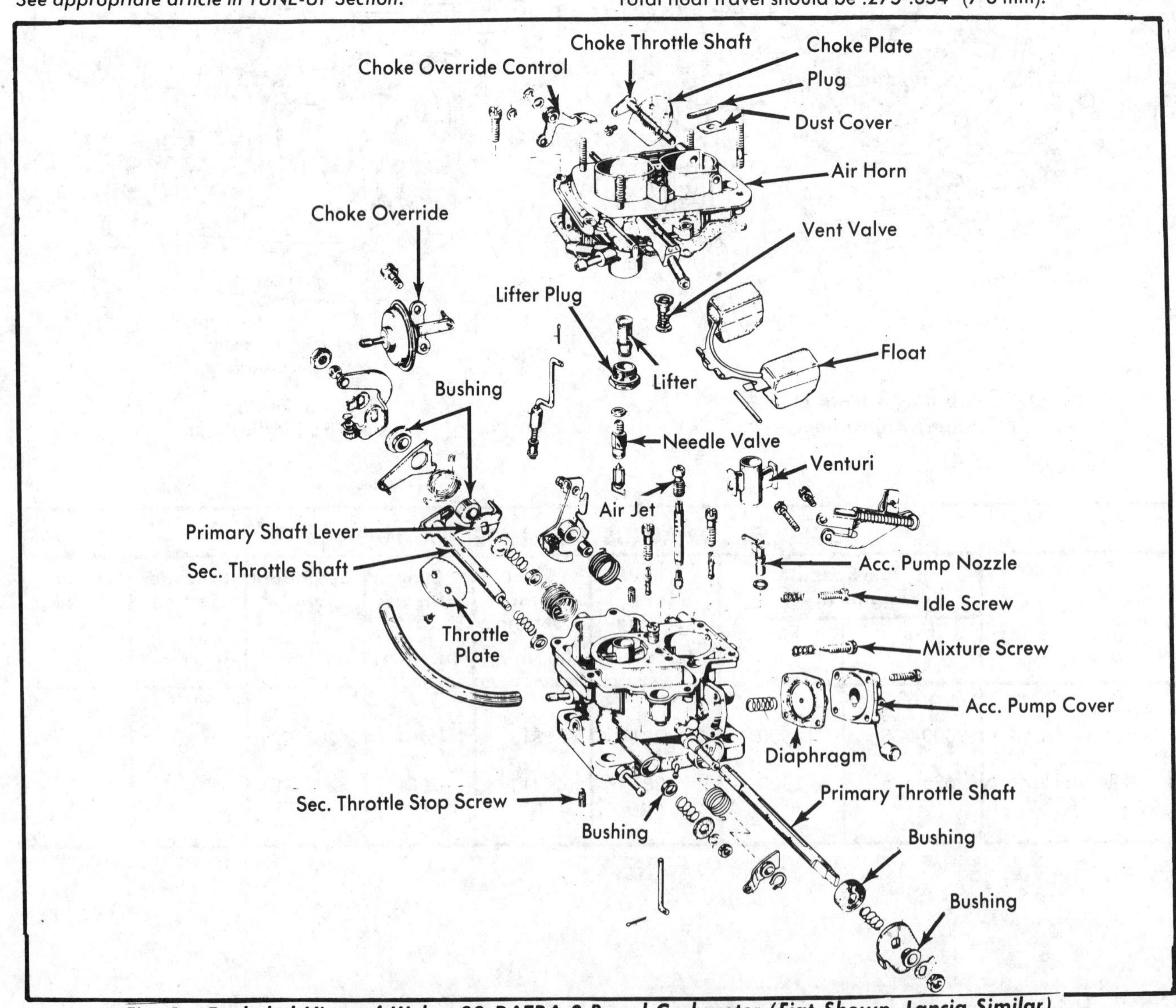

Fig. 1 ***Exploded View of Weber 32 DATRA 2-Barrel Carburetor (Fiat Shown, Lancia Similar)***

WEBER 32 DIR 2-BARREL

Renault
R-5

DESCRIPTION

The Weber 32 carburetor is a two barrel downdraft type. It is equipped with a manual choke and carburetor base is heated by engine coolant flowing through it. Fuel filter is a metal screen type located in carburetor fuel inlet.

CARBURETOR IDENTIFICATION

Application	Carb. No.
Renault R-5	
Federal	32 DIR 56
California	32 DIR 55
High Altitude	32 DIR 53

ADJUSTMENTS

HOT (SLOW) IDLE RPM

See appropriate article in TUNE-UP Section.

IDLE MIXTURE

See appropriate article in TUNE-UP Section.

COLD (FAST) IDLE RPM

See appropriate article in TUNE-UP Section.

FLOAT LEVEL & FLOAT DROP (TRAVEL)

Float level and drop are checked and adjusted with float bowl removed. Place float bowl in a vertical position (see illustration). Allow weight of float to close needle valve without allowing ball to enter valve. Measure dimension "A" (see illustration) to check float level. Measurement should be .281" (7 mm). If necessary, adjust by bending float arm. Measure dimension "B" (see illustration) to check float drop. Measurement should be .315" (8 mm). If necessary, adjust by bending float arm tab.

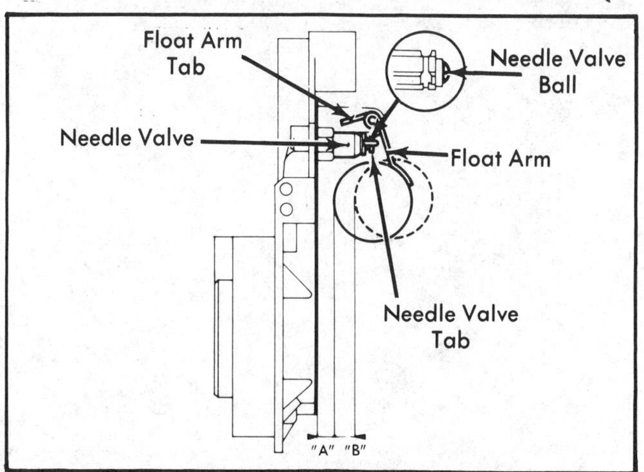

Fig. 1 Float Level & Drop Adjustment

INITIAL THROTTLE VALVE OPENING ADJUSTMENT

With choke valve completely closed, measure throttle valve opening. Measurement should be .047" (1.2 mm). If necessary, adjust opening by loosening lock nut and turning adjustment screw at choke cam.

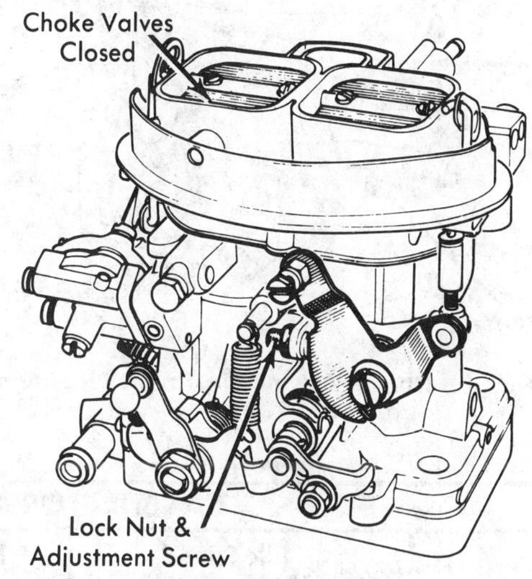

Fig. 2 Initial Throttle Valve Opening Adjustment

INITIAL CHOKE VALVE OPENING ADJUSTMENT

NOTE — *Two adjustments are required. Both mechanical and vacuum adjustments are necessary.*

Mechanical — With choke valve fully closed, push on sleeve until it contacts cam lever. Measure opening at bottom of choke valve. Measurement should be as noted in Specifications Table at end of article. If adjustment is needed, bend link as shown in *Fig. 3*.

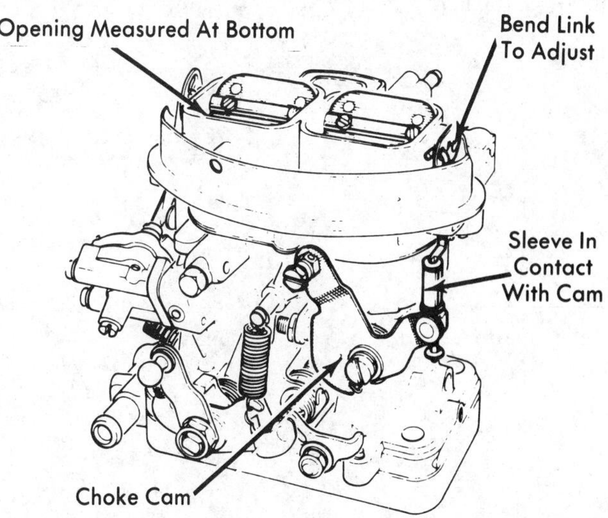

Fig. 3 Choke Valve Adjustment (Mechanical)

1977 Weber Carburetors

WEBER 32 DIR 2-BARREL (Cont.)

Vacuum – Push diaphragm link in as far as possible. Now close choke plates with choke arm until spring on link is slightly compressed. Measure opening at bottom of choke valve. Measurement should be to specifications. If adjustment is needed, remove screw from end of diaphragm and turn set screw until opening is correct.

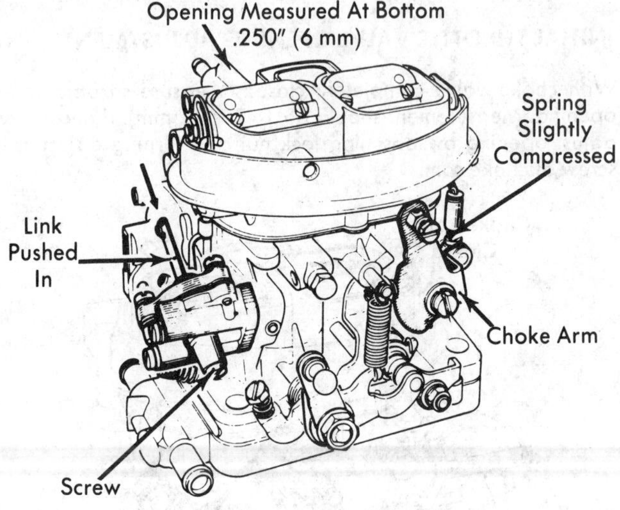

Fig. 4 Choke Valve Adjustment (Vacuum)

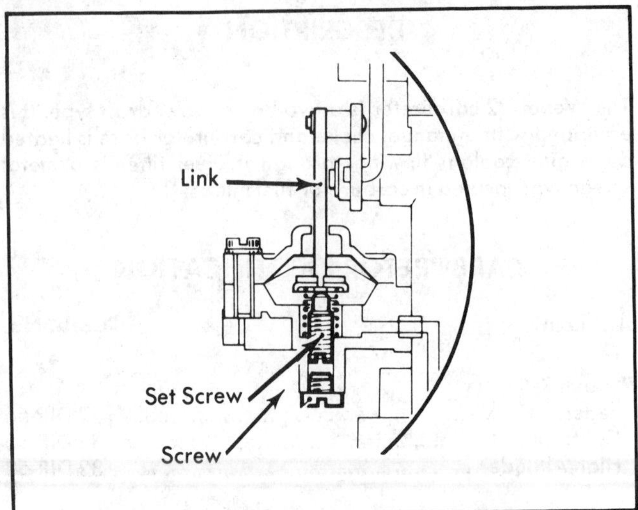

Fig. 5 Choke Valve Adjustment (Vacuum) Set Screw Adjustment

CARBURETOR ADJUSTMENT SPECIFICATIONS

Carb. No.	Idle Speed (Engine RPM)		Float Level Setting In. (mm)	Float Drop Setting In. (mm)	Choke Plate (Vacuum) In. (mm)	Choke Plate (Mech.) In. (mm)	Unloader Setting In. (mm)	Vacuum Break In. (mm)
	Hot	Fast						
DIR 53	750-800①	1500②	.281 (7)	.313 (8)	.234 (6)	.203 (5)	.....	.....
DIR 55	750-800	1500②	.281 (7)	.313 (8)	.234 (6)	.203 (5)	.....	.....
DIR 56	750-800	1500②	.281 (7)	.313 (8)	.281 (7)	.157 (4)	.....	.....

① – With air pump – 750-850 RPM
② – ±100 RPM

ZENITH-STROMBERG CD TYPE 1-BARREL

Jaguar XJ6
Mercedes Benz 230
M.G. (All)
Triumph (All)

DESCRIPTION

Stromberg CD type carburetor is a constant depression carburetor, which operates on the principle of varying effective areas of choke and jet openings. This variation depends upon the degree of throttle opening, engine speed and engine load requirements. California models of Triumph and Mercedes-Benz with single carburetors, have automatic chokes, while all other models have twin carburetors and manual chokes. The M.G. Midget with catalytic converter is equipped with a water temperature controlled choke.

The Mercedes 230 incorporates many changes for 1977. An idle shut off valve is now built into the intake manifold and a solenoid valve has been added to vent the float chamber. The thermo-vacuum valve for the automatic choke has been discontinued. Choke housing has an additional air adjustment screw for adjusting air/fuel mixture more accurately when choke is in operation. A new mixture enrichment valve aids in cold starting and the coolant heating for the carburetor has been eliminated. The method in which the carburetor is mounted has been slightly changed to do away with the insulator. Federal versions of this carburetor have an altitude compensation feature added and a safety cap has been added to the fuel mixture screw on the California versions.

CARBURETOR IDENTIFICATION

Application	Type No.
Jaguar XJ6	
All Models	175 CD2SET
Mercedes-Benz	
230	175CDTU
M.G.	
Midget	150 CD4T
MGB	175 CD5T
Triumph	
Spitfire	
Federal	150 CD4
Calif.	150 CD4T
TR-7	175 CDFEVX

ADJUSTMENTS

HOT (SLOW) IDLE RPM

See appropriate article in TUNE-UP Section.

IDLE MIXTURE

See appropriate article in TUNE-UP Section.

COLD (FAST) IDLE RPM

See appropriate article in TUNE-UP Section.

FLOAT HEIGHT

With float cover removed and carburetor body inverted, measure distance from gasket surface of body to highest point of float. This distance should be .624-.663" (16-17 mm). **NOTE** — *Use care to prevent misaligning floats when making adjustment. If necessary to adjust, bend float tab that contacts fuel inlet needle.*

ALTITUDE COMPENSATION
FEDERAL MERCEDES 230 ONLY

1) Two markinqs are found on small handwheel attached to carburetor. These markings are "NORMAL" and "4000 ft.". When handwheel is moved clockwise, fuel nozzle is moved upwards. This effectively leans out fuel mixture.

2) Set handwheel to "NORMAL" for vehicle operations at levels lower than 4000 ft. Set wheel to "4000 ft." for vehicle operation above that level.

3) Recheck vehicle idle speed and CO% level after resetting altitude compensator.

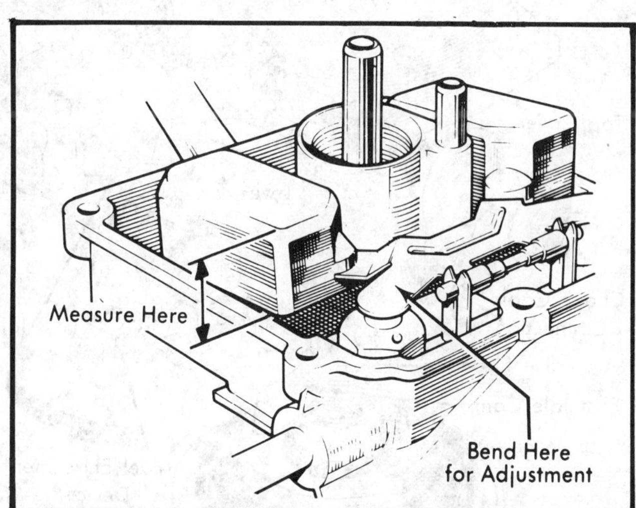

Fig. 1 Float Level Adjustment Points

OVERHAUL

NOTE — *The following overhaul procedure is based upon M.G. Midget suggested procedures, but may be generally applicable to all Stromberg CD type carburetors. Certain variations exist in external components and some models will have automatic chokes, but all carburetors (of this type) are generally similiar in their internal workings.*

1) With carburetor removed, unscrew the damper cap. Reach in through air filter side of carburetor bore and with finger, raise piston while carefully lifting oil retainer cap (on damper rod). Pull plug out of bottom of float chamber and drain fuel and oil from carburetor. Remove "O" ring on float bowl plug. Remove screws securing float chamber to bottom of carburetor. Remove float assembly by gently prying float shaft out of clip on carburetor body. Remove needle valve and washer. Remove screws securing top cover to body. Remove top cover, spring and air valve assembly.

ZENITH-STROMBERG CD TYPE 1-BARREL (Cont.)

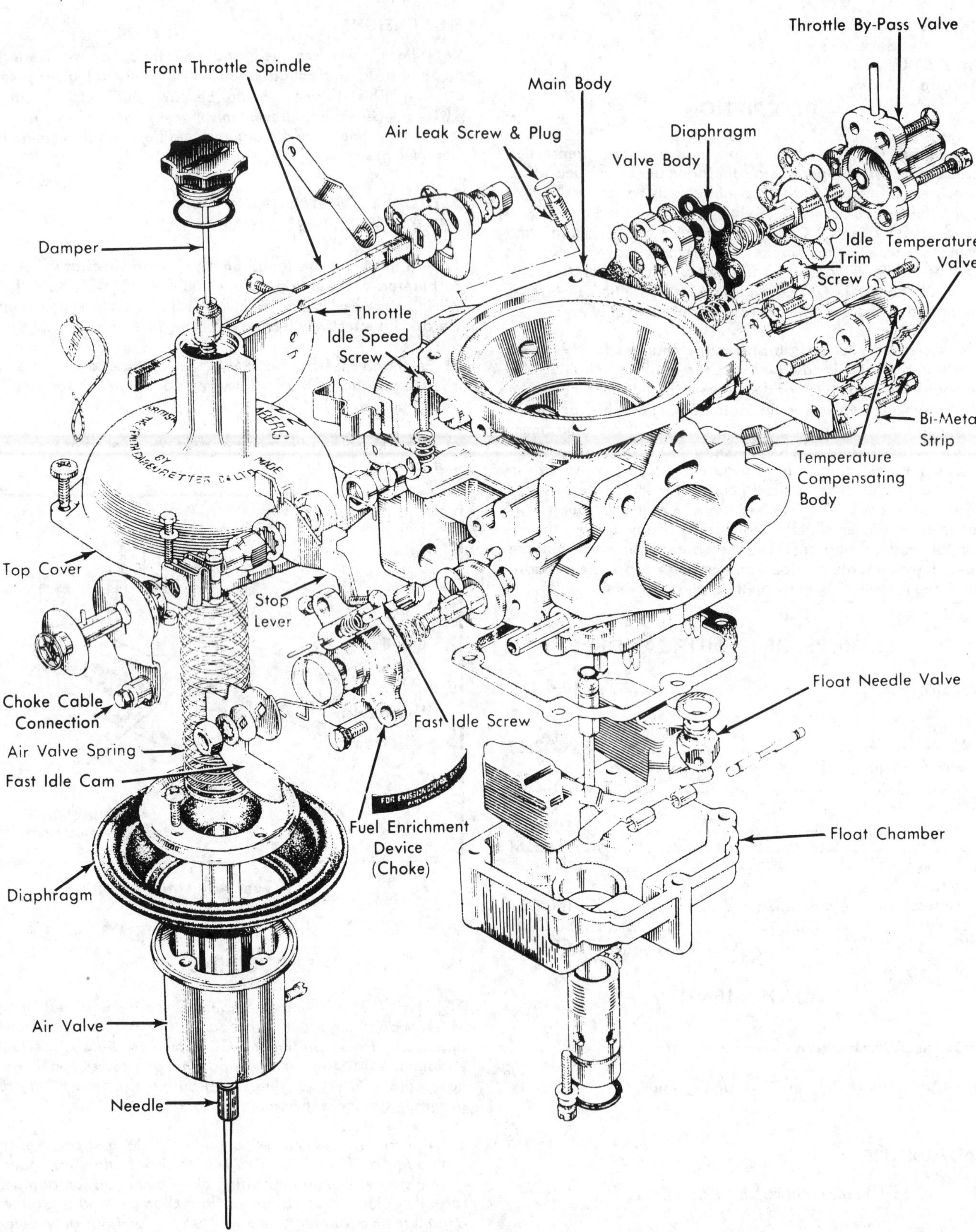

Fig. 2 Exploded View of Stromberg CDSE Carburetor

ZENITH-STROMBERG CD TYPE 1-BARREL (Cont.)

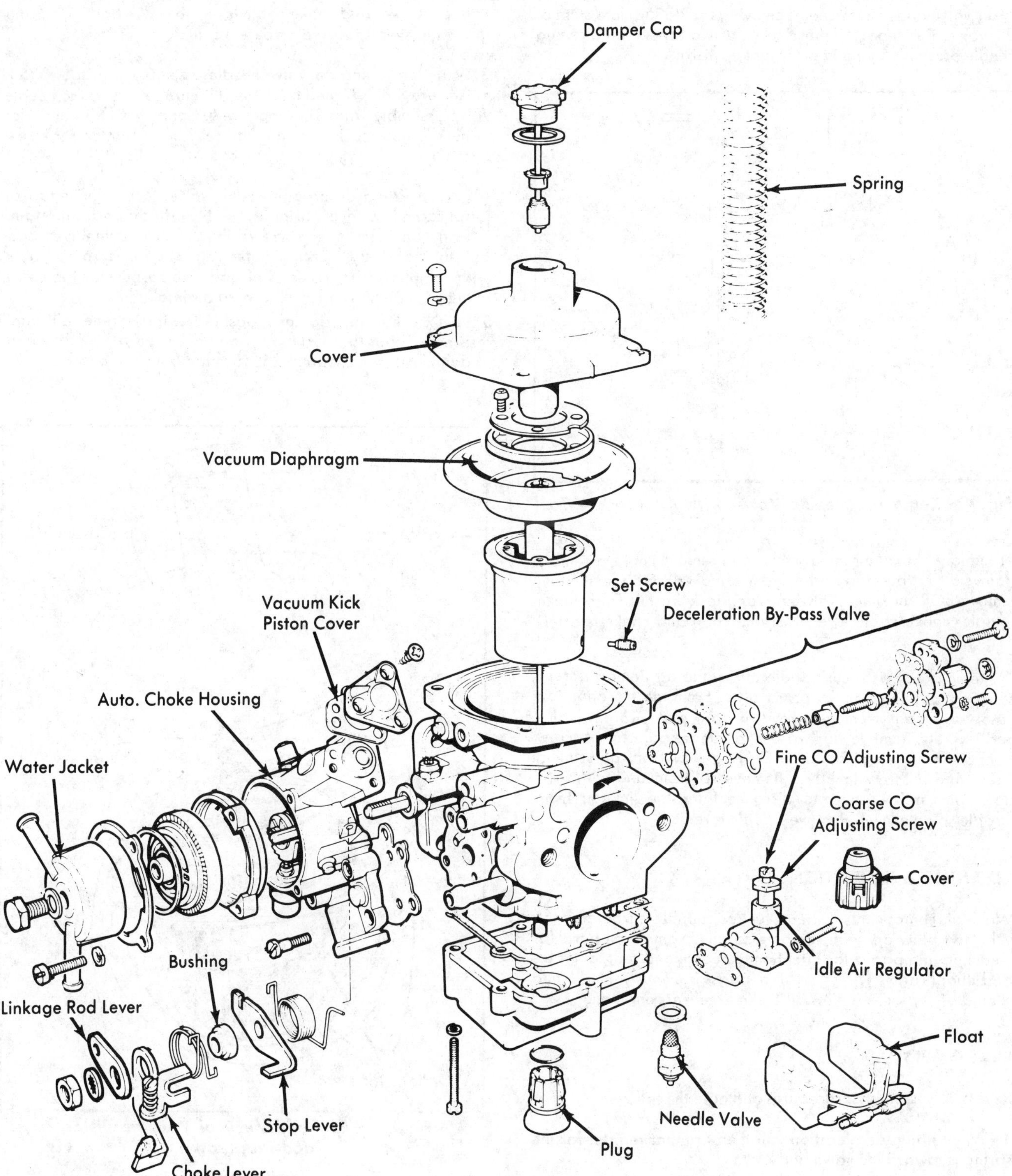

Fig. 3 Exploded View of CD4 Carburetor Assembly

ZENITH-STROMBERG CD TYPE 1-BARREL (Cont.)

2) From air valve assembly, remove screws securing diaphragm and retaining ring. Loosen set screw holding needle in air valve and insert needle removing tool (S353) into stem of air valve. Turn tool counterclockwise two turns, withdrawing needle assembly by pulling straight upward.

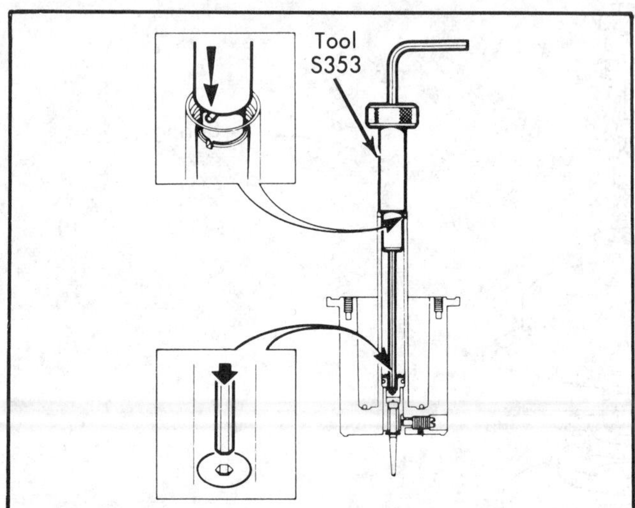

Fig. 4 Removing Needle Valve with Appropriate Tool

3) Remove choke retaining screws and remove choke assembly from side carburetor body. From removed choke assembly, remove EGR air bleed valve, nut and lock washer from choke spindle, choke cable lever, fast idle cam, and choke (starter) disc.

4) Remove screws securing idle air regulator. Remove screws securing deceleration by-pass valve. From deceleration by-pass valve body, remove screws in base plate, spring, valve and gaskets. Remove star washer to release adjustment screw from valve housing. Remove "O" ring seal from adjustment screw and unscrew lock nut. Remove split pin and withdraw clevis pin and washers to disconnect throttle linkage from throttle spindle lever. Remove throttle lever.

CLEANING & INSPECTION

Wash all components in clean fuel or suitable carburetor solvent and blow dry with compressed air. Examine all parts for wear, paying particular attention to needle and seat, air valve and diaphragm. **NOTE** — *The parts previously mentioned should be replaced, unless all are in excellent condition.*

REASSEMBLY

Reverse disassembly procedures and note the following:

1) When fitting deceleration valve, ensure that register for the spring is toward the valve body.

2) Refit disc assembly to choke body, ensuring that lug with detent ball is between slot of disc and largest series of holes. Refit cam lever and choke cable lever (to choke body) ensuring that cam lever is located on detent ball.

3) When installing air valve needle assembly with tool S353, make sure tool is turned clockwise to engage threads of needle valve assembly with adjusting screw. Continue to turn until slot in needle housing is aligned with set screw. Tighten set screw carefully.

4) When fitting diaphragm to air valve, locate inner tag of diaphragm into recess of air valve. Now fit diaphragm retaining ring and secure with screws. Fit air valve assembly to carburetor body, by locating outer tag and rim of diaphragm with complimentary recesses of body. Fit carburetor top cover with bulge on housing neck toward air intake.

5) Fill carburetor damper dashpot with engine oil until resistence is felt to insertion of damper piston when screw cap of damper piston is about .25" (6 mm) above top cover.

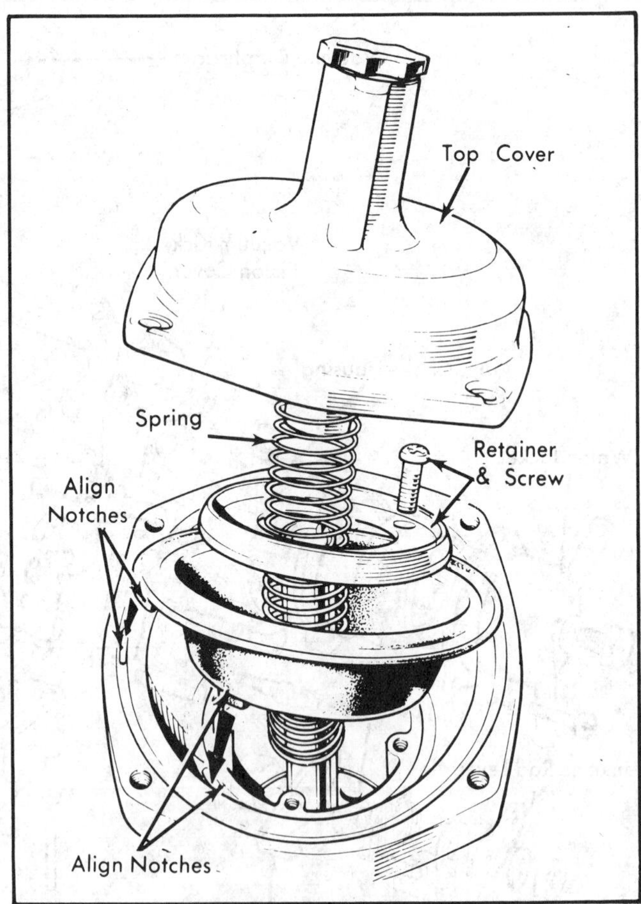

Fig. 5 Expanded View of Vacuum Piston and Diaphragm

ZENITH-STROMBERG 4-BARREL

Mazda Cosmo
Mazda RX-3 SP
Mazda RX-4

DESCRIPTION

Carburetor is of four barrel, two stage design. Primary stage includes idle system, slow speed circuit, accelerator pump system, and main metering system. In addition, fluid from sub-zero starting device, if equipped, and oil from metering oil pump is admitted into primary stage. Secondary stage contains secondary vacuum diaphragm operating system, stepping circuit, and main metering system. Choking is accomplished by semi-automatic choke. Carburetor also contains fuel return circuit and electric idle switch.

ADJUSTMENT

HOT (SLOW) IDLE RPM

See appropriate article in TUNE-UP Section.

COLD (FAST) IDLE RPM

See appropriate article in TUNE-UP Section.

IDLE MIXTURE

See appropriate article in TUNE-UP Section.

FLOAT LEVEL

With engine operating, check fuel level in float bowl sight glass. If fuel level is not within specified limits, remove air horn and adjust as follows:

Invert air horn and allow float to lower by its own weight. Measure distance from air horn gasket surface to top of float. If clearance is not to specifications, adjust by bending float level tab.

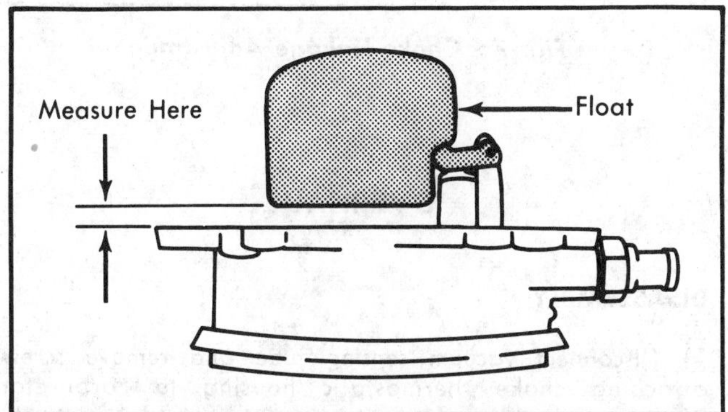

Fig. 1 Making Float Level Measurement for Adjustment

FLOAT DROP

With air horn removed and held upright, measure clearance between air horn gasket surface and bottom of float. If clearance is not to specifications, adjust by bending float drop tang.

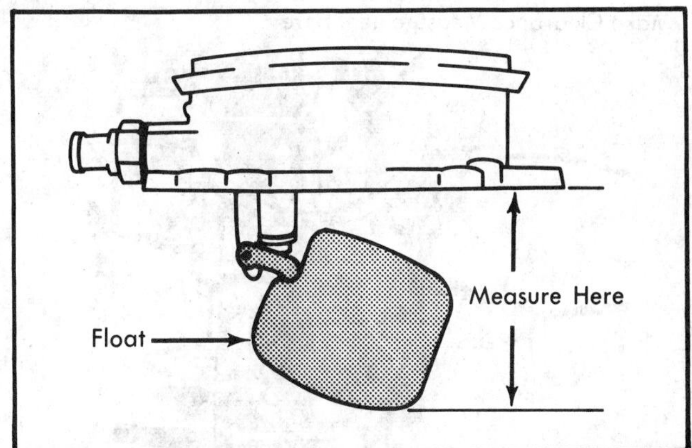

Fig. 2 Making Float Drop Measurement for Adjustment

ACCELERATOR PUMP

NOTE — *Accelerator pump is adjusted by manufacturer and should only be adjusted when it is apparent that factory setting has been disturbed.*

1) Remove carburetor and position over drip pan. Fill a burette or other cubic centimeter measuring device with 10-22 cc of fuel. Attach and hold burette in position as shown in *Fig. 3*.

2) Operate carburetor linkage to wide open throttle (WOT) 10 times and check that correct amount of fuel has been drawn from burette.

3) Check position actuating rod in pump arm and/or pump piston condition.

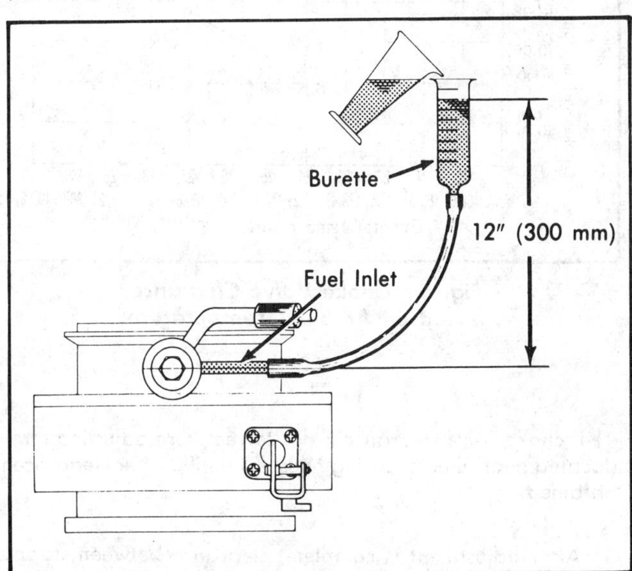

Fig. 3 Tool Hook Up for Accelerator Pump Discharge Test

CHOKE VALVE OPENING

1) Apply about 15.7 in Hg (400 mm Hg) to vacuum diaphragm. Pull out choke lever link and hold in position.

2) Check choke valve clearance as shown in *Fig. 4*.

ZENITH-STROMBERG 4-BARREL (Cont.)

Fig. 4 Choke Valve Clearance Measurement Point

3) Measure temperature surrounding bimetal, then compare with specifications shown in *Fig. 5*. **NOTE** — *Temperature surrounding the general area of choke is referred to as AMBIENT temperature.*

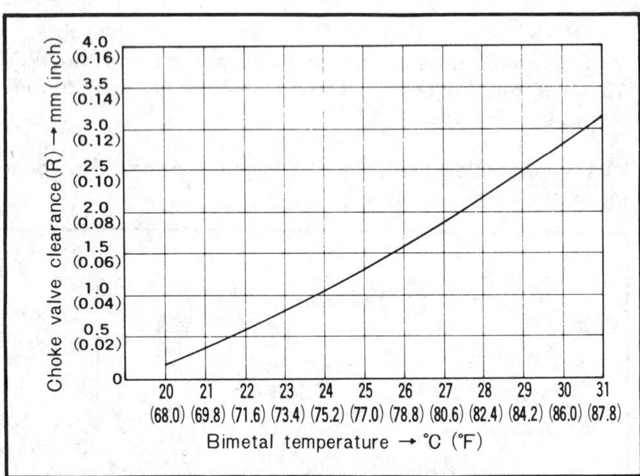

Fig. 5 Choke Valve Clearance Based on Ambient Temperature

4) If choke valve clearance is not correct, turn adjusting screw (located near bimetal spring housing) until proper clearance is obtained.

5) After adjustment is complete, clearance between stopper and bimetal spring lever should be about .169-.185" (4.3-4.7 mm).

VACUUM BREAK DIAPHRAGM

Push diaphragm stem in until seated, then measure distance of travel when stem is released. If amount of travel is not to specifications, adjust diaphragm-to-choke lever connecting rod.

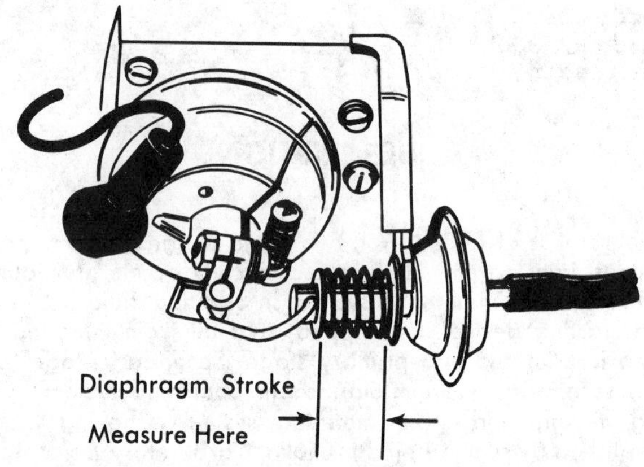

Fig. 6 Vacuum Break Diaphragm Adjustment

CHOKE LINKAGE (FAST IDLE)

With carburetor removed and inverted, actuate choke lever link by pulling outward to its full travel. With choke lever link actuated (fully) measure gap between primary throttle valve and throttle bore. If gap is not to specifications, adjust by bending choke connecting rod.

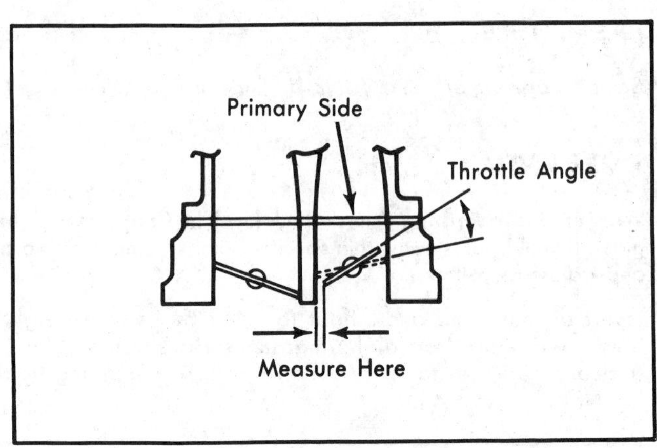

Fig. 7 Choke Linkage Adjustment

OVERHAUL

DISASSEMBLY

1) Disconnect vacuum sensing tube and remove screws attaching choke thermostatic housing to carburetor. Disconnect throttle safety return spring by turning counter lever counterclockwise. Remove throttle return spring.

2) From air horn, disconnect choke connecting rod by removing cotter pin, plain washer and spring. Remove accelerator pump connecting rod by removing cotter pin. Remove bolt attaching fuel inlet fitting and remove fitting and filter. Remove screws which attach air horn to main body. Remove air horn being careful not to tear gasket.

ZENITH-STROMBERG 4-BARREL (Cont.)

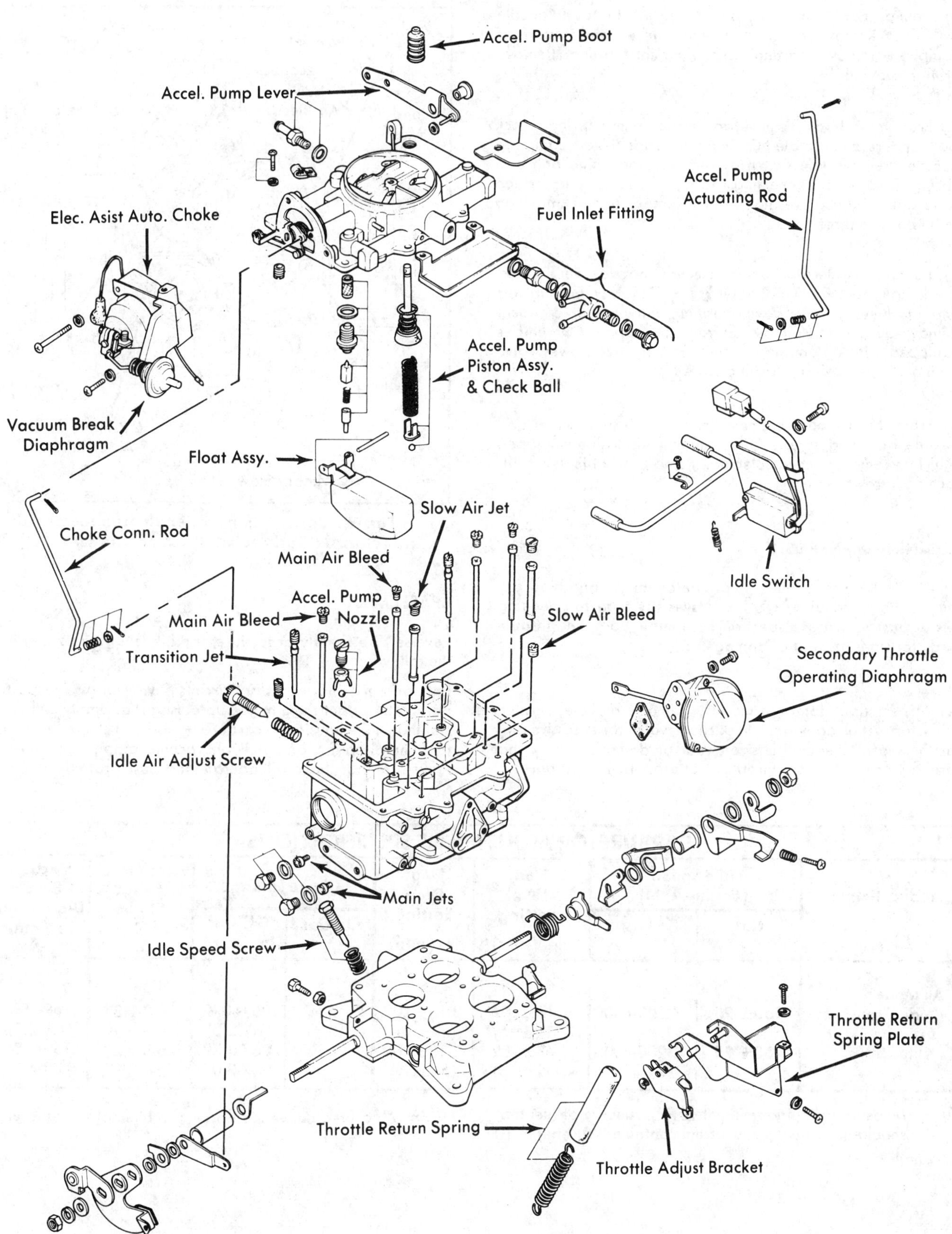

Fig. 8 Exploded View of Zenith-Stromberg Carburetor Assembly RX-4 Shown

ZENITH-STROMBERG 4-BARREL (Cont.)

3) From air horn, remove float retaining pin, float and needle assembly. Remove accelerator pump lever and piston. If equipped, remove starting assist fluid inlet fitting. Remove primary slow air bleeds.

4) From main body, remove accelerator pump spring, check ball and retainer plate. On manual transmission equipped vehicles, remove idle switch by removing attaching bolt and spring. Disconnect connecting rod from secondary operating diapragm and remove diaphragm. Remove screws attaching main body to throttle body.

5) Remove accelerator pump injection nozzle, weight and check ball from main body. **NOTE** — *Before removing jets and air bleeds, write down position and number of each.* Remove all jets and air bleeds from main body. On vehicles equipped with automatic transmissions, remove power valve solenoid by removing attaching screws.

6) From throttle body, remove mixture adjusting screw and throttle adjusting screw. On manual transmission equipped vehicles, remove richer solenoid. Remove throttle lever attaching hardware.

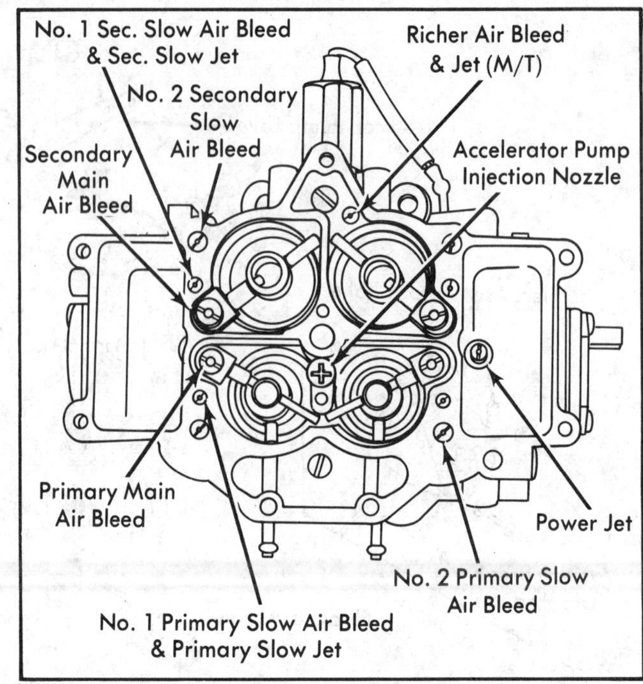

Fig. 9 Jet Location in Zenith-Stromberg 4-Barrel Carburetor (RX-3 SP Shown)

CLEANING & INSPECTION

1) Wash all parts in suitable carburetor solvent and blow dry with compressed air. **NOTE** — *Never use wire for cleaning jets or passageways.* Inspect air horn, main body and throttle body for signs of wear or damage.

2) Inspect float for deformation, damage or holes. Inspect filter for rust or damage. Check choke valve for excessive play at the shaft. Check all jets for wear or damage. Check that primary and secondary throttles seat properly in their bores.

REASSEMBLY

Reverse disassembly procedure, use all new gaskets and note the following:

Both primary and secondary circuits have their own respective parts; do not get them mixed up during reassembly. When installing choke housing to carburetor body, fit choke shaft lever to bimetal spring and pull on vacuum diaphragm shaft to make sure that choke will operate and close properly.

CARBURETOR ADJUSTMENT SPECIFICATIONS

Application	Idle Speed (Engine RPM)		Float Level Setting In. (mm)	Float Drop Setting In. (mm)	Choke Linkage		Accelerator Pump Stroke ①	Vacuum Break Diaphragm In. (mm) ②
	Hot	Fast			On Car	Off Car In. (mm)		
All Models								
Man. Trans.	750± 25	3200-4000	.47± .02 (12± .5)	2.13± .02 (54± .5)	.....	.067-.079 (1.7-2.0)	6.8-9.2	.169-.185 (4.3-4.7)
Auto. Trans.	750± 25	3200-4000	.47± .02 (12± .5)	2.13± .02 (54± .5)	.....	.067-.079 (1.7-2.0)	6.8-9.2	.169-.185 (4.3-4.7)

① — Measured in cubic centimeters (cc). Amount of fuel that should have been drawn from container (burette) in 10 strokes.

② — Measured between stopper and bimetal spring lever.

BOSCH AFC FUEL INJECTION SYSTEM

BMW 530i & 630CSi
Datsun 280Z & 810
Renault R-17 Gordini
Volkswagen Type 1 & 2

DESCRIPTION

The Bosch Air Flow Controlled (AFC) fuel injection system is electronic and uses sensors to detect engine conditions. These sensors send signals to the Electronic Control Unit (ECU) and the ECU then determines amount of fuel and length of time that fuel is to be injected into the engine.

An air flow meter, mounted between the throttle chamber and air cleaner, measures amount of intake air. Fuel injector open-valve time is based on amount of intake air required for one rotation of engine. System maintains a constant fuel pressure and accurately balances air/fuel mixture under all operating conditions. System consists of air flow meter, various sensors and switches, air cleaner assembly, Electronic Control Unit, throttle chamber, air and pressure regulators, injectors and connecting wires, lines and hoses.

In 1977, BMW models added a high altitude compensation feature which should be hooked up if vehicle is to be operated above 4,000 feet. The altitude feature is automatic on other models.

OPERATION

Fuel under pressure from electric fuel pump, flows through a filter and pulsation damper (some models) and is injected into intake manifold branch to mix with incoming air. A pressure regulator controls fuel pressure so that a difference of 36.3 psi exists constantly between fuel pressure and intake manifold vacuum. To aid in cold engine starting, a cold start valve is activated by a thermotime switch to increase quantity of fuel to be injected.

Each engine cylinder is supplied fuel by an injector. Ignition signal from ignition coil determines frequency of injections while the ECU determines length of each injection.

Air is drawn in through air cleaner and is measured by the air flow meter. Air then travels through throttle chamber and into intake manifold. A throttle valve in the chamber controls air flow while driving. At idle, throttle valve is almost closed and air is drawn through a by-pass port in throttle chamber. Idle speed adjusting screw controls quantity of air intake at idle. During warm-up operation, extra air is passed through air regulator to increase engine RPM.

AIR FLOW METER & POTENTIOMETER

The throttle valve housing provides method for air to enter engine under controlled conditions. Throttle valve sliding switch is a potentiometer which functions as sensor for informing control unit (ECU) of throttle valve position. Datsun models also have a fuel pump relay contact in potentiometer section of air flow meter. Fuel pump contact turns ON only after flap in air flow meter turns 8° or more. Contact turns OFF when flap returns to less than 8° rotation.

INTAKE AIR SENSOR

The intake air sensor provides the control unit with voltage signals. The intensity of these signals, depends upon intake air volume and air temperature. The incoming air moves the stator flap against the force of the return spring. As more air is drawn in, stator flap opens even more. This rotary motion of the stator flap actuates a special potentiometer (both are physically connected together) and thus varies the strength of the signal sent to the electronic control unit (ECU). Connected to the stator flap is a dampening flap which prevents rapid oscillations of the stator flap. One of the contacts on the potentiometer operates the fuel pump as the stator flap is opened by air flow. Temperature Sensor I is an intergal part of the potentiometer and its operation modifies the signal sent to the ECU.

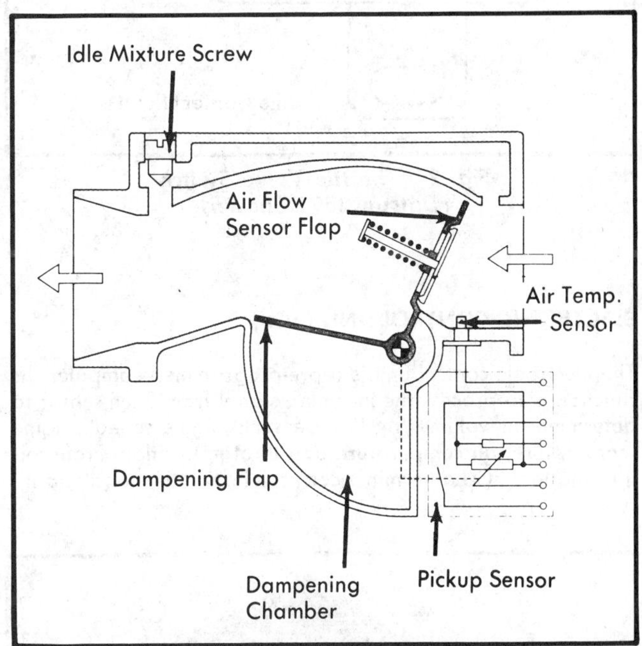

Fig. 1 Air Flow Meter and Air Flow Sensor Pickup

TEMPERATURE SENSOR II

This sensor provides the ECU with engine temperature information relating to cold starting and warm-up enrichment operation. The temperature sensing unit uses a thermister which is sensitive in the lower temperature ranges. Electrical resistance of the thermister decreases as coolant temperature rises.

THROTTLE SWITCH

Throttle valve switch is attached to throttle chamber. Accelerator pedal movement activates the switch which has two sets of contact points. One monitors idle position and the other monitors full throttle position. Full throttle contacts close only after throttle valve opens more than 34°. Throttle switch compensates for enrichment at idle and after idle, and at full throttle positions. Idle circuit of switch also is responsible for sending out the fuel cut-off signal.

BOSCH AFC FUEL INJECTION SYSTEM (Cont.)

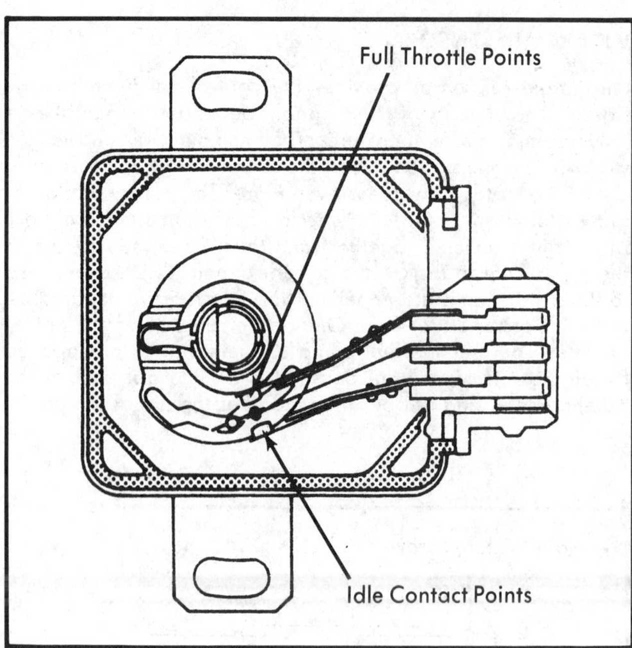

Fig. 2 Throttle Valve Switch (Datsun 280Z Shown)

ELECTRONIC CONTROL UNIT (ECU)

The electronic control unit is a pre-programmed computer. Its function is to process the incoming signal from each sensor to determine air volume (by flow sensor), engine speed, engine temperature, air temperature and throttle position. From this information, ECU determines correct injection time and quantity.

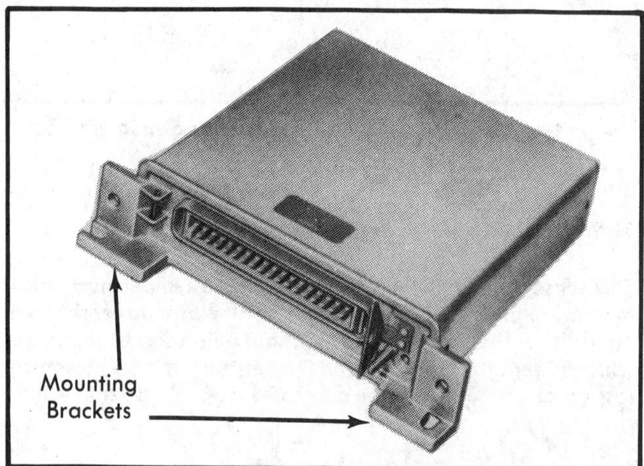

Fig. 3 Electronic Control Unit (ECU)

PRESSURE REGULATOR

Pressure controls fuel pressure and maintains a constant difference between fuel pressure and intake vacuum. This difference is about 36.3 psi and provides sufficient pressure to handle any driving condition.

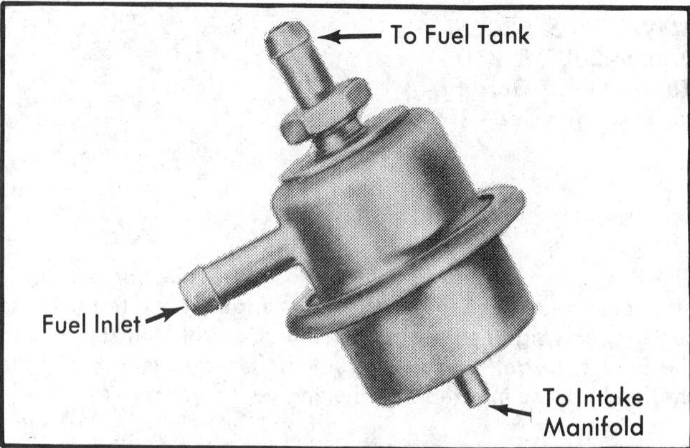

Fig. 4 Typical View of Pressure Regulator

AUXILIARY AIR REGULATOR

To provide for cold starting and engine warm-up, more air and fuel are required. The auxiliary air regulator is fully open when engine is cold and therefore provides additional air required. As engine warms up, the gate valve is closed by operation of the electrically heated bi-metal spring.

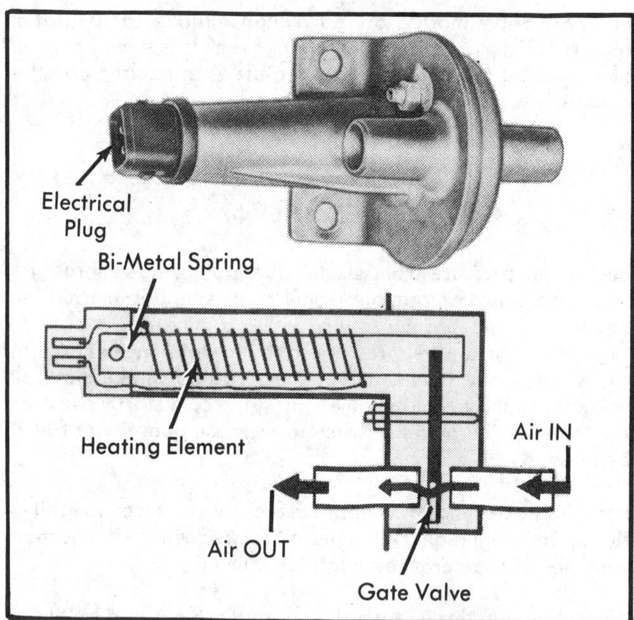

Fig. 5 Auxiliary Air Regulator

THERMO-TIME SWITCH

The thermo-time switch controls the time the cold start valve is switched on. This time limit is usually between 5 and 20 seconds depending upon engine. The time switch has a bimetal contact, surrounded by a heating coil. The heating coil receives current during cranking. The bimetal contact breaks the ground circuit of the cold start valve whenever the heating coil is about 95°F or when the delay time is up. Delay time is shortened as temperature raises.

PRE-RESISTORS

The purpose of the pre-resistor (if they are used) is mainly to reduce the response time of the injectors. The pre-resistors are connected in series between the injectors and the dual relay.

BOSCH AFC FUEL INJECTION SYSTEM (Cont.)

DUAL RELAY

The dual relay is composed of two relays which control current supply for entire electronic fuel injection system and which disengages system (electrically) from battery when ignition is turned to off position. When ignition switch is on, the main relay points close, providing voltage to the ECU and pre-resistors (if used) of the electronic fuel injection system. The other relay (within the dual relay), controls current to the electric fuel pump. These points close during cranking and when points of air flow valve are closed. This design is to cut off current to fuel pump in the event that engine stops (air flow meter closed).

TESTING

NOTE – *This fuel injection system maintains constant fuel pressure in fuel lines and component parts at all times. Be sure to relieve pressure before attempting to open system at any point for testing. Do not allow fuel to flow onto engine or electrical parts. Do not allow open flame in area while testing fuel system components.*

FUEL PRESSURE

Volkswagen – 1) Remove air sensor and air cleaner assembly. Connect suitable pressure gauge (US 1076 or equivalent) to injector supply line. Detach vacuum hose which connects air distributor and pressure regulator. Connect plug to removed intake air sensor.

2) Turn on ignition. Slightly open stator flap by hand until pump contacts close and read fuel pressure shown on pressure gauge. **NOTE** – *Normal pressure should be between 31-44 psi, with vacuum hose detached.* If pressure is not to specifications, replace pump.

BMW, Datsun & Renault – 1) Relieve pressure in fuel line then connect a fuel pressure gauge in the cold start valve line on BMW and Datsun models or in the line to pressure regulator on Renault models. Start engine and check pressure against following specifications.

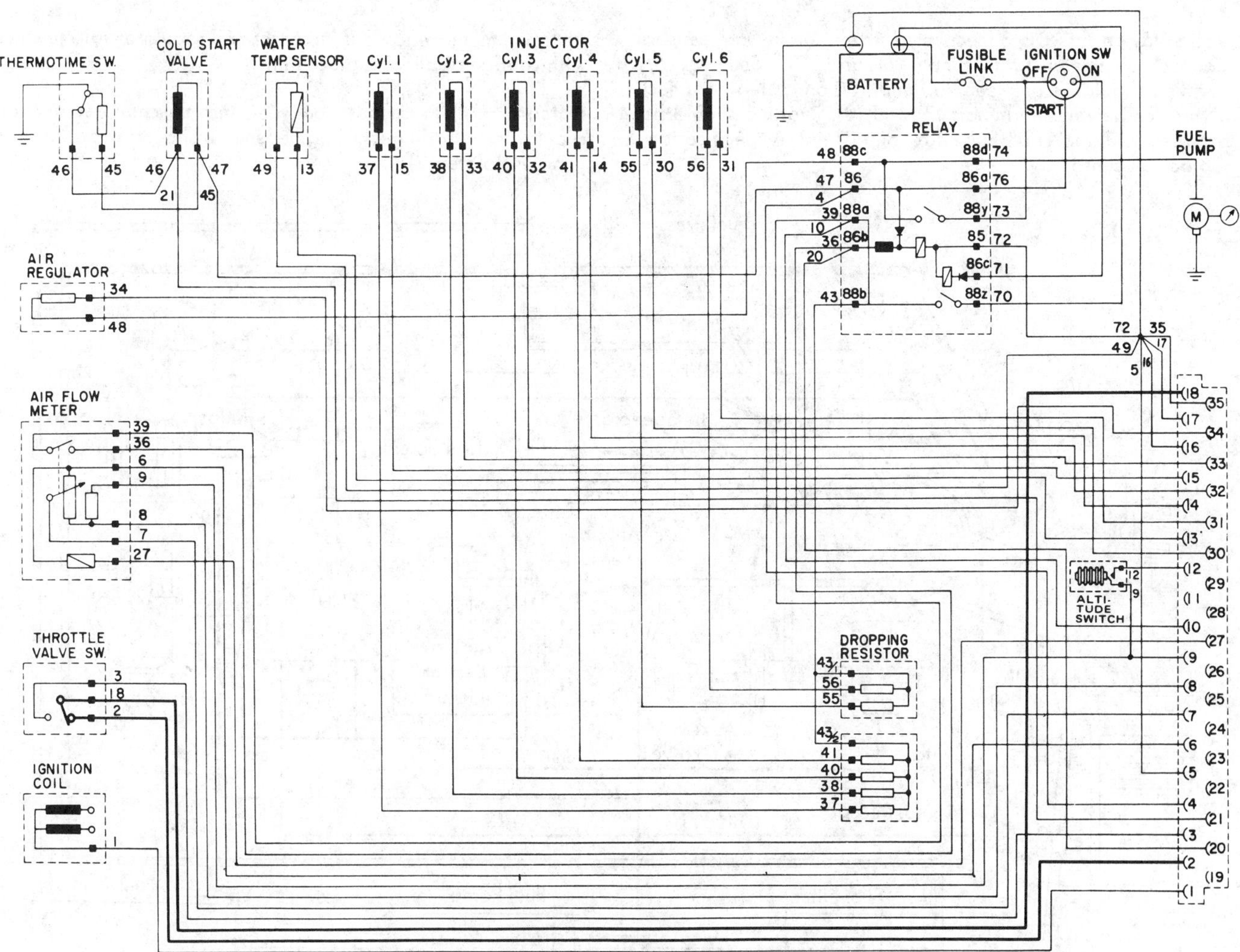

Fig. 6 Electronic Fuel Injection Electrical Diagram Showing Electrical Terminal Numbers for Testing (Datsun 280Z Shown – Others Similar)

BOSCH AFC FUEL INJECTION SYSTEM (Cont.)

Fuel Pressure Specifications

Application	Pressure
BMW	33.4-39 psi (2.2-2.7 kg/cm²)
Datsun	37 psi (2.55 kg/cm²)
Renault	29-32 psi (2-2.2 kg/cm²)

2) If pressures are not as specified, adjust pressure regulator on Renault or replace on BMW and Datsun. If pressures are still incorrect, check for leaking fuel lines and/or replace fuel pump.

TEMPERATURE SENSOR I (INTAKE AIR SENSOR)

Datsun – Disconnect battery ground cable, air flow meter, and record outside air (ambient air) temperature. Measure resistance between terminals 27 and 6, on air flow meter electrical connector. As point of reference, at 50°F. the resistance should be between 3250 and 4150 ohms or at 120°F. the resistance should be between 740 and 940 ohms. If resistance is completely outside of this range, replace temperature sensor and air flow meter as an assembly.

Volkswagen – Disconnect plug from intake air sensor. Connect ohmmeter to terminals (6) and (9). *(See Fig. 6).* Reading should be between 200 and 800 ohms. Now connect ohmmeter between terminals (7) and (8). Reading should be between 120 and 200 ohms. If reading is not to specification, replace air sensor.

BMW & Renault – Both manufactures recommend replacement of temperature sensor (BMW recommends replacing both the sensor and control valve) if sensor is defective.

THROTTLE VALVE SLIDING SWITCH

All Models – Disconnect plug from throttle switch (on throttle body) and connect ohmmeter between middle contact and rear contact. Slowly open throttle by hand. Ohmmeter should move from infinity to zero ohm reading; if not replace throttle sliding switch.

AUXILIARY AIR REGULATOR

All Models Exc. Datsun – **1)** Remove auxiliary air regulator and connect ohmmeter to both terminals of regulator. Reading should be about 30 ohms.

2) Apply compressed air to regulator; passage must be open while engine is cold.

3) Connect battery voltage to both terminals. As temperature increases, opening in regulator should become smaller.

4) If ohmmeter reading is incorrect or if regulator fails to close with voltage applied, replace unit.

Datsun – **1)** Pinch hose between throttle chamber and air regulator with fingers. Engine speed should drop. If not, proceed to Step **2)**.

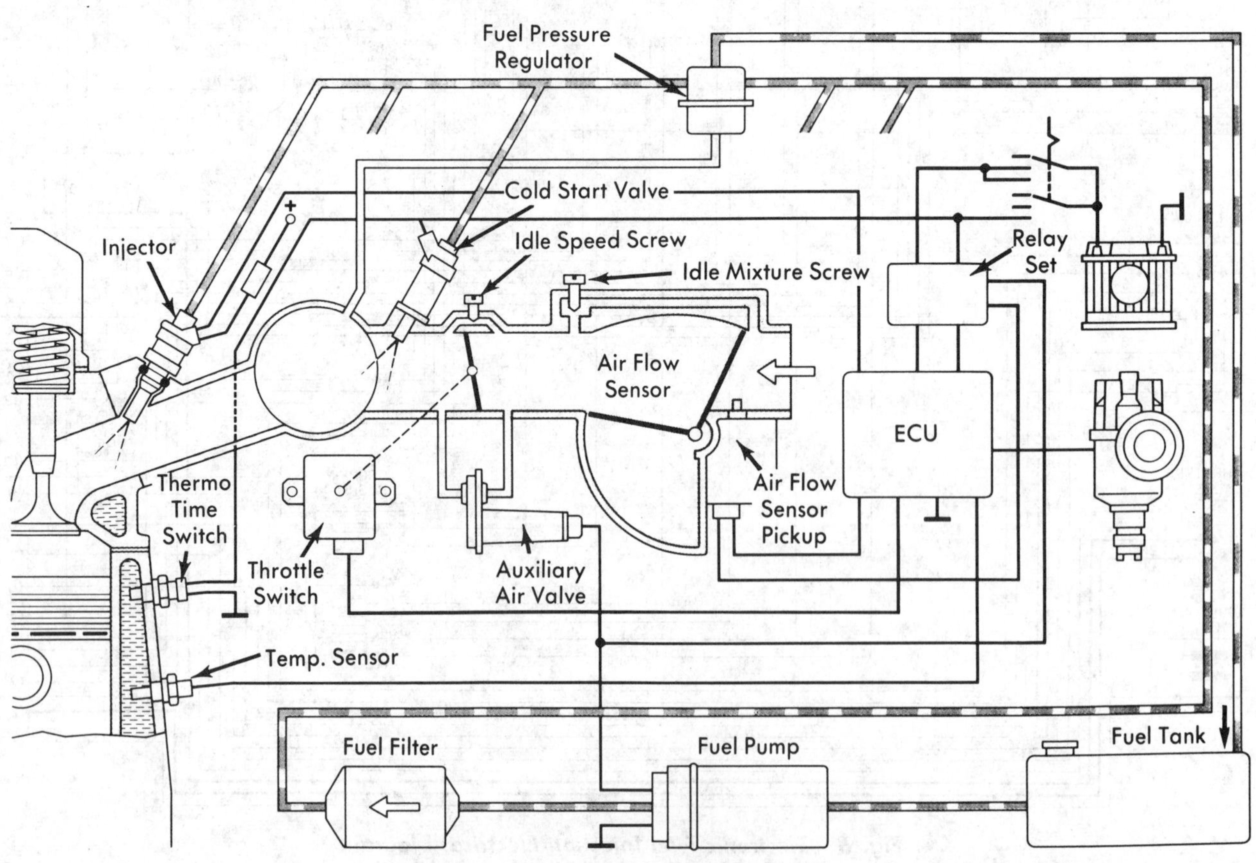

Fig. 7 Typical Diagram of Bosch AFC Fuel Injection System

BOSCH AFC FUEL INJECTION SYSTEM (Cont.)

2) Unhook hoses at each end of regulator. Visually check to see if air regulator valve opens. Valve should open farther as temperature increases.

3) Check continuity of air regulator at electrical connector. If continuity does not exist, air regulator is defective and should be replaced.

4) Check smoothness of operation by carefully prying air regulator valve open with a flat bladed screwdriver and then close valve again. Replace valve if operation is not smooth.

THERMO-TIME SWITCH

All Models – Unhook battery ground cable. Disconnect plug from cold start valve and connect ohmmeter between the two terminals. **NOTE** – *If temperature of sensor is below 59° F, ohmmeter should indicate ZERO ohms. If engine temperature is above 71° F, ohmmeter should read infinity.* Measure resistance between terminal No. 45 and switch body. Reading should be 70-86 ohms.

COLD START VALVE

All Models Exc. Datsun – Connect pressure gauge to injector supply line. Operate starter to build up fuel pressure. Unhook plug from cold start valve. Connect wires from negative (–) terminal of coil to cold start valve. Observe fuel pressure reading. It should slowly decrease. If the pressure does not drop, replace cold start valve.

Datsun – 1) Unhook battery ground cable. Detach cold start valve harness connector. Attach jumper wires from each connector terminal to positive (+) and negative (–) terminals of battery as shown in *Fig. 8*. Unhook wire at "S" terminal of starter.

2) Release pressure in fuel system by connecting other terminals of jumper wires to cold start valve connector for 2 or 3 seconds.

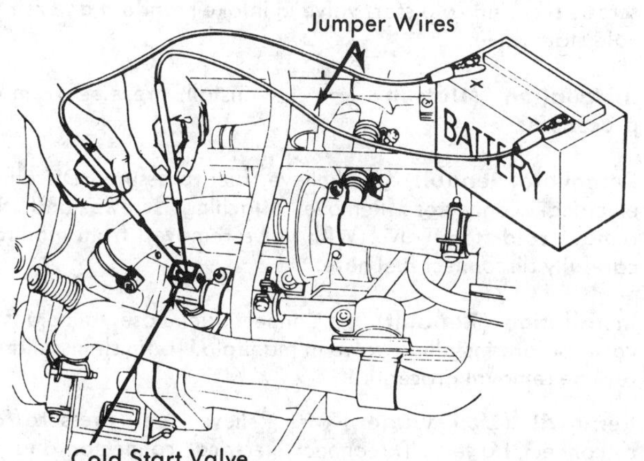

Fig. 8 Releasing Fuel Pressure at Cold Start Valve

3) Remove (2) screws holding cold start valve to intake manifold. Remove clip and disengage fuel hose from valve. Take care to contain fuel spillage from valve.

4) Place cold start valve into glass container of over 20 cc capacity. Block remaining opening at top of container with a rag.

5) Connect battery ground cable. Turn ignition switch to START position. Cold start valve should NOT inject fuel.

NOTE – *Prior to applying test voltaage to relay, install inline fuse in series with lead wire to avoid circuit damage. If possible, use a 7 Volt tester in place of a 12 volt tester.*

6) Turn ignition switch OFF. Connect jumper wire between cold start valve and battery terminals. Ensure cold start valve is in container and container is covered with rag.

7) Cold start valve should now inject fuel. If not, replace.

TEMPERATURE SENSOR II (ENGINE COOLANT SENSOR)

All Models – Disconnect plug and connect ohmmeter between temperature sensor and ground. Reading should be between 500-2500 ohms. **NOTE** – *Sensor is temperature sensitive, as temperature increases, ohm reading will decrease.* As point of reference, ohmmeter reading should be about 2500 ohms (or less) at 68°F.

DECELERATION VALVE

All Models (Exc. Datsun) – 1) Check vacuum controlled valves by detaching hose from deceleration valve to intake air sensor at sensor. Start engine and run at about 3000 RPM.

2) Close throttle suddenly. If no suction is present at end of disconnected hose at instant of throttle closing, replace deceleration valve.

3) Check electrically controlled decel valves by, first turning ignition switch ON. Remove wire from decel valve to ATF pressure switch at switch.

4) Ground disconnected wire and listen for "click". If no click is heard, replace decel valve or pressure switch and recheck using above procedure.

REMOVAL & INSTALLATION

NOTE – *This fuel injection system maintains constant fuel pressure in fuel lines and component parts at all times. Be sure to relieve pressure before attempting to open system at any point for testing. Do not allow fuel to flow onto engine or electrical parts. Do not allow open flame or sparks in area while servicing or testing fuel system components.*

AIR FLOW METER & AIR CLEANER (AFC SYSTEM)

Removal (BMW) – Disconnect electrical plug and loosen clamps on both sides of air flow meter. Remove air cleaner and lift air flow meter out of its holder. **NOTE** – *Use only air flow meter with yellow dot, as replacement part.*

Installation (BMW) – Reverse removal Procedure.

Removal (Datsun) – Disconnect battery ground cable. Disconnect rubber hose from both sides of air flow meter. Disconnect air flow meter ground cable and remove three bolts securing air flow meter bracket. Move air flow meter upward. Disconnect electrical connector and remove air flow meter.

Installation (Datsun) – To install, reverse removal procedure.

BOSCH AFC FUEL INJECTION SYSTEM (Cont.)

Removal (Renault) – At time of publication, no specific removal procedure was available.

Removal (Volkswagen) – 1) Remove air cleaner top and filter, then carefully remove electrical connector from sensor. Loosen hose clamp then disconnect elbow duct from sensor.

2) Remove nuts securing air cleaner body to vehicle chassis. Remove sensor and air cleaner body as a unit. Now remove sensor from air cleaner body.

Installation (Volkswagen) – To install sensor, reverse removal procedure. Make sure sensor is properly adjusted after installation.

THROTTLE VALVE HOUSING

Removal (BMW) – Remove throttle valve housing cover. Disconnect electrical plug of throttle valve sliding switch. Disconnect vacuum control hose and red electrical cut-off valve hose, at collector. Disconnect warm air hose. Disconnect accelerator linkage and engine vent hose. Disconnect ignition control vacuum hose. Remove cylinder head cover and unscrew lower left stud.

Installation (BMW) – To ease installation problems, saw slot in end of stud which was removed on installation. Replace gasket and reverse removal procedure.

Removal (Datsun) – Disconnect battery ground cable. Remove distributor cap and remove rubber hoses from throttle chamber. Remove throttle valve switch and disconnect B.C.D.D. device. Disconnect rod from auxiliary throttle shaft. Remove four screws securing throttle chamber to intake manifold. Throttle chamber can now be removed together with B.C.D.D. device and dashpot.

Installation (Datsun) – To install, reverse removal procedure.

Removal (Renault) – At time of publication, no specific removal procedure was available.

Removal (Volkswagen) – 1) Remove intake air sensor and air cleaner as a unit. Loosen clamp and remove elbow ducting from top of throttle valve housing.

2) Disconnect throttle return spring from bracket on EGR valve body. Remove EGR inlet pipe, then remove EGR valve. Disconnect throttle linkage from throttle valve housing.

3) Disconnect vacuum hoses from throttle valve housing, mark hoses for correct positioning during installation. Disconnect electrical connector from throttle switch. Remove screws securing throttle valve housing to manifold and remove throttle valve housing.

Installation (Volkswagen) – To install throttle valve housing, reverse removal procedure. Always use a new gasket when installing housing.

CONTROL UNIT (ECU)

Removal (BMW) – Press back on clip (located on wire end of electrical connector) and swing cable assembly to right side. Remove screws retaining control unit.

Installation (BMW) – Reverse removal procedure.

Removal (Datsun) – Turn ignition switch OFF or disconnect battery negative (–) cable. Remove (3) bolts securing control unit cover to left dash side panel. Remove cover and (3) bolts securing control unit to dash side panel bracket and remove control unit.

Installation (Datsun) – Reverse removal procedure.

Removal (Renault) – 1) ECU is located in passenger compartment beneath defroster nozzles on passenger side. Disconnect air hose at right defroster nozzle.

2) Disconnect rubber band holders and tilt ECU forward, then remove metal holder. Loosen clamp and slide holder out of ECU. Remove plug from ECU and remove ECU.

Installation (Renault) – To install ECU, reverse removal procedure.

Removal (Volkswagen) – ECU is located on the right side of rear seat luggage compartment (behind rear seat). Remove ECU cover. Disconnect cable plug and position it where there will be no chance of damage to plug pins either physically or electrically. Remove mounting strap and then ECU.

Installation (Volkswagen) – To install ECU, reverse removal procedure. Make sure cable plug is carefully and fully engaged in ECU.

COLD START VALVE

Removal (BMW) – Remove electrical connector and retaining screws. Remove cold start valve.

Installation (BMW) – Reverse removal procedure.

Removal (Datsun) – Disconnect ground cable from battery. Disconnect ground lead wire (black) from fuel pump. Disconnect lead wire from "S" terminal of starter. Remove two screws securing cold start valve to intake manifold and remove cold start valve.

Installation (Datsun) – To install, reverse removal procedure.

Removal (Renault) – Relieve fuel pressure. Disconnect electrical connector. Remove attaching screws and then remove cold start valve. With valve removed from manifold, carefully disconnect fuel hose.

Installation (Renault) – Connect fuel hose to cold start valve before installing valve in manifold. To finish installation, reverse removal procedure.

Removal (Volkswagen) – Relieve fuel pressure and disconnect battery. Disconnect electrical connector and fuel hoses at cold start valve. Remove screws securing cold start valve to air distributor and remove valve with gasket.

Installation (Volkswagen) – To install cold start valve, reverse removal procedure.

AUXILIARY AIR REGULATOR

Removal (BMW) – Disconnect air hoses attached to auxiliary air regulator. **NOTE** – *Auxiliary air regulator is*

BOSCH AFC FUEL INJECTION SYSTEM (Cont.)

installed in the coolant system. When removing auxiliary air regulator from coolant system, either have another regulator ready for immediate installation or drain coolant system below level of regulator. Remove screws securing regulator to block and remove regulator.

Installation (BMW) – To install auxiliary air regulator, reverse removal procedure.

Removal (Datsun) – Disconnect battery ground cable. Disconnect electrical connector from regulator and remove hose clamp. Remove two set screws.

Installation (Datsun) – Reverse removal procedure.

Removal (Renault) – Auxiliary air regulator is located in the coolant system. When removing regulator either have another regulator ready for immediate installation or drain coolant below level of regulator. Disconnect air hoses at auxiliary air regulator. Remove screws securing regulator to engine and remove regulator.

Installation (Renault) – To install auxiliary air regulator, reverse removal procedure.

Removal (Volkswagen) – Disconnect air hoses and the electrical connector at auxiliary air regulator. Remove screws securing regulator to engine block then remove auxiliary air regulator.

Installation (Volkswagen) – To install auxiliary air regulator, reverse removal procedure. Always use a new gasket upon installation.

THERMO-TIME SWITCH

Removal (BMW) – From beneath pressure regulator, remove electrical connector to thermo-time switch. Drain sufficient coolant to allow removal of switch (below level of switch). Use socket and remove switch.

Installation (BMW) – Reverse removal procedure.

Removal (Datsun) – Remove radiator cap, drain coolant to level below thermostat housing. Disconnect water hose from thermostat housing. Disconnect battery ground cable. Disconnect lead wires from thermal transmitter and remove transmitter. Disconnect thermo-time switch and remove by turning switch counterclockwise.

Installation (Datsun) – Reverse removal procedure.

Removal (Renault) – Drain coolant level to below level of thermo-time switch. Disconnect electrical connector and remove screws securing switch. Remove thermo-time switch.

Installation (Renault) – To install thermo-time switch, reverse removal procedure. Use a new gasket with switch and then refill coolant system.

Removal (Volkswagen) – Disconnect electrical connection then remove screws securing switch. Then remove thermo-time switch.

Installation (Volkswagen) – To install thermo-time switch, reverse removal procedure.

PRESSURE REGULATOR

Removal (BMW) – Relieve pressure in fuel system and disconnect battery. Disconnect intake pipe of number four cylinder. Disconnect pressure regulator fuel lines. Disconnect vacuum hose at collector and remove pressure regulator.

Installation (BMW) – To install pressure regulator, reverse removal procedure. When installing intake pipe onto cylinder head, use a new gasket.

Removal (Datsun) – Disconnect negative battery cable, ground lead wire from fuel pump and lead wire from "S" terminal of starter motor. Remove two screws securing cold start valve and remove cold start valve. Remove vacuum hose connecting pressure regulator to intake manifold and remove pressure regulator.

Installation (Datsun) – To install, reverse removal procedure.

Removal (Renault) – Relieve fuel pressure and disconnect battery. Clamp both fuel hoses, to prevent fuel spillage, then disconnect fuel hoses from pressure regulator. Remove retaining screw and remove pressure regulator.

Installation (Renault) – To install pressure regulator, reverse removal procedure.

Removal (Volkswagen) – 1) Disconnect battery and relieve pressure in fuel system. Disconnect vacuum hose from regulator. Clamp fuel hoses, to prevent fuel leakage, then disconnect fuel hoses from regulator.

2) From underneath vehicle, remove nut securing pressure regulator to engine front cover. Remove pressure regulator.

Installation (Volkswagen) – To install pressure regulator, reverse removal procedure.

INJECTORS

Removal (BMW) – Disconnect battery and relieve pressure in fuel system. Disconnect and plug fuel lines to injector(s) being removed. Disconnect electrical connections. Remove retaining screws and remove injector(s).

Installation (BMW) – To install injectors, reverse removal procedure.

Removal (Datsun) – Disconnect battery negative cable and ground wire (black) to fuel pump. Disconnect lead wire from "S" terminal of starter. Remove two screws securing cold start valve to intake manifold and remove valve. Disconnect electrical connector to injectors. Remove fuel feed line and remove screws securing front fuel feed line to injectors. To remove rear injectors, remove bolts securing fuel feed line to intake manifold. **NOTE** – *When removing any injector, place suitable container or rag under injector to prevent fuel from spilling on engine.*

Removal (Renault) – Disconnect battery and relieve pressure in fuel system. Disconnect electrical connection and remove fuel line to injectors to be removed. Remove screw securing injector and remove injector with retainer. Cover injector hole to prevent dirt from entering intake manifold.

BOSCH AFC FUEL INJECTION SYSTEM (Cont.)

Installation (Renault) – To install injectors, reverse removal procedure. Be sure to use new rubber grommets and washers.

Removal (Volkswagen) – 1) Remove the large air duct between fan housing and heat exchangers on exhaust system. Disconnect battery and relieve pressure in fuel system.

2) Disconnect electrical connector and fuel lines from injectors to be removed. Remove screw securing injector to intake manifold. Remove injector with seals and retainer plate.

Installation (Volkswagen) – To install injectors, reverse removal procedure.

ADJUSTMENTS

FUEL PRESSURE REGULATOR

Renault – Connect pressure gauge in fuel line. Start engine and run at idle speed. Loosen lock nut on pressure regulator and turn hex screw to adjust fuel pressure to specifications. Turning screw clockwise increases pressure and counterclockwise decreases pressure.

BMW, Datsun & Volkswagen – These manufactures do not give fuel pressure regulator adjustment procedures.

HOT (SLOW) IDLE RPM

See appropriate article in TUNE-UP Section.

IDLE MIXTURE

See appropriate article in TUNE-UP Section.

THROTTLE VALVE SWITCH

BMW & Renault – 1) Throttle valve switch should start to operate when throttle valve is opened 2° from its normally closed position.

2) To check and adjust throttle valve switch, suitable testing equipment should be used. On BMW use Bosch tester No. 0684100202; on Renault, use tester EFAW 228S 10.

3) Use tester manufactures instructions for switch positions on tester. Readings on tester should show zero resistance for off, infinity resistance for part throttle and zero resistance for full throttle.

4) If throttle switch does not perform as described, loosen throttle switch screws. Rotate throttle valve switch clockwise until needle on tester moves from an infinity reading to a zero reading. Then rotate throttle switch counterclockwise one graduation (one graduation equals 2°). Tighten throttle valve switch screws. Recheck operation of switch.

Datsun – 1) Disconnect battery ground cable. Remove throttle valve switch connector.

2) Connect ohmmeter between terminals 2 and 18. Continuity should exist when throttle valve is in IDLE position and should NOT exist when valves opens about 4°. *See Fig. 7.*

3) Now connect ohmmeter between terminals 3 and 18. Gradually open throttle valve from fully closed position.

4) Ohmmeter reading should be at its lowest point at about 34° of throttle valve rotation. If ohmmeter reading is greater at all other valve positions, throttle valve switch is functioning properly.

Volkswagen – 1) Remove throttle valve housing. Hold throttle valve in fully closed position.

2) Turn throttle valve switch in open throttle direction until slight resistance is felt.

3) Tighten mounting screws to throttle valve switch.

4) Ensure that throttle valve is not held open after making adjustment.

5) Now open throttle valve slowly. Just before full throttle is reached, needle of ohmmeter should move from infinity to zero ohms.

6) Check EGR contact by connecting ohmmeter to terminals 42 and 44. Open throttle valve slowly.

7) Ohmmeter should move from zero to infinity. Just prior to reaching full open throttle, ohmmeter should return to zero ohms.

BOSCH CIS INJECTION SYSTEM – AUDI & VOLKSWAGEN

Audi Fox & 100LS
Volkswagen
Dasher
Rabbit
Scirocco

DESCRIPTION & OPERATION

The Bosch Continuous Injection System (CIS) is a mechanically operated system. It injects fuel to each cylinder in amounts determined by the volume of air flow through the air intake system. Intake air required by the engine is metered by an air flow sensor located in the air inlet. Sensor is activated by a circular plate attached to an arm and pivot assembly which is extremely sensitive to air flow. This sensor plate is raised or lowered by the incoming flow of air, and in turn, raises or lowers a plunger in the fuel distributor. This plunger acts to increase or decrease amount of fuel to be injected at each cylinder.

Main components of the CI System are: Control Pressure Regulator, Air Sensor, Fuel Distributor, Thermo-Time Switch, Auxiliary Air Regulator, Cold Start Valve and Injectors, Electric Fuel Pump, Fuel Accumulator, Auxiliary Air Valve and a fuel filtering system.

TESTING

AIR/FUEL MIXTURE CONTROL (AIR FLOW SENSOR)

Audi & VW – 1) Operate starter for short period or run engine at idle. Turn ignition OFF after fuel pressure has built up and stabilized. Remove air duct assembly.

2) Lift sensor plate with magnet or by hand slightly off seated position. Gradually raise plate to limit of upward travel.

3) Even resistance should be felt over entire travel of sensor plate. No tight or binding spots should be evident.

4) Ensure sensor plate is centered in inlet cone. If adjustment is needed, use suitable tool (1109 or equivalent) or insert a .004" (.10 mm) feeler gauge around outside of sensor plate while in seated position. Centering bolt should be slightly loosened. Retighten bolt after adjustment.

5) When sensor plate is pushed down quickly there should be no resistance felt. If binding or sticking is evident, replace sensor unit.

6) If sensor plate lever is hard to move in upward direction but moves freely when pushed down, control plunger is sticking or binding. Remove fuel distributor and clean the control plunger in appropriate solvent.

7) Reinstall plunger and recheck. Replace fuel distributor if plunger still sticks or binds.

8) To adjust sensor plate position for height in cone, loosen fuel line to control pressure regulator where line is connected to fuel distributor.

NOTE – *Fuel is under pressure and some fuel will escape when fitting is loosened at fuel distributor. Wrap cloth around fitting to avoid spillage of fuel in engine area.*

9) Upper edge of sensor plate must be even with edge of air cone. *(See Fig. 1)*. If too high, adjust sensor plate.

10) Plate may be positioned slightly lower but not more than .019" (.5 mm).

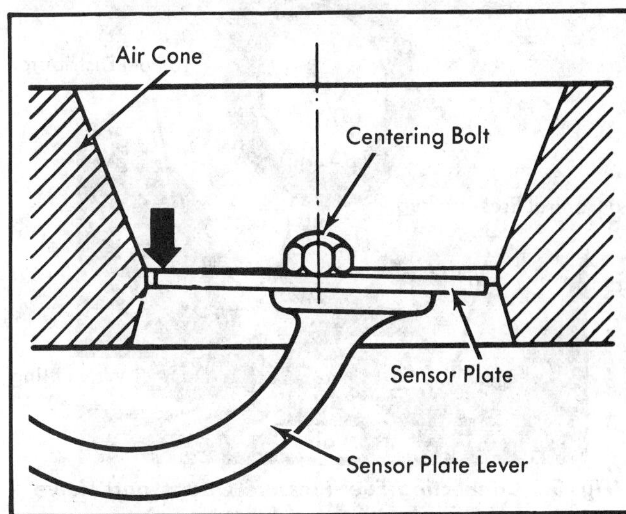

Fig. 1 Sensor Plate Position

11) Adjust by bending wire bracket beneath sensor plate. *(See Fig. 2)*.

12) Check idle speed and CO% and readjust after making sensor plate adjustment.

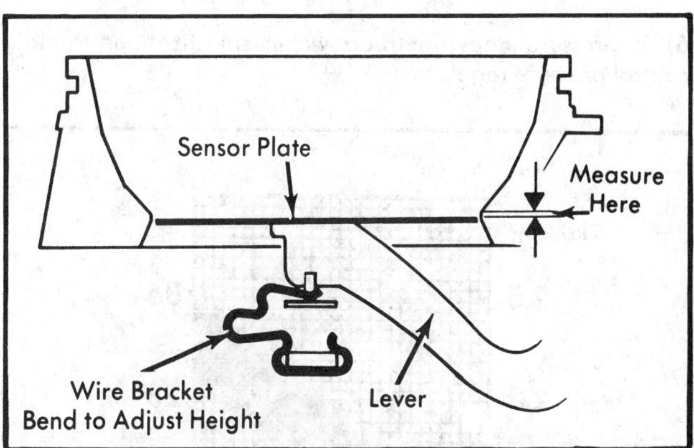

Fig. 2 Adjusting Location for Sensor Plate Height

COLD ENGINE CONTROL PRESSURE TEST

NOTE – *Before pressure test can be done, it will be necessary to install fuel pressure gauge and valve (VW 1318 or P378).*

1) Install pressure gauge and valve in fuel line between fuel distributor and control pressure regulator.

2) Valve assembly should be on control pressure regulator side of gauge. *(See Fig. 3)*.

BOSCH CIS INJECTION SYSTEM – AUDI & VOLKSWAGEN (Cont.)

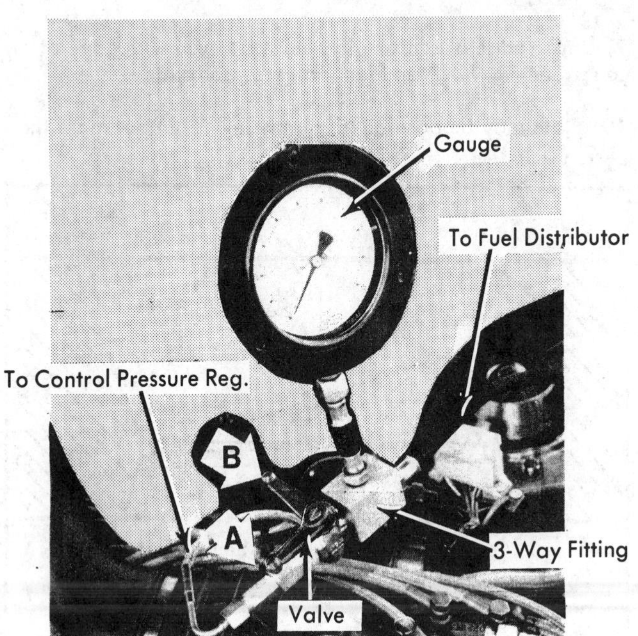

Fig. 3 Connecting Fuel Pressure Gauge and Valve To Test Control Pressure

3) Set valve lever to position "A" as shown in *Fig. 3*.

4) Unplug electrical connector from control pressure regulator. Start engine and idle for maximum of 1 minute.

5) Note control pressure and refer to graph in *Fig. 4*. At normal room temperature, about 68° F (20° C), pressure should read between 18-24 psi (1.3-1.7 kg/cm²).

6) If pressure does not read within specifications, replace control pressure regulator.

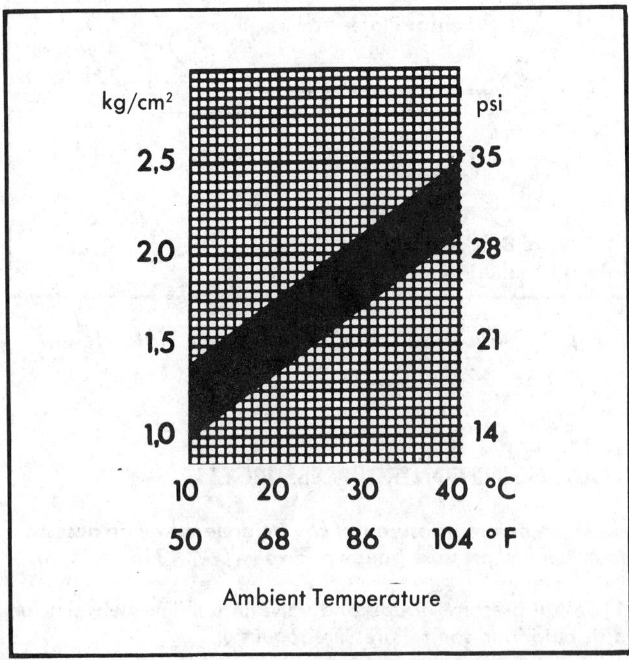

Fig. 4 Graph Showing Cold Control Pressure at Various Temperatures

WARM ENGINE CONTROL PRESSURE TEST

NOTE — *Connect pressure testing gauge and lever as outlined in cold engine test.*

1) Be sure control pressure regulator electrical plug is correctly plugged in. Place valve lever on tester in position "A" as shown in *Fig. 3*.

2) Start engine and idle until fuel pressure stabilizes. Reading should be 48-54 psi (3.4-3.8 kg/cm²). If not, replace control pressure regulator.

FUEL PRESSURE TESTING

NOTE — *Connect pressure testing gauge and lever as outlined in cold engine test.*

1) Ensure electric fuel pump activates when ignition switch is turned ON and that fuel filter is clean.

2) Set valve lever to position "B" as shown in *Fig 3*. Start engine and run at idle.

3) System fuel pressure should be 66-74 psi (4.5-5.2 kg/cm²). If not, clean and check fuel distributor pressure relief valve. If this does not bring fuel pressure within specifications, replace fuel distributor.

COLD START INJECTION VALVE & THERMO-TIME SWITCH

1) Unplug electrical connector from cold start valve but do not disconnect fuel line.

2) Remove cold start valve from engine and place into fuel resistant container with nozzle pointing down into container.

3) Connect jumper wire from one terminal of cold start valve to ignition coil terminal #15 (hot terminal). Connect another jumper wire from remaining terminal on cold start valve to a good ground.

4) Activate electric fuel pump by removing fuel pump relay and bridging relay plate terminals marked 13 and 14 with a fused (8 amp) jumper wire.

5) Turn ignition switch ON. Fuel should spray from cold start valve into container in a steady cone-shaped pattern.

6) Turn ignition switch OFF (pumps will still run). Wipe nozzle of cold start valve dry with clean cloth. No drops of fuel should form on tip of valve within one minute.

7) If cold start valve leaks or does not perform to specifications, replace it.

8) To check thermo-time switch, engine must be cold (coolant temperature below 95° F/35° C).

9) Remove electrical plug from cold start valve on end of intake manifold. Connect test light across harness plug terminals.

BOSCH CIS INJECTION SYSTEM – AUDI & VOLKSWAGEN (Cont.)

10) To prevent engine from starting during test, install jumper wire from ignition coil terminal #1 to ground.

11) Operate starter. Test light should come ON for 1-8 seconds. If not, replace thermo-time switch.

AUXILIARY AIR VALVE

NOTE – *Test must be performed on cold engine.*

1) Remove vacuum hose from auxiliary air regulator and plug hose.

2) With aid of mirror and light, observe gate valve inside air valve opening. Valve should be OPEN.

3) Run engine at idle to warm up. Observe gate valve as engine warms up. Valve should close after 5 minutes. If not, replace auxiliary air valve.

CONTROL PRESSURE REGULATOR FOR WARM RUNNING COMPENSATION

1) Unplug electrical connector from control pressure regulator.

2) Check resistance in regulator by connecting ohmmeter across the two electrical terminals in regulator socket. Resistance should be about 20 ohms. If not, replace control pressure regulator.

3) Remove ohmmeter and plug in harness connector.

INJECTOR NOZZLES

NOTE – *Do not allow open flame or sparks in area while testing and servicing fuel system components, to avoid possibility of fire or explosion.*

1) Remove injector but leave fuel line attached. Point injector nozzle into fuel resistant container.

2) Remove fuel pump relay and bridge relay plate terminals marked 13 and 14 with a fused (8 amp) jumper wire. This will activate fuel pump.

3) Remove bellows from air intake sensor unit. Turn ignition switch ON.

4) Lift sensor plate with magnet or pliers. Observe that injector fuel spray pattern is steady and cone-shaped.

5) Turn ignition switch OFF. Hold injector horizontally. No fuel should drip from injector nozzle. If injector does not perform to specifications, replace it. Repeat test for each injector.

NOTE – *When reinstalling injectors, dampen rubber seal with fuel. Ensure injectors are fully pressed into seat.*

REMOVAL & INSTALLATION

MIXTURE CONTROL UNIT

CAUTION – *On all models, disconnect battery ground cable and relieve fuel pressure before removinq mixture control unit.*

1) Disconnect air duct from air sensor and throttle valve housing.

2) Clean all connections completely and disconnect.

3) Remove mixture control unit from console. Ensure that no fuel spills onto engine or electrical components.

4) To install, reverse removal procedure. Use new gasket beneath upper section of air sensor.

FUEL DISTRIBUTOR

CAUTION – *On all models, disconnect battery ground cable and relieve fuel pressure before removing fuel distributor.*

1) Clean and remove fuel lines at fuel distributor. Remove fuel distributor retaining bolts.

2) Carefully lift fuel distributor up and away. Use care to avoid control plunger falling out from underside of fuel distributor.

3) If control plunger has been removed, dampen with fuel before installing. **NOTE** – *Small shoulder of plunger must be inserted first.*

4) Install fuel distributor using new O-rings.

CONTROL PRESSURE REGULATOR FOR WARM RUNNING COMPENSATION

CAUTION – *On all models, disconnect battery ground cable and relieve fuel pressure before removing control pressure regulator.*

1) Clean fuel lines and disconnect. Remove electrical connections to regulator.

2) Remove (2) screws securing regulator to intake manifold.

3) To install, reverse removal procedure.

AUXILIARY AIR REGULATOR

1) Remove vacuum hose connections to valve. Remove electrical connection(s).

2) Remove (2) screws holding regulator valve to intake manifold.

3) To install, reverse removal procedure.

THERMO-TIME SWITCH

1) Relieve any cooling system pressure and drain enough coolant from system to bring level below that of time switch.

2) Switch is located on coolant adaptor on engine block. Unplug electrical harness plug from thermo-time switch.

3) Using a deep socket (to avoid damaging electrical terminals on top of switch), remove thermo-time switch.

4) To install switch, reverse removal procedure. Suitable sealing compound may be needed to ensure proper seal of new switch.

BOSCH CIS INJECTION SYSTEM – AUDI & VOLKSWAGEN (Cont.)

COLD START VALVE

CAUTION – *On all models, disconnect bettery ground cable and relieve fuel pressure before removing cold start valve.*

1) Cold start valve is bolted to intake manifold behind throttle valve housing. Clean around fuel line and remove line from valve.

2) Remove electrical connector from cold start valve.

3) Remove bolt(s) holding cold start valve and lift out valve.

4) To install, reverse removal procedure.

INJECTORS

CAUTION – *On all models, disconnect battery ground cable and relieve fuel pressure before removing injectors.*

1) Clean fuel line connection at injector thoroughly. Remove fuel line from injector with special tool (P384) or equivalent.

2) Pull steadily upward on injector to remove.

3) To install, reverse removal procedure ensuring that O-rings are dampened with fuel prior to installation.

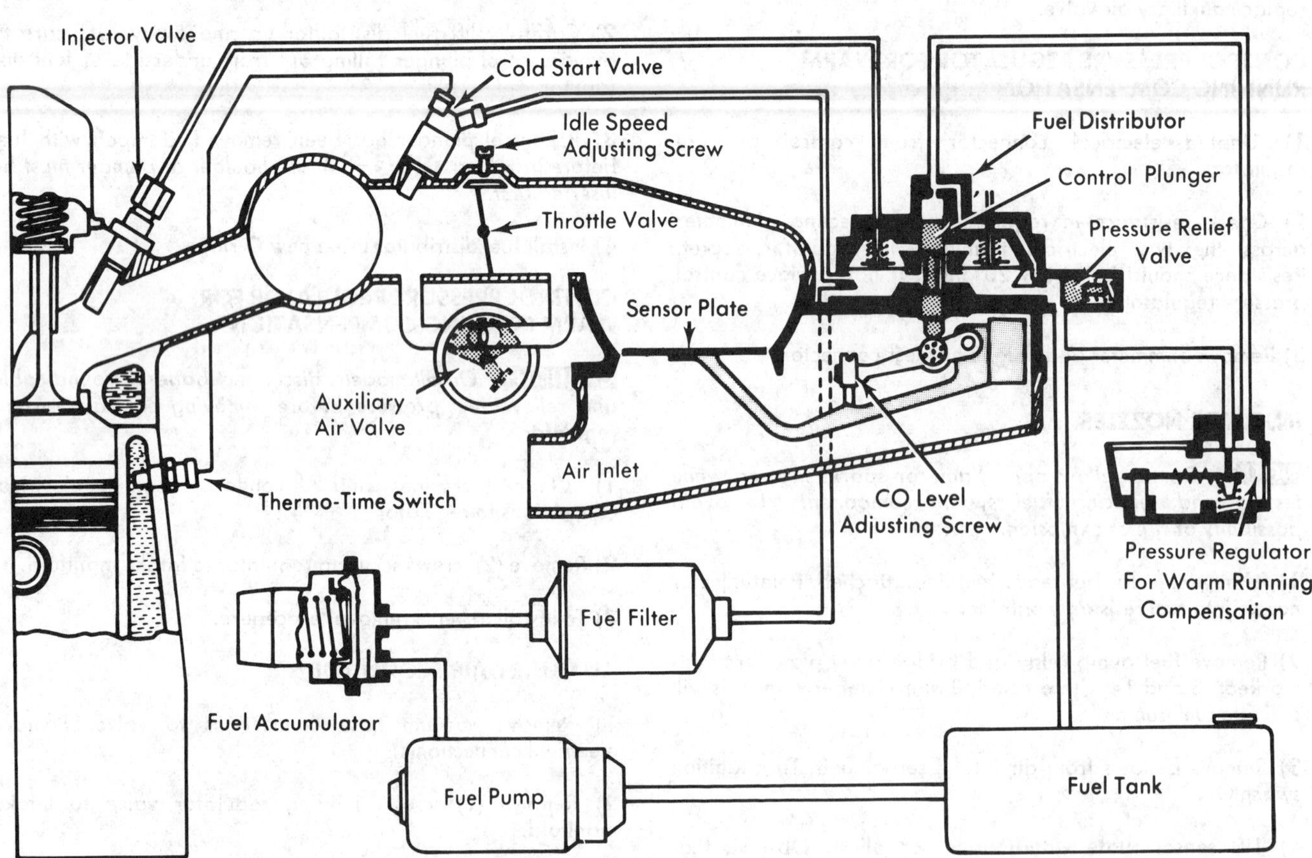

Fig. 5 Functional Diagram of Audi & Volkswagen CIS Fuel Injection System

BOSCH CIS INJECTION SYSTEM – BMW MODELS

BMW 320i

DESCRIPTION & OPERATION

The Bosch Continuous Injection System (CIS) is a mechanical system. It injects fuel to each cylinder in amounts determined by the volume of air flow through the air intake system. Intake air required by the engine is metered by an air flow sensor located in the air inlet. Sensor is activated by a circular plate attached to an arm and pivot assembly which is extremely sensitive to air flow. This sensor plate is raised or lowered by the incoming flow of air, and in turn, raises or lowers a plunger in the fuel distributor. This plunger acts to increase or decrease amount of fuel to be injected at each cylinder.

Main components of the CI System are: Control Pressure Regulator, Air Sensor, Fuel Distributor, Thermo-Time Switch, Auxiliary Air Regulator, Cold Start Valve and Injectors, Electric Fuel Pump, Fuel Accumulator, Auxiliary Air Valve, a fuel filtering system and Vacuum Regulator.

TESTING

AIR/FUEL MIXTURE CONTROL (AIR FLOW SENSOR)

BMW – 1) Detach and remove intake cowl at mixture control unit and throttle housing.

2) Turn ignition switch ON for about 5 seconds, then turn it OFF again. During this time, raise sensor plate by using magnet or pliers. As plate is slowly raised, resistance felt should be even throughout range of travel.

3) When sensor plate is quickly pushed down, no resistance should be felt. Do not allow plate to scrape on wall of air cone. If necessary to center sensor plate, loosen centering bolt in middle of plate and adjust.

4) Check sensor plate height. Plate should be even with beginning of taper in air cone. If plate is no more than .019" (.5 mm) deeper than edge of tapered area, adjustment is not needed.

5) To adjust height of sensor plate, remove mixture control unit and bend spring beneath plate assembly.

6) If sensor plate is too high in air cone, engine will diesel or run on. If plate is too low, poor cold or warm engine starting will result.

7) Check for sticking or binding fuel control piston (plunger) in fuel distributor. Remove fuel distributor, remove plunger and clean thoroughly with gasoline.

8) Plunger binding or sticking is evident when resistance to sensor plate movement is uneven.

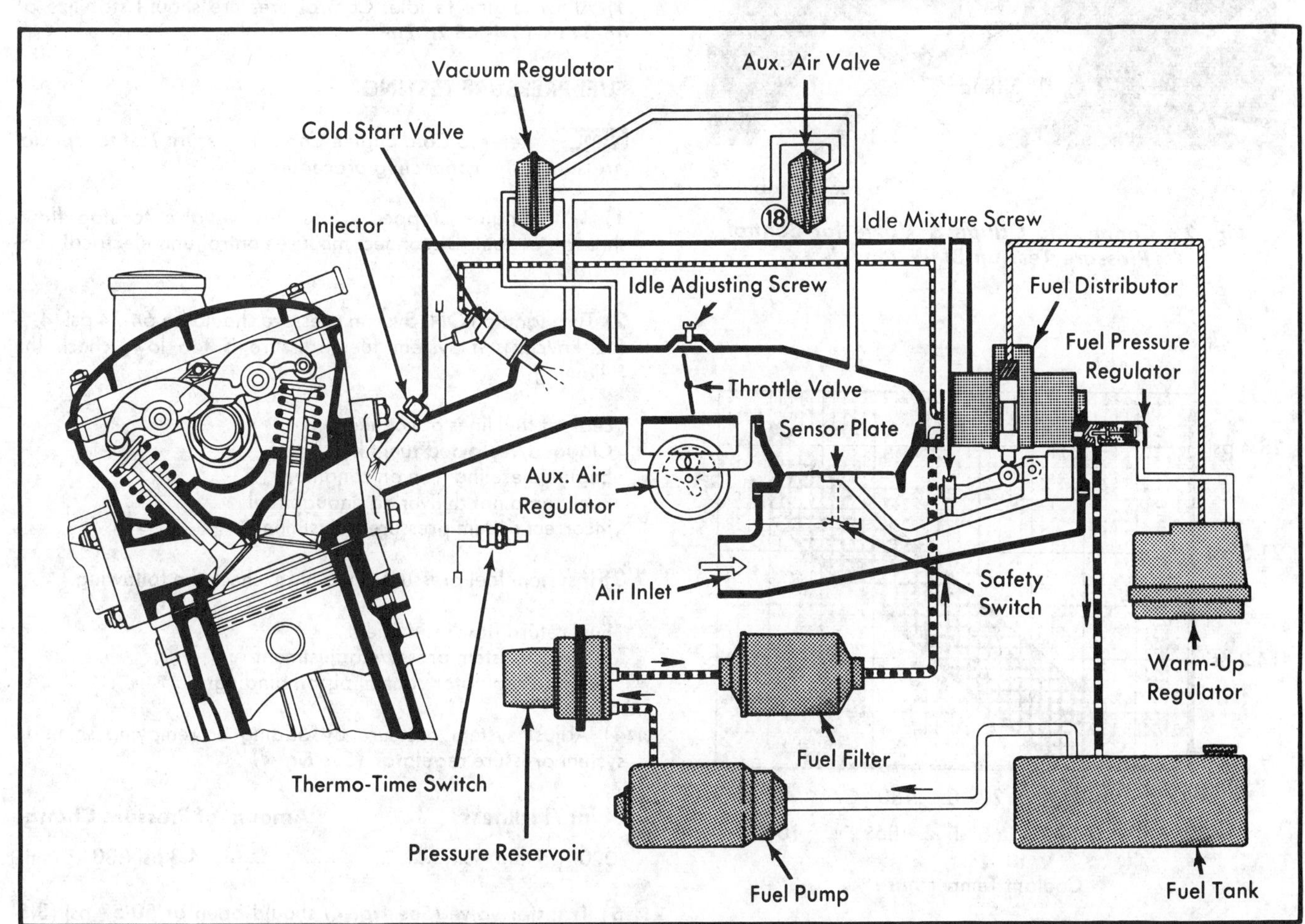

Fig. 1 System Diagram of Bosch CIS System Used on BMW

BOSCH CIS INJECTION SYSTEM – BMW MODELS (Cont.)

COLD ENGINE CONTROL PRESSURE TEST

NOTE – *Before pressure test can be done, it will be necessary to install a fuel pressure gauge, 2-way valve and 3-way "T" fitting in fuel line between fuel distributor and control pressure regulator.*

1) Install valve so that it is between gauge and control pressure regulator. *(See Fig. 2).* Hang gauge from convenient point above level of units to be tested.

2) Unplug electrical connector at auxiliary air regulator to avoid overheating unit. Disconnect electrical connector at mixture control unit. Turn ignition ON.

3) Set 2-way valve for flow-through operation (open).

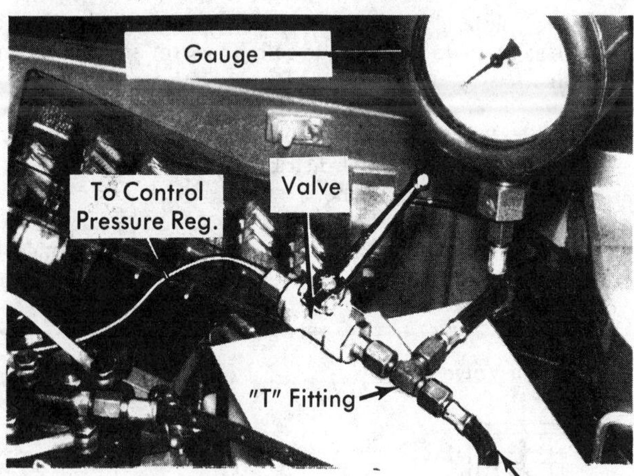

Fig. 2 Connecting Gauge & Valve for Control Pressure Test on BMW Models

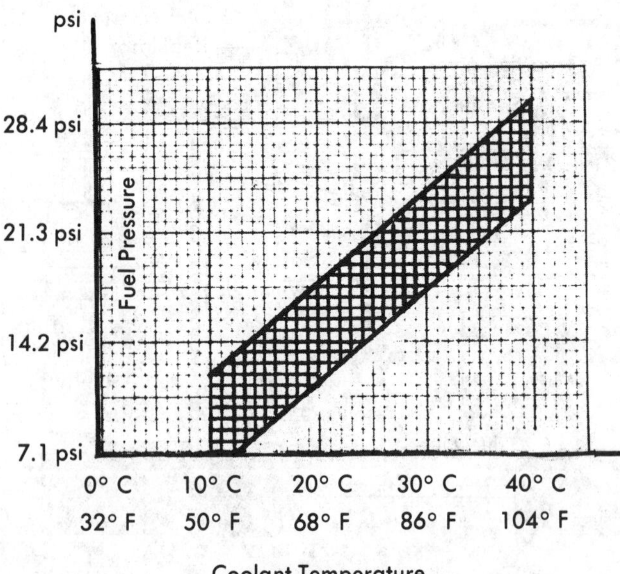

Fig. 3 Graph Showing Fuel Pressure & Temperature Relationship

4) Control pressure is dependant upon coolant temperature. Refer to *Fig. 3* graph for temperature and pressure relationship.

5) If fuel pressure reads too low, warm-up regulator is defective and should be replaced. If fuel pressure reads too high, regulator is defective or fuel return flow is insufficient or restricted. Turn OFF ignition.

WARM ENGINE CONTROL PRESSURE TEST

NOTE – *Connect special pressure tester as outlined in cold engine testing.*

1) Open 2-way valve for flow-through operation. Disconnect electrical connector to mixture control unit.

2) Turn ignition ON. Do not start engine. Control pressure should rise steadily for about 3 minutes to 48-54 psi (3.4-3.8 kg/cm^2).

3) If not, check for voltage at electrical connector. If voltage is satisfactory, heating coil is defective. Replace warm-up regulator.

4) Install air inlet assembly. Reconnect electrical connectors to auxiliary air regulator and mixture control unit. Start engine.

5) Allow engine to idle. Control pressure should stabilize at 48-54 psi (3.4-3.8 kg/cm^2).

FUEL PRESSURE TESTING

NOTE – *Refer to Cold Engine Control Pressure Test for special pressure tester connecting procedure.*

1) With engine stopped, close 2-way valve to stop flow-through of fuel. Disconnect mixture control unit electrical connector.

2) Turn ignition ON. System pressure should be 64-74 psi (4.5-5.2 kg/cm^2). If system fuel pressure is too low, check the following:

Leak at fuel lines or connections
Clogged/restricted fuel filter
Engine dieseling (run on condition)
Fuel pump not delivering enough fuel
Incorrect system pressure adjustment

3) If system fuel pressure is too high, check the following:

Fuel return flow insufficient
Incorrect system pressure adjustment
Pressure regulator control piston binding

4) Adjust system pressure by adding or removing shims to system pressure regulator. *(See Fig. 4).*

Shim Thickness	Amount of Pressure Change
.020" (.5 mm)	4.3 psi (.30 kg/cm^2)

5) Transfer valve *(See Fig. 4)* should open at 50-57 psi (3.5-4.0 kg/cm^2). If not, engine will be difficult to start. Check by replacing valve and restarting engine.

BOSCH CIS INJECTION SYSTEM – BMW MODELS (Cont.)

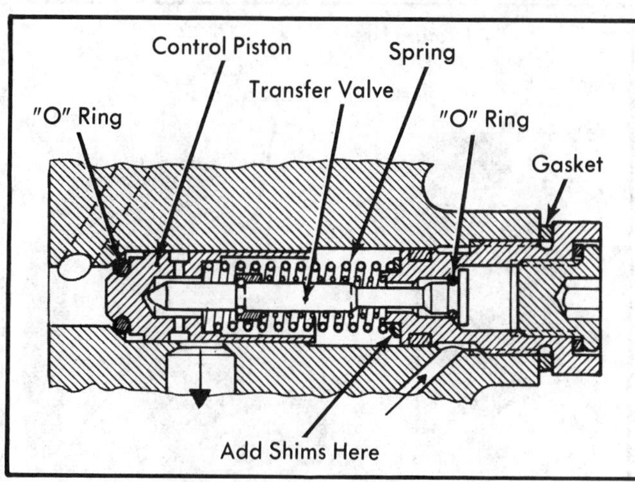

Fig. 4 System Pressure Regulator Adjustment (Located in Fuel Distributor Housing)

SYSTEM PRESSURE REGULATOR TEST

NOTE – *Refer to Cold Engine Control Pressure Test for pressure tester connecting procedure.*

1) Open 2-way valve for flow-through operation. Turn ignition ON.

2) Unplug electrical connector at mixture control unit, and then plug it in again.

3) Turn ignition OFF. Observe cut-off pressure on gauge. Pressure should not drop below 24 psi (1.7 kg/cm^2) for several minutes.

4) If pressure drops too soon, check the following:

One or both "O" rings in pressure regulator leaking
Warm-up regulator or supply line leaking
Fuel pump check valve leaking
Pressure reservoir leaks

5) Repair or replace parts as necessary and recheck system.

COLD START INJECTION VALVE & THERMO-TIME SWITCH

1) Disconnect electrical plug at thermo-time switch. Connect brown/black wire (W) to ground. *(See Fig. 5).*

2) Disconnect wire from lowest terminal of starter solenoid to prevent engine from starting during test.

3) Remove cold start valve. Remove fuel pump relay from relay plate. Apply battery voltage to terminal marked 87 on relay plate. This will activate fuel pump.

4) Cold start valve should spray fuel. If not, replace cold start valve and recheck.

5) Replace fuel pump relay. Reattach all electrical connectors.

6) Check thermo-time switch by disconnecting electrical plug at thermo-time switch. Connect test light to battery positive terminal (+) and terminal "W" of time switch *(See Fig. 5).*

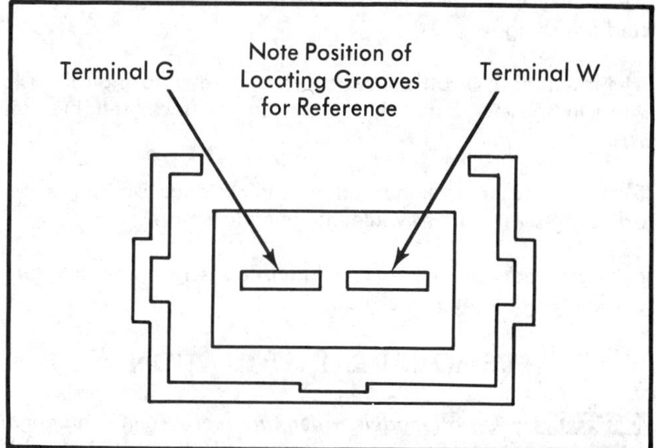

Fig. 5 Cold Start Valve Terminal Locations for Testing

7) Test light should come ON at coolant temperatures below 95° F (35° C) and should NOT come on when coolant temperature is above that level. Light should not remain on for more than 8 seconds. If switch is defective, replace it.

AUXILIARY AIR VALVE

1) Engine must be cold to perform this test. Start engine.

2) Engine speed should be higher than specified engine speed for fast idle for a brief period. Normal idle speed should be 850-950 RPM.

3) If no increase in idle speed is evident, or idle speed fails to return to normal level after a few minutes, replace auxiliary air valve.

INJECTOR NOZZLES

1) Install pressure tester (13 3 060 or equivalent) to measure fuel pressure applied to injector. *See Cold Engine Control Pressure Test.*

2) Remove injection valves. Carefully lift sensor plate with magnet or pliers.

3) Observe injector tips. Injectors are good if no more than one drop leaks from tip every 15 seconds. Replace defective injectors.

4) Open 2-way valve for flow-through operation. Turn ignition ON. Disconnect mixture control unit plug. Lift sensor plate for about 4 seconds maximum.

5) System pressure should not drop more than 4 psi (.3 kg/cm^2). If pressure drop is more than 4 psi, check the following:

Fuel filter restricted or blocked
Poor fuel pump delivery rate
Fuel level in fuel tank too low

THROTTLE ADJUSTMENT

1) Disconnect accelerator cable.

2) Loosen lock nut and screw on adjuster stand. Adjust distance between stop and lever to .039-.058" (1-1.5 mm).

BOSCH CIS INJECTION SYSTEM – BMW MODELS (Cont.)

3) When correct clearance has been achieved, tighten lock nut and adjusting screw.

4) Now loosen throttle lever shaft set screw. Position throttle valve in housing so that there is no play or slack. Retighten set screw.

5) Now loosen lock nut on adjuster stand. Do not allow adjusting screw to turn while loosening lock nut.

6) With lock nut loose, turn adjusting screw one full turn clockwise and tighten lock nut.

REMOVAL & INSTALLATION

CAUTION – *On all models, when any fuel system component is being serviced or removed, disconnect battery ground cable and relieve fuel system pressure. Do not allow open flame or sparks in area due to danger of fire and explosion.*

MIXTURE CONTROL UNIT

1) Remove intake cowl. Loosen (3) screws on top of fuel distributor. Bend wire fuel line clips open and remove wire holder.

2) Carefully lift off top of fuel distributor. Do not allow control piston to fall out bottom. Disconnect mixture control unit electrical plug and remove all vacuum hoses.

3) Loosen (2) bracket nuts on side of control unit and lift out mixture control unit assembly.

NOTE – *Whenever venturi is to be replaced, take notice that there are two different shapes numbered as to application. Federal vehicles use Bosch No. 0 438 120 030; California vehicles use Bosch No. 0 438 120 039.*

4) Reverse removal procedure to install mixture control unit. Be sure to replace gasket between upper and lower halves of unit and replace "O" ring seal beneath fuel distributor at control piston opening.

FUEL DISTRIBUTOR

1) Relieve fuel pressure and disconnect all fuel lines at fuel distributor. Remove (3) screws on top of distributor unit.

2) Carefully lift fuel distributor off of mixture control unit, using care not to drop control piston from beneath distributor housing.

3) When installing fuel distributor, be sure to replace "O" ring beneath distributor head around control piston opening. Check control piston for dirt or any damage. Clean piston in new gasoline thoroughly before installing.

WARM-UP REGULATOR (CONTROL PRESSURE REGULATOR)

1) Disconnect fuel control line and fuel return line fittings at regulator.

2) Unplug electrical connector. Remove altitude control line (if equipped). Remove retaining bolt and remove warm-up regulator. *(See Fig. 6).*

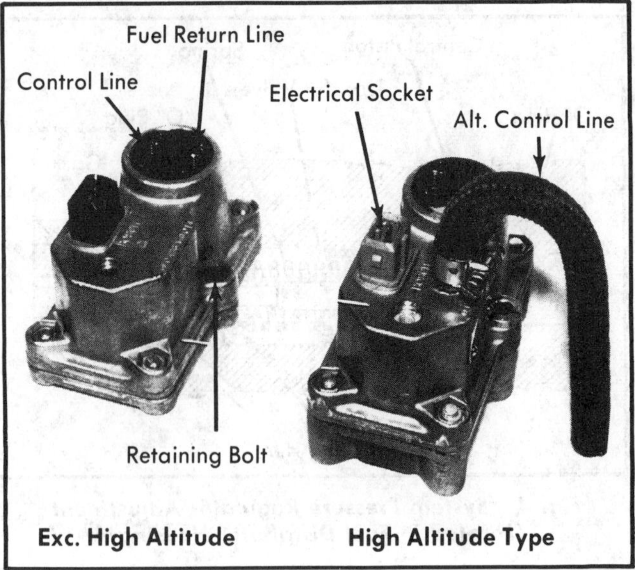

Fig. 6 Warm-Up (Control Pressure) Regulators on BMW

AUXILIARY AIR REGULATOR

1) Disconnect electrical plug from end of regulator.

2) Detach (2) hoses and remove. Remove auxiliary air regulator from cylinder head cover.

THERMO-TIME SWITCH

1) Remove electrical plug from time switch. Lower coolant level.

2) Remove time switch from engine using deep socket or suitable tool to avoid damaging electrical connections on top of switch. When installing, use appropriate sealer on threads.

COLD START VALVE

1) Clean thoroughly around fuel connection. Remove fuel line at fitting.

2) Detach electrical connector. Remove attaching bolt(s) or Allen screws and remove cold start valve.

3) To install, reverse removal procedure, ensuring that valve is firmly seated and connections are tight.

INJECTORS

1) Remove intake cowl and intake pipes at No. 2 and No. 3 cylinders.

2) Using suitable tool (screwdriver), gently lift injectors out of intake. Remove injectors from fuel lines and mark location of each injector.

3) To install, ensure insulator is properly seated in opening in intake. Press rubber "O" ring type seal in place in intake opening. Insert injector.

4) Install new gaskets when reinstalling intake pipes.

BOSCH CIS INJECTION SYSTEM – MERCEDES BENZ

Mercedes Benz
280
450
6.9

DESCRIPTION & OPERATION

The Bosch Continuous Injection System (CIS) is a mechanically operated system. Amount of fuel that is continuously injected to each cylinder is determined from air flow by the air sensor plate. This sensor plate is raised or lowered by the air flowing through the intake system to the engine. This, in turn, raises or lowers a plunger in the fuel distributor which increases or decreases amount of fuel to be injected at each cylinder.

Main components of the system are: Control Pressure Regulator, Air Sensor assembly, Fuel Distributor, Thermo-Time Switch, Auxiliary Air Regulator, Cold Start Valve, Injectors, Electric Fuel Pump, Fuel Accumulator, Auxiliary Air Valve, and a fuel filtering system.

TESTING

AIR/FUEL MIXTURE CONTROL (AIR FLOW SENSOR)

1) Check sensor plate lever for freedom of movement. Remove safety valve plug, turn ON ignition to build up fuel control pressure.

2) Turn ignition OFF and push sensor plate down by hand. Even resistance should be felt over entire range of travel. Release sensor plate suddenly. No binding should be evident. Sensor plate should quickly return and lever should follow more slowly.

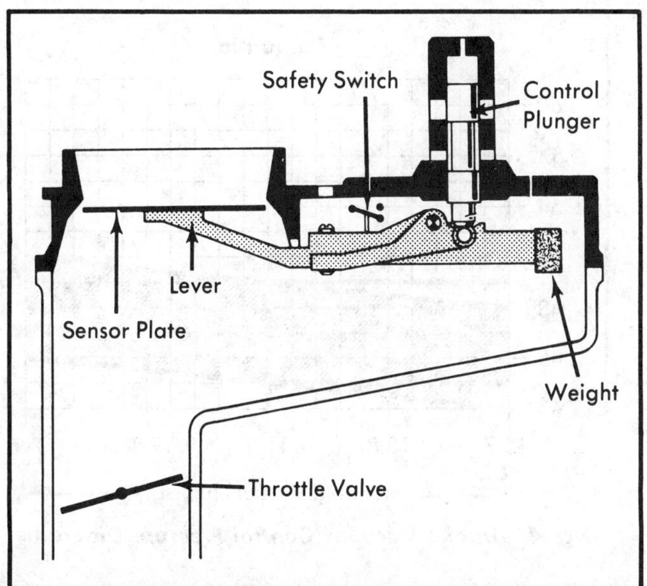

Fig. 1 Air Flow Sensor & Control Plunger Assembly (Mixture Control Unit)

COLD ENGINE CONTROL PRESSURE TEST

NOTE – *Before pressure testing can be done, it will be necessary to install special testing guage and 3-way valve assembly. Mercedes Benz recommends unit No. 100 589 13 21 00 for this procedure. Gauge installation will remain the same for all pressure testing operations.*

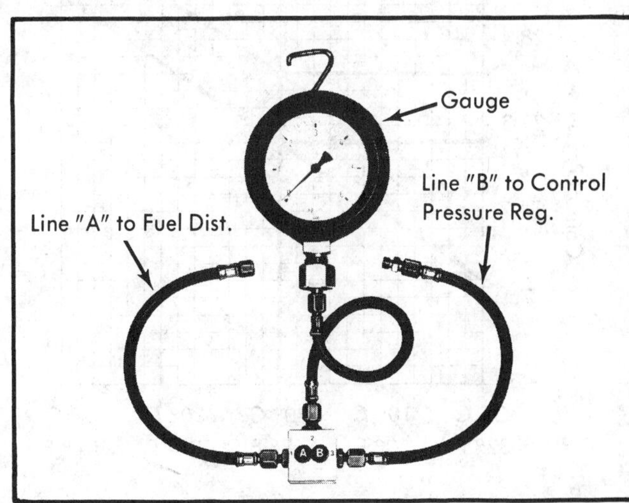

Fig. 2 Pressure Testing Gauge & Valve Assembly

1) Install tester assembly in fuel line between fuel distributor and control pressure regulator as directed in *Fig. 2*. Ensure engine is cold for this test.

2) Open valves for lines "A" and "B" on tester. Start engine and idle. QUICKLY read control pressure. Pressure should agree with pressure shown on graph in *Fig. 3* for ambient (surrounding) temperature.

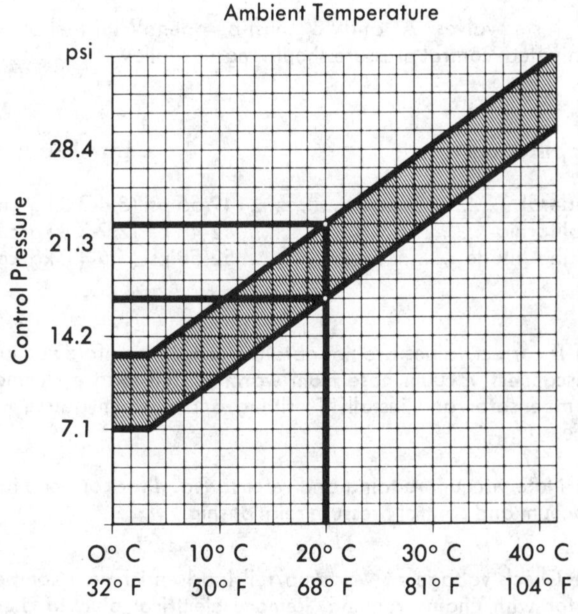

Fed. & Calif.

Fig. 3 Temperature/Control Pressure Graph

BOSCH CIS INJECTION SYSTEM – MERCEDES BENZ (Cont.)

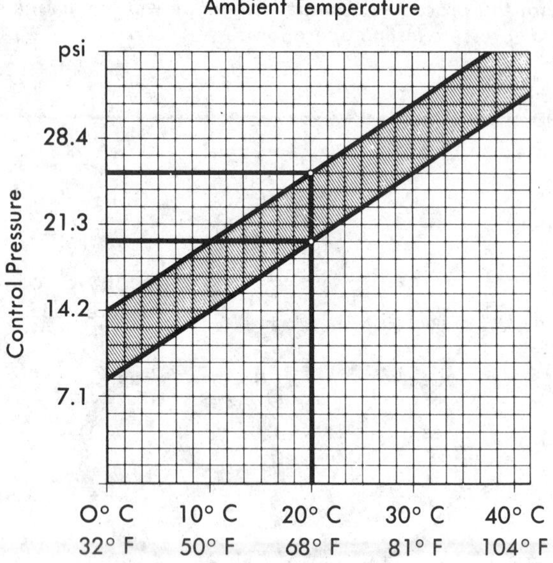

High Altitude

Fig. 3A Temperature/Control Pressure Graph

3) If correct value is not obtained, replace the warm-up/full load enrichment compensator. Reinstall plug to warm-up compensator.

WARM ENGINE CONTROL PRESSURE TEST

NOTE – *See Cold Engine Test for correct pressure tester installation.*

1) Tester valves "A" and "B" must be open. With fuel pumps activated, control pressure should read as follows:

Application	Control Pressure
Federal	49-55 psi (3.4-3.8 kg/cm²)
California	42-48 psi (2.9-3.3 kg/cm²)
High Altitude	52-58 psi (3.6-4.0 kg/cm²)

2) If correct values are not obtained, check manifold vacuum. Disconnect vacuum hose from warm-up/full load enrichment compensator and install "T" fitting and vacuum gauge into line.

3) Note vacuum reading and refer to *Fig. 4* for correct intake vacuum and control pressure relationship.

4) Check voltage at warm-up/full load enrichment compensator with engine running. Remove electrical plug to check. Voltage should be minimum of 13.5 volts.

5) Check warm-up heating coil with ohmmeter. Reading should be about 35 ohms. If not, replace the compensator.

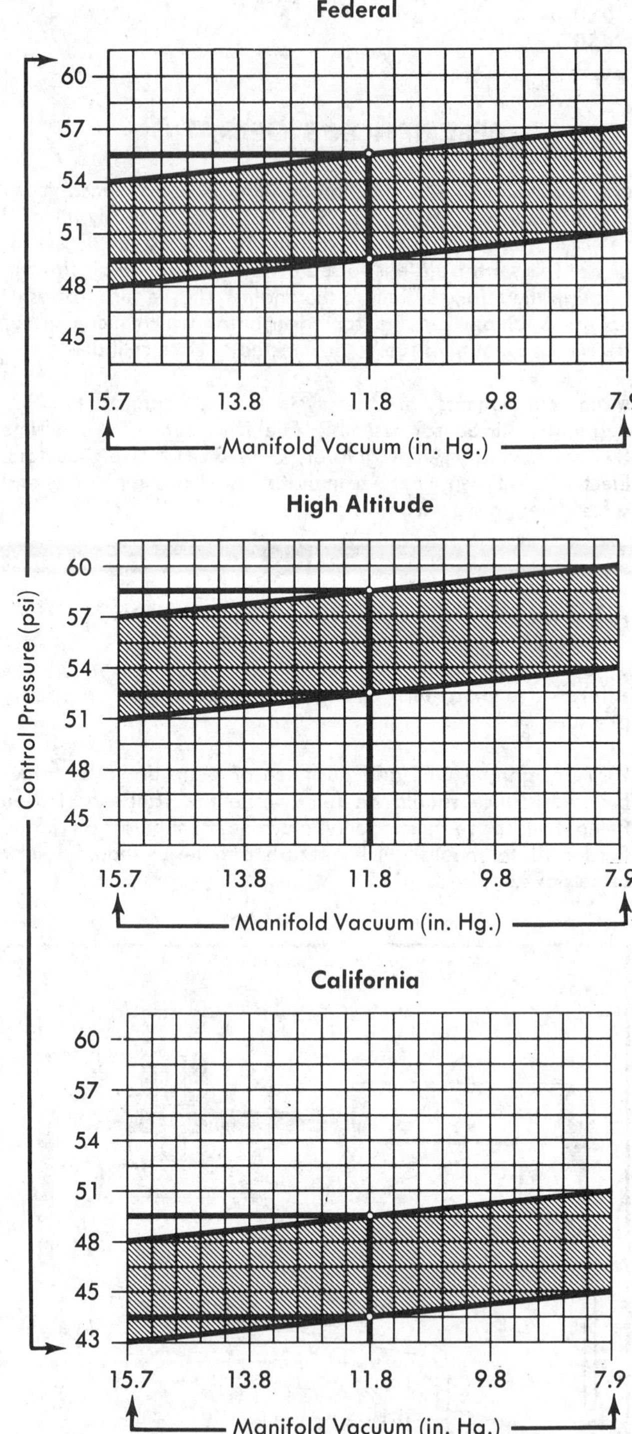

Fig. 4 Intake Vacuum/Control Pressure Diagrams

6) To check full load enrichment, remove vacuum line at compensator. Control pressure should drop to 41-46 psi (2.8-3.2 kg/cm²). If not, replace compensator.

7) Turn OFF engine. Remove pressure tester assembly. Avoid fuel spillage on engine. Reconnect fuel lines and electrical connectors. Run engine and check for leaks.

BOSCH CIS INJECTION SYSTEM – MERCEDES BENZ (Cont.)

SYSTEM PRESSURE TEST

NOTE – *Tester installation is the same as for Cold Engine Control Pressure Test.*

1) Close valve "B" on tester. Primary system pressure should be 75-84 psi (5.2-5.8 kg/cm²). If not, check the following:

Fuel pump delivery may not be enough
Primary system pressure regulator may not be adjusted correctly

PRIMARY SYSTEM PRESSURE REGULATOR ADJUSTMENT

1) Relieve system fuel pressure. Remove fuel return line at fuel distributor and plug line.

2) Remove pressure regulator from fuel distributor. Use care to avoid losing compression spring and shims *(See Fig. 5)*.

3) Regulator plunger may stick inside fuel distributor. Plunger can be removed with magnet or pencil.

4) In order to add or remove shims to change system pressure, regulator must be disassembled. Push compression spring back and remove retaining ring. Remove valve stem after removing hex socket plug.

5) Install new "O" rings and compression springs contained in repair kit. Adjusting shims are placed under outer heavy compression spring to increase pressure. Shims are available in thicknesses of .004" (.1 mm), .006" (.15 mm), .012" (.3 mm), .016" (.4 mm), and .020" (.5 mm). A shim thickness of .004" (.1 mm) will result in a pressure change of about 2.9 psi (.2 kg/cm²).

6) Reverse disassembly procedure to assemble regulator. Be sure to lubricate "O" rings prior to installation. Recheck system pressure and add or remove shims as necessary to obtain correct pressure reading of 75-84 psi (5.2-5.8 kg/cm²).

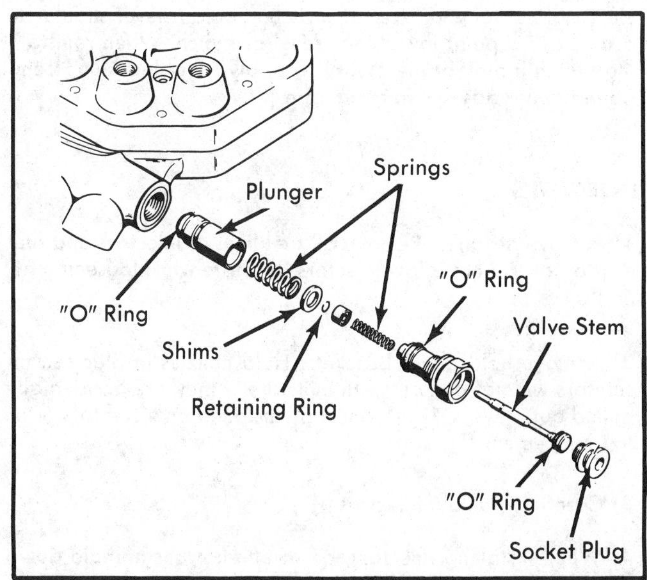

Fig. 5 Exploded View of System Pressure Regulator

COLD START VALVE & THERMO-TIME SWITCH

1) Disconnect fuel line at cold start valve. Remove valve. Loosen fuel line on fuel distributor and turn so that cold start valve can later be reconnected. Point cold start valve down into fuel resistant container. Disconnect safety switch plug.

2) Turn ignition ON. Connect a jumper wire from cold start valve to positive (+) terminal of battery. Valve should spray a cone-shaped pattern of fuel. **CAUTION** – *Connect jumper wire to cold start valve first to prevent electric arcing.*

NOTE – *When coolant temperature is below 59° F (15° C), jumper wire is not needed. Instead, reconnect harness plug.*

3) Now disconnect jumper wire from valve. Using clean cloth, wipe excess fuel from tip of valve. No fuel should leak out of nozzle.

4) Turn ignition OFF. Install cold start valve using new gasket. Reconnect safety switch plug and cold start valve plug.

5) Thermo-time switch is responsible for activating cold start valve at temperatures below 59° F (15° C). Actuating period increases with decreasing temperatures to a maximum of 12 seconds at −4° F (−20° C).

6) At coolant temperatures below 59° F, connect voltmeter to cold start valve terminal. Operate starter. Voltmeter should indicate 10 volts for amount of time that thermo-time switch is closed.

7) At coolant temperatures above 59° F, switch can be checked with an ohmmeter. Disconnect thermo-time switch plug. Connect test lead to terminal marked "W" in plug (brown/black wire), and other lead to ground. Reading should be about 270 ohms.

8) Connect test lead to other terminal in plug. Ohmmeter should read about 62 ohms. If not, replace switch.

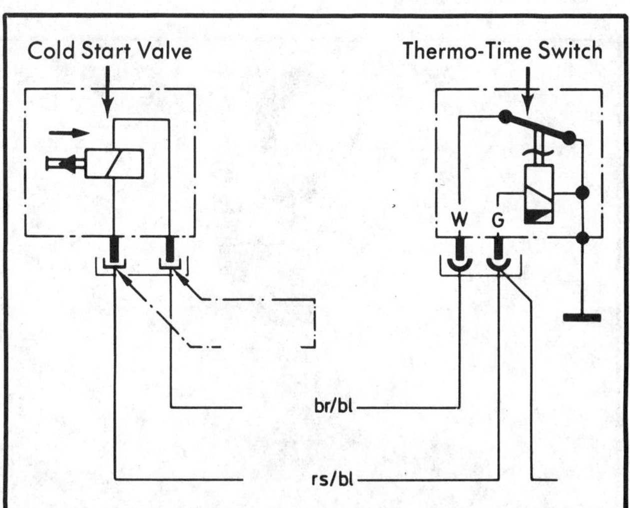

Fig. 6 Testing Thermo-Time Switch

BOSCH CIS INJECTION SYSTEM – MERCEDES BENZ (Cont.)

AUXILIARY AIR VALVE

1) When engine is initially cold started, engine speed should be about 800-1000 RPM. Engine speed should then increase to about 1200-1300 RPM.

2) As coolant temperature warms up to 158° F (70° C), engine RPM should again drop to normal range. Air valve is operating correctly if engine performs to these specifications.

INJECTOR NOZZLES

NOTE – *Manufacturer recommends using testing tool (EFEP 60 H or Bosch No. 0 681 200 502) for this test. If not available, use pressure gauge assembly No. 100 589 13 21 00.*

1) Remove air filter assembly. Unscrew fuel lines at injector nozzles. Ensure nozzles do not rotate when unscrewing fittings. Catch escaping fuel with cloth.

2) Remove hold down brackets. Hold nozzles in place to avoid pulling out nozzles and insulators. Pull out injectors while keeping insulators in place in opening of intake. If insulators accidently come out, new "O" rings must be installed before placing them back into intake.

3) Connect injector nozzles to tester. Bleed pressure line with shut-off valve open and pressure line nut loose. Several strokes of hand lever should be sufficient for bleeding.

4) Tighten pressure line nut. With shut-off valve still open, depress hand lever slowly to build up pressure to maximum of 22 psi (1.5 kg/cm^2). If injector leaks (solid stream from nozzle), replace it with a new one.

5) Close shut-off valve on tester and flush out valve with several rapid hand lever strokes. Open shut-off valve and slowly build up pressure with hand lever. Leak test again.

6) No fuel droplets should form within 15 seconds. Replace injectors that do not meet specifications. After installation, start engine and check for fuel leaks.

Fig. 7 EFEP60 H Injection Nozzle Tester

REMOVAL & INSTALLATION

NOTE – *On all models, disconnect battery ground cable and relieve fuel pressure before opening fuel system at any point. Do not allow open flame or sparks in area while servicing fuel system components due to danger of fire and explosion.*

MIXTURE CONTROL UNIT

Air Flow Sensor Housing – 1) Remove air filter. Remove all fuel and injection lines at injection nozzles and fuel distributor.

2) Plug all disconnected fuel supply and return lines. Remove safety switch connector. Remove retaining bolts and nuts on air flow sensor housing. Remove housing with gasket.

3) When installing housing, use new gasket. Torque hex head bolts and nuts to 6.5-7.2 ft. lbs. Reconnect all fuel lines and wiring. Start engine and check for leakage.

Fuel Distributor – 1) Remove air filter. Remove all fuel supply lines at fuel distributor and injectors. Plug disconnected lines.

2) Unscrew fitting for control pressure line on fuel distributor. Remove (3) retaining screws and remove distributor.

NOTE – *Use care not to drop control plunger from beneath fuel distributor.*

3) Install fuel distributor using reversed removal procedure. Use new "O" ring (lubricated) and carefully install distributor. Reinstall all lines. Check sensor plate and lever for freedom of movement. Check control plunger for sticking or binding. Start engine and check for leaks. Adjust idle speed if necessary.

THERMO-TIME SWITCH

When removing thermo-time switch, use care not to damage electrical contacts on top of switch. Coolant level should be drained to a point lower than level of switch. When reinstalling switch it may be necessary to apply suitable sealing compound to threads to avoid leakage.

INJECTORS

1) Remove air filter. Remove all fuel lines at injectors and fuel distributor. Do not allow injectors to rotate while loosening fittings.

2) Remove hold down brackets. Hold nozzles in place so insulators will not pull out with injectors. If they are accidentally pulled out, new "O" rings must be installed on insulators prior to replacement.

3) Carefully pull out injectors.

4) When installing injectors, be sure that noses on hold down brackets face to the LEFT. Do not allow injectors to rotate while tightening fittings. Run engine and check for leaks.

BOSCH CIS INJECTION SYSTEM – MERCEDES BENZ (Cont.)

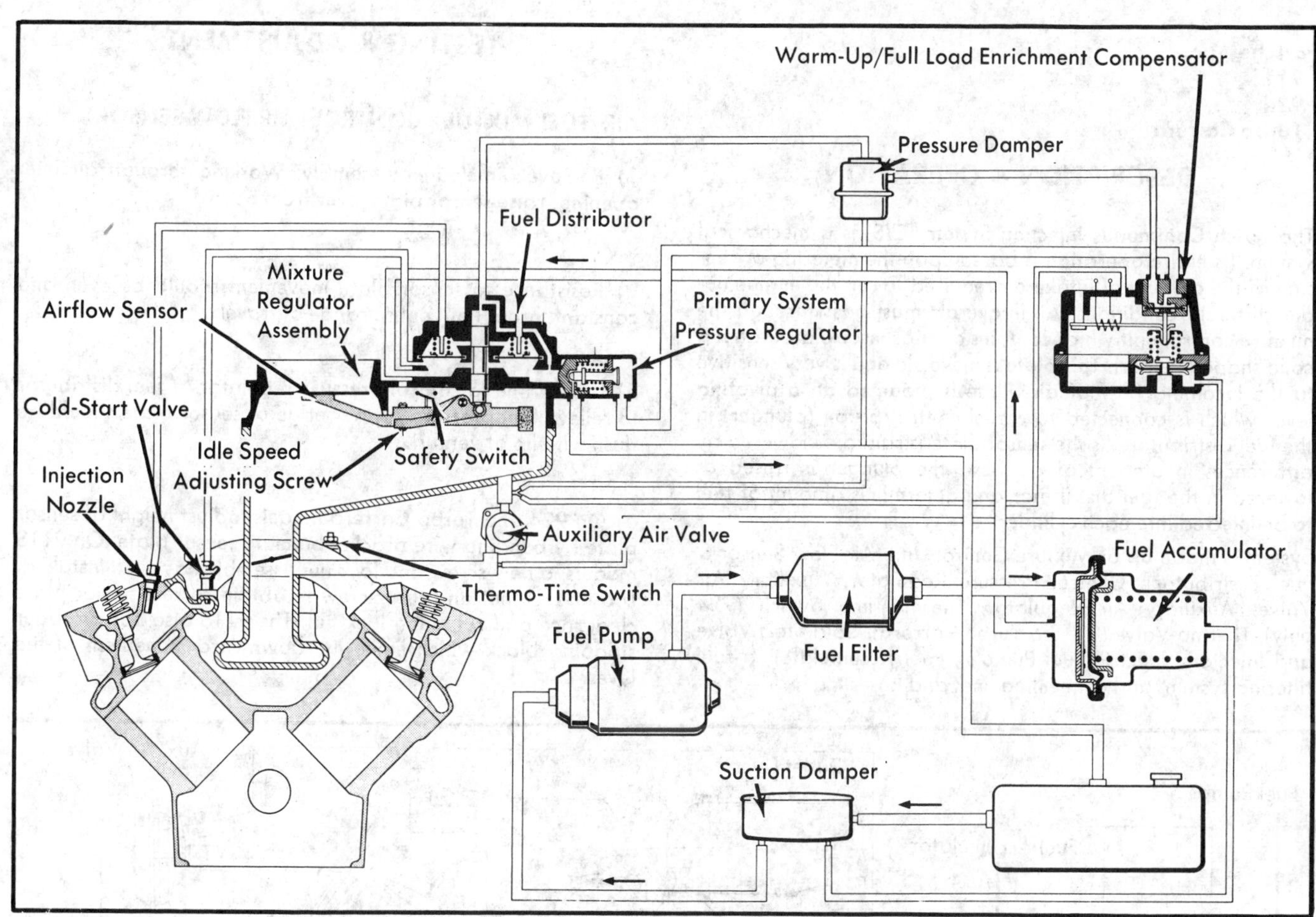

Fig. 8 Diagram of Mercedes-Benz CIS Injection System

BOSCH CIS INJECTION SYSTEM – PORSCHE

Porsche
911S
924
Turbo Carrera

DESCRIPTION & OPERATION

The Bosch Continuous Injection System (CIS) is a mechanical system. Its entire operation is based upon the metering or sensing of the amount of intake air required to run the engine under different conditions. All intake air must pass through the mixture control unit which contains an air sensor plate within a cone shaped venturi. This plate is movable and is very sensitive to the incoming flow of air. Plate is mounted on a pivoting lever which is connected to a fuel control piston (plunger) in the fuel distributor. As the sensor plate is raised or lowered by differences in amount of air flow, the plunger is raised or lowered in the fuel distributor and determines amount of fuel to be injected into each cylinder.

System is made up of Mixture Control Unit (Air Flow Sensor & Fuel Distributor), Control Pressure Regulator, Auxiliary Air Valve, Auxiliary Air Regulator, Thermo-Time Switch (924 only), Thermo-Valve (911S & Turbo Carrera), Cold Start Valve and Injectors, Electric Fuel Pump(s), Fuel Accumulator, a fuel filtering system, and connecting lines and hoses.

TESTING & ADJUSTMENT

AIR/FUEL MIXTURE CONTROL (AIR FLOW SENSOR)

1) Remove air cleaner assembly. Working through air inlet opening, raise sensor plate lever from below.

2) Resistance to sensor plate movement should be even and constant throughout entire range of travel.

3) Loosen line to control pressure regulator at fuel distributor to relieve fuel pressure. Upper edge of sensor plate should be flush with lip of venturi.

4) On 924 and Turbo Carrera models, adjust height of sensor plate by bending wire bracket beneath sensor plate. On 911S models, a new screw and lock nut assembly has been installed. Loosen lock nut and turn screw to obtain correct sensor plate clearance and retighten lock nut. The 911S also has a rubber stopping block which limits the downward movement of the lever.

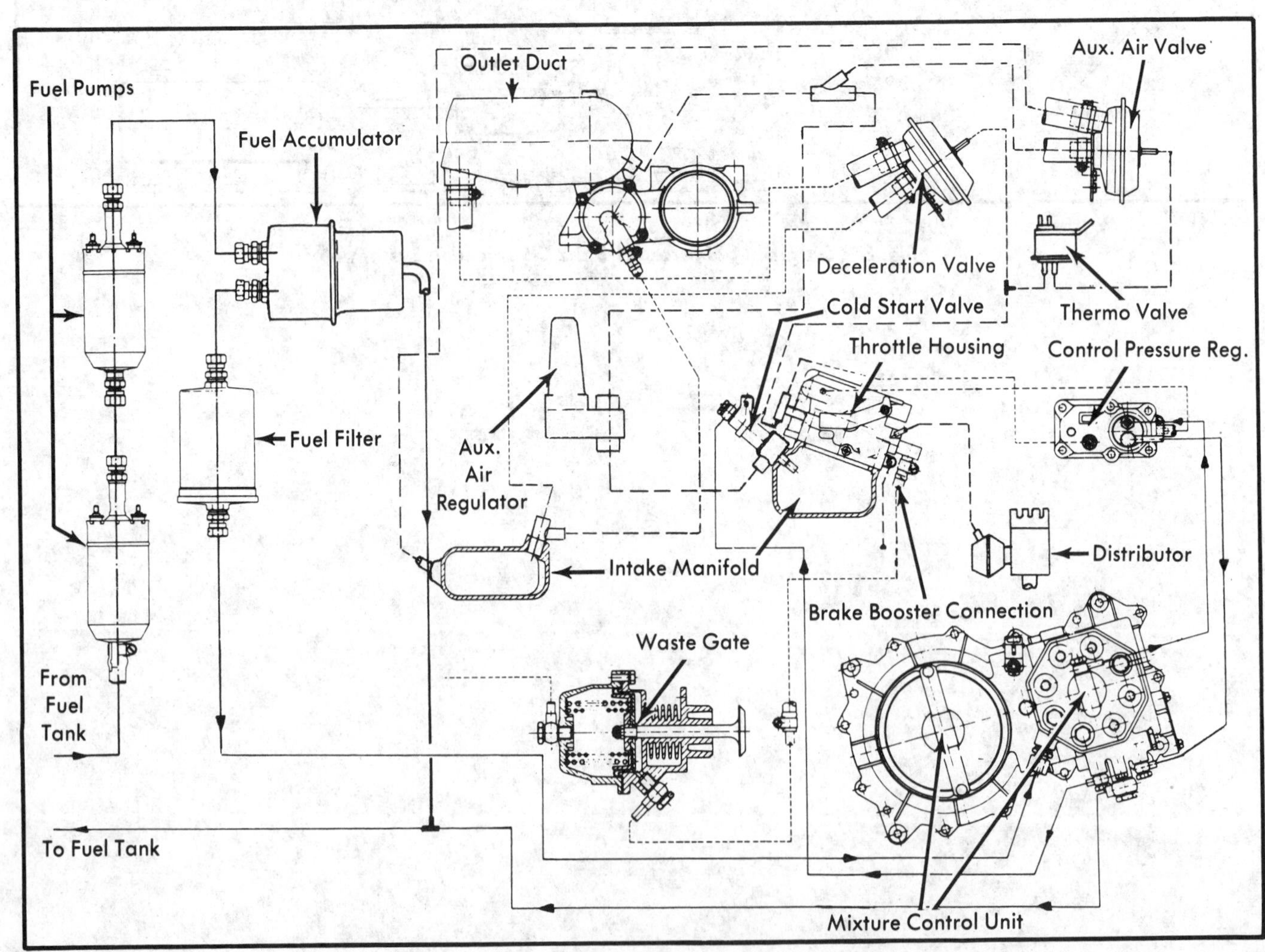

Fig. 1 CIS System on Porsche Turbo Carrera

BOSCH CIS INJECTION SYSTEM – PORSCHE (Cont.)

5) Now check sensor plate position with control pressure applied. Turn ignition ON and remove electrical plug on air flow sensor. If sensor plate drops slightly by a maximum of .04" (1 mm), operation is satisfactory. Plate may not move at all under control pressure and this condition is also satisfactory. If necessary, replace leaf spring on sensor plate stop.

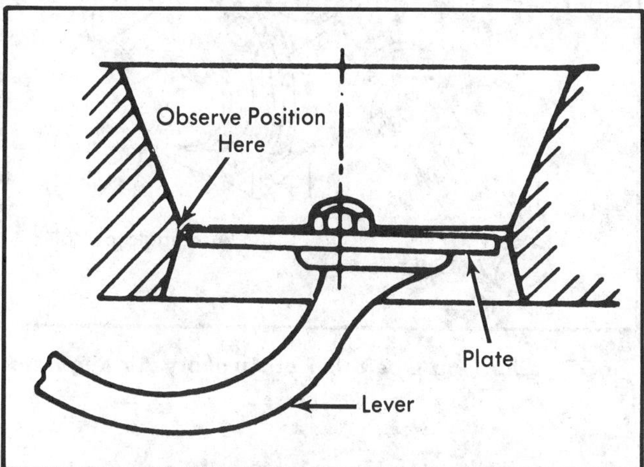

Fig. 2 Correct Sensor Plate Positioning

6) To center sensor plate within air cone, loosen and remove retaining bolt. Coat bolt threads with Loctite or suitable compound and install bolt finger tight.

7) Using a feeler gauge, center sensor plate so that a .004" (.10 mm) gap exists between plate and air cone wall at all points around the circle. Tighten retaining bolt to 43-48 in. lbs. (50-55 cmkg). Recheck gap after tightening.

COLD ENGINE CONTROL PRESSURE TEST

NOTE – *Before this fuel pressure test can be made, it is necessary to install a special 3-way pressure testing valve and gauge. Tool (P 378 or equivalent) can be used for all control pressure tests. Engine must be cold for this test.*

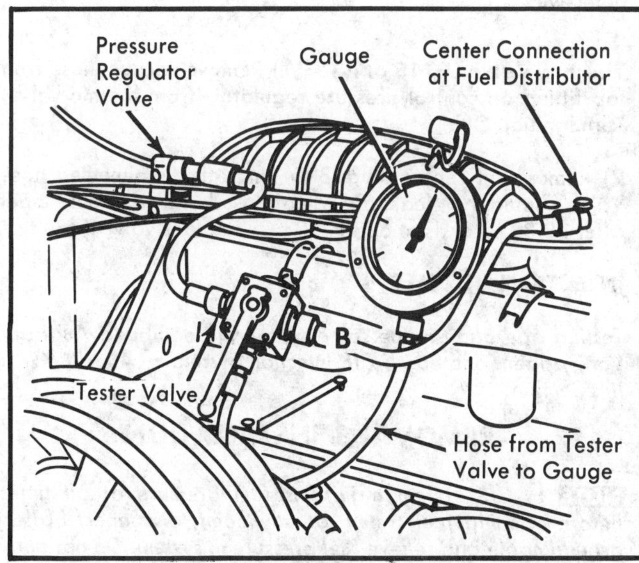

Fig.3 Pressure Tester Assembly for Checking Control Pressure

1) Ensure that all air has been bled from tester lines. Turn ignition ON. Remove air sensor and control regulator plugs. With valve lever on tester pointing toward gauge, read control pressure.

2) Gauge should read 18-24 psi (1.3-1.7 kg/cm²) at room temperature of about 68° F (20° C). If not, replace control pressure regulator.

WARM ENGINE CONTROL PRESSURE TEST

NOTE – *Pressure tester installation is the same as for Cold Engine Test. Engine can be warm or cold for this test.*

Porsche 911S & 924 – 1) Place tester valve lever so it points to gauge. Ensure control pressure regulator (warm-up regulator) plug is in place. Disconnect electrical plug at air flow sensor.

2) Turn ignition ON. Allow warm-up regulator to heat up. When indicator on gauge stops rising, take reading. Pressure should be 50-55.5 psi (3.5-3.9 kg/cm²). If not, replace regulator.

Turbo Carrera – 1) Tester valve lever should point to gauge. Disconnect mixture control unit electrical connector.

2) Control pressure should increase slowly to 38-44 psi (2.7-3.1 kg/cm²). Time will vary with ambient temperature.

If pressure does not reach this level, control pressure regulator is defective.

SYSTEM FUEL CONTROL PRESSURE

NOTE – *Tester hook-up is the same as for Cold and Warm Engine testing.*

911S & 924 – 1) Ensure fuel supply, fuel pump(s) and filter are in good working order for this test. Move tester valve lever to position "B" *(See Fig. 3).*

2) Disconnect electrical plug at air flow sensor terminal. Turn ignition ON.

3) Pressure should be 65-75 psi (4.6-5.3 kg/cm²). If not, pressure can be adjusted by adding or removing shims beneath outer spring in system pressure regulator. Pressure regulator is located in fuel distributor housing.

Turbo Carrera – Procedures are the same as for 911S and 924, except that system pressure should be 85-95 psi (6.0-6.7 kg/cm²).

COLD START VALVE & THERMO-TIME SWITCH

1) Ensure engine is cold. Remove cold start valve. Do not disconnect wire or fuel line. Disconnect hot lead at ignition coil. Point cold start valve down into fuel resistant container *(See Fig. 4).*

2) Turn ON ignition and have assistant operate starter. Valve must spray even cone shaped pattern for about 1-8 seconds. If not, replace cold start valve.

BOSCH CIS INJECTION SYSTEM – PORSCHE (Cont.)

3) Check valve for leaks by turning ignition ON again. Remove electrical plug at air flow sensor. Fuel pump(s) should still be operating.

4) With clean cloth, wipe cold start valve tip dry. No fuel should leak from valve within one minute. Replace valve if defective.

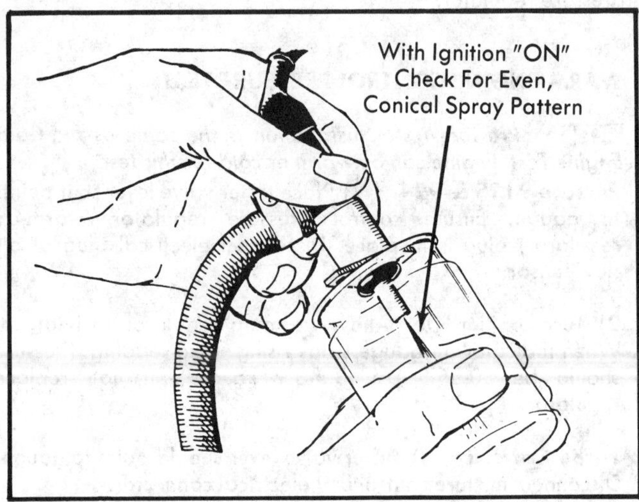

Fig. 4 Testing Cold Start Valve

5) To check thermo-time switch (exc. Turbo Carrera), remove electrical plug at cold start valve. Connect voltmeter to the plug.

6) Disconnect hot lead at ignition coil and operate starter. Voltmeter should deflect for about 1-8 seconds. Replace thermo-time switch if defective.

NOTE – *Ensure that coolant temperature is below 95° F (35° C) when performing test. Above that temperature, thermo-time switch does not operate and cannot be tested with voltmeter.*

AUXILIARY AIR VALVE (TURBO CARRERA ONLY)

NOTE – *Turbo Carrera has a new thermo-valve installed which acts on the auxiliary air valve. A "T" fitting in deceleration valve line leads to the air valve through the electric thermo-valve.*

1) Thermo-valve should be open when cold. When engine is cold started, idle speed should increase to ensure quick warm-up of thermo reactors.

2) Thermo-valve slowly heats and cuts off vacuum to air valve. The engine idle speed should drop to normal RPM as the auxiliary air valve closes. Thermo-valve is operating correctly if above conditions are met.

AUXILIARY AIR REGULATOR

1) Detach hose at regulator. Using mirror and flashlight, check to see that air passage in regulator is open.

2) Disconnect electrical plug at air flow sensor. Turn Ignition ON. Air passage in regulator should close after 5 minutes. If not, replace regulator.

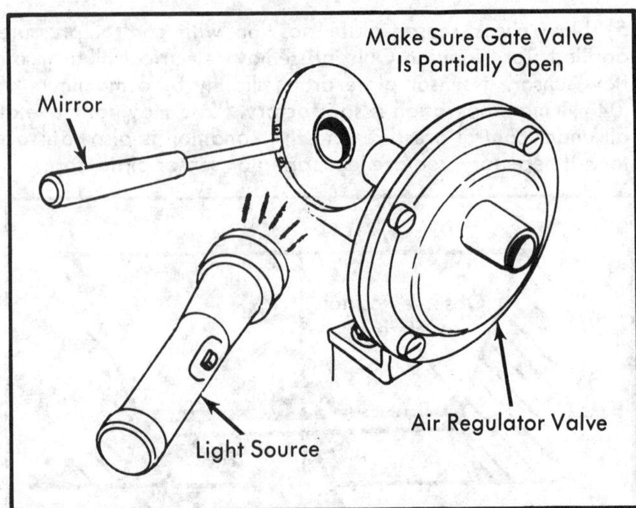

Fig. 5 Checking Operation of Auxiliary Air Regulator

CONTROL PRESSURE REGULATOR (WARM-UP COMPENSATOR)

NOTE – *911S models have a thermo-valve installed. Valve is placed to the vacuum retard line by a "T" fitting. Vacuum passes through the thermo-valve (electrically heated) to the control pressure regulator.*

1) Ensure engine oil temperature is above 120° F (50° C) and that engine is fully warmed up. Disconnect wires at warm-up regulator.

2) Remove plug at air flow sensor and turn ignition ON. Using voltmeter, check voltage at disconnected regulator plug. Voltage should be a minimum of 11.5 volts.

3) Using ohmmeter, check resistance of heating coil. Reading should be about 20 ohms. Replace warm-up regulator if defective.

Thermo-Valve (911S only) – 1) Remove vacuum hose from top fitting on control pressure regulator (from thermo-valve). Turn ignition ON.

2) Remove air sensor plug. Blow through disconnected hose. Valve should not leak air when closed. Valve should open after 20-33 seconds at 68° F (20° C). Replace valve if faulty.

INJECTION NOZZLES

Testing operation is the same as for CIS equipped Audi and Volkswagen. See Bosch CIS Injection System – Audi & VW in this Section.

REMOVAL & INSTALLATION

NOTE – *CIS system maintains fuel pressure at all times. Before opening fuel system at any point, disconnect battery ground cable and relieve fuel pressure in system. Do not allow open flame or sparks in area while servicing fuel system components due to danger of fire and explosion.*

BOSCH CIS INJECTION SYSTEM – PORSCHE (Cont.)

MIXTURE CONTROL UNIT

1) Remove rubber boot from air sensor. Clean around all fuel line fittings. Remove fuel line fittings from fuel distributor.

2) Detach wire plugs, loosen (6) Allen bolts and remove mixture control unit.

3) Reverse removal procedure to install, using new gaskets for housing and a new "O" ring beneath fuel distributor, if removed.

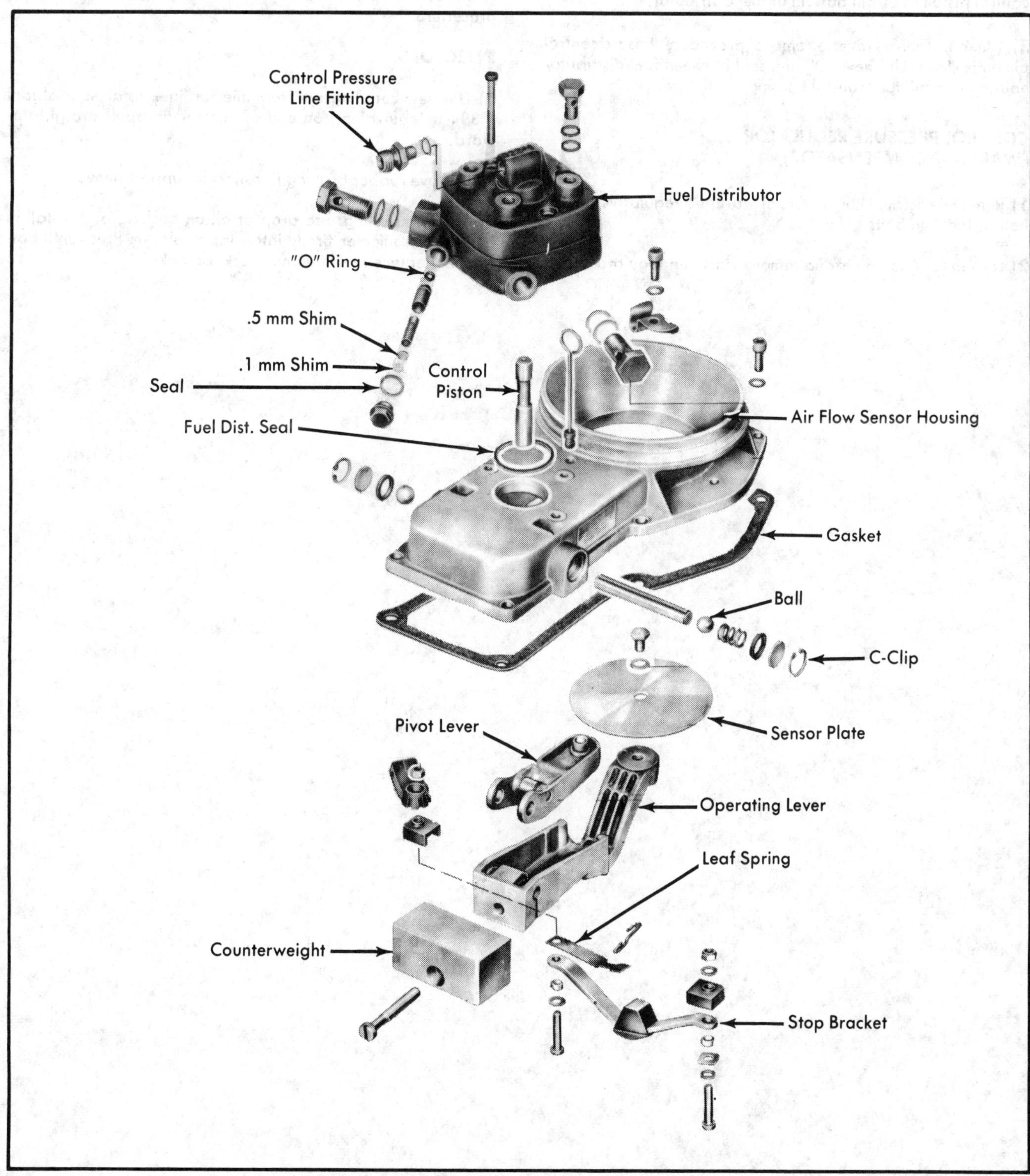

Fig. 6 Exploded View of Mixture Control Unit (924 Model Shown – Others Similar)

BOSCH CIS INJECTION SYSTEM – PORSCHE (Cont.)

FUEL DISTRIBUTOR

1) Clean area around fuel fittings and remove. Remove (3) retaining screws from top of fuel distributor.

2) Carefully lift fuel distributor off. Use care not to drop control piston out from bottom of fuel distributor.

3) When installing, reverse removal procedure. Ensure control piston is clean. Use new "O" ring seal between fuel distributor housing and mixture control housing.

CONTROL PRESSURE REGULATOR (WARM-UP COMPENSATOR)

1) Remove electrical connectors at warm-up regulator. Loosen hollow fuel line bolts.

2) Loosen (2) Allen bolts and remove warm-up regulator.

3) When replacing the regulator, torque hollow bolts to 7 ft. lbs (lower bolt) and 11 ft. lbs. (upper bolt).

AUXILIARY AIR VALVE

Pull wire plug off regulator and loosen hose clamps. Remove Allen screws and regulator. To install, reverse removal procedure.

INJECTORS

1) Unscrew coupling nut from injector line. Install special tool (P384 or equivalent) on end of injector and pull straight upward.

2) Remove rubber bushing if it sticks in support sleeve.

3) When installing, use drop of oil on bushing and install in head. Press injector firmly into support sleeve. Press until bottomed. Replace fuel line and check for leaks.

BOSCH CIS INJECTION SYSTEM – SAAB & VOLVO

Saab 99 (Federal Only)
Volvo
260 Series
240 Series (Federal)

DESCRIPTION & OPERATION

This is a mechanical system which determines the amount of fuel to be injected into each cylinder by measuring the amount of intake air required to run the engine. Once the volume of air being drawn into the engine is known, the system can inject the correct amount of fuel to achieve a balanced air/fuel mixture. An air flow sensor, made up of a round plate and lever assembly, moves up and down in relation to the air being brought into the engine. This assembly, in turn, raises or lowers a fuel control plunger or piston in the fuel distributor, resulting in exact measurement of fuel allowed to the injectors.

System is composed of an Air Flow Sensor, Fuel Distributor, Air Cleaner and Fuel Filter Assemblies, Warm-Up Regulator, Throttle Valve Housing, Cold Start Valve, Thermo-Time Switch, Injectors, Auxiliary Air Valve and Deceleration Valve.

TESTING

AIR/FUEL MIXTURE CONTROL (AIR FLOW SENSOR)

1) Ensure ignition switch is OFF. At seated position, sensor plate should be even with bottom edge of air venturi.

2) If plate is slightly lower than the edge of venturi by no more than .02" (.5 mm), it is acceptable. If adjustment is needed, bend wire clip beneath sensor plate and lever.

3) Ensure that sensor plate is centered in venturi. Use centering tool (#8392474 – Saab) or equivalent to center sensor plate, If tool is not available, loosen retaining bolt in center of plate, adjust plate so that .010" (.25 mm) clearance exists at all points around plate. Use suitable compound such as Loctite on threads of centering bolt to prevent it from vibrating loose during engine operation.

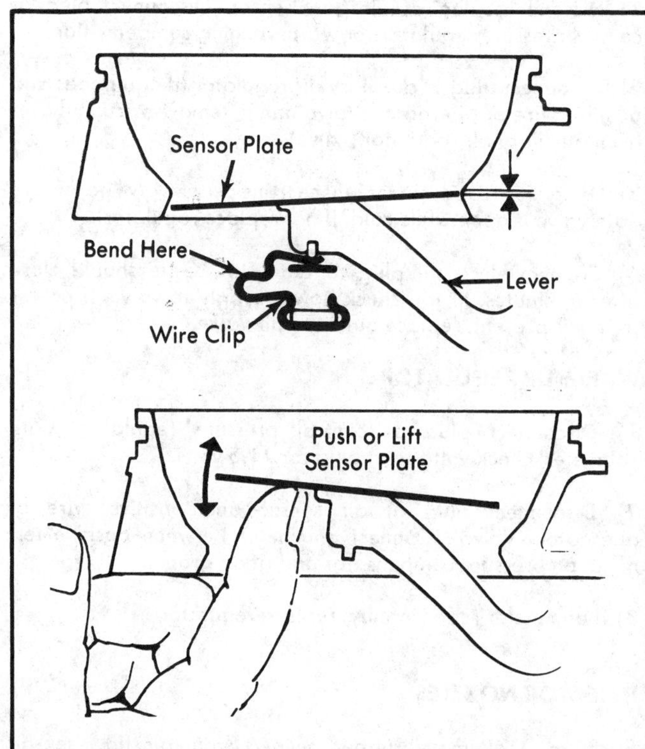

Fig. 1 Sensor Plate & Adjustment

4) On Volvo models, either push sensor plate up from beneath or lift with magnet or pliers. Check for binding or seizing throughout entire range of plate travel. **NOTE** – *Control pressure will cause some resistance when sensor plate is raised. Do not confuse this resistance with seizure or binding.* If either condition is found, repair or replace as necessary.

COLD ENGINE CONTROL PRESSURE TEST

NOTE – *Engine must be cold for this test. Connect pressure testing gauge and valve as shown in Fig. 2 for all following pressure tests. Ensure tester has been bled of air in lines before proceeding with test.*

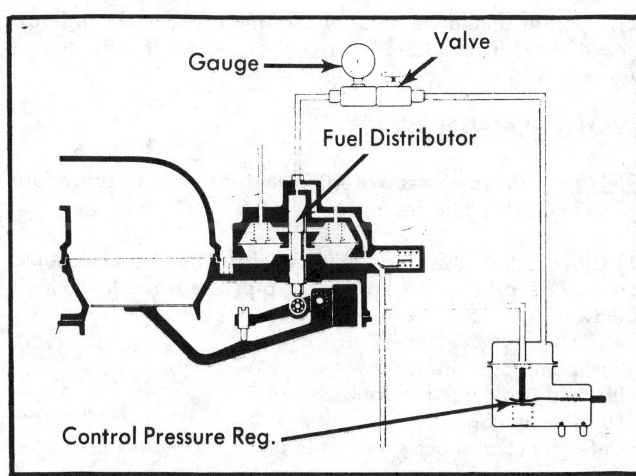

Fig. 2 Correct Connection of Pressure Testing Equipment (Saab Shown – Volvo Similar)

1) Disconnect electrical plug at air flow sensor. This isolates the safety circuit and allows fuel pumps to run with ignition

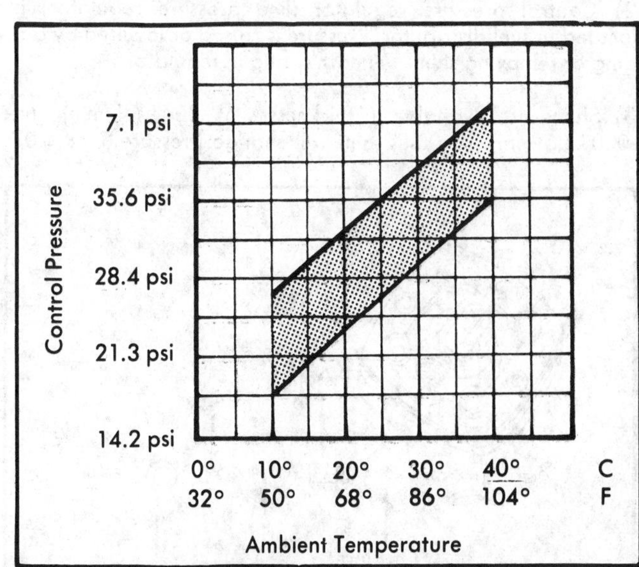

Fig. 3 Graph Showing Relationship Between Ambient Temperature & Cold Control Pressure

BOSCH CIS INJECTION SYSTEM – SAAB & VOLVO (Cont.)

ON and engine not running. Ensure testing equipment is properly installed.

2) Open tester valve, unhook plug at warm-up regulator, and turn ignition switch ON.

3) Pressure reading on gauge should be in agreement with graph shown in *Fig. 3*.

4) If pressure level is not correct, replace warm-up regulator.

WARM ENGINE CONTROL PRESSURE TEST

NOTE – *See Cold Engine Test for correct testing equipment installation procedure.*

1) Valve on tester should be OPEN. Connect warm-up regulator plug. Turn ignition ON and allow pressure to stabilize.

2) Pressure should be 48.5-54 psi (3.4-3.8 kg/cm^2) on Saab and 49.7-55.3 psi (3.5-3.9 kg/cm^2) on Volvo. If not, replace warm-up regulator.

SYSTEM PRESSURE TEST

NOTE – *Use same testing equipment installation procedure given in Cold Engine Testing.*

1) Close tester valve. Turn ignition switch ON. Pressure should be 64-72.5 psi (4.5-5.1 kg/cm^2). If pressure is too low, check following:

Fuel pump pressure too low
Blocked strainer in fuel tank
Fuel line leakage
Defective control pressure regulator

If pressure reads too high, check the following:

Fuel return line blocked
Control pressure regulator defective

2) Control pressure regulator (line pressure regulator) is located in fuel distributor. Pressure is raised or lowered by adding or removing shims beneath spring in regulator.

3) Shims are available in thicknesses of .004" (.1 mm) and .020" (.5 mm). A .004" shim will change pressure 1 psi (.07 kg/cm^2) and a .020" shim will cause a pressure change of 5 psi (.35 kg/cm^2).

4) Remove regulator. Add or replace shims as necessary and assemble regulator. *(See Fig. 4)*. Test line pressure.

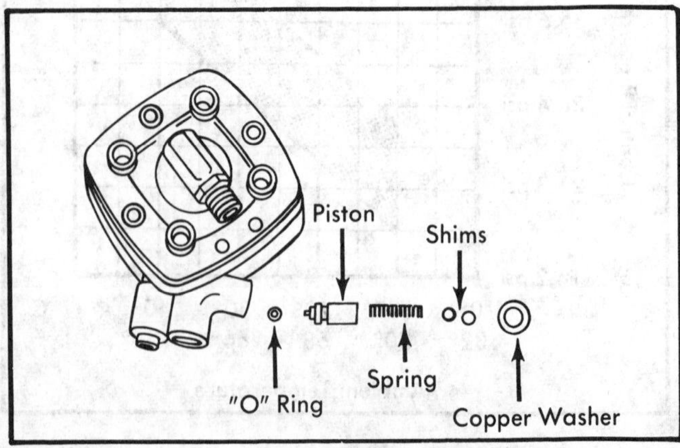

Fig. 4 Exploded View of Line Pressure Regulator

COLD START VALVE & THERMO-TIME SWITCH

NOTE – *Engine coolant temperature should be below 95° F (35° C) for this test.*

1) Remove cold start valve and point nozzle into fuel resistant container. Remove plug at air flow sensor (Saab only).

2) Do not disconnect fuel line from valve. Turn ignition switch ON. Fuel should spray in even conical pattern into container. If not, clean or replace cold start valve.

3) Fuel should spray from valve for no longer than 30 seconds (Saab) or 12 seconds (Volvo).

4) Wipe tip of valve dry with clean cloth. No fuel should leak from nozzle.

5) If no fuel sprays from valve at all, check for voltage at valve plug. If voltage is present, thermo-time switch is defective and should be replaced.

6) With engine coolant temperature below 113° F (45° C), check for voltage to cold start valve when starter is being operated. Thermo-time switch should close when engine is started. If switch does not operate properly, replace.

AUXILIARY AIR VALVE

NOTE – *Engine must be cold for this test.*

1) Disconnect plug at air flow sensor. Disconnect plug at control pressure regulator for warm running compensation.

2) Disconnect plug at auxiliary air regulator (if equipped) and positive wire of alternator (Volvo only). Remove vacuum hoses from auxiliary air regulator (valve).

3) Using light and mirror, inspect inside of valve to ensure gate valve is open while cold. If not replace regulator.

4) Connect electrical plug to regulator. Gate should close after 5 minutes. If not, check power supply to valve. If power supply is present, replace auxiliary air valve.

WARM-UP REGULATOR

1) Disconnect plug at control pressure regulator. With voltmeter, check voltage at plug for 11.5 volts.

2) Disconnect plug at air sensor and positive wire of alternator (Volvo). Connect ohmmeter between positive terminal on pressure compensator and good ground.

3) If ohmmeter reads infinity, replace regulator.

INJECTOR NOZZLES

Saab – 1) Remove rubber bellows from air flow sensor. Unscrew injection valves from intake manifold. Place valves in

BOSCH CIS INJECTION SYSTEM — SAAB & VOLVO (Cont.)

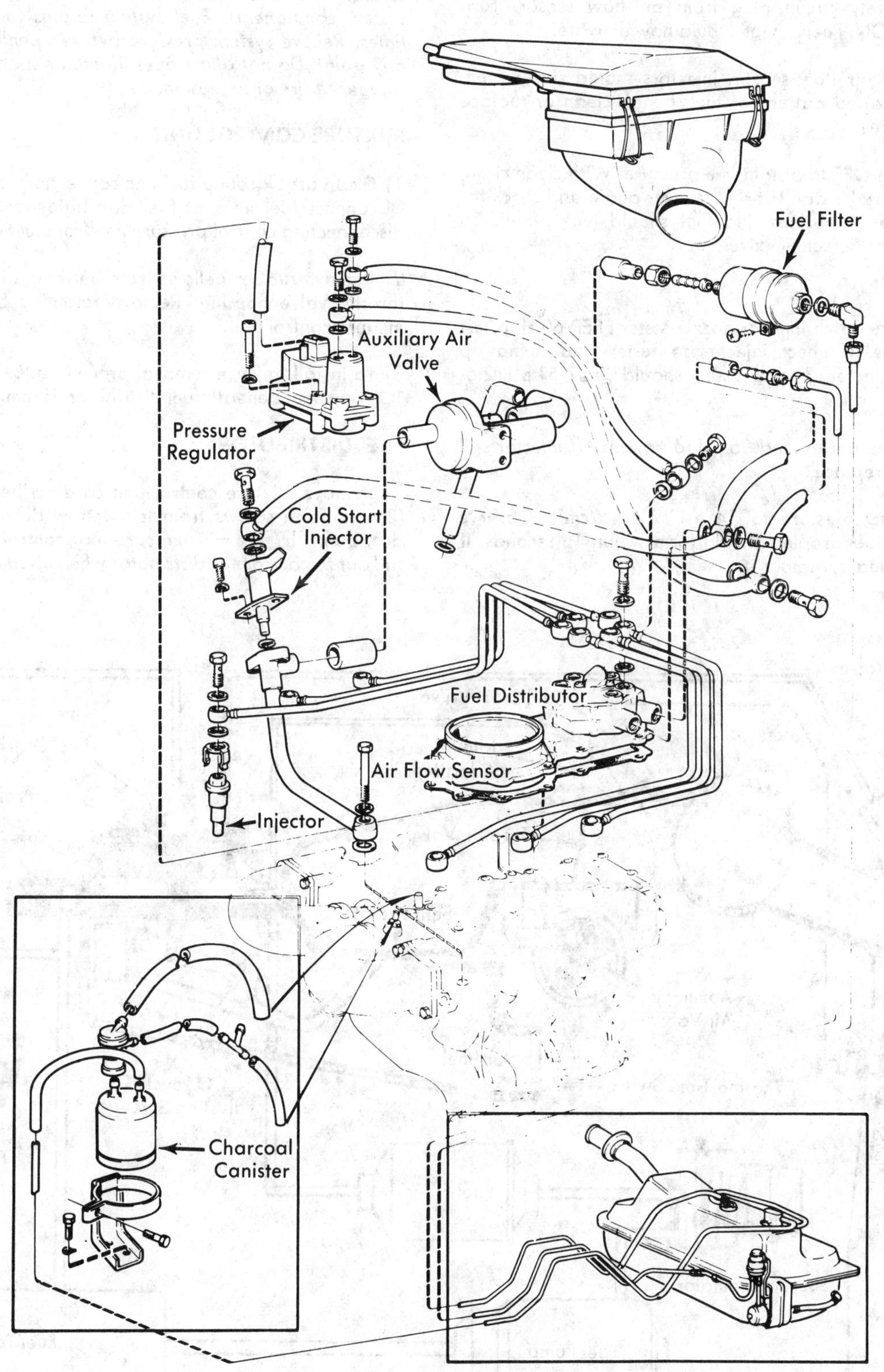

Fig. 5 Diagram of Volvo 260 Series CIS Injection (240 Series Similar)

BOSCH CIS INJECTION SYSTEM — SAAB & VOLVO (Cont.)

suitable fuel resistant container. Do not disconnect fuel lines to valves.

2) Remove safety circuit plug from air flow sensor. Turn ignition switch ON. Fuel pumps should now activate.

3) Lift lever in air flow sensor. Injectors should spray even, steady cone shaped pattern of fuel. If not, clean or replace defective injectors.

4) Turn ignition OFF to obtain line pressure. With clean cloth, wipe injector nozzles dry. Lift sensor lever again and check for leakage at tip of nozzles. No fuel should leak within 15 seconds. Replace defective valves.

Volvo — 1) Use Bosch injector nozzle tester EFEP 60 H to test injector nozzles. Connect injector to tester and pump up pressure until injector opens. Pressure should be 37-51 psi (2.6-3.6 kg/cm²).

CAUTION — *Do not exceed 85 psi (6 kg/cm²). If injector still does not open, replace.*

2) Lower pump pressure to 34 psi (2.4 kg/cm²). Observe nozzle tip. No fuel droplets should form within 15 seconds. If injector nozzle leaks, replace it.

REMOVAL & INSTALLATION

NOTE — *Remove battery ground cable prior to removing fuel system components. Fuel system retains fuel pressure at all times. Relieve system pressure before opening fuel system at any point. Do not allow open flame or sparks in area due to danger of fire or explosion.*

MIXTURE CONTROL UNIT

1) Clean area around fuel line connections on fuel distributor. Disconnect fuel lines at fuel distributor and injectors before disconnecting control pressure line from fuel distributor.

2) Remove rubber bellows from between air flow sensor and throttle valve housing. Remove retaining bolts and remove mixture control unit.

3) To install, reverse removal procedure. Be sure to use a new "O" ring seal beneath fuel distributor, if removed.

FUEL DISTRIBUTOR

1) Remove mixture control unit as described above. Remove (3) attaching screws from top of fuel distributor and lift off distributor. **NOTE** — *Take care that control plunger does not fall out the bottom of distributor when lifted off.*

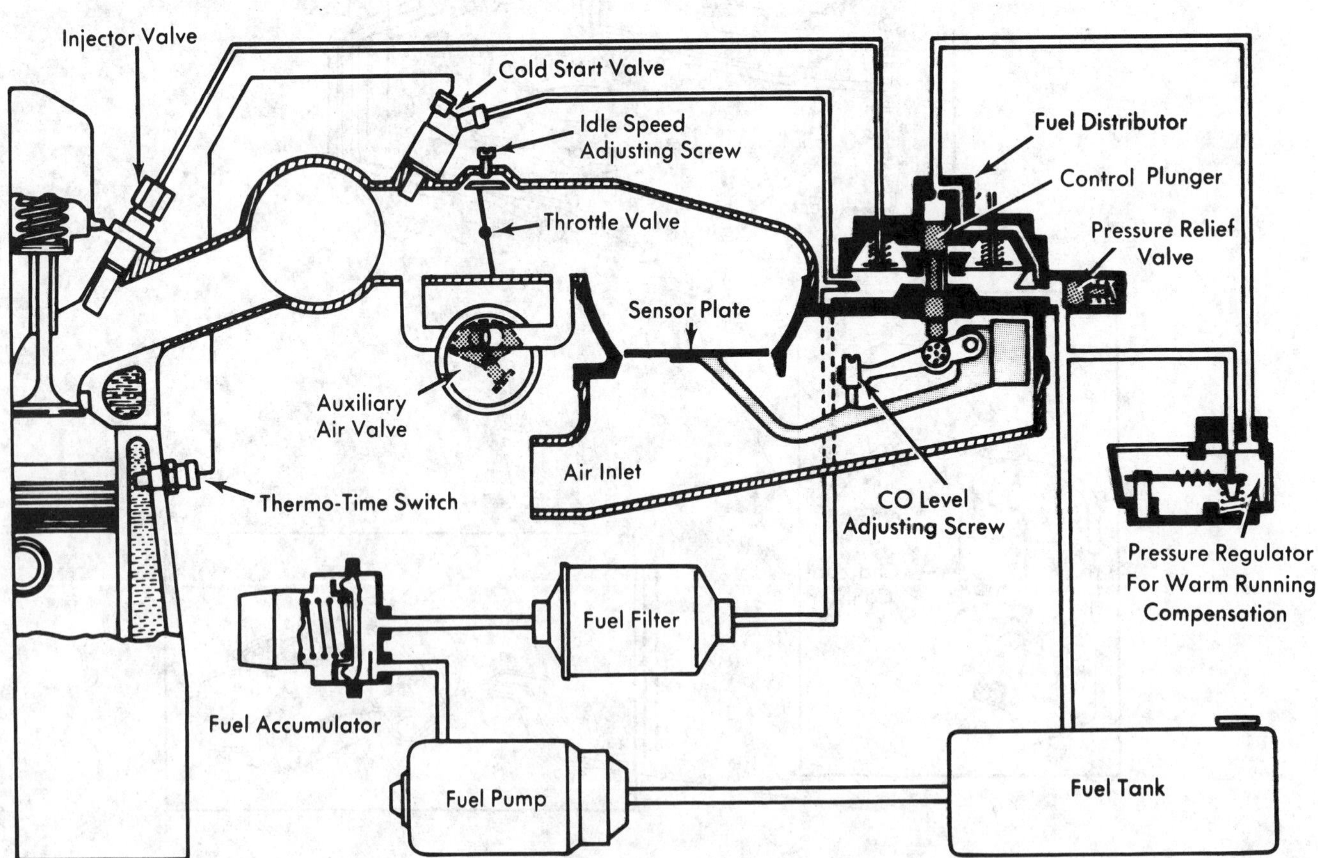

Fig. 6 Diagram of Saab 99 CIS Injection System

BOSCH CIS INJECTION SYSTEM – SAAB & VOLVO (Cont.)

2) When installing distributor, use new "O" ring seal beneath housing. Torque retaining bolts to 2.3-2.7 ft. lbs. **NOTE** – *Fuel distributor should not be disassembled. If defective, replace as a unit.*

WARM-UP REGULATOR (CONTROL PRESSURE REGULATOR)

1) Clean area around fuel fittings on regulator. Remove fuel lines.

2) Disconnect electrical plug at warm-up regulator. Remove attaching bolt(s) and remove regulator.

3) Reverse removal procedure to install. Ensure fittings are tight and do not leak.

AUXILIARY AIR VALVE

1) Pull off vacuum hoses at valve. Disconnect electrical connector and unscrew the auxiliary air valve.

2) To install, reverse removal procedure.

THERMO-TIME SWITCH

1) Drain coolant from cooling system until it is below level of time switch.
2) Disconnect electrical plug at switch. Be sure to use a deep socket to remove switch so as not to damage terminals on top of switch.

3) Reverse removal procedure to install switch. Be sure to refill cooling system.

COLD START VALVE

1) Disconnect electrical plug at cold start valve. Clean around fuel fittings and remove fuel lines.

2) Remove retaining screws and remove cold start valve.

3) To install, reverse removal procedure. Ensure that fittings are tight and do not leak.

INJECTORS

1) Clean area around fuel line fittings at injector. Remove fuel lines. Be sure to hold injector to prevent it from turning while fuel lines are being removed.

2) Remove screws from retaining plate and carefully pull injector straight up and out of opening. If insulators are used, do not pull them out with the injector.

3) To install, reverse removal procedure. Ensure insulators are firmly in place and that new "O" ring has been installed on insulator if it has been removed. Press injector firmly into place and tighten fuel lines. Do not allow injector to turn while installing fuel lines. Check for leaks.

BOSCH LAMBDA CIS INJECTION SYSTEM

Saab 99 (Calif. Only)
Volvo 240 Series (California)

DESCRIPTION

The Bosch Lambda CIS System consists of a conventional CIS fuel injection system with the addition of an oxygen sensor (located in the exhaust manifold), a modulating valve (frequency valve), a throttle valve switch (Saab models only), a relay switch, and an Electronic Control Unit (ECU). The final component completing the Lambda system is a three way catalytic converter. This catalytic converter consists of a honey combed ceramic material coated with rhodium and platinum.

OPERATION

The Lambda CIS System operates the same as the conventional CIS system with the addition of more precise fuel metering. This closer tolerance of injected fuel is controlled by the oxygen sensor which sends impulses to the ECU which in turn sends control impulses to the modulating valve. The modulating valve controls the time the injectors are injecting fuel. The final component in the Lambda system is the three way catalytic converter. This special converter further reduces the three most prevalent pollutants, CO, HC and NOx.

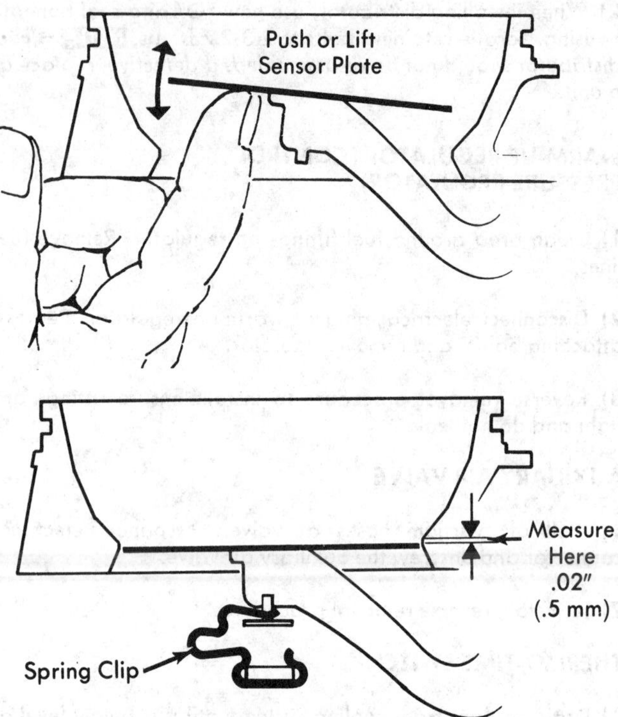

Fig. 1 Checking Operation of Air Flow Sensor Plate

TESTING

AIR FUEL MIXTURE CONTROL (AIR FLOW SENSOR)

Saab – 1) Remove air duct from top of air flow sensor. Turn on ignition for about five seconds and then switch off. Remaining pressure in fuel system will press control plunger against sensor plate lever. Lift sensor plate by hand (use magnet if necessary). Same amount of resistance should be noticeable on control plunger over entire range of travel.

2) With rapid downward movement, control plunger should follow lever more slowly. If sensor plate is hard to move, replace entire sensor unit. If control plunger is hard to move, replace fuel distributor.

3) Check spring stop of sensor plate in air sensor. **NOTE** – *Fuel system must be depressurized for this inspection.* Loosen control line connection at control pressure regulator warm running device and relieve remaining pressure.

4) Wrap cloth around this connection to catch escaping fuel. Visually check that upper edge of sensor plate is flush with start of venturi edge. If necessary, setting of spring stop can be adjusted by bending wire clip.

Volvo – 1) With fuel system depressurized, check that lower edge of sensor plate is no more that .02" (.5 mm) lower than venturi lower edge. If adjustment is necessary, bend flexible wire clip.

2) Lift sensor plate by hand (use magnet if necessary) to check for plate binding or seizing. **NOTE** – *Control pressure will cause some resistance when sensor plate is raised, do not confuse this resistance with seizure or binding.* If either condition is encountered, replace or repair sensor plate as necessary.

PRESSURE TESTING COLD ENGINE

NOTE – *Before pressure test can be accomplished, it will be necessary to install special pressure testing manifold. Use tester 8392516 for Saab or tester 999 5011 for Volvo.*

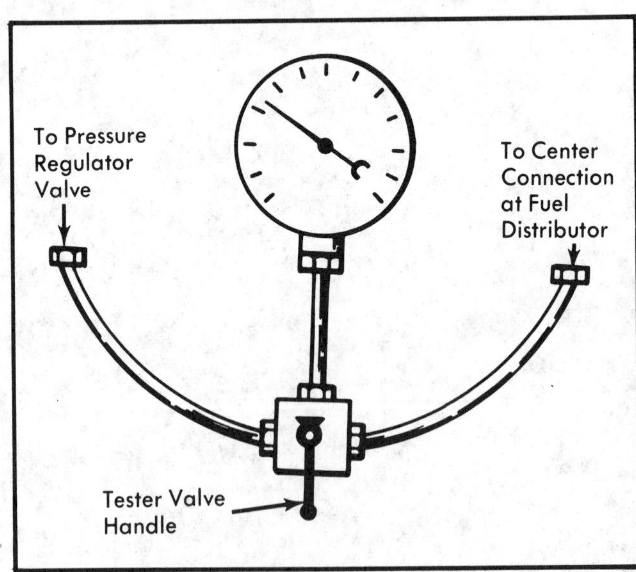

Fig. 2 Tester for Testing Fuel Pressures

Tester Installation – 1) Disconnect top center (fuel pressure) line of fuel distributor and connect one end of special tester to fuel distributor (where fuel pressure line was disconnected) and connect other end of tester to free end of fuel line removed from fuel distributor.

BOSCH LAMBDA CIS INJECTION SYSTEM (Cont.)

NOTE — *This places tester IN fuel line from control pressure regulator for warm running compensation to fuel distributor.*

2) Before testing fuel pressure, it will be necessary to bleed tester. As preparation for bleeding; on Saab, disconnect wire to control pressure regulator for warm running compensation, on Volvo, disconnect wire to air fuel mixture control valve (air flow sensor).

3) Turn ignition switch on and let gauge hang lower than hose connections to engine. To bleed tester, repeatedly open and close valve on Saab or turn handle of tester toward fuel distributor for about 10 seconds then back to neutral position a few times on Volvo. Now place pressure tester higher than hose connections.

Pressure Test, Saab & Volvo — 1) With tester installed and electrical connector disconnected as described in tool installation, proceed as follows:

2) To check cold control pressure, open valve on Saab or turn lever to center position on Volvo. Disconnect warm up regulator electrical connector and turn on ignition.

3) Cold control pressure should be a minimum of 20 psi (1.2 kg/cm²) at 50°F (10°C). Cold control pressure should increase 5.7 psi (.4 kg/cm²) for every 18°F (10°C) increase in ambient temperature.

4) Reconnect wire to control pressure regulator. Pressure should be 52.5±2.8 psi (3.7±.2 kg/cm²). If pressure is not to specifications, test electrical connection at control pressure regulator for voltage. If voltage is present, replace warm up regulator.

PRESSURE TESTING WARM ENGINE

NOTE — *Connect pressure tester as outlined in Testing Cold Engine.*

Saab — 1) With pressure tester installed and bled, open gauge and reconnect plug to warm up regulator. Leave ignition switched on until rest pressure is present. Rest pressure should be 24-34 psi (1.7-2.4 kg/cm²). If pressure is substantially different, replace warm up regulator.

2) Now close pressure gauge valve and switch on ignition. Line pressure should be 64-74 psi (4.5-5.2 kg/cm²). If line pressure should differ considerable, check following: fuel pump output pressure, fuel strainer in tank, fuel line for leaks, line pressure regulator, blockage of fuel return line and adjustment of mixture control unit.

3) To check fuel pump pressure, place a pressure gauge in-line between fuel tank and fuel distributor. Pressure gauge must have a capacity above 120 psi (8.5 kg/cm²) Fuel pressure should be above 80 psi (5.6 kg/cm²) with a maximum of 120 psi (8.5 kg/cm²).

Volvo — Turn ignition switch on and connect electrical connection to control pressure regulator. Within three minutes pressure should reach 52.5±2.8 psi (3.7±.2 kg/cm²). If pressure fails to come within specified limit, replace control pressure regulator.

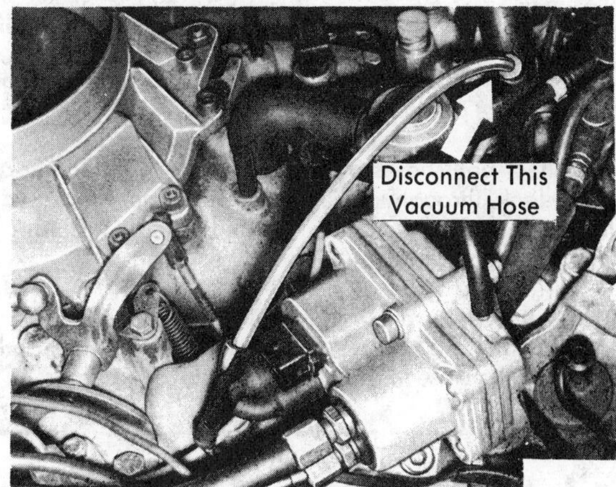

Fig. 3 Testing Warm-up/Full Load Enrichment Compensator

COLD START INJECTION VALVE & THERMO-TIME SWITCH

Saab & Volvo — 1) With cold start valve removed and held over suitable container, turn on ignition switch and check that cold start valve sprays fuel in a conical pattern.

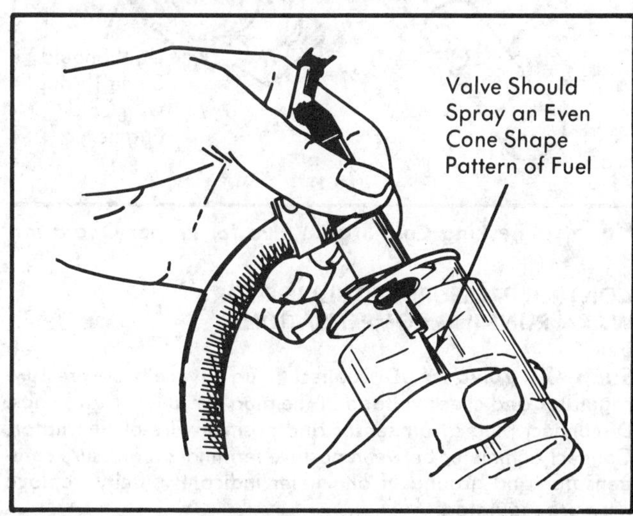

Fig. 4 Checking Auxiliary Air Valve for Correct Operation

NOTE — *Cold start valve operation is controlled by a thermo-time switch. As a point of reference, at engine temperature of −4°F (−20°C) valve should spray fuel for 12 seconds on Saab and 7.5 seconds on Volvo. At 113°F (45°C) cold start valve should cease to spray any fuel.*

2) If engine is within temperature range that it should spray fuel but no fuel is sprayed out when ignition is turned on, use test light to check for voltage at cold start valve wires. If no voltage is present, thermo-time switch is bad and should be replaced.

NOTE — *Caution should be exercised in condemning thermo-time switch, because if engine coolant temperature is above 113°F (45°C), then no fuel would be sprayed out.*

AUXILIARY AIR VALVE

NOTE — *This test can only be performed on a cold engine.*

BOSCH LAMBDA CIS INJECTION SYSTEM (Cont.)

Saab & Volvo – **1**) Disconnect plug at control pressure regulator for warm running compensation. Disconnect plug to air flow sensor (mixture control unit), auxiliary air regulator and positive wire of alternator.

2) Disconnect both hoses of auxiliary air regulator and use mirror to look through auxiliary air regulator. Gate valve should be open on cold engine. If valve is not at least partially open, replace regulator.

3) Now, connect electrical plug to auxiliary air regulator and check that within five minutes, regulator gate valve is closed. If regulator fails to close in five minutes, replace regulator.

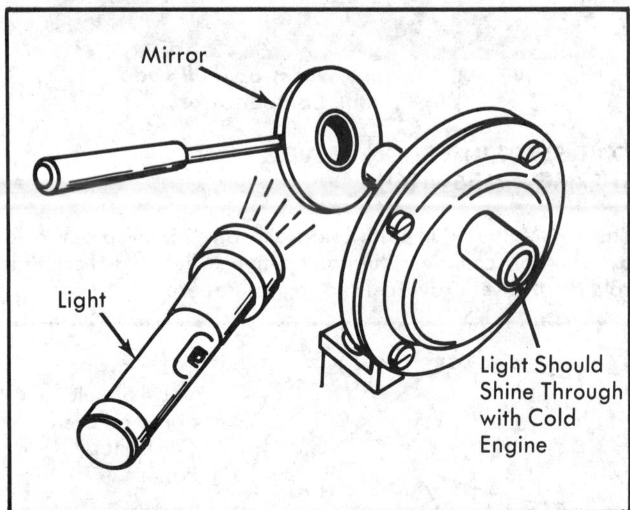

Fig. 5 Checking Cold Start Valve for Proper Operation

CONTROL PRESSURE REGULATOR FOR WARM RUNNING COMPENSATION

Saab & Volvo – Disconnect plug at control pressure regulator and check voltage at the plug for at least 11.5 volts. Disconnect plug at air sensor and positive wire of alternator. Connect ohmmeter between positive terminal on pressure compensator and ground. If ohmmeter indicates infinity, replace pressure regulator.

INJECTOR NOZZLES

Saab – **1**) Remove rubber bellows (large tube from air cleaner to air flow sensor) from air flow sensor. Remove injection valve(s) from intake manifold and place in a suitable container (leave fuel lines connected).

2) Disconnect the safety circuit plug from air flow sensor. Turn ignition switch on, this starts fuel pump operating.

3) Lift air flow sensor plate and check spray pattern from injector nozzle(s). Spray should be a finely atomized cone pattern. If spray pattern is incorrect, clean or replace injectors as necessary.

4) Next check injectors for leakage. Turn ignition switch off and wipe injectors dry with a clean dry cloth. Lift air flow sensor plate. It should take more than 15 seconds for any drops to form on injectors. If drops form more quickly, clean or replace injectors as necessary.

Volvo – **1**) Use Bosch injector nozzle tester EFEP 60 H to test injector nozzles. Connect injector nozzle to tester and pump up pressure until injector opens. Pressure should be 37-51 psi (2.6-3.6 kg/cm^2). **NOTE** – *Pressure should never exceed 85 psi (6 kg/cm^2).*

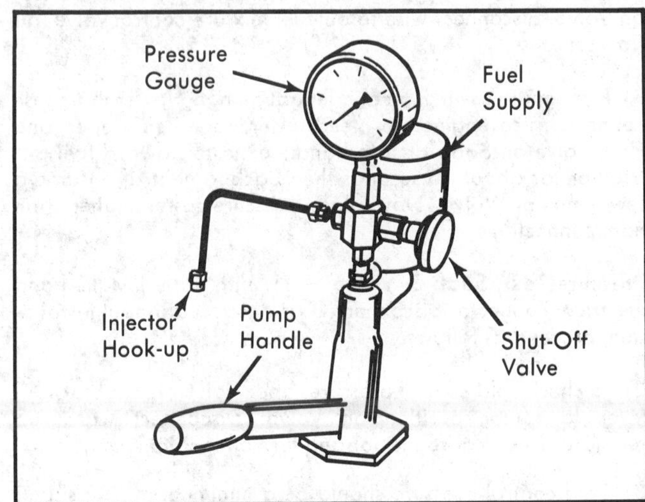

Fig. 6 Bosch Injector Tester (EFEP 60 H)

2) Lower pump pressure to 34 psi C2.4 kgcm^2) by turning hand wheel out. Injector nozzle leak should not exceed 1 drop in 15 seconds.

REMOVAL & INSTALLATION

FUEL PUMP

CAUTION – *On all models, disconnect battery ground cable and relieve fuel pressure prior to removing fuel pump.*

Saab – **1**)Roll back carpet in trunk compartment. Remove rear floor panel and remove circular floor plate on top of pump. Make sure battery is disconnected to prevent fire hazard.

2) Disconnect electrical connections to pump and disconnect hose connections to pump. Hold pump by means of open end wrench. Use special tool 8392433 (large circular spanner wrench). Turn pump mounting counterclockwise to nearest groove, to unlock bayonet socket.

3) Lift out pump unit saving "O" ring. **NOTE** – *Pump can only be removed in one position because one bayonet toungue is wider than all others.*

4) To install fuel pump, reverse removal procedure.

Volvo – **1**) Make sure battery is disconnected. Clean all hose connections. Use hose crimping device to block fuel inlet hose. Remove fuel inlet hose from pump outlet, and pump from its bracket (near gas tank).

2) Disconnect plug at fuel pump and fuel accumulator hoses. Separate bracket and rubber cushion from fuel pump and accumulator. To install fuel pump, reverse removal procedure.

BOSCH LAMBDA CIS INJECTION SYSTEM (Cont.)

MIXTURE CONTROL UNIT

CAUTION — *On all models, disconnect battery ground cable and relieve fuel pressure before removing mixture control unit.*

Saab — 1) Throughly clean area around fuel connections on fuel distributor. Disconnect the fuel lines from fuel distributor. Disconnect lines to injection valve before disconnecting control pressure line from fuel distributor.

2) Remove rubber bellows from between air flow sensor and throttle valve housing. Remove retaining bolts and remove mixture control unit.

3) To install mixture control unit, reverse disassembly procedure.

Volvo — Clean around fuel connections carefully, before removing any fuel line. Remove rubber bellows and strap for injection lines. Remove injection lines and control pressure line from fuel distributor. Remove mixture control unit. To install, reverse removal procedure.

FUEL DISTRIBUTOR

CAUTION — *On all models, disconnect battery ground cable and relieve fuel pressure prior to removing fuel distributor.*

Saab — 1) With mixture control unit removed from vehicle, remove fuel distributor as a unit. **NOTE** — *When separating fuel distributor from mixture control unit, make sure that control plunger does not fall out or damage will result to control plunger.*

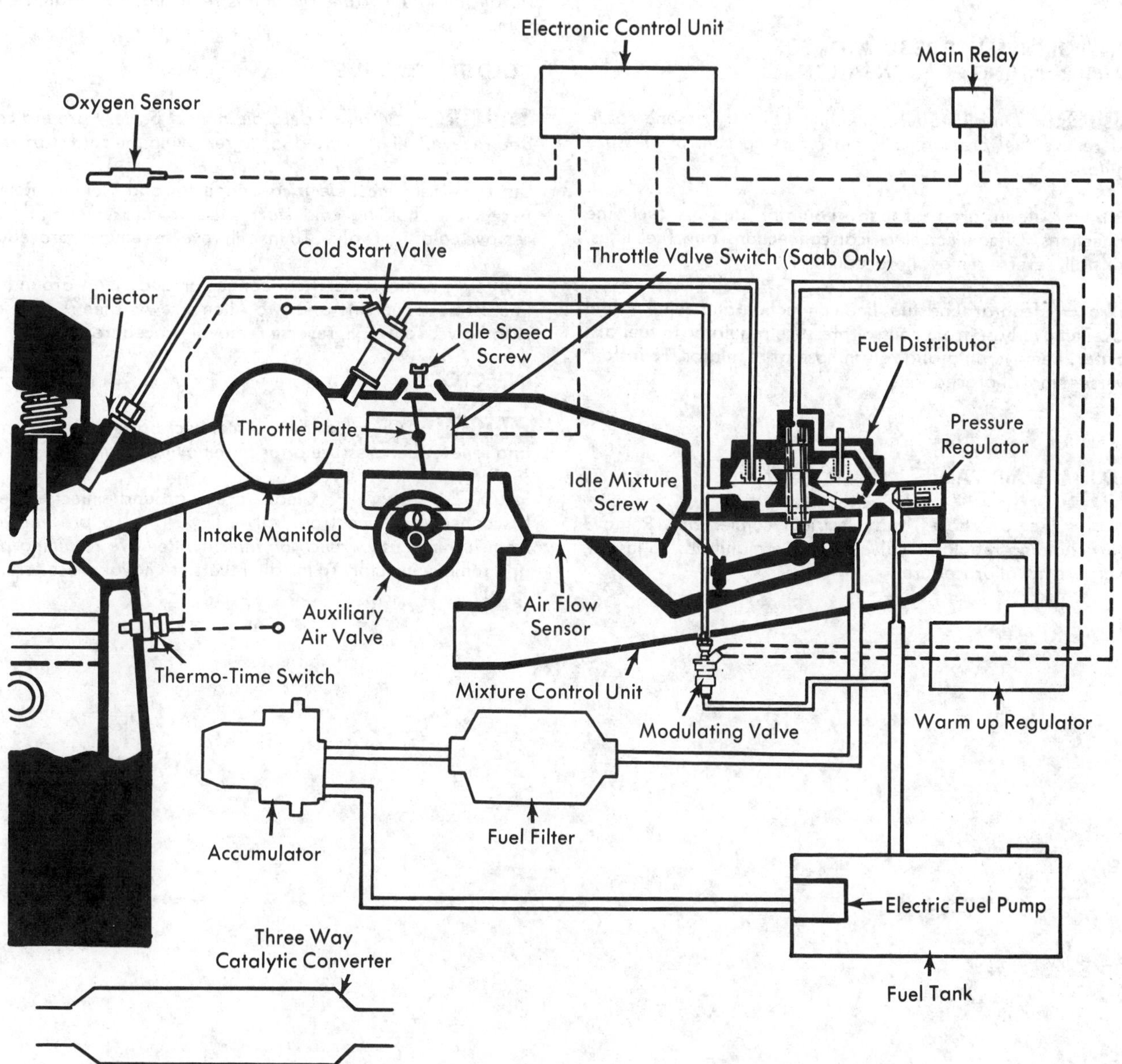

Fig. 7 Functional Schematic of Lambda CIS Fuel Injection System for Saab and Volvo

BOSCH LAMBDA CIS INJECTION SYSTEM (Cont.)

CAUTION — *DO NOT disassemble the fuel distributor. Fuel distributor contains springs with different thickness shims under each spring. These shims are used by the factory to adjust spring pressure to keep output pressure for each injector the same.*

2) To install fuel distributor, reverse removal procedure noting the following. Make sure control plunger is held up in fuel distributor and does not drop down. Check movement of Mixture Control Unit, it should not bind or stick.

Volvo — With mixture control unit removed from vehicle, place fuel distributor in vise (carefully) and remove three screws from top of fuel distributor. **NOTE** — *When removing fuel distributor from mixture control unit, take care that control plunger does not fall out or damage to control plunger will result.* To install, reverse removal procedure.

CONTROL PRESSURE REGULATOR FOR WARM RUNNING COMPENSATION

CAUTION — *On all models, disconnect battery ground cable and relieve fuel pressure prior to removing control pressure regulator.*

Saab — Clean area around regulator and its fuel line connections. Disconnect electrical connections and fuel lines. To install, reverse removal procedure.

Volvo — Clean around fuel line connection and remove fuel lines. Remove hose from control pressure regulator to fuel distributor. Remove plug and return hose at regulator. To install, reverse removal procedure.

AUXILIARY AIR VALVE

Saab — Remove hoses and electrical connections. Remove screws holding regulator valve to intake manifold. To install, reverse removal procedure.

Volvo — Disconnect and plug hoses to regulator valve. Remove retaining screws and electrical connection. To install, reverse removal procedure.

THERMO-TIME SWITCH

Saab — The thermo-time switch is located in the head between the intake manifold runners. Disconnect the electrical connector. Use a socket with sufficient depth to prevent damage to electrical contacts on top of switch. **NOTE** — *It will be necessary to either drain coolant below level of thermo-time switch or have a new switch ready to install the moment the old one is removed.* To install, reverse removal procedure.

Volvo — Disconnect electrical connector. Use a socket with sufficient depth to prevent damaging electrical contacts on top of switch. **NOTE** — *It will be necessary to either drain coolant below level of thermo-time switch or have new switch ready to install the moment the old one is removed.* To install, reverse removal procedure.

COLD START VALVE

CAUTION — *On all models, disconnect battery ground cable and relieve fuel pressure prior to removing the cold start valve.*

Saab — Disconnect electrical connector and fuel line. Remove two screws holding cold start valve to intake manifold and remove cold start valve. To install, reverse removal procedure.

Volvo — Remove electrical connector and clean around fuel line. Remove fuel line and two Allen screws. Then remove cold start valve. To install, reverse removal procedure.

INJECTORS

CAUTION — *On all models, disconnect battery ground cable and relieve fuel pressure prior to removing the injectors.*

Saab & Volvo — Clean area around injector valve. Disconnect fuel line from valve. **NOTE** — *To prevent valve from turning, use wrench on injector.* Remove retaining plate and remove injector. To install, reverse removal procedure.

LUCAS-JAGUAR ELECTRONIC INJECTION SYSTEM

Jaguar XJS & XJ12

DESCRIPTION

Lucas manifold pressure controlled (MPC) injection system is a pulsed, port injection system with one injector per cylinder. The amount of fuel injected depends upon engine load, speed and atmospheric pressure. Manifold pressure control regulator (MPC) measures the amount of pressure differential in the intake manifold and transmits an electric signal to electronic control unit (ECU). This signal modifies all other signals sent to ECU by the other sensors. The ECU electronically analyzes all sensor information and transmits a signal to the injectors, which determines the amount of time each injector will be open. This Bosch electronic injection system consists of three sub-assemblies; fuel delivery, air induction system, and electronic sensing and control. Major components of fuel delivery system include: twin fuel tanks, fuel vibration damper, fuel pump, change-over valves, fuel rails, injectors, fuel pressure regulator, fuel cooler and fuel filter. Major components of the electronic sensing and control are: ECU, power amplifier, thermo-time switch, incoming air and engine coolant temperature sensors, cold start injector valve, MPC (manifold pressure control sensor), throttle switch, distributor trigger unit, main relay, and pump relay.

TESTING

NOTE – *Failure of any component in the system, effects balance of entire system. Installation of any new component will not automatically restore system to normal state of balance since the new component will have slightly different characteristics than original part being replaced. Although balancing the system is accomplished by the ECU, a certain amount of time is required for ECU to make this adjustment (normal road test will be sufficient time). This period of time required for the system to reach equalibrium is also required when replacing ECU.*

FUEL PUMP

1) Switch on ignition, pump should run one or two seconds and then stop. Switch off ingnition and operate change-over switch to select other tank. Switch on ignition and pump should operate for one or two seconds, then stop. Switch off ignition. If pump operates as described, test procedure is complete, however if pump either does not run or does not stop, proceed as follows:

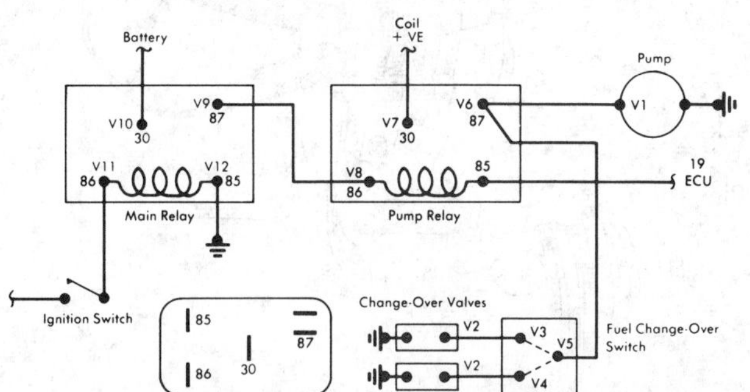

Fig. 1 Diagram of Fuel Pump Circuit for Testing

2) Check inertia switch (located on right front kick pad) by removing screws attaching switch to kick pad and checking that both cables are secure. Pull cables off switch and check continuity across switch terminals. Pull button out and check that an open circuit exists. Push button inward and check that resistance is either zero or less than 5 ohms. If inertia switch checks out good, ground pump relay terminal 85, switch on ignition and check circuitry as follows:

3) Use voltmeter to check voltage at test point V1. If battery voltage is present, faulty pump or bad ground connection is indicated. If no voltage is present at test point V1, make sure changeover switch is selecting correct tank and continue testing. Check voltage at test point V2. If voltage is present, faulty changeover valve or bad ground connection is indicated. If no voltage at V2, faulty switch or wiring connection is indicated. Now check voltage at test point V3 and V4. If voltage is present, an open circuit in wire to changeover valve(s) is indicated. If no voltage is present, make sure test is being carried out at correct changeover position and continue testing.

4) Check voltage at test point V5. If voltage is present, faulty switch is indicated. If necessary, replace switch and continue testing. Check voltage at V6. If voltage is present, an open circuit between terminal 87 and changeover switch is indicated. If no voltage at test point V6 check voltage at V7. If voltage is present at V7, pump relay is not energized or pump contacts are bad. If no voltage is present, check voltage at test point V8. If voltage is present, faulty pump relay is indicated. If no voltage was present at test point V8, continue testing.

5) Check voltage at test point V9. If voltage is present, an open circuit exists between test point V8 and V9. If no voltage is present at test point V9, check for voltage at test point V10. If voltage is present at this test point, main relay is not energized or contacts are faulty. If no voltage is present, check power supply from battery and continue testing. Check for voltage at test point V11. If no voltage is present, check battery voltage supplied through ignition switch via inertia switch. If voltage was present, proceed with testing. At test point V12 disconnect ground lead and connector and check for battery voltage at terminal 85. If no voltage, replace main relay. If voltage is present, check cable and ground connection from terminal 85. If relay energizes, check for battery voltage at terminal 87. If still no voltage, or relay does not energize, replace relay.

ELECTRONIC CONTROL UNIT (ECU)

Due to the complexity of the ECU unit, Jaguar recommends the use of their "EPITEST" test unit. When using this tester, follow manufactures operating instructions. The only other method of checking out an ECU is to replace a suspected bad ECU with a known good unit and test drive the vehicle. There is no field repairs for ECU's. If ECU is bad, it should be replaced.

FUEL PRESSURE REGULATOR

1) Depressurize fuel system. Loosen pipe clamp securing left-hand cold start injector to fuel rail and pull pipe from rail. Connect pressure gauge to fuel rail and tighten pipe clamp. Pull negative "VE" lead from ignition coil and switch on ignition. Connect pump relay terminal 85 to ground. Check pressure gauge reading, it should be 28.5-30 psi. **NOTE** – *Pressure reading may drop slowly though either regulator valve or pump non-return valve. A slow steady drop is permissable, but a fast drop should be investigated.*

LUCAS-JAGUAR ELECTRONIC INJECTION SYSTEM (Cont.)

2) Operate fuel tank change-over valve and repeat step **1)**. Remove ground connection to terminal 85 of pump relay. **NOTE** — *If satisfactory pressure readings are not obtained, it will be necessary to either adjust the pressure regulator or repair the leak-down condition, before proceeding with test procedure. If satisfactory results were obtained, loosen pipe clamp and remove pressure gauge from fuel rail. Reconnect cold start injector supply pipe and tighten pipe clamp. Switch off ignition.*

MANIFOLD PRESSURE CONTROL VALVE (MPC)

Pull connector off of pressure control valve and use ohmmeter to check the following resistances: **Between terminals 7 and 15, resistance should be 85-95 ohms. Between terminals 8 and 10, resistance should be 346-354 ohms. Between all terminals and ground, resistance should be infinity. If readings are outside these values, replace MPC.**

INJECTORS

Injector Windings — Use ohmmeter to measure resistance of each injector winding. This can be accomplished by disconnecting electrical connection to each injector and measuring across both terminals. Resistance should be 2.4 at 68°F (20°C). Now check for short circuit between ground and windings by connecting ohmmeter from injector terminals to ground (injector body). Resistance should be infinity. If injector fails either of these tests, replace that injector.

Electrical Pulses and Cable — **1)** Injectors are connected in two groups to power amplifier and each group is divided into parallel sets of three (see table).

Group 1		Group 2	
1A	6B	6A	1B
5A	2B	2A	5B
3A	4B	4A	3B

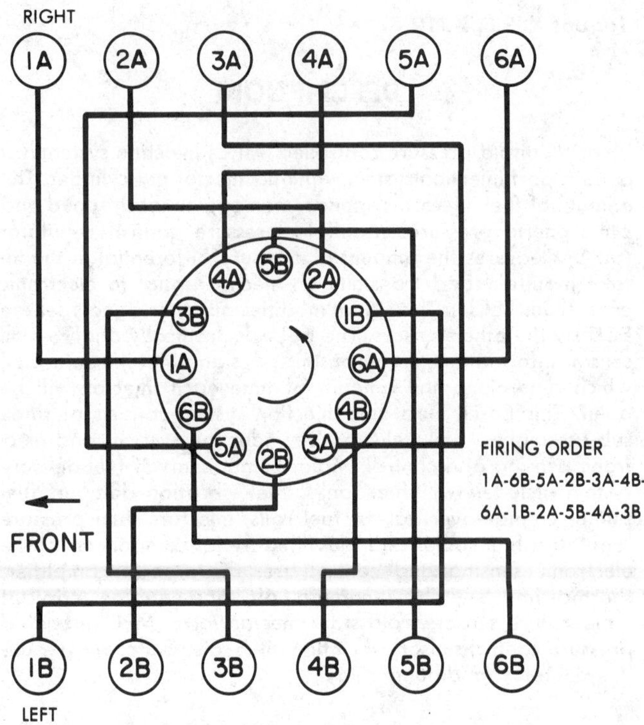

Fig. 3 Firing Order Illustration

2) Disconnect coolant temperature sensor and terminal 85 of pump relay. Disconnect injectors electrical connection. Connect voltmeter or test light across terminals of each injector electrical plug. **NOTE** — *Start with injector at cylinder 1A.* Crank engine, test light should flash or meter should deflect as amplifier pulses. Repeat test for all injectors in first set of group 1, before continuing with second set of group 1, then test group 2 etc. **NOTE** — *If only one result (injector) per set is incorrect, check for faulty connection of that injector. If all*

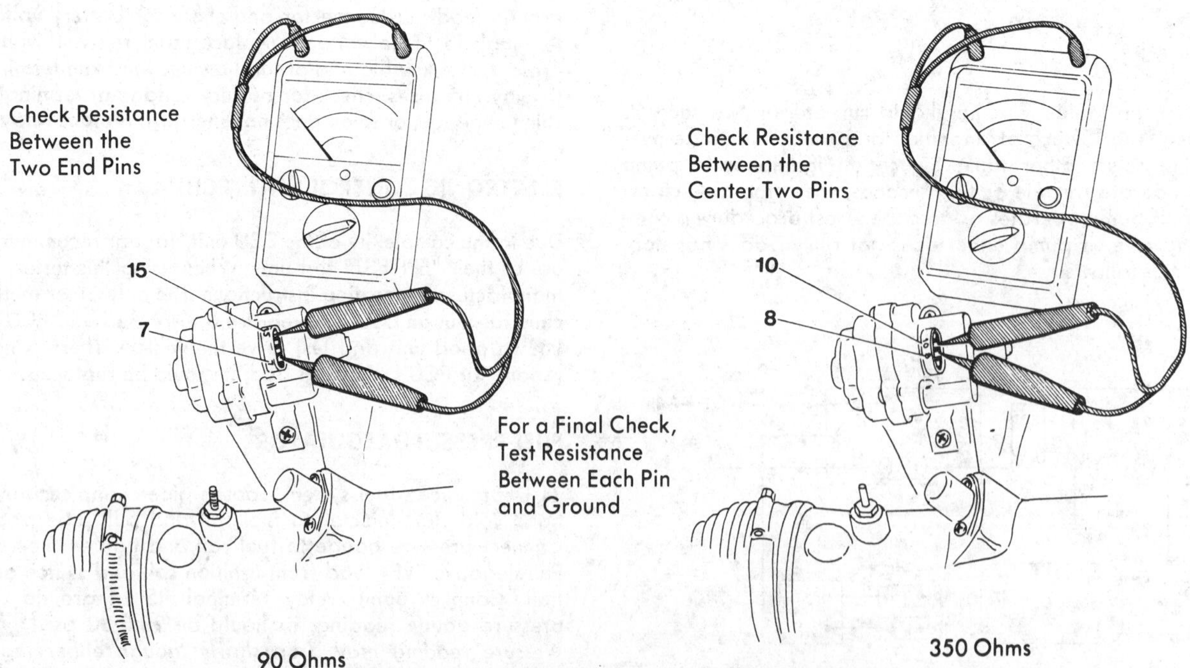

Fig. 2 Test Connections for Manifold Pressure Sensor Test

LUCAS-JAGUAR ELECTRONIC INJECTION SYSTEM (Cont.)

three results (injectors) in same set are incorrect, either amplifier is faulty or faulty connection is indicated. If all six results (injectors) are incorrect, defect could be faulty connection of cable, bad amplifier or bad ECU.

NOTE — *Before performing the delivery test, take all precautions against fire and explosion; because fuel vapor will be present in engine compartment during test procedure.*

Delivery Test — **1)** Remove two set screws securing each fuel rail to intake manifold. Remove two nuts and spring washers securing each injector clamp to ram pipes. Raise fuel rail as far as possible and support with blocks of wood. **NOTE** — *Take care not to strain pipe joints and locate a container beneath each injector to catch discharged fuel.* Pull negative "VE" connection off of ignition coil and connector on thermo-time switch.

2) Crank engine and observe that each injector sprays fuel. If one injector is not operating, check that injector electrical connection and if necessary replace that injector. If three injectors are not operating, suspect power amplifier. If six injectors are not functioning, either power amplifier or ECU should be replaced. After testing is complete, reverse disassembly procedure.

COLD START INJECTION VALVE

NOTE — *When testing cold start system, fuel vapors will be present in engine compartment, therefore you should take all precautions necessary to prevent fire or explosion.*

Preparations For Testing — Remove cold start injector valves from intake manifold. Place suitable container beneath each cold start valve, to catch discharged fuel. Disconnect negative "VE" connection at ignition coil.

Engine Below 58°F (15°C) — **1)** Switch on ignition and check that injectors do not leak. Crank engine one or two revolutions and make sure that injectors spray fuel. If each injector does operate, reverse preparations for testing. If any injector fails to operate properly, continue tests.

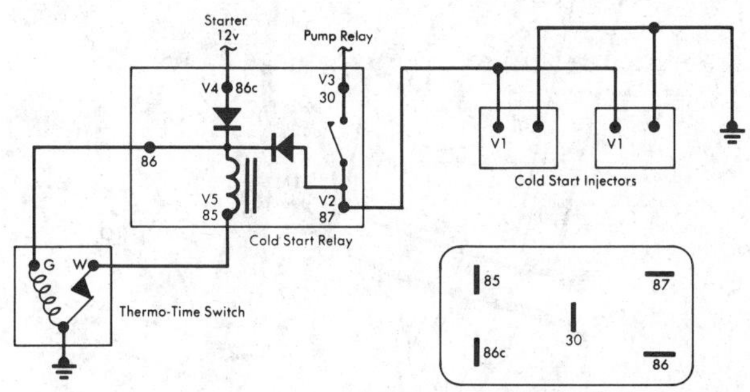

Fig. 4 Diagram of Cold Start Circuit for Testing

2) At test point V1 (on diagram), check for battery voltage. If battery voltage is present when cranking engine and injectors still do not spray, check electrical connections to each injector. If both positive and negative connections are good, the injector is bad and should be replaced. If no voltage was present at test point V1, check for voltage at test point V2.

3) If voltage is present at V2, check cables between cold start injector relay and cold start injectors. If no voltage was present at V2, check for voltage at V3. If no voltage is present at V3, check supply voltage from pump relay. If voltage was present at V3, cold start relay is not functioning properly. Check for voltage at V4.

4) If no voltage was present at V4, check supply voltage from starter relay. If voltage was present at V4, disconnect terminal 85 of cold start relay and check for voltage at terminal 86. If no voltage is present, replace relay. If voltage is present, bridge terminal 85 to ground and relay should energize. Now check voltage at terminal 87, if no volatge, replace relay. If voltage present at 87, check cable and connections to thermo-time switch. If cables are in good condition and making proper connections, continue test procedure.

5) Replace cold start injectors and all cables and connections. Crank engine and check for voltage at terminal 87. Voltage at terminal 87 should be zero. If voltage present at terminal 87, disconnect terminal 85. Crank engine and recheck for voltage at terminal 87. If terminal 87 has no voltage, thermo-time switch should be replaced. If voltage is present at 87, replace relay. **NOTE** — *If injectors spray fuel while voltage at 87 is zero, injector should be replaced.*

COOLANT TEMEPRATURE SENSOR

Disconnect battery and pull connector from sensor. Connect ohmmeter between the terminals and note the resistance reading. Compare reading obtained with following table, which is based upon temperature. Check each terminal to ground and make sure resistance is infinity.

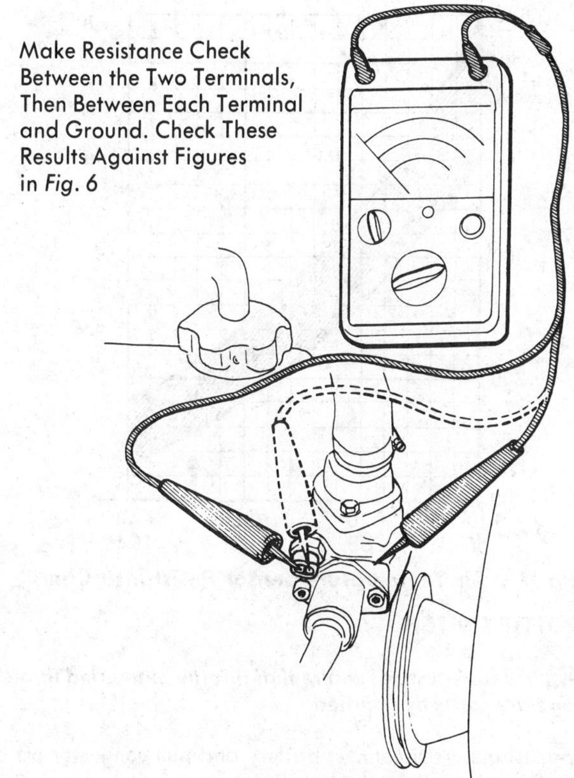

Fig. 5 Test Connections and Equipment for Evaluating Engine Coolant Temperature Sensor

LUCAS-JAGUAR ELECTRONIC INJECTION SYSTEM (Cont.)

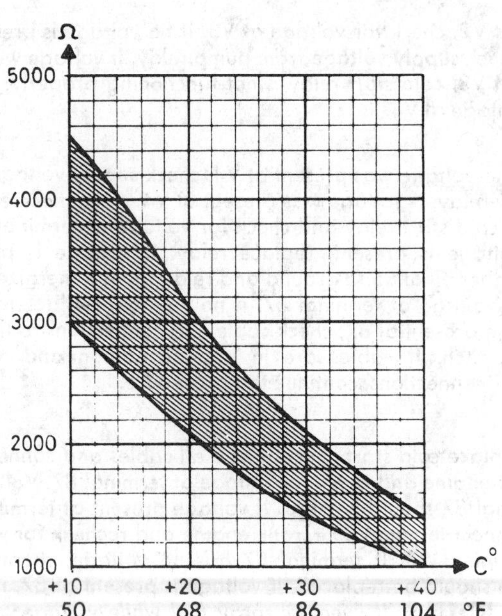

Fig. 6 Engine Coolant Temperature Sensor Resistance Chart

AIR TEMPERATURE SENSOR

Disconnect battery and pull electrical connector off sensor. Connect ohmmeter between the terminals and note reading. Compare reading with table to determine whether or not sensor is functioning properly. If reading is outside of range, replace sensor.

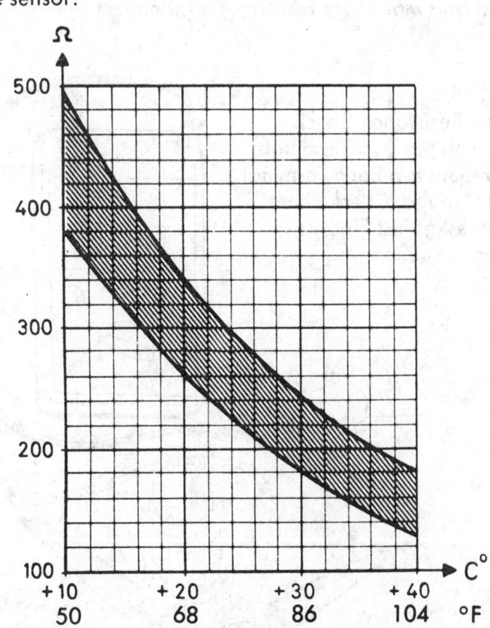

Fig. 7 Air Temperature Sensor Resistance Chart

THROTTLE SWITCH

NOTE — *Before testing, ensure that throttle plates and throttle linkage are correctly adjusted.*

Preparations — Disconnect battery and pull connector off of throttle switch.

Idle Position — Connect ohmmeter between terminals 12/47 (ground) and terminal 17 of throttle switch *(See Fig. 9)*. Meter reading should be very low resistance or zero. If reading is not very low, adjust throttle switch.

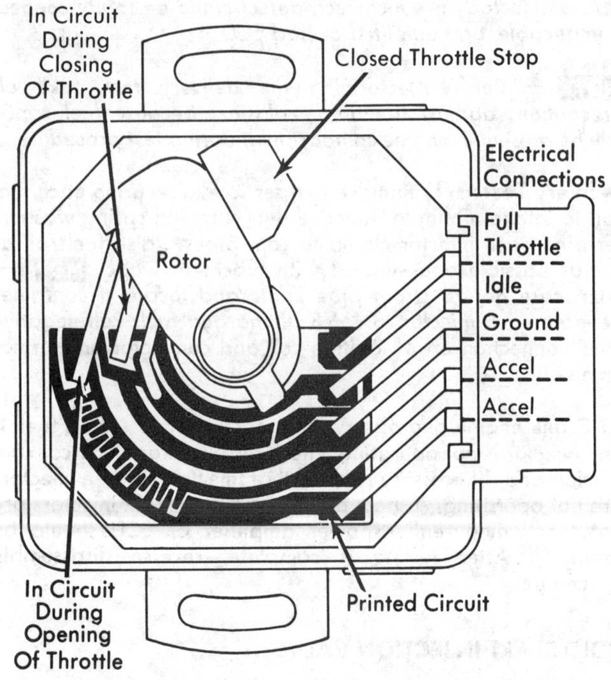

Fig. 8 Diagram of Throttle Position Switch

Temporare Enrichment (Acceleration) — Connect ohmmeter between terminals 9 and 12/47 (ground). Watch ohmmeter and turn throttle by hand. Meter needle should swing smoothly between very low resistance and very high resistance (to point on open circuit). If meter does not swing smoothly, replace throttle switch.

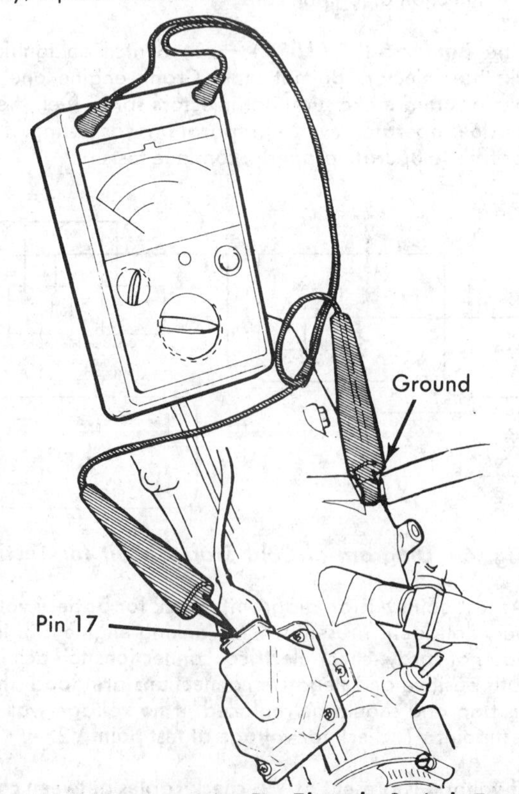

Fig. 9 Test Connections For Throttle Switch Testing

LUCAS-JAGUAR ELECTRONIC INJECTION SYSTEM (Cont.)

AUXILIARY AIR VALVE

Remove auxiliary air valve and fully close adjustment screw. Immerse valve bulb in container of boiling water. With bulb immerased, watch valve action, through side port. Valve should move smoothly to closed position. Quickly blow through a hose attached to side port, no air should pass. Allow blub to cool. Valve should move smoothly to open position. If valve performance is not satisfactory, replace with new unit. If valve action is acceptable, reset adjustment screw and install valve.

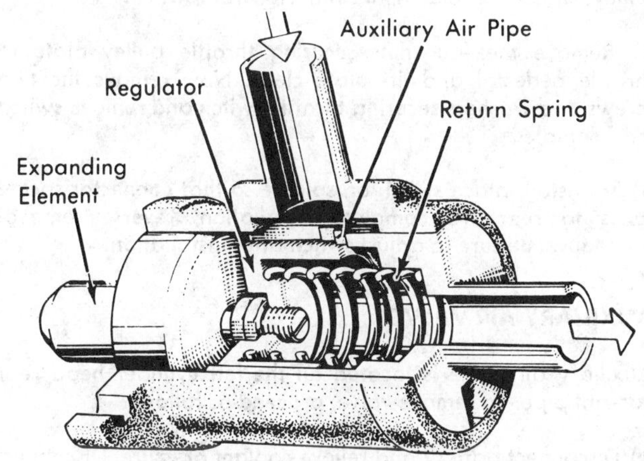

Fig. 10 Cutaway View of Auxiliary Air Valve

THERMO-TIME SWITCH

NOTE – *Engine should either be below 32°F (0°C) or in cold condition. If coolant is above 50°F (10°C), connect ohmmeter between terminal "W" of switch and ground. Reading should be either very high or infinity.*

Pull connector from thermo-time switch and use ohmmeter across terminals. Reading should be very low or zero ohms. Use stop watch and apply voltage to terminal "G" of switch. Note delay time according to coolant temperature (see table). If time delay is clearly outside of specifications given in table, replace unit.

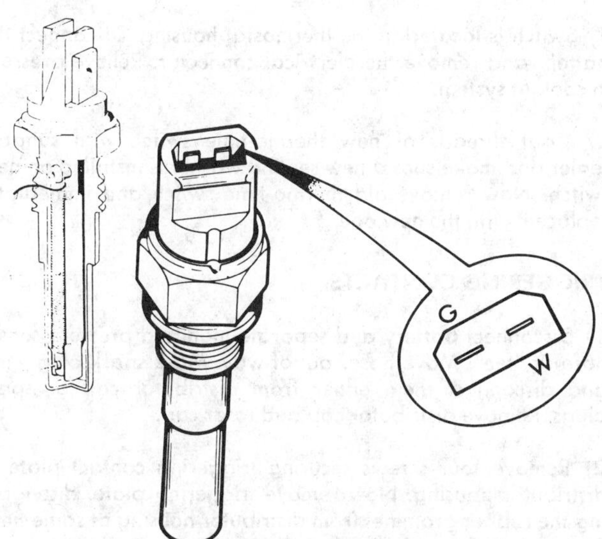

Fig. 11 Thermo-Time Switch with Details of Electrical Connections

Coolant Temperature °F	Delay (Seconds)
-4	8
14	5.7
32	3.5
50	1.2
59	0

DISTRIBUTOR TRIGGER UNIT

Disconnect cable from pump relay terminal 85. Disconnect negative "VE" terminal from ignition coil. Seperate in-line connector to distributor trigger unit. Connect ohmmeter between terminals 21 and 12 on distributor side of in-line connector. Crank engine, ohmmeter should show even swing between low resistance (a current limiting resistor is fitted inside trigger unit) and very high resistance. Transfer ohmmeter to terminals 22 and 12, an identical result should be obtained. If meter display reading remains steady during cranking or if the swing is uneven or intermittent, the trigger unit should be replaced.

REMOVAL & INSTALLATION

NOTE – *On all procedures where the fuel lines are to be disconnected, the fuel system should be relieved of its pressure. To do this, disconnect the cable (connection 85) from ECU to pump relay (see Fig. 1 for location of cable).* Switch on ignition and crank engine. Engine may run for a few seconds until fuel pressure is reduced. Switch off ignition and reconnect cable to terminal 85 of pump relay.

FUEL PUMP

Fuel pump is located beneath the trunk compartment floor, to remove fuel pump proceed as follows:

1) Disconnect battery and remove spare tire. Clamp fuel lines on both sides of pump, then disconnect hoses from pump.

2) Disconnect electrical plug from pump. Remove screws attaching pump to mounting bracket then remove clamp from pump body. To install fuel pump, reverse removal procedure.

ELECTRONIC CONTROL UNIT (ECU)

The ECU is located in the trunk compartment up against the rear seat panel. The ECU has an idle CO adjustment knob on it, this knob should NOT be moved. If it is, the CO level will have to be readjusted.

1) Disconnect battery. At the front end of trunk compartment (toward front of vehicle), remove the ECU cover. Disconnect ECU retainer band or clamp.

2) Remove the cable clamp screws and clip. Remove the end cover. Locate handle on cable harness plug and withdraw plug. To install, reverse removal procedure. Also, check the idle CO level.

LUCAS-JAGUAR ELECTRONIC INJECTION SYSTEM (Cont.)

FUEL PRESSURE REGULATOR

There are two fuel pressure regulators, one located between the third and forth intake manifold runners on each side of engine.

1) Depressurize system and disconnect battery. Remove screws securing regulator bracket. Carefully lift regulator and bracket up. Take note of how regulator is installed in bracket (which line goes to pump and which goes to fuel rails).

2) Clamp fuel lines, then disconnect fuel lines from regulator. Then disconnect regulator from bracket. To install, reverse removal procedure. Be sure to install regualtor in bracket the same way it was removed, inlet to fuel pump and outlet to fuel rails.

MANIFOLD PRESSURE CONTROL VALVE (MPC)

Manifold pressure control valve is located on the top left side of the radiator. To remove valve, proceed as follows: Disconnect battery and unplug electrical connector from valve. Disconnect hose from valve and then remove screws securing valve to bracket. To install, reverse removal procedure.

INJECTORS

1) Depressurize system and disconnect battery. Clamp fuel line between filter and fuel rails. Disconnect electrical plug from injector(s) to be removed.

2) Remove screws securing fuel rail to intake manifold, then release clips attaching supply fuel rail to return fuel rail. Remove the 12 screws attaching injectors to intake manifold.

3) Carefully lift fuel rail, with injectors, clear of intake manifold. Plug injector holes and wipe up any spilled fuel. Now disconnect injector(s) from fuel rail as needed. As injector(s) are removed, note the location of the electrical socket. This will aid in installation.

4) To install, reverse removal procedure and note the following. Install new "O" rings on all injectors. Make sure the electrical plug is located in the right direction (as removed).

COLD START VALVE

Depressurize system and disconnect battery. Clamp fuel line and remove electrical connector. Remove screws securing cold start valve and remove valve. **NOTE** – *There are two cold start valves on the Jaguar V12 engine.* To install, reverse removal procedure.

COOLANT TEMPERATURE SENSOR

1) Disconnect battery and remove pressure from coolant system by loosening radiator cap. Disconnect electrical connector from sensor. **NOTE** – *Since the sensor is mounted in the block below the coolant level, it will be necessary to either drain part of the coolant or have another sensor (or other suitable plug) ready to install the moment the old sensor is removed.* Remove coolant temperature sensor.

2) When installing new sensor be sure to coat threads with a suitable sealing compound.

AIR TEMPERATURE SENSOR

Air temperature sensor is located in the left side air cleaner. Disconnect electrical connector and remove sensor. To install, reverse removal procedure.

THROTTLE SWITCH

1) Throttle switch is located beneath throttle pulley. Disconnect battery and remove throttle cross rods from throttle pulley. Disconnect electrical connector from switch.

2) Remove the four nuts securing throttle pulley plate to throttle pedestal and lift plate clear. Now remove the two screws and washers securing throttle switch and remove switch from spindle.

3) To install, place switch on spindle so that connector socket faces to rear. To complete installation, reverse removal procedure. Be sure to adjust switch after installation.

AUXILIARY AIR VALVE

Auxiliary air valve is located on the left cylinder head rear coolant pipe. To remove valve, proceed as follows:

1) Disconnect battery and relieve coolant pressure. Disconnect air hoses connected to air valve. Disconnect air valve from coolant pipe.

2) Clean gasket material from coolant pipe. Scribe a mark on adjusting screw and on air valve. Now count the number of turns it takes to fully seat adjusting screw.

3) On the new auxiliary air valve, seat adjusting screw then turn out the number of turns counted in step **2)**. To complete installation, reverse removal procedure.

THERMO-TIME SWITCH

NOTE – *Replacement of the thermo-time switch must be done on a cold engine only.*

1) Switch is located in the thermostat housing. Disconnect the battery and remove the electrical connector. Relieve pressure in coolant system.

2) Coat threads of new thermo-time switch with suitable sealer and make sure a new sealing washer is installed on new switch. Now remove old thermo-time switch and immediatly replace it with the new one.

TRIGGERING CONTACTS

1) Disconnect battery and separate manifold pressure sensor hose at "tee". Move hoses out of way. Mark spark plug wires and disconnect them either from distributor cap or spark plugs. Remove distributor cap and rotor cap.

2) Remove four screws securing triggering contact plate to distributor housing. Now remove triggering plate, disengaging the rubber grommet from distributor housing at same time. Disconnect triggering contact cable from pump relay.

3) To install triggering contacts, reverse removal procedure.

LUCAS-JAGUAR ELECTRONIC INJECTION SYSTEM (Cont.)

ADJUSTMENTS

HOT (SLOW) IDLE RPM

See appropriate article in TUNE-UP Section.

IDLE MIXTURE

See appropriate article in TUNE-UP Section.

FUEL PRESSURE REGULATOR

NOTE — *Fuel pressure regulator should only be adjusted after complete system has been throughly checked.*

1) Remove bolts securing both pressure regulators to intake manifold. Crimp off fuel line between "B" bank pressure regulator inlet and fuel rail. Loosen hose clamp securing left-hand cold start injector supply line to fuel rail and remove line from rail. Connect pressure gauge to fuel rail and tighten hose clamp.

2) Start engine and loosen lock nuts on both pressure regulators. Set adjusting bolt on bank "A" regulator, until pressure gauge reads 29.6 psi (2.1 kg/cm^2). Release crimp on "B" bank regulator and transfer to "A" bank regulator. Set adjusting bolt on "B" bank regulator to read 29.6 psi (2.1 kg/cm^2) on pressure gauge.

3) Release crimp on "A" bank inlet line to pressure regulator, tighten lock nuts on both regulators and install bolts securing both pressure regulators to intake manifold. Switch off ignition, depressurize fuel system and remove pressure gauge. Switch on ignition and check for leaks.

THROTTLE SWITCH

1) Disconnect battery, remove cross rods from throttle pulley and pull connector off of throttle switch. Remove four nuts and washer securing throttle pulley plate to throttle pedestal and lift plate clear. Loosen two screws securing throttle switch. Insert .030" feeler gauge between pulley and closed throttle stop.

2) Connect ohmmeter between terminals 12 and 17 of throttle switch. Turn throttle switch slowly until meter just flips over to very low resistance (short circuit) and tighten two screws securing throttle switch. Remove feeler gauge and meter should read very high resistance when pulley is against closed stop. Reassemble and adjust throttle linkage, if necessary.

THROTTLE LINKAGE

Testing — 1) In order to determine whether or not throttle linkage needs adjusting, perform the following tests: Make sure throttle return springs are correctly attached and that throttle pulley moves freely, coming to rest against the closed stop position. Check that throttle butterfly valve (closed) stop position screw has not been moved.

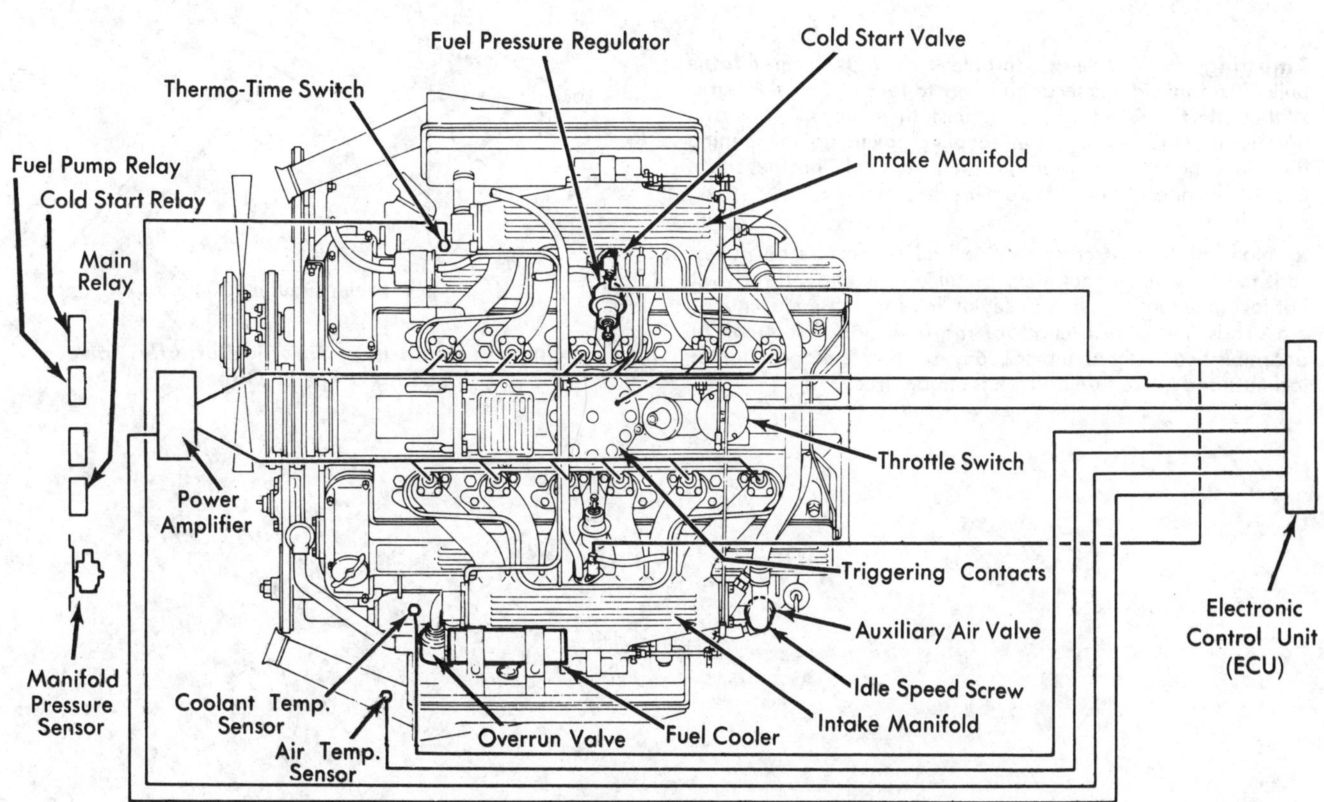

Fig. 12 Top View of Jaguar Fuel Injection System

LUCAS-JAGUAR ELECTRONIC INJECTION SYSTEM (Cont.)

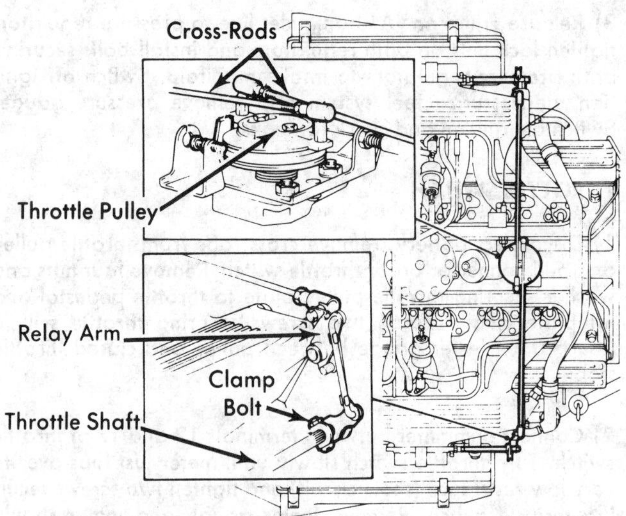

Fig. 13 Throttle Linkage with Detail of Linkage Connections

NOTE – *If throttle butterfly stop screw has been tampered with, do not continue this test and adjustment procedure until the throttle butterfly valves have been properly adjusted.*

2) Check that throttle Pulley can be rotated to full open position and that throttle butterfly valve arm is touching the throttle housing. If these conditions are not as specified, then it will be necessary to adjust the throttle linkage.

Adjusting – **1)** Release throttle cross-rods from throttle pulley. Loosen clamps securing levers to rear of throttle shafts. With butterfly valves closed against their stops, relay arm against its stop and play in coupling taken up in opening direction, tighten clamp-to-lever on rear of throttle shaft. Repeat this operation for the other side of engine.

2) Now try to refit cross-rods to ball connectors on pulley; rods must locate without moving pulley or linkage. If rods will not locate without moving pulley or linkage, loosen locknut on cross-rods and adjust length of rod until attachment can be accomplished without moving any part of linkage. Tighten locknuts and make sure ball joints remain free.

3) Loosen locknut on throttle pulley and back out stop screw to full extent of travel. Hold throttle relay arm pulley fully open and check that butterfly stop arms are against throttle housing. Adjust stop to just touch throttle pulley and tighten locknut. Check operation of throttle switch and kickdown switch.

THROTTLE BUTTERFLY VALVE ADJUSTMENT

CAUTION – *Any adjustment must be carried out on both butterfly valves. It is not recommended to adjust one valve only.*

Remove both air cleaners, loosen locknut on throttle butterfly stop screw and turn in screw until butterfly valve is completely closed. Insert .004" feeler gauge between top of valve and housing, to hold valve open. Set stop screw to just touch stop arm and tighten locknut with feeler gauge still in position. Press stop arm against stop screw and withdraw feeler gauge. Repeat same operation on other side of engine. Seal threads of adjusting screws with blob of paint and refit air cleaners.

NOTE – *After adjusting throttle butterfly linkage, check throttle linkage, operation of throttle switch and kickdown switch operation.*

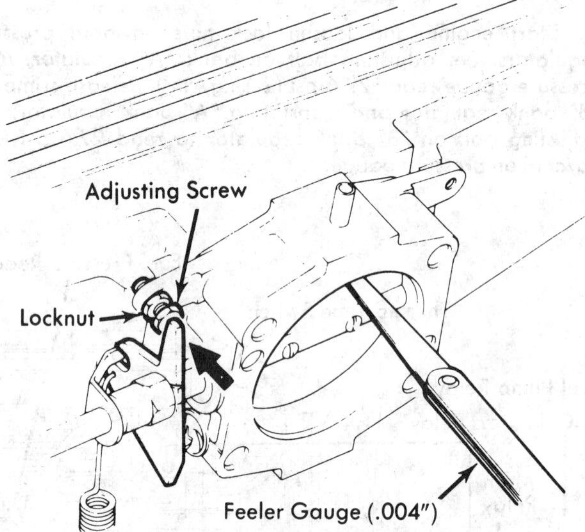

Fig. 14 Measuring Throttle Butterfly Valve (Using a Feeler Gauge)

BOSCH DIESEL INJECTION – MERCEDES-BENZ

Mercedes-Benz
240D
300D

DESCRIPTION

Fuel injection system consists of the following components. See *Fig. 1:*

- Pre-filter
- Main Fuel Filter
- Fuel Injection Pump with Fuel Pump
- Mechanical Centrifugal Governor
- Automatic Altitude Compensating Device
- Vacuum Control Unit
- Injection Nozzles
- Glow Plugs
- Key-starting System

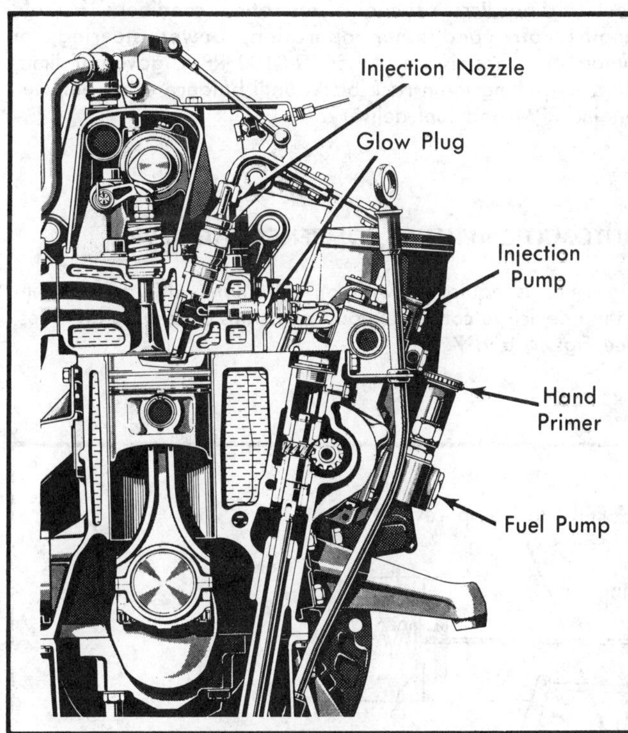

Fig. 1 Components of 1977 Bosch Diesel Fuel Injection System for Mercedes-Benz

Fuel is pumped from fuel tank, through a pre-filter and main fuel filter into suction chamber of injection pump. Pump's camshaft operates injection pump plungers, which force fuel through delivery valves, reverse-flow dampening valves, and pressure lines to fuel injection nozzles.

When pressure stroke is completed, spring-loaded valves close pressure lines. Plungers return to original position.

TESTING

Manufacturer recommends that ALL tests be conducted on an injection pump test stand, using tests sheets furnished by manufacturer.

SYSTEM COMPONENTS

FUEL INJECTION PUMP

Injection pumps used on 240D and 300D Diesel engines are similar. *See Fig. 2.* Major difference is the number of pumping elements, five on 300D and four on 240D – one for each cylinder.

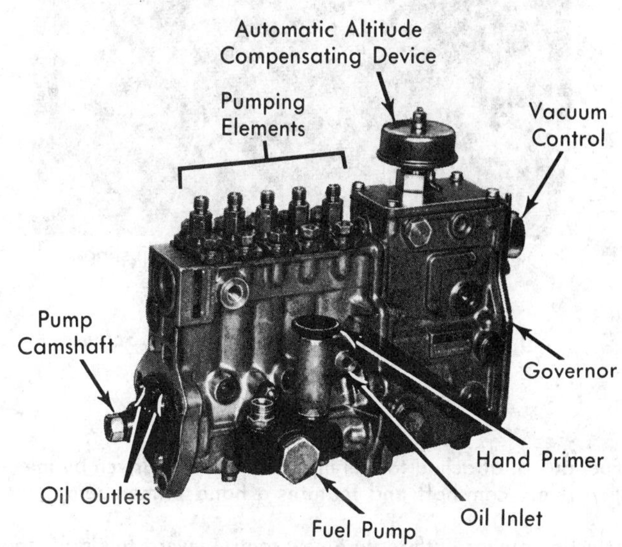

Fig. 2 Fuel Injection Pump Components

Built-in mechanical centrifugal governor has eliminated need for previously-used throttle valve in intake manifold. Engine shut-off is achieved by vacuum control unit. Pumps are lubricated by engine lubrication system. Note oil inlet and outlets. *See Fig. 2.*

An automatic altitude compensating device has been added to governor housing to meet exhaust emission standards at varying altitudes.

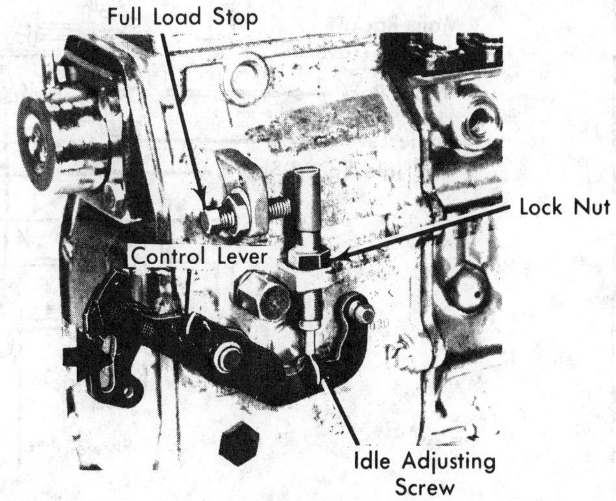

Fig. 3 Control Lever and Adjusting Screws for Mercedes-Benz 240D

BOSCH DIESEL INJECTION – MERCEDES-BENZ (Cont.)

Fig. 4 Control Lever and Adjusting Screws for Mercedes-Benz 300D

Fuel pump, attached to fuel injection pump, is driven by injection pump camshaft and features a hand primer pump.

Injection pumps both feature new control levers, full load stop screws and idle adjusting screws. *See Figs. 3 and 4.* On 240D engine, control pressure rod for automatic transmission is connected to control lever. *See arrow in Fig. 3.*

GOVERNOR

Governor is an idle-maximum RPM governor. *See Fig. 5* Springs are designed and adjusted so no regulating takes place in intermediate range except for compensation. Between idle and maximum RPM cutout, main rack is operated only by accelerator pedal. Pedal is connected through linkage with fulcrum lever of governor.

When engine RPM increases, flyweights move outward as soon as centrifugal force exceeds spring pressure. Movement of flyweights is transmitted through the angle lever, adjusting screws and control lever to main rack.

When reaching maximum RPM, main rack is moved toward the cutout position, reducing the amount of fuel and limiting engine RPM. As engine RPM decreases, the function is reversed.

Through governor action, engine RPM is held constant at idle speed, regardless of engine operating conditions – cold engine, air conditioner operation, power steering, or automatic transmission. At 5000-5100 RPM, governor limits RPM by pulling main rack back, until balance exists between engine RPM and fuel delivery.

AUTOMATIC ALTITUDE COMPENSATING DEVICE

Governor is equipped with an automatic altitude compensating device to control exhaust emissions at varying altitudes. *See Figs. 6 and 7.*

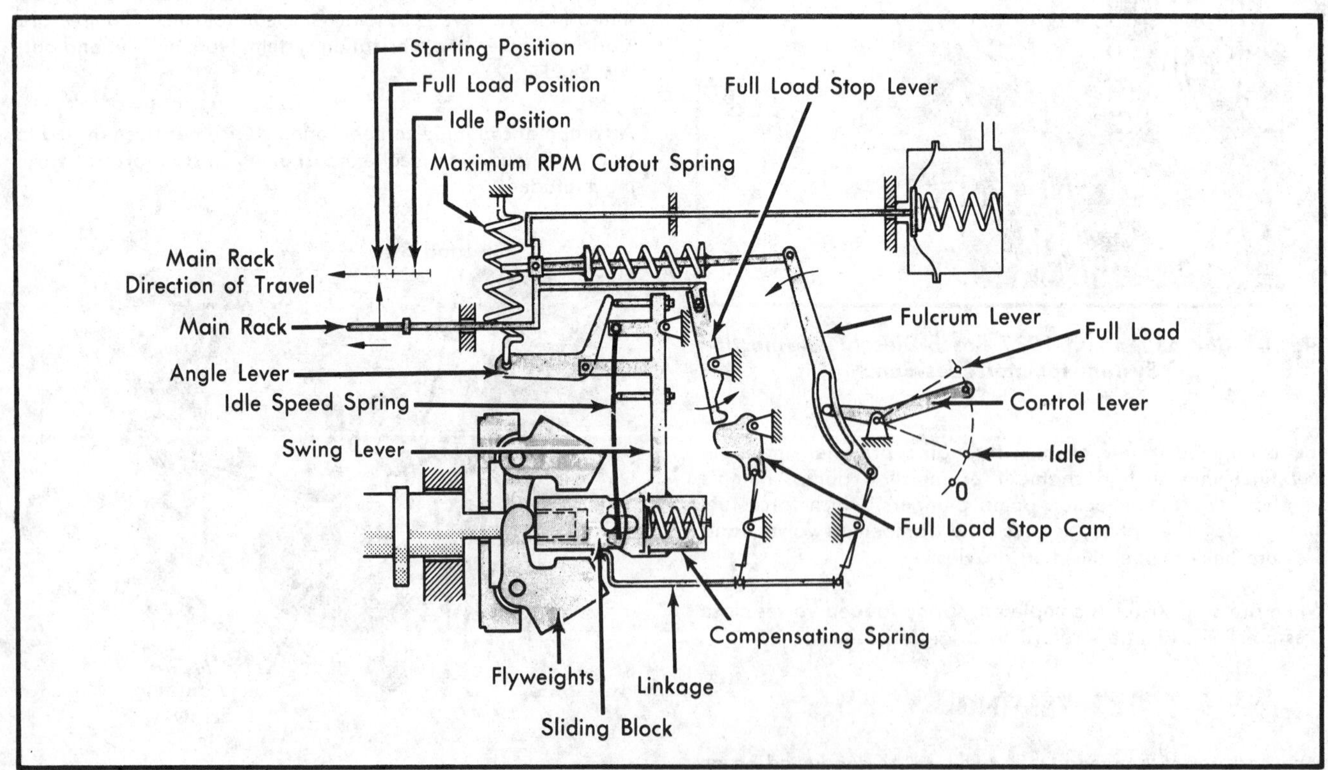

Fig. 5 Typical Governor Linkage for Mercedes-Benz (Start Position Illustrated)

BOSCH DIESEL INJECTION – MERCEDES-BENZ (Cont.)

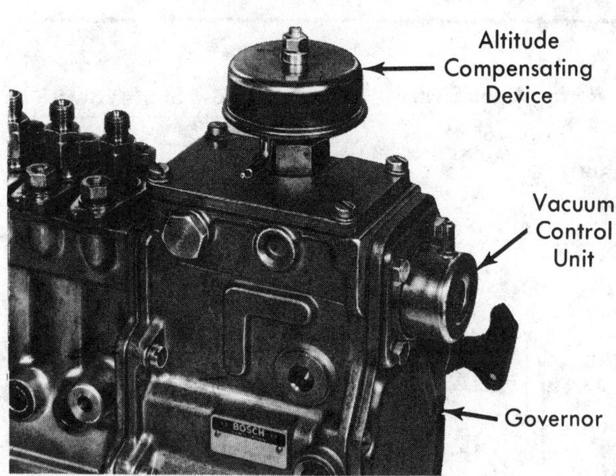

Fig. 6 Automatic Altitude Compensating Device and Vacuum Control Unit

With increasing altitude, atmospheric pressure is decreased. This causes two aneroid (non-fluid) compensators to expand. At specified atmospheric pressure, internal force of compensators becomes greater than pretension of aneroid compression spring. Push rod moves downward, moving linkage. This causes main rack to move in direction "D", causing less fuel to be injected. See *Fig. 7*.

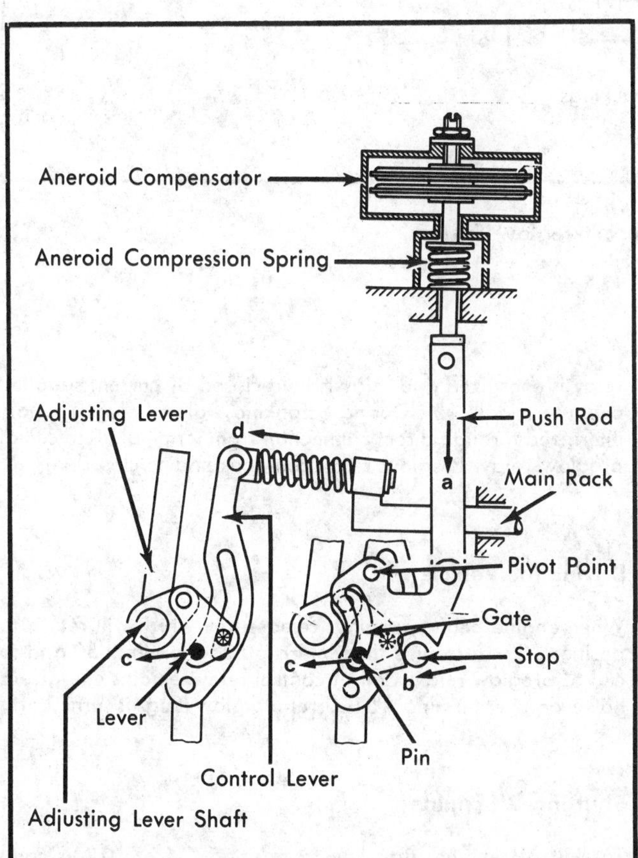

Fig. 7 Diagram of Automatic Altitude Compensating Device and Linkage

As adjusting lever moves closer to idle stop, compensating adjustment in partial load range is gradually reduced. At idle it is almost completely eliminated. At low altitudes, governor settings are not affected by compensators.

MAIN FUEL FILTER

Main fuel filter is composed of a throwaway-type filter element, which is part of lower filter housing. See *REMOVAL AND INSTALLATION.*

INJECTION NOZZLES

Injection nozzles are used to spray fuel into the cylinder under the proper pressure and spray pattern for optimum combustion. See *Fig. 8*.

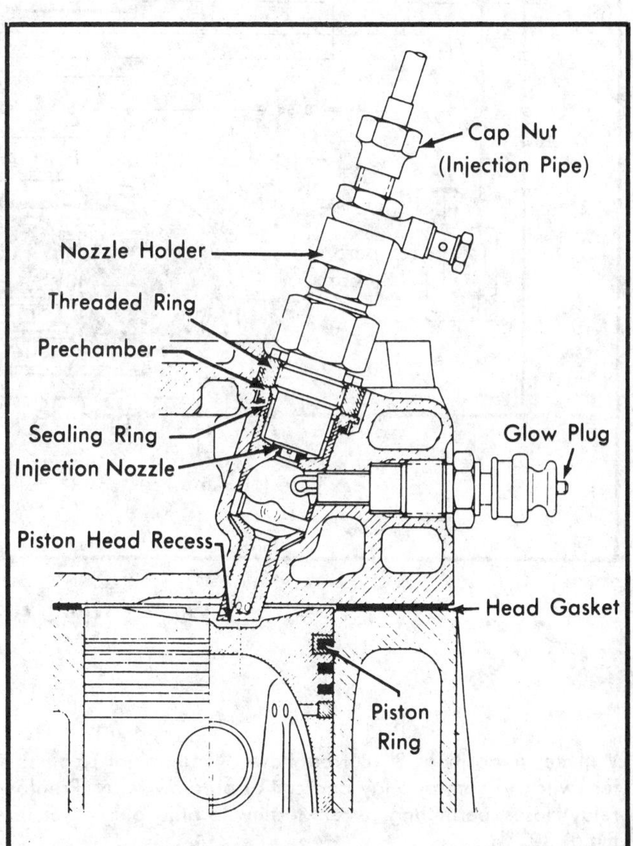

Fig. 8 Fuel Injection Nozzle, Holder and Glow Plug

KEY-STARTING SYSTEM

Starting the Engine

To start engine, turn key to position "2" of starter switch. When indicator light in bottom of speedometer goes out, preglow time is optimum for ignition. See *Fig. 9*.

NOTE – *If engine does not start immediately, preglow system remains energized for approximately 2 minutes and then shuts down to prevent battery drain. Use care when working in engine compartment during this time, as resistor wires are very hot.*

BOSCH DIESEL INJECTION – MERCEDES-BENZ (Cont.)

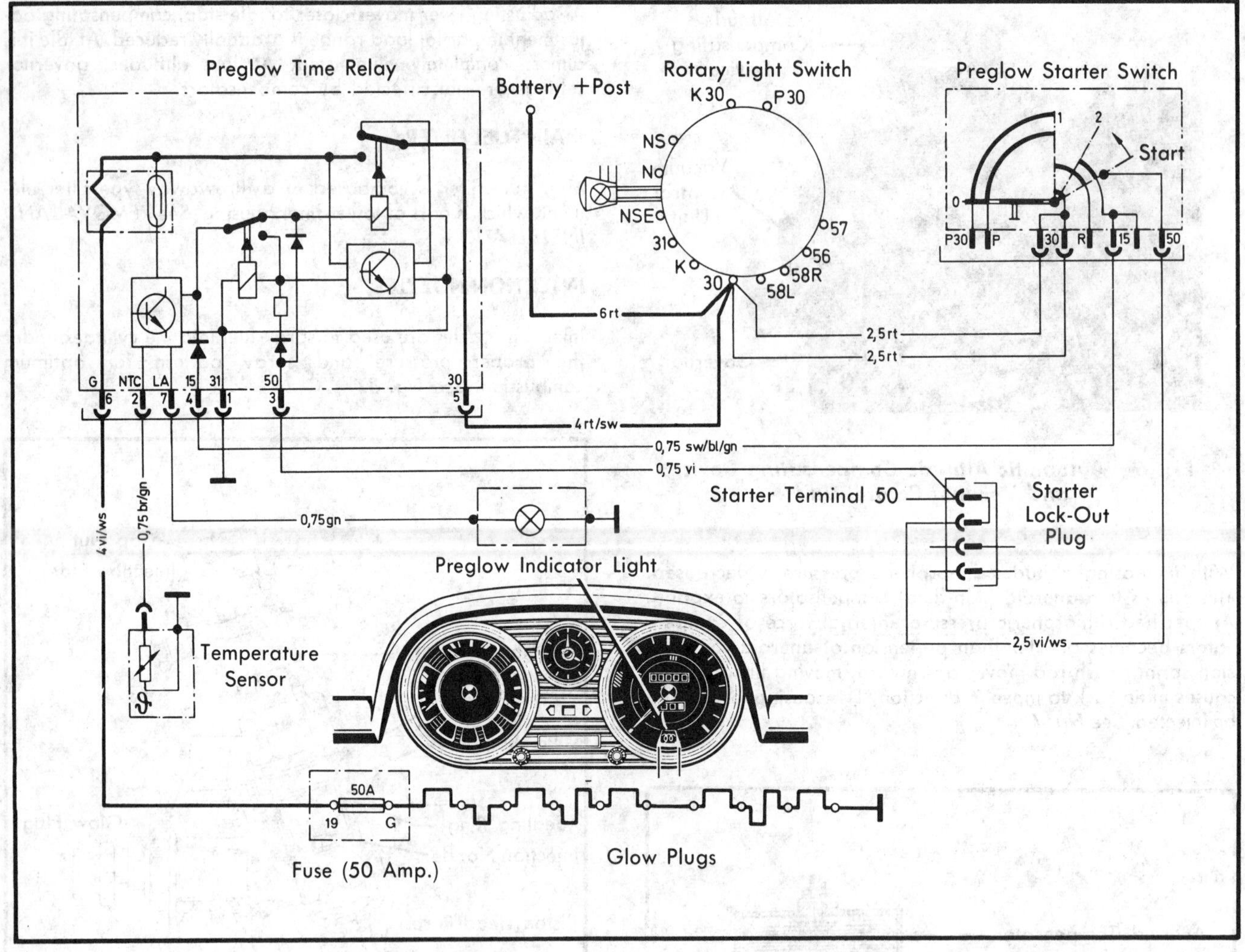

Fig. 9 Wiring Diagram of Preglow System

With key in position "2", current flows over terminal 15 of starter switch to control relay and coil of preglow relay. Preglow relay closes, permitting current to flow to glow plugs over terminal 30.

System is equipped with a temperature sensor, which turns off dash-mounted indicator light when most favorable preglow temperature is sensed. System is protected by a 50 ampere fuse box in engine compartment.

If temperature is below 59°F (15°C) and engine is cold, depress accelerator. This releases main rack in injection pump into its starting position. Turn starter switch key clockwise to "start" position. After engine starts, release accelerator pedal, allowing main rack to return to idle position. At higher temperatures and with engine warm, accelerator pressure is not required.

With starter switch in "start" position, current is supplied to solenoid switch of starter and to preglow time relay over terminal 50. Two circuits are then energized. The coil of control relay is energized and relay is held closed by current supplied over terminal 15. During cranking, glow plugs remain energized through direct connection from terminal 50 to coil of preglow relay. Preglow relay contact remains closed.

Driving the Vehicle

When engine begins running, release key which will return to position "2". Current is then interrupted to terminal 50 and to coil of preglow relay. Coil of control relay remains energized, however, over terminal 15. Current to glow plugs is turned off.

Shutting Off Engine

To shut off engine, turn key to position "1" or "0". A cam-operated valve, attached to starter switch opens, connecting the vacuum line from the vacuum pump to the injection pump. See *Fig. 10*.

BOSCH DIESEL INJECTION – MERCEDES-BENZ (Cont.)

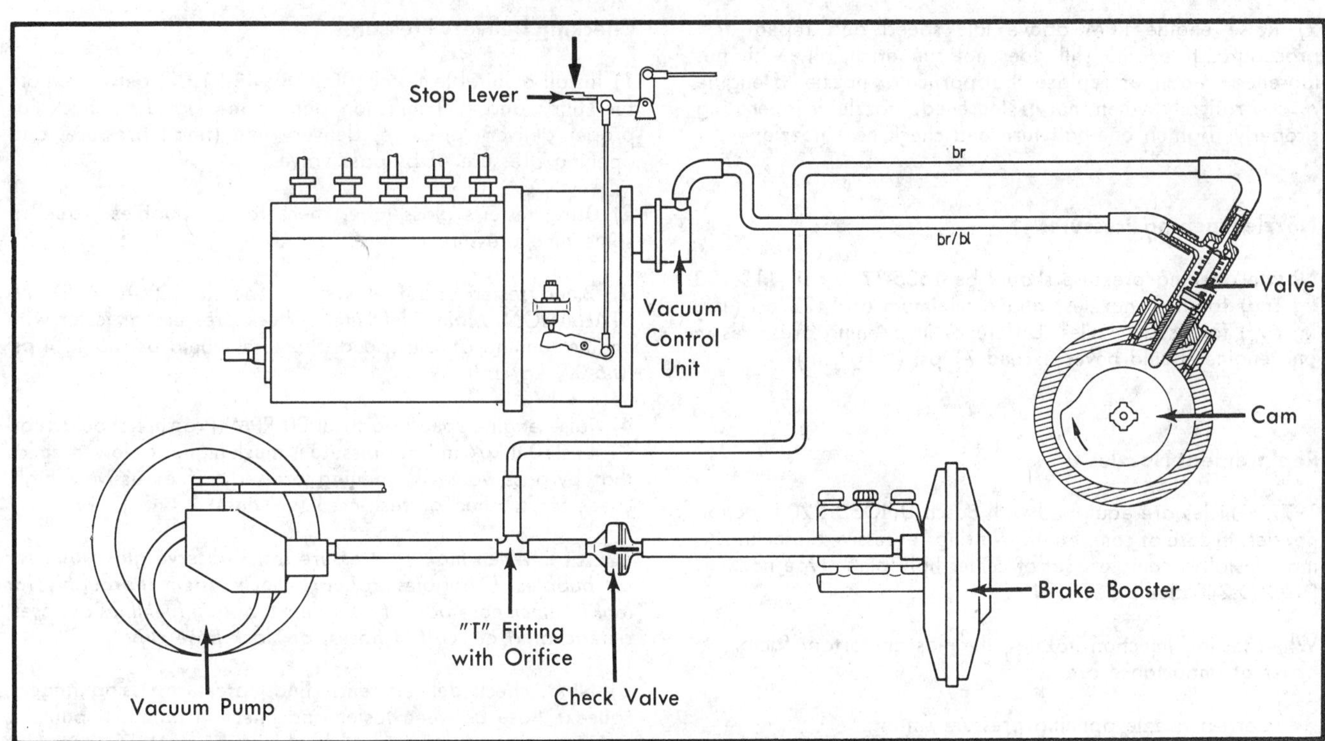

Fig. 10 Vacuum Diagram Showing Vacuum Pump, Valve, and Vacuum Control Unit on Injection Pump

Diaphragm of pump-mounted vacuum control unit reacts, pulling main rack to "stop" position.. If engine fails to stop, push "stop" lever on cylinder head. This manually moves main rack to "stop" position. *See REMOVAL AND INSTALLATION, VACUUM CONTROL UNIT and Fig. 11.*

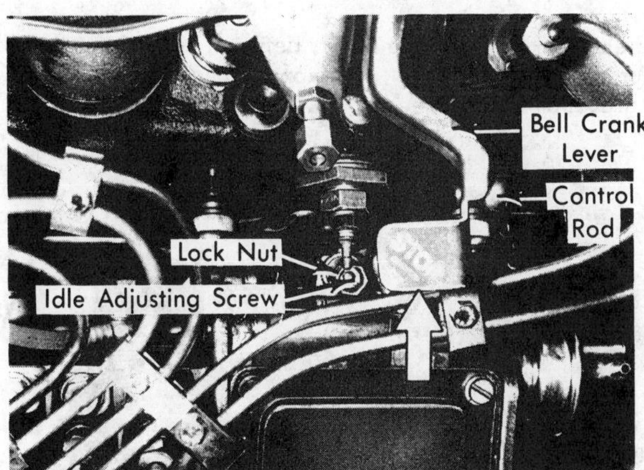

Fig. 11 Manual "Stop" Lever Controlling Injection Pump Main Rack

Starting Lock Position

To lock engine, so vehicle cannot be started by towing or coasting downhill, remove key or turn key to position "1" or "0". Vacuum control unit will then pull main rack to "stop" position.

REVERSE FLOW DAMPENING VALVE

The disc-type reverse flow dampening valve is crimped into place above each delivery valve compression spring. Valves permit free fuel flow toward injection nozzles, opening in direction of nozzles.

Closing needle valve in nozzle causes a pressure wave to return toward injection pump. Since delivery valve is already closed, pressure wave would normally return to injection nozzle and open it briefly again. This would cause higher HC content of exhaust gases.

Pressure wave is eliminated, however, by orifice in dampening valve disc, preventing secondary injection.

SERVICING COMPONENTS

INJECTION NOZZLES

If exhaust gives off intermittent clouds of black smoke, this usually means one or more nozzles are operating unevenly. If exhaust offers a rumbling noise, it usually indicates one cylinder is partly or completely out of action. *See Fig. 8.* To check injection nozzles:

1) At idle, loosen each injection pipe cap nut (in turn) one-half turn. If sound of engine does not change, part of problem is a defective nozzle or inadequate sealing between pipe union and nozzle holder.

BOSCH DIESEL INJECTION – MERCEDES-BENZ (Cont.)

2) Raise engine RPM above idle speed and repeat test procedure. If engine still does not run erratically with nut loosened, repair or replace that particular nozzle. If engine runs erratically when nut is loosened, nozzle is operating properly. Tighten one-half turn and check next nozzle.

Nozzle Opening Pressures

Nozzle opening pressure should be 1635-1750 psi (115-123 kg/cm²) for new nozzles, and a minimum of 1422 psi (100 kg/cm²) for used nozzles. Difference in opening pressures in one engine should never exceed 71 psi (5 kg/cm²).

Replacement Nozzles

1977 vehicles are equipped with Bosch DNOSD 220 injection nozzles. In case of complaints involving "excessive diesel knocking", install a complete set of center hole pintle-type nozzles, DNOSD 240. See *DIESEL KNOCK*.

When testing injection nozzles, the most important factors in order of importance are:

- Correct nozzle opening pressure setting.
- Tightness of valve seat to minimum 280 psi (19.7 kg/cm²) below opening pressure of nozzle.
- Correct spray pattern.

Always install new seal between nozzle and prechamber. Tighten nozzles to specified torque. Use accurate torque wrench so seals and nozzles are not damaged. Coked-up seals speed clogging of nozzle throttling gaps, causing distorted spray pattern and diesel knock.

FUEL PUMP

Fuel pump must deliver fuel under constant pressure and without bubbles. Insufficient pressure could cause engine problems. Pressure is kept constant by a by-pass valve which does not open until specified pressure is reached.

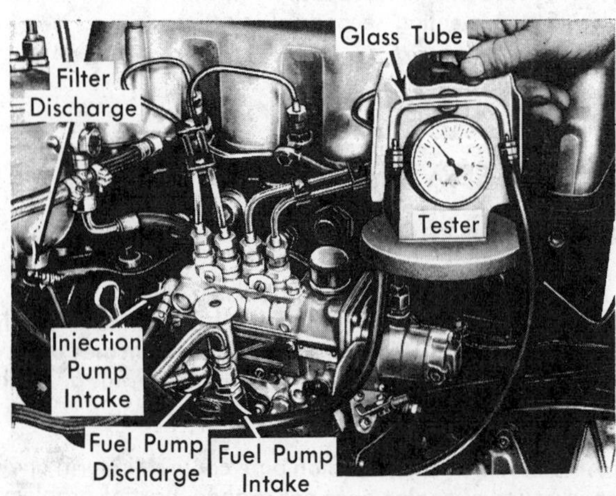

Fig. 12 Pressure Tester (000 589 49 21 00) Hook-Up (Earlier Model Injection Pump Shown)

Checking Delivery Pressures

1) Install a suitable tester (000 589 49 21 00) between main fuel filter and fuel injection pump. *See Fig. 12.* Check for proper delivery pressure, delivery end (final) pressure, and opening pressure of by-pass valve.

2) Using tester's glass tube, check for air bubbles in fuel at same time pressure is read.

3) Bleed tester and fuel system. *See REMOVAL AND INSTALLATION, Main Fuel Filter.* Check pressure at tester with engine running at idle speed. Pressure should be 8.5-11.4 psi (0.6-0.8 kg/cm²).

4) Raise engine speed up to 3000 RPM. Pressure should read 11.4 psi (0.8 kg/cm²). If pressure is much higher or lower, check that by-pass valve is opening properly. If excessively high, check for crushed or restricted fuel lines.

NOTE – *When making pressure tests, observe glass tube for air bubbles. If bubbles appear, check system thoroughly for leaks. Check hose porosity, hairline cracks in fuel lines or hoses, deteriorated or scuffed hoses, or slack hose clips.*

5) Next, check delivery end (final) pressure. Using fingers, squeeze hose between tester and injection pump. If pump is working properly, pressure should be at least 15.6 psi (1.1 kg/cm²) at idle and at least 18.5 psi (1.3 kg/cm²) at 3000 RPM.

6) If pressure is lower than specified, either the valve requires replacing, or pump requires repair or replacement.

7) If pressure is higher than specified, and opening pressure of by-pass valve is greater than 11.4 psi (0.8 kg/cm²), remove, clean and check by-pass valve for leaks. Replace valve if necessary.

LEAKING FUEL LINE FITTINGS

If external fuel leakage occurs between pipe connection fitting (union) and adjusting plate of injection pump, install new "grooved" fittings. *See Fig. 13.*

Fig. 13 Old Style and New "Grooved" Style Connection Fittings (Unions)

BOSCH DIESEL INJECTION – MERCEDES-BENZ (Cont.)

1) If pump is equipped with non-grooved fittings, replace ALL fittings with new "grooved" fittings. If equipped with "grooved" fittings, replace only leaking fittings.

NOTE – *Do not loosen adjusting plate, as this would require recalibration of injection pump on a test stand.*

2) Whenever new fittings are installed or fittings are removed for any purpose, install new copper gaskets under delivery valve carriers. Grooved end of valve carrier should be installed downward. Reinstall other valve components previously removed.

3) Oil fitting threads and tighten to 29-36 ft. lbs. (4-5 mkg), using one continuous motion.

4) Install injection lines and operate hand primer until by-pass valve opens (audible sound). Run engine and check for further leaks.

DIESEL KNOCK

Diesel knock can be traced to mechanical causes, diesel fuel properties, or a combination of both. Knock is a pinging noise caused by excessive combustion pressure.

To eliminate or reduce knock, use fuel best suited for your area and check and correct the following:

- Beginning of fuel delivery to assure optimum compression temperature and air charge.
- Valve lash.
- Correct nozzle spray pattern and opening pressure.
- Reverse flow dampening valve for proper operation.
- Insufficient compression pressure (compression check and cylinder leak test).

CHECKING GLOW PLUGS

Glow plugs provide ignition during starting. Use dash-mounted indicator light to locate faulty glow plugs.

1) Hold starting switch key in preglow position "2". Using screwdriver, have assistant short plugs to ground, one at a time. Each plug should spark if working properly. When grounded in this manner indicator light should be "lit."

2) If light stays on, when ground is disconnected, a short to ground exists in system. Check for leads touching cylinder head and then for carbon-fouled plug electrodes.

3) If leads appear correct, turn key to preglow position "2". Disconnect one glow plug power lead at a time, starting from ground end. Indicator light will go out when faulty plug is disconnected.

4) Check grounding of glow plug bus bar. Be sure control rods do not rest against bus bar or glow plugs.

5) Remove glow plugs with special tool (617 589 00 03 00). Ream bores with suitable reamer (636 589 03 53 00). Prevent dust from entering prechamber by greasing reamer prior to use.

6) Visually check glow plugs for damage from burning, cracks, or foreign metallic particles. If glow plug is burned out, check next plug in circuit also, since a short between threaded glow plug body and outer electrode or between outer electrode and cylinder head may result from metallic particles.

7) Remove all dirt or deposits from threaded bore.

DEFECTIVE VACUUM CONTROL UNIT

On 5-cylinder 300D engine, engine oil can enter vacuum system through a defective diaphragm in the vacuum control unit. Sometimes vacuum pump has been mistakenly blamed. If complaints are received that engine does not shut off or shuts off with difficulty, check vacuum control unit first:

1) Remove brown and blue line from vacuum control unit. Check for traces of oil. If present, replace unit and oil-filled vacuum lines. Also repair vacuum pump and replace brake booster if oil is found at connecting fitting for vacuum line.

2) If no traces of oil are found at control unit or in vacuum lines, start engine and run at idle. Pull off brown vacuum line from "T" fitting between vacuum pump and brake booster. See *Fig. 10.* Check for vacuum. If none present, remove and check "T" fitting and clean with compressed air.

3) If vacuum is present, connect vacuum control unit directly to "T" fitting (by-pass the valve). Pump is now free to act directly upon diaphragm of control unit. If engine does not shut off immediately, replace control unit.

NOTE – *When installing new unit, be sure control linkage in pump governor is properly engaged and is not holding main rack in full-load position.*

4) If engine shuts off immediately, vacuum control unit is not to blame. Problem could then be jammed vacuum valve in steering lock.

5) Be sure all vacuum lines are connected as shown in *Fig. 10.* Start engine, check vacuum control unit, valve in steering lock and injection pump for leaks.

INJECTION TIMER DRIVE

240D and 300D engines have an injection timer drive installed in the end of intermediate gear shaft. Drive is now pressure-lubricated (previously splash-lubricated).

Use care in servicing engines, as bores in bearing bushing have been eliminated in new design. Never use a new injection timer and bearing bushing with earlier version intermediate gear shafts, since no oil would reach bearing bushing.

However, the new intermediate gear shaft may be used along with previous injection timer and bearing bushing. Never install only a bearing bushing separately.

BOSCH DIESEL INJECTION – MERCEDES-BENZ (Cont.)

REMOVAL AND INSTALLATION

FUEL INJECTION PUMP

Removal – 1) Remove battery and battery frame. Clean pump and fuel lines to prevent entrance of dirt into system. Disconnect all injection, vacuum, fuel and oil lines at injection pump. Plug injection lines and fuel hose unions at pump.

2) Detach connecting rods and all cables from pump.

3) Remove mounting nuts at rear support and front flange, using a 13 mm (45° rebent) box wrench. Lift injection pump rearward from crankcase.

NOTE – *If drive collar is to be replaced, observe markings on flange, collar, and pump shaft for reassembly reference.*

Installation – 1) Remove plug and fill injection pump with ½ pint of engine oil. Turn crankshaft in direction of rotation until 45° BTDC mark aligns with pointer. Piston of No. 1 cylinder must be in compression stroke.

2) Slide coupling sleeve onto drive collar of injection pump. Now, slide coupling forward onto drive shaft in crankcase.

3) Set injection pump to "start delivery" position by turning pump shaft until drive collar tooth gap aligns with pump shaft and pump flange marks. See Fig. 14.

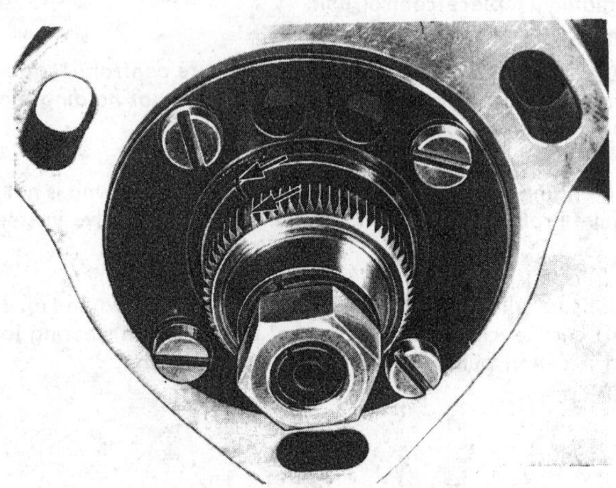

Fig. 14 Aligning Marks on Injection Pump Shaft Drive Collar and Flange

4) When applying light counterclockwise pressure (opposite direction of rotation) to drive collar, cam pressure action causes drive collar to jump back two teeth to cam base circle. Second tooth must then coincide with marking on injection pump housing.

NOTE – *Before installing pump, be sure piston of No. 1 cylinder is in compression stroke and crankshaft is 45° BTDC.*

5) Apply grease to either side of new paper gaskets and place gaskets on crankcase. Install injection pump in coupling sleeve. Be sure stud bolts are centrally positioned within slotted holes. This permits later alignment in either direction.

NOTE – *After aligning injection pump, there must be a clearance of 3.15" (80 mm) between crankcase and center of injection line fitting. This is to permit glow plug removal.*

6) Place washers in position and slightly tighten injection pump nuts.

NOTE – *Use special spacer washer (116 990 14 40) and M8 x 16 hex head screw to fasten rear support bracket.*

Checking for Start of Delivery

1) Turn crankshaft further in direction of rotation, until 24° BTDC mark aligns with pointer. Piston of No. 1 cylinder must again be in compression stroke position.

2) Screw out pipe connection fitting (union) of first pumping element and remove valve parts. Reinstall fitting and attach overflow pipe.

NOTE – *During test adjust control lever on injection pump to full throttle (full-load) position.*

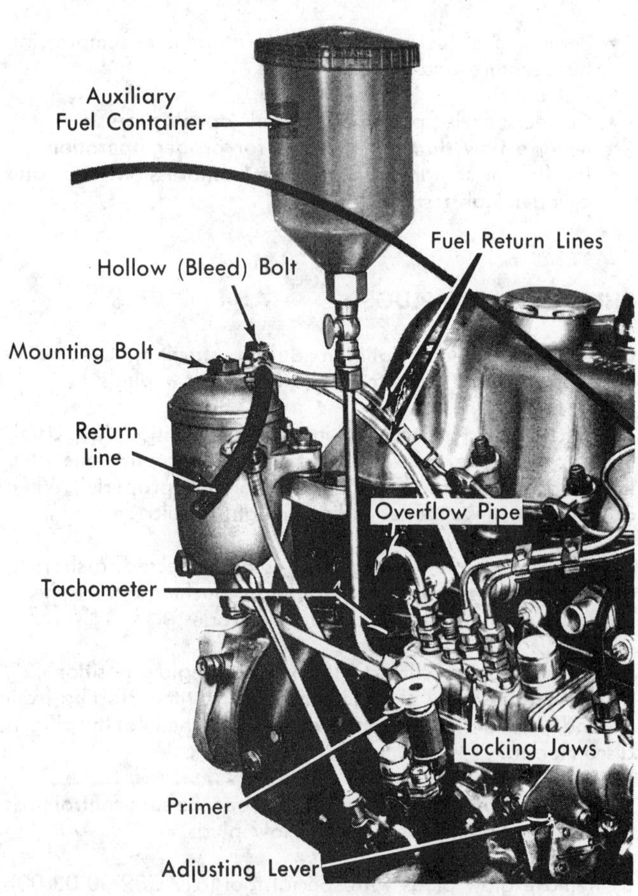

Fig. 15 Installing Auxiliary Fuel Container on Injection Pump (Typical)

BOSCH DIESEL INJECTION – MERCEDES-BENZ (Cont.)

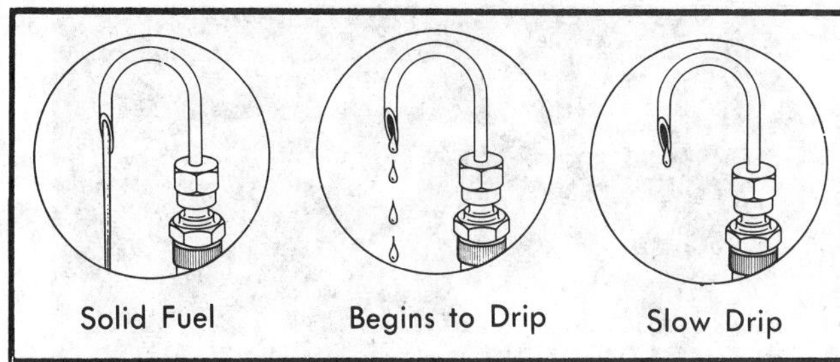

Fig. 16 Checking Fuel Dripping From Overflow Pipe

3) Connect auxiliary fuel container (000 589 05 23 00) to injection pump. See *Fig. 15.* Turn engine over slowly in normal direction of rotation until fuel stream from overflow pipe stops dripping. See *Fig. 16.*

NOTE – *Another drop may follow 10-15 seconds later, but this is normal.*

4) Start of delivery should occur when pipe stops dripping Crankshaft pointer should then be on 24° BTDC mark. Turn crankshaft two more full turns. Fuel should stop dripping again at end of second full turn. If so, tighten injection pump in this position.

5) If crankshaft position does not prove true, loosen injection pump mounting nuts and turn pump TOWARD engine to advance start of delivery and AWAY FROM engine to retard start of delivery. When adjustment is correct, tighten mounting nuts of pump and recheck position.

6) Remove overflow pipe and connection fitting (union). Reinstall valve parts using new gasket. Tighten fitting to 29-36 ft. lbs. (4-5 mkg) in one continuous motion. Remove auxiliary fuel container.

7) Connect all fuel, vacuum and lubricating oil lines. Install all control rods, cables, and other parts previously removed. Adjust as necessary.

8) Bleed fuel system and install battery and battery frame. Bring engine to operating temperature. Check all connections for leaks. Check idle speed and adjust as necessary. See *ADJUSTMENTS.*

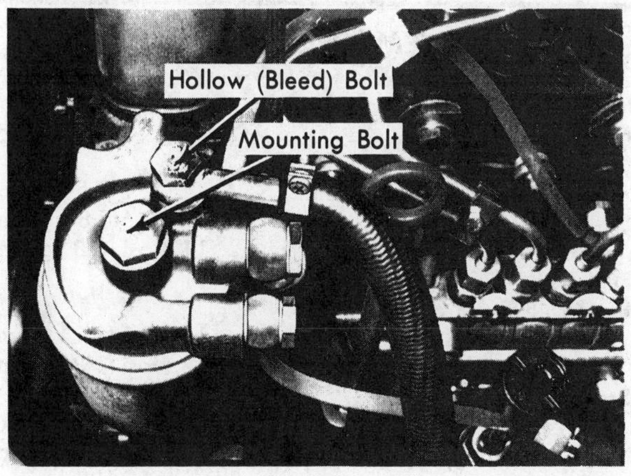

Fig. 17 Removing, Installing and Bleeding Fuel Filter

FUEL FILTER

Every 37,500 miles, the main fuel filter and lower housing should be replaced. Loosen mounting bolt. See *Fig. 17.* Pull downward on one-piece element and lower housing.

Install new lower housing and element. Tighten mounting bolt. After installation, bleed fuel filter and fuel injection pump.

Bleeding Fuel Filter

Loosen hollow bolt. See *Fig. 17.* Pump hand primer pump until fuel emerges free of bubbles. Retighten hollow bolt.

Bleeding Injection Pump

Pump hand primer until by-pass valve on injection pump opens. You will hear a buzzing sound when this occurs. Run engine and check for leaks.

VACUUM CONTROL UNIT

Removal – **1)** Unscrew lower right-hand mounting screw from vacuum control unit. See *Fig. 18.*

Fig. 18 Removing and Installing Vacuum Control Unit

2) Depress "stop" lever on cylinder head cover. Measure position of main rack by inserting punch into screw bore until it touches main rack. Mark this position on punch.

3) Unscrew remaining three mounting screws and remove control unit.

Installation – **1)** Install new gasket and steel ring. Make sure tang on vacuum control unit engages in main rack. Install last three mounting screws removed.

2) Insert punch in lower right-hand screw bore. Check main rack position with mark on punch. When punch touches main rack, press lightly on punch and move control lever on injection pump from "stop" position to "full load" stop. Punch must follow the main rack smoothly. If correct, install remaining screw.

BOSCH DIESEL INJECTION – MERCEDES-BENZ (Cont.)

AUTOMATIC ALTITUDE COMPENSATING DEVICE

NOTE – *Do not attempt to remove upper cover of governor housing. Governor linkage is assembled to altitude compensating device.*

Removal – Hold altitude compensating device by small nut, while loosening larger nut. See *Fig. 19*. Unscrew altitude compensating device and remove shims.

Installation – Using previously removed shims, screw compensating device into place. Be sure vent tube is positioned at lowest point to drain off any possible condensation. Hold small nut and tighten large nut.

Fig. 19 Removing and Installing Automatic Altitude Compensating Device

ADJUSTMENTS

IDLE SPEED AND IDLE SPEED REGULATOR

1) Check throttle linkage for free movement and wear. Run engine until oil temperature reaches 140-176° F (60-80° C). Turn idle speed regulator knob on dashboard as far as it will go. Distance between collar and spring should be .040" (1.0 mm). *See Fig. 20*. Adjust as necessary, making sure spring is properly adjusted.

2) Depress "stop" lever. *See Fig. 11*. Bowden cable of cruise control should rest tension-free against bell crank. If necessary, adjust cable with adjusting nut. Release "stop" lever. Cable should have play.

3) Disconnect control rod at bell crank lever. Check idle speed with tachometer. Loosen lock nut. *See Figs. 3 and 4*. Using adjusting screw, adjust idle speed to 650-750 RPM. Reconnect control rod free of tension. Adjust throttle linkage, if necessary.

4) Place automatic transmission selector lever in a driving position. Turn on air conditioner and turn power steering to full lock position. Engine must run smoothly. If necessary, readjust idle speed.

5) Depress accelerator pedal slightly. Simultaneously, turn idle speed regulator knob counterclockwise to "stop." Release accelerator pedal. Engine speed should be 1000-1100 RPM. If necessary, readjust idle speed by turning adjusting screw.

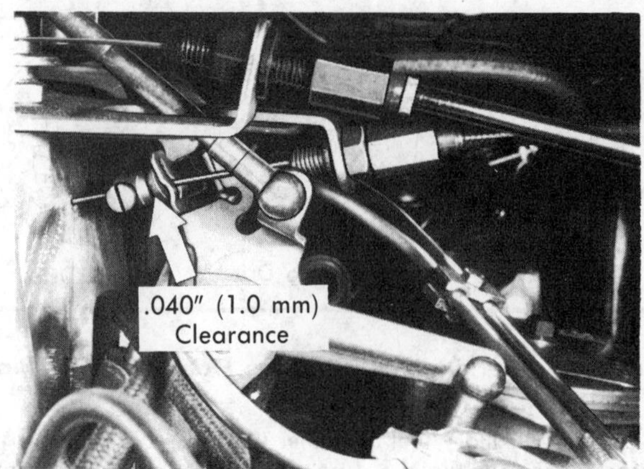

Fig. 20 Measuring Distance Between Collar and Spring

6) Let engine run for a short period. If engine speed increases by itself, reduce engine speed with adjusting screw.

CAUTION – *If engine speed is adjusted higher, it will be above controlled idle speed range of governor. Engine speed could automatically increase up to maximum RPM (without load).*

TIGHTENING SPECIFICATION

Application	Ft. Lbs. (mkg)
Rocker Arm Cover	3.6 (0.5)
Glow Plugs	36.0 (5.0)
Precombustion Chamber	118.5 (16.5)
Nozzle-to-Holder	54.0 (7.5)
Nozzle Holder-to-Head	54.0 (7.5)
Nozzle Holder Connector	54.0 (7.5)
Injection Pump Shaft Nut	50.6 (7.0)
Connecting Fitting (Union)	29.0-36.0 (4.0-5.0)
Injection Pipe Cap Nuts	18.0 (2.5)

SYSTEM SPECIFICATIONS

Idle Speed	650-750 RPM
Fuel Pump Delivery Pressure	
Idle Speed	8.5-11.4 psi (0.6-0.8 kg/cm^2)
3000 RPM	11.4 psi (0.8 kg/cm^2)
Fuel Pump Final Delivery Pressure	
Idle Speed	15.6 psi (1.1 kg/cm^2)
3000 RPM	18.5 psi (1.3 kg/cm^2)
Start of Delivery	24° BTDC (In Compression Stroke)
Nozzle Opening Pressure	1635-1750 psi (115-123 kg/cm^2)

BOSCH DIESEL INJECTION – PEUGEOT

Peugeot 504 Diesel

DESCRIPTION

Peugeot diesel injection system consists of a fuel filter which incorporates a priming pump, Bosch rotary type injection pump, Peugeot deferred injection device, four injectors and four glow plugs. The rotary pump incorporates a single piston feed pump, a hydraulically controlled automatic advance and a speed regulator which acts as a governor. The fuel filter incorporates a by-pass circuit with vapor seperating cartridge and hand operated priming pump. The injectors incorporate a fuel return line as well as fuel feed line. The glow plug system incorporates an indicator light on the instrument panel to signal when to start the engine.

TESTING

FUEL CIRCUIT

NOTE – *Following test should be performed whenever engine stalls or runs irratically at idle speed, when engine lacks power or whenever fuel circuit is suspected as being cause of improper engine operation.*

1) Use a clear nylon tube 4" (100 mm) long with inside diameter of .32" (8 mm), two hose clamps and copper tube 1" (25 mm) long with outside diameter of .32" (8 mm). Remove fuel inlet hose from injection pump inlet fitting. Insert clear tube over injection pump inlet fitting. Insert one end of copper tube into fuel inlet hose and other end into clear tube. Secure hose connections with hose clamps.

Fig. 1 Testing Fuel Circuit

2) Start engine and watch clear tubing. Bubbles in fuel should not appear until engine reaches 3000 RPM. If bubbles appear at idle or speeds below 3000 RPM, it will be necessary to conduct further tests to determine where fuel system is admitting air.

3) If air is present at idle or speeds below 3000 RPM, shut off engine and move clear tubing to inlet side of fuel filter. Again run engine to determine presence of air bubbles in fuel system. If air is still present, continue testing as outlined until air leak is discovered. Repair air leak and bleed system.

INJECTORS

NOTE – *Injectors can only be checked with special equipment furnished either by manufacturer of vehicle or manufacturer of injector.*

If an injector is being replaced, make sure both the new injector and its holder are correct for that particular engine and pump.

REMOVAL & INSTALLATION

NOTE – *The following procedure can only be performed using special tools as indicated.*

INJECTION PUMP

Removal – **1)** Disconnect the battery and turn ignition switch to "ON" (or "Marche") position. On top of injection pump, disconnect stop control cable, fast idle control cable, and accelerator control cable. Remove rubber hose connected to top of injection pump.

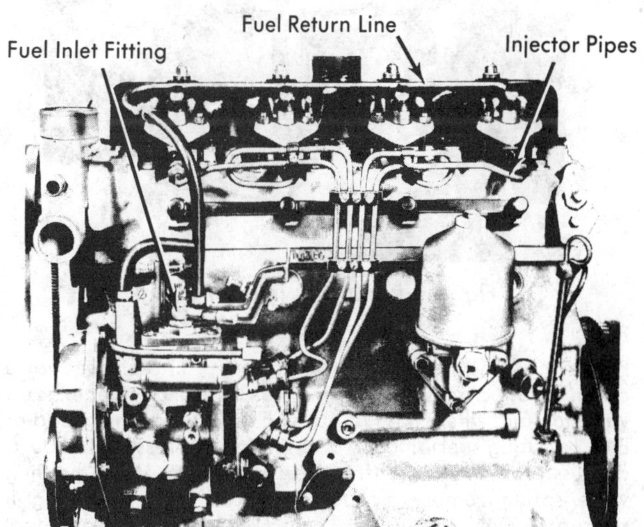

Fig. 2 Injection System with Control Cable Removed

Fig. 3 Pump with Injector Pipes Removed

BOSCH DIESEL INJECTION – PEUGEOT (Cont.)

2) Remove fuel inlet hose and outlet couplings from injection pump. Remove complete injector pipe assembly, leave couplings on pump and injector holder (on head) and plug or cap all couplings. Remove pump rear support from cylinder block.

3) On pump driven by timing **chain**, use special Allen wrench (8.0117 D) to remove two screws holding pump to timing cover. On pump driven by timing **gears**, remove bolt and two screws holding pump intermediate flange to timing gear housing. On lower screw use 6 mm Allen wrench. To remove pump, move it backward while pivoting it toward engine.

Fig. 4 Removing Injector Pump

Preparing Engine For Installation – 1) Remove valve cover. Rotate crankshaft to bring No. 1 (rear) cylinder exhaust valve to point where it is just opening (exhaust opening lead or E.O. L.). Using special tool (valve spring compressor) 8.0105 Y, depress No. 4 cylinder (front) exhaust valve. While holding valve spring compressed, remove rocker arm by sliding it rearward with the valve contact face up. Release tool pressure. **NOTE** – *Do not pull upward on push-rod.*

Fig. 5 Removing Rocker Arm of No. 4 Exhaust

2) Now bring No. 1 (rear) piston up to point where intake valve is just opening and exhaust valve is just closing. Using special tool 8.0105 Y, again compress No. 4 cylinder exhaust valve and remove valve keepers. Release tool pressure. **NOTE** – *Make sure that valve moves freely and allow it to rest on top of piston.* Remove glow plug connector bar and remove No. 3 and No. 4 cylinder glow plugs.

3) On front rocker-valve cover stud, attach G1 support from special tool kit 8.0110 GY. From same tool kit, assemble support A1 onto support A2. Slide this assembly over top of G1 support and attach dial indicator (8.1504). Place actuating foot of dial indicator on top of No. 4 cylinder exhaust valve.

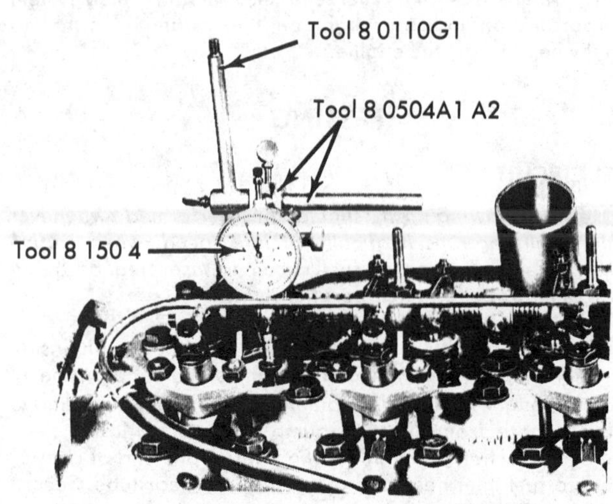

Fig. 6 Preparing Engine for Installation of Pump

Calibrate (set) dial indicator to zero at TDC. Rotate crankshaft **counterclockwise** until **dial indicator** has completed four complete turns. Now rotate crankshaft in normal direction of rotation (clockwise) until dial indicator gives reading (see table) to correspond with particular pump to be installed.

Valve Setting BTDC

Application①	Specification In. (mm)
EP/VM AR5-7-8	.055 (1.40)
EP/VM AR10-12	.057 (1.46)
EP/VA CR 173	.020 (.51)

① – Pump designation number.

Preparing EP/VM Pump For Installation – 1) On injection pump, install drive gear and tighten torque attaching bolt to 47 ft. lbs. (6.5 m/kg). **NOTE** – *On pumps driven by timing gear (as opposed to chain) make sure two Allen screws fastening pump on support flange are centered in slotted holes.*

2) Use copper gasket and install adapter support screw of special tool 6.0168 into fuel inlet of injection pump. Insert probe (under tension) of special tool 6.0168 into pump body through support screw. Use 3 mm Allen wrench to tighten tool on support screw.

BOSCH DIESEL INJECTION – PEUGEOT (Cont.)

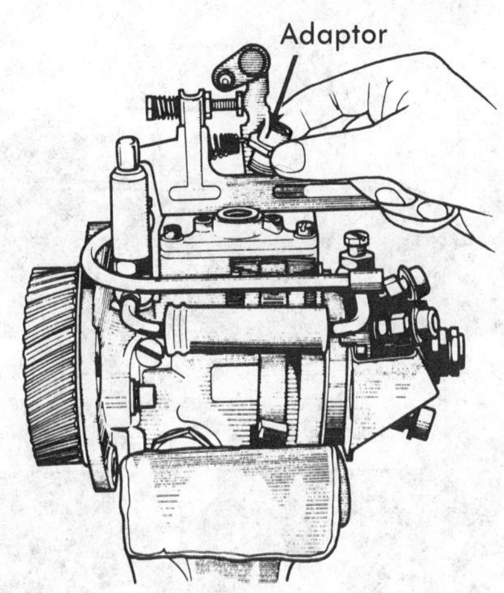

Fig. 7 Installing Adaptor on EP/VM Pump

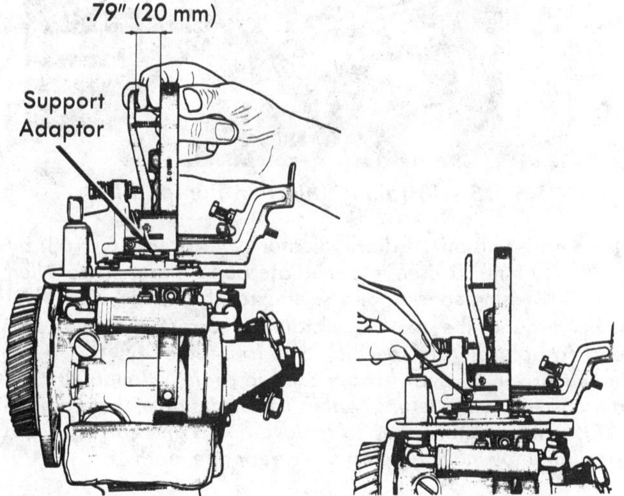

Fig. 8 Fitting Special Tool EP/VM Pump

3) Install dial indicator (special tool 8.0117 A) onto top of special tool (see illustration). Check that spring loaded handle (which touches dial indicator) has free movement.

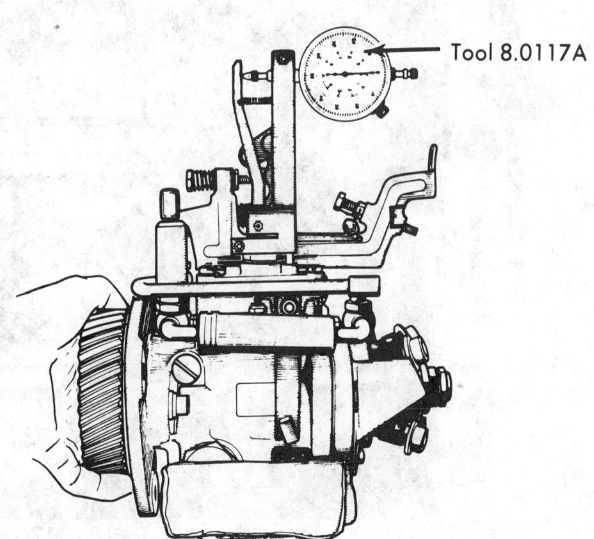

Fig. 9 Installing Special Dial Indicator

4) On pumps which are installed on engine with chain timing gears, center double-toothed side of gear with No. 4 outlet coupling (see illustration).

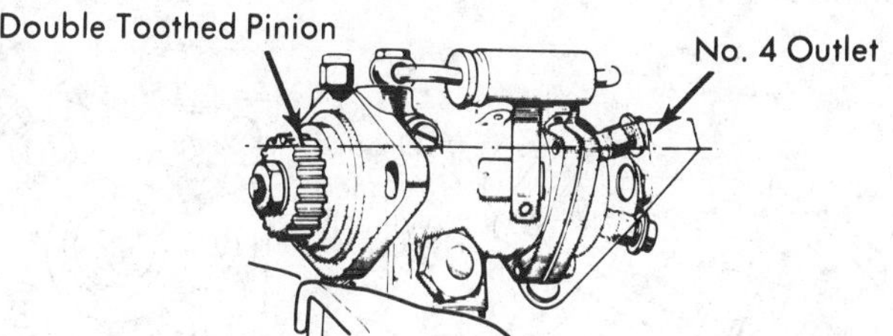

Fig. 10 Chain Driven Injection Pump

5) On pumps which are installed on engines with timing gears, center timing mark (dot on face of gear) with axis of outlet coupling marked "D" (see illustration).

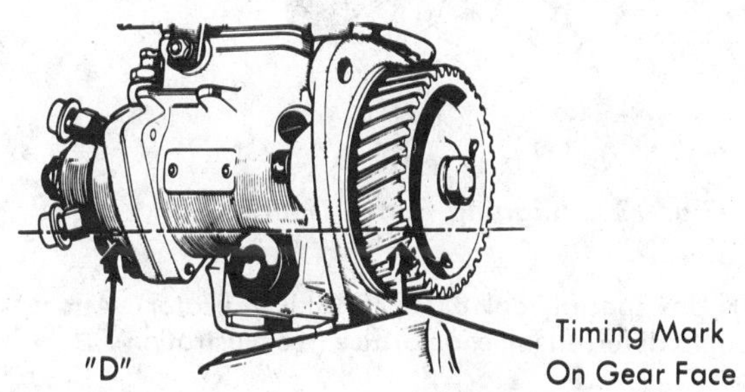

Fig. 11 Gear Driven Injection Pump

6) On all pumps, set dial indicator to zero at BDC. This is accomplished by moving drive gear back and forth until lowest reading is obtained and then zeroing dial indicator. Now rotate drive gear in direction of normal rotation until exact instant where dial indicator begins to register start of upstroke (approximately .0008" or .02 mm).

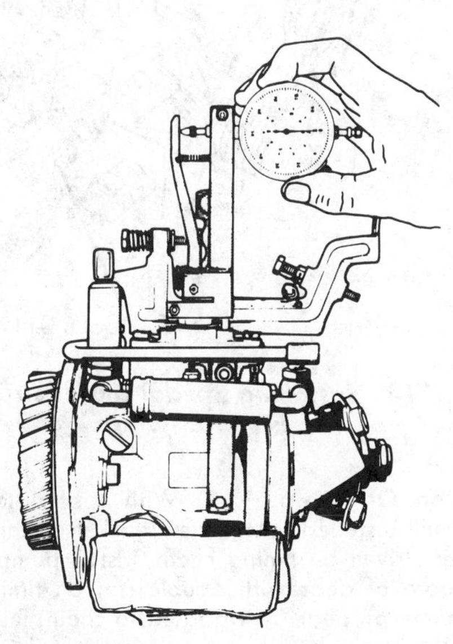

Fig. 12 Setting Special Dial Indicator

BOSCH DIESEL INJECTION – PEUGEOT (Cont.)

Preparing EP/VAC Pump For Installation – **1**) Remove deferred injection accumulator. Rotate pump drive shaft to bring pump piston timing groove opposite discharge connection marked "B".

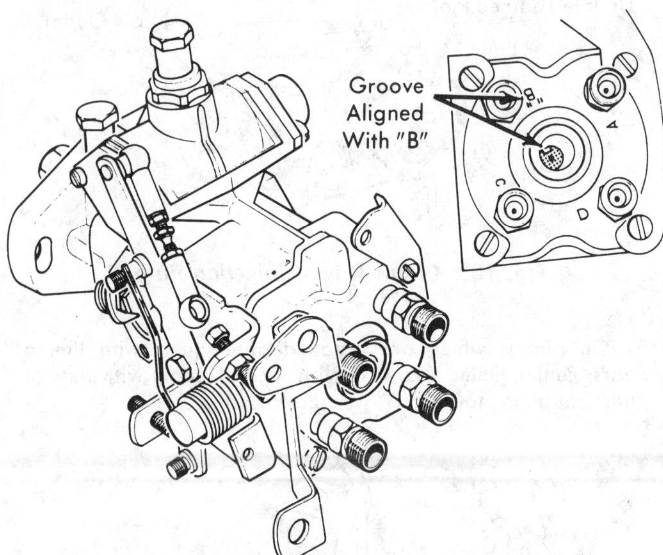

Fig. 13 Aligning Pump Timing Marks on EP/VAC

2) Use special tool 8.0117F (dial indicator). Attach special tool to deferred injection orifice (see illustration).

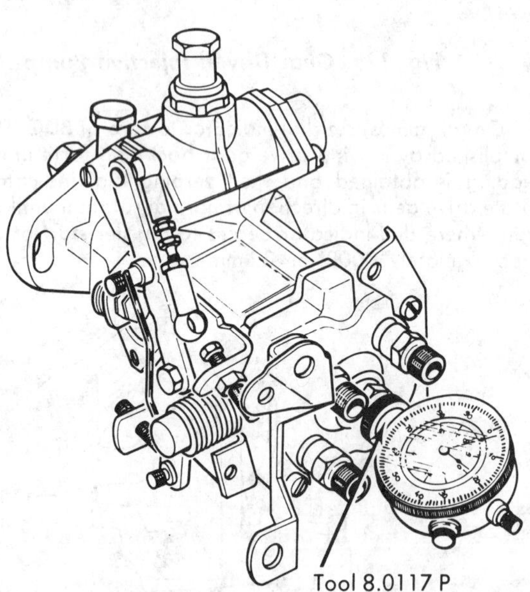

Fig. 14 Installing Special Dial Indicator on EP/VAC Pump

Installation Of Pump – **1**) With special tools (dial indicators) still installed, install new gasket on injection pump. On pumps driven by timing chain, install pump by aligning double tooth of gear with double slot on timing gear. On pumps driven by gear (as opposed to chain) install pump by applying slight outward rotation to pump body as pump is inserted into timing case flange. Tighten bolts holding pump assembly to timing case flange.

Fig. 15 Installing Injection Pump (All)

2) Release tension on dial indicator (special tool 6.0168) by .157" (4.0 mm). Loosen intermediate pump flange (two Allen screws) by using special long Allen wrench (8.0117 D). Swivel pump around it's axis to obtain a correct dial indicator reading according to specific pump (see table). **NOTE** – *On models driven by gear (as opposed to chain), if unable to obtain correct pump setting within limits of slotted hole adjustment, it will be necessary to remove pump and correct pump installation by moving pump drive gear one tooth.*

Fig. 16 Adjusting Injection Pump Timing

BOSCH DIESEL INJECTION — PEUGEOT (Cont.)

Pump Setting

Application	In. (mm)
EP/VM AR 5 & 7	.0148 (.38)
EP/VM AR 8, 10 & 12	.0215 (.55)
EP/VA CR 173	.0253 (.65)

3) To recheck pump setting, bring engine up to TDC and check that engine dial indicator reading is zero. Now rotate engine in opposite direction of rotation (**counterclockwise**) until engine dial indicator has completed **exactly seven** revolutions. **NOTE** — *During last revolution, pump dial indicator should be in BDC range and reading zero.* Now rotate engine in normal direction and check that engine and pump dial indicator settings are correct for that particular pump (see table).

Fig. 17 Rechecking Pump Setting

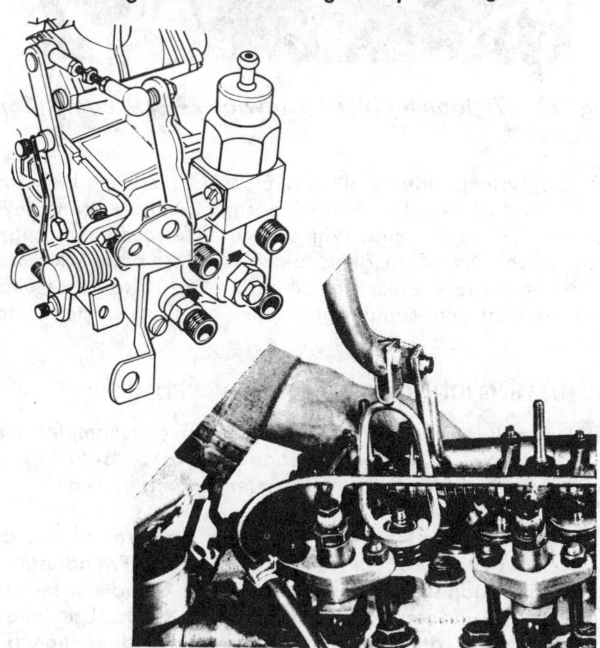

Fig. 18 Installing Rocker Arm on No. 4 Exhaust

Timing Specifications

Application	①Piston Setting BTDC In. (mm)	②Pump Lift In. (mm)
EP/VM AR 5 & 7	.055 (1.40)	.0148 (.38)
EP/VM AR 8	.055 (1.40)	.0215 (.55)
EP/VM 10 & 12	.057 (1.46)	.0215 (.55)
EP/VA CR 173	.020 (.51)	.0253 (.65)

① — Reading on engine dial indicator.

② — Reading on pump dial indicator.

4) Bring engine to TDC and remove all tools. On EP/VAC pumps, install deferred injection accumulator using two new sealing washers. Tighten accumulator to 36 ft. lbs. (5 mkg). Using special tool (spring compressor) 8.0105 Y, install valve spring with keepers. Rotate crankshaft **counterclockwise** until No. 1 (rear) cylinder exhaust valve just begins to open. Move rocker arm forward tilting valve contact face downward (normal position). With rocker arm correctly positioned above exhaust valve, release tool 8.0105 Y pressure and remove tool.

5) Check valve clearances of engine and readjust if necessary. Install and connect all equipment removed on disassembly. With reassembly complete, bleed fuel system to remove all trapped air.

INJECTOR

NOTE — *Cleanliness is of utmost importance when working with injectors. Before removing injector holder from engine, clean area around injector holder.*

Removal — Disconnect battery and remove injector pressure pipe. Disconnect fuel return line. Remove flange, injector holder and gasket. **NOTE** — *If replacing injector, it is of extreme importance that correct injector for that engine-injection pump combination, be used.*

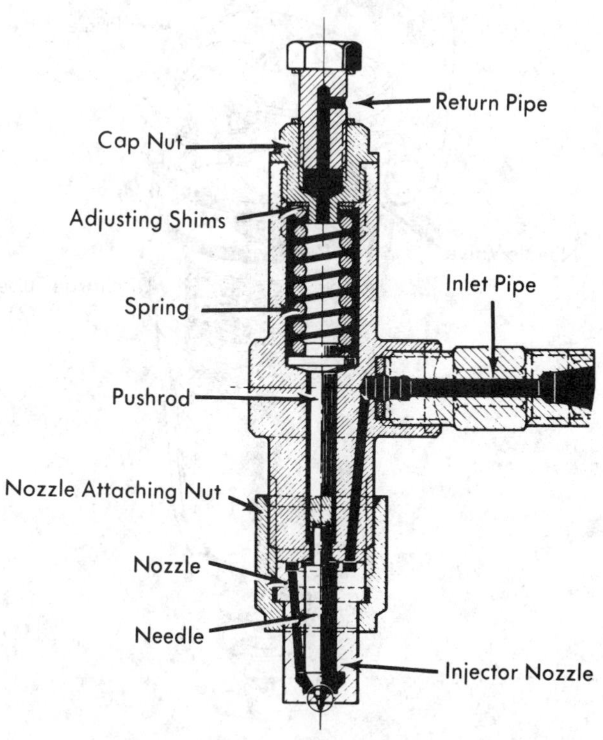

Fig. 19 Injector Assembly

BOSCH DIESEL INJECTION – PEUGEOT (Cont.)

Installation – Use new copper gasket (PD 1981.05) and position flange on injector holder. **NOTE** – *Do not tighten.* Screw injector pipe couplings on by hand, first on pump then on injector holder. Lightly tighten couplings on pump and injector to 18 ft. lbs. (2.5 mkg) Tighten flange nuts to 14 ft. lbs. (2.0 mkg). Connect return pipe. **NOTE** – *In event of leaky coupling, do not tighten further. Unscrew coupling and retighten to specifications.*

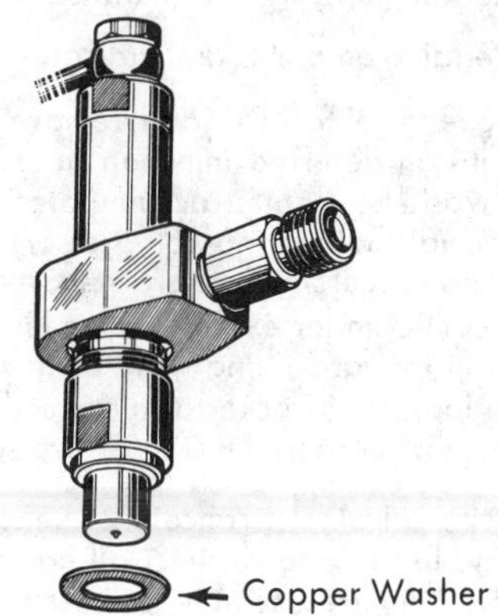

Fig. 20 Injector Holder

MAINTENANCE & ADJUSTMENTS

BLEEDING SYSTEM

On top of fuel filter, loosen needle valve and actuate primer lever. Tighten needle valve when water has drained through drain tube. Loosen air bleed screw and actuate lever. When resistence is felt, tighten air bleed screw.

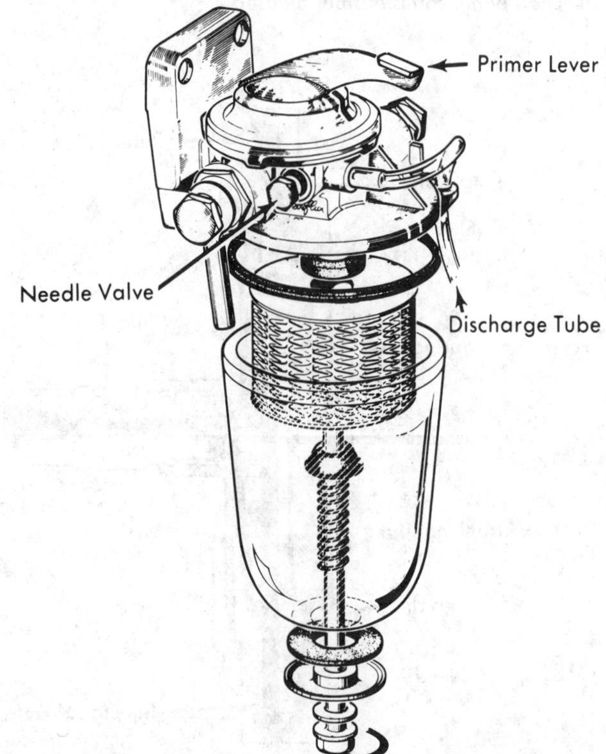

Fig. 21 Fuel Filter Assembly

PRIMING SYSTEM

1) On both EP/VM and EP/VAC pump systems, loosen needle valve (1) on top of fuel filter. Actuate primer lever (2) until fuel flows through discharge tube (3). Tighten needle valve. Loosen air bleed screw (4). Again actuate primer lever until resistence is felt, then tighten bleed screw (4).

Fig. 22 Priming Pump (Top of Fuel Filter)

2) On systems equipped with EP/VM pumps, loosen injection pump bleed screw and actuate pump lever until fuel flows bubble free. Tighten bleed screw on top of injection pump.

Fig. 23 Tightening Bleed Screw on EP/VM Pump (Top)

3) On systems equipped with EP/VAC pumps, place stop lever (on dash panel) in "STOP" position. Acutate primer lever (on filter) 30 or 40 times. With stop lever released, switch ignition switch "ON". Turn idling control (on dash panel) clockwise to maximum idle. Press starter button for 10 to 15 seconds, then preheat until signal light comes on. Press starter button again.

ADJUSTING IDLING SPEED ON EP/VM PUMPS

NOTE – *It is necessary to use friction drive tachometer, such as Jaegar No. 42.839 with friction disc No. 87.645. To read corrected idle RPM, divide tachometer reading by two.*

1) With engine at normal operating temperature, release accelerator cable. Loosen lock nut on fast idle RPM adjustment and loosen adjusting screw several turns. On idle speed adjustment rod, loosen lock nut on front of pump. Use Jaegar tachometer (or other friction tachometer) with friction disc applied to fan drive belt.

BOSCH DIESEL INJECTION – PEUGEOT (Cont.)

Fig. 24 Idle Adjustment on EP Pump

2) Adjust idle speed to 730 RPM by turning idle adjustment rod (3). Unscrew fast idle speed adjusting screw until engine speed increases. Tighten fast idle stop screw one turn and tighten lock nut. Secure accelerator cable ensuring that pedal travel corresponds to full depression of lever (4).

3) On dash panel, turn fast idel control cable to minimum position and connect fast idling control cable by bottoming cable clamp against slide link. **NOTE** – *Never use fast idle stop screw to adjust idle speed.*

ADJUSTING IDLING SPEED ON EP/VAC PUMPS

NOTE – *Idling adjustment is accomplished under setting of deferred injection device.*

ADJUSTING DEFERRED INJECTION DEVICE ON EP/VM PUMPS

1) With engine at normal operating temperature, turn idle control on dash panel to minimum position. Disconnect link rod where it connects to deferred injection accumulator lever. Push accumulator lever to fully open position (minimum engine speed). Adjust idle speed to 730 RPM with .08" (2.0 mm) throttle lever free travel.

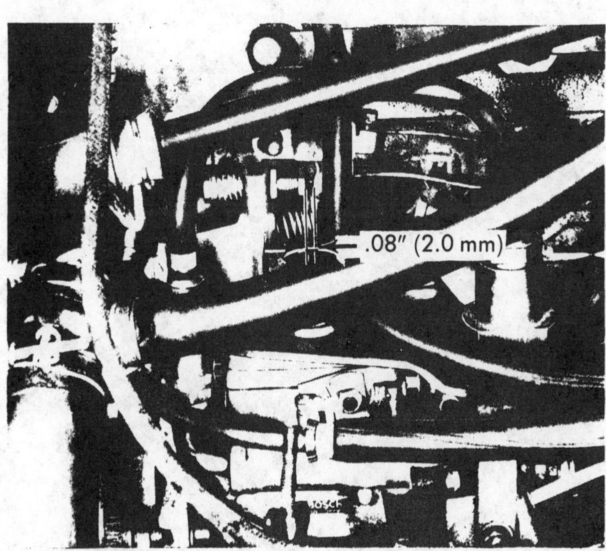

Fig. 25 Throttle Stop Adjustment on EP Pump

2) Push accumulator lever back toward accumulator until engine speed just begins to increase. This point is easily ascertained by increase in engine noise. Adjust length of link rod so that it just attaches to accumulator lever at point where engine speed begins to increase. **NOTE** – *Correct adjustment will be evident by existence of .039" (1.0 mm) clearance between throttle stop and throttle lever.*

Fig. 26 Accumulator Initial Operation Adjustment on EP/VM

3) Correct position can also be determined by running characteristics of engine. If link is too long, accumulator is out of circuit. If link is too short, engine speed is increased at idle, vehicle will have poor acceleration and exhaust will exhibit smoke.

ADJUSTING DEFERRED INJECTION DEVICE ON EP/VAC PUMPS

1) With engine at normal operating temperature, place idle control on dash panel in minimum position. Loosen lock nuts on accumulator rod and disconnect accumulator rod at accumulator actuating lever. Push accumulator lever to full open position (which is evident by minimum engine speed). Adjust idle stop screw to obtain idle speed of 730 RPM.

2) Move accumulator lever toward (b) accumulator until engine speed just begins to increase. This position is also evident by increase in engine noise. Mark one side of center adjusting nut on acutator rod (see illustration). Adjust length of rod to allow installation of rod end on accumulator lever without changing position of accumulator actuating lever. **NOTE** – *One complete turn of adjusting nut equals about .08" (2.0 mm).*

BOSCH DIESEL INJECTION – PEUGEOT (Cont.)

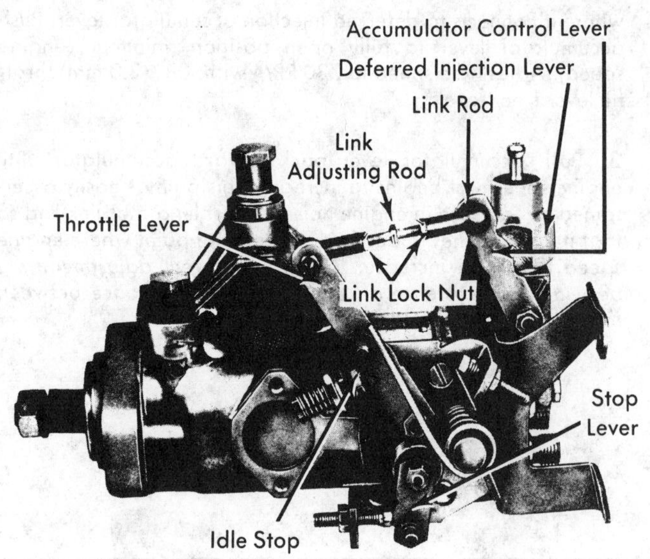

Fig. 27 Adjustments on EP/VAC Pump

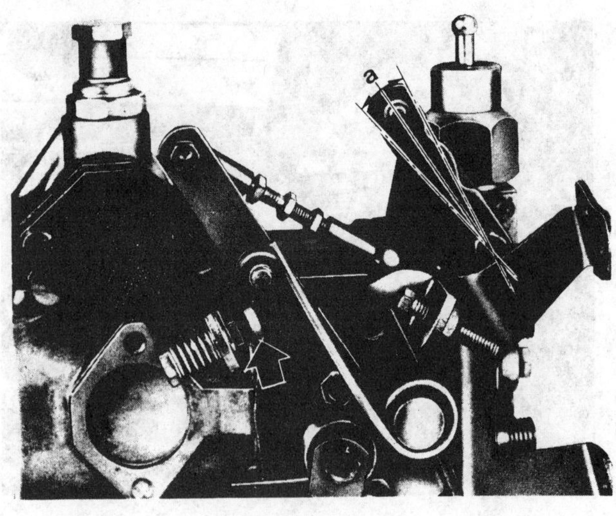

Fig. 28 Adjusting EP/VAC Accumulator

BOSCH DIESEL INJECTION – VOLKSWAGEN

Volkswagen Rabbit

DESCRIPTION

Fuel injection system (*Figs. 1 and 2*) consists of the following components:

- Fuel tank.
- Fuel filter.
- Distributor-type injection pump.
- Glow plugs.
- Throttle pintle injection nozzles.
- Car application speed governor.

A vane-type fuel pump, built into the injection pump, supplies fuel from tank to fuel filter to injection pump. Injection pump supplies fuel to nozzles under high pressure, according to 1-3-4-2 firing sequence. Excess fuel is returned to fuel tank by return lines.

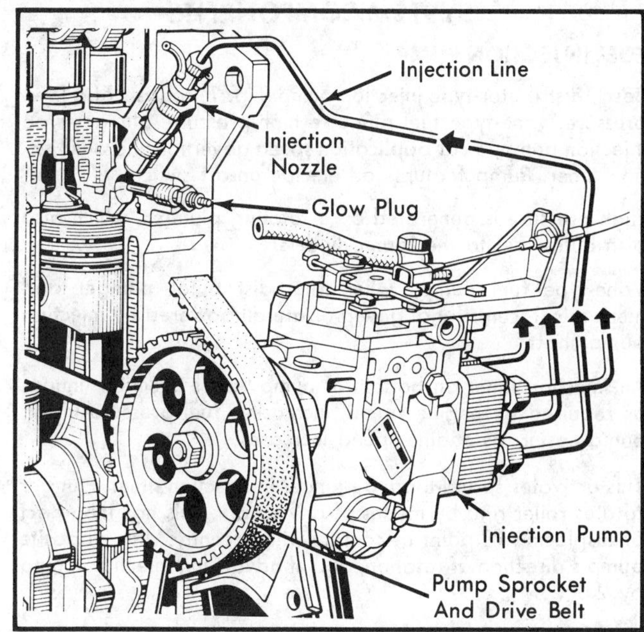

Fig. 2 Fuel System Components for Volkswagen Diesel

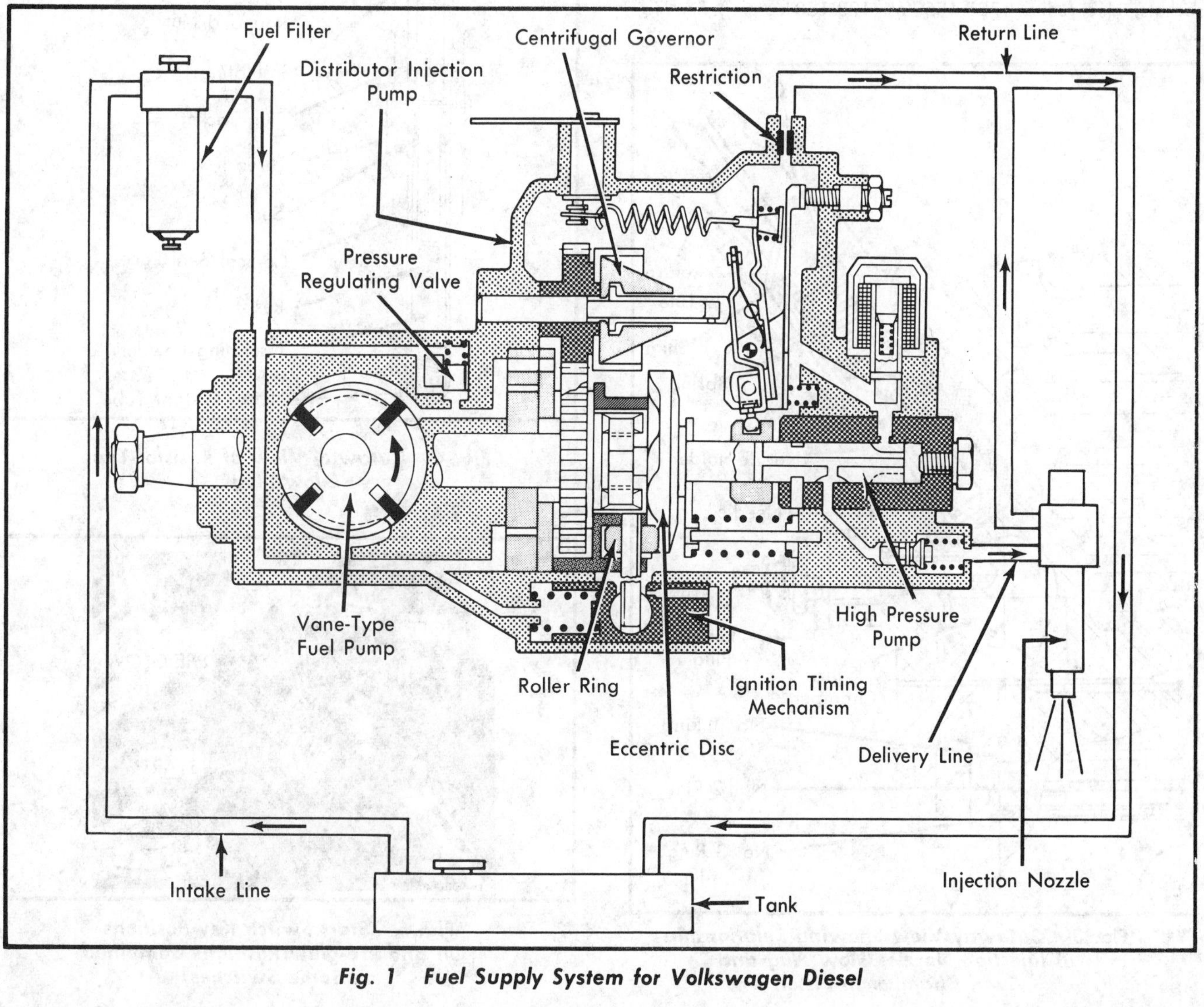

Fig. 1 Fuel Supply System for Volkswagen Diesel

BOSCH DIESEL INJECTION – VOLKSWAGEN (Cont.)

SYSTEM COMPONENTS

FUEL INJECTION PUMP

Bosch distributor-type injection pump (*Fig. 1*) consists of a low-pressure, vane-type fuel pump, a high-pressure, plunger-type injection pump, a car application speed governor and an injection timer. Pump features an electric on-off switch.

High pressure is generated by a rotating plunger, which also distributes fuel to the four cylinders.

Vane-type fuel pump, roller ring, distributor plunger and mechanical, centrifugal governor are all powered by injection pump shaft.

An injection timer on bottom of pump varies injection timing, as required by engine speed, increasing fuel pressure inside pump casing as engine speed increases.

This activates spring-loaded plunger in injection timer. Plunger rotates roller ring by means of driving pin. This has the effect of displacing its point of contact with eccentric disc, opposite pump's direction of rotation, and of advancing injection timing by 2.5°.

INJECTION NOZZLES

Bosch DNOSD 193 injection nozzles, mounted in KDA SD 27/4 sockets, inject fuel at 1700-1850 psi (123-130 kg/cm²). *See Fig. 3.*

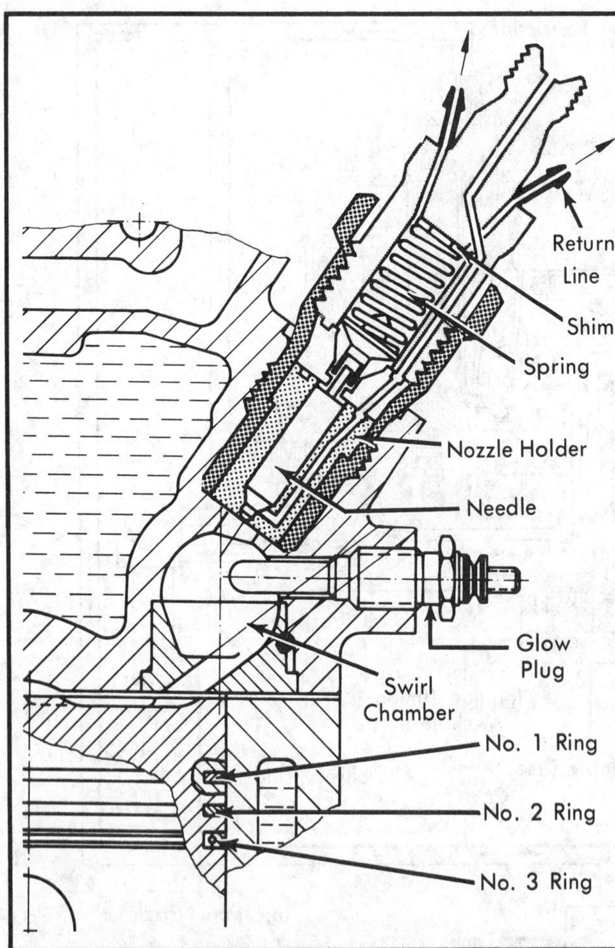

Fig. 3 Cutaway View Showing Relationship of Injection Nozzle, Glow Plug and Swirl Chamber to Piston

A pressurized mist of fuel is injected into a round swirl chamber. Fuel swirls around chamber, mixing with hot air, compressed at a 23:1 ratio.

Combustion begins in rich swirl chamber, continues on through small passageway, and into leaner, main chamber. As peak cylinder pressures build in swirl chamber, rather than main chamber, loads on connecting rods and crankshaft are reduced.

GLOW PLUGS

Fast, easy starting is assured by resistor-type glow plugs, installed in swirl chambers. *See Figs. 3 and 4.* Glow plugs have stubby-finger design rather than wire-type design used on many Diesel engines. Heat is applied to swirling fuel upon injection.

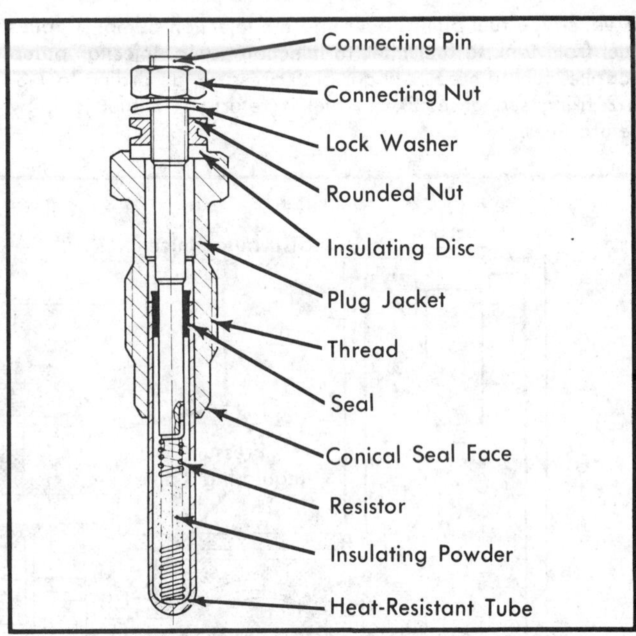

Fig. 4 Cutaway View of Resistor-Type Glow Plug

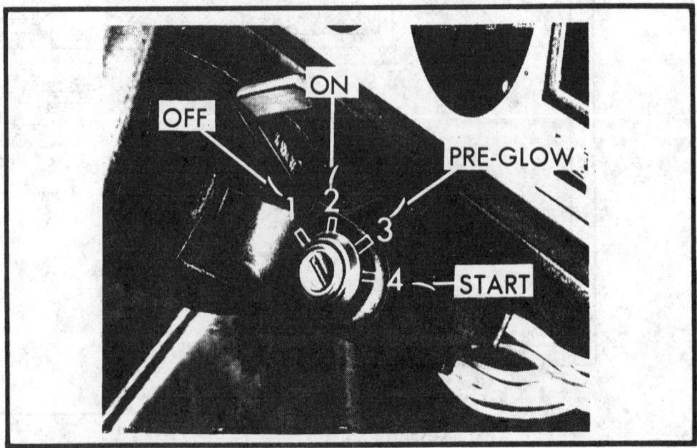

Fig. 5 Start Switch Key Positions (On and Pre-glow Positions Combined on Some Switches)

BOSCH DIESEL INJECTION – VOLKSWAGEN (Cont.)

To start a cold engine, pull out cold start knob, located left of steering column. Turn start switch key to pre-glow position. See *Fig. 5*.

NOTE – *Some switches combine the on and pre-glow positions.*

Glow plug light on dash will come on. When light goes out (approximately 15 seconds in warm climates; 60 seconds in cold), turn key to start position.

NOTE – *When temperature is below freezing, accelerator must be fully depressed during starting. Pre-glowing is not necessary if engine is already warm.*

After engine starts and runs for two minutes, push cold start knob fully inward. To stop engine, turn key to off position.

CAR APPLICATION SPEED GOVERNOR

A mechanical, car application speed governor provides acceleration similar to a well-groomed spark ignition engine. See *Figs. 1 and 6*. Low speed range of modified part-load governor was expanded to also govern maximum engine speed.

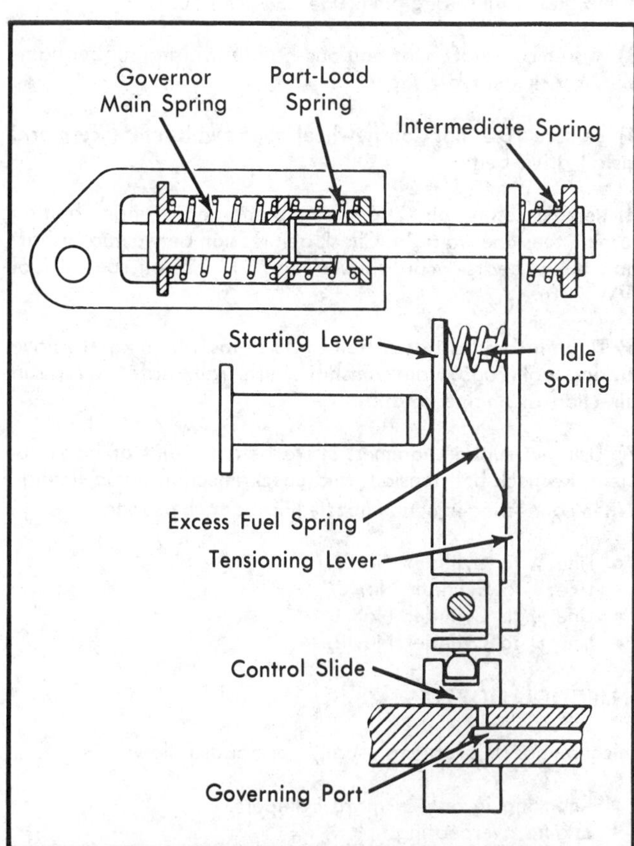

Fig. 6 Position and Function of Springs in Mechanical Car Application Speed Governor

When operating at low speeds, governor assures smooth load absorption on starting.

Governor operates at starting, idling, and full-load ranges. At part-load speed range, governor has no effect, the injection pump being controlled directly by the accelerator.

Operating range is determined by type of springs used and geometry of governor levers. See *Fig. 6*.

FUEL FILTER

Early model fuel filters were equipped with hand primer pump and vent screw for bleeding fuel system. See *Fig. 7*.

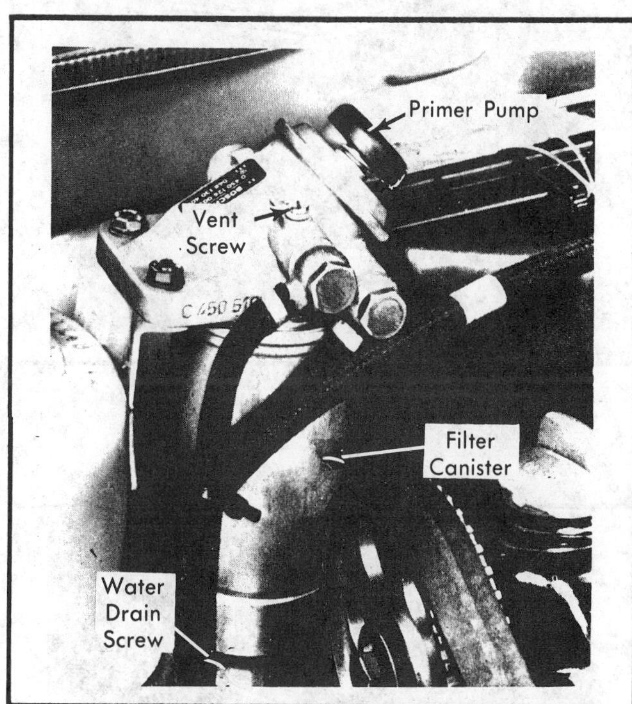

Fig. 7 Early Model Fuel Filter With Primer Pump

Later model filter has no primer pump. Regardless, which filter is used, bleeding is unnecessary. Vane-type fuel pump supplies fuel at starting speeds and is capable of automatically bleeding fuel supply system.

SERVICING COMPONENTS

FUEL INJECTION PUMP

NOTE – *When working on injection system, keep all components clean. Clean all injection line unions before loosening.*

If injection pump is faulty, it must be replaced. Special test equipment is necessary for making repairs.

Removal – **1)** Remove belt cover and cylinder head cover.

2) Turn engine until No. 1 cylinder is at TDC. See *Fig. 8*. Lock camshaft in position with locking tool (2065).

3) Remove drive belt.

BOSCH DIESEL INJECTION – VOLKSWAGEN (Cont.)

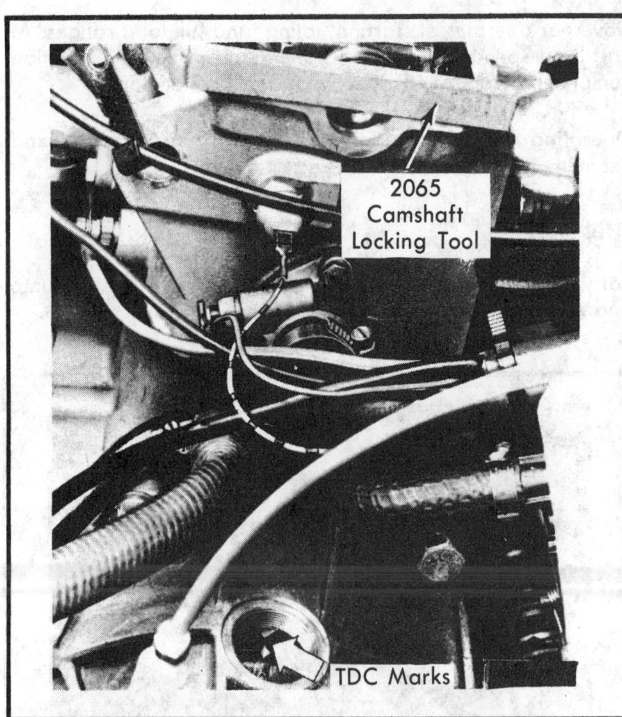

Fig. 8 Adjusting No. 1 Cylinder to TDC and Locking Camshaft

Fig. 9 Pulling Fuel Injection Pump Gear

4) Loosen (but do not remove) injection pump gear nut. Attach puller (VW 203b). *See Fig. 9.* Be sure jaws are at right angles to cross bar and point in direction of spindle rotation. Carefully apply tension to puller. Using a light hammer, strike puller bolt lightly, until gear loosens from injection pump shaft taper.

5) Remove puller and nut. Take gear off by hand.

6) Remove all fuel lines from pump. Cover unions with clean cloth. Disconnect wire from stop control on pump and remove accelerator cable.

7) Remove bolts from injection pump mounting plate. Support and remove pump.

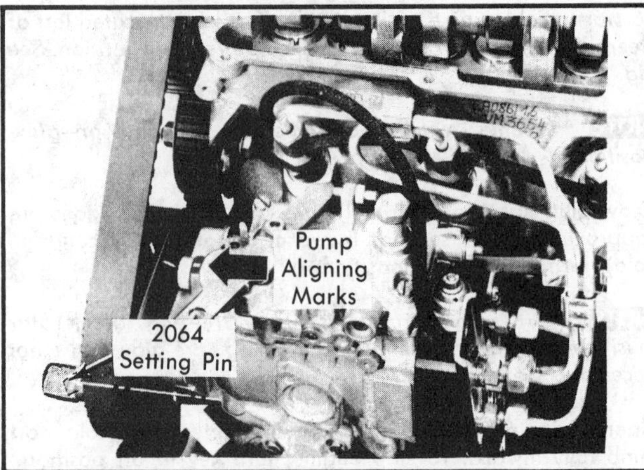

Fig. 10 Aligning Reference Marks When Installing Injection Pump Gear

Installation – **1)** Install pump, aligning marks on pump and mounting plate. *See Fig. 10.* Torque mounting bolts to 18 ft. lbs. (2.5 mkg).

2) Install pump gear, turning it until mark on gear aligns with mounting plate mark. Torque nut to 33 ft. lbs. (4.5 mkg). Lock pump gear with setting pin (2064). *See Fig. 10.*

3) Loosen camshaft gear bolt one-half turn. Using rubber hammer, knock gear off taper.

4) Be sure TDC mark on flywheel aligns with reference mark. Install drive belt.

5) Remove setting pin (2064) from pump gear. Tension belt by turning tensioner to right. Check belt tension between camshaft and pump gears. Scale should read "11-12" on special tool (VW 210).

6) Tighten camshaft gear bolt to 33 ft. lbs. (4.5 mkg). Remove locking tool (2065) from camshaft. Turn crankshaft two turns in direction of engine rotation.

7) Using a rubber hammer, strike belt at point of measurement. Recheck belt tension, and check injection pump timing. When connecting injection nozzle lines, attach as follows:

- Line A to Cylinder No. 1.
- Line B to Cylinder No. 3.
- Line C to Cylinder No. 4.
- Line D to Cylinder No. 2.

INJECTION NOZZLES

Injection nozzle problems usually appear as follows:

- Knocking in one or more cylinders.
- Engine overheating.
- Loss of power.
- Smoky black exhaust.
- Increased fuel consumption.

To locate faulty injection nozzles, loosen line union on each injection nozzle (one at a time) with engine running at fast idle. If engine speed remains constant with line removed, that nozzle is defective.

BOSCH DIESEL INJECTION – VOLKSWAGEN (Cont.)

Removal – **1)** Detach injector line or lines.

2) Use special tool (US 2775) to remove injection nozzles.

Installation – **1)** Install a new heat shield with recess pointing upward.

2) Torque injection nozzles to 51 ft. lbs. (7.0 mkg) and lines to 18 ft. lbs. (2.5 mkg).

NOTE – *Bleeding is not required.*

FUEL FILTER

To replace filter, remove old canister and install new one. Bleeding is not required.

On early models, bleeding can be accomplished, if desired, by loosening vent screw on top of filter. See *Fig. 7*. Operate primer pump until fuel appears free of air bubbles. Then tighten vent screw and start engine.

NOTE – *If engine will not start, loosen line unions on two injection nozzles. Crank engine without using glow plugs. When fuel appears at unions, tighten unions and start engine.*

If water is present in system, loosen vent screw and open water drain screw on bottom of filter. Operate primer pump until clean fuel appears. Tighten water drain screw. Operate primer pump again until fuel appears free of air bubbles at vent screw. Tighten vent screw.

NOTE – *Later model has no primer pump. Such bleeding should not prove necessary with either filter.*

ADJUSTMENTS

ADJUSTING ACCELERATOR CABLE

Be sure ball pin on pump lever is pointing upward and is in line with mark on edge of elongated hole. See *white arrow in Fig. 11*. Accelerator cable should be attached at upper hole (black arrow) in bracket.

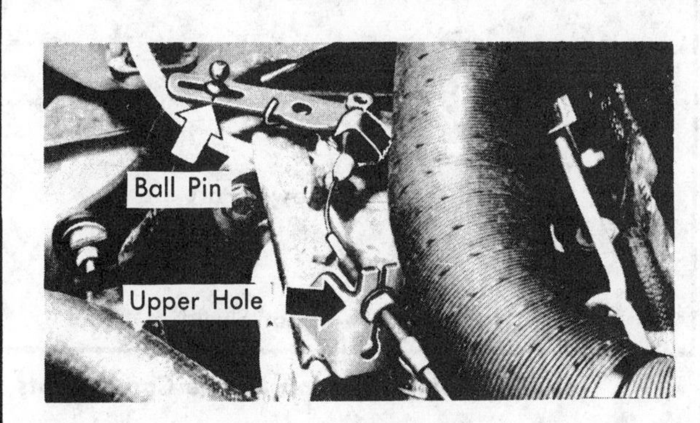

Fig. 11 Checking Accelerator Cable Attaching Points

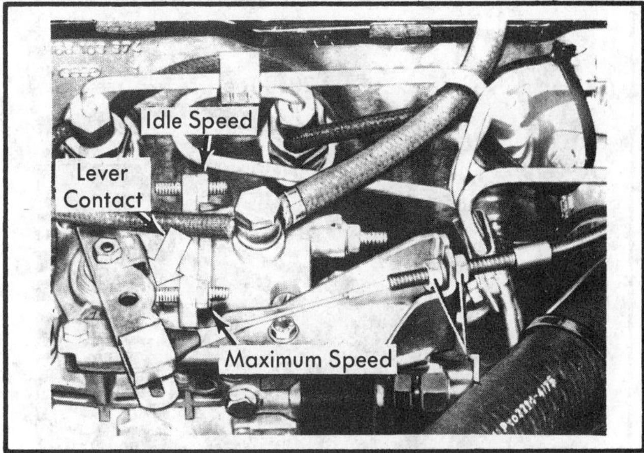

Fig. 12 Adjusting Points for Accelerator Cable, Idle Speed, and Maximum Speed

Place pedal in full throttle position. Adjust cable with nuts until pump lever contacts stop free of strain. See *white arrow in Fig. 12*.

ADJUSTING COLD STARTING CABLE

Insert washer onto cable. See *Fig. 13*. Install cable in bracket with rubber bushing.

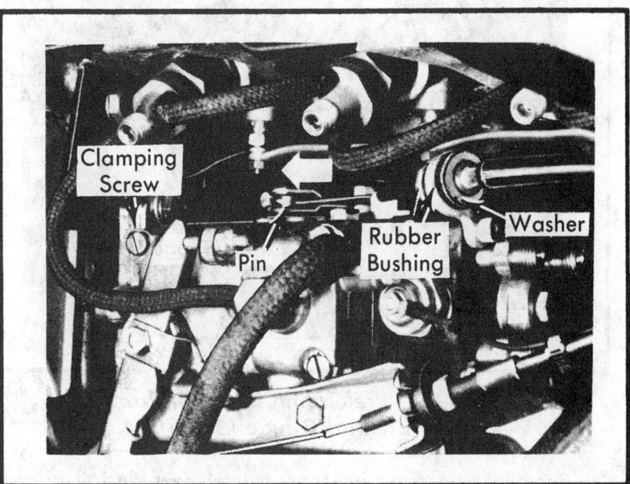

Fig. 13 Adjusting Cold Starting Cable To Provide 2.5° Timing Advance

Insert cable in pin and install lock washer. Move lever as far as possible in direction of arrow. Pull cable tight and secure pin with clamping screw.

NOTE – *When cold start knob (left of steering column) is pulled out, timing of fuel injection pump is advanced 2.5°, improving starting.*

ADJUSTING INJECTION PUMP TIMING

1) Turn engine until TDC mark on flywheel is in line with boss on bell housing and the marks on pump and mounting plate are aligned. See *Figs. 8 and 10*.

BOSCH DIESEL INJECTION – VOLKSWAGEN (Cont.)

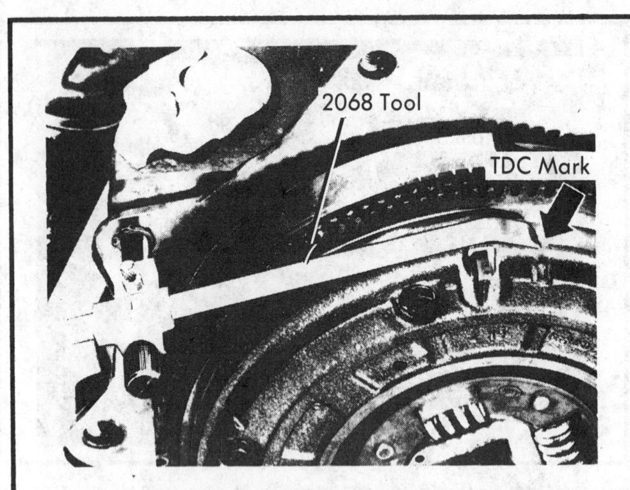

Fig. 14 Setting No. 1 Cylinder at TDC With Engine Removed

NOTE – *If engine is removed from vehicle, turn engine until TDC mark on flywheel aligns with end of setting bar (2068). See Fig. 14.*

Fig. 15 Preloading Injection Pump With Dial Gauge (2066)

2) Remove plug from injection pump cover. Install adapter and dial gauge (2066) in plug hole. See *Fig. 15*. Preload gauge to .097" (2.5 mm).

3) Turn engine counterclockwise (opposite normal rotation) until gauge needle stops moving. Zero gauge with .039" (1 mm) preload.

4) Turn engine clockwise (normal rotation) until TDC on flywheel is aligned with reference mark. Gauge should read .032" (0.83 mm).

NOTE – *If necessary, loosen mounting plate and support bolts. Set lift to .032" (0.83 mm) by turning pump.*

CHECKING VALVE TIMING

See *CHECKING VALVE TIMING* in *ENGINE* Section.

MEASURING ENGINE SPEED

Use the following tools when measuring engine speed:

- Adapter (VW 1324).
- Bosch Dwell-Tach (EFAW 166C).
- Sun Dwell-Tach (TDT-12) as alternate.

ADJUSTING IDLE SPEED

1) Operate engine until oil temperature reaches 122-158° F (50-70° C).

2) Set engine speed to 770-870 RPM, by turning idle adjusting screw. See *Fig. 12.*

3) Lock screw in place and seal it.

ADJUSTING MAXIMUM SPEED

1) Operate engine until oil temperature reaches 122-158° F (50-70° C).

2) Open throttle fully and set speed at 5400-5450 RPM. See *Fig. 12.*

3) Lock screw in place and seal it.

CHECKING INJECTION NOZZLES

1) To disassemble, place upper part of nozzle in vise and loosen lower part.

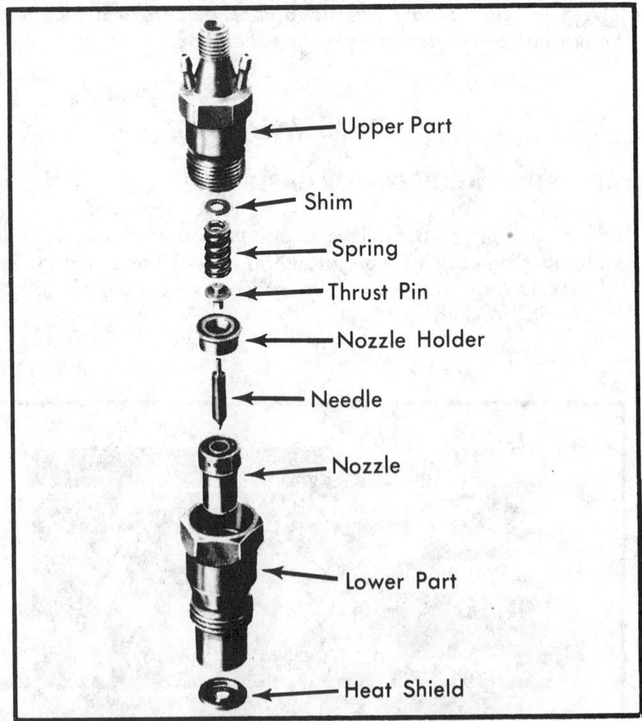

Fig. 16 Inspecting Injection Nozzle Components

2) To prevent parts from falling out, reverse position with lower part of nozzle in vise. Remove parts carefully. See *Fig. 16.*

BOSCH DIESEL INJECTION – VOLKSWAGEN (Cont.)

NOTE – *When disassembling, keep all individual parts together. Do not interchange parts from one nozzle to another.*

3) To reassemble, reverse procedure. Tighten upper and lower parts to 51 ft. lbs. (7.0 mkg) torque.

TESTING

TESTING INJECTION NOZZLES

CAUTION – *Do not expose hands to injector spray during testing, as working pressure will cause fuel oil to penetrate skin.*

Nozzles should be tested for:

- Spray formation.
- Noise.
- Breaking pressure.
- Leakage.

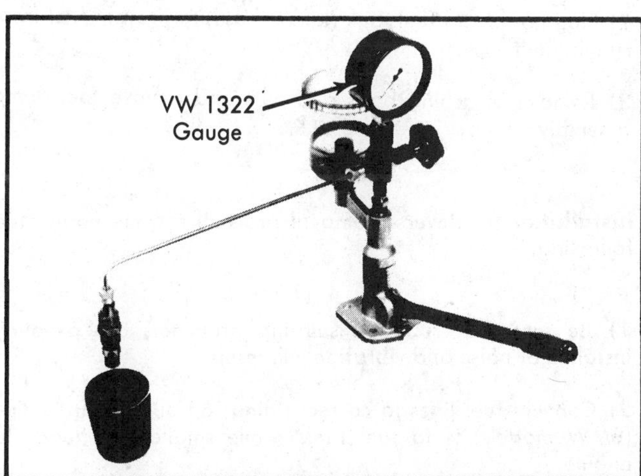

Fig. 17 Testing Injection Nozzles for Spray Formation, Noise, Breaking Pressure, and Leakage

Spray Formation Test

Isolate gauge (VW 1322). *See Fig. 17.* Use short, rapid strokes of testing pump lever (4-6 strokes per second). Spray should be even and stop cleanly. Nozzles should not drip.

Noise Test

Isolate gauge (VW 1322). *See Fig. 17.* Use long, slow strokes of testing pump lever (1-2 strokes per second). If nozzle is working properly it will "ping" as fuel emerges.

Breaking Pressure Test

1) With gauge (VW 1322) working, move pump lever down slowly. *See Fig. 17.* Watch pressure at which injector works.

2) Adjust, if necessary, by changing shims until working pressure reaches 1700-1850 psi (123-130 kg/cm²).

3) Using a thicker shim increases pressure. Using thinner shim decreases pressure.

NOTE – *A shim thickness of .0019" (0.05 mm) increases pressure by 71 psi (5.0 kg/cm²). Shims are available in thicknesses of .039-.070" (1.00-1.95 mm) in .0019" (0.05 mm) steps.*

Leakage Test

With gauge working, press pump lever down slowly and hold pressure at about 1564 psi (110 kg/cm²) for 15 seconds. *See Fig. 17.* No fuel should leak from nozzle tip.

CHECKING GLOW PLUGS

1) To check glow plug condition, remove glow plug wire and bus bar connector.

2) Connect test lamp to positive battery connector and in turn to each glow plug. *See Fig. 18.*

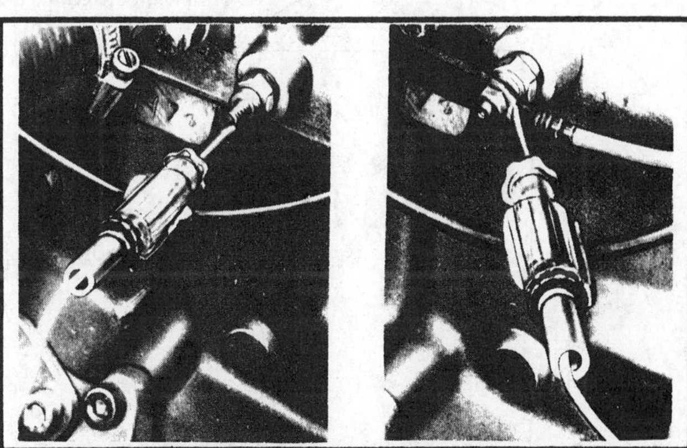

Fig. 18 Checking Glow Plug Condition (Left) and Current Supply to Plug (Right)

3) If lamp lights up, glow plug is good. If not, glow plug is defective.

4) To check current supply to glow plug, reinstall wires and bus bar connector. Connect test lamp between glow plug of No. 4 cylinder and ground. *(See Fig. 18).* Turn ignition key to pre-glow position. Test lamp should light if current is present.

SYSTEM SPECIFICATIONS

Injection Nozzle Pressure	1700-1850 psi (123-130 kg/cm²)
Leakage Pressure	①1564 psi (110 kg/cm²)
Injection Pump Timing	②.032" (0.83 mm)

① – Pressure must hold for 15 seconds.
② – Plunger stroke at engine TDC.

TIGHTENING SPECIFICATIONS

Application	Ft. Lbs. (mkg)
Injection Pump Mounting Bolts	18 (2.5)
Fuel Injection Line Unions	18 (2.5)
Fuel Injection Pump Gear Nut	33 (4.5)
Camshaft Gear Bolt	33 (4.5)
Injection Nozzle-to-Socket	51 (7.0)
Nozzle (Upper-to-Lower Part)	51 (7.0)

BENDIX ELECTRIC FUEL PUMPS

LUV

DESCRIPTION

The Bendix electric fuel pump is shaped like a cylinder and is made up of both electrical and mechanical parts. An electrically activated plunger and diaphragm assembly draws fuel through the inlet side of the pump from the fuel tank and pumps it out the outlet fitting towards the carburetor. The lower housing contains a small magnet to remove metal particles from the fuel.

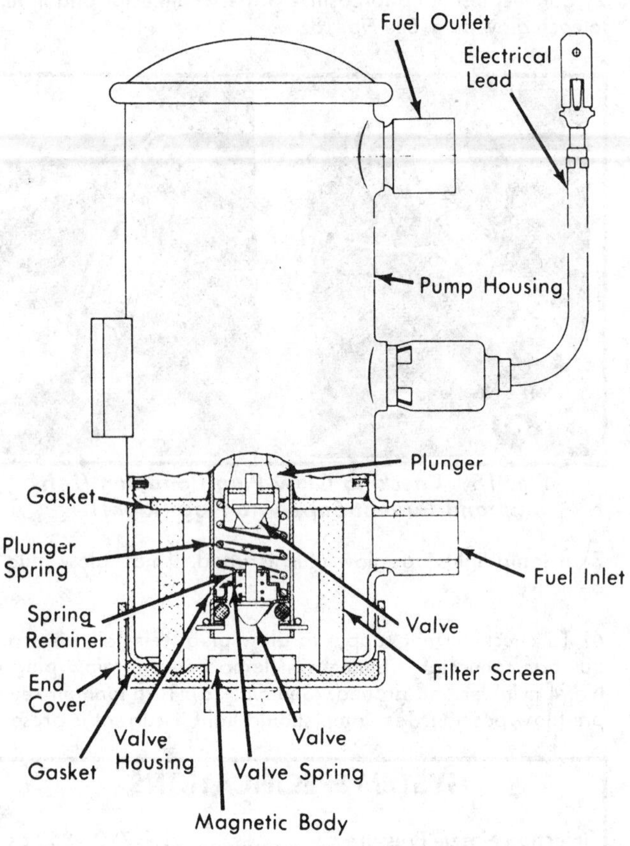

*Fig. 1 **Bendix Fuel Pump Assembly***

OPERATION

Pump operates by the rapid, constant alternating movement of the pump piston, which rides in a brass tube inside the pump. Springs, magnets and electromagnets work together to ensure the continued movement of the plunger and diaphragm mechanism. In this manner, suction is applied through the inlet fitting to draw fuel into the pump. At the same time, pressure is applied to the fuel to force it out from the pump into the lines leading to the carburetor or injection system.

The Bendix electric fuel pump has a removable fuel filter inside the end cover and this should be periodically taken out and cleaned.

CLEANING & INSPECTION

Remove bottom pump cover *(See Fig. 1)* by turning hex bolt counterclockwise. Remove filter. Clean and dry with air. Clean bottom cover and inspect gasket. Install new gasket if needed, reinstall bottom cover and check for leaks with engine running.

REMOVAL & INSTALLATION

NOTE – *Disconnect negative battery cable. Relieve any fuel pressure which may be in the system. DO NOT allow smoking, open flame or sparks in area while servicing fuel system components.*

Removal – 1) Disconnect electrical lead and rubber hoses at fuel pump side.

2) Plug hose from fuel tank (larger hose) to prevent fuel from running out.

3) Remove attaching bolts and nuts and remove fuel pump assembly.

Installation – Reverse removal procedure while noting the following:

1) Be sure that rubber insulating grommets are properly installed or noise and vibration will result.

2) Connect fuel lines to correct fittings on pump. Larger line (BMW models) is to fuel tank, while smaller line leads to engine.

3) Be careful when installing electrical lead. Tabs on pump must fit properly with slots in connector.

4) Check for leaks with engine running.

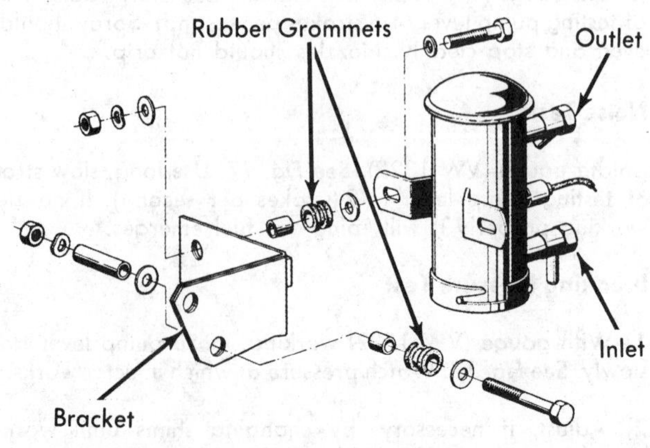

*Fig. 2 **Bendix Electric Fuel Pump Mounting***

BOSCH ELECTRIC FUEL PUMPS

BMW
Datsun 280Z
Jaguar XJS
Mercedes-Benz
Peugeot
Porsche
Volkswagen
Volvo

DESCRIPTION

Bosch electric fuel pumps are roller cell, positive displacement pumps and operate on 12 volts. Output pressure is limited to about 28 psi by one or more fuel regulators on most models. Pumps with a return line have an internal pressure relief valve which is designed to open between 43 and 65 psi depending on model application. Porsche Turbo Carrera uses two pumps mounted in series, and the combined output should be about 1700 cc of fuel in 30 seconds. Single pump applications should pump about 715 cc of fuel in 30 seconds.

OPERATION

Two methods of fuel control are used by Bosch pumps:

1) On pumps which have no fuel return line, fuel is taken from inlet, through pump to delivery connection. In this type both rotor and brushes are immersed in fuel. To maintain uniform fuel pressure, a ball valve is located in delivery connection. In addition, pump has a pressure relief by-pass which disconnects suction and delivery lines at approximately 73.5 psi. Delivery rate is approximately 2.11 quarts per minute at 2500 RPM.

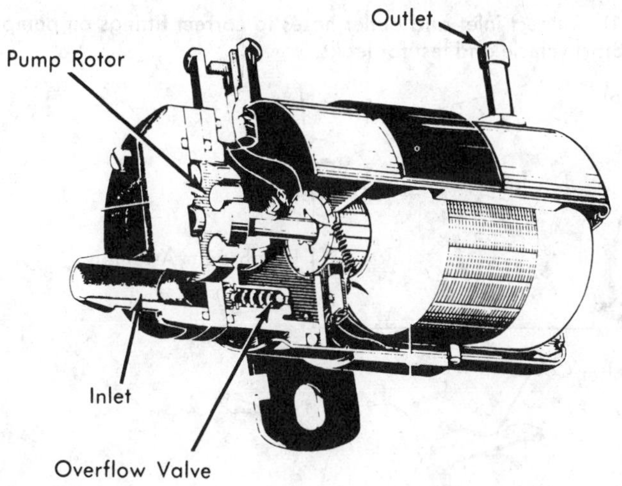

Fig. 1 Non-Return Line Type of Fuel Pump

2) On pumps which have a fuel return line, fuel is circulated through pump rotor and brushes. On this type, all fuel line connections are on one end of fuel pump. When pump starts operating and there is air in pump, air is vented by a spiral groove around the side of a spring loaded valve. When air has been vented and fuel pressure increases, the spring loaded valve actuates, shutting off fuel return line and opening fuel delivery line. If fuel pump pressure goes beyond proper operating pressure, 64 psi (4.5 kp/sq. cm.), spring loaded valve opens further and allows excess pressure and fuel to be returned to fuel tank.

On both return and non-return line pumps, when ignition is switched "ON", pump runs for one to two seconds and stops, preventing flooding before engine starts. Now pump operates only when starter is engaged or engine is running. Bosch fuel pumps are sealed and no repair or disassembly is possible.

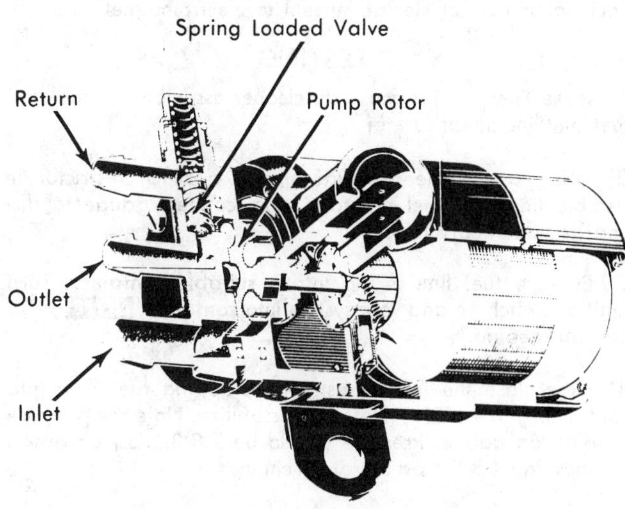

Fig. 2 Return Line Type Fuel Pump

REMOVAL & INSTALLATION

CAUTION — *Do not allow smoking, open flame or sparks in area while servicing fuel system components. Danger of fire or explosion exists.*

Removal — **1)** On fuel injected models, fuel pressure must be relieved before removing any components. Disconnect battery.

2) Remove spare tire (Jaguar models) for access to fuel pump cover. Porsche models have fuel pump(s) mounted on front axle carrier. On Jaguar models, remove pump cover from battery tray (2 screws), roll back carpet and release pump cover to floor clips.

3) On all models, disconnect inlet and outlet fuel lines, making note of position for reassembly. Plug lines to prevent fuel spillage.

4) On models with retaining band, remove attaching screws and loosen band (some models; band will come off with pump). Unhook electrical connector and remove fuel pump assembly.

Installation — Reverse removal procedure while noting the following:

1) Be sure rubber grommets and insulation are installed correctly or noise and vibration will result.

2) Hook all fuel lines and return lines to proper fittings and be sure they are tight to avoid air and/or fuel leaks.

3) Route fuel lines so they will not vibrate or rub against other body parts.

4) Test system for leaks with engine running.

1977 Electric Fuel Pumps

MAZDA ELECTRIC FUEL PUMPS

Courier
Mazda

DESCRIPTION

Mazda electric fuel pump is a pulsating diaphragm type. Check valves are used to control fuel flow direction and contact points control electric current to electromagnet.

TESTING

Pressure Test – **1**) Remove air cleaner assembly. Unhook the fuel inlet line at carburetor

2) Using a suitable pressure gauge, a pinch restrictor in flexible line and fuel resistant hose, connect gauge to discharge side of carburetor.

3) Be sure fuel line is fed into a suitable container. Turn ignition switch on and vent system into container. **NOTE** – *Do not start engine.*

4) Now close the in-line restrictor, stopping fuel flow into container and wait for pressure to stabilize. Note the pressure reading on gauge. Pressure should be 2.8-3.6 psi on piston engines and 4.3-5.4 psi on rotary engines.

5) If pressure is not within specifications, replace pump. Electric pump is a sealed unit and cannot be repaired.

Volume Test – **1**) Using the same equipment outlined under *Pressure Test* in this section, ensure that container is large enough to hold about 1½ quarts.

2) Turn ignition switch on and open hose restrictor. Fuel output volume should be 1 qt. in one minute for Courier models; .8 qts. per minute for Mazda 808(1600); 1.2 qts. in one minute for the rotary engines.

REMOVAL & INSTALLATION

Removal – **1**) Disconnect battery. On Courier models pump is mounted on left frame side rail near fuel tank. Remove fuel pump shield from frame, disconnect inlet and outlet hoses at pump, remove attaching bolts and remove pump.

2) On Mazda sedan and coupe models, disconnect fuel pump wire at snap junction in trunk. On Mazda wagon models, remove left rear side trim panel and disconnect wire to pump.

3) On Mazda 808(1600) models, jack up rear of vehicle and support with safety stands. Remove pump shield from body and remove nuts attaching fuel pump to mounting bracket.

4) Disconnect inlet and outlet hoses at pump and remove pump assembly.

5) All other Mazda models have fuel pump installed in trunk behind the partition board. Remove board, disconnect wire to pump and remove pump cover. Disconnect inlet and outlet hoses at pump and unbolt and remove pump from vehicle.

Installation – Reverse removal procedure while noting the following :

1) Ensure all rubber grommets and insulation are properly replaced to avoid noise and vibration.

2) If pump is grounded by external wire, be sure wire is tightly connected to good ground.

3) Check fuel line routing to ensure lines are not rubbing or vibrating against other body parts.

4) Connect inlet and outlet hoses to correct fittings on pump. Start vehicle and test for leaks.

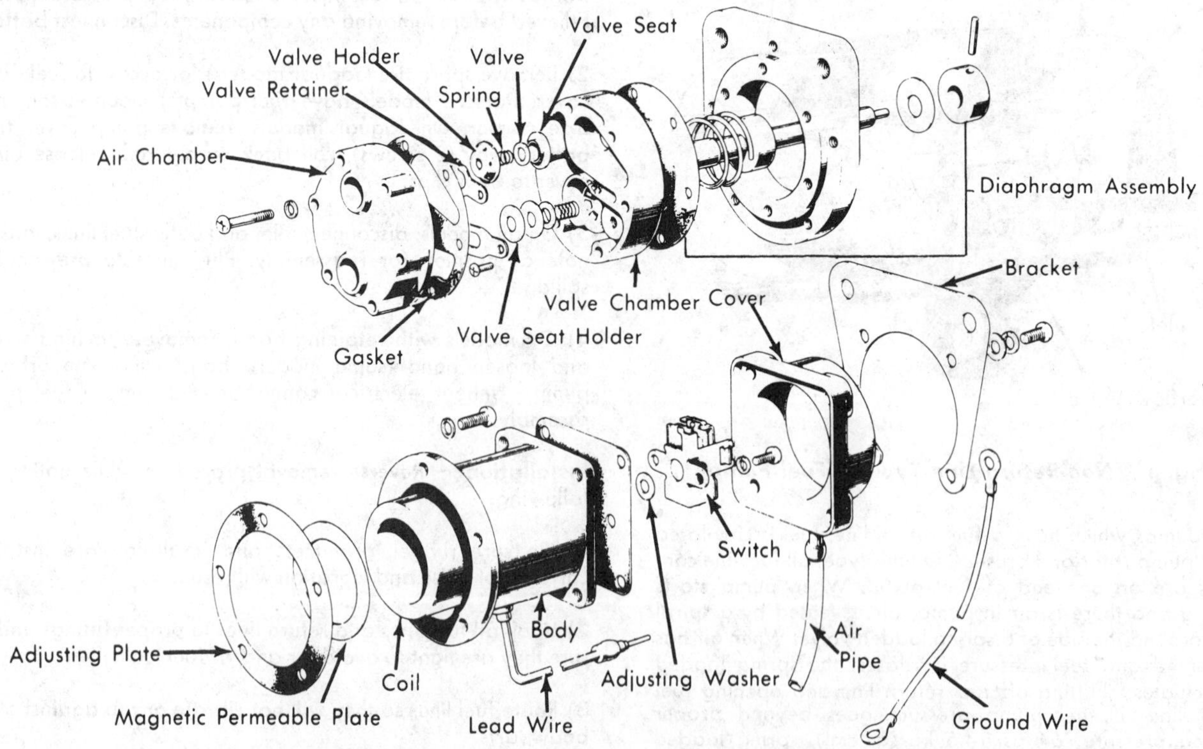

Fig. 1 Exploded View of Typical Mazda Fuel Pump

S.U. AUF TYPE ELECTRIC FUEL PUMPS

Jaguar XJ6, XJ12
MGB

DESCRIPTION

The S.U. Auf type of electric fuel pump is a pulsating diaphragm design. Current is controlled through adjustable contact points and this pump operates on 12 volts. Internal disc valves are used to control fuel flow direction.

MGB and Jaguar XJ6 models use a single pump while Jaguar XJ12 models use a dual pump arrangement. This pump system should maintain a line pressure at the carburetor or injector of 2.8-3.8 psi and should pump a volume of about (1) pint in 30 seconds. Unit can be identified by a tag attached to the pump body.

ADJUSTMENTS

CONTACT PLATE POSITIONING

1) Points are correctly positioned when they contact each other on the center of the curved point and wipe across evenly.

2) Lower rocker points. Check that contact plate on top of pedestal rests on narrow pedestal bridge. Contact plate should be square with rocker points. Contact plate points should be slightly forward of rocker points.

3) If adjustment is required, use contact plate attaching screw to adjust to proper position.

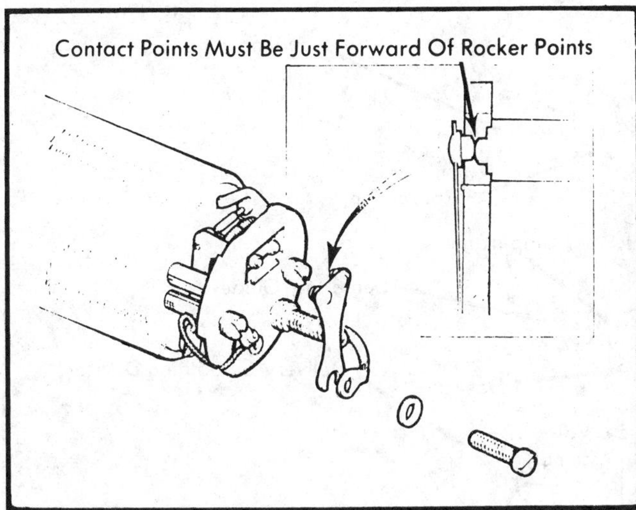

Fig. 1 Correct Contact Point Alignment

SETTING CONTACT GAPS

1) Ensure rocker points are touching contact plate points. Measure distance contact points are pushed (lifted) above pedestal when cycled. Lift should be .035" (.9 mm).

2) Adjust by bending upper rocker finger beneath pedestal.

3) Now check gap between lower rocker finger and housing. Gap should be .070" (1.8 mm). To adjust, upper rocker finger may again need to be bent. **NOTE** — *Both adjustments require bending same upper rocker finger. Be careful because this finger is used to set both adjustments and they must be proportioned correctly.*

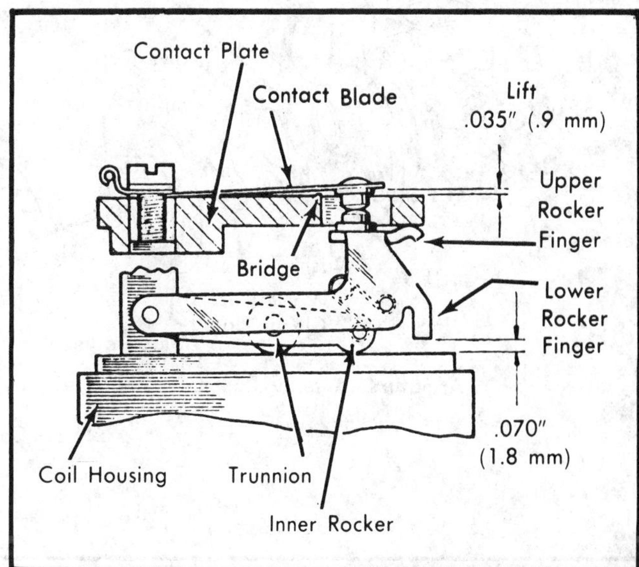

Fig. 2 Adjusting Contact Gaps

REMOVAL & INSTALLATION

Removal — 1) Disconnect battery. On Jaguar models, remove spare wheel and remove (7) screws securing fuel pump cover. **NOTE** — *Do not remove center screw at front edge of cover.* On MGB, remove pump guard inside trunk, disconnect electrical lead and loosen pump retaining clip.

2) On all models, disconnect fuel lines at pump fittings and plug lines to prevent fuel leakage. **NOTE** — *MGB pump is located beneath vehicle.*

3) On MGB models, disconnect breather tube and slide pump away from clip. On Jaguar models, release both banjo bolts on pump, remove strapping around pump and hose, and detach ground strap at pump body. Now remove (1) screw and washer securing pump clamp, lift pump assembly away from clamp and disconnect electrical lead. **NOTE** — *Use care not to damage insulation around pump body.*

Installation — Reverse disassembly steps while making note of the following:

1) On Jaguar models, ensure that seals at banjo connectors are in good condition.

2) On all models, ensure that insulation and rubber grommets (if equipped) are in good condition and placed properly to avoid noise and vibration.

3) Make sure that fuel lines are routed so as not to rub or scrape against other body parts.

4) Tighten all lines and fittings to avoid air and/or fuel leaks. Check system for leaks with engine running.

S.U. AUF TYPE ELECTRIC FUEL PUMPS (Cont.)

Delivery Flow Smoothing Device
Inlet Air Bottle Cover
Outlet Valve
Ground Terminal
Rocker Assembly
Valve Cap
Impact Washer
Pin
Terminal Stud
Contact Plate
Condenser
End Cover
Ball
Vent Valve
Filter
Washer
Valve Cap Clamp Plate
Diaphragm & Spindle Assembly
Armature Centering Roller
Pedestal
Coil Housing
Insulating Sleeve
Brass Nut
Sealing Band
Condenser Clip

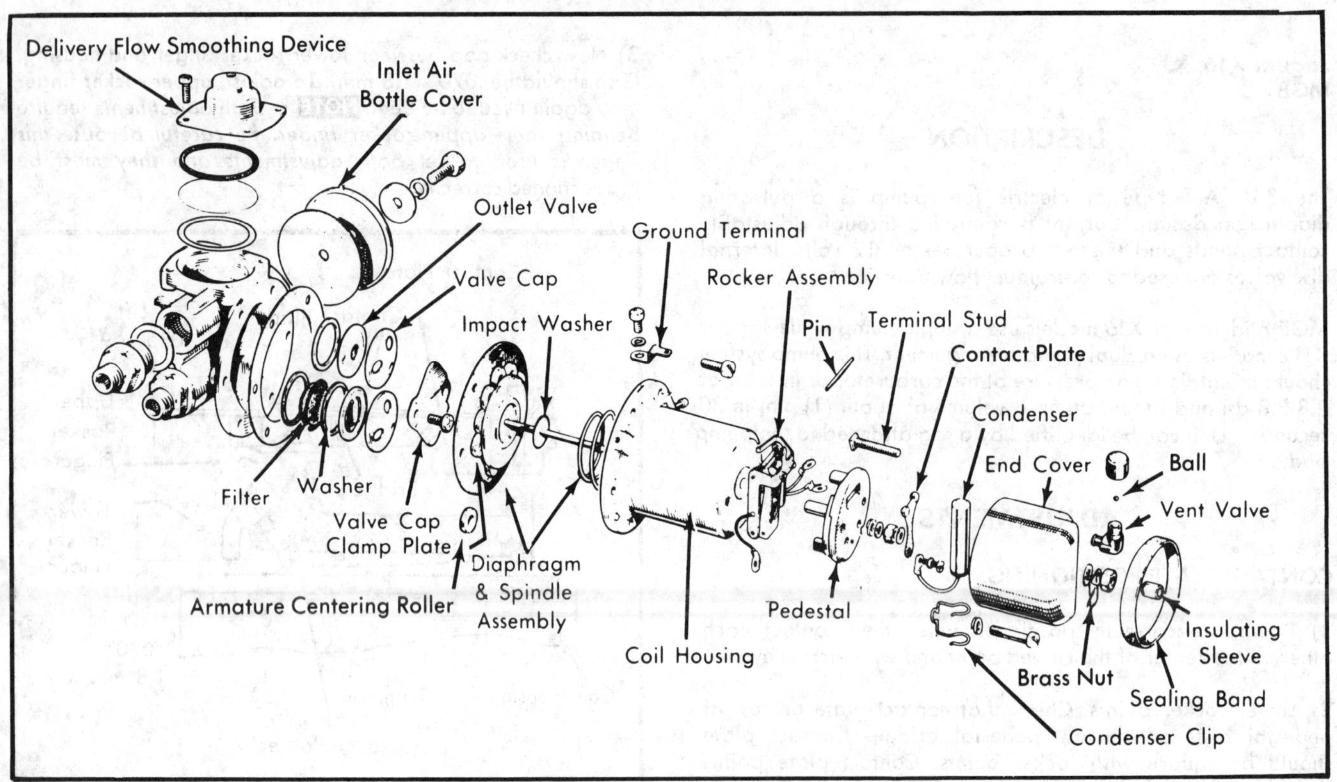

Fig. 3 S.U. AUF 400 Series Fuel Pump (Jaguar XJ12 Shown)

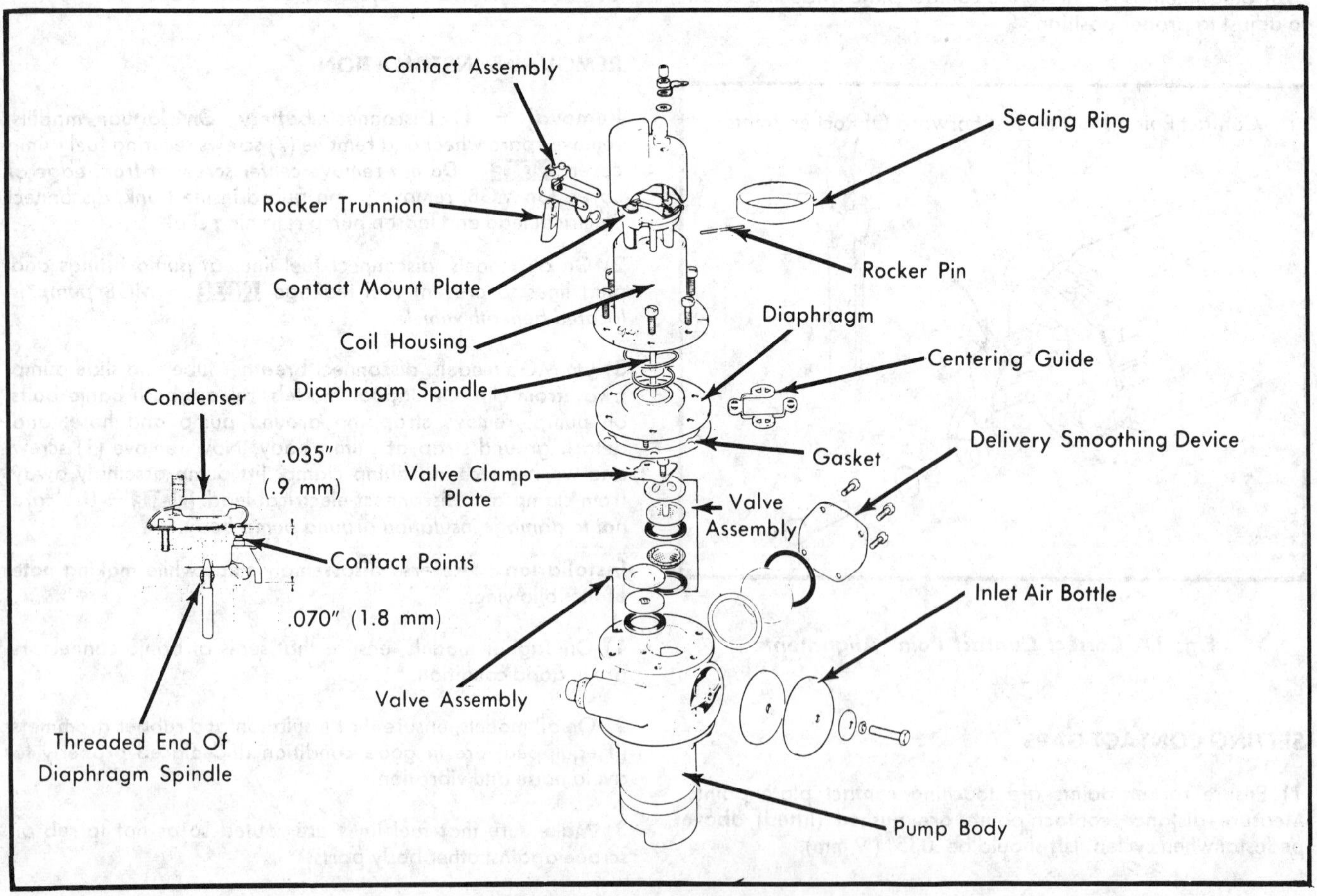

Contact Assembly
Sealing Ring
Rocker Trunnion
Rocker Pin
Contact Mount Plate
Diaphragm
Coil Housing
Centering Guide
Condenser
Diaphragm Spindle
Delivery Smoothing Device
.035" (.9 mm)
Valve Clamp Plate
Gasket
Valve Assembly
Contact Points
Inlet Air Bottle
.070" (1.8 mm)
Valve Assembly
Threaded End Of Diaphragm Spindle
Pump Body

Fig. 4 S.U. AUF 300 Series Fuel Pump (Jaguar XJ6 & MGB Shown)

TOYOTA ELECTRIC FUEL PUMPS

Corona
Celica
Pickup

DESCRIPTION

Fuel pump is located inside gas tank and is serviced only as a unit. See *Fig. 1*. If electric pump becomes defective, it must be replaced.

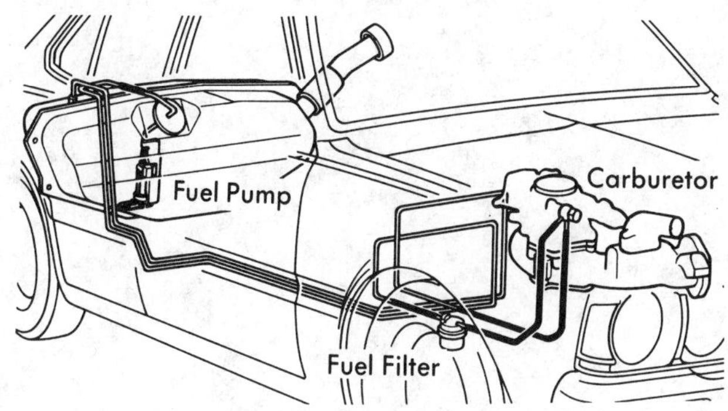

Fig. 1 Toyota Electric Fuel Pump System

Fuel pump assembly is composed of pump, filter, cover, cushion, and relief valve. See *Fig. 2*. Fuel pump operates when starter is turning and when oil pressure is present.

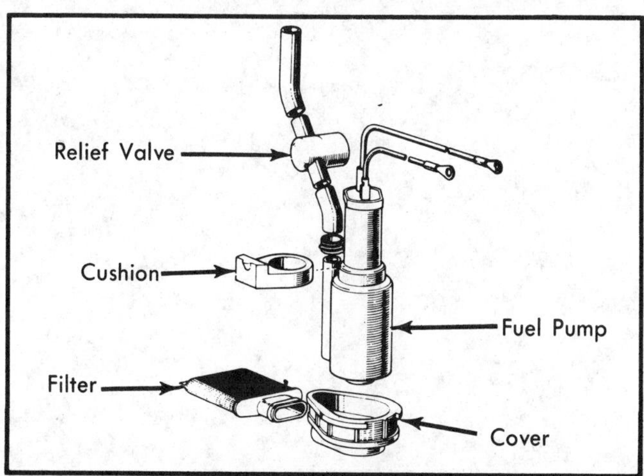

Fig. 2 Exploded View of Electric Fuel Pump

TESTING

CAUTION — *Do not operate electric fuel pump unless it is immersed in gasoline. Do not attempt to test pump without resistor.*

PUMP OPERATION CHECK

1) Check oil pressure switch operation.

2) Disconnect connector from oil pressure switch, to operate fuel pump relay. See *Fig. 3*.

3) Turn ignition key to ON position.

4) Check pump for steady, smooth operation. Replace pump if abnormal noise is present. If pump does not run, check pump resistor, relay and pump.

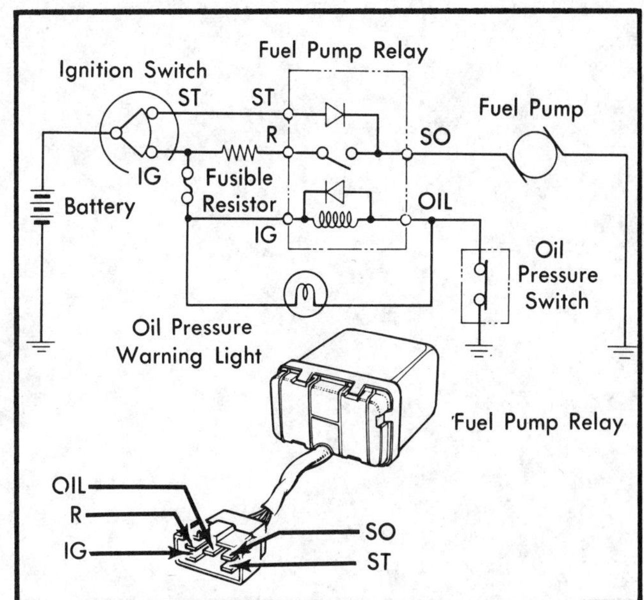

Fig. 3 Fuel Pump Control System Circuit

DISCHARGE CAPACITY TEST

1) Connect a short test hose to fuel filter outlet.

2) Turn ignition key to ON position. Measure discharge capacity. Pump should discharge 1.3 qts. (1.2 L) per minute.

3) If below specification, check fuel lines, hoses, and filter for restrictions. Replace fuel pump, if necessary.

DISCHARGE PRESSURE TEST

1) Connect pressure gauge to fuel filter outlet.

2) Turn ignition key to ON position. Measure discharge pressure at gauge. Reading should be 2.1-4.3 psi (0.15-0.30 kg/cm^2). If not within specified limits, check fuel level. Replace pump if necessary.

COMPLETING TESTS

After tests, necessary repairs or replacement of parts, turn off ignition. Reconnect fuel hoses and lead to oil pressure switch.

REMOVAL AND INSTALLATION

Removal — Remove fuel pump from tank. On pickup, remove fuel tank. Remove negative battery cable.

Installation — Install fuel pump into tank, using a new gasket. Reconnect electrical leads and fuel lines. Connect negative battery cable and check fuel system for leaks.

FUEL PUMP RESISTOR TEST

Check for continuity between two terminals of resistor connector. If no continuity, replace resistor and check fuel pump. Resistance of 1.4 ohms required.

Section 3
ELECTRICAL

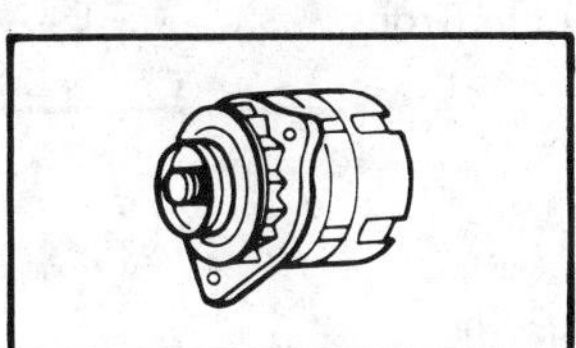

Contents

DISTRIBUTOR APPLICATIONS Page

DISTRIBUTOR SPECIFICATIONS

DISTRIBUTORS & IGNITION SYSTEMS

ALTERNATORS & REGULATORS Page

STARTERS

STARTER CONTROLS

SWITCHES, GAUGES & SPEEDOMETER

NOTE — ALSO SEE GENERAL INDEX.

1977 Distributor Applications

APPLICATION TABLES

ARROW/COLT	FEDERAL	CALIF.
Mitsubishi		
1600 cc Std.	T3T0 3875	T3T0 4278
1600 cc W/SS①	T3T0 5771	T3T0 5672
2000 cc	T3T0 4575	T3T0 4874

① – Equipped with Silent Shaft.

AUDI

	FEDERAL	CALIF.
Bosch①		
Fox		
Man. Trans.	049 905 205A	049 905 205A
Auto. Trans.	056 905 205C	056 905 205C
100LS		
Man. Trans.	058 905 205A	058 905 205A
Auto. Trans.	176 032	176 032

① – Bosch basic part number 0231.

BMW

	FEDERAL	CALIF.
Bosch①		
320i	170 214	170 214
530i	305 059	305 070
630CSi	305 059	305 070

① – Bosch basic part number 0231

CAPRI II

	FEDERAL	CALIF.
Bosch/Motorcraft		
2300 cc①		
Man. Trans.	D7FZ-D	D7FZ-E
Auto. Trans.	D7FZ-C	D7FZ-J
2800 cc		
Man. Trans.	305 052	
Auto. Trans.	308 012	308 010

① – Distributor specifications are not available for Ford part numbers.

COURIER

	FEDERAL	CALIF.
Ford/Motorcraft①		
1800 cc	D77Z-C	
2300 cc	D77Z-B	D77Z-A

① – Distributor Specifications are not available.

DATSUN

	FEDERAL	CALIF.
Hitachi		
200SX		
Man. Trans.	D4A5-14	D4F5-06
Auto. Trans.	D4A6-03	D4F4-07

DATSUN (Cont.)	FEDERAL	CALIF.
280Z		
Man. Trans.	D6F5-02	D6F4-03
Auto. Trans.	D6F5-03	D6F4-03
710		
Man. Trans.		D4A5-14
Auto. Trans.	D4A6-03	D4F4-07
810		
Man. Trans.	D6F6-01	D6F5-02
Auto. Trans.	D6F4-03	D6F4-03
B210		
Man. Trans.	D4A5-13	D4F5-03
Auto. Trans.		D4A5-05
F10	D4A5-13	D4F5-04
Pickup		
Man. Trans.		D4A4-07
Auto. Trans.	D4A4-06	D4F4-03

FIAT

	FEDERAL	CALIF.
Ducellier		
128 & X1/9	4480A	44880A
Marelli		
124 & 131	S144CAY	S144CAY

HONDA①

	FEDERAL	CALIF.
Hitachi		
Accord	657 773	657 791
CVCC		
Man. Trans. (Exc. Fed. Sedan)	657 773	657 791
Auto. Trans.	657 773	657 791
Man. Trans.(Sedan)	663 811	
Civic		
Man. Trans.	657 772	657 791
Auto. Trans.	657 773	657 791

① – Honda basic part number 30100.

JAGUAR

	FEDERAL	CALIF.
Lucas		
XJS	41675	41675
XJ6①		
Man. Trans.	41343	41343
Auto. Trans.	41617	41617
XJ12	41677	41677

① – No specifications available.

LANCIA

	FEDERAL	CALIF.
Marelli		
Beta	S144CBY	S144CBY

LUV

	FEDERAL	CALIF.
Nippondenso		
All Models	029 100 3281	029 100 3281

APPLICATION TABLES (Cont.)

MAZDA	FEDERAL	CALIF.
Mazda/Mitsubishi		
GLC	8028 18 200	8028 18 200
808-1300 cc	3710 18 200	3710 18 200
808-1600 cc		
Man. Trans.	3928 18 200	3725 18 200A
Auto. Trans.	3928 18 200	3770 18 200A
Pickup	3790 18 200	3790 18 200
RX3		
Man. Trans.	8649 18 200B	8649 18 200B
Auto. Trans.	8650 18 200	8650 18 200
RX4	8735 18 200	8735 18 200
Cosmo	8235 18 200	8235 18 200

① – Mazda part numbers.

MERCEDES-BENZ		
Bosch		
230①	179 137	170-137
280 Series②	304 001	304 001
450 Series②	405 002	405 002

① – Bosch basic part number 0231.
② – Bosch basic part number 0237

MG		
Lucas		
Midget	41697	41698
MGB		
W/Cat. Conv.	41693	41695
W/O Cat. Conv.	41692	

OPEL		
Nippondenso		
All Models	029 100 3281	029 100 3281

PEUGEOT		
Bosch①		
604	402 008	402 008
Ducellier		
504	590166	590166

① – Bosch basic part number 0237.

PORSCHE		
Bosch①		
911S & Carrera	184 004	184 004
924②	047 905 205	047 905 205

① – Bosch basic part number 0231.
② – Porsche part number.

RENAULT	FEDERAL	CALIF.
Ducellier		
R-5	4441	525003
R-12/17GTL	4546	4546
R-17 Gordini	525089	525089

SAAB		
Bosch①		
99	170 145	170 145

① – Bosch basic part number 0231.

SUBARU		
Nippondenso		
Man. Trans.	029 100 3700	029 100 4270
Hitachi		
Auto. Trans.	D4H6-01	D4H6-01

TOYOTA		
Nippondenso①		
3K-C Engine		
Man. Trans.	24013	24013
Auto. Trans.	24013	24013
2T-C Engine		
Man. Trans.	26230	26230
Auto. Trans.	26240	26240
20R Engine	38020	38040
2F Engine	61021	61060

① – Nippondenso basic part number 19100.

TRIUMPH		
Lucas		
Spitfire	41593	41593
TR7	41601	41603

VOLKSWAGEN		
Bosch①		
Type 1		
Man. Trans.	176 044	176 044
Auto. Trans.	176 053	176 053
Type 2 (Bus)	168 005	170 093
Rabbit & Scirocco	176 057	176 057
Dasher	176 057	176 057

① – Bosch basic part number 0231.

VOLVO		
Bosch①		
240 Series	003 003	003 003
260 Series	406 001	406 001

① – Bosch basic part number 0237

BOSCH DISTRIBUTOR ADVANCE & RETARD SPECIFICATIONS

NOTE — *FOR DISTRIBUTOR RPM & DEGREES, DIVIDE SPECIFICATIONS BY 2*

Distributor Part No.	Rot. ①	Centrifugal Advance (Engine Degrees @ RPM)					Vacuum Advance (Engine Degrees @ In. of Hg)				Vacuum Retard (Engine Degrees @ In. of Hg)			
047 905 205②	.....	0 1000	12 1600	18 2000	28 3000	36 4000	0 2.2	2 2.9	....	2 11.8	0 2.2	2 2.9	6 5.9	8 11.8
049 905 205A③	.....	0 1400	17 2000	19 2400	27 4800	28 5200	0 9	....	....	6 11	0 6	....	....	9 9.6
056 905 205C③	.....	0 1250	17 2100	21 3000	....	28 5000	0 8.8	....	....	13 13.9	0 7.3	....	....	10.9 9
058 905 205A③	.....	0 1100	3 1300	10 1600	29 3200	31 3400	0 3	....	....	4 4	0 4.5	....	....	11 7.5
0231 168 005	.....	0 100	14 1600	16 2000	24 3000	26 4000	0 3.9	4 5.9	....	6 7.9	....	....	....	....
0231 170 093	.....	0 1000	14 1600	17 2000	24 3000	25 4000	0 3.9	4 5.9	....	6 7.9	....	....	....	....
0231 170 137	.....	0 800	19 2000	22 3000	34 4000	39 5000	0 5.5	3 7.9	....	13 11.8	....	....	....	....
0231 170 145	.....	0 800	7 2000	19 3000	23 4000	28 5000	0 1.6	4 7.9	6 11.8	7.5 15.7	....	....	....	....
0231 170 214	.....	0 1000	18 2000	26 2600	34 4000	36 5000	....	....	....	....	0 3.9	11 7.9	....	13 11.8
0231 176 032	.....	0 1100	10 1400	18 2000	30 3000	34 4000	0 3.3	....	....	5 7.9	0 3.3	4 5.5	....	6 11.8
0231 176 044	.....	0 1000	12 1400	16 2000	22 3000	24 4000	0 3.9	3 5.9	....	4 7.9	0 1.6	2 3.9	3 5.9	4 7.9
0231 176 053	.....	0 1000	12 1400	16 2000	22 3000	24 4000	0 3.7	4 5.9	....	7 7.9	0 2.4	2 3.9	....	4 7.9
0231 176 057	.....	0 800	18 2000	24 3000	28 4000	31 5000	0 7.9	3 9.8	....	4 11.8	0 3.9	2 5.9	....	5 7.9
0231 184 004	.....	0 1200	10 2000	18 2400	22 4000	28 6000	....	....	....	....	0 1.6	3 2.4	....	6 3.9
0231 305 052	.....	0 800	8 1600	14 2200	20 3000	21 4000	0 3.9	3.5 5.9	....	4.5 7.9	....	....	....	....
0231 305 059	.....	0 800	7 1500	12 2000	....	15 4000	....	....	....	....	0 3.1	3 4.7	7 7.8	9 11.8
0231 305 070	.....	0 800	6 1400	8 2000	14 3000	18 4000	....	....	....	....	0 3.9	4 7.9	....	7 11.8
0231 308 010	.....	0 800	10 1600	14 2200	19 3000	21 4000	0 3.9	4 5.9	....	4.5 7.9	0 3.9	2 7.9	4 9.8	7 15.7
0231 308 012	.....	0 800	8 1600	14 2200	19 3000	21 4000	0 3.9	4 5.9	....	4.5 7.9	0 3.9	2 7.9	4 9.8	4.5 11.8
0237 003 003	.....	0 800	14 2000	20 3000	26 4000	31 5000	0 3.9	3 5.9	....	5 11.8	0 3.9	2 5.9	....	5 11.8

BOSCH DISTRIBUTOR ADVANCE & RETARD SPECIFICATIONS (Cont.)

NOTE — *FOR DISTRIBUTOR RPM & DEGREES, DIVIDE SPECIFICATIONS BY 2*

Distributor Part No.	Rot. ①	Centrifugal Advance (Engine Degrees @ RPM)					Vacuum Advance (Engine Degrees @ In. of Hg)				Vacuum Retard (Engine Degrees @ In. of Hg)			
0237 304 001	.....	0 1200	8 2600	12 3200	14 3600	15 4000	0 3.9	4 5.9	....	6 7.9	0 1.6	5 3.5	8 4.7	10 7.9
0237 402 008	.....	0 800	14 2000	18 2500	22 3000	28 4000	0 3.9	3 7.9	6 11.8	8 15.7	....	....	....	....
0237 405 002	.....	0 1000	8 1500	14 2000	20 2500	24 4000	0 3.4	2.5 5.5	....	6 7.9	0 3.3	2.5 5.5	....	5 7.9
0237 406 001	.....	0 800	16 2000	22 3000	30 4000	29 5000	0 3.9	6 7.9	....	8 11.8	0 3.9	4 5.9	....	6 7.9

① — C (Clockwise), CC (Counterclockwise), viewed from rotor end.
② — Porsche part number is given.
③ — Audi part number is given.

DUCELLIER DISTRIBUTOR ADVANCE & RETARD SPECIFICATIONS

NOTE — *FOR DISTRIBUTOR RPM & DEGREES, DIVIDE SPECIFICATIONS BY 2*

Distributor Part No.	Rot. ①	Centrifugal Advance (Engine Degrees @ RPM)					Vacuum Advance (Engine Degrees @ In. of Hg)				Vacuum Retard (Engine Degrees @ In. of Hg)			
4441	C	0 1000	14 2750	....	....	23 5200	0 3	7 8	....	22 13	....	....	....	....
4480A②	C	0 1000	8 1500	11.5 2000	17.5 3000	28 4800	0 4	3.5 6	7 8	10 10	0 7	5 10	10 13	....
4480A	C	0 1000	8.5 1500	11.5 2000	17.5 3000	23 4000	3.5 4	7 6	10 8	10 10	5.5 4	10 7	....	....
4546③	C	0 1100	14 1400	....	....	36 5000	0 1	5 1.5	....	9 2	....	....	....	....
4546	C	0 1100	14 1400	....	....	36 5000	8 1	....	....	9 1.5	....	....	....	....
525003	C	0 1100	14 2750	....	....	23 5200	0 3	7 8	....	11 13	....	....	....	....
525089	C	0 1100	8 1500	....	....	26 4900	0 3	8 4.5	17 7	22 9.5	0 3	4 4	9 5	12 6
590166	C	0 1000	14 3000	....	....	26 5000	0 3.9	....	....	5.5 11.8	....	....	....	....

① — C (Clockwise), CC (Counterclockwise), viewed from rotor end.
② — Specifications for Model 128 Calif. only.
③ — Specifications for Model R-17GTL Calif. only.

1977 Distributor Applications

HITACHI DISTRIBUTOR ADVANCE & RETARD SPECIFICATIONS

NOTE — *FOR DISTRIBUTOR RPM & DEGREES, DIVIDE SPECIFICATIONS BY 2*

Distributor Part No.	Rot. ①	Centrifugal Advance (Engine Degrees @ RPM)					Vacuum Advance (Engine Degrees @ In. of Hg)				Vacuum Retard (Engine Degrees @ In. of Hg)			
D4A4-06	CC	0 1100	....	....	....	11 4600	0 5.9	....	....	3 9.8	....	....	....	....
D4A4-07	CC	0 1200	....	....	....	22 3900	0 6.7	....	....	6.5 11.8	....	....	....	....
D4A5-05	CC	0 1100	....	....	....	28 4600	0 6.7	....	....	6.5 11.8	....	....	....	....
D4A5-13	CC	0 1100	....	....	....	28 4600	0 4.1	....	....	15 15.4	....	....	....	....
D4A5-14	CC	0 1200	....	....	....	22 3900	0 2.7	....	....	10 7.6	....	....	....	....
D4A6-03	CC	0 1200	....	....	....	22 3900	0 3.5	....	....	4 6.3	....	....	....	....
D4F4-03	CC	0 1200	....	....	....	22 3900	0 5.9	....	....	3 9.8	....	....	....	....
D4F4-04	CC	0 1100	....	....	....	22 22	0 5.9	....	....	3 9.8	....	....	....	....
D4F4-07	CC	0 1200	....	....	....	22 3900	0 3.5	....	....	3 5.5	....	....	....	....
D4F5-03	CC	0 1100	....	....	....	28 4600	0 4.1	....	....	15 15.4	....	....	....	....
D4F5-04	CC	0 1100	....	....	....	28 4600	0 4.1	....	....	15 15.4	....	....	....	....
D4F5-05	CC	0 1100	....	....	....	28 4300	0 6.7	....	....	9 11.8	....	....	....	....
D4F5-06	CC	0 1200	....	....	....	22 3900	0 2.8	....	....	10 7.7	....	....	....	....
D4H6-01	CC	0 1000	14 2400	....	....	28 4800	0 9.7	....	....	10 11.8	0 2.9	....	....	7.5 10.8
D6F4-03	CC	0 1200	....	....	....	17 2500	0 7.9	....	....	7.5 13.8	....	....	....	....
D6F5-02	CC	0 1200	....	....	....	17 2500	0 5.9	....	....	9 11.6	....	....	....	....
D6F5-03	CC	0 1200	....	....	....	17 2500	0 5.9	....	....	5 9.8	....	....	....	....
D6F6-01	CC	0 1200	....	....	....	17 2500	0 2.7	....	....	12.5 9.4	....	....	....	....
657 772②	CC	8 1500	16 2500	....	....	21 3300	0 6	....	....	12 13	0 3.5	....	....	7 5
657 773	CC	0 1000	12 2000	22 3000	....	31 4000	0 5.9	....	....	7.5 12	0 11.8	....	....	2.5 2.8
657 791	CC	0 1250	6 2000	10 2500	20 3800	18 5000	0 6	6 8	9 11	12 13.5	0 2.5	2 3.5	4 4	7 4.5
663 811	CC	0 1100	11 1800	16 2500	21 3200	25 5000	0 7.8	9 9.8	15 11.8	17 13.7	....	....	....	....

① — C (Clockwise), CC (Counterclockwise), viewed from rotor end.

② — Honda basic part number 30100.

LUCAS DISTRIBUTOR ADVANCE & RETARD SPECIFICATIONS

NOTE — *FOR DISTRIBUTOR RPM & DEGREES, DIVIDE SPECIFICATIONS BY 2*

Distributor Part No.	Rot. ①	Centrifugal Advance (Engine Degrees @ RPM)					Vacuum Advance (Engine Degrees @ In. of Hg)				Vacuum Retard (Engine Degrees @ In. of Hg)			
41593	CC	0 1200	10 1600	13 2600	14 3200	14 5000	....	....	....	....	0 1	6 15	....	6 15
41601	CC	0 880	3 1500	9 2100	14 3800	16 4500	....	....	....	....	0 0	12 11	....	12 15
41603	CC	0 880	8 1500	11 2100	19 3800	22 4500	....	....	....	....	0 3	10 11	....	14 15
41675	CC	0 900	24 2000	31 4000	....	36 6200	0 6	....	....	4 10	....	....	....	....
41677	CC	0 800	3 1200	14 2000	18 2600	26 7000	0 7	....	....	8 10	....	....	....	....
41692	CC	18 2000	32 4000	....	....	36 5000	0 3	....	....	24 11	....	....	....	....
41693	CC	15 2000	30 3500	....	....	35 4500	0 3	....	....	24 11	....	....	....	....
41695	CC	15 2000	30 3500	....	....	35 4500	0 5	....	....	14 11	....	....	....	....
41697	CC	4 1200	10 1500	....	....	17 3300	0 5	....	....	22 10	....	....	....	....
41698	CC	4 1200	10 1500	....	....	17 3300	....	....	....	....	0 5	....	....	12 10

① — C (Clockwise), CC (Counterclockwise), viewed from rotor end.

MARELLI DISTRIBUTOR ADVANCE SPECIFICATIONS

NOTE — *FOR DISTRIBUTOR RPM & DEGREES, DIVIDE SPECIFICATIONS BY 2*

Distributor Part No.	Rot. ①	Centrifugal Advance (Engine Degrees @ RPM)					Vacuum Advance (Engine Degrees @ In. of Hg)				Vacuum Retard (Engine Degrees @ In. of Hg)			
S144CAY	C	0 1000	13 1600	21 2000	30 3000	37 3600	....	....	....	....	....	....	....	....
S144CBY	C	0 1000	20 2000	30 3000	....	36 3600	....	....	....	....	....	....	....	....

① — C (Clockwise), CC (Counterclockwise), viewed from rotor end.

MAZDA DISTRIBUTOR ADVANCE SPECIFICATIONS

NOTE – *FOR DISTRIBUTOR RPM & DEGREES, DIVIDE SPECIFICATIONS BY 2*

Distributor Part No.	Rot. ①	Centrifugal Advance (Engine Degrees @ RPM)					Vacuum Advance (Engine Degrees @ In. of Hg)				Vacuum Retard (Engine Degrees @ In. of Hg)			
3710 18 200	.....	0	.....	.....	.....	25	0	.....	.....	6	.....	.....	.....	.....
		1200	.....	.....	.....	5500	12.6	.....	.....	19.3	.....	.....	.....	.....
3725 18 200A	.....	0	.....	.....	.....	22	0	.....	.....	18	.....	.....	.....	.....
		1100	.....	.....	.....	4000	9.4	.....	.....	18.9	.....	.....	.....	.....
3770 18 200A	.....	0	.....	.....	.....	22	0	.....	.....	18	.....	.....	.....	.....
		1100	.....	.....	.....	4000	12.6	.....	.....	22	.....	.....	.....	.....
3790 18 200														
Leading	.....	0	.....	.....	.....	20	.....	.....	.....	.....	.....	.....	.....	.....
		1000	.....	.....	.....	3500	.....	.....	.....	.....	.....	.....	.....	.....
Trailing	.....	0	.....	.....	.....	20	.....	.....	.....	.....	.....	.....	.....	.....
		1000	.....	.....	.....	3500	.....	.....	.....	.....	.....	.....	.....	.....
3928 18 200	.....	0	.....	.....	.....	22	0	.....	.....	7.5	.....	.....	.....	.....
		1100	.....	.....	.....	4000	10.6	.....	.....	19.7	.....	.....	.....	.....
8028 18 200	.....	0	.....	.....	.....	25	0	.....	.....	12	.....	.....	.....	.....
		1200	.....	.....	.....	5500	17.3	.....	.....	31	.....	.....	.....	.....
8235 18 200														
Leading	.....	0	.....	.....	.....	25	0	.....	.....	10	.....	.....	.....	.....
		1000	.....	.....	.....	4000	3.9	.....	.....	31.4	.....	.....	.....	.....
Trailing	.....	0	.....	.....	.....	25	0	.....	.....	35	.....	.....	.....	.....
		1000	.....	.....	.....	4000	7.8	.....	.....	31.4	.....	.....	.....	.....
8649 18 200B														
Leading	.....	0	.....	.....	.....	20	0	.....	.....	30	.....	.....	.....	.....
		1000	.....	.....	.....	3000	7.8	.....	.....	31.4	.....	.....	.....	.....
Trailing	.....	0	.....	.....	.....	20	0	.....	.....	30	.....	.....	.....	.....
		1000	.....	.....	.....	3000	15.6	.....	.....	31.4	.....	.....	.....	.....
8650 18 200														
Leading	.....	0	.....	.....	.....	20	0	.....	.....	30	.....	.....	.....	.....
		1000	.....	.....	.....	3000	7.8	.....	.....	31.4	.....	.....	.....	.....
Trailing	.....	0	.....	.....	.....	20	0	.....	.....	30	.....	.....	.....	.....
		1000	.....	.....	.....	3000	15.6	.....	.....	31.4	.....	.....	.....	.....
8735 18 200														
Leading	.....	0	.....	.....	.....	25	0	.....	.....	10	.....	.....	.....	.....
		1000	.....	.....	.....	4000	3.9	.....	.....	31.4	.....	.....	.....	.....
Trailing	.....	0	.....	.....	.....	25	0	.....	.....	35	.....	.....	.....	.....
		1000	.....	.....	.....	4000	3.9	.....	.....	31.4	.....	.....	.....	.....

① – C (Clockwise), CC (Counterclockwise), viewed from rotor end.

MITSUBISHI DISTRIBUTOR ADVANCE & RETARD SPECIFICATIONS

NOTE – *FOR DISTRIBUTOR RPM & DEGREES, DIVIDE SPECIFICATIONS BY 2*

Distributor Part No.	Rot. ①	Centrifugal Advance (Engine Degrees @ RPM)					Vacuum Advance (Engine Degrees @ In. of Hg)				Vacuum Retard (Engine Degrees @ In. of Hg)			
T3T03875	C	0 1000	....	....	....	20 4400	0 3.2	....	....	23 11.2	....	....	....	....
T3T04278	C	0 1000	....	....	....	20 4400	0 3.2	....	....	20 14.2	0 7.9	....	....	10 10.7
T3T04575	C	0 1200	....	....	....	20 6000	0 3.2	....	....	23 11	....	....	....	....
T3T04874	C	0 1200	....	....	....	20 6000	0 3.2	....	....	20 14.2	0 9.5	....	....	10 12
T3T05672	C	0 1000	....	....	....	20 4000	0 3.2	....	....	20 14.2	0 7.9	....	....	10 10.7
T3T05771	C	0 1000	....	....	....	20 4400	0 3.2	....	....	23 11.2	....	....	....	....

① – C (Clockwise), CC (Counterclockwise), viewed from rotor end

NIPPONDENSO DISTRIBUTOR ADVANCE & RETARD SPECIFICATIONS

NOTE – *FOR DISTRIBUTOR RPM & DEGREES, DIVIDE SPECIFICATIONS BY 2*

Distributor Part No.	Rot. ①	Centrifugal Advance (Engine Degrees @ RPM)					Vacuum Advance (Engine Degrees @ In. of Hg)				Vacuum Retard (Engine Degrees @ In. of Hg)			
029 100 3281	CC	0 1200	6 2000	16 3000	22 4000	25 5000	0 3.9	3 5.9	4 7.9	5 11.8	....	....	....	....
029 100 3700	CC	0 1000	6 1680	14 2400	28 4800	29 6000	0 4	....	....	16 12	0 4	....	....	20 14
029 100 4270	CC	0 1000	14 2400	....	....	28 4800	0 19.7	....	....	10 11.8	0 2.9	....	....	7.5 10.8
24013②	C	0 1000	23 3400	....	....	28 5400	0 4.3	6 7.8	....	9 10.2	....	....	....	....
26230②	C	0 1100	16 2400	24 4200	....	23.8 6000	0 3.5	3 4.7	....	9 11.8	....	....	....	....
26240②	C	0 1100	16 2400	20 3300	....	19.7 6000	0 3.5	4 5.9	....	9 10.2	0 2.7	....	....	5 5.9
38020②	C	0 1100	1.9 1300	9.4 2000	13.6 2600	20.8 6000	0 3.9	1.7 4.7	11.8 6.7	14 15.7	....	....	....	....
38040②	C	0 1100	9.4 2000	13.6 2600	18.9 4400	20.8 6000	0 3.9	1.5 4.7	8.6 10.2	10 14.9	....	....	....	....
61021②	C	0 1200	13 1800	20 3800	....	19.4 6000	....	....	....	....	0 3.9	....	....	5 6.3
61060②	C	0 1000	20 3200	....	....	19.6 6000	0 3.9	....	....	5 6.3	0 3.1	....	....	5 5.5

① – C (Clockwise), CC (Counterclockwise), viewed from rotor end.
② – Toyota basic part number 19100.

BOSCH SINGLE BREAKER DISTRIBUTOR

Audi
BMW
Mercedes Benz
Porsche
Saab
Volkswagen

DESCRIPTION

Single breaker, fully automatic type distributor. Centrifugal advance is accomplished with conventional weights and springs. Vacuum advance and/or vacuum retard units are diaphragm type and actuate the movable portion of breaker plate assembly. Vacuum units may be single or dual diaphragm. **NOTE** – *On some distributors, dual diaphragm unit may provide vacuum retard only (vacuum advance side of unit not used).*

Engine Speed Governor – Some distributors may use a specially designed rotor which also functions as a governor. When an engine speed for which this rotor is calibrated is exceeded, a centrifugal weight in rotor shifts position to ground ignition circuit. **CAUTION** – *Do not attempt to correct speed restriction by bending ground contact or any of the mechanical parts.* Replace rotor if damaged or out of calibration.

Triggering Contacts – Bosch distributors used on engines with electronically controlled fuel injection systems, have triggering contacts which provide the electronic control unit with information concerning engine speed. These contacts (mounted on an insert), are located below the centrifugal advance mechanism and actuated by a cam on distributor shaft. To remove insert with triggering contacts, remove both retaining screws and pull insert straight out. **CAUTION** – *Do not attempt to adjust contacts in any way.*

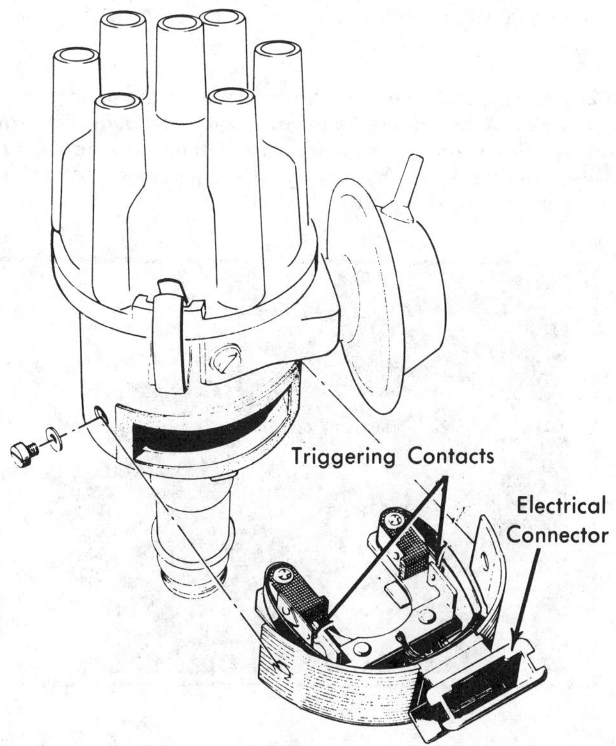

Fig. 1 Triggering Contacts

SPECIFICATIONS

Point Gap & Cam Angle – *See Tune-Up Data on Car Model Tune-Up Pages.*

Centrifugal & Vacuum Advance (Or Retard) – *See Specification Tables in this section.*

ADJUSTMENT

Point Gap, Alignment, & Cam Angle – With rubbing block on high point of cam lobe, insert a feeler gauge blade between contacts and check reading against specification. To correct, loosen retaining screw and move stationary contact point until correct gap is obtained, then tighten screw. Align points if necessary by bending stationary contact support only. Check cam angle with a dwell meter; compare indicated reading with specification and correct if necessary.

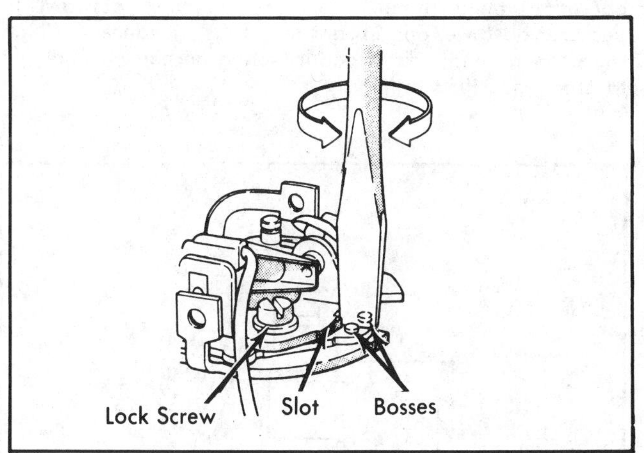

Fig. 2 Adjusting the Contact Points

Breaker Arm Spring Tension – To check spring tension, place hook end of spring scale as close as possible to the movable breaker point. Pull scale at a right angle (90 degrees) to the movable arm and note reading just as points begin to open.

Centrifugal Advance – 1) Check distributor in test stand according to test equipment manufacturers instructions. Operate distributor both up and down the RPM range and check advance at all RPM settings specified. Adjust or replace springs, weights or cam as necessary.

2) If distributor has adjustable driving collar for centrifugal advance (see illustration), disassemble distributor and lift distributor shaft out (breaker cam assembly need not be removed from shaft). Adjustment is made by altering spring tension in centrifugal advance. Loosen screws retaining driving collar. If driving collar is turned in direction of rotation, the advance curve rises; turning driving collar in opposite direction of rotation will lower the curve. **CAUTION** – *Centrifugal advance curve must not be adjusted by bending the spring clamps of driving collar.*

BOSCH SINGLE BREAKER DISTRIBUTOR (Cont.)

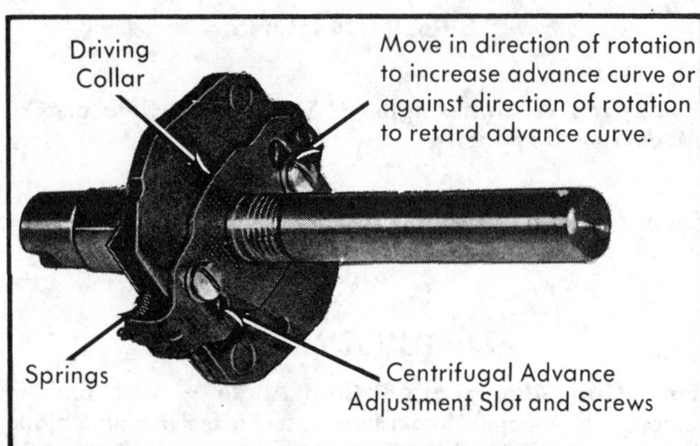

Fig. 3 Centrifugal Advance Adjustment (Driving Collar)

3) If distributor does not have adjustable driving collar, adjustment may be made by bending spring anchor tabs to modify spring tension (see illustration). To adjust for low speed operation, bend primary spring anchor tab outward to decrease advance, and inward to increase advance. For high speed operation, bend secondary spring anchor tab in or out to obtain specified settings.

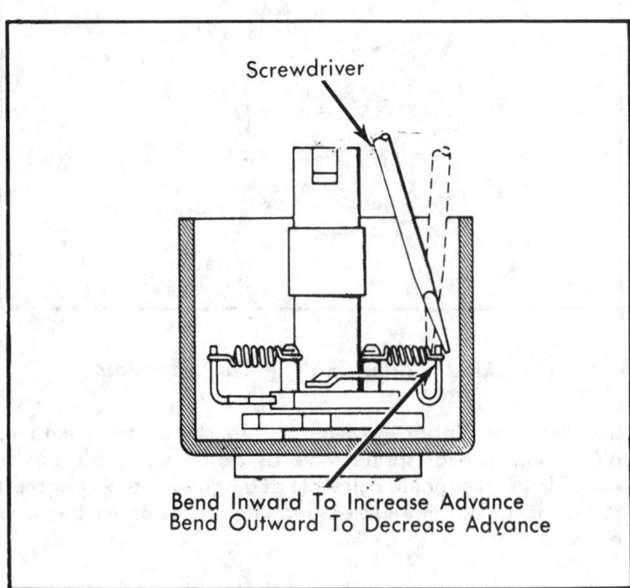

Fig. 4 Centrifugal Advance Adjustment (Spring Anchor Tabs)

Vacuum Advance – 1) With distributor in test stand, check advance at vacuum settings shown in specifications. If tests indicate vacuum diaphragm unit is inoperative, out of calibration, or leaking, replace vacuum unit.

2) Most types of vacuum diaphragm units are factory pre-set and cannot be adjusted. However, on some dual diaphragm vacuum units, the vacuum advance may be increased or decreased by turning an Allen screw located in end of diaphragm unit.

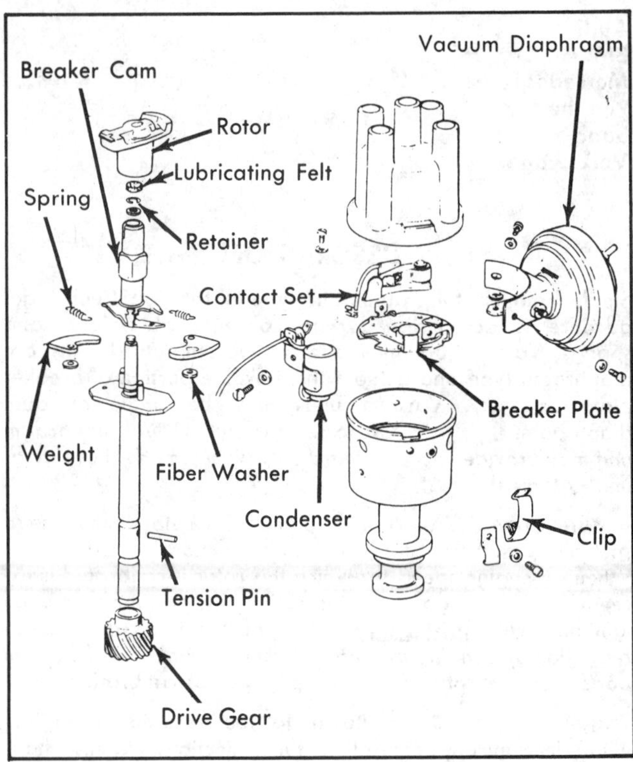

Fig. 5 Disassembled View of Bosch Distributor

Vacuum Retard – 1) With distributor in test stand, check retard at vacuum setttings shown in specifications. If tests indicate vacuum diaphragm unit is inoperative, out of calibration, or leaking, replace vacuum unit.

2) Most types of vacuum diaphragm units are factory pre-set and cannot be adjusted. However, on some dual diaphragm units, the maximum vacuum retard setting may be raised or lowered if necessary by turning an eccentric, located at side of vacuum unit (see illustration).

Fig. 6 Adjusting Maximum Vacuum Retard (Eccentric Location)

BOSCH SINGLE BREAKER DISTRIBUTOR (Cont.)

OVERHAUL

NOTE — *All parts should be marked or set aside separately in groups so that same combination can be reinstalled.*

Disassembly — 1) Disconnect and remove vacuum unit. Remove breaker points and condenser, then remove breaker plate assembly. Remove insert with triggering contacts (if equipped). Note positioning of centrifugal advance parts and mark for reassembly reference. Disconnect and remove centrifugal advance springs (do not distort). Using two screwdrivers, carefully pry upward on the lower edge of breaker cam to disengage cam retaining ring. Lift cam, washer, retaining ring and lubricating felt pad from shaft, then remove advance weights.

2) Drive out retaining pin, then remove coupling (or gear) from end of distributor shaft. NOTE — *Before removing coupling (if equipped),note relationship of coupling offset key to rotor locating slot as viewed from coupling end, then mark position of coupling on end of shaft for reassembly reference.* Remove shaft from distributor housing.

Reassembly — Install centrifugal weights and breaker cam on distributor shaft, then install advance springs. Secure breaker cam with washer and retaining ring, then install lubricating felt pad. Install shaft in distributor housing. Complete reassembly by reversing disassembly procedure.

BOSCH TRANSISTORIZED BREAKERLESS IGNITION SYSTEM

Mercedes Benz
Peugeot
Porsche
Volvo

DESCRIPTION & OPERATION

Bosch Transistorized Ignition System includes an electronic control module, a breakerless distributor, and a high output coil. Inside the distributor a trigger wheel rotates past a magnetic pick-up coil and stator winding. This builds up and then collapses a magnetic field producing a low voltage electrical signal. This signal passes to the module which controls the dwell angle and at the same time interrupts the ignition primary current to the coil. The interruption of primary current induces the high secondary coil output voltage to the spark plugs. Standard centrifugal and vacuum advance units are used and models with electronic fuel injection incorporate a set of triggering contacts in the distributor housing

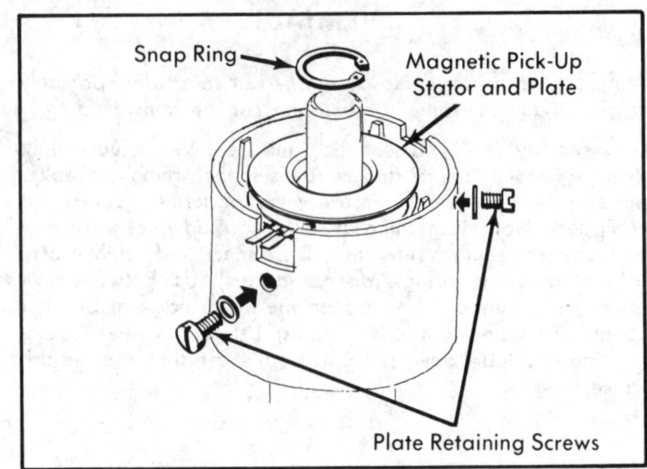

Fig. 2 Removing or Installing Pick-Up, Stator, and Carrier Plate

TESTING

NOTE – *Use full page diagnosis chart for testing ignition system. Repair or replace components as indicated by chart.*

OVERHAUL

DISASSEMBLY

1) Remove distributor cap, rotor and dust cover. Remove vacuum unit screws and lock clasp screws. **CAUTION** – *Keep screws with the component they attach, as screws are different lengths and damage could occur if installed in wrong position.* Remove screws securing electrical leads and remove leads by carefully pulling straight out.

2) Remove trigger wheel snap ring and then shims. Remove carrier plate attaching screws. Remove trigger wheel and small lock pin. Remove snap ring and lift carrier plate straight up off shaft. Remove three screws to separate stator winding from carrier plate.

3) Disconnect springs to centrifugal governor. Mark drive shaft relation to distributor shaft then secure drive shaft in a soft-jawed vise. Carefully tap on distributor housing using a plastic mallet until circlip releases. If equipped, remove triggering contacts and attaching screws.

4) Remove resilient ring then mark location of flange to distributor shaft. Support distributor shaft and using a pin punch, remove pin. Remove flange and distributor shaft. Remove lock springs for centrifugal weights then remove weights.

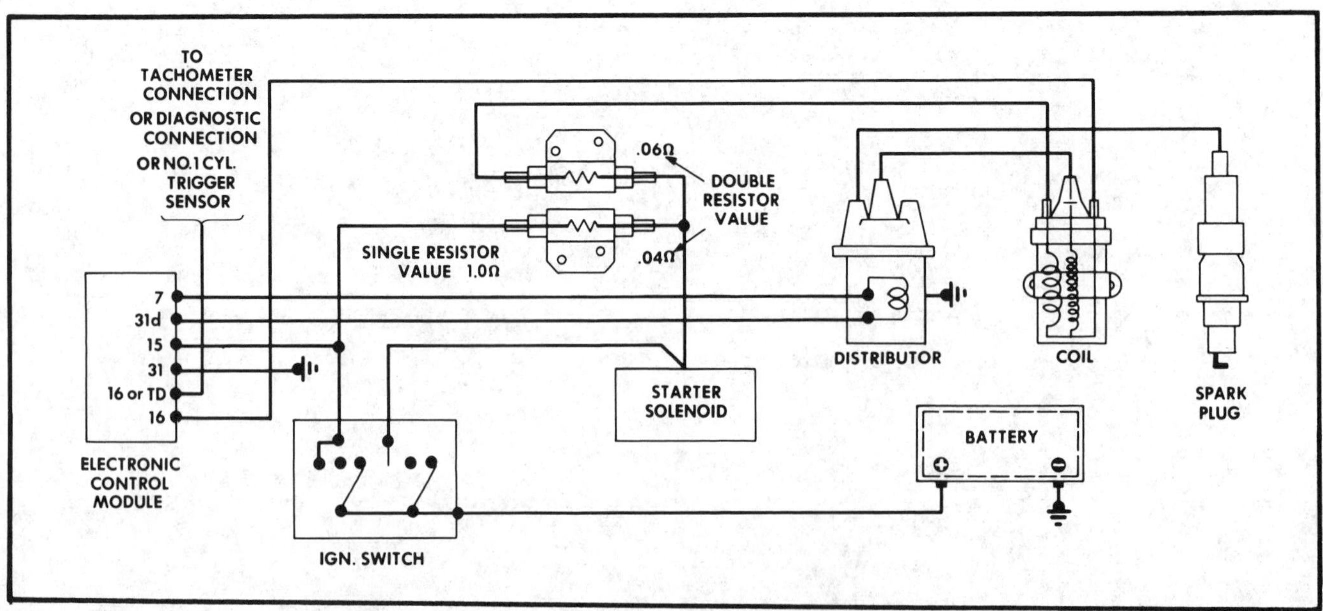

Fig. 1 Wiring Diagram of Typical Bosch Transistorized Ignition System

BOSCH TRANSISTORIZED BREAKERLESS IGNITION SYSTEM (Cont.)

TESTING BOSCH BREAKERLESS IGNITION

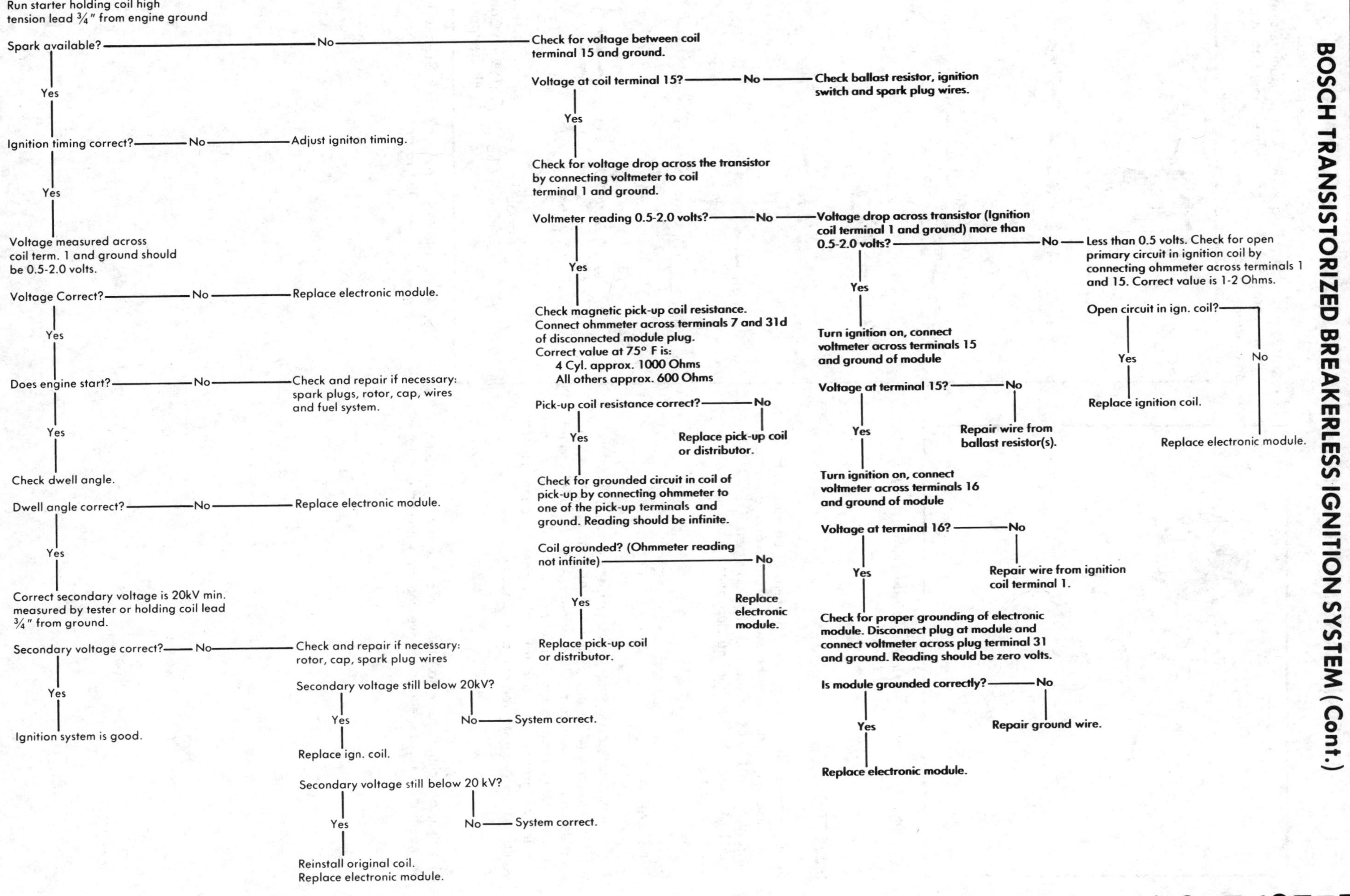

BOSCH TRANSISTORIZED BREAKERLESS IGNITION SYSTEM (Cont.)

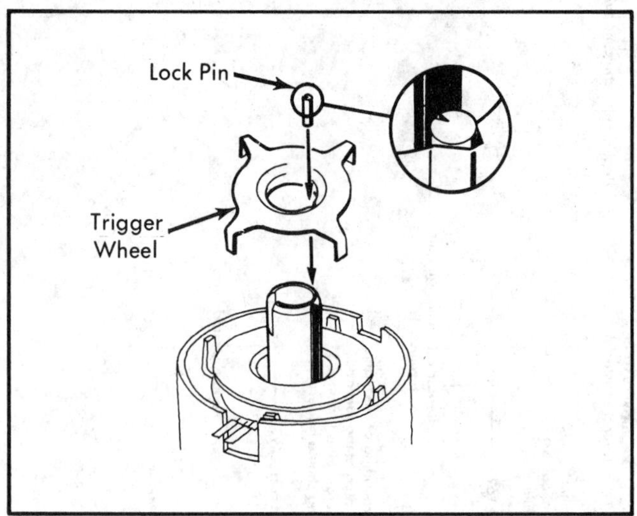

Fig. 3 Installing Trigger Wheel (Armature) and Lock Pin

INSPECTION

Springs for weights must not be deformed or damaged. Holes in centrifugal governor weights must not be oval or deformed. Distributor shaft to cam clearance should not exceed .004" (.1 mm). Distributor shaft to housing clearance should not exceed .008" (.2 mm).

REASSEMBLY

1) To reassemble distributor, reverse disassembly procedure while noting the following: Place a light coat of grease on weights and breaker cam. Oil distributor shaft before installing shaft in housing. Soak felt lubricator in oil. Place small amount of grease on fiber tabs of triggering contacts (if equipped) before installing contacts in housing.

2) When attaching stator to plate, the connector pins should be positioned opposite and above the attachment ear for carrier plate. Install lock pin with lift facing ridge on distributor shaft. Slot on trigger wheel should be opposite ridge on distributor shaft.

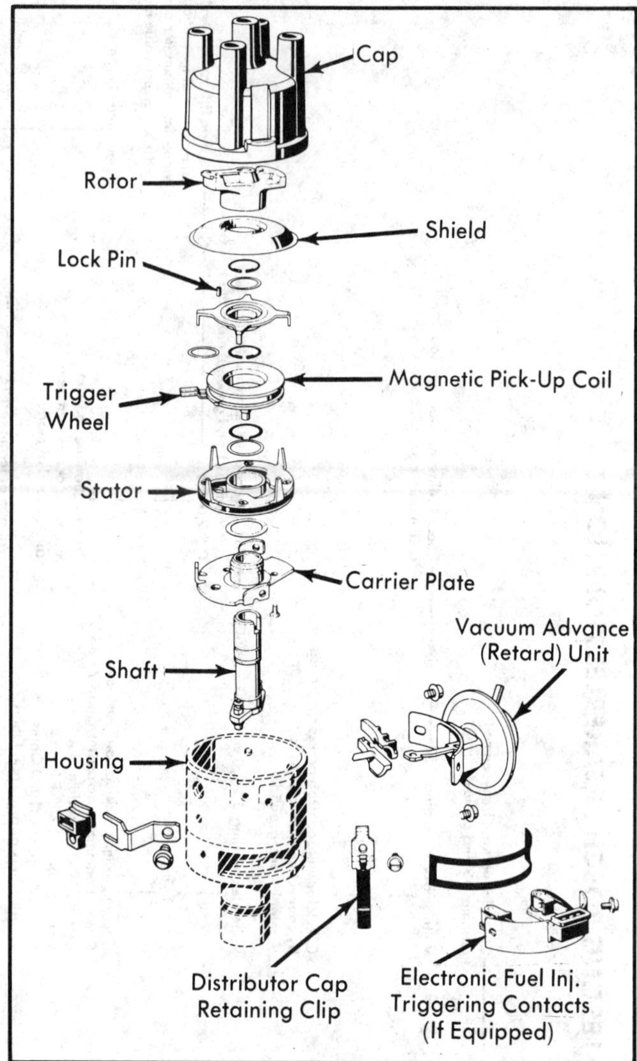

Fig. 4 Exploded View of Bosch Breakerless Distributor

DUCELLIER DISTRIBUTORS

Fiat
128 & X1/9
Peugeot
504 Model
Renault
All Models

DESCRIPTION

Single breaker, fully automatic type distributor. Centrifugal advance is conventional type with weights and springs. Unit may or may not be equipped with vacuum advance device.

SPECIFICATIONS

Point Gap, Cam Angle & Breaker Arm Spring Tension – *See Tune-Up Data on Car Model Tune-Up Pages.*

Centrifugal & Vacuum Advance – *See Specification Tables in this section.*

ADJUSTMENT

Point Gap, Alignment, & Cam Angle – With rubbing block on high point of cam lobe, insert a feeler gauge blade between contacts and check reading against specification. To correct, loosen retaining screw and move stationary contact point until correct gap is obtained, then tighten screw. Align points if necessary by bending stationary contact support only. Check cam angle using a dwell meter; compare indicated reading with specification and correct if necessary.

Breaker Arm Spring Tension – To check spring tension, place hook end of spring scale as close as possible to the movable breaker point. Pull scale at a right angle (90 degrees) to the movable arm and note reading just as points begin to open.

Centrifugal Advance – Check distributor in test stand according to test equipment manufacturers instructions. Operate distributor both up and down the RPM range and check advance at all RPM settings specified. If not within specifications, adjust by bending spring anchor tabs to modify tension, or replace springs.

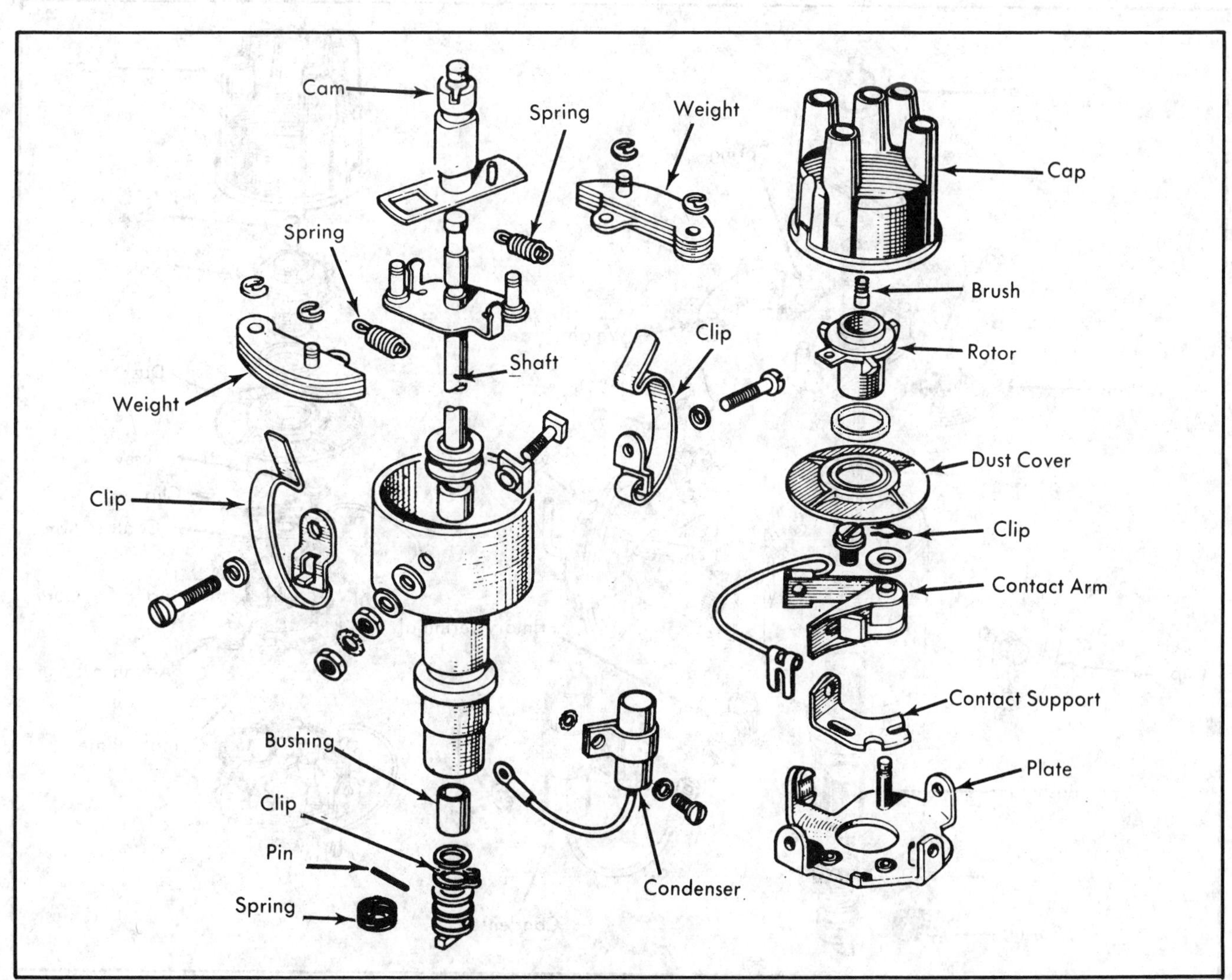

Fig. 1 Disassembled View of Ducellier Distributor Without Vacuum Unit

DUCELLIER DISTRIBUTORS (Cont.)

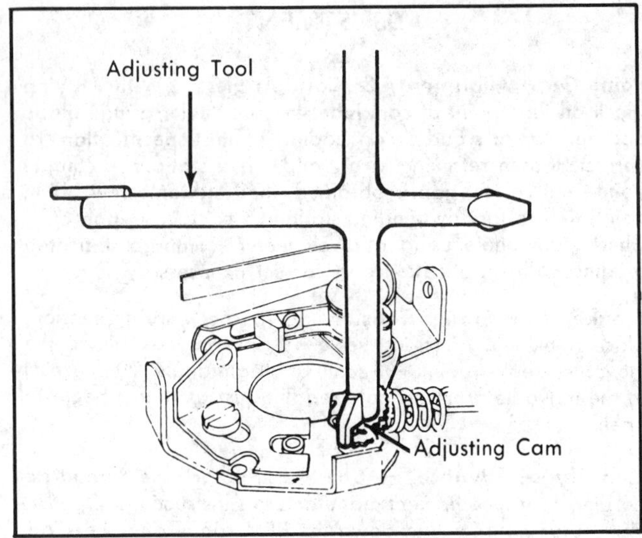

Fig. 2 Adjusting Vacuum Advance (Renault is Shown)

Vacuum Advance – With distributor in test stand, check advance at vacuum settings shown in specifications. Adjust if necessary by altering the adjusting cam setting (see illustration). If tests indicate vacuum diaphragm unit is inoperative, out of calibration, or leaking, replace vacuum unit.

OVERHAUL

Disassembly – **NOTE** – *All parts should be marked or set aside separately in groups so that same combination can be reinstalled.* Remove rotor, dust cover (if equipped), and condenser. Remove vacuum diaphragm unit (if equipped), then remove breaker plate assembly. Remove pin retaining spring, then remove pin, coupling, and related parts from end of distributor shaft. Remove shaft from distributor housing. Note positioning of cam, springs and weights on distributor shaft, then remove cam attaching screw and remove cam, governor springs and weights.

Reassembly – Reassemble distributor in reverse order of disassembly.

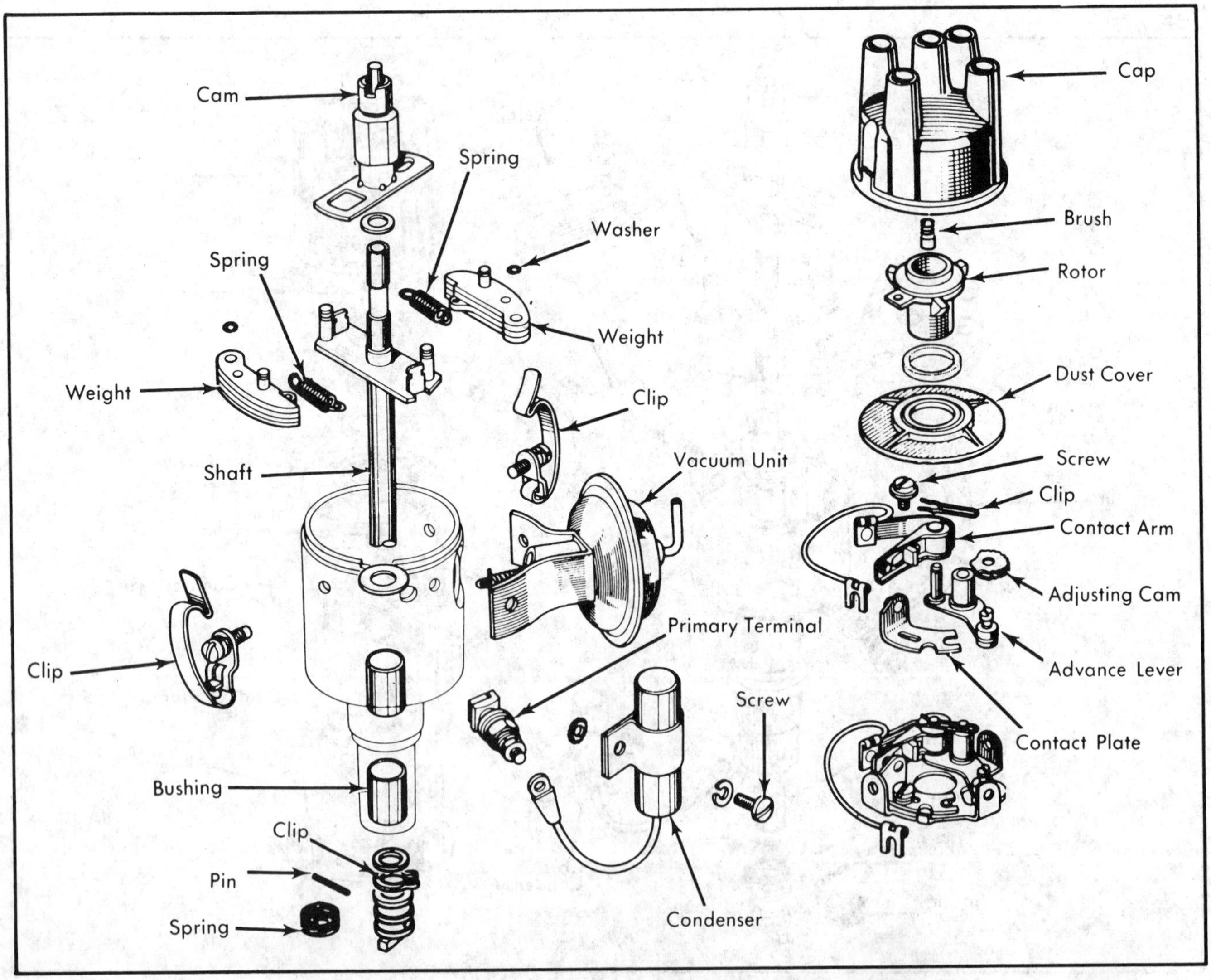

Fig. 3 Disassembled View of Ducellier Distributor with Vacuum Unit

HITACHI SINGLE BREAKER DISTRIBUTOR

Datsun
All Federal Models Exc. 280Z
Honda
All Models

DESCRIPTION

Single breaker, fully automatic type of conventional design. Breaker plate assembly consists of a fixed lower plate, with breaker points mounted on movable upper plate. Centrifugal advance is conventional type with weights and springs. Vacuum advance (or retard) is controlled by a vacuum diaphragm unit mounted on distributor housing and linked to the movable portion of the breaker plate assembly.

NOTE — *Distributor operation with either vacuum advance or vacuum retard is the same except that on distributors with vacuum retard, the breaker plate rotates in the reverse direction.*

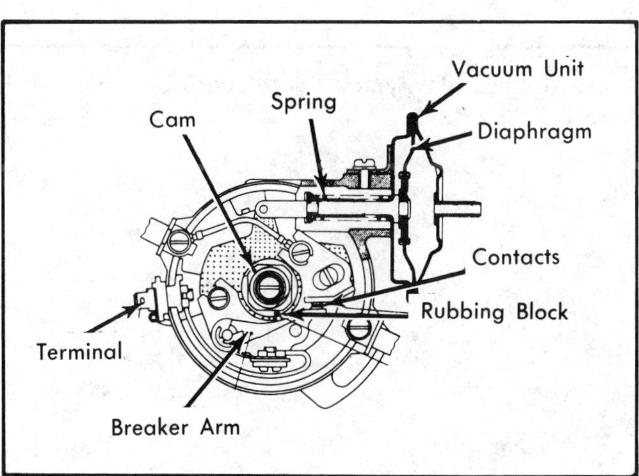

Fig. 1 Typical Vacuum Advance System

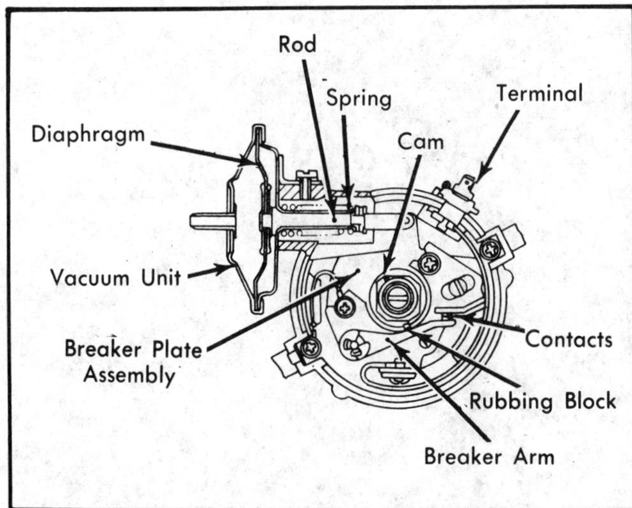

Fig. 2 Typical Vacuum Retard System

SPECIFICATIONS

Point Gap, Cam Angle & Breaker Arm Spring Tension — *See Tune-Up Data on Car Model Tune-Up Pages.*

Centrifugal & Vacuum Advance (Or Retard) — See *Specification Tables in this section.*

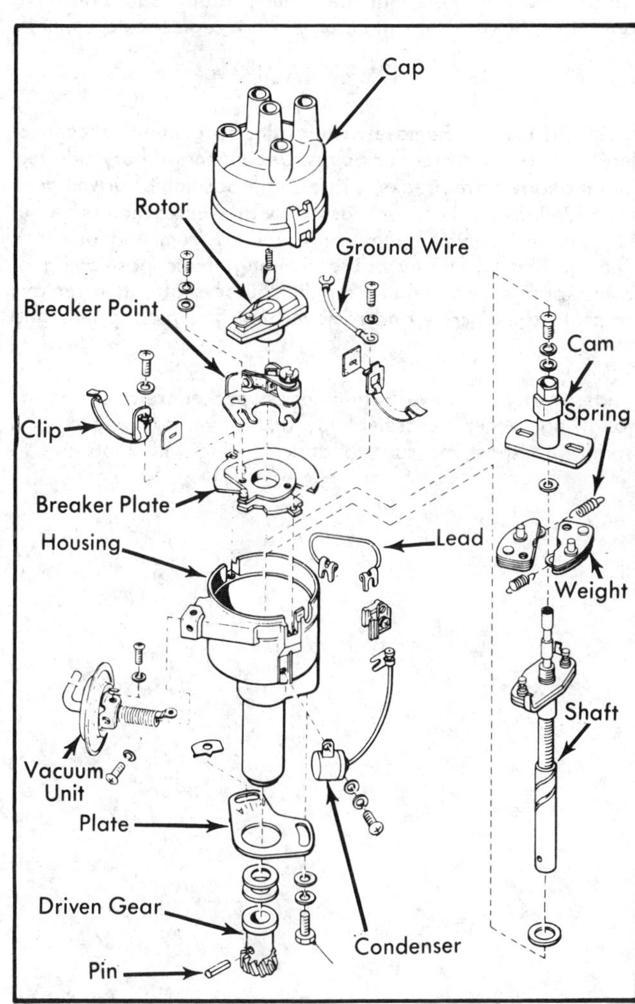

Fig. 3 Disassembled View of Distributor

ADJUSTMENT

Point Gap, Alignment, & Cam Angle — With rubbing block on high point of cam lobe, insert a feeler gauge blade between contacts and check reading against specification. To correct, loosen retaining screw and move stationary contact point until correct gap is obtained, then tighten screw. Align points if necessary by bending stationary contact support only. Check cam angle using a dwell meter; compare indicated reading with specification and correct if necessary.

Breaker Arm Spring Tension — To check spring tension, place hook end of spring scale as close as possible to the movable breaker point. Pull scale at a right angle (90 degrees) to the movable arm and note reading just as points begin to open.

HITACHI SINGLE BREAKER DISTRIBUTOR (Cont.)

Centrifugal Advance – Check distributor in a test stand according to test equipment manufacturers instructions. Operate distributor both up and down the RPM range and check advance at all RPM settings specified.

Vacuum Advance (Or Retard) – With distributor in test stand, check advance (or retard) at vacuum settings shown in specifications. If tests indicate vacuum diaphragm unit is inoperative, out of calibration, or leaking, replace vacuum unit.

OVERHAUL

Disassembly – Remove vacuum diaphragm unit. Disconnect lead and remove breaker points. Disconnect primary side terminal and remove breaker plate. Mark position of driven gear (or coupling) on shaft for reassembly reference, then drive out roll pin and remove gear (or coupling) from end of shaft. Remove shaft from distributor housing. Note positioning of cam, springs and weights on distributor shaft, then remove cam attaching screw and remove cam, governor springs and weights.

Reassembly – Reverse disassembly procedure and note the following: When reassembling cam, governor weights and springs to shaft, be sure to attach spring with loop end to governor weight, the pin of which is fitted into the longer slot in cam plate. Attach the spring with rectangular hook end to governor weight, the pin of which is fitted into the shorter slot. See *illustration*.

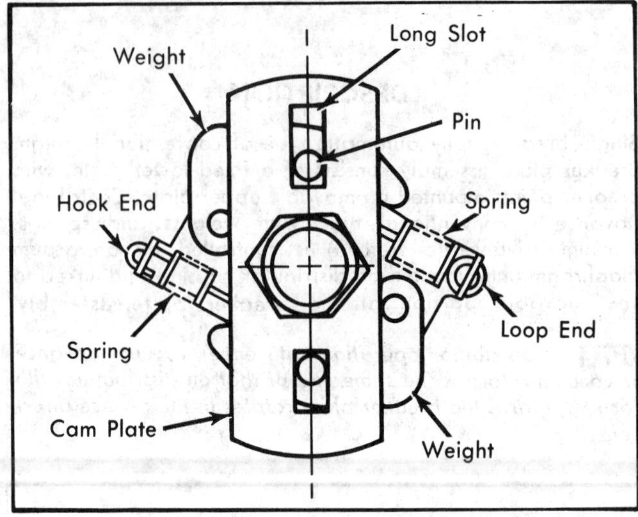

Fig. 4 Typical Centrifugal Advance

HITACHI ELECTRONIC IGNITION SYSTEM

Datsun
All Calif. & 280Z Models
Subaru
Calif. with Auto. Trans.

DESCRIPTION

Hitachi's electronic distributor consists of a housing, rotor, and distributor cap. A reluctor and pickup coil replace the breaker points and cam of a conventional distributor. A transistor ignition unit makes and breaks the electrical current in the primary circuit of the ignition coil with the duty control circuit of this unit setting the rate at which current is broken. This creates what is equal to dwell angle in a conventional distributor.

SPECIFICATIONS

Air Gap & Cam Angle – *See Tune-Up Data on Car Model Tune-Up Pages.*

Centrifugal & Vacuum Advance – *See Specification Tables in this section.*

ADJUSTMENTS

Air Gap – Air gap should be adjusted to specifications by aligning high point on reluctor with pole piece on pickup coil, then loosen pickup coil screws. Using a feeler gauge, move pickup coil to obtain specified air gap. On dual pickup distributors, check the cam-to-contactor clearance as it may be affected by changing the air gap. Clearance should be .012" (.3 mm) and contactor should touch highest point of cam.

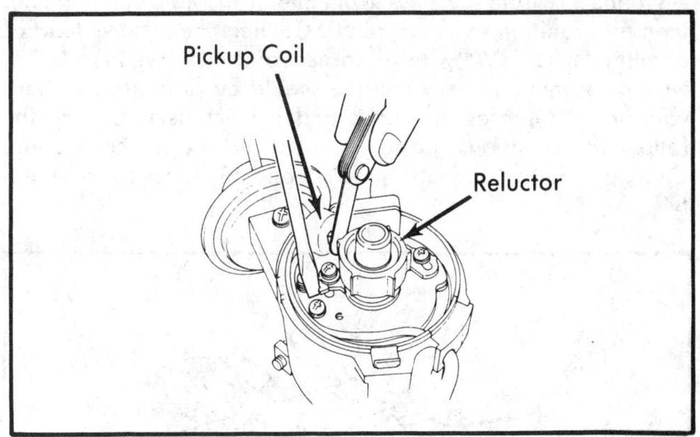

Fig. 1 Adjusting the Air Gap

Phase Angle (Dual Pickup) – With water temperature switch for advanced side disconnected and shorted, timing set to specifications and engine idling, check that phase difference is six degrees. If not, correct by loosening adjuster plate screws ½ to 2 turns. Turn adjuster plate until correct phase angle is obtained. Turning adjusting plate clockwise increases phase angle and counterclockwise decreases phase angle.

NOTE – *Graduations on adjuster plate refer to crankshaft degrees. One graduation equals four crankshaft degrees.*

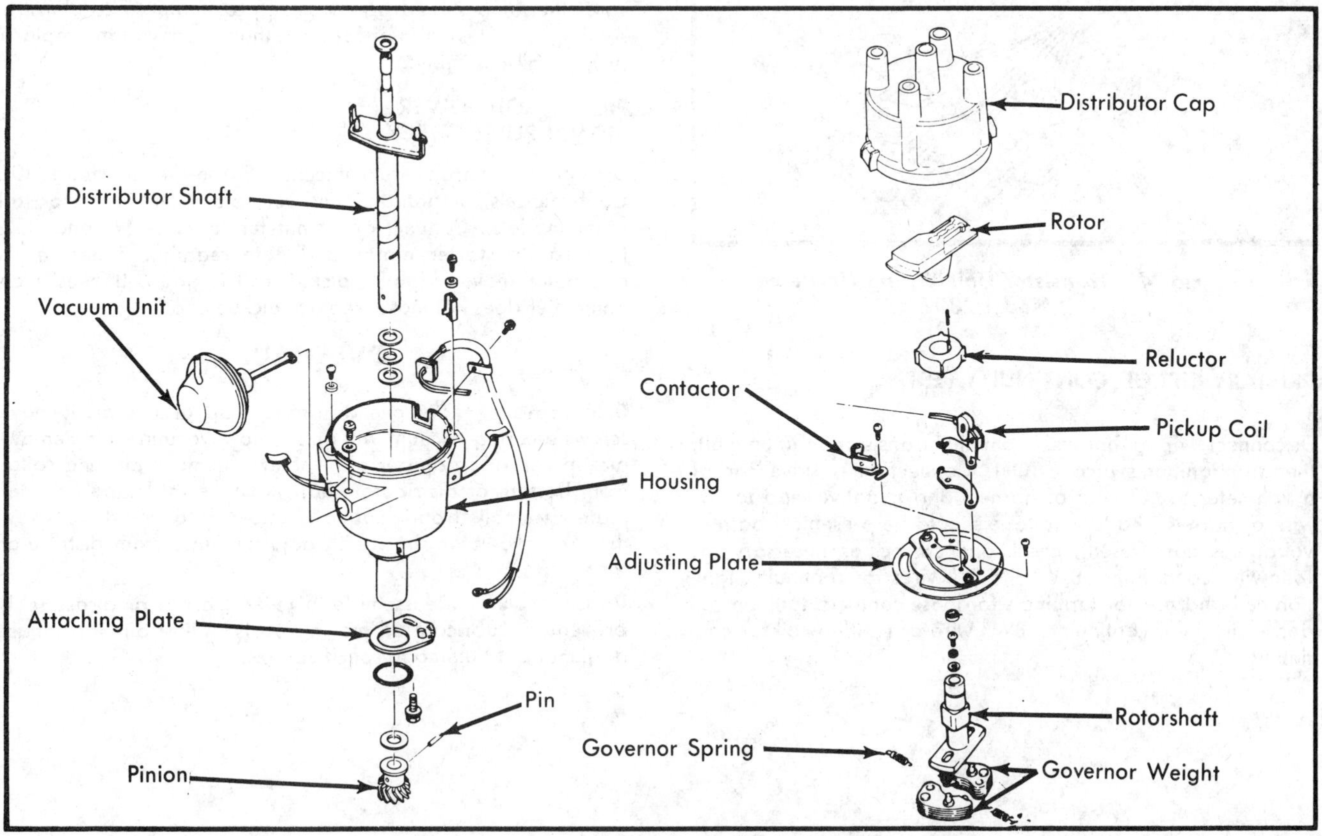

Distributor Shaft
Vacuum Unit
Housing
Attaching Plate
Pin
Pinion
Distributor Cap
Rotor
Reluctor
Contactor
Pickup Coil
Adjusting Plate
Rotorshaft
Governor Spring
Governor Weight

Fig. 2 Exploded View of Distributor

HITACHI ELECTRONIC IGNITION SYSTEM (Cont.)

TESTING

POWER SUPPLY WIRING & BATTERY TEST

Disconnect wiring harness from the transistor ignition unit, then turn ignition switch to "ON". Connect the positive lead of a voltmeter to "BW" wire of harness and negative lead to "B" wire of harness. Battery voltage should be present. If battery voltage is not present, check and correct as necessary the following conditions: Battery cables for proper connection. Charge condition of battery. "BW" and "B" wires for continuity.

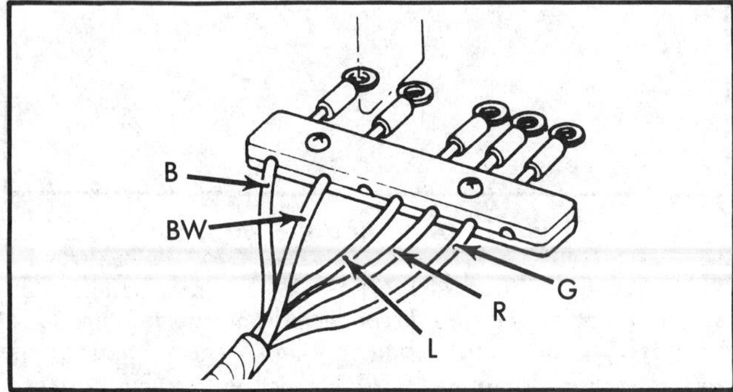

Fig. 3 Transistor Wiring Harness Unit for Datsun 200SX, B210, F10, 810 & P/U

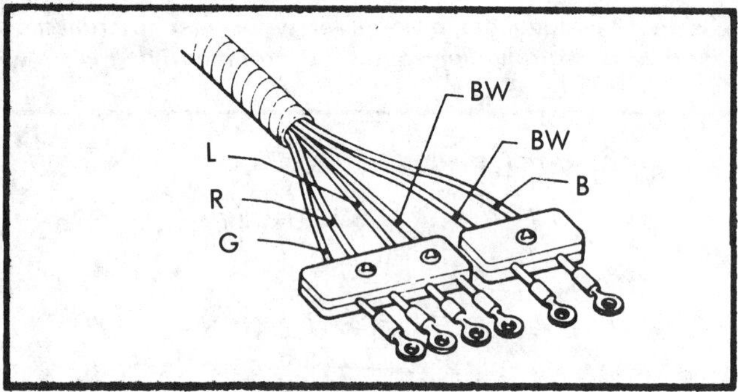

Fig. 4 Transistor Unit Wiring Harness Model 280Z

PRIMARY CIRCUIT CONTINUITY TEST

Disconnect wiring harness from the transistor ignition unit, then turn ignition switch to "ON". Connect the positive lead of a voltmeter to "L" wire of harness and negative lead to "B" wire of harness. Battery voltage should be present. If battery voltage is not present, check and correct as necessary the following conditions: "BW" and "L" wires for continuity. Ignition coil and resistor terminals for loose contacts. Ignition coil and resistor for continuity. "BW" wire of ignition coil for continuity.

IGNITION COIL & RESISTOR TEST

Disconnect engine harness from ignition coil external resistor terminals. Connect an ohmmeter to terminals of resistor and note reading. If reading is more than 1.8 ohms, coil requires replacement.

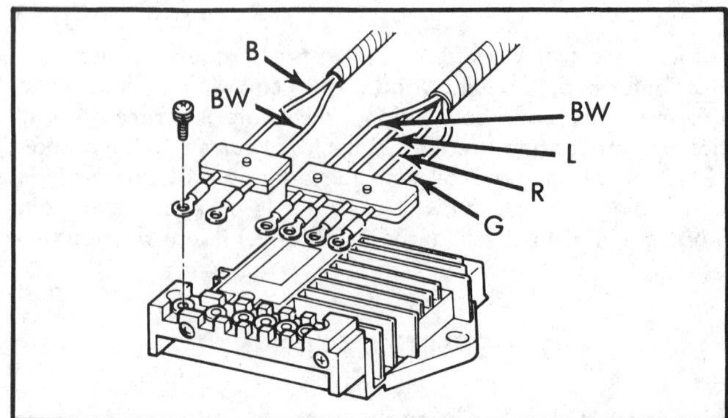

Fig. 5 Transistor Unit Wiring Harness for 710 Models

PICKUP COIL CONTINUITY CHECK

Disconnect wiring harness from the transistor ignition unit. Connect an ohmmeter to wires "R" and "G", then note reading. Ohmmeter should read approximately 720 ohms. If reading is far less than or far more than specifications, replace pickup coil assembly. On 280Z Federal models check the advance side of pickup coil by connecting an ohmmeter to "R" and "G" wires. Reading should again be approximately 720 ohms. If reading is far less than or far more than specifications, replace pickup coil assembly.

PICKUP COIL POWER SIGNAL PULSE CHECK

Disconnect electronic fuel injection harness connector (280Z Calif. models) or anti-dieseling solenoid valve connector (all other models). Connect an ohmmeter to wires "R" and "G", then rotate starter motor and note reading. If needle on ohmmeter moves slightly, pickup coil is good. If needle on ohmmeter does not move, replace pickup coil.

OVERHAUL

Disassembly – Remove distributor cap and rotor. Remove screws securing vacuum unit and remove vacuum unit. Remove pickup coil and adjuster plate screws. Remove pin and collar from bottom of distributor shaft. Remove shaft and adjuster plate assembly from housing. Remove rotor shaft set screw then remove rotor shaft with adjuster plate from distributor shaft.

Reassembly – Reassemble in reverse order of disassembly procedure. Lubricate all moving parts. Adjust air gap, phase angle, and set timing to specifications.

LUCAS "OPUS" ELECTRONIC IGNITION SYSTEM

Jaguar
All Models
MG
Midget
MGB
Triumph
Spitfire
TR7

DESCRIPTION

Lucas "OPUS" (Oscillating Pick-Up System) electronic ignition includes an amplifier unit mounted on distributor on MG, Triumph, and Jaguar XJ6, or externally mounted on XJ12 and XJS; a ballast resistor wire, except on XJ12 and XJS which use a ballast resistor unit; an ignition coil; a drive resistor on MG, Triumph, and XJ6; and a breakerless distributor.

Distributor – 1) Consists of a centrifugal advance mechanism, a retard-type vacuum unit, a high-tension rotor, electronic timing rotor, and a pick-up module assembly.

2) The timing rotor and pick-up module, working in conjunction with a separate amplifier unit, replace the contact breaker and cam of a conventional distributor. Timing rotor is a glass-filled nylon disc with small ferrite rods embedded into its outer edge, the number and spacing of rods corresponding with the number of cylinders and firing angles of the engine. An air gap (adjustable to specified limits) exists between rotor and ferrite core of the stationary pick-up module. The pick-up module assembly comprises a magnetically balanced small transformer, with primary (input) and secondary (output) windings. **CAUTION** – *Pick-up module is magnetically balanced during manufacture and setting must not be altered. The sealed ferrite adjusting screw must not be disturbed.*

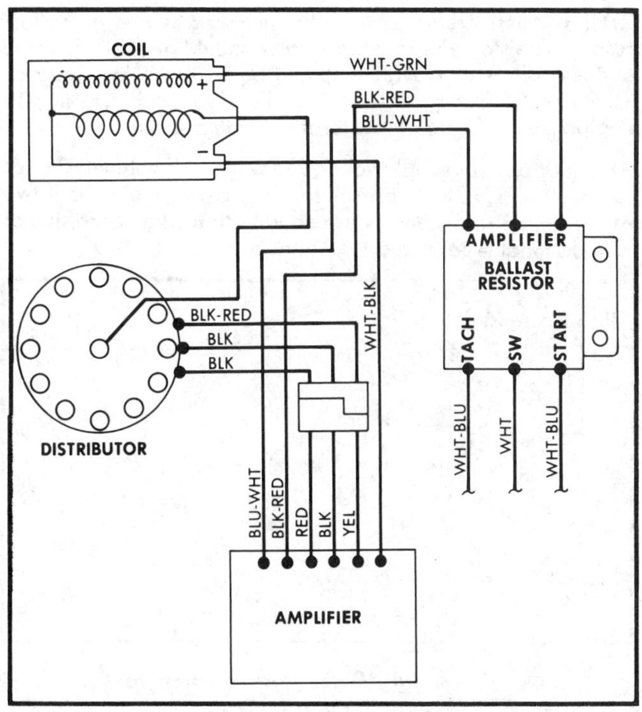

Fig. 1 Wiring Diagram of Jaguar XJ12 and XJS Lucas "OPUS" Ignition System

3) Automatic control of retard-ignition timing is provided by a vacuum unit which varies the static timing position of pick-up module in relation to the ferrite rods in timing rotor. The distributor timing rotor and pick-up module generate an electronic timing signal, which is fed to the amplifier unit via external cables. **CAUTION** – *The length of this triple-core extruded type cable must not be altered, and the cables must not be separated or replaced by loose individual cables.*

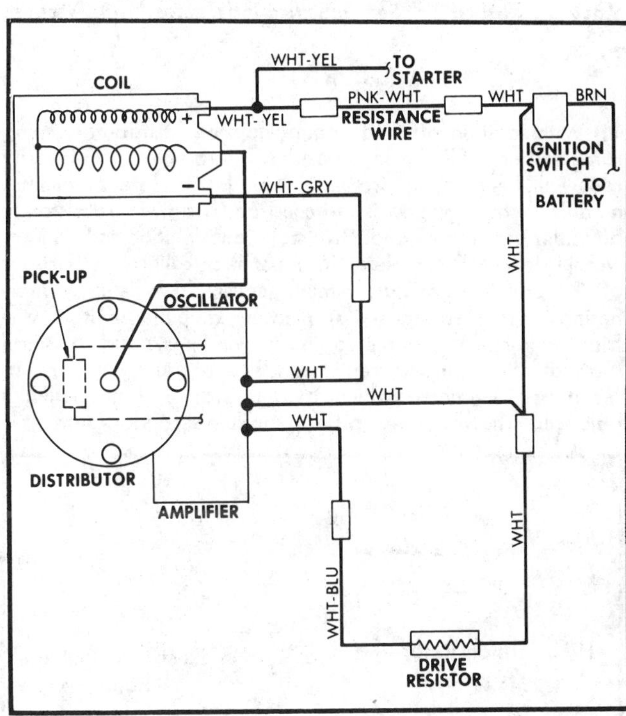

Fig. 2 Wiring Diagram of Triumph TR7 Lucas "OPUS" Ignition System Spitfire, MG and XJ6 Similar

Amplifier Unit – Interprets timing signals from distributor. A power transistor incorporated in the printed circuit then functions as an electronic switch in primary circuit of ignition coil. Unit is connected to ignition coil via a ballast resistance unit and external cables.

Drive Resistor – An externally mounted unit which functions as part of the amplifier. External mounting is required because of size and heat dissipation requirements.

Ballast Resistor Unit (XJ12, XJS) – Includes three resistors enclosed in an aluminum heat sink. Two of the resistors are wired in series to coil primary winding and the third resistor functions with a transistor in the amplifier.

Ballast Resistor Wire (XJ6, MG, Triumph) – Connected in series between ignition switch and coil primary winding.

Ignition Coil – A specially designed fluid-cooled, high-performance, ballast-ignition coil. Coil terminals are marked "+" and "–" and have different types of connectors to prevent incorrect cable connection. **CAUTION** – *The "OPUS" coil is NOT interchangeable with any other type.*

LUCAS "OPUS" ELECTRONIC IGNITION SYSTEM (Cont.)

SPECIFICATIONS

Pick-Up Module Gap & Cam Angle – *See Tune-Up Data on Car Model Tune-Up Pages.*

Centrifugal Advance – *See Specification Tables in this section.*

Vacuum Retard – *See Specification Tables in this section.*

OPERATION

1) With ignition off and engine stopped, distributor timing rotor will normally be in a position where none of the ferrite rods will be in close proximity with ferrite core of pick-up module. When ignition is switched on, a power transistor in amplifier unit is in a conductive state, and ignition coil primary winding circuit is complete via the emitter/collector electrodes of the power transistor. Simultaneously, a pulsating alternating current voltage is applied by amplifier unit to distributor pick-up module primary windings, and a small residual alternating current voltage is produced at pick-up secondary windings, which at this stage is magnetically balanced. The voltage at pick-up module secondary terminals is applied to amplifier unit, but residual voltage at this stage is insufficient to have any effect on transistor circuits, which control the switching off of the power transistor in the output stage of amplifier unit.

2) When engine is cranked, one of the ferrite rods in the rotor, now brought into close proximity with ferrite core of module causes "magnetic unbalancing" of module core, resulting in an increase in voltage at module output terminals. This "unbalancing" and voltage increases to maximum as rotor rod passes center and upper legs of the module "E" shaped core. Maximum voltage is then applied to amplifier unit, where it is rectified. The resulting direct current is then used to operate the transistor circuits which control switching off of the power transistor in the output stage. With power transistor switched off, its emitter/collector electrodes cease to conduct, and coil primary winding is disconnected which causes a rapid collapse of the primary winding magnetic field through the secondary windings of ignition coil, resulting in a high-tension voltage being produced at ignition coil.

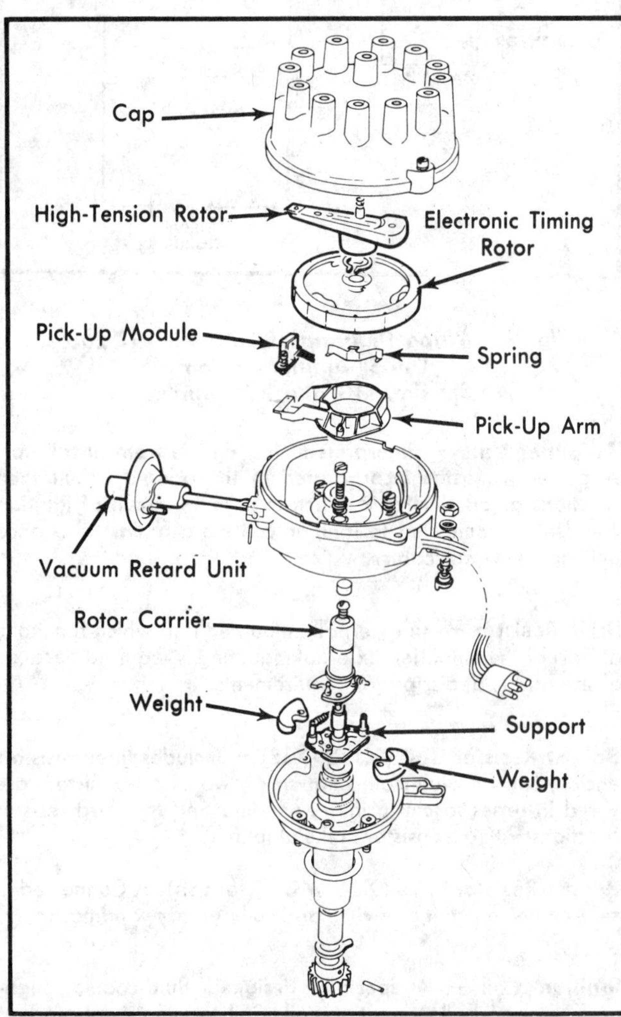

Fig. 3 Exploded View of Lucas Breakerless Distributor Used on Jaguar XJ12 and XJS

TESTING

NOTE – *It is important that the following tests be made in order outlined below.*

Battery (Circuit Test) – Battery should be fully charged. Disconnect lead from coil terminal marked "–", then connect voltmeter between battery ground terminal and frame. Operate starter, voltmeter reading should not exceed 0.5 volts. If higher voltage is registered, correct faulty connection between frame and battery.

Ignition Coil (Applied Voltage Test) – **1)** Connect voltmeter between coil "+" terminal and ground. With ignition switch ON, voltmeter should read 4-6 volts.

2) If voltmeter reads below 4 volts, check value of ballast resistor. Resistor wire resistance value should be 1.3-1.5 Ohms. Ballast resistor block values should be 7.6-9.2 Ohms (resistor 1), 0.72-0.80 Ohms (resistor 2), and 0.9-1.0 Ohms (resistor 3). Replace resistor wire or resistor if not within specifications.

3) Check battery supply voltage to resistor. If voltmeter reads above 6 volts, remove distributor cap, crank engine until two of the timing rotor sensors are equally spaced on each side of pick-up module core. Recheck voltage.

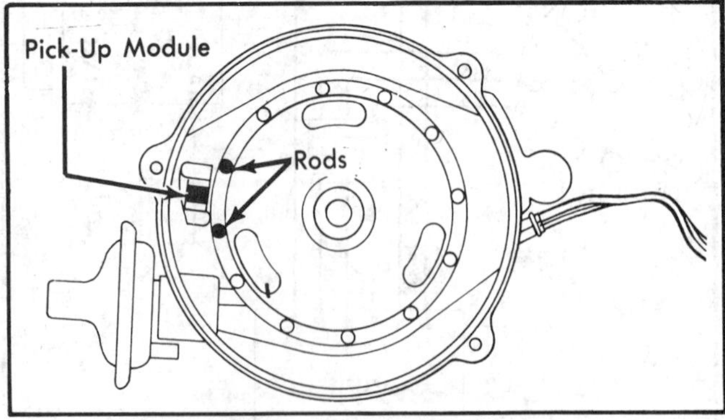

Fig. 4 Timing Rotor Rod Location for Applied Voltage Test

4) Check ignition coil for continuity and resistance of primary winding between "+" and "–" terminals. Replace coil if outside limits of 0.8-1.0 ohms, or if open circuited.

LUCAS "OPUS" ELECTRONIC IGNITION SYSTEM (Cont.)

Ignition Coil (Voltage Drop Test) – Connect voltmeter between "–" terminal of coil and ground. DO NOT disconnect coil wires. Switch on ignition and note meter reading. Replace amplifier unit if above 2 volts.

Amplifier Unit (Switching Action Test) – Remove distributor cap, then crank engine until one of the ferrite rods is in line with timing mark on module. Connect voltmeter between "–" terminal of coil and ground. DO NOT disconnect coil wires. Switch on ignition and note meter reading. If below battery voltage (12 volts), test amplifier unit, then test pick-up module.

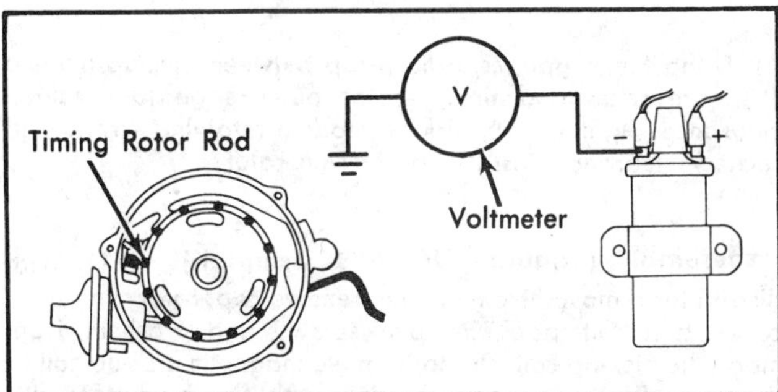

Fig. 5 Connections for Testing Amplifier Switching Action

Amplifier Unit Test – Crank engine until two of the ferrite rods in the timing rotor are equally spaced on each side of pick-up module core. Disconnect lead from "SW" terminal of ballast unit. Connect an ammeter (0-20A range) in series with lead and terminal. Switch on ignition, ammeter should read 5-6.5 amperes. Separate connector between distributor and amplifier unit. Connect outside terminals of amplifier plug alternately to center terminal. Ammeter reading should remain unchanged. If reading increases by more than 0.5 ampere, replace amplifier unit.

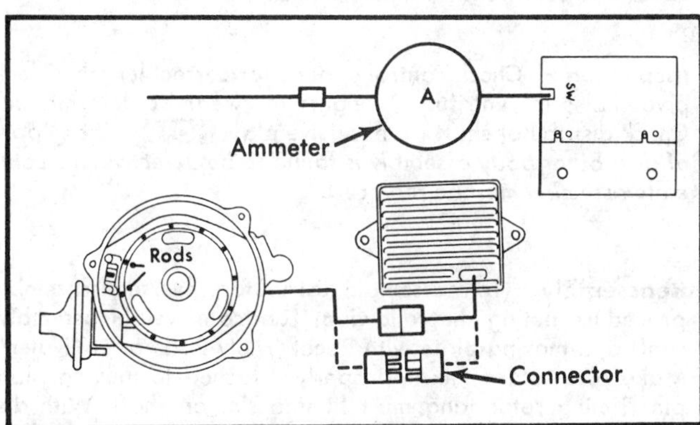

Fig. 6 Connections for Amplifier Unit Test

Pick-Up Module Test – 1) Connect one lead of ohmeter to center terminal of pick-up module connector, and other lead alternately to each of the outside terminals.

2) Primary (input) winding resistance, measured between center terminal and outer terminal (red wire) should be 2.5 ohms nominal at 68°F (20°C).

3) Secondary (output) winding resistance, measured between center terminal and outer terminal (black wire), should be 0.9 ohms nominal at 68°F (20°C).

4) If readings shown above are obtained, remove pick-up module and check sealed adjusting screw near bottom leg of "E" shaped core. Replace module assembly if seal is broken.

5) If readings are not as shown above, replace module assembly.

6) On models with drive resistor, check for 9-10 Ohms resistance by testing across drive resistor terminals. Replace drive resistor if not within specifications.

ADJUSTMENT

Pick-Up Module Gap & Cam Angle – Slightly loosen two screws retaining pick-up module to pick-up arm. Using feeler gauges, adjust gap between pick-up module "E" core faces and timing rotor outer edge to .020-.022" (.50-.55 mm) XJ12 and XJS, or .014-.016" (.25-.40 mm) all other models. Tighten pick-up retaining screws and recheck clearance. Check cam angle with a dwell meter and correct if necessary.

Centrifugal Advance – Check distributor in test stand according to test equipment manufacturers instructions. Operate distributor both up and down the RPM range and check advance at all RPM settings specified.

Vacuum Retard – With distributor in test stand, check retard at vacuum settings shown in specifications. If tests indicate vacuum diaphragm unit is inoperative, out of calibration, or leaking, replace vacuum unit.

OVERHAUL

Disassembly (Jaguar XJ12 and XJS) – 1) Remove distributor cap. Crank engine to align No. 1 cylinder mark on timing rotor with mark on pick-up module. Disconnect vacuum hose to retard unit and electrical lead plug. Release three Allen screws (accessible through slots in micro housing) and remove distributor. **CAUTION** - *Do not crank engine with distributor removed.*

2) Remove high-tension rotor, then remove snap ring, wave washer, and electronic timing rotor. Lift vacuum unit operating rod from peg on pick-up arm. Pry cable grommet from distributor housing. Remove pick-up arm bearing spring. Slide pick-up arm sideways to disengage it from bearing, then lift from micro housing while pulling cable through hole. Detach pick-up module.

3) Drive out roll pin and remove vacuum unit from micro housing. Remove three spring loaded screws and lift micro housing from distributor body. Remove felt pad and screw from top of rotor carrier shaft. Remove control springs from retaining posts, lift rotor carrier shaft from distributor shaft, then remove centrifugal weights.

LUCAS "OPUS" ELECTRONIC IGNITION SYSTEM (Cont.)

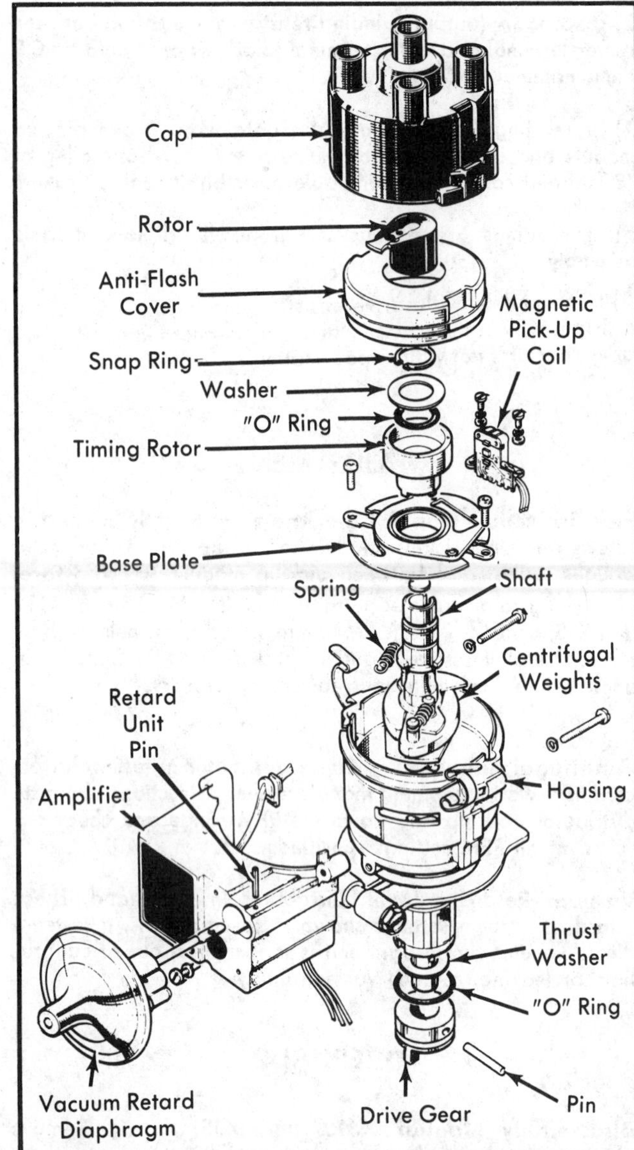

Fig. 7 Exploded View of Lucas Breakerless Distributor Used on MG, MGB, Triumph and Jaguar XJ6

Inspection – Check control springs for correct length. Check pivot holes in centrifugal weights for wear or deformation. Check distributor shaft for excessive play. **NOTE** – *If any part of distributor body assembly is found to be defective, the complete assembly must be replaced.*

Reassembly – **1)** Lubricate centrifugal advance mechanism with Mobilgrease No. 2 or equivalent, then install weights on pivot posts. Lubricate bore of rotor carrier shaft with clean engine oil, install on distributor shaft, then install retaining screw and felt oil pad. Install control springs.

2) **NOTE** – *Be sure the three Allen screws and plain washers are in place through slots in distributor body base.* Install micro housing on distributor body, being sure micro adjustment eccentric peg engages in slot. Tighten micro housing to body using screws, plain washers and springs (tighten screws to just short of coil binding).

3) Loosely secure pick-up module to pick-up arm. Pass pick-up module connector and cable out through hole in micro housing and install pick-up arm on rotor carrier shaft. Install bearing spring. Engage wide part of cable grommet in hole and pry into position. Place vacuum unit in position and install new roll pin. Connect vacuum operating rod to peg on pick-up arm. Install electronic timing rotor and secure with wave washer and snap ring.

4) Using feeler gauges, adjust gap between pick-up module "E" core faces and timing rotor outer edge to specified clearance. Tighten both pick-up module retaining screws and recheck clearance. Install high-tension rotor.

Disassembly (Jaguar XJ6, MG, Triumph) – **1)** With distributor removed from engine, remove cap, rotor, anti-flash cover and felt pad. Remove screws and washers from magnetic pick-up coil. Do not remove magnetic pick-up coil at this time. Remove screws securing amplifier module to distributor. Carefully disengage retard link from moving plate pin, then remove the two cover clips.

2) Pull out wire grommet, then remove amplifier module and magnetic pick-up coil (amplifier and coil are connected by wires). Tap out retard unit pin and then remove retard unit. Remove snap ring, washer and "O" ring. Carefully remove timing rotor.

3) Remove screws securing base plate then remove base plate. Remove drive gear pin, drive gear and thrust washer. Make sure shaft is free of burrs, then remove shaft. Remove distance collar and centrifugal weight springs.

Inspection – Check control springs for correct length. Check pivot holes in centrifugal weights for wear or deformation. Check distributor shaft for excessive play. **NOTE** – *If any part of distributor body assembly is found to be defective, the complete assembly must be replaced.*

Reassembly – To reassemble distributor, reverse disassembly procedure noting the following: Lubricate weight assembly, shaft and moving plate with Rocol "Moly Pad" or equivalent. Make sure retard link is properly attached to moving plate pin. Timing rotor tang must fit into slot on shaft. With distributor assembled and replaced in vehicle, set air gap and ignition timing to specifications.

MARELLI DISTRIBUTORS

Fiat 124 & 131
Lancia

DESCRIPTION

Distributors may be single or dual breaker type. Centrifugal advance is accomplished with conventional weights and springs which may be located either beneath breaker plate, or at top of distributor shaft above cam. On distributor with top mounted centrifugal advance, the rotor also serves as a cover for the advance mechanism. Distributors may or may not be equipped with a vacuum advance device.

Dual-Breaker – Each point set operates independently; one set for normal operation, and the other set for cold starting only. The second set provides additional spark advance. A control circuit activates the advance breaker set for cold start operation and then switches ignition circuit to the other breaker set for normal operation.

SPECIFICATIONS

Point Gap, Cam Angle & Breaker Arm Spring Tension – *See Tune-Up Data on Car Model Tune-Up Pages.*

Centrifugal & Vacuum Advance – *See Specification Tables in this section.*

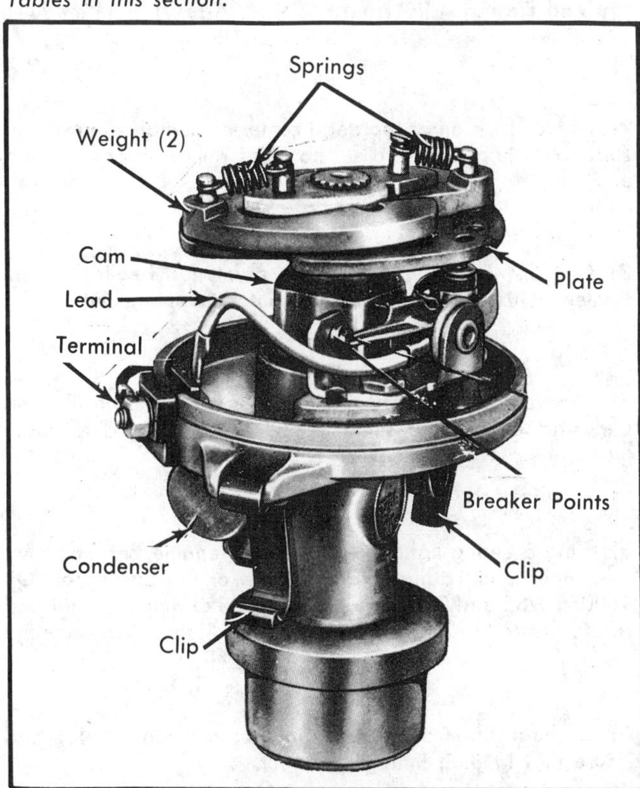

Fig. 1 Distributor Assembly with Centrifugal Advance Under Rotor

ADJUSTMENT

Point Gap, Alignment, & Cam Angle – With rubbing block on high point of cam lobe, insert a feeler gauge blade between contacts and check reading against specification. To correct, loosen retaining screw and move stationary contact point until correct gap is obtained, then tighten screw. Align points if necessary by bending stationary contact support only. Check cam angle using a dwell meter; compare indicated reading with specification and correct if necessary. If distributor is equipped with dual breaker points, adjust each set separately to obtain the specified dwell.

Breaker Arm Spring Tension – To check spring tension, place hook end of spring scale as close as possible to the movable breaker point. Pull scale at a right angle (90 degrees) to the movable arm and note reading just as points begin to open.

Centrifugal Advance – Check distributor in test stand according to test equipment manufacturers instructions. Operate distributor both up and down the RPM range and check advance at all RPM settings specified.

Vacuum Advance – With distributor in test stand, check advance at vacuum settings shown in specifications. If tests indicate vacuum diaphragm unit is inoperative, out of calibration, or leaking, replace vacuum unit.

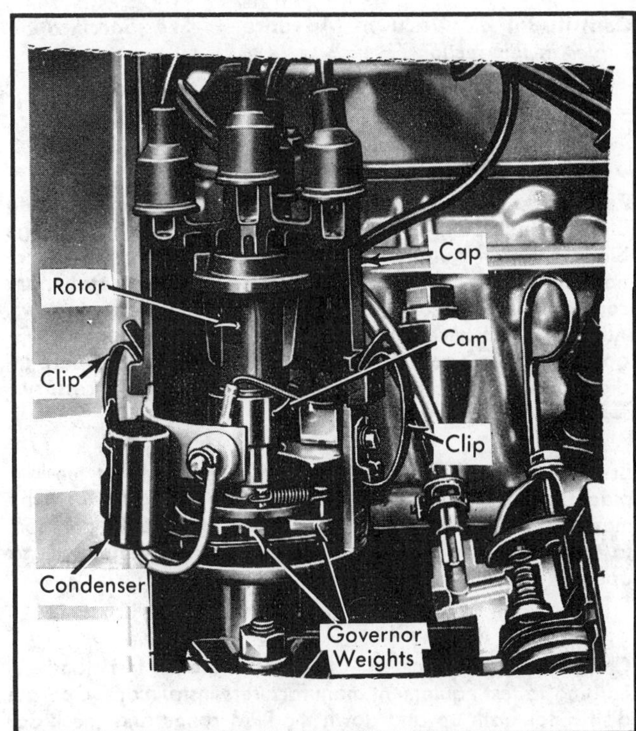

Fig. 2 Distributor Assembly with Centrifugal Advance Below Breaker Plate

MITSUBISHI PISTON ENGINE BREAKER TYPE DISTRIBUTOR

Arrow
All Models
Colt
All Models
Mazda
1300cc Calif. Model Only
808 (1600cc)
GLC (Calif.)

NOTE – *All other Mazda piston engine models use the Mitsubishi Transistorized Ignition system.*

DESCRIPTION

Mitsubishi distributors are fully automatic and of conventional design. Breaker plate assembly consists of a fixed lower plate, with breaker points mounted on movable upper plate. Centrifugal advance is conventional type with weights and springs. Vacuum advance is controlled by a vacuum diaphragm unit mounted on distributor housing and linked to movable portion of breakerplate assembly.

SPECIFICATIONS

Point Gap, Cam Angle & Breaker Arm Spring Tension – *See Tune-Up Data on Car Model Tune-Up Pages.*

Centrifugal & Vacuum Advance – *See Specification Tables in this section.*

ADJUSTMENT

Point Gap, Alignment, & Cam Angle – With rubbing block on high point of cam lobe, insert a suitable feeler gauge blade between contacts and check reading against specification. To correct, loosen retaining screws and move stationary contact point until correct gap is obtained, then tighten screws. Align points if necessary by bending stationary contact support only. Check cam angle using a dwell meter; compare indicated reading with specification and correct if necessary.

Breaker Arm Spring Tension – To check spring tension, place hook end of spring scale as close as possible to the movable breaker point. Pull scale at a right angle (90 degrees) to the movable arm and note reading just as points begin to open.

Centrifugal Advance – Check distributor in test stand according to test equipment manufacturers instructions. Operate distributor both up and down the RPM range and check advance at all RPM settings specified.

Vacuum Advance – With distributor in test stand, check advance at vacuum settings shown in specifications. If tests indicate vacuum diaphragm unit is inoperative, out of calibration, or leaking, replace vacuum unit.

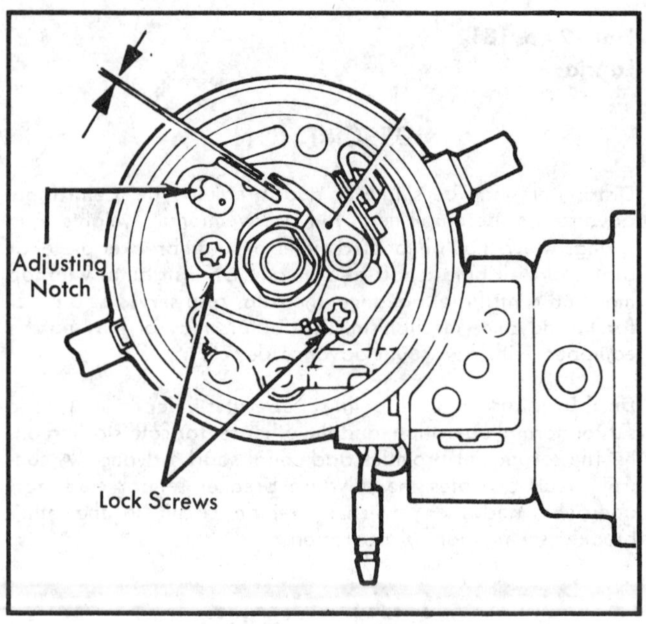

Fig. 1 Adjusting Point Gap on Colt and Arrow Models (Mazda Models Similar)

Ignition Timing Adjustment (Colt & Arrow) – **1)** Set dwell angle.

2) Set No. 1 piston at top dead center on compression stroke. Turn crankshaft pulley to set notch of pulley to basic timinq position.

3) Turn distributor where breaker points just begin to open, tighten adjusting screw and distributor mounting nut.

4) Remove rubber plug from distributor vacuum control chamber, start engine and set at proper RPM. (Dual diaphragm type only).

5) Using a timing light, on 1600cc STD engine, set timing by using the timing adjuster on the side of the distributor. On 1600cc w/SS and 2000cc, loosen distributor mounting nut and rotate distributor until timing is correct. Tighten nut securely.

6) On dual diaphragm distributor, replace rubber plug and insure that ignition timing is correct.

Ignition Timing Adjustment (Mazda) – Connect timing light to number one cylinder spark plug. Start engine and set idle to specifications. Loosen distributor bolt and rotate distributor until mark on crankshaft aligns with indicator on timing cover. Tighten distributor bolt.

MITSUBISHI PISTON ENGINE BREAKER TYPE DISTRIBUTOR (Cont.)

OVERHAUL

Disassembly — 1) Remove rotor, condensor, cam lubricating felt, breaker point assembly, vacuum diaphragm and breaker plate.

2) Mark position of driven gear on shaft for reassembly reference. Drive out retaining pins and remove rear, thrust collar, washers and "O" ring from shaft.

3) Remove shaft from distributor housing.

4) Note positioning of cam, springs and weights on distributor shaft for reassembly reference, then remove cam attaching screw and remove cam, governor springs and weights.

Reassembly — Reassemble distributor in reverse order of disassembly.

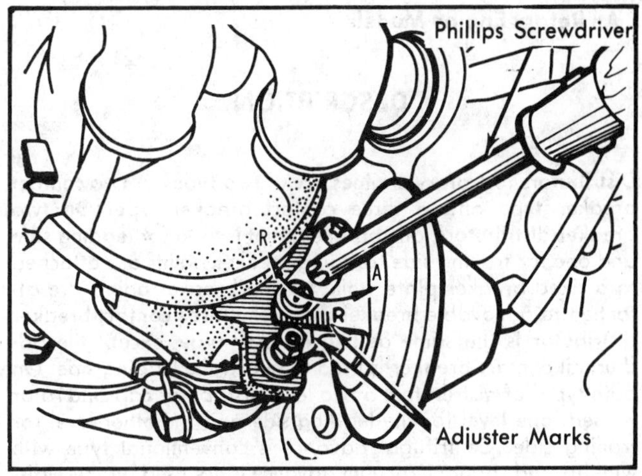

Fig. 2 Adjusting Ignition Timing on Colt and Arrow Model (1600cc Engine Shown)

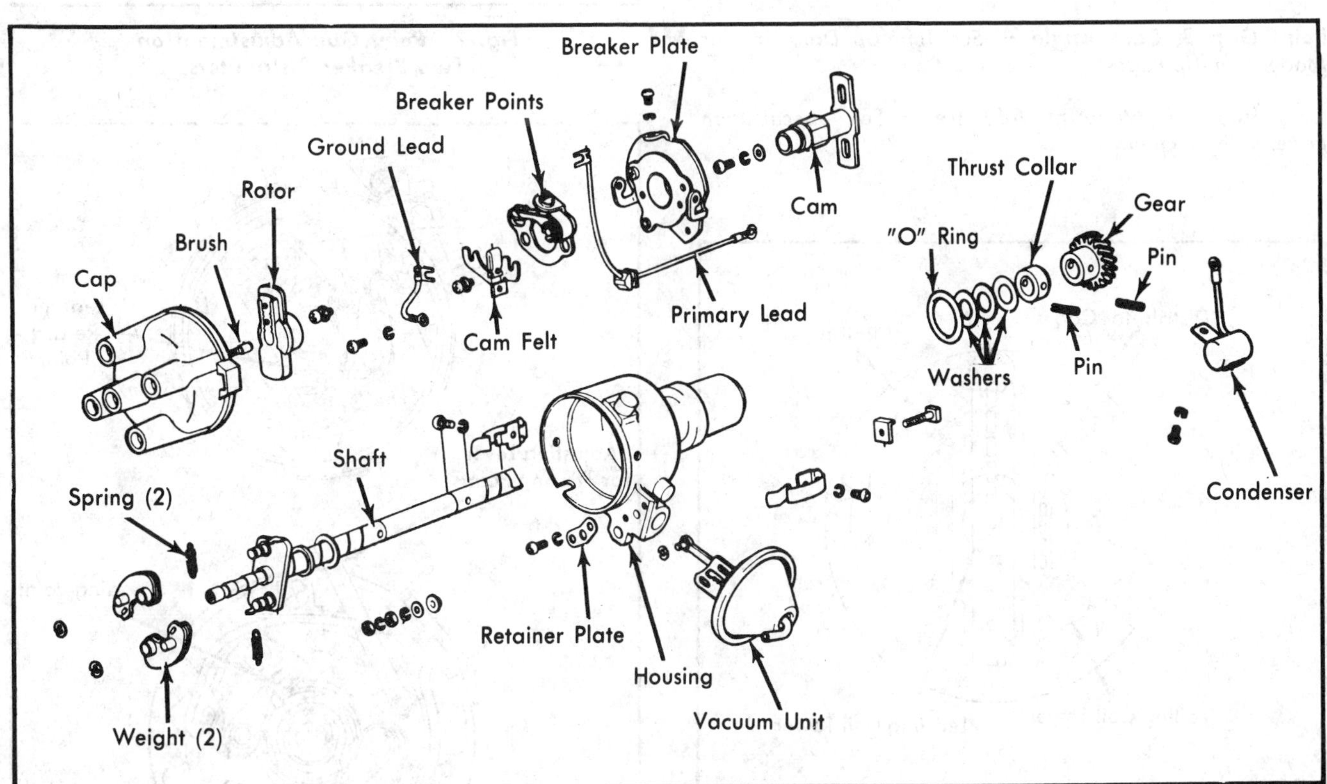

Fig. 3 Exploded View of Typical Mitsubishi Distributor

MITSUBISHI ROTARY ENGINE BREAKER TYPE DISTRIBUTOR

Mazda
All Rotary Engine Models

DESCRIPTION

Distributors for rotary engines are of two types. A two contact breaker type and a three contact breaker type. On two breaker distributors, one breaker point is used for leading side and one for trailing side. Leading breaker points are attached to a fixed breaker plate while trailing breaker points are attached to a movable breaker plate. The three contact breaker distributor is the same as two breaker type, except the additional contact breaker is used to retard the leading side. On both types of distributors a two level distributor cap and rotor is used, one level for the leading side and the other level for trailing side. Centrifugal advance is conventional type with weights and springs. Vacuum advance is not used on these distributors.

SPECIFICATIONS

Point Gap & Cam Angle — *See Tune-Up Data on Car Model Tune-Up Pages.*

Centrifugal & Vacuum Advance — *See Specification Pages in this section.*

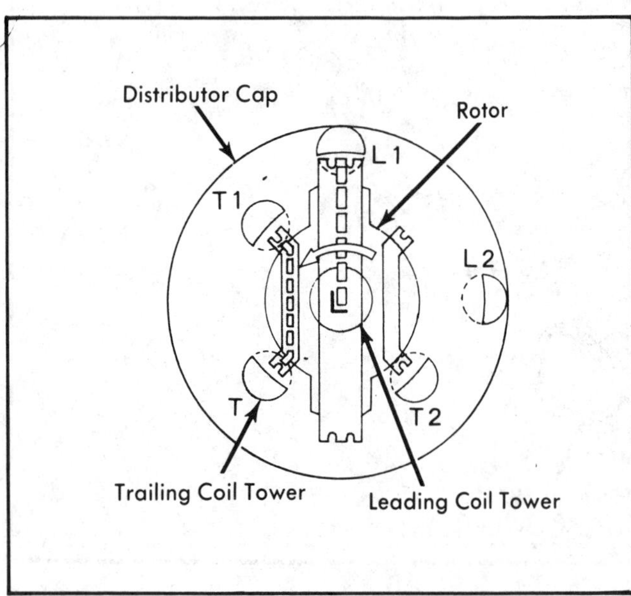

Fig. 1 Rotor/Distributor Cap Relationship

ADJUSTMENT

Point Gap, Alignment, & Cam Angle — With rubbing block on high point of cam lobe, insert a feeler gauge blade between contacts and check reading against specifications. To correct, loosen retaining screw and move stationary contact point until correct gap is obtained, then tighten screw. Align points if necessary by bending stationary contact support only. Check cam angle using a dwell meter; compare indicated reading with specification and correct if necessary.

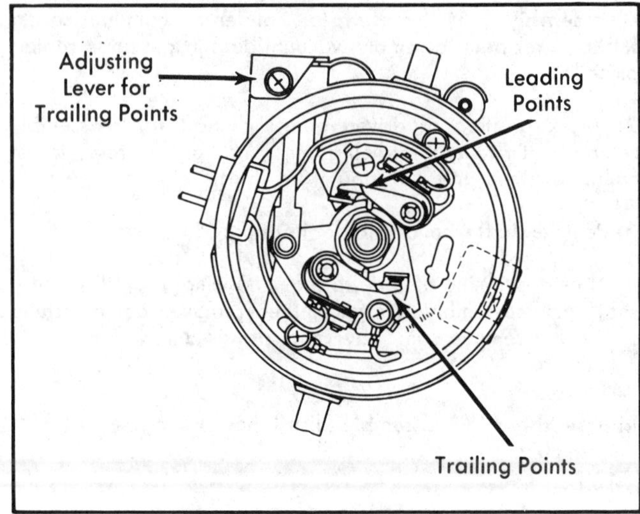

Fig. 2 Point Gap Adjustment on Two Breaker Distributors

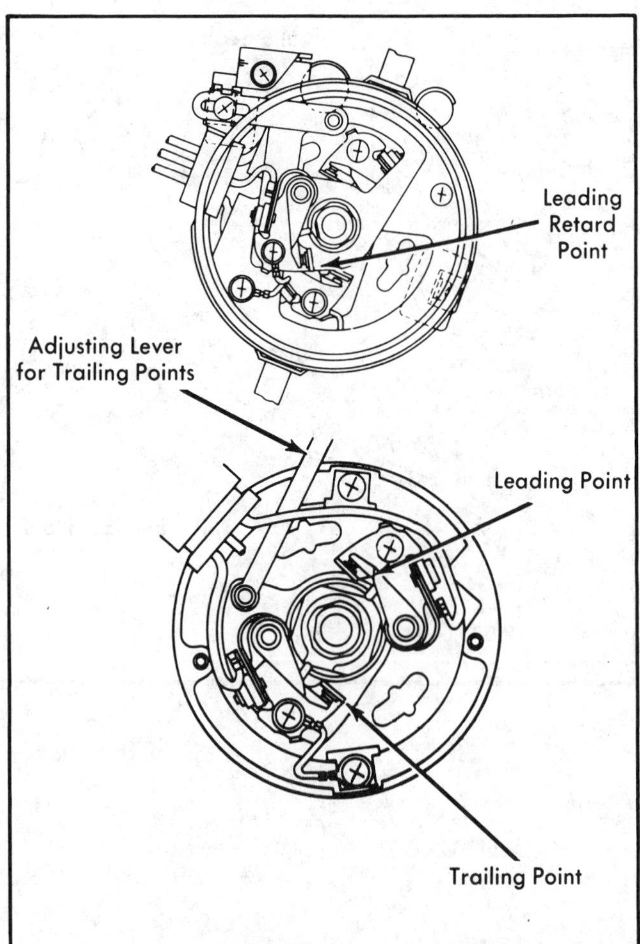

Fig. 3 Point Gap Adjustment on Three Breaker Distributors

MITSUBISHI ROTARY ENGINE BREAKER TYPE DISTRIBUTOR (Cont.)

Breaker Arm Spring Tension – To check spring tension, place hook end of spring scale as close as possible to the movable breaker point. Pull scale at a right angle to the movable arm and note reading just as points begin to open, reading should be 1.1-1.4 lbs. (.5-.65 kg).

Centrifugal Advance – Check distributor in test stand according to test equipment manufacturers' instructions. Operate distributor both up and down the RPM range and check advance at all RPM settings specified.

OVERHAUL

Disassembly – Remove distributor cap and rotor. Remove clip securing external adjusting lever for adjusting trailing timing, then remove adjusting lever and bracket. Remove condensers, primary wires and breaker points. Remove screws securing breaker plate and remove breaker plate. Remove cam set screws and cam. Remove pin retaining gear to distributor shaft, and remove gear with washers. Remove distributor shaft in upward direction, then remove weights by removing springs and clips.

Reassembly – Reassemble distributor in reverse order of disassembly. Adjust points and timing to specifications.

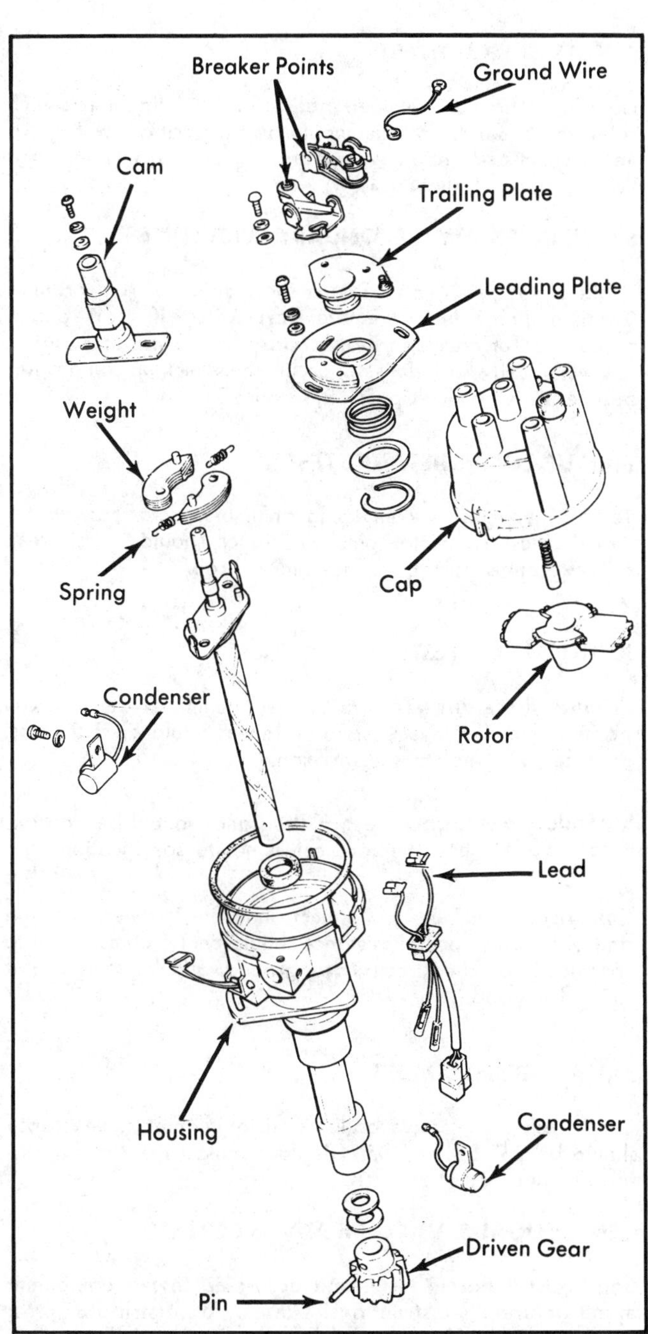

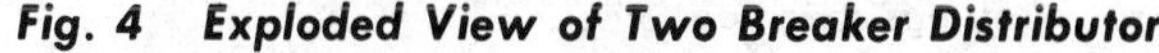

Fig. 4 Exploded View of Two Breaker Distributor

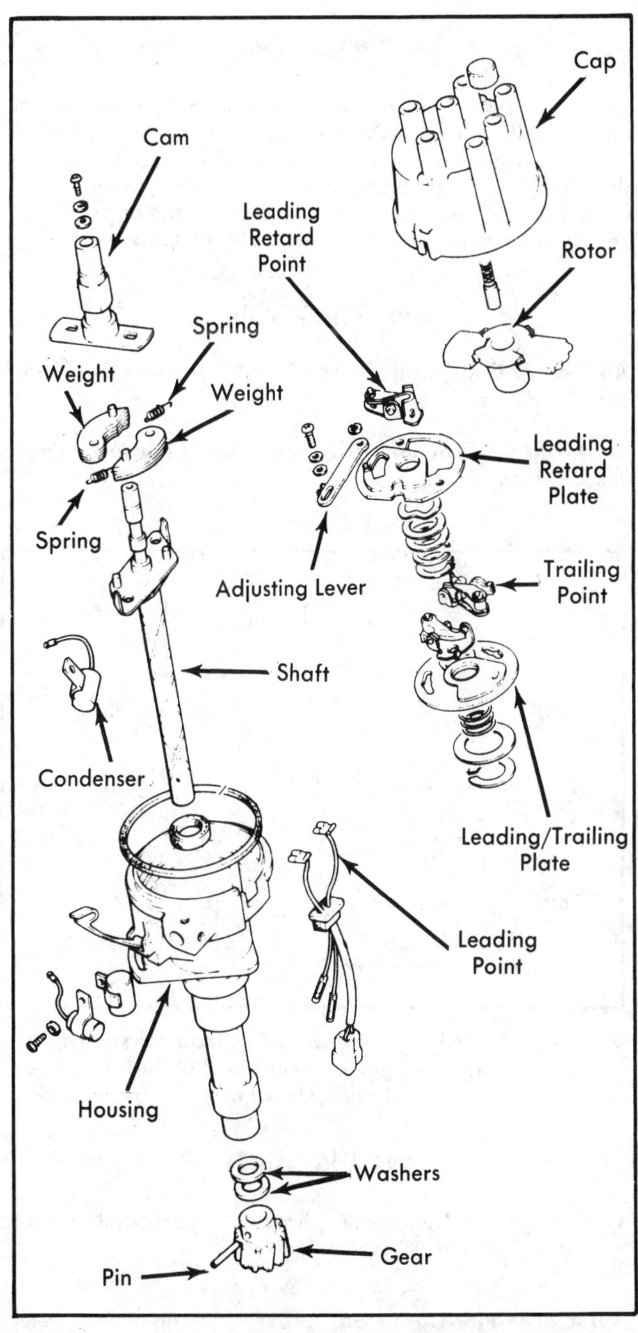

Fig. 5 Exploded View of Three Breaker Distributor

MITSUBISHI TRANSISTORIZED BREAKERLESS IGNITION SYSTEM

Mazda
GLC & 1300cc Federal Models

NOTE – *California models use the standard Mitsubishi breaker type distributor.*

DESCRIPTION

Mitsubishi Transistorized Ignition System includes a breakerless distributor, ignition coil, ignitor (electronic module), ballast resistor, and ignition switch. The distributor utilizes a reluctor (trigger wheel), magnetic pick-up coil, and standard type centrifugal advance weights and vacuum advance units.

OPERATION

The reluctor, turning with the distributor shaft, passes by the pick-up coil. This makes and breaks a magnetic field which produces a low voltage electrical signal. The ignitor receives this signal and turns on and then turns off the ignition primary current to the coil. This action induces the ignition secondary voltage back to the distributor and on to the spark plugs.

SPECIFICATIONS

Air Gap & Cam Angle – *See Tune-Up Data on Car Model Tune-Up Pages.*

Centrifugal & Vacuum Advance – *See Specification Pages in this section.*

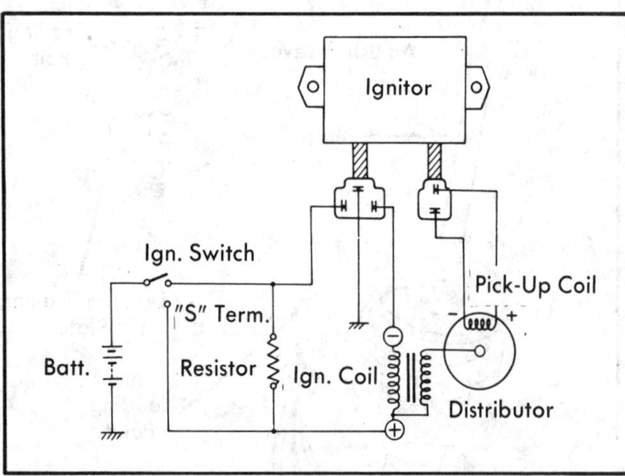

Fig. 1 Wiring Diagram of Mazda Mitsubishi Transistorized Breakerless Distributor Ignition System

ADJUSTMENT

Cam Angle – Cam angle (dwell) is automatically set and manual adjustment is not required.

Reluctor-to-Pick-Up Air Gap – Check air gap between reluctor teeth and magnetic pick-up coil using a .010-.014" (0.25-0.36mm) flat feeler gauge. If not to specification, loosen retaining screws and move breaker plate to adjust air gap. Recheck to insure that air gap is equal at each reluctor tooth.

TESTING

CAUTION – *Insure all wire connections are correct as reverse battery polarity within the system will damage ignitor. Do not disconnect battery while engine is running or transistors may be damaged. Do not allow water to enter ignitor. If a tachometer is connected to system, connect tachometer positive lead to coil negative terminal.*

PRIMARY CIRCUIT TEST

Connect voltmeter between ballast resistor (ignition switch side) and ground. Voltage should be near battery voltage. If not, inspect and repair wiring and connectors between ignition switch and ballast resistor.

SPARK INTENSITY (SECONDARY CIRCUIT) TEST

Hold coil high tension cable a short distance from ground. Crank engine using a remote start switch. If spark occurs repeat test for each spark plug wire at the distributor and at spark plugs. If spark does not occur, check pick-up coil air gap and perform the Pick-Up Coil Resistance Test.

PICK-UP COIL RESISTANCE TEST

Test pick-up coil by connecting ohmmeter across distributor wire harness connector pins. Resistance should be between 670-790 ohms. If not, replace pick-up coil.

IGNITION COIL TESTS

Primary Resistance Test – Connect ohmmeter between coil positive and negative posts. Resistance should be 1.5 ohms. Replace coil if not to specifications.

Secondary Resistance Test – Resistance should be approximately 9,000 ohms. Replace coil if not to specification.

Coil Insulation Test – Connect ohmmeter between ground and coil positive post. Resistance should be 1.6 ohms. If not to specifications, check coil case ground and replace coil if ground is good.

BALLAST RESISTOR TEST

Check resistance across ballast resistor terminals. Resistance should be 0.9 ±0.09 Ohms. Replace ballast resistor if not to specification.

CENTRIFUGAL & VACUUM ADVANCE TESTS

Check distributor in test stand according to test equipment manufacturers' instructions. Refer to distributor test specifications in this section and check advance at all RPM and vacuum settings specified.

MITSUBISHI TRANSISTORIZED BREAKERLESS IGNITION SYSTEM (Cont.)

OVERHAUL

Disassembly – **1**) With distributor removed from vehicle, remove distributor cap and rotor. Remove screws retaining pick-up coil to breaker plate. Remove pick-up coil and wire harness from distributor.

2) Remove screws retaining vacuum advance unit to distributor housing and remove vacuum unit.

3) Using a pin punch remove lock pin from distributor drive gear. Remove gear and washers from shaft.

4) Remove screws retaining breaker plate to housing. Push shaft with breaker plate out through top of distributor housing.

5) Remove reluctor from distributor shaft after removing reluctor retaining screw. Remove governor weights by removing governor springs.

Reassembly – Reassemble distributor in reverse order of disassembly. Adjust reluctor-to-pick-up coil air gap.

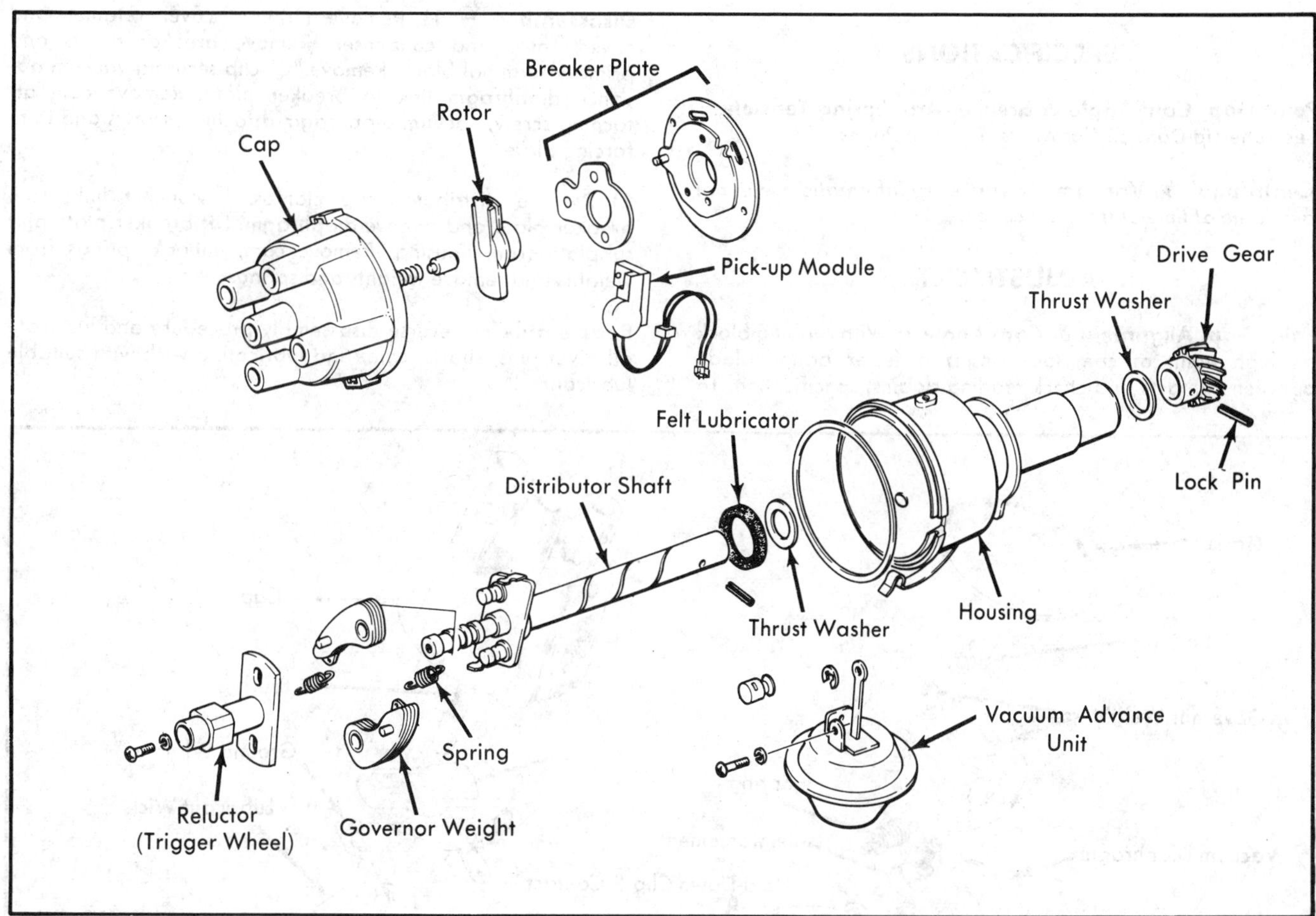

Fig. 2 ***Exploded View of Mitsubishi Distributor.***

MOTORCRAFT SINGLE BREAKER DISTRIBUTOR

Courier
1800cc

DESCRIPTION

Distributor is of single breaker, fully automatic design. Breaker plate assembly consists of a fixed lower plate, with breaker points mounted on movable upper plate. Centrifugal advance is conventional type with weights and springs. Vacuum advance is controlled by a vacuum diaphragm unit mounted on distributor housing and linked to movable portion of breaker plate assembly.

SPECIFICATIONS

Point Gap, Cam Angle & Breaker Arm Spring Tension – *See Tune-Up Data on Car Model Tune-Up Pages.*

Centrifugal & Vacuum Advance – *Information was not available at time of this publication.*

ADJUSTMENT

Point Gap, Alignment & Cam Angle – With rubbing block on high point of cam lobe, insert a feeler gauge blade between contacts and check reading against specification. To correct, loosen retaining screw and move stationary contact point until correct gap is obtained, then tighten screw. Align points if necessary by bending stationary contact support only. Check cam angle using a dwell meter; compare indicated reading with specification and correct if necessary.

Breaker Arm Spring Tension – To check spring tension, place hook end of spring scale as close as possible to the movable breaker point. Pull scale at a right angle (90°) to the movable arm and note reading just as points begin to open.

OVERHAUL

Disassembly – **1**) Remove terminal cover retainer and cover, rotor and condenser. Remove breaker points and primary terminal block. Remove "C" clip securing vacuum advance diaphragm link to breaker plate. Remove cam attaching screw, vacuum diaphragm attaching screws and reinforcing plate.

2) Remove distributor cap clamps. Disconnect link from breaker plate and remove diaphragm. Lift breaker plate and subplate from housing. Remove cam, unhook springs from weights and remove weights and springs.

Reassembly – Reverse disassembly procedure and lubricate all pivot pins, shafts, cam, and lubricating wick with suitable lubricant.

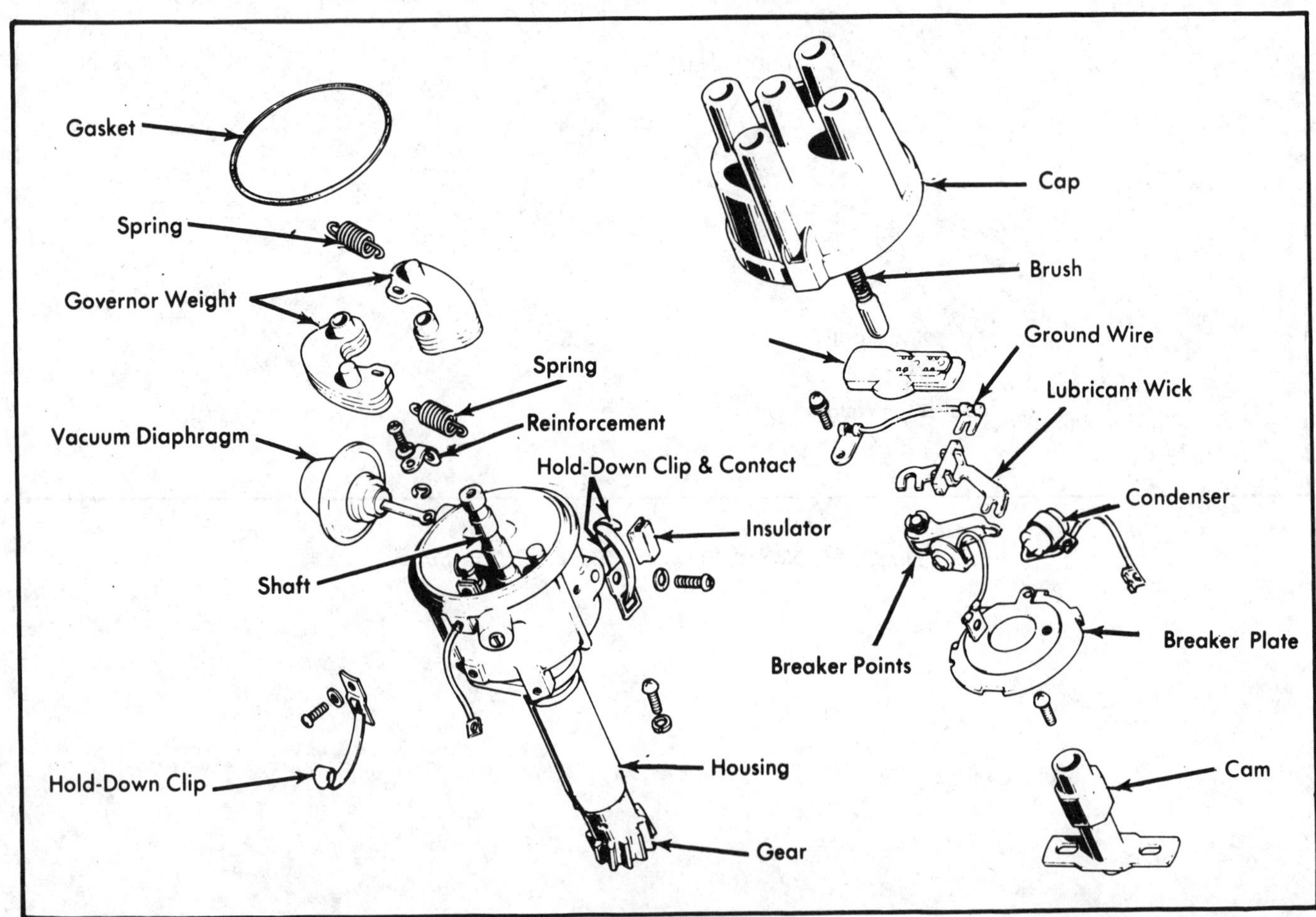

Fig. 1 Exploded View of Motorcraft Single Breaker Point Distributor

MOTORCRAFT SOLID STATE IGNITION

Courier 2300cc

DESCRIPTION

Courier Solid State Ignition consists of an electronic control module, coil, and distributor. When ignition switch is on, primary circuit is on and coil is energized. As distributor shaft rotates the distributor generates signals causing module to break the primary current and induce secondary voltage in coil. A timing circuit in module turns primary circuit on again to energize coil for next spark cycle. The dwell varies with engine speed and can not be altered, so measurement and adjustment is not required.

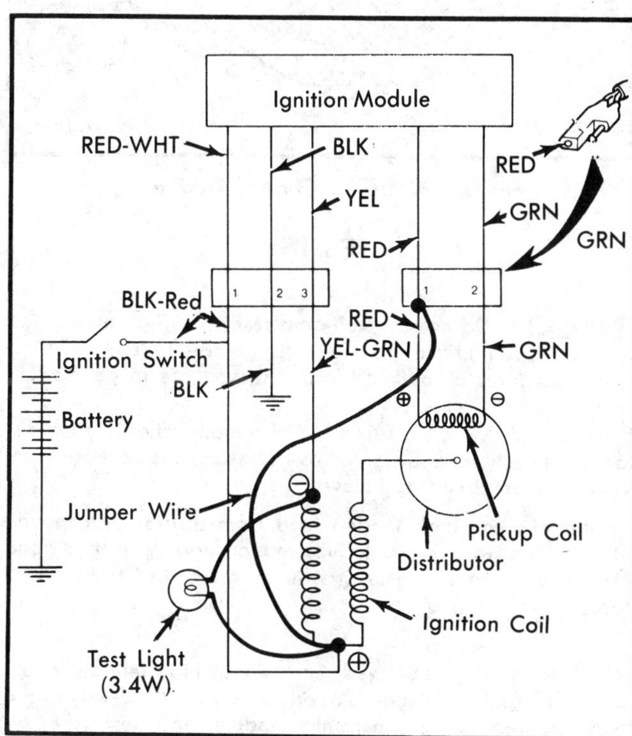

Fig. 1 Wiring Diagram of Module Test for 2.3 Liter Courier

TESTING

NOTE — *Insure that battery is fully charged and in good condition before making any tests.*

HIGH VOLTAGE SPARK TEST

1) Connect a remote starter switch in starting circuit and remove high tension wire from center of distributor cap.

2) Turn on ignition switch and hold the high tension lead 0.2-0.4 inch from a good ground. Crank engine, if no spark or a weak spark, perform following tests:

CONNECTORS AND WIRES

Inspect all connectors, wires and related equipment.

COIL RESISTANCE

Turn ignition switch to "OFF" position, check the resistance of primary and secondary coil circuits. Primary circuit should be 0.9±0.09 ohms and secondary 8.0±1.2K ohms. If not within specifications, replace coil.

ARMATURE GAP

Insure that a tooth of the armature is lined up with the magnetic pickup. Use a feeler gauge to check gap which should be 0.016±0.008 inch. If gap is not within specifications, replace the distributor.

NOTE — *No adjustments are to be made to ignition system except initial ignition timing and spark plug gap.*

REMOVAL & INSTALLATION

DISTRIBUTOR

Removal — 1) Remove distributor cap, rubber cap from timing chain cover and vacuum hose from distributor vacuum.

2) Scribe marks between distributor body and cylinder block, and on distributor body indicating position of rotor. Scribe mark showing position of cam gear to cam gear indicator. (Primarily used for installation.)

3) Disconnect wiring, remove lock plate bolt, then pull distributor from cylinder block.

NOTE — *Do not crank engine after distributor has been removed.*

Installation — 1) If engine has been cranked, turn crankshaft where number one piston is coming up on compression stroke. The mark on the cam gear should be in line with the cam gear indicator. The TDC mark on crankshaft pulley in line with pointer on timing chain cover.

2) If engine has not been cranked, install distributor reversing removal procedure.

MOTORCRAFT SOLID STATE IGNITION

Capri II

DESCRIPTION & OPERATION

Motorcraft Solid State Ignition used on Capri utilizes a Bosch Breakerless distributor and Motorcraft electronic control module and coil. When ignition switch is on, primary circuit is on and coil is energized. As distributor shaft rotates the distributor generates signals causing module to break the primary current and induce secondary voltage in coil. A timing circuit in module turns primary circuit on again to energize coil for next spark cycle. The dwell varies with engine speed and can not be altered, so measurement and adjustment is not required.

Electronic Module – Module contains seven color coded wires as shown in *Fig. 2*. Module receives power from ignition switch through Red wire while engine is running and through White wire while engine is cranking. Orange and Purple wires transmit signals from distributor while Green wire receives primary ignition current from coil which is then transmitted to ground at distributor through Black wire. System protection is provided through Blue wire, which is a fusible link. The electronic module cannot be repaired.

Distributor – The Solid State distributor is similar in appearance to conventional distributors with the following differences: The cam and advance plate assembly has been replaced by a sleeve and advance plate assembly. The spring loaded upper and lower breaker plate assembly is replaced by a base plate mounted to base casting and fitted with a magnetic pickup assembly secured by a retaining ring. The breaker cam is replaced by an armature with poles and secured to sleeve and plate assembly. Movement of these poles passing by core of magnetic pickup assembly signals module to turn primary current off. Diaphragm assembly has a different rod. The shaft gear, weights, springs, cap and rotor have not been changed.

Coil – Coil is oil filled and can easily be identified by tower terminals which are labelled "BAT" (battery) and "DEC" (distributor electronic control). Solid state system coil and standard coils cannot be interchanged.

System Protection – System is protected against electrical currents produced or used by any vehicle component during normal operation. **NOTE** – *Damage to ignition system can occur if proper testing procedures are not followed.*

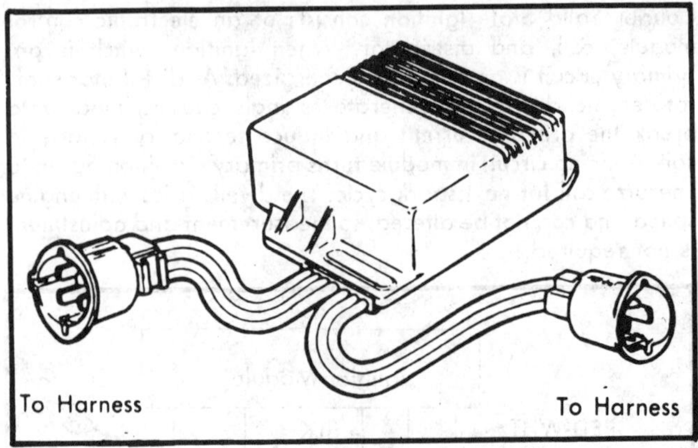

Fig. 1 Electronic Control Module

TESTING

CAUTION – *Do not use volt-amp test procedure or any test equipment that utilizes a knife switch on battery terminal. Only test procedures as outlined in this section are to be used.*

If the ignition system is suspected of a malfunction, inspect for loose connections and tighten as necessary, then check secondary ignition circuit as follows:

1) Remove coil high tension lead from distributor cap and turn ignition switch on. Hold high tension lead 3/16" from a good ground and crank engine. If spark is good then trouble is in secondary circuit.

2) If no spark is observed, ensure that high tension lead is good. If high tension lead is good, disconnect the 3-way and 4-way connectors at electronic module and test (see test procedure tables) system at harness connectors. **NOTE** – *Do not make tests at module terminals.* If all of the following tests comply with specifications, replace electronic module with a

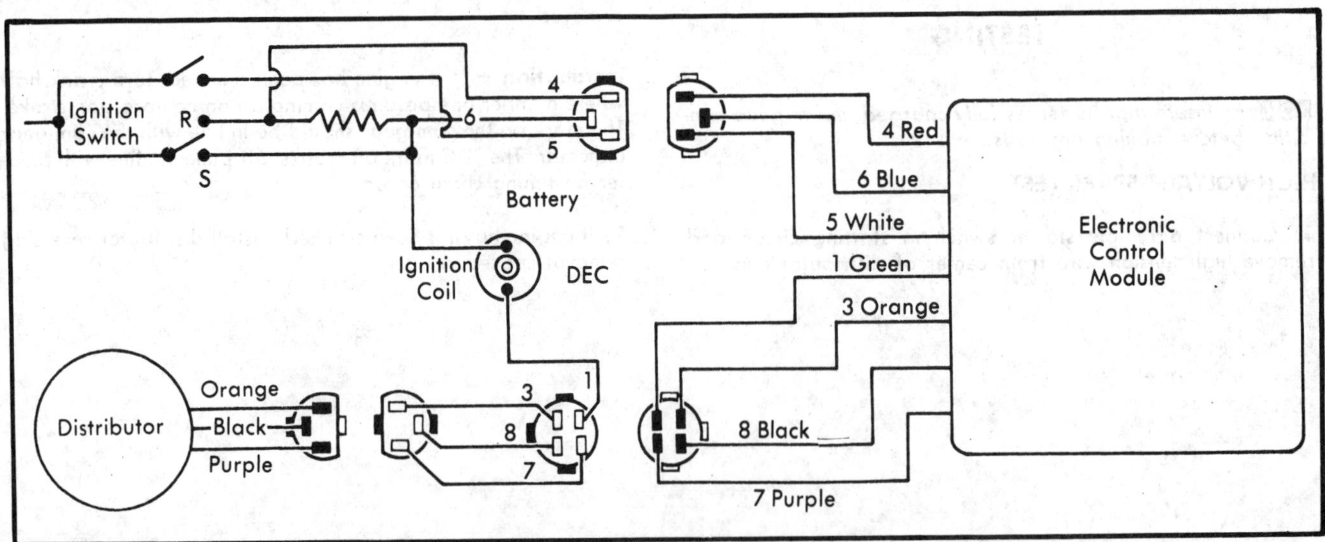

Fig. 2 Schematic of Breakerless Ignition System

MOTORCRAFT SOLID STATE IGNITION (Cont.)

new module and test to see if there is spark. If there is spark with new module and not with old module, replace old module.

NOTE – *When testing module operation, it is not necessary to remove old module. Just unplug old module and plug in new module. New module does not require mounting to function.*

MODULE BIAS TEST

With key on, measure voltage at pin #4 (Red wire) to engine ground. If observed voltage is less than battery voltage, repair voltage feed wire (Red wire) to the module.

BATTERY SOURCE TEST

Without disconnecting coil, connect voltmeter between coil BAT terminal and engine ground. Connect a jumper wire from coil DEC terminal to a good ground. Turn all lights and accessories off and ignition on. A voltmeter reading between 4.9 and 7.9 volts indicates primary circuit from battery to coil is satisfactory. If reading is less than 4.9 volts, inspect primary wiring and resistance wire for worn insulation, broken strands and loose or corroded terminals. If reading is greater than 7.9 volts, check and replace resistance wire as necessary.

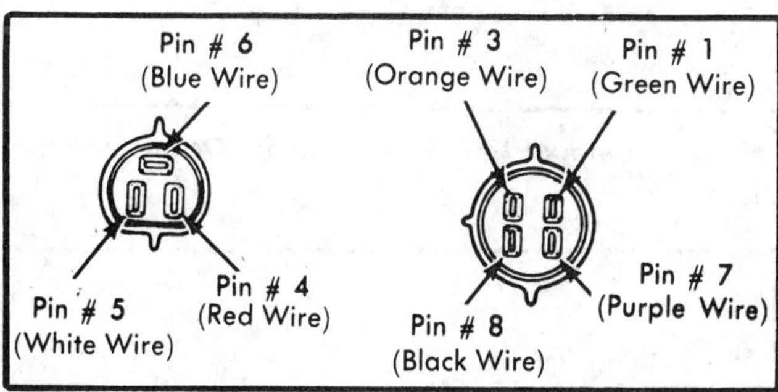

Fig. 3 Harness Connector Pins

CRANKING TEST

With engine cranking, measure voltage from pin #5 to engine ground. If voltage is not between 8 and 12 volts, repair voltage feed wire (White wire) to the module.

STARTING CIRCUIT TEST

If reading is not over 6 volts, the ignition by-pass circuit is open or grounded from either the starter solenoid or the ignition switch to pin #5. Check primary connections at coil.

DISTRIBUTOR HARDWARE TEST

Disconnect distributor 3-way pigtail. With voltmeter on 2.5 volts scale and connected between pin #3 and pin #7 and engine cranking, meter needle should oscillate. If meter does not oscillate, remove distributor cap and check for visual damage or incorrect assembly. Armature must be tight on sleeve and roll pin, aligning armature, in position. Iron stator must not be broken and armature must rotate when engine is cranking. If internal components are all good and voltmeter still will not oscillate, replace magnetic pickup (stator assembly).

MAGNETIC PICKUP (STATOR ASSEMBLY) TEST

With key off, there should be no continuity between pin #3 and pin #7. Check resistance between pin #8 and engine ground to read zero ohms. Check resistance between pin #3 and engine ground; then, between pin #7 and engine ground. Both readings should be more than 70,000 ohms. If it fails any of the tests , the distributor magnetic pickup is inoperative and must be replaced.

IGNITION COIL TEST

With key off, check secondary resistance between pin #4 and coil tower to be 7,000 to 13,000 ohms. Check primary resistance between pin #1 and pin #6 to be 1.0-2.0 ohms. If coil is within limits but the coil is still suspected, test coil on a standard coil tester. If reading differs from the original test, check for a defective harness.

SHORT TEST

If resistance between pin #1 and engine ground is less than 4.0 ohms, check for a short to ground at coil "DEC" terminal or in primary wiring (Green wire) to coil.

PRIMARY RESISTANCE WIRE TEST

Resistance between pin #4 and pin #6 should be 1-2 ohms. If not within limits, replace ignition resistance wire.

OVERHAUL

NOTE – *Overhaul of the Bosch distributor is not recommended by the manufacturer. With the exception of the rotor and cap, if components of the distributor are found defective or damaged, the distributor must be replaced.*

NIPPONDENSO BREAKER TYPE DISTRIBUTORS

LUV
Opel
Subaru
Man. Trans.
Toyota
Semi-transistorized
(exc. Celica Calif.)

DESCRIPTION

Single breaker, fully automatic type of conventional design. Breaker points are mounted on movable portion of breaker plate assembly. Centrifugal advance is conventional type with weights and springs. Vacuum advance (or retard) is controlled by a vacuum diaphragm unit mounted on distributor housing and linked to movable portion of breaker plate assembly. Vacuum advance unit may incorporate a vernier adjustment (octane selector), so that small adjustments may be made to suit varying grades of fuel, or to satisfy tuning requirements.

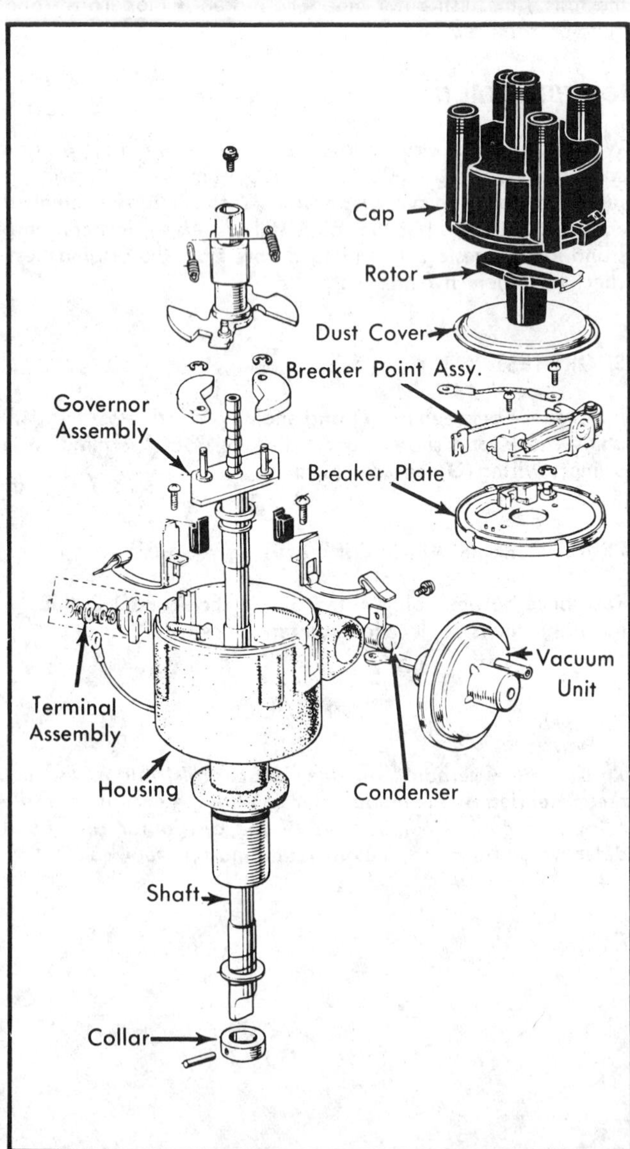

Fig. 1 Disassembled View of Breaker Type Distributor

NOTE – *Toyota uses a semitransistorized ignition system which utilizes breaker points with a transistorized ignitor. Ignitor assembly is mounted externally from the distributor and turns the primary current "ON" and "OFF" increasing breaker point durabilty. See Fig. 3 and Fig. 4.*

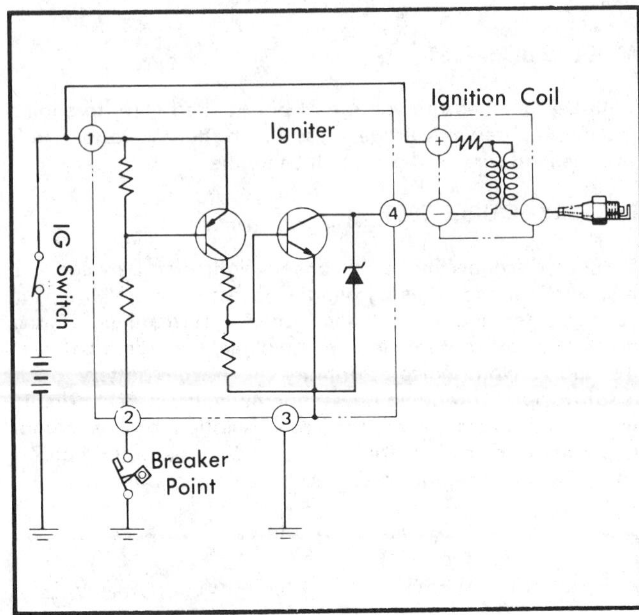

Fig. 2 Standard Line Adjustment for Octane Selector

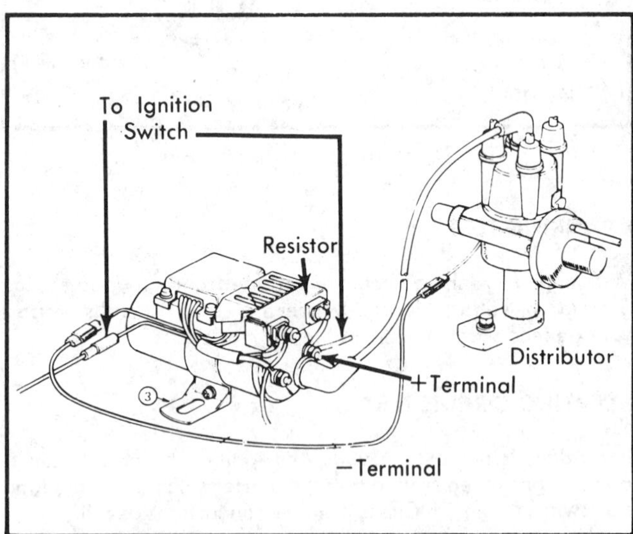

Fig. 3 Toyota Semitransistorized Wiring Diagram

SPECIFICATIONS

Point Gap, Cam Angle & Breaker Arm Spring Tension – *See Tune-Up Data on Car Model Tune-Up Pages.*

Centrifugal & Vacuum Advance (Or Retard) – *See Specification Tables in this section.*

NIPPONDENSO BREAKER TYPE DISTRIBUTORS

ADJUSTMENT

Point Gap, Alignment, & Cam Angle – With rubbing block on high point of cam lobe, insert a feeler gauge blade between contacts and check reading against specification. To correct, loosen retaining screws and move stationary contact point until correct gap is obtained, then tighten screws. Align points if necessary by bending stationary contact support only. Check cam angle using a dwell meter; compare indicated reading with specification and correct if necessary.

Breaker Arm Spring Tension – To check spring tension, place hook end of spring scale as close as possible to the movable breaker point. Pull scale at a right angle (90 degrees) to the movable arm and note reading just as points begin to open.

Centrifugal Advance – Check distributor in test stand according to test equipment manufacturers instructions. Operate distributor both up and down the RPM range and check advance at all RPM settings specified.

Vacuum Advance (Or Retard) – With distributor in test stand, check advance (or retard) at vacuum settings shown in specifications. If tests indicate vacuum diaphragm unit is inoperative, out of calibration, or leaking, replace vacuum unit.

Vernier (Octane Selector) Adjuster – Standard position of octane selector is obtained by turning vernier adjuster until setting line shown in illustration is just barely visible, and the center line is aligned with setting mark on housing.

Disassembly – 1) Remove rotor, dust cover, and breaker point assembly. Remove vacuum advance unit retaining screw and adjuster cap, then disconnect unit from breaker plate and remove. If necessary, remove terminal insulator and attaching hardware, noting sequence for reassembly reference. Remove cap hold-down springs if necessary, noting difference in springs and location of each.

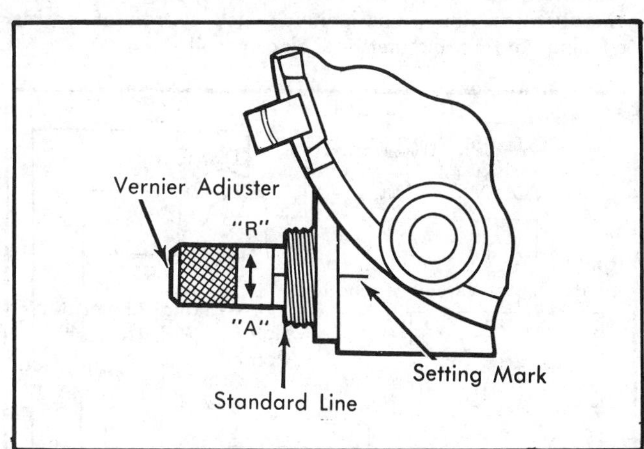

Fig. 4 Typical Toyota Semitransistorized Connections

2) – **NOTE** – *During disassembly, record the quantity, type, sequence, and thickness of washers in use at each location for later reference.* Remove breaker plate assembly. Note positioning of cam, springs and weights on distributor shaft, then remove cam attaching screw and remove cam, governor springs and weights. Mark position of driven gear on shaft for reassembly reference. Remove retaining pin(s), then remove gear (and spacing collar, if so equipped) from end of shaft. Remove shaft from distributor housing.

Reassembly – Reassemble distributor in reverse order of disassembly.

NIPPONDENSO TRANSISTORIZED IGNITION SYSTEM

Toyota
Celica GT for Calif.

DESCRIPTION

Nippondenso Transistorized Ignition System includes a breakerless distributor, special ignition coil, ignition signal generating mechanism and ignition switch. Distributor consists of timing rotor, a magnet and pick up coil.

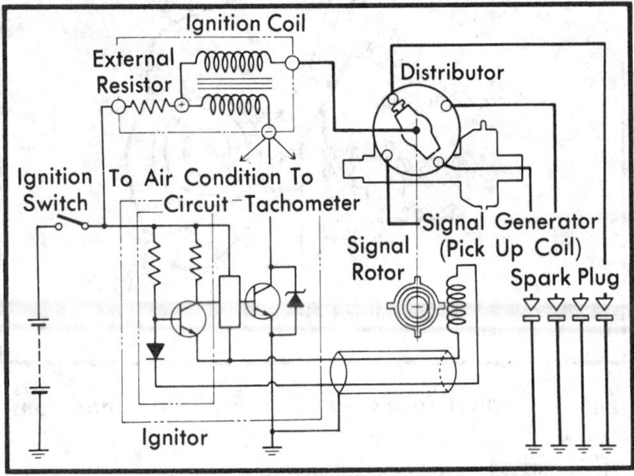

Fig. 1 Wiring Diagram of Nippondenso Transistorized Ignition System

OPERATION

1) The distributor pick up unit consists of a signal rotor and signal generator. As the air gap changes, the amount of flux varies which determines the amount of voltage produced across the signal generator pick up coil terminals.

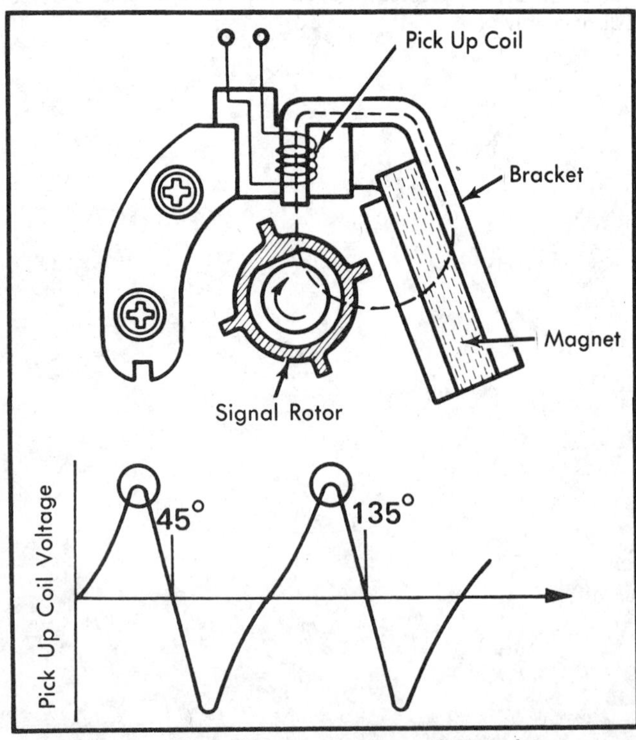

Fig. 2 High Voltage Position of Signal Rotor

2) When the distributor signal rotor is at the position shown in *Fig. 2*, the pick up coil generated voltage will be high restricting flow of current from the battery.

3) When rotor turns and a tooth passes the pick up coil, *Fig. 3*, the pick up coil generated voltage drops to zero allowing battery current flow to the pick up coil. High voltage is induced in the secondary coil and spark is released to the spark plug.

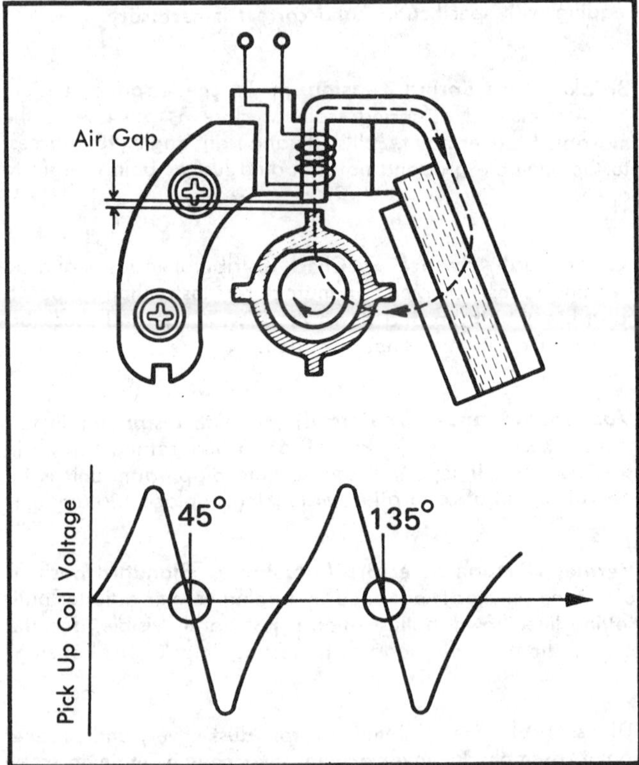

Fig. 3 Low Voltage (Firing Position) of Signal Rotor

4) The ignitor is the ignition sensing unit. It senses the distributor ignition signal, determines ignition timing and ignition coil current passage time.

ADJUSTMENT

Timing Rotor-to-Pick Up Coil Projection – Using a flat feeler gauge check air gap. Air gap should be .008-.016" (0.2-0.4 mm). If not, loosen screws and adjust to specification.

TESTING

CAUTION – *Insure all wire connections are correct as reverse battery polarity within the system will damage ignitor. Do not disconnect battery while engine is running or transistors may be damaged. Do not allow water to enter ignitor. If a tachometer is connected to system, connect tachometer positive lead to coil negative terminal.*

NIPPONDENSO TRANSISTORIZED IGNITION SYSTEM

IGNITION COIL TESTS

NOTE – *All tests are made with an ohmmeter and if the resistance for any test is not within specification, replace coil*

Primary Coil Resistance – Between terminal c and e, 1.35 to 1.65 ohms.

Secondary Coil Resistance – Between terminal c and d, 12,-800 to 15,200 ohms.

Resistor Resistance – Between terminal a and b, 1.3 to 1.7 ohms.

Insulation Resistance – Between terminal c and f, infinity.

SIGNAL GENERATOR TEST

Check resistance across signal generator terminals with an ohmmeter. Resistance should be 130 to 190 ohms.

IGNITOR TEST

No Load Voltage Test – **1)** Turn ignition switch to "ON" position.

2) Check voltage between ignition coil negative (–) terminal and resistor terminal using a voltmeter. Voltage should be 12 volts.

Voltage Test with Load – **1)** Disconnect wiring connector from distributor.

2) Use a 1 to 10 ohm range ohmmeter to provide resistance to the two terminals of the ignitor as illustrated. *Fig. 5.*

CAUTION – *Do not intermix positive (+) and negative (–) terminals of the ohmmeter.*

3) Turn ignition switch to "ON" position.

4) Check voltage between ignition coil negative (–) terminal and resistor terminal using a voltmeter. Voltage should be nearly zero.

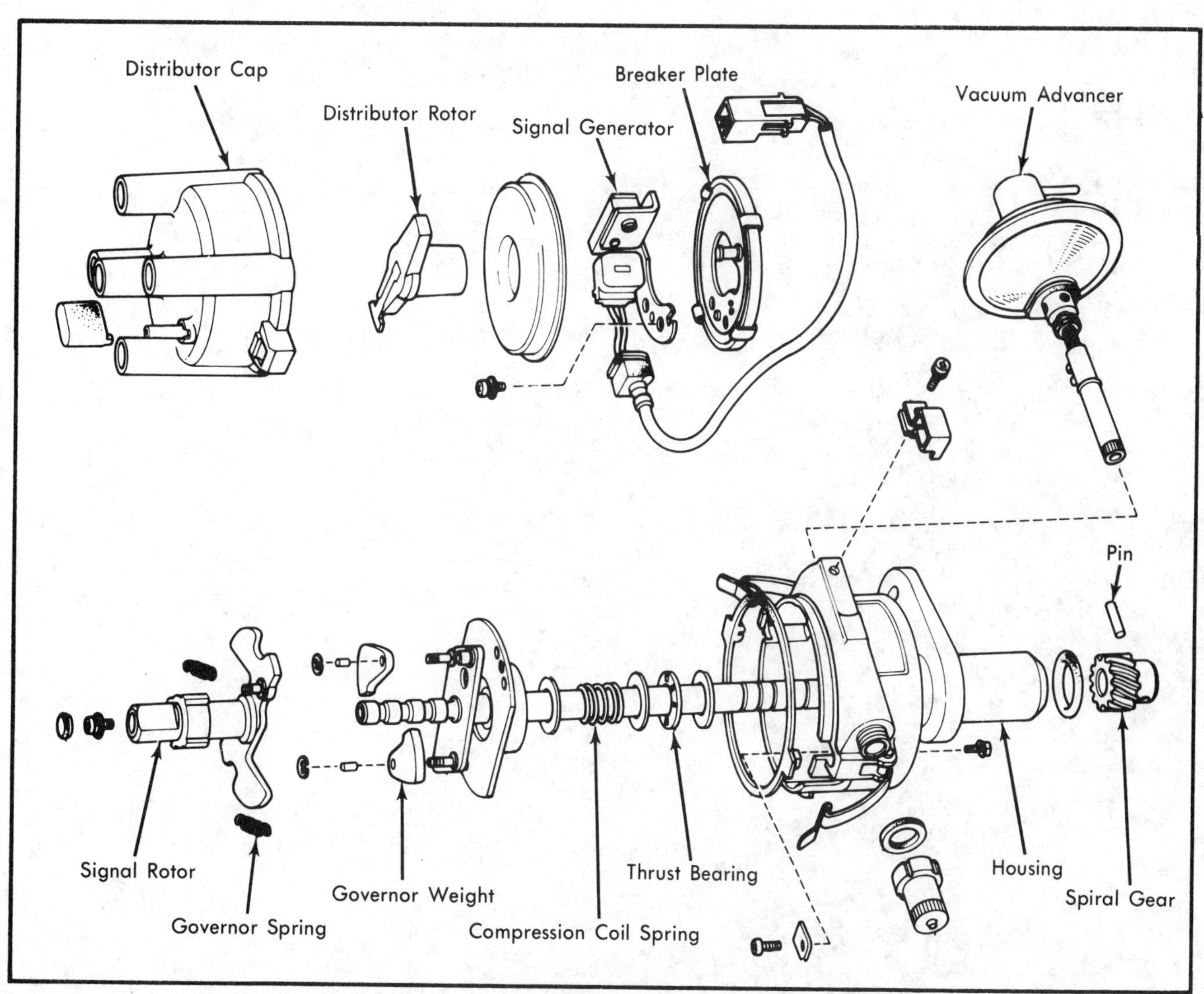

Fig. 4 Exploded View of Nippondenso Fully Transistorized Distributor

NIPPONDENSO TRANSISTORIZED IGNITION SYSTEM

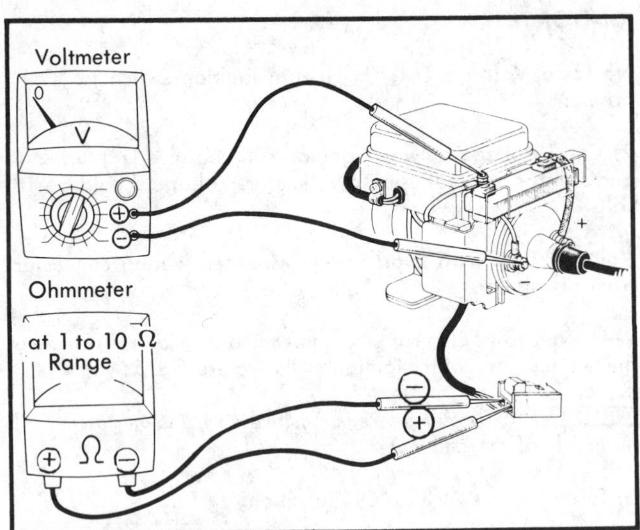

Fig. 5 Connections for Voltage Load Test

OVERHAUL

Disassembly — 1) With distributor removed from vehicle, remove distributor cap, rotor and dust cover. Remove signal generator, breaker plate, wire connector and vacuum advancer from distributor.

2) Grind shank of gear removing flare from head of pin. Using a pin punch, drive out pin and remove gear from shaft.

3) Loosen two screws on bottom side of distributor housing and carefully remove shaft using a plastic hammer for tapping to prevent damage.

4) Remove governor spring, loosen screw at end of governor shaft and remove signal rotor from distributor. Remove governor snap ring and weight.

Reassembly — Reassemble distributor in reverse order of disassembly. Adjust timing-to-pick up coil projection air gap.

BOSCH ALTERNATORS

Audi
BMW
Capri
Lancia
Mercedes-Benz
Porsche
Saab
Volkswagen
Volvo

▶ CHANGES, CAUTIONS, CORRECTIONS

▶ *BATTERY INSTALLATION, BATTERY CHARGING, OR USING A BOOSTER BATTERY TO START ENGINE* – Reversed polarity or excessive voltage will result in damage to alternator system. Note the following to prevent damage:

Battery Installation – Negative battery terminal must be connected to ground. Positive terminal must be connected to starter lead. DO NOT reverse battery leads.

Battery Charging – If a Quick Charger is used, both battery cables must be disconnected from the battery. DO NOT use a Quick Charger to provide starting voltage.

Booster Battery (For Engine Start) – Booster battery must be connected with negative lead to negative terminal of battery and positive lead to positive terminal of battery. DO NOT reverse battery leads.

DESCRIPTION

Bosch alternators are conventional three-phase, self-rectifying type alternators. Nine rectifier diodes are connected to the stator windings (three to each phase lead). The diodes change the alternator A.C. voltages to D.C. voltages coming out of the "B+" and the "D+" terminals of the alternator.

NOTE – *In reference to application table, N-1 and K-1 are identical parts.*

APPLICATION (Cont.)

Model	Type No.	Part No.
Audi	K1(RL)14V 55A 20	.....
BMW		
320i	K1(RL)14V 55A 20	.....
530i	.....	①0 120 489 503
630CSi	.....	①0 120 489 503
Capri		
4 Cyl.	.....	②D7RY-A35
		②D7RY-B45
		②D7RY-C55
V6	.....	②D6RY-C35
		②D6RY-H45
		②D6RY-D55
Lancia	.....	①082331598
Mercedes-Benz		
All Models	K1(RL)14V 55A 20	.....
Porsche		
4 Cyl.	.....	①0 120 450 001

APPLICATION (Cont.)

Model	Type No.	Part No.
Saab	K1(RL)14V 55A 20	.....
Volkswagen		
Type 1	.....	①0120 489 565
Type 2	N1-14V 65A 15	.....
Scirocco		
W/A.C.	.....	①0 120 489 520
All Others	.....	①0 120 489 500
Dasher & Rabbit		
W/A.C.	K1(RL)14V 55A 20	.....
All Others	.....	①0 120 489 581 or 582
Volvo	K1(RL)14V 55A 20	.....

① – Bosch part number.
② – Ford part number.

NOTE – *Bosch has a 65 amp. alternator which is installed on Volkswagen vehicles with factory installed air conditioning.*

SPECIFICATIONS

Alternator①	Amp Output @RPM	Max. Current
K1(RL)14V 35A 20	23 @2000	35A
K1(RL)14V 45A 20	30 @2050	45A
K1(RL)14V 55A 20	36 @2000	55A
K1(RL)14A 55A 22	36 @2200	55A

① – Charging voltage is 14 volts.

Field Coil Resistance – 4.0 ohms + 10% measured at slip rings at normal ambient temperature.

Stator Windings Resistance – Specification is .2 ohms +10% (except Capri II) measured between the phase output terminals. Specification for Capri II is .25-.28 ohms on models without air conditioning and .14-.16 ohms on models with air conditioning.

ON VEHICLE TESTING

NOTE – *Off vehicle testing is explained as part of Overhaul procedure in this article.*

WIRING CONTINUITY TEST
Disconnect terminal plug from rear of alternator and connect a voltmeter negative terminal to ground. With ignition "ON", connect positive lead to each of the connector wires, in turn. Voltmeter should read battery voltage as each positive connection is made. If proper voltage is not read, trace each wire to find fault.

VOLTAGE DROP TEST – GROUND SIDE
Connect voltmeter between negative terminal of battery and alternator housing. Start engine and run at approximately 3000 RPM. If voltmeter reading exceeds .25 Volts, a high resistance in negative side of charging circuit is indicated. If so, check for loose, dirty, or corroded connections.

BOSCH ALTERNATORS (Cont.)

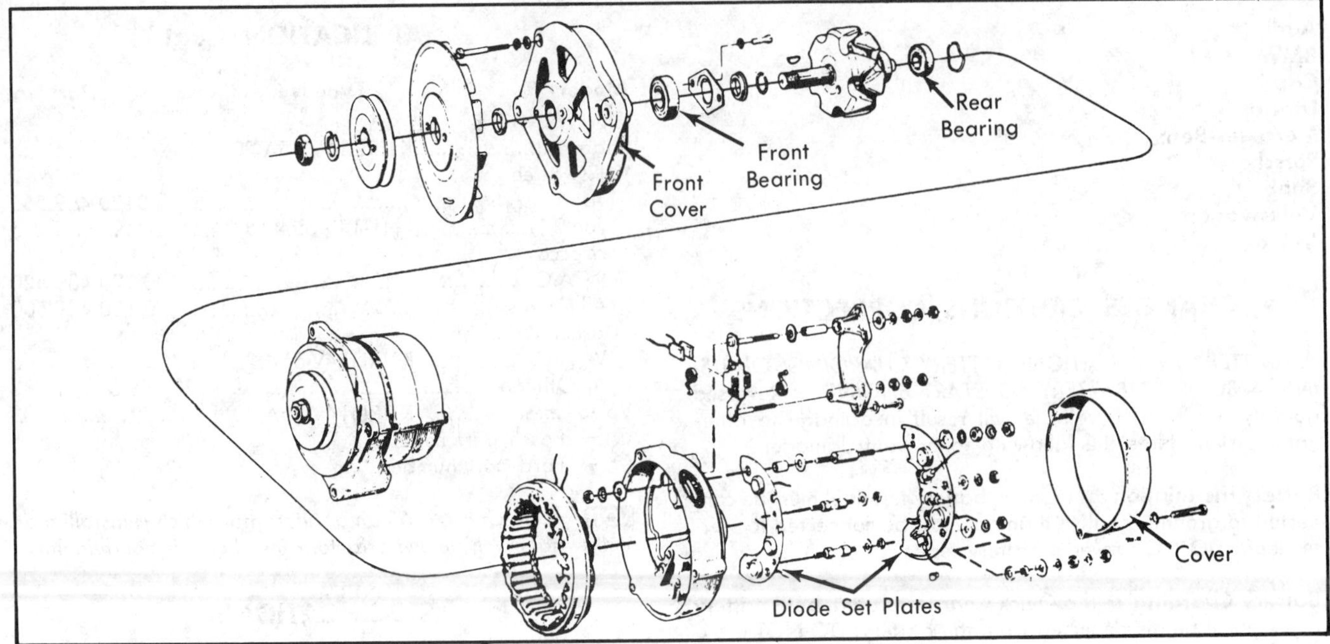

Fig. 1 Disassembled View of Bosch Alternator

OUTPUT TEST

Disconnect terminal plug from rear of alternator and connect ammeter, in series, between alternator center terminal and corresponding socket in terminal plug. Also connect a jumper lead between the "D+" terminal and its corresponding socket in terminal plug. Start engine and run at approximately 3000 RPM. Turn on headlights and leave on for five minutes. Ammeter should read maximum alternator amperage at normal operating temperature.

REGULATOR CONTROL VOLTAGE TEST

Connect a voltmeter between main terminals of battery. Connect an ammeter, in series, between "B+" terminal of alternator and corresponding terminal of connector plug. Connect a jumper lead between alternator "D+" terminal and corresponding terminal of connector plug. Start engine and increase speed to approximately 3000 RPM. Run engine until charging rate falls below 10 amps. The voltmeter should then read 14.1-14.4 Volts. If these readings are not obtained, replace regulator.

NOTE – *The test cables should not be removed or the load excessively reduced during the testing procedure. Considerable load variations may damage the diodes. The control lamp should not go on at any time during the test.*

OVERHAUL

DISASSEMBLY

NOTE – *On 0 120 400 600 series alternators, lift carbon brushes with a hook and secure them, prior to disassembly (see illustration).*

1) Remove nut, pulley, hub and key. Mark location of alternator in blower housing. Unscrew brush plate assembly and remove from alternator. Remove bolts from end frame, then remove frame and field rotor. Press rotor out of end frame. Press ball bearing off rotor. Remove insulating conduit from wires and cut wires as close to soldered joints as possible.

2) The diodes may be tested at this point, prior to further disassembly. Care should be exercised with insulating bushings under positive diode carrier. To remove negative carrier, extract threaded studs. When one rectifying diode has been damaged due to short circuiting, the three complementing diodes must be replaced also. Unscrew nuts on both "B+" terminal bolts and lift positive diode carrier (heat sink) up and back.

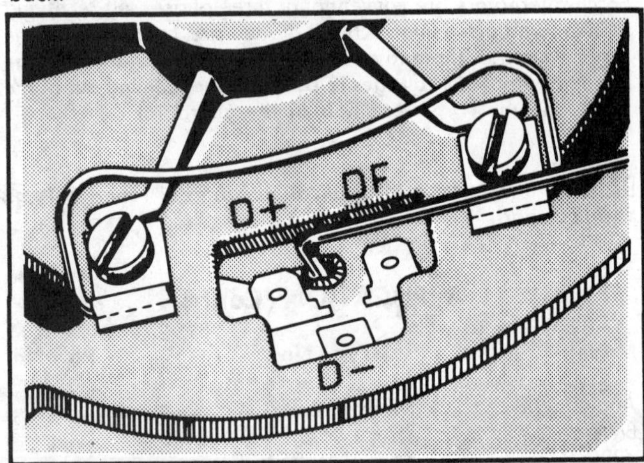

Fig. 2 Lifting Carbon Brushes on 0120 400 600 Series

TESTING & REPAIRING

Diode Assemblies – Test diodes with a suitable alternator tester (EFAW 192) before dismantling slip ring end frame further. **CAUTION** – *Do not lay positive diode carrier on housing or false reading will be obtained.* Disconnect conductor from "D+" to the exciter diodes at the exciter diodes heat sink. Unscrew spring and brush holder and remove from alternator. Unsolder stator lead and negative diode connections. Unscrew exciter diodes heat sink and remove together with positive diodes heat sink.

NOTE – *Before further testing, lightly clean all components in gasoline or trichlorethylene, but do not soak.*

BOSCH ALTERNATORS (Cont.)

Stator – Test stator for short circuits to ground, using suitable tester (EFAW 84). Test voltage should be 40V AC. Measure resistance of stator windings between phase connections. See *Specifications for proper value*.

Rotor – **1**) Test claw pole rotor for short circuits to ground. Test voltage should be 40V AC. Measure resistance of exciter (field coil) in rotor with ohmmeter. See *Specifications for proper value*. Turn down slip rings on a lathe, using suitable tailstock chuck (EFAW 75 or GDF 85 R 3).

2) After turning, check concentricity of slip rings with dial gauge. Runout should not exceed .001" (.03 mm). Minimum diameter of slip rings may be 1.25" (31.5 mm). Maximum runout of pole wheel must not exceed .002" (.05 mm).

Diode Replacement – **1**) On all except 0 120 400 600 series alternators, set diode plate on press die and force diodes out with plunger. Place diode plate (without diodes) onto suitable guide pilot (EFLJ 57/0/5) and set diode seat with suitable sleeve (EFLJ 57/0/3). Smear silicone oil on diode seat, place diode plate on press die and press diodes into position. After pressing in, test all diodes.

2) On 0 120 400 600 series alternators, set slip ring end frame on press die and force out defective diode. Coat diode seat with silicone oil and press in new diode. Test all diodes after replacement.

Fig. 3 Installing Diodes

Drive End Frame – Check ball bearings for wear and replace as necessary. Lubricate bearings on one side. Press ball bearing into drive end frame with shielded side downward. Screw on retainer plate. Press ball bearing onto rotor (slip ring end), then press drive end frame onto rotor.

Carbon Brushes – Unsolder and replace carbon brushes. Do not allow solder to run into copper strands of brush leads. Minimum brush length is .55" (14 mm). After installation of new brushes, test for free movement.

REASSEMBLY & TESTING

1) On all except 0 120 400 600 series alternators (steps **1** through **4**), fit negative diodes heat sink and clamps. Screw in double end bolts (shorter threads outward). **NOTE** – *Left clamp is longer than right.* Replace insulating washers and bushings. Test terminal bolt "B+" for short circuit to ground. Test voltage should be 80V AC.

2) Position positive diodes heat sink (carrier) and secure with insulating and spring washers. **NOTE** – *Use insulating cap No. 1 120 502 000 instead of insulating washer on bolt next to terminal marked "D+/61".* Tighten hex nuts.

3) Place stator in slip ring end frame. Draw positive and negative diode leads together and slip through an insulating sleeve. Push sleeve over lead of exciter diode and stator connection cable. Crimp a metal ring around end of leads and solder. Cut off any excess wire protruding through ring. Reposition wiring and attach in holding clamps.

4) Slide insulating sleeve over exciter diode terminal. Insulating sleeves of stator connection lead must project over edge of negative diodes heat sink. Clamp connections firmly.

5) On 0 120 400 600 series alternators (steps **5** through **7**), test both "B+" terminal bolts for short circuit to ground. Test voltage should be 80V AC. Before fitting exciter diodes heat sink (carrier), solder three positive diode terminal leads onto heat sink from below.

6) After fitting exciter diodes heat sink, solder stator leads, negative and exciter diodes to the "COMB". **NOTE** – *Use caution, do not overheat negative diodes.* Install brush holder. Raise and secure carbon brushes before installing. Screw conductor "D+" onto exciter diodes heat sink.

7) Place wave spring washer into ball bearing fit. Rub ball bearing seat with suitable lubricant. Insert rotor with drive end bearing into slip ring end frame and secure with screws. Position positive diodes heat sink and secure. Springs are to be set onto carbon brushes by pressing on brush with a screwdriver. Brush springs pressure will seat brushes automatically.

8) Rub suitable lubricant into ball bearing seat of slip ring end frame. Install claw pole rotor with drive end frame. Check position of stator relative to end frame. Position brush holder plate. Tighten screws. Install fan belt pulley. Coat newly installed positive diodes with chlorinated rubber lacquer.

BOSCH REGULATORS

Audi
BMW
Capri
Mercedes Benz
Lancia
Porsche
Saab
Volkswagen
Volvo

NOTE — *For models using integral alternator regulators, see Bosch Alternators in this section.*

DESCRIPTION

Bosch alternator regulators are provided in two types, vibrating contact points or transistorized solid state. The vibrating contact regulator is two contact, single field units. The field coil of the alternator is grounded and voltage contacts of the regulator are in series with the field. Vibrator types are models AD(N), AB, & AE. Transistorized models are EA, ED, & EE.

TESTING

ON CAR TEST

Vibrator Type — Install a battery post adapter at the positive post of the battery. Connect voltmeter across battery. Connect a tachometer to ignition system. Make sure all electrical acessories are turned off. Start engine with battery post adapter switch closed; open switch as soon as engine is started. With engine speed at 4000 RPM, after voltage reading stabilizes, any reading between 13.7 and 14.8 volts is satisfactory.

Transistorized (Solid State) — **1**) For type ED 14 V 3, regulated voltage should be 13.7 to 14.6 with a 10 amp. load current.

2) For type EE 14 V 3, regulated voltage should be 13.7 to 14.6 with a load current of 5 to 7 amps.

3) For type ED 14 V 2, regulated voltage should be 13.9 to 14.9 with load current of 5 amps.

4) For ED 14 V 3 (Only part numbers 0192062 002 and 0192062 003) regulated voltage should be 13.7 to 14.5.

ADJUSTMENT

VIBRATOR TYPE

If voltage reading is out of limits, remove regulator cover and adjust voltage regulator armature spring tension to obtain a middle reading of 14.0 volts. If reading fluctuates, voltage contacts are dirty. Replace regulator cover and recheck voltage setting. A steady voltage reading between 13.5 and 14.5 volts indicates regulator is in good condition.

TRANSISTOR TYPE

Adjust alternator current and voltage to balance by altering the load resistance and readjust the alternator speed if necessary. Adjust to 14.0 volts.

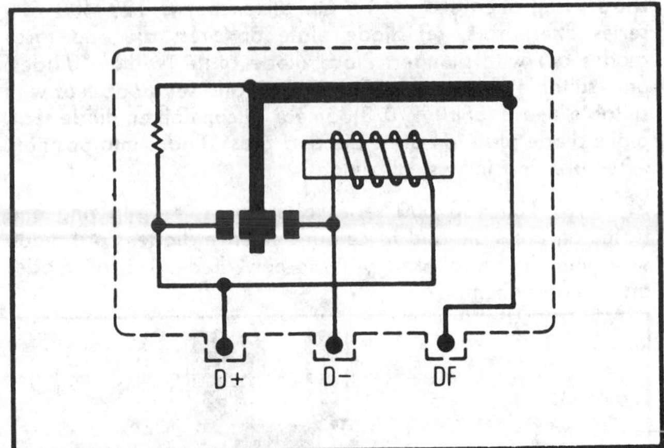

Fig. 1 Bosch Vibrator Type Alternator Regulator

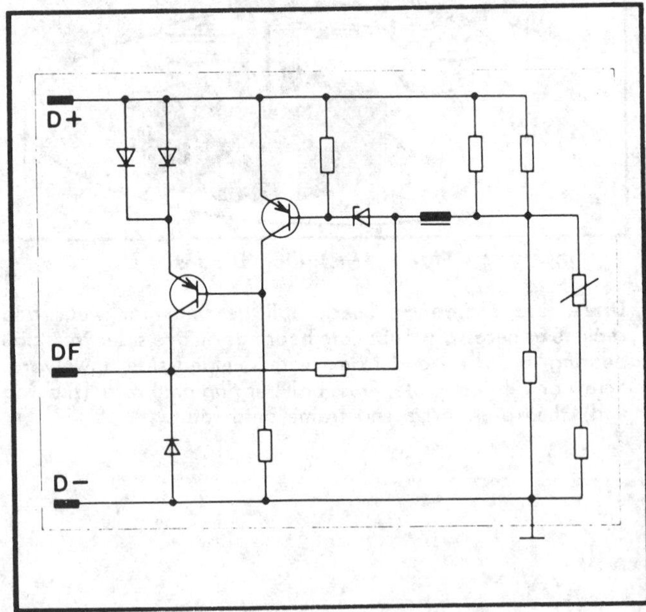

Fig. 2 Typical Bosch Transistorized Voltage Regulator Wiring Diagram

HITACHI ALTERNATORS

Datsun
LUV
Subaru

▶ CHANGES, CAUTIONS, CORRECTIONS

▶ *BATTERY INSTALLATION, BATTERY CHARGING, OR USING A BOOSTER BATTERY FOR ENGINE START* – Reversed polarity or excessive voltage will result in extensive damage to alternator system. Note the following to prevent damage:

Battery Installation – Negative battery terminal must be connected to ground. Positive terminal must be connected to starter lead. DO NOT reverse battery leads.

Battery Charging – If a Quick Charger is used, both battery cables must be disconnected from the battery. DO NOT use a Quick Charger to provide starting voltage.

Booster Battery (For Engine Start) – Booster battery must be connected with negative lead to negative battery terminal and positive lead to positive battery terminal. DO NOT reverse battery leads.

DESCRIPTION

Hitachi alternators are conventional three-phase, self-rectifying type alternators. Six diodes (three positive and three negative) are used to rectify current.

APPLICATION

Model	Hitachi No.
Datsun	
B210 & F10	LT150-26
200SX, 610 & 710	LT150-25
280Z	LT160-23C
620 Pickup	
W/O Air Conditioning	LT135-36B
W/Air Conditioning	LT138-01B
810	LT160-39
LUV	LT135-30
Subaru	LT150-21

SPECIFICATIONS

Output@2500 Alternator RPM

Alternator	Amps	Volts
LT135-36B	35	14
LT135-01B	38	14
LT135-30	28	14
LT138-01B	38	14
LT150-21	40	14
LT150-25	37.5	14
LT150-26	37.5	14
LT160-23C	42	14
LT160-39	42	14

Nominal Output

Alternator	Amps	Volts
LT135-36B	35	12
LT135-01B	35	12
LT135-30	35	12
LT138-01B	38	12
LT150-21	50	12
LT150-25	50	12
LT150-26	50	12
LT160-23	60	12
LT160-23C	60	12

Resistance Values (Ohms)

Alternator	Stator Coil	Rotor Coil
LT135-36B	0.17	4.4
LT135-01B	0.17	4.4
LT135-30	0.13	4.3
LT150-21		
LT150-25		
LT150-26		
LT160-23	0.17	4.4
LT160-23C	0.17	4.4
LT160-39		

TESTING

NOTE – *Some testing is described as part of Overhaul procedure in this article. The following testing is performed with alternator on the vehicle.*

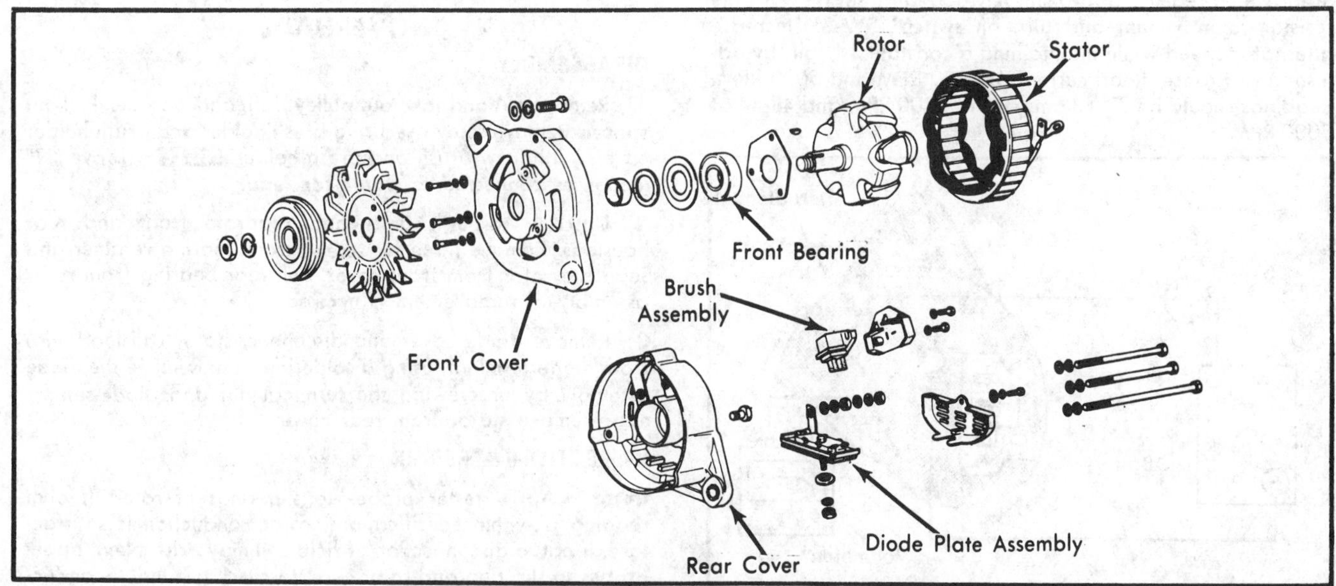

Fig. 1 Disassembled View of Hitachi Alternator

HITACHI ALTERNATORS (Cont.)

ALTERNATOR SPEED TEST

Datsun Models – Ensure battery has a full charge, then connect a 30-volt voltmeter as shown in illustration, and test as follows:

1) Detach connectors at alternator. Connect a test probe from voltmeter positive terminal to "N" or "BAT" terminal. Connect other test probe to ground. Check that voltmeter registers battery voltage.

2) Turn on headlights to high beam. Start engine and increase speed to approximately 1000 RPM and observe voltmeter. If voltmeter registers below 12.5 volts, alternator is defective. If above 12.5 volts, alternator is good.

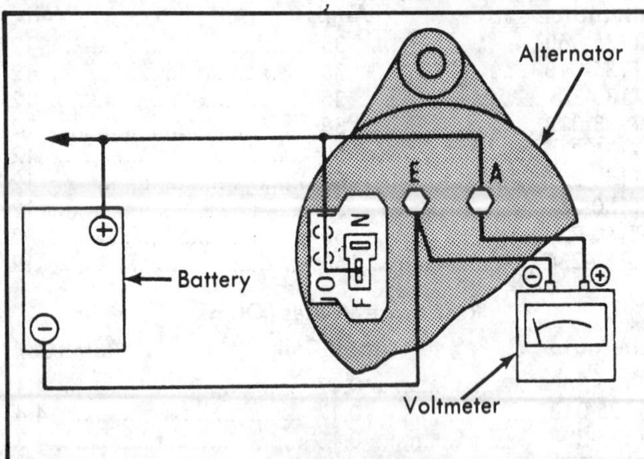

Fig. 2 Alternator Testing Connections for Datsun

Subaru Models – 1) Connect a voltmeter and leads to battery as shown in *Fig. 3*. Operate the alternator and turn off the switch "SW" when alternator speed reaches approximately 800 RPM. Increase speed in small increments while watching voltmeter deflection and read alternator speed when at 14 volts. Speed should be approximately 1000 RPM.

2) Make test connections using a 30-50 ampere variable resistor, battery, ammeter, and voltmeter as shown in *Fig. 4*. Operate alternator with switch "SW-1" closed. When alternator speed reaches approximately 800 RPM, set the variable resistor to maximum and turn on switch "SW-2". Increase alternator speed while maintaining a constant 14 volts by adjusting resistance. Read current at 2500 RPM and 5000 RPM. Readings should be 37-43 amperes at 2500 RPM and 48-54 at 5000 RPM.

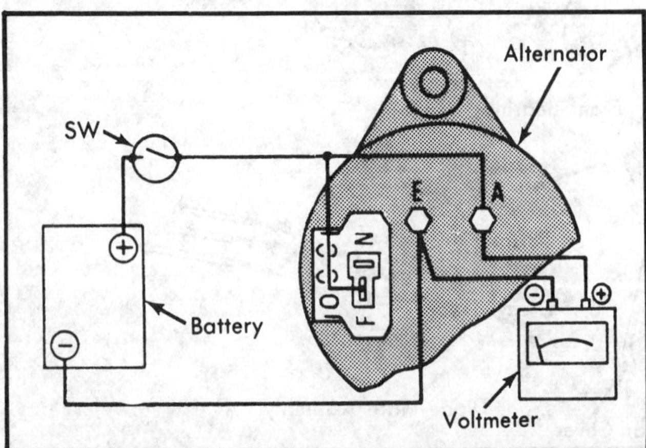

Fig. 3 Alternator Testing Connections for Subaru

RESISTANCE & CONTINUITY TESTING

All Models – 1) Measure resistance, using an ohmmeter, across "F" and "E" terminals for rotor coil resistance. Rotor coil circuit is normal if resistance is 4-5 ohms. If resistance is high, there is poor contact between brushes and commutator. If no continuity exists between "F" and "E" terminals, there is either an open rotor coil circuit, brush sticking or a broken lead wire. If resistance is low, it indicates a rotor coil layer short or grounded circuit.

2) **NOTE** – *The following test will not indicate a open state of the diodes. Tester will indicate a continuity regardless of diode conditions if tester leads are connected to the terminals with polarities reversed.* Connect positive lead of tester to alternator "N" terminal and tester negative lead to alternator "A" terminal. If continuity is observed on the tester, there exists one or more shorted positive diodes.

3) Next, connect tester positive lead to alternator "E" terminal and tester negative lead to alternator "N" terminal. If continuity is present, it indicates that one or more of the negative diodes are shorted.

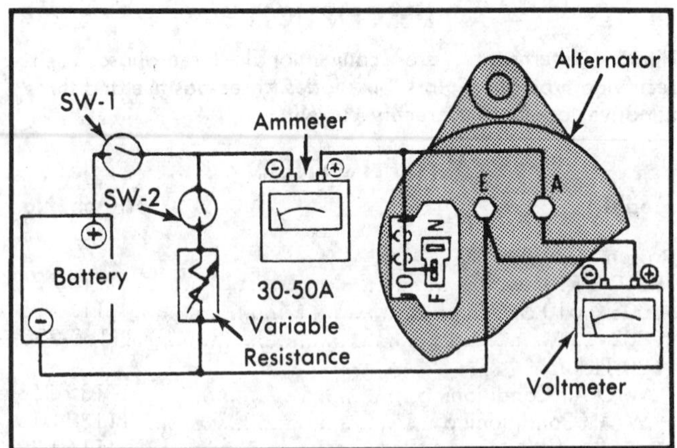

Fig. 4 Alternator Test Connections for Subaru

OVERHAUL

DISASSEMBLY

1) Remove nut and take out pulley, fan, and washers. Pull out spacer. Remove screws securing brush holder and brush holder cover. Withdraw brush and brush holder. **NOTE** – *Leave "N" lead wire connected to stator coil lead.*

2) Unscrew through bolts and separate front and rear housings. Remove three set screws from bearing retainer and separate rotor from front cover. Pull rear bearing from rotor assembly, if replacement is necessary.

3) Remove diode cover and disconnect stator coil lead wire from diode terminal, using a soldering iron. Remove the diode assembly by unscrewing the terminal nut and diode-setting nuts. Remove stator from rear cover.

INSPECTION & REPAIR

Rotor – Apply tester probes to slip rings of rotor. If ohm reading is within specifications, rotor conduction is satisfactory. If not, a disconnection of field coil may exist. Next, apply probes to slip ring and rotor core, to check ground. If conduction exists, replace rotor assembly.

HITACHI ALTERNATORS (Cont.)

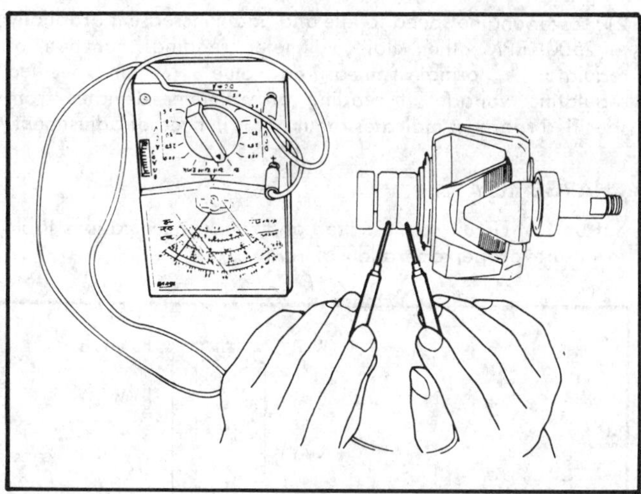

Fig. 5 Rotor Field Coil Conduction Test

Stator— The stator is normal when there is conduction between individual stator coil terminals. When there is no conduction between terminals, cable is broken; replace stator assembly. If each lead wire of stator coil (including neutral wire) is not conductive with stator core, condition is satisfactory. If conduction exists, stator is grounded and must be replaced.

Diodes — **1**) Perform a conduction test on all diodes, in both directions, using an ohmmeter. Test the conduction between each terminal and plate. Diode installed on "+" plate is a positive diode which allows current to flow from terminal to "+" plate only; current does not flow from "+" plate to the terminal. A diode installed on the "−" plate is a negative diode and allows current to flow from the "−" plate to the terminal only; current does not flow from the terminal to the "−" plate.

2) If current flows in both directions, the diode is short-circuited. If current does not flow in either direction, the diode is open. If any diode is defective, replace the entire diode assembly (individual diodes are not serviceable).

Brushes & Brush Springs — Inspect movement of brushes for smoothness. Clean brush holder if necessary. Check brushes for cracks and wear. Replace if beyond limits shown. Check brush spring for corrosion and damage. Determine if springs exhibit proper tension. Test brush holder for continuity between each holder; replace if continuity exists.

Brush & Spring Data

Alternator	Brush Wear Limit	①Spring Pressure
LT135-36B	.31"(7.5 mm)	9-12.2 oz.
LT138-01B	.31"(7.5 mm)	9-12.2 oz.
LT150-30	.28"(7.0 mm)	9-12.2 oz.
LT150-21	.28"(7.0 mm)	9-12.2 oz.
LT150-25	.31"(7.5 mm)	9-12.2 oz.
LT150-26	.31"(7.5 mm)	9-12.2 oz.
LT160-23C	.31"(7.5 mm)	9-12.2 oz.

① — Measure with .08" (2 mm) protrusion from holder.

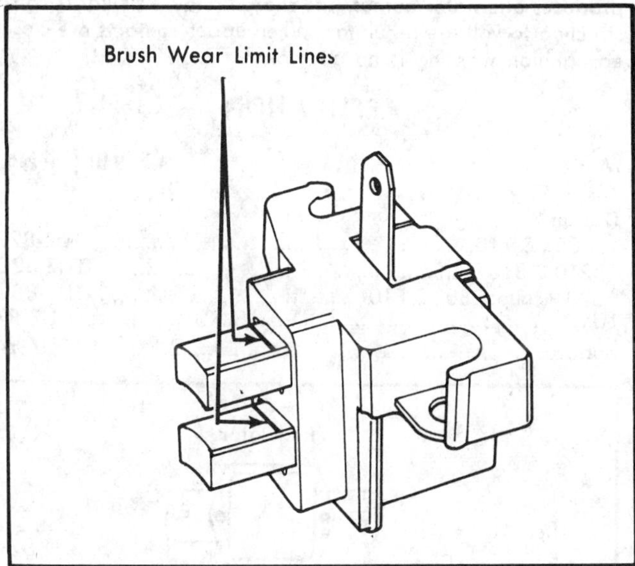

Fig. 6 View of Assembled Brushes

REASSEMBLY

Reinstall diode assembly and stator to rear cover. Connect lead wires of stator coil to terminals of diode assembly. **NOTE** — *Solder quickly to avoid damage to diodes.* Reinstall diode cover. Reinstall rotor to front cover. Place assembly in vise and replace pulley and components. Insert and tighten housing through bolts. Assemble brushes to brush holder and insert holder into alternator. Perform, as previously described.

HITACHI REGULATORS

Datsun
LUV
Subaru

DESCRIPTION

The regulator system consists basically of a voltage regulator and a charge relay. The voltage regulator has two sets of contact points, a lower set and upper set, to control alternator voltage. An armature plate placed between the two sets of contacts moves upward, downward, or vibrates. The lower contacts, when closed, complete the field circuit direct to ground. The upper contacts, when closed, complete field circuit to ground through a resistance (field coil), and thereby produces alternator output. The charge relay is similar in construction to voltage regulator. When upper contacts are closed, ignition warning lamp goes on.

APPLICATION

Model	Hitachi No.
Datsun	
200SX & 710	TLIZ-82B
B210 & 810	TLIZ-82C
620 Pickup, 280Z & F10	TLIZ-85C
LUV	TLIZ-87
Subaru	TLIZ-94

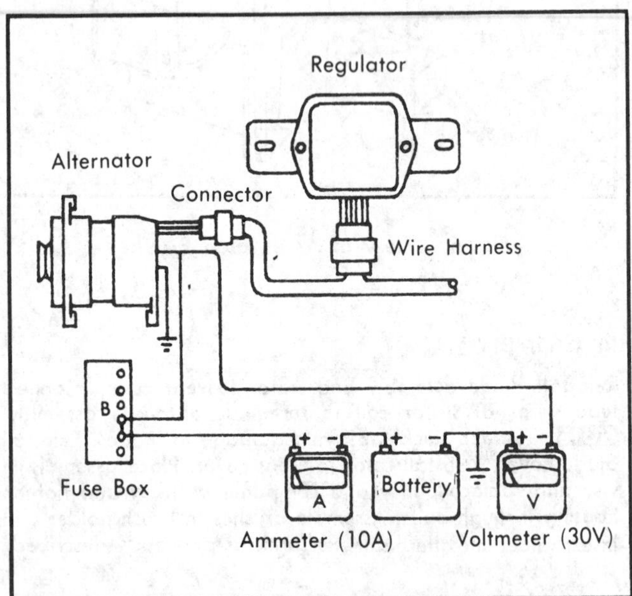

Fig. 1 Test Connections for Voltage Regulator

TESTING

VOLTAGE REGULATOR

1) Connect voltmeter and ammeter as illustrated. Start and maintain engine speed at 2500 RPM for a few minutes, then check to make sure that reading of ammeter is 5 amps or less. If ammeter remains higher than 5 amps, disconnect battery in use and connect a battery known to be fully charged. Recheck to be sure reading of ammeter is lower than 5 amps.

2) Lower engine speed to idle and again increase it gradually to 2500 RPM, then note voltmeter reading. Function of regulator is normal if measured value is within specified regulating voltage. If reading of voltmeter deviates from specified range, it indicates regulator is in need of adjustment.

CHARGE RELAY

Set up test circuit as illustrated and check specifications table to ensure proper operation of relay.

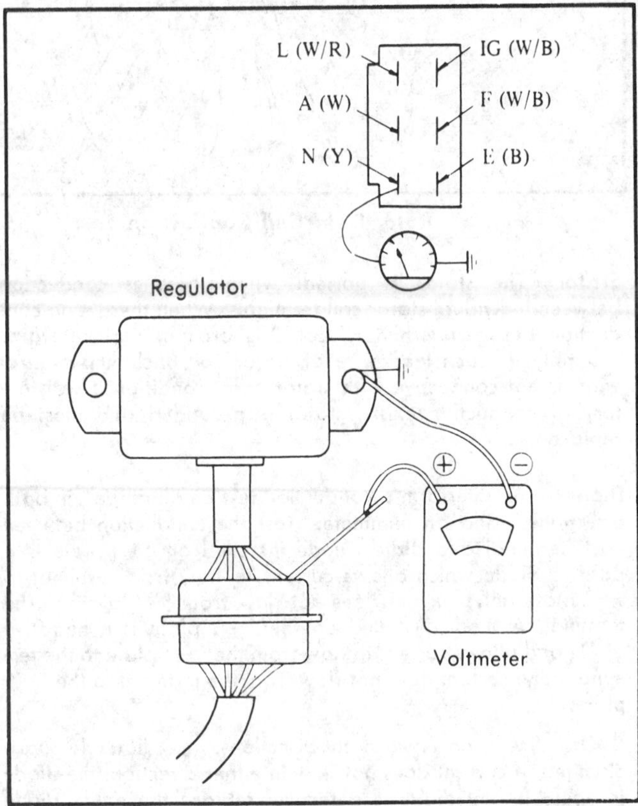

Fig. 2 Test Connections for Charge Relay

ADJUSTMENT

NOTE – *Charge relay is adjusted in same manner as voltage regulator.*

1) Disconnect and remove voltage regulator from vehicle. If contact points are roughened, smooth with fine sand paper. Check and adjust gaps: core gap first, then point gap. **NOTE** – *Adjustment of yoke gap is unnecessary on some models.*

2) Adjust core gap by loosening screws attaching contact set to yoke. Move contact set upward or downward as required. Adjust point gap by loosening screw attaching upper contact. Move upper contact up or down as required to set gap to specification.

3) Adjust regulated voltage by means of adjusting screw. Turn screw in to increase regulated voltage or out to decrease voltage. When correct voltage adjustment is obtained, secure with lock nut. When adjustment procedure is complete, reinstall regulator and perform on car check.

HITACHI REGULATORS (Cont.)

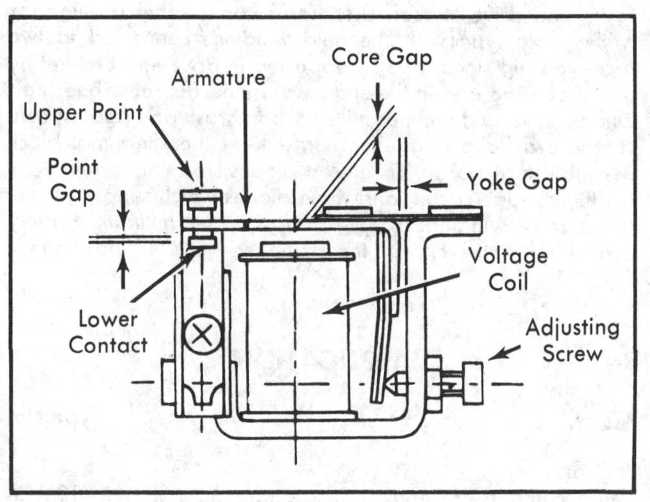

Fig. 3 Adjustment Points for Voltage Regulator

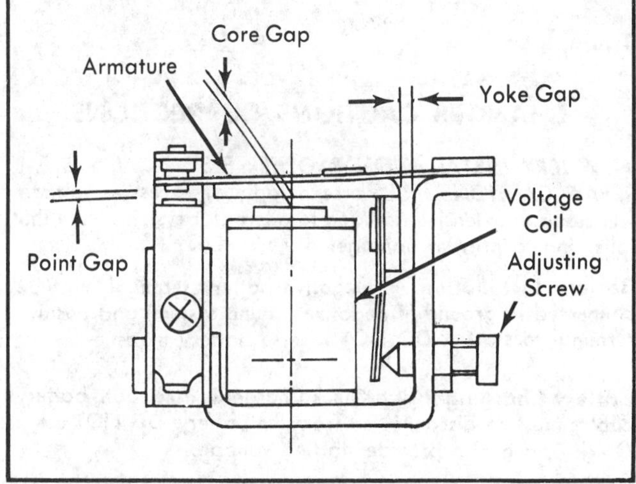

Fig. 4 Adjustment Points for Charge Relay

VOLTAGE REGULATOR SPECIFICATIONS

Regulator	Battery Voltage	Regulated Voltage	Voltage Coil Resistance (Ohms)	Yoke Gap In. (mm)	Core Gap In. (mm)	Point Gap In. (mm)
TLIZ-82B & 82C	12	14.3-15.3	10.5	①	.024-.039(.6-1.0)	.014-.018(.35-45)
TLIZ-85C	12	14.3-15.3	10.5	①	.024-.039(.6-1.0)	.014-.018(.35-.45)
TLIZ-87	12	13.8-14.8	10.3	①	.024-.039(.6-1.0)	.012-.000(.3-.4)
TLIZ-94	12	14.0-15.0	10.3	.035(,89)	.024-.039(.6-1.0)	.012-.016(.3-.4)

① — No yoke gap adjustment required.

VOLTAGE RELAY SPECIFICATIONS

Regulator	Released Voltage	Voltage Coil Resistance (Ohms)	Yoke Gap In. (mm)	Core Gap In. (mm)	Point Gap In. (mm)
TLIZ-82B & 82C	4.2-5.2②	37.8	①	.031-.039(.79-1.0)	.016-.024 (.41-.61)
TLIZ-85C	4.2-5.2②	37.8	①	.031-.039(.79-1.0)	.016-.024(.41-.61)
TLIZ-87	5③	31.9	①	.031-.039(.79-1.0)	.016-.024(.41-.61)
TLIZ-94	8-10	31.9	.035(.89)	.031-.039(.79-.1.0)	.016-.024(.41-.61)

① — No yoke gap adjustment required.
② — Measured at "N" terminal
③ — Measured at "A" terminal.

LUCAS ALTERNATOR WITH INTEGRAL REGULATOR

Jaguar
MG
Triumph

▸ CHANGES, CAUTIONS, CORRECTIONS

▸ *BATTERY INSTALLATION & OTHER ELECTRICAL SYSTEM REPAIR CAUTIONS* — Reverse polarity or excessive voltage will result in extensive damage to alternator system. Note the following to prevent damage:

Battery Installation — Negative battery terminal must be connected to ground (if negative ground system) and positive terminal to starter. DO NOT reverse battery leads.

Battery Charging — If a Quick Charger is used, both battery cables must be disconnected from the battery. DO NOT use a Quick Charger to provide starting voltage.

Circuit Interruption — Battery must NEVER be disconnected while alternator is running.

Alternator Removal — Always disconnect battery ground before replacement of alternator.

High Voltage — DO NOT use a high voltage source to test diodes.

Booster Battery (For Engine Start)— Booster battery must be connected with negative lead to negative terminal of battery and positive lead to positive terminal of battery. DO NOT reverse battery leads.

DESCRIPTION

Lucas "ACR" model alternators have an integral voltage regulator mounted in the slip ring end bracket. The stator consists of star-connected, three phase windings on a ring end cover and drive end bracket. The rotor is either an eight or twelve pole type with the field windings connected to two face-type slip rings, and is supported in drive-end bracket by a ball bearing and in the end cover by needle roller bearings. One positive and one negative carbon brush ride against concentric brass slip rings. The heatsink-rectifier, terminal block assembly incorporate six silicon diodes, forming a full wave rectifier bridge circuit, and three diodes which supply current to the rotor windings. **NOTE** — *Up to a ten milliamp battery drain is normal, even with the ignition in the "OFF" position.*

APPLICATION

Model	Type No.
Jaguar	
XJ-6 Without Air Cond.	18 ACR
XJ-6 With Air Cond.	20 ACR
XJ-12, XJS	20 ACR
MG	16 ACR
Triumph	
Spitfire 1500	16 ACR
TR-7	20 ACR

SPECIFICATIONS

Alternator	Nominal Output Amps @ RPM	Voltage
16 ACR	34 @ 6000	12
18 ACR	43 @ 6000	12
20 ACR	66 @ 6000	12

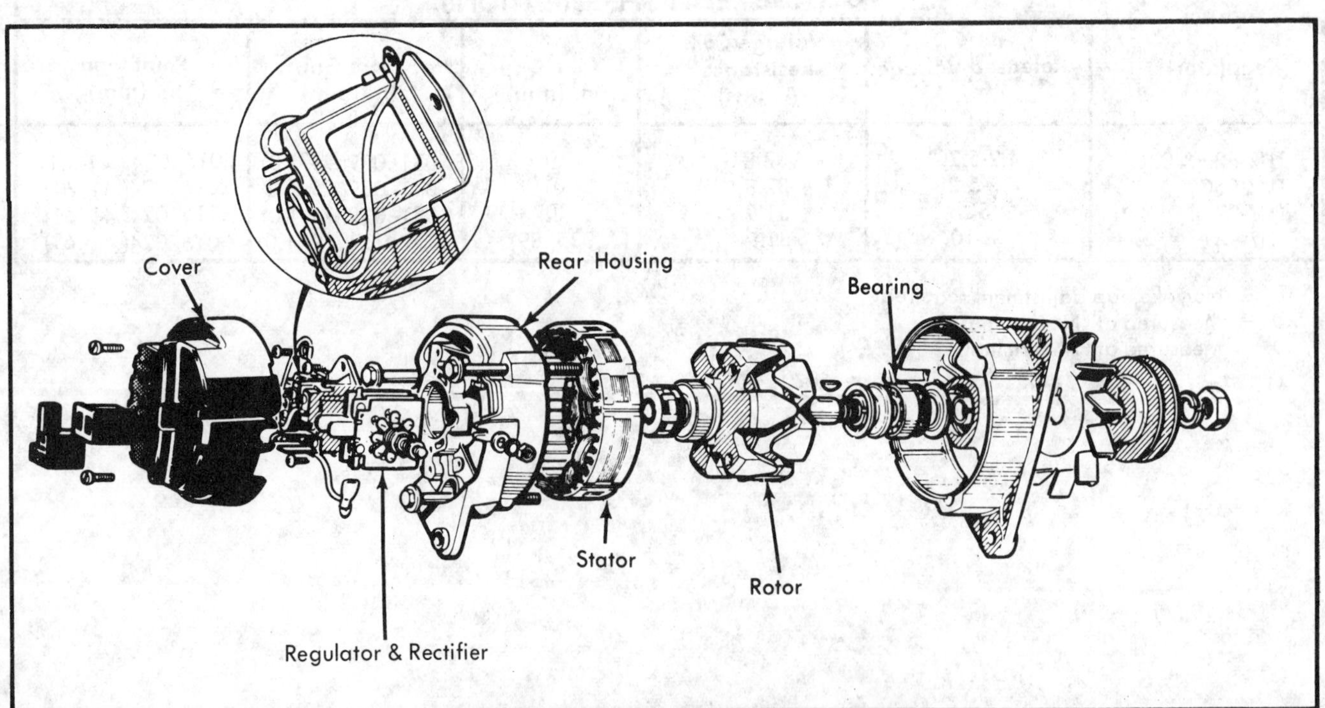

Fig. 1 Disassembled View of Lucas Integral Alternator Regulator Assembly

LUCAS ALTERNATOR WITH INTEGRAL REGULATOR (Cont.)

TESTING

ON CAR TESTING

Testing Alternator Output With Regulator Inoperative – **1)** Disconnect alternator harness connector. Unscrew molded cover from rear of alternator. Link together regulator negative terminal and "F" terminal. Connect an external test circuit as shown in lower half of illustration. **CAUTION** – *Be aware of proper connections to avoid reversed polarity.*

2) **NOTE** – *Variable resistor across battery terminals must not be left connected any longer than necessary to complete the test.* Start engine and run at 800 RPM (1500 alternator RPM). The test circuit bulb should now be out.

3) Inscrease engine speed to 3200 RPM (6000 alternator RPM) and adjust variable resistance until voltmeter reads 14 volts. Ammeter reading should then be approximately specified rated output. If obvious variance from specifications is encountered, alternator necessitates removal and overhaul or replacement.

Regulator Test – **NOTE** – *The following test assumes alternator is satisfactory.* – **1)** Disconnect variable resistor and remove link bridging regulator negative and "F" terminals. With remainder of test circuit still connected, start engine and run up to 3200 RPM (6000 alternator RPM), until ammeter registers output current of less than 10 amps. Voltmeter should then read 13.6-14.4 volts. Any variation necessitates regulator replacement.

2) If regulator is still shown to be satisfactory, disconnect entire external test circuit and reconnect alternator harness connector. Attach a low-range voltmeter between either positive alternator terminal and positive battery terminal.

3) Turn on headlights, start engine and increase engine speed to 3200 RPM. Record voltmeter reading. Transfer voltmeter connection to alternator frame and negative battery terminal. Record reading. If reading exceeds 0.5 volt on positive side or 0.25 volt on negative side, there is a high resistance in charging circuit which must be traced and corrected. See *further testing on Overhaul procedure.*

OVERHAUL

DISASSEMBLY

1) Unscrew cover retaining screws and remove cover. Unsolder three stator connections from rectifier pack, noting positions. Remove two brush molding securing screws, loosen rectifier pack retaining nuts, and withdraw brush molding and rectifier pack.

2) Remove three through bolts. Remove bearing, by slipping a tube over slip ring molding until it is even with outer track of slip ring end bearing, then drive bearing from its housing. Remove shaft nut, pulley, and shaft key. Press rotor from drive end bracket. Remove circlip retaining the drive end bearing and remove bearing. Unsolder field connections from slip ring assembly and withdraw assembly from rotor shaft. Remove slip ring end bearing.

Regulator Removal – Disconnect colored tag lead connectors from brush box and detach ground lead after removing lower mounting screw or brush box retaining screw. Remove other retaining screw and withdraw regulator.

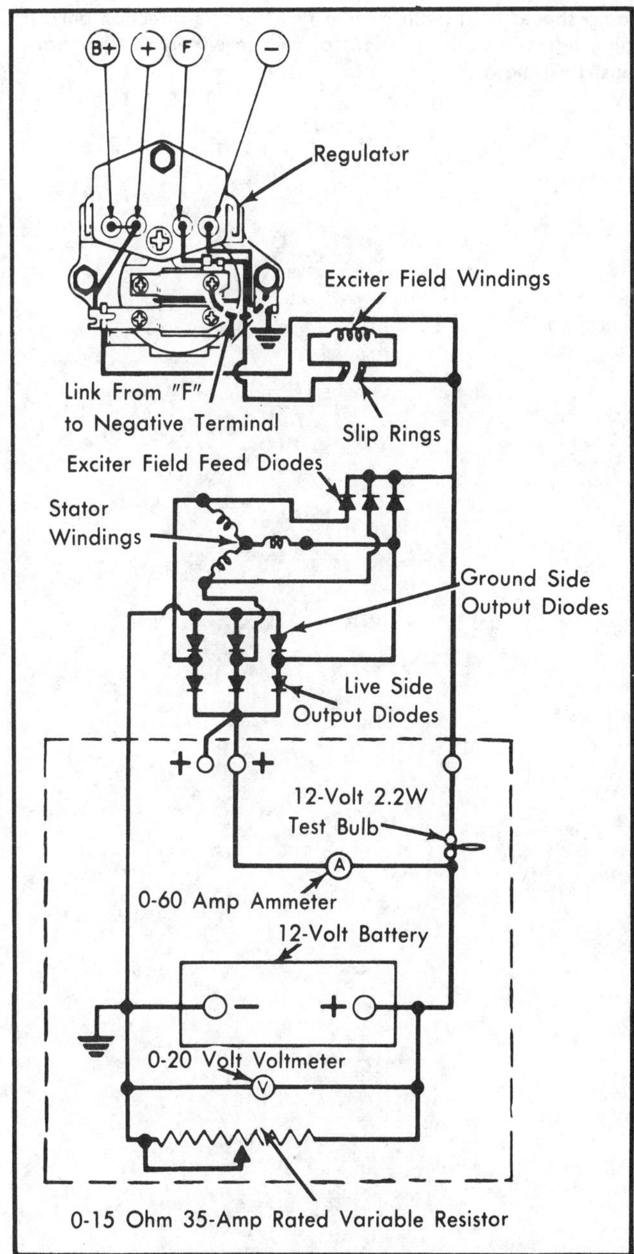

Fig. 2 Alternator Output Test Circuit

LUCAS ALTERNATOR WITH INTEGRAL REGULATOR (Cont.)

TESTING

Rotor – Connect an ohmmeter and read resistance of field coil (across slip rings). Using a 110-volt A.C. supply and 15-watt test lamp, check for insulation between one of the slip rings and any rotor pole. If lamp lights, rotor is shorted.

Stator – Connect 12-volt battery and 36-watt test lamp to two of the stator connections. Then repeat test using any other combination of two of the three connections. If lamp fails to light in either test, stator has an open coil. Using a 110-volt A.C. supply and a 15-watt test lamp, check for insulation between any one of the three stator connections and stator laminations. If lamp lights, stator should be replaced.

Diodes – Connect a 12-volt battery and a 1.5-watt test lamp in turn to each of the nine diode pins and its corresponding heat sink on the rectifier pack, then reverse the connections. Lamp should light (with current flow) in one direction only. If lamp lights in both directions or fails in either, rectifier pack must be renewed.

PARTS REPLACEMENT

Diodes – If a defective diode is detected, the rectifier pack must be replaced as a unit.

Brushes – If length of brush protruding beyond brush box molding is .2" (5 mm) or less, the brush must be replaced. Check brush spring pressure, using a push type spring gauge. Gauge should register 9-13 oz. when brush is pushed back flush with housing. If reading is outside limits, place brush assembly.

REASSEMBLY

Reverse disassembly procedure, noting the following: When installing slip ring end bearing, ensure it is fitted with open side facing rotor and that it is seated fully. When replacing rotor to drive end bracket, support inner track of bearing with suitable piece of tubing. DO NOT use drive end bracket as the only support for bearing when fitting rotor.

MARELLI ALTERNATORS

Fiat
All Models

▶ CHANGES, CAUTIONS, CORRECTIONS

▶ *ELECTRICAL SYSTEM REPAIRING CAUTION* – Reversed polarity or excessive voltage will result in extensive damage to alternator system. Note the following to prevent damage:

Battery Installation – Negative battery terminal must be connected to ground (negative ground systems only), and positive terminal connected to starter. DO NOT reverse battery leads.

Battery Charging – If a Quick Charger is used, both battery cables must be disconnected from battery. DO NOT use a Quick Charger to provide starting voltage.

Circuit Interruption – The battery must never be disconnected while alternator is running.

Alternator Removal – Always disconnect battery ground before alternator removal and replacement.

High Voltage – DO NOT use a high voltage source to test diodes.

Booster Battery (For Engine Start) – Booster battery must be connected with negative lead to negative terminal and positive lead to positive terminal. DO NOT reverse battery leads.

DESCRIPTION

Marelli alternators are conventional three-phase, self-rectifying type alternators. Six silicone rectifier diodes are connected to form a full-wave, three phase rectifying bridge. The three negative rectifier diodes are pressed directly in the end frame. Three positive diodes are located in a heat sink which is insulated from the end frame. The 60 amp. alternator models also have three energizing diodes pressed into a support assembly.

APPLICATION

Model	Fiat No.
124	A 12M 124/12/42M
128	A124/14V/60A
131 & X1/9	
W/O Air Conditioning	A 124/14V/44A
W/Air Conditioning	A 124/14V/60A

TROUBLE SHOOTING

INDICATOR LIGHT ON WITH IGNITION SWITCH IN OFF POSITION

Output current and voltage will be slightly lower than specifications. One or more positive diodes are shorted.

INDICATOR LIGHT ON AT LOW RPM

Stator winding has a phase open.

NO OUTPUT VOLTAGE

Rotor winding is open.

INDICATOR LIGHT ON WITH ENGINE RUNNING

One or more negative and energizing diodes shorted.

HIGH OUTPUT VOLTAGE

One energizing diode open. Improper operation of voltage regulator.

INDICATOR LIGHT GLOWS DIMLY WITH KEY ON OR ENGINE RUNNING

Faulty connection in ignition system. Brushes stuck in housing or worn excessively.

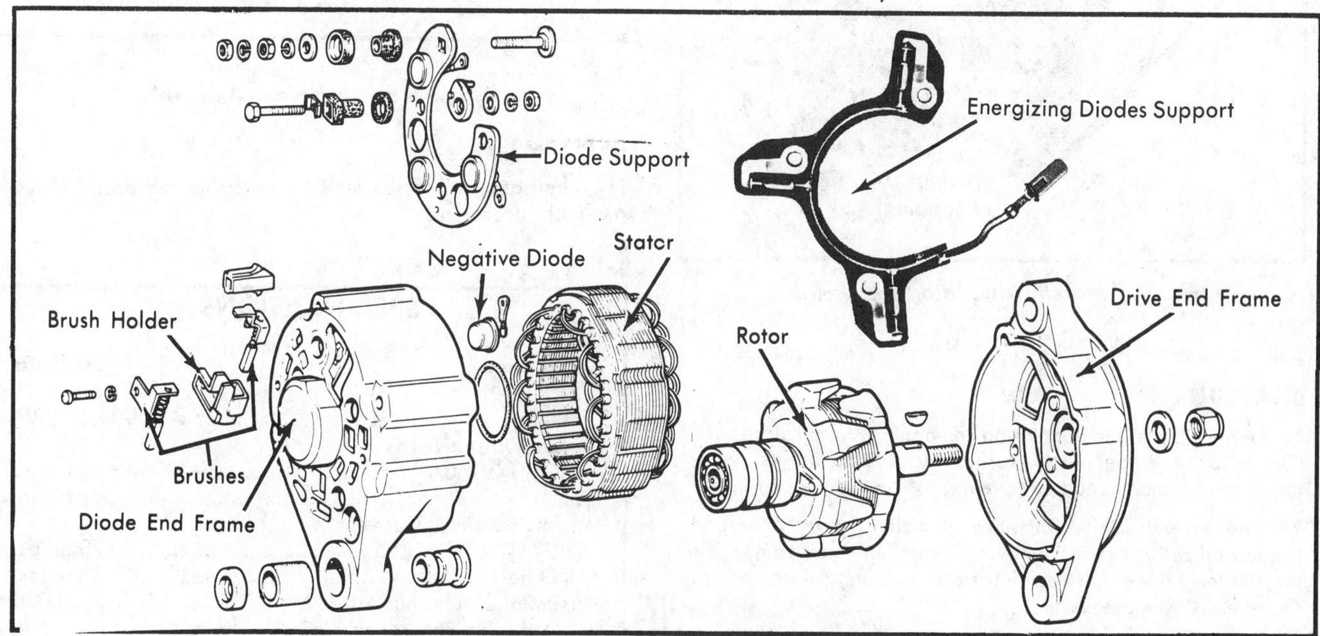

Fig. 1 Disassembled View of Marelli Alternator (the A 124 /14V/60A Type is Shown)

MARELLI ALTERNATORS (Cont.)

TESTING

BENCH TESTING

Rotor Field Winding Resistance – Connect ohmmeter leads to terminal 67 of alternator and to a good ground. If resistance is not within specifications, rotor field winding is open.

Stator Phase Winding Resistance (A 124/14V/44A only) – Use an ohmmeter to check the resistance across each phase of armature winding. Resistance should be almost zero. If resistance is high, an open exists in one of the windings.

Diode Checks – 1) Connect leads of an ohmmeter to terminal 30 and stator winding connector. Check resistance, then reverse leads and recheck. Both readings should show high resistance with one reading being slightly higher than the other. If both readings are low, a positive diode is bad.

2) Check resistance between ground and stator winding connector. Reverse leads and check reading. If both readings are low, a negative diode is bad.

3) Check resistance between energizing diode plug and stator winding connector. Reverse leads and check reading. If both readings are low, an energizing diode is bad.

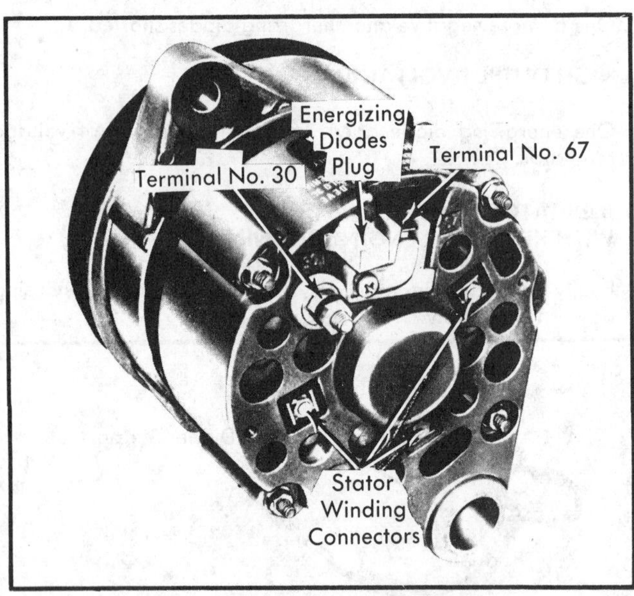

Fig. 2 Marelli Alternator Test Points

OVERHAUL

DISASSEMBLY

1) Remove drive and ventilation components from rotor shaft. Remove brush holder (with brushes) by backing out its mounting screw on diode end head. Remove Woodruff key on shaft.

2) Unscrew nuts of the four through bolts, remove drive end frame and rotor. Before removing stator, unscrew from inside (of housing), three nuts securing stator winding phase ends to diode ends. Remove stator.

3) To disassemble diode end frame, unscrew the nut of terminal "30". The frame with negative diodes and the support with positive diodes will thus be separated.

TESTING

Stator Winding Resistance – With stator disassembled from alternator and leads disconnected, connect ohmmeter probes between each pair of stator leads. Ohmmeter must show equal readings for each pair of stator leads. Replace stator if readings are not equal.

Rotor Winding Resistance – Rotor resistance can be checked with an ohmmeter. Connect leads across slip rings at 68°F (see specifications).

Brushes – The spring pressure on slip ring brushes should be about one pound (0.43 kg), with new brushes in operation position.

PARTS REPLACEMENT

Brushes – To ensure best results, brushes should be replaced with a new brush holder as a complete assembly. Before installing holder assembly, clean all parts of grease and carbon dust, lubricate bearings with suitable grease (Fiat MR 3).

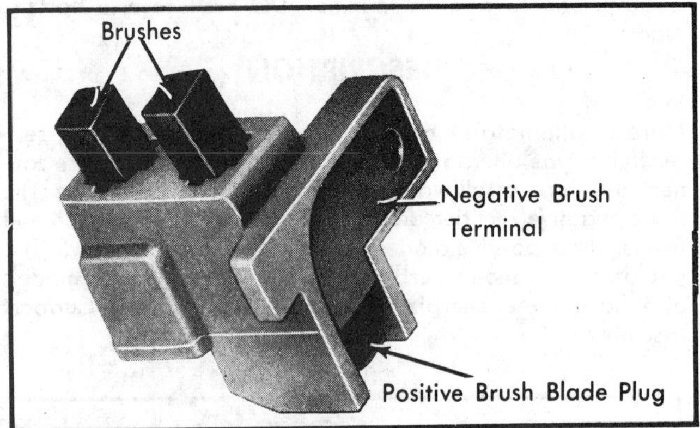

Fig. 3 Brush Holder Assembly

REASSEMBLY

The alternator is reassembled by reversing the order of disassembly procedure.

SPECIFICATIONS

Application	Test Data
Cut-In Speed @12V (68°F)	1000±50 RPM
Current Output @14V	
A 124/14V/60A	60 amps. min.
All Others	44 amps. min.
Maximum Output Current	
A 124/14V/60A	70 amps.
All Others	53 amps.
Maximum Continuous Alt. RPM	13,000
Field Winding Resistance @68°F	
A 124/14V/60A	2.6±.05 ohms
All Others	4.3±.2 ohms

MARELLI REGULATORS

Fiat
All Models

▶ CHANGES, CAUTIONS, CORRECTIONS

▶ *SERVICE PRECAUTIONS* — When replacing regulator, and during bench testing, be careful not to exchange the wire to plug "15" with wire to plug "67" (see illustration). Current passing through contacts would be high enough to melt second stage contacts before fuse in lead "15" would blow.

▶ *HANDLING* — During installation, removal, and handling, protect regulator from blows which might damage the resistors and upset adjustments.

▶ *GROUNDING* — During checks on vehicle and on bench, see that regulator is well grounded. If grounding is poor or open, alternator voltage will rise to an abnormally high value, which may damage battery and electrical equipment.

▶ *CAPACITORS* — NEVER install radio noise suppressor on regulator plug "67" as operation of contacts will be adversely affected.

▶ *COVER GASKET* — Should gasket require replacement, use only a gasket of same original material. Unsuitable gasket could release harmful volatile substances into regulator which will foul contacts.

▶ *SUPPLY CIRCUITS* — DO NOT connect electrical accessories directly in circuit between alternator and voltage regulator (i.e., cable between terminal "30" of alternator ignition switch, plug "15" of regulator, or cable between ignition switch and voltage regulator), since alternator voltage would rise and affect life of battery and electrical equipment.

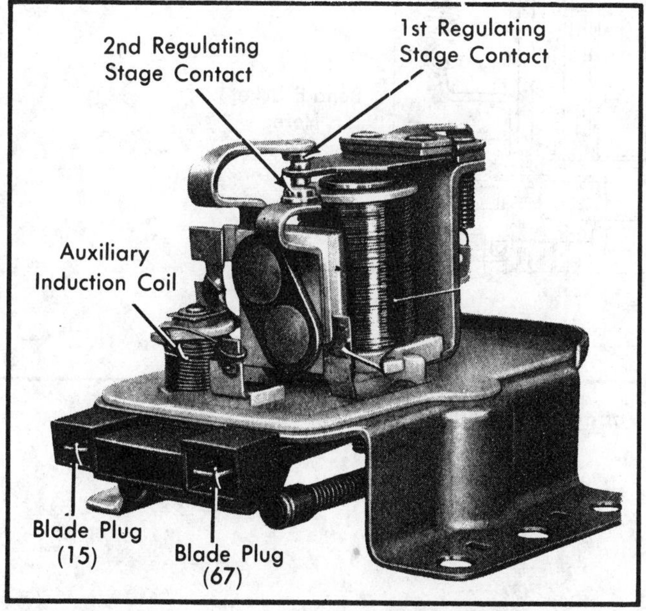

Fig. 1 Marelli Voltage Regulator

DESCRIPTION

Fiat voltage regulators are of the dual stage vibrating contact type. An induction auxiliary coil, considerably smaller than the magnetizing coil, is mounted near contact side of the yoke. In addition to two regulating resistors, an additional resistor works in series with the main voltage coil. The regulator is grounded through the mounting flanges. Resistors are protected from impacts by a metal shield secured to mounting flange.

APPLICATION

Model	Part No.
124	RC2/12B
128	RC 2/12E
131 & X1/9 W/O A.C.	RC 2/12D
131 & X1/9 W/A.C.	RC 2/12E

SPECIFICATIONS

Application	Specification
Alternator Test RPM	
All Models	5000 RPM
1st Stage Testing (Amps)	
RC 2/12E Regulator	40-45
All Others	25-35
2nd Stage Testing (Amps)	
RC 2/12B Regulator	2-12
All Others	10-14
2nd Stage Testing (Volts)	
All Models	14.2±.3
Resistance Values (Ohms)	
Plug "15" & Ground	
RC 2/12B Regulator	27.7±2
All Others	27.2±2
Plug "15" & "67" W/Contacts Open	
RC 2/12E Regulator	3.7±.2
All Others	5.6±.3
Armature Air Gap	
Point "A"	.055-.063"
Point "B"	.014-.022"

TESTING

BENCH TESTING

1) Install alternator and regulator on test bench equipped with gradual speed control. Connect ammeter, voltmeter, and rheostat as shown in illustration. Regulator must be placed vertically, with terminals "15" and "67" at base. Regulator must be checked without removing cover.

2) **CAUTION** — *DO NOT operate regulator with switch "I" open (battery disconnected) since this will damage regulator contacts.* Operate voltage regulator in an ambient temperature of 122±5.4°F for 30 minutes (thermal stabilization). Start with rheostat fully inserted, then adjust current output to one sixth of maximum alternator output. Alternator should be operated slowly at first and then be SLOWLY brought up to 5000 RPM.

3) **NOTE** — *Suitable thermostatic equipment must be available in order to maintain regulator at specified temperature throughout test.* Operate alternator at 5000 RPM. Adjust rheostat for specified current output. See specifications.

MARELLI REGULATORS (Cont.)

4) Check first stage immediately after second stage, and ensure that the conditions specified in step 2) are still met. At 5000 RPM, adjust rheostat until specifications are met for 1st Stage Testing. Regulated voltage should be .2-.7 volts (model 124) or 0-.5 volts (all other models) less than the voltage recorded for the second stage. **NOTE** — *When testing the first and second stages, check that regulated voltage is stable, without any sudden surges or drops.*

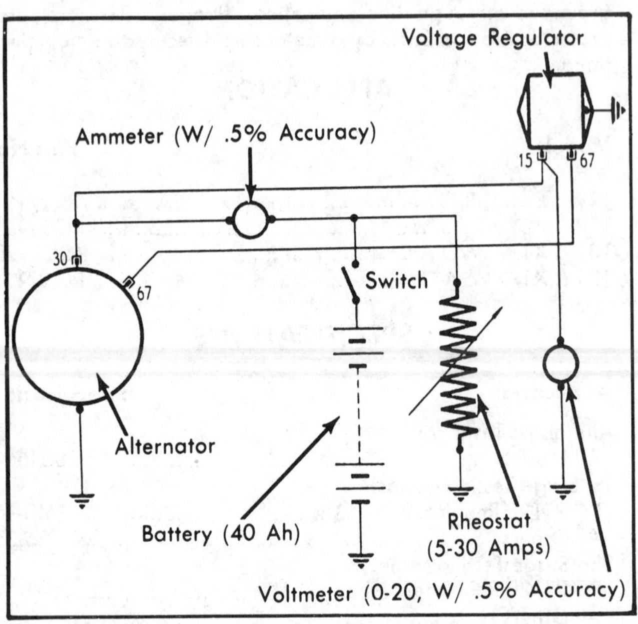

Fig. 2 Circuit for Conducting Bench Test

ADJUSTMENT

VOLTAGE REGULATOR

1) Disconnect positive battery cable then remove dust cover on voltage regulator. Inspect contact points for pitting and burn marks, then clean minor pitting and burn marks. **NOTE** — *Extreme damage to points requires regulator replacement.* Use a feeler gauge to check measurements at point "A" and "B" as shown in *Fig. 3*.

2) If clearances are not within specifications, remove the regulator from vehicle. Loosen nut and adjust gaps by moving the slotted arms indicated in *Fig. 3.* until clearances are within specifications. Tighten nut and recheck clearances.

3) Install regulator in vehicle and connect battery cable. Run engine until normal operating temperature is reached, then connect a voltmeter positive lead to positive battery post and negative lead to a good ground. Voltmeter should read 13.9-14.5 volts at 2500 RPM with all electrical components off. If reading is not within specifications carefully apply slight pressure to lower spring bracket to adjust. Bending bracket down increases reading while bending bracket up decreases reading. **NOTE** — *Bend bracket a very small amount as a slight change will adjust voltage.* Disconnect voltmeter and install dust cover.

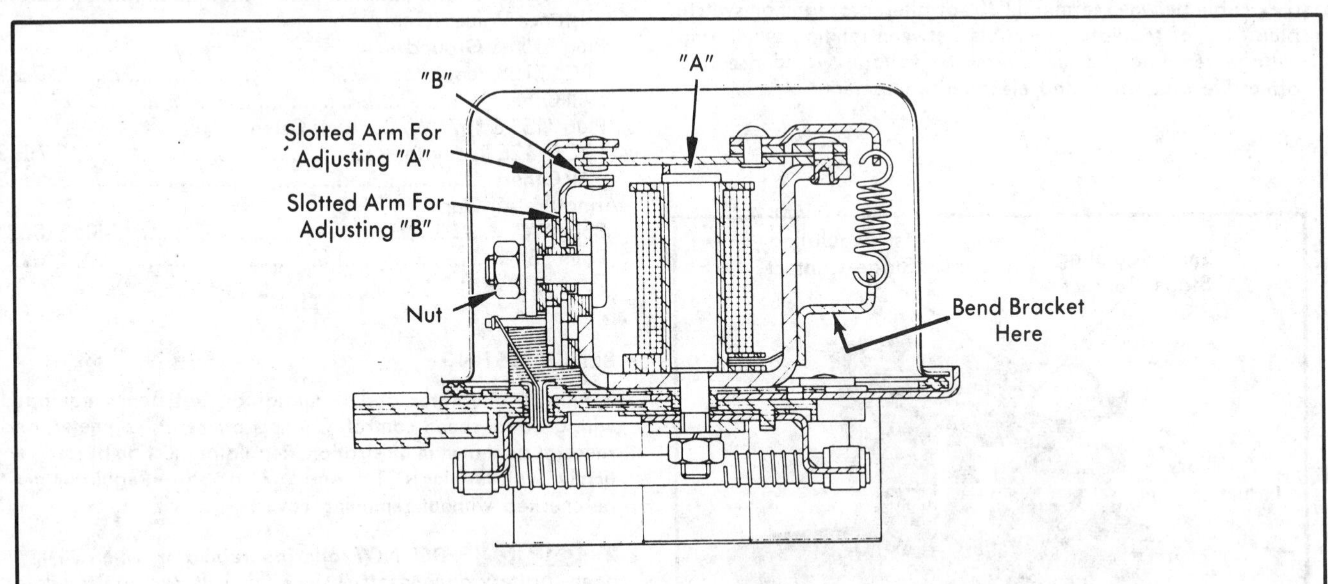

Fig. 3 Adjusting Voltage Regulator

MITSUBISHI ALTERNATORS

Arrow
Colt
Courier
Mazda

▶ CHANGES, CAUTIONS, CORRECTIONS

▶ *BATTERY INSTALLATION, BATTERY CHARGING, OR USING A BOOSTER BATTERY FOR ENGINE START* — Reverse polarity or excessive voltage will result in extensive damage to alternator system. Note the following to prevent damage:

Battery Installation — Negative battery terminal must be connected to ground (negative ground system) and positive battery terminal must be connected to starter. DO NOT reverse battery leads.

Battery Charging — If a Quick Charger is used, both battery cables must be disconnected from the battery. DO NOT use a Quick Charger to provide starting voltage.

Circuit Interruption — Battery must NEVER be disconnected when alternator is running.

High Voltage — DO NOT use a high voltage source to test diodes.

Booster Battery (For Engine Start) — Booster battery must be connected with negative lead to negative battery terminal and positive lead to positive battery terminal. DO NOT reverse battery leads.

DESCRIPTION

Mitsubishi alternators are conventional three-phase, self-rectifying type units containing six diodes (three positive and three negative) which are used to rectify current.

APPLICATION

Model	Part No.
Arrow & Colt	
1600cc	AH2045K1
2000cc	AH2045G1
Courier	①D47Z-10346-A
Mazda	
RX-3, 808 (1300cc)	1011 18 300
RX-4, Cosmo	8735 18 300
808 (1600cc)	0453 18 300A
Rotary Pickup	0571 18 300A
GLC	0483 18 300

① — Ford Part Number.

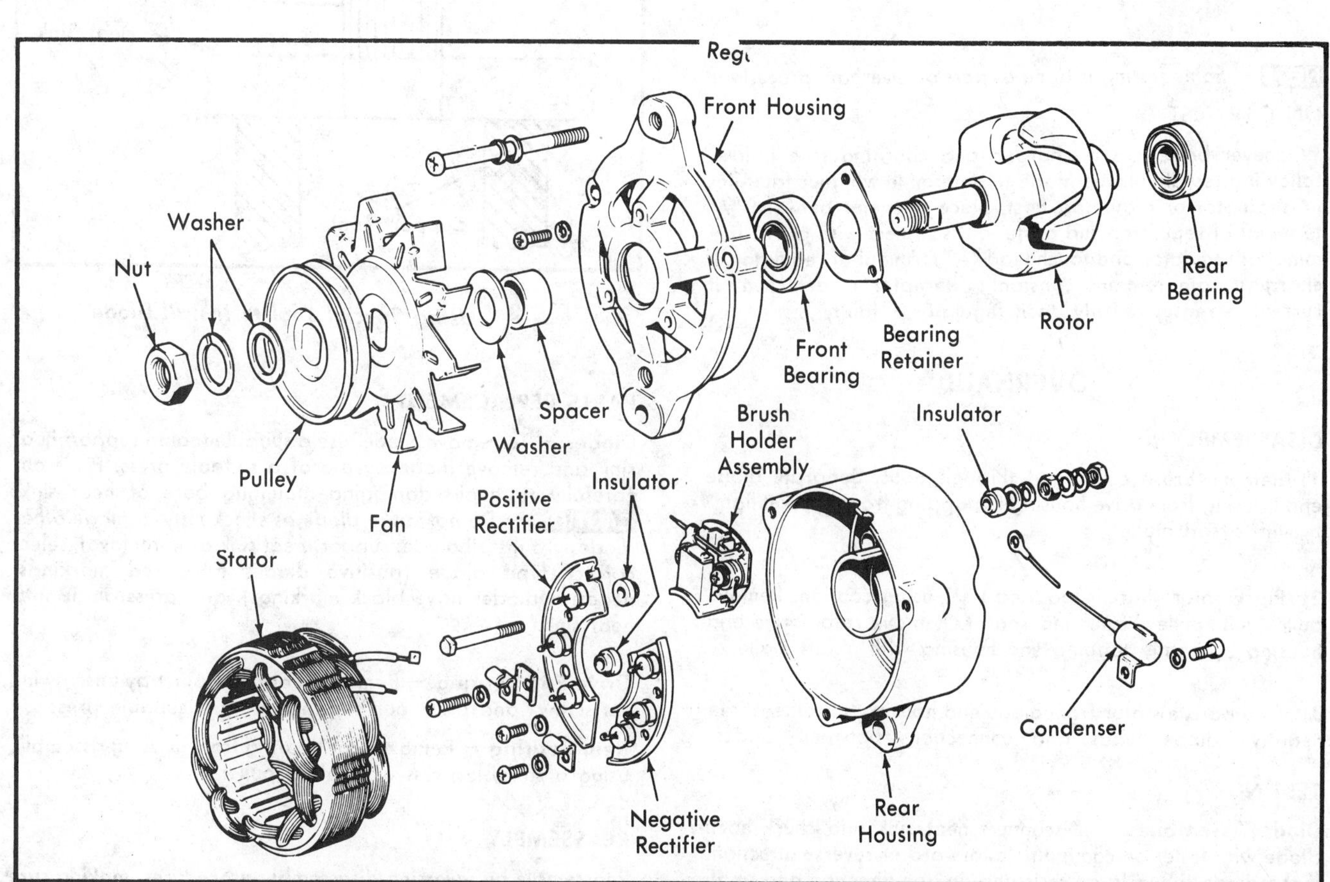

Fig. 1 Exploded View of Mitsubishi Alternator

MITSUBISHI ALTERNATORS (Cont.)

SPECIFICATIONS

Nominal Output at 2500 RPM

Application	Amps.	Voltage
AH2045G1	45	12
AH2045K1	45	12
1011 18 300	40	14
0453 18 300A	50	14
0571 18 300A	40	14
8735 18 300	56	14
D47Z-10346-A	35	14.5

Coil Resistance (Ohms)

Application	Rotor	Stator
Arrow & Colt	4.7	①
Courier	5-6	①
Mazda		
W/1600 cc Engine	5-6	①
All Others	4-6	①

① – Test must show current continuity, no given value.

Brush Wear Limit – To wear limit line (one third of original length).

Brush Spring Pressure – Standard value is 12-16 ozs. If less than 7.8 ozs. replace.

TESTING

NOTE – *Some testing is done as part of Overhaul procedure.*

ON CAR TEST

Whenever battery is discharged and charging rate is low, following test should be made to determine whether fault lies in alternator or regulator. First, place ammeter between "A" terminal of regulator and battery. Disconnect wire at "F" terminal of regulator and touch lead "A" terminal of regulator. If charging rate remains constant, alternator is defective. If current increases greatly, then regulator is faulty.

OVERHAUL

DISASSEMBLY

1) Remove brush cover and through bolts. Separate diode end housing from drive housing by tapping front bracket lightly with a soft mallet.

2) Place rotor shaft in padded vise, using caution. Remove pulley nut, pulley, fan, and spacer. Remove rotor drive end housing by lightly tapping end housing with a soft mallet.

3) To separate stator from diode end housing, unsolder three negative diode leads and connections between diodes.

TESTING

Diode Assemblies – Disconnect heat sink and check each diode with tester on continuity in forward or reverse direction. If the diode shows large resistance in one direction and small resistance in other direction, diode is normal. If it shows small resistance in both directions it is shorted. If large resistance is shown in both directions, diode is open.

CAUTION – *If excessive temperature is allowed, diode will become inoperative.*

Field Continuity – Check continuity between field coil and slip ring. No continuity indicates broken wire; field coil must be replaced.

Field Coil Ground – Check continuity between slip ring and shaft (core). If there is continuity, coil or slip ring is grounded and must be replaced.

Stator Coil Ground – Check to ensure no continuity between stator coil leads and stator core.

Stator Coil Continuity – Check continuity between leads of stator coil. If there is no continuity, coil has broken wire and must be replaced.

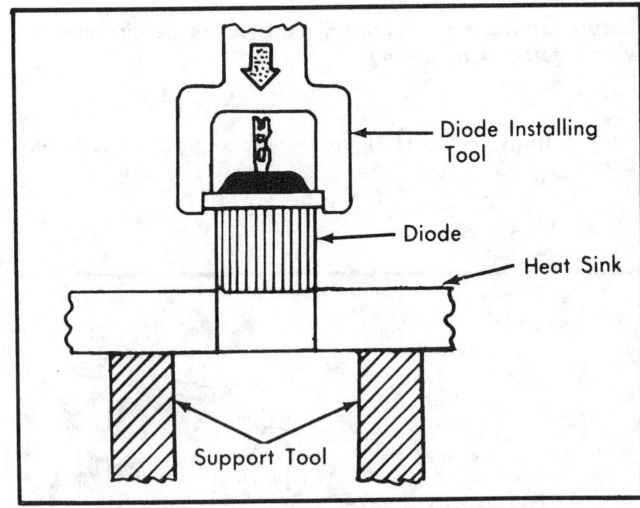

Fig. 2 Using Special Tool to Install Diode

PARTS REPLACEMENT

Diodes – To remove diode, use a suitable tool to support heat sink and remove diode by use of a suitable press. Press out carefully to avoid damaging mounting bore of heat sink. **CAUTION** – *Do not strike diode as shock may damage other diodes.* To install diode, support heat sink as in removal, select correct type diode (positive diodes have red markings; negative diodes have black markings), and press diode into heat sink.

Drive End Bearing – Remove bearing retainer by unscrewing set screws and press out bearing, using a suitable press.

Rear Bearing – Remove rear bearing from housing assembly, using a suitable press or bearing puller.

REASSEMBLY

Reassemble by reversing disassembly procedures, making sure polarity of diodes is correct.

MITSUBISHI REGULATORS

Arrow
Colt
Courier
Mazda

DESCRIPTION

Regulator consists of two elements: constant-voltage relay and pilot lamp relay. Both relays consist of an electromagnet, contacts, frame, moving element and coil side plate. This regulator has a temperature compensation gradient as an improvement over the constant voltage charging system. It has functions for automatically compensating the adjusted value of the constant-voltage relay so that the adjusted value will be lower in summer and higher in winter.

APPLICATION

Model	Part No.
Arrow & Colt	RQB-2D
Courier	D27Z-10316-A
Mazda	0453 18 391

TESTING

To check adjusted value of constant voltage relay, connect a voltmeter between terminal "A" and E" of the regulator. Place generator at no load by disconnecting one of the battery terminals during operation at idling speed, then increase alternator speed to approximately 4000 RPM (Approximately 2000 engine RPM). In this condition, satisfactory voltage is 14.5-15.8 volts.

ADJUSTMENT

Adjust voltage of the constant voltage relay by bending end of coil side plate up or down as shown in illustration. If plate is bent up, the adjusted value becomes higher. If it is bent down, value becomes lower. Adjust pilot lamp relay by same method.

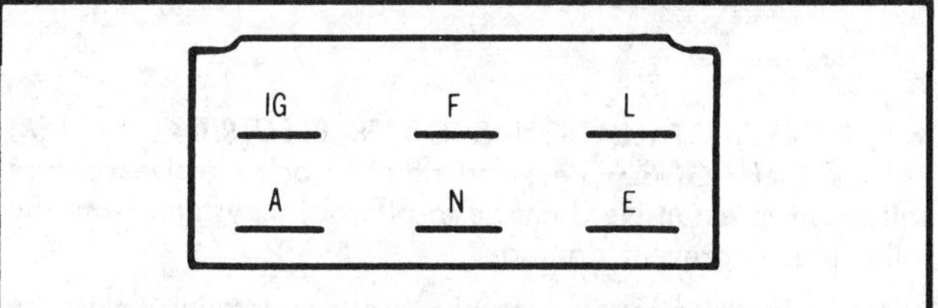

Fig. 1 Regulator Harness Connector

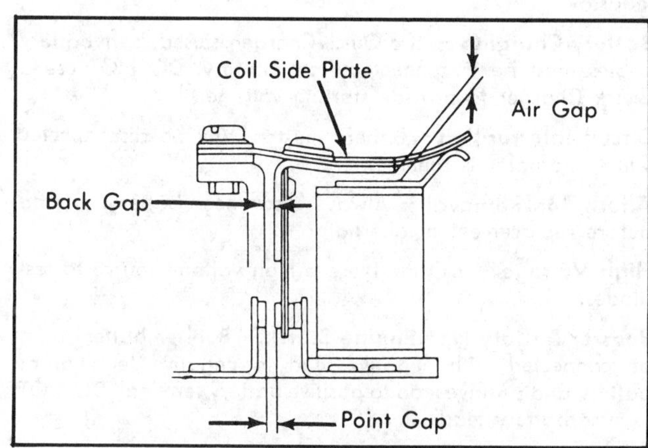

Fig. 2 Voltage Adjustment Point

MITSUBISHI ALTERNATOR REGULATOR SPECIFICATIONS

Reg. No.	VOLTAGE REGULATOR				PILOT LAMP RELAY		
	Output Volts	Air Gap in. (mm)	Back Gap in. (mm)	Point Gap in. (mm)	Air Gap in. (mm)	Back Gap in. (mm)	Point Gap in. (mm)
RQB-2D	14.5-15.3	.032-.047 (.81-1.2)	.032-.043 (.81-1.1)	.012-.016 (.31-.41)	.035-.047 (.89-1.2)	.030-.043 (.76-1.1)	.030-.043 (.76-1.1)
045318391	13.5-14.5	.028-.051 (.71-1.3)	.028-.059 (.71-1.5)	.012-.018 (.31-.45)	.039-.051 (.89-1.4)	.028-.059 (.71-1.5)	.020-.035 (.71-1.1)
D27Z-A	14-15	.....	.....	.....	.....	.....	.....

NIPPONDENSO ALTERNATORS

Honda
Opel
Toyota

► CHANGES, CAUTIONS, CORRECTIONS

► *BATTERY INSTALLATION & OTHER ELECTRICAL SYSTEM REPAIR CAUTIONS* – Reversed polarity or excessive voltage will result in extensive damage to alternator system. Note the following to prevent damage:

Battery Installation – Negative battery terminal must be connected to ground (negative ground systems) and positive terminal must be connected to starter. DO NOT reverse battery leads.

Battery Charging – If a Quick Charger is used, both battery cables must be disconnected from battery. DO NOT use a Quick Charger to provide starting voltage.

Circuit Interruption – Battery must NEVER be disconnected while alternator is running.

Alternator Removal – Always disconnect battery ground before replacement of alternator.

High Voltage – DO NOT use a high voltage source to test diodes.

Booster Battery (For Engine Start) – Booster battery must be connected with negative lead to negative terminal of battery and positive lead to positive battery terminal. DO NOT reverse battery leads.

DESCRIPTION

Nippondenso alternators are conventional, three-phase, self-rectifying type alternators. Six diodes (three positive and three negative) are used to rectify current.

APPLICATION

Model	Amps①	Part No.
Honda		
Accord	50	314-6-671
Civic, CVCC	40	31100-671-014
Opel	40	94201052
Toyota②		
3K-C	40	24020
2TC	40	36071
2F		
Standard	40	60010, 60071
With A/C	50	60020
Heavy Duty	50	60030, 60040
W/Vac. Pump	55	60080
20R		
Standard	40	34031
With A/C	45	38021

① – Rated output at 14 volts at 3000 RPM (Toyota), 2000 RPM (Honda) and 1400 RPM (Opel).

② – All Toyota part numbers are preceded by 27020.

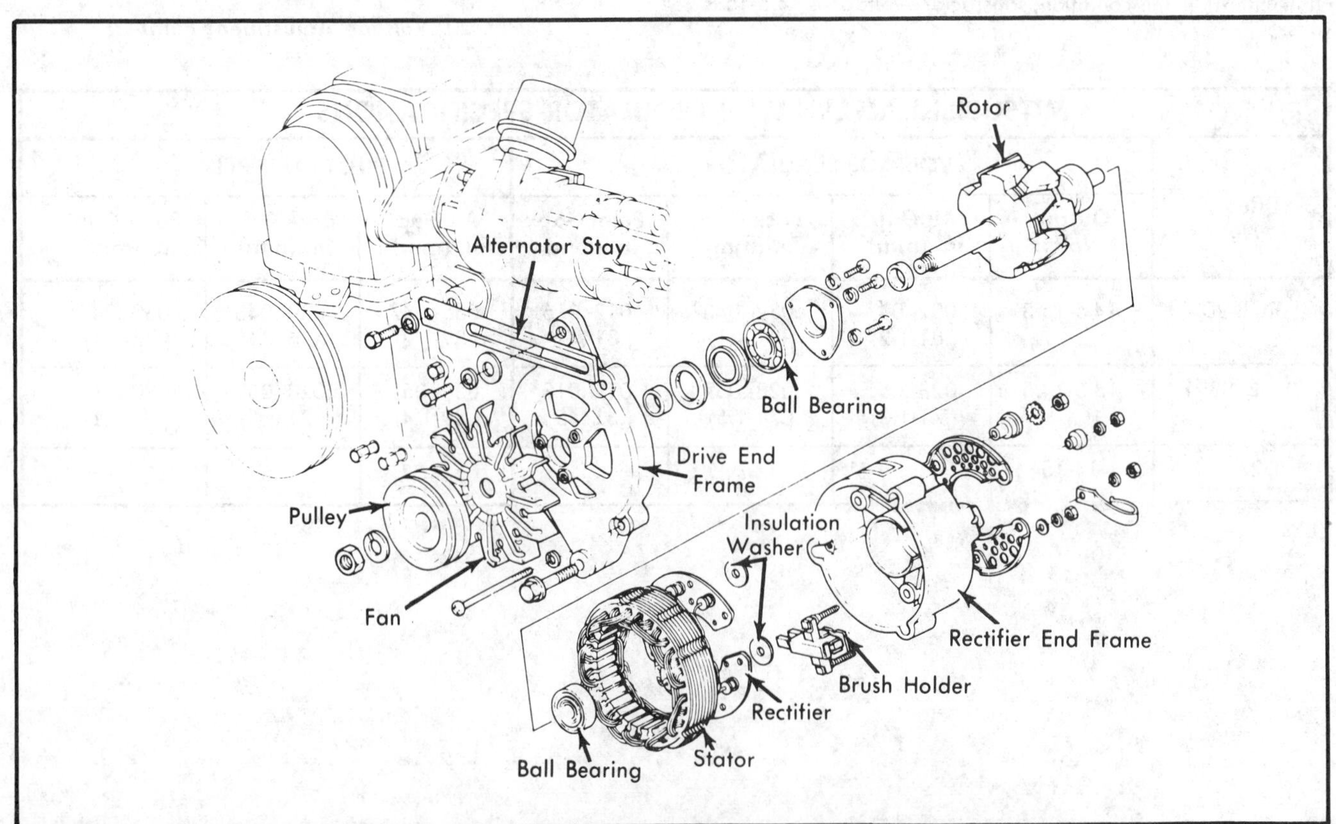

Fig. 1 Disassembled View of Nippondenso Alternator.

NIPPONDENSO ALTERNATORS (Cont.)

SPECIFICATIONS

Coil Resistance (Ohms)

Application	Rotor
All Models	4.1-4.3

Minimum Brush Length

Application	In.(mm)
All Models	.22 (5.5)

TESTING

ON CAR TEST

Preliminary Inspection – Check alternator mounting and belt tension. Inspect turn signal fuse and gauge fuse. Check alternator and regulator wire connections for tightness.

No Load Test – 1) Connect a suitable test meter (09081-00010 alternator tester for models with special connector from regulator, or a common regulator tester) as shown in illustrations. Start engine and increase speed gradually to 2000-2300 RPM. Read "B" terminal voltage. Voltage should be 13.5-14.8 with a current draw of not more than 10 amps. If current is over specifications, battery is discharged or internally shorted.

2) If voltage reading is not steady, it indicates regulator points are dirty, or defective connection exists at "F" terminal.

3) If voltage reading is too high, it indicates the following problems: Regulator low speed gap is too wide. High speed point gap is too wide. High speed point resistance is too high. Open circuit regulator coil or voltage relay coil. Open circuited regulator coil or voltage relay coil. Open circuited regulator "N" terminal or "B" terminal. Low speed point contact tension too heavy. Loose regulator ground connection.

"F" Terminal Voltage Test – 1) With regulator tester, stop engine, disconnect alternator wiring connector, turn ignition switch to "ON" and measure voltage between "F" and "E" terminals of connector. Voltage should be 12 volts. If voltage is zero or very low, note the following possible causes; blown fuse, regulator "IG" terminal open, or regulator high speed points are burned.

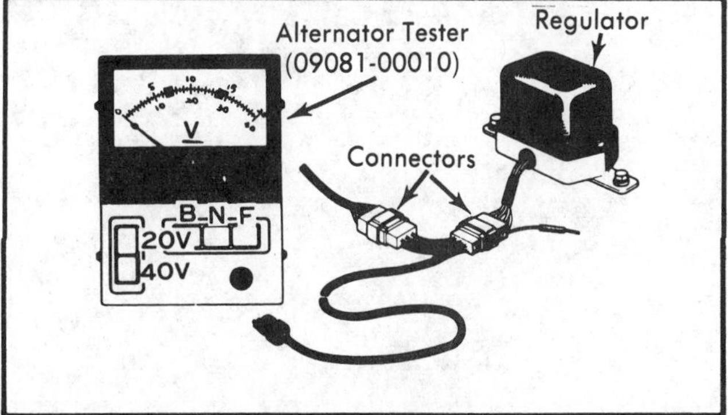

Fig. 2 Connections for Testing Alternator Using Tester 09081-00010

2) With alternator tester (09081-00010) connected and engine idling, press switch "F" on tester. Gradually increase engine speed to 2300 RPM. Needle on tester should deflect in small steps from 12-7 volts, 6-4 volts and 3-1 volts. If voltage does not drop as specified, regulator is defective or out of adjustment.

Regulator Circuit Resistance – Disconnect regulator connector plug and check resistance between regulator "IG" and "F" terminals with an ohmmeter. If there is any resistance, the low speed contact in regulator is defective.

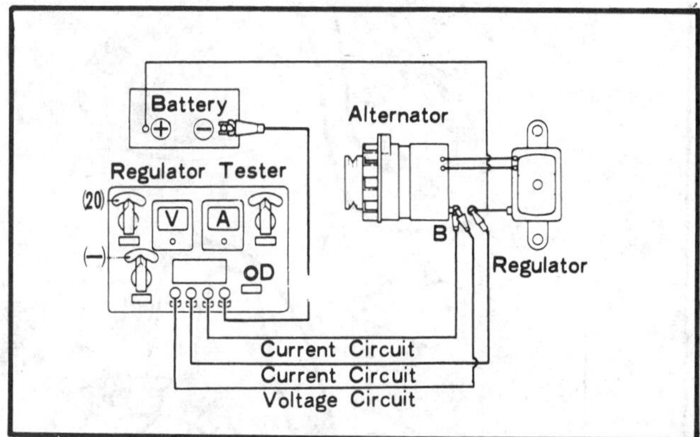

Fig. 3 Connections for Testing Regulator

Load Test – With regulator tester connected as shown in illustration, start engine and turn on all lights and accessories. Run engine at 1100 RPM. Read amperage and voltage. It should be as specified. If battery is fully charged and reading is low, discharge battery by cranking engine (without spark) for about 15 seconds. Now if amperage is low, the rectifiers are open, shorted, or stator coil is open or shorted.

OVERHAUL

DISASSEMBLY

1) Remove three retaining screws and insert screwdrivers into notches in drive end frame, pry with screwdrivers to separate drive end frame from stator. If necessary, tap lightly on drive end frame with a mallet.

2) Secure rotor core in padded vise, remove pulley attaching nut, and withdraw pulley, fan, and spacer. Remove rotor from drive end frame, utilizing a press. Remove bearing retainer from drive end frame, then remove bearing, felt cover and felt ring.

3) Remove four rectifier holder securing nuts and two brush holder securing screws; separate stator with rectifier holders and brush holders from rectifier end frame. Remove brush lead terminal and stator coil "N" terminal from brush holder, utilizing a small screwdriver. **CAUTION** – *When removing brush holder assembly, do not remove it by cutting "N" terminal lead or melting the solder.*

TESTING

Rotor – Check rotor for open field windings by connecting an ohmmeter across the slip rings. Coil resistance should be approximately as specified. Next check bearing and replace if necessary. Check slip rings for rough condition.

NIPPONDENSO ALTERNATORS (Cont.)

Stator – Use ohmmeter to check stator coil for ground. To check stator for open circuit, stator leads must be disconnected from diode leads. To disconnect leads from diodes, unsolder as quickly as possible and with a low-watt iron. Check four leads of stator coil for conduction between each lead. If ohmmeter shows no conduction, stator coil is open and must be replaced. Resistance should be zero.

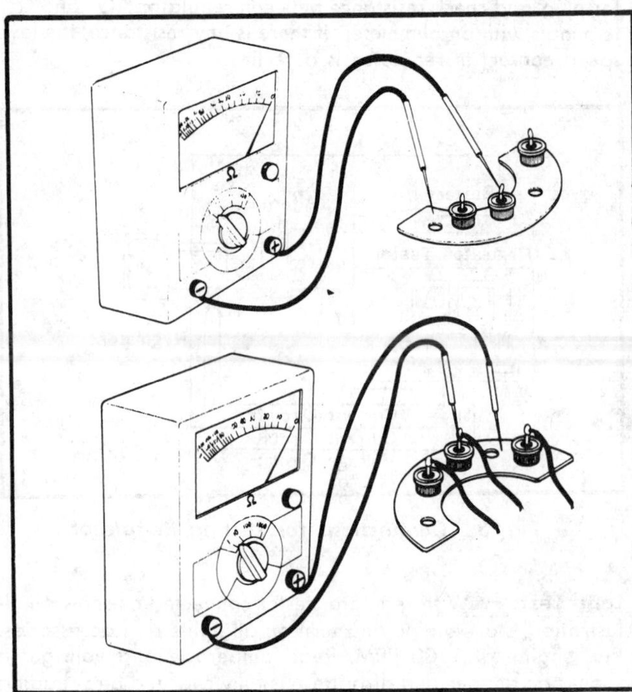

Fig. 4 Testing the Diodes

Diode Test – With diode assembly on bench, make test connections as illustrated, using an ohmmeter. Contact diode plate with one probe and contact each of the three diode leads with the other probe. Note ohmmeter reading, then reverse probes and repeat test. Check both positive and negative diodes in this manner. All diodes should show a low reading in one direction and no reading in opposite direction. If any one rectifier is defective, always replace positive or negative holder assembly.

PARTS REPLACEMENT

Brushes – Check for cracks and wear. If brushes are worn beyond specifications, replace. Brushes should slide smoothly. Install new brush spring when replacing brush. Solder brush lead wire keeping protruded length to .51" (13 mm).

NOTE – *Brush length for Heavy Duty alternators is .73" (18.5 mm).*

REASSEMBLY

Reassemble alternator by reversing disassembly procedure, noting the following points:

1) Press brushes, against spring tension, into brush holder. Insert a wire through access hole in rectifier and frame, and into hole in brush holder. This will prevent brushes from falling. Remove wire after assembly to end frame is completed.

2) Pack multipurpose grease into rear bearing and press bearing onto rotor shaft.

3) Install felt ring and felt cover so that convex surface of cover will face toward pulley side onto drive end frame. Next pack multipurpose grease into bearing and install bearing.

NIPPONDENSO REGULATORS

Honda
Opel
Toyota

DESCRIPTION

Nippondenso regulators are of two designs: a single element type and a two element type. Two element types consists of a voltage regulator and voltage relay. The single element type has a voltage regulator only.

APPLICATION

Model	Part No.
Honda	
Accord	31100-671-004
Civic, CVCC	31400-657-672
Opel	
All Models	94208462
Toyota	
2F	2700-60080
All Others	2700-38010

TESTING

VOLTAGE REGULATOR

Connect tests meters to voltage regulator circuit as shown in illustrations. Vary alternator RPM and check voltmeter reading. Increase alternator RPM and check voltage when ammeter registers 1/2 of maximum rated alternator output. Voltage should be 13.8-14.8 volts. Adjust alternator speed to 3,000 RPM, voltage output should again be 13.8-14.8 volts. If voltage is not within specified range, adjust voltage regulator by bending arm to obtain correct setting.

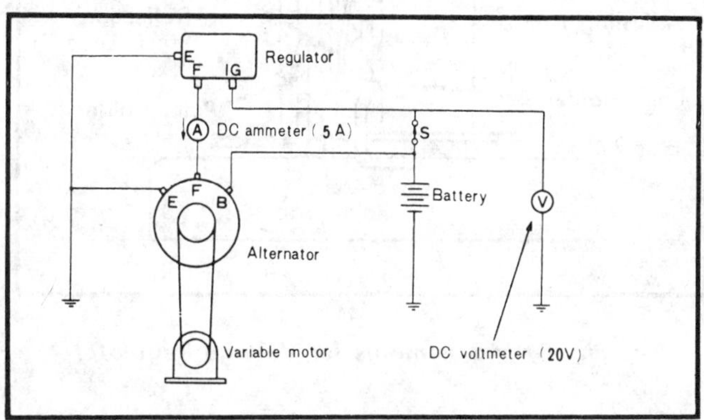

Fig. 1 Test Circuit for Single Element Type

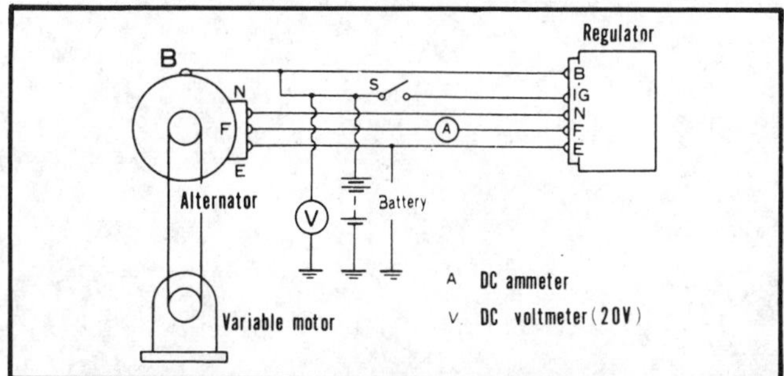

Fig. 2 Test Circuit for Two Element Type

VOLTAGE RELAY

Charge Warning Lamp Type – Connect test meters as shown in *Fig. 3 thru 6*. Increase alternator RPM gradually and note voltage when charge lamp goes out. Cut-in voltage should be 4.0-5.8 volts. If voltage is not as specified, bend voltage relay adjusting arm to obtain correct setting.

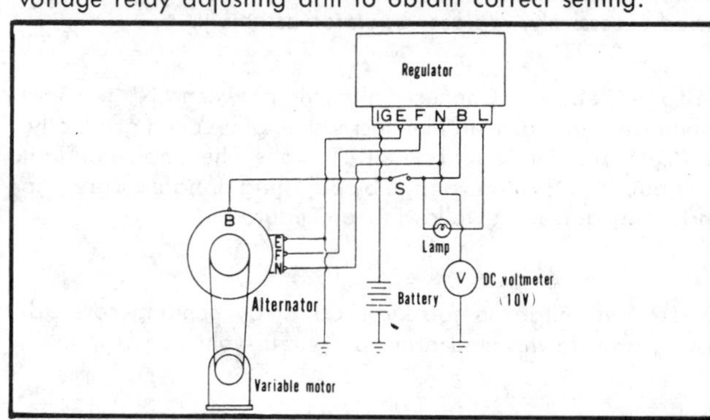

Fig. 3 Test Circuit for Relay-Warning Lamp Type

Ammeter Type – Connect test meters as shown in *Fig. 4 thru 6*. Increase alternator RPM gradually and note voltage. Voltage should be 4.5-5.8 volts. If necessary, adjust voltage by bending adjusting arm.

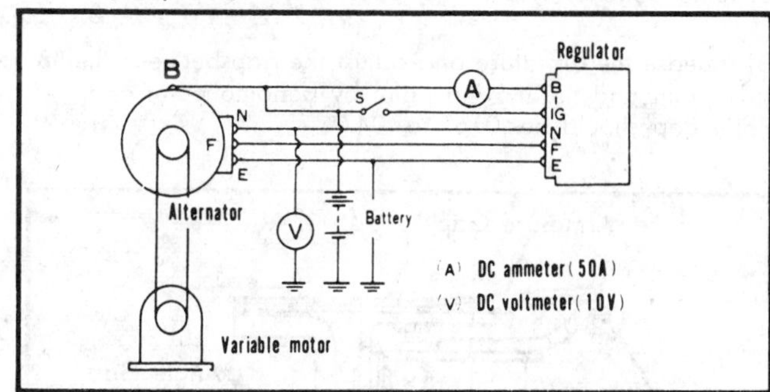

Fig. 4 Test Circuit for Relay-Ammeter Type

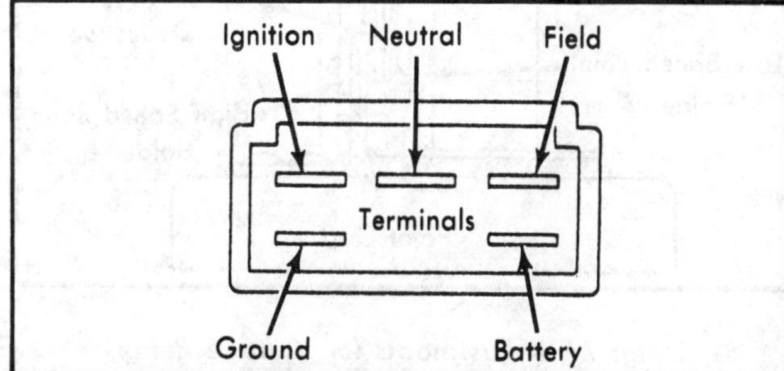

Fig. 5 Terminal Position for Two Element Type Regulator Wiring Connector.

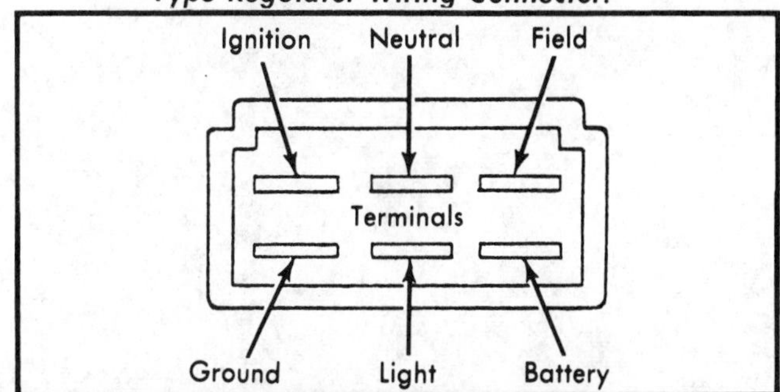

Fig. 6 Terminal Position for Two Element Regulator with Warning Lamp Circuit.

NIPPONDENSO REGULATORS (Cont.)

ADJUSTMENT

NOTE – *Adjustments are not applicable to sealed units. If points are slightly oxidized or pitted, dress contacts with suitable emery cloth (about 400 grit). If points are oxidized or pitted excessively, replace regulator assembly.*

Voltage Relay – Connect voltmeter between "N" terminal (white wire) and ground then increase engine speed gradually. Voltmeter reading should be 4.0-5.8 volts when indicator light goes out. Adjust cut-in voltage by adjusting armature core gap and point gap using following procedures.

1) If cut-in voltage is too high, adjust by bending core adjusting arm down. Bend arm up if cut-in voltage is too low.

2) If adjustment of core arm does not correct cut-in voltage, proceed with point gap adjustment. Disconnect negative cable from battery. Check armature core gap with armature depressed until moving point is in contact with "B" side point. Armature core gap should be .012" or more. Adjust by bending point arm "B".

3) Release the armature and adjust the gap between the "B" side point and the moving point by bending point arm "A". Point gap should be .016" to .047".

4) After point gap adjustment, recheck cut-in voltage. If not within 4.0-5.8 volts, repeat cut-in voltage adjustment.

Voltage Regulator – If the no load regulated voltage is not within the 13.8-14.8 volt range, adjust regulator as follows.

1) If regulated voltage is too high, adjust by bending armature adjusting arm down. If voltage is too low, bend arm up.

2) If core arm adjustment will not correct regulated voltage, proceed to point gap adjustment.

3) Disconnect battery ground cable. Depress armature arm until the moving point contacts "B" side point. Bend point arm "B" to obtain armature gap of .012" or more.

4) Release armature and adjust gap between "B" side point and moving point by bending point arm "A". Gap should be .012" to .018".

5) After gap adjustment is made, recheck no load regulated voltage under operating test. Repeat core arm adjustment if necessary.

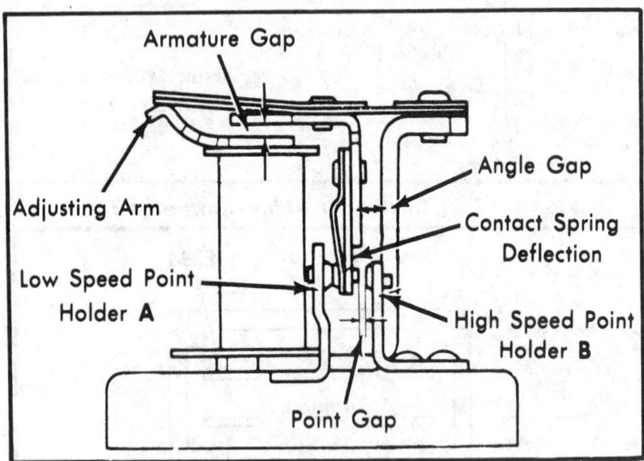

Fig. 7 Adjustments for Voltage Relay

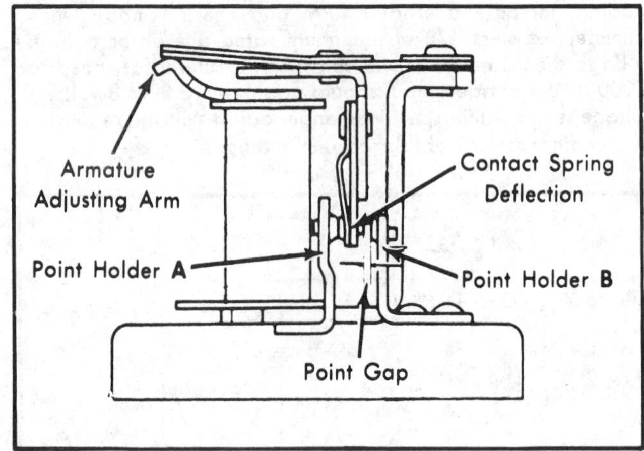

Fig. 8 Adjustments for Voltage Regulator

SEV MARCHAL ALTERNATORS

Renault
Saab
Volvo

DESCRIPTION

Alternator is a conventional three-phase, self-rectifying type. Six silicon rectifier diodes are connected to form a full-wave, three-phase rectifying bridge. Three exciter diodes are connected to stator windings and have a common junction point.

► *BATTERY INSTALLATION, BATTERY CHARGING, OR USING A BOOSTER BATTERY FOR ENGINE START* – Reversed polarity or excessive voltage will result in extensive damage to alternator system. Note the following to prevent damage:

Battery Installation – Negative battery terminal must be connected to ground and positive terminal must be connected to starter. DO NOT reverse polarity.

Battery Charging – If a Quick Charger is used, both battery cables must be disconnected from the battery. DO NOT use a Quick Charger to provide starting voltage.

Circuit Interruption – Battery and/or regulator must NEVER be disconnected while alternator is running

Alternator Removal – Always disconnect battery ground before removal and replacement of alternator.

High Voltage – DO NOT use a high voltage source to test diodes.

Exciter Terminals – NEVER ground the exciter terminals of the alternator or regulator.

APPLICATION

Model	Part No.
Renault 5	A13 R154
Saab 99	S.E.V. 71212002
Volvo 260 Series	S.E.V. 7160410

SPECIFICATIONS

Application	Data
Output @ 3000 Alternator RPM	48 amps.
Output @ 5000 Alternator RPM	55 amps.
Rotor Resistance between Slip Rings	3.7-4.3 ohms
Stator Windings Resistance	.18 ohms±10%
Minimum Brush Protrusion from Holder	.16"(4 mm)

OVERHAUL

DISASSEMBLY

1) Remove brush holder attaching screws and carefully remove brush holder. Scribe a mark on end frames for reassembly reference, then remove four through bolts. Separate end frames by inserting two screwdrivers into notches on sides of alternator. **CAUTION** – *Do not insert screwdrivers deeper than .08" (2 mm) or damage may occur to stator windings.*

2) Remove nuts and washers for positive and negative diode holders from end frame. Carefully remove stator from end frame. Hold rotor in a vise using special wood blocks so no damage will occur to rotor. Remove nut, washer, pulley, fan, key and spacer. **NOTE** – *Check which way spacer faces for reassembly reference.*

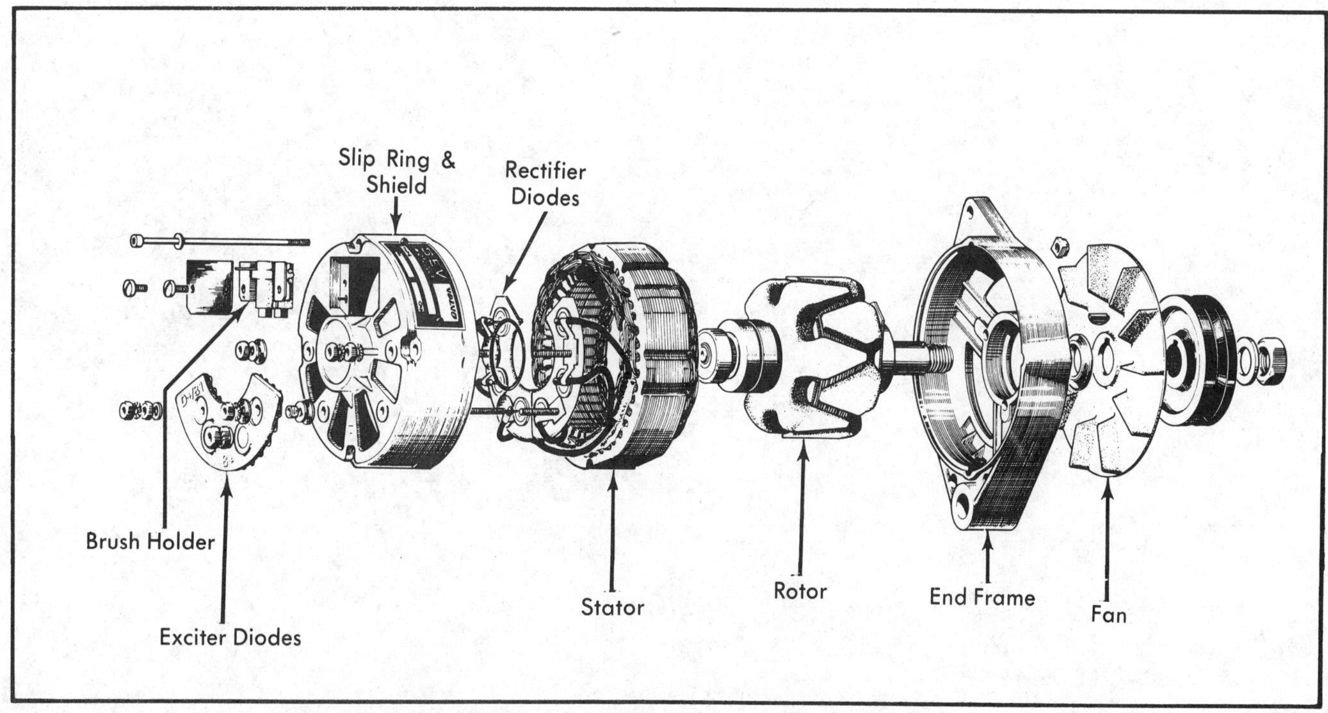

Fig. 1 Exploded View of Alternator

SEV MARCHAL ALTERNATORS (Cont.)

3) Remove three attaching screws for bearing cap, then push rotor shaft from end frame. Press bearing from end frame. Use a puller to remove bearing from slip ring end of rotor.

BENCH TESTING

Rotor — Check resistance of winding across slip rings using an ohmmeter. If resistance is not within specifications replace rotor. Use a 40V/40W test lamp to check for insulation between one of the slip rings and any rotor pole. If lamp lights, rotor is shorted.

Stator — Using an ohmmeter connect probes between each pair of stator leads with leads disconnected. All readings should be within specifications or stator should be replaced. Use a 40V/40W test lamp and check for a short by connecting one probe to iron core of stator and other probe to each of the three disconnected leads. If lamp lights replace stator.

Diodes — 1) Perform a conduction test on all diodes, in both directions, using an ohmmeter. Test the conduction between each terminal and plate with terminals disconnected. Positive diodes should allow current to flow from terminal to plate, but not from plate to terminal. Negative diodes should allow current to flow from the plate to terminal, but not from terminal to plate.

2) If current flows in both directions, the diode is shorted. If current does not flow in either direction, the diode is open. If any diode is defective, replace the entire diode assembly as individual diodes are not serviceable.

REASSEMBLY

1) Press on inner race of bearing to position bearing on slip ring end of rotor shaft. Press on outer race to press bearing into end frame. Install bearing cap and three attaching screws. Press end frame with bearing assembly firmly onto rotor shaft. Install spacer, key, fan, pulley, washer and nut onto rotor shaft. Tighten nut to 29 ft. lbs.

2) Install insulating washers and sleeves onto positive diode holder, then install stator to end frame while inserting brush holder through opening in end frame. Install nuts and washers to secure diode holders. Check that "O" ring in end frame bearing seat does not block vent hole.

3) Assemble two end frames along with stator and rotor assemblies together, then secure with four through bolts. Install brush holder attaching screws and tighten.

SEV MOTOROLA ALTERNATORS

Porsche
Volkswagen

▶ CHANGES, CAUTIONS, CORRECTIONS

*▶ **BATTERY INSTALLATION & OTHER ELECTRICAL REPAIRS CAUTION*** – Reversed polarity or excessive voltage will result in extensive damage to alternator system. Note the following to prevent damage:

Battery Installation – Negative battery terminal must be connected to ground (negative ground system) and positive terminal must be connected to starter. DO NOT reverse battery leads.

Battery Charging – If a Quick Charger is used, both battery cables must be disconnected from the battery. DO NOT use a Quick Charger to provide starting voltage.

Circuit Interruption – The battery must NEVER be disconnected while alternator is running.

Alternator Removal – Always disconnect battery ground before replacement of alternator.

High Voltage – DO NOT use a high voltage source to test diodes.

Booster Battery (For Engine Start) – Booster battery must be connected with negative lead to negative battery terminal and positive lead to positive battery terminal. DO NOT reverse battery leads.

Field Terminal – NEVER ground field energizing terminal on alternator, regulator, or connecting lead.

Voltage Regulator – NEVER operate voltage regulator without a good ground connection or immediate damage will result.

DESCRIPTION

SEV Motorola alternators are conventional three-phase, self-rectifying type alternators. Six silicon diodes (three positive and three negative) are used to rectify AC current.

APPLICATION

Model	Rating	Part No.
Porsche		
911 & Carerra	70 Amps	①911 603 12000
Volkswagen		
Type 1	55 Amps	②043 903 023E

① – Porsche part number.
② – Volkswagen part number

SPECIFICATIONS

Nominal Output

Application	Voltage
Porsche	14
Volkswagen	12

TESTING

ON CAR TEST

Connect alternator as shown in *Fig. 1*. Check that current through field winding (rotor) is 3.0-3.5 ampreres. If current is not within specifications, check field winding condition and brush holder. Run engine speed to 1500 RPM. Alternator should then produce the specified current. Measure voltage at terminal "B+" and at terminal "61". Voltage should be .8-.9 volts more at terminal "61". If not, isolation diodes are faulty and should be replaced.

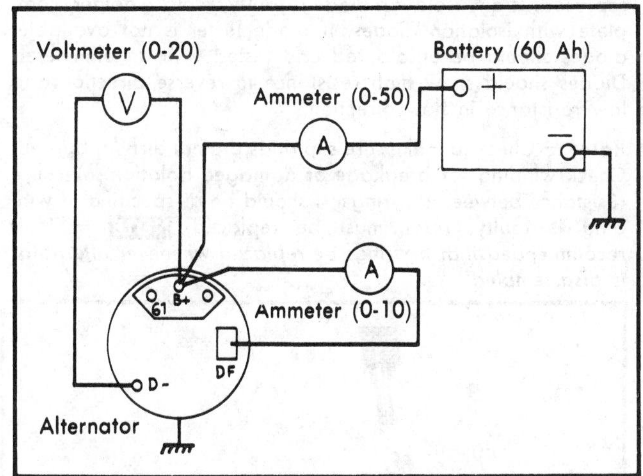

Fig. 1 Test Connections for Alternator

OVERHAUL

NOTE – *On Volkswagen voltage regulator, remove two screws and regulator. Alternators then disassemble in the same manner.*

DISASSEMBLY

1) Remove two screws holding brush holder and remove isolation plate (if equipped). Carefully lift out brush holder.

2) Hold pulley with belt in a vise with soft jaws, and remove the nut and washer. Lift off pulley, fan, key and spacer washer.

3) Remove nuts and washers on terminal 61 and the corresponding terminal on other side of isolation diode. Mark drive shield, stator and slip ring end shield for correct reassembly position.

SEV MOTOROLA ALTERNATORS (Cont.)

4) Remove four attaching screws. Remove rotor and drive end shield with help of two screwdrivers, which are inserted in two sockets between stator and drive end shield. **CAUTION** – *The screwdrivers may not be inserted deeper than 1/16" (2 mm); otherwise stator may be damaged.*

5) Release three screws holding support plate of drive end bearing. Release bearing by knocking end of shaft against a piece of wood.

6) Remove nuts and washers for the diode holder for negative diodes. Remove stator and diode holders for slip ring end shield.

TESTING

Stator – Check stator for short-circuiting. If one or more of the coils are burned, there must be a short-circuit in stator. Connect test lamp (12 volt, 2-5 watt) between stator plates and a terminal on stator (see illustration). If lamp lights, isolation between stator winding and stator plates must be burned, in which case stator should be replaced. **NOTE** – *Use only test lamp as specified. DO NOT use a 110-volt or 220-volt test lamp on this or any alternator test procedure.*

Diodes – Check diodes with a diode tester. If any of the rectified diodes are shorted or open, the diode holder must be replaced. If any isolation diode is faulty, replace holder, complete with isolation diodes. If diode tester is not available, diodes should be unsoldered and tested with an ohmmeter. Diodes should show high resistance in reverse direction and low resistance in flow direction.

Rotor – Check to make sure slip rings are not dirty or burned. Check winding for breakage or damaged isolation. Measure resistance between slip rings. It should be as specified. If winding is faulty, rotor must be replaced. **NOTE** – *It is recommended that bearings be replaced whenever alternator is disassembled.*

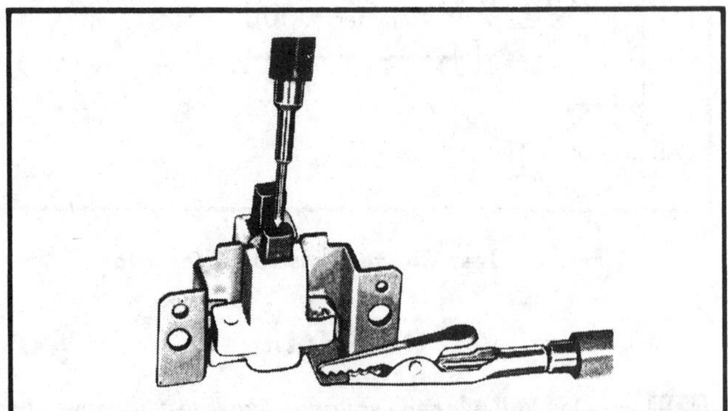

Fig. 2 Checking the Brush Holder

Brush Holder – Connect a test lamp between the brushes. Lamp should not light. Next connect test lamp between "DF" terminal and the "+" brush. Lamp should give steady light even if brush or terminal cable is moved (see illustration). Connect test lamp between brush holder frame and "–" brush. Lamp should give steady light. If test results are not satisfactory or brush length is less than 3/16" (5 mm), replace brush holder. **NOTE** – *Brush length is measured between brush contact surface and holder, with brush resting against spring.*

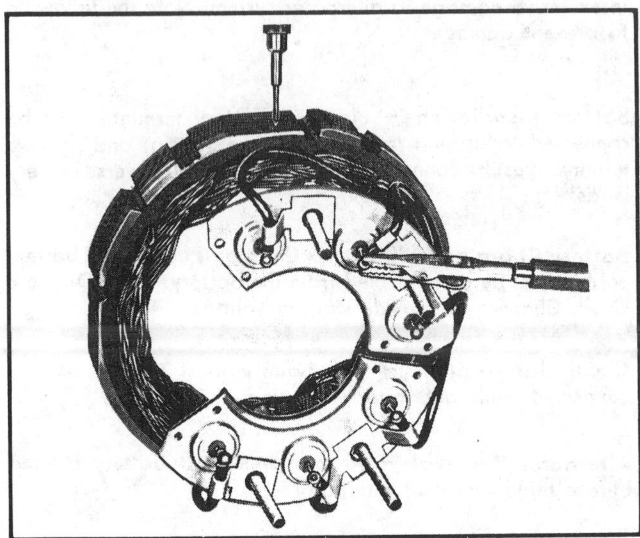

Fig. 3 Checking the Stator

PARTS REPLACEMENT

Diodes – Mark leads connecting stator to diodes, then unsolder leads. Place new diode holder in exact position of holder being replaced. Solder new leads, holding with pliers (this is to conduct heat from soldering point, to avoid damaging new diode). Use a minimum 100-watt, well-heated soldering iron. Never change places of diode holders. Positive holder is isolated from frame by means of isolation washers and sleeves and its diodes are marked in red. Negative diode holder is not isolated and its diodes are marked in black.

REASSEMBLY

Alternator is reassembled by reversing disassembly procedures while noting the following: Rotor must be pressed into drive end shield. Connect a test lamp between "B+" terminal and alternator frame, then reverse connections. Lamp should light only in one direction. After completion of reassembly, test run alternator on bench, using same procedure as described for On Car Testing.

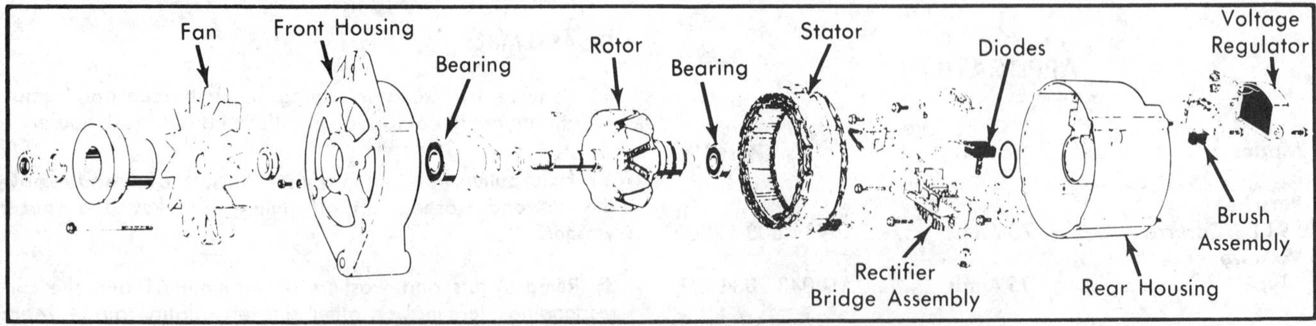

Fig. 4 Disassembled View of S.E.V. Motorola Alternator (Volkswagen Shown)

SEV MOTOROLA REGULATORS

Porsche

▶ CHANGES, CAUTIONS, CORRECTIONS

▶ *SERVICE CAUTION — When servicing alternator or regulator, note following precautions to avoid damage to components:*

Field Terminal — Never ground field energizing terminal on alternator, regulator or connecting lead.

Voltage Regulator — Never operate voltage regulator without a good ground connection. Immediate damage will result.

Alternator — Do not ground output terminal. Always disconnect battery negative cable before removing wire from alternator output terminal. Do not attempt to polarize alternator as polarization is not required and any attempt to polarize will damage voltage regulator and wiring harness.

DESCRIPTION

SEV Motorola alternators use either an electronic or mechanical type voltage regulator. The electronic unit contains neither mechanical contacts or relays, and requires no adjustments or maintenance. It is sealed, and if found to be defective requires replacement. The mechanical voltage regulator has fixed upper and lower contacts and the center contact is moveable.

APPLICATION

Model	Part No.
Porsche	
911 & Carerra	911 603 90100

TESTING

ON CAR TEST

1) Connect alternator and regulator as shown in illustration. For an accurate test, drive vehicle or operate system (on bench) for about 45 minutes at 30 miles per hour or more. This will allow regulator to reach its normal operating temperature.

2) Run alternator at 5000 RPM (engine speed at 2500 RPM) for 15 seconds. Voltage with no load should be as shown in specifications.

3) Load alternator with 10-15 amperes (for example, high beam headlights). Record voltage reading. The voltage should also be as shown in specifications.

4) The following chart gives voltage values for other ambient temperatures. If voltage is outside tolerance limits, regulator must be replaced.

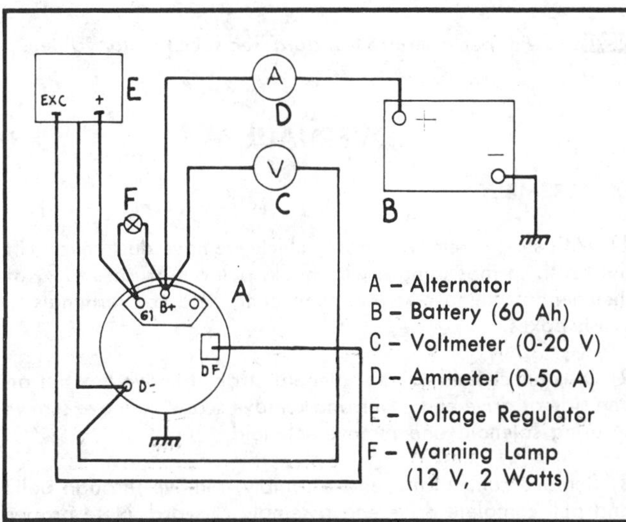

Fig. 1 Regulator Test Circuit

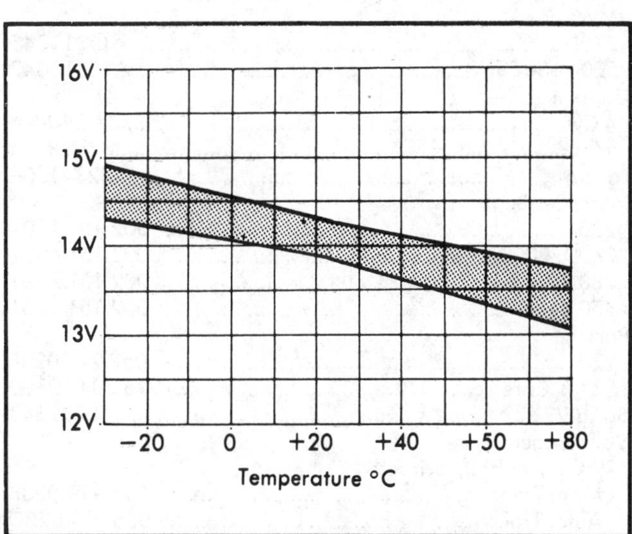

Fig. 2 Voltage-Temperature Variation with Regulator Warm.

BOSCH

Audi
BMW
Capri II
Lancia
Mercedes-Benz
Porsche
Saab
Volkswagen
Volvo

DESCRIPTION

Starter is a brush type, series wound, electric motor, equipped with an overrunning clutch (inner-wedge or outer-wedge type). Unit may or may not be equipped with a solenoid. Field frame is enclosed by commutator end frame and drive bushing and carries the pole shoes and field coils. A spline, located on drive end of armature, carries overrunning clutch and pinion assembly. Armature shaft is supported in sintered bronze bushings in the commutator end frame and drive end housings (these bushings are packed with lubricant at assembly and require no further lubrication).

APPLICATION

Model	Manufacturer Part No.
Audi	
100LS	058 911 023F
Fox	056 911 023B
BMW	
320i	①311045
530i, 630CSi	①311042
Capri II	
4 Cyl.	D7RY-A
V6	D7RY-A
Lancia	82301308
Mercedes-Benz	
230	002 151 1101
240D, 300D	002 151 6901
280	002 151 7101
450 Series	002 151 4301
Porsche	
924	059 911 023F
911 & Carerra	916 604 10100
Saab 99	8309643
Volkswagen	
Dasher, Rabbit, Scirocco	
Man. Trans.	055 911 023B
Auto. Trans.	056 911 023D
All Others	
Man. Trans.	113 911 023
Auto. Trans.	311 911 023D
Volvo	
4 Cyl.	464316-9
V6	464317-7

① — Basic Bosch Part No. 0 001.

TESTING

Lock Test— Mount starter in a test stand to allow starter torque measurement (follow manufacturers instructions). With voltage adjusted to specifications, ammeter reading and starter torque should be within specifications.

Free Running Test— With starter in test bench, take readings of starter current, voltage and RPM. Readings should be within specifications.

NOTE — *Starter must be mounted to prevent meshing of pinion and ring gear even in engaged position. If starter has warmed up during previous tests, RPM will be higher.*

SPECIFICATIONS

Brush Spring Tension

Application	lbs. (Kg)
208 xxx	2.54-2.98 (1150-1350)
211 xxx	2.54-2.98 (1150-1350)
211 9xx	2.38-2.69 (1080-1220)
212 xxx	2.38-2.69 (1080-1220)
311 xxx	2.54-2.87 (1150-1300)
312 1xx	1.76-1.98 (800-900)
313 xxx	2.54-2.87 (1150-1300)
362 xxx	2.54-2.87 (1150-1300)

Min. Brush Length

Application	In. (mm)
312 1xx	.394 (10)
362 xxx	.611 (15.5)
All Other Starters	.520 (13)

NOTE — *For performance test data, see specification table.*

OVERHAUL

DISASSEMBLY

1) With starter removed from vehicle, remove dust cover. Lift out brush springs using a wire hook, pull out brushes to ¾ of their length. Remove screws connecting field coil terminals to brush boxes.

2) Disconnect field coil to solenoid strap, remove hex nut on one side of drive end cover and remove screw. Remove screws securing solenoid and remove solenoid.

3) Remove commutator end assembly, remove through bolts and pull complete drive end assembly forward. Note proper location of washers for reassembly.

4) Remove yoke lever, then from armature shaft, remove cotter pin and left hand threaded castle nut. Remove snap ring and discard.

5) Remove drive assembly, intermediate bearing with bushing and armature brake, spring plate washer unit or washer spring jaw unit, depending on the model.

CLEANING & INSPECTING

Clean all parts using carbontetrachloride or suitable cleaning agent, inspect parts for wear or damage. After inspecting parts apply thin coat of oil to running surfaces.

BOSCH (Cont.)

PARTS REPLACEMENT & TESTING

Brushes & Springs – Check brush spring pressure with suitable spring scale. Check brushes for minimum length. If replacement is necessary, replace all brushes.

Armature – Check coil and commutator to shaft (or core) for short circuit, with 110 volt ac control lamp. Control lamp should not illuminate (slight illumination is possible due to dampness). Check coil to commutator for short circuit with a 6 volt DC control lamp, touching every coil on armature and its corresponding bar, brightness of lamp should not change. Check coils on armature for short circuit between windings using a growler.
Check out of round of commutator to core, it should not exceed .00197" (0.5 mm). Commutator should have a smooth greyish-blue surface with no grooves or burned spots otherwise, it must be turned. Minimum commutator diameter is 1.32" (33.5 mm). After turning commutator, undercut insulation to a depth of .0197-.0236" (0.5-0.8 mm), decrease diameter by .0039" (0.1 mm). Do not use emery cloth, turn on a lathe only.

Housing– Check field coils for shorted or open circuits. Remove burned or damaged coils, mark location of coils and pole shoes for installation. Replace pole shoes with coils, using a suitable pole shoe screwdriver and mandrel.

Drive Assembly– Replace drive when damaged or teeth are worn. Disassemble as follows: Pull Pinion with left hand (turning to left), then pull guide discs toward commutator, also giving these a left hand turn. Mark all parts for reassembly. Remove intermediate bearing, spring, spring seat and plate from armature shaft. Carefully remove spring ring using a screwdriver and pushing stop ring back.

Take off inner and outer spring, guiding piece, locking piece, disc and thrust ring from drive cup. Remove spring ring from drive cup. Remove pinion with clutch discs, taking care not to lose disc. Remove stamping marks between stop ring and spring ring. Slacken clutch nut from pinion by twisting, being careful of small springs inside nut. If pinion, stop disc or plate is damaged, force out ring so new parts may be installed.

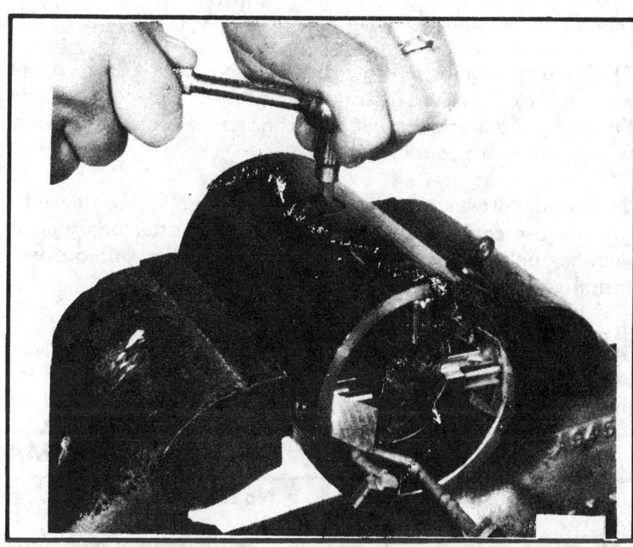

Fig. 1 Removing Pole Shoes

Bushings – Self-lubricating bushings should be replaced only when worn or damaged. Force out bushings, using a suitable mandrel, remove burrs and clean hole. Before pressing in new

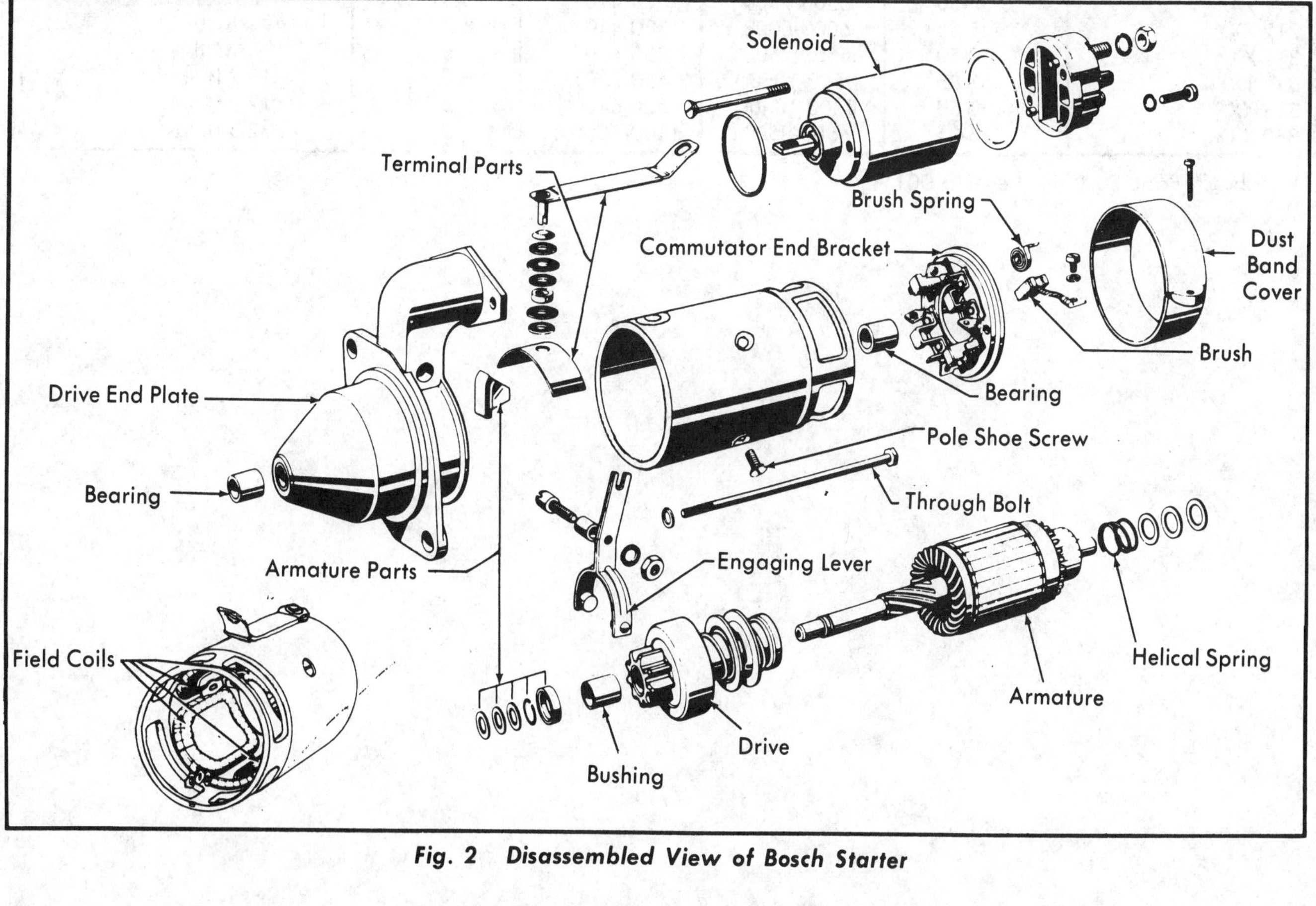

Fig. 2 Disassembled View of Bosch Starter

BOSCH (Cont.)

bushing, soak bushing in a suitable oil for not less than 30 minutes. After replacing, cross check inner diameter of bushing by pulling a smoothing mandrel through.

REASSEMBLY

NOTE – *When reassembling use all new gaskets. When reassembly is complete, paint all main joints on starter (including solenoid) with gum-lac or equivalent.*

1) Clamp armature in a suitable holding fixture, line up armature brake unit and intermediate bearing. The bent ends of the spring plate washer unit must engage into holes of cupped washer of intermediate bearing.

2) Push drive over armature shaft, then push spring ring into groove. Use conical piece to froce ring over after adjusting it with hex bolts so that tube pushes spring straight into groove. Install castle nut and adjust with cotter pin.

3) Insert yoke lever, slipping drive end assembly over drive, being sure guide pins on fork are between guiding discs and that fork is in center of casting throat. Replace rubber seal to joint of drive end housing (on starters with intermediate bearing only).

4) Install intermediate bearing to drive end assembly and install through bolts in the reverse manner of their removal. Be certain intermediate bearing is properly seated to drive end assembly. Check armature brake spring ends to ensure proper positioning.

5) Insert armature with drive assembly into housing, do not damage field coils. Install washers on armature shaft as they were marked at disassembly, replace commutator end assembly. Check play of armature, should be .004-.006". Adjust with shims if necessary.

6) Hook in joint fork of solenoid, pushing back engagement fork. Be certain rubber seal is installed between solenoid and drive end and copper washer on bearing bolt. Attach solenoid and field coil terminal to solenoid.

7) Connect field coil terminal to brush box and install brushes. Make sure leads of brushes do not interfere with cover. Fasten dust cover being certain to install gasket, bend tongues of lock washers.

STARTER PERFORMANCE SPECIFICATIONS

Model①	No Load Test		Lock Test		
	Amps.	RPM	Amps.	Volts	Torque
208 XXX	35-55	6000-8000	320-410	8.5	9 ft. lbs.
211 XXX	30-50	6000-9000	300-390	9.0	8.7 ft. lbs.
211 9XX	30-50	6500-9500	320-410	8.5	8.3 ft. lbs.
212 XXX	35-55	6000-8000	320-410	8.5	9 ft. lbs.
311 XXX	30-50	5500-7500	350-450	8.5	13 ft. lbs.
312 1XX	55-85	8500-10500	650-730	6.0	13.7 ft. lbs.
313 XXX	50-80	8300-10300	520-610	6.5	12.3 ft. lbs.
362 XXX	65-95	6500-8500	1100-1300	7.0	32.5 ft. lbs.

① – Bosch Basic Part Number is 0 001

DUCELLIER & PARIS RHONE

Peugeot
Renault

DESCRIPTION

Starter is a 12-volt, four-pole unit of conventional design. Solenoid assembly is mounted on starter case. Starters have a overrunning clutch (pinion-free wheel assembly) connected by a shift lever to the solenoid plunger.

APPLICATION

Application①	Ducillier No.	Paris Rhone No.
Peugeot		
604		
LHD	6237	D9 E14
RHD	6238	D9 E15
Renault		
R-5		D8 E121
R-12		D10 E64
R17 GTL		D10 E64
R-17 Gordini		D10 E65

① – Specifications for Peugeot 504 and Diesel are not available at this time.

TESTING

PERFORMANCE TEST

Lock Test – To perform lock test, follow instructions and procedures outlined in instruction manual furnished with tester. Use a fully charged battery and carry out the test at a temperature of 77°F. Ammeter reading and starter torque should be within limits (see specifications).

LOCK TEST SPECIFICATIONS

Starter No.①	Amps.	Torque (Ft. Lbs.)
6237, 6238	440	10.8
D9 E14, D9 E15	450	11.6
D8 E121	400	9

① – Specifications not available for part numbers not shown.

OVERHAUL

DISASSEMBLY

1) Remove two nuts on through bolts. Remove the rear shield.

2) Lift out brushes and retaining shaft for connecting fork between the solenoid and pinion. Remove bolts securing solenoid and remove solenoid.

3) Remove the body and armature.

PARTS REPLACEMENT & TESTING

Brushes – Inspect brush length and if less than 5/16" on Paris Rhone models or 19/64" on Ducellier models, replace the brushes.

Commutator – If commutator surface is scored, rough or burnt, dress with a lathe just enough to remove defective area and polish with a strip of fine emery paper. Check insulation undercut depth and it must be .02" deep.

Armature – Check armature for open, shorted or grounded circuits. Inspect armature shaft for bend; if bend is excessive replace armature. **NOTE** – *Do not attempt to straighten a bent shaft.*

Bearings – Inspect bearings for excessive wear and clearance between armature shaft and bearing. Replace as necessary.

Pinion-Free Wheel Assembly – If it is necessary to change the pinion assembly, remove the stop collar, slide assembly off and replace with a new pinion assembly. Reinstall stop collar and snap ring.

REASSEMBLY

Clean all parts and coat the sliding surface of armature shaft, splines, and bushings with multipurpose grease. Reassemble in the reverse order of disassembly while noting the following:

1) After completing reassembly, disconnect the field terminal from solenoid. Connect solenoid to battery and measure clearance of pinion gear to stop collar. Clearance should be .02-.099".

2) If clearance is not within limits, adjust by screwing the plunger fork or adjusting screw in or out to change clearance. Solenoid must be removed to adjust plunger fork (if equipped).

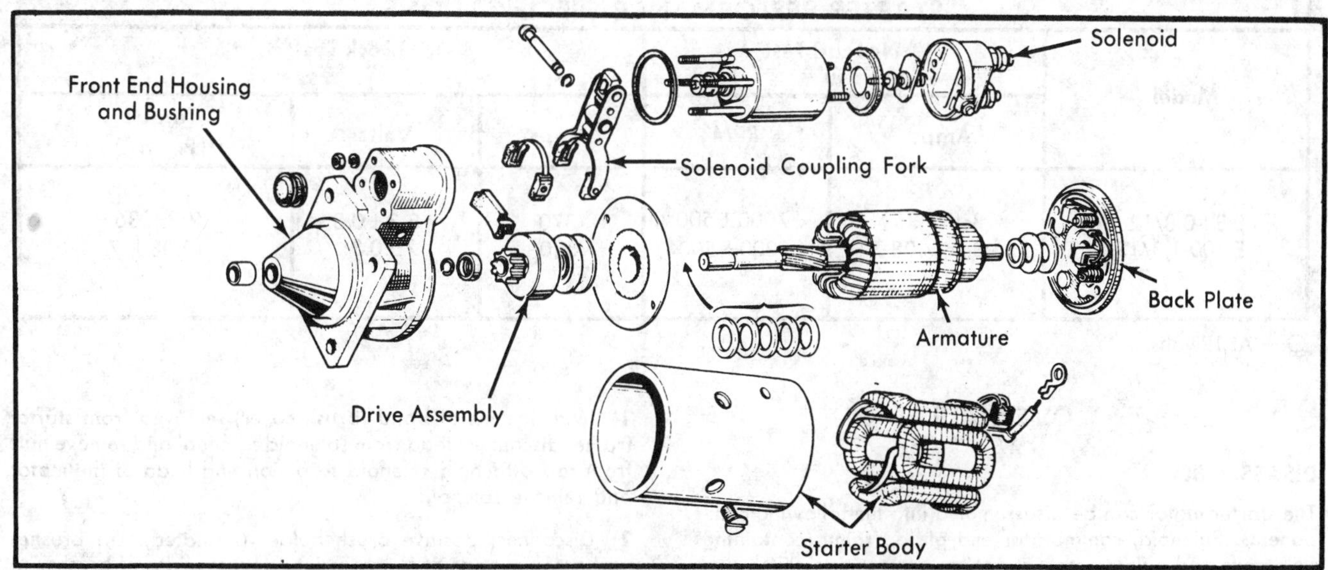

Fig. 1 Disassembled View of Paris Rhone Starter

FIAT

Fiat
All Models

DESCRIPTION

Fiat starter is a 12 volt system with four poles and field windings are in series. Overrunning clutch pinion drive mounted directly on armature shaft. Pinion drive and battery connection to starter motor are controlled by a solenoid mounted on starter frame.

APPLICATION

Model Application	Fiat No.
128 & X1/9 Models	E 84-0.8/12
124 & 131 Models	E 100-1.3/12

TESTING

PERFORMANCE TESTS

Cranking Amperage Draw – Mount starter on starter test stand. Make wiring connections as shown in illustration. Starter test stand should have a ring gear and a brake dynomometer. Ring gear should have minimum pinion/ring ratio of 1.0-10. If test stand is not equipped with correct pinion/ring ratio, follow manufacturers instructions in use of test stand. Test should be made with ambiant temperature of 77°F. Observe amperage draw, voltage reading, and delivered torque while operating starter and check against specifications.

No Load Test – With starter mounted on test stand so pinion cannot contact ring gear, operate starter. Amperage draw, voltage reading and armature RPM should be within specifications.

Stall (Lock) Test – With starter mounted in test stand and ring gear locked, adjust test stand rheostat to values specified (see specifications) and observe torque on dial indicator.

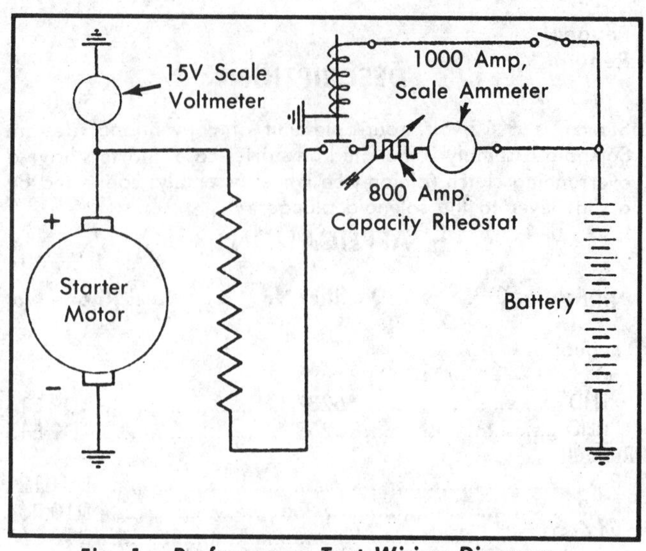

Fig. 1 Performance Test Wiring Diagram

CRANKING SPECIFICATIONS

Starter No.	Amps @RPM	Torque (Ft. Lbs.)
E 84-0.8/12	170@1950±100①	2.89±.14
E 100-1.3/12	280@1600±100②	5.78±.14

① – At 10.3 volts.
② – At 9.5 volts.

Brush Spring Tension – E 84-0.8/12 – 2.5-2.9 lbs. (1.15-1.3 kg); E 100-1.3/12 – 2.2±.2 lbs. (1±0.1 kg).

Rotation (Pinion End) – Clockwise.

Armature End Play – E 84-0.8/12 – .0039-.0197" (0.1-0.5 mm); E 100-1.3/12 – .003-.027" (0.07-0.70 mm).

STARTER PERFORMANCE SPECIFICATIONS

Model	No Load Test ①		Lock Test		
	Amps.	RPM	Amps.	Volts	Torque (Ft. Lbs.)
E 84-0.8/12	Below 35	7000±500	370	8.3±0.3	7.9±.36
E 100-1.3/12	Below 28	5200±500	530	7±0.3	12.58±.7

① – At 12 volts.

OVERHAUL

DISASSEMBLY

The starter motor can be disassembled into the following components: Solenoid, commutator end plate, frame (containing field coils and pole pieces), armature, overrunning clutch and pinion drive gear, and pinion end housing.

1) With the metal band (brush cover) removed from starter frame, disconnect lead from solenoid terminal and remove nuts from rod attaching solenoid to pinion end head of the motor and remove solenoid.

2) Disconnect positive brush holder (insulated). Lift brushes and arrange ends of brush springs against sides of brushes to hold them off commutator.

FIAT (Cont.)

3) Remove nuts on tie-rods of the two supports, and remove brush holder bracket. Be careful not to lose thrust washers (one fibre, and one steel) on the pin.

4) Slide frame off pinion end. Take out split pin from engaging lever pivot and remove pivot.

5) The armature and thrust washers can be taken out with drive and fork lever. Remove the snap ring from armature shaft and remove drive parts in their proper order.

CLEANING

Do not immerse starter components in solvent. Use compressed air to blow dirt and worn brush dust from field coils and armature. Use cleaning brush dipped in solvent to clean drive unit, then blow dry with air.

PARTS REPLACEMENT

Field Coils – Mount starter frame in press-type screwdriver stand and remove pole piece attaching screws. Remove pole pieces and field coils. Prior to installing new coils, heat windings to 122°F in order to obtain added flexibility and facilitate seating the coils under pole shoes. Use press-type screwdriver stand to completely tighten attaching screws. After installation is completed, measure pole shoes inner diameter. To assure proper air gap between pole shoes and armature, inner diameter must be between 2.175-2.182" (55.25-55.42 mm) on starter No. E 84-0.8/12 and between 2.675-2.677" (67.95-68.00 mm) on starter No. E 100-1.3/12. Do not bore out inner diameter to obtain specified diameter. If diameter is not within tolerance, coils and shoes have been improperly installed.

REASSEMBLY

Lubricate inner splined face of drive assembly with SAE 10 motor oil before installing drive on armature shaft. Reverse disassembly procedure to complete overhaul.

TROUBLE SHOOTING & DIAGNOSIS

Starter Inoperative – Battery terminals corroded. Starter switch or battery terminals loose. Battery discharged or defective. Worn brushes (not contacting commutator). Starter switch (solenoid) contacts burned or worn. Commutator segment dislodged by centrifugal force.

Starter Operation Sluggish – Worn brushes. Part of field or armature windings shorted. Poor battery cable connections. Battery charge low, or defective cell.

Starter Motor Noisy – Worn armature shaft bushing. Pinion gear disengagement exceptionally late (worn or defective overrunning clutch).

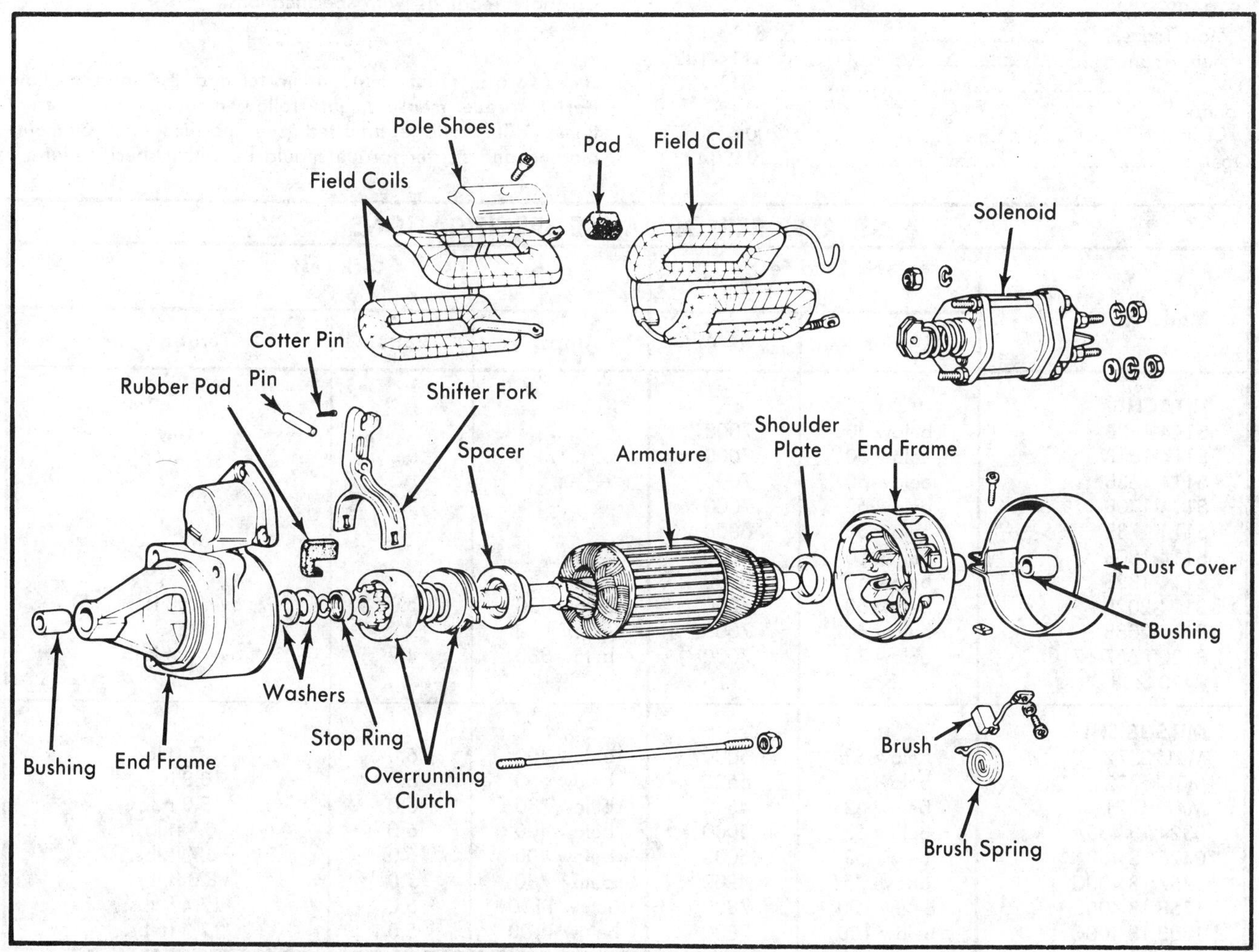

Fig. 2 Disassembled View of Fiat Starter Motor

HITACHI & MITSUBISHI

Arrow
Colt
Datsun
Honda
LUV
Mazda
Opel

DESCRIPTION

Starter is a 12-volt, four-pole unit of conventional design. Magnetic switch assembly is mounted on gear case. Starters have a overrunning clutch connected by a shift lever to magnetic switch plunger. Brushes and springs are retained inside yoke assembly by holders.

APPLICATION

Hitachi

Model	Part No.
Datsun	
B210	
Man. Trans.	S114-160B
Auto. Trans.	S114-163B
F10	
Man. Trans.	S114-161B
Auto. Trans.	S114-208B
200SX, 710 & P/U 620 Man. Trans.	S114-170B
Auto. Trans.	S114-180B
810, 280Z	
Man. Trans.	S114-173B
Auto. Trans.	S114-182B
LUV	S114-202
Honda	
Civic	31200 657 671
Opel	94204338

Mitsubishi

Model	Part No.
Arrow & Colt	
1600cc	
Man. Trans.	M3T12572
Auto. Trans.	M3T15772
2000cc	
Man. Trans.	M3T15772
Auto. Trans.	M4T14771
Mazda	
1300cc	0324 18 400A
1600cc	0426 18 400A
RX-3 Auto. Trans.	1883 18 400
All Others	
Man. Trans.	1757 18 400C
Auto. Trans.	1758 18 400C

TESTING

PERFORMANCE TESTS

No Load Tests – Connect starter in series with a 12 volt battery, being certain ammeter used is capable of 1000 ampere reading. Connect voltmeter to starter (see illustration). Compare readings with specifications.

Lock (Torque) Test – Mount starter in a test stand to allow starter torque measurement (follow manufacturers instructions). With voltage adjusted (see specifications), ammeter reading and starter torque should be within specifications.

STARTER PERFORMANCE SPECIFICATIONS

Model	No Load Test		Lock Test		
	Amps.	RPM	Amps.	Volts	Torque
HITACHI					
S114-160B	below 60	7000	.....	.....	.....
S114-161B	below 60	7000	.....	.....	.....
S114-163B	below 60	7000	.....	.....	.....
S114-170B	below 60	7000	.....	.....	.....
S114-173B	below 60	6000	.....	.....	.....
S114-180B	below 60	6000	.....	.....	.....
S114-182B	below 60	6000	.....	.....	.....
S114-202B	below 60	6000	below 330	5.0	over 5.8 ft.lbs.
S114-208B	below 60	7000	.....	.....	.....
31200-657-671①	below 70	7000	below 380	4.9	over 5.4 ft.lbs.
94204338②	.....	.....	.....	.....	.....
MITSUBISHI					
M3T12572	below 53	5000	below 400	6.0	6.7 ft.lbs.
M3T15772	below 55	6500	below 560	6.0	10.8 ft.lbs.
M4T14771	below 62	4500	below 730	6.0	18.0 ft.lbs.
0324 18 400A	below 53	5000	below 400	6.0	6.7 ft.lbs.
0426 18 400A	below 53	5000	below 400	6.0	6.7 ft.lbs.
1757 18 400C	above 75	4900	below 780	5.0	8.0 ft.lbs.
1758 18 400C	below 100	7800	below 1100	5.0	17.4 ft.lbs.
1883 18 400C	below 100	7800	below 1100	5.0	17.4 ft.lbs.

① – Honda part number.
② – Buick part number.

HITACHI & MITSUBISHI (Cont.)

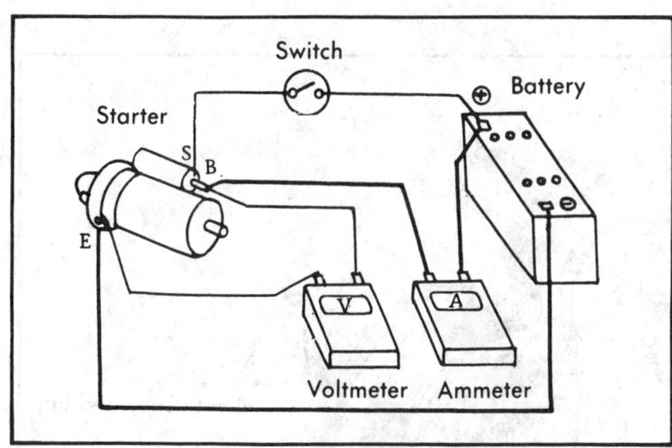

Fig. 1 Connections for No Load Test

OVERHAUL

DISASSEMBLY

1) Loosen nut securing connecting plate to magnetic switch "M" terminal, remove screws securing magnetic switch and remove switch assembly. Remove two through bolts and brush cover assembly, then tap yoke assembly with a wooden hammer and remove it. Remove armature assembly shift lever.

2) Remove pinion stop ring from end of armature shaft by pushing stop ring to the clutch side. Remove snap ring and then remove stop ring with overrunning clutch. Remove overrunning clutch assembly from armature shaft.

PARTS REPLACEMENT & TESTING

Brushes & Springs – Check brush spring tension using a suitable spring scale (see specifications). Check brush contact surface condition. If brush contact is loose, replace brush. If brush length is less than specified, replace brushes. Check lead clip and wire connection, check condition of brush holders and spring clip, repair or replace parts as necessary.

Brush Spring Tension

Application	Lbs. (Kg)
Arrow, Colt	3.3 (1.5)
Datsun	3.1-4.0 (1.4-1.8)
Honda, LUV, Mazda, Opel	3.5 (1.6)

Brush Length (Minimum)

Application	In. (mm)
Arrow, Colt, Mazda	.45 (11.5)
Datsun	.47 (12.0)
Honda	.16 (4.0)
LUV, Opel	.47 (12.0)

Armature – Check external condition of armature. Measure shaft for distortion or bending, using a dial indicator gauge. Replace armature shaft if bending exceeds .0031" on Datsun, .006" on Luv and .004" on all other models.

Commutator – Inspect commutator for roughness, if surface is pitted or grooved, it should be sanded lightly with no. 500 emery paper. Also check commutator for being out-of-round. If out-of-round is more than .0079", or insulating mica depth is less than .0079" from the cummutator surface, turn commutator in a lathe until out-of-round is less than .002". Insulating mica should be undercut to depth of .0197-.0315". Wear limit of commutator diameter is .0787", if excessively worn, it must be replaced.

Field Coil – Check field coil continuity by connecting test probe of a circuit tester or a resistance counter to the field coil positive terminal and positive brush holder, if tester shows no continuity, field circuit or coil is open. Check for grounded field coils by placing one probe of a circuit tester on yoke and other probe to field coil positive terminal, if resistance is read, field coils are grounded.

Overrunning Clutch Assembly – Inspect pinion assembly and sleeve. Sleeve should slide freely along armature shaft spline and if damage or resistance is noted, replace assembly. Inspect pinion teeth for excessive rubbing, replace as necessary. Check flywheel ring gear for damage or wear.

Magnetic Switch Assembly – After checking starter motor, magnetic switch assembly should also be checked. Connect jumper cables between negative battery terminal and starting motor "M" terminal, and positive battery terminal and starting motor "S" terminal, connecting ignition switch in series (see illustration). With ignition switch on, measure distance between the pinion front edge and pinion stopper (see illustration). Clearance should be .012-.059" on Hitachi starters and .02-.08" on Mitsubishi starters. If not within specifications, adjust by changing washer between magnetic switch and gear case.

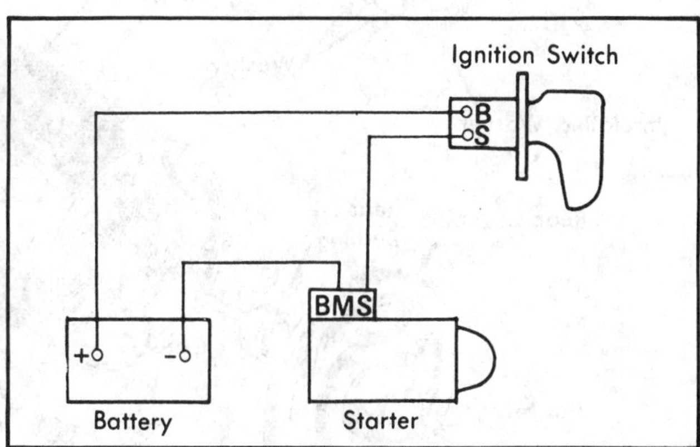

Fig. 2 Circuit for Testing Magnetic Switch Assembly

Pinion Case Bearing – Inspect bearing for wear and check side play. Clearance between bearing and armature shaft should not exceed .0079". If limit is exceeded, replace bearing. Clearance with new bearing installed should be .001-.004" on Hitachi starters and .002-.004" on Mitsubishi starters.

NOTE – *Be sure bearing is installed so that end of bearing is flush with gear case end plane.*

HITACHI & MITSUBISHI (Cont.)

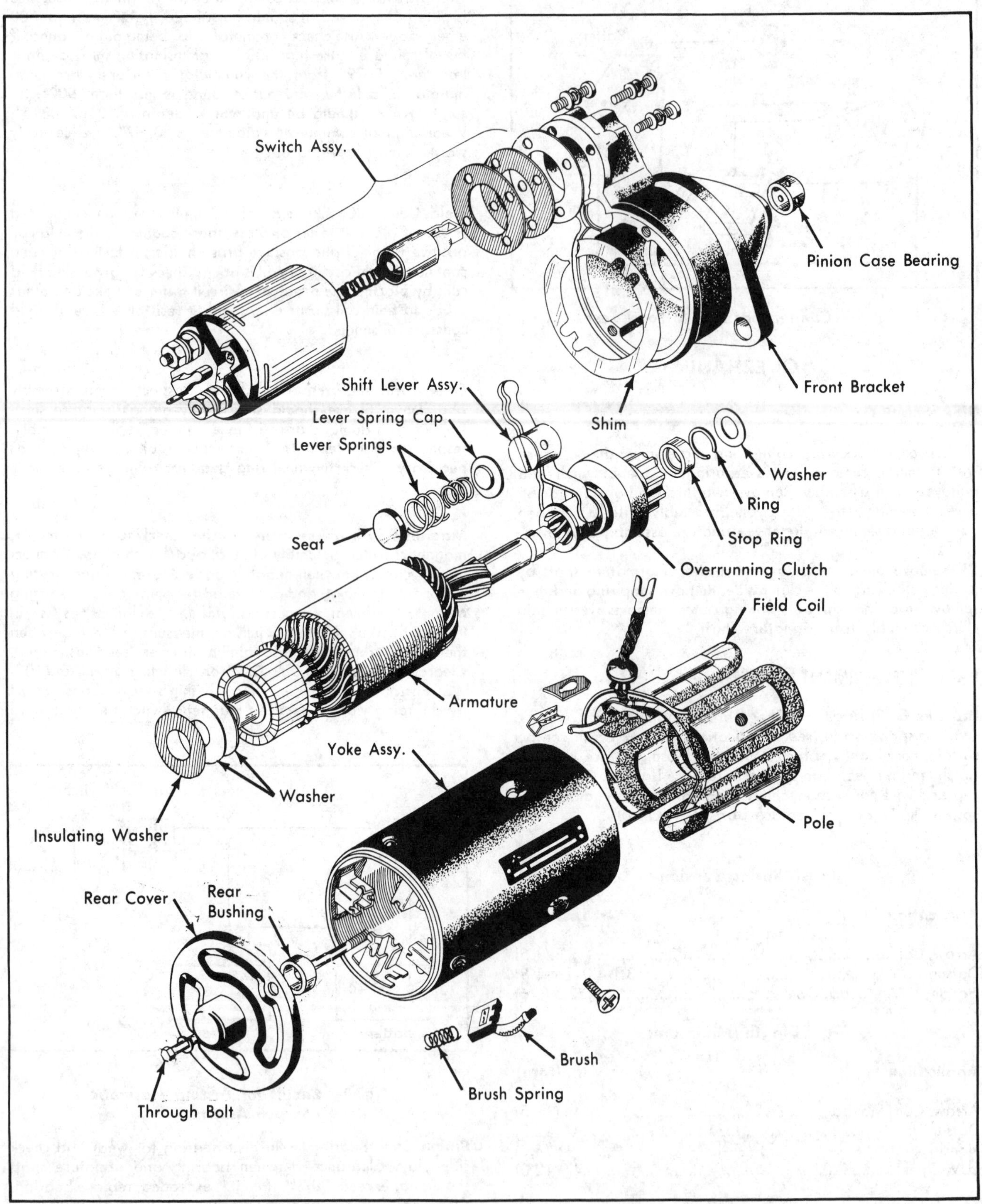

Fig. 3 Disassembled View of a Typical Mitsubishi Starter

HITACHI & MITSUBISHI (Cont.)

CLEANING & INSPECTION

Clean all disassembled parts, being careful not to use a grease dissolving solvent on overrunning clutch, armature assembly, magnetic switch assembly or field coils, as damage could result. Check all parts for damage or excessive wear, replace as required.

REASSEMBLY

To reassemble, reverse disassembly procedure and be certain to fill rear case with grease and to lightly oil rear cover metal bearing and pinion.

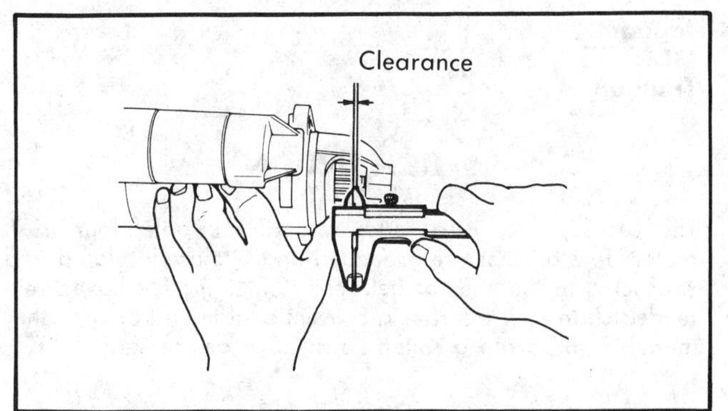

Fig. 4 Measuring Pinion Edge-to-Pinion Stopper Clearance

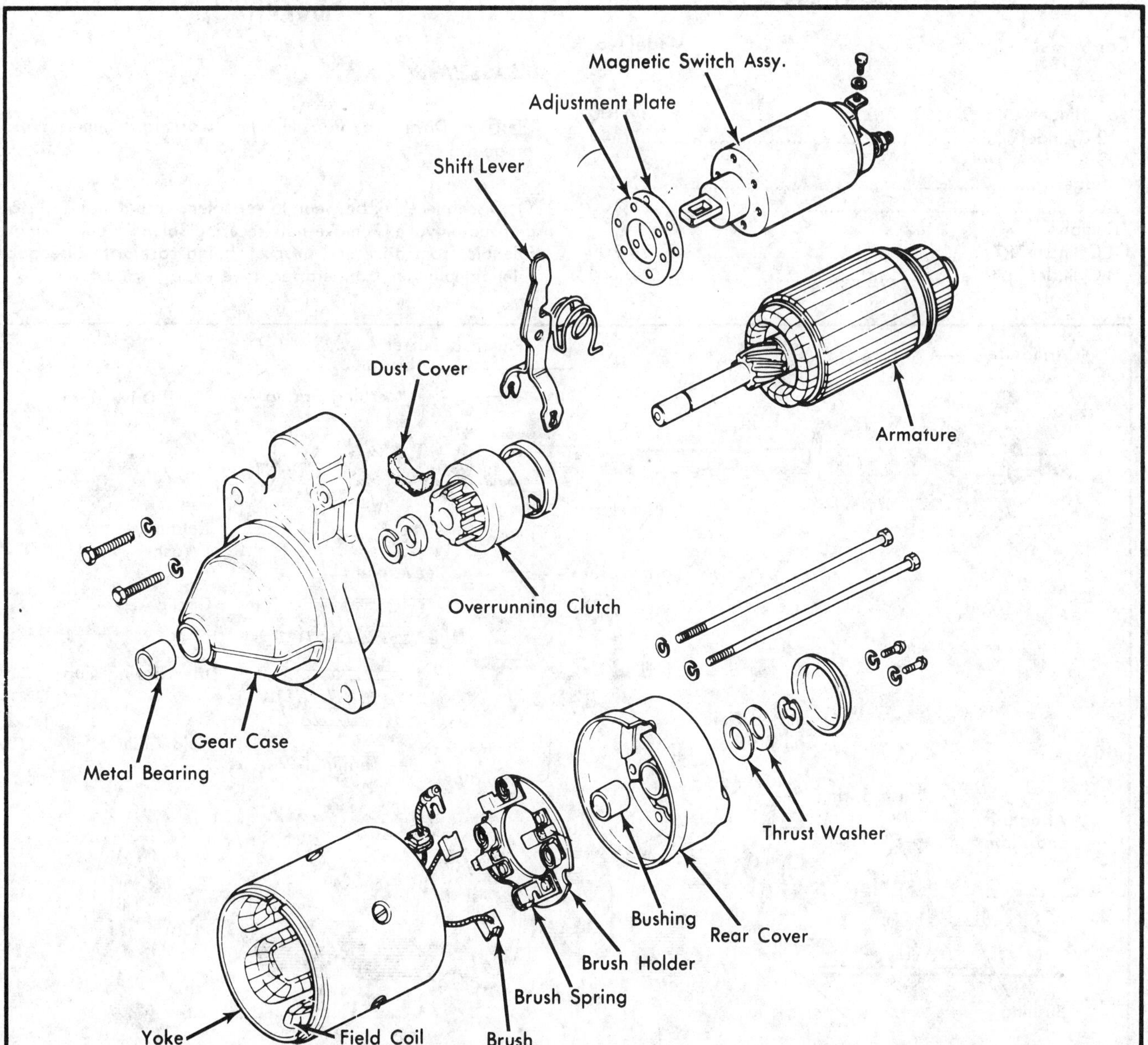

Fig. 5 Disassembled View of a Typical Hitachi Starter

LUCAS

Jaguar
MG
Triumph

DESCRIPTION

The Lucas starter is a series wound, four-pole, four-brush motor. Two brushes are grounded and two are insulated and connected to the ends of field coils. Some models have an extended shaft which carries a conventional inertia drive. Other models incorporate a roller clutch drive on the shaft.

APPLICATION

Car Model	Model No.
Jaguar	
6 Cylinder	3M100
12 Cylinder	M45
MG	
Midget	M35J
MGB	2M100
Triumph	
4 Cylinder TR7	2M100
4 Cylinder Spitfire	M35J

TESTING

PERFORMANCE TESTS

No Load Test – With starter on bench and using a good 12-volt battery, connect an ammeter in series to starter. Starter should rotate smoothly. See specifications for RPM, and current draw.

Lock Test – To perform lock test, follow instructions and procedures outlined in instruction manual furnished with tester. With starter locked in test stand, and voltage adjusted to specified figure, ammeter reading and starter torque should be as specified (see specifications).

OVERHAUL

DISASSEMBLY

NOTE – *Disregard Step 1) when working on inertia drive models.*

1) Disconnect link between lower solenoid terminal and starting motor yoke. Remove nuts securing solenoid unit. Remove solenoid from drive end bracket, being careful to disengage solenoid plunger from starter drive engagement lever.

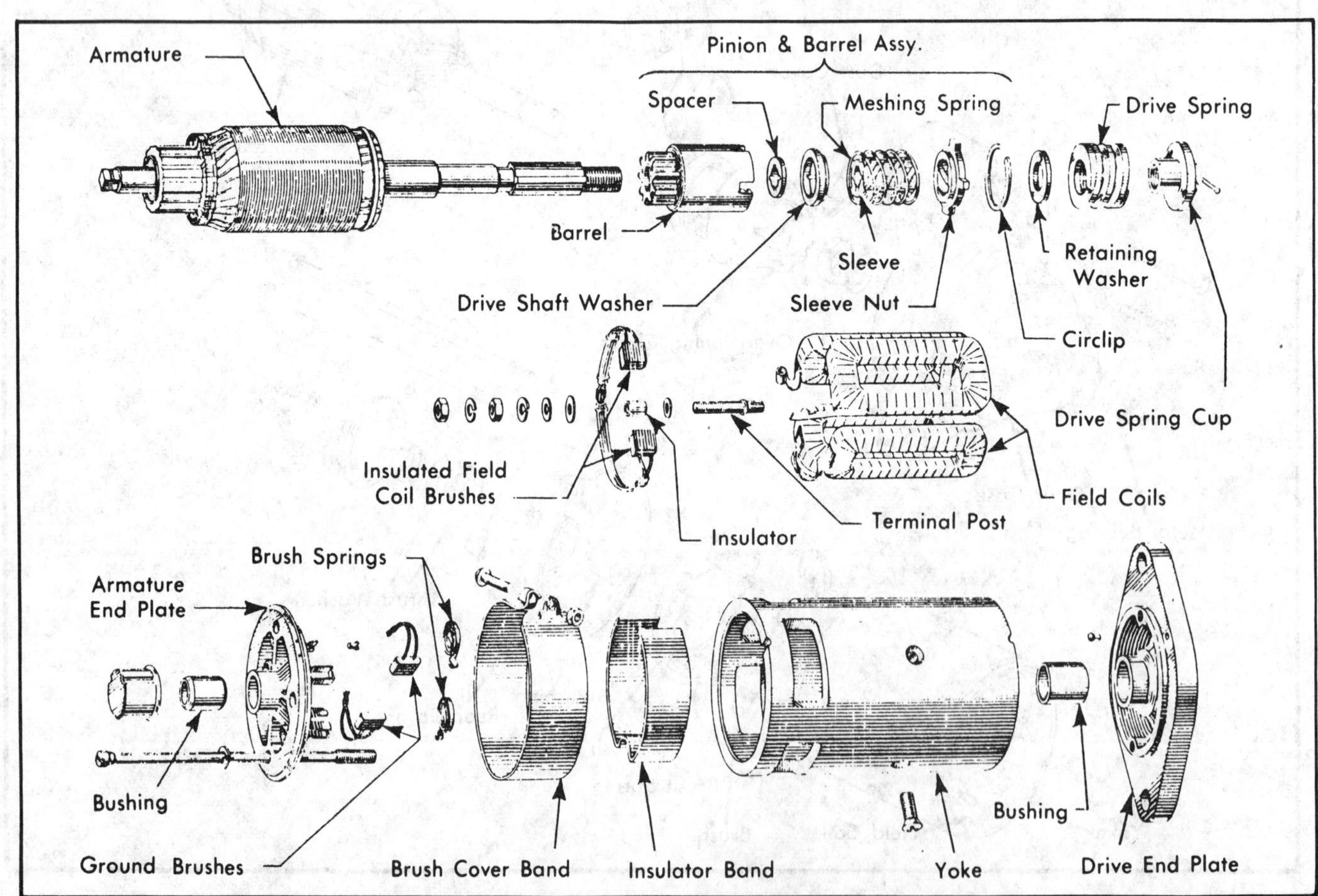

Fig. 1 Exploded View of Lucas Inertia Starter

LUCAS (Cont.)

2) Remove metal band cover, hold back brush springs and remove brushes from their holders. Remove the two through bolts and remove commutator end bracket from yoke.

3) On inertia type starters, remove drive end bracket with armature and drive from yoke. If it is necessary to remove drive end bracket from armature, it can be removed after the drive is dismantled.

4) On all other models, extract rubber seal from drive end bracket. Remove nut securing eccentric pin on which drive engagement lever pivots and remove pin. Separate drive end bracket from armature and intermediate bracket assembly. Remove washer from end of armature shaft extension and slide assembly and engagement lever off shaft. Remove intermediate bracket retaining ring from armature shaft extension and slide bracket and brake assembly off shaft.

PARTS REPLACEMENT & TESTING

Armature – Check armature for open, shorted, or grounded circuits. Check for lifted commutator segments and loose turns in armature winding. A damaged armature must always be replaced and no attempt should be made to machine armature core or to true a distorted shaft. A scored armature may indicate a bent shaft or a loose pole shoe.

Commutator – Clean commutator with a cloth moistened in gasoline and if this is not effective, carefully polish with a strip of fine glass paper while rotating armature. To correct a badly worn commutator, disassemble starter as previously described and remove armature from end bracket. Mount armature in a lathe and rotate at high speed, taking a light cut on commutator with a very sharp tool. Do not remove more metal than is absolutely necessary. **NOTE** – *Insulators, between commutator segments, must not be undercut.*

Brushes & Springs – Check that brushes move freely in holders by holding back brush springs and pulling gently on the flex connectors. If movement is sluggish, remove brush from holder and clean sides with a gasoline moistened cloth. Replace brushes and springs when they have reached minimum specifications in specification table.

Starter Model	Min. Brush Length	Min. Spring Tension
M35J	3/8"	28 ozs.
M45PE	5/16"	30 ozs.
2M100/PE	3/8"	36 ozs.
3M100	5/16"	30 ozs.

Field Coils – Check for open or grounded coils using test lamp or voltmeter and battery, connected in series. If coil is found to be defective, replace all coils as they should not be serviced individually. Mark yoke and pole shoes so shoes may be installed in original position. Remove fiber insulating washers and sleeve from field coil terminal post and remove insulating band from commutator end of yoke. Install a suitable tool (Pole Piece Expander) in starter and expand tool against pole pieces. Remove pole piece screws. Remove field coils and pole pieces from yoke. Carefully unsolder the field coil tappings from terminal post. To install, reverse removal procedure.

Bushings – 1) Armature shaft is supported by three bushings. Commutator and driving end brackets each carry porous bronze bushings, while intermediate bracket carries a graphite-impregnated brass bushing. Bushings which are worn to the extent that they allow excessive side play of the armature must be replaced.

2) The drive end bushing and intermediate bracket bushings can be pressed out. The commutator end bracket bushing is removed by inserting a suitable tap and withdrawing the tap with the bushing attached. New bushings are installed using a shouldered highly polished mandrel of same diameter as shaft to be fitted in the bushing. **CAUTION** – *Do not ream bronze bushings, as the porosity of the bushing may be altered.*

3) Before installing a new porous bronze bushing, it should be immersed in clean engine oil for 24 hours. This process can be speeded up in case of an emergency, by heating oil to 212°F (100°C) and allowing bushing to soak for two hours. Allow oil to cool before removing bushings from oil.

REASSEMBLY

Clean all parts with a clean cloth and reassemble in the reverse order of disassembly while noting the following:

1) To facilitate installing the solenoid unit to drive end plate, ease drive assembly forward along armature shaft.

2) Set pinion movement before tightening the eccentric pivot pin securing nut. After completing reassembly, connect the small center terminal on the solenoid unit by way of a switch to a 12-volt battery. Connect other side of battery to one of the solenoid studs. Close switch (throwing drive assembly forward into the engaged position) and measure the distance between

STARTER PERFORMANCE SPECIFICATIONS

Model	No Load Test		Lock Test		
	Amps.	RPM	Amps.	Volts	Torque
M35J	below 65	8000-10,000	350-375	7.5	over 7 ft.lbs.
M45PE	below 100	5000-7000	below 940	6.5	over 29 ft. lbs.
2M100/PE	below 40	5000-7000	below 463	7.0	over 14.4 ft. lbs.
3M100	below 65	5000-7000	515-545	7.0	over 16.5 ft.lbs.

LUCAS (Cont.)

the pinion and the washer on the armature shaft extension. Make this measurement with the pinion pressed lightly towards armature to take up slack in engagement linkage. Measurement should be .005-.015".

3) To adjust, turn pivot pin until the correct measurement is obtained. The arc of the adjustment is 180° and the arrow on pivot pin should be set between the arrows on the drive end bracket. Tighten pivot pin locking nut.

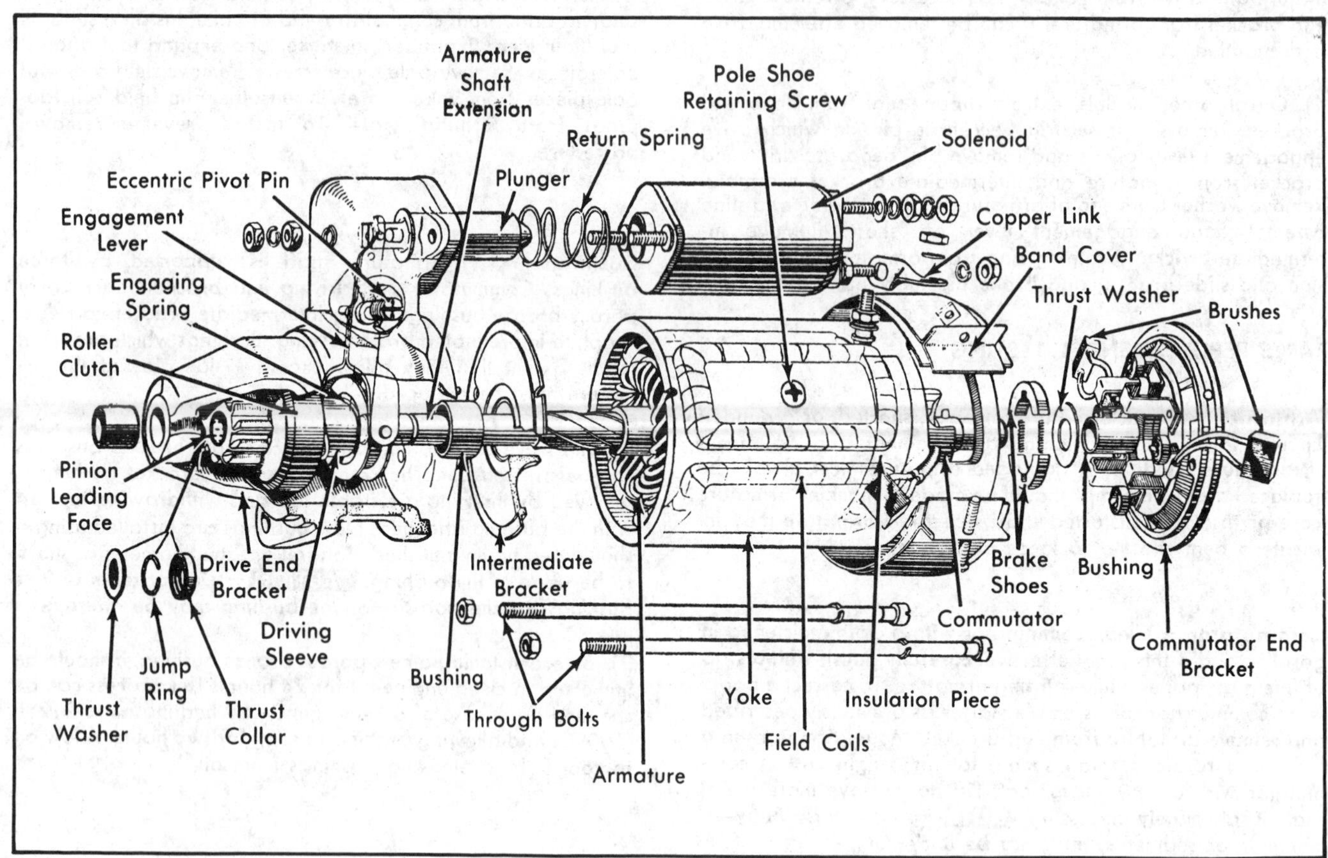

Fig.2 Exploded View of Lucas Pre-Engaged Starter

NIPPONDENSO DIRECT DRIVE

Courier
Subaru
All Models
Toyota

DESCRIPTION

The Nippondenso starter has four pole pieces and four sets of field coils. Four commutator brushes are installed; two are grounded, and two are insulated and are connected to the ends of field coils. Field coil is connected with armature coil through brushes and commutator segments in series. Starter clutch is engaged to armature shaft with helical splines. The turning of the pinion is due to these helical splines which result in a smooth engagement of pinion and flywheel.

APPLICATION

Model	Part No.
Courier	①D77Z
Subaru	
Man. Trans.	2970
Auto. Trans. (Calif.)	4210
Auto. Trans. (Fed.)	4721
Toyota	
2F Engine	60041, 60061
3K-C Engine	24022
20R Engine	
Federal	36050
Calif.	33020

① — Ford part number.

TESTING

PERFORMANCE TESTS

No Load Test — With starter on bench, and using a fully charged 12-volt battery, make connections as shown. The starter should rotate smoothly. See specification chart for RPM, voltage, and current draw.

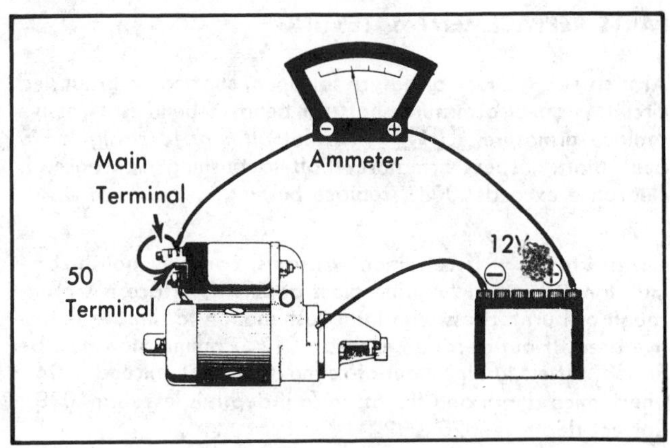

Fig. 1 Circuit for No Load Test

Lock Test — To perform lock test follow instructions and procedures outlined in instruction manual furnished with tester. With starter locked in test stand, and voltage adjusted to specified figure, ammeter reading and starter torque should be within limits (see specifications).

OVERHAUL

DISASSEMBLY

1) Disconnect field coil wire from starter solenoid main terminal and remove the two solenoid attaching bolts. Remove solenoid by moving it up and down to unhook unit from drive lever.

2) Remove bearing cover and pull out armature shaft lock plate, washer, seal and spring.

3) Remove through bolts, commutator end frame, brush holder and yoke.

4) Remove drive lever set bolt, rubber piece, plate, armature and drive lever from housing.

5) Remove pinion stop collar from armature shaft end, and remove starter clutch.

STARTER PERFORMANCE SPECIFICATIONS

Model	No Load Test ①		Lock Test		
	Amps.	RPM	Amps.	Volts	Torque
D77Z	below 50	over 5000	.....	.....	.....
2970	below 50	over 5000	below 600	7.7	over 9.4 ft.lbs.
4210	below 50	over 5000	below 600	7.7	over 9.4 ft.lbs.
4721	below 60	over 5000	below 600	7.0	over 13.0 ft.lbs.
60041	below 50	over 5000	.....	.....	.....
60061	below 50	over 5000	.....	.....	.....
33020	below 50	over 5000	.....	.....	.....
36050	below 50	over 5000	.....	.....	.....

① — At 11 volts on Subaru and Courier; 11.5 volts on Toyota.

NIPPONDENSO DIRECT DRIVE (Cont.)

PARTS REPLACEMENT & TESTING

Armature – Check armature for open, shorted or grounded circuits. Inspect armature shaft for bend; if bend is excessive replace armature. **NOTE** – *Do not attempt to straighten a bent shaft.* Inspect armature shaft to bushing clearance. If clearance exceeds .008", replace bushing.

Commutator – If condition warrants, carefully polish commutator with a strip of fine glass paper. If surface is scored, rough or burnt, dress with lathe just enough to remove defective area. If out-of-round exceeds .012", commutator must be turned. After turning, out-of-round must not exceed .004". Check mica depth and file off mica if depth is less than .008". Correct depth is .020-.032".

Brushes & Springs – 1) Check brush holder insulation. Connect one lead of ammeter to brush holder positive side and other lead to negative side of brush holder. If tester needle moves, the brush holder is shorted due to defective insulator. Replace brush holder.

2) Check brush length and if less than .39" (Toyota 3K-C engines), .51" (Toyota 2F engines) or .47" (all others), replace brushes. Be sure brushes move freely in holders and if movement is sluggish, clean brushes and holders.

3) Check brush spring tension and if less than 21 ozs. replace springs. New brush springs should have a tension of 37-48 ozs.

Starter Solenoid – Test pull-in motion of solenoid by connecting test leads to the "50" terminal and the main "F" terminal. Apply 8 volts. Plunger should be pulled in. If switch does not pull in, it is defective. Disconnect the "F" terminal lead only. If plunger remains pulled in, then switch is satisfactory. Test plunger returning movement by connecting the battery positive lead to the "F" terminal and the negative lead to the switch body. Depress plunger by hand and release it. If plunger returns to its original position with 12 volts, switch is satisfactory.

Field Coils – Check field coils for open circuit using a circuit tester. Connect one test prod to field coil lead and the other prod to soldered portion of brush lead. If meter does not register, field coil is open. Repair or replace as necessary. Check field for ground by connecting one test prod to field coil and other lead to starter housing. If meter registers, coil is

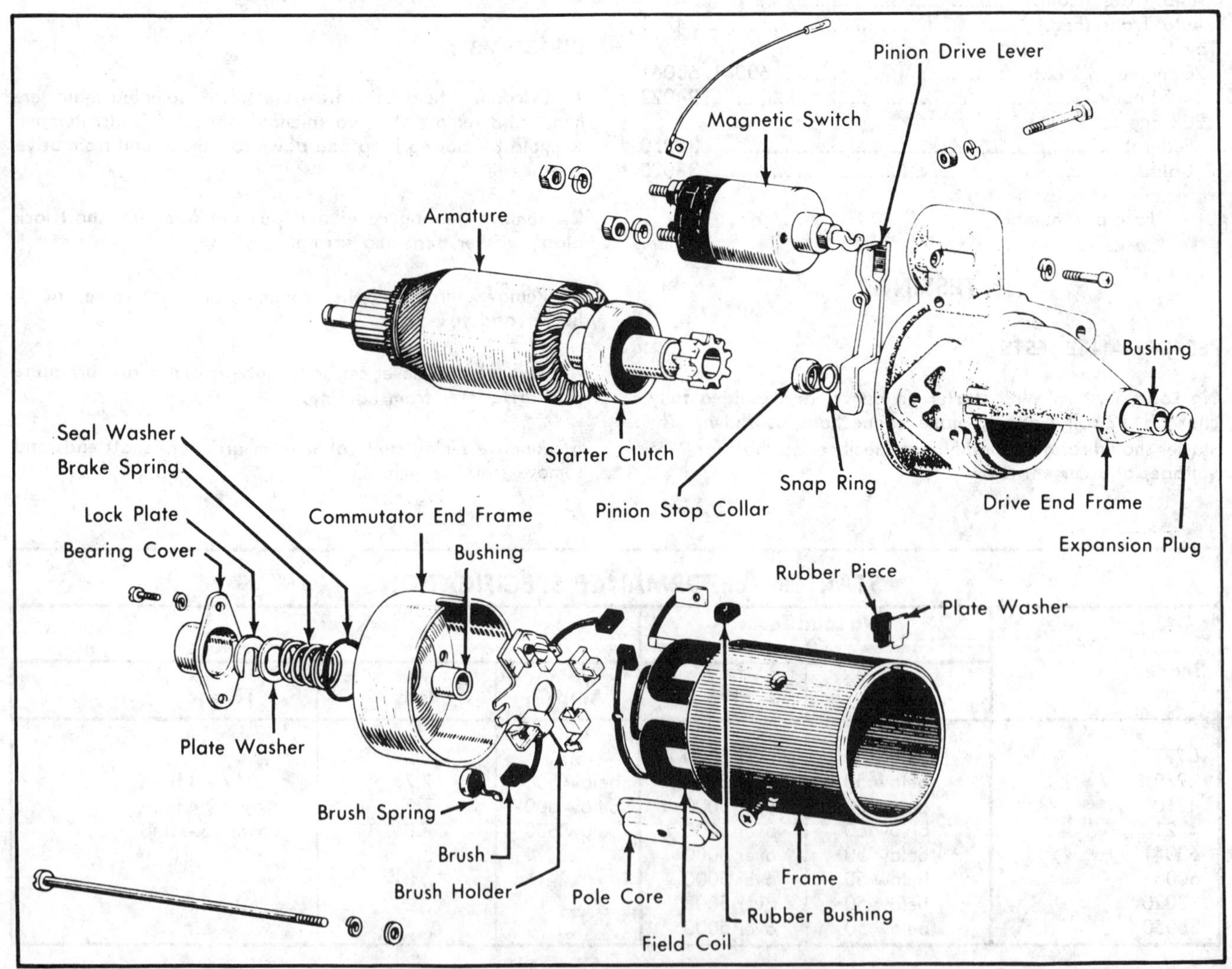

Fig. 2 Disassembled View of Starter Motor

NIPPONDENSO DIRECT DRIVE (Cont.)

grounded. Remove field coil and repair or replace as necessary.

REASSEMBLY

Clean all parts and coat the sliding surface of armature shaft splines, starter clutch bushing, drive lever and moving stud with multipurpose grease. Reassemble in the reverse order of disassembly while noting the following: After completing reassembly, operate starter under a no load condition and check clearance between pinion gear and pinion stop collar. If clearance is not within specifications, adjust length of solenoid plunger shaft. Standard length of shaft is 1.34". To increase clearance, lengthen plunger. To decrease clearance, shorten plunger length.

Pinion Gear Clearance

Application	Clearance
Ford Courier	.080-.160"
Subaru	.004-.160"
Toyota	.040-.160"

NIPPONDENSO REDUCTION GEAR

Honda
CVCC Models
Toyota
2T-C

DESCRIPTION

Starter is a 12 volt, four brush, solenoid actuated, gear reduction type and is equipped with an overrunning clutch. Brushes are held in place by coiled springs of the brush holder located in the switch assembly housing. Starters used on the Toyota 2T-C engines have two ratings, 1 kilowatt and 1.4 kilowatt. Testing and service is the same on all starters.

APPLICATION

Model	Part No.
Honda	
CVCC Engine	31200-657-025
Toyota ①	
2T-C Engine	
1KW Calif.	26062
1KW Fed.	26042
1.4KW	26052

① — Toyota basic part number is 28100.

TESTING

PERFORMANCE TESTS

No Load Tests — With starter motor connected to a 12 volt battery, connect an ammeter in series (*Fig. 1*) with starter. Connect voltmeter in parallel with battery. Compare readings with specifications.

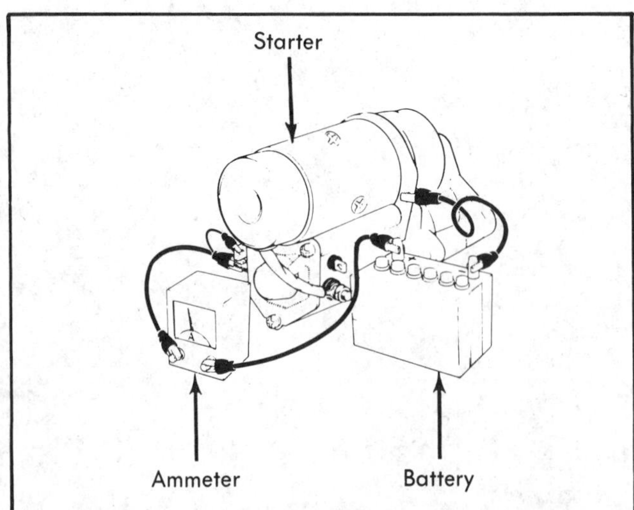

Fig. 1 Ammeter Hook-Up for No Load Test (Toyota Shown)

Cranking Test (Honda Only) — With starter in vehicle, disconnect battery ground cable and connect one ammeter connector to negative battery post and the other ammeter connector to the ground cable. Connect one voltmeter connector to the ground cable and the other connector to the battery positive post. Crank engine and observe readings. Readings should be a maximum of 160 amps at 9.6 volts.

No Load Specifications

Application	RPM	Amps@Voltage
Honda	3000	90 @ 11.5
Toyota		
2T-C		
1KW	3500	90 @ 11.5
1.4KW	4000	90 @ 11.5

OVERHAUL

DISASSEMBLY

1) With starter removed from vehicle, disconnect wire(s) to magnetic switch. Remove bolts and remove field frame with armature from magnetic switch. Remove "O" ring and felt seal.

2) Remove screws and then remove starter gear housing from magnetic switch. Pull out clutch assembly and gears. Remove ball from clutch shaft hole or from magnetic switch. Remove brushes from brush holder then pull armature out of field frame.

PARTS REPLACEMENT & TESTING

Brushes & Springs — Measure brush length and replace if less than specified. Check brush spring tension with suitable spring scale and replace if tension is less than 2.6 lbs. (1.2 kg) or more than 4.3 lbs. (1.96 kg). Check insulation between the plus and minus brush holders, repair or replace if continuity is shown. Check condition of brush holders and spring clip, repair or replace parts as necessary.

Brush Length

Application	In. (mm)
Honda	.394-.571 (10-14.5)
Toyota	.394-.571 (10-14.5)

Commutator — Inspect commutator for roughness, if surface is pitted or grooved, it should be sanded lightly with a no. 500 emery paper. Also check commutator for being out-of-round. If out-of-round is more than .002" (.05 mm), turn commutator in a lathe until out-of-round is less than .002" (.05 mm). Insulating mica should be undercut to a depth of .024-.035" (.6-.9 mm) if it is less than .008" (.2 mm). Wear or cutting limit of commutator is 1.14" (29 mm).

Armature Coil — Check commutator and armature coil core for continuity, if continuity exists, replace armature. Check armature with an armature tester (growler) for shorts, if shorts exist, replace armature. Check for continuity between segments on commutator, if no continuity exists replace armature.

Field Coil — Check field coil for open circuits. There should be continuity between lead wire and field coil brush lead, if not, replace field coil. Check for no continuity between field coil end and end frame, if continuity exists, replace field coil.

Overrunning Clutch Assembly — Inspect gear teeth for wear and damage. Replace gears if damaged. Also, if gears are damaged, check flywheel ring gear. Rotate pinion. Pinion should rotate freely in a clockwise direction and lock up in a counterclockwise direction.

NIPPONDENSO REDUCTION GEAR (Cont.)

Bearings – Turn each bearing by hand, replace bearings if they stick or have a high resistance to turning.

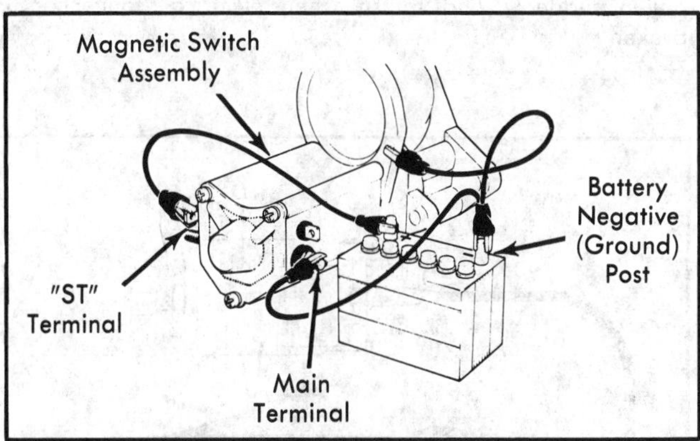

Fig. 2 Magnetic Switch Pull-In Coil Hook-Up

Magnetic Switch Assembly – Connect a 12 volt battery to magnetic switch "ST" terminal, main terminal and ground (*Fig. 2*). Plunger should extend firmly, if not, replace magnetic switch. Next disconnect battery from main terminal. (*Fig. 3*) Plunger should remain extended, if not, replace magnetic switch.

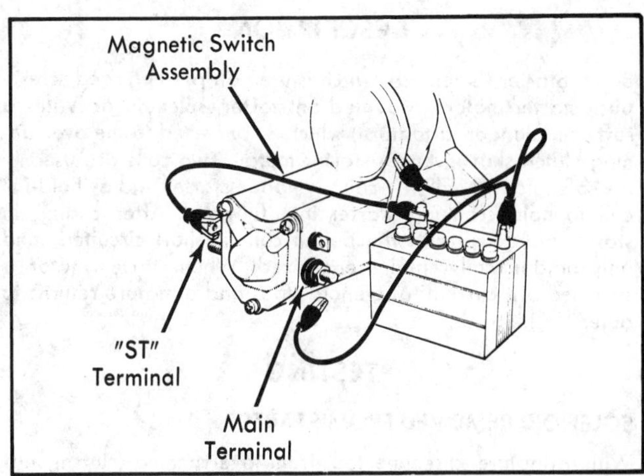

Fig. 3 Magnetic Switch Hold-In Test Hook-Up

REASSEMBLY

To reassembly, reverse disassembly procedure and note the following: Use a high temperature grease on bearings, gears and clutch assembly. **NOTE** – *Apply grease to clutch shaft hole and insert ball.*

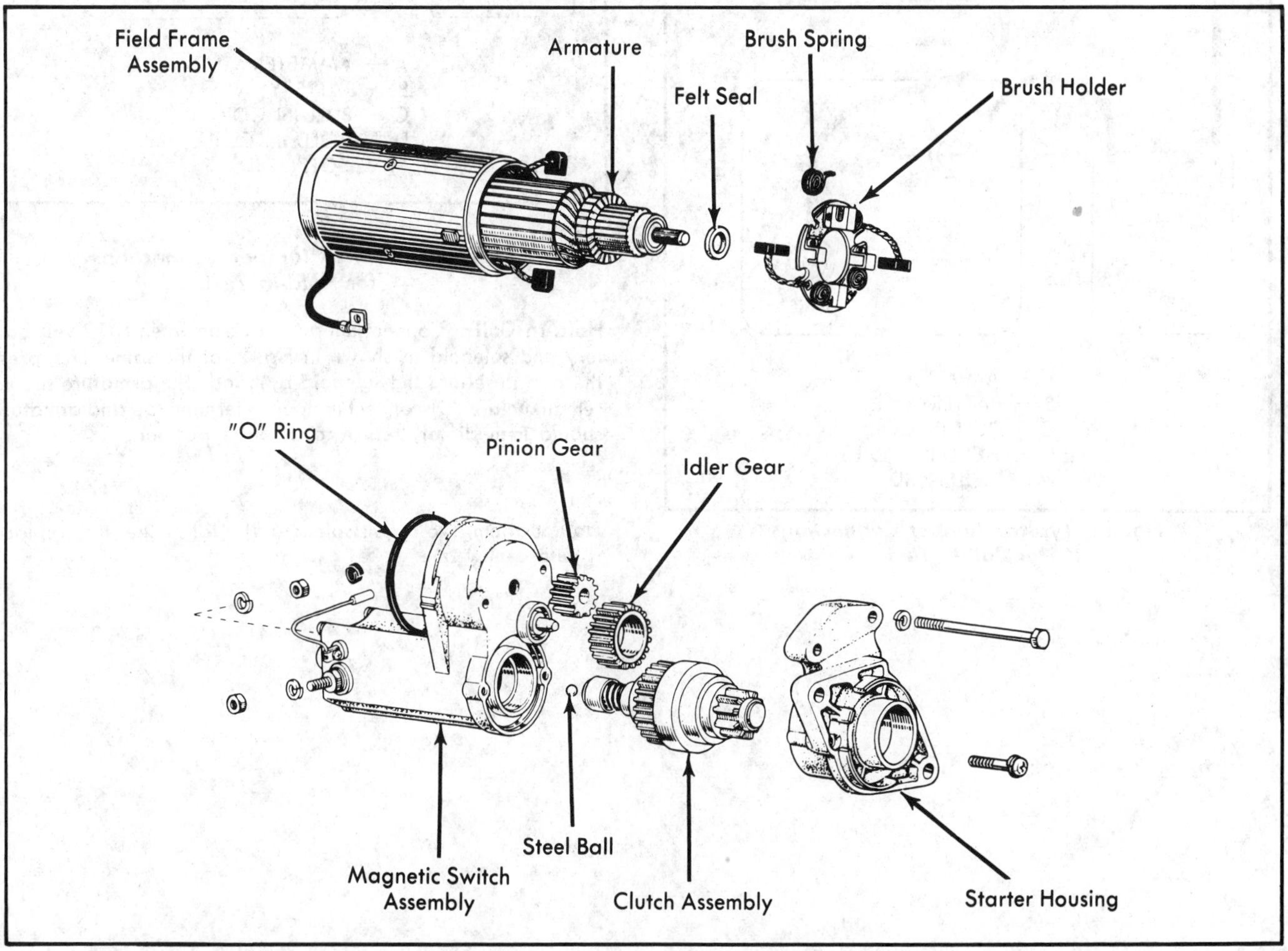

Fig. 4 Exploded View of Nippondenso Reduction Gear Starter

BOSCH

DESCRIPTION

Bosch Starter (Solenoid) switch is used on pre-engaged screw-push starter motors. Mounted on starter, solenoid activates a soft iron plunger (armature) which is connected to the overrunning clutch shift lever, in starter motor. Two coils are used in the solenoid. A "pull-in" coil to engage starter and a "hold-in" coil to hold cranking starter into flywheel. After cutting in starter motor current, the pull-in coil is short circuited, and only hold-in coil remains energized. When starter motor is switched off, current to solenoid stops and armature returns to outer position.

TESTING

SOLENOID REMOVED FROM STARTER

With armature disconnected from overrunning clutch shift lever, armature must move freely in and out of solenoid. If corroded, clean thoroughly before proceeding with tests.

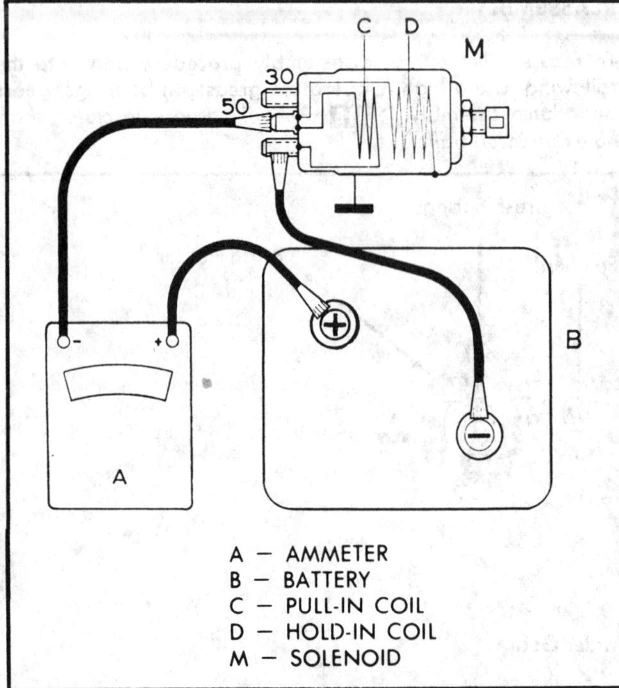

Fig. 1 Typical Jumper Connections for Pull-In Test

Pull-In Coil — Connect jumper wires between a 12 volt battery and the solenoid as shown in *Fig. 1*. The armature should pull-in suddenly and return when electrical connection is broken

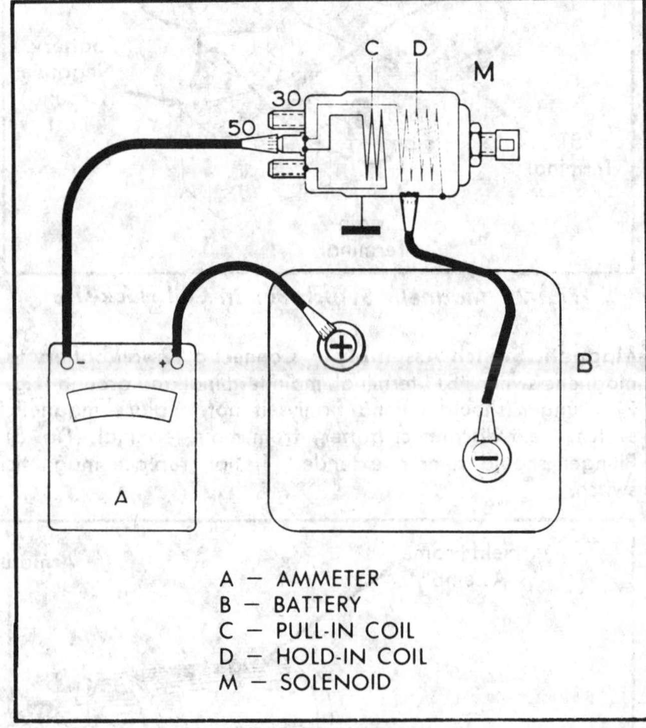

Fig. 2 Typical Jumper Connections for Hold-In Test

Hold-In Coil — Connect jumper wires between a 12 volt battery and solenoid as shown in *Fig. 2*, at the same time, press the armature into the solenoid by hand. The armature should remain held-in. Disconnect jumper to terminal 50 and armature should immediately return to its outer position.

Do not attempt to repair solenoid. If it fails either test, replace it with a new one.

HITACHI & MITSUBISHI

DESCRIPTION

The starter solenoid is mounted directly to the starter yoke (gear case). Current flows through "Series" (Pull-in) and "Shunt" (Hold-in) coils to excite the solenoid. A plunger, inside the solenoid is pulled into the solenoid, in turn pulling the shift lever that engages the starter pinion gear with the engine flywheel ring gear. When the contacts of the solenoid close, the starter cranks the engine and the pull-in coil is cut out. The magnetic force of the hold-in coil holds the plunger in until the engine starts. When the ignition is switched from START to ON, the starting current is broken and the pull-in coil demagnitizes the hold-in coil and the plunger returns to its original position.

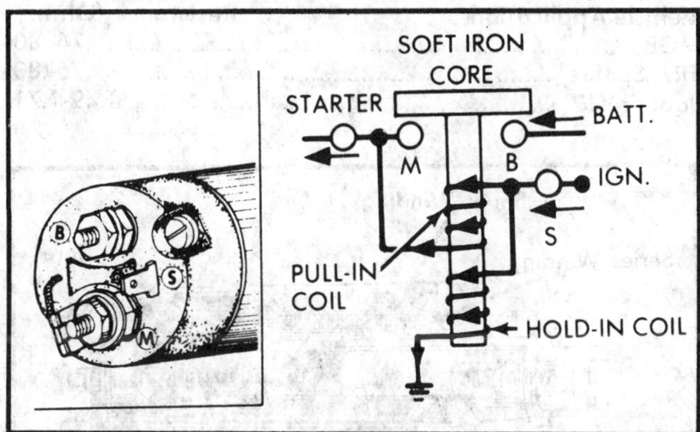

Fig. 1 Starting Circuit Diagram and Solenoid Terminals

TESTING

Clean solenoid plunger and sleeve with fine sand paper and alcohol and blow off with air before performing tests.

NOTE – *Make tests with solenoid removed from starter, or remove starter to solenoid lead before testing.*

Pull-in Coil Test – Using a 12 volt battery, connect a jumper wire between the negative battery post and the "S" terminal. Connect a second jumper to the positive battery post, and just touch the "M" (MT) terminal. Plunger should pull-in immediately.

Hold-in Coil Test – Connect a ground lead between the "M" (MT) terminal and the solenoid case. Apply 8 volts to the "S" terminal, this will pull-in the plunger. Disconnect lead to "M" (MT) terminal and the plunger should remain held in.

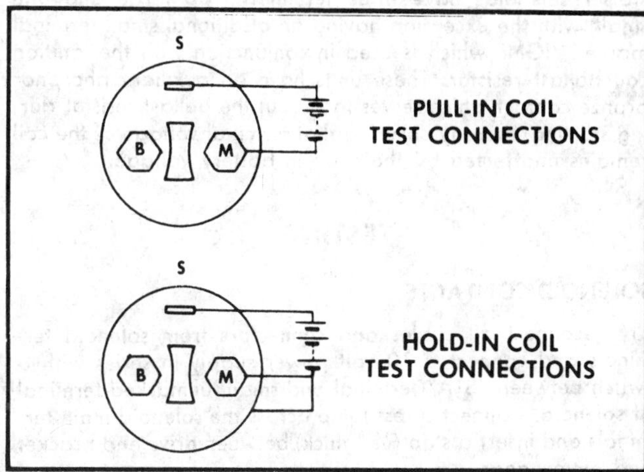

Fig. 2 Test connections for Pull-In Coil and Hold-In Coil

Return Test – Push plunger into solenoid by hand. Apply 12 volts between the "M" (MT) terminal and the solenoid case. If solenoid case is short circuited the plunger will be attracted. If nothing happens, the solenoid is satisfactory.

Pinion Gear Clearance – The clearance between the pinion gear and stop collar should be .012-.059" (.305-1.52 mm) on Hitachi and .02-.08" (.51-2.03 mm) on Mitsubishi. This is adjusted by placing shims between solenoid and starter yoke.

LUCAS

DESCRIPTION

Starter solenoids are electro-magnetic actuators mounted externally on the yokes of pre-engaged starting motors. These solenoids contain a soft iron plunger (linked to engaging lever), starter switch contacts and a coil with two windings (a heavy gauge pull-in winding and lighter gauge hold-in winding). Initially, both windings are energized in parallel when starter device is operated, but the pull-in winding is shorted out by the starter switch contacts at the instant of closure. Solenoids described here are sealed in a rolled steel outer case or body and cannot be disassembled. Most ground return starter solenoids have three terminals (two large and one small) with the exception having an additional small terminal marked "IGN" which is used in conjunction with the ignition coil ballast resistor. These units have an auxiliary phosphor bronze contact which serves to cut out the ballast resistor during starting, thereby ensuring that terminal voltage of the coil remains unaffected by the drop in battery voltage.

TESTING

SOLENOID CONTACTS

1) Disconnect all cables and connectors from solenoid terminals and connect a 10 volt power supply in series with a switch between "STA" terminal and small, unmarked terminal of solenoid. Connect a test lamp across the solenoid main terminals and insert a stop (⅛" thick) between drive end bracket and pinion gear.

2) Close switch to energize series windings and test lamp should light, indicating contacts are closed. Open switch and remove pinion stop. Close switch and hold pinion gear in engaged position. Open switch and light should go out indicating that contacts have opened.

WINDING CONTINUITY

Connect ohmmeter between "STA" terminal and a good ground on solenoid body. A reading of 1.01-1.07 ohms should be obtained. If reading is not to specifications, replace solenoid.

PULL-IN WINDING

Connect ohmmeter between small unmarked terminal of solenoid and "STA" terminal. If resistance is not within specifications, closing (series) winding are bad, replace solenoid.

Vehicle Application	Resistance (Ohms)
MGB	.25-.27
TR7, Spitfire	.25-.27
Jaguar V12	.36-.42

HOLD-ON WINDING

Connect ohmmeter between small unmarked terminal of solenoid and a good ground on solenoid body. If resistance is not within specifications, hold-on (shunt) windings are bad, replace solenoid.

Vehicle Application	Resistance (Ohms)
MGB	.76-.80
TR7, Spitfire	.76-.80
Jaguar V12	1.49-1.71

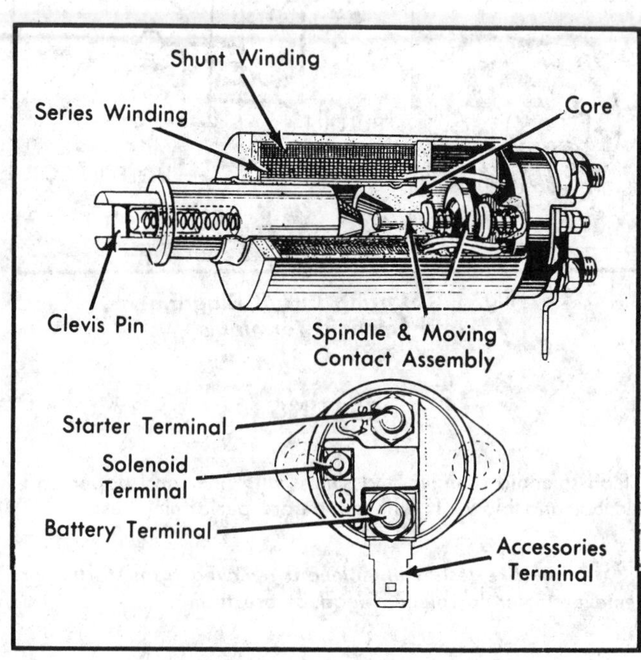

Fig. 1 Lucas Starter Solenoid

NIPPONDENSO

DESCRIPTION

The starter solenoid is an electromagnetic switch, activating a plunger by means of a "pull-in" coil and a "hold-in" coil. The plunger is pulled in, which engages the starter, and then is held in, while the engine starts. When the hold-in coil is activated the pull-in coil is short circuited and only the hold-in coil remains effective. When the current flow to the starter is stopped, the hold-in force is lost and the plunger returns to its rest position.

TESTING

All tests should be performed with the starter assembled and the "M" (field) lead from the starter disconnected at the solenoid.

NOTE — *If plunger and or sleeve are corroded, clean with fine sand paper and alcohol, and blow out with air before performing tests.*

Pull-In Test — Apply 8 volts momentarily between the "S" terminal and the "M" terminal of the solenoid. If the plunger is pulled in strongly the pull-in coil is satisfactory.

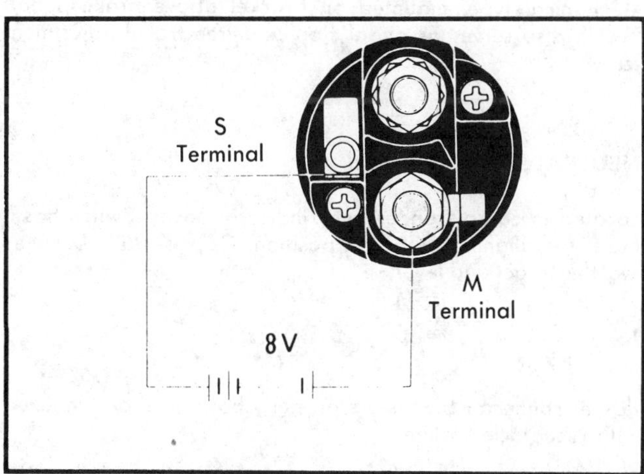

Fig. 1 Test Connections for Pull-In Coil

Hold-In Test — Connect leads from an 8 volt source onto the solenoid case and to the "M" terminal. Connect a jumper wire between "M" terminal and the "S" terminal. This will pull-in the plunger. Disconnect the jumper wire from the "M" terminal and if the plunger remains held in, the hold-in coil is satisfactory.

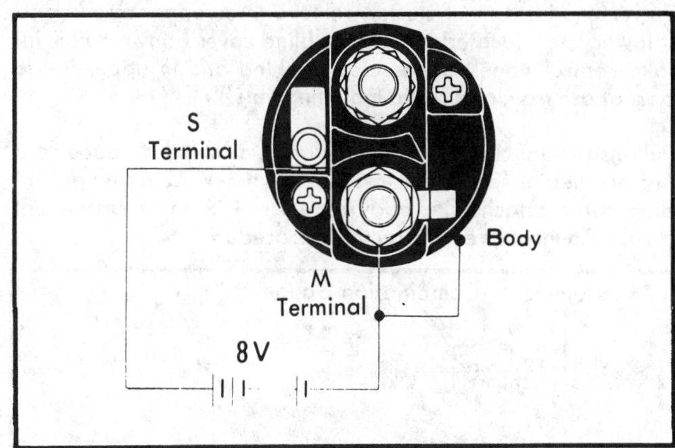

Fig. 2 Test Connections for Hold-In Coil

Plunger Return Test — Apply 12 volts between "M" terminal and solenoid case. Pull out starter pinion gear with fingers until it stops. If plunger returns to original position when pinion is released, solenoid is satisfactory.

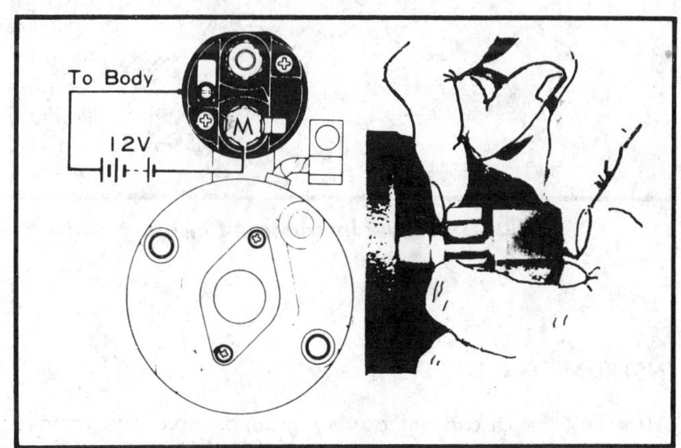

Fig. 3 Test Connections for Plunger Return

Solenoid Resistance Values

Pull-In Coil — About 0.4 ohms
Hold-In Coil — About 1.1 ohms

ARROW

INSTRUMENT CLUSTERS

To remove instrument cluster, remove three upper screws and a lower screw located behind the blind cover above the air intake control panel, three screws behind and in upper inside part of ash tray, and radio mounting nuts.

Pull instrument cluster a small distance, disconnect gauge connectors, heater fan connectors, speedometer cable and grounding cable attached to body by a screw. Remove instrument cluster. To install, reverse removal procedure.

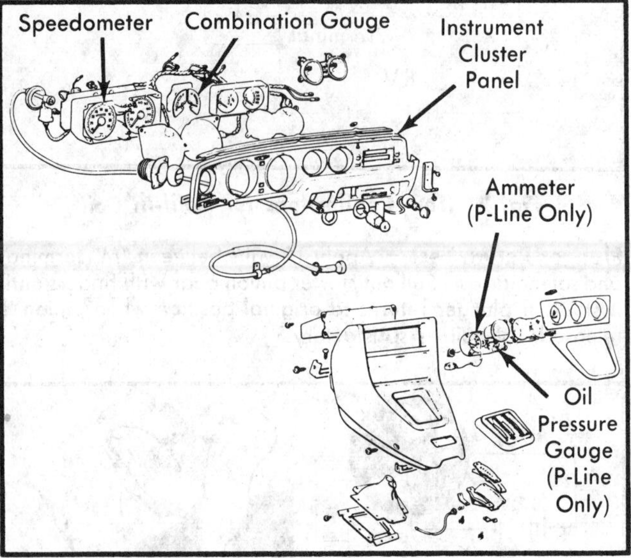

Fig. 1 Arrow Instrument Cluster

SPEEDOMETER & GAUGE

After removing instrument panel, remove bezel and lens. Loosen attaching screws and remove speedometer and combination gauge.

HAZARD WARNING & TURN SIGNAL FLASHER

Located at lower center of instrument panel. A separate flasher unit is used for hazard warning and turn signals.

IGNITION SWITCH

To replace ignition switch, remove column cover and pull out switch assembly.

STOP LIGHT SWITCH

Mechanical type, mounted on bracket above brake pedal. Switch also serves as pedal stop and free travel adjustment screw.

NEUTRAL SAFETY SWITCH

Located in console under gear indicator cover. Switch has a mark for aligning with "N" position. Gap is .059" between switch contact and lever.

AUDI

INSTRUMENT CLUSTER

Audi Fox — Disconnect battery ground cable and remove lower instrument panel trim. Disconnect speedometer shaft at speedometer and multiple plug at back of cluster. Disconnect left and right mounting springs using suitable long nose pliers. Remove cluster by pulling it forward.

Audi 100 — After removing battery ground cable, proceed as follows:

1) Remove instrument panel padding. Remove two hex nuts from cluster cover and remove cover, washers and foam rubber strips.

2) Pull instrument cluster assembly straight out. Disconnect multiple plug and (if equipped) tachometer cable. Disconnect speedometer cable and remove cluster.

SPEEDOMETER, CLOCK & GAUGES

Speedometer, clock and all gauges may be removed after first removing instrument cluster from panel.

HAZARD WARNING & TURN SIGNAL FLASHER

Single, plug-in type unit mounted on fuse block. Plug-in connectors can be installed in only one position. Be sure that flasher connector blades are properly positioned and indexed with receptacle sockets.

IGNITION SWITCH

Audi Fox — Disconnect battery ground cable and remove steering wheel, switch holder cap and upper and lower instrument panel trim. Proceed as follows:

1) A punch mark is on the steering lock housing in the area of the lock cylinder guide. Drill carefully through the housing at this location with a number 31 (3 mm) drill. Guide a punch into this hole and press in lock cylinder spring. Pry out lock cylinder with a screwdriver. **NOTE** — *Steering wheel lock pin must not be engaged in jaws of steering column when removing cylinder.*

2) If the ignition key is not available and lock pin is engaged, drill off the shear screw heads. When installing lock cylinder, make sure that projection on lock cylinder is seated in groove of ignition lock housing so that spring will engage.

Audi 100 — Disconnect battery ground cable and proceed as follows:

1) Remove steering wheel and steering wheel trim. Unscrew combination switch.

AUDI (Cont.)

2) Center punch shear screws that hold ignition switch clamp together and drill through screws with a number 31 (3 mm) drill.

3) Insert proper size screw extractor into drilled holes and remove shear screws and lower portion of switch clamp. Remove switch and lock from steering column. To install, reverse removal procedure, using new shear screws.

STOP LIGHT SWITCH

Switch is hydraulically operated by brake fluid pressure and is attached to end of brake master cylinder.

BMW

INSTRUMENT CLUSTER

320i – Remove steering wheel. Detach lower center instrument panel trim and disconnect speedometer cable. Unscrew knurled nut at base of instrument cluster and pull out instrument cluster. Disconnect wiring at connector.

530i – Remove center, lower instrument panel trim and disconnect speedometer cable. Loosen knurled nut above steering column and upper steering column screws. Pull out cluster and disconnect all wiring.

630CSi – Disconnect negative (–) battery cable and remove steering wheel. Detach lower center instrument panel trim and remove mask from inquiry unit. Detach printed circuit board leaving wiring attached. Remove light and fog light switch, and disconnect wiring at back of switch. Remove left air control knob and cover. Loosen screws on instrument cluster, steering wheel control base and disconnect speedometer cable. Press down on instrument cluster upper section and steering column far enough to allow removal of instrument cluster at an angle.

SPEEDOMETER & GAUGES

Speedometer and all guages may be removed after first removing instrument cluster.

IGNITION SWITCH

Disconnect battery ground cable. Remove lower steering column trim panel and lower center section of instrument panel trim. Turn ignition switch to "Halt" position and remove screws from steering lock holder. Note wiring position and disconnect wiring. To install, reverse removal procedure.

STOP LIGHT SWITCH

Mechanical type mounted on brake pedal bracket. Adjust switch so that specified amount of contact button is visible.

Application	Plunger Length
320i,530i & 630CSi	.20-.24" (5-6 mm)

CAPRI

INSTRUMENT CLUSTER

1) Disconnect battery ground cable and remove lower steering column shroud. Release clip securing upper steering column shroud. Remove ashtray.

2) Remove hazard flasher switch and disconnect wiring. Remove turn signal switch and allow it to hang on wiring. Remove screws securing lower dash trim panel and pull trim panel forward and down. Disconnect wiring to clock and cigarette lighter and remove trim panel.

3) Pull off instrument panel light control knob. Remove lower screws securing instrument cluster, pull cluster downward and disconnect seat belt warning light wiring and oil pressure line union. Remove screws securing cluster to panel and disconnect speedometer cable and wiring. Remove cluster.

SPEEDOMETER & GAUGES

Speedometer and all gauges may be removed after first removing instrument cluster.

HAZARD WARNING & TURN SIGNAL FLASHER

Disconnect battery ground cable and pull instrument cluster from panel to gain access to flasher. Remove flasher and wiring.

IGNITION SWITCH

Remove upper and lower steering column shrouds and disconnect wiring from ignition switch. Ensure that switch is in "0" position and remove screws securing switch to lock and remove switch. Remove screws securing left and right lower dash trim panels and lower panels. Move turn signal switch out of way and disconnect wiring from ignition switch. Remove screws holding steering column to dash and turn column to gain access to headless bolts. Remove lock from steering column by drilling out headless bolts or removing bolts with screw extractor.

STOP LIGHT SWITCH

Mechanical type mounted on bracket at brake pedal lever.

CAPRI II (Cont.)

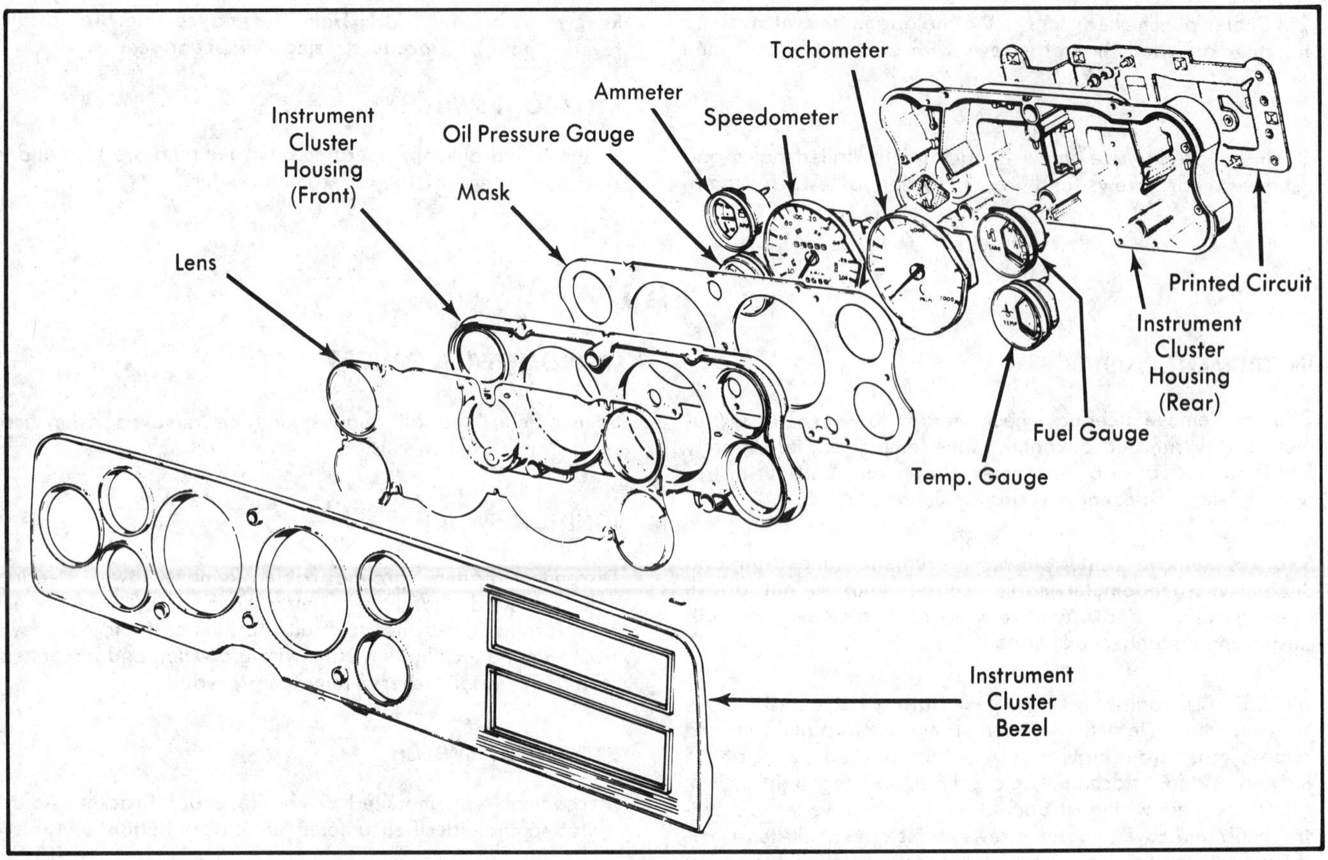

Tachometer
Ammeter
Speedometer
Instrument Cluster Housing (Front)
Oil Pressure Gauge
Mask
Lens
Printed Circuit
Instrument Cluster Housing (Rear)
Fuel Gauge
Temp. Gauge
Instrument Cluster Bezel

Fig. 2 Capri II Instrument Cluster

COLT

INSTRUMENT CLUSTER

To remove instrument cluster, loosen three screws at upper part and two screws at lower part of instrument cluster. Loosen screws holding heater knob, ash tray and cigarette lighter. Remove blind cover on right side of glove box and remove attaching screws on side of cluster. Remove harness cover and disconnect headlight switch.

Pull the instrument cluster panel forward, disconnect multiple connector, radio connections, heater fan and gauge connectors. Remove instrument cluster assembly.

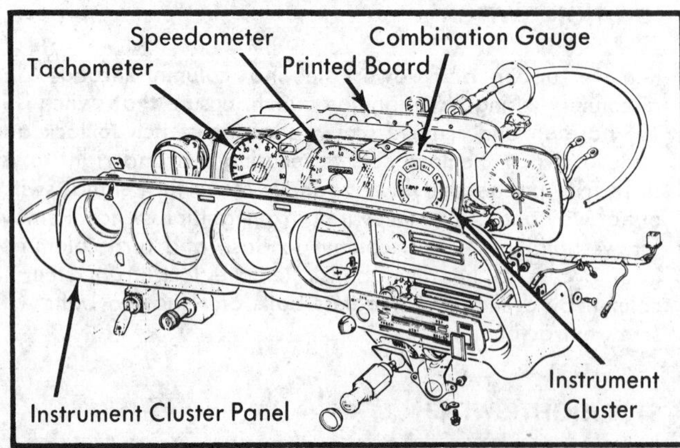

Fig. 3 Colt Instrument Cluster

SPEEDOMETER & GAUGES

Speedometer and all gauges may be removed after first removing instrument cluster.

HAZARD WARNING & TURN SIGNAL FLASHER

Located at lower center of instrument panel. A separate flasher is used for hazard warning and turn signals.

IGNITION SWITCH

To replace ignition switch, remove column cover and pull out switch assembly.

STOP LIGHT SWITCH

Mechanical type, mounted on brace above brake pedal. Switch also serves as a brake pedal free travel adjustment screw.

NEUTRAL SAFETY SWITCH

Located in console under gear indicator cover. Switch has a mark for aligning with "N" position. Gap is .059" between switch contact and lever.

COURIER

INSTRUMENT CLUSTER

Disconnect battery ground cable. Remove four screws securing cluster to instrument panel. Pull cluster out sufficiently to gain access and disconnect speedometer cable and wiring. Remove cluster from vehicle.

SPEEDOMETER & GAUGES

Speedometer and all gauges may be removed after first removing instrument cluster.

HAZARD WARNING FLASHER

Flasher is located to the left of the steering column beneath instrument panel.

TURN SIGNAL FLASHER

Flasher is located to the right of the steering column beneath instrument panel.

IGNITION SWITCH

Disconnect battery ground cable. Reach behind instrument panel and disconnect wiring from switch. While holding switch from back, remove black retaining nut and remove switch.

STOP LIGHT SWITCH

Mechanical type mounted on bracket at top of brake pedal.

DATSUN

INSTRUMENT CLUSTER

200SX – 1) Disconnect battery ground cable. Remove steering wheel and shell cover. Remove all knobs and nuts.

2) Remove upper and lower screws from instrument cluster. Pull cluster forward and disconnect wiring connectors, speedometer cable and remove rear window defogger switch. Remove instrument cluster.

B210 – 1) Disconnect battery ground cable and remove shell covers. **NOTE** – *To facilitate removal of cluster, remove steering wheel and turn signal switch.* Pull out ashtray and remove ashtray cover. Remove switch knobs and retaining rings.

2) Remove radio knobs and retaining knobs, if equipped. Remove nine screws securing cluster cover to dash (four on upper side, three under cover, one at ash tray outer case and one in glove box). Pull cluster cover out slightly and disconnect wiring. Remove cluster cover.

3) Remove four instrument cluster retaining screws and pull cluster out slightly. Disconnect wiring and speedometer cable. Remove instrument cluster assembly.

F-10 – Disconnect battery, speedometer cable and remove ash tray. Disconnect heater control cables and all wire harness connectors.

NOTE – *Tag wires for correct installation.*

Remove steering column bracket bolts, loosen instrument panel upper attaching screws, remove side panel bolts and bolts attaching instrument panel to pedal bracket. Draw instrument panel out backwards. To install, reverse removal procedure.

610 – Remove steering column shrouds and cluster cover. Remove two retaining screws and pull cluster cover forward, disconnect all wiring and speedometer cable. Remove cluster cover from panel. Remove odometer knob, if equipped, remove attaching screws and instrument cluster.

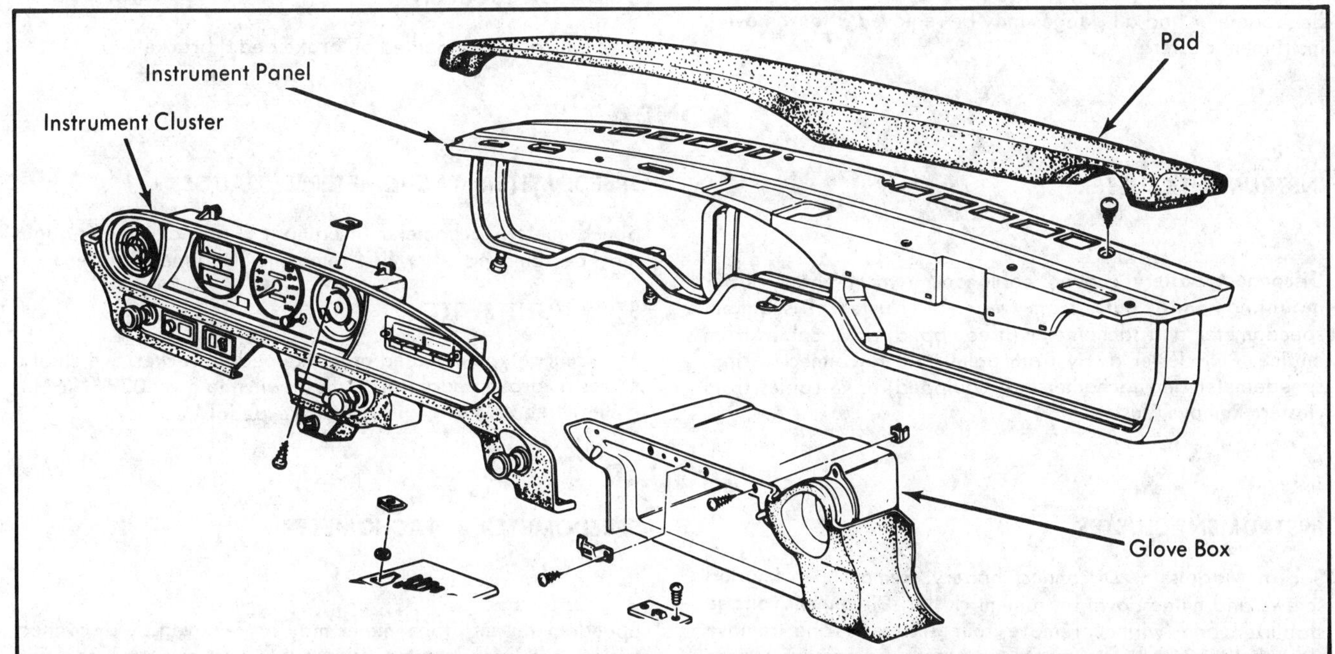

Fig. 4 Typical Datsun Instrument Cluster (Model 710 Shown)

DATSUN (Cont.)

620 Pickup — Disconnect battery ground cable. Remove screws securing cluster to instrument panel and from under panel remove screw securing cluster to dash. Withdraw cluster slightly, then from behind cluster disconnect speedometer cable and wiring. Remove screws securing cluster cover to cluster and remove cluster assembly.

710 — **1)** Disconnect battery and remove steering column shrouds. **NOTE** — *To facilitate removal of cluster, remove steering wheel and turn signal switch.* Remove wiper switch and light control switch knob and retaining rings, two retaining screws and remove lower center cover.

2) Remove ashtray and disconnect wiring to cluster. Remove ten screws from cluster cover (five on upper edge, three below cover, one on ashtray cover and one under lower center cover). Disconnect speedometer cable and fibre optics and remove cluster cover. Remove odometer knob and six screws securing cluster. Remove instrument cluster.

810 — **1)** Disconnect battery ground cable. Remove knobs and nuts on radio switch and choke control wire. Remove ash tray.

2) Remove screws and shell covers from steering column. Disconnect main harness connectors, screws retaining cluster and remove instrument cluster.

280Z — **1)** Disconnect battery. Remove steering wheel and screws securing garnish to panel. Remove garnish. Remove screws securing upper instrument to cowl top panel, finisher to instrument and detach finisher. Remove floor console, air control screws, floor tunnel screws, side ventilator control bracket screws and screws from each side of lower instrumsnt panel.

2) Disconnect speedometer cable and instrument harness as follows:

- Junction Block
- Combination Switch
- Ignition Switch
- Stop Light Switch
- Flasher Units
- Door Switch

To install, reverse removal procedure.

SPEEDOMETER & GAUGES

All Exc. 280Z Models — Speedometer and all gauges may be removed after removing instrument cluster.

280Z Models — Speedometer, tachometer and all gauges are removed individually from instrument panel. All units are secured at back with wing nuts. To remove center gauges, first remove center console trim.

IGNITION SWITCH

All Models — Remove steering column shrouds and disconnect wiring. Remove switch retainer screw at bottom of lock and remove switch. To remove lock assembly, drill out shear bolts and remove assembly.

FIAT

INSTRUMENT CLUSTER

Disconnect battery. Remove five screws holding cluster to panel, slide cluster forward and disconnect electrical connectors and speedometer cable. Remove instrument cluster.

SPEEDOMETER & GAUGES

Speedometer and all gauges may be removed after removing instrument cluster.

IGNITION SWITCH

Ignition switch is keyed and has four positions. Key can be removed with engine running. Key can also be fitted with an anti-theft device which locks the steering shaft.

STOP LIGHT SWITCH

Mechanical type mounted on brake pedal bracket.

HONDA

INSTRUMENT CLUSTER

Disconnect battery ground cable and remove three cluster mounting wing nuts from rear of cluster. Disconnect speedometer and tachometer (if equipped) drive cables from engine. Pull cluster away from panel and disconnect wiring, speedometer and tachometer (if equipped) drive cables from cluster. Remove cluster.

SPEEDOMETER, TACHOMETER & GAUGES

Speedometer, tachometer (if equipped) and all other gauges may be removed after first removing instrument cluster.

STOP LIGHT SWITCH

Mechanical type mounted on brake pedal bracket. Switch also serves as brake pedal stop. Adjust switch to give .039-.196" (1-5 mm) freeplay at center of brake pedal.

JAGUAR

INSTRUMENT CLUSTER

Sedan Models — Disconnect battery. Remove two knurled screws and hinge down instrument cluster. Disconnect voltage stabilizer and wiring, remove four setscrews and remove cluster. Individual instruments may now be removed from cluster.

SPEEDOMETER & TACHOMETER

Speedometer and tachometer may be removed by disconnect wiring and speedometer drive cable and releasing securing clamps.

JAGUAR (Cont.)

HAZARD WARNING & TURN SIGNAL FLASHERS

Two separate flashers are used and are located under center of instrument panel.

IGNITION SWITCH

Disconnect battery and remove steering wheel. Remove switch cover and steering column covers. Remove dash casing and disconnect switch wiring. Remove upper steering column. Withdraw retaining screw from switch body and remove switch unit. Remove shear bolt using a suitable tool. To install, reverse removal procedure and use new shear bolts.

STOP LIGHT SWITCH

Mechanical type mounted on brake pedal bracket.

LANCIA

INSTRUMENT CLUSTER

Disconnect battery positive cable and speedometer drive cable from the gear box differential unit. Remove all knurled knobs and screws securing instrument cluster to the dashboard. Lower steering wheel and remove instrument cluster. To install, reverse removal procedure.

SPEEDOMETER & GAUGES

Remove ring nuts and extract trip distance recorder knob with cable and instrument light switch. Release the plastic retainers and remove the rim from the instrument cluster. Remove desired instrument. To install, reverse removal procedure.

IGNITION SWITCH

Remove lower steering column casing and loosen upper casing. Disconnect multiple connectors. Remove bolt securing ignition switch to anti-theft locking device, insert ignition key and turn to "GAR" position and remove key. Depress locking spring pin and remove ignition switch complete with cables. To install, reverse removal procedure.

STOP LIGHT SWITCH

Mechanical type mounted on brake pedal bracket.

LUV

INSTRUMENT CLUSTER

To remove the instrument cluster, it is necessary to first detach and remove the speedometer cable and position it out of way. Now, remove the wing nuts from the rear of the instrument cluster, to free the cluster assembly, and pull cluster only part way out. Then, disconnect all necessary wiring. Remove instrument cluster assembly from panel.

SPEEDOMETER & GAUGES

Speedometer and all gauges may be removed after first removing instrument cluster.

STOP LIGHT SWITCH

Stop light switch is mechanical type mounted on brake pedal bracket and requires .079 to .110" free travel.

MAZDA

INSTRUMENT CLUSTER

All (Exc. P/U) – Disconnect battery. Remove steering wheel, steering column cover and combination cover. Remove choke assembly, radio knobs and attaching nuts; screws attaching center panel and remove center panel. Disconnect wiring connectors from combination meter and speedometer cable. Remove nuts holding instrument cluster and remove cluster. To install, reverse removal procedures.

SPEEDOMETER & GAUGES

Speedometer and all gauges can be removed when cluster is removed.

IGNITION SWITCH

Remove steering wheel and steering column cover. Remove the combination switch and disconnect wiring connector. Remove screw attaching the contact housing to the steering lock body and remove ignition switch contact housing. To install, reverse removal procedure.

STOP LIGHT SWITCH

Mechanical type mounted on brake pedal bracket and is used for pedal adjustment. Adjust for free pedal travel of .280 to .350" (7.0 to 9.0 mm)

MERCEDES-BENZ

INSTRUMENT CLUSTER

Instrument cluster is held in a recess by a rubber section. Remove instrument plate glass, prying out and lifting up, using a non-metalic device to prevent damage to the glass.

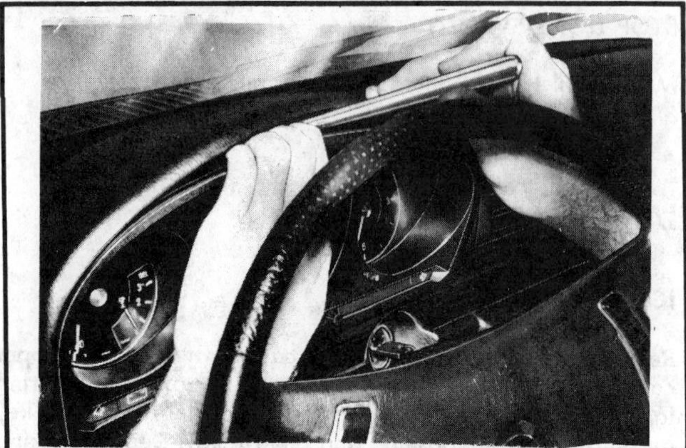

Fig. 5 Instrument Cluster Removal

Remove the speedometer shaft from the cable strap under the left floormat. Pull instrument cluster out, loosen speedometer shaft, electrical connections and oil pressure line. Remove the instrument cluster sideways and to the right. To install, reverse removal procedure.

SPEEDOMETER & GAUGES

Speedometer and all gauges can easily be removed after removing instrument cluster.

STOPLIGHT SWITCH

Mechanical type mounted on brake pedal bracket and is used for pedal adjustment. Switch contact button should extend for .236 to .315" (6 to 8 mm) from housing and free pedal travel should be .590 to .798" (15 to 20 mm).

MG

SPEEDOMETER

MG Midget — 1) Disconnect battery and speedometer cable from the speedometer. Remove center console retaining screws and move console back and aside toward the steering column.

2) Remove two knurled retaining nuts from behind speedometer and the knurled nut retaining the trip remote control in its bracket. Pull speedometer forward from dash.

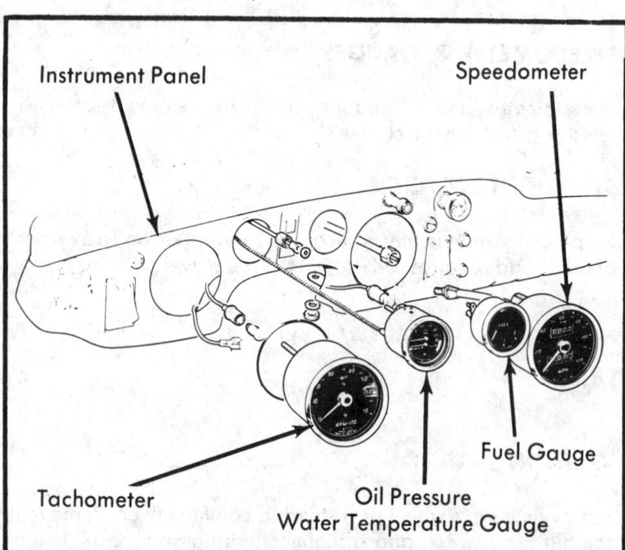

Fig. 6 MG Midget Instrument Cluster

MGB — 1) Disconnect the battery. Remove lower left hand instrument panel cover. Unscrew the knurled nut and disconnect speedometer cable.

2) Push in and turn speedometer clockwise for 30 degrees until the three studs located on the body of the speedometer are aligned with the cut-aways in the dash. Pull speedometer forward from the dash and disconnect wiring.

TACHOMETER

All Models — Disconnect the battery and remove the lower left hand instrument panel cover. Push in and turn 30 degrees until the three studs on the body of the tachometer are aligned with the cut-aways in the dash. Pull tachometer forward from dash and disconnect the wiring.

GAUGES

To remove fuel, oil pressure and temperature gauges, remove components listed below to gain access to unit, then unscrew knurled nuts. Pull instrument from dash and disconnect wiring.

To Remove	First Remove
Fuel Gauge	
MG Midget	Speedometer
MGB	None
Oil Pressure Gauge (MGB)	Tachometer
Temperature Gauge (MGB)	Heater Control
Combination Gauge (MG Midget)	Tachometer

IGNITION SWITCH

MG Midget — Disconnect battery. Remove steering column then remove left and right hand cowls. Turn ignition switch to position "1". Drill out retaining shear bolts and remove steering lock and ignition switch. Disconnect wiring.

MGB — Remove both halves of switch cowl and two switch retaining screws. Disconnect switch wiring at snap connectors and remove switch complete with wiring.

STOP LIGHT SWITCH

All Models — Mechanical type mounted on brake pedal bracket. Free movement adjustment is .125" (3 mm).

OPEL

INSTRUMENT CLUSTER

Disconnect battery ground cable and remove steering wheel. Disconnect speedometer cable, remove wing nut and instrument cluster retaining screws. Rotate cluster outward, disconnect two electrical connectors and remove instrument cluster. To install, reverse removal procedure.

SPEEDOMETER & GAUGES

Speedometer and all gauges can be removed after first removing instrument cluster.

STOP LIGHT SWITCH

Mechanical, mounted on brake pedal bracket.

PORSCHE

INSTRUMENT CLUSTER

924 Models – Disconnect battery and remove center console. Remove screw in glove compartment and detach side padding plates. Loosen instrument panel mounting under loudspeaker insert. Remove side metal screws and steering wheel. Loosen steering column switch mounting screw and remove switch. Remove instrument panel.

SPEEDOMETER, TACHOMETER & GAUGES

924 Models – Disconnect battery. Put hand underneath instrument panel to back of instrument to be removed. Press instrument forward out of instrument panel. Disconnect wiring or speedometer cable.

NOTE – *Remove tachometer and combination gauge before removing speedometer.*

911 Models – Connecting terminals and wires of all instruments are accessible from luggage compartment side of instrument panel after luggage compartment carpet is removed.

1) Disconnect and detach all cables and wire from instrument that is to be removed. In case of speedometer, also remove drive shaft knurled nut and withdraw shaft from speedometer.

2) Remove small knurled nuts securing instrument, remove retaining clamp and take instrument out from passenger compartment side.

TURN SIGNAL FLASHER (911 MODELS)

Flasher is located adjacent to fuse block in luggage compartment, and is a plug in type.

STOP LIGHT SWITCH

To adjust switch, loosen jam nut and adjusting screw. Clamp a piece of sheet metal .16" (4 mm) thick between brake pedal lever and pedal stop at brake pedal center. Turn adjusting screw until brake lights operate. Remove switch and lock adjusting screw. Reinstall switch and check switch operation.

RENAULT

INSTRUMENT CLUSTER

R-5 Models – Disconnect battery cable and speedometer cable in engine compartment. Unclip instrument panel cowel and remove. Press left and right side clips until support plate is cleared and remove instrument panel. Disconnect two electrical junction blocks and speedometer cable.

R-12 Models – Disconnect battery and two junction blocks on cluster. Disconnect speedometer cable. Lift the two retaining clips and pull cluster out, freeing mounting lugs from holders.

R-17 Models – Disconnect battery. Unscrew two knurled nuts on fuse block bracket and tilt it. Unscrew four retaining clip screws (located in each corner of cluster) by first removing radio speaker grill to gain access to right hand screws. Insert a screwdriver between cluster and instrument panel to free inside clip located at bottom center of cluster. Pull out cluster and disconnect all wiring and speedometer cable.

SPEEDOMETER & GAUGES

Speedometer and all gauges may be removed after instrument cluster is removed.

STOP LIGHT SWITCH

Mechanically operated switch attached to the steering column.

SAAB

INSTRUMENT CLUSTER

99 Models – Remove safety padding. Remove four self tapping screws. Disconnect speedometer cable and wiring. Remove bulb holders. Lift out instrument cluster.

SPEEDOMETER & GAUGES

99 Models – Speedometer and all gauges may be removed after first removing instrument cluster.

TURN SIGNAL FLASHER

Located under instrument panel on left hand side of steering column.

STOP LIGHT SWITCH

Mechanical type mounted on brake pedal bracket.

Switches, Gauges & Instrument Panels

SUBARU

INSTRUMENT CLUSTER

1) Remove radio knobs and nuts. Remove ashtray, then remove bolt in ashtray opening. Remove lighting and wiper switch knobs and nuts, heater shutter control knobs, heater control knobs and hanger spring for speedometer cable.

2) Disconnect speedometer cable and wiring harness plug from back of cluster. Disconnect wiring to cigarette lighter (if equipped). Remove cluster from instrument panel.

SPEEDOMETER & GAUGES

Speedometer and all gauges may be removed after first removing instrument cluster.

TACHOMETER

To remove tachometer, remove meter visor by removing two screws. Remove tachometer mounting screws, disconnect wiring harness and remove tachometer.

HAZARD WARNING & TURN SIGNAL FLASHER

Located under instrument panel.

STOP LIGHT SWITCH

Mechanical type mounted on brake pedal bracket. Adjust switch so there is .24-.55" (6-14 mm) free pedal movement before switch turns on brake lights.

TOYOTA

INSTRUMENT CLUSTER

Corolla – Disconnect battery and speedometer cable. Remove instrument panel center and right mouldings. Remove cluster securing screw and two nuts behind cluster. Slowly pull out instrument cluster and disconnect wiring.

Pickup – Loosen steering column clamp bolts. Remove three screws securing cluster. Pull out cluster slightly and disconnect speedometer cable and wiring. Remove cluster.

Corona – Disconnect battery and remove instrument trim panel. Remove side ventilator knob and clock knob (if equipped). Loosen five bolts securing cluster housing. Disconnect speedometer cable and wiring and remove cluster.

Celica – Remove heater knobs and heater control panel. Remove screws securing cluster trim panel and pull out lower part of trim panel. Disconnect all wiring from instrument cluster trim panel and remove panel. Disconnect speedometer cable and remove instrument cluster.

Land Cruiser – Disconnect speedometer cable and remove cluster attaching screws. On 55 series models only, remove steering column clamp attaching bolts. Pull cluster, disconnect wiring and remove cluster.

SPEEDOMETER & GAUGES

All Models – Speedometer and all gauges may be removed after first removing instrument cluster.

TURN SIGNAL FLASHER

Celica & Corona – Mounted under right hand side of dash.

Corolla – Located on fuse block mounting bracket.

Pickup & Land Cruiser – Located behind instrument cluster.

IGNITION SWITCH

Celica, Corona & Corolla – Remove upper and lower steering column covers. Set ignition key to "ACC" position and while pushing lock pin, remove key cylinder. Disconnect wiring and remove switch. Steering column lock may be removed using a screw extractor.

Pickup – Disconnect battery and remove steering column cover. Disconnect wiring, remove switch mounting screw and remove switch.

Land Cruiser – Remove steering column bracket, upper contact ring housing and ignition switch assembly. To install, reverse removal procedure making certain to align the convex part with the concave part.

STOP LIGHT SWITCH

Mechanical type mounted on brake pedal bracket. Free travel should be .120 to .240" (3 to 6 mm).

TRIUMPH

INSTRUMENT CLUSTER

Spitfire – Disconnect battery and remove heater control knobs. Remove four screws and cup washers and lower cluster. Remove bulb holders, disconnect wiring and remove cluster.

TR7 – Remove radio speaker grill and top instrument panel trim pad. Remove steering column shrouds, loosen odometer reset knob and remove knob with cable. Loosen clock reset knob and remove with cable. Disconnect speedometer cable, remove retaining screws and pull out instrument cluster slightly. Disconnect all wiring and remove cluster.

TACHOMETER

Spitfire & TR7 – Tachometer may be removed after removing instrument cluster.

SPEEDOMETER

Spitfire – Disconnect battery. Lower center dash, remove tachometer and depress lever releasing catch from annular groove in the boss. Detach speedometer cable, unscrew trip reset and remove two knurled nuts. Disconnect two connectors, bulb holders and remove speedometer.

TRIUMPH (Cont.)

TR7 – Speedometer may be removed after removing instrument cluster.

GAUGES

Spitfire & TR7 – All gauges may be removed after removing instrument cluster.

IGNITION SWITCH

Spitfire – Remove steering column. Remove switch cover and column anti-torque strap. Use a small chisel to unscrew two shear head bolts. If this fails, remove using a screw extractor. When installing switch, use new shear bolts.

TR7 – Remove steering column shrouds. Use a small chisel to unscrew two shear bolts. If this fails, remove using a screw extractor. When installing switch, use new shear bolts.

STOP LIGHT SWITCH

Mechanical type mounted on brake pedal bracket.

VOLKSWAGEN

INSTRUMENT CLUSTER

Type 1 (Beetle) – Disconnect battery ground cable. Remove five screws securing cluster. **NOTE** – *Cluster screws are covered by small strips on left and right and by a cap in the center.* Disconnect speedometer cable and wiring, remove cluster.

Type 2 (Bus) – Disconnect battery ground cable. Remove cluster securing screws and tilt cluster outward. Disconnect speedometer cable and wiring and remove cluster.

Rabbit & Scirocco – Remove trim plate for fresh air control and remove radio or glove box. Disconnect speedometer cable and wiring. Remove retaining screw on right side of cluster (visible after radio or glove box is removed) and remove cluster.

Dasher – Disconnect battery ground cable and speedometer cable. Using long nosed pliers, detach springs securing left and right sides of cluster then swing cluster outward.

SPEEDOMETER

All Models – Speedometer can be removed after removing instrument cluster and speedometer retaining screws.

HAZARD WARNING & TURN SIGNAL FLASHER

Type 1 – Flashers are mounted seperately on a bracket above the fuse box. Relays can be reached by removing the access panel from rear of the front luggage compartment.

All Other Models – Flasher is a plug-in unit on fuse block.

IGNITION SWITCH

All Exc. Type 2 – Disconnect battery ground cable, turn signal switch plug and ignition switch plug. Remove steering wheel and turn signal switch. Remove switch retainer, press ignition switch plug upward out of guide and disconnect wires. Pull lock cylinder with key outward far enough so that lock cylinder may be depressed through hole with piece of stiff wire. While depressing cylinder, pull out cylinder by pulling on key.

Type 2 – Disconnect battery ground cable. Remove ignition switch housing and disconnect wiring behind instrument panel. If necessary, drill out blind hole using a 1/8" (3 mm) drill. Press down retaining spring with drill or piece of stiff wire and pull lock cylinder out of housing with key. When installing, if hole was drilled, close hole with piece of wire which can only be removed by drilling.

STOP LIGHT SWITCH

Hydraulic type mounted on brake master cylinder.

VOLVO

INSTRUMENT CLUSTER

All Models – Disconnect battery ground cable and proceed as follows:

1) Remove steering column shrouds. Loosen bracket screw and allow bracket to drop down steering column. Remove instrument cluster mounting screws. Disconnect speedometer cable.

2) Take hold of back side of speedometer and press upwards until snap lock on upper edge releases. Lift cluster forward and disconnect wiring and tachometer drive cable (if equipped). Cluster can now be removed.

SPEEDOMETER & GAUGES

All Models – Speedometer and all gauges can be removed after removing instrument cluster.

HAZARD WARNING & TURN SIGNAL FLASHER

240 Series – Flasher is mounted behind left side kick panel.

260 Series – Flasher is mounted behind instrument cluster.

IGNITION SWITCH

240 & 260 Series – Disconnect battery cable. Remove noise insulation panel and center side panel. Disconnect terminal block for the ignition switch. Using a stubby screwdriver, remove ignition switch.

STOP LIGHT SWITCH

Mechanical type mounted on brake pedal bracket. Adjust switch to provide .16" (4 mm) clearance between brake pedal and end of switch plunger.

Section 4
WIRING DIAGRAMS

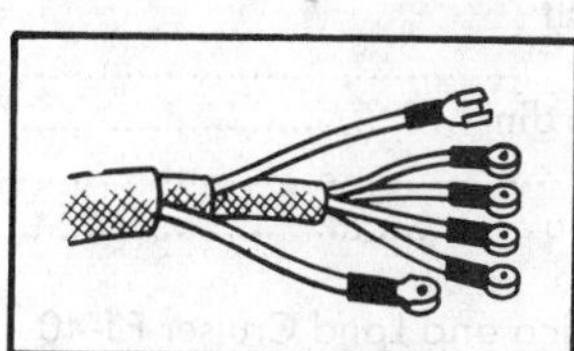

Contents

CHASSIS WIRING

NOTE — ALSO SEE GENERAL INDEX.

Contents (Cont.)

NOTE — ALSO SEE GENERAL INDEX

Contents (Cont.)

FUSES & CIRCUIT BREAKERS

ARRANGEMENT OF DATA

The Wiring Diagram Section contains chassis wiring diagrams spread across two pages for efficient reading. The diagrams are arranged alphabetically by car model or make.

Appearing on each wiring diagram is a legend of Accessory Power Feeds. The letters preceding the titles of the accessory circuits are codes which are also shown somewhere on the diagram. These codes indicate where the sub-system wiring connects to car chassis wiring system.

Also contained in this section are Fuel Injection wiring diagrams and diagrams for various sub-systems.

NOTE — ALSO SEE GENERAL INDEX

1977 Arrow

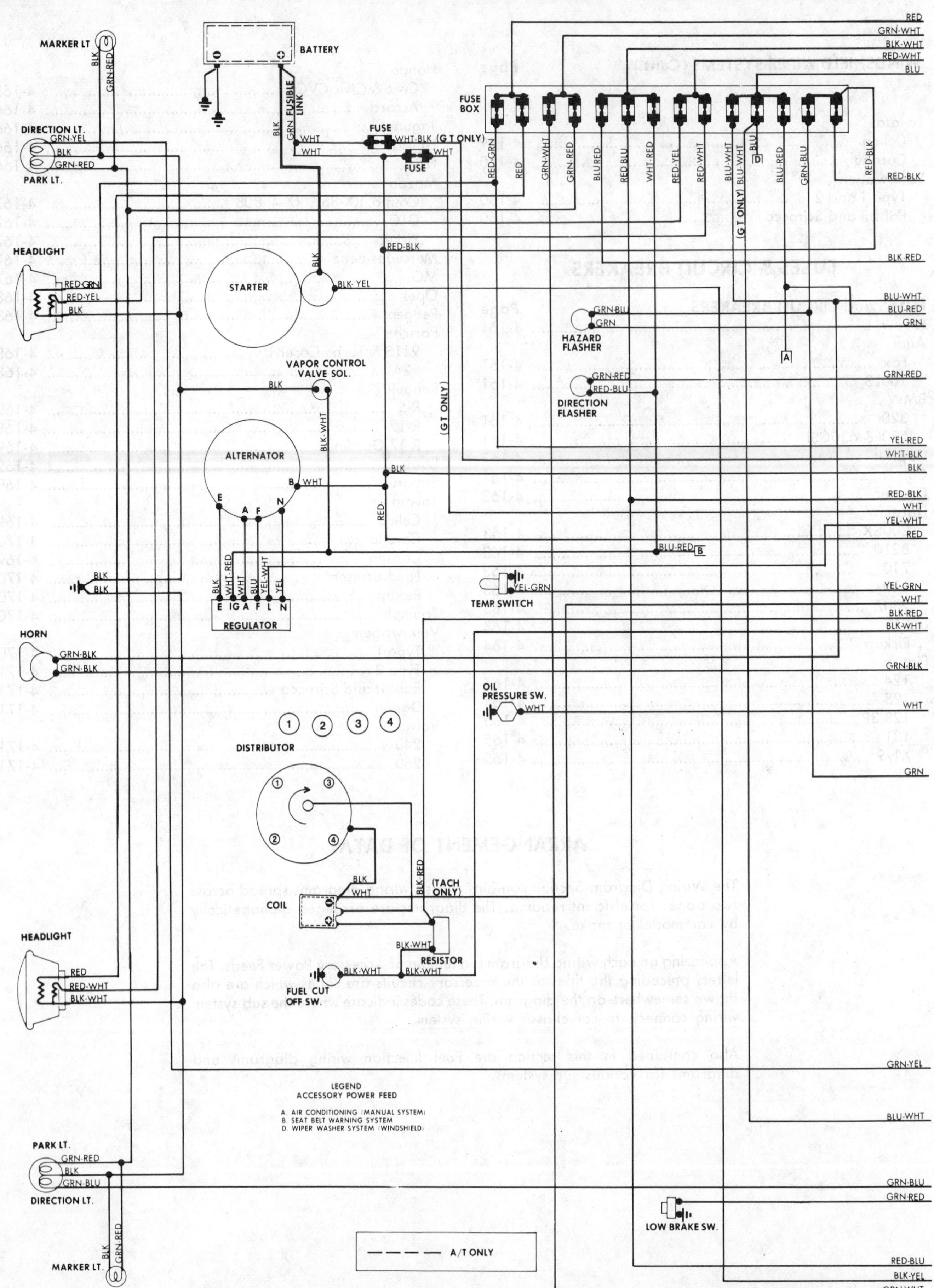

MARKER LT
BATTERY
FUSIBLE LINK
FUSE BOX
DIRECTION LT.
PARK LT.
FUSE
WHT-BLK (G T ONLY)
(G T ONLY)
HEADLIGHT
STARTER
HAZARD FLASHER
DIRECTION FLASHER
VAPOR CONTROL VALVE SOL.
ALTERNATOR
TEMP SWITCH
REGULATOR
HORN
OIL PRESSURE SW.
DISTRIBUTOR
COIL
(TACH ONLY)
RESISTOR
FUEL CUT OFF SW.
LOW BRAKE SW.
A/T ONLY
LEGEND
ACCESSORY POWER FEED
A. AIR CONDITIONING (MANUAL SYSTEM)
B. SEAT BELT WARNING SYSTEM
D. WIPER WASHER SYSTEM (WINDSHIELD)

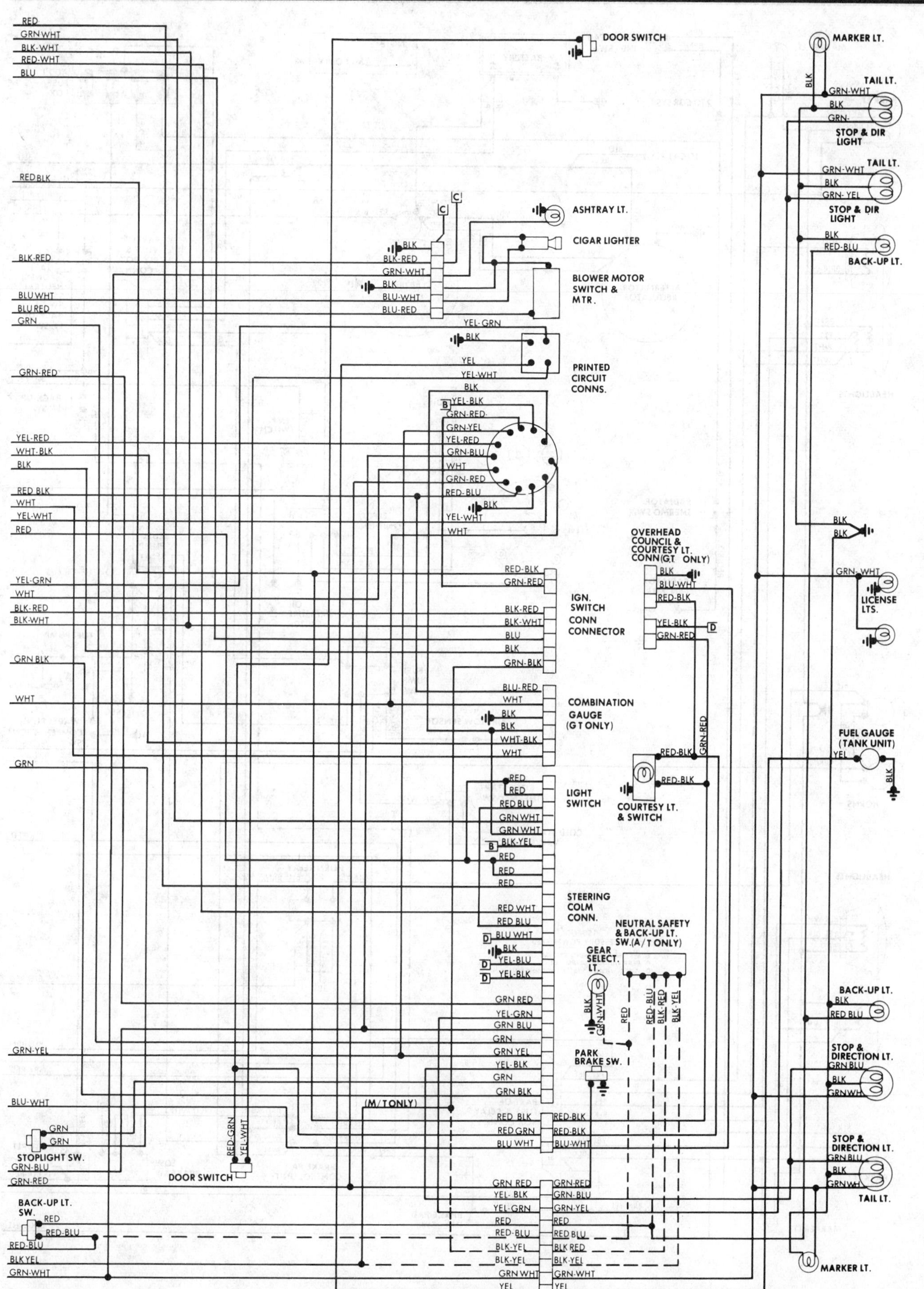
DOOR SWITCH
MARKER LT.
TAIL LT.
STOP & DIR LIGHT
TAIL LT.
STOP & DIR LIGHT
ASHTRAY LT.
CIGAR LIGHTER
BLOWER MOTOR SWITCH & MTR.
BACK-UP LT.
PRINTED CIRCUIT CONNS.
OVERHEAD COUNCIL & COURTESY LT. CONN(G.T. ONLY)
LICENSE LTS.
IGN. SWITCH CONN CONNECTOR
COMBINATION GAUGE (G T ONLY)
FUEL GAUGE (TANK UNIT)
LIGHT SWITCH
COURTESY LT. & SWITCH
STEERING COLM CONN.
NEUTRAL SAFETY & BACK-UP LT. SW.(A/T ONLY)
GEAR SELECT. LT.
PARK BRAKE SW.
BACK-UP LT.
STOP & DIRECTION LT.
STOP & DIRECTION LT.
TAIL LT.
(M/T ONLY)
STOPLIGHT SW.
DOOR SWITCH
BACK-UP LT. SW.
MARKER LT.

1977 Audi

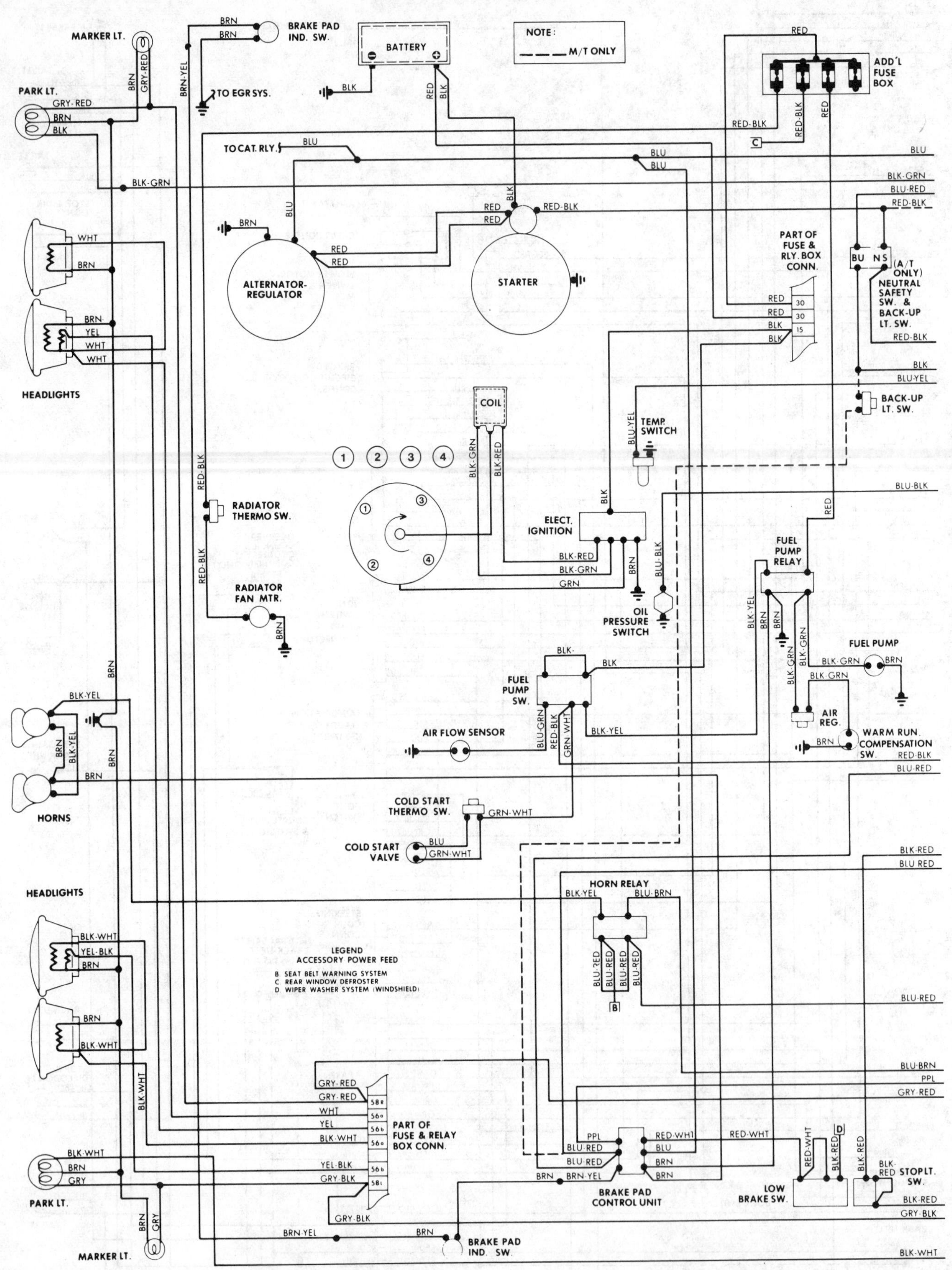

MARKER LT.
BRAKE PAD IND. SW.
BATTERY
NOTE: — — — M/T ONLY
ADD'L FUSE BOX
PARK LT.
TO EGR SYS.
TO CAT. RLY.
ALTERNATOR-REGULATOR
STARTER
PART OF FUSE & RLY. BOX CONN.
(A/T ONLY) NEUTRAL SAFETY SW. & BACK-UP LT. SW.
HEADLIGHTS
COIL
TEMP. SWITCH
BACK-UP LT. SW.
RADIATOR THERMO SW.
ELECT. IGNITION
FUEL PUMP RELAY
RADIATOR FAN MTR.
OIL PRESSURE SWITCH
FUEL PUMP
FUEL PUMP SW.
AIR REG.
AIR FLOW SENSOR
WARM RUN. COMPENSATION SW.
HORNS
COLD START THERMO SW.
COLD START VALVE
HEADLIGHTS
HORN RELAY
LEGEND
ACCESSORY POWER FEED
B SEAT BELT WARNING SYSTEM
C REAR WINDOW DEFROSTER
D WIPER WASHER SYSTEM (WINDSHIELD)
PART OF FUSE & RELAY BOX CONN.
BRAKE PAD CONTROL UNIT
LOW BRAKE SW.
STOPLT. SW.
PARK LT.
MARKER LT.
BRAKE PAD IND. SW.

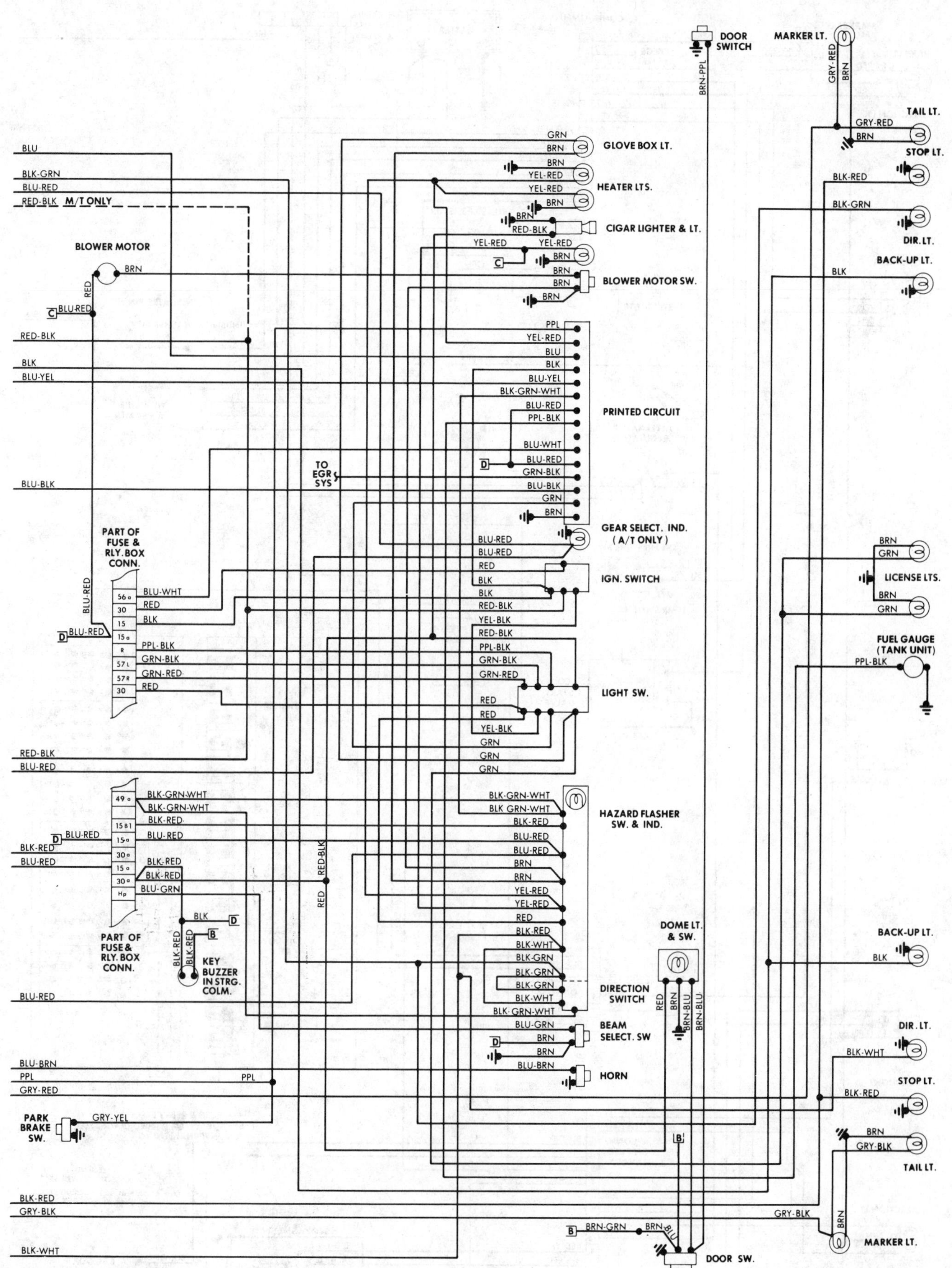
DOOR SWITCH
MARKER LT.
TAIL LT.
STOP LT.
GLOVE BOX LT.
HEATER LTS.
CIGAR LIGHTER & LT.
DIR. LT.
BACK-UP LT.
BLOWER MOTOR SW.
BLOWER MOTOR
PRINTED CIRCUIT
TO EGR SYS
GEAR SELECT. IND. (A/T ONLY)
IGN. SWITCH
LICENSE LTS.
FUEL GAUGE (TANK UNIT)
PART OF FUSE & RLY. BOX CONN.
LIGHT SW.
HAZARD FLASHER SW. & IND.
DOME LT. & SW.
KEY BUZZER IN STRG. COLM.
DIRECTION SWITCH
BEAM SELECT. SW
HORN
PARK BRAKE SW.
BACK-UP LT.
DIR. LT.
STOP LT.
TAIL LT.
MARKER LT.
DOOR SW.
BLU
BLK-GRN
BLU-RED
RED-BLK M/T ONLY
RED-BLK
BLK
BLU-YEL
BLU-BLK
BLU-BRN
PPL
GRY-RED
GRY-YEL
BLK-RED
GRY-BLK
BLK-WHT
BRN-GRN
BRN-PPL
BRN-BLU

1977 Audi

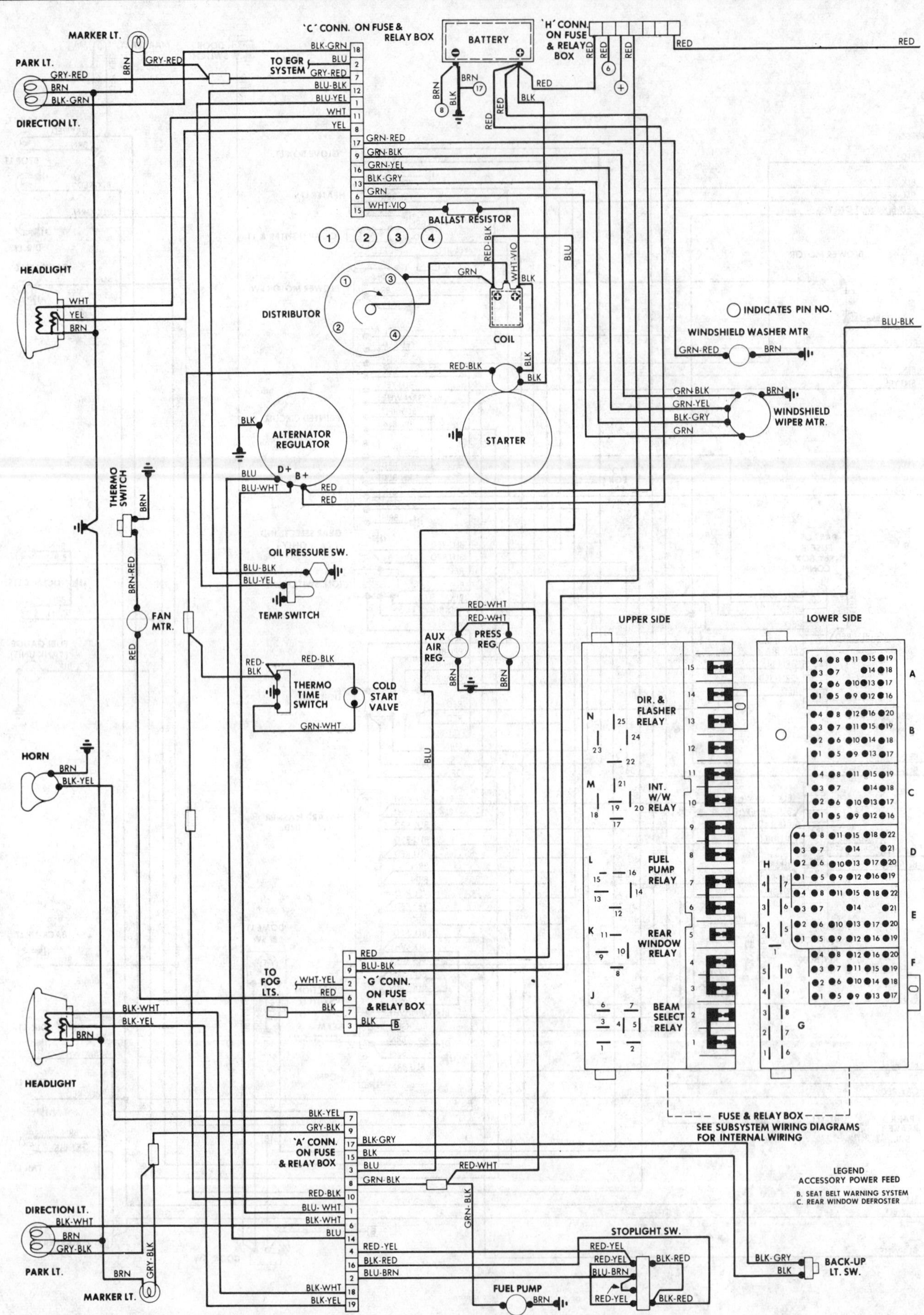

MARKER LT.
PARK LT.
DIRECTION LT.
HEADLIGHT
THERMO SWITCH
FAN MTR.
HORN
HEADLIGHT
DIRECTION LT.
PARK LT.
MARKER LT.
'C' CONN. ON FUSE & RELAY BOX
TO EGR SYSTEM
BATTERY
'H' CONN. ON FUSE & RELAY BOX
BALLAST RESISTOR
DISTRIBUTOR
COIL
ALTERNATOR REGULATOR
STARTER
OIL PRESSURE SW.
TEMP. SWITCH
AUX AIR REG.
PRESS REG.
THERMO TIME SWITCH
COLD START VALVE
TO FOG LTS.
'G' CONN. ON FUSE & RELAY BOX
'A' CONN. ON FUSE & RELAY BOX
FUEL PUMP
STOPLIGHT SW.
BACK-UP LT. SW.
INDICATES PIN NO.
WINDSHIELD WASHER MTR
WINDSHIELD WIPER MTR.
UPPER SIDE
LOWER SIDE
DIR. & FLASHER RELAY
INT. W/W RELAY
FUEL PUMP RELAY
REAR WINDOW RELAY
BEAM SELECT RELAY
FUSE & RELAY BOX
SEE SUBSYSTEM WIRING DIAGRAMS FOR INTERNAL WIRING
LEGEND
ACCESSORY POWER FEED
B. SEAT BELT WARNING SYSTEM
C. REAR WINDOW DEFROSTER

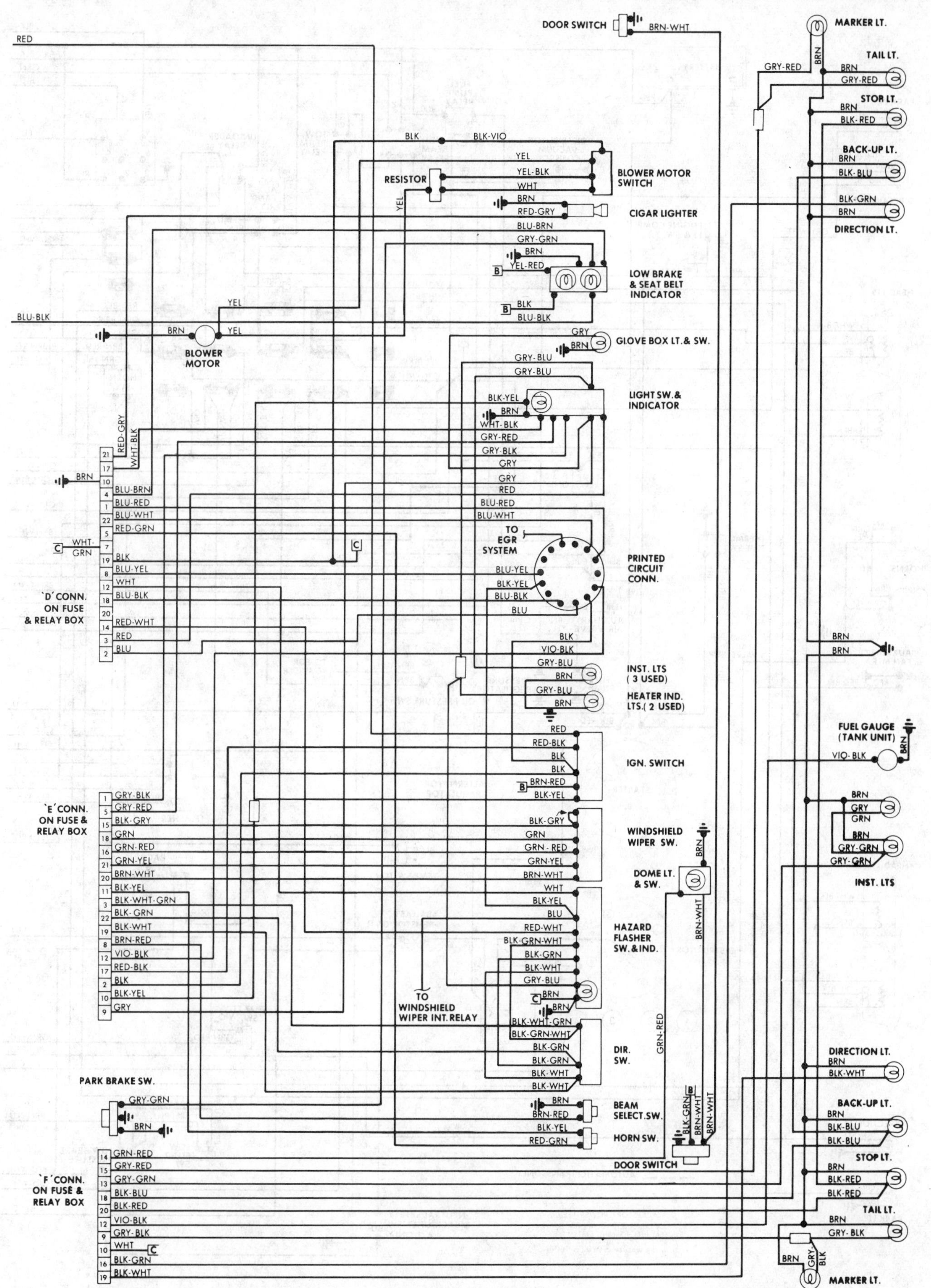

DOOR SWITCH
BRN-WHT
MARKER LT.
TAIL LT.
STOP LT.
BACK-UP LT.
DIRECTION LT.
BLOWER MOTOR SWITCH
RESISTOR
CIGAR LIGHTER
LOW BRAKE & SEAT BELT INDICATOR
BLOWER MOTOR
GLOVE BOX LT. & SW.
LIGHT SW. & INDICATOR
TO EGR SYSTEM
PRINTED CIRCUIT CONN.
'D' CONN. ON FUSE & RELAY BOX
INST. LTS (3 USED)
HEATER IND. LTS. (2 USED)
FUEL GAUGE (TANK UNIT)
IGN. SWITCH
'E' CONN. ON FUSE & RELAY BOX
WINDSHIELD WIPER SW.
DOME LT. & SW.
INST. LTS
HAZARD FLASHER SW. & IND.
TO WINDSHIELD WIPER INT. RELAY
DIR. SW.
PARK BRAKE SW.
BEAM SELECT. SW.
HORN SW.
DOOR SWITCH
'F' CONN. ON FUSE & RELAY BOX

1977 BMW

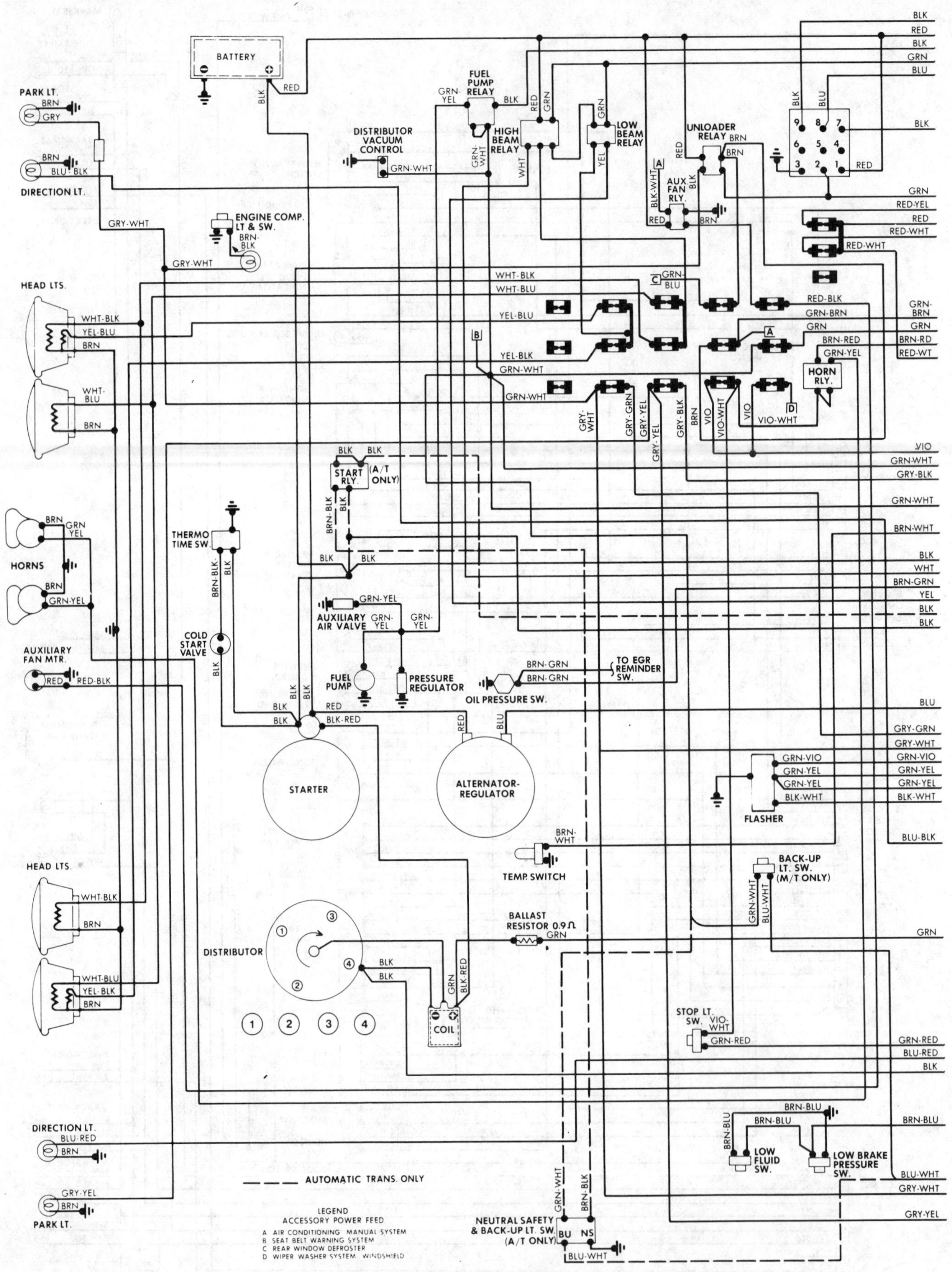

BATTERY
PARK LT.
DIRECTION LT.
HEAD LTS.
HORNS
AUXILIARY FAN MTR.
FUEL PUMP RELAY
DISTRIBUTOR VACUUM CONTROL
HIGH BEAM RELAY
LOW BEAM RELAY
UNLOADER RELAY
AUX FAN RLY.
HORN RLY.
ENGINE COMP. LT & SW.
START RLY. (A/T ONLY)
THERMO TIME SW.
COLD START VALVE
AUXILIARY AIR VALVE
FUEL PUMP
PRESSURE REGULATOR
OIL PRESSURE SW.
TO EGR REMINDER SW.
STARTER
ALTERNATOR-REGULATOR
FLASHER
TEMP SWITCH
BACK-UP LT. SW. (M/T ONLY)
BALLAST RESISTOR 0.9Ω
DISTRIBUTOR
COIL
STOP LT. SW.
LOW FLUID SW.
LOW BRAKE PRESSURE SW.
NEUTRAL SAFETY & BACK-UP LT. SW. (A/T ONLY)
AUTOMATIC TRANS. ONLY
LEGEND
ACCESSORY POWER FEED
A AIR CONDITIONING MANUAL SYSTEM
B SEAT BELT WARNING SYSTEM
C REAR WINDOW DEFROSTER
D WIPER WASHER SYSTEM WINDSHIELD

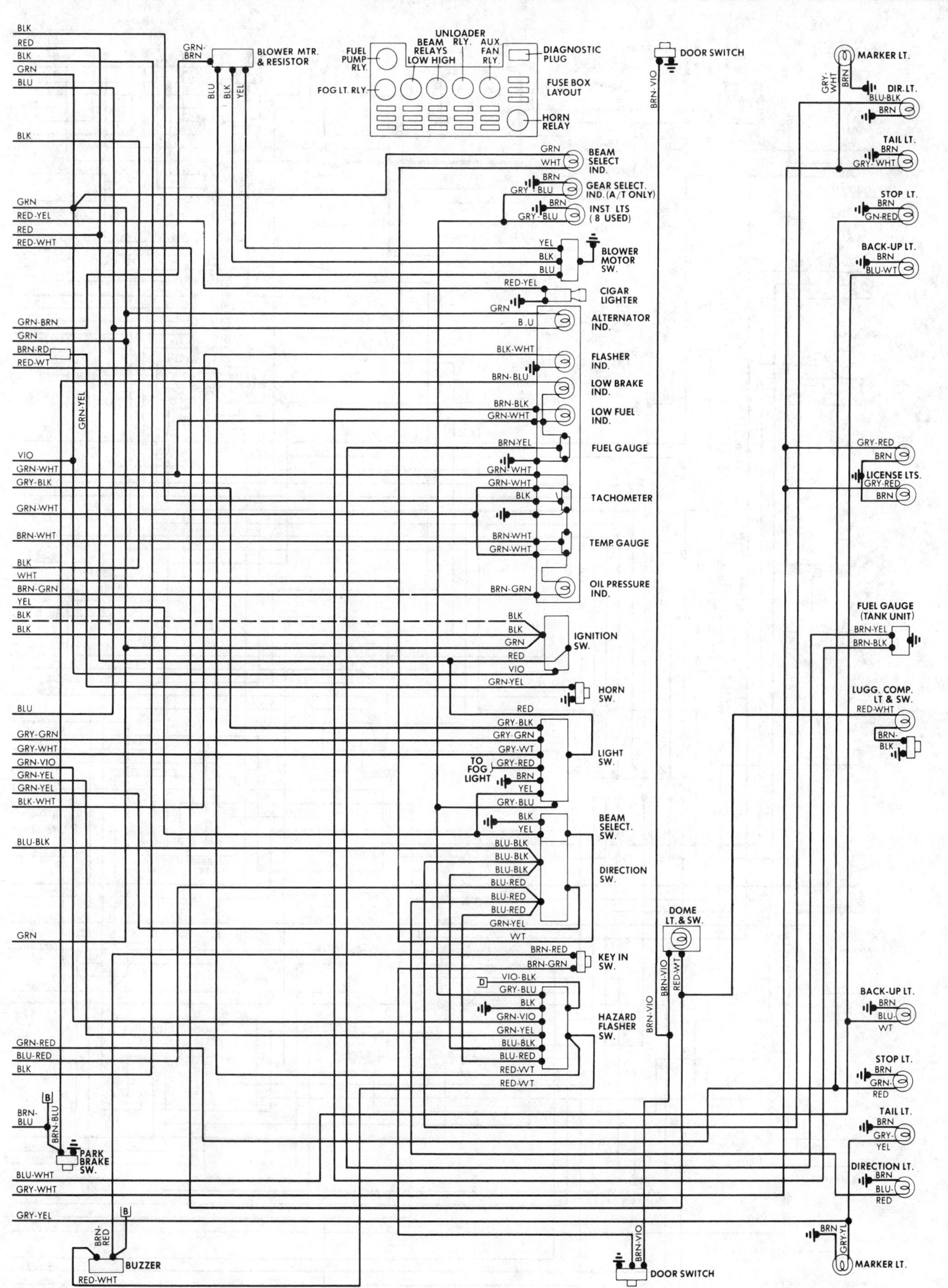
BLOWER MTR. & RESISTOR
FUEL PUMP RLY.
UNLOADER RLY.
BEAM RELAYS LOW HIGH
AUX. FAN RLY.
DIAGNOSTIC PLUG
FOG LT. RLY.
FUSE BOX LAYOUT
HORN RELAY
DOOR SWITCH
MARKER LT.
DIR. LT.
TAIL LT.
STOP LT.
BACK-UP LT.
BEAM SELECT IND.
GEAR SELECT. IND. (A/T ONLY)
INST LTS (8 USED)
BLOWER MOTOR SW.
CIGAR LIGHTER
ALTERNATOR IND.
FLASHER IND.
LOW BRAKE IND.
LOW FUEL IND.
FUEL GAUGE
TACHOMETER
TEMP GAUGE
OIL PRESSURE IND.
LICENSE LTS.
FUEL GAUGE (TANK UNIT)
IGNITION SW.
HORN SW.
LUGG. COMP. LT & SW.
LIGHT SW.
TO FOG LIGHT
BEAM SELECT. SW.
DIRECTION SW.
DOME LT. & SW.
KEY IN SW.
HAZARD FLASHER SW.
BACK-UP LT.
STOP LT.
TAIL LT.
DIRECTION LT.
PARK BRAKE SW.
MARKER LT.
BUZZER
DOOR SWITCH

1977 BMW

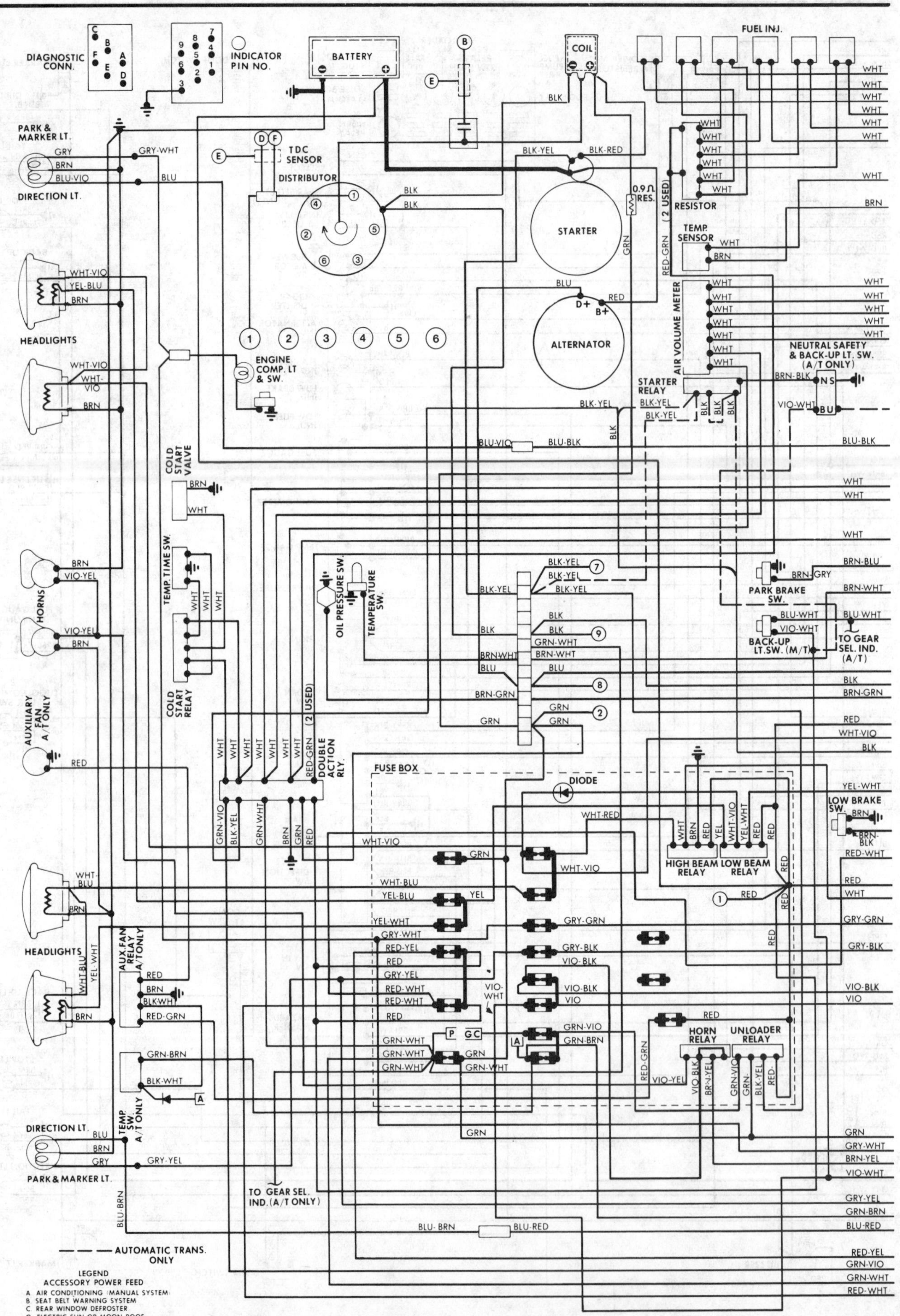

DIAGNOSTIC CONN.
INDICATOR PIN NO.
BATTERY
COIL
FUEL INJ.
PARK & MARKER LT.
DIRECTION LT.
TDC SENSOR
DISTRIBUTOR
STARTER
0.9Ω RES. (2 USED)
RESISTOR
TEMP. SENSOR
AIR VOLUME METER
ALTERNATOR
HEADLIGHTS
ENGINE COMP. LT & SW.
NEUTRAL SAFETY & BACK-UP LT. SW. (A/T ONLY)
STARTER RELAY
COLD START VALVE
TEMP. TIME SW.
OIL PRESSURE SW.
TEMPERATURE SW.
PARK BRAKE SW.
BACK-UP LT. SW. (M/T)
TO GEAR SEL. IND. (A/T)
HORNS
COLD START RELAY
AUXILIARY FAN A/T ONLY
DOUBLE ACTION RLY. (2 USED)
FUSE BOX
DIODE
LOW BRAKE SW.
HIGH BEAM RELAY
LOW BEAM RELAY
AUX. FAN RELAY A/T ONLY
HORN RELAY
UNLOADER RELAY
TEMP. SW. A/T ONLY
TO GEAR SEL. IND. (A/T ONLY)
– – – AUTOMATIC TRANS. ONLY
LEGEND
ACCESSORY POWER FEED
A. AIR CONDITIONING (MANUAL SYSTEM)
B. SEAT BELT WARNING SYSTEM
C. REAR WINDOW DEFROSTER
G. ELECTRIC SUN OR MOON ROOF
P. POWER WINDOW CONTROL SYSTEM

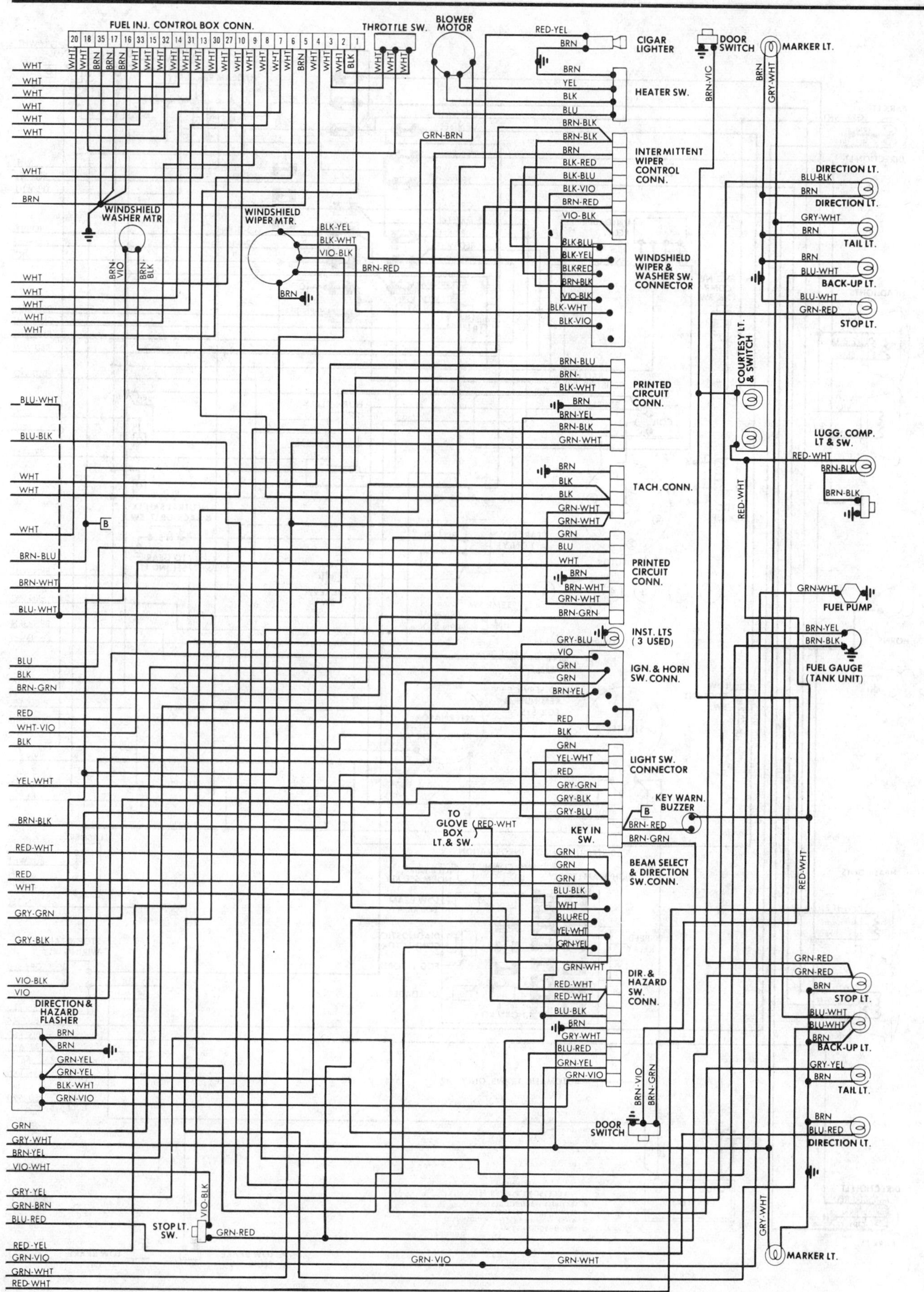
FUEL INJ. CONTROL BOX CONN.
THROTTLE SW.
BLOWER MOTOR
CIGAR LIGHTER
DOOR SWITCH
MARKER LT.
HEATER SW.
INTERMITTENT WIPER CONTROL CONN.
DIRECTION LT.
TAIL LT.
BACK-UP LT.
STOP LT.
WINDSHIELD WASHER MTR
WINDSHIELD WIPER MTR.
WINDSHIELD WIPER & WASHER SW. CONNECTOR
COURTESY LT. & SWITCH
PRINTED CIRCUIT CONN.
LUGG. COMP. LT & SW.
TACH. CONN.
PRINTED CIRCUIT CONN.
FUEL PUMP
INST. LTS (3 USED)
FUEL GAUGE (TANK UNIT)
IGN. & HORN SW. CONN.
LIGHT SW. CONNECTOR
KEY WARN. BUZZER
TO GLOVE BOX LT. & SW.
KEY IN SW.
BEAM SELECT & DIRECTION SW. CONN.
DIRECTION & HAZARD FLASHER
DIR. & HAZARD SW. CONN.
STOP LT.
BACK-UP LT.
TAIL LT.
DIRECTION LT.
DOOR SWITCH
STOP LT. SW.
MARKER LT.

1977 BMW

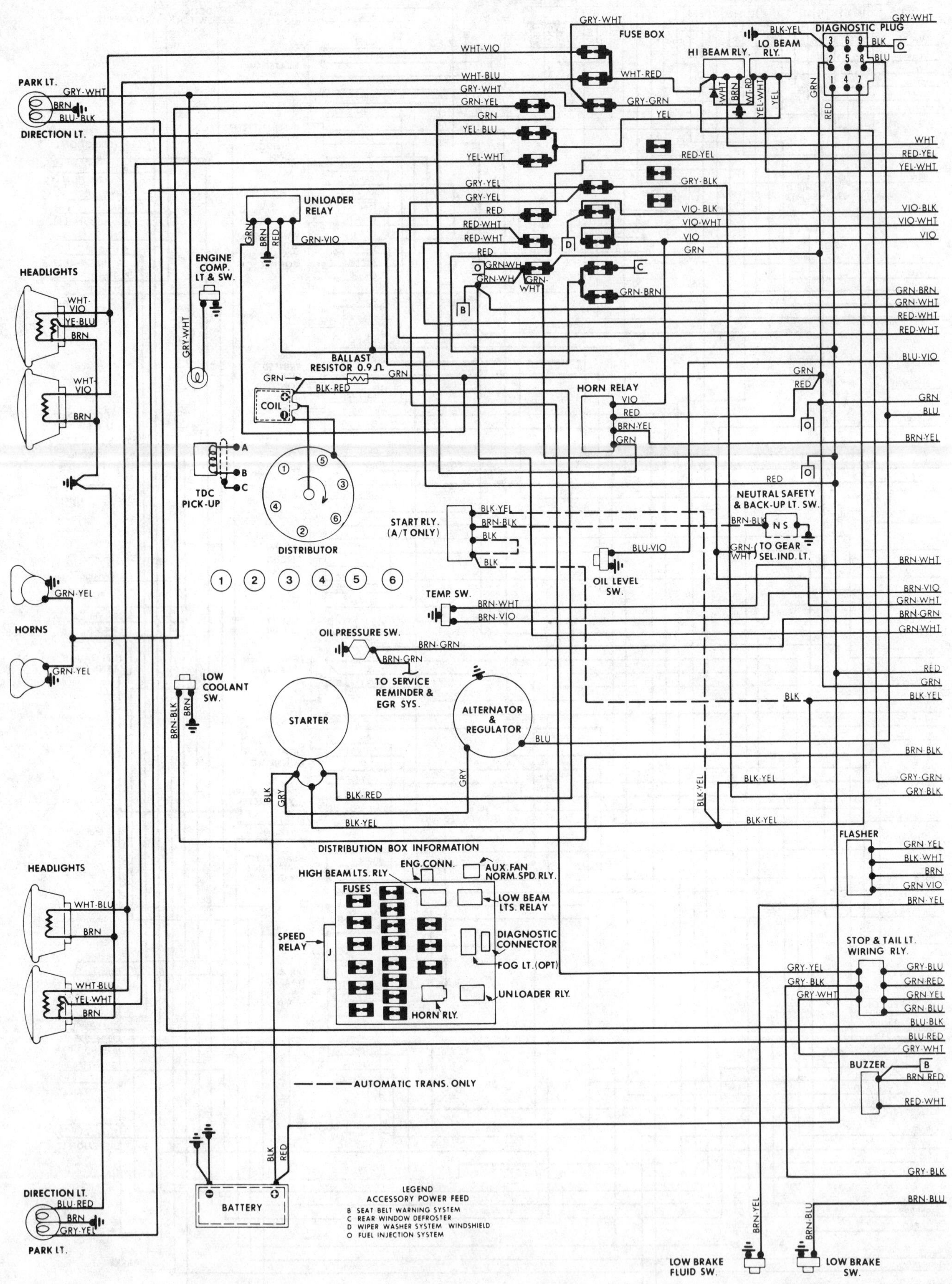

PARK LT.
DIRECTION LT.
HEADLIGHTS
HORNS
FUSE BOX
HI BEAM RLY.
LO BEAM RLY.
DIAGNOSTIC PLUG
UNLOADER RELAY
ENGINE COMP. LT & SW.
BALLAST RESISTOR 0.9 Ω
COIL
HORN RELAY
TDC PICK-UP
DISTRIBUTOR
START RLY. (A/T ONLY)
NEUTRAL SAFETY & BACK-UP LT. SW.
TO GEAR SEL. IND. LT.
OIL LEVEL SW.
TEMP. SW.
OIL PRESSURE SW.
TO SERVICE REMINDER & EGR SYS.
LOW COOLANT SW.
STARTER
ALTERNATOR & REGULATOR
DISTRIBUTION BOX INFORMATION
ENG. CONN.
AUX. FAN NORM. SPD. RLY.
HIGH BEAM LTS. RLY
FUSES
LOW BEAM LTS. RELAY
DIAGNOSTIC CONNECTOR
SPEED RELAY
FOG LT. (OPT)
UNLOADER RLY.
HORN RLY.
FLASHER
STOP & TAIL LT. WIRING RLY.
BUZZER
AUTOMATIC TRANS. ONLY
BATTERY
LEGEND
ACCESSORY POWER FEED
B SEAT BELT WARNING SYSTEM
C REAR WINDOW DEFROSTER
D WIPER WASHER SYSTEM WINDSHIELD
O FUEL INJECTION SYSTEM
LOW BRAKE FLUID SW.
LOW BRAKE SW.

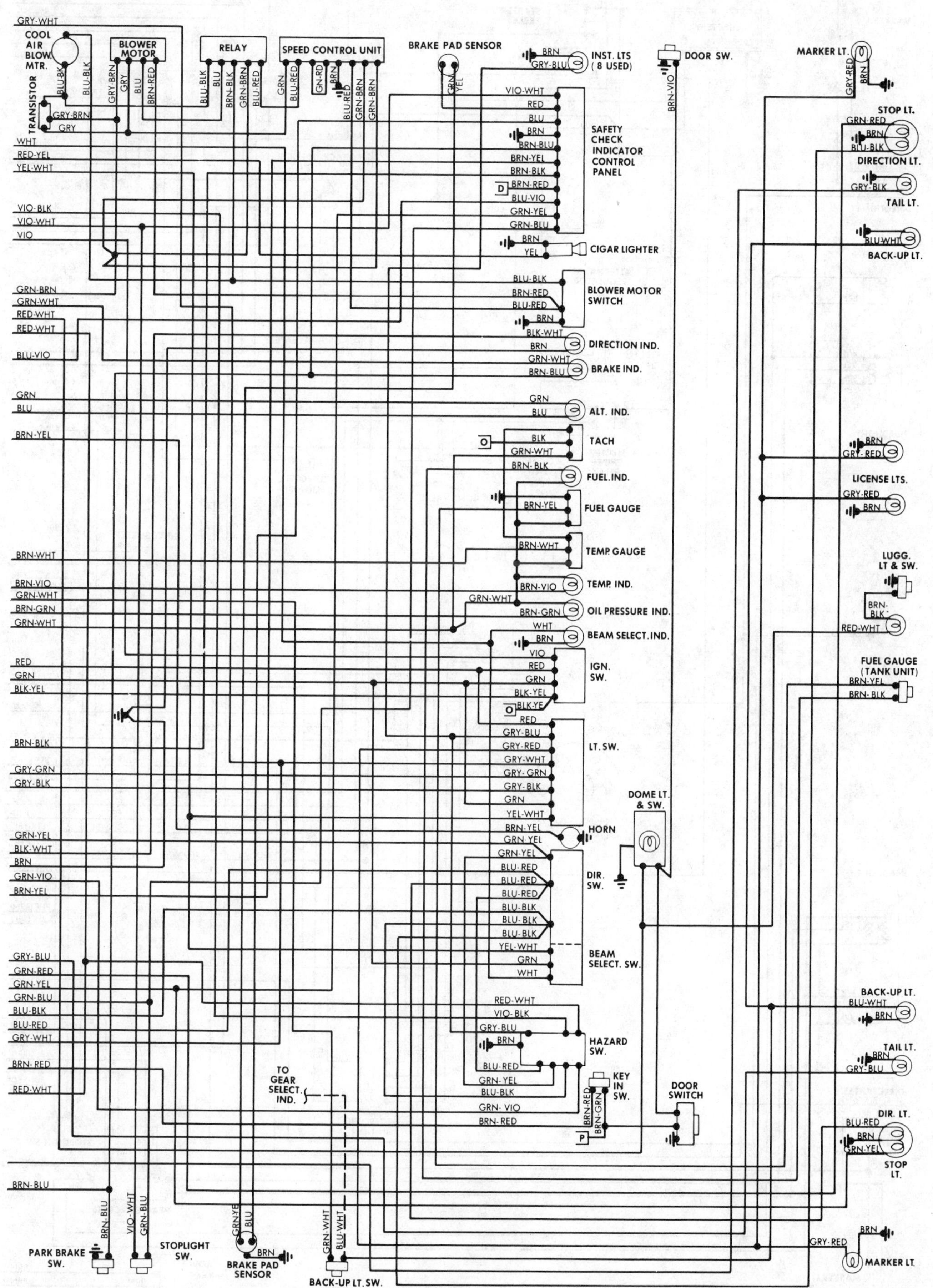
COOL AIR BLOW. MTR.
TRANSISTOR
BLOWER MOTOR
RELAY
SPEED CONTROL UNIT
BRAKE PAD SENSOR
INST. LTS (8 USED)
DOOR SW.
MARKER LT.
SAFETY CHECK INDICATOR CONTROL PANEL
STOP LT.
DIRECTION LT.
TAIL LT.
BACK-UP LT.
CIGAR LIGHTER
BLOWER MOTOR SWITCH
DIRECTION IND.
BRAKE IND.
ALT. IND.
TACH
FUEL. IND.
LICENSE LTS.
FUEL GAUGE
TEMP. GAUGE
LUGG. LT & SW.
TEMP. IND.
OIL PRESSURE IND.
BEAM SELECT. IND.
IGN. SW.
FUEL GAUGE (TANK UNIT)
LT. SW.
DOME LT. & SW.
HORN
DIR. SW.
BEAM SELECT. SW.
BACK-UP LT.
HAZARD SW.
TAIL LT.
KEY IN SW.
TO GEAR SELECT. IND.
DOOR SWITCH
DIR. LT.
STOP LT.
PARK BRAKE SW.
STOPLIGHT SW.
BRAKE PAD SENSOR
BACK-UP LT. SW. (M/T)
MARKER LT.

1977 Capri

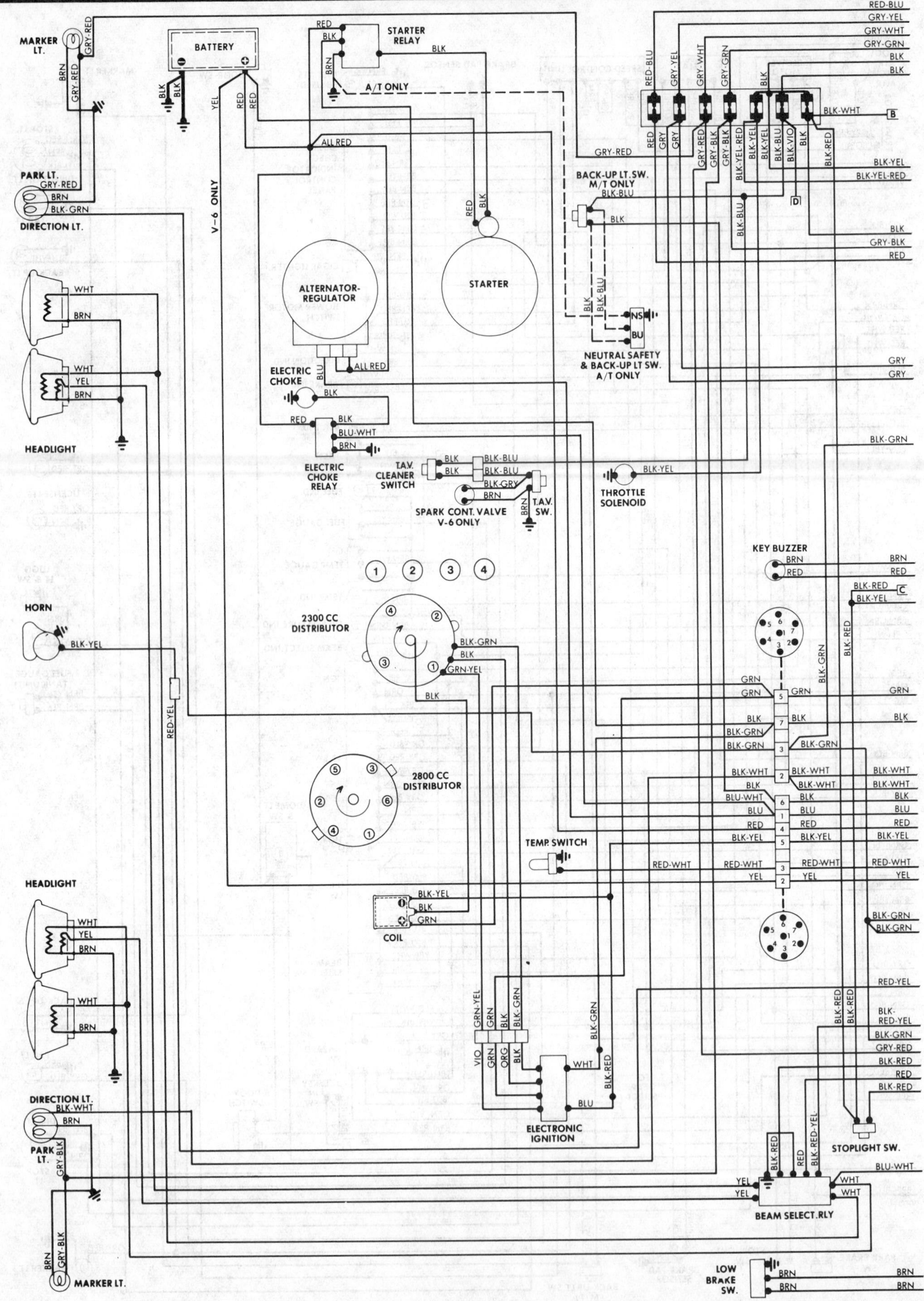
MARKER LT.
BATTERY
STARTER RELAY
A/T ONLY
PARK LT.
DIRECTION LT.
V-6 ONLY
ALL RED
ALTERNATOR-REGULATOR
STARTER
BACK-UP LT. SW. M/T ONLY
NS
BU
NEUTRAL SAFETY & BACK-UP LT SW. A/T ONLY
ELECTRIC CHOKE
ELECTRIC CHOKE RELAY
T.A.V. CLEANER SWITCH
SPARK CONT. VALVE V-6 ONLY
T.A.V. SW.
THROTTLE SOLENOID
HEADLIGHT
KEY BUZZER
HORN
2300 CC DISTRIBUTOR
2800 CC DISTRIBUTOR
TEMP. SWITCH
COIL
ELECTRONIC IGNITION
STOPLIGHT SW.
BEAM SELECT. RLY
LOW BRAKE SW.
DIRECTION LT.
PARK LT.
MARKER LT.
B
C
D
RED-BLU
GRY-YEL
GRY-WHT
GRY-GRN
BLK
BLK-WHT
GRY-RED
BLK-YEL
BLK-YEL-RED
GRY-BLK
RED
GRY
BLK-GRN
BRN
BLK-RED
GRN
BLU
RED-WHT
YEL
RED-YEL
BLK-RED-YEL
BLU-WHT
WHT

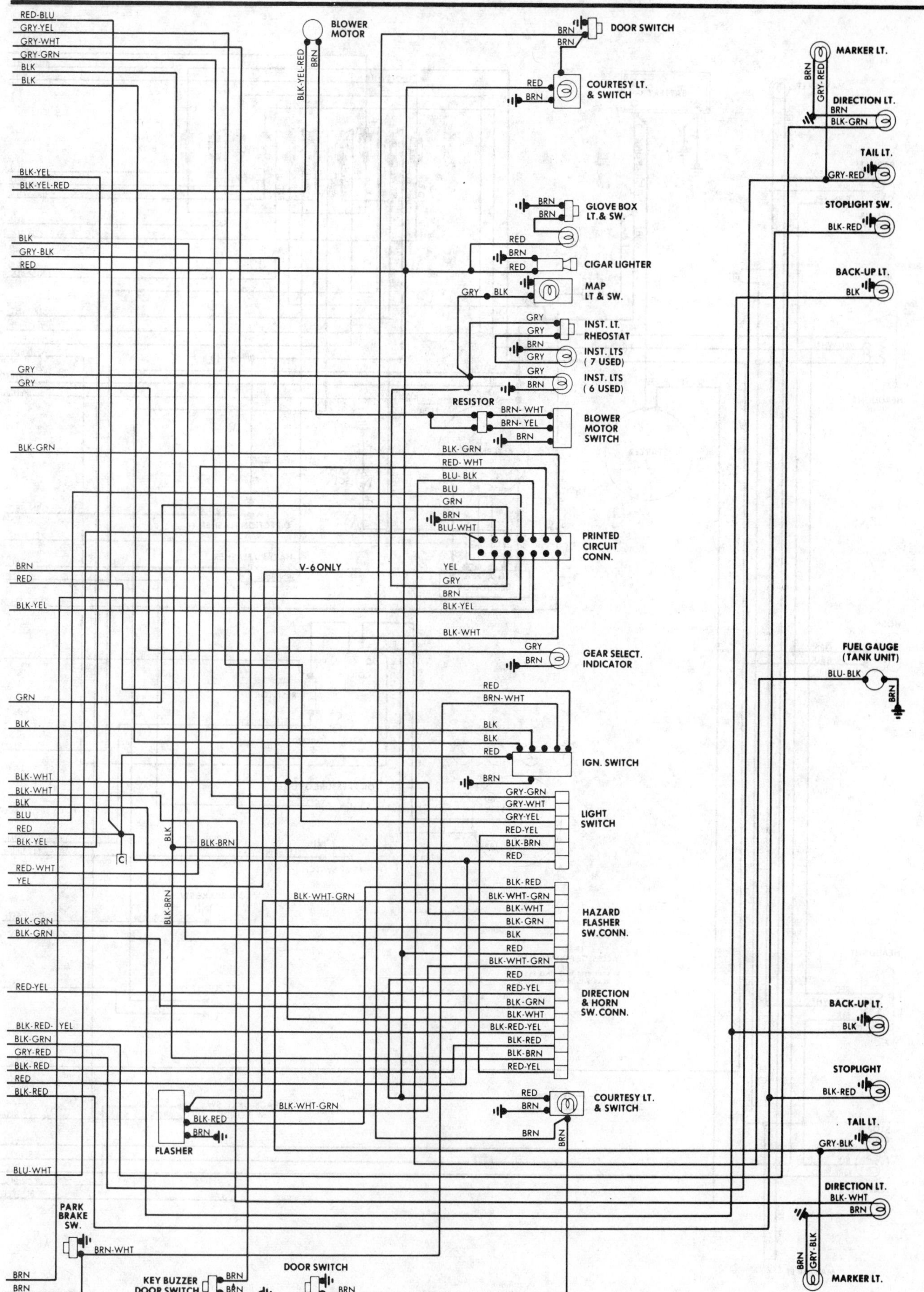
BLOWER MOTOR
DOOR SWITCH
COURTESY LT. & SWITCH
MARKER LT.
DIRECTION LT.
TAIL LT.
STOPLIGHT SW.
GLOVE BOX LT. & SW.
CIGAR LIGHTER
MAP LT & SW.
BACK-UP LT.
INST. LT. RHEOSTAT
INST. LTS (7 USED)
INST. LTS (6 USED)
RESISTOR
BLOWER MOTOR SWITCH
PRINTED CIRCUIT CONN.
V-6 ONLY
GEAR SELECT. INDICATOR
FUEL GAUGE (TANK UNIT)
IGN. SWITCH
LIGHT SWITCH
HAZARD FLASHER SW. CONN.
DIRECTION & HORN SW. CONN.
BACK-UP LT.
STOPLIGHT
COURTESY LT. & SWITCH
TAIL LT.
FLASHER
DIRECTION LT.
PARK BRAKE SW.
KEY BUZZER DOOR SWITCH
DOOR SWITCH
MARKER LT.
RED-BLU
GRY-YEL
GRY-WHT
GRY-GRN
BLK
BLK-YEL
BLK-YEL-RED
GRY-BLK
RED
GRY
BLK-GRN
BRN
GRN
BLK-WHT
BLU
RED-WHT
YEL
RED-YEL
BLK-RED-YEL
GRY-RED
BLK-RED
BLU-WHT
BRN-WHT
BRN-YEL
RED-WHT
BLU-BLK
BLK-BRN
BLK-WHT-GRN
GRY-BLK

1977 Colt

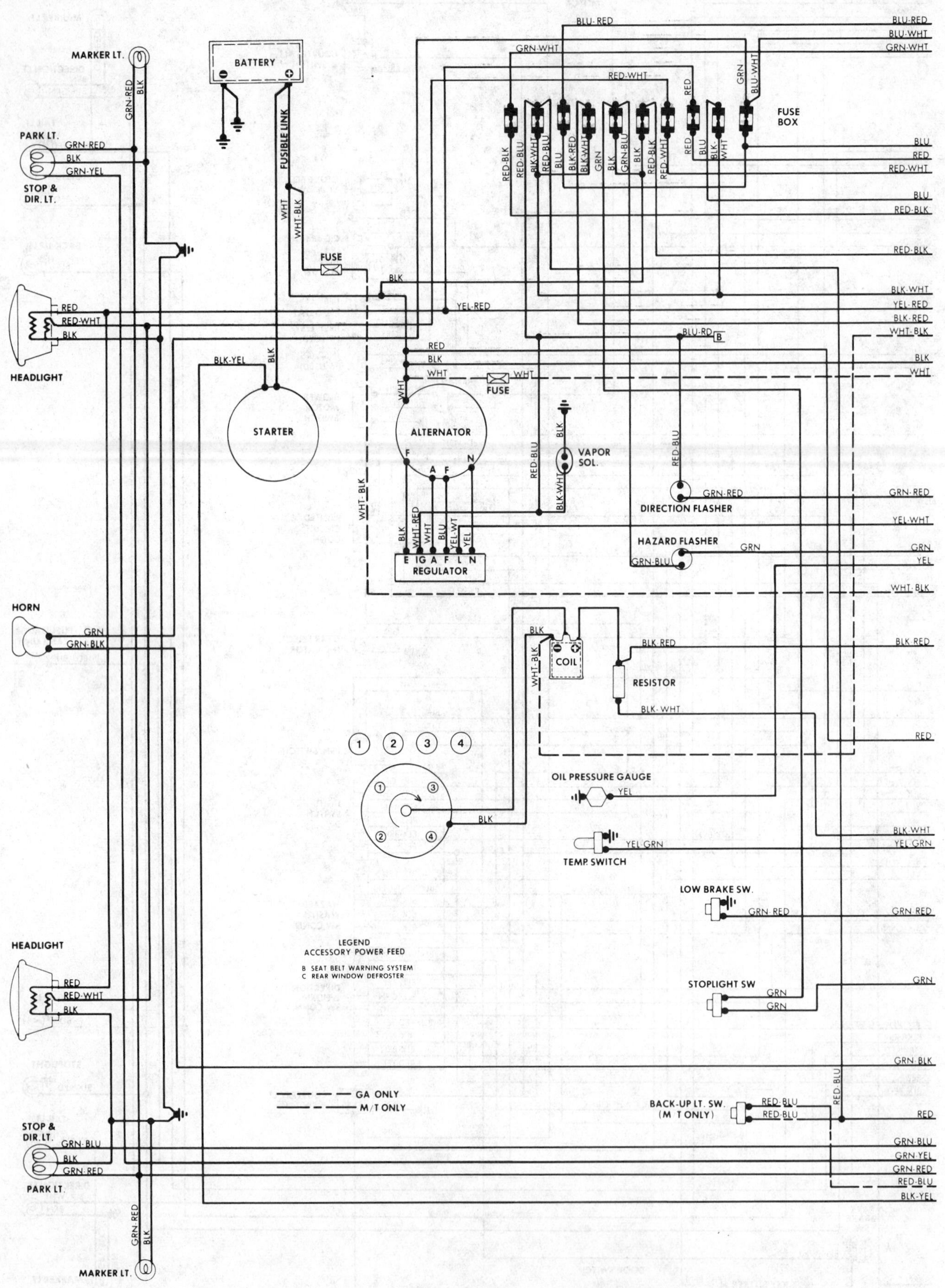

MARKER LT.
PARK LT.
STOP & DIR. LT.
HEADLIGHT
HORN
BATTERY
FUSIBLE LINK
FUSE
STARTER
ALTERNATOR
REGULATOR
VAPOR SOL.
FUSE BOX
DIRECTION FLASHER
HAZARD FLASHER
COIL
RESISTOR
OIL PRESSURE GAUGE
TEMP. SWITCH
LOW BRAKE SW.
STOPLIGHT SW
BACK-UP LT. SW. (M/T ONLY)
LEGEND
ACCESSORY POWER FEED
B SEAT BELT WARNING SYSTEM
C REAR WINDOW DEFROSTER
GA ONLY
M/T ONLY

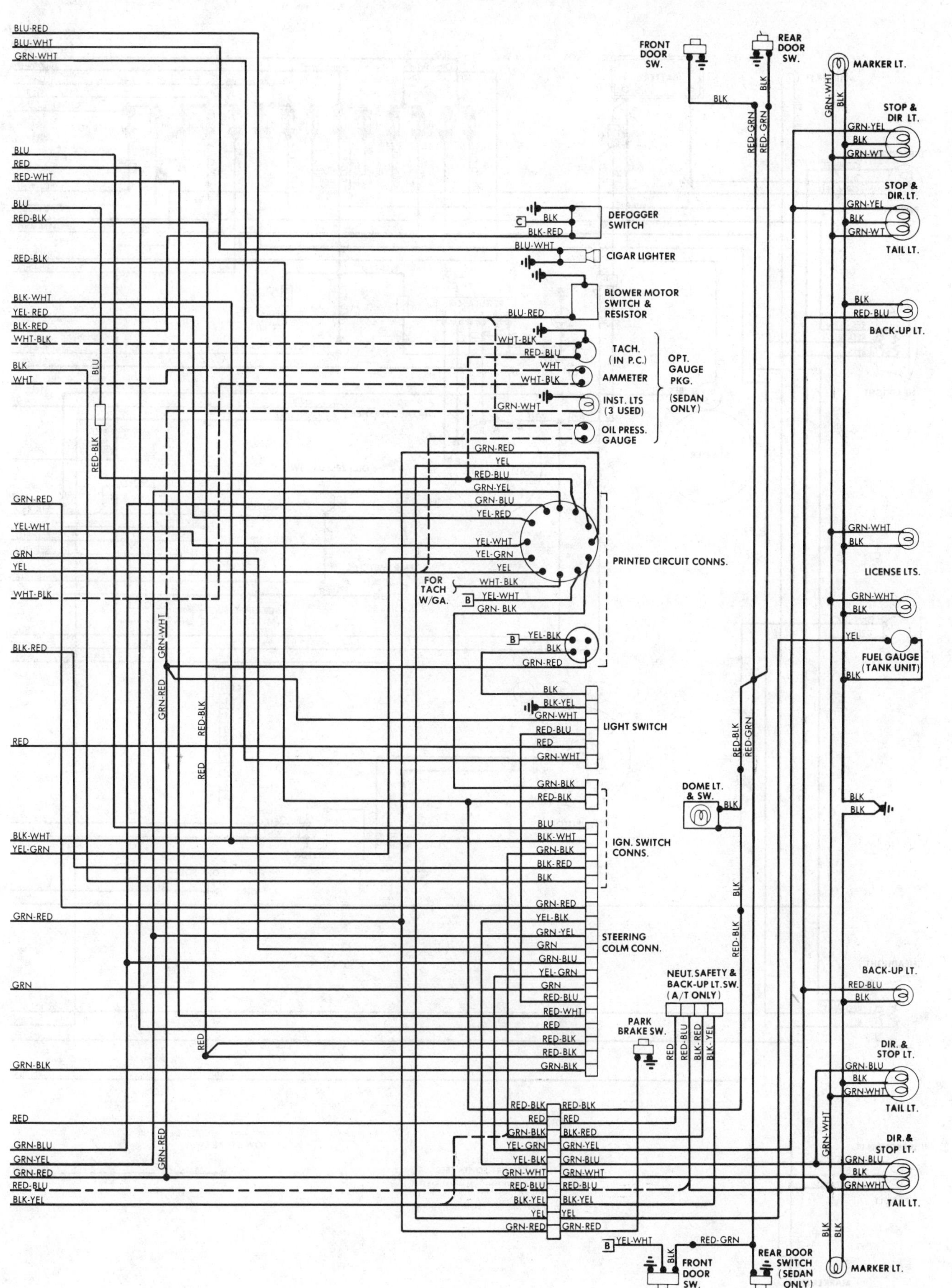
FRONT DOOR SW.
REAR DOOR SW.
MARKER LT.
STOP & DIR LT.
STOP & DIR. LT.
TAIL LT.
DEFOGGER SWITCH
CIGAR LIGHTER
BLOWER MOTOR SWITCH & RESISTOR
BACK-UP LT.
TACH. (IN P.C.)
AMMETER
INST. LTS (3 USED)
OIL PRESS. GAUGE
OPT. GAUGE PKG. (SEDAN ONLY)
PRINTED CIRCUIT CONNS.
FOR TACH W/GA.
LICENSE LTS.
FUEL GAUGE (TANK UNIT)
LIGHT SWITCH
DOME LT. & SW.
IGN. SWITCH CONNS.
STEERING COLM CONN.
NEUT. SAFETY & BACK-UP LT. SW. (A/T ONLY)
PARK BRAKE SW.
DIR. & STOP LT.
FRONT DOOR SW.
REAR DOOR SWITCH (SEDAN ONLY)

1977 Colt

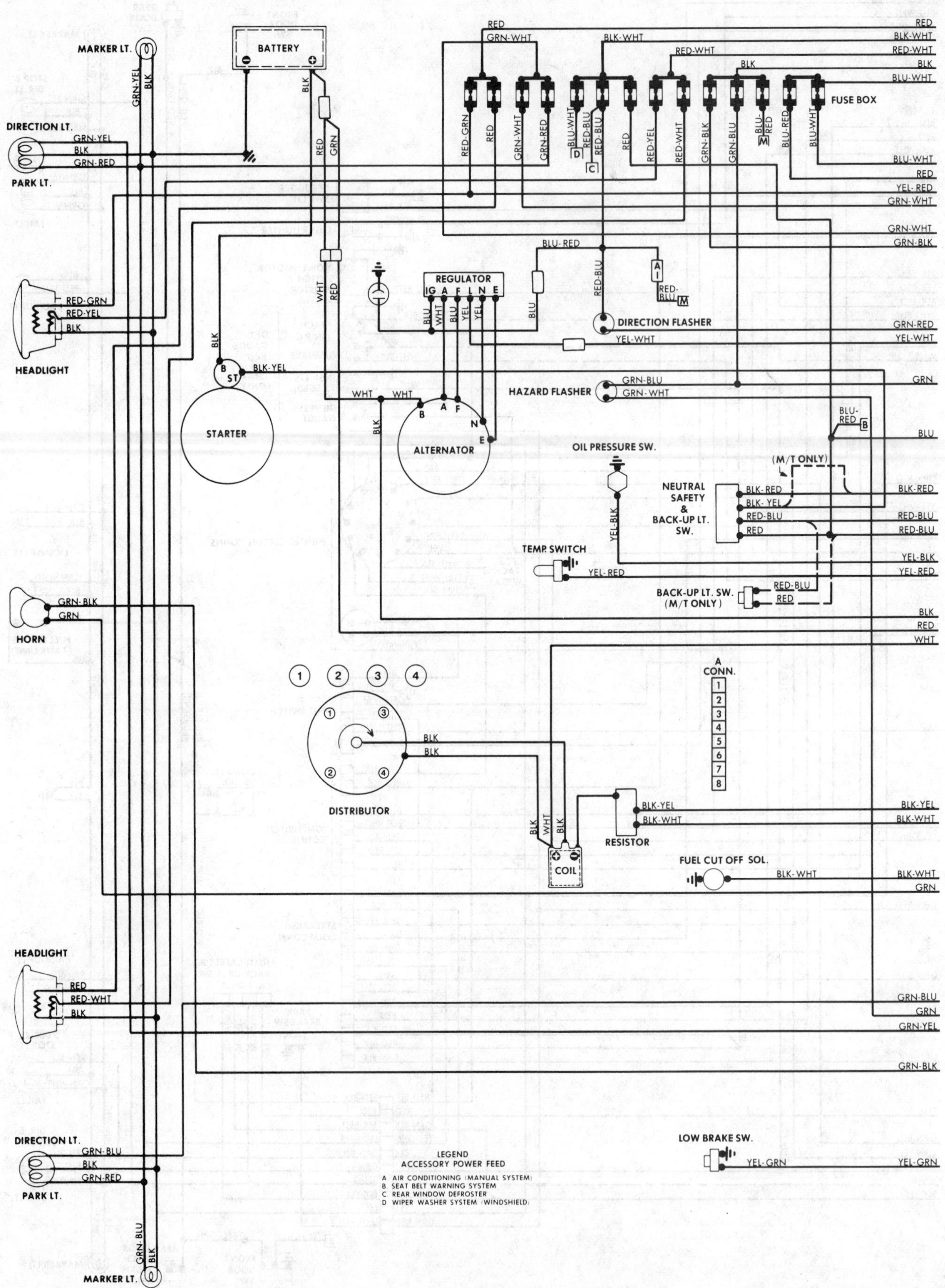
MARKER LT.
BATTERY
DIRECTION LT.
PARK LT.
HEADLIGHT
REGULATOR
IG A F L N E
FUSE BOX
DIRECTION FLASHER
HAZARD FLASHER
STARTER
ALTERNATOR
OIL PRESSURE SW.
NEUTRAL SAFETY & BACK-UP LT. SW.
(M/T ONLY)
TEMP SWITCH
BACK-UP LT. SW. (M/T ONLY)
HORN
DISTRIBUTOR
A CONN.
RESISTOR
COIL
FUEL CUT OFF SOL.
LOW BRAKE SW.
LEGEND
ACCESSORY POWER FEED
A AIR CONDITIONING (MANUAL SYSTEM)
B SEAT BELT WARNING SYSTEM
C REAR WINDOW DEFROSTER
D WIPER WASHER SYSTEM (WINDSHIELD)

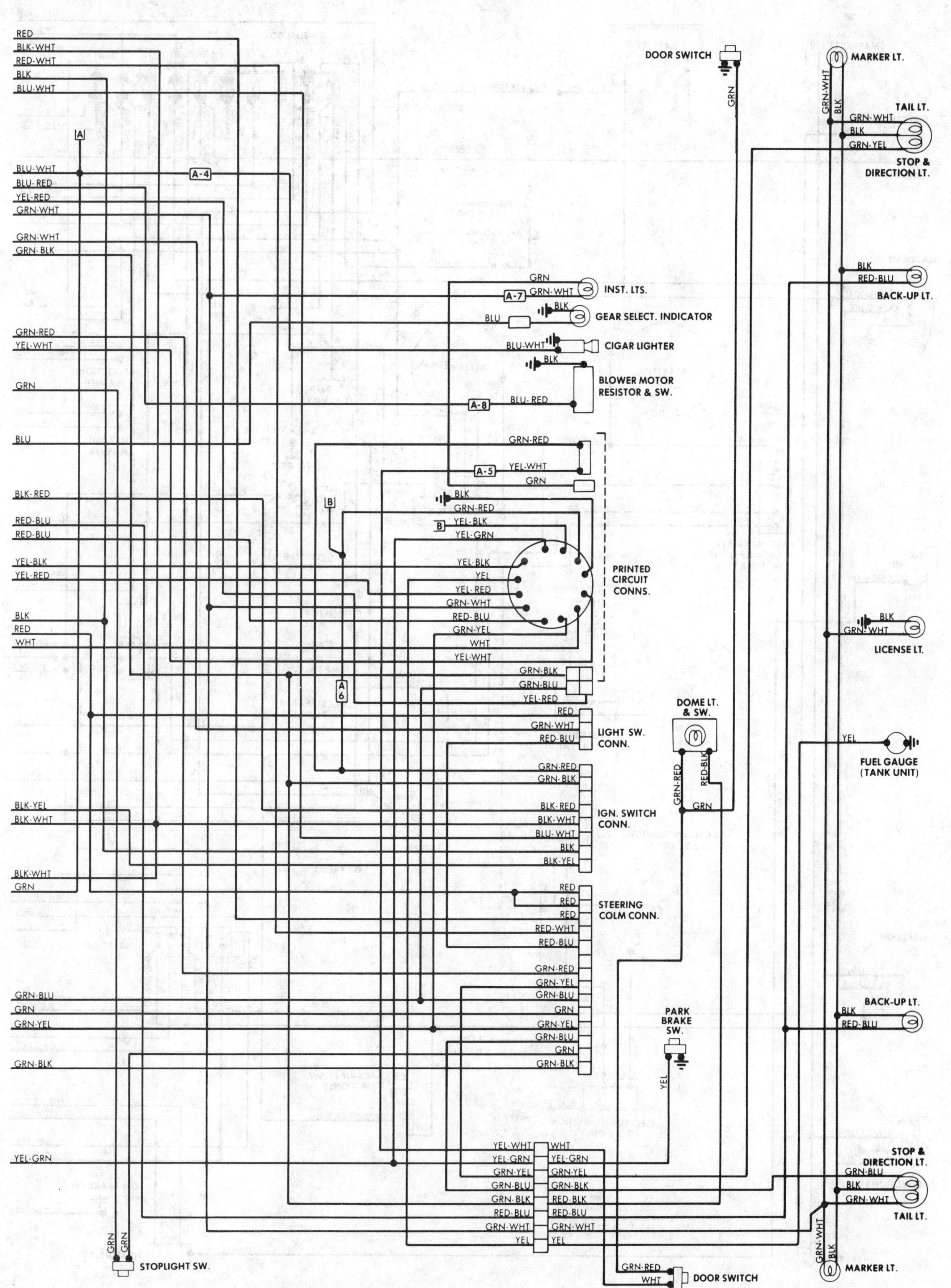

DOOR SWITCH
MARKER LT.
TAIL LT.
STOP & DIRECTION LT.
INST. LTS.
GEAR SELECT. INDICATOR
CIGAR LIGHTER
BLOWER MOTOR RESISTOR & SW.
BACK-UP LT.
PRINTED CIRCUIT CONNS.
LICENSE LT.
DOME LT. & SW.
LIGHT SW. CONN.
FUEL GAUGE (TANK UNIT)
IGN. SWITCH CONN.
STEERING COLM CONN.
PARK BRAKE SW.
BACK-UP LT.
STOP & DIRECTION LT.
TAIL LT.
MARKER LT.
DOOR SWITCH
STOPLIGHT SW.

1977 Courier

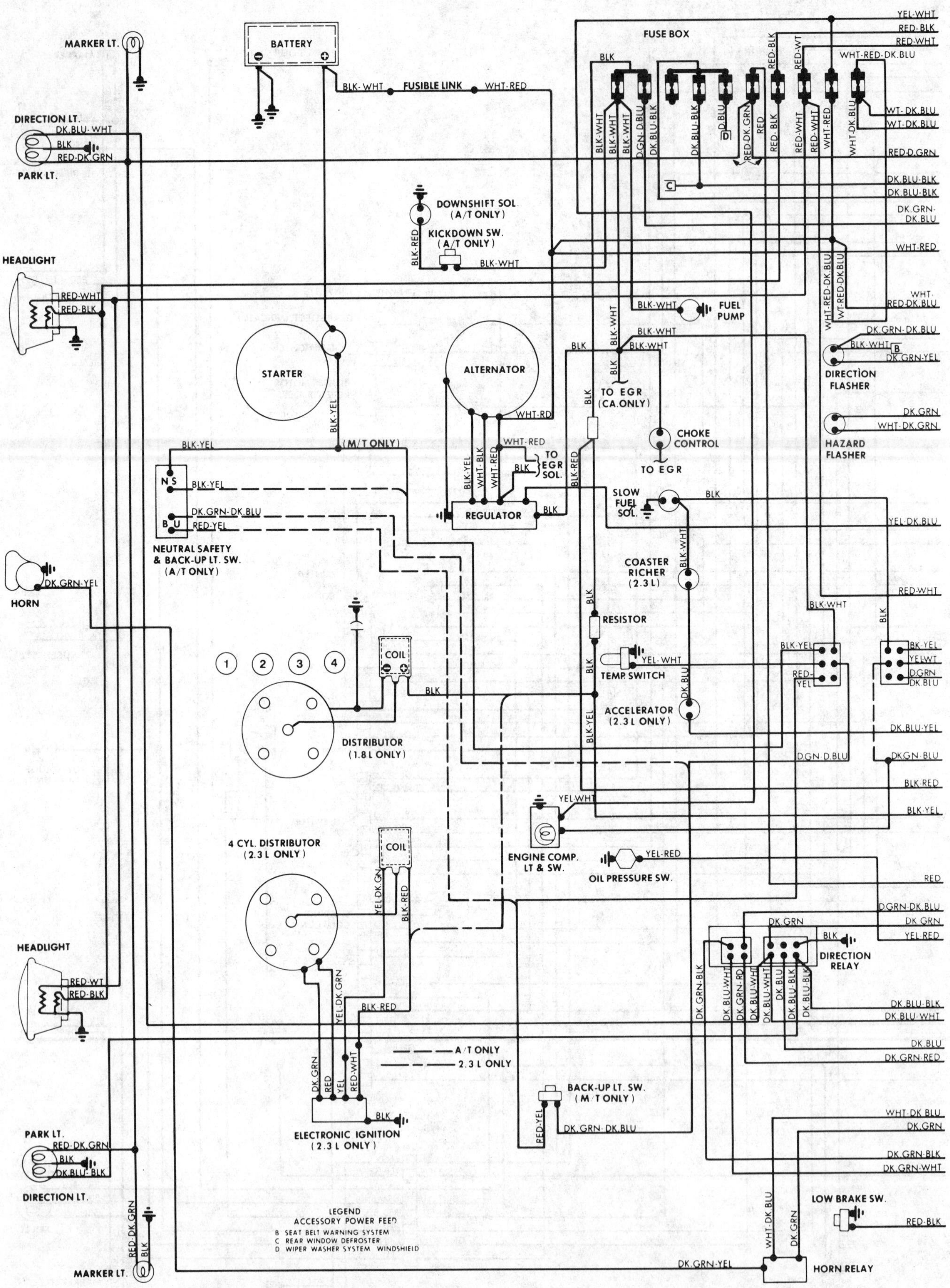

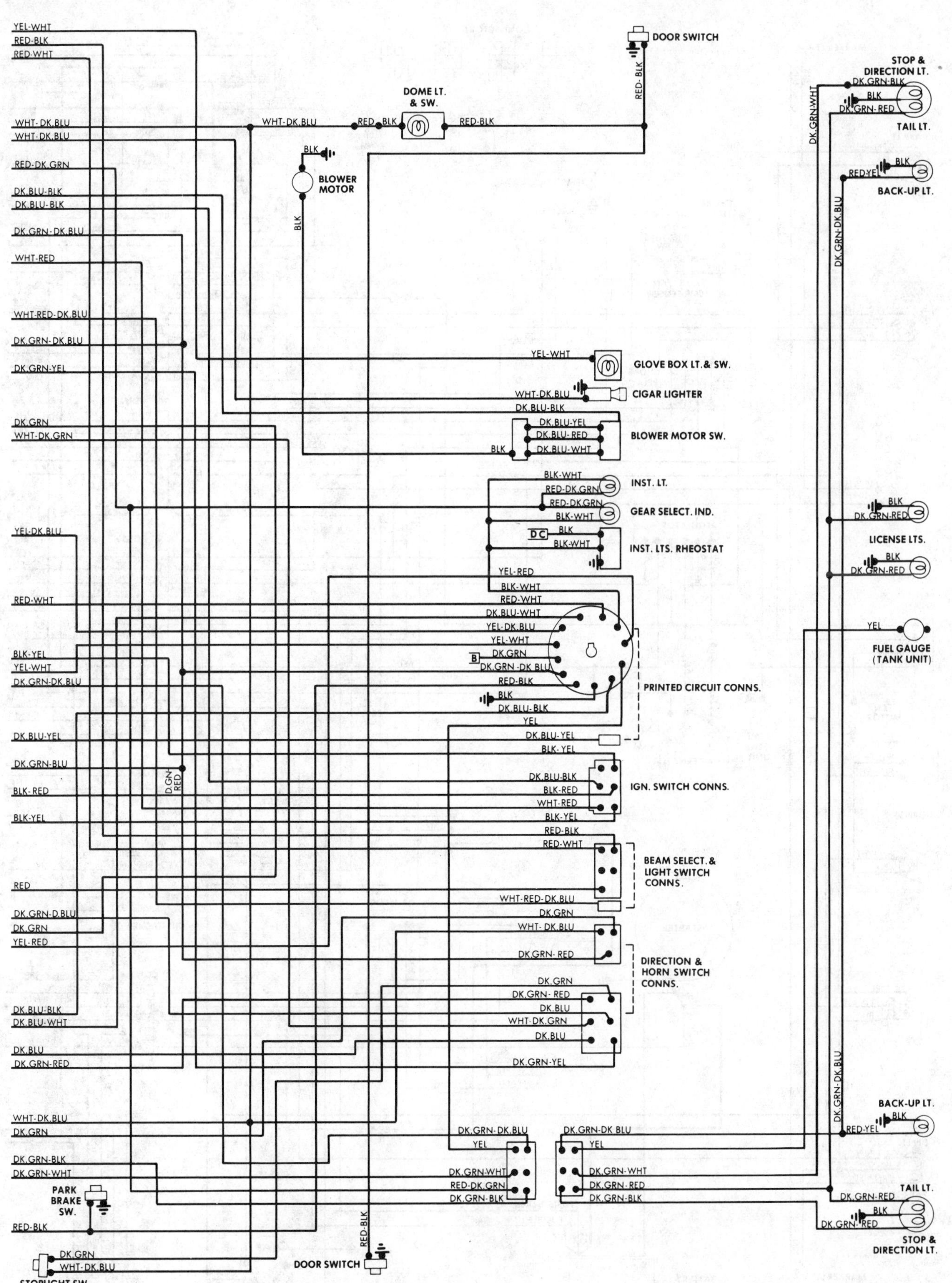

DOOR SWITCH
DOME LT. & SW.
BLOWER MOTOR
STOP & DIRECTION LT.
TAIL LT.
BACK-UP LT.
GLOVE BOX LT. & SW.
CIGAR LIGHTER
BLOWER MOTOR SW.
INST. LT.
GEAR SELECT. IND.
INST. LTS. RHEOSTAT
LICENSE LTS.
FUEL GAUGE (TANK UNIT)
PRINTED CIRCUIT CONNS.
IGN. SWITCH CONNS.
BEAM SELECT. & LIGHT SWITCH CONNS.
DIRECTION & HORN SWITCH CONNS.
PARK BRAKE SW.
STOPLIGHT SW.

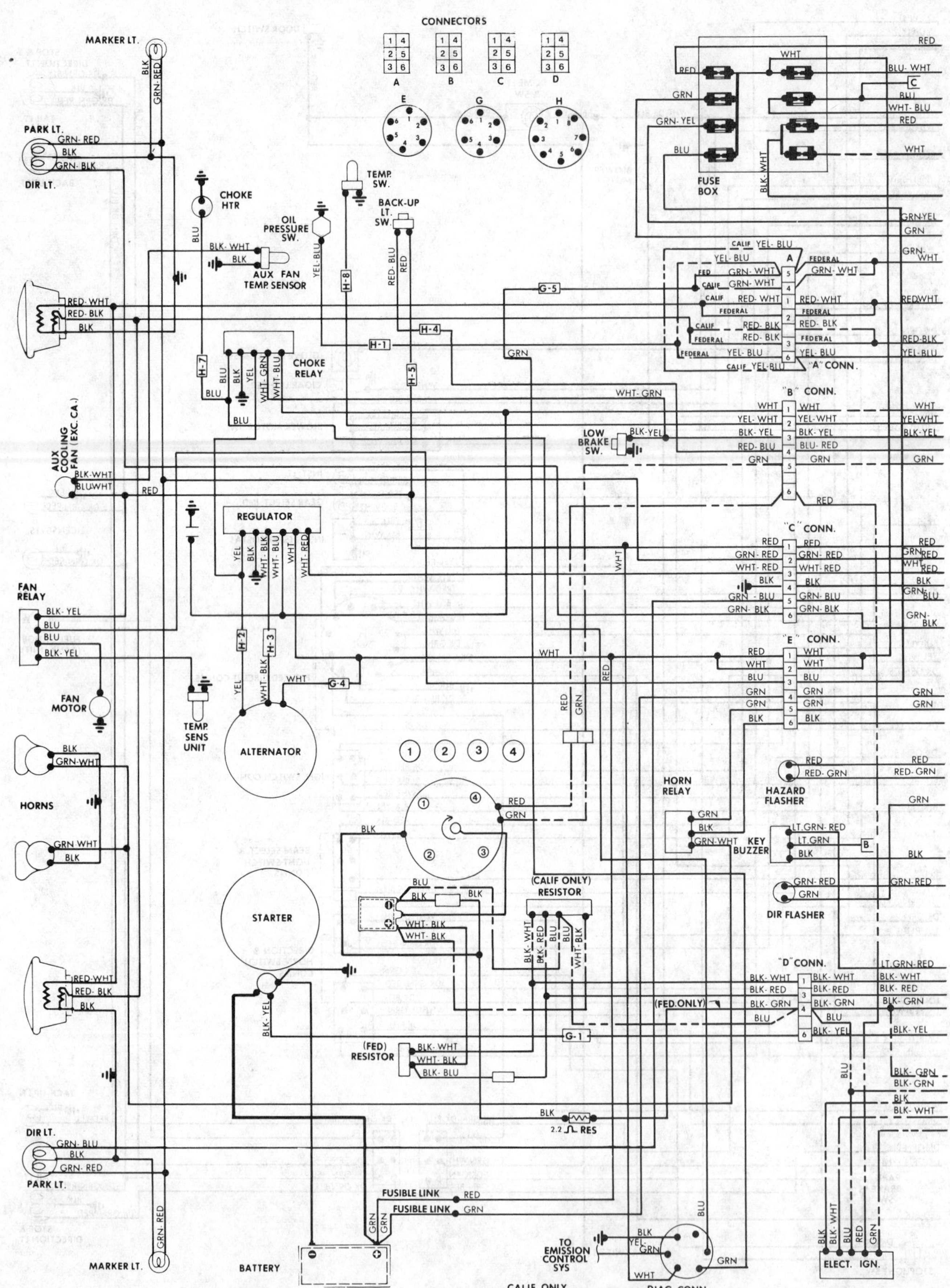

CONNECTORS
A
B
C
D
E
G
H
MARKER LT.
PARK LT.
DIR LT.
CHOKE HTR
TEMP. SW.
OIL PRESSURE SW.
BACK-UP LT. SW.
AUX FAN TEMP. SENSOR
CHOKE RELAY
AUX COOLING FAN (EXC. CA.)
REGULATOR
FAN RELAY
FAN MOTOR
TEMP. SENS UNIT
ALTERNATOR
HORNS
STARTER
FUSE BOX
"A" CONN.
"B" CONN.
"C" CONN.
"E" CONN.
"D" CONN.
LOW BRAKE SW.
HORN RELAY
HAZARD FLASHER
KEY BUZZER
DIR FLASHER
(CALIF ONLY) RESISTOR
(FED) RESISTOR
(FED. ONLY)
2.2 Ω RES
FUSIBLE LINK
BATTERY
TO EMISSION CONTROL SYS
DIAG. CONN.
CALIF ONLY
ELECT. IGN.

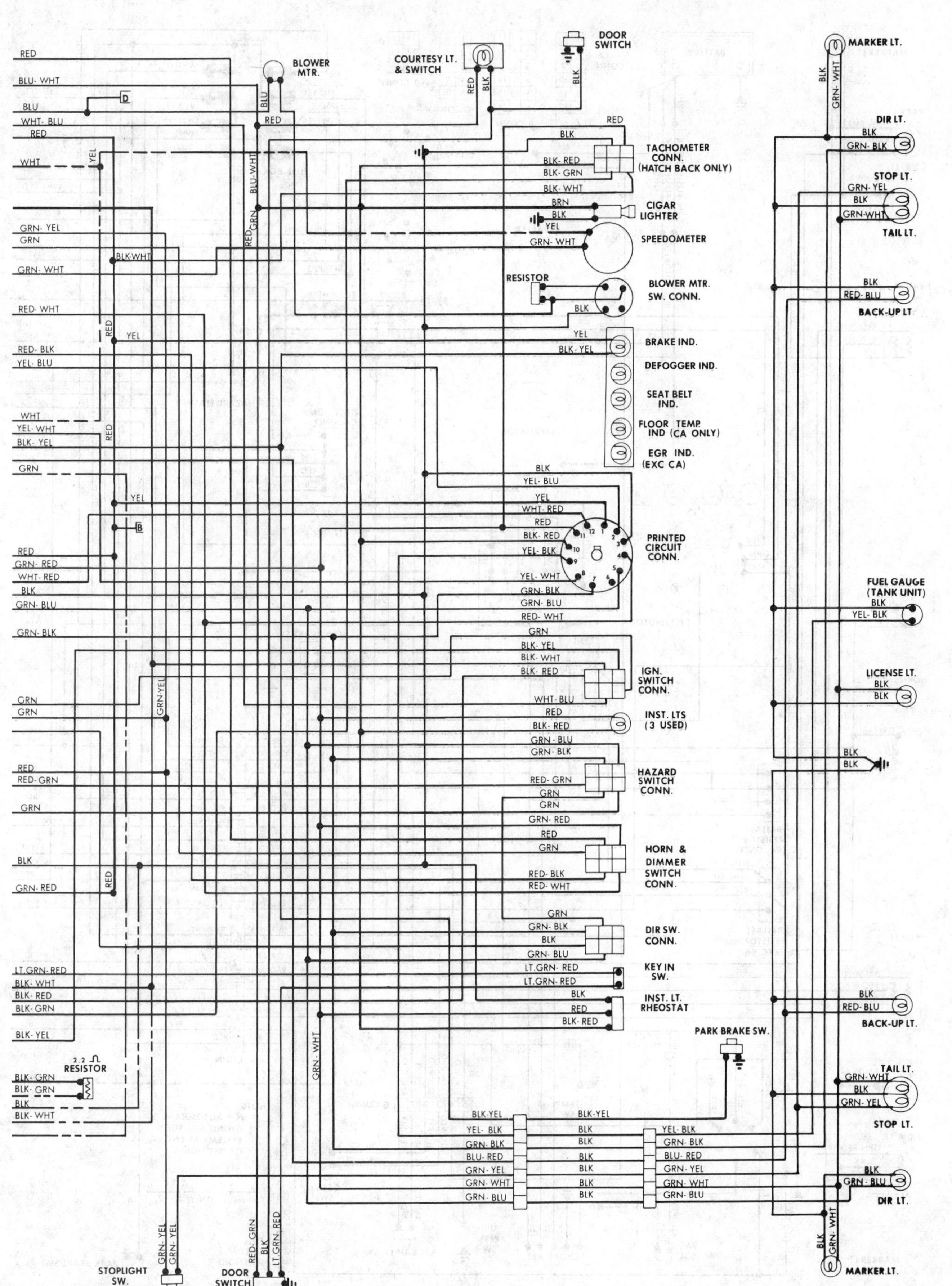
BLOWER MTR.
COURTESY LT. & SWITCH
DOOR SWITCH
MARKER LT.
DIR LT.
TACHOMETER CONN. (HATCH BACK ONLY)
STOP LT.
CIGAR LIGHTER
TAIL LT.
SPEEDOMETER
RESISTOR
BLOWER MTR. SW. CONN.
BACK-UP LT.
BRAKE IND.
DEFOGGER IND.
SEAT BELT IND.
FLOOR TEMP. IND (CA ONLY)
EGR IND. (EXC CA)
PRINTED CIRCUIT CONN.
FUEL GAUGE (TANK UNIT)
IGN. SWITCH CONN.
LICENSE LT.
INST. LTS (3 USED)
HAZARD SWITCH CONN.
HORN & DIMMER SWITCH CONN.
DIR SW. CONN.
KEY IN SW.
INST. LT. RHEOSTAT
PARK BRAKE SW.
2.2 Ω RESISTOR
STOPLIGHT SW.
DOOR SWITCH

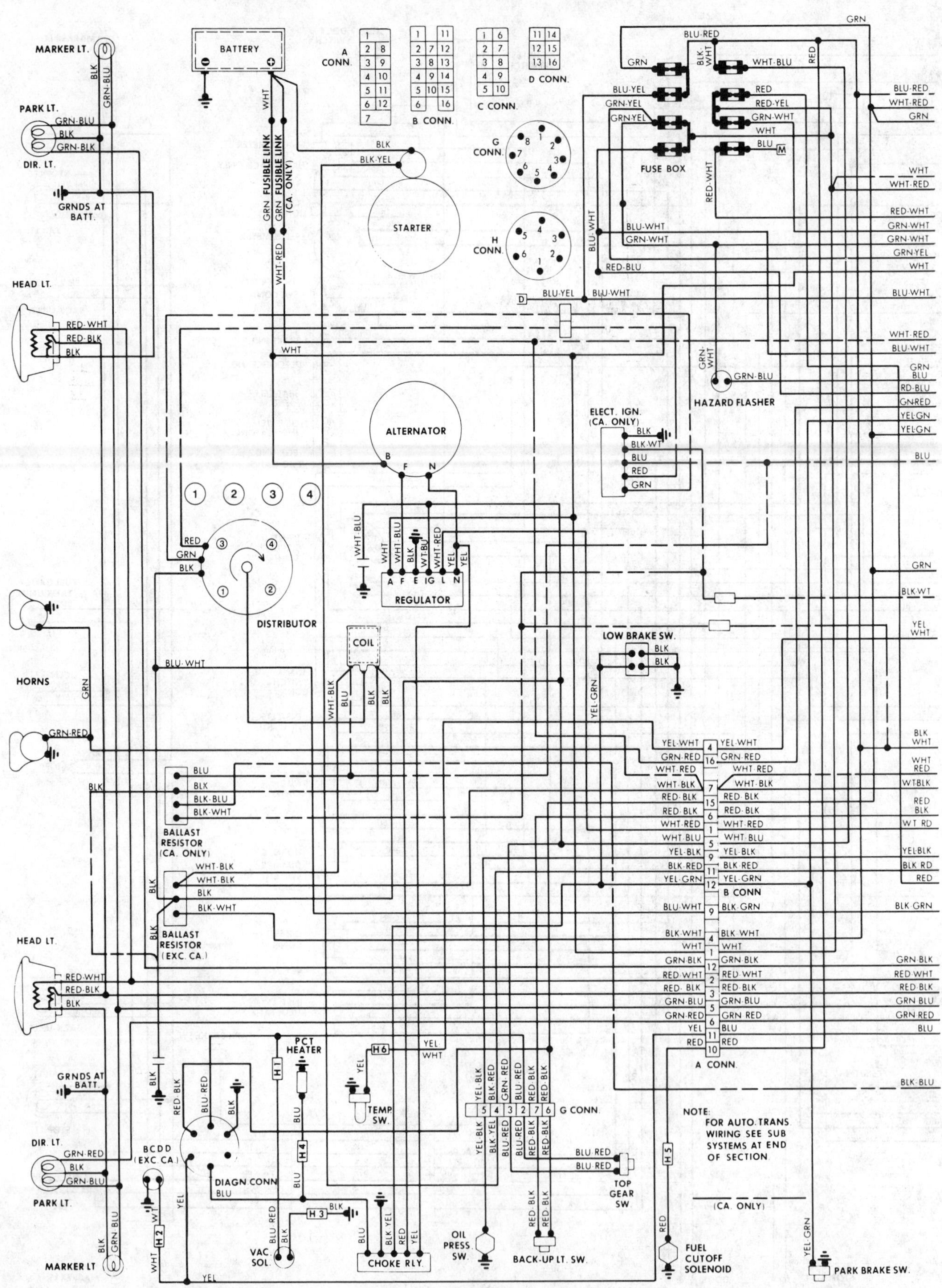
MARKER LT.
PARK LT.
DIR. LT.
GRNDS AT BATT.
HEAD LT.
HORNS
BATTERY
A CONN.
B CONN.
C CONN.
D CONN.
G CONN.
H CONN.
STARTER
GRN FUSIBLE LINK
GRN FUSIBLE LINK (CA. ONLY)
FUSE BOX
HAZARD FLASHER
ALTERNATOR
ELECT. IGN. (CA. ONLY)
DISTRIBUTOR
REGULATOR
COIL
LOW BRAKE SW.
BALLAST RESISTOR (CA. ONLY)
BALLAST RESISTOR (EXC. CA.)
PCT HEATER
TEMP. SW.
BCDD (EXC. CA.)
DIAGN. CONN
VAC. SOL.
CHOKE RLY.
OIL PRESS. SW.
BACK-UP LT. SW.
TOP GEAR SW.
FUEL CUTOFF SOLENOID
PARK BRAKE SW.
NOTE: FOR AUTO. TRANS WIRING SEE SUB SYSTEMS AT END OF SECTION
(CA. ONLY)

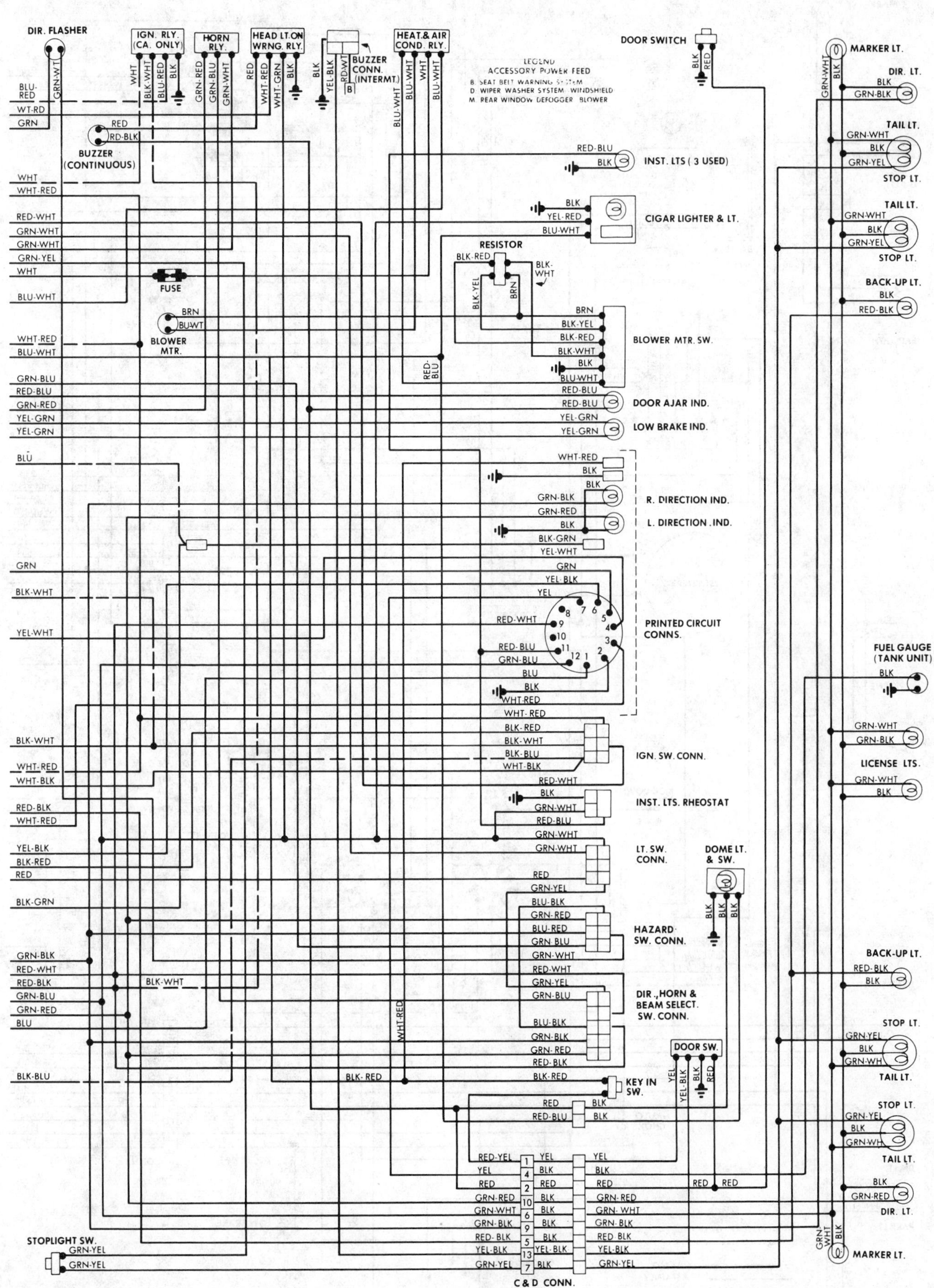
DIR. FLASHER
IGN. RLY. (CA. ONLY)
HORN RLY.
HEAD LT. ON WRNG. RLY.
BUZZER CONN. (INTERMT.)
HEAT.& AIR COND. RLY.
DOOR SWITCH
MARKER LT.
DIR. LT.
LEGEND
ACCESSORY POWER FEED
B SEAT BELT WARNING SYSTEM
D WIPER WASHER SYSTEM WINDSHIELD
M REAR WINDOW DEFOGGER BLOWER
BUZZER (CONTINUOUS)
TAIL LT.
STOP LT.
INST. LTS (3 USED)
CIGAR LIGHTER & LT.
RESISTOR
FUSE
BACK-UP LT.
BLOWER MTR.
BLOWER MTR. SW.
DOOR AJAR IND.
LOW BRAKE IND.
R. DIRECTION IND.
L. DIRECTION IND.
PRINTED CIRCUIT CONNS.
FUEL GAUGE (TANK UNIT)
IGN. SW. CONN.
LICENSE LTS.
INST. LTS. RHEOSTAT
LT. SW. CONN.
DOME LT. & SW.
HAZARD SW. CONN.
DIR., HORN & BEAM SELECT. SW. CONN.
DOOR SW.
KEY IN SW.
STOPLIGHT SW.
C & D CONN.

1977 Datsun

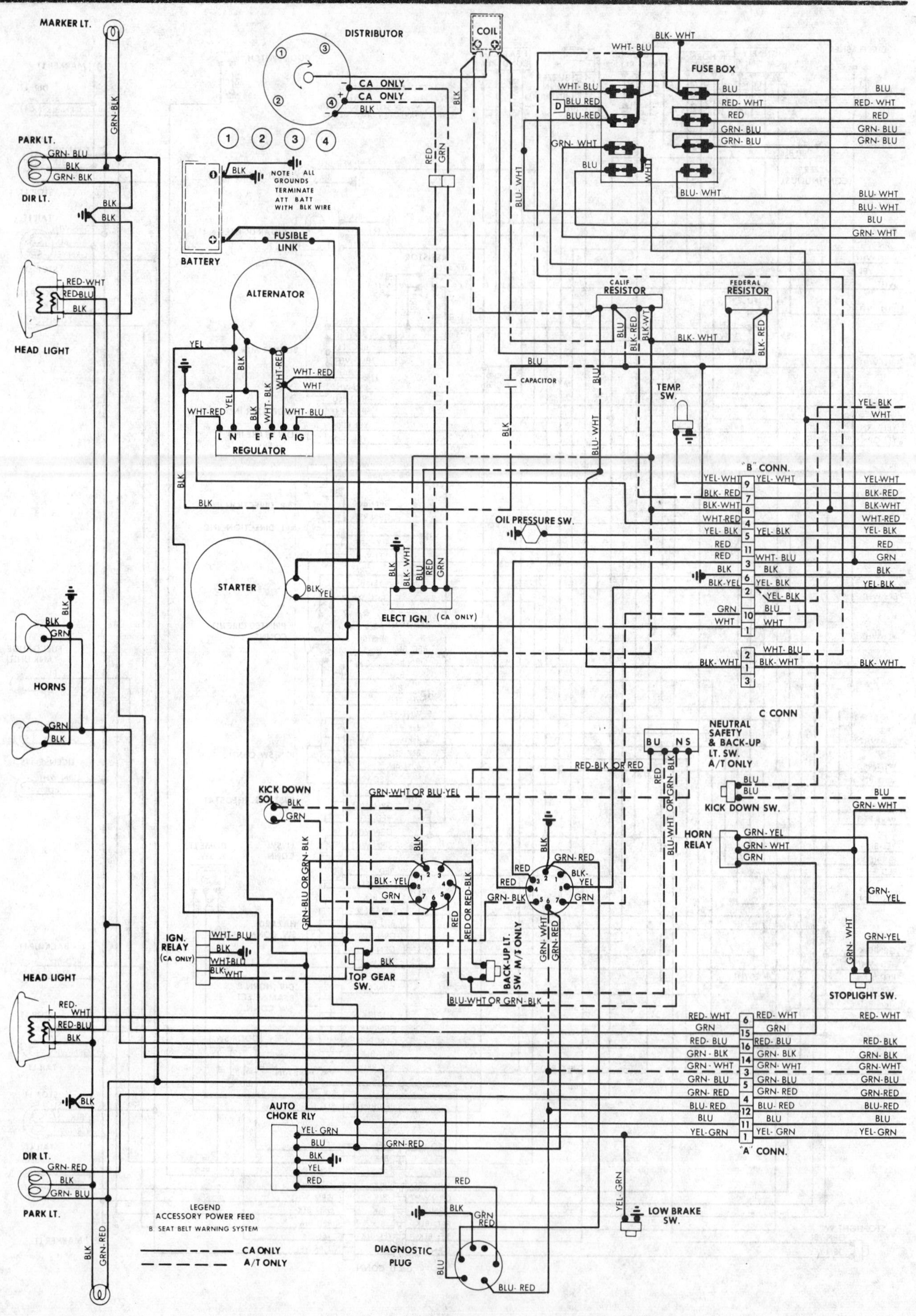

MARKER LT.
PARK LT.
DIR LT.
HEAD LIGHT
HORNS
DISTRIBUTOR
CA ONLY
COIL
BATTERY
NOTE: ALL GROUNDS TERMINATE ATT BATT WITH BLK WIRE
FUSIBLE LINK
ALTERNATOR
REGULATOR
FUSE BOX
CALIF RESISTOR
FEDERAL RESISTOR
CAPACITOR
TEMP. SW.
"B" CONN.
OIL PRESSURE SW.
STARTER
ELECT IGN. (CA ONLY)
C CONN
NEUTRAL SAFETY & BACK-UP LT. SW. A/T ONLY
KICK DOWN SOL
KICK DOWN SW.
HORN RELAY
IGN. RELAY (CA ONLY)
TOP GEAR SW.
BACK-UP LT. SW. M/T ONLY
STOPLIGHT SW.
"A" CONN.
AUTO CHOKE RLY
LOW BRAKE SW.
DIAGNOSTIC PLUG
LEGEND
ACCESSORY POWER FEED
B SEAT BELT WARNING SYSTEM
CA ONLY
A/T ONLY

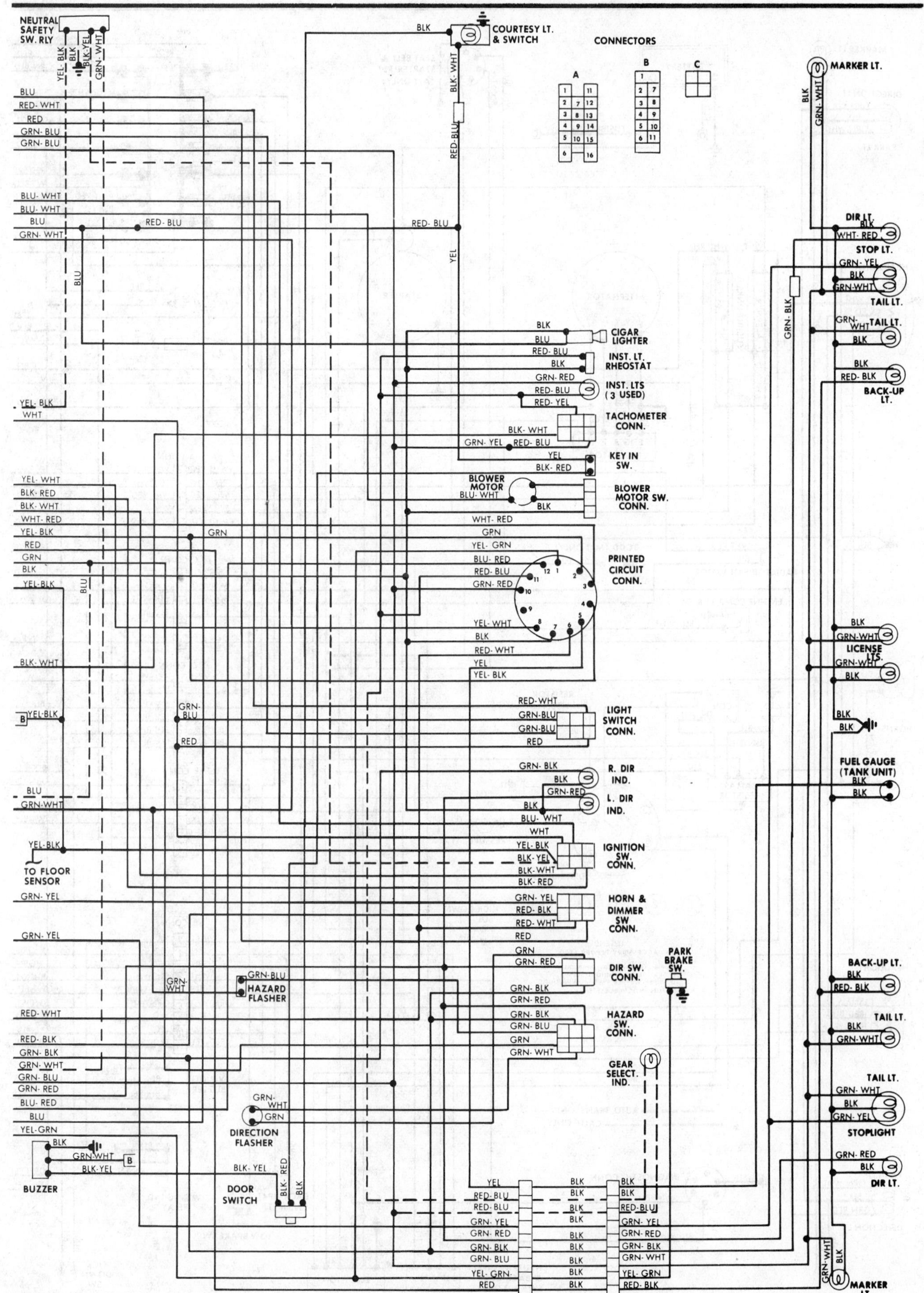
NEUTRAL SAFETY SW. RLY
COURTESY LT. & SWITCH
CONNECTORS
A
B
C
MARKER LT.
DIR LT.
STOP LT.
TAIL LT.
CIGAR LIGHTER
INST. LT. RHEOSTAT
INST. LTS (3 USED)
TACHOMETER CONN.
BACK-UP LT.
KEY IN SW.
BLOWER MOTOR
BLOWER MOTOR SW. CONN.
PRINTED CIRCUIT CONN.
LICENSE LTS.
LIGHT SWITCH CONN.
R. DIR IND.
L. DIR IND.
FUEL GAUGE (TANK UNIT)
TO FLOOR SENSOR
IGNITION SW. CONN.
HORN & DIMMER SW CONN.
PARK BRAKE SW.
HAZARD FLASHER
DIR SW. CONN.
HAZARD SW. CONN.
GEAR SELECT. IND.
STOPLIGHT
DIRECTION FLASHER
BUZZER
DOOR SWITCH

1977 Datsun

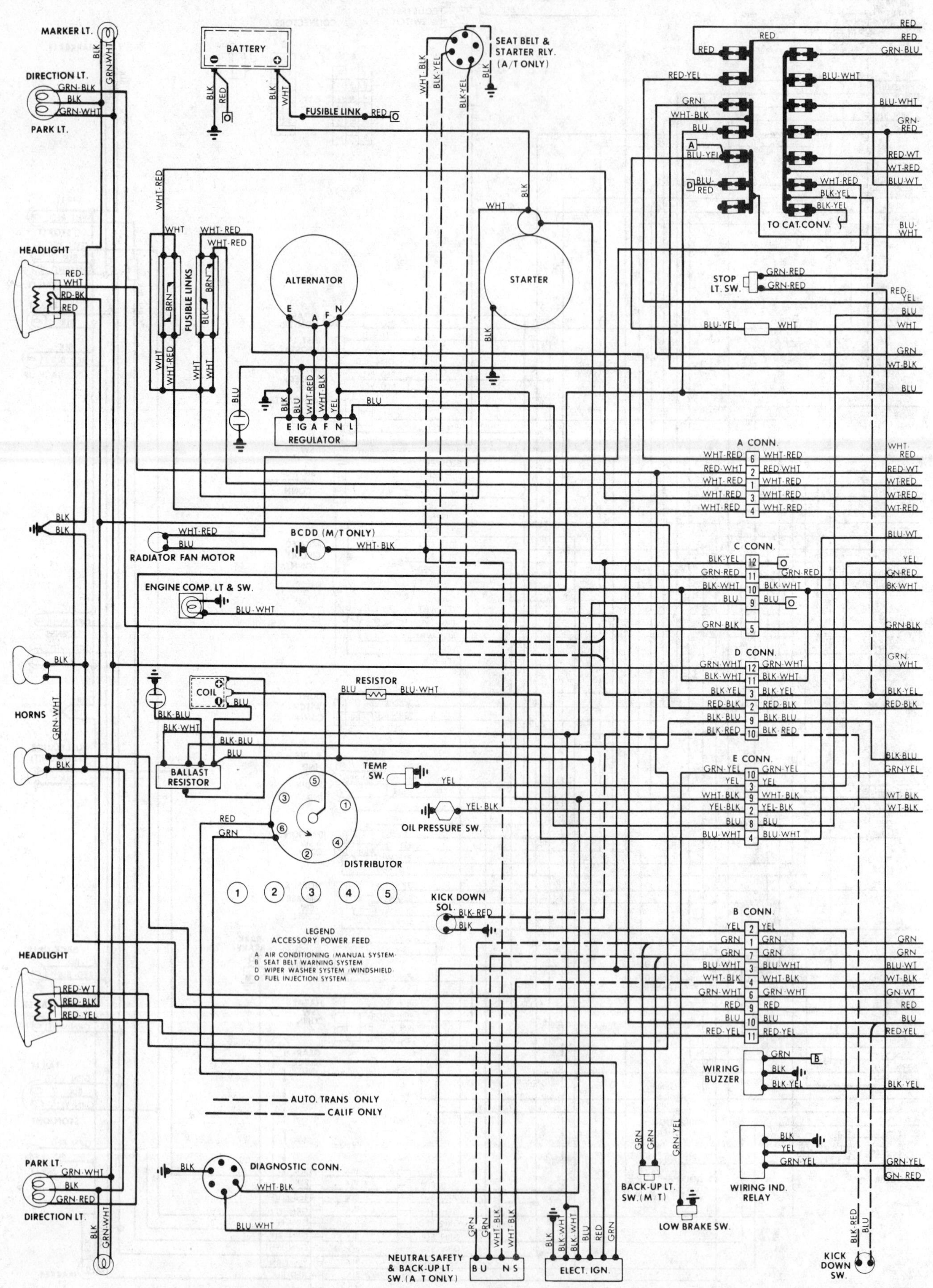
MARKER LT.
DIRECTION LT.
PARK LT.
BATTERY
FUSIBLE LINK
SEAT BELT & STARTER RLY. (A/T ONLY)
TO CAT. CONV.
HEADLIGHT
FUSIBLE LINKS
ALTERNATOR
STARTER
STOP LT. SW.
REGULATOR
A CONN.
RADIATOR FAN MOTOR
BCDD (M/T ONLY)
C CONN.
ENGINE COMP. LT & SW.
D CONN.
HORNS
COIL
RESISTOR
BALLAST RESISTOR
TEMP. SW.
E CONN.
OIL PRESSURE SW.
DISTRIBUTOR
KICK DOWN SOL.
B CONN.
LEGEND
ACCESSORY POWER FEED
A AIR CONDITIONING (MANUAL SYSTEM)
B SEAT BELT WARNING SYSTEM
D WIPER WASHER SYSTEM (WINDSHIELD)
O FUEL INJECTION SYSTEM
HEADLIGHT
WIRING BUZZER
AUTO. TRANS ONLY
CALIF ONLY
PARK LT.
DIAGNOSTIC CONN.
DIRECTION LT.
BACK-UP LT. SW. (M/T)
LOW BRAKE SW.
WIRING IND. RELAY
KICK DOWN SW.
NEUTRAL SAFETY & BACK-UP LT. SW. (A/T ONLY)
ELECT. IGN.

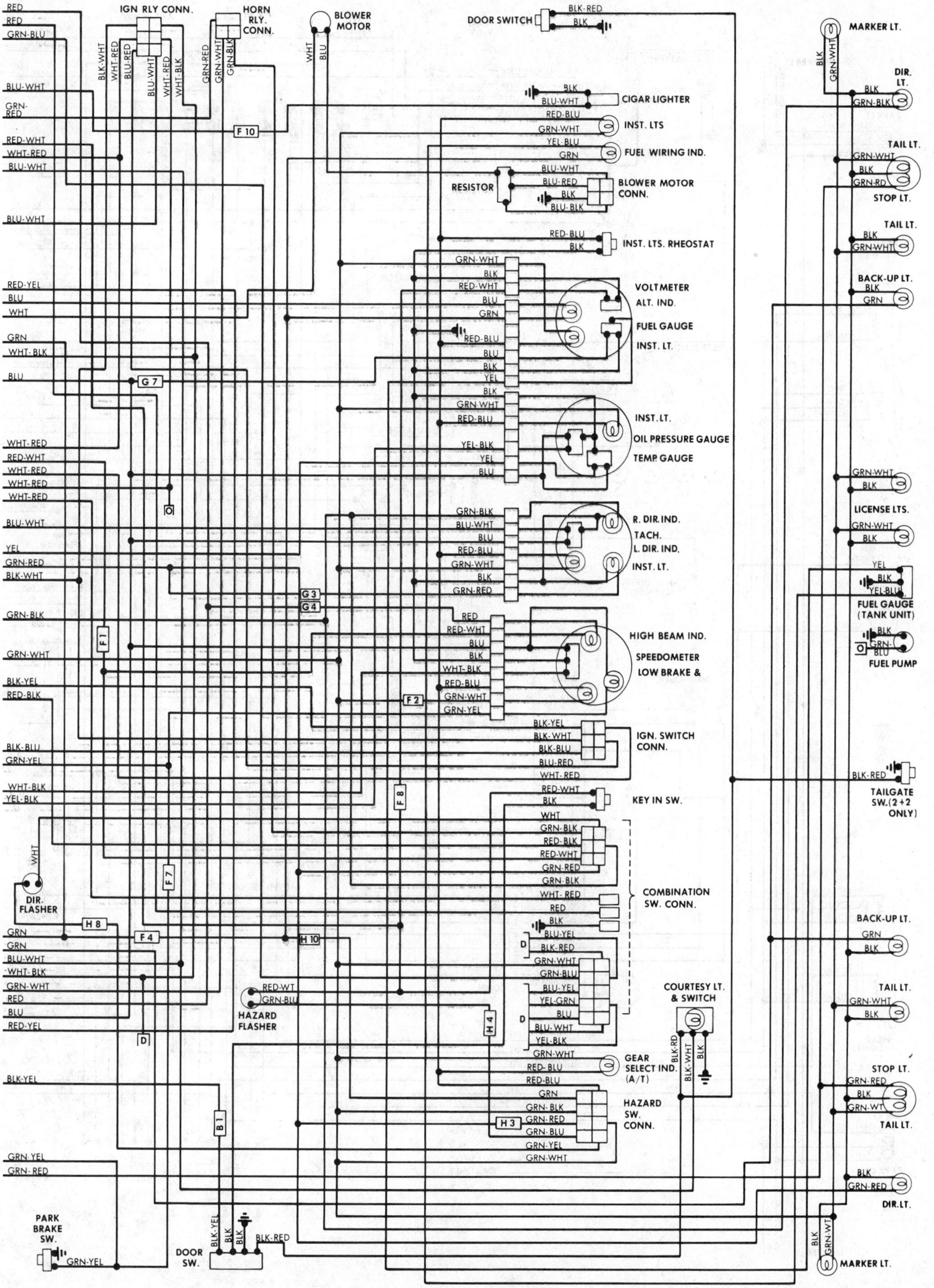

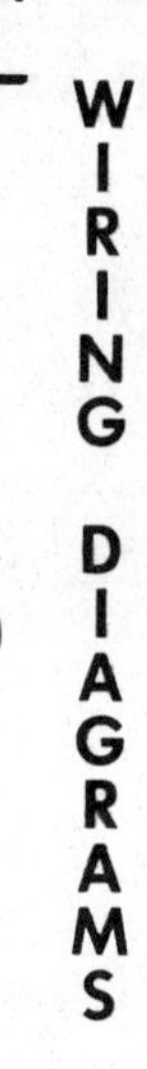

IGN RLY CONN.
HORN RLY. CONN.
BLOWER MOTOR
DOOR SWITCH
MARKER LT.
DIR. LT.
CIGAR LIGHTER
INST. LTS
FUEL WIRING IND.
RESISTOR
BLOWER MOTOR CONN.
TAIL LT.
STOP LT.
INST. LTS. RHEOSTAT
TAIL LT.
BACK-UP LT.
VOLTMETER
ALT. IND.
FUEL GAUGE
INST. LT.
INST. LT.
OIL PRESSURE GAUGE
TEMP. GAUGE
LICENSE LTS.
R. DIR. IND.
TACH.
L. DIR. IND.
INST. LT.
FUEL GAUGE (TANK UNIT)
FUEL PUMP
HIGH BEAM IND.
SPEEDOMETER
LOW BRAKE &
IGN. SWITCH CONN.
TAILGATE SW. (2+2 ONLY)
KEY IN SW.
COMBINATION SW. CONN.
DIR. FLASHER
BACK-UP LT.
TAIL LT.
COURTESY LT. & SWITCH
HAZARD FLASHER
GEAR SELECT IND. (A/T)
STOP LT.
TAIL LT.
HAZARD SW. CONN.
DIR. LT.
PARK BRAKE SW.
DOOR SW.
MARKER LT.
F 10
G 7
G 3
G 4
F 1
F 2
F 8
F 7
H 8
F 4
H 10
H 4
H 3
B 1

1977 Datsun

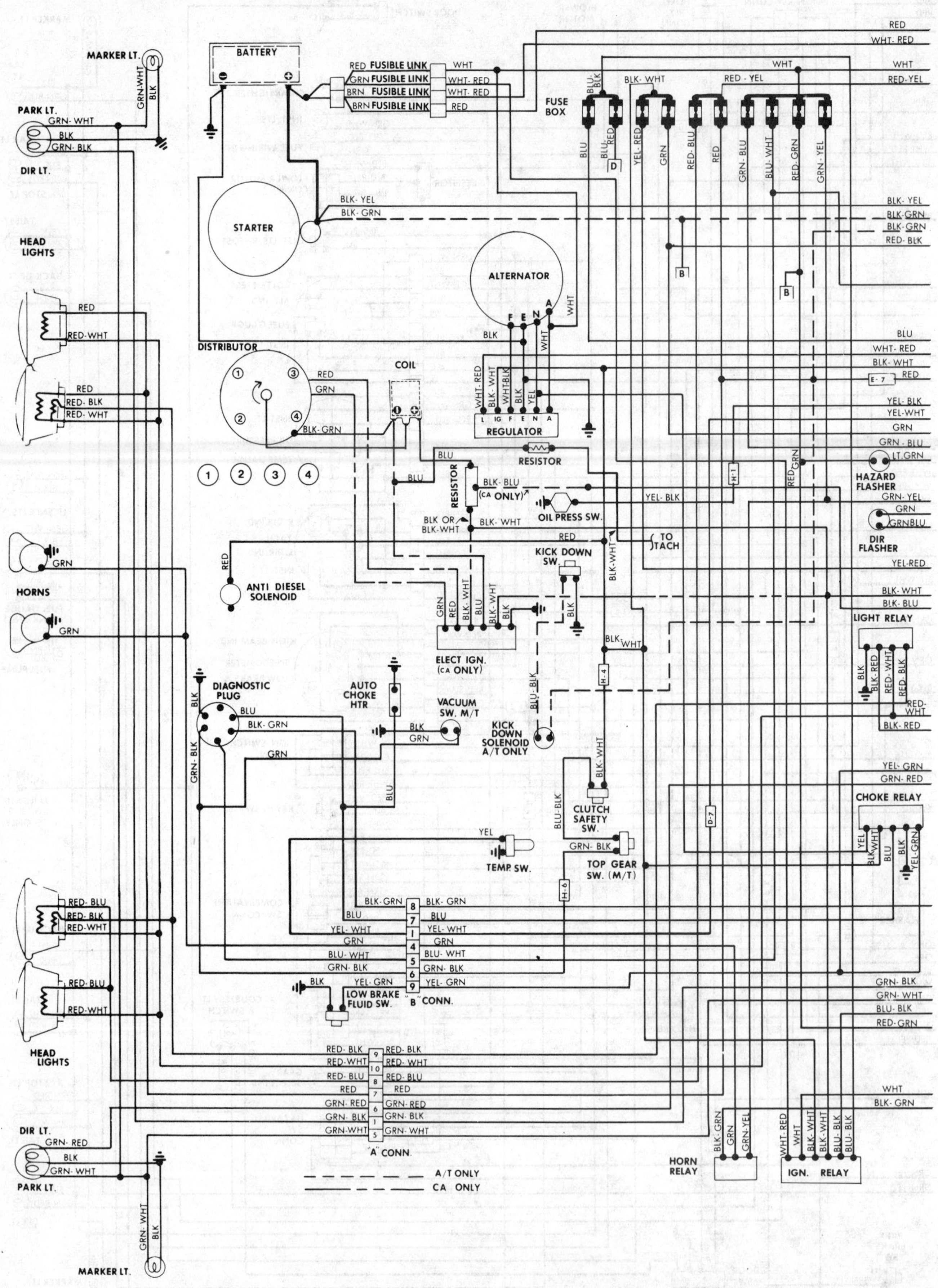

MARKER LT.
PARK LT.
DIR LT.
HEAD LIGHTS
BATTERY
FUSIBLE LINK
FUSE BOX
STARTER
ALTERNATOR
DISTRIBUTOR
COIL
REGULATOR
RESISTOR
OIL PRESS SW.
TO TACH
KICK DOWN SW.
HAZARD FLASHER
DIR FLASHER
ANTI DIESEL SOLENOID
HORNS
ELECT IGN. (CA ONLY)
LIGHT RELAY
DIAGNOSTIC PLUG
AUTO CHOKE HTR
VACUUM SW. M/T
KICK DOWN SOLENOID A/T ONLY
CLUTCH SAFETY SW.
CHOKE RELAY
TEMP. SW.
TOP GEAR SW. (M/T)
LOW BRAKE FLUID SW.
"B" CONN.
"A" CONN.
HORN RELAY
IGN. RELAY
A/T ONLY
CA ONLY

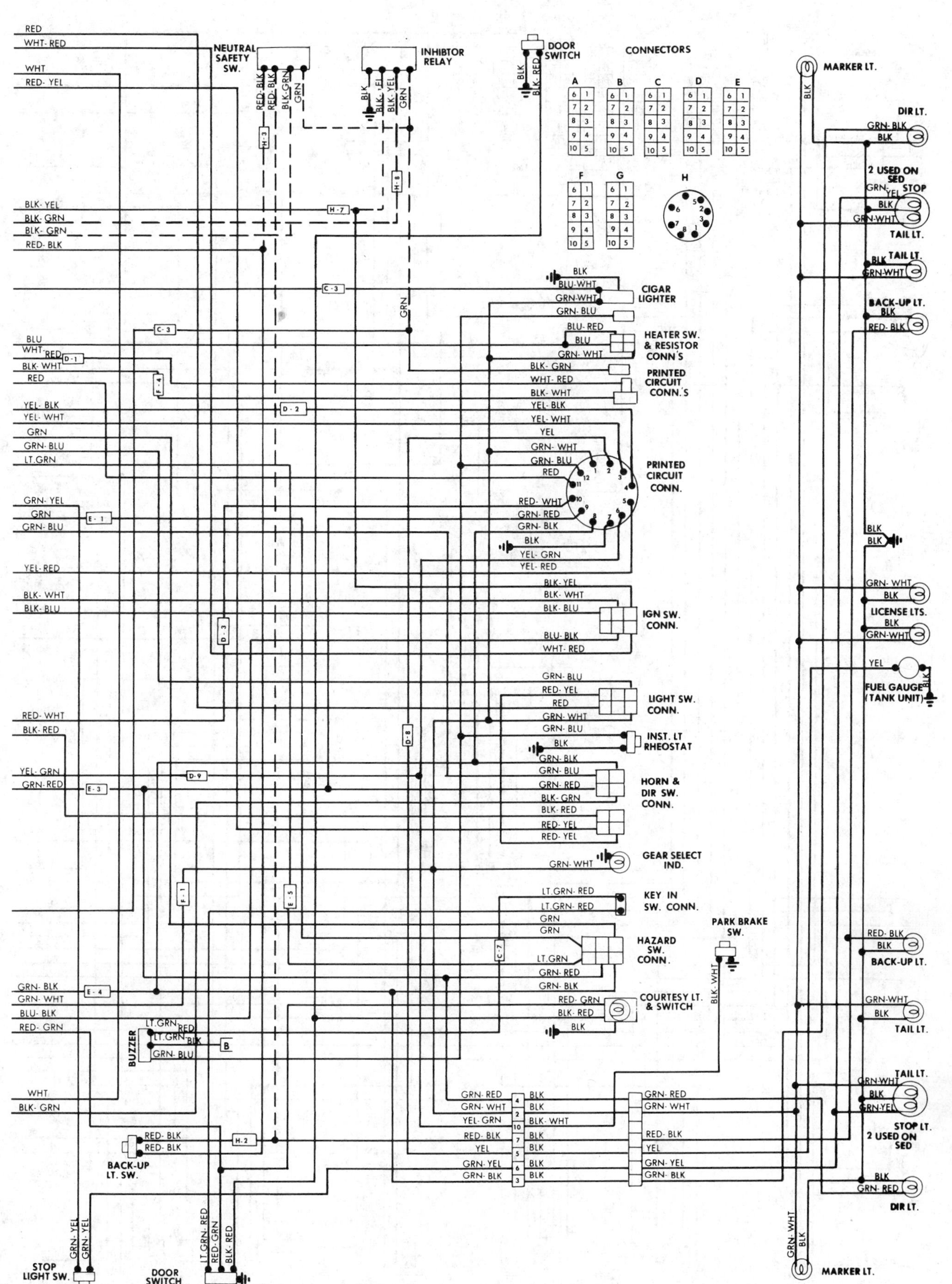
NEUTRAL SAFETY SW.
INHIBITOR RELAY
DOOR SWITCH
CONNECTORS
MARKER LT.
DIR LT.
2 USED ON SED
STOP
TAIL LT.
BACK-UP LT.
CIGAR LIGHTER
HEATER SW. & RESISTOR CONN'S
PRINTED CIRCUIT CONN.'S
PRINTED CIRCUIT CONN.
LICENSE LTS.
IGN SW. CONN.
FUEL GAUGE (TANK UNIT)
LIGHT SW. CONN.
INST. LT RHEOSTAT
HORN & DIR SW. CONN.
GEAR SELECT IND.
KEY IN SW. CONN.
PARK BRAKE SW.
HAZARD SW. CONN.
COURTESY LT. & SWITCH
BUZZER
BACK-UP LT. SW.
STOP LIGHT SW.
DOOR SWITCH
STOP LT. 2 USED ON SED

1977 Datsun

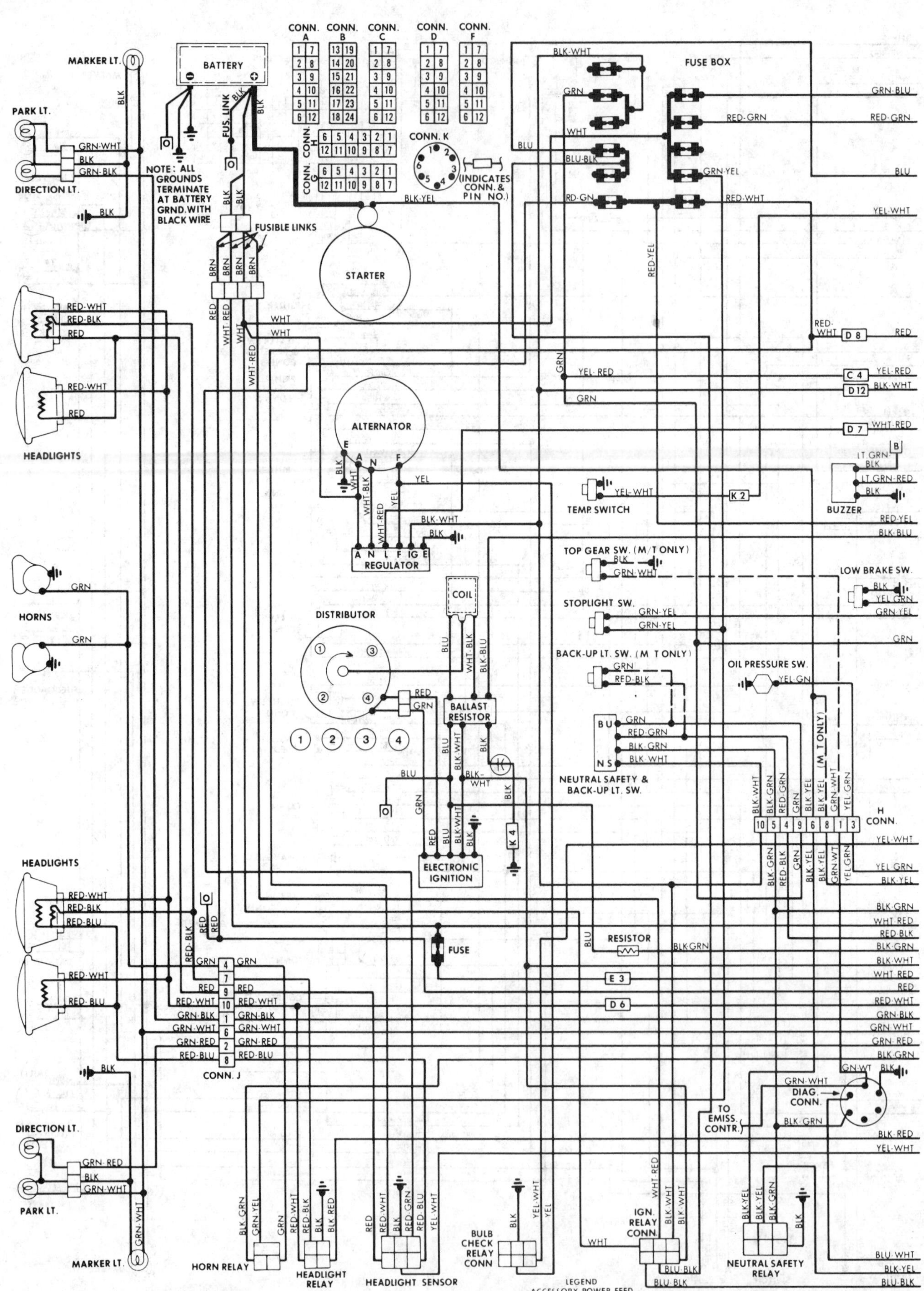

MARKER LT.
BATTERY
PARK LT.
DIRECTION LT.
NOTE: ALL GROUNDS TERMINATE AT BATTERY GRND. WITH BLACK WIRE
FUS. LINK
FUSIBLE LINKS
CONN. A
CONN. B
CONN. C
CONN. D
CONN. F
CONN. H
CONN. G
CONN. K
(INDICATES CONN. & PIN NO.)
STARTER
FUSE BOX
HEADLIGHTS
ALTERNATOR
REGULATOR
TEMP SWITCH
BUZZER
TOP GEAR SW. (M/T ONLY)
LOW BRAKE SW.
STOPLIGHT SW.
HORNS
DISTRIBUTOR
COIL
BALLAST RESISTOR
BACK-UP LT. SW. (M T ONLY)
OIL PRESSURE SW.
NEUTRAL SAFETY & BACK-UP LT. SW.
(M/T ONLY)
H CONN.
ELECTRONIC IGNITION
RESISTOR
FUSE
CONN. J
DIAG. CONN.
TO EMISS. CONTR.
HORN RELAY
HEADLIGHT RELAY
HEADLIGHT SENSOR
BULB CHECK RELAY CONN
IGN. RELAY CONN.
NEUTRAL SAFETY RELAY
LEGEND
ACCESSORY POWER FEED
A AIR CONDITIONING MANUAL SYSTEM
B SEAT BELT WARNING SYSTEM
D WIPER WASHER SYSTEM WINDSHIELD
O FUEL INJECTION SYSTEM

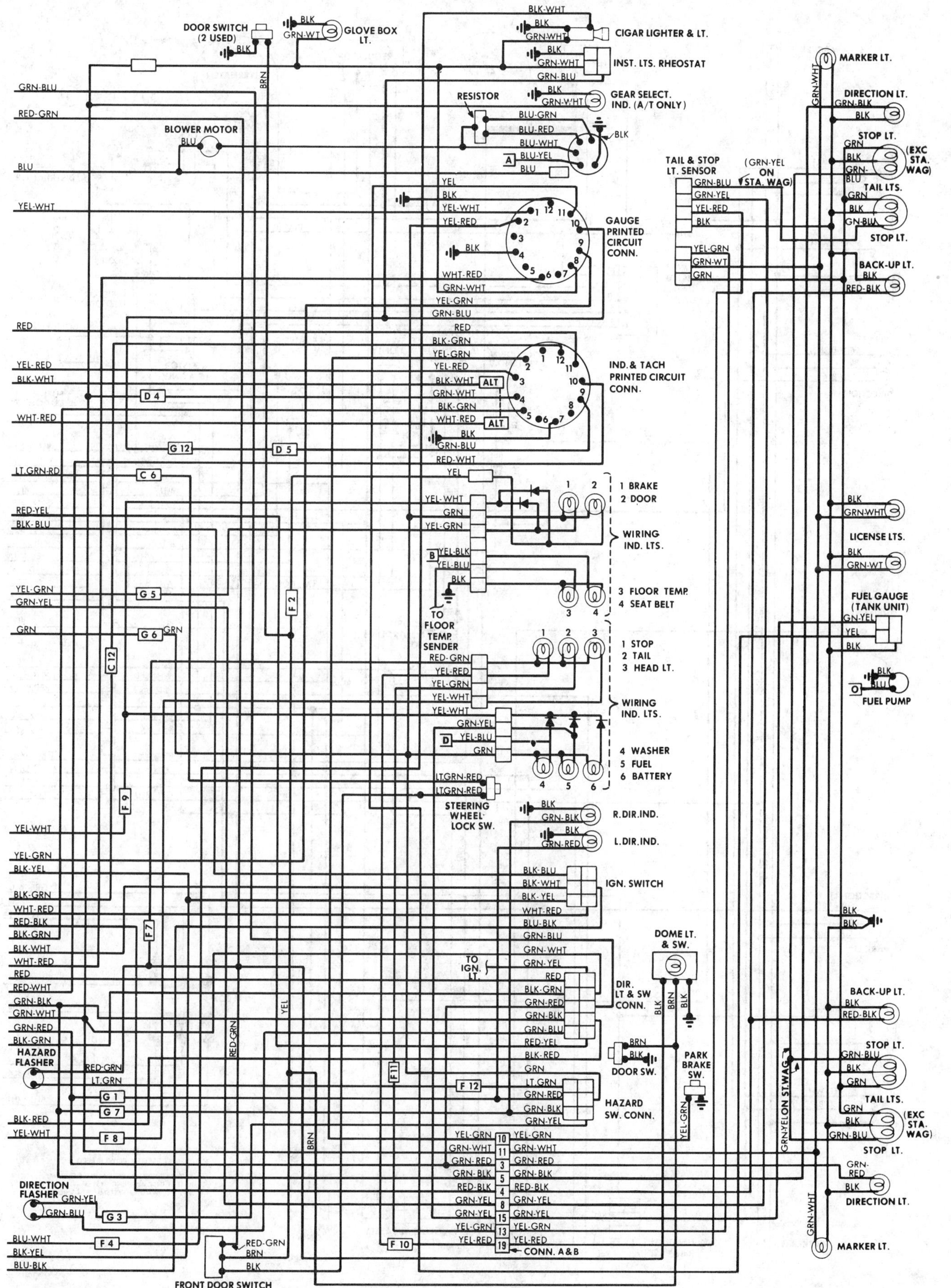

DOOR SWITCH (2 USED)
GLOVE BOX LT.
CIGAR LIGHTER & LT.
INST. LTS. RHEOSTAT
GEAR SELECT. IND. (A/T ONLY)
RESISTOR
BLOWER MOTOR
GAUGE PRINTED CIRCUIT CONN.
IND. & TACH PRINTED CIRCUIT CONN.
1 BRAKE
2 DOOR
WIRING IND. LTS.
3 FLOOR TEMP.
4 SEAT BELT
TO FLOOR TEMP. SENDER
1 STOP
2 TAIL
3 HEAD LT.
4 WASHER
5 FUEL
6 BATTERY
STEERING WHEEL LOCK SW.
R. DIR. IND.
L. DIR. IND.
IGN. SWITCH
TO IGN. LT.
DOME LT. & SW.
DIR. LT & SW CONN.
DOOR SW.
PARK BRAKE SW.
HAZARD SW. CONN.
HAZARD FLASHER
DIRECTION FLASHER
FRONT DOOR SWITCH
CONN. A & B
TAIL & STOP LT. SENSOR
(GRN-YEL ON STA. WAG)
MARKER LT.
DIRECTION LT.
STOP LT.
(EXC STA. WAG)
TAIL LTS.
BACK-UP LT.
LICENSE LTS.
FUEL GAUGE (TANK UNIT)
FUEL PUMP
GRN-YEL ON ST. WAG

1977 Datsun

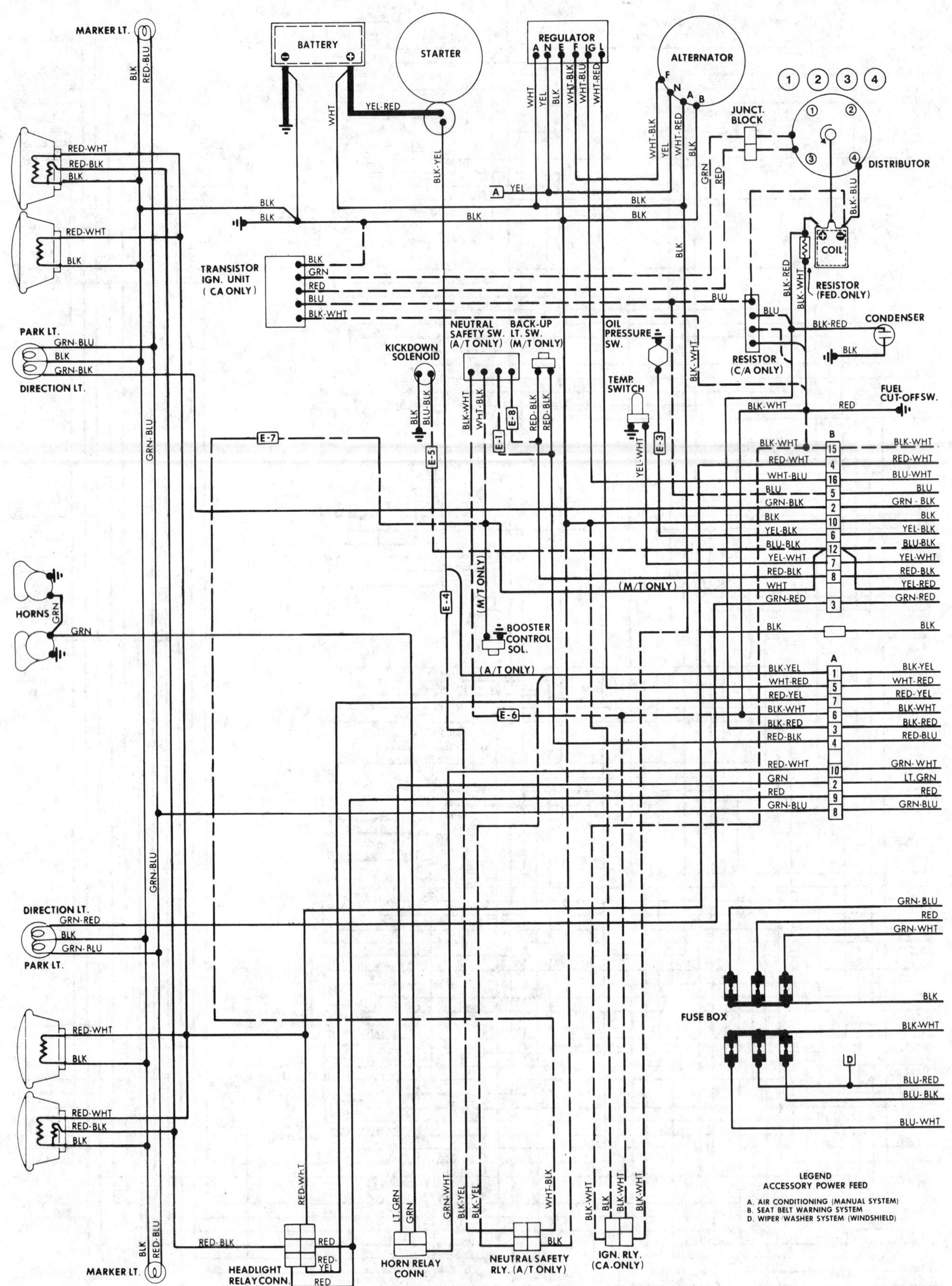
MARKER LT.
BATTERY
STARTER
REGULATOR
A N E F IG L
ALTERNATOR
JUNCT. BLOCK
DISTRIBUTOR
COIL
RESISTOR (FED. ONLY)
TRANSISTOR IGN. UNIT (CA ONLY)
CONDENSER
RESISTOR (C/A ONLY)
PARK LT.
DIRECTION LT.
KICKDOWN SOLENOID
NEUTRAL SAFETY SW. (A/T ONLY)
BACK-UP LT. SW. (M/T ONLY)
OIL PRESSURE SW.
TEMP. SWITCH
FUEL CUT-OFF SW.
HORNS
BOOSTER CONTROL SOL.
(A/T ONLY)
(M/T ONLY)
FUSE BOX
HEADLIGHT RELAY CONN.
HORN RELAY CONN.
NEUTRAL SAFETY RLY. (A/T ONLY)
IGN. RLY. (CA. ONLY)
LEGEND
ACCESSORY POWER FEED
A. AIR CONDITIONING (MANUAL SYSTEM)
B. SEAT BELT WARNING SYSTEM
D. WIPER/WASHER SYSTEM (WINDSHIELD)

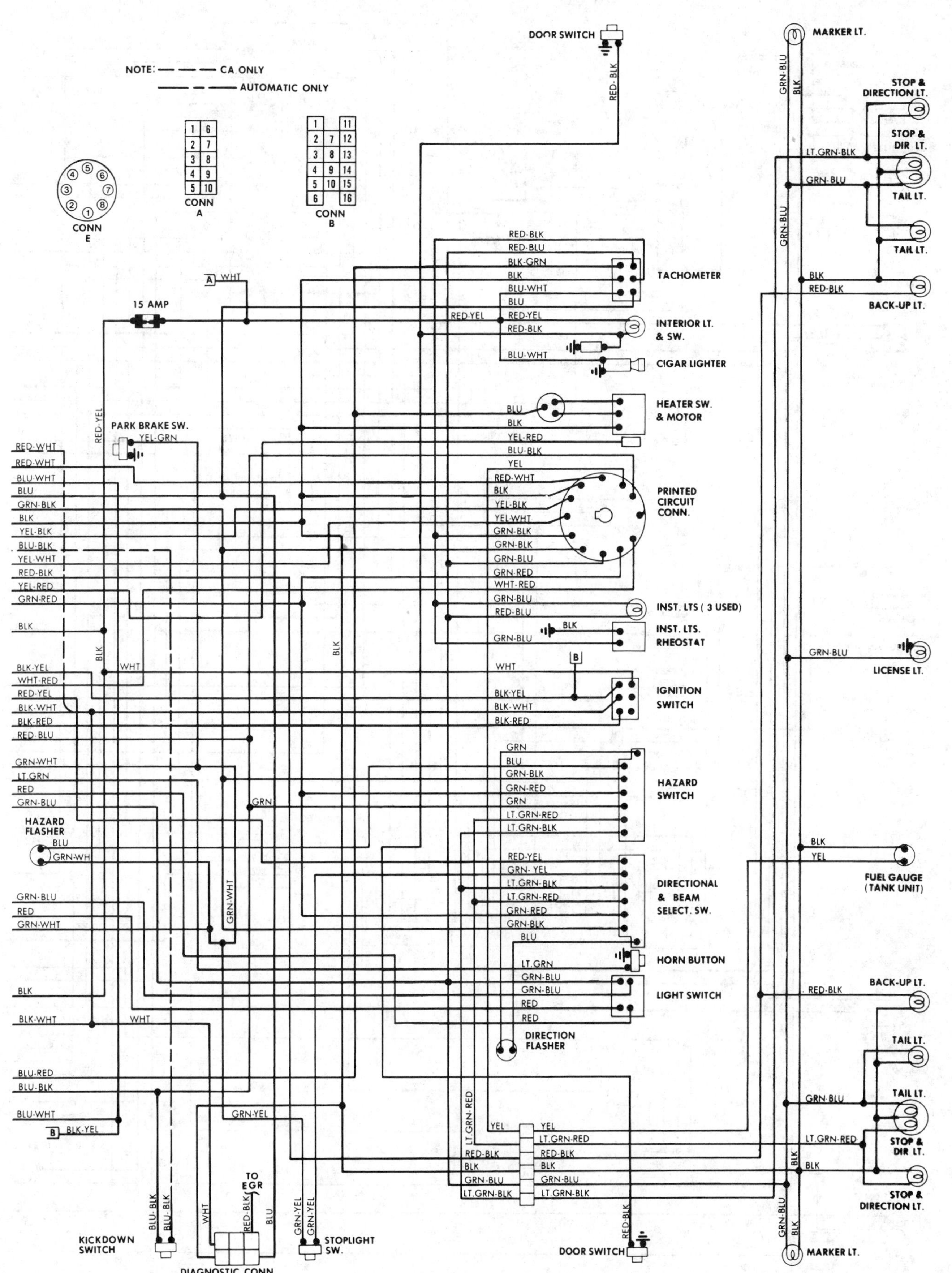
NOTE: — — — CA ONLY
— — — AUTOMATIC ONLY
CONN E
CONN A
CONN B
DOOR SWITCH
MARKER LT.
STOP & DIRECTION LT.
STOP & DIR LT.
TAIL LT.
TAIL LT.
BACK-UP LT.
TACHOMETER
INTERIOR LT. & SW.
CIGAR LIGHTER
15 AMP
HEATER SW. & MOTOR
PARK BRAKE SW.
PRINTED CIRCUIT CONN.
INST. LTS (3 USED)
INST. LTS. RHEOSTAT
LICENSE LT.
IGNITION SWITCH
HAZARD SWITCH
HAZARD FLASHER
FUEL GAUGE (TANK UNIT)
DIRECTIONAL & BEAM SELECT. SW.
HORN BUTTON
LIGHT SWITCH
BACK-UP LT.
DIRECTION FLASHER
TAIL LT.
TAIL LT.
STOP & DIR LT.
STOP & DIRECTION LT.
TO EGR
KICKDOWN SWITCH
STOPLIGHT SW.
DIAGNOSTIC CONN.
DOOR SWITCH
MARKER LT.

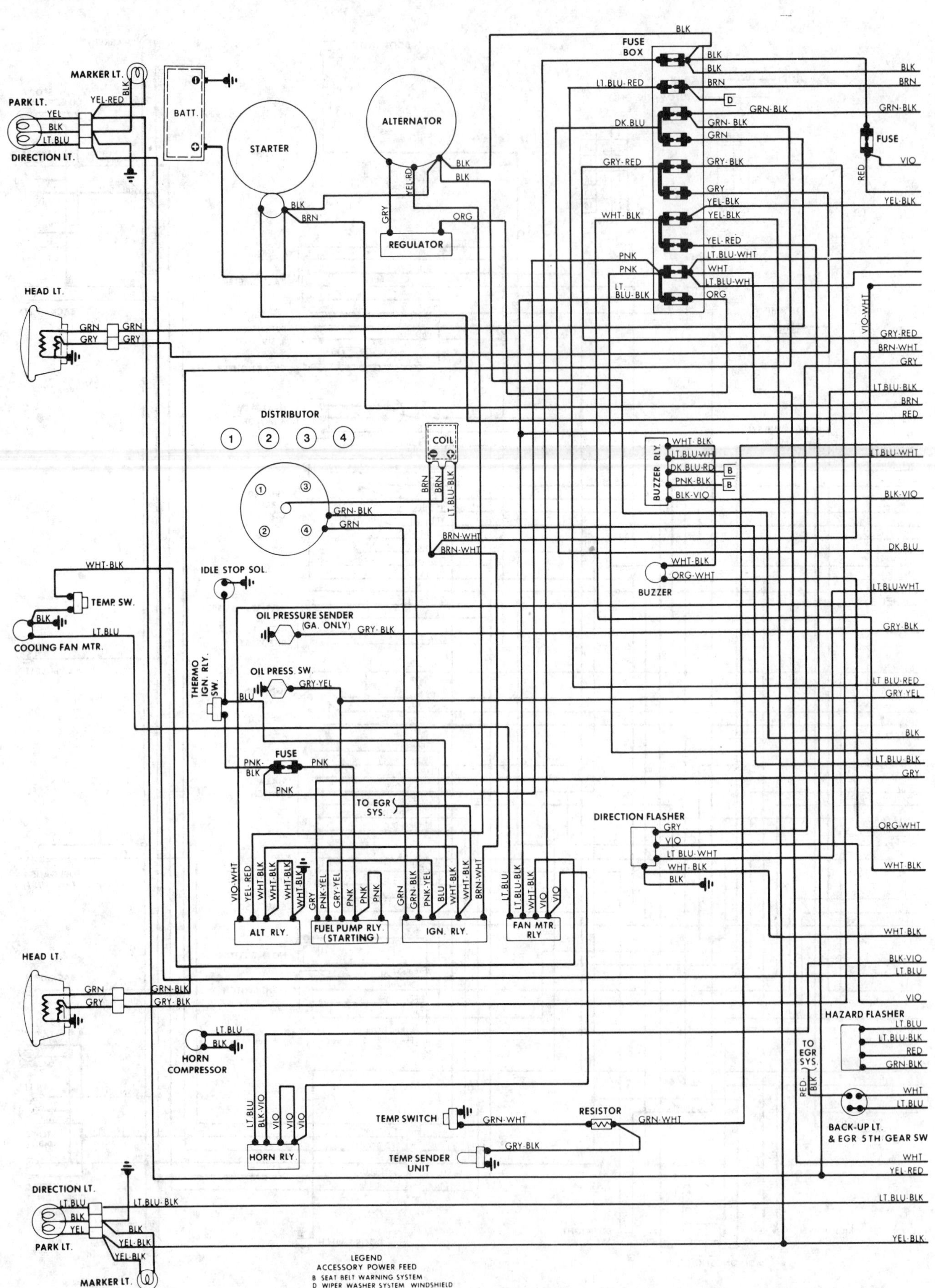
MARKER LT.
PARK LT.
DIRECTION LT.
BATT.
STARTER
ALTERNATOR
REGULATOR
FUSE BOX
FUSE
HEAD LT.
DISTRIBUTOR
COIL
BUZZER RLY.
BUZZER
IDLE STOP SOL.
TEMP. SW.
COOLING FAN MTR.
OIL PRESSURE SENDER (GA. ONLY)
OIL PRESS. SW.
THERMO IGN. RLY. SW.
TO EGR SYS.
DIRECTION FLASHER
ALT RLY.
FUEL PUMP RLY. (STARTING)
IGN. RLY.
FAN MTR. RLY
HAZARD FLASHER
HORN COMPRESSOR
HORN RLY.
TEMP SWITCH
RESISTOR
TEMP. SENDER UNIT
BACK-UP LT. & EGR 5TH GEAR SW
LEGEND
ACCESSORY POWER FEED
B SEAT BELT WARNING SYSTEM
D WIPER WASHER SYSTEM WINDSHIELD

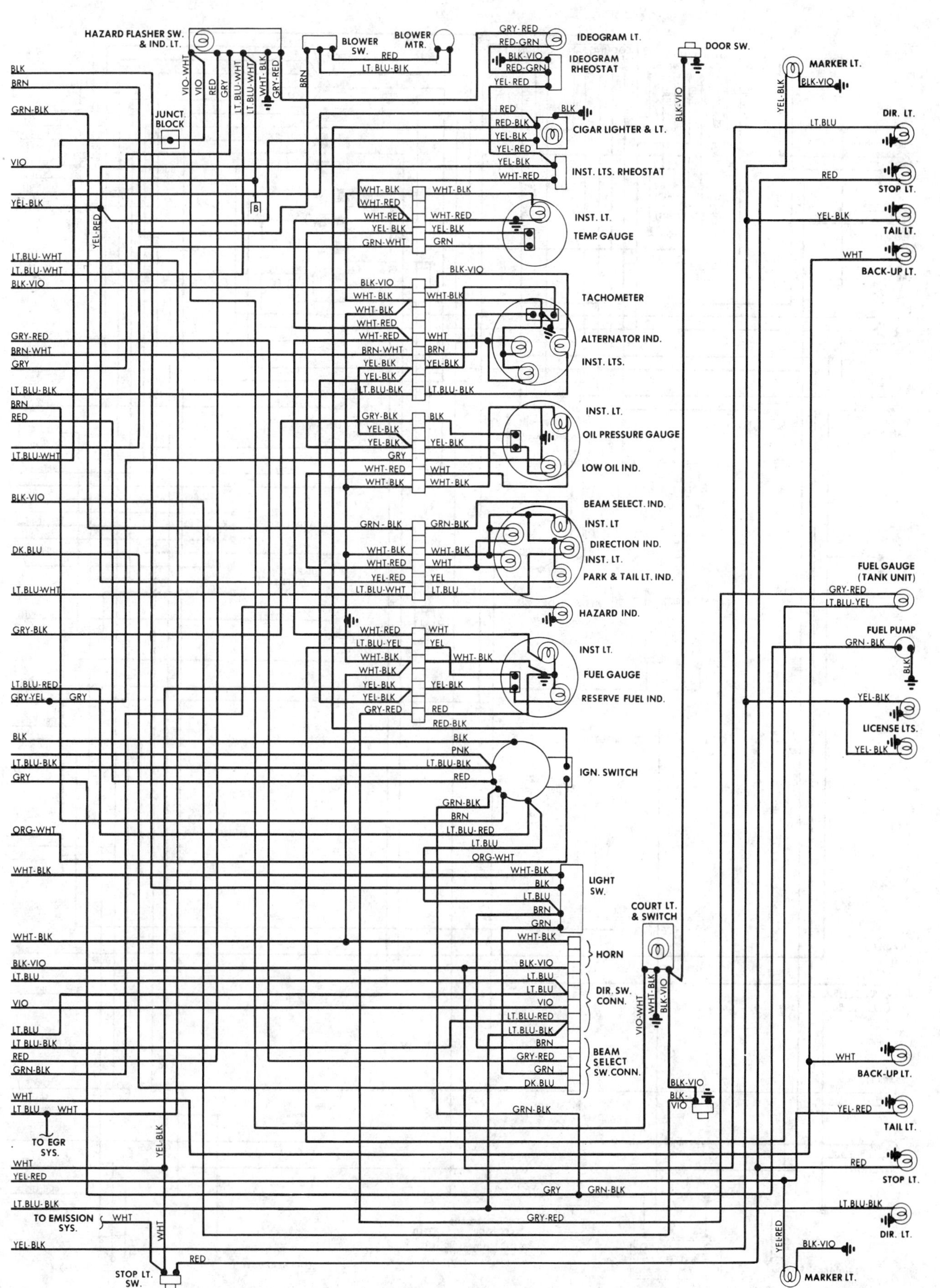

HAZARD FLASHER SW. & IND. LT.
BLOWER SW.
BLOWER MTR.
IDEOGRAM LT.
IDEOGRAM RHEOSTAT
DOOR SW.
MARKER LT.
JUNCT. BLOCK
CIGAR LIGHTER & LT.
DIR. LT.
INST. LTS. RHEOSTAT
STOP LT.
INST. LT.
TEMP. GAUGE
TAIL LT.
BACK-UP LT.
TACHOMETER
ALTERNATOR IND.
INST. LTS.
INST. LT.
OIL PRESSURE GAUGE
LOW OIL IND.
BEAM SELECT. IND.
INST. LT
DIRECTION IND.
INST. LT.
PARK & TAIL LT. IND.
FUEL GAUGE (TANK UNIT)
HAZARD IND.
FUEL PUMP
INST LT.
FUEL GAUGE
RESERVE FUEL IND.
LICENSE LTS.
IGN. SWITCH
LIGHT SW.
COURT LT. & SWITCH
HORN
DIR. SW. CONN.
BEAM SELECT SW. CONN.
BACK-UP LT.
TAIL LT.
STOP LT.
DIR. LT.
MARKER LT.
TO EGR SYS.
TO EMISSION SYS.
STOP LT. SW.

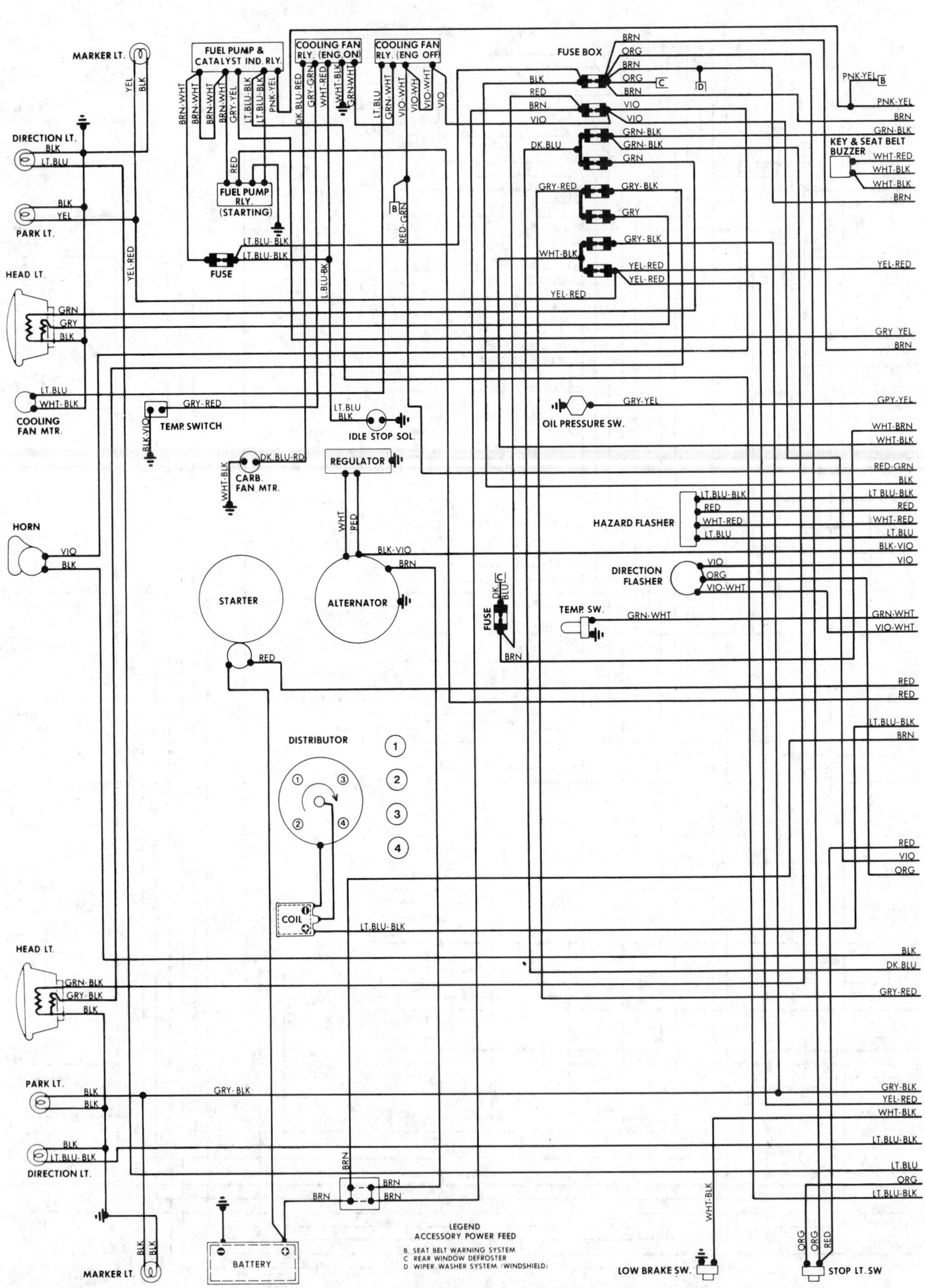
MARKER LT.
FUEL PUMP & CATALYST IND. RLY.
COOLING FAN RLY. (ENG ON)
COOLING FAN RLY. (ENG OFF)
FUSE BOX
DIRECTION LT.
PARK LT.
HEAD LT.
FUEL PUMP RLY. (STARTING)
FUSE
KEY & SEAT BELT BUZZER
COOLING FAN MTR.
TEMP. SWITCH
IDLE STOP SOL.
OIL PRESSURE SW.
CARB. FAN MTR.
REGULATOR
HORN
HAZARD FLASHER
DIRECTION FLASHER
STARTER
ALTERNATOR
TEMP. SW.
DISTRIBUTOR
COIL
HEAD LT.
PARK LT.
DIRECTION LT.
BATTERY
MARKER LT.
LEGEND
ACCESSORY POWER FEED
B. SEAT BELT WARNING SYSTEM
C. REAR WINDOW DEFROSTER
D. WIPER WASHER SYSTEM (WINDSHIELD)
LOW BRAKE SW.
STOP LT. SW

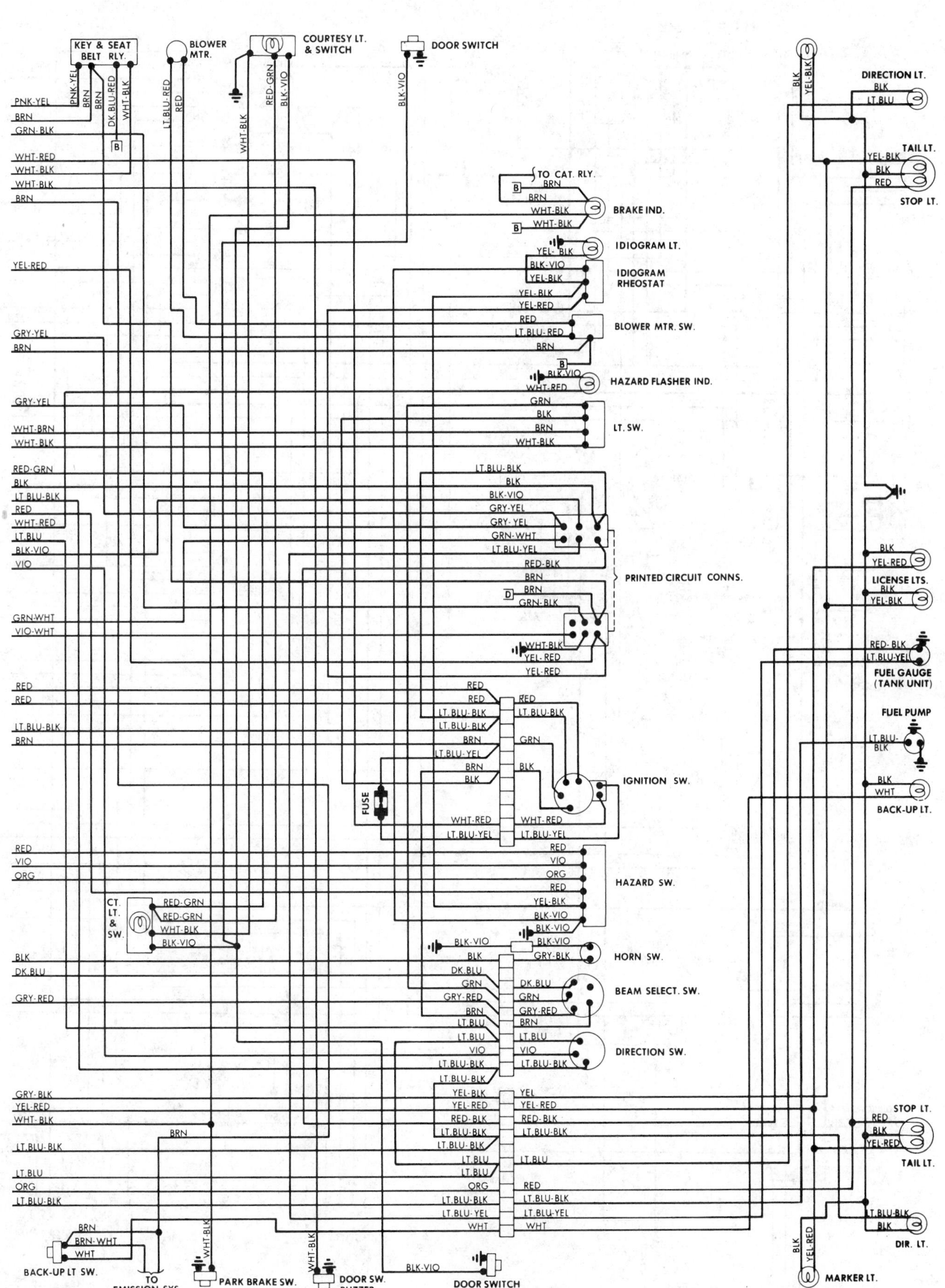
KEY & SEAT BELT RLY.
BLOWER MTR.
COURTESY LT. & SWITCH
DOOR SWITCH
DIRECTION LT.
TAIL LT.
STOP LT.
TO CAT. RLY.
BRAKE IND.
IDIOGRAM LT.
IDIOGRAM RHEOSTAT
BLOWER MTR. SW.
HAZARD FLASHER IND.
LT. SW.
PRINTED CIRCUIT CONNS.
LICENSE LTS.
FUEL GAUGE (TANK UNIT)
FUEL PUMP
IGNITION SW.
FUSE
BACK-UP LT.
HAZARD SW.
CT. LT. & SW.
HORN SW.
BEAM SELECT. SW.
DIRECTION SW.
STOP LT.
TAIL LT.
DIR. LT.
MARKER LT.
BACK-UP LT SW.
TO EMISSION SYS.
PARK BRAKE SW.
DOOR SW. BUZZER
DOOR SWITCH

1977 Fiat

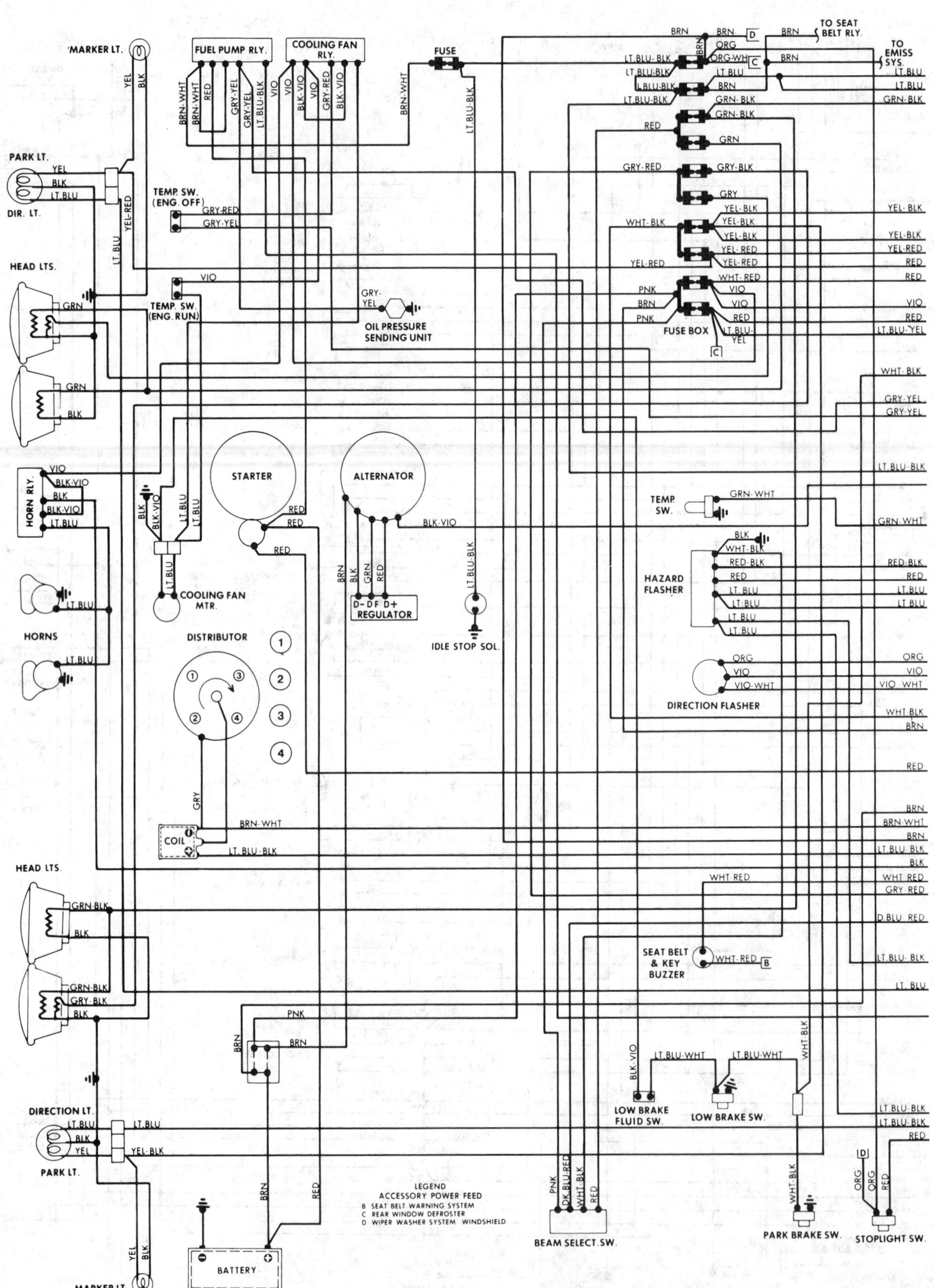
MARKER LT.
FUEL PUMP RLY.
COOLING FAN RLY.
FUSE
TO SEAT BELT RLY.
TO EMISS SYS.
PARK LT.
DIR. LT.
TEMP. SW. (ENG. OFF)
HEAD LTS.
TEMP. SW. (ENG. RUN)
OIL PRESSURE SENDING UNIT
FUSE BOX
HORN RLY.
STARTER
ALTERNATOR
TEMP. SW.
HAZARD FLASHER
COOLING FAN MTR.
D- DF D+ REGULATOR
IDLE STOP SOL.
HORNS
DISTRIBUTOR
DIRECTION FLASHER
COIL
HEAD LTS.
SEAT BELT & KEY BUZZER
LOW BRAKE FLUID SW.
LOW BRAKE SW.
DIRECTION LT.
PARK LT.
LEGEND
ACCESSORY POWER FEED
B SEAT BELT WARNING SYSTEM
C REAR WINDOW DEFROSTER
D WIPER WASHER SYSTEM WINDSHIELD
BATTERY
BEAM SELECT. SW.
PARK BRAKE SW.
STOPLIGHT SW.
MARKER LT

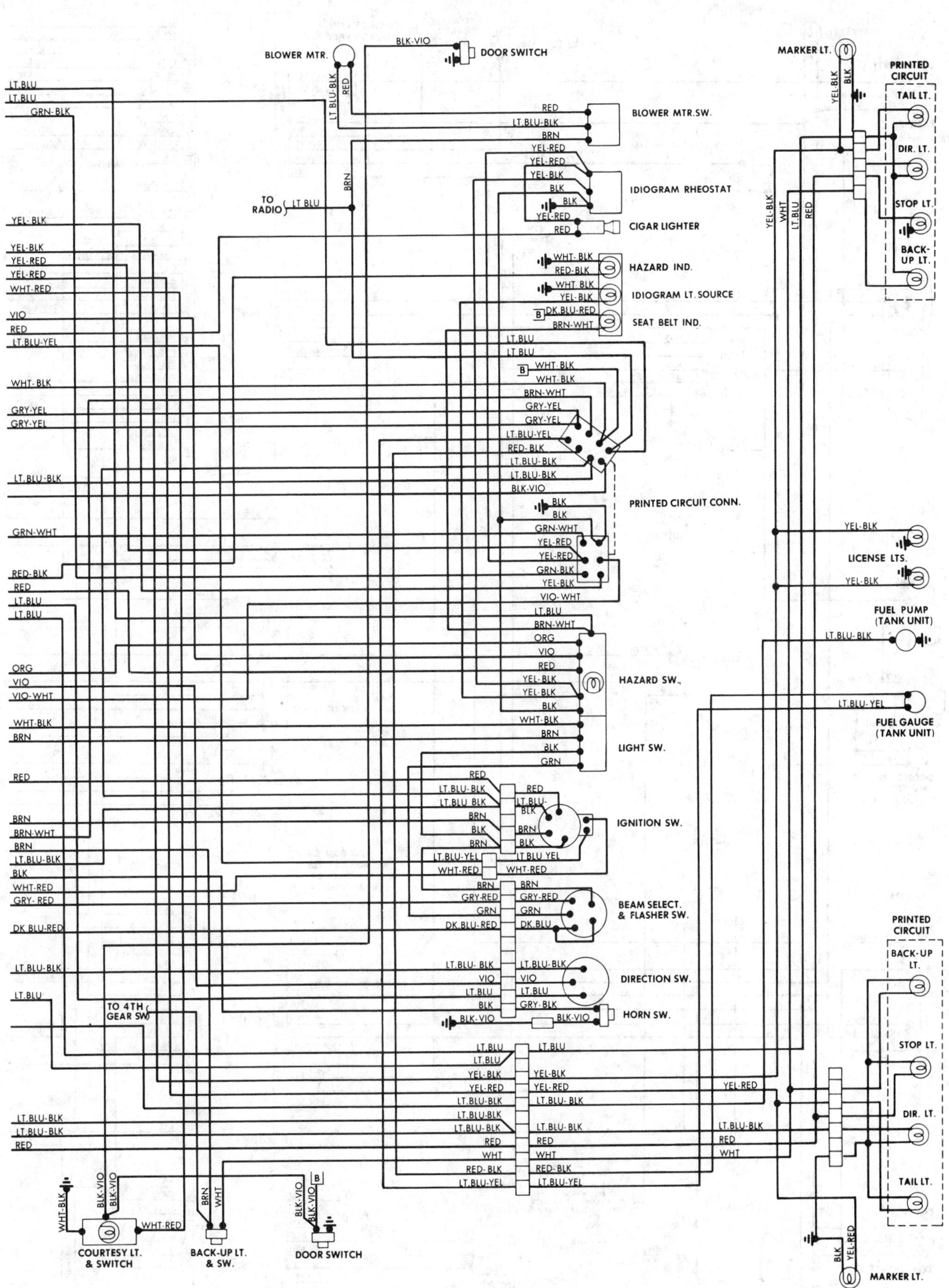
BLOWER MTR.
DOOR SWITCH
BLOWER MTR. SW.
IDIOGRAM RHEOSTAT
TO RADIO
CIGAR LIGHTER
HAZARD IND.
IDIOGRAM LT. SOURCE
SEAT BELT IND.
PRINTED CIRCUIT CONN.
HAZARD SW.
LIGHT SW.
IGNITION SW.
BEAM SELECT. & FLASHER SW.
DIRECTION SW.
HORN SW.
TO 4TH GEAR SW.
COURTESY LT. & SWITCH
BACK-UP LT. & SW.
DOOR SWITCH
MARKER LT.
PRINTED CIRCUIT
TAIL LT.
DIR. LT.
STOP LT.
BACK-UP LT.
LICENSE LTS.
FUEL PUMP (TANK UNIT)
FUEL GAUGE (TANK UNIT)
PRINTED CIRCUIT
BACK-UP LT.
STOP LT.
DIR. LT.
TAIL LT.
MARKER LT.

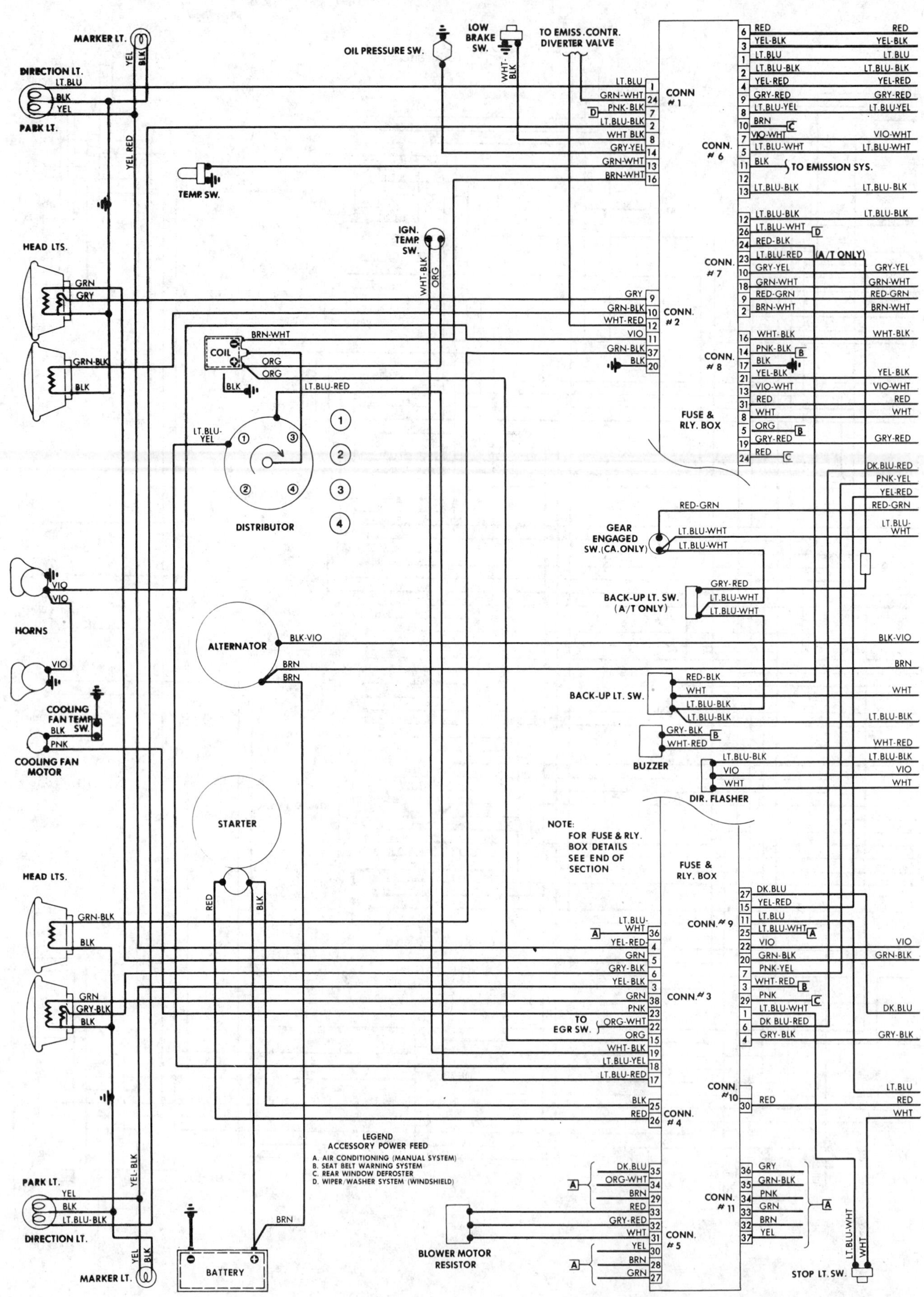
MARKER LT.
DIRECTION LT.
PARK LT.
OIL PRESSURE SW.
LOW BRAKE SW.
TO EMISS. CONTR. DIVERTER VALVE
TEMP. SW.
HEAD LTS.
IGN. TEMP. SW.
COIL
DISTRIBUTOR
HORNS
ALTERNATOR
COOLING FAN TEMP. SW.
COOLING FAN MOTOR
STARTER
BATTERY
CONN #1
CONN. #2
CONN. #3
CONN. #4
CONN. #5
CONN. #6
CONN. #7
CONN. #8
CONN. #9
CONN. #10
CONN. #11
FUSE & RLY. BOX
TO EMISSION SYS.
(A/T ONLY)
GEAR ENGAGED SW. (CA. ONLY)
BACK-UP LT. SW. (A/T ONLY)
BACK-UP LT. SW.
BUZZER
DIR. FLASHER
NOTE: FOR FUSE & RLY. BOX DETAILS SEE END OF SECTION
TO EGR SW.
BLOWER MOTOR RESISTOR
STOP LT. SW.
LEGEND
ACCESSORY POWER FEED
A. AIR CONDITIONING (MANUAL SYSTEM)
B. SEAT BELT WARNING SYSTEM
C. REAR WINDOW DEFROSTER
D. WIPER/WASHER SYSTEM (WINDSHIELD)

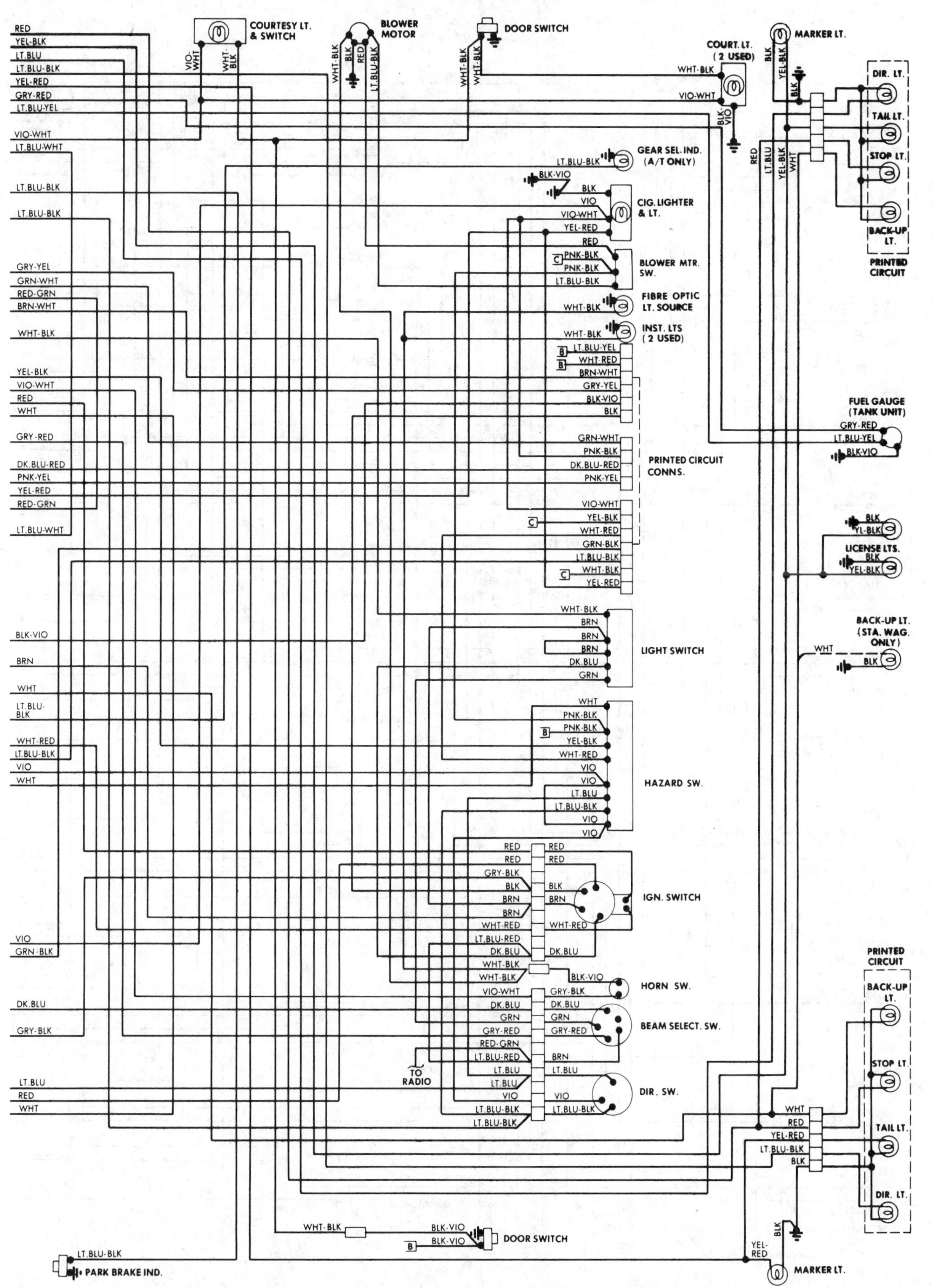
COURTESY LT. & SWITCH
BLOWER MOTOR
DOOR SWITCH
MARKER LT.
COURT. LT. (2 USED)
DIR. LT.
TAIL LT.
STOP LT.
BACK-UP LT.
PRINTED CIRCUIT
GEAR SEL. IND. (A/T ONLY)
CIG. LIGHTER & LT.
BLOWER MTR. SW.
FIBRE OPTIC LT. SOURCE
INST. LTS (2 USED)
PRINTED CIRCUIT CONNS.
FUEL GAUGE (TANK UNIT)
LICENSE LTS.
BACK-UP LT. (STA. WAG. ONLY)
LIGHT SWITCH
HAZARD SW.
IGN. SWITCH
HORN SW.
BEAM SELECT. SW.
DIR. SW.
TO RADIO
PRINTED CIRCUIT
BACK-UP LT.
STOP LT.
TAIL LT.
DIR. LT.
DOOR SWITCH
PARK BRAKE IND.
MARKER LT.

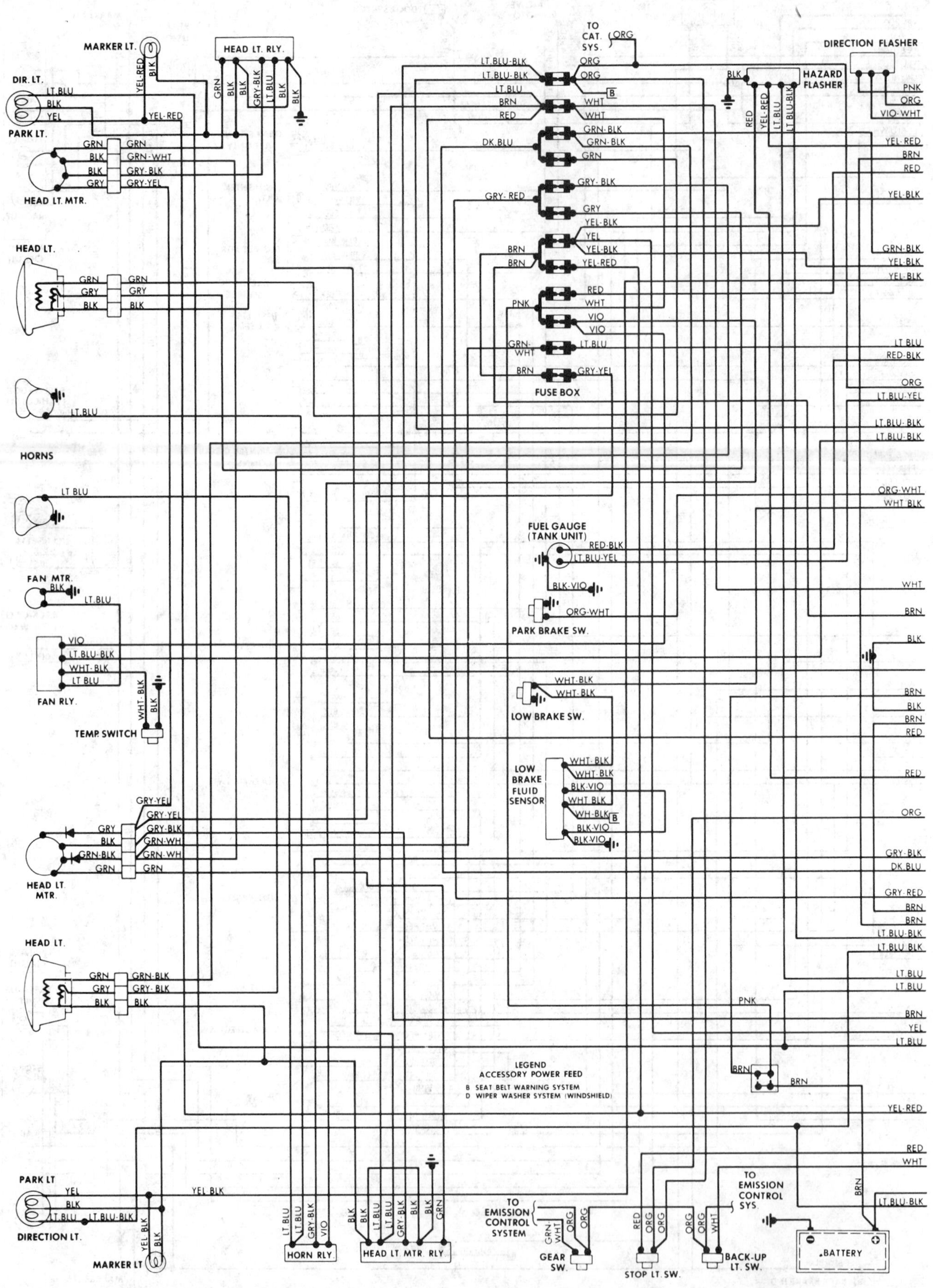
MARKER LT.
HEAD LT. RLY.
DIR. LT.
PARK LT.
HEAD LT. MTR.
HEAD LT.
HORNS
FAN MTR.
FAN RLY.
TEMP. SWITCH
HEAD LT. MTR.
HEAD LT.
PARK LT
DIRECTION LT.
MARKER LT
HORN RLY.
HEAD LT MTR RLY.
TO CAT. SYS.
FUSE BOX
HAZARD FLASHER
DIRECTION FLASHER
FUEL GAUGE (TANK UNIT)
PARK BRAKE SW.
LOW BRAKE SW.
LOW BRAKE FLUID SENSOR
LEGEND
ACCESSORY POWER FEED
B SEAT BELT WARNING SYSTEM
D WIPER WASHER SYSTEM (WINDSHIELD)
TO EMISSION CONTROL SYSTEM
GEAR SW.
STOP LT. SW.
TO EMISSION CONTROL SYS.
BACK-UP LT. SW.
BATTERY

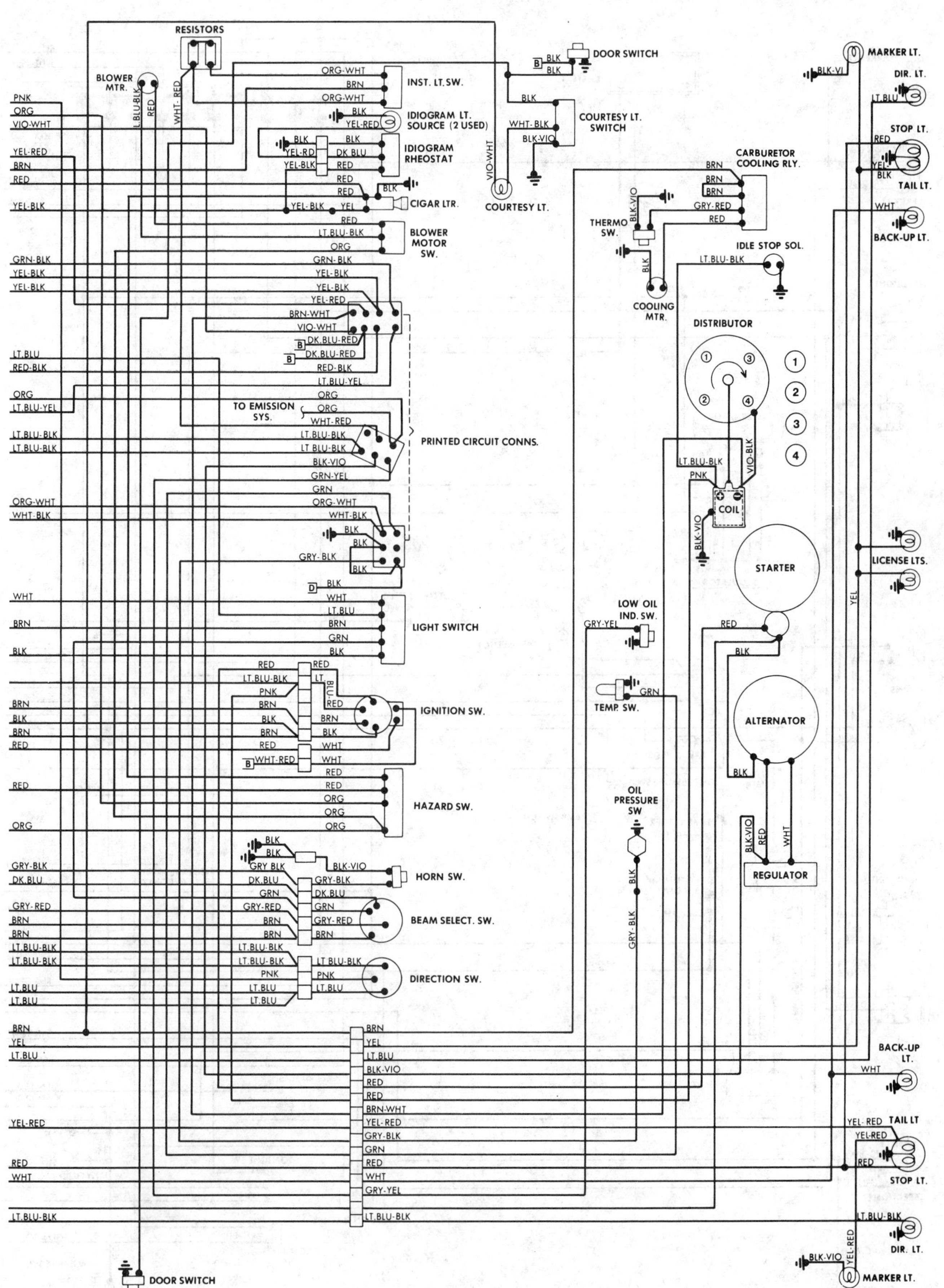
RESISTORS
BLOWER MTR.
DOOR SWITCH
INST. LT. SW.
IDIOGRAM LT. SOURCE (2 USED)
IDIOGRAM RHEOSTAT
COURTESY LT. SWITCH
COURTESY LT.
CIGAR LTR.
BLOWER MOTOR SW.
CARBURETOR COOLING RLY.
THERMO SW.
IDLE STOP SOL.
COOLING MTR.
DISTRIBUTOR
TO EMISSION SYS.
PRINTED CIRCUIT CONNS.
COIL
STARTER
LIGHT SWITCH
LOW OIL IND. SW.
TEMP. SW.
ALTERNATOR
IGNITION SW.
HAZARD SW.
OIL PRESSURE SW
REGULATOR
HORN SW.
BEAM SELECT. SW.
DIRECTION SW.
MARKER LT.
DIR. LT.
STOP LT.
TAIL LT.
BACK-UP LT.
LICENSE LTS.
DOOR SWITCH

1977 Honda

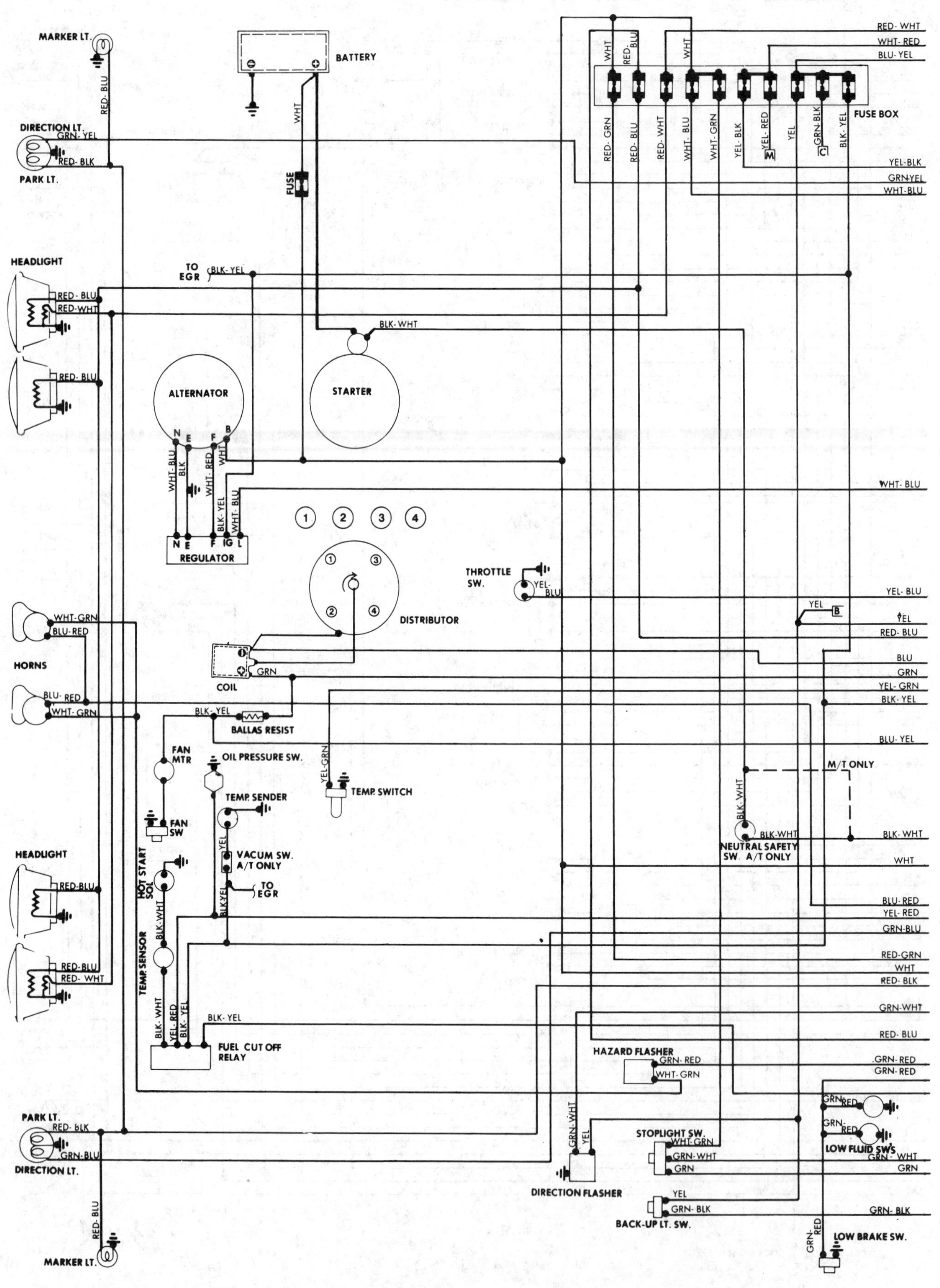

MARKER LT.
RED-BLU
DIRECTION LT.
GRN-YEL
RED-BLK
PARK LT.
BATTERY
WHT
FUSE
HEADLIGHT
TO EGR
BLK-YEL
RED-BLU
RED-WHT
BLK-WHT
ALTERNATOR
STARTER
N E F B
WHT-BLU
BLK
WHT-RED
BLK-YEL
WHT-BLU
N E F IG L
REGULATOR
1 2 3 4
DISTRIBUTOR
THROTTLE SW.
YEL-BLU
WHT-GRN
BLU-RED
HORNS
COIL
GRN
BALLAS RESIST
FAN MTR
OIL PRESSURE SW.
TEMP. SENDER
TEMP. SWITCH
YEL-GRN
FAN SW
VACUM SW. A/T ONLY
TO EGR
HOT START SOL
TEMP SENSOR
FUEL CUT OFF RELAY
YEL-RED
FUSE BOX
RED-WHT
WHT-RED
BLU-YEL
RED-GRN
WHT-GRN
YEL-BLK
YEL-RED
YEL
GRN-BLK
BLK-YEL
GRN-YEL
WHT-BLU
YEL-BLU
RED-BLU
BLU
YEL-GRN
M/T ONLY
NEUTRAL SAFETY SW. A/T ONLY
WHT
YEL-RED
GRN-BLU
RED-BLK
GRN-WHT
GRN-RED
HAZARD FLASHER
STOPLIGHT SW.
LOW FLUID SW'S
DIRECTION FLASHER
BACK-UP LT. SW.
LOW BRAKE SW.

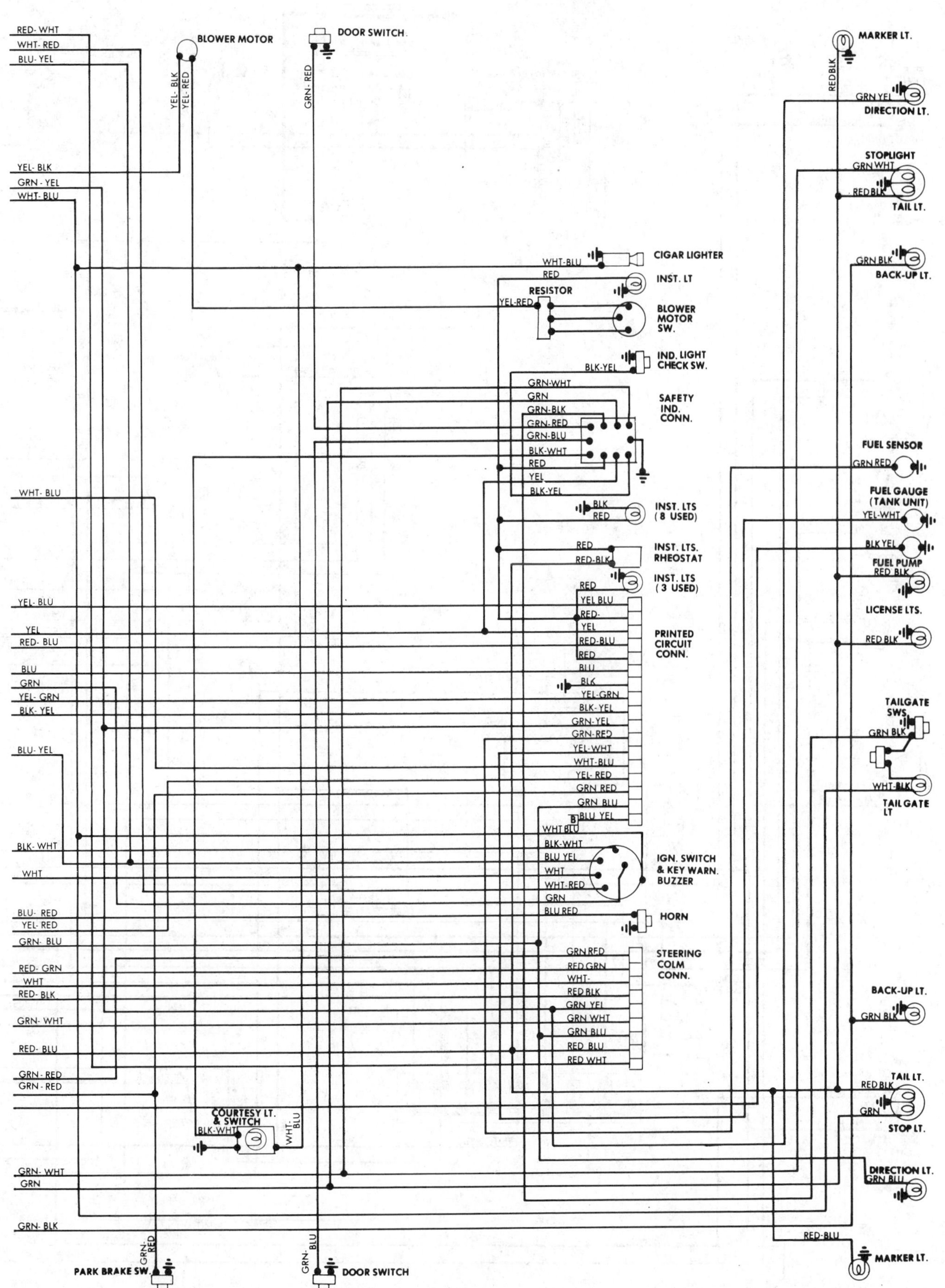

BLOWER MOTOR
DOOR SWITCH
MARKER LT.
DIRECTION LT.
STOPLIGHT
TAIL LT.
CIGAR LIGHTER
INST. LT
RESISTOR
BLOWER MOTOR SW.
BACK-UP LT.
IND. LIGHT CHECK SW.
SAFETY IND. CONN.
FUEL SENSOR
FUEL GAUGE (TANK UNIT)
FUEL PUMP
INST. LTS (8 USED)
INST. LTS. RHEOSTAT
INST. LTS (3 USED)
LICENSE LTS.
PRINTED CIRCUIT CONN.
TAILGATE SWS
TAILGATE LT
IGN. SWITCH & KEY WARN. BUZZER
HORN
STEERING COLM CONN.
BACK-UP LT.
TAIL LT.
STOP LT.
COURTESY LT. & SWITCH
DIRECTION LT.
MARKER LT.
PARK BRAKE SW.
DOOR SWITCH

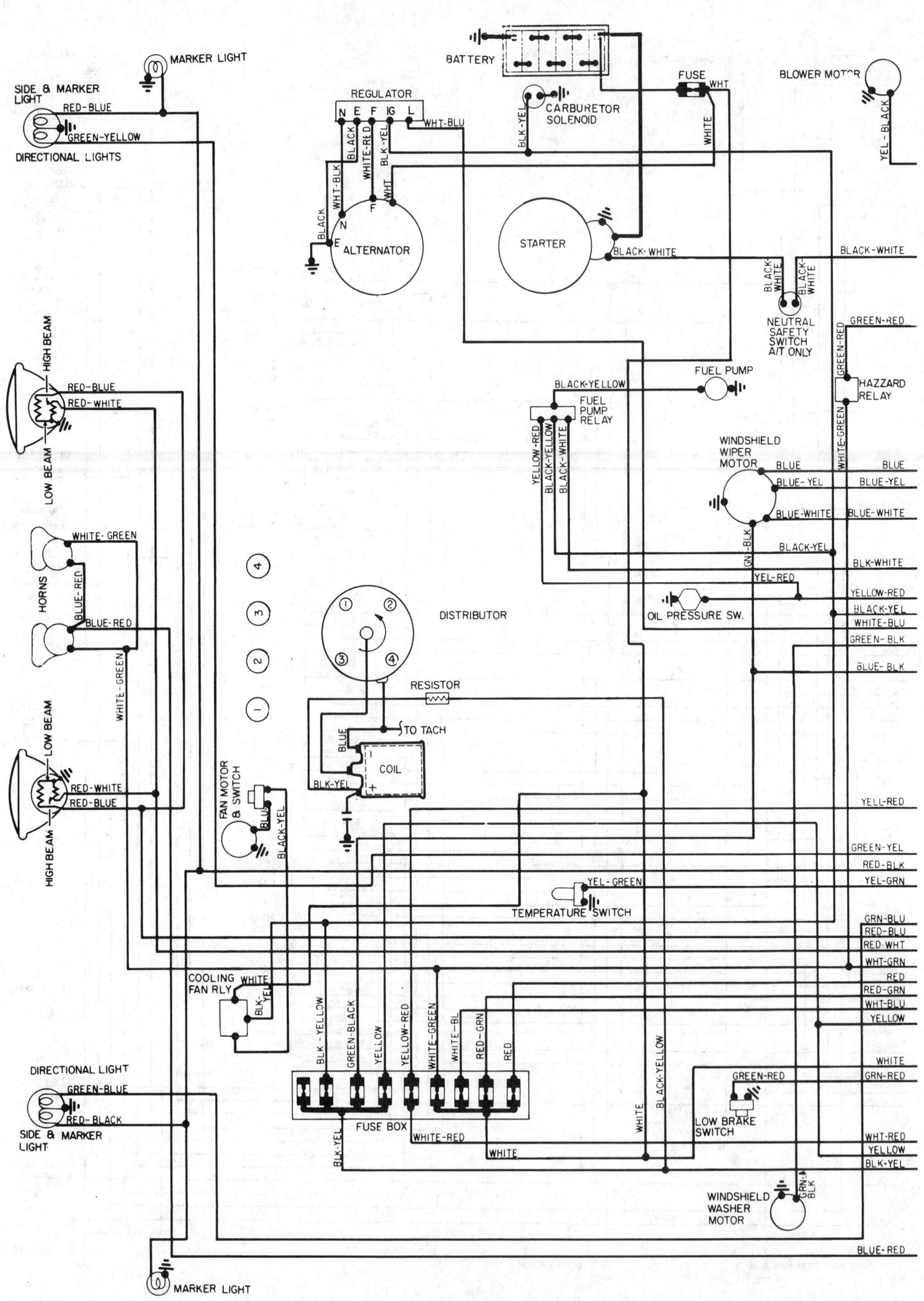
MARKER LIGHT
SIDE & MARKER LIGHT
RED-BLUE
GREEN-YELLOW
DIRECTIONAL LIGHTS
BATTERY
REGULATOR
N E F IG L
WHT-BLU
CARBURETOR SOLENOID
FUSE
WHT
BLOWER MOTOR
YEL-BLACK
ALTERNATOR
STARTER
BLACK-WHITE
NEUTRAL SAFETY SWITCH A/T ONLY
GREEN-RED
HIGH BEAM
LOW BEAM
RED-WHITE
FUEL PUMP
BLACK-YELLOW
FUEL PUMP RELAY
HAZZARD RELAY
WINDSHIELD WIPER MOTOR
BLUE
BLUE-YEL
BLUE-WHITE
WHITE-GREEN
HORNS
BLUE-RED
BLACK-YEL
BLK-WHITE
YEL-RED
YELLOW-RED
OIL PRESSURE SW.
WHITE-BLU
GREEN-BLK
BLUE-BLK
DISTRIBUTOR
RESISTOR
TO TACH
COIL
FAN MOTOR & SWITCH
BLK-YEL
YELL-RED
GREEN-YEL
RED-BLK
YEL-GRN
YEL-GREEN
TEMPERATURE SWITCH
GRN-BLU
RED-BLU
RED-WHT
WHT-GRN
RED
RED-GRN
WHT-BLU
YELLOW
COOLING FAN RLY
WHITE
BLK-YELLOW
GREEN-BLACK
YELLOW-RED
WHITE-GREEN
WHITE-BL
FUSE BOX
WHITE-RED
DIRECTIONAL LIGHT
GREEN-BLUE
RED-BLACK
SIDE & MARKER LIGHT
LOW BRAKE SWITCH
WHT-RED
BLK-YEL
WINDSHIELD WASHER MOTOR
GRN-BLK
BLUE-RED
MARKER LIGHT

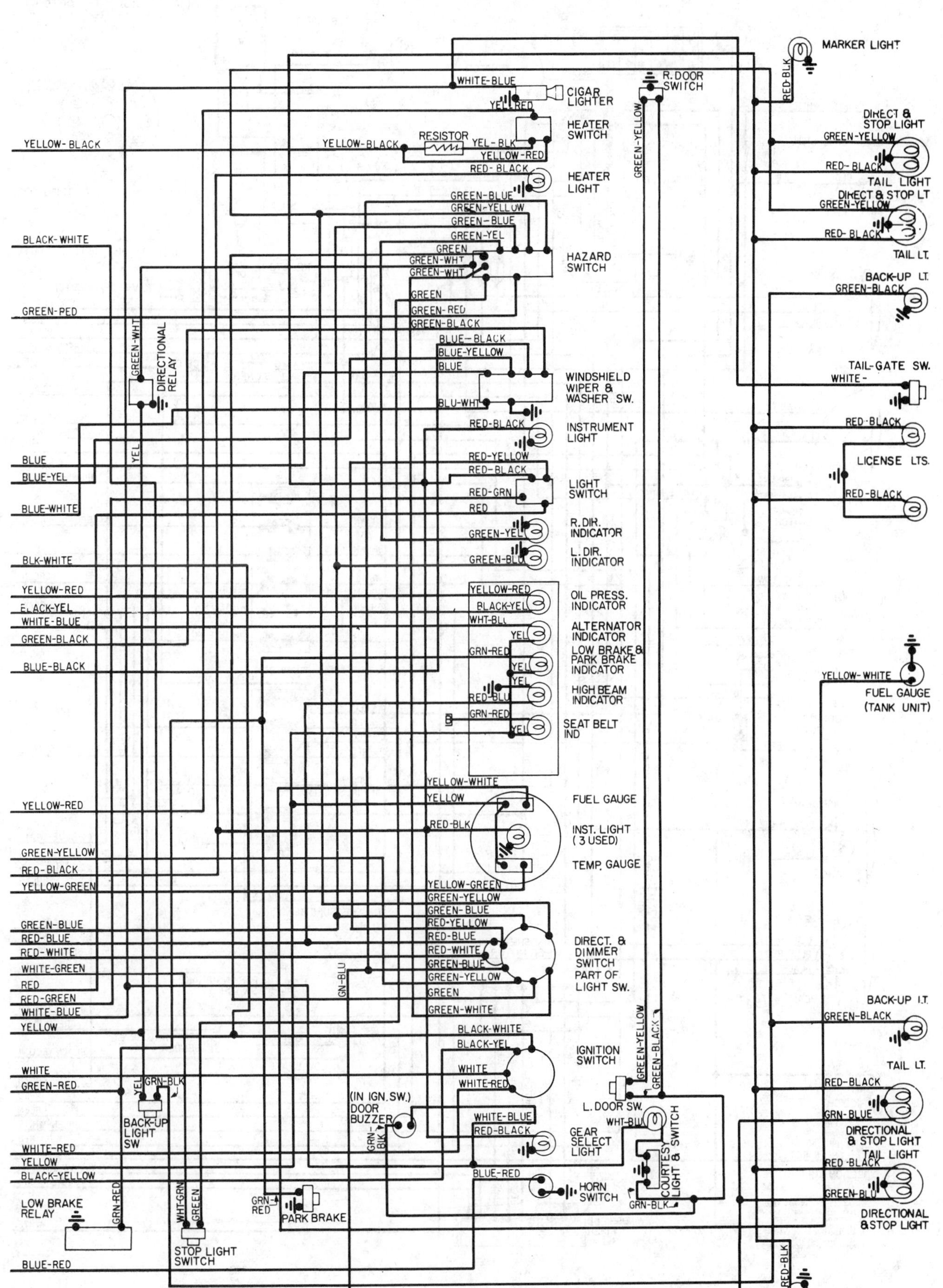
MARKER LIGHT
R. DOOR SWITCH
CIGAR LIGHTER
HEATER SWITCH
RESISTOR
HEATER LIGHT
HAZARD SWITCH
DIRECTIONAL RELAY
WINDSHIELD WIPER & WASHER SW.
INSTRUMENT LIGHT
LIGHT SWITCH
R. DIR. INDICATOR
L. DIR. INDICATOR
OIL PRESS. INDICATOR
ALTERNATOR INDICATOR
LOW BRAKE & PARK BRAKE INDICATOR
HIGH BEAM INDICATOR
SEAT BELT IND
FUEL GAUGE
INST. LIGHT (3 USED)
TEMP. GAUGE
DIRECT. & DIMMER SWITCH PART OF LIGHT SW.
IGNITION SWITCH
(IN IGN. SW.) DOOR BUZZER
L. DOOR SW.
COURTESY LIGHT & SWITCH
GEAR SELECT LIGHT
HORN SWITCH
BACK-UP LIGHT SW
LOW BRAKE RELAY
STOP LIGHT SWITCH
PARK BRAKE
DIRECT & STOP LIGHT
TAIL LIGHT
DIRECT & STOP LT
TAIL LT.
BACK-UP LT.
TAIL-GATE SW.
LICENSE LTS.
FUEL GAUGE (TANK UNIT)
BACK-UP LT.
TAIL LT.
DIRECTIONAL & STOP LIGHT
TAIL LIGHT
DIRECTIONAL & STOP LIGHT
MARKER LIGHT
YELLOW-BLACK
BLACK-WHITE
GREEN-RED
BLUE
BLUE-YEL
BLUE-WHITE
BLK-WHITE
YELLOW-RED
BLACK-YEL
WHITE-BLUE
GREEN-BLACK
BLUE-BLACK
YELLOW-RED
GREEN-YELLOW
RED-BLACK
YELLOW-GREEN
GREEN-BLUE
RED-BLUE
RED-WHITE
WHITE-GREEN
RED
RED-GREEN
WHITE-BLUE
YELLOW
WHITE
GREEN-RED
WHITE-RED
YELLOW
BLACK-YELLOW
BLUE-RED

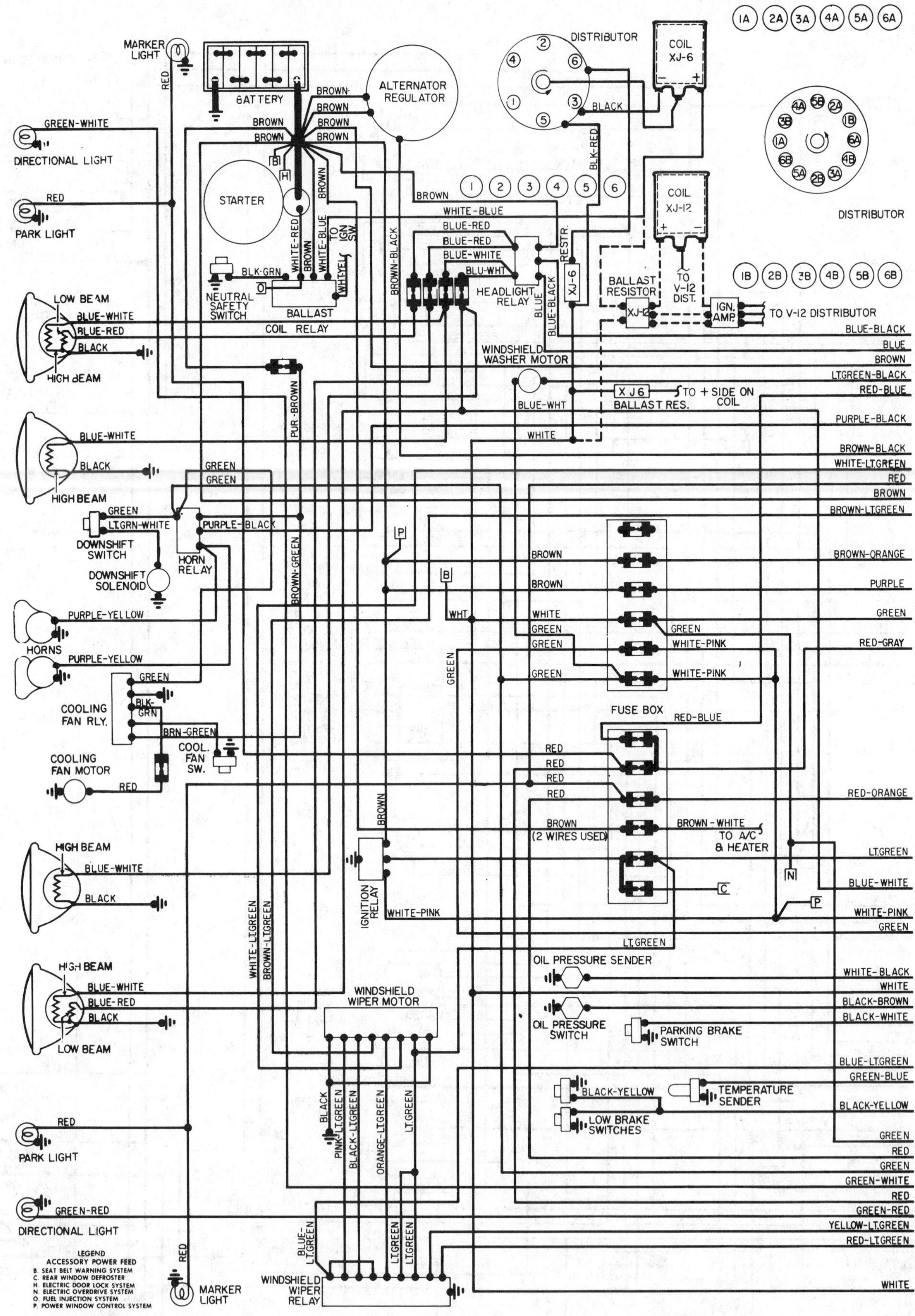

MARKER LIGHT
RED
BATTERY
BROWN
ALTERNATOR REGULATOR
DISTRIBUTOR
COIL XJ-6
BLACK
BLK-RED
1A 2A 3A 4A 5A 6A
1B 2B 3B 4B 5B 6B
GREEN-WHITE
DIRECTIONAL LIGHT
PARK LIGHT
STARTER
WHITE-RED
WHITE-BLUE
TO IGN SW
BROWN-BLACK
BLUE-RED
BLUE-WHITE
BLU-WHT
RESTR.
XJ-6
COIL XJ-12
BALLAST RESISTOR
XJ12
TO V-12 DIST.
IGN. AMP.
TO V-12 DISTRIBUTOR
BLK-GRN
WHT-YEL
NEUTRAL SAFETY SWITCH
BALLAST
COIL RELAY
HEADLIGHT RELAY
BLUE
BLUE-BLACK
LOW BEAM
HIGH BEAM
BLACK
WINDSHIELD WASHER MOTOR
PUR-BROWN
BLUE-WHT
XJ6 BALLAST RES.
TO + SIDE ON COIL
LT.GREEN-BLACK
RED-BLUE
PURPLE-BLACK
WHITE
WHITE-LT.GREEN
BROWN-LT.GREEN
GREEN
LT.GRN-WHITE
DOWNSHIFT SWITCH
DOWNSHIFT SOLENOID
HORN RELAY
BROWN-GREEN
P
B
WHT
BROWN-ORANGE
PURPLE
PURPLE-YELLOW
HORNS
WHITE-PINK
RED-GRAY
COOLING FAN RLY.
BLK-GRN
BRN-GREEN
COOL. FAN SW.
COOLING FAN MOTOR
FUSE BOX
RED-ORANGE
BROWN (2 WIRES USED)
BROWN-WHITE
TO A/C & HEATER
IGNITION RELAY
LT.GREEN
N
C
WHITE-LT.GREEN
BROWN-LT.GREEN
OIL PRESSURE SENDER
WHITE-BLACK
BLACK-BROWN
BLACK-WHITE
WINDSHIELD WIPER MOTOR
OIL PRESSURE SWITCH
PARKING BRAKE SWITCH
BLUE-LT.GREEN
GREEN-BLUE
BLACK-YELLOW
TEMPERATURE SENDER
LOW BRAKE SWITCHES
PINK-LT.GREEN
BLACK-LT.GREEN
ORANGE-LT.GREEN
GREEN-RED
YELLOW-LT.GREEN
RED-LT.GREEN
WINDSHIELD WIPER RELAY
LEGEND
ACCESSORY POWER FEED
B. SEAT BELT WARNING SYSTEM
C. REAR WINDOW DEFROSTER
H. ELECTRIC DOOR LOCK SYSTEM
N. ELECTRIC OVERDRIVE SYSTEM
O. FUEL INJECTION SYSTEM
P. POWER WINDOW CONTROL SYSTEM

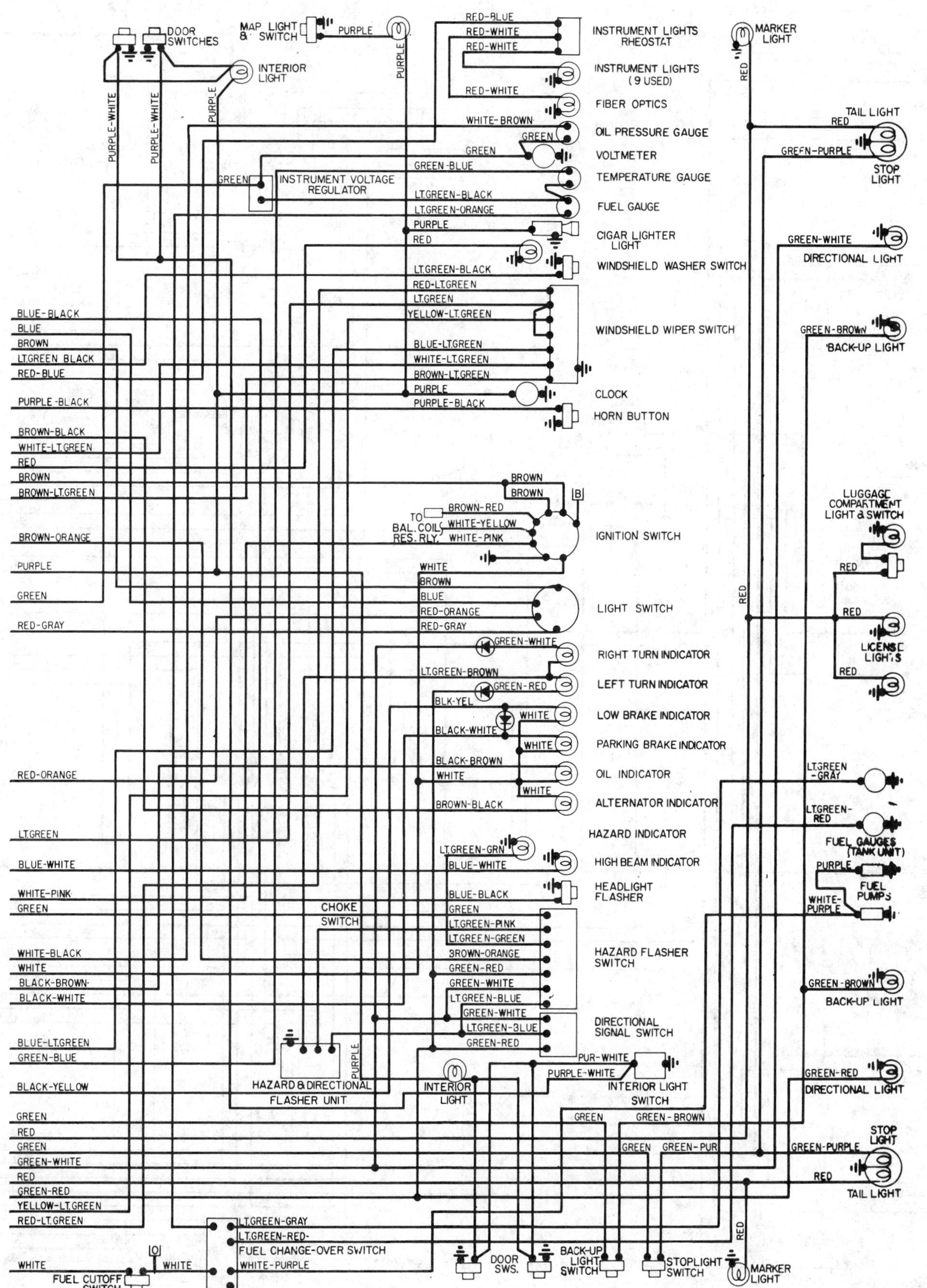
DOOR SWITCHES
MAP LIGHT & SWITCH
INTERIOR LIGHT
INSTRUMENT LIGHTS RHEOSTAT
INSTRUMENT LIGHTS (9 USED)
FIBER OPTICS
OIL PRESSURE GAUGE
VOLTMETER
TEMPERATURE GAUGE
FUEL GAUGE
INSTRUMENT VOLTAGE REGULATOR
CIGAR LIGHTER LIGHT
WINDSHIELD WASHER SWITCH
WINDSHIELD WIPER SWITCH
CLOCK
HORN BUTTON
TO BAL. COIL RES. RLY.
IGNITION SWITCH
LIGHT SWITCH
RIGHT TURN INDICATOR
LEFT TURN INDICATOR
LOW BRAKE INDICATOR
PARKING BRAKE INDICATOR
OIL INDICATOR
ALTERNATOR INDICATOR
HAZARD INDICATOR
HIGH BEAM INDICATOR
HEADLIGHT FLASHER
CHOKE SWITCH
HAZARD FLASHER SWITCH
DIRECTIONAL SIGNAL SWITCH
HAZARD & DIRECTIONAL FLASHER UNIT
INTERIOR LIGHT
INTERIOR LIGHT SWITCH
FUEL CHANGE-OVER SWITCH
FUEL CUTOFF SWITCH
DOOR SWS.
BACK-UP LIGHT SWITCH
STOPLIGHT SWITCH
MARKER LIGHT
TAIL LIGHT
STOP LIGHT
DIRECTIONAL LIGHT
BACK-UP LIGHT
LUGGAGE COMPARTMENT LIGHT & SWITCH
LICENSE LIGHTS
FUEL GAUGES (TANK UNIT)
FUEL PUMPS
BLUE-BLACK
BLUE
BROWN
LT.GREEN BLACK
RED-BLUE
PURPLE-BLACK
BROWN-BLACK
WHITE-LT.GREEN
RED
BROWN-LT.GREEN
BROWN-ORANGE
PURPLE
GREEN
RED-GRAY
RED-ORANGE
LT.GREEN
BLUE-WHITE
WHITE-PINK
WHITE-BLACK
WHITE
BLACK-BROWN
BLACK-WHITE
BLUE-LT.GREEN
GREEN-BLUE
BLACK-YELLOW
GREEN-WHITE
GREEN-RED
YELLOW-LT.GREEN
RED-LT.GREEN

1977 Jaguar

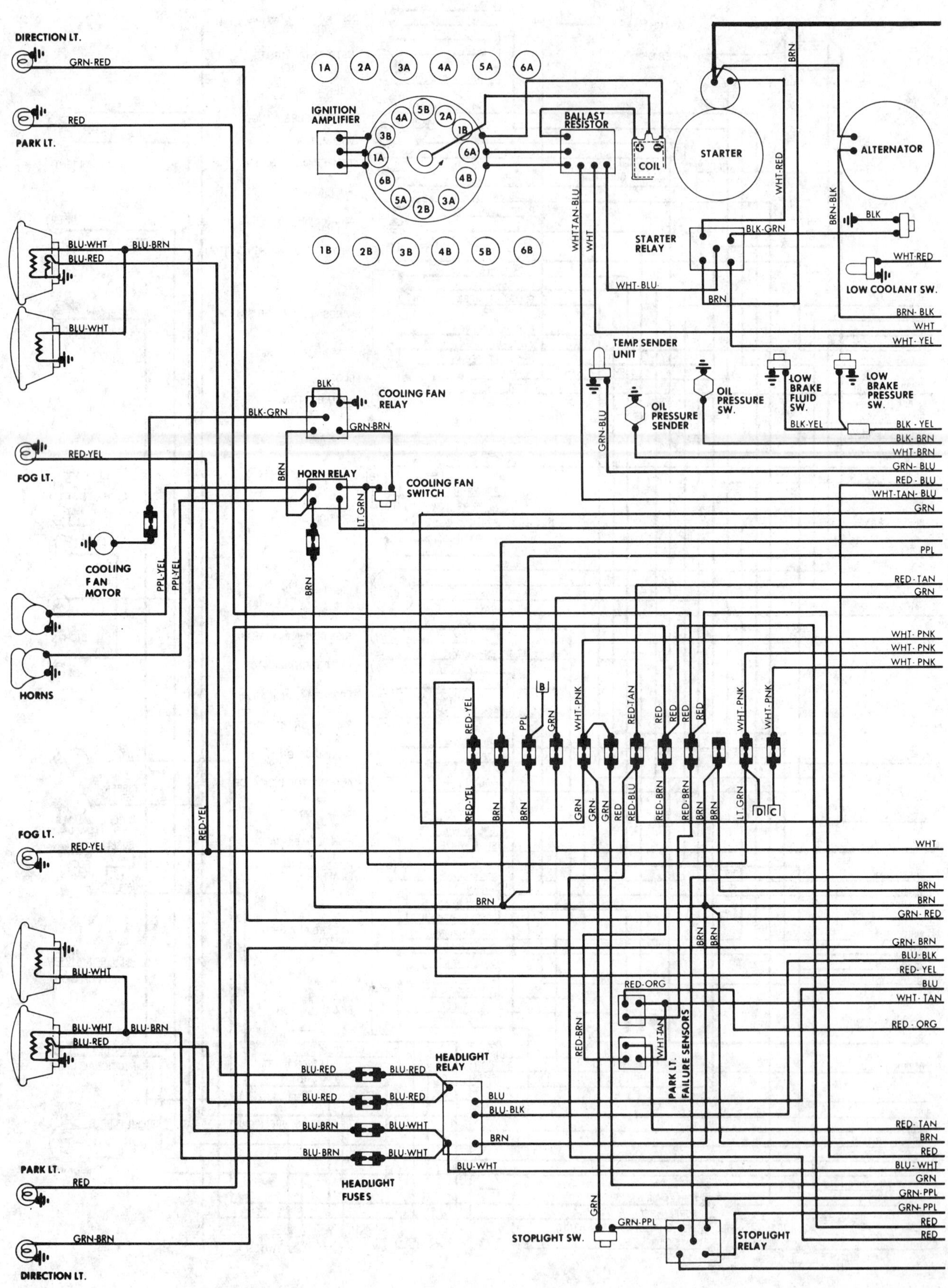
DIRECTION LT.
GRN-RED
RED
PARK LT.
IGNITION AMPLIFIER
BALLAST RESISTOR
COIL
STARTER
ALTERNATOR
STARTER RELAY
LOW COOLANT SW.
TEMP. SENDER UNIT
OIL PRESSURE SENDER
OIL PRESSURE SW.
LOW BRAKE FLUID SW.
LOW BRAKE PRESSURE SW.
COOLING FAN RELAY
HORN RELAY
COOLING FAN SWITCH
FOG LT.
COOLING FAN MOTOR
HORNS
HEADLIGHT RELAY
HEADLIGHT FUSES
PARK LT. FAILURE SENSORS
STOPLIGHT SW.
STOPLIGHT RELAY
PARK LT.
DIRECTION LT.

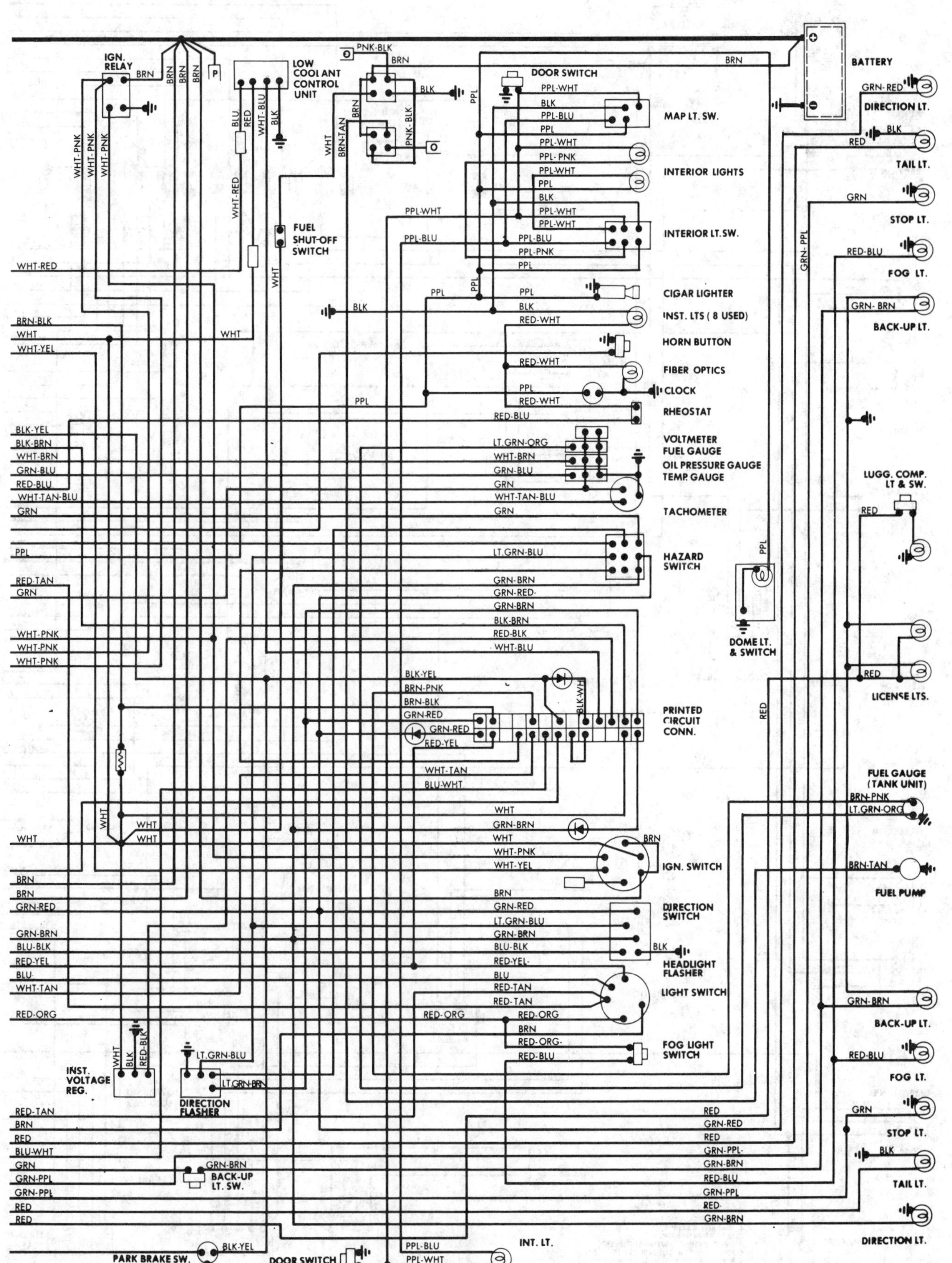
IGN. RELAY
LOW COOLANT CONTROL UNIT
DOOR SWITCH
BATTERY
MAP LT. SW.
INTERIOR LIGHTS
INTERIOR LT. SW.
FUEL SHUT-OFF SWITCH
CIGAR LIGHTER
INST. LTS (8 USED)
HORN BUTTON
FIBER OPTICS
CLOCK
RHEOSTAT
VOLTMETER
FUEL GAUGE
OIL PRESSURE GAUGE
TEMP. GAUGE
TACHOMETER
HAZARD SWITCH
DOME LT. & SWITCH
PRINTED CIRCUIT CONN.
IGN. SWITCH
DIRECTION SWITCH
HEADLIGHT FLASHER
LIGHT SWITCH
FOG LIGHT SWITCH
INST. VOLTAGE REG.
DIRECTION FLASHER
BACK-UP LT. SW.
PARK BRAKE SW.
DOOR SWITCH
INT. LT.
DIRECTION LT.
TAIL LT.
STOP LT.
FOG LT.
BACK-UP LT.
LUGG. COMP. LT & SW.
LICENSE LTS.
FUEL GAUGE (TANK UNIT)
FUEL PUMP
BACK-UP LT.
FOG LT.
STOP LT.
TAIL LT.
DIRECTION LT.

1977 Lancia

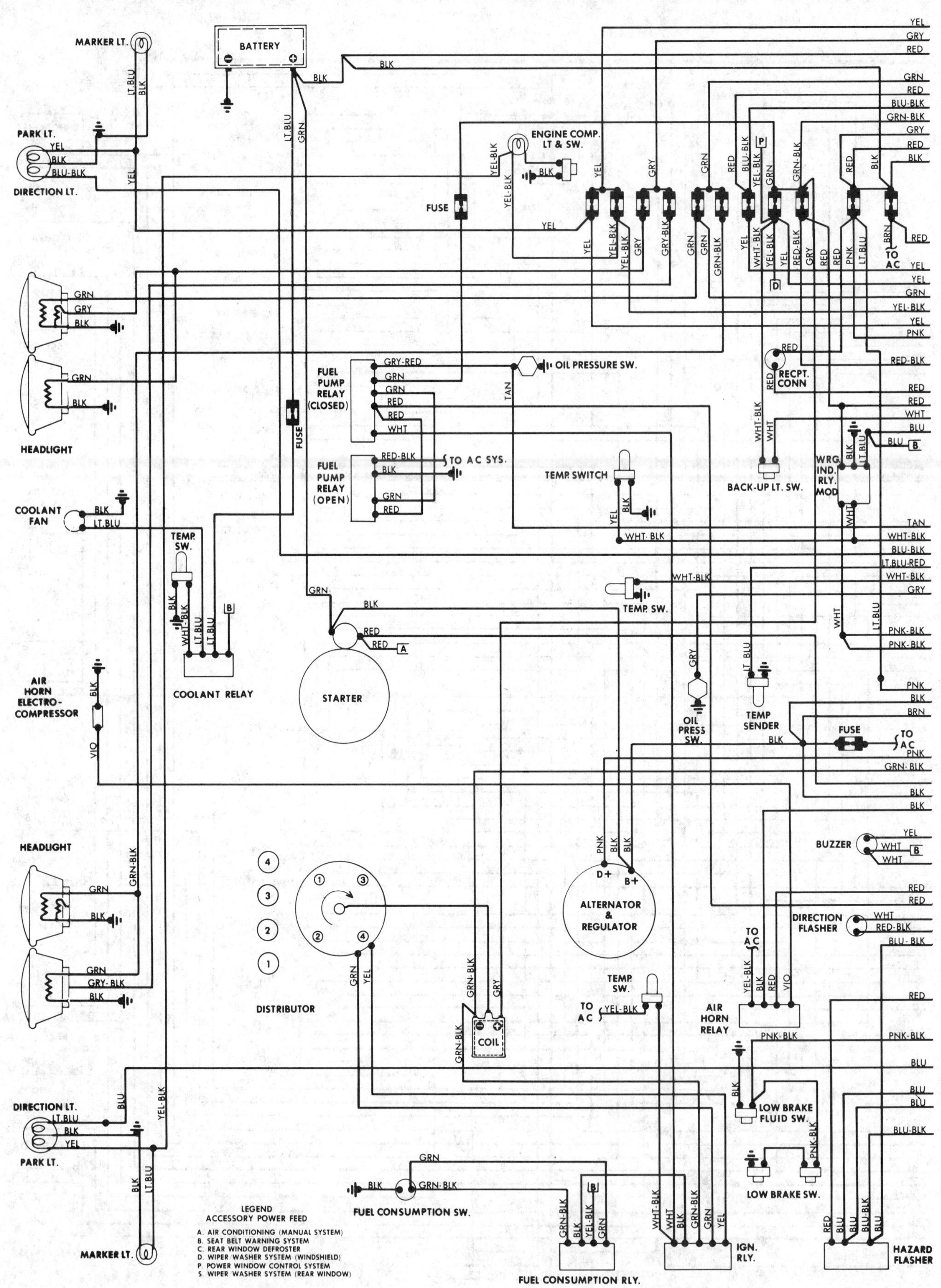
MARKER LT.
BATTERY
PARK LT.
DIRECTION LT.
ENGINE COMP. LT & SW.
FUSE
HEADLIGHT
FUEL PUMP RELAY (CLOSED)
OIL PRESSURE SW.
RECPT. CONN
FUEL PUMP RELAY (OPEN)
TO AC SYS.
TEMP. SWITCH
BACK-UP LT. SW.
WRG. IND. RLY. MOD
COOLANT FAN
TEMP. SW.
COOLANT RELAY
STARTER
AIR HORN ELECTRO-COMPRESSOR
OIL PRESS SW.
TEMP SENDER
TO AC
BUZZER
ALTERNATOR & REGULATOR
DIRECTION FLASHER
DISTRIBUTOR
COIL
AIR HORN RELAY
LOW BRAKE FLUID SW.
LOW BRAKE SW.
FUEL CONSUMPTION SW.
IGN. RLY.
HAZARD FLASHER
FUEL CONSUMPTION RLY.
LEGEND
ACCESSORY POWER FEED
A. AIR CONDITIONING (MANUAL SYSTEM)
B. SEAT BELT WARNING SYSTEM
C. REAR WINDOW DEFROSTER
D. WIPER WASHER SYSTEM (WINDSHIELD)
P. POWER WINDOW CONTROL SYSTEM
S. WIPER WASHER SYSTEM (REAR WINDOW)

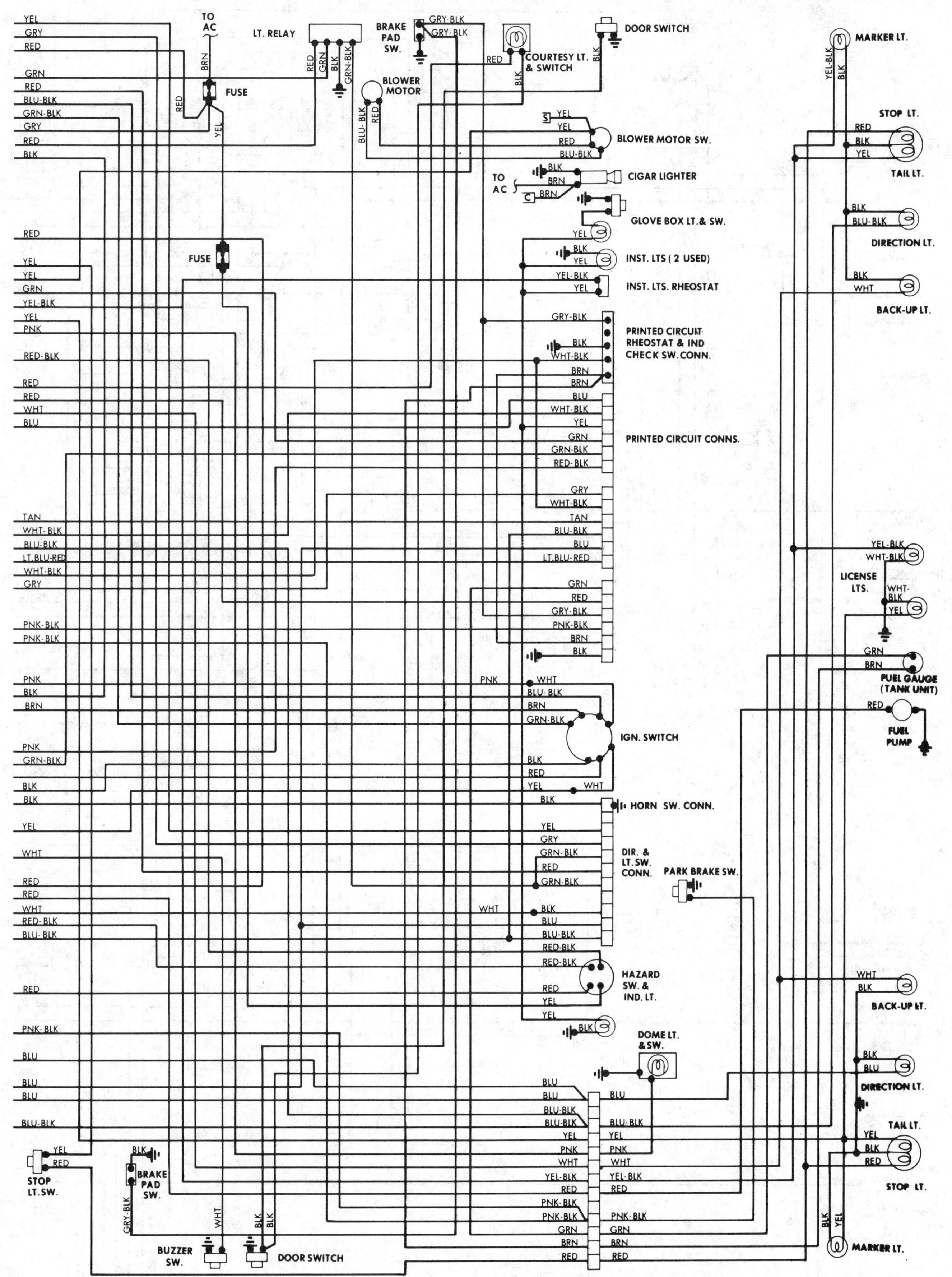

TO AC
LT. RELAY
BRAKE PAD SW.
DOOR SWITCH
COURTESY LT. & SWITCH
BLOWER MOTOR
FUSE
BLOWER MOTOR SW.
CIGAR LIGHTER
GLOVE BOX LT. & SW.
INST. LTS (2 USED)
INST. LTS. RHEOSTAT
PRINTED CIRCUIT RHEOSTAT & IND CHECK SW. CONN.
PRINTED CIRCUIT CONNS.
IGN. SWITCH
HORN SW. CONN.
DIR. & LT. SW. CONN.
PARK BRAKE SW.
HAZARD SW. & IND. LT.
DOME LT. & SW.
STOP LT. SW.
BUZZER SW.
MARKER LT.
STOP LT.
TAIL LT.
DIRECTION LT.
BACK-UP LT.
LICENSE LTS.
FUEL GAUGE (TANK UNIT)
FUEL PUMP

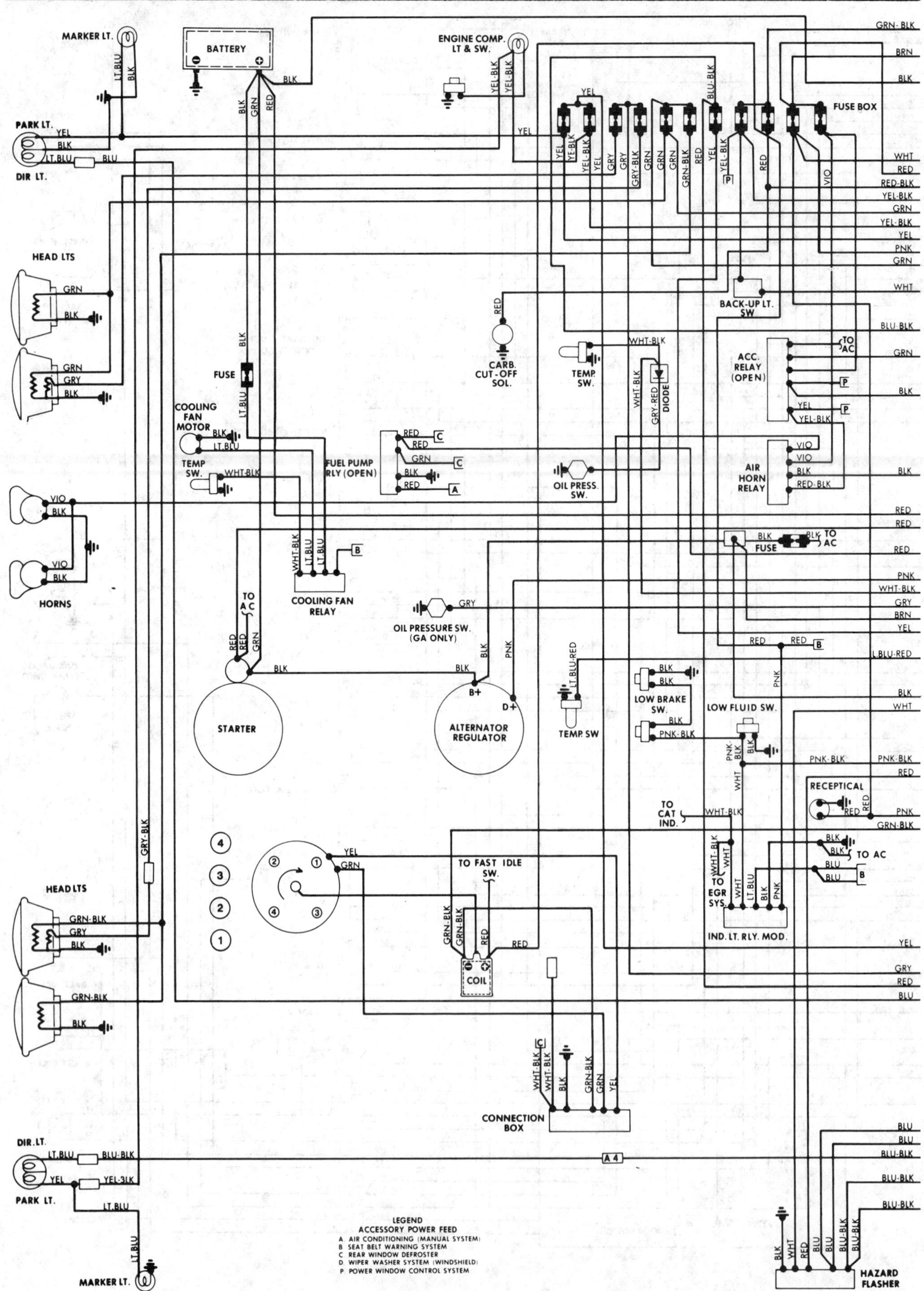
MARKER LT.
BATTERY
ENGINE COMP. LT & SW.
FUSE BOX
PARK LT.
DIR LT.
HEAD LTS
BACK-UP LT. SW
CARB. CUT-OFF SOL.
TEMP. SW.
DIODE
ACC. RELAY (OPEN)
TO AC
FUSE
COOLING FAN MOTOR
TEMP SW.
FUEL PUMP RLY (OPEN)
OIL PRESS. SW.
AIR HORN RELAY
HORNS
COOLING FAN RELAY
TO A C
OIL PRESSURE SW. (GA ONLY)
STARTER
ALTERNATOR REGULATOR
TEMP. SW
LOW BRAKE SW.
LOW FLUID SW.
RECEPTICAL
TO CAT IND.
TO EGR SYS.
IND. LT. RLY. MOD.
TO FAST IDLE SW.
COIL
HEAD LTS
CONNECTION BOX
DIR. LT.
PARK LT.
MARKER LT.
HAZARD FLASHER
LEGEND
ACCESSORY POWER FEED
A AIR CONDITIONING (MANUAL SYSTEM)
B SEAT BELT WARNING SYSTEM
C REAR WINDOW DEFROSTER
D WIPER WASHER SYSTEM (WINDSHIELD)
P POWER WINDOW CONTROL SYSTEM

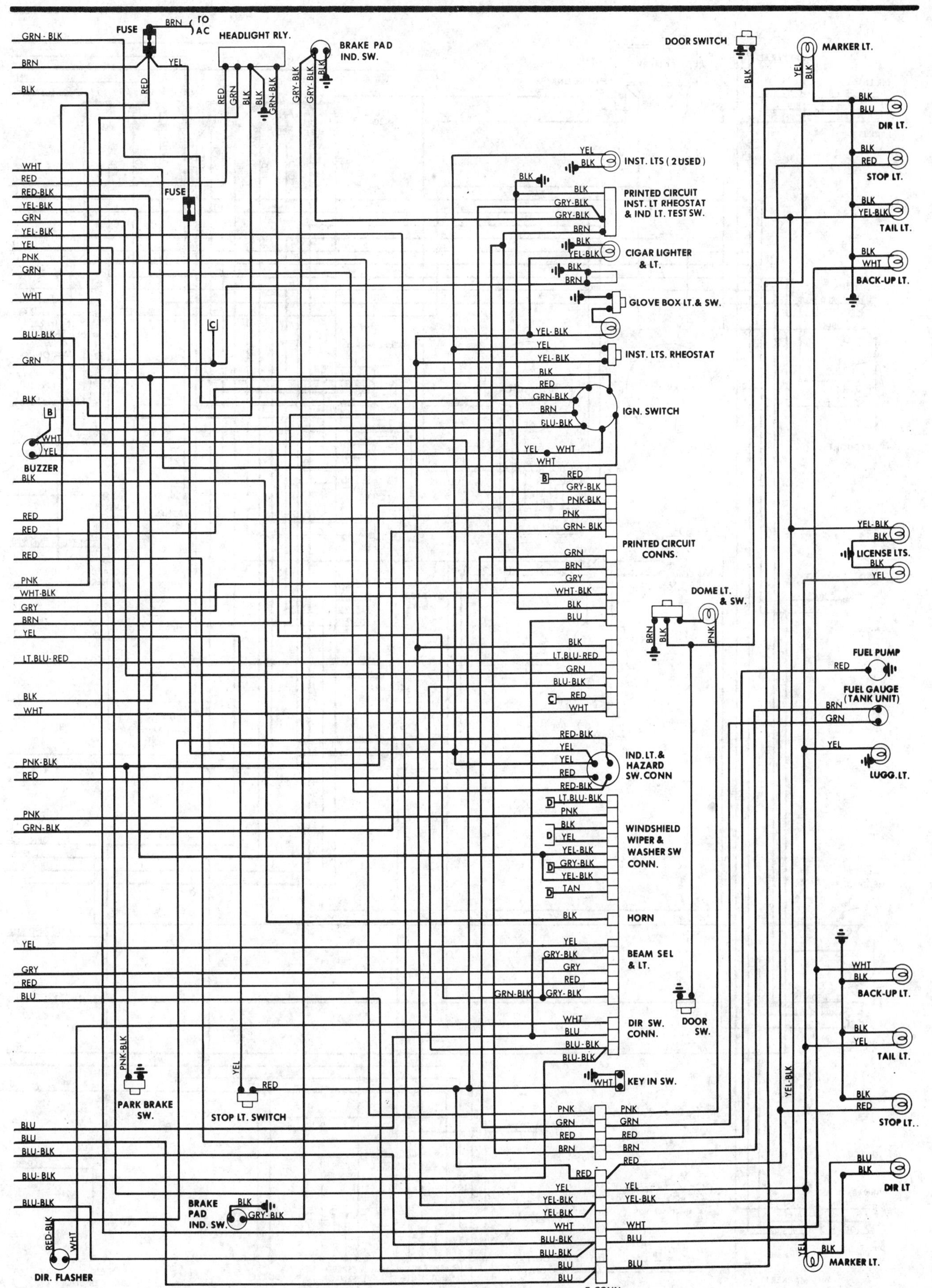
FUSE
BRN
TO AC
HEADLIGHT RLY.
BRAKE PAD IND. SW.
DOOR SWITCH
MARKER LT.
DIR LT.
STOP LT.
TAIL LT.
BACK-UP LT.
INST. LTS (2 USED)
PRINTED CIRCUIT INST. LT RHEOSTAT & IND LT. TEST SW.
CIGAR LIGHTER & LT.
GLOVE BOX LT. & SW.
INST. LTS. RHEOSTAT
IGN. SWITCH
BUZZER
PRINTED CIRCUIT CONNS.
LICENSE LTS.
DOME LT. & SW.
FUEL PUMP
FUEL GAUGE (TANK UNIT)
LUGG. LT.
IND. LT. & HAZARD SW. CONN
WINDSHIELD WIPER & WASHER SW CONN.
HORN
BEAM SEL & LT.
DIR SW. CONN.
DOOR SW.
KEY IN SW.
PARK BRAKE SW.
STOP LT. SWITCH
BRAKE PAD IND. SW.
DIR. FLASHER
E-CONN.

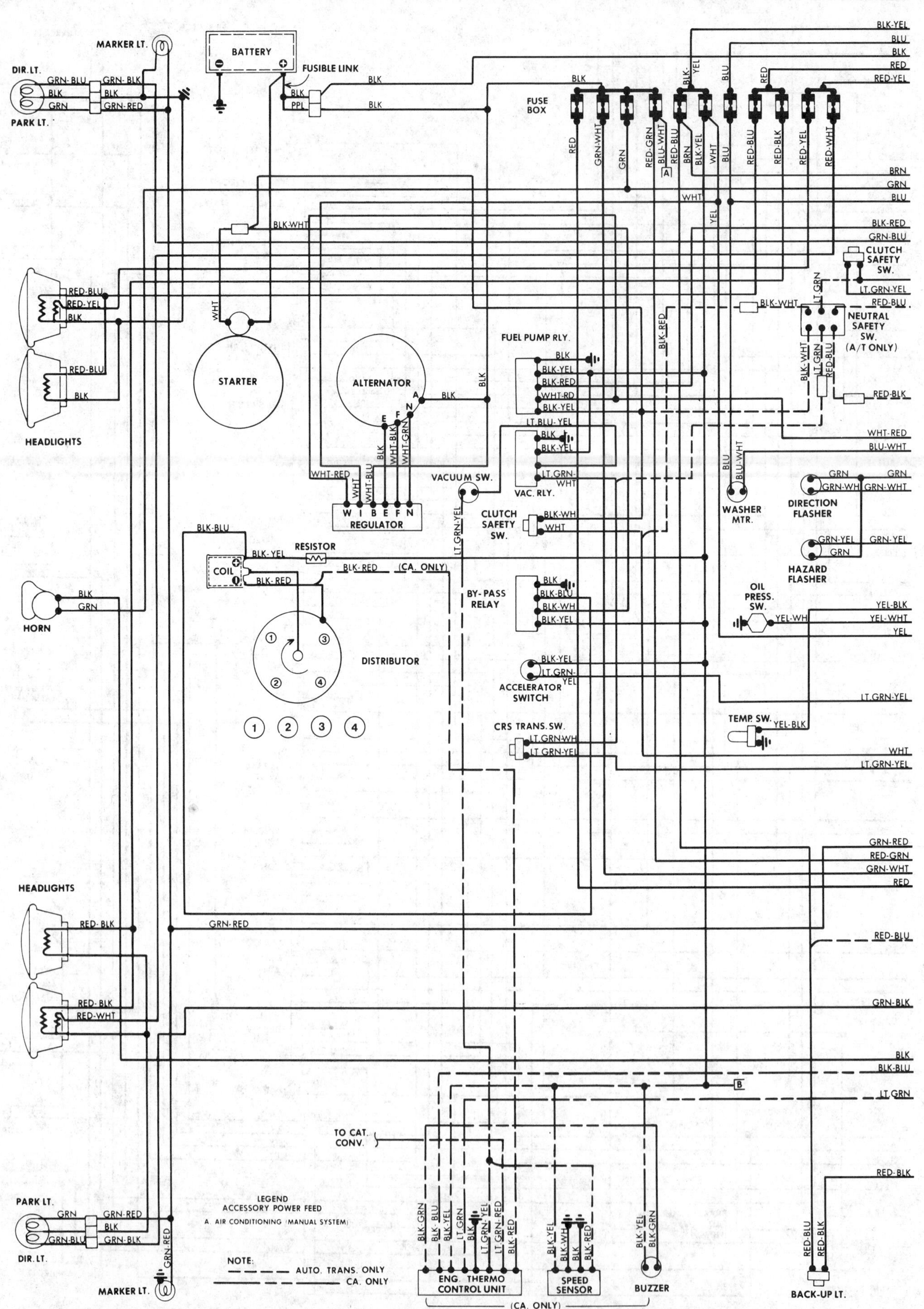

MARKER LT.
DIR. LT.
PARK LT.
BATTERY
FUSIBLE LINK
FUSE BOX
HEADLIGHTS
STARTER
ALTERNATOR
REGULATOR
W I B E F N
FUEL PUMP RLY.
VAC. RLY.
VACUUM SW.
CLUTCH SAFETY SW.
NEUTRAL SAFETY SW. (A/T ONLY)
COIL
RESISTOR
(CA. ONLY)
BY-PASS RELAY
DISTRIBUTOR
HORN
ACCELERATOR SWITCH
CRS TRANS. SW.
WASHER MTR.
DIRECTION FLASHER
HAZARD FLASHER
OIL PRESS. SW.
TEMP. SW.
TO CAT. CONV.
ENG. THERMO CONTROL UNIT
SPEED SENSOR
BUZZER
BACK-UP LT.
LEGEND
ACCESSORY POWER FEED
A AIR CONDITIONING (MANUAL SYSTEM)
NOTE:
AUTO. TRANS. ONLY
CA. ONLY

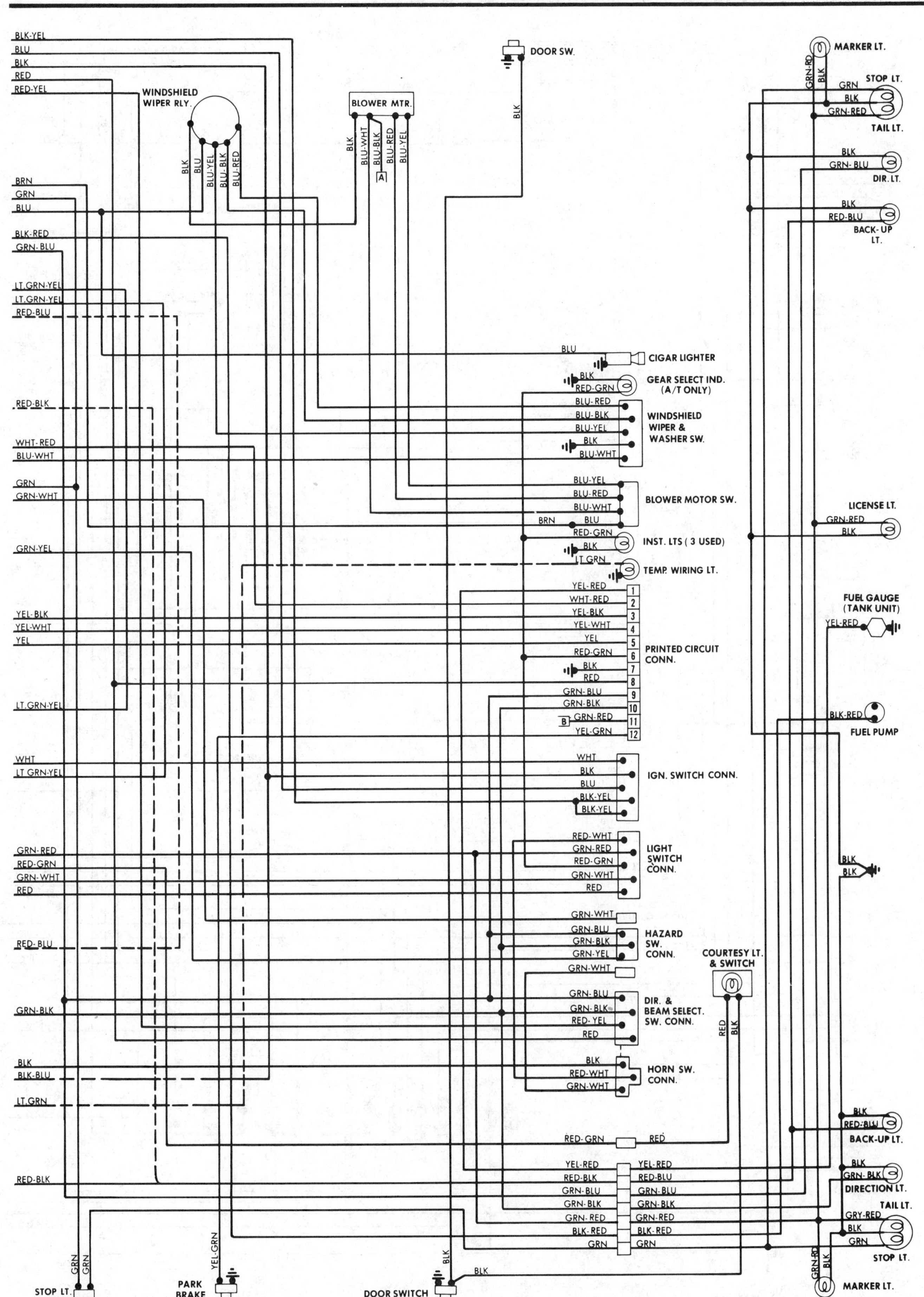
WINDSHIELD WIPER RLY.
BLOWER MTR.
DOOR SW.
MARKER LT.
STOP LT.
TAIL LT.
DIR. LT.
BACK-UP LT.
CIGAR LIGHTER
GEAR SELECT IND. (A/T ONLY)
WINDSHIELD WIPER & WASHER SW.
BLOWER MOTOR SW.
INST. LTS (3 USED)
TEMP. WIRING LT.
LICENSE LT.
FUEL GAUGE (TANK UNIT)
PRINTED CIRCUIT CONN.
FUEL PUMP
IGN. SWITCH CONN.
LIGHT SWITCH CONN.
HAZARD SW. CONN.
COURTESY LT. & SWITCH
DIR. & BEAM SELECT. SW. CONN.
HORN SW. CONN.
BACK-UP LT.
DIRECTION LT.
TAIL LT.
STOP LT.
MARKER LT.
STOP LT. SW.
PARK BRAKE SW.
DOOR SWITCH

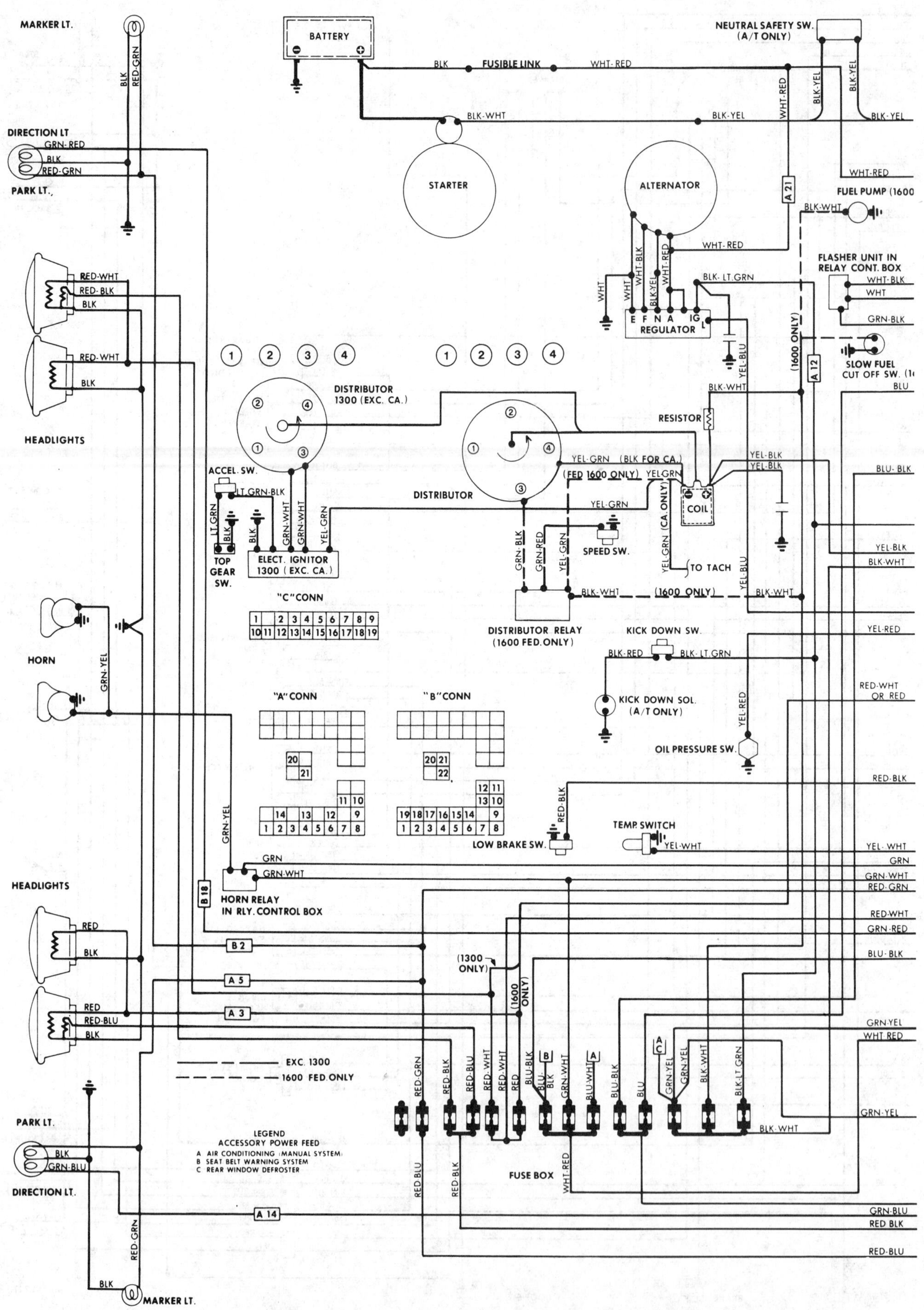
MARKER LT.
BATTERY
NEUTRAL SAFETY SW. (A/T ONLY)
FUSIBLE LINK
DIRECTION LT
PARK LT.
STARTER
ALTERNATOR
FUEL PUMP (1600
FLASHER UNIT IN RELAY CONT. BOX
REGULATOR
SLOW FUEL CUT OFF SW.
HEADLIGHTS
DISTRIBUTOR 1300 (EXC. CA.)
RESISTOR
DISTRIBUTOR
COIL
ACCEL. SW.
TOP GEAR SW.
ELECT. IGNITOR 1300 (EXC. CA.)
SPEED SW.
TO TACH
DISTRIBUTOR RELAY (1600 FED. ONLY)
KICK DOWN SW.
KICK DOWN SOL. (A/T ONLY)
OIL PRESSURE SW.
"C" CONN
"A" CONN
"B" CONN
HORN
TEMP. SWITCH
LOW BRAKE SW.
HORN RELAY IN RLY. CONTROL BOX
EXC. 1300
1600 FED. ONLY
FUSE BOX
LEGEND
ACCESSORY POWER FEED
A AIR CONDITIONING (MANUAL SYSTEM)
B SEAT BELT WARNING SYSTEM
C REAR WINDOW DEFROSTER

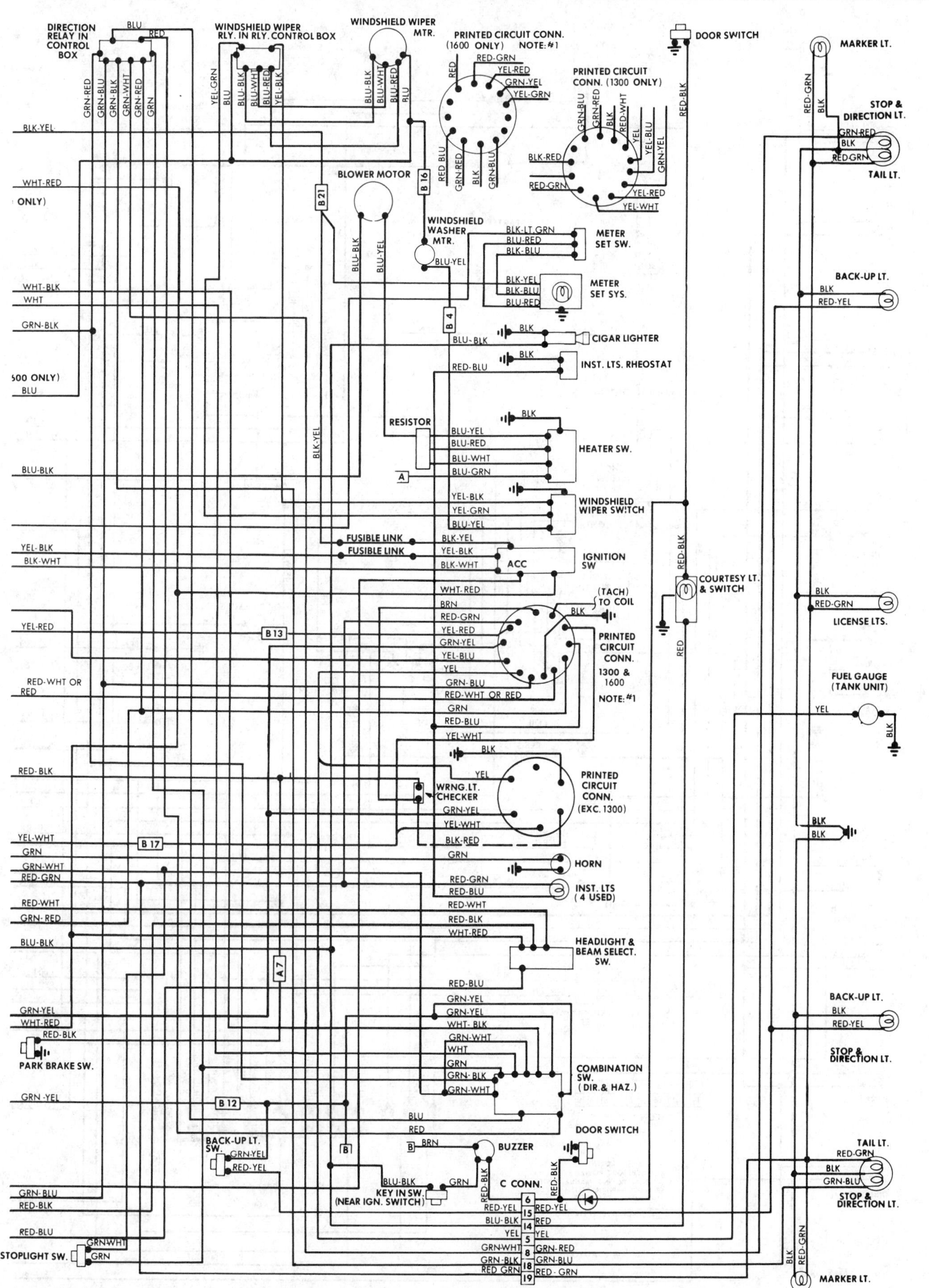
DIRECTION RELAY IN CONTROL BOX
WINDSHIELD WIPER RLY. IN RLY. CONTROL BOX
WINDSHIELD WIPER MTR.
PRINTED CIRCUIT CONN. (1600 ONLY) NOTE: #1
PRINTED CIRCUIT CONN. (1300 ONLY)
DOOR SWITCH
MARKER LT.
STOP & DIRECTION LT.
TAIL LT.
BLOWER MOTOR
WINDSHIELD WASHER MTR.
METER SET SW.
METER SET SYS.
BACK-UP LT.
CIGAR LIGHTER
INST. LTS. RHEOSTAT
RESISTOR
HEATER SW.
WINDSHIELD WIPER SWITCH
FUSIBLE LINK
FUSIBLE LINK
ACC
IGNITION SW
COURTESY LT. & SWITCH
(TACH) TO COIL
PRINTED CIRCUIT CONN. 1300 & 1600 NOTE: #1
LICENSE LTS.
FUEL GAUGE (TANK UNIT)
PRINTED CIRCUIT CONN. (EXC. 1300)
WRNG. LT. CHECKER
HORN
INST. LTS (4 USED)
HEADLIGHT & BEAM SELECT. SW.
PARK BRAKE SW.
COMBINATION SW. (DIR. & HAZ.)
DOOR SWITCH
BACK-UP LT. SW.
BUZZER
C CONN.
KEY IN SW. (NEAR IGN. SWITCH)
STOPLIGHT SW.
BACK-UP LT.
STOP & DIRECTION LT.
TAIL LT.
STOP & DIRECTION LT.
MARKER LT.
ONLY)
500 ONLY)
RED-WHT OR RED
B 21
B 16
B 4
B 13
B 17
A 7
B 12

1977 Mazda

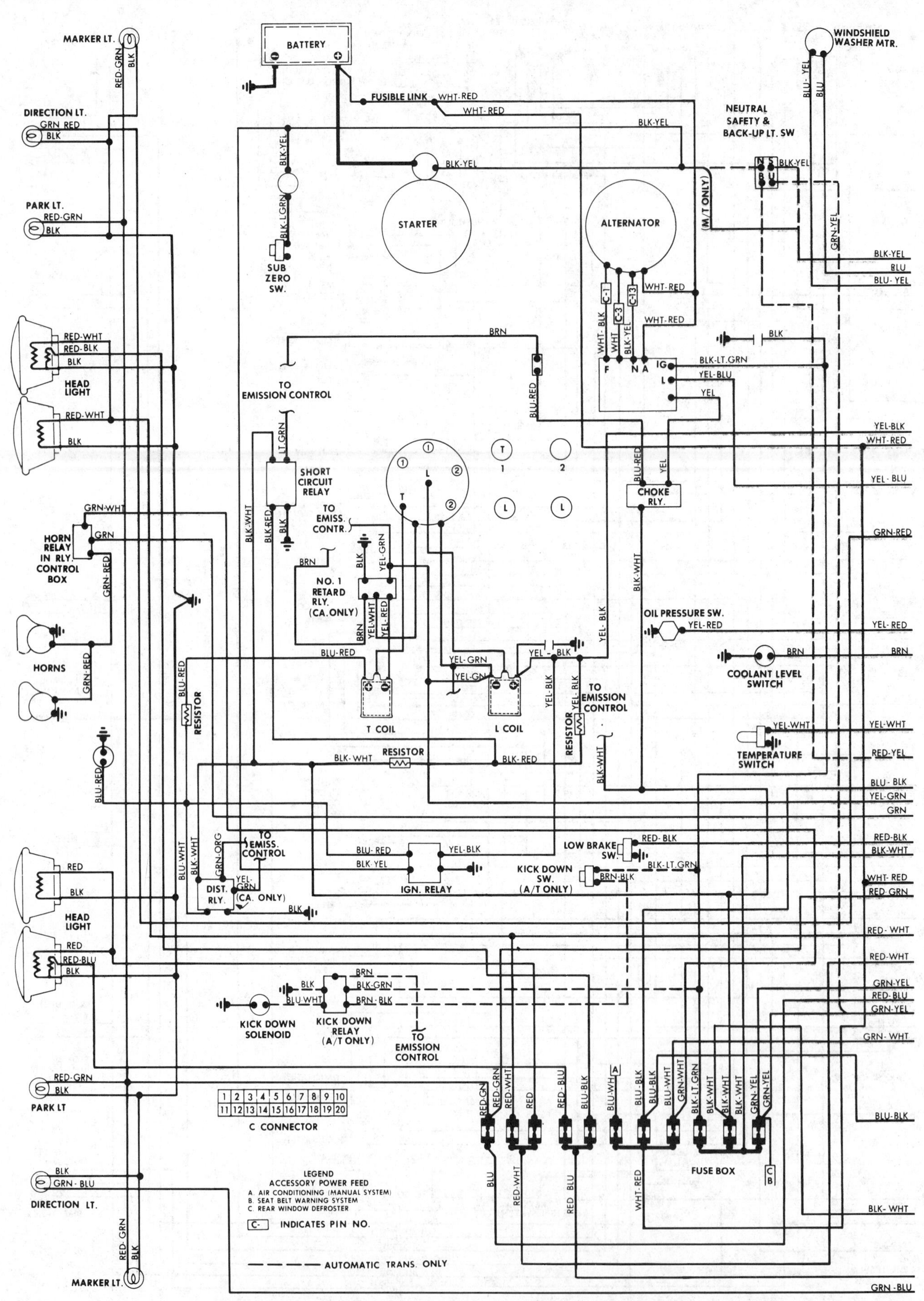
MARKER LT.
BATTERY
FUSIBLE LINK
WINDSHIELD WASHER MTR.
DIRECTION LT.
NEUTRAL SAFETY & BACK-UP LT. SW
PARK LT.
STARTER
ALTERNATOR
(M/T ONLY)
SUB ZERO SW.
HEAD LIGHT
TO EMISSION CONTROL
SHORT CIRCUIT RELAY
CHOKE RLY.
HORN RELAY IN RLY. CONTROL BOX
TO EMISS. CONTR.
NO. 1 RETARD RLY. (CA. ONLY)
OIL PRESSURE SW.
HORNS
COOLANT LEVEL SWITCH
RESISTOR
T COIL
L COIL
TO EMISSION CONTROL
TEMPERATURE SWITCH
TO EMISS. CONTROL
LOW BRAKE SW.
KICK DOWN SW. (A/T ONLY)
DIST. RLY.
(CA. ONLY)
IGN. RELAY
HEAD LIGHT
KICK DOWN SOLENOID
KICK DOWN RELAY (A/T ONLY)
TO EMISSION CONTROL
PARK LT
C CONNECTOR
FUSE BOX
LEGEND
ACCESSORY POWER FEED
A. AIR CONDITIONING (MANUAL SYSTEM)
B. SEAT BELT WARNING SYSTEM
C. REAR WINDOW DEFROSTER
C- INDICATES PIN NO.
DIRECTION LT.
AUTOMATIC TRANS. ONLY
MARKER LT.

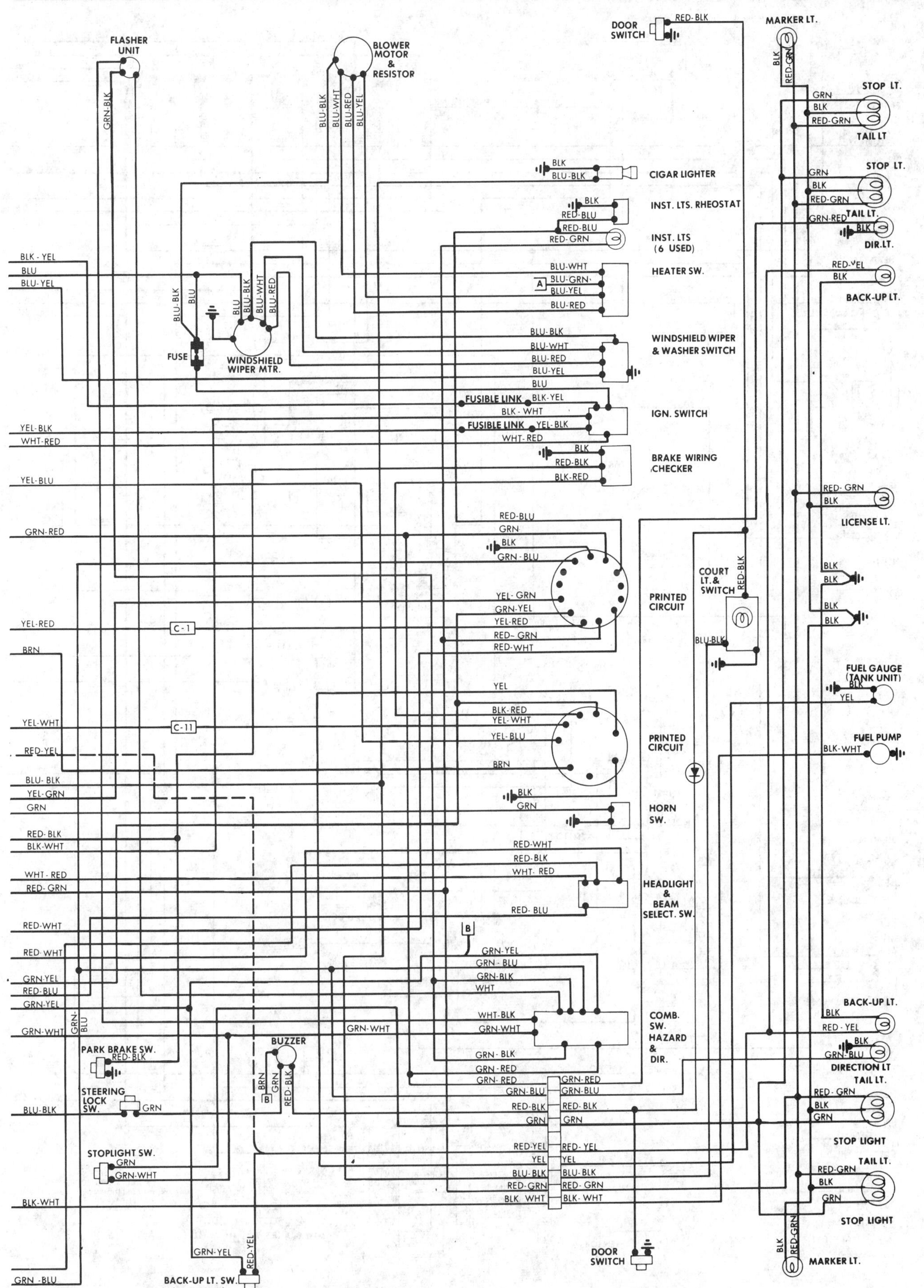

FLASHER UNIT
GRN-BLK
BLOWER MOTOR & RESISTOR
BLU-BLK
BLU-WHT
BLU-RED
BLU-YEL
DOOR SWITCH
RED-BLK
MARKER LT.
BLK
RED-GRN
STOP LT.
GRN
BLK
RED-GRN
TAIL LT
STOP LT.
GRN
BLK
RED-GRN
TAIL LT.
GRN-RED
BLK
DIR.LT.
BLK
BLU-BLK
CIGAR LIGHTER
BLK
RED-BLU
INST. LTS. RHEOSTAT
RED-BLU
RED-GRN
INST. LTS (6 USED)
BLK-YEL
BLU
BLU-YEL
BLU-BLK
BLU
BLU-BLK
BLU-WHT
BLU-RED
BLU
FUSE
WINDSHIELD WIPER MTR.
BLU-WHT
A
BLU-GRN
BLU-YEL
BLU-RED
HEATER SW.
RED-YEL
BLK
BACK-UP LT.
BLU-BLK
BLU-WHT
BLU-RED
BLU-YEL
BLU
WINDSHIELD WIPER & WASHER SWITCH
FUSIBLE LINK
BLK-YEL
BLK-WHT
FUSIBLE LINK
YEL-BLK
WHT-RED
IGN. SWITCH
YEL-BLK
WHT-RED
BLK
RED-BLK
BLK-RED
BRAKE WIRING CHECKER
YEL-BLU
RED-GRN
BLK
LICENSE LT.
GRN-RED
RED-BLU
GRN
BLK
GRN-BLU
COURT LT. & SWITCH
RED-BLK
PRINTED CIRCUIT
BLK
BLK
BLK
BLK
YEL-GRN
GRN-YEL
YEL-RED
RED-GRN
RED-WHT
YEL-RED
C-1
BRN
BLU-BLK
FUEL GAUGE (TANK UNIT)
BLK
YEL
YEL
BLK-RED
YEL-WHT
YEL-BLU
PRINTED CIRCUIT
YEL-WHT
C-11
RED-YEL
BRN
FUEL PUMP
BLK-WHT
BLU-BLK
YEL-GRN
GRN
BLK
GRN
HORN SW.
RED-BLK
BLK-WHT
RED-WHT
RED-BLK
WHT-RED
WHT-RED
RED-GRN
HEADLIGHT & BEAM SELECT. SW.
RED-BLU
RED-WHT
B
RED-WHT
GRN-YEL
GRN-BLU
GRN-BLK
WHT
GRN-YEL
RED-BLU
GRN-YEL
WHT-BLK
GRN-WHT
GRN-WHT
COMB. SW. HAZARD & DIR.
GRN-WHT
GRN-BLU
BACK-UP LT.
BLK
RED-YEL
BLK
GRN-BLU
DIRECTION LT
PARK BRAKE SW.
RED-BLK
BUZZER
BRN
GRN
RED-BLK
GRN-BLK
GRN-RED
GRN-RED
GRN-RED
GRN-BLU
GRN-BLU
TAIL LT.
RED-GRN
BLK
GRN
STEERING LOCK SW.
GRN
BLU-BLK
RED-BLK
RED-BLK
GRN
GRN
STOP LIGHT
STOPLIGHT SW.
GRN
GRN-WHT
RED-YEL
RED-YEL
YEL
YEL
BLU-BLK
BLU-BLK
RED-GRN
RED-GRN
BLK-WHT
BLK-WHT
TAIL LT.
RED-GRN
BLK
GRN
STOP LIGHT
BLK-WHT
GRN-YEL
RED-YEL
DOOR SWITCH
BLK
RED-GRN
MARKER LT.
GRN-BLU
BACK-UP LT. SW. (M/T ONLY)

1977 Mazda

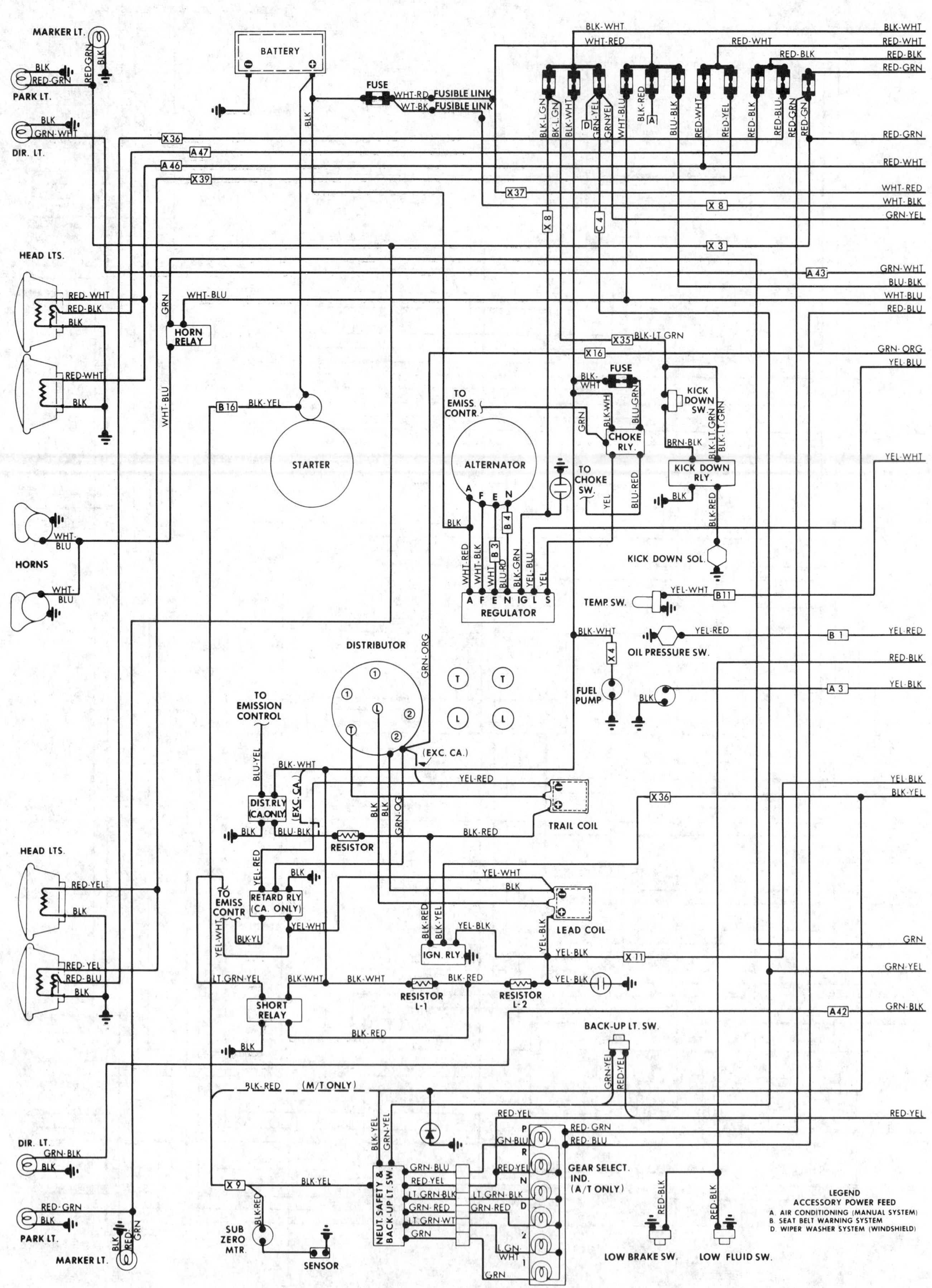

MARKER LT.
PARK LT.
DIR. LT.
BATTERY
FUSE
FUSIBLE LINK
FUSIBLE LINK
HEAD LTS.
HORN RELAY
STARTER
ALTERNATOR
TO EMISS. CONTR.
CHOKE RLY.
TO CHOKE SW.
KICK DOWN SW.
KICK DOWN RLY.
KICK DOWN SOL.
REGULATOR
TEMP. SW.
OIL PRESSURE SW.
FUEL PUMP
HORNS
DISTRIBUTOR
TO EMISSION CONTROL
DIST. RLY (CA. ONLY)
RESISTOR
TRAIL COIL
HEAD LTS.
TO EMISS CONTR
RETARD RLY. (CA. ONLY)
IGN. RLY.
LEAD COIL
SHORT RELAY
RESISTOR L-1
RESISTOR L-2
BACK-UP LT. SW.
(M/T ONLY)
DIR. LT.
PARK LT.
MARKER LT.
SUB ZERO MTR.
SENSOR
NEUT. SAFETY & BACK-UP LT. SW.
GEAR SELECT. IND. (A/T ONLY)
LOW BRAKE SW.
LOW FLUID SW.
LEGEND
ACCESSORY POWER FEED
A. AIR CONDITIONING (MANUAL SYSTEM)
B. SEAT BELT WARNING SYSTEM
D. WIPER WASHER SYSTEM (WINDSHIELD)

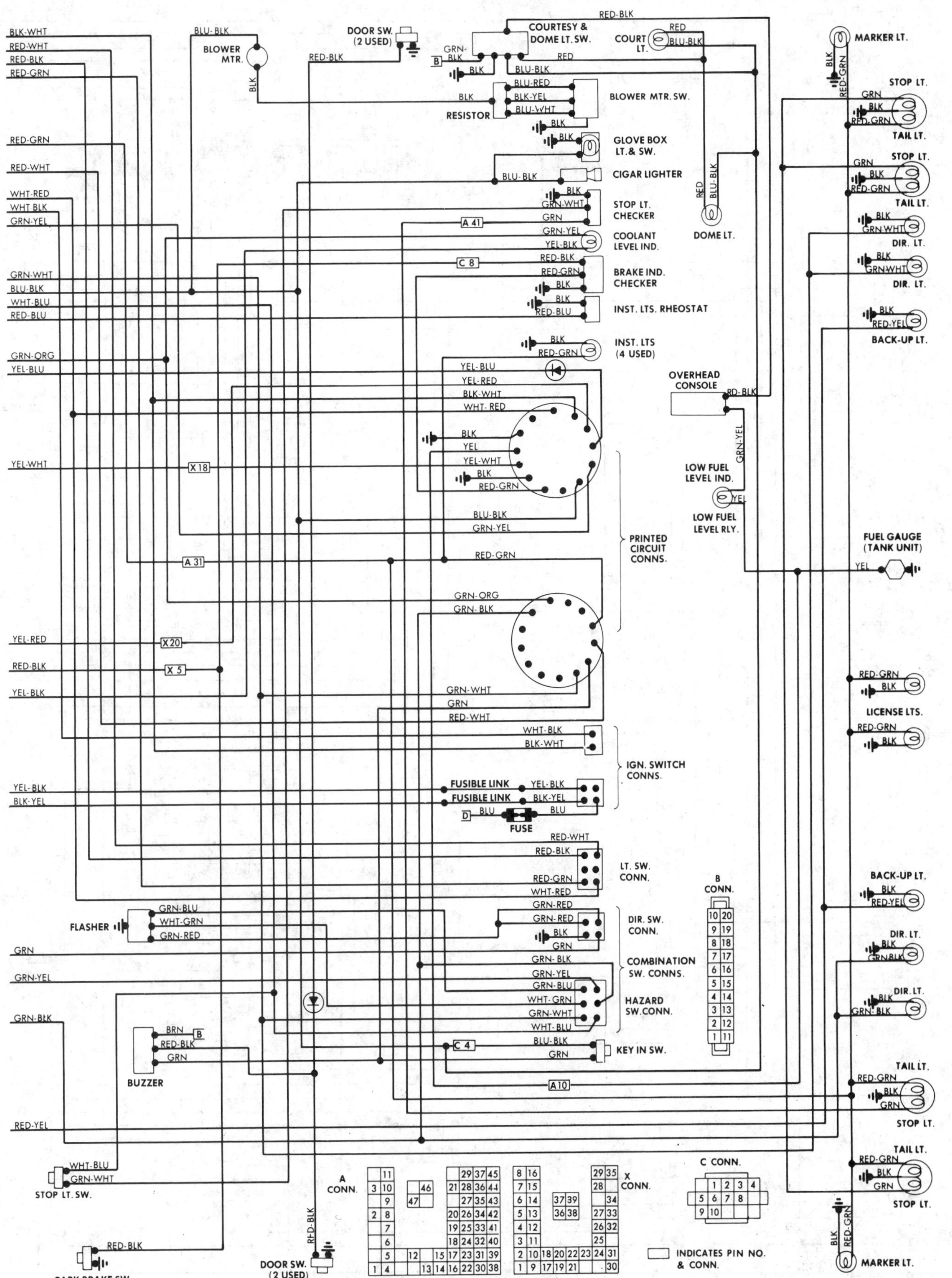
BLOWER MTR.
DOOR SW. (2 USED)
COURTESY & DOME LT. SW.
COURT LT.
MARKER LT.
STOP LT.
TAIL LT.
BLOWER MTR. SW.
RESISTOR
GLOVE BOX LT. & SW.
CIGAR LIGHTER
STOP LT. CHECKER
COOLANT LEVEL IND.
DOME LT.
DIR. LT.
BRAKE IND. CHECKER
INST. LTS. RHEOSTAT
BACK-UP LT.
INST. LTS (4 USED)
OVERHEAD CONSOLE
LOW FUEL LEVEL IND.
LOW FUEL LEVEL RLY.
FUEL GAUGE (TANK UNIT)
PRINTED CIRCUIT CONNS.
LICENSE LTS.
IGN. SWITCH CONNS.
FUSIBLE LINK
FUSE
LT. SW. CONN.
B CONN.
FLASHER
DIR. SW. CONN.
COMBINATION SW. CONNS.
HAZARD SW. CONN.
KEY IN SW.
BUZZER
STOP LT. SW.
A CONN.
X CONN.
C CONN.
INDICATES PIN NO. & CONN.
PARK BRAKE SW.

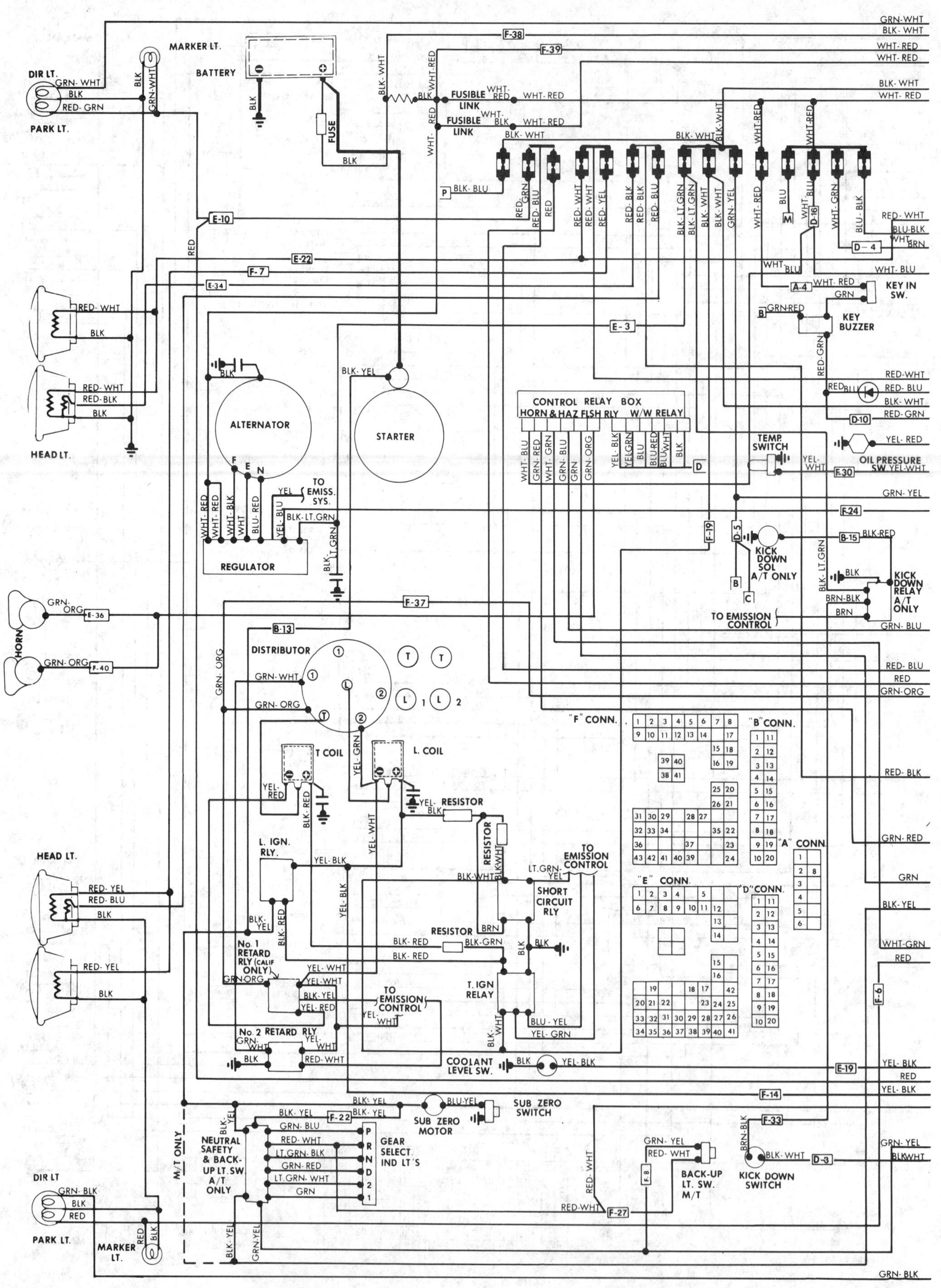
MARKER LT.
BATTERY
DIR LT.
PARK LT.
FUSE
FUSIBLE LINK
FUSIBLE LINK
ALTERNATOR
STARTER
REGULATOR
HEAD LT.
HORN
DISTRIBUTOR
T COIL
L. COIL
RESISTOR
L. IGN. RLY.
TO EMISSION CONTROL
SHORT CIRCUIT RLY
No. 1 RETARD RLY (CALIF ONLY)
T. IGN RELAY
No. 2 RETARD RLY
COOLANT LEVEL SW.
SUB ZERO MOTOR
SUB ZERO SWITCH
NEUTRAL SAFETY & BACK-UP LT. SW. A/T ONLY
M/T ONLY
GEAR SELECT. IND LT'S
BACK-UP LT. SW. M/T
KICK DOWN SWITCH
CONTROL RELAY BOX
HORN & HAZ FLSH RLY
W/W RELAY
KEY IN SW.
KEY BUZZER
TEMP. SWITCH
OIL PRESSURE SW
KICK DOWN SOL A/T ONLY
KICK DOWN RELAY A/T ONLY
TO EMISSION CONTROL
"F" CONN.
"B" CONN.
"A" CONN.
"E" CONN.
"D" CONN.

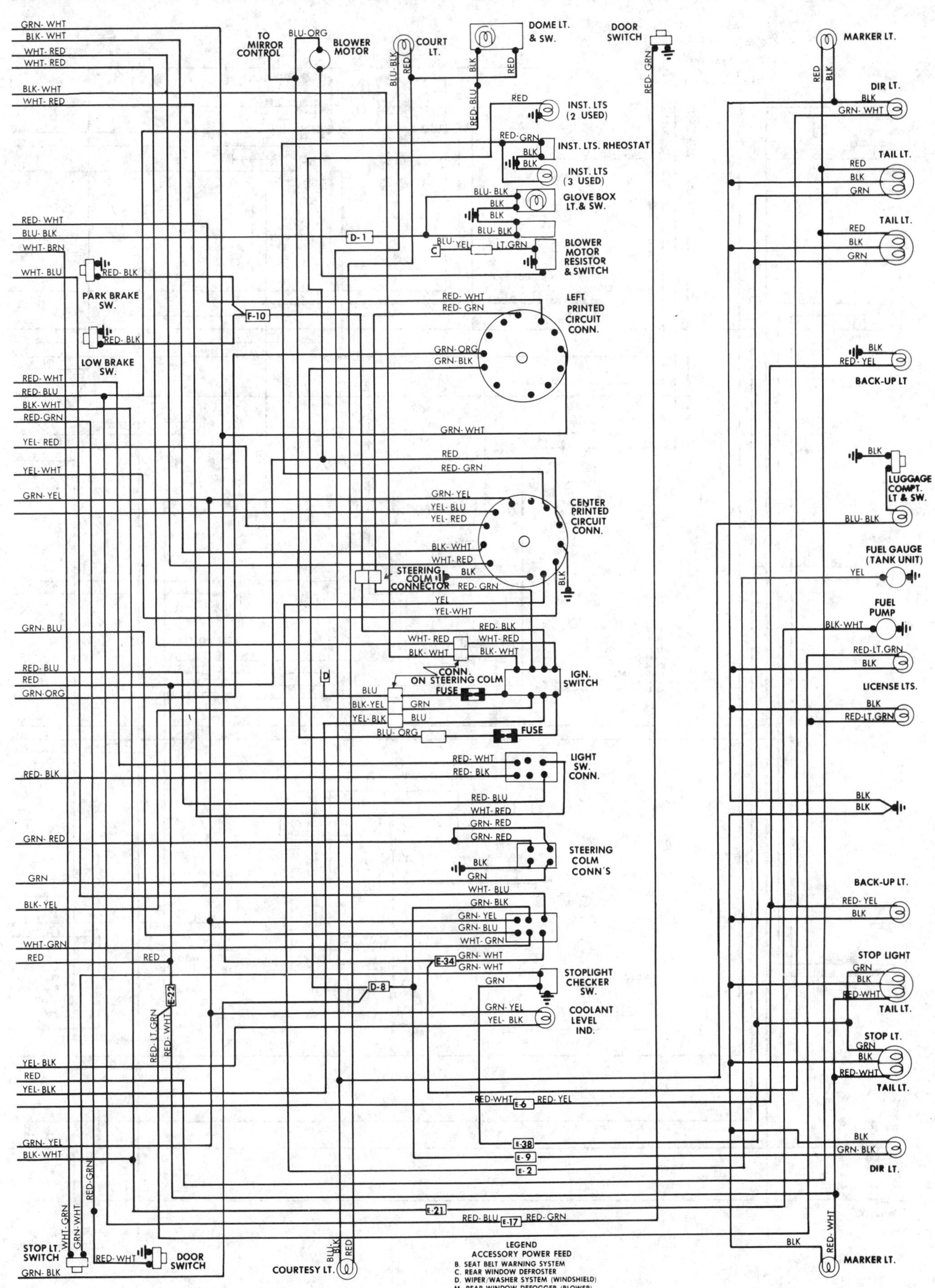

TO MIRROR CONTROL
BLOWER MOTOR
COURT LT.
DOME LT. & SW.
DOOR SWITCH
MARKER LT.
DIR LT.
INST. LTS (2 USED)
INST. LTS. RHEOSTAT
INST. LTS (3 USED)
TAIL LT.
GLOVE BOX LT.& SW.
BLOWER MOTOR RESISTOR & SWITCH
PARK BRAKE SW.
LEFT PRINTED CIRCUIT CONN.
LOW BRAKE SW.
BACK-UP LT
LUGGAGE COMPT. LT & SW.
CENTER PRINTED CIRCUIT CONN.
FUEL GAUGE (TANK UNIT)
STEERING COLM CONNECTOR
FUEL PUMP
CONN. ON STEERING COLM
IGN. SWITCH
FUSE
LICENSE LTS.
LIGHT SW. CONN.
STEERING COLM CONN'S
BACK-UP LT.
STOP LIGHT
STOPLIGHT CHECKER SW.
COOLANT LEVEL IND.
STOP LT.
DIR LT.
STOP LT. SWITCH
DOOR SWITCH
COURTESY LT.
MARKER LT.
LEGEND
ACCESSORY POWER FEED
B. SEAT BELT WARNING SYSTEM
C. REAR WINDOW DEFROSTER
D. WIPER/WASHER SYSTEM (WINDSHIELD)
M. REAR WINDOW DEFOGGER (BLOWER)
P. POWER WINDOW CONTROL SYSTEM

1977 Mazda

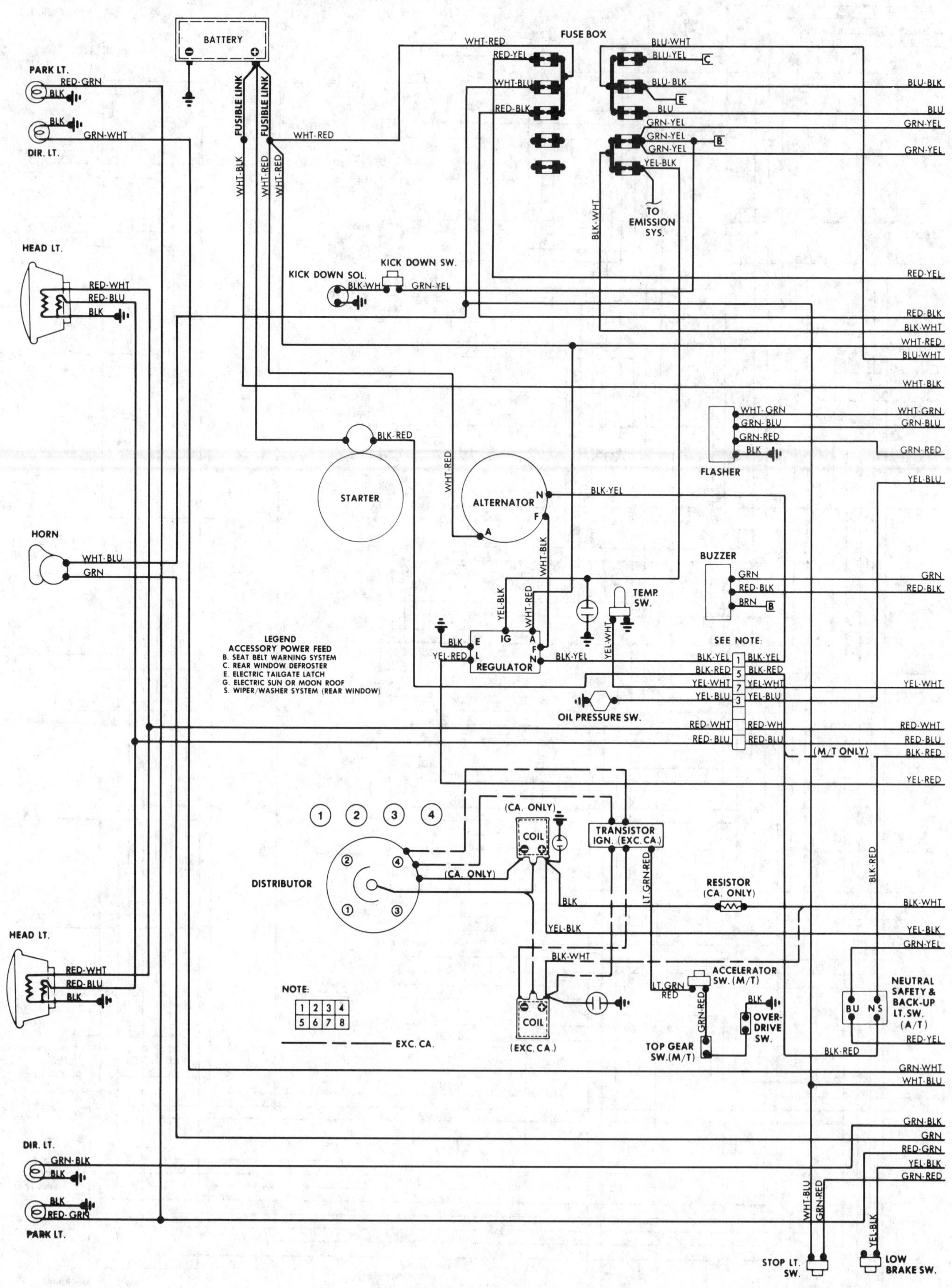

BATTERY
FUSIBLE LINK
FUSIBLE LINK
FUSE BOX
PARK LT.
DIR. LT.
HEAD LT.
KICK DOWN SW.
KICK DOWN SOL.
TO EMISSION SYS.
FLASHER
STARTER
ALTERNATOR
HORN
BUZZER
TEMP. SW.
REGULATOR
LEGEND
ACCESSORY POWER FEED
B. SEAT BELT WARNING SYSTEM
C. REAR WINDOW DEFROSTER
E. ELECTRIC TAILGATE LATCH
G. ELECTRIC SUN OR MOON ROOF
S. WIPER/WASHER SYSTEM (REAR WINDOW)
SEE NOTE:
OIL PRESSURE SW.
(M/T ONLY)
(CA. ONLY)
COIL
TRANSISTOR IGN. (EXC. CA.)
DISTRIBUTOR
(CA. ONLY)
RESISTOR (CA. ONLY)
HEAD LT.
NOTE:
1 2 3 4
5 6 7 8
EXC. CA.
COIL
(EXC. CA.)
ACCELERATOR SW. (M/T)
OVER-DRIVE SW.
TOP GEAR SW. (M/T)
NEUTRAL SAFETY & BACK-UP LT. SW. (A/T)
DIR. LT.
PARK LT.
STOP LT. SW.
LOW BRAKE SW.

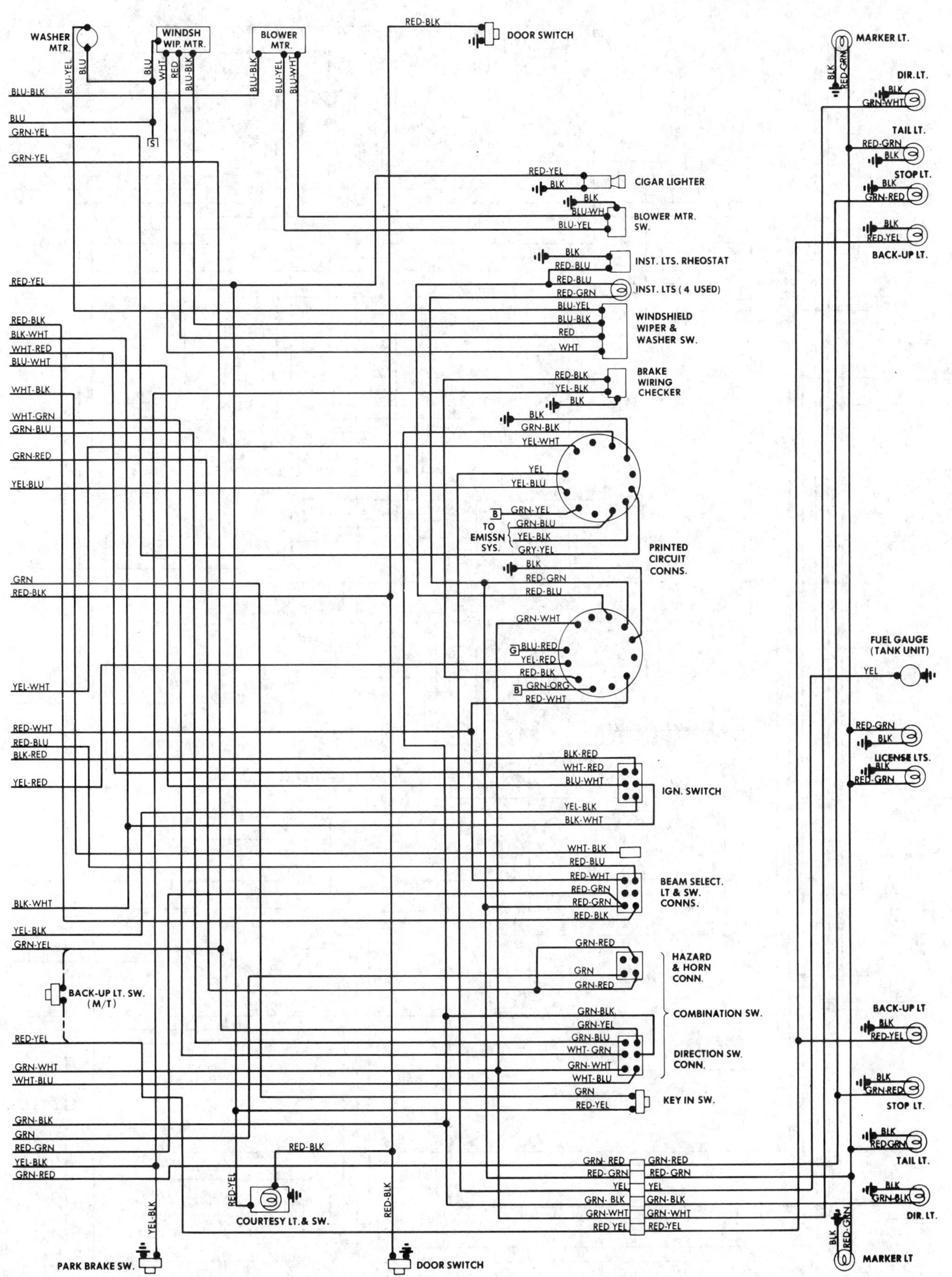
WASHER MTR.
WINDSH WIP. MTR.
BLOWER MTR.
DOOR SWITCH
MARKER LT.
DIR. LT.
TAIL LT.
STOP LT.
BACK-UP LT.
CIGAR LIGHTER
BLOWER MTR. SW.
INST. LTS. RHEOSTAT
INST. LTS (4 USED)
WINDSHIELD WIPER & WASHER SW.
BRAKE WIRING CHECKER
TO EMISSN SYS.
PRINTED CIRCUIT CONNS.
FUEL GAUGE (TANK UNIT)
LICENSE LTS.
IGN. SWITCH
BEAM SELECT. LT & SW. CONNS.
HAZARD & HORN CONN.
COMBINATION SW.
DIRECTION SW. CONN.
KEY IN SW.
BACK-UP LT. SW. (M/T)
COURTESY LT. & SW.
PARK BRAKE SW.
DOOR SWITCH
BACK-UP LT
STOP LT.
TAIL LT.
DIR. LT.
MARKER LT

1977 Mazda

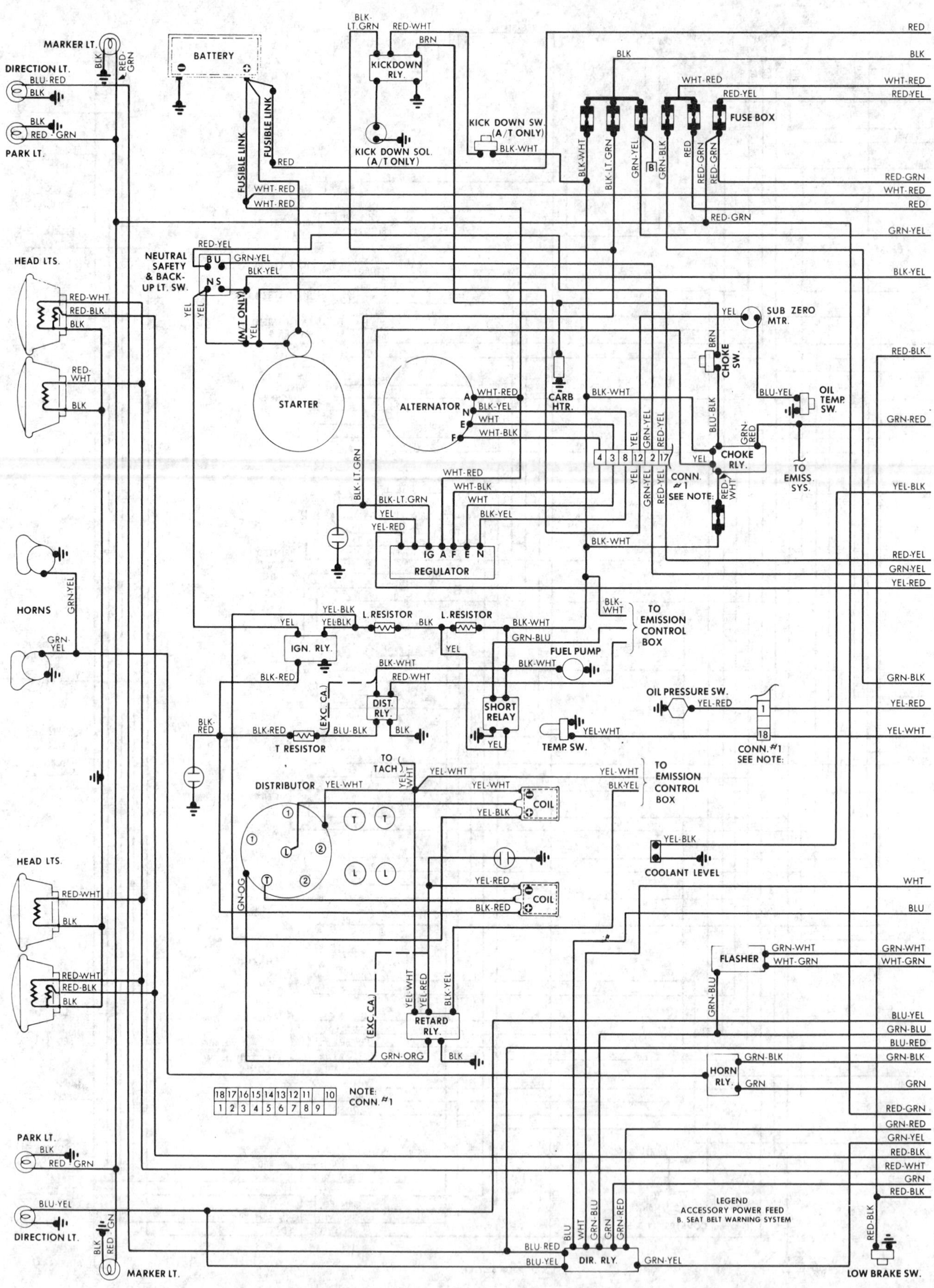

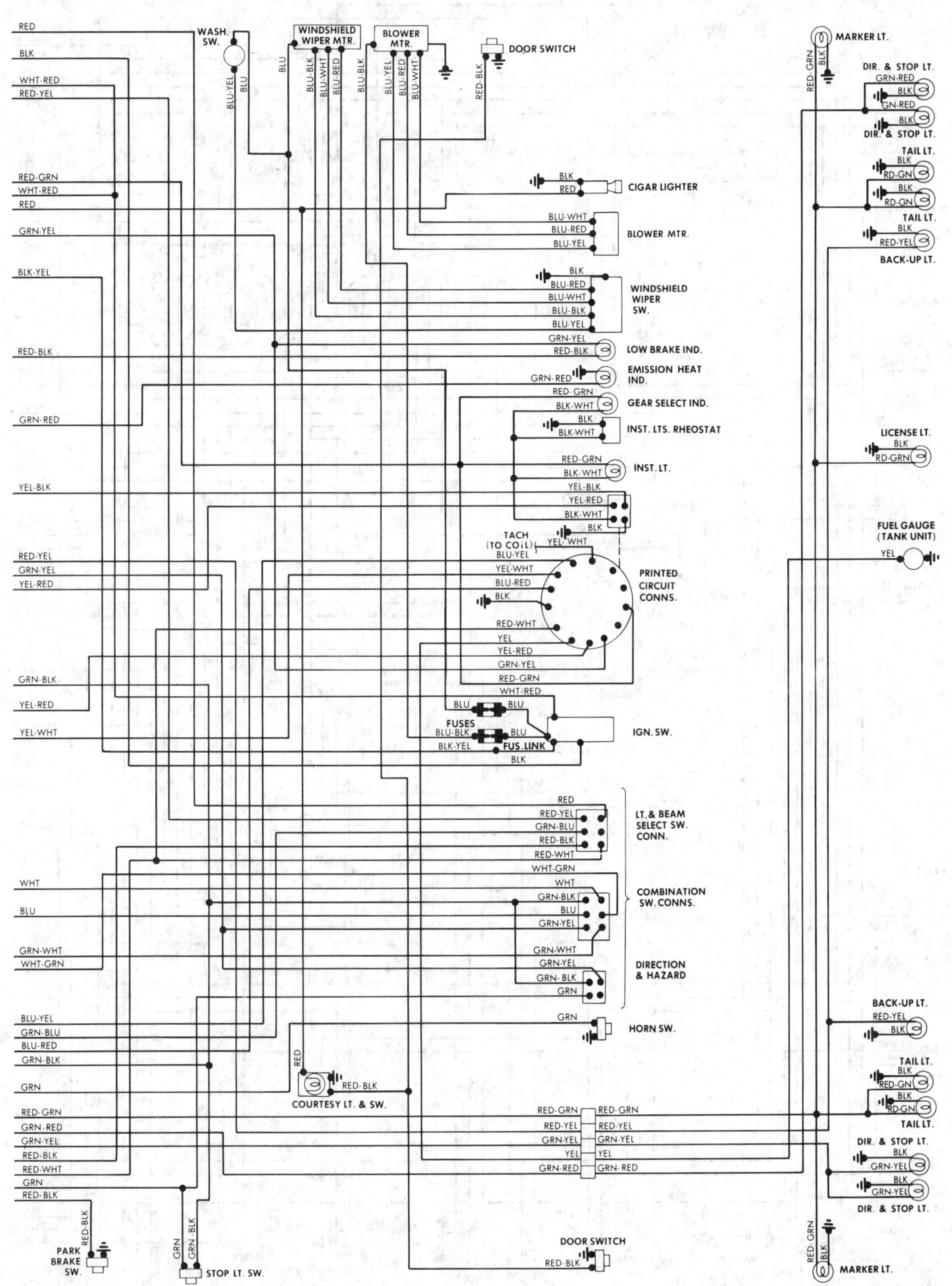
WASH. SW.
WINDSHIELD WIPER MTR.
BLOWER MTR.
DOOR SWITCH
MARKER LT.
DIR. & STOP LT.
TAIL LT.
BACK-UP LT.
CIGAR LIGHTER
BLOWER MTR.
WINDSHIELD WIPER SW.
LOW BRAKE IND.
EMISSION HEAT IND.
GEAR SELECT IND.
INST. LTS. RHEOSTAT
INST. LT.
LICENSE LT.
FUEL GAUGE (TANK UNIT)
TACH (TO COIL)
PRINTED CIRCUIT CONNS.
FUSES
FUS. LINK
IGN. SW.
LT. & BEAM SELECT SW. CONN.
COMBINATION SW. CONNS.
DIRECTION & HAZARD
HORN SW.
COURTESY LT. & SW.
PARK BRAKE SW.
STOP LT. SW.
DOOR SWITCH
MARKER LT.

1977 Mercedes-Benz

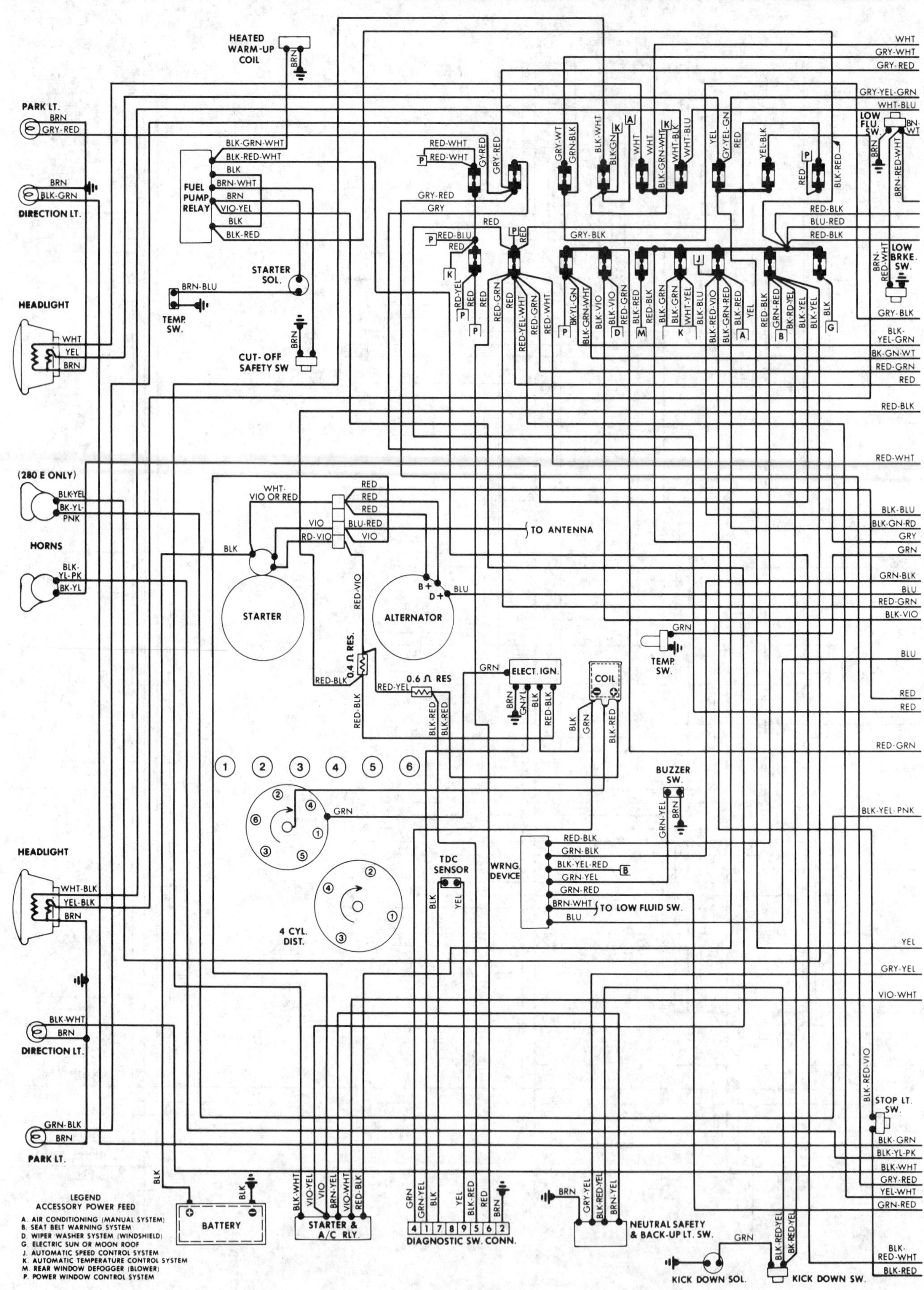

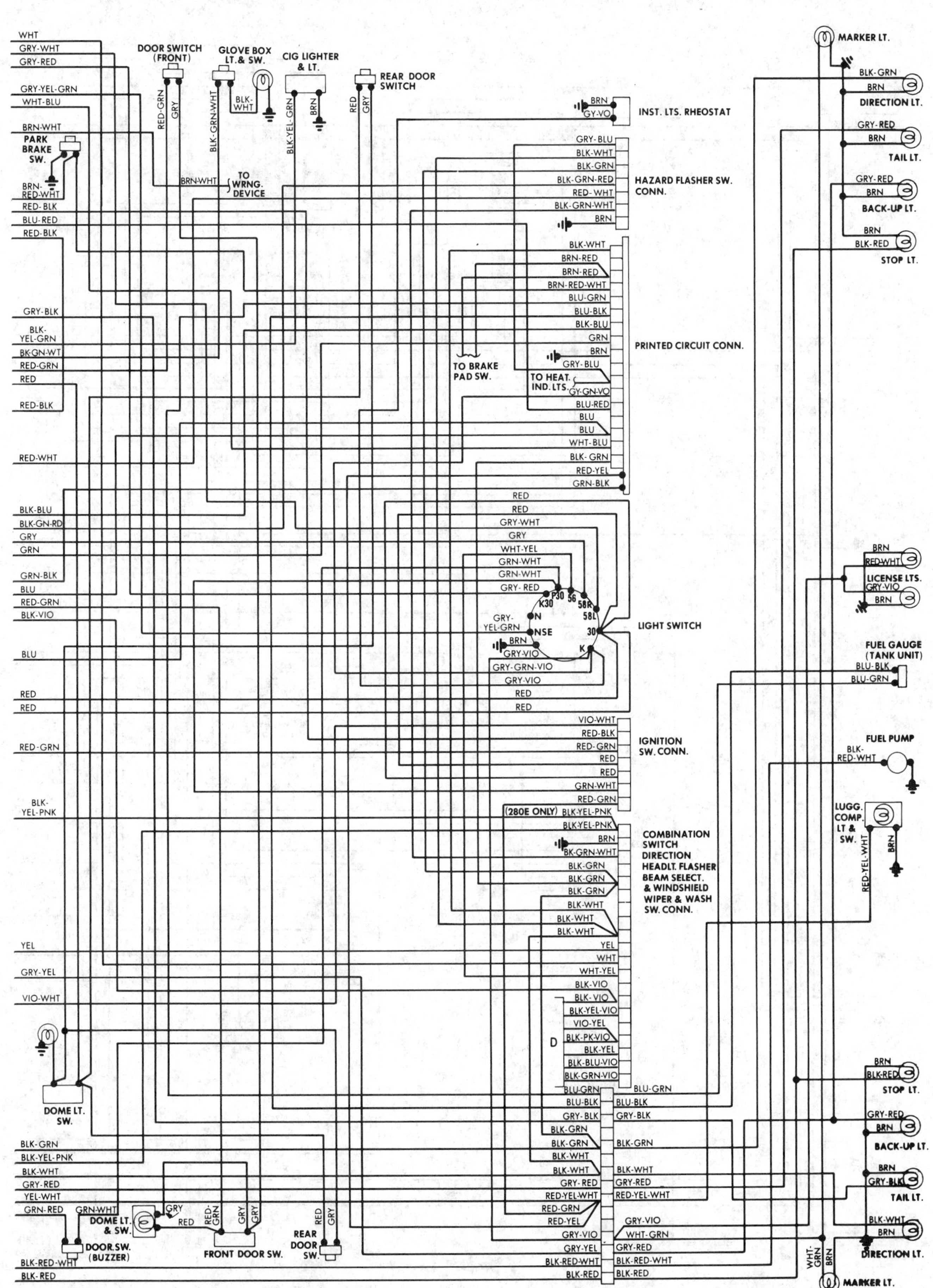

DOOR SWITCH (FRONT)
GLOVE BOX LT. & SW.
CIG LIGHTER & LT.
REAR DOOR SWITCH
MARKER LT.
DIRECTION LT.
INST. LTS. RHEOSTAT
TAIL LT.
PARK BRAKE SW.
TO WRNG. DEVICE
HAZARD FLASHER SW. CONN.
BACK-UP LT.
STOP LT.
PRINTED CIRCUIT CONN.
TO BRAKE PAD SW.
TO HEAT. IND. LTS.
LICENSE LTS.
LIGHT SWITCH
FUEL GAUGE (TANK UNIT)
FUEL PUMP
IGNITION SW. CONN.
LUGG. COMP. LT & SW.
(280E ONLY)
COMBINATION SWITCH DIRECTION HEADLT. FLASHER BEAM SELECT. & WINDSHIELD WIPER & WASH SW. CONN.
DOME LT. SW.
DOME LT. & SW.
DOOR SW. (BUZZER)
FRONT DOOR SW.
REAR DOOR SW.

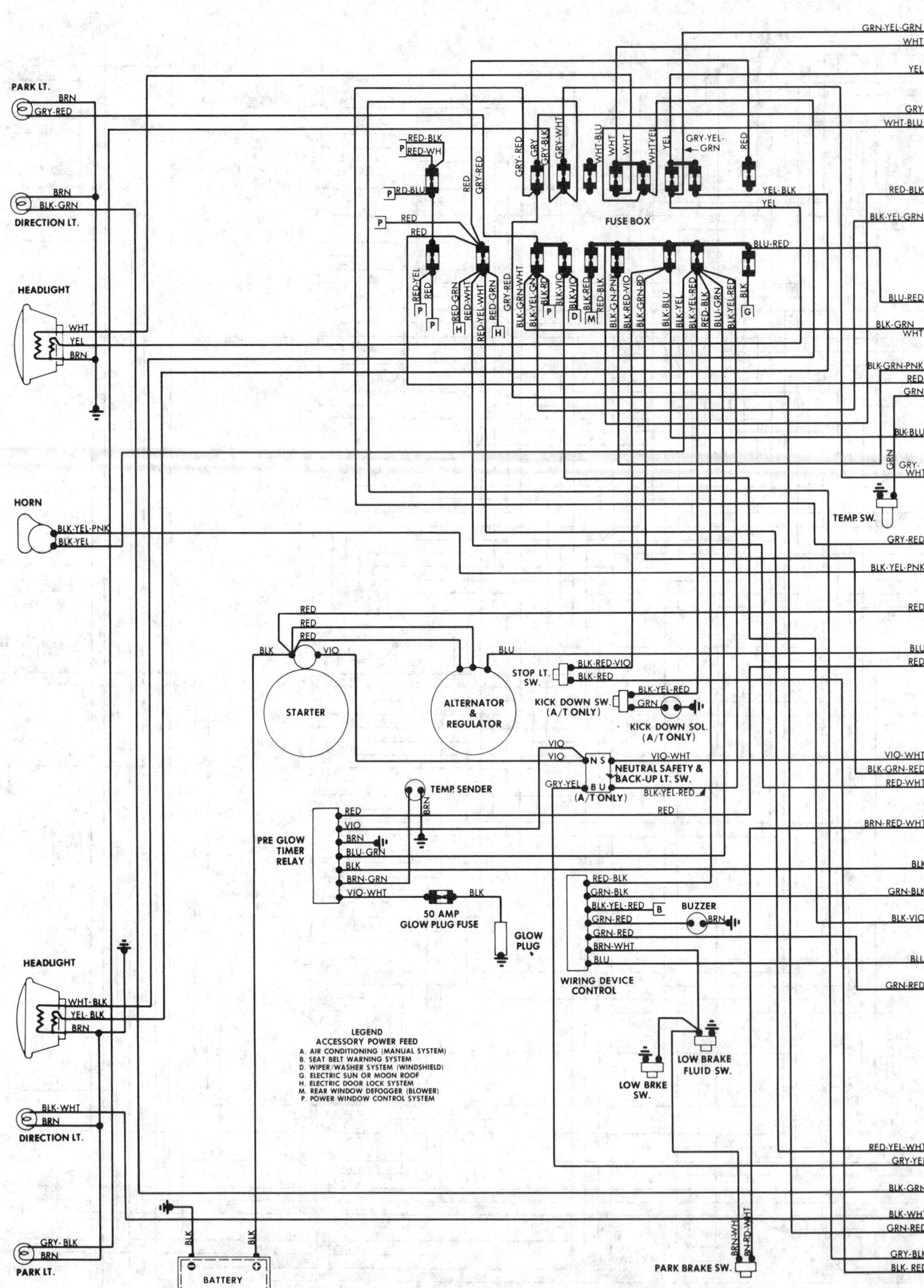
PARK LT.
DIRECTION LT.
HEADLIGHT
HORN
FUSE BOX
TEMP. SW.
STARTER
ALTERNATOR & REGULATOR
STOP LT. SW.
KICK DOWN SW. (A/T ONLY)
KICK DOWN SOL. (A/T ONLY)
NEUTRAL SAFETY & BACK-UP LT. SW. (A/T ONLY)
TEMP. SENDER
PRE GLOW TIMER RELAY
50 AMP GLOW PLUG FUSE
GLOW PLUG
BUZZER
WIRING DEVICE CONTROL
LOW BRAKE FLUID SW.
LOW BRKE SW.
PARK BRAKE SW.
BATTERY
LEGEND
ACCESSORY POWER FEED
A. AIR CONDITIONING (MANUAL SYSTEM)
B. SEAT BELT WARNING SYSTEM
D. WIPER/WASHER SYSTEM (WINDSHIELD)
G. ELECTRIC SUN OR MOON ROOF
H. ELECTRIC DOOR LOCK SYSTEM
M. REAR WINDOW DEFOGGER (BLOWER)
P. POWER WINDOW CONTROL SYSTEM

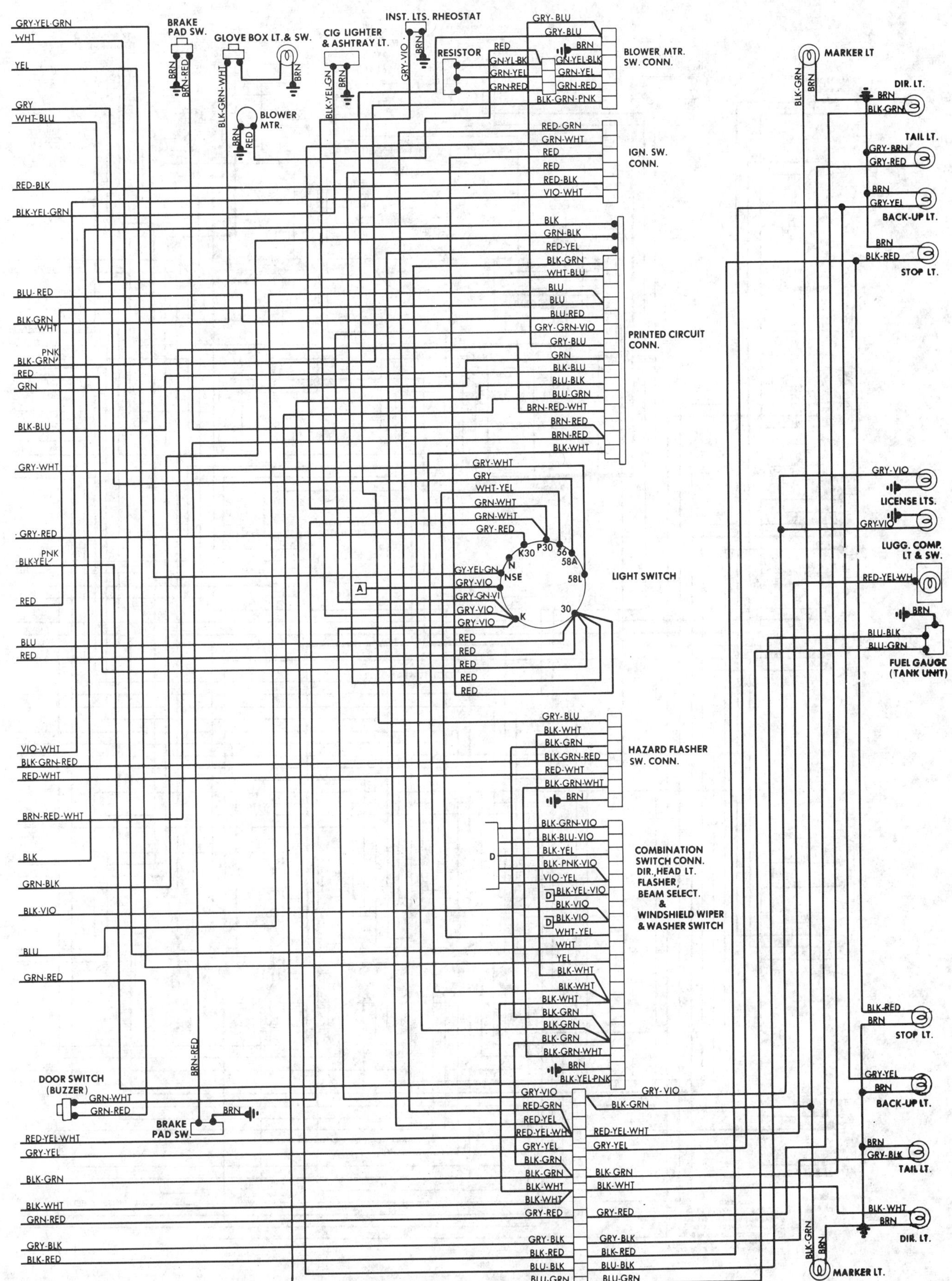
BRAKE PAD SW.
GLOVE BOX LT. & SW.
CIG LIGHTER & ASHTRAY LT.
INST. LTS. RHEOSTAT
RESISTOR
BLOWER MTR.
BLOWER MTR. SW. CONN.
IGN. SW. CONN.
PRINTED CIRCUIT CONN.
LIGHT SWITCH
HAZARD FLASHER SW. CONN.
COMBINATION SWITCH CONN. DIR., HEAD LT. FLASHER, BEAM SELECT. & WINDSHIELD WIPER & WASHER SWITCH
DOOR SWITCH (BUZZER)
MARKER LT
DIR. LT.
TAIL LT.
BACK-UP LT.
STOP LT.
LICENSE LTS.
LUGG. COMP. LT & SW.
FUEL GAUGE (TANK UNIT)

1977 Mercedes-Benz

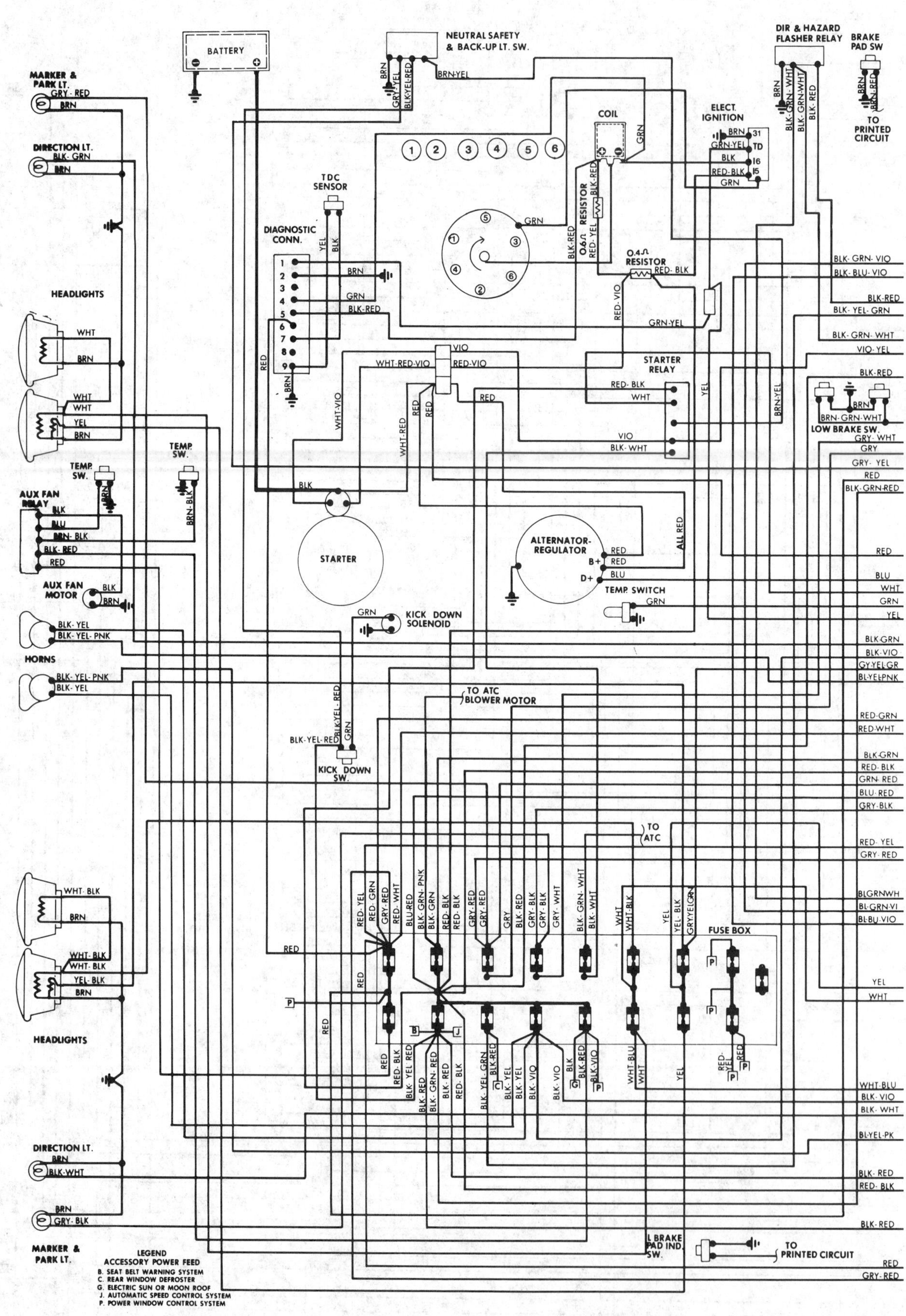

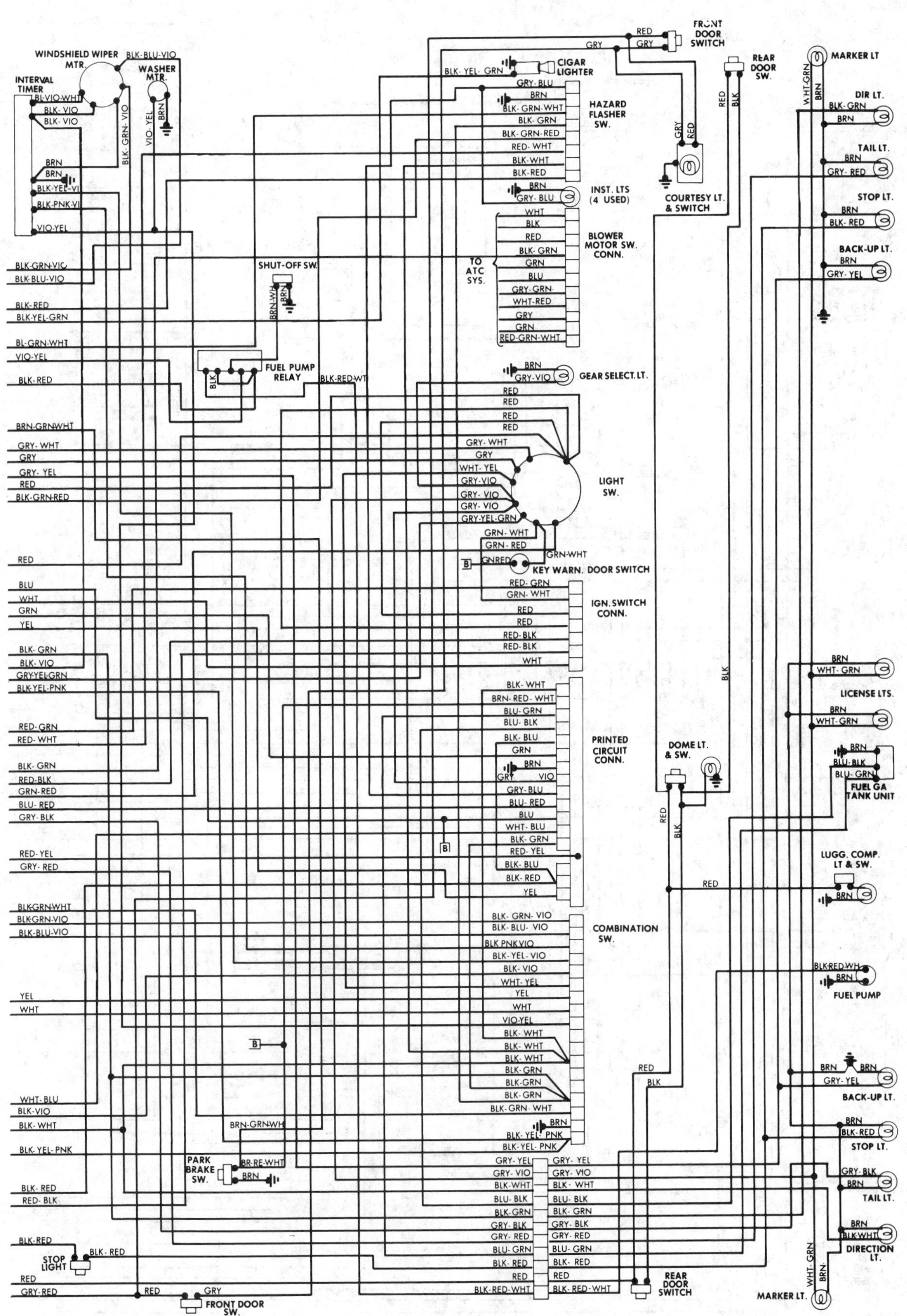
WINDSHIELD WIPER MTR.
WASHER MTR.
INTERVAL TIMER
SHUT-OFF SW.
FUEL PUMP RELAY
FRONT DOOR SWITCH
CIGAR LIGHTER
HAZARD FLASHER SW.
INST. LTS (4 USED)
BLOWER MOTOR SW. CONN.
TO ATC SYS.
GEAR SELECT LT.
LIGHT SW.
KEY WARN. DOOR SWITCH
IGN. SWITCH CONN.
PRINTED CIRCUIT CONN.
COMBINATION SW.
PARK BRAKE SW.
STOP LIGHT
FRONT DOOR SW.
REAR DOOR SW.
COURTESY LT. & SWITCH
DOME LT. & SW.
REAR DOOR SWITCH
MARKER LT
DIR LT.
TAIL LT.
STOP LT.
BACK-UP LT.
LICENSE LTS.
FUEL GA TANK UNIT
LUGG. COMP. LT & SW.
FUEL PUMP
BACK-UP LT.
STOP LT.
TAIL LT.
DIRECTION LT.
MARKER LT.

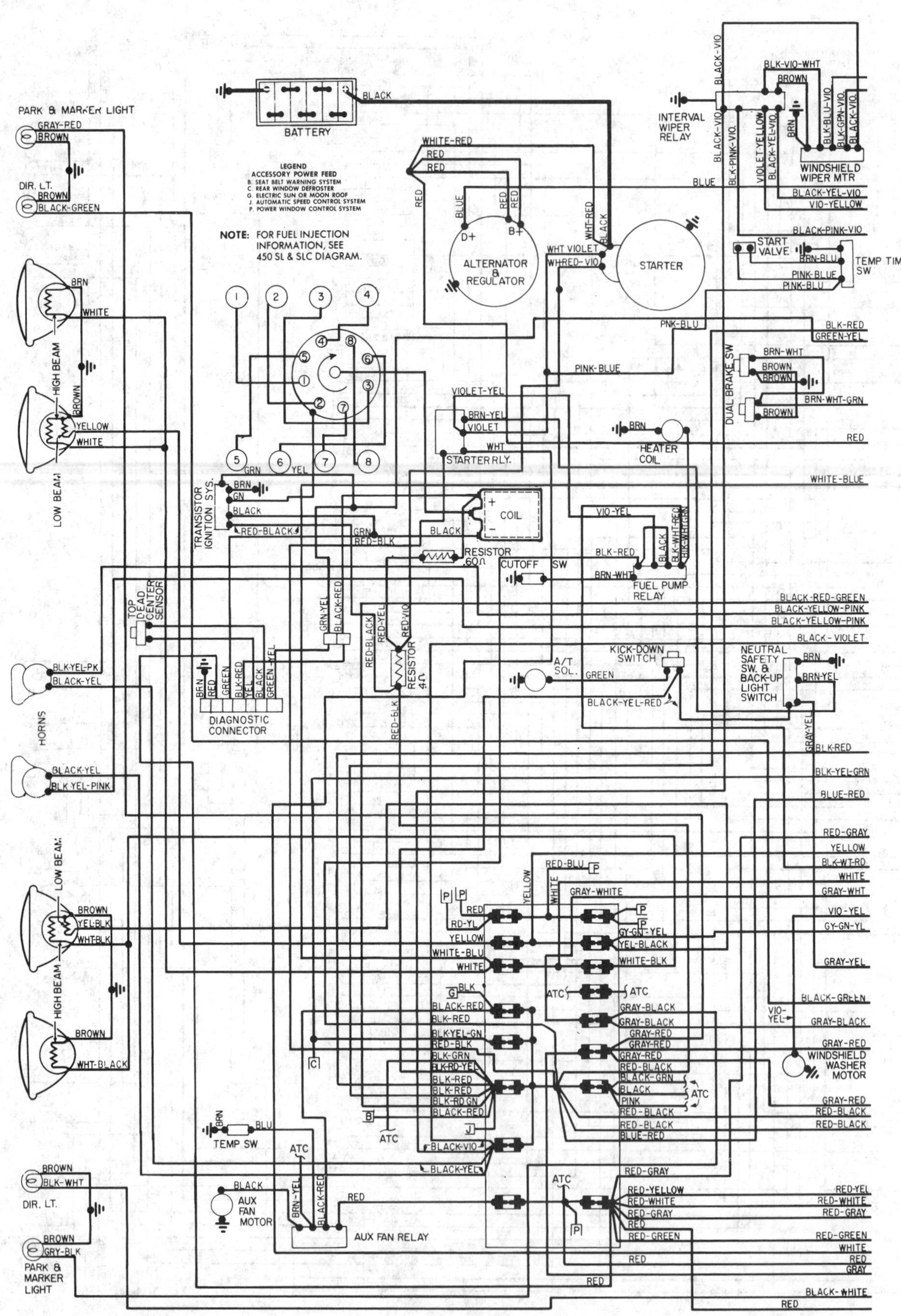

PARK & MARKER LIGHT
DIR. LT.
HIGH BEAM
LOW BEAM
BATTERY
LEGEND
ACCESSORY POWER FEED
B. SEAT BELT WARNING SYSTEM
C. REAR WINDOW DEFROSTER
G. ELECTRIC SUN OR MOON ROOF
J. AUTOMATIC SPEED CONTROL SYSTEM
P. POWER WINDOW CONTROL SYSTEM
NOTE: FOR FUEL INJECTION INFORMATION, SEE 450 SL & SLC DIAGRAM.
ALTERNATOR & REGULATOR
STARTER
INTERVAL WIPER RELAY
WINDSHIELD WIPER MTR
START VALVE
TEMP TIME SW
DUAL BRAKE SW
HEATER COIL
STARTER RLY.
TRANSISTOR IGNITION SYS.
COIL
RESISTOR .60Ω
CUTOFF SW
FUEL PUMP RELAY
TOP DEAD CENTER SENSOR
RESISTOR .4Ω
DIAGNOSTIC CONNECTOR
KICK-DOWN SWITCH
A/T SOL.
NEUTRAL SAFETY SW. & BACK-UP LIGHT SWITCH
HORNS
WINDSHIELD WASHER MOTOR
TEMP SW
AUX FAN MOTOR
AUX FAN RELAY
ATC

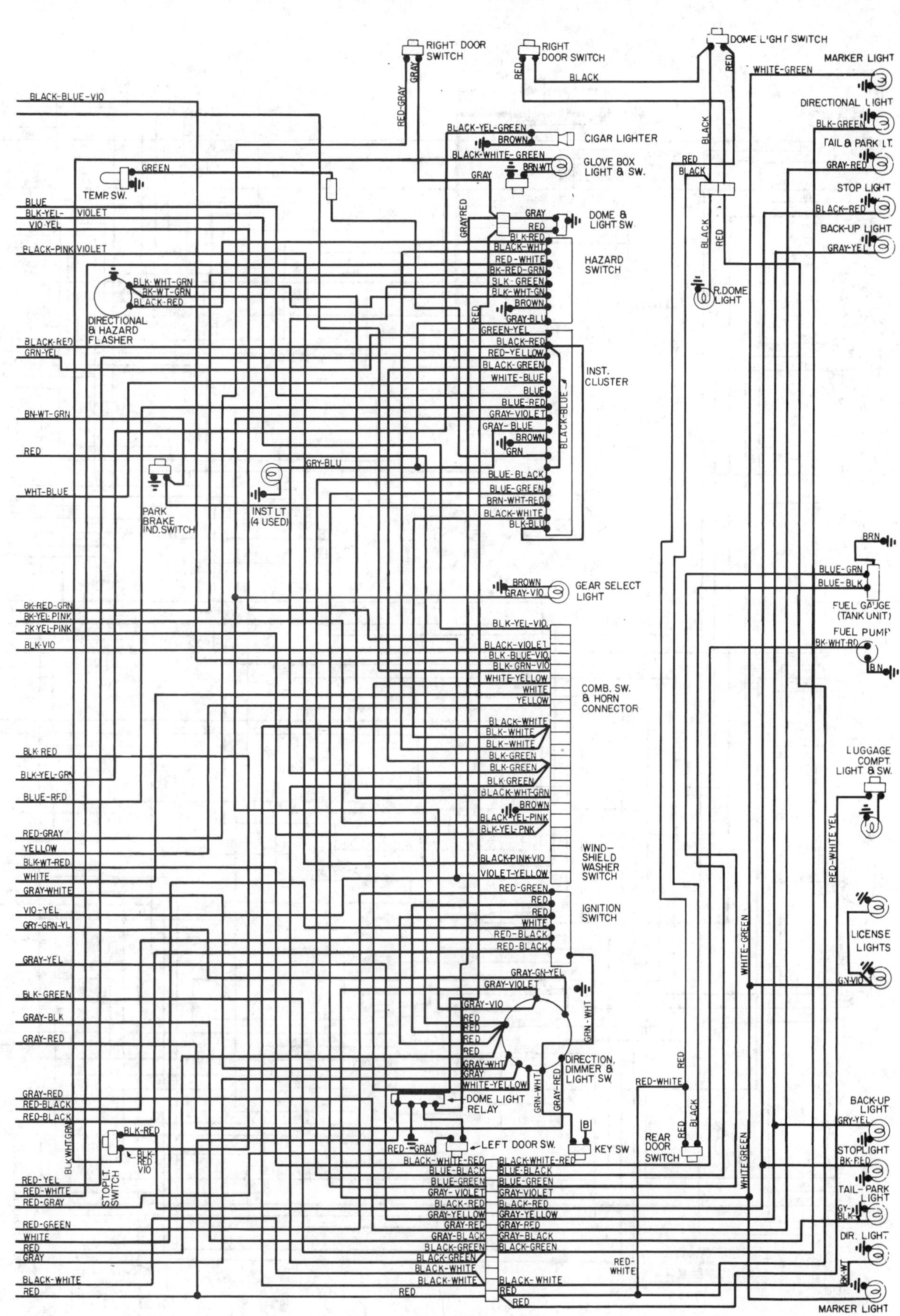
RIGHT DOOR SWITCH
RIGHT DOOR SWITCH
DOME LIGHT SWITCH
MARKER LIGHT
DIRECTIONAL LIGHT
TAIL & PARK LT.
STOP LIGHT
BACK-UP LIGHT
CIGAR LIGHTER
GLOVE BOX LIGHT & SW.
TEMP. SW.
DOME & LIGHT SW.
HAZARD SWITCH
DIRECTIONAL & HAZARD FLASHER
R. DOME LIGHT
INST. CLUSTER
PARK BRAKE IND. SWITCH
INST LT (4 USED)
GEAR SELECT LIGHT
FUEL GAUGE (TANK UNIT)
FUEL PUMP
COMB. SW. & HORN CONNECTOR
LUGGAGE COMPT. LIGHT & SW.
WIND-SHIELD WASHER SWITCH
IGNITION SWITCH
LICENSE LIGHTS
DIRECTION, DIMMER & LIGHT SW.
DOME LIGHT RELAY
LEFT DOOR SW.
KEY SW
REAR DOOR SWITCH
STOPLT. SWITCH
BACK-UP LIGHT
STOPLIGHT
TAIL-PARK LIGHT
DIR. LIGHT
MARKER LIGHT

1977 Mercedes-Benz

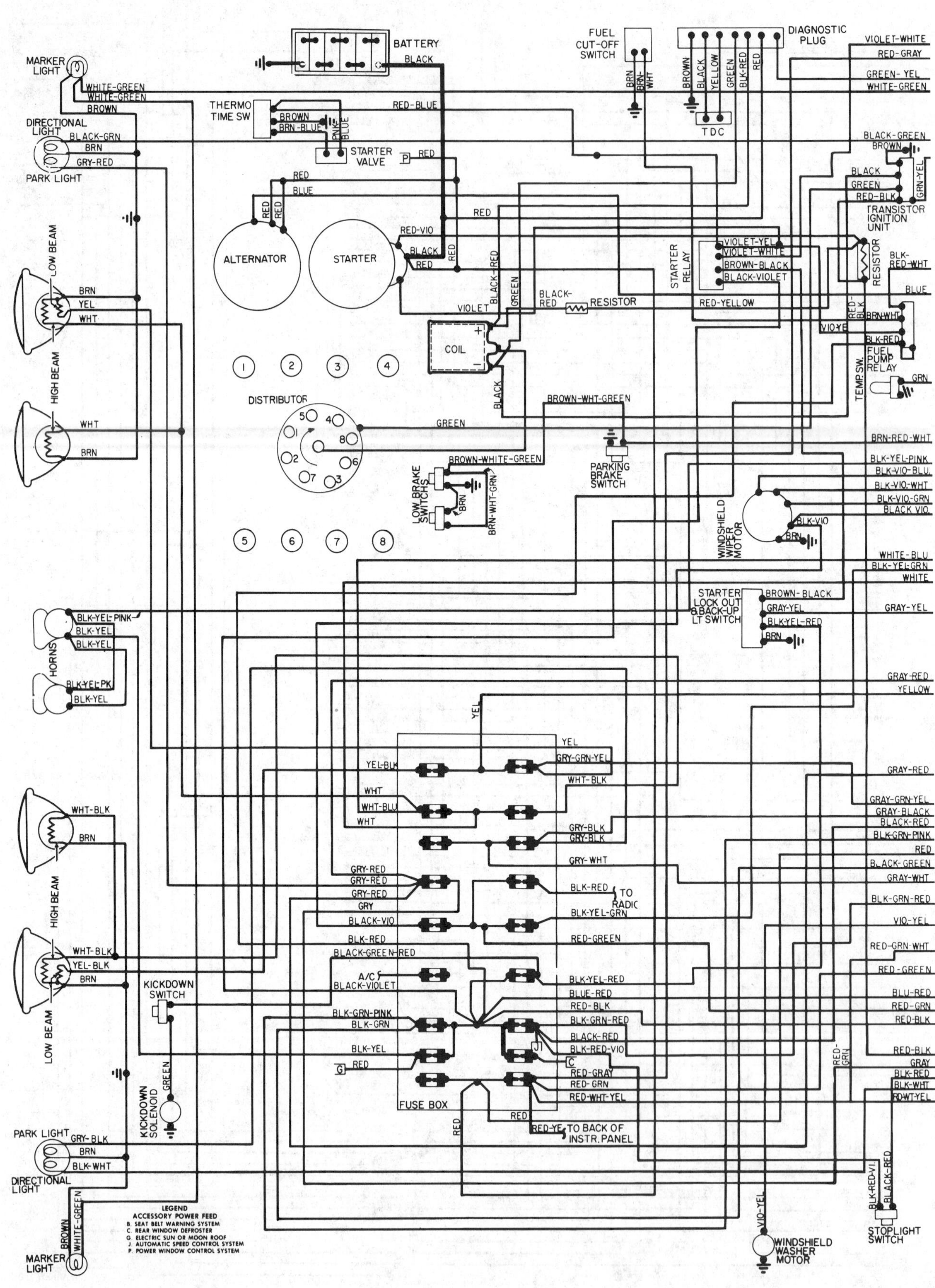

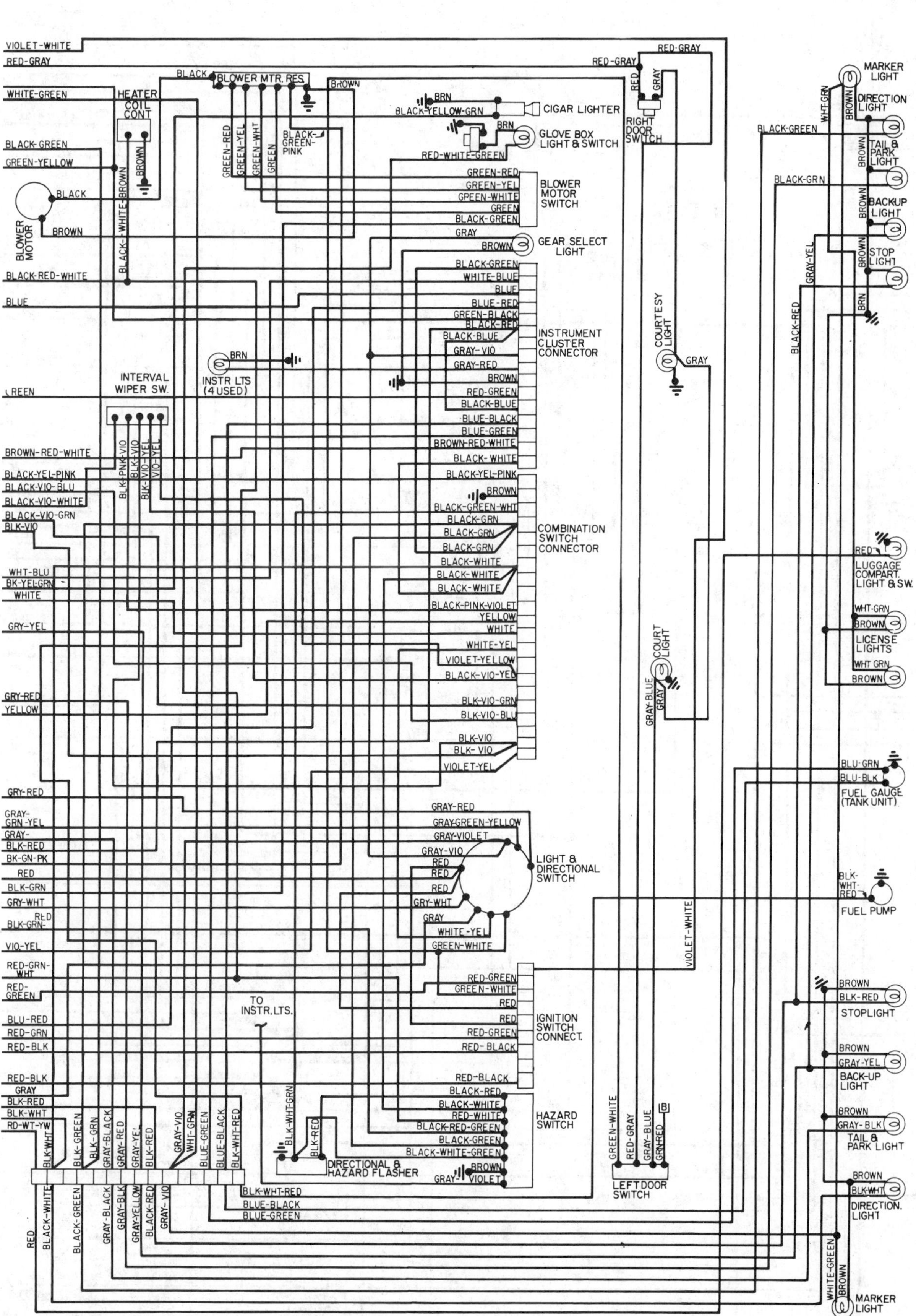

BLOWER MTR. RES.
HEATER COIL CONT
BLOWER MOTOR
CIGAR LIGHTER
GLOVE BOX LIGHT & SWITCH
BLOWER MOTOR SWITCH
GEAR SELECT LIGHT
INSTRUMENT CLUSTER CONNECTOR
INSTR LTS (4 USED)
INTERVAL WIPER SW.
COMBINATION SWITCH CONNECTOR
LIGHT & DIRECTIONAL SWITCH
IGNITION SWITCH CONNECT.
TO INSTR. LTS.
HAZARD SWITCH
DIRECTIONAL & HAZARD FLASHER
RIGHT DOOR SWITCH
COURTESY LIGHT
COURT LIGHT
LEFT DOOR SWITCH
MARKER LIGHT
DIRECTION LIGHT
TAIL & PARK LIGHT
BACKUP LIGHT
STOP LIGHT
LUGGAGE COMPART. LIGHT & SW.
LICENSE LIGHTS
FUEL GAUGE (TANK UNIT)
FUEL PUMP
STOPLIGHT
BACK-UP LIGHT
TAIL & PARK LIGHT
DIRECTION. LIGHT
MARKER LIGHT

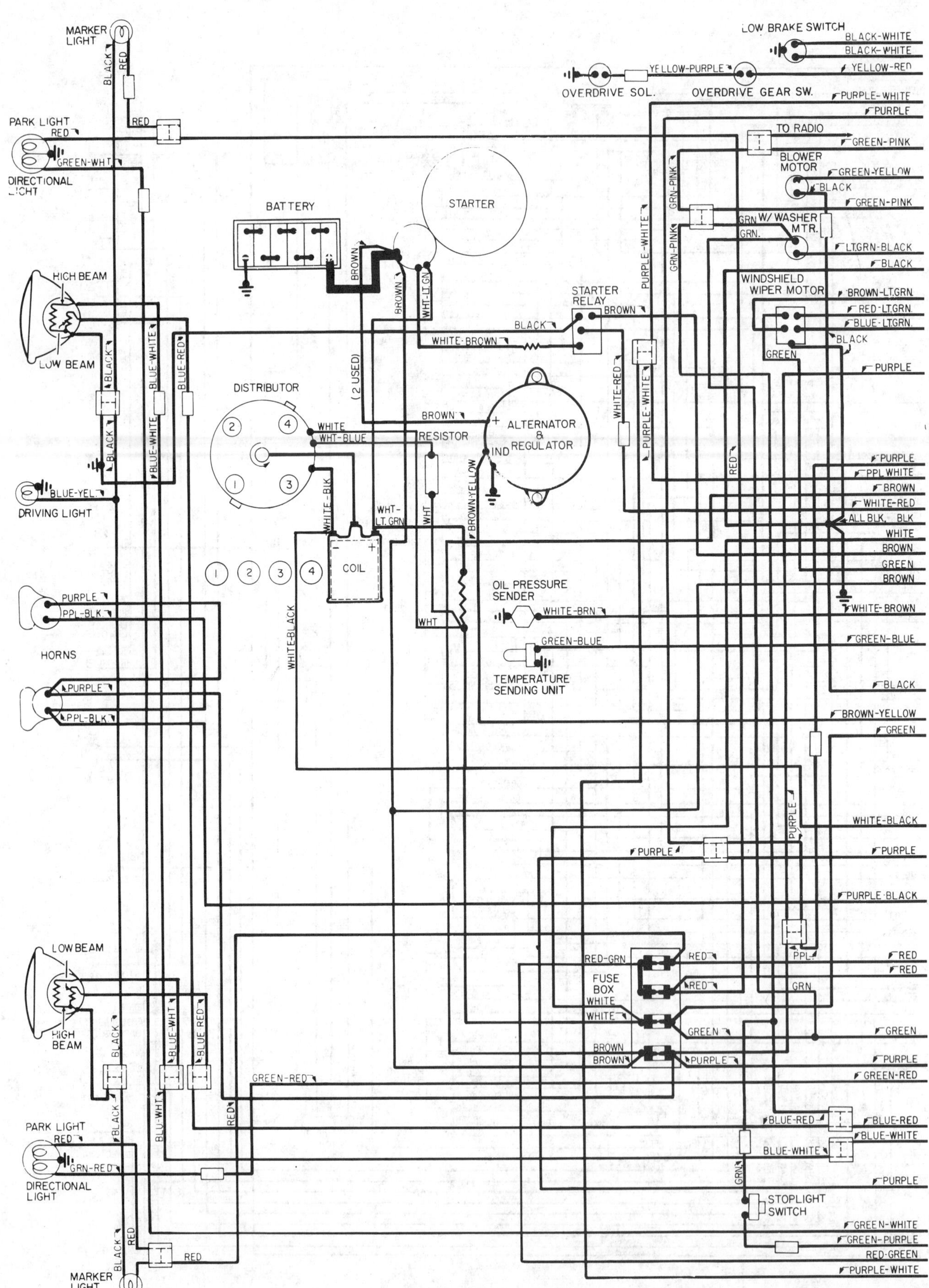
MARKER LIGHT
PARK LIGHT
DIRECTIONAL LIGHT
HIGH BEAM
LOW BEAM
DRIVING LIGHT
HORNS
LOW BEAM
HIGH BEAM
PARK LIGHT
DIRECTIONAL LIGHT
MARKER LIGHT
BATTERY
STARTER
DISTRIBUTOR
RESISTOR
COIL
ALTERNATOR & REGULATOR
STARTER RELAY
OIL PRESSURE SENDER
TEMPERATURE SENDING UNIT
OVERDRIVE SOL.
OVERDRIVE GEAR SW.
LOW BRAKE SWITCH
TO RADIO
BLOWER MOTOR
W/ WASHER MTR.
WINDSHIELD WIPER MOTOR
FUSE BOX
STOPLIGHT SWITCH
(2 USED)

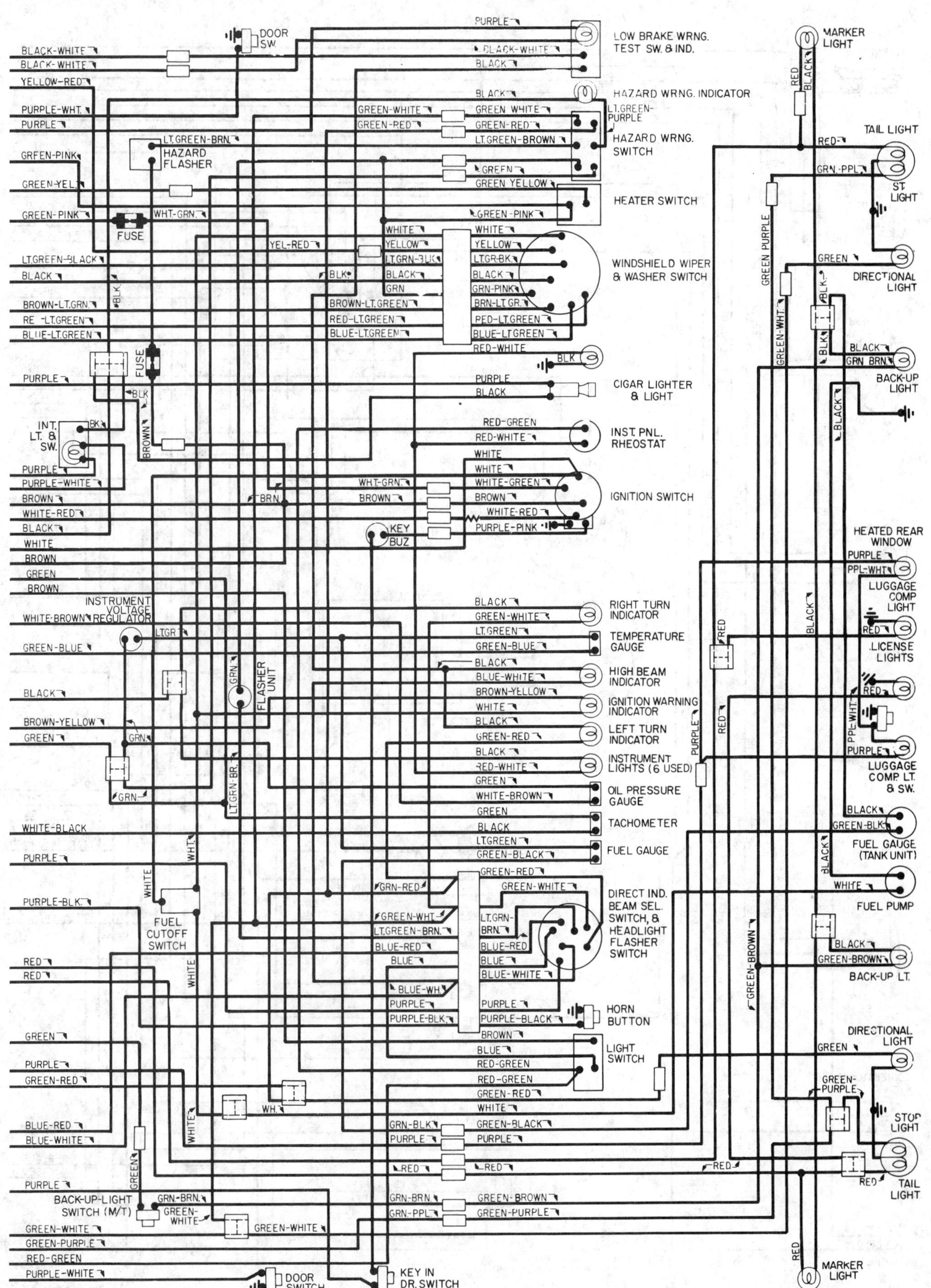

LOW BRAKE WRNG. TEST SW. & IND.
HAZARD WRNG. INDICATOR
HAZARD WRNG. SWITCH
HEATER SWITCH
WINDSHIELD WIPER & WASHER SWITCH
CIGAR LIGHTER & LIGHT
INST. PNL. RHEOSTAT
IGNITION SWITCH
RIGHT TURN INDICATOR
TEMPERATURE GAUGE
HIGH BEAM INDICATOR
IGNITION WARNING INDICATOR
LEFT TURN INDICATOR
INSTRUMENT LIGHTS (6 USED)
OIL PRESSURE GAUGE
TACHOMETER
FUEL GAUGE
DIRECT IND. BEAM SEL. SWITCH, & HEADLIGHT FLASHER SWITCH
HORN BUTTON
LIGHT SWITCH
DOOR SW.
HAZARD FLASHER
FUSE
INT. LT. & SW.
KEY BUZ
INSTRUMENT VOLTAGE REGULATOR
FLASHER UNIT
FUEL CUTOFF SWITCH
BACK-UP-LIGHT SWITCH (M/T)
DOOR SWITCH
KEY IN DR. SWITCH
MARKER LIGHT
TAIL LIGHT
ST. LIGHT
DIRECTIONAL LIGHT
BACK-UP LIGHT
HEATED REAR WINDOW
LUGGAGE COMP LIGHT
LICENSE LIGHTS
LUGGAGE COMP. LT. & SW.
FUEL GAUGE (TANK UNIT)
FUEL PUMP
BACK-UP LT.
DIRECTIONAL LIGHT
STOP LIGHT
TAIL LIGHT
MARKER LIGHT

1977 MG

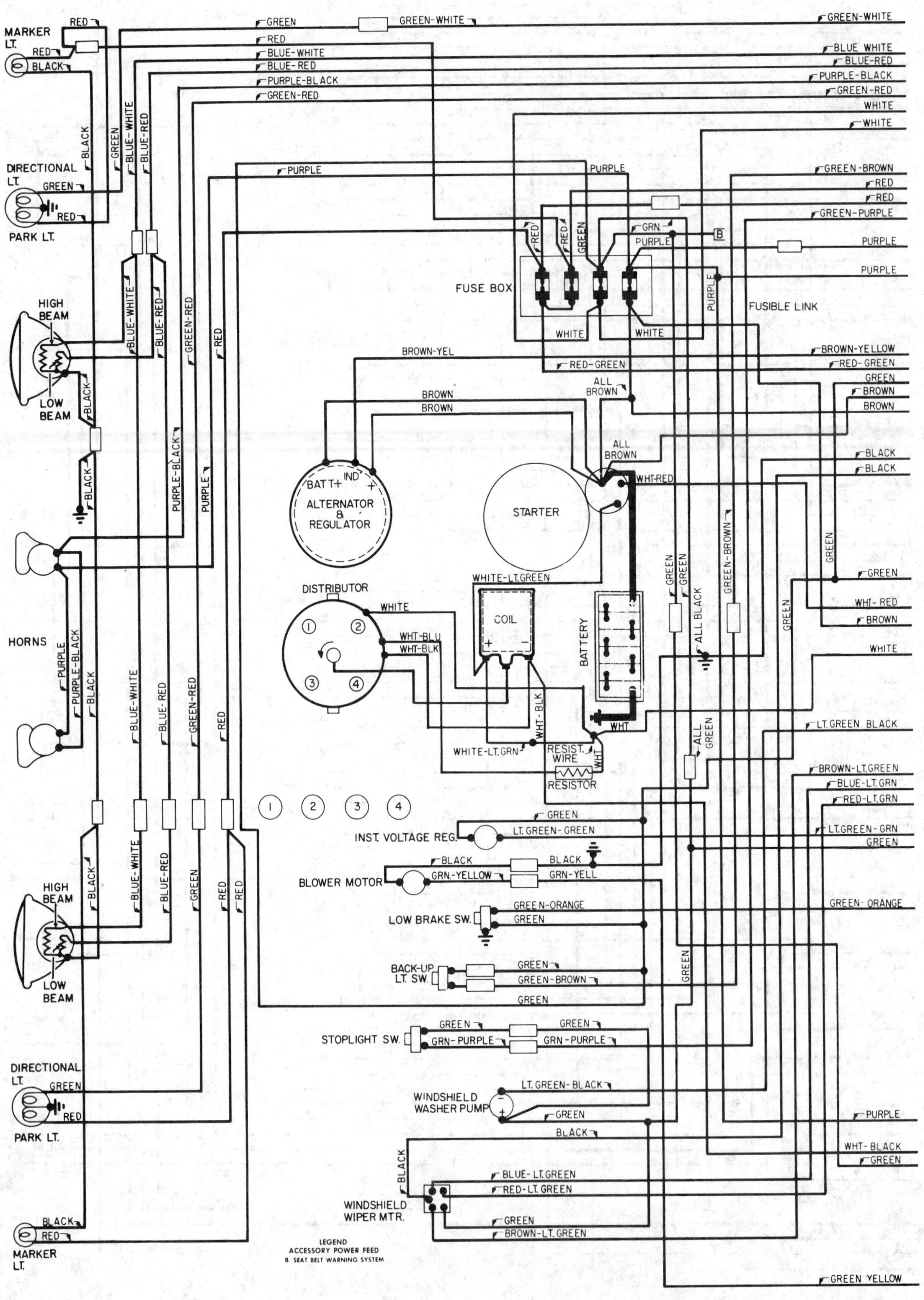
MARKER LT.
DIRECTIONAL LT.
PARK LT.
HIGH BEAM
LOW BEAM
HORNS
FUSE BOX
FUSIBLE LINK
ALTERNATOR & REGULATOR
STARTER
DISTRIBUTOR
COIL
BATTERY
RESIST. WIRE
RESISTOR
INST. VOLTAGE REG.
BLOWER MOTOR
LOW BRAKE SW.
BACK-UP LT. SW.
STOPLIGHT SW.
WINDSHIELD WASHER PUMP
WINDSHIELD WIPER MTR.
LEGEND
ACCESSORY POWER FEED
B. SEAT BELT WARNING SYSTEM

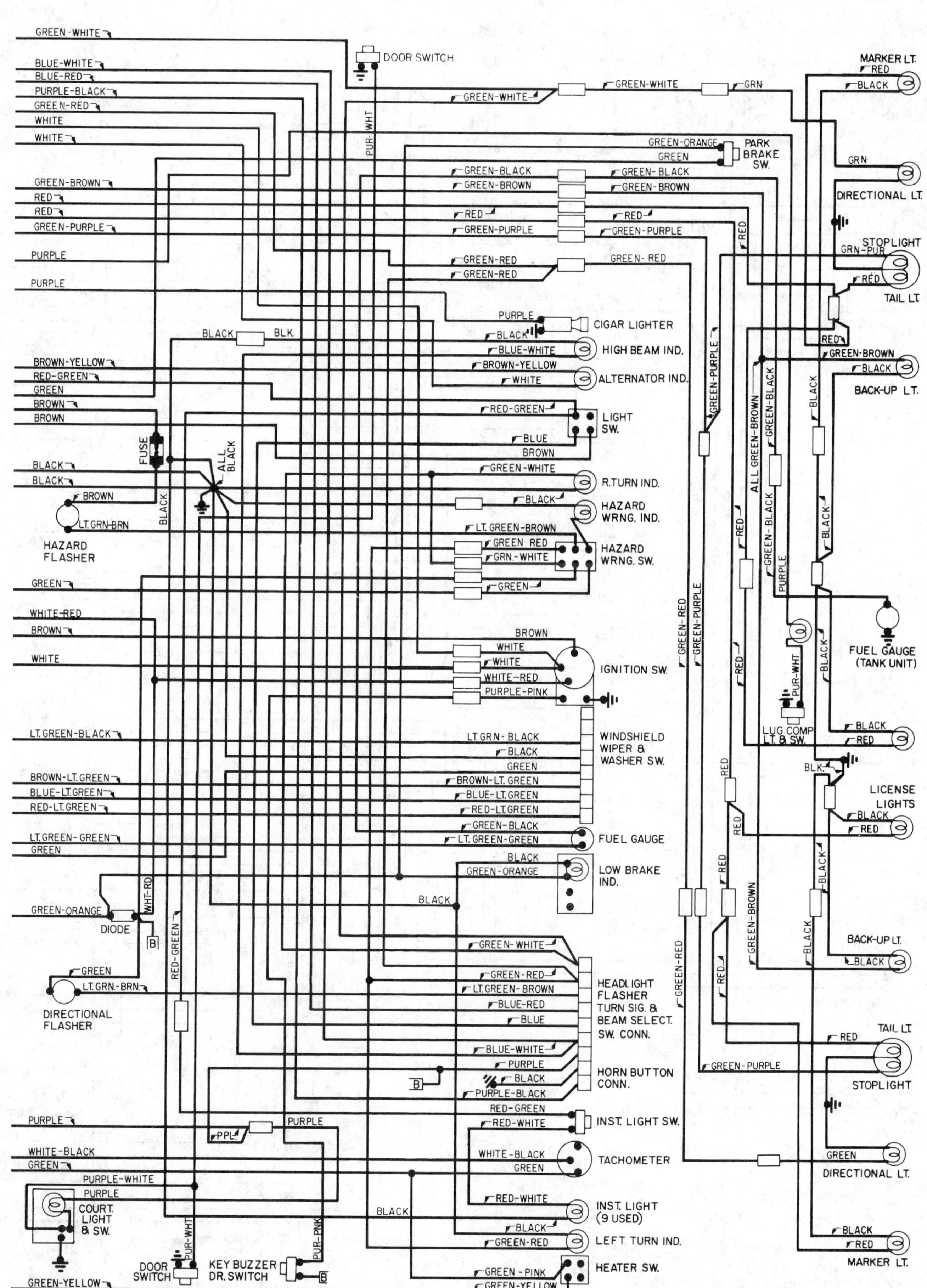
DOOR SWITCH
MARKER LT.
PARK BRAKE SW.
DIRECTIONAL LT.
STOPLIGHT
TAIL LT.
CIGAR LIGHTER
HIGH BEAM IND.
ALTERNATOR IND.
BACK-UP LT.
LIGHT SW.
R.TURN IND.
HAZARD WRNG. IND.
HAZARD WRNG. SW.
HAZARD FLASHER
FUSE
ALL BLACK
FUEL GAUGE (TANK UNIT)
IGNITION SW.
WINDSHIELD WIPER & WASHER SW.
LUG COMP LT. & SW.
LICENSE LIGHTS
FUEL GAUGE
LOW BRAKE IND.
DIODE
BACK-UP LT.
DIRECTIONAL FLASHER
HEADLIGHT FLASHER TURN SIG. & BEAM SELECT SW. CONN.
HORN BUTTON CONN.
TAIL LT.
STOPLIGHT
INST. LIGHT SW.
TACHOMETER
DIRECTIONAL LT.
COURT. LIGHT & SW.
INST. LIGHT (9 USED)
LEFT TURN IND.
MARKER LT.
DOOR SWITCH
KEY BUZZER DR. SWITCH
HEATER SW.

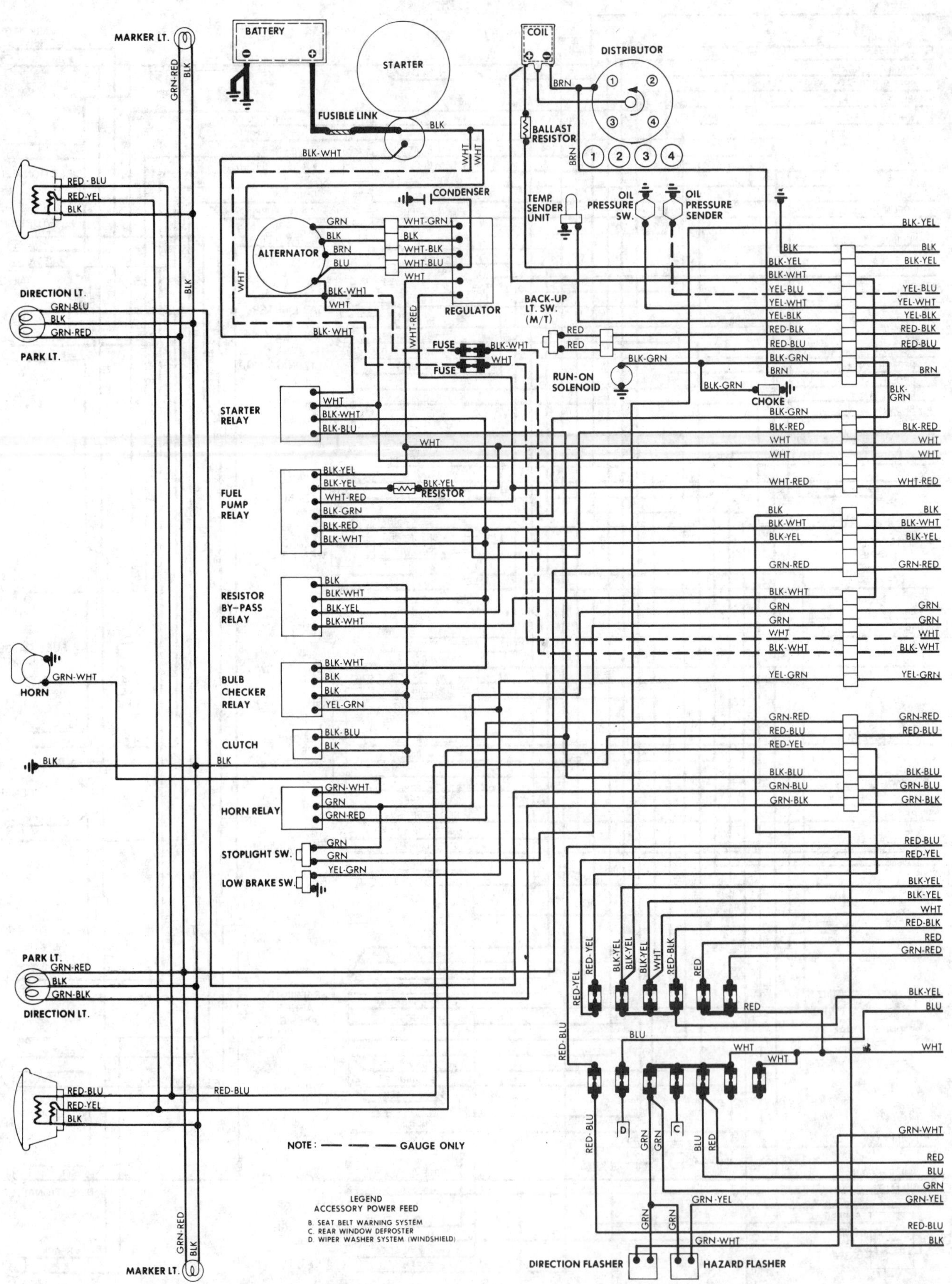
MARKER LT.
BATTERY
STARTER
FUSIBLE LINK
COIL
DISTRIBUTOR
BALLAST RESISTOR
CONDENSER
ALTERNATOR
REGULATOR
TEMP. SENDER UNIT
OIL PRESSURE SW.
OIL PRESSURE SENDER
BACK-UP LT. SW. (M/T)
RUN-ON SOLENOID
CHOKE
FUSE
DIRECTION LT.
PARK LT.
STARTER RELAY
FUEL PUMP RELAY
RESISTOR
RESISTOR BY-PASS RELAY
HORN
BULB CHECKER RELAY
CLUTCH
HORN RELAY
STOPLIGHT SW.
LOW BRAKE SW.
PARK LT.
DIRECTION LT.
MARKER LT.
DIRECTION FLASHER
HAZARD FLASHER
NOTE: — — — GAUGE ONLY
LEGEND
ACCESSORY POWER FEED
B. SEAT BELT WARNING SYSTEM
C. REAR WINDOW DEFROSTER
D. WIPER WASHER SYSTEM (WINDSHIELD)

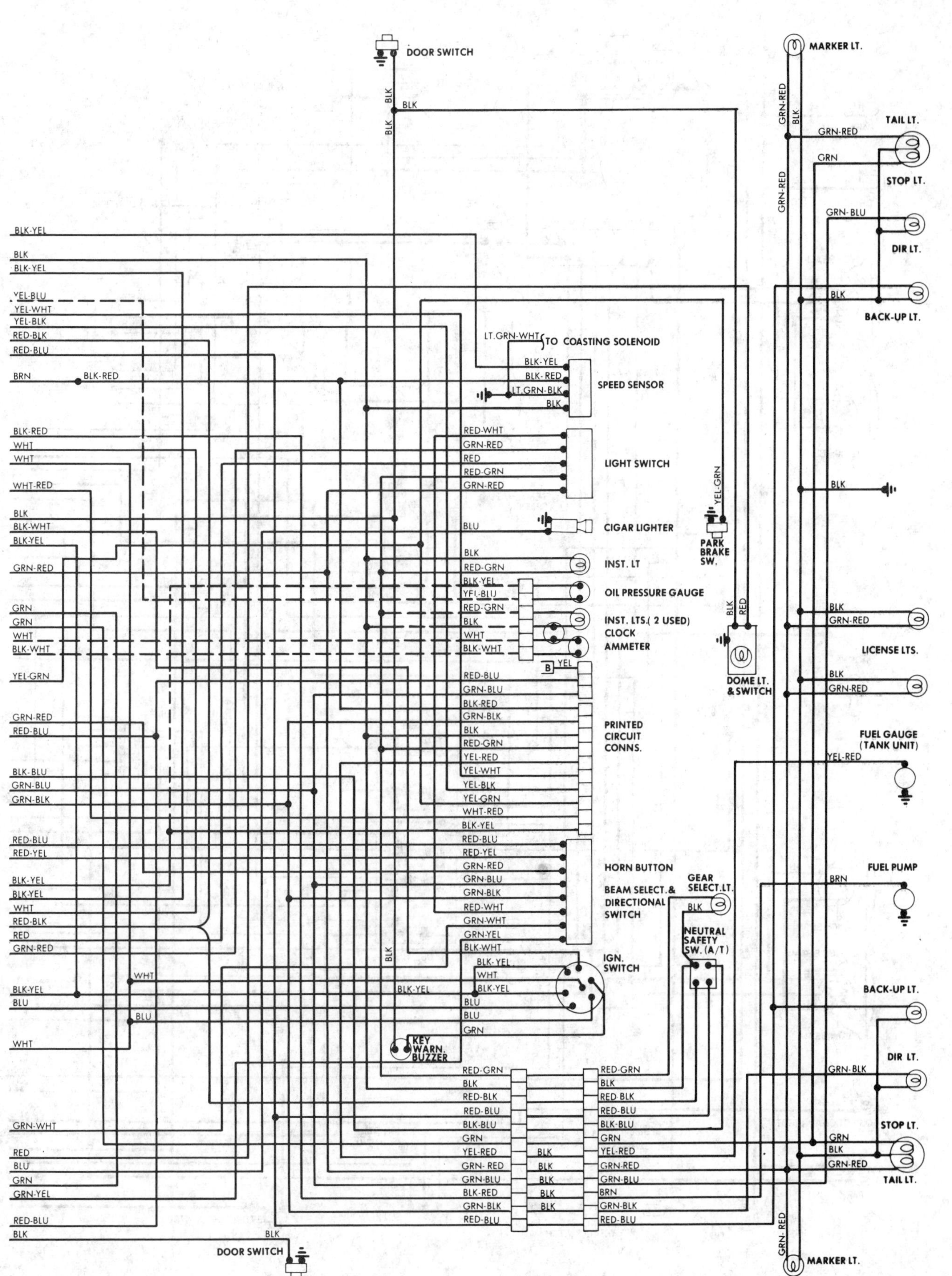
DOOR SWITCH
MARKER LT.
TAIL LT.
STOP LT.
DIR LT.
BACK-UP LT.
TO COASTING SOLENOID
SPEED SENSOR
LIGHT SWITCH
CIGAR LIGHTER
PARK BRAKE SW.
INST. LT
OIL PRESSURE GAUGE
INST. LTS.(2 USED)
CLOCK
AMMETER
DOME LT. & SWITCH
LICENSE LTS.
PRINTED CIRCUIT CONNS.
FUEL GAUGE (TANK UNIT)
FUEL PUMP
HORN BUTTON
GEAR SELECT.LT.
BEAM SELECT.& DIRECTIONAL SWITCH
NEUTRAL SAFETY SW. (A/T)
IGN. SWITCH
KEY WARN. BUZZER
BACK-UP LT.
DIR LT.
STOP LT.
TAIL LT.
MARKER LT.
DOOR SWITCH

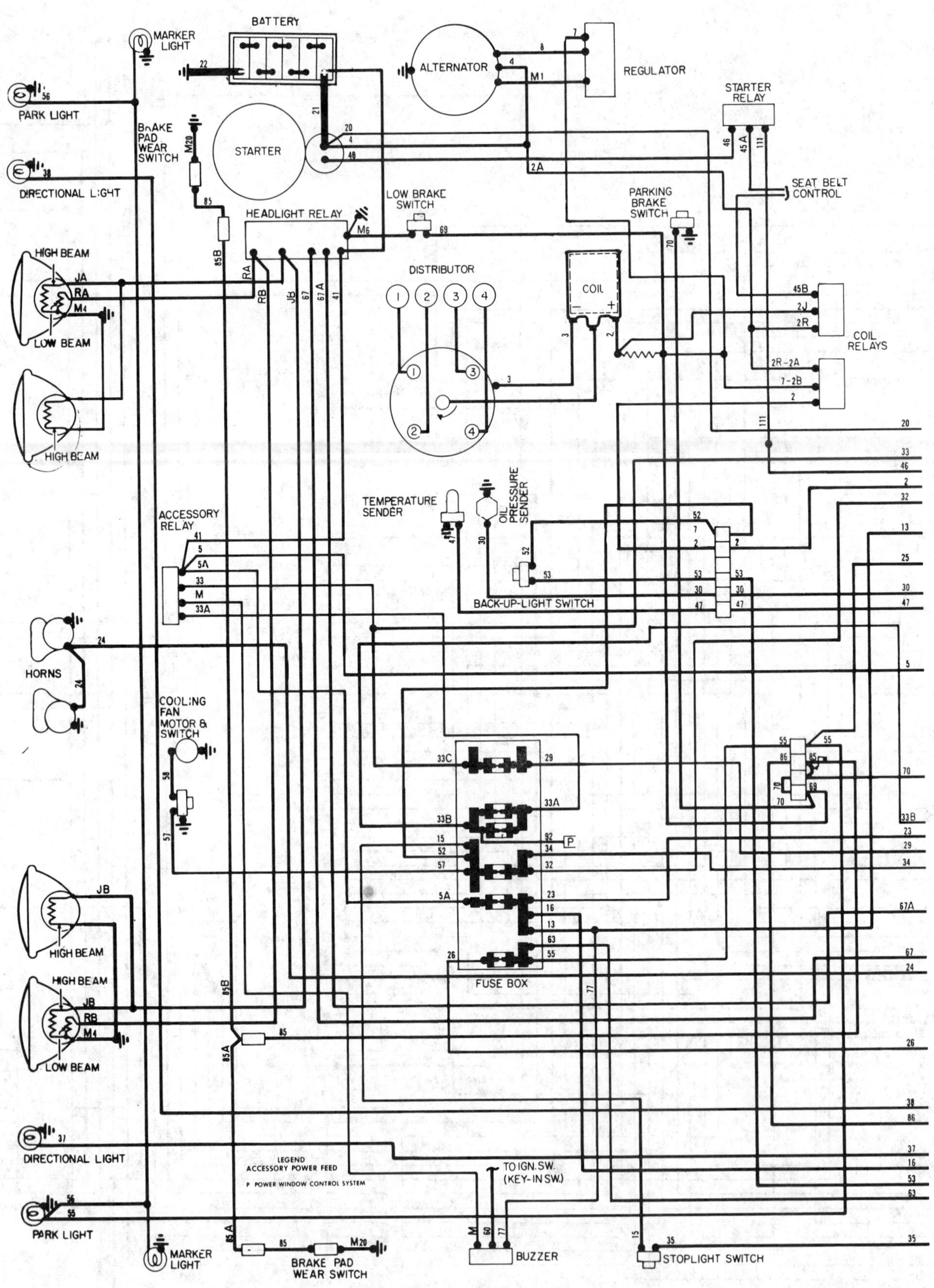
BATTERY
MARKER LIGHT
ALTERNATOR
REGULATOR
STARTER RELAY
PARK LIGHT
BRAKE PAD WEAR SWITCH
STARTER
DIRECTIONAL LIGHT
SEAT BELT CONTROL
LOW BRAKE SWITCH
PARKING BRAKE SWITCH
HEADLIGHT RELAY
HIGH BEAM
LOW BEAM
DISTRIBUTOR
COIL
COIL RELAYS
TEMPERATURE SENDER
OIL PRESSURE SENDER
ACCESSORY RELAY
BACK-UP-LIGHT SWITCH
HORNS
COOLING FAN MOTOR & SWITCH
FUSE BOX
LEGEND
ACCESSORY POWER FEED
P POWER WINDOW CONTROL SYSTEM
TO IGN. SW. (KEY-IN SW.)
BUZZER
STOPLIGHT SWITCH

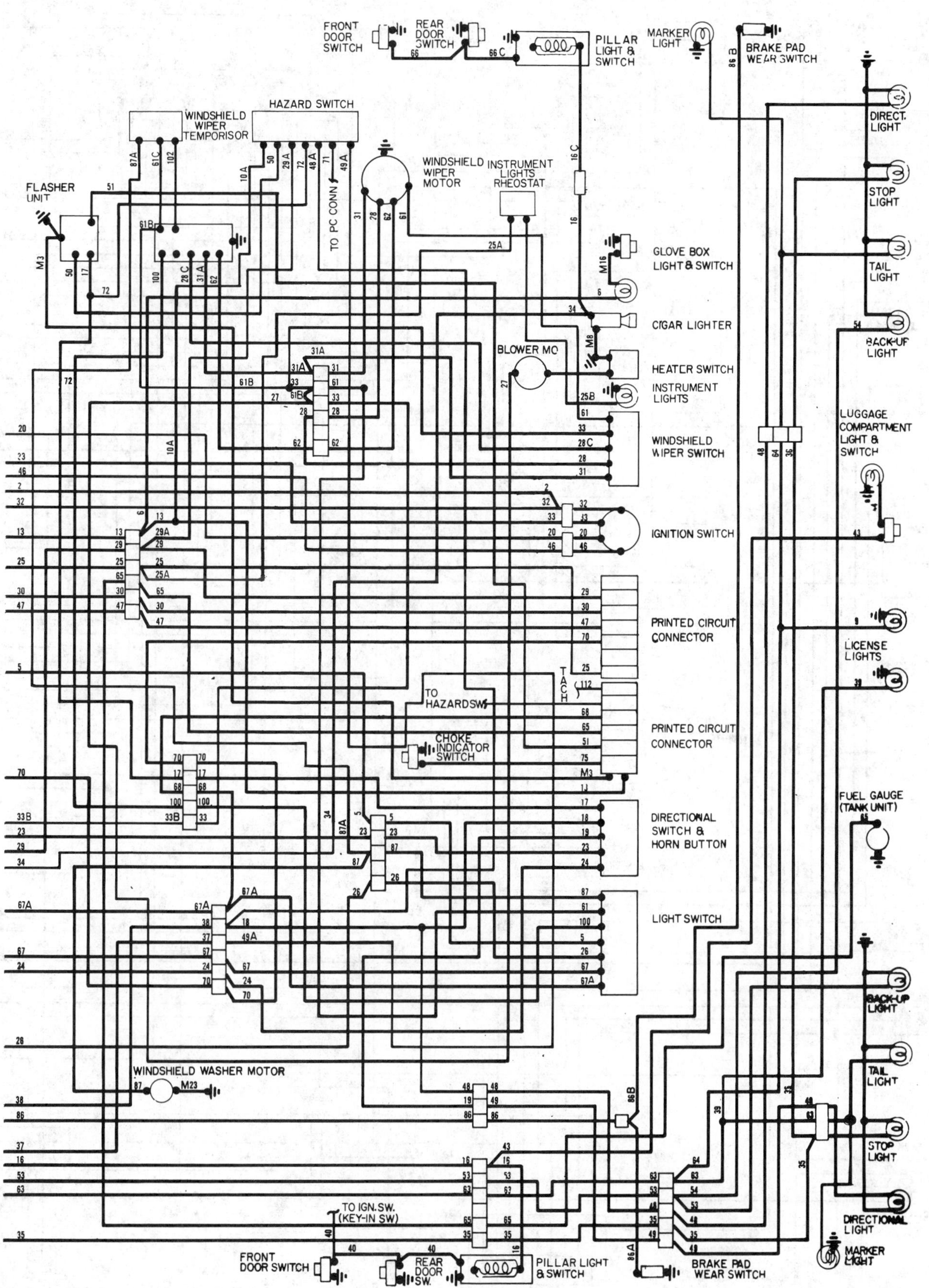
FRONT DOOR SWITCH
REAR DOOR SWITCH
PILLAR LIGHT & SWITCH
MARKER LIGHT
BRAKE PAD WEAR SWITCH
DIRECT. LIGHT
STOP LIGHT
TAIL LIGHT
BACK-UP LIGHT
WINDSHIELD WIPER TEMPORISOR
HAZARD SWITCH
FLASHER UNIT
WINDSHIELD WIPER MOTOR
INSTRUMENT LIGHTS RHEOSTAT
TO PC CONN
GLOVE BOX LIGHT & SWITCH
CIGAR LIGHTER
BLOWER MO
HEATER SWITCH
INSTRUMENT LIGHTS
WINDSHIELD WIPER SWITCH
LUGGAGE COMPARTMENT LIGHT & SWITCH
IGNITION SWITCH
PRINTED CIRCUIT CONNECTOR
LICENSE LIGHTS
TACH
TO HAZARD SW
CHOKE INDICATOR SWITCH
PRINTED CIRCUIT CONNECTOR
FUEL GAUGE (TANK UNIT)
DIRECTIONAL SWITCH & HORN BUTTON
LIGHT SWITCH
BACK-UP LIGHT
TAIL LIGHT
WINDSHIELD WASHER MOTOR
STOP LIGHT
TO IGN. SW. (KEY-IN SW)
DIRECTIONAL LIGHT
MARKER LIGHT
FRONT DOOR SWITCH
REAR DOOR SW.
PILLAR LIGHT & SWITCH
BRAKE PAD WEAR SWITCH

1977 Peugeot

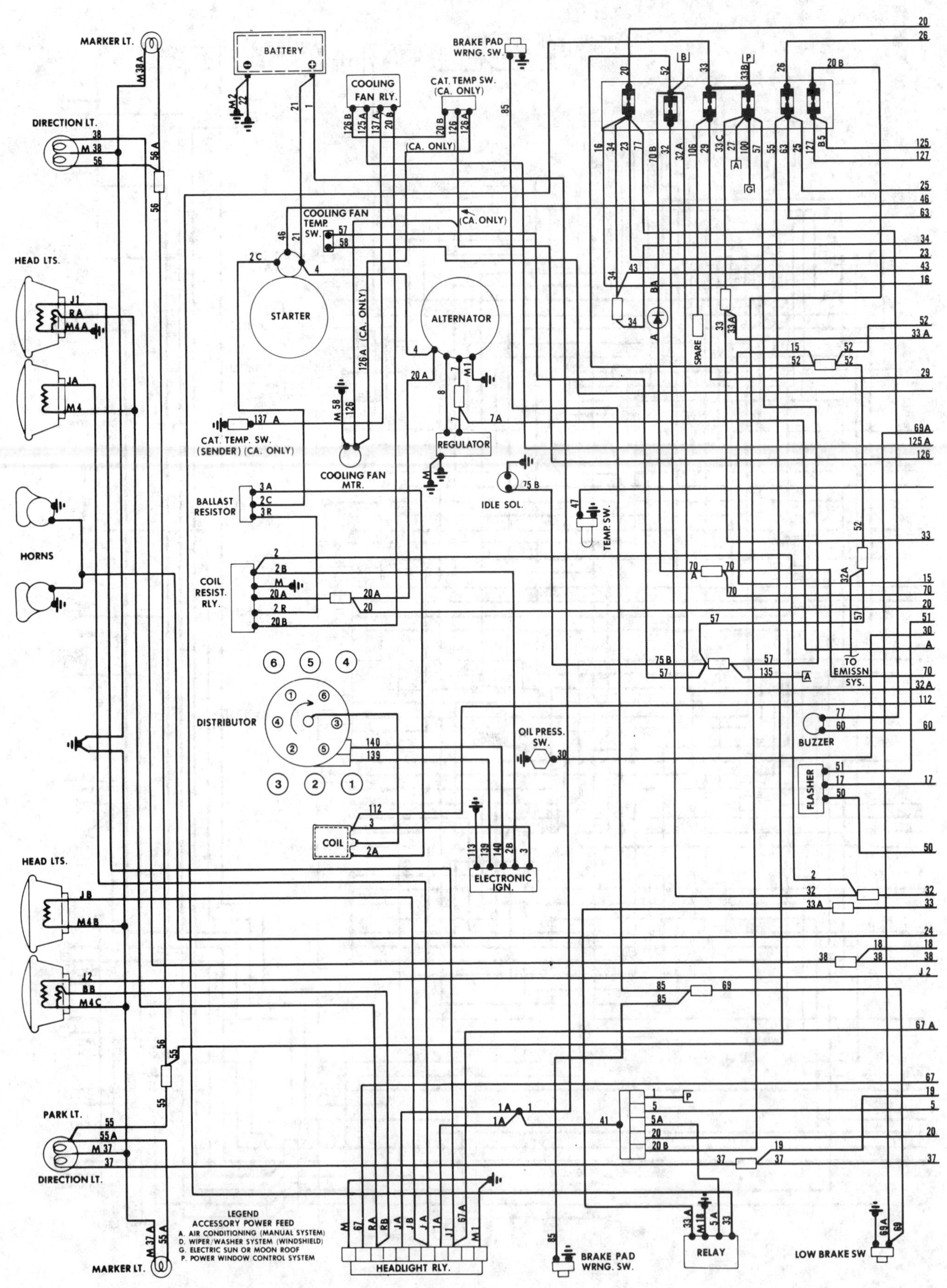

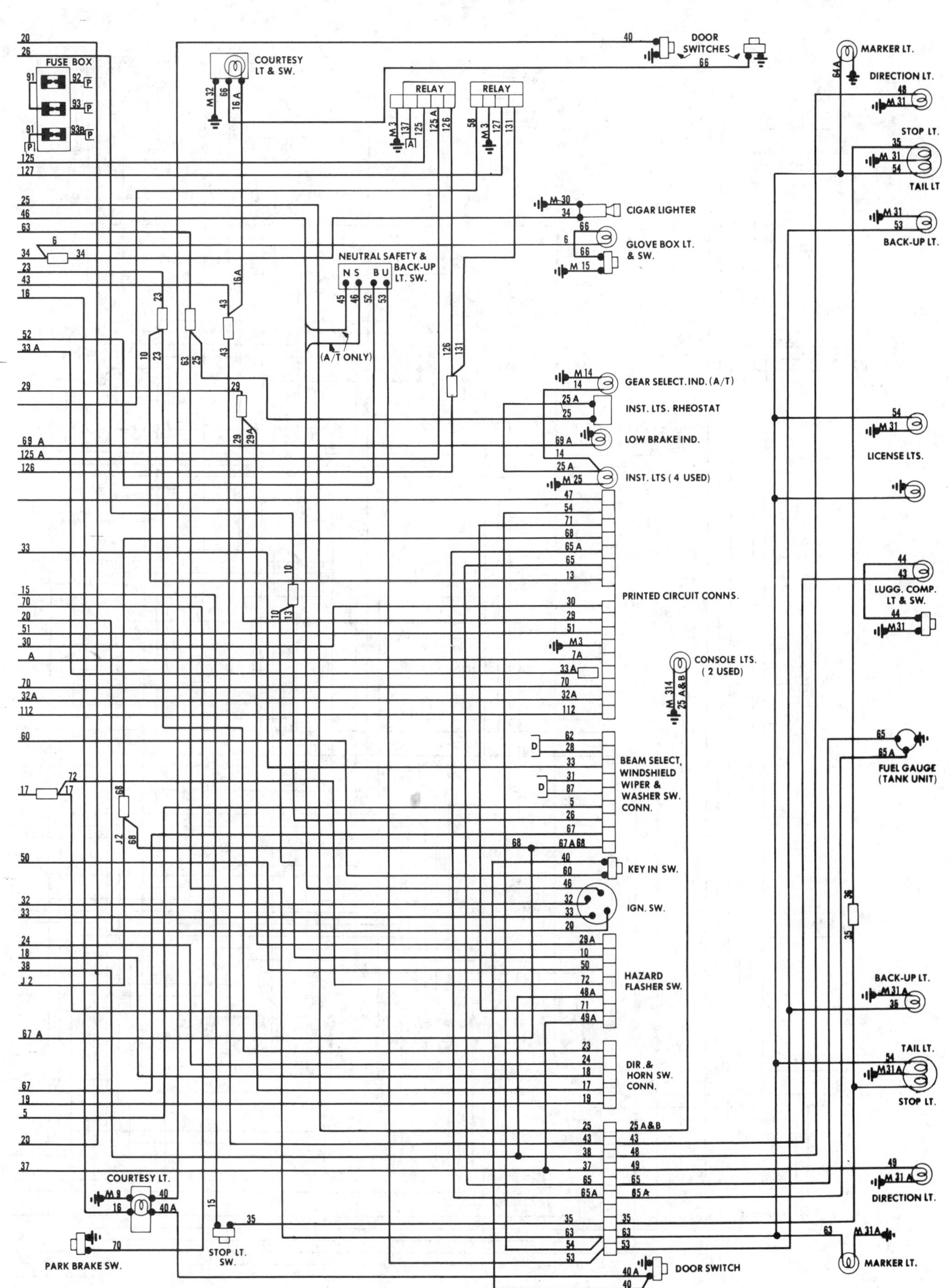
FUSE BOX
COURTESY LT & SW.
RELAY
RELAY
DOOR SWITCHES
MARKER LT.
DIRECTION LT.
STOP LT.
TAIL LT
CIGAR LIGHTER
BACK-UP LT.
GLOVE BOX LT. & SW.
NEUTRAL SAFETY & BACK-UP LT. SW.
(A/T ONLY)
GEAR SELECT. IND. (A/T)
INST. LTS. RHEOSTAT
LOW BRAKE IND.
INST. LTS (4 USED)
LICENSE LTS.
PRINTED CIRCUIT CONNS.
LUGG. COMP. LT & SW.
CONSOLE LTS. (2 USED)
FUEL GAUGE (TANK UNIT)
BEAM SELECT, WINDSHIELD WIPER & WASHER SW. CONN.
KEY IN SW.
IGN. SW.
HAZARD FLASHER SW.
BACK-UP LT.
DIR. & HORN SW. CONN.
TAIL LT.
STOP LT.
COURTESY LT.
DIRECTION LT.
PARK BRAKE SW.
STOP LT. SW.
DOOR SWITCH
MARKER LT.

1977 Porsche

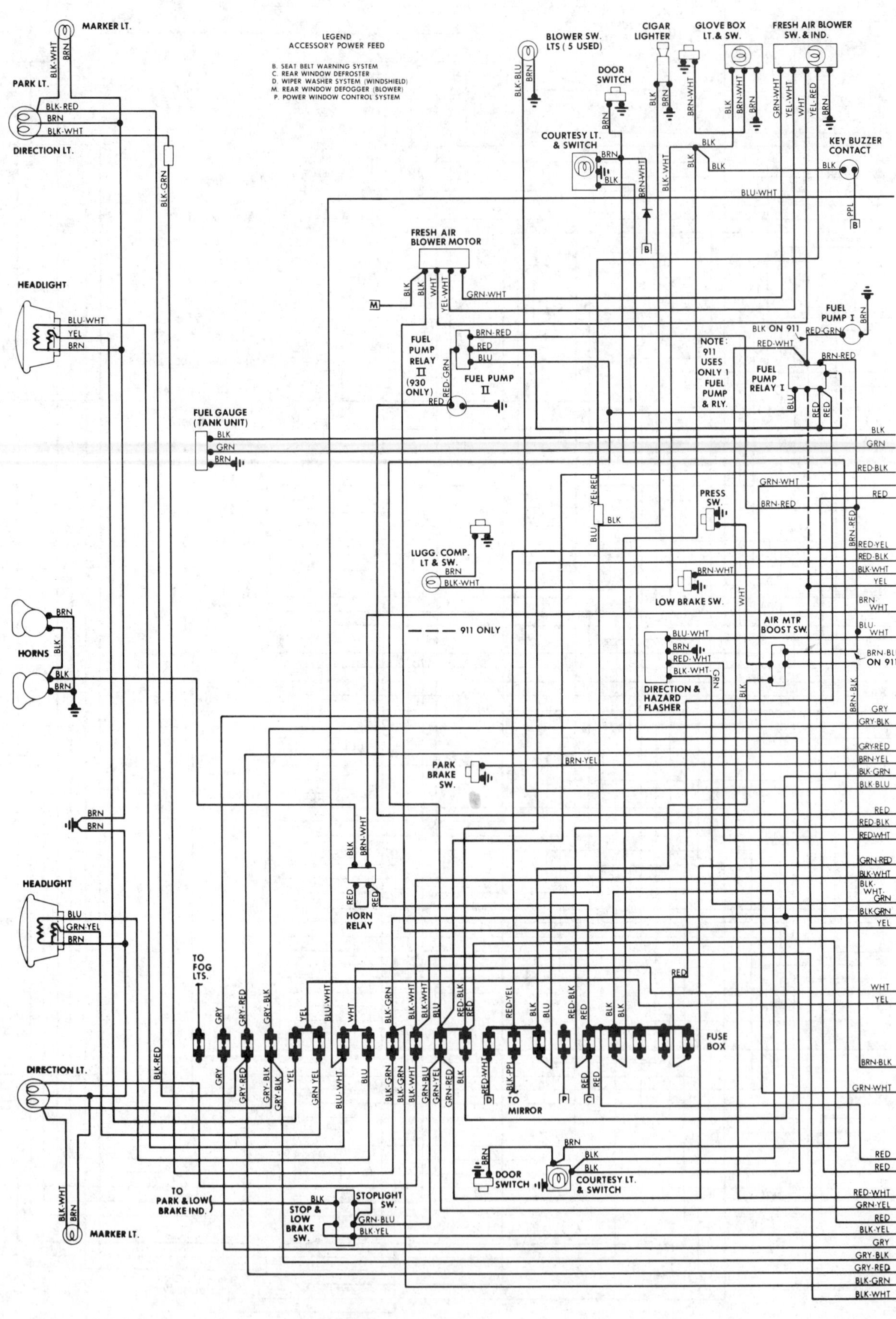

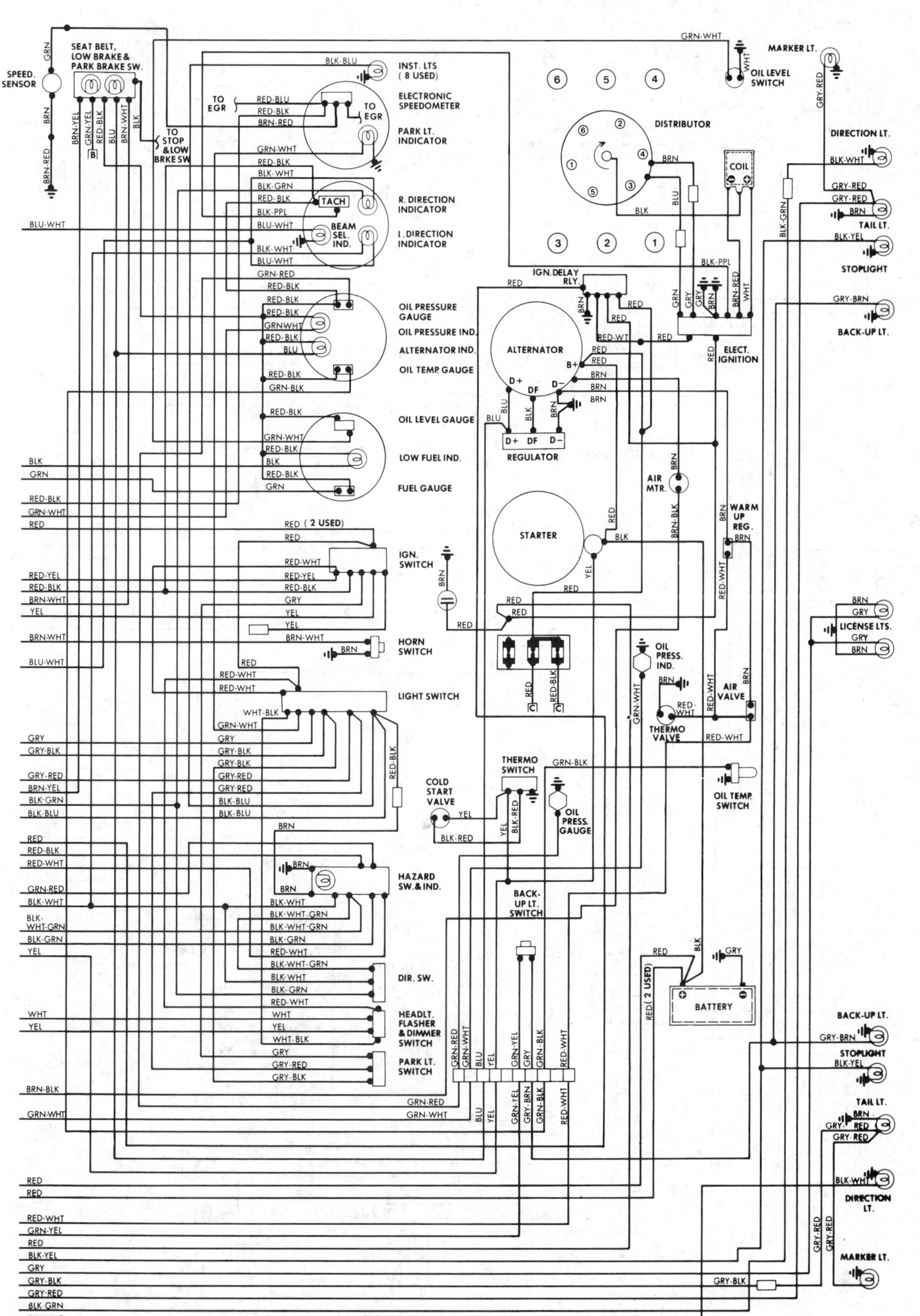

SPEED. SENSOR
SEAT BELT, LOW BRAKE & PARK BRAKE SW.
TO STOP & LOW BRKE SW
TO EGR
INST. LTS (8 USED)
ELECTRONIC SPEEDOMETER
PARK LT. INDICATOR
TACH
R. DIRECTION INDICATOR
BEAM SEL. IND.
L. DIRECTION INDICATOR
OIL PRESSURE GAUGE
OIL PRESSURE IND.
ALTERNATOR IND.
OIL TEMP. GAUGE
OIL LEVEL GAUGE
LOW FUEL IND.
FUEL GAUGE
IGN. SWITCH
HORN SWITCH
LIGHT SWITCH
COLD START VALVE
HAZARD SW. & IND.
DIR. SW.
HEADLT. FLASHER & DIMMER SWITCH
PARK LT. SWITCH
MARKER LT.
OIL LEVEL SWITCH
DISTRIBUTOR
COIL
IGN. DELAY RLY.
ALTERNATOR
REGULATOR
ELECT. IGNITION
AIR MTR.
STARTER
WARM UP REG.
OIL PRESS. IND.
AIR VALVE
THERMO VALVE
THERMO SWITCH
OIL TEMP. SWITCH
OIL PRESS. GAUGE
BACK-UP LT. SWITCH
BATTERY
DIRECTION LT.
TAIL LT.
STOPLIGHT
BACK-UP LT.
LICENSE LTS.
MARKER LT.

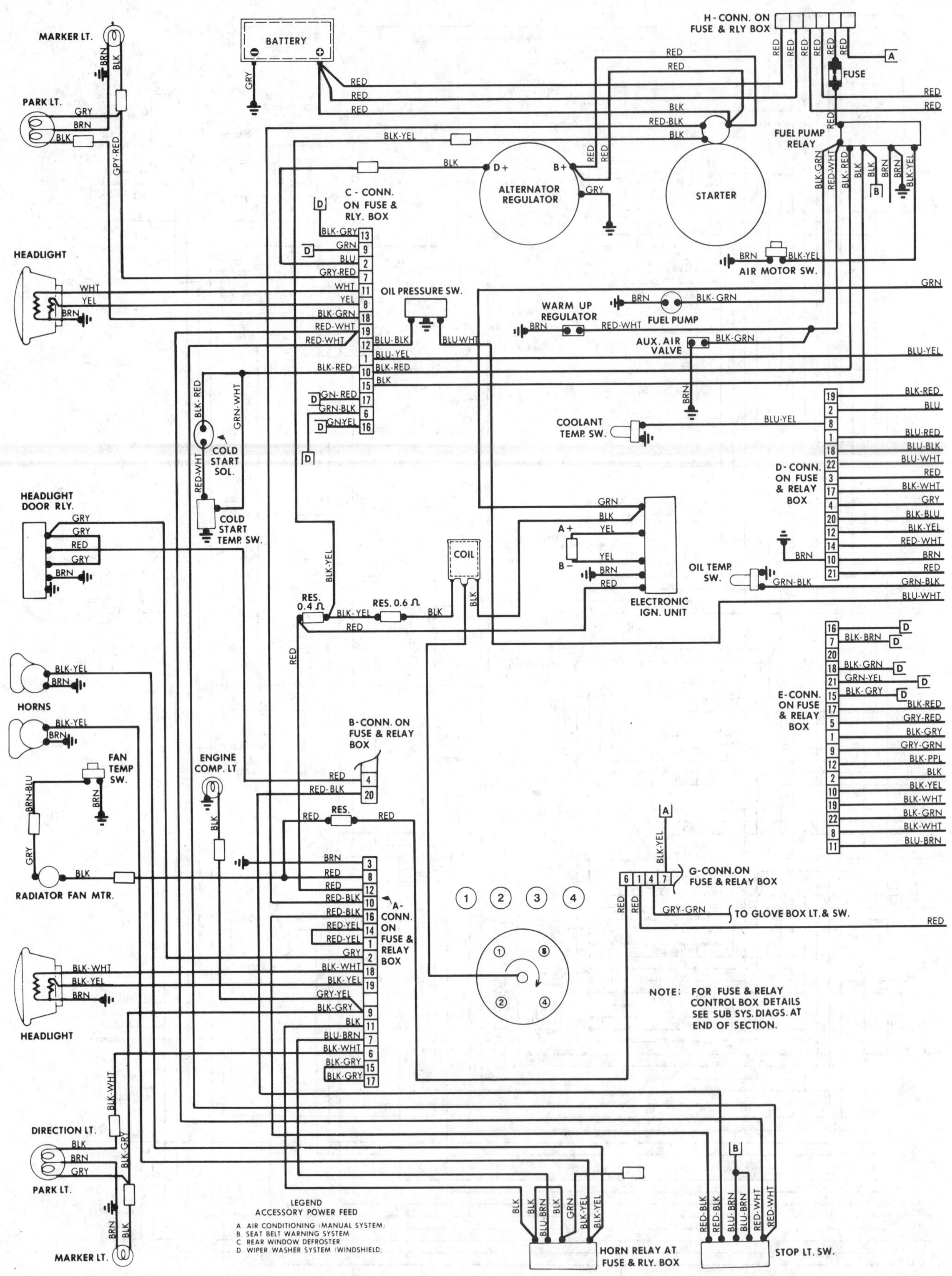
MARKER LT.
PARK LT.
HEADLIGHT
HEADLIGHT DOOR RLY.
HORNS
FAN TEMP SW.
RADIATOR FAN MTR.
HEADLIGHT
DIRECTION LT.
PARK LT.
MARKER LT.
BATTERY
C - CONN. ON FUSE & RLY. BOX
ALTERNATOR REGULATOR
STARTER
H - CONN. ON FUSE & RLY BOX
FUSE
FUEL PUMP RELAY
AIR MOTOR SW.
OIL PRESSURE SW.
WARM UP REGULATOR
FUEL PUMP
AUX. AIR VALVE
COLD START SOL.
COLD START TEMP. SW.
COOLANT TEMP. SW.
D- CONN. ON FUSE & RELAY BOX
COIL
RES. 0.4 Ω
RES. 0.6 Ω
ELECTRONIC IGN. UNIT
OIL TEMP. SW.
E-CONN. ON FUSE & RELAY BOX
B-CONN. ON FUSE & RELAY BOX
ENGINE COMP. LT
RES.
A-CONN. ON FUSE & RELAY BOX
G-CONN. ON FUSE & RELAY BOX
TO GLOVE BOX LT. & SW.
NOTE: FOR FUSE & RELAY CONTROL BOX DETAILS SEE SUB SYS. DIAGS. AT END OF SECTION.
HORN RELAY AT FUSE & RLY. BOX
STOP LT. SW.
LEGEND
ACCESSORY POWER FEED
A AIR CONDITIONING (MANUAL SYSTEM)
B SEAT BELT WARNING SYSTEM
C REAR WINDOW DEFROSTER
D WIPER WASHER SYSTEM (WINDSHIELD)

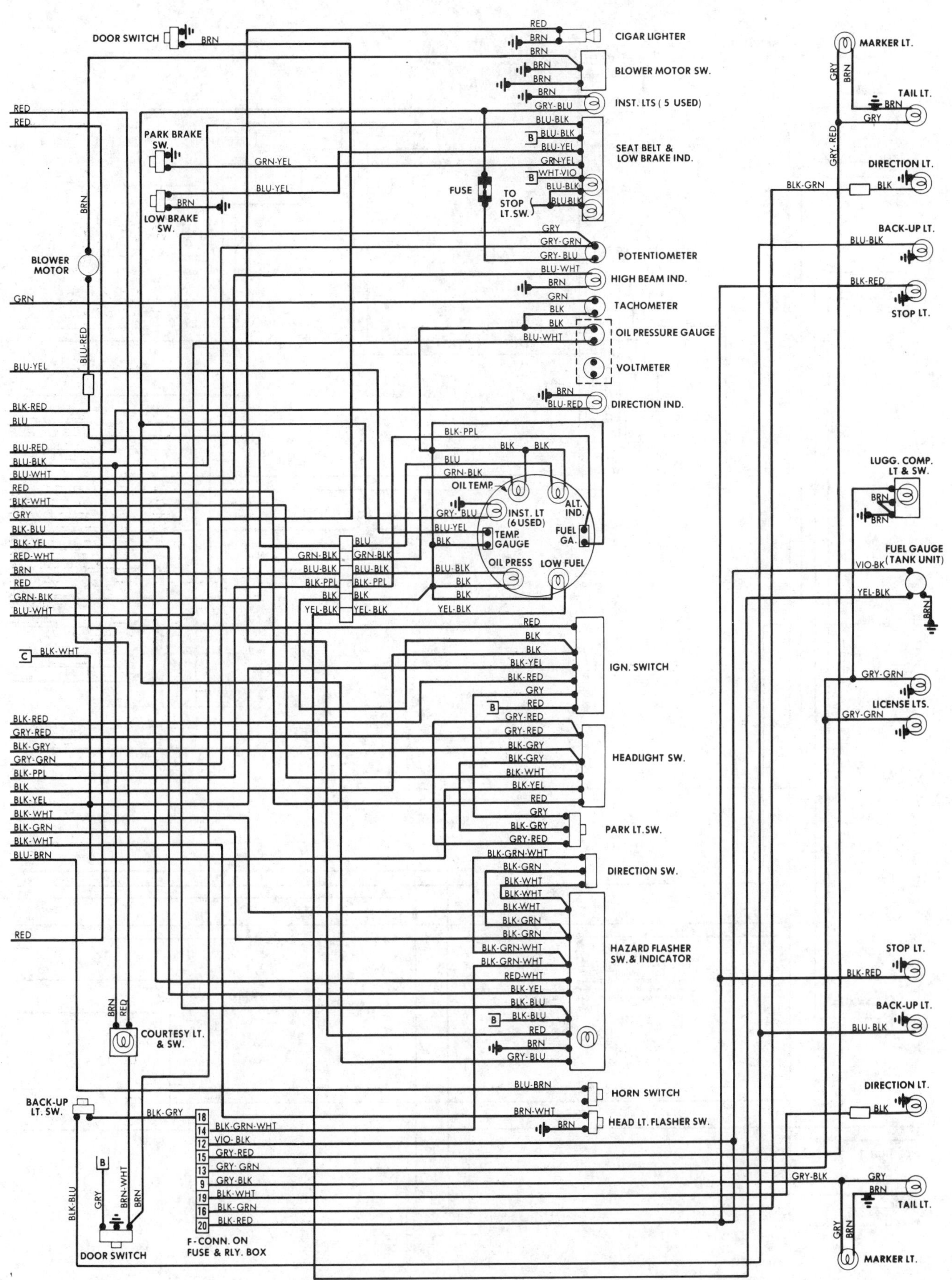
DOOR SWITCH
CIGAR LIGHTER
BLOWER MOTOR SW.
INST. LTS (5 USED)
PARK BRAKE SW.
SEAT BELT & LOW BRAKE IND.
FUSE
TO STOP LT. SW.
LOW BRAKE SW.
BLOWER MOTOR
POTENTIOMETER
HIGH BEAM IND.
TACHOMETER
OIL PRESSURE GAUGE
VOLTMETER
DIRECTION IND.
OIL TEMP.
INST. LT (6 USED)
ALT. IND.
TEMP. GAUGE
FUEL GA.
OIL PRESS
LOW FUEL
IGN. SWITCH
HEADLIGHT SW.
PARK LT. SW.
DIRECTION SW.
HAZARD FLASHER SW. & INDICATOR
COURTESY LT. & SW.
HORN SWITCH
HEAD LT. FLASHER SW.
BACK-UP LT. SW.
F-CONN. ON FUSE & RLY. BOX
MARKER LT.
TAIL LT.
DIRECTION LT.
BACK-UP LT.
STOP LT.
LUGG. COMP. LT & SW.
FUEL GAUGE (TANK UNIT)
LICENSE LTS.

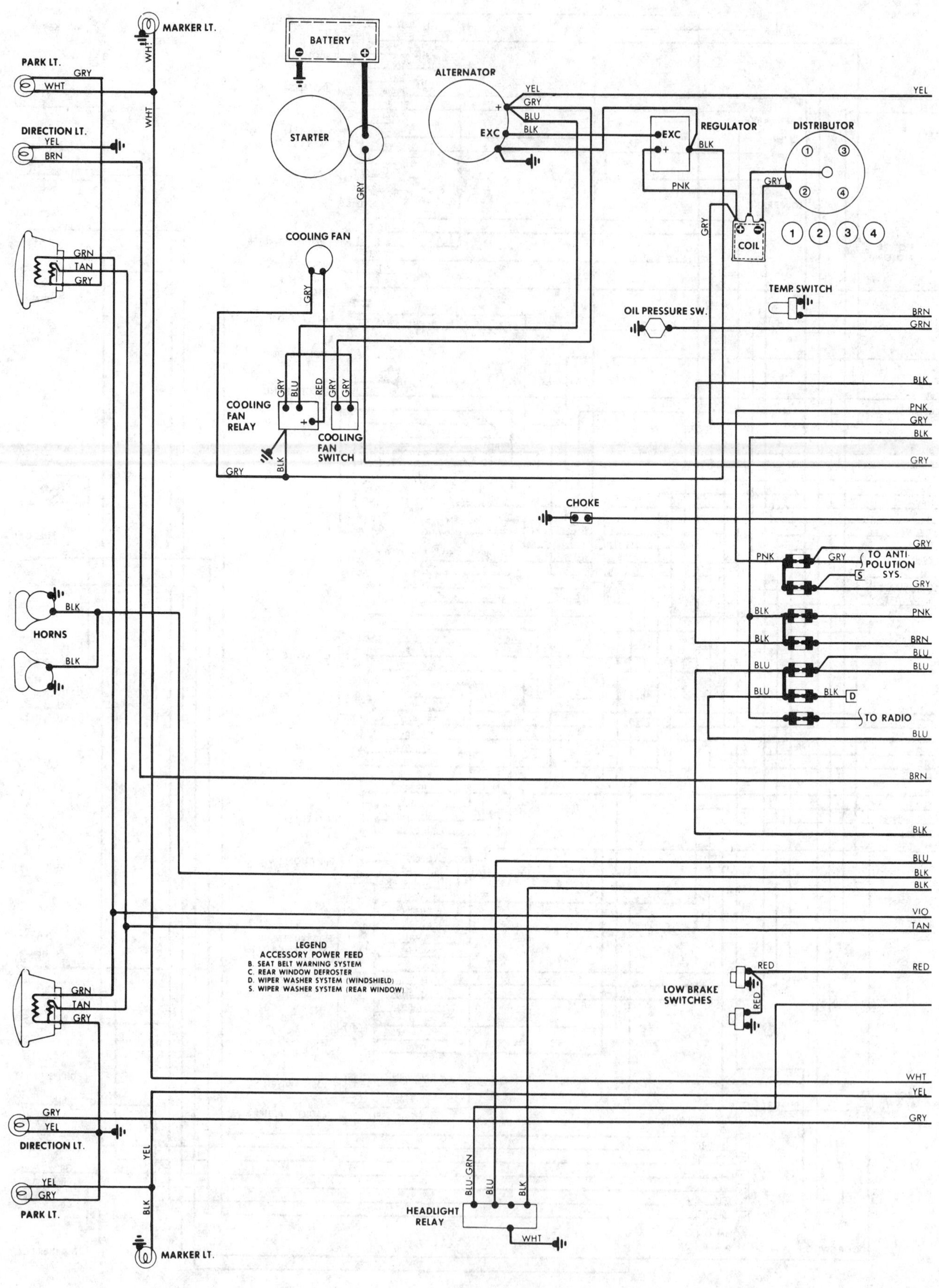
MARKER LT.
PARK LT.
DIRECTION LT.
BATTERY
STARTER
ALTERNATOR
EXC
REGULATOR
DISTRIBUTOR
COIL
COOLING FAN
COOLING FAN RELAY
COOLING FAN SWITCH
TEMP. SWITCH
OIL PRESSURE SW.
CHOKE
TO ANTI POLUTION SYS.
TO RADIO
HORNS
LEGEND
ACCESSORY POWER FEED
B. SEAT BELT WARNING SYSTEM
C. REAR WINDOW DEFROSTER
D. WIPER WASHER SYSTEM (WINDSHIELD)
S. WIPER WASHER SYSTEM (REAR WINDOW)
LOW BRAKE SWITCHES
HEADLIGHT RELAY
DIRECTION LT.
PARK LT.
MARKER LT.

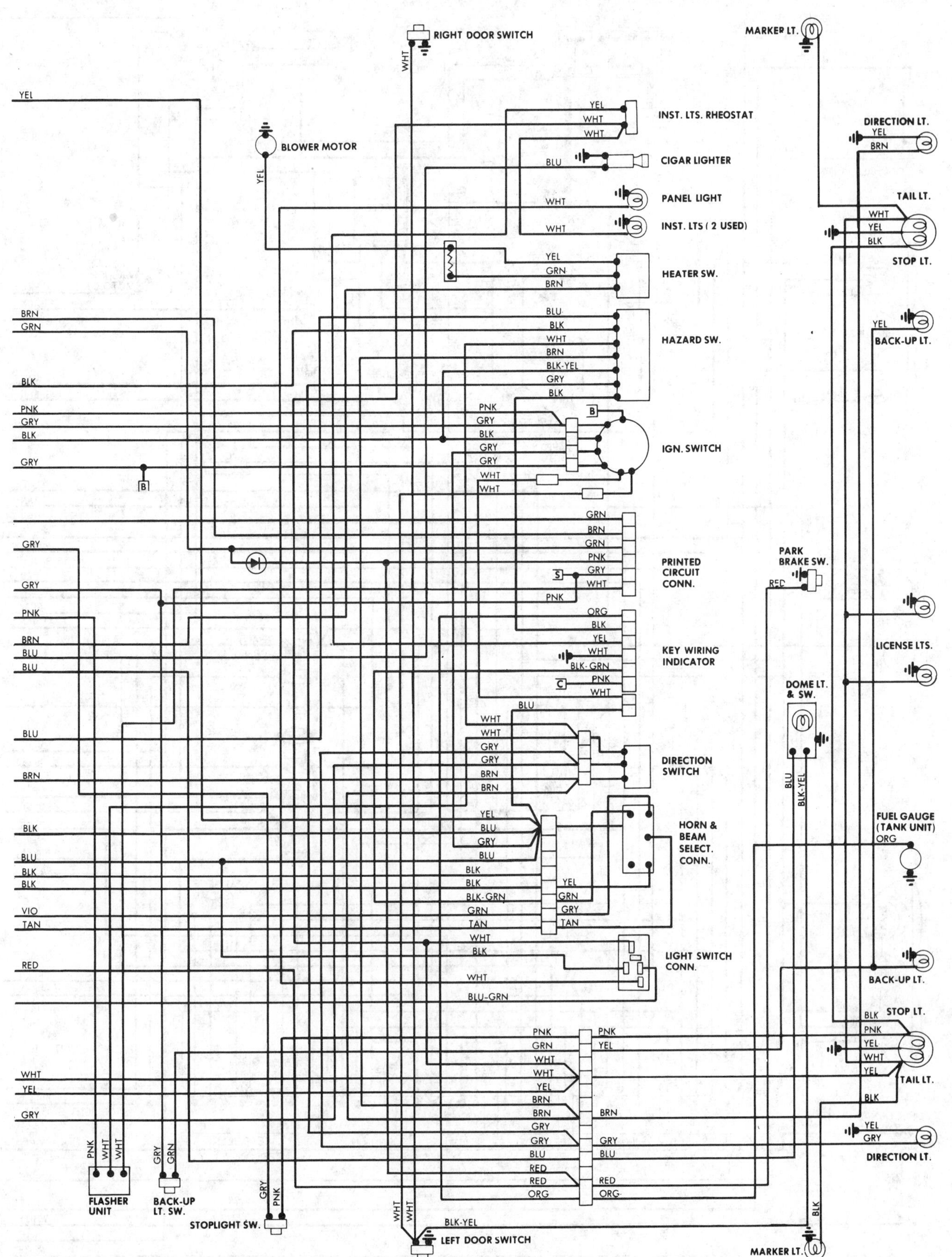
RIGHT DOOR SWITCH
MARKER LT.
INST. LTS. RHEOSTAT
BLOWER MOTOR
CIGAR LIGHTER
PANEL LIGHT
INST. LTS (2 USED)
DIRECTION LT.
TAIL LT.
STOP LT.
HEATER SW.
HAZARD SW.
BACK-UP LT.
IGN. SWITCH
PRINTED CIRCUIT CONN.
PARK BRAKE SW.
KEY WIRING INDICATOR
LICENSE LTS.
DOME LT. & SW.
DIRECTION SWITCH
HORN & BEAM SELECT. CONN.
FUEL GAUGE (TANK UNIT)
LIGHT SWITCH CONN.
BACK-UP LT.
STOP LT.
TAIL LT.
DIRECTION LT.
FLASHER UNIT
BACK-UP LT. SW.
STOPLIGHT SW.
LEFT DOOR SWITCH
MARKER LT.

1977 Renault

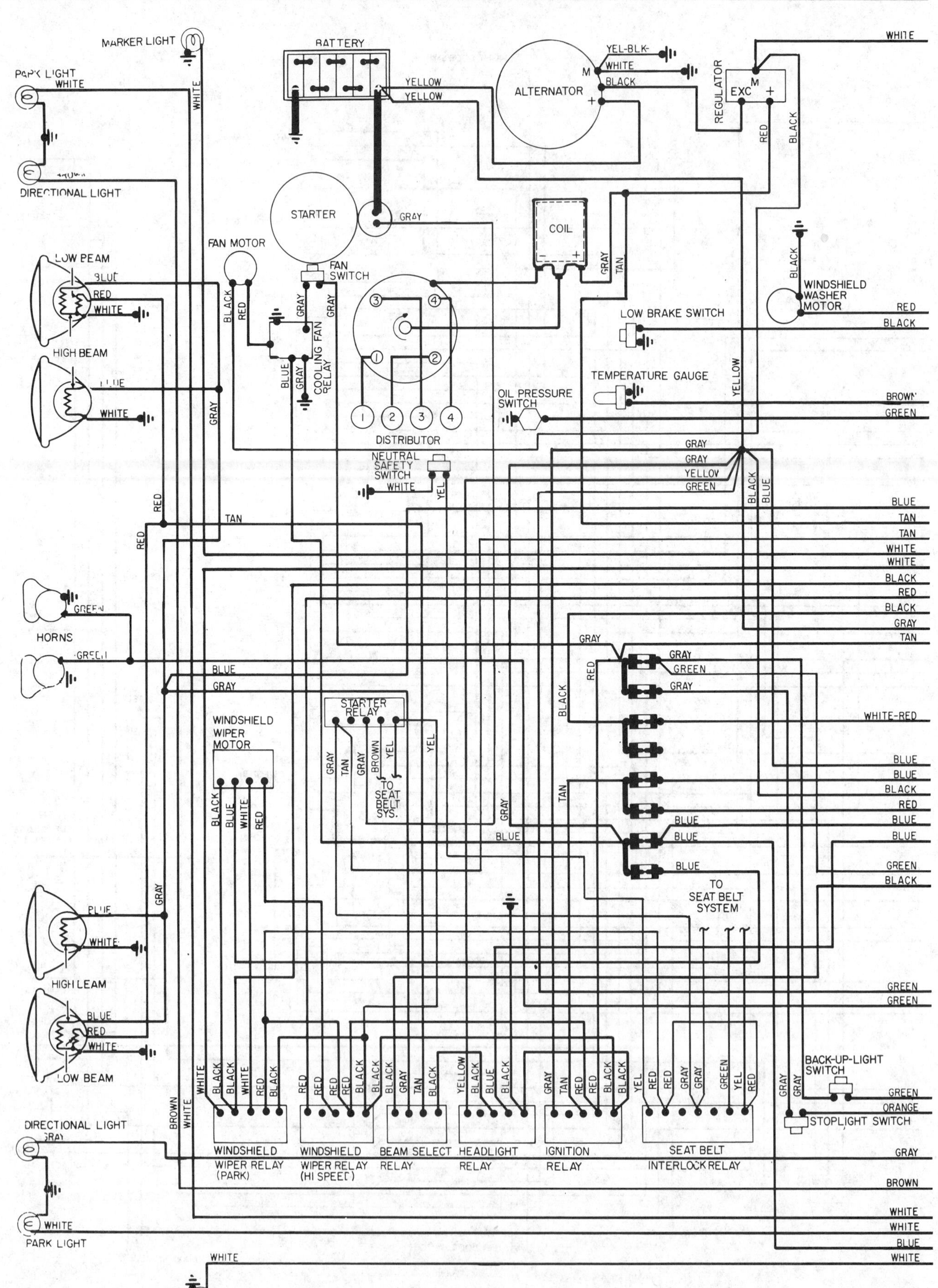

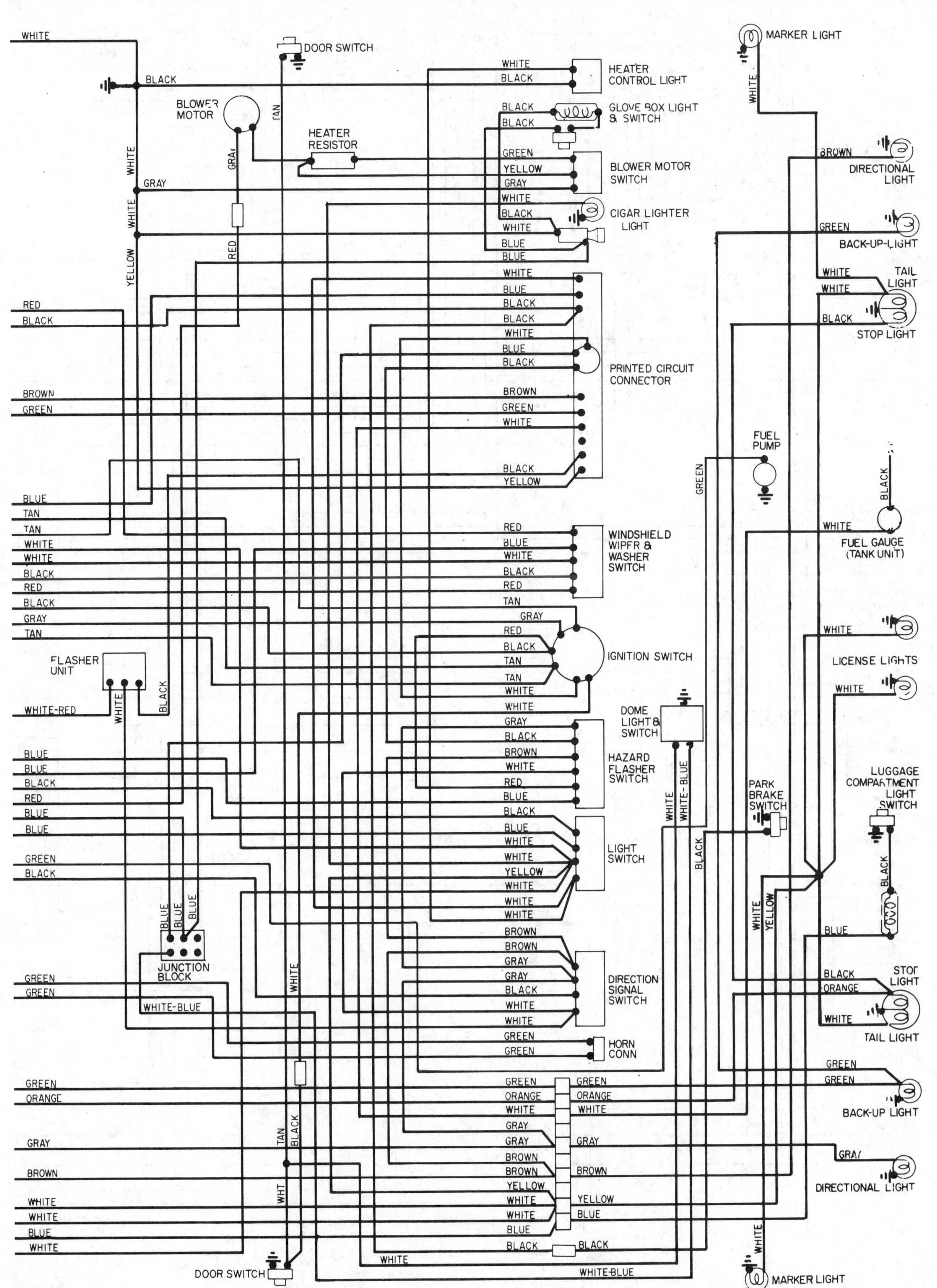
DOOR SWITCH
BLOWER MOTOR
HEATER RESISTOR
HEATER CONTROL LIGHT
GLOVE BOX LIGHT & SWITCH
BLOWER MOTOR SWITCH
CIGAR LIGHTER LIGHT
PRINTED CIRCUIT CONNECTOR
WINDSHIELD WIPER & WASHER SWITCH
IGNITION SWITCH
FLASHER UNIT
DOME LIGHT & SWITCH
HAZARD FLASHER SWITCH
LIGHT SWITCH
JUNCTION BLOCK
DIRECTION SIGNAL SWITCH
HORN CONN
DOOR SWITCH
MARKER LIGHT
DIRECTIONAL LIGHT
BACK-UP LIGHT
TAIL LIGHT
STOP LIGHT
FUEL PUMP
FUEL GAUGE (TANK UNIT)
LICENSE LIGHTS
PARK BRAKE SWITCH
LUGGAGE COMPARTMENT LIGHT SWITCH
STOP LIGHT
TAIL LIGHT
BACK-UP LIGHT
DIRECTIONAL LIGHT
MARKER LIGHT

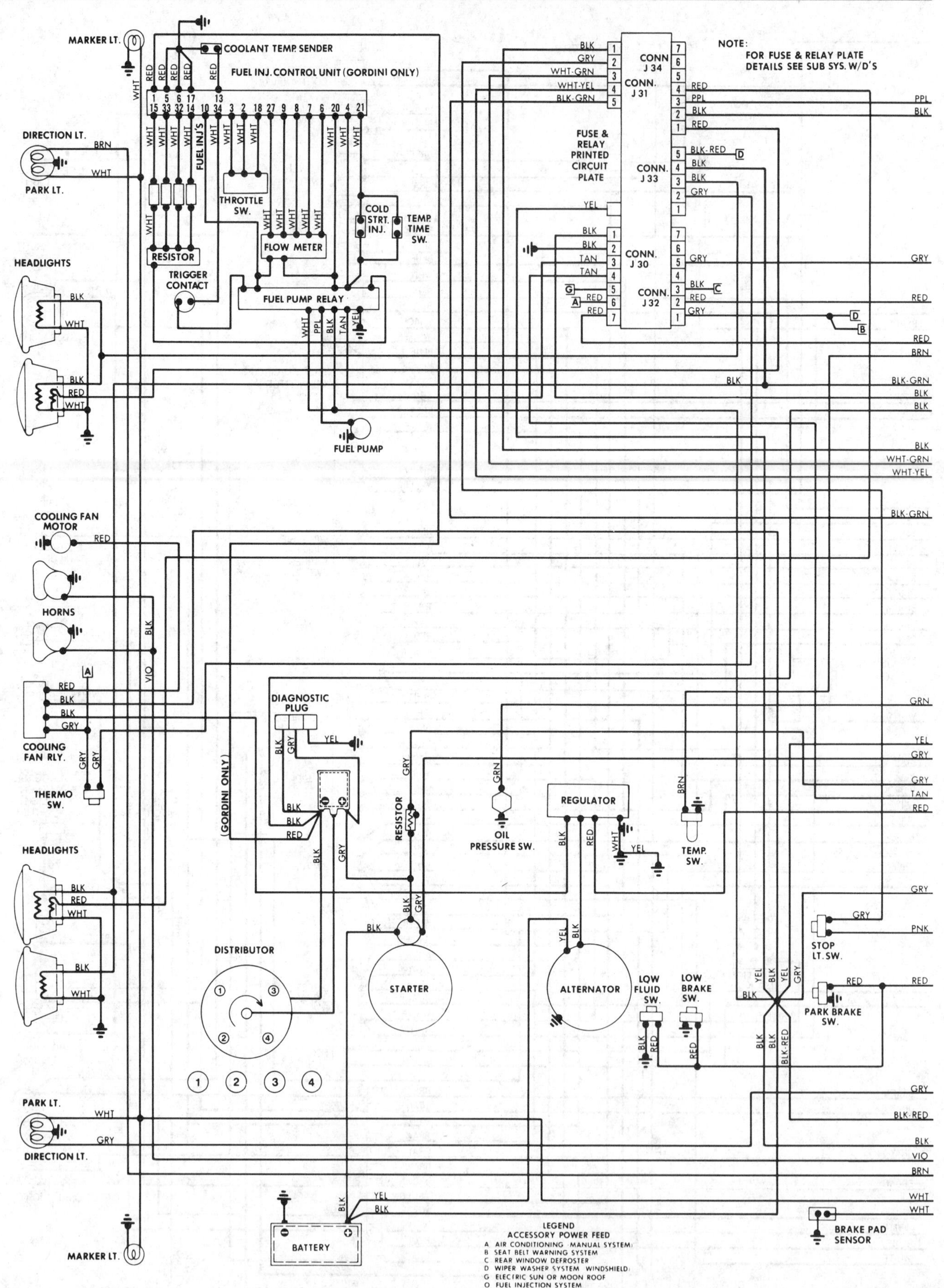
MARKER LT.
COOLANT TEMP. SENDER
FUEL INJ. CONTROL UNIT (GORDINI ONLY)
DIRECTION LT.
PARK LT.
FUEL INJ'S
THROTTLE SW.
COLD STRT. INJ.
TEMP. TIME SW.
RESISTOR
FLOW METER
TRIGGER CONTACT
FUEL PUMP RELAY
HEADLIGHTS
FUEL PUMP
NOTE:
FOR FUSE & RELAY PLATE DETAILS SEE SUB SYS. W/D'S
CONN J 34
CONN. J 31
FUSE & RELAY PRINTED CIRCUIT PLATE
CONN. J 33
CONN. J 30
CONN. J 32
COOLING FAN MOTOR
HORNS
COOLING FAN RLY.
THERMO SW.
DIAGNOSTIC PLUG
(GORDINI ONLY)
RESISTOR
OIL PRESSURE SW.
REGULATOR
TEMP. SW.
STOP LT. SW.
DISTRIBUTOR
STARTER
ALTERNATOR
LOW FLUID SW.
LOW BRAKE SW.
PARK BRAKE SW.
PARK LT.
DIRECTION LT.
BATTERY
BRAKE PAD SENSOR
MARKER LT.
LEGEND
ACCESSORY POWER FEED
A AIR CONDITIONING (MANUAL SYSTEM)
B SEAT BELT WARNING SYSTEM
C REAR WINDOW DEFROSTER
D WIPER WASHER SYSTEM (WINDSHIELD)
G ELECTRIC SUN OR MOON ROOF
O FUEL INJECTION SYSTEM

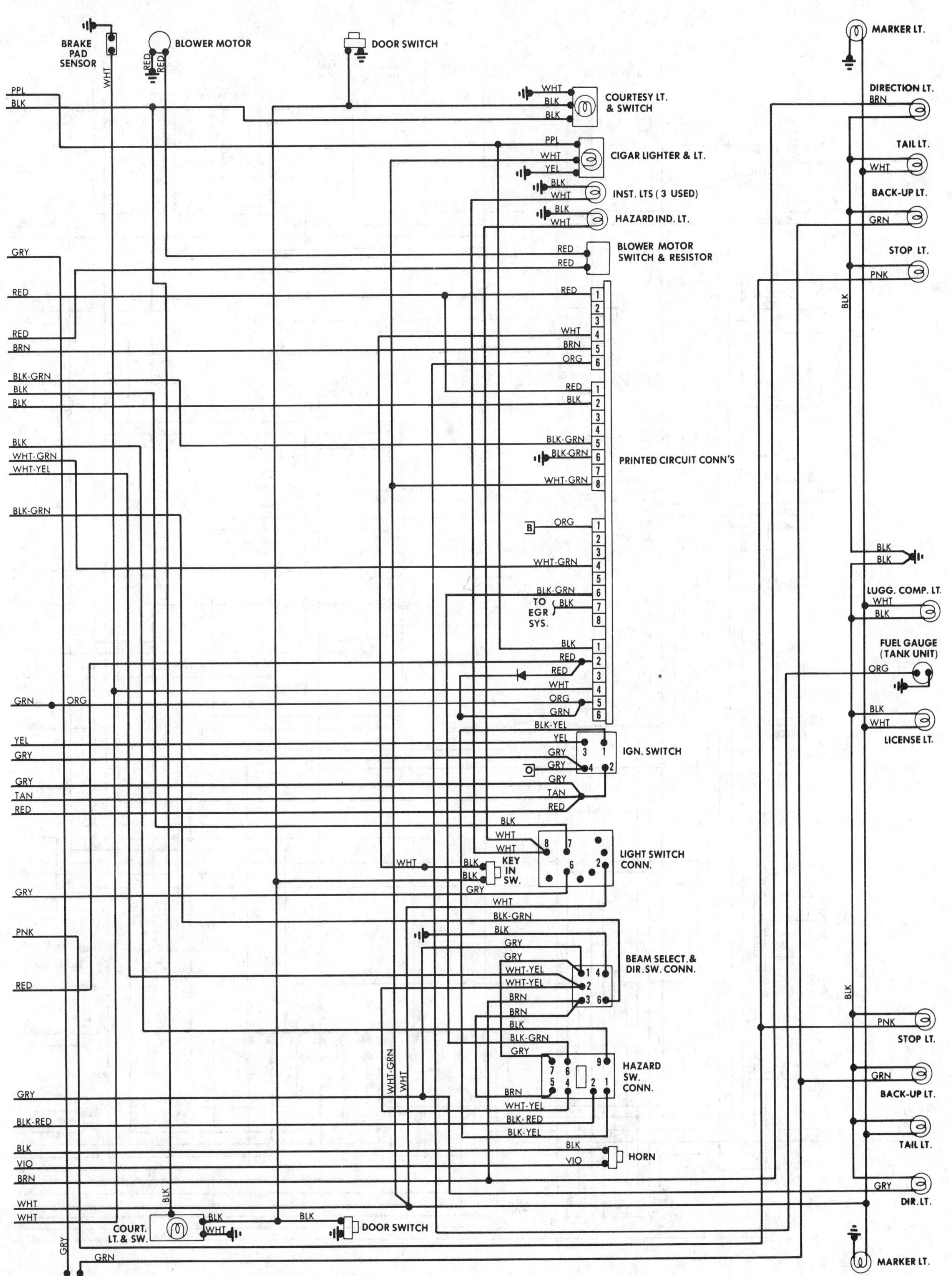
BRAKE PAD SENSOR
BLOWER MOTOR
DOOR SWITCH
MARKER LT.
COURTESY LT. & SWITCH
DIRECTION LT.
CIGAR LIGHTER & LT.
TAIL LT.
INST. LTS (3 USED)
BACK-UP LT.
HAZARD IND. LT.
BLOWER MOTOR SWITCH & RESISTOR
STOP LT.
PRINTED CIRCUIT CONN'S
TO EGR SYS.
LUGG. COMP. LT.
FUEL GAUGE (TANK UNIT)
LICENSE LT.
IGN. SWITCH
LIGHT SWITCH CONN.
KEY IN SW.
BEAM SELECT. & DIR. SW. CONN.
STOP LT.
HAZARD SW. CONN.
BACK-UP LT.
TAIL LT.
HORN
DIR. LT.
COURT. LT. & SW.
DOOR SWITCH
MARKER LT.
BACK-UP LT. SW.

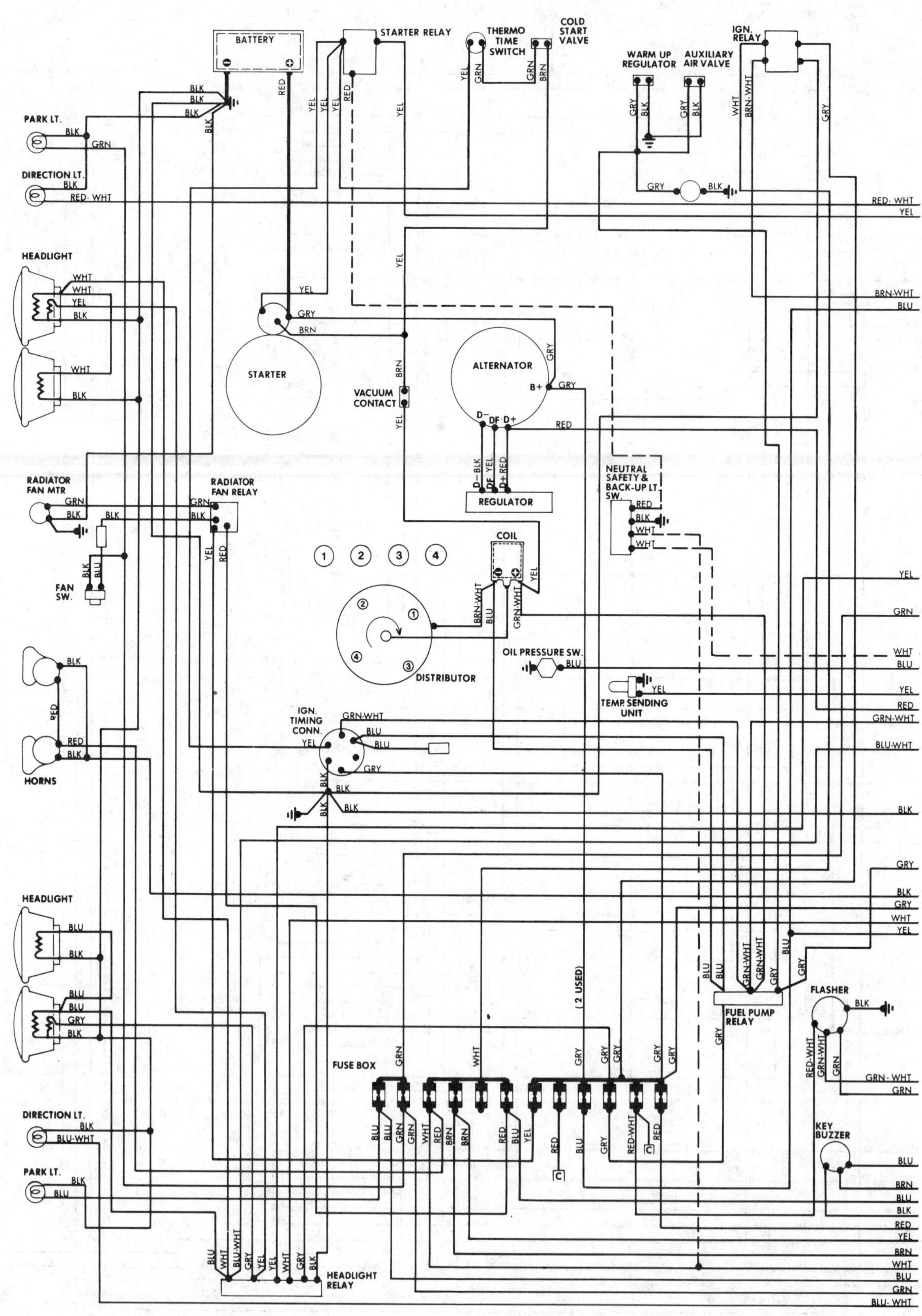
BATTERY
STARTER RELAY
THERMO TIME SWITCH
COLD START VALVE
IGN. RELAY
WARM UP REGULATOR
AUXILIARY AIR VALVE
PARK LT.
DIRECTION LT.
HEADLIGHT
STARTER
ALTERNATOR
VACUUM CONTACT
REGULATOR
NEUTRAL SAFETY & BACK-UP LT. SW.
RADIATOR FAN MTR
RADIATOR FAN RELAY
FAN SW.
COIL
DISTRIBUTOR
OIL PRESSURE SW.
TEMP SENDING UNIT
HORNS
IGN. TIMING CONN.
FUEL PUMP RELAY
FLASHER
(2 USED)
FUSE BOX
KEY BUZZER
HEADLIGHT RELAY

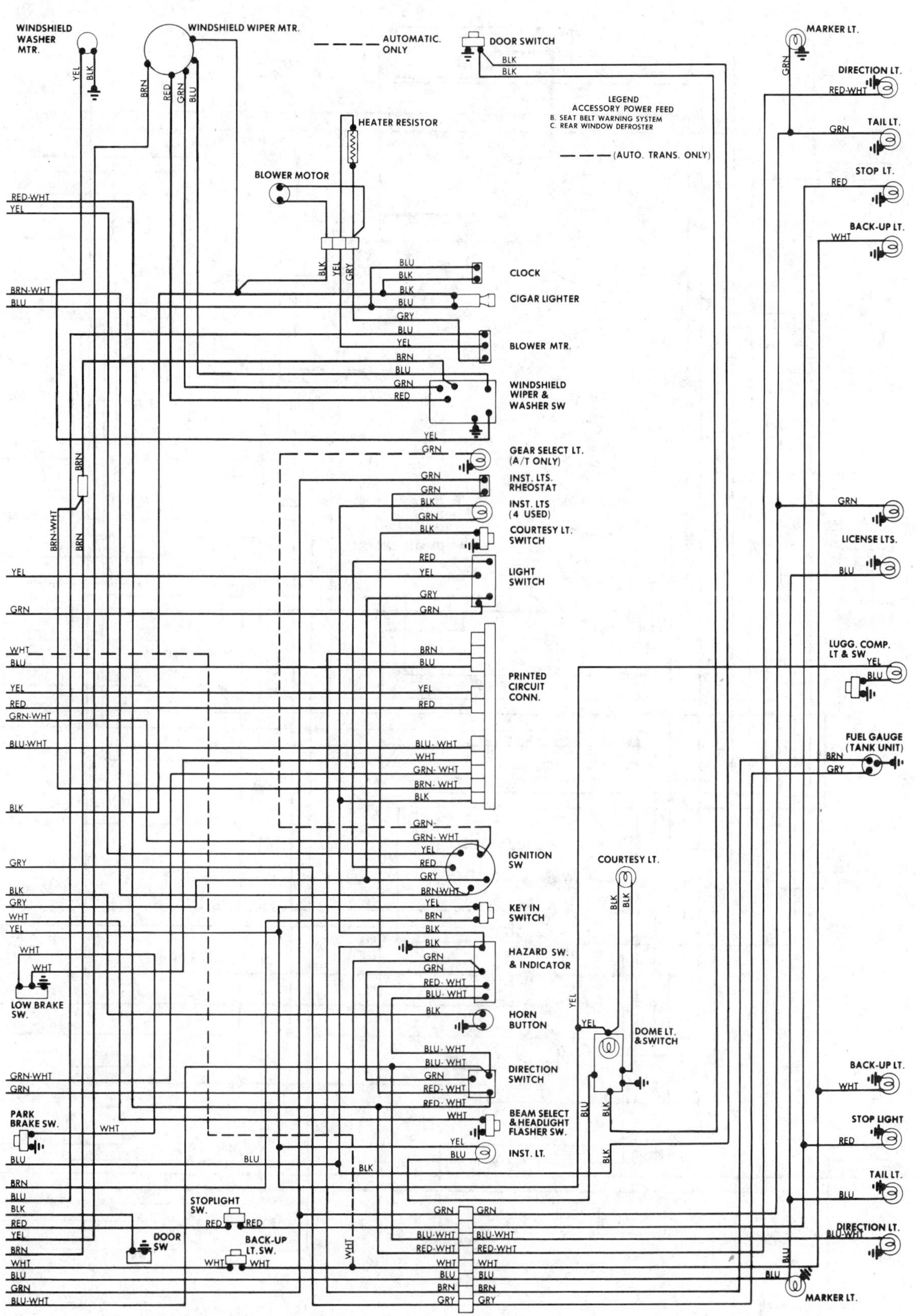
WINDSHIELD WASHER MTR.
WINDSHIELD WIPER MTR.
AUTOMATIC ONLY
DOOR SWITCH
MARKER LT.
DIRECTION LT.
LEGEND
ACCESSORY POWER FEED
B. SEAT BELT WARNING SYSTEM
C. REAR WINDOW DEFROSTER
(AUTO. TRANS. ONLY)
HEATER RESISTOR
TAIL LT.
STOP LT.
BLOWER MOTOR
BACK-UP LT.
CLOCK
CIGAR LIGHTER
BLOWER MTR.
WINDSHIELD WIPER & WASHER SW
GEAR SELECT LT. (A/T ONLY)
INST. LTS. RHEOSTAT
INST. LTS (4 USED)
COURTESY LT. SWITCH
LICENSE LTS.
LIGHT SWITCH
LUGG. COMP. LT & SW
PRINTED CIRCUIT CONN.
FUEL GAUGE (TANK UNIT)
IGNITION SW
COURTESY LT.
KEY IN SWITCH
HAZARD SW. & INDICATOR
LOW BRAKE SW.
HORN BUTTON
DOME LT. & SWITCH
DIRECTION SWITCH
BACK-UP LT.
STOP LIGHT
PARK BRAKE SW.
BEAM SELECT & HEADLIGHT FLASHER SW.
INST. LT.
TAIL LT.
STOPLIGHT SW.
DOOR SW
BACK-UP LT. SW.
DIRECTION LT.
MARKER LT.

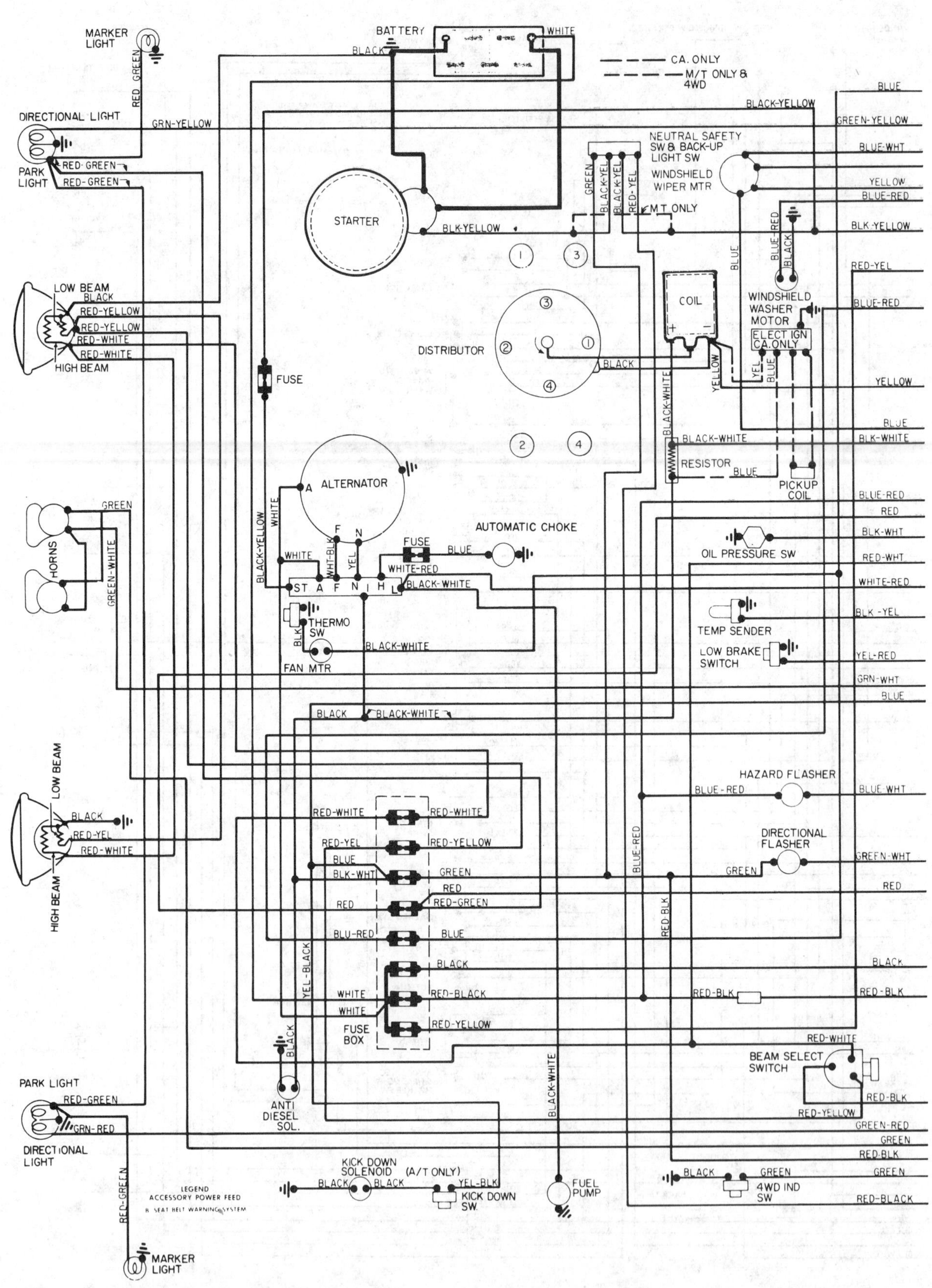

MARKER LIGHT
DIRECTIONAL LIGHT
PARK LIGHT
BATTERY
BLACK
WHITE
CA. ONLY
M/T ONLY & 4WD
GRN-YELLOW
RED-GREEN
RED GREEN
STARTER
BLK-YELLOW
NEUTRAL SAFETY SW & BACK-UP LIGHT SW
WINDSHIELD WIPER MTR
M T ONLY
GREEN
BLACK-YEL
RED-YEL
BLUE
BLACK-YELLOW
GREEN-YELLOW
BLUE-WHT
YELLOW
BLUE-RED
BLUE-RED
LOW BEAM
HIGH BEAM
RED-YELLOW
RED-WHITE
FUSE
DISTRIBUTOR
COIL
WINDSHIELD WASHER MOTOR
ELECT IGN CA. ONLY
RED-YEL
BLACK-WHITE
RESISTOR
PICKUP COIL
ALTERNATOR
AUTOMATIC CHOKE
WHITE-RED
BLACK-YELLOW
WHITE
WHT-BLK
YEL
THERMO SW
FAN MTR
OIL PRESSURE SW
TEMP SENDER
LOW BRAKE SWITCH
RED
BLK-WHT
RED-WHT
WHITE-RED
BLK-YEL
YEL-RED
GRN-WHT
HORNS
GREEN-WHITE
HAZARD FLASHER
DIRECTIONAL FLASHER
GREEN-WHT
RED-GREEN
BLU-RED
YEL-BLACK
RED-BLACK
RED-BLK
FUSE BOX
ANTI DIESEL SOL.
BEAM SELECT SWITCH
RED-WHITE
RED-YELLOW
GREEN-RED
GRN-RED
KICK DOWN SOLENOID (A/T ONLY)
YEL-BLK
KICK DOWN SW
FUEL PUMP
4WD IND SW
RED-BLACK
LEGEND
ACCESSORY POWER FEED
SEAT BELT WARNING SYSTEM

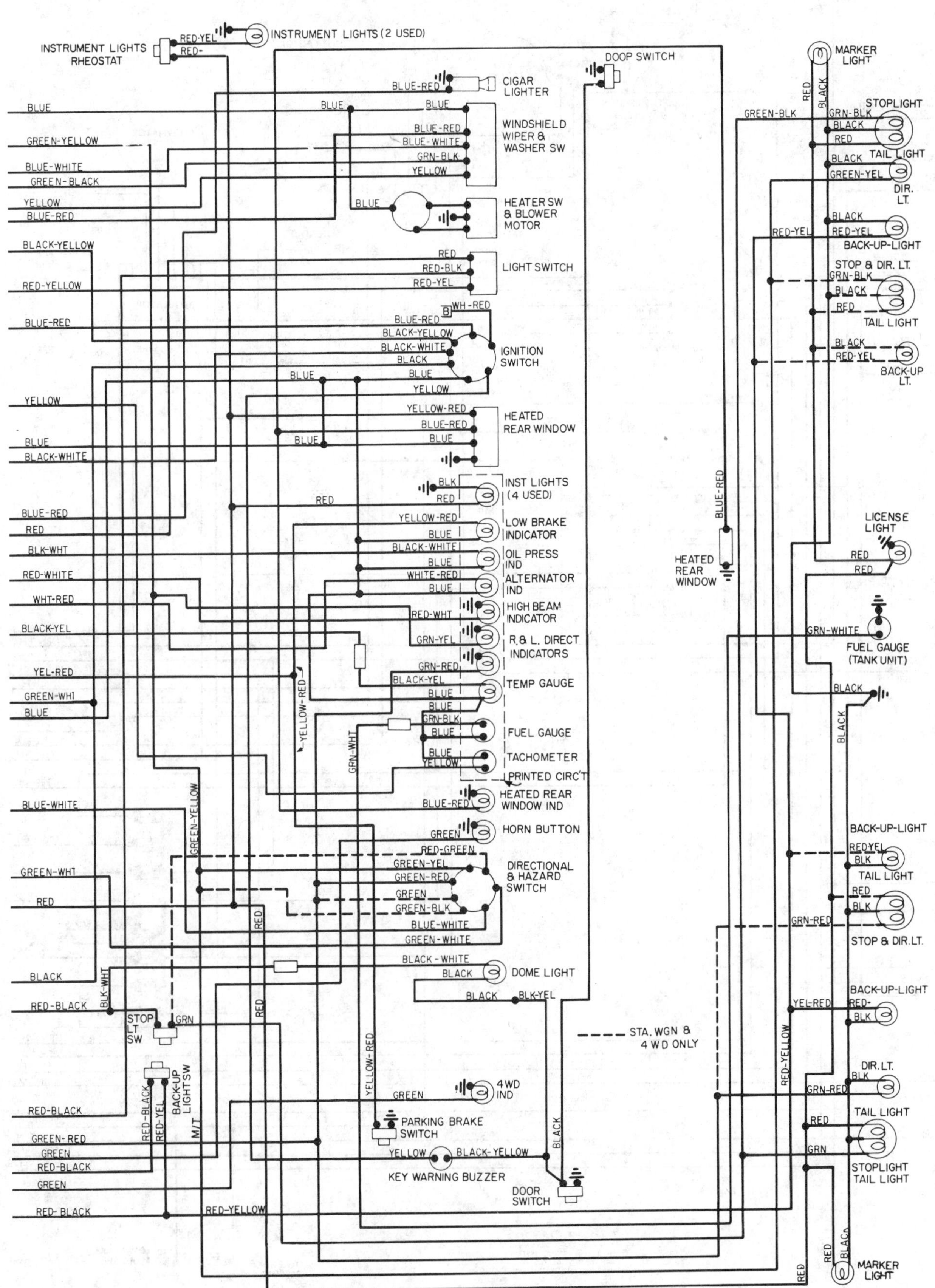
INSTRUMENT LIGHTS RHEOSTAT
INSTRUMENT LIGHTS (2 USED)
DOOP SWITCH
CIGAR LIGHTER
WINDSHIELD WIPER & WASHER SW
HEATER SW & BLOWER MOTOR
LIGHT SWITCH
IGNITION SWITCH
HEATED REAR WINDOW
INST LIGHTS (4 USED)
LOW BRAKE INDICATOR
OIL PRESS IND
ALTERNATOR IND
HIGH BEAM INDICATOR
R & L DIRECT INDICATORS
TEMP GAUGE
FUEL GAUGE
TACHOMETER
PRINTED CIRC'T
HEATED REAR WINDOW IND
HORN BUTTON
DIRECTIONAL & HAZARD SWITCH
DOME LIGHT
STOP LT SW
BACK-UP LIGHT SW
M/T
STA. WGN & 4 WD ONLY
4WD IND
PARKING BRAKE SWITCH
KEY WARNING BUZZER
DOOR SWITCH
MARKER LIGHT
STOPLIGHT
TAIL LIGHT
DIR. LT.
BACK-UP-LIGHT
STOP & DIR. LT.
TAIL LIGHT
BACK-UP LT.
HEATED REAR WINDOW
LICENSE LIGHT
FUEL GAUGE (TANK UNIT)
BACK-UP-LIGHT
TAIL LIGHT
STOP & DIR. LT.
BACK-UP-LIGHT
DIR. LT.
TAIL LIGHT
STOPLIGHT TAIL LIGHT
MARKER LIGHT
SUBARU

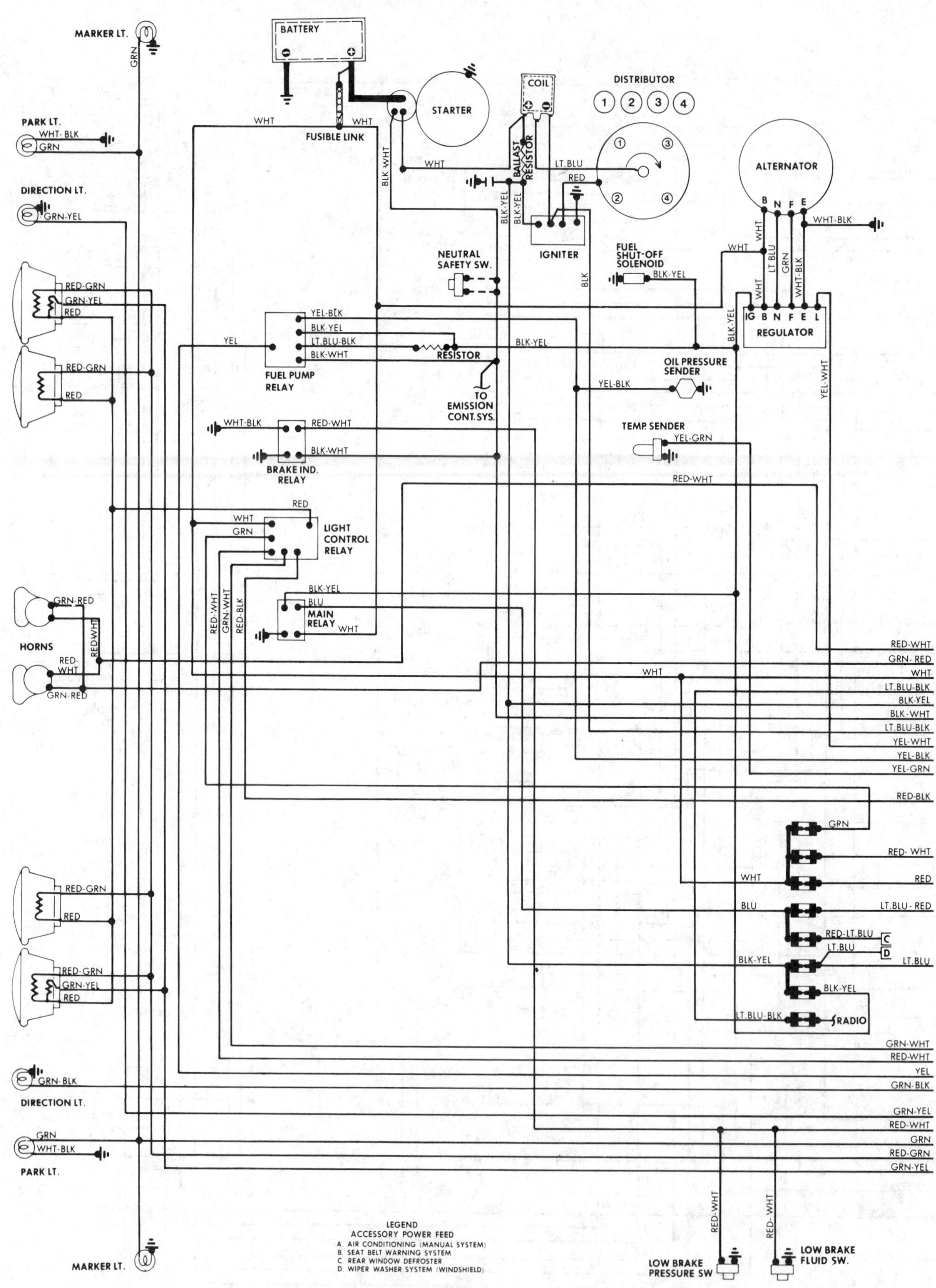
MARKER LT.
BATTERY
STARTER
COIL
DISTRIBUTOR
FUSIBLE LINK
PARK LT.
DIRECTION LT.
BALLAST RESISTOR
IGNITER
ALTERNATOR
NEUTRAL SAFETY SW.
FUEL SHUT-OFF SOLENOID
REGULATOR
FUEL PUMP RELAY
RESISTOR
TO EMISSION CONT. SYS.
OIL PRESSURE SENDER
TEMP. SENDER
BRAKE IND. RELAY
LIGHT CONTROL RELAY
MAIN RELAY
HORNS
RADIO
DIRECTION LT.
PARK LT.
MARKER LT.
LEGEND
ACCESSORY POWER FEED
A. AIR CONDITIONING (MANUAL SYSTEM)
B. SEAT BELT WARNING SYSTEM
C. REAR WINDOW DEFROSTER
D. WIPER WASHER SYSTEM (WINDSHIELD)
LOW BRAKE PRESSURE SW
LOW BRAKE FLUID SW.

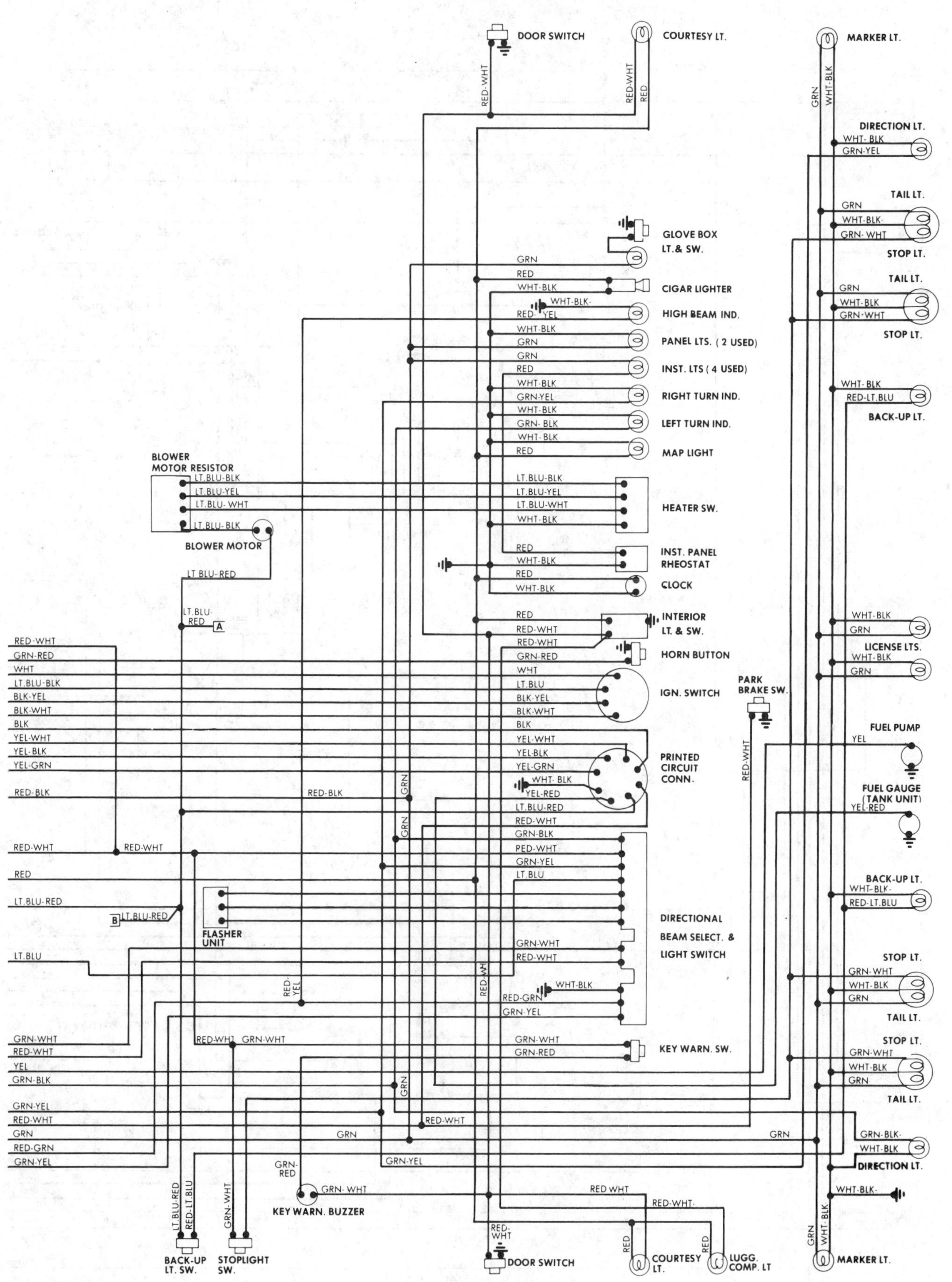
DOOR SWITCH
COURTESY LT.
MARKER LT.
DIRECTION LT.
TAIL LT.
STOP LT.
GLOVE BOX LT.& SW.
CIGAR LIGHTER
HIGH BEAM IND.
PANEL LTS. (2 USED)
INST. LTS (4 USED)
RIGHT TURN IND.
LEFT TURN IND.
MAP LIGHT
BACK-UP LT.
BLOWER MOTOR RESISTOR
HEATER SW.
BLOWER MOTOR
INST. PANEL RHEOSTAT
CLOCK
INTERIOR LT. & SW.
HORN BUTTON
LICENSE LTS.
IGN. SWITCH
PARK BRAKE SW.
FUEL PUMP
PRINTED CIRCUIT CONN.
FUEL GAUGE (TANK UNIT)
FLASHER UNIT
DIRECTIONAL BEAM SELECT. & LIGHT SWITCH
KEY WARN. SW.
KEY WARN. BUZZER
BACK-UP LT. SW.
STOPLIGHT SW.
COURTESY LT.
LUGG. COMP. LT

1977 Toyota

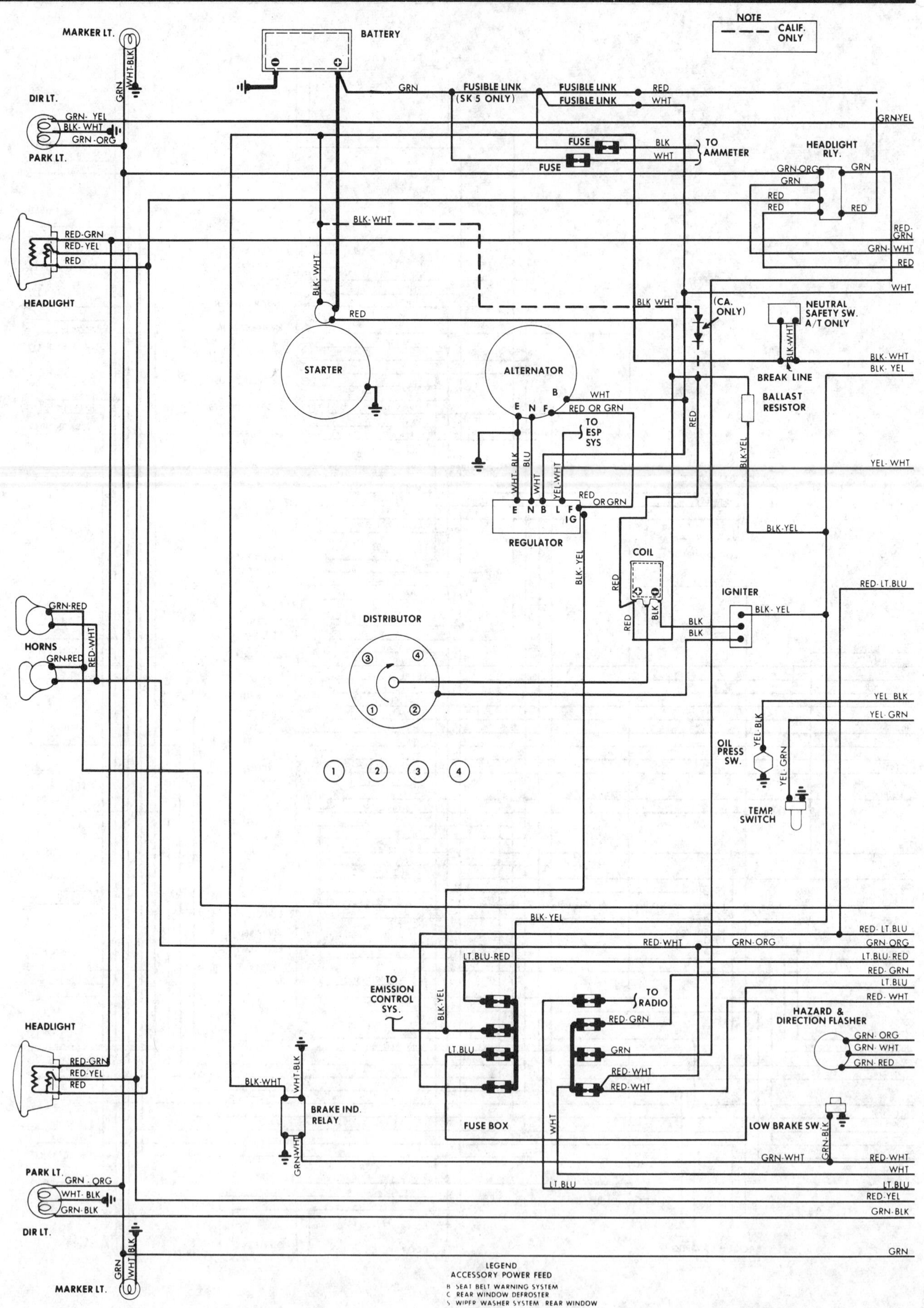
NOTE
CALIF. ONLY
MARKER LT.
BATTERY
DIR LT.
PARK LT.
FUSIBLE LINK
(SK 5 ONLY)
FUSE
TO AMMETER
HEADLIGHT RLY.
HEADLIGHT
STARTER
ALTERNATOR
(CA. ONLY)
NEUTRAL SAFETY SW. A/T ONLY
BREAK LINE
BALLAST RESISTOR
TO ESP SYS
REGULATOR
COIL
IGNITER
DISTRIBUTOR
HORNS
OIL PRESS SW.
TEMP. SWITCH
TO EMISSION CONTROL SYS.
TO RADIO
HAZARD & DIRECTION FLASHER
BRAKE IND. RELAY
FUSE BOX
LOW BRAKE SW.
LEGEND
ACCESSORY POWER FEED
B SEAT BELT WARNING SYSTEM
C REAR WINDOW DEFROSTER
S WIPER WASHER SYSTEM REAR WINDOW

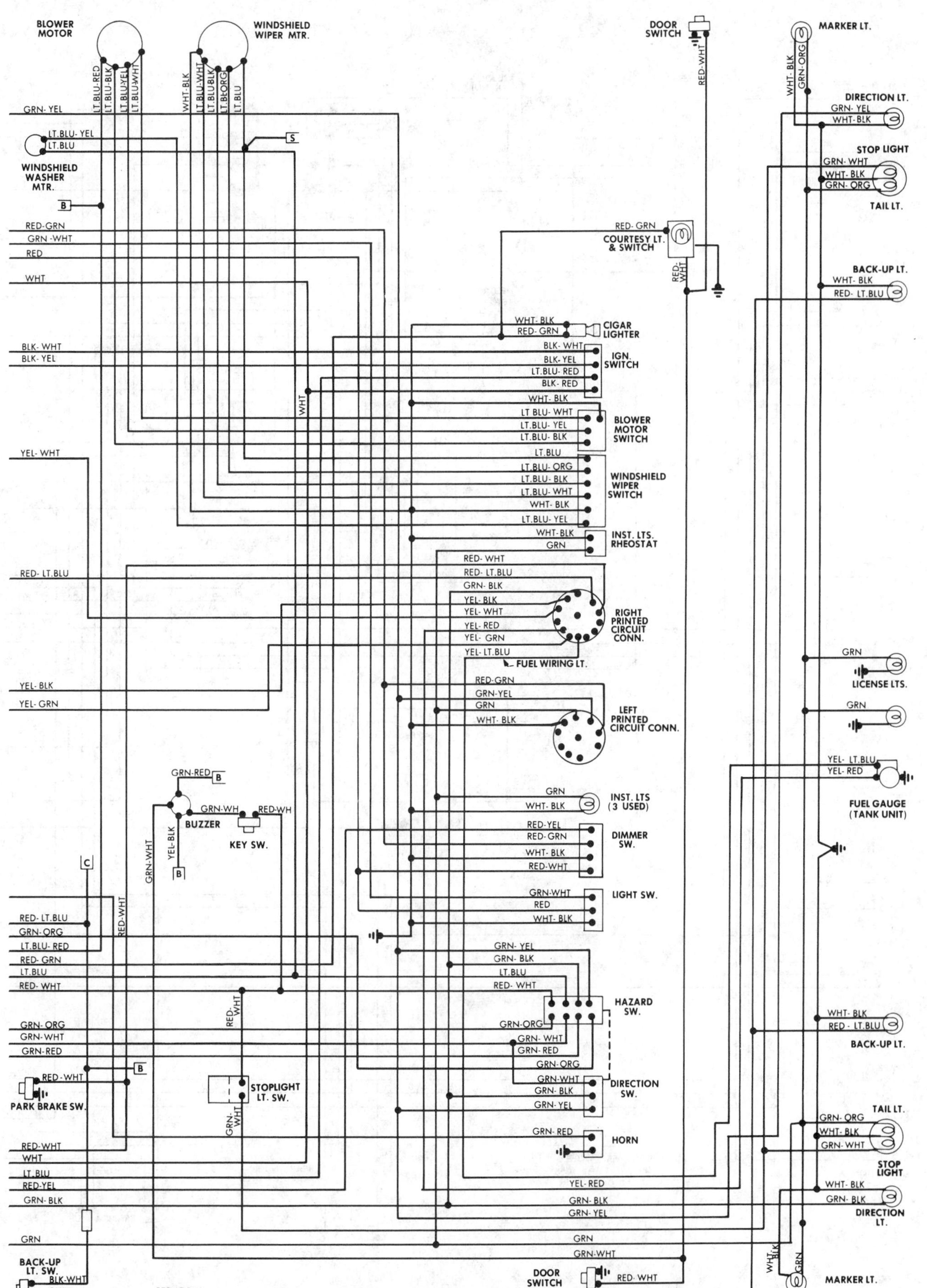
BLOWER MOTOR
WINDSHIELD WIPER MTR.
WINDSHIELD WASHER MTR.
DOOR SWITCH
MARKER LT.
DIRECTION LT.
STOP LIGHT
TAIL LT.
COURTESY LT. & SWITCH
BACK-UP LT.
CIGAR LIGHTER
IGN. SWITCH
BLOWER MOTOR SWITCH
WINDSHIELD WIPER SWITCH
INST. LTS. RHEOSTAT
RIGHT PRINTED CIRCUIT CONN.
FUEL WIRING LT.
LEFT PRINTED CIRCUIT CONN.
LICENSE LTS.
FUEL GAUGE (TANK UNIT)
INST. LTS (3 USED)
BUZZER
KEY SW.
DIMMER SW.
LIGHT SW.
HAZARD SW.
DIRECTION SW.
HORN
STOPLIGHT LT. SW.
PARK BRAKE SW.
BACK-UP LT. SW.
DOOR SWITCH
STOP LIGHT
DIRECTION LT.
MARKER LT.

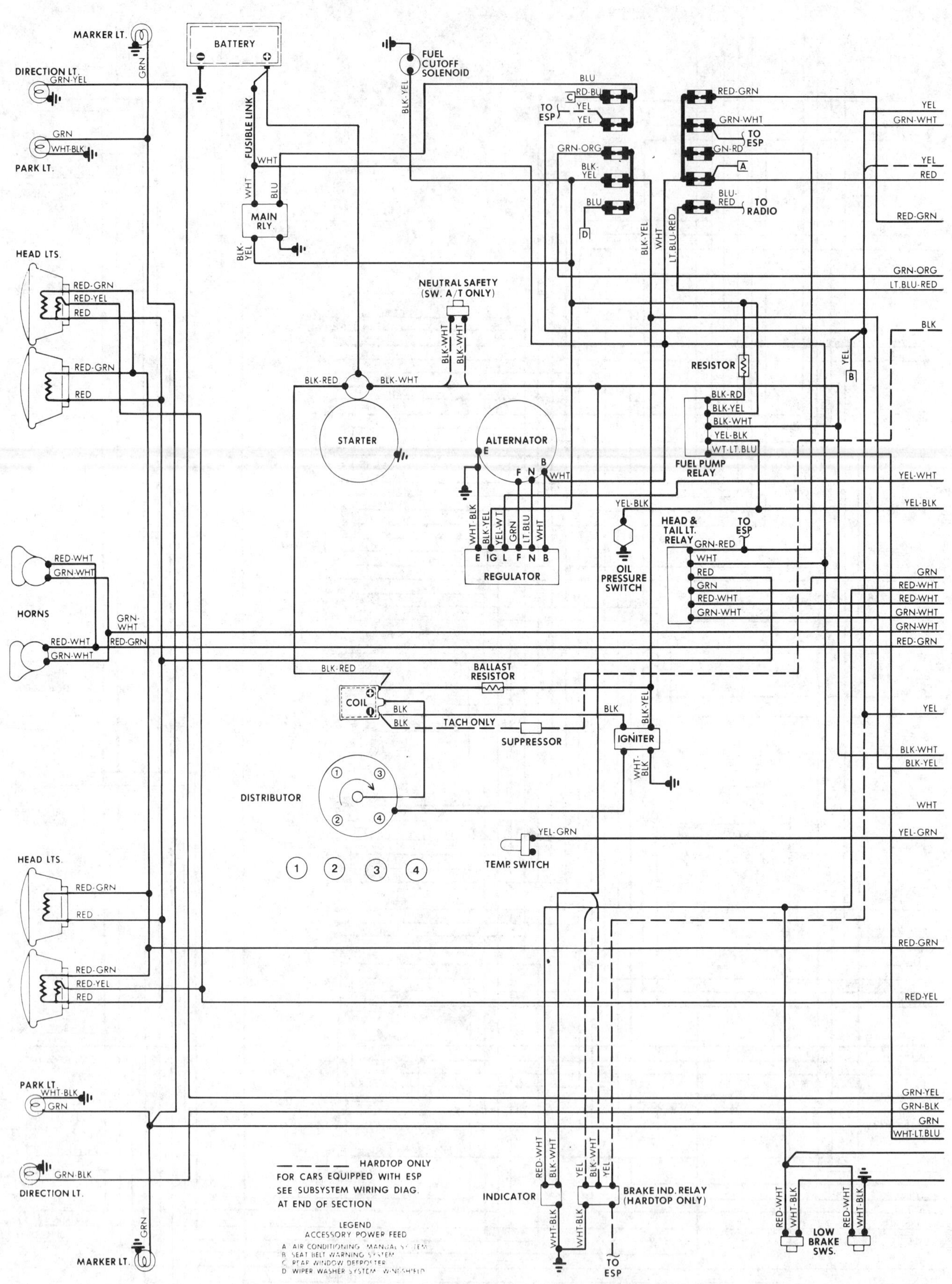
MARKER LT.
BATTERY
FUEL CUTOFF SOLENOID
DIRECTION LT.
PARK LT.
FUSIBLE LINK
MAIN RLY.
TO ESP
TO RADIO
HEAD LTS.
NEUTRAL SAFETY (SW. A/T ONLY)
RESISTOR
STARTER
ALTERNATOR
FUEL PUMP RELAY
REGULATOR
OIL PRESSURE SWITCH
HEAD & TAIL LT. RELAY
HORNS
BALLAST RESISTOR
COIL
TACH ONLY
SUPPRESSOR
IGNITER
DISTRIBUTOR
TEMP. SWITCH
HEAD LTS.
PARK LT.
DIRECTION LT.
MARKER LT.
HARDTOP ONLY
FOR CARS EQUIPPED WITH ESP SEE SUBSYSTEM WIRING DIAG. AT END OF SECTION
LEGEND
ACCESSORY POWER FEED
INDICATOR
BRAKE IND. RELAY (HARDTOP ONLY)
LOW BRAKE SWS.

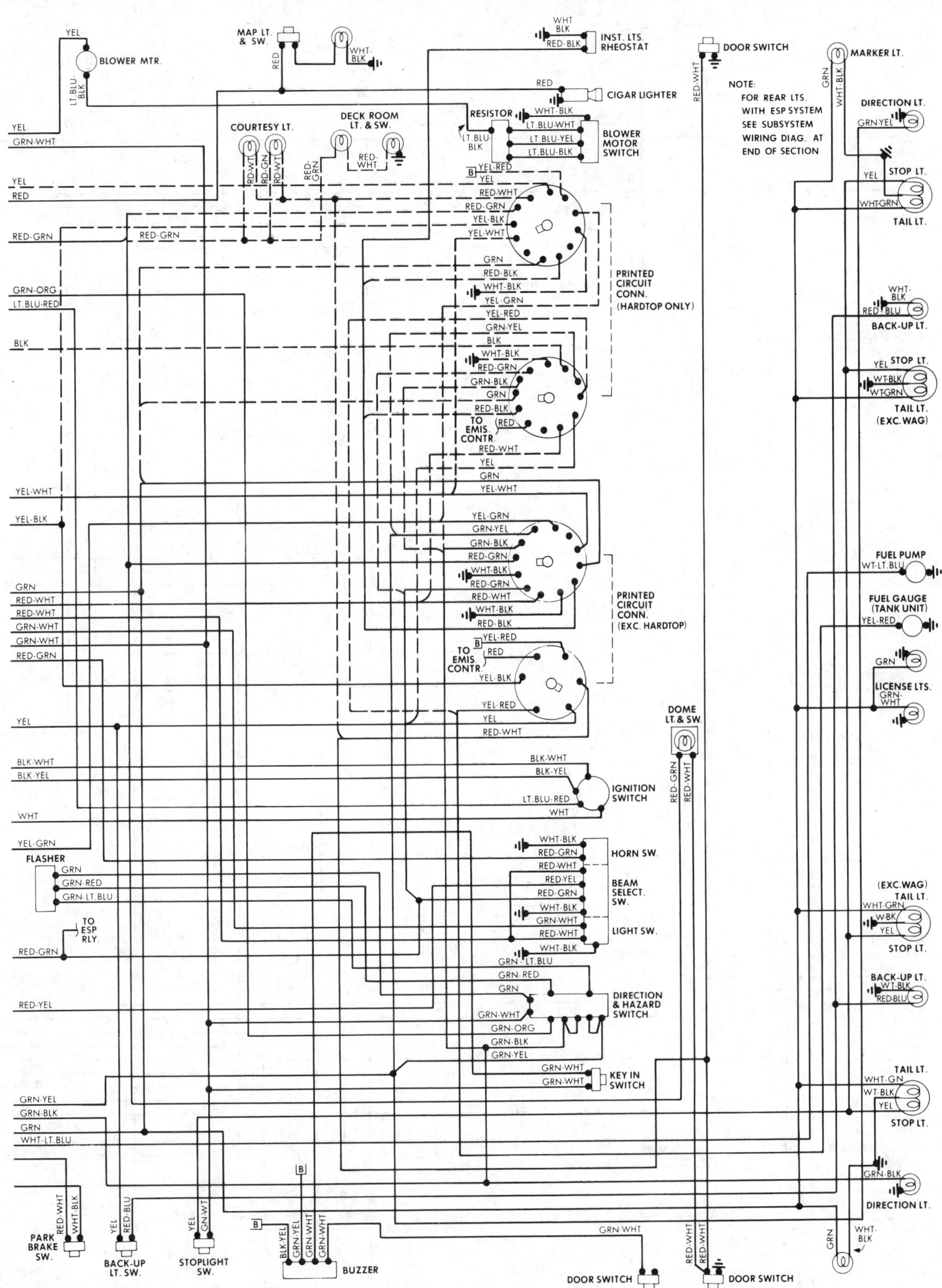

BLOWER MTR.
MAP LT. & SW.
INST. LTS. RHEOSTAT
DOOR SWITCH
MARKER LT.
CIGAR LIGHTER
NOTE: FOR REAR LTS. WITH ESP SYSTEM SEE SUBSYSTEM WIRING DIAG. AT END OF SECTION
DIRECTION LT.
RESISTOR
BLOWER MOTOR SWITCH
COURTESY LT.
DECK ROOM LT. & SW.
STOP LT.
TAIL LT.
PRINTED CIRCUIT CONN. (HARDTOP ONLY)
BACK-UP LT.
TAIL LT. (EXC. WAG)
TO EMIS. CONTR.
FUEL PUMP
FUEL GAUGE (TANK UNIT)
PRINTED CIRCUIT CONN. (EXC. HARDTOP)
LICENSE LTS.
DOME LT. & SW.
IGNITION SWITCH
FLASHER
HORN SW.
BEAM SELECT. SW.
LIGHT SW.
TO ESP RLY.
(EXC. WAG) TAIL LT.
DIRECTION & HAZARD SWITCH
KEY IN SWITCH
PARK BRAKE SW.
BACK-UP LT. SW.
STOPLIGHT SW.
BUZZER
DOOR SWITCH

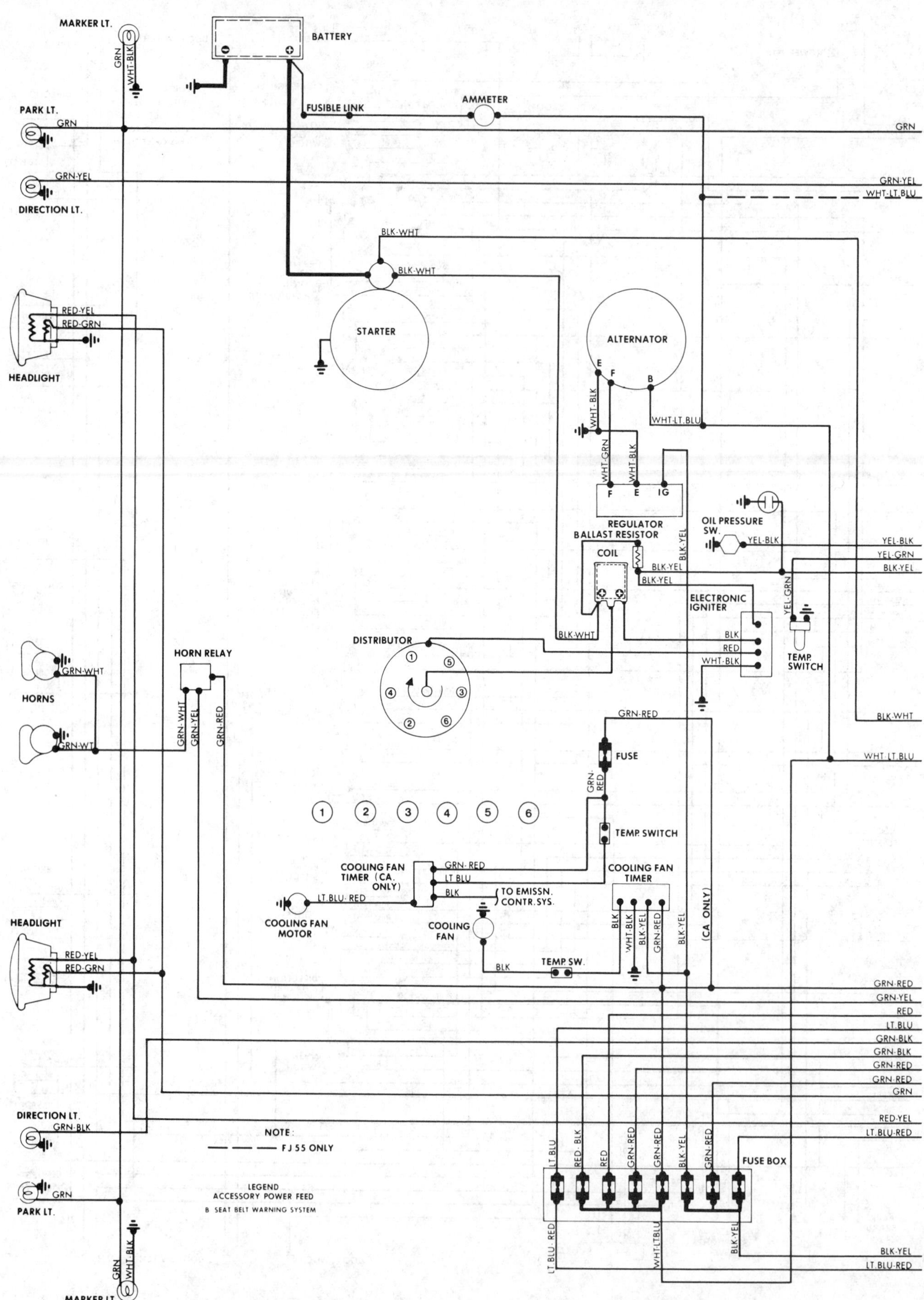
MARKER LT.
BATTERY
FUSIBLE LINK
AMMETER
PARK LT.
GRN
GRN-YEL
WHT-LT.BLU
DIRECTION LT.
BLK-WHT
STARTER
ALTERNATOR
E
F
B
HEADLIGHT
RED-YEL
RED-GRN
WHT-BLK
WHT-GRN
REGULATOR
BALLAST RESISTOR
COIL
OIL PRESSURE SW.
YEL-BLK
YEL-GRN
BLK-YEL
ELECTRONIC IGNITER
DISTRIBUTOR
HORN RELAY
HORNS
GRN-WHT
GRN-RED
BLK
RED
WHT-BLK
TEMP. SWITCH
FUSE
COOLING FAN TIMER (CA. ONLY)
LT BLU
LT.BLU-RED
TO EMISSN. CONTR. SYS.
COOLING FAN MOTOR
COOLING FAN
TEMP. SW.
COOLING FAN TIMER
(CA ONLY)
GRN-BLK
LT.BLU
RED-BLK
WHT-LT.BLU
FUSE BOX
NOTE:
— — — FJ 55 ONLY
LEGEND
ACCESSORY POWER FEED
B SEAT BELT WARNING SYSTEM

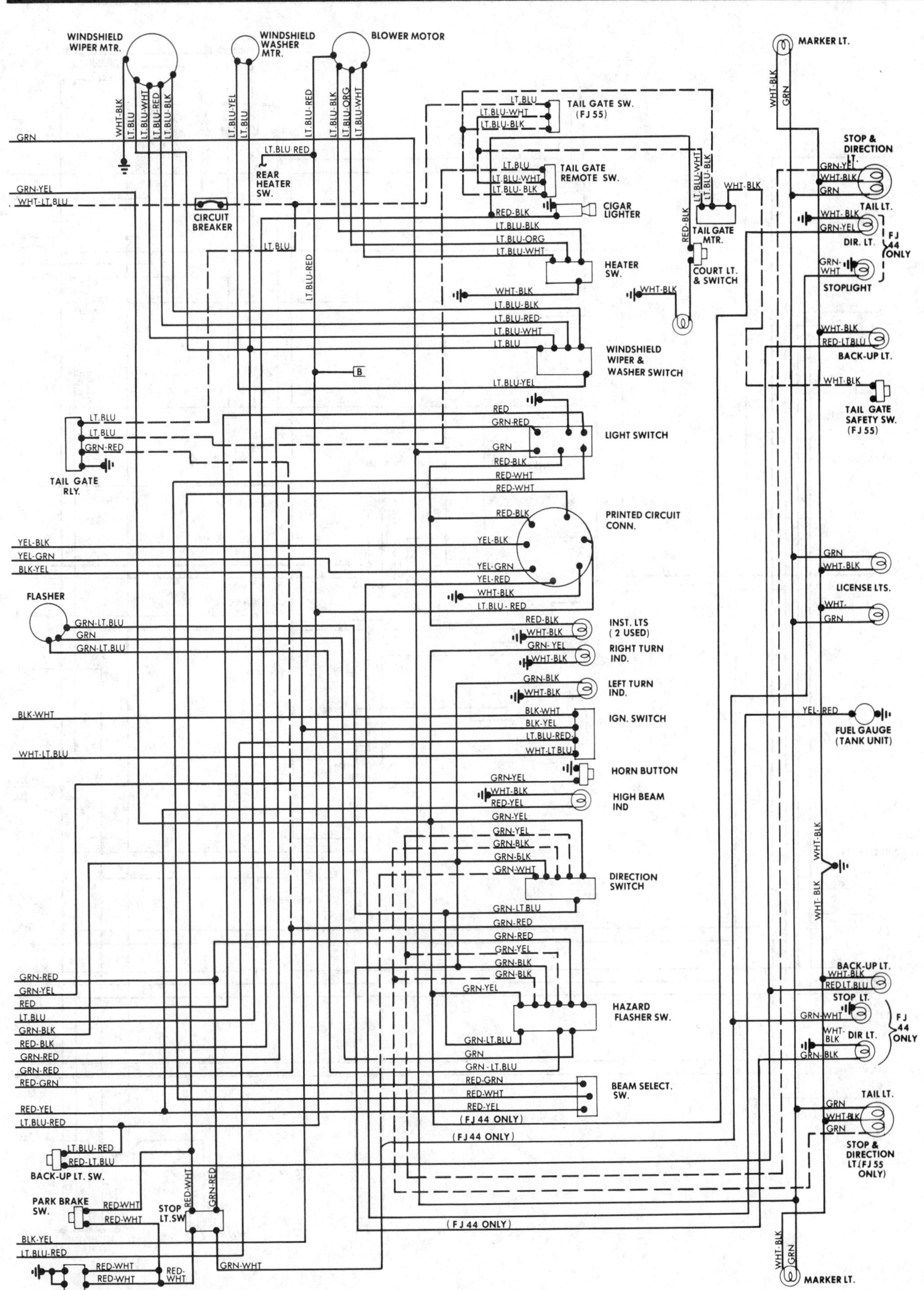
WINDSHIELD WIPER MTR.
WINDSHIELD WASHER MTR.
BLOWER MOTOR
MARKER LT.
TAIL GATE SW. (FJ 55)
TAIL GATE REMOTE SW.
REAR HEATER SW.
CIRCUIT BREAKER
CIGAR LIGHTER
TAIL GATE MTR.
COURT LT. & SWITCH
HEATER SW.
STOP & DIRECTION LT.
TAIL LT.
DIR. LT.
FJ 44 ONLY
STOPLIGHT
BACK-UP LT.
WINDSHIELD WIPER & WASHER SWITCH
TAIL GATE SAFETY SW. (FJ 55)
LIGHT SWITCH
TAIL GATE RLY.
PRINTED CIRCUIT CONN.
LICENSE LTS.
FLASHER
INST. LTS (2 USED)
RIGHT TURN IND.
LEFT TURN IND.
IGN. SWITCH
FUEL GAUGE (TANK UNIT)
HORN BUTTON
HIGH BEAM IND
DIRECTION SWITCH
HAZARD FLASHER SW.
BEAM SELECT. SW.
(FJ 44 ONLY)
STOP & DIRECTION LT. (FJ 55 ONLY)
BACK-UP LT. SW.
PARK BRAKE SW.
STOP LT. SW
LOW BRAKE SW.

1977 Toyota

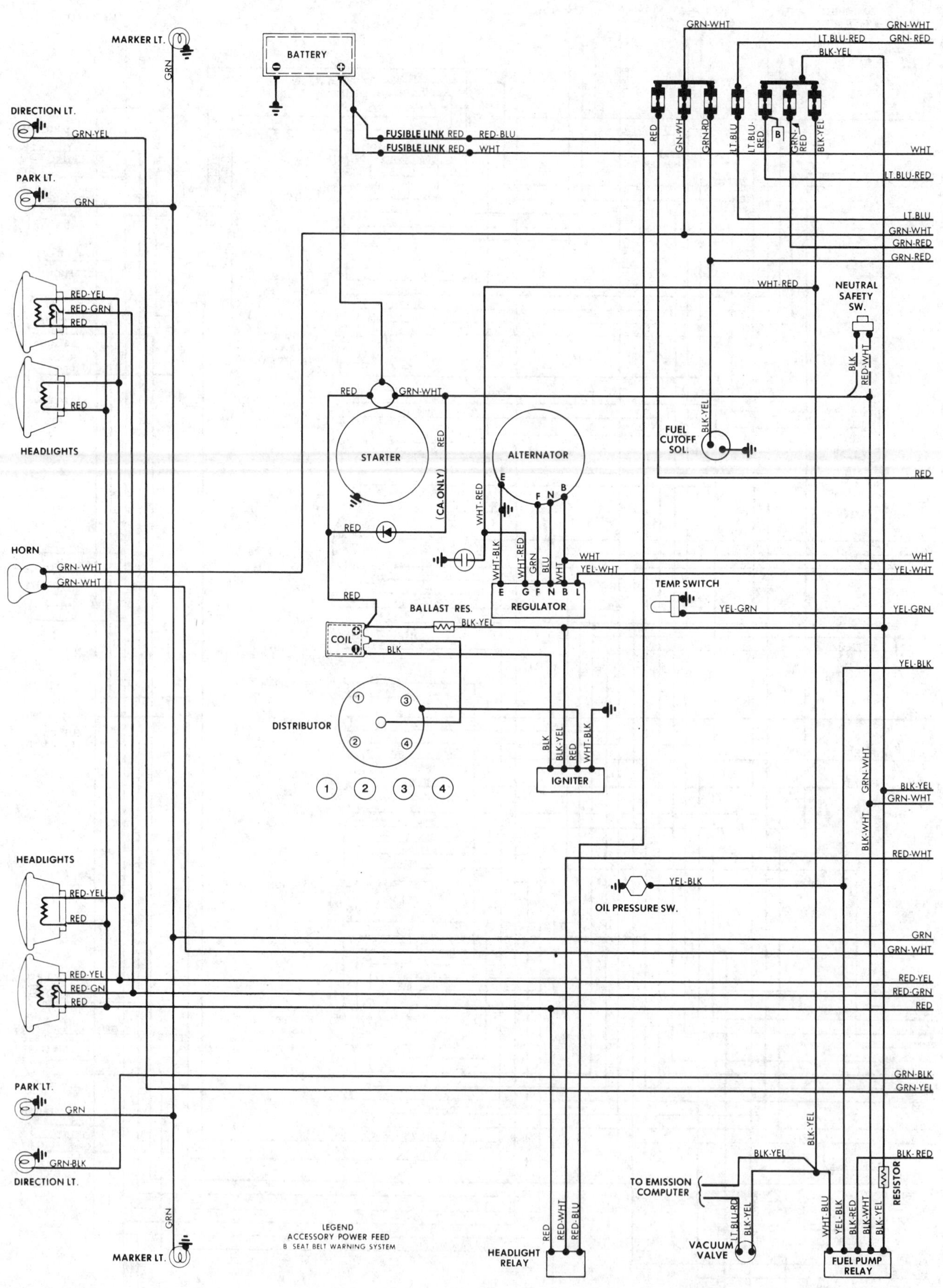
MARKER LT.
BATTERY
DIRECTION LT.
FUSIBLE LINK
PARK LT.
HEADLIGHTS
NEUTRAL SAFETY SW.
STARTER
ALTERNATOR
FUEL CUTOFF SOL.
(CA. ONLY)
HORN
REGULATOR
TEMP. SWITCH
BALLAST RES.
COIL
DISTRIBUTOR
IGNITER
HEADLIGHTS
OIL PRESSURE SW.
PARK LT.
DIRECTION LT.
TO EMISSION COMPUTER
RESISTOR
LEGEND
ACCESSORY POWER FEED
B SEAT BELT WARNING SYSTEM
HEADLIGHT RELAY
VACUUM VALVE
FUEL PUMP RELAY

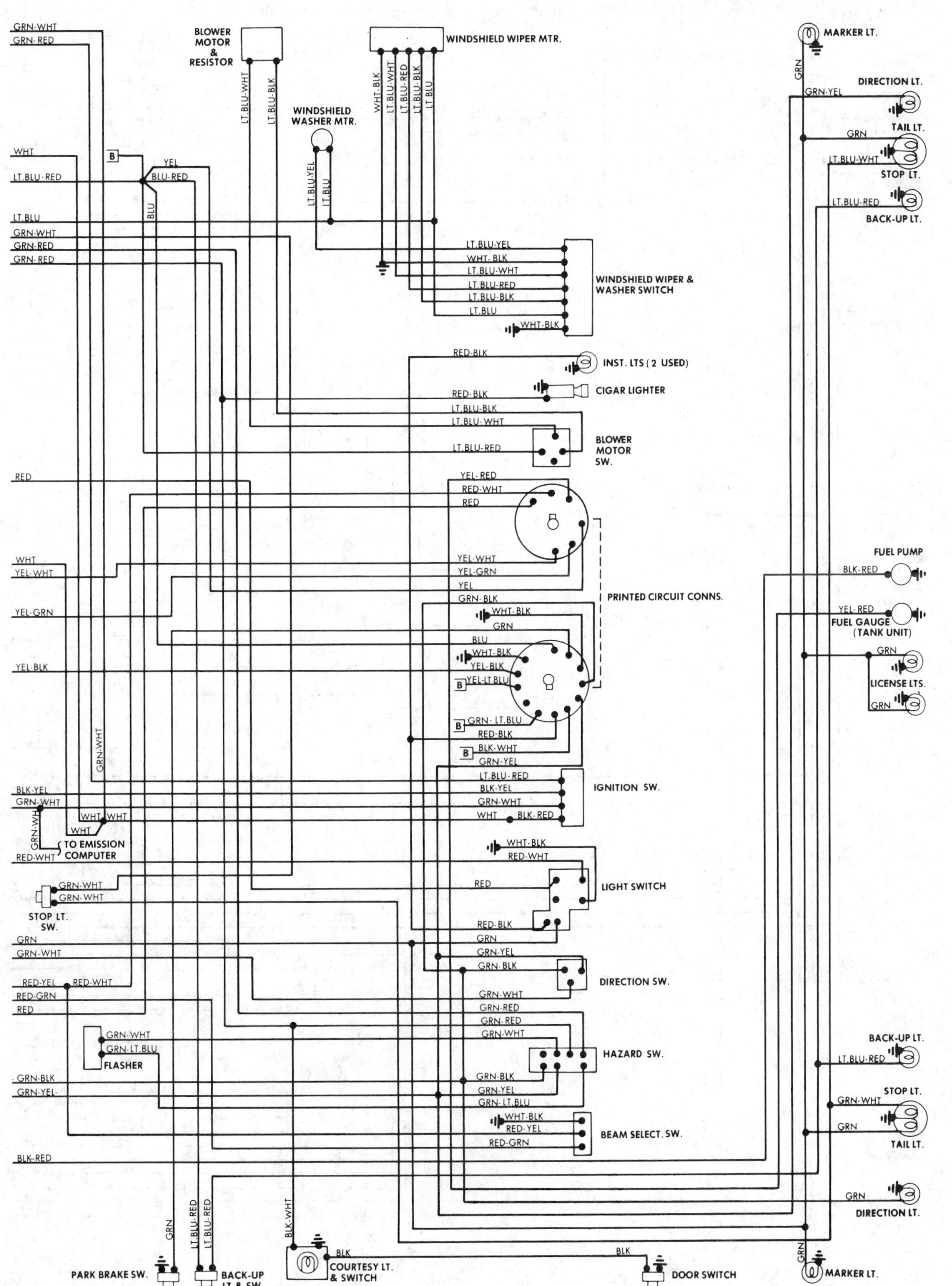
BLOWER MOTOR & RESISTOR
WINDSHIELD WIPER MTR.
WINDSHIELD WASHER MTR.
MARKER LT.
DIRECTION LT.
TAIL LT.
STOP LT.
BACK-UP LT.
WINDSHIELD WIPER & WASHER SWITCH
INST. LTS (2 USED)
CIGAR LIGHTER
BLOWER MOTOR SW.
PRINTED CIRCUIT CONNS.
FUEL PUMP
FUEL GAUGE (TANK UNIT)
LICENSE LTS.
IGNITION SW.
TO EMISSION COMPUTER
LIGHT SWITCH
STOP LT. SW.
DIRECTION SW.
HAZARD SW.
FLASHER
BEAM SELECT. SW.
PARK BRAKE SW.
BACK-UP LT. & SW.
COURTESY LT. & SWITCH
DOOR SWITCH

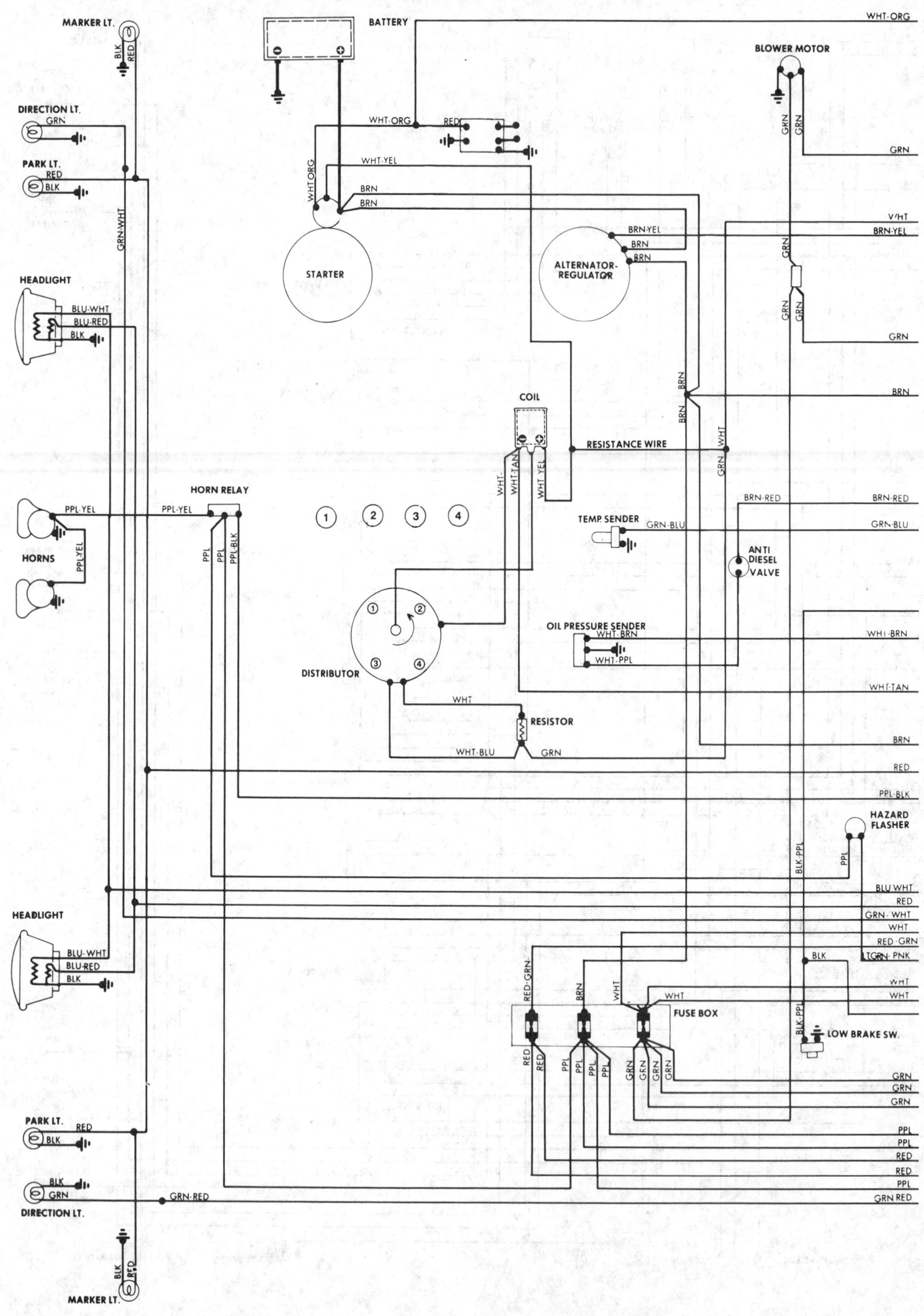
MARKER LT.
BATTERY
BLOWER MOTOR
DIRECTION LT.
PARK LT.
STARTER
ALTERNATOR-REGULATOR
HEADLIGHT
COIL
RESISTANCE WIRE
HORN RELAY
TEMP. SENDER
ANTI DIESEL VALVE
HORNS
OIL PRESSURE SENDER
DISTRIBUTOR
RESISTOR
HAZARD FLASHER
HEADLIGHT
FUSE BOX
LOW BRAKE SW.
PARK LT.
DIRECTION LT.
MARKER LT.

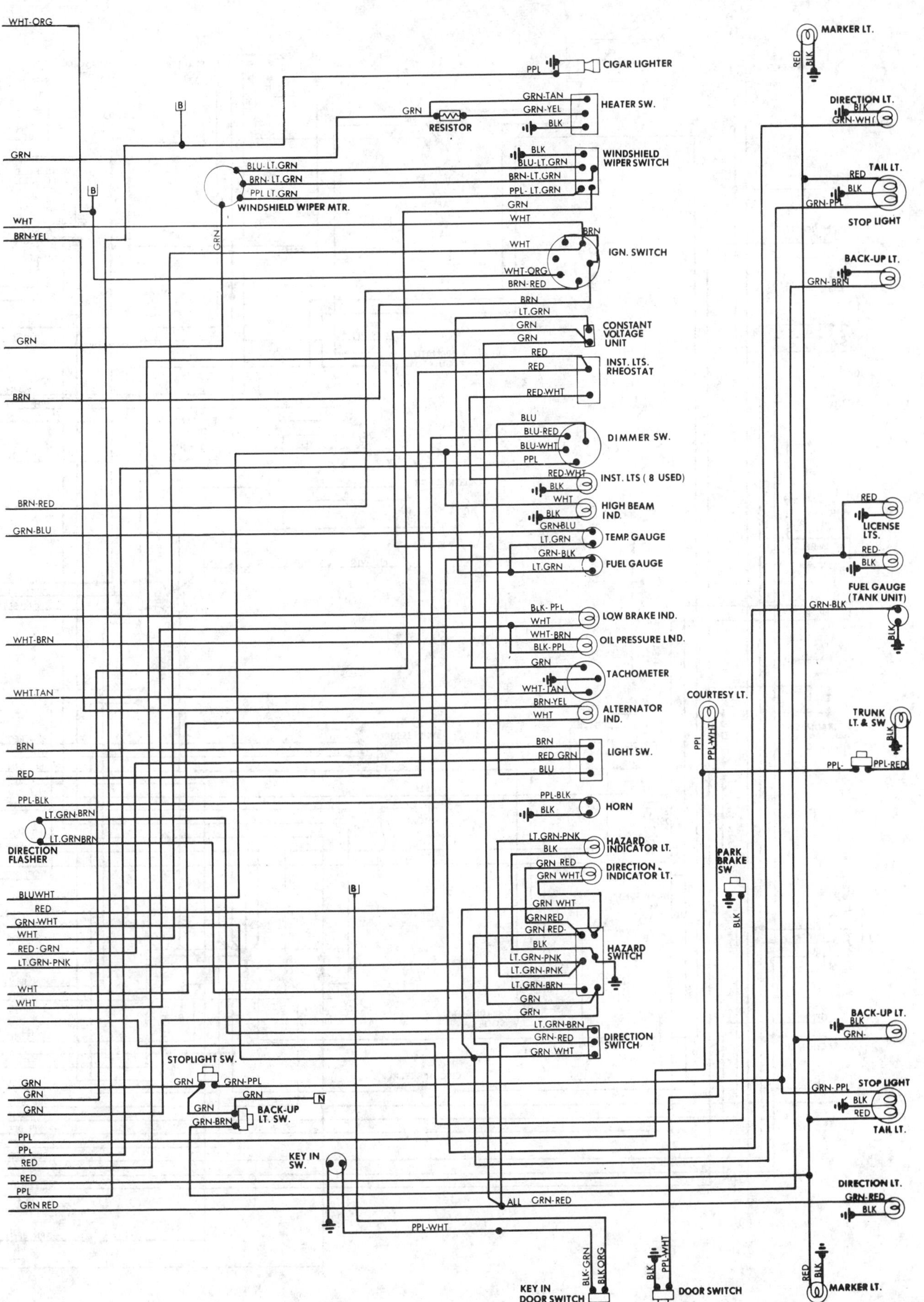

CIGAR LIGHTER
HEATER SW.
RESISTOR
WINDSHIELD WIPER SWITCH
WINDSHIELD WIPER MTR.
IGN. SWITCH
CONSTANT VOLTAGE UNIT
INST. LTS. RHEOSTAT
DIMMER SW.
INST. LTS (8 USED)
HIGH BEAM IND.
TEMP. GAUGE
FUEL GAUGE
LOW BRAKE IND.
OIL PRESSURE IND.
TACHOMETER
ALTERNATOR IND.
LIGHT SW.
HORN
HAZARD INDICATOR LT.
DIRECTION INDICATOR LT.
HAZARD SWITCH
DIRECTION SWITCH
DIRECTION FLASHER
STOPLIGHT SW.
BACK-UP LT. SW.
KEY IN SW.
KEY IN DOOR SWITCH
DOOR SWITCH
COURTESY LT.
PARK BRAKE SW
MARKER LT.
DIRECTION LT.
TAIL LT.
STOP LIGHT
BACK-UP LT.
LICENSE LTS.
FUEL GAUGE (TANK UNIT)
TRUNK LT. & SW

1977 Triumph

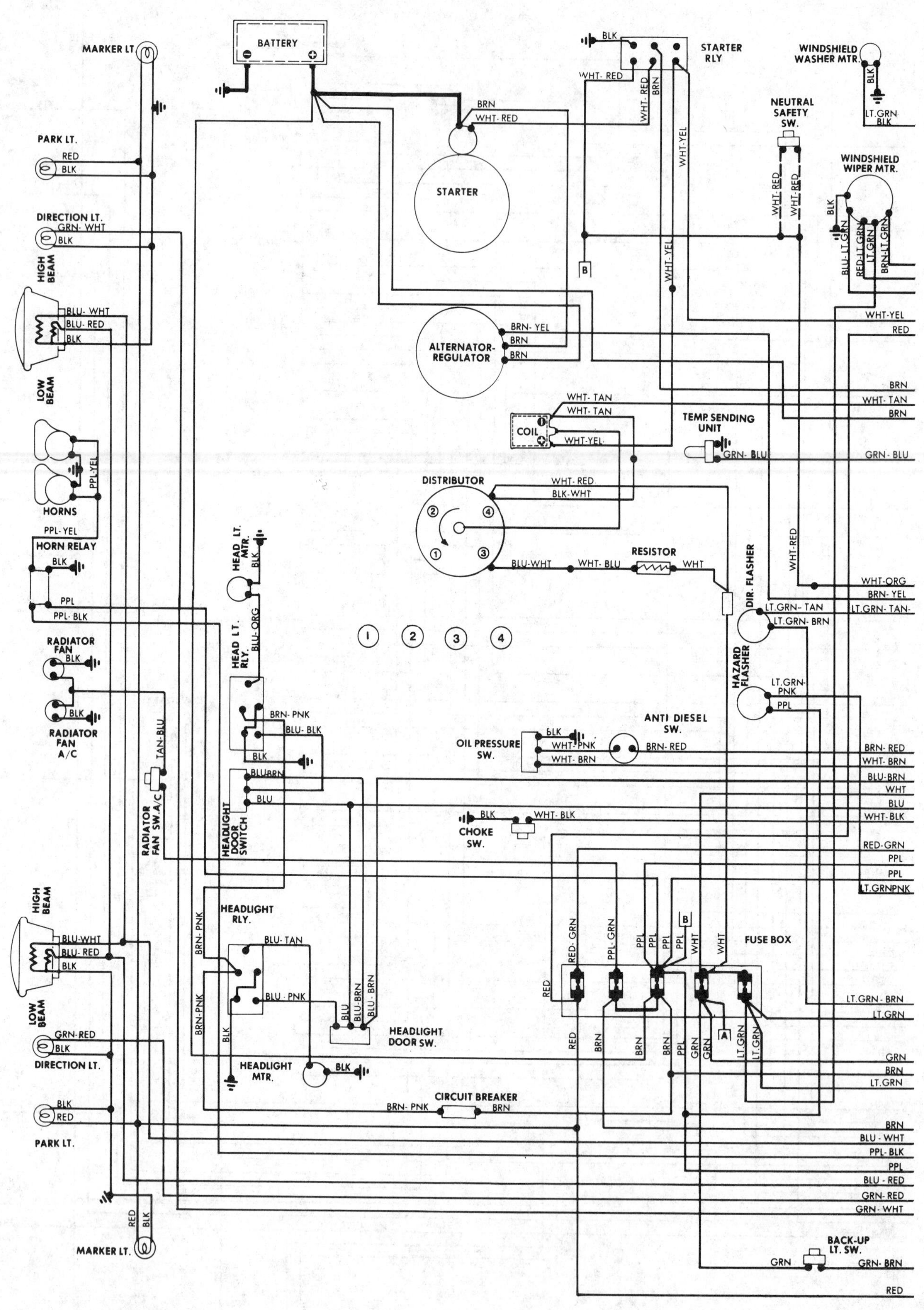

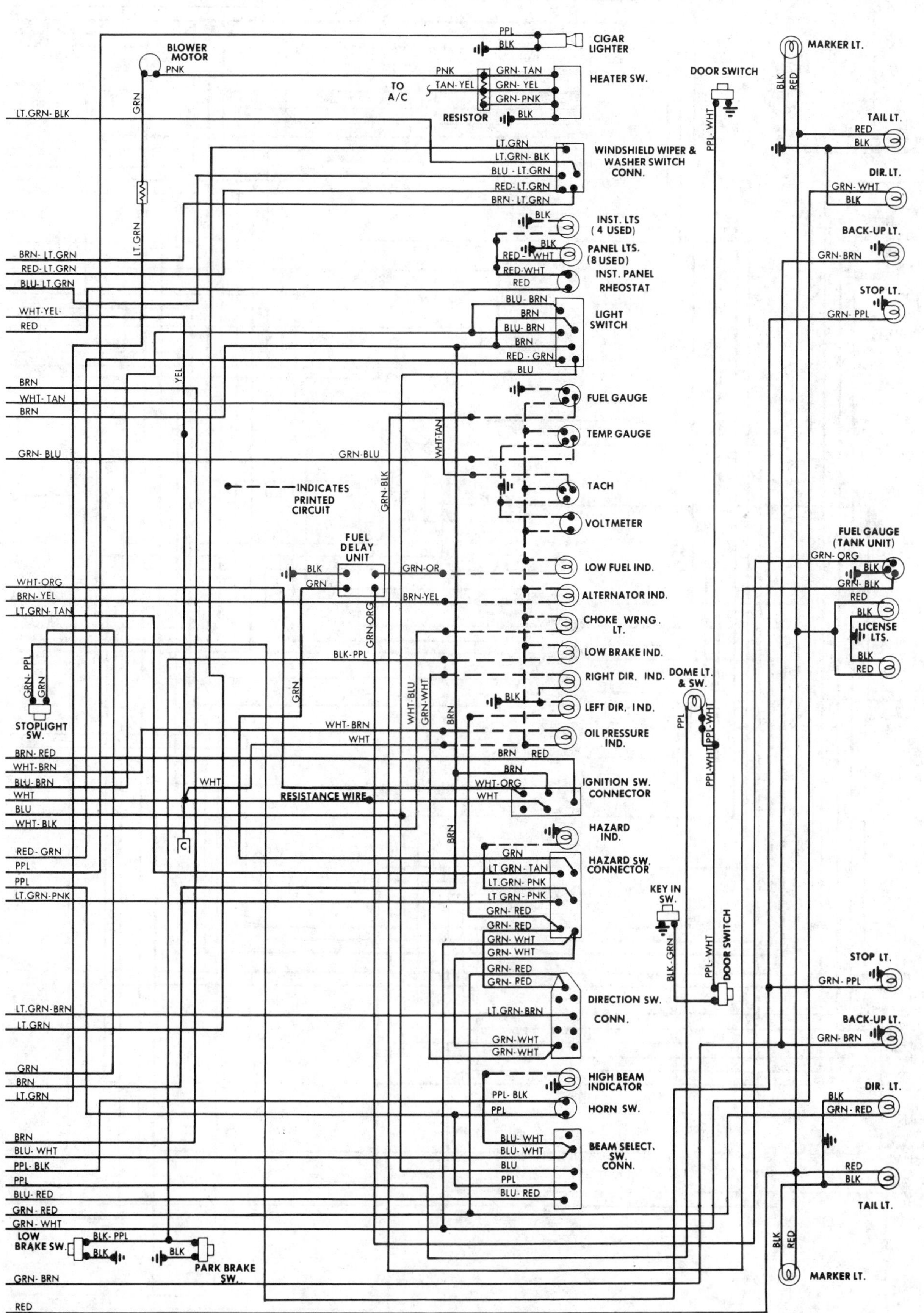
BLOWER MOTOR
CIGAR LIGHTER
HEATER SW.
TO A/C
RESISTOR
WINDSHIELD WIPER & WASHER SWITCH CONN.
INST. LTS (4 USED)
PANEL LTS. (8 USED)
INST. PANEL RHEOSTAT
LIGHT SWITCH
FUEL GAUGE
TEMP. GAUGE
TACH
VOLTMETER
INDICATES PRINTED CIRCUIT
FUEL DELAY UNIT
LOW FUEL IND.
ALTERNATOR IND.
CHOKE WRNG. LT.
LOW BRAKE IND.
RIGHT DIR. IND.
LEFT DIR. IND.
OIL PRESSURE IND.
STOPLIGHT SW.
RESISTANCE WIRE
IGNITION SW. CONNECTOR
HAZARD IND.
HAZARD SW. CONNECTOR
DIRECTION SW. CONN.
HIGH BEAM INDICATOR
HORN SW.
BEAM SELECT. SW. CONN.
LOW BRAKE SW.
PARK BRAKE SW.
DOOR SWITCH
DOME LT. & SW.
KEY IN SW.
MARKER LT.
TAIL LT.
DIR. LT.
BACK-UP LT.
STOP LT.
FUEL GAUGE (TANK UNIT)
LICENSE LTS.

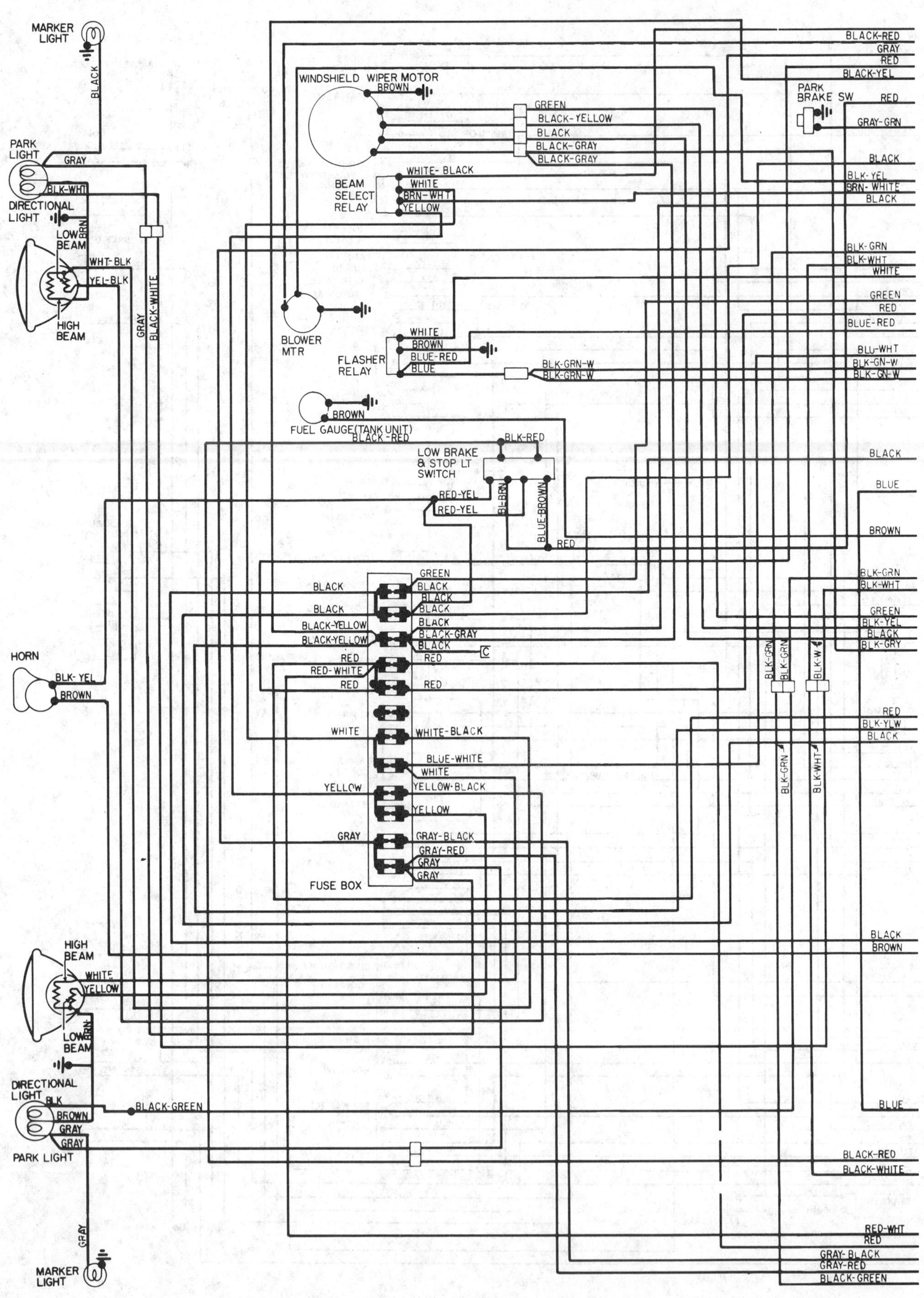
MARKER LIGHT
BLACK
PARK LIGHT
GRAY
BLK-WHT
DIRECTIONAL LIGHT
LOW BEAM
BRN
WHT-BLK
YEL-BLK
HIGH BEAM
GRAY
BLACK-WHITE
WINDSHIELD WIPER MOTOR
BROWN
GREEN
BLACK-YELLOW
BLACK
BLACK-GRAY
BLACK-GRAY
WHITE-BLACK
WHITE
BRN-WHT
YELLOW
BEAM SELECT RELAY
BLOWER MTR
WHITE
BROWN
BLUE-RED
BLUE
FLASHER RELAY
BLK-GRN-W
BLK-GRN-W
BROWN
FUEL GAUGE (TANK UNIT)
BLACK-RED
BLK-RED
LOW BRAKE & STOP LT SWITCH
RED-YEL
RED-YEL
BL-BRN
BLUE-BROWN
RED
GREEN
BLACK
BLACK
BLACK
BLACK
BLACK-YELLOW
BLACK
BLACK-YELLOW
BLACK-GRAY
BLACK
C
RED
RED
RED-WHITE
RED
RED
WHITE
WHITE-BLACK
BLUE-WHITE
WHITE
YELLOW
YELLOW-BLACK
YELLOW
GRAY
GRAY-BLACK
GRAY-RED
GRAY
GRAY
FUSE BOX
HORN
BLK-YEL
BROWN
HIGH BEAM
WHITE
YELLOW
LOW BEAM
BRN
DIRECTIONAL LIGHT
BLK
BROWN
GRAY
GRAY
BLACK-GREEN
PARK LIGHT
GRAY
MARKER LIGHT
BLACK-RED
GRAY
RED
BLACK-YEL
PARK BRAKE SW
RED
GRAY-GRN
BLACK
BLK-YEL
BRN-WHITE
BLACK
BLK-GRN
BLK-WHT
WHITE
GREEN
RED
BLUE-RED
BLU-WHT
BLK-GN-W
BLK-GN-W
BLACK
BLUE
BROWN
BLK-GRN
BLK-WHT
GREEN
BLK-YEL
BLACK
BLK-GRY
BLK-GRN
BLK-GRN
BLK-W
RED
BLK-YLW
BLACK
BLK-GRN
BLK-WHT
BLACK
BROWN
BLUE
BLACK-RED
BLACK-WHITE
RED-WHT
RED
GRAY-BLACK
GRAY-RED
BLACK-GREEN

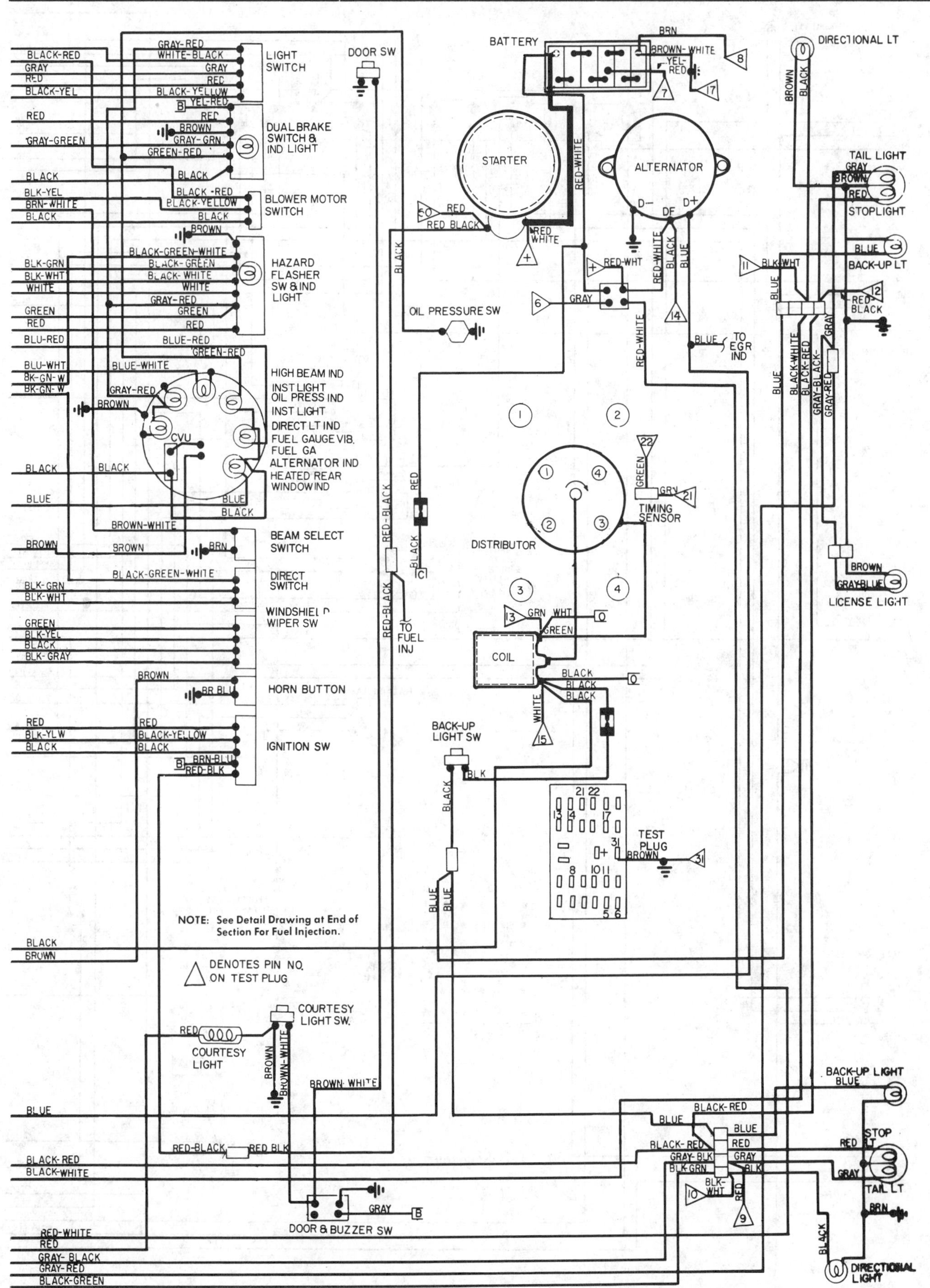

LIGHT SWITCH
DOOR SW
BATTERY
DIRECTIONAL LT
DUAL BRAKE SWITCH & IND LIGHT
STARTER
ALTERNATOR
TAIL LIGHT
STOPLIGHT
BLOWER MOTOR SWITCH
BACK-UP LT
HAZARD FLASHER SW & IND LIGHT
OIL PRESSURE SW
TO EGR IND
HIGH BEAM IND
INST LIGHT
OIL PRESS IND
INST LIGHT
DIRECT LT IND
FUEL GAUGE VIB.
FUEL GA
ALTERNATOR IND
HEATED REAR WINDOW IND
CVU
TIMING SENSOR
DISTRIBUTOR
BEAM SELECT SWITCH
DIRECT SWITCH
LICENSE LIGHT
WINDSHIELD WIPER SW
TO FUEL INJ
COIL
HORN BUTTON
IGNITION SW
BACK-UP LIGHT SW
TEST PLUG
NOTE: See Detail Drawing at End of Section For Fuel Injection.
DENOTES PIN NO. ON TEST PLUG
COURTESY LIGHT SW.
COURTESY LIGHT
BACK-UP LIGHT
STOP LT
TAIL LT
DOOR & BUZZER SW
DIRECTIONAL LIGHT

1977 Volkswagen

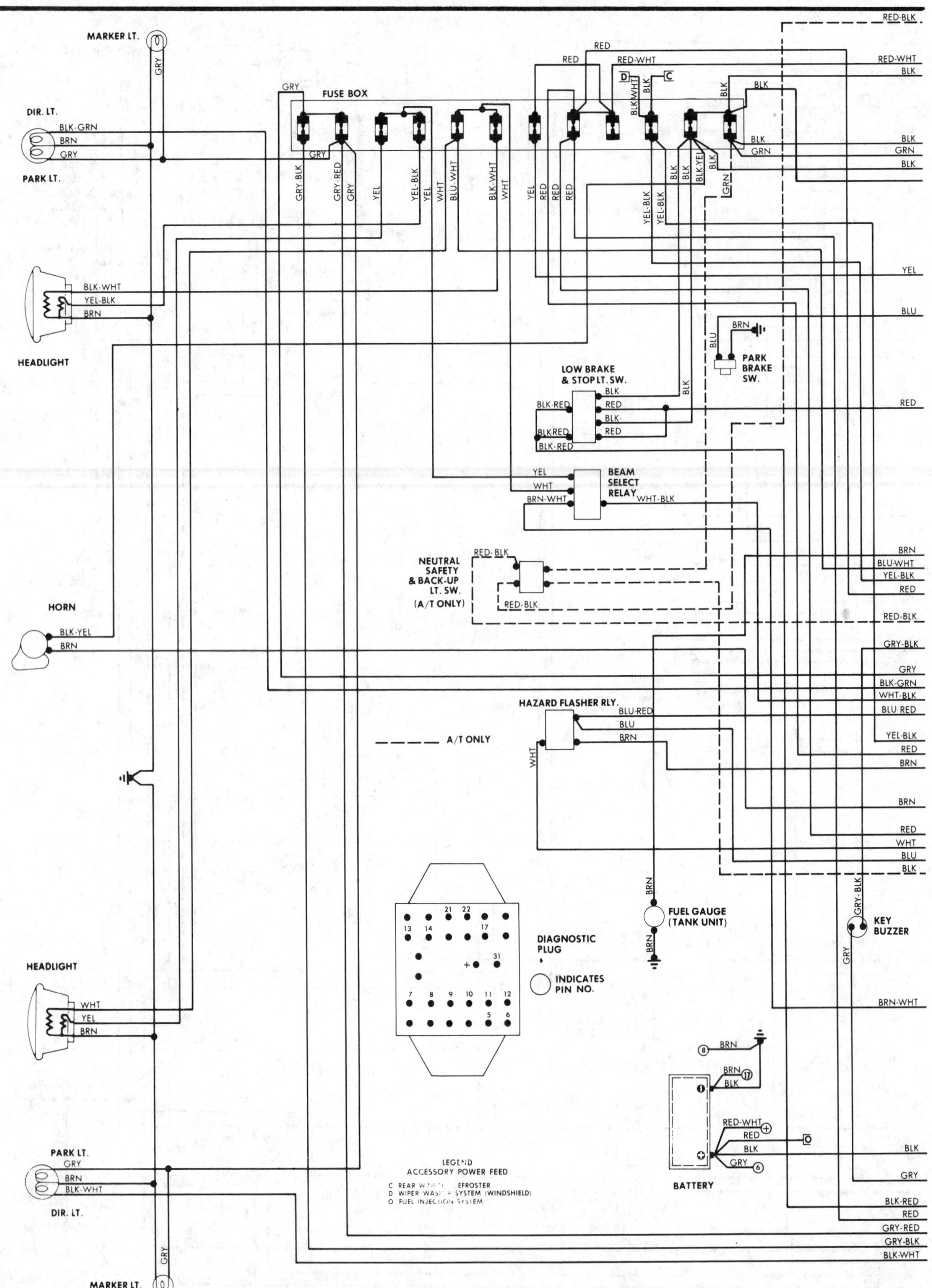

1977 Volkswagen

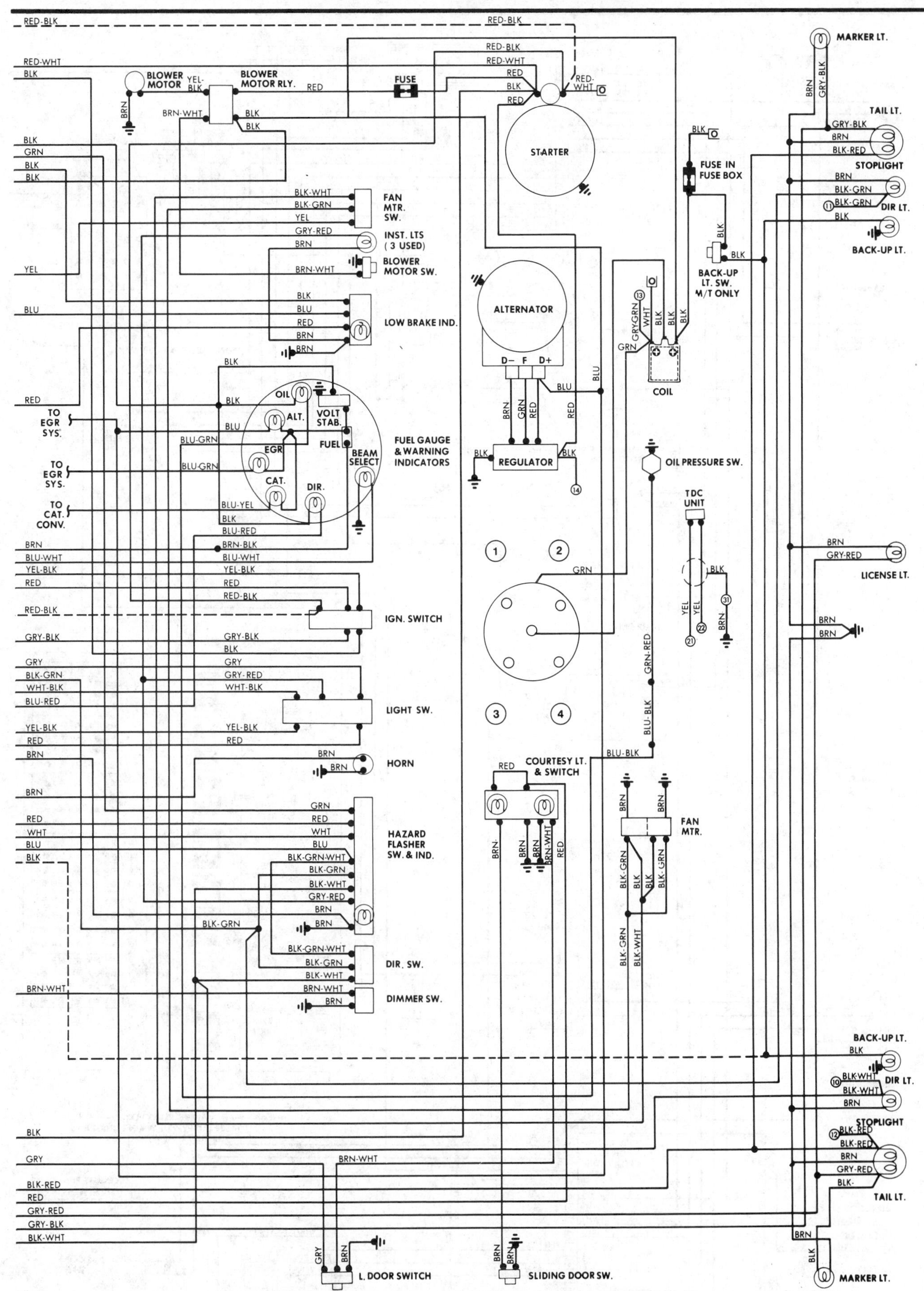

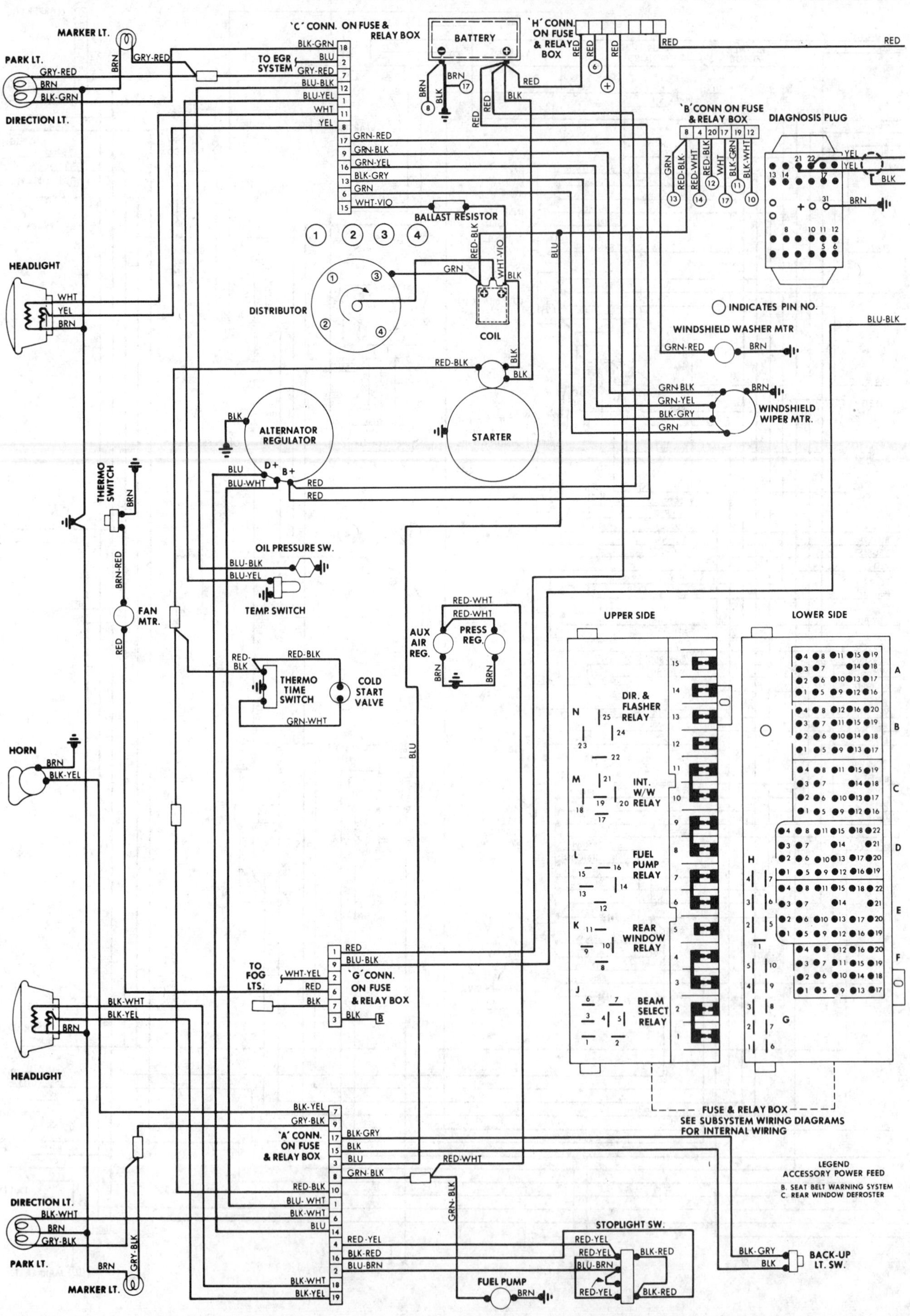
MARKER LT.
PARK LT.
DIRECTION LT.
'C' CONN. ON FUSE & RELAY BOX
TO EGR SYSTEM
BATTERY
'H' CONN. ON FUSE & RELAY BOX
'B' CONN ON FUSE & RELAY BOX
DIAGNOSIS PLUG
BALLAST RESISTOR
HEADLIGHT
DISTRIBUTOR
COIL
INDICATES PIN NO.
WINDSHIELD WASHER MTR
WINDSHIELD WIPER MTR.
ALTERNATOR REGULATOR
STARTER
THERMO SWITCH
OIL PRESSURE SW.
TEMP. SWITCH
FAN MTR.
AUX AIR REG.
PRESS REG.
THERMO TIME SWITCH
COLD START VALVE
UPPER SIDE
LOWER SIDE
DIR. & FLASHER RELAY
INT. W/W RELAY
FUEL PUMP RELAY
REAR WINDOW RELAY
BEAM SELECT RELAY
HORN
TO FOG LTS.
'G' CONN. ON FUSE & RELAY BOX
HEADLIGHT
FUSE & RELAY BOX
SEE SUBSYSTEM WIRING DIAGRAMS FOR INTERNAL WIRING
'A' CONN. ON FUSE & RELAY BOX
LEGEND
ACCESSORY POWER FEED
B. SEAT BELT WARNING SYSTEM
C. REAR WINDOW DEFROSTER
STOPLIGHT SW.
BACK-UP LT. SW.
FUEL PUMP
DIRECTION LT.
PARK LT.
MARKER LT.

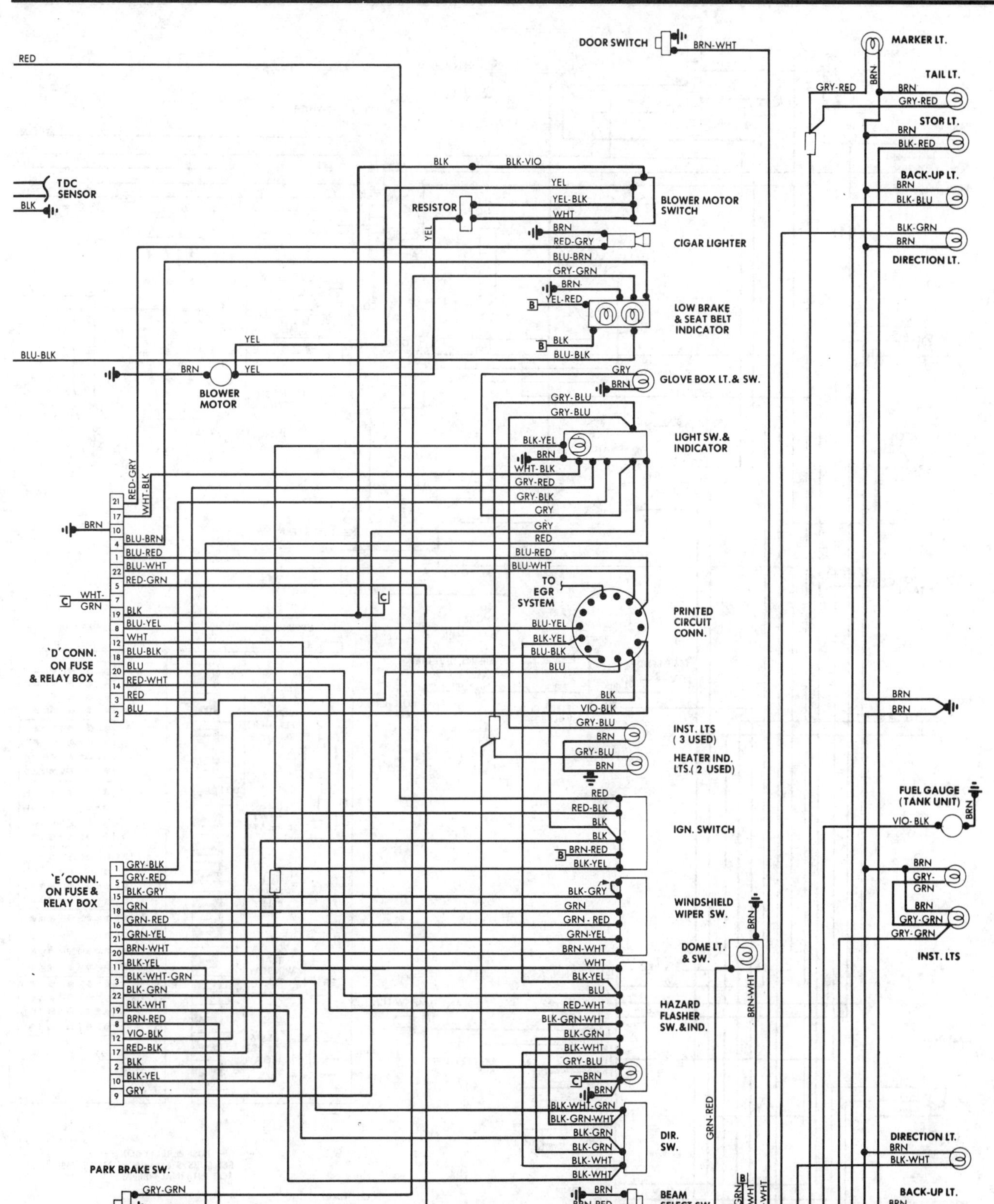
DOOR SWITCH
MARKER LT.
TAIL LT.
STOP LT.
BACK-UP LT.
TDC SENSOR
RESISTOR
BLOWER MOTOR SWITCH
CIGAR LIGHTER
DIRECTION LT.
LOW BRAKE & SEAT BELT INDICATOR
BLOWER MOTOR
GLOVE BOX LT. & SW.
LIGHT SW. & INDICATOR
TO EGR SYSTEM
PRINTED CIRCUIT CONN.
'D' CONN. ON FUSE & RELAY BOX
INST. LTS (3 USED)
HEATER IND. LTS. (2 USED)
FUEL GAUGE (TANK UNIT)
IGN. SWITCH
'E' CONN. ON FUSE & RELAY BOX
WINDSHIELD WIPER SW.
DOME LT. & SW.
INST. LTS
HAZARD FLASHER SW. & IND.
DIR. SW.
PARK BRAKE SW.
BEAM SELECT. SW.
HORN SW.
DOOR SWITCH
'F' CONN. ON FUSE & RELAY BOX
MARKER LT.

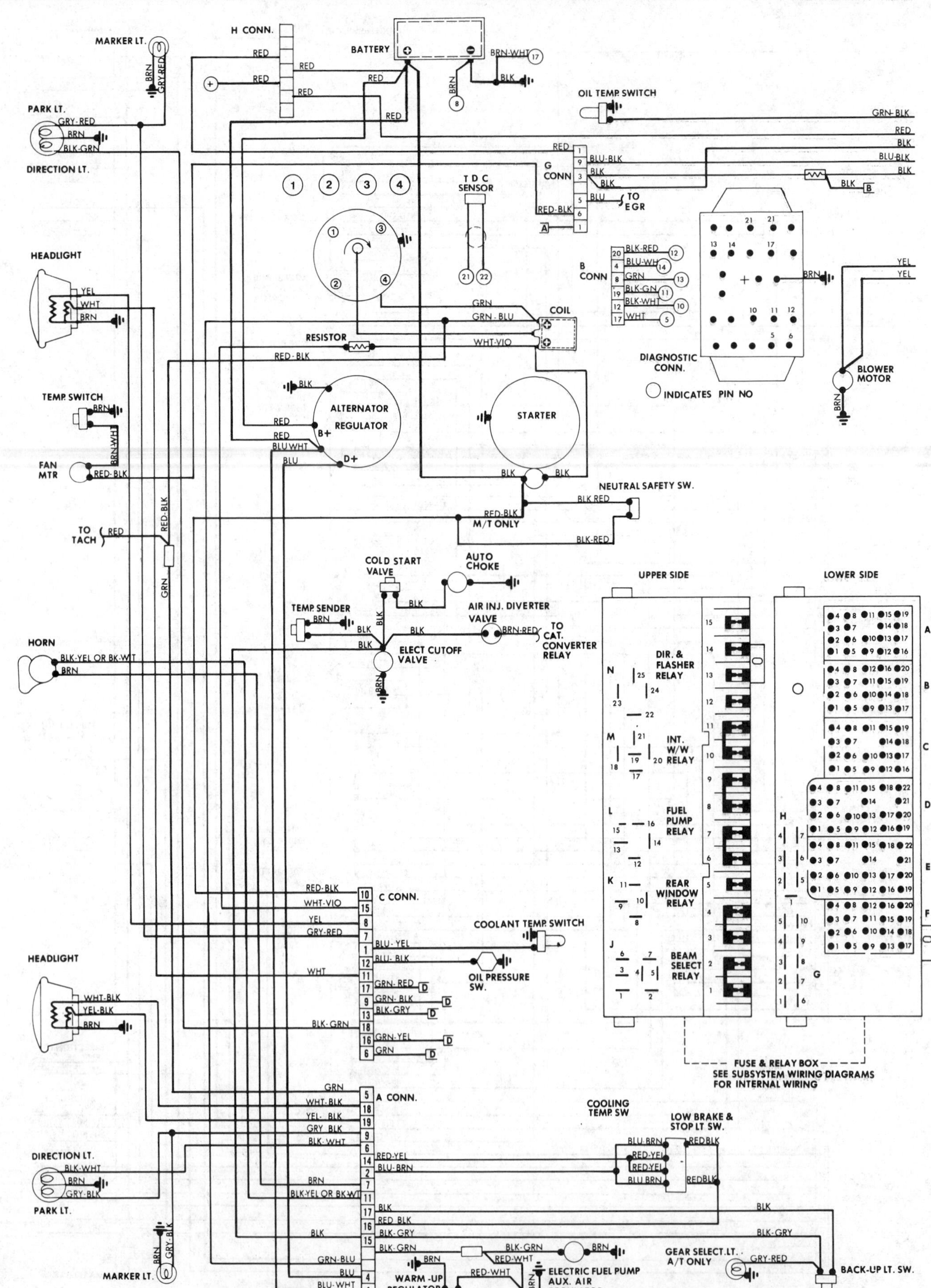
MARKER LT.
H CONN.
BATTERY
PARK LT.
DIRECTION LT.
OIL TEMP. SWITCH
G CONN
TDC SENSOR
TO EGR
B CONN
HEADLIGHT
COIL
RESISTOR
DIAGNOSTIC CONN.
INDICATES PIN NO
BLOWER MOTOR
TEMP. SWITCH
ALTERNATOR REGULATOR
STARTER
FAN MTR
NEUTRAL SAFETY SW.
M/T ONLY
TO TACH
COLD START VALVE
AUTO CHOKE
UPPER SIDE
LOWER SIDE
TEMP. SENDER
AIR INJ. DIVERTER VALVE
TO CAT. CONVERTER RELAY
HORN
ELECT CUTOFF VALVE
DIR. & FLASHER RELAY
INT. W/W RELAY
FUEL PUMP RELAY
REAR WINDOW RELAY
BEAM SELECT RELAY
C CONN.
COOLANT TEMP. SWITCH
OIL PRESSURE SW.
HEADLIGHT
FUSE & RELAY BOX
SEE SUBSYSTEM WIRING DIAGRAMS FOR INTERNAL WIRING
A CONN.
COOLING TEMP. SW
LOW BRAKE & STOP LT SW.
DIRECTION LT.
PARK LT.
GEAR SELECT LT. A/T ONLY
BACK-UP LT. SW.
MARKER LT.
WARM-UP REGULATOR
ELECTRIC FUEL PUMP AUX. AIR REGULATOR

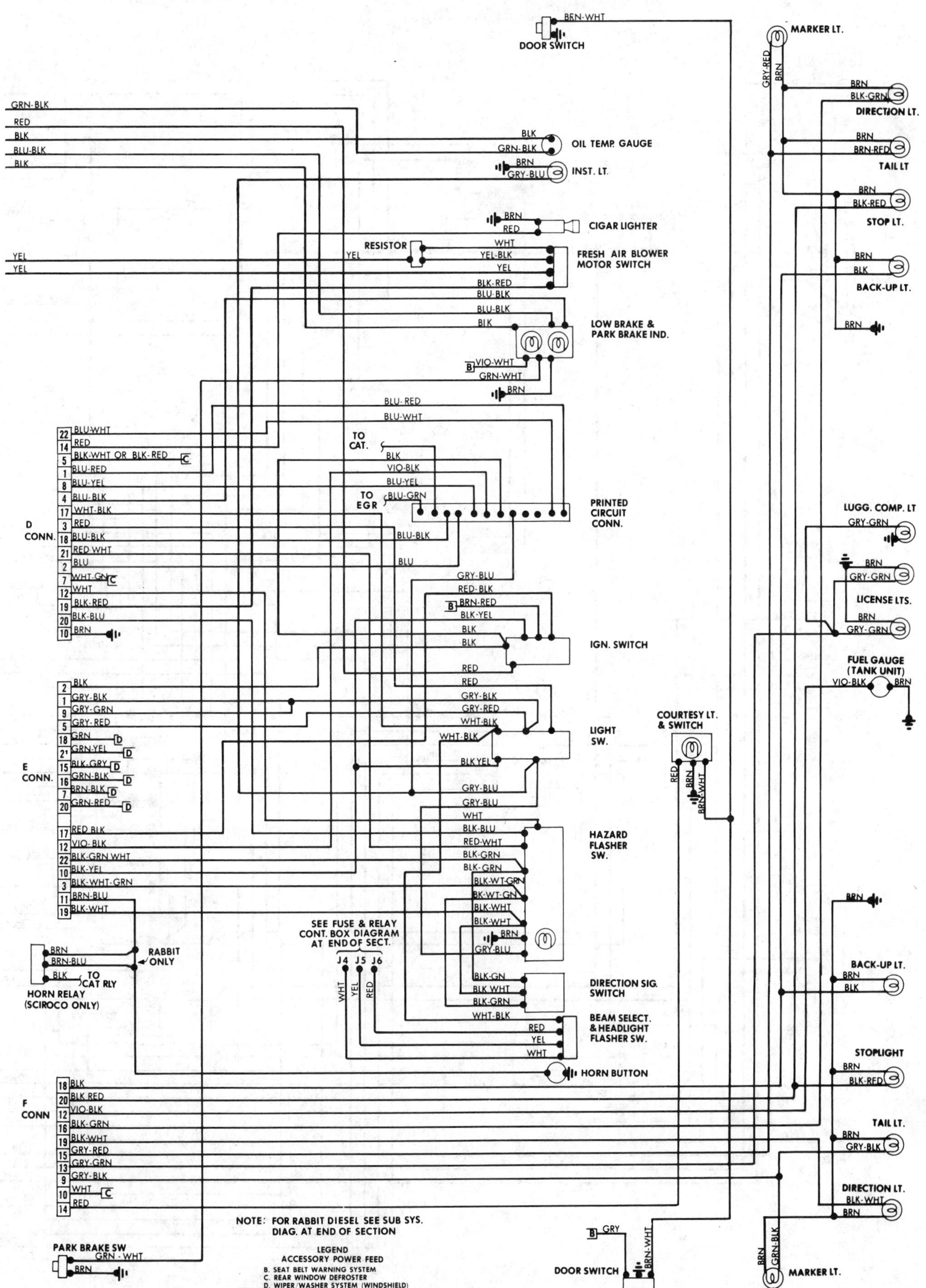
DOOR SWITCH
MARKER LT.
DIRECTION LT.
OIL TEMP. GAUGE
INST. LT.
TAIL LT
STOP LT.
CIGAR LIGHTER
RESISTOR
FRESH AIR BLOWER MOTOR SWITCH
BACK-UP LT.
LOW BRAKE & PARK BRAKE IND.
TO CAT.
TO EGR
PRINTED CIRCUIT CONN.
D CONN.
LUGG. COMP. LT
LICENSE LTS.
IGN. SWITCH
FUEL GAUGE (TANK UNIT)
COURTESY LT. & SWITCH
LIGHT SW.
E CONN.
HAZARD FLASHER SW.
SEE FUSE & RELAY CONT. BOX DIAGRAM AT END OF SECT.
J4 J5 J6
RABBIT ONLY
TO CAT RLY
HORN RELAY (SCIROCO ONLY)
DIRECTION SIG. SWITCH
BEAM SELECT. & HEADLIGHT FLASHER SW.
HORN BUTTON
STOPLIGHT
F CONN
TAIL LT.
DIRECTION LT.
NOTE: FOR RABBIT DIESEL SEE SUB SYS. DIAG. AT END OF SECTION
LEGEND
ACCESSORY POWER FEED
B. SEAT BELT WARNING SYSTEM
C. REAR WINDOW DEFROSTER
D. WIPER/WASHER SYSTEM (WINDSHIELD)
PARK BRAKE SW
DOOR SWITCH
MARKER LT.

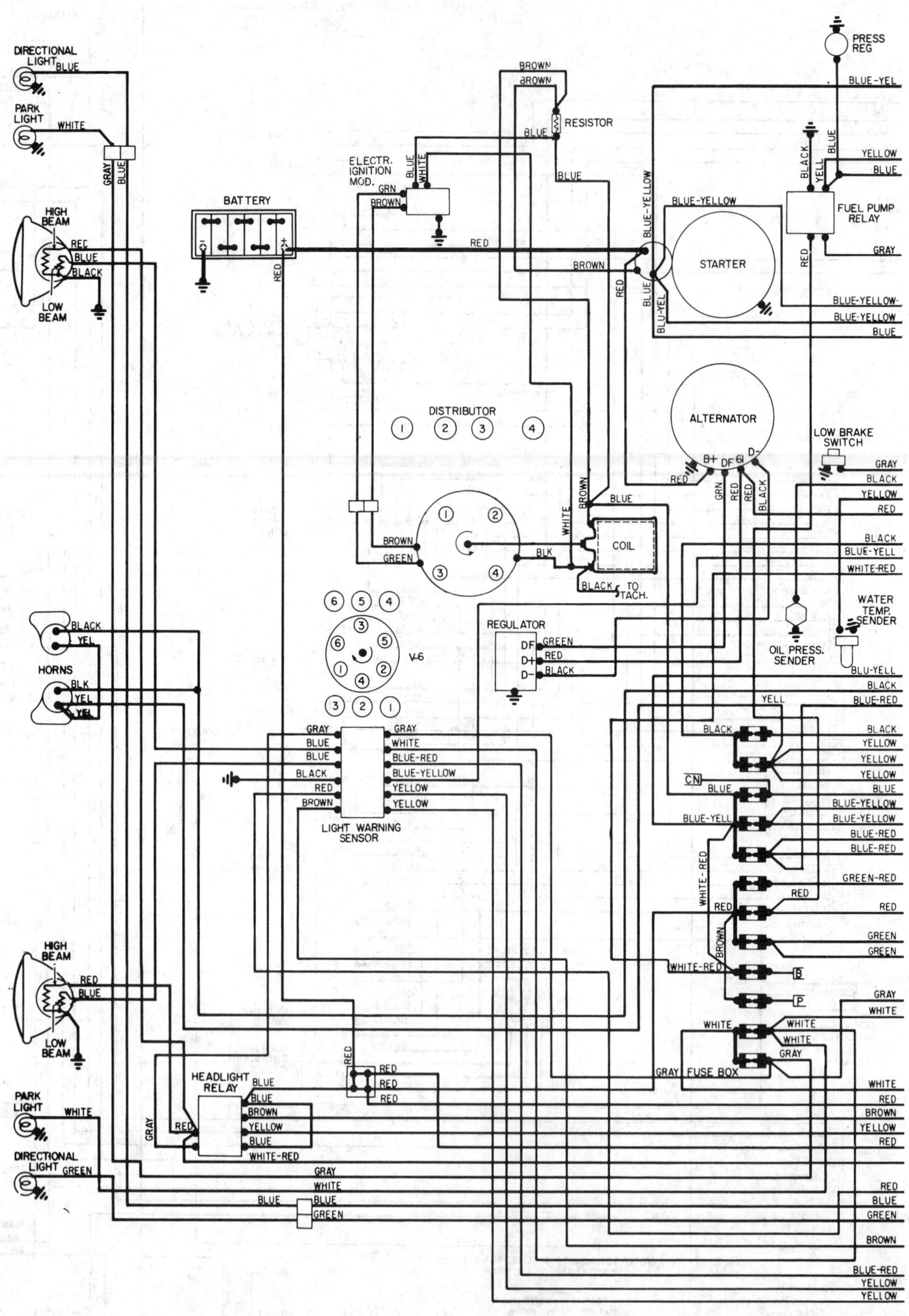
DIRECTIONAL LIGHT
PARK LIGHT
HIGH BEAM
LOW BEAM
BATTERY
ELECTR. IGNITION MOD.
RESISTOR
STARTER
FUEL PUMP RELAY
PRESS REG
DISTRIBUTOR
ALTERNATOR
LOW BRAKE SWITCH
COIL
TO TACH.
REGULATOR
OIL PRESS. SENDER
WATER TEMP. SENDER
HORNS
V-6
LIGHT WARNING SENSOR
HEADLIGHT RELAY
FUSE BOX

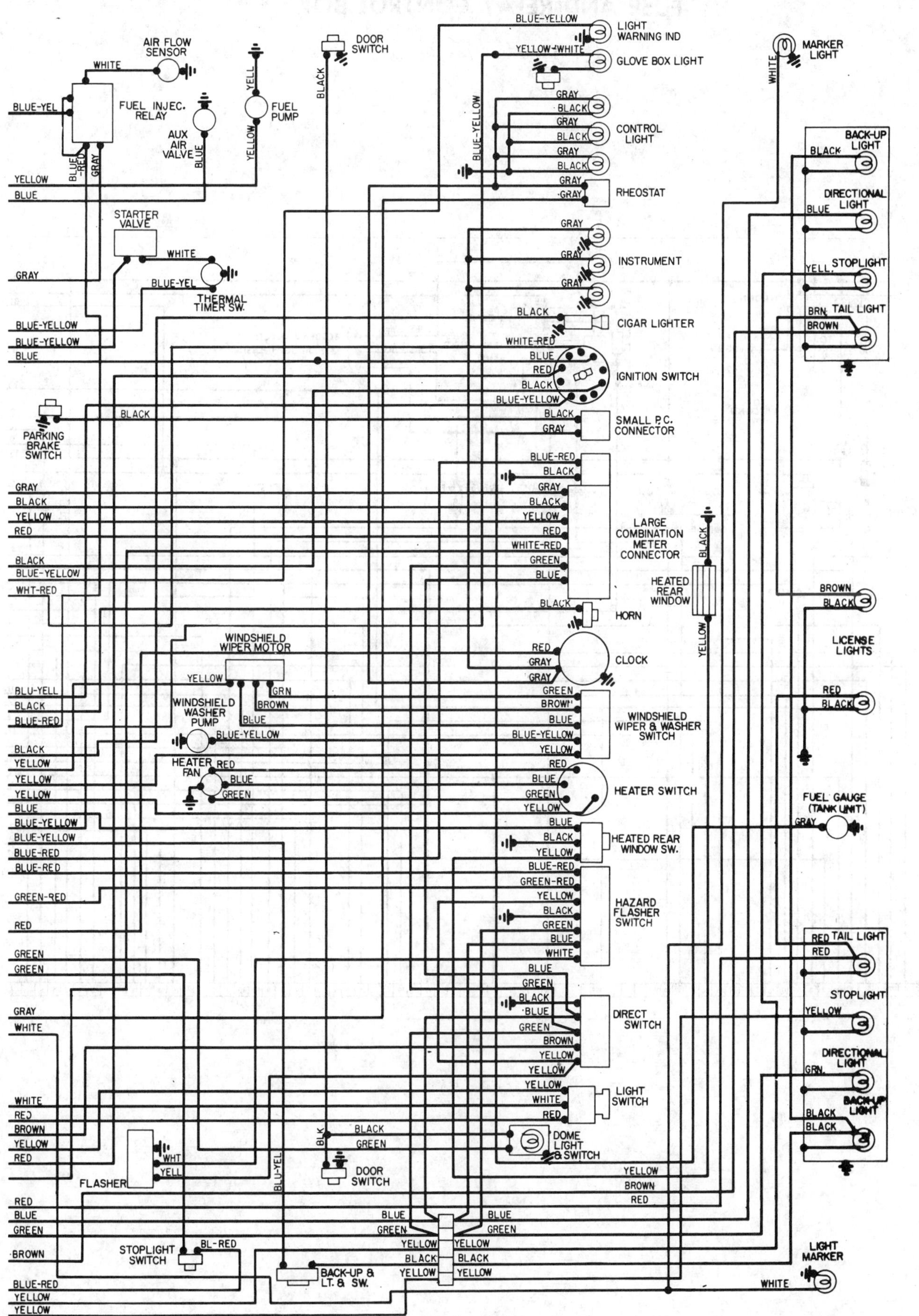

AIR FLOW SENSOR
FUEL INJEC. RELAY
AUX AIR VALVE
FUEL PUMP
DOOR SWITCH
LIGHT WARNING IND
GLOVE BOX LIGHT
CONTROL LIGHT
RHEOSTAT
INSTRUMENT
CIGAR LIGHTER
IGNITION SWITCH
SMALL P.C. CONNECTOR
LARGE COMBINATION METER CONNECTOR
HORN
CLOCK
WINDSHIELD WIPER & WASHER SWITCH
HEATER SWITCH
HEATED REAR WINDOW SW.
HAZARD FLASHER SWITCH
DIRECT SWITCH
LIGHT SWITCH
DOME LIGHT & SWITCH
MARKER LIGHT
BACK-UP LIGHT
DIRECTIONAL LIGHT
STOPLIGHT
TAIL LIGHT
HEATED REAR WINDOW
LICENSE LIGHTS
FUEL GAUGE (TANK UNIT)
LIGHT MARKER
STARTER VALVE
THERMAL TIMER SW.
PARKING BRAKE SWITCH
WINDSHIELD WIPER MOTOR
WINDSHIELD WASHER PUMP
HEATER FAN
FLASHER
STOPLIGHT SWITCH
BACK-UP & LT. & SW.

FUSE AND RELAY CONTROL BOX

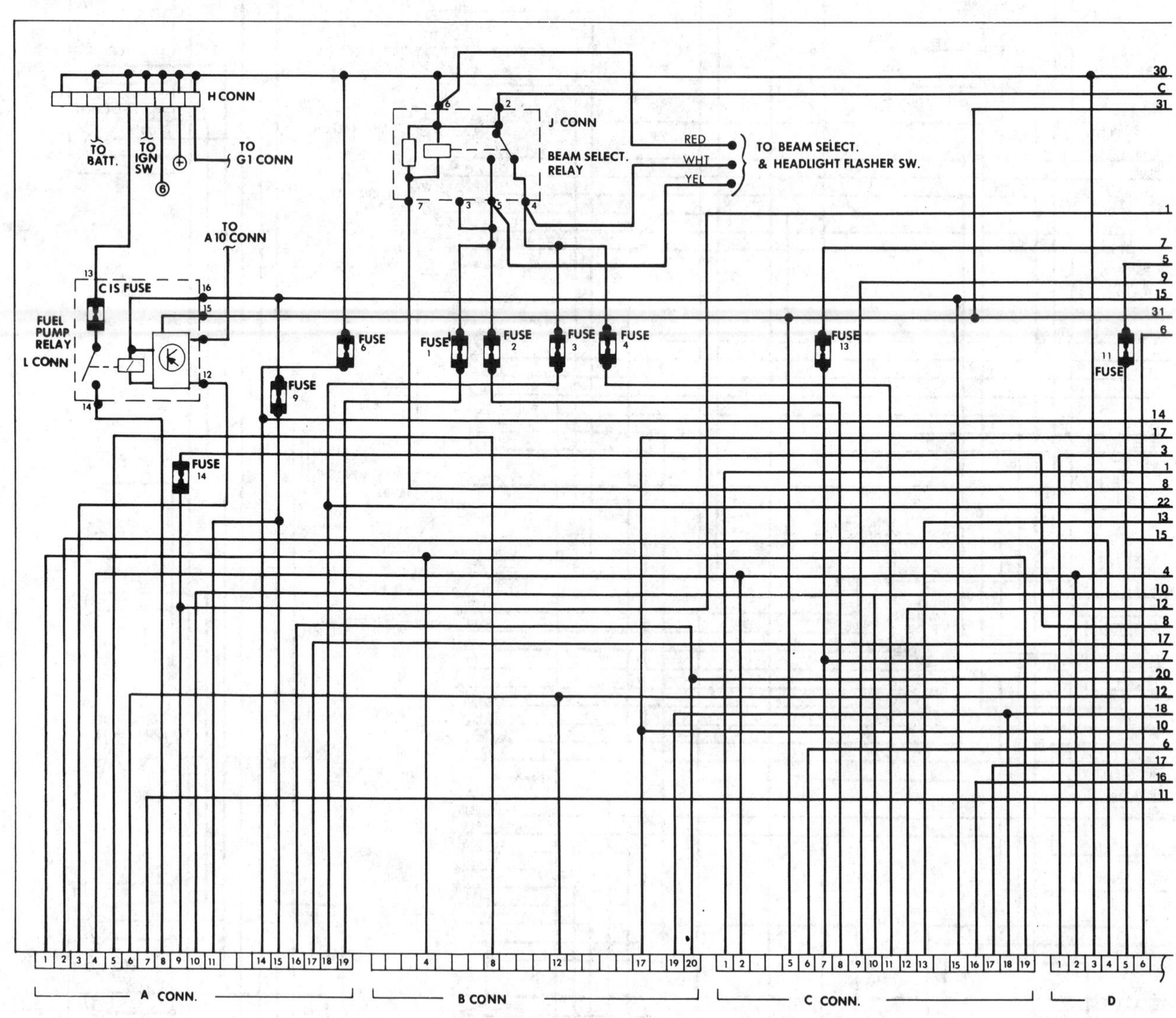

Fuse and Relay Control Box
Audi Fox, Volkswagen Dasher, Rabbit and Scirocco

FUSE AND RELAY CONTROL BOX

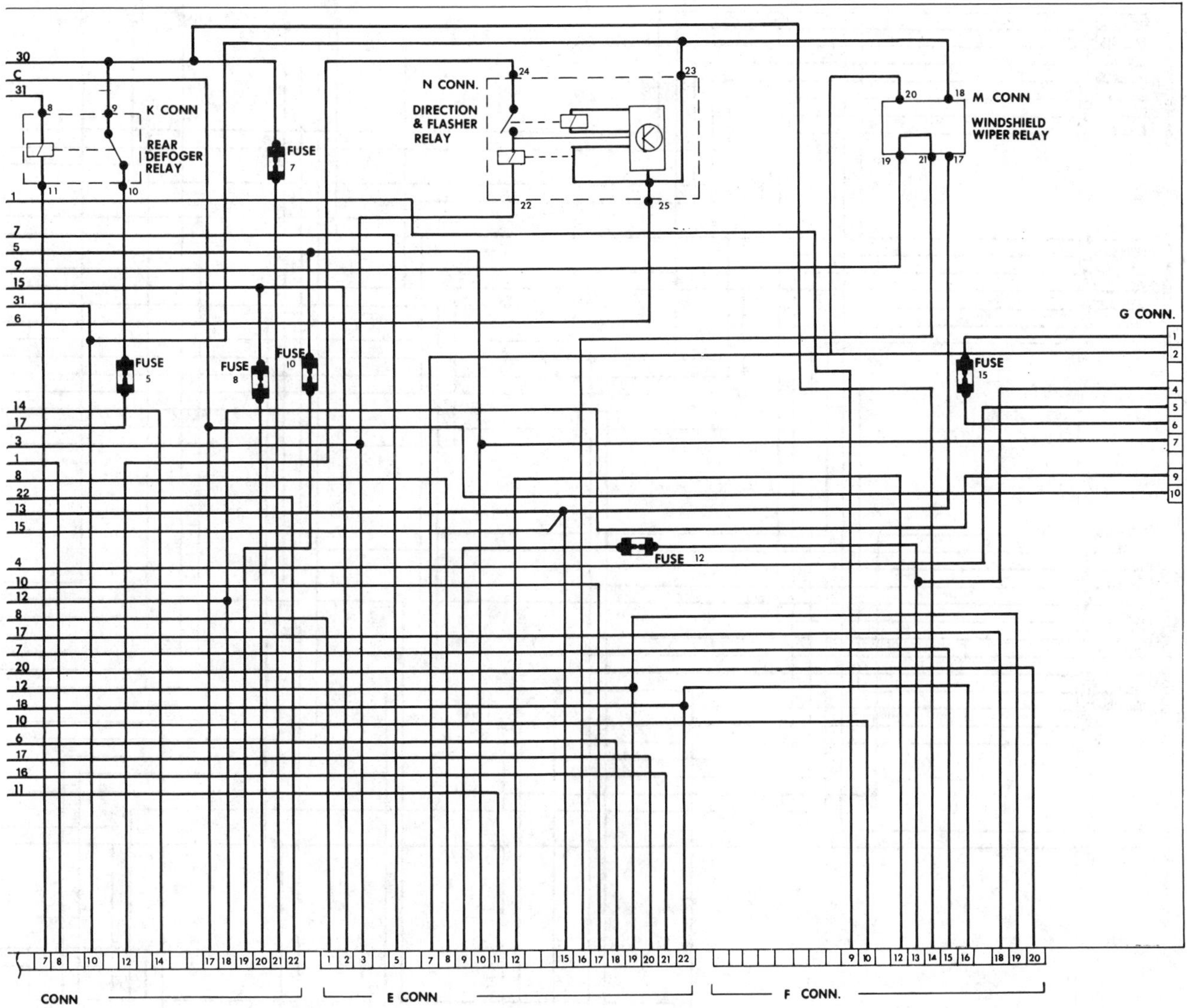

Fuse and Relay Control Box
Audi Fox, Volkswagen Dasher, Rabbit and Scirocco

FUSE AND RELAY CONTROL BOX

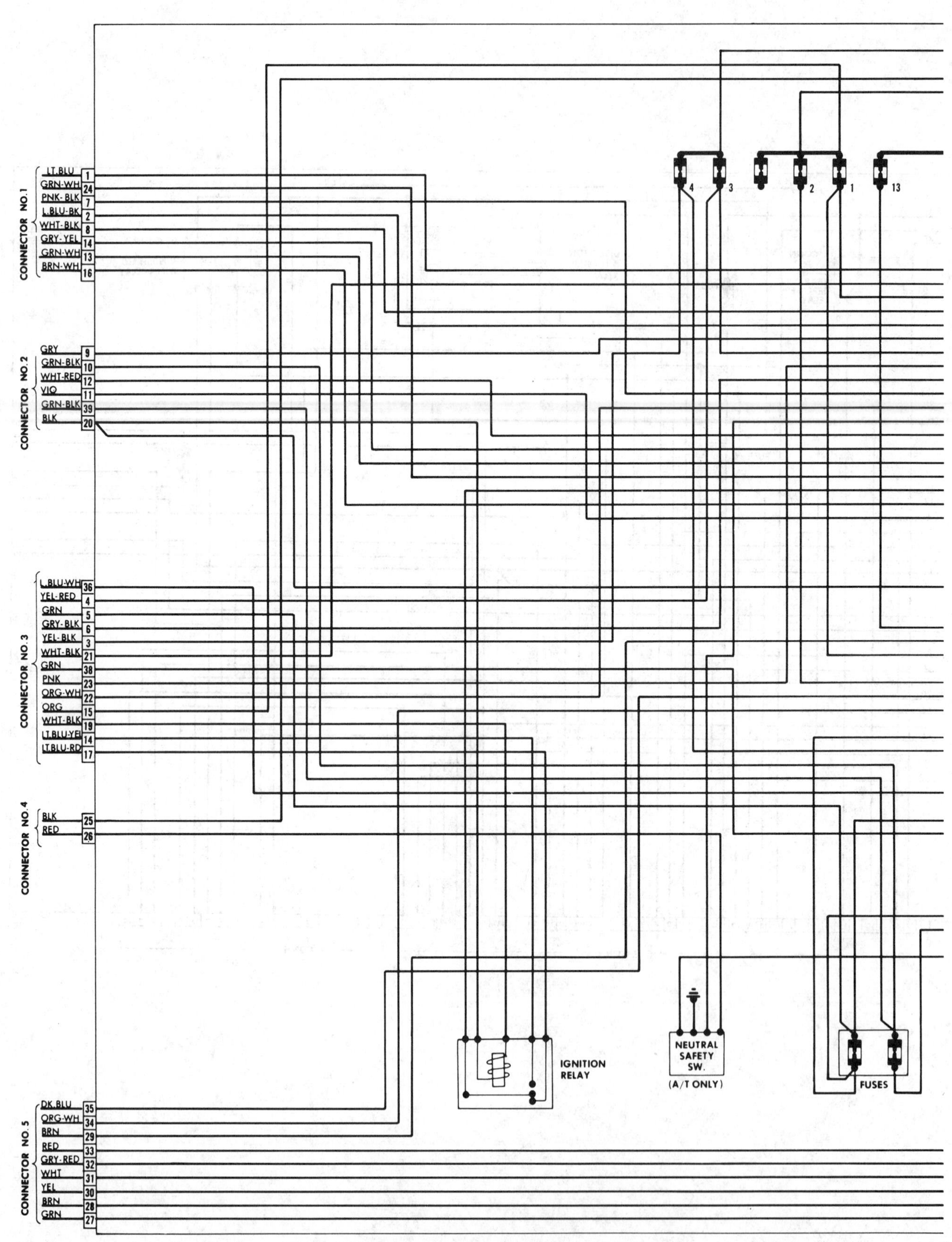

Fuse and Relay Control Box
Fiat 131

FUSE AND RELAY CONTROL BOX

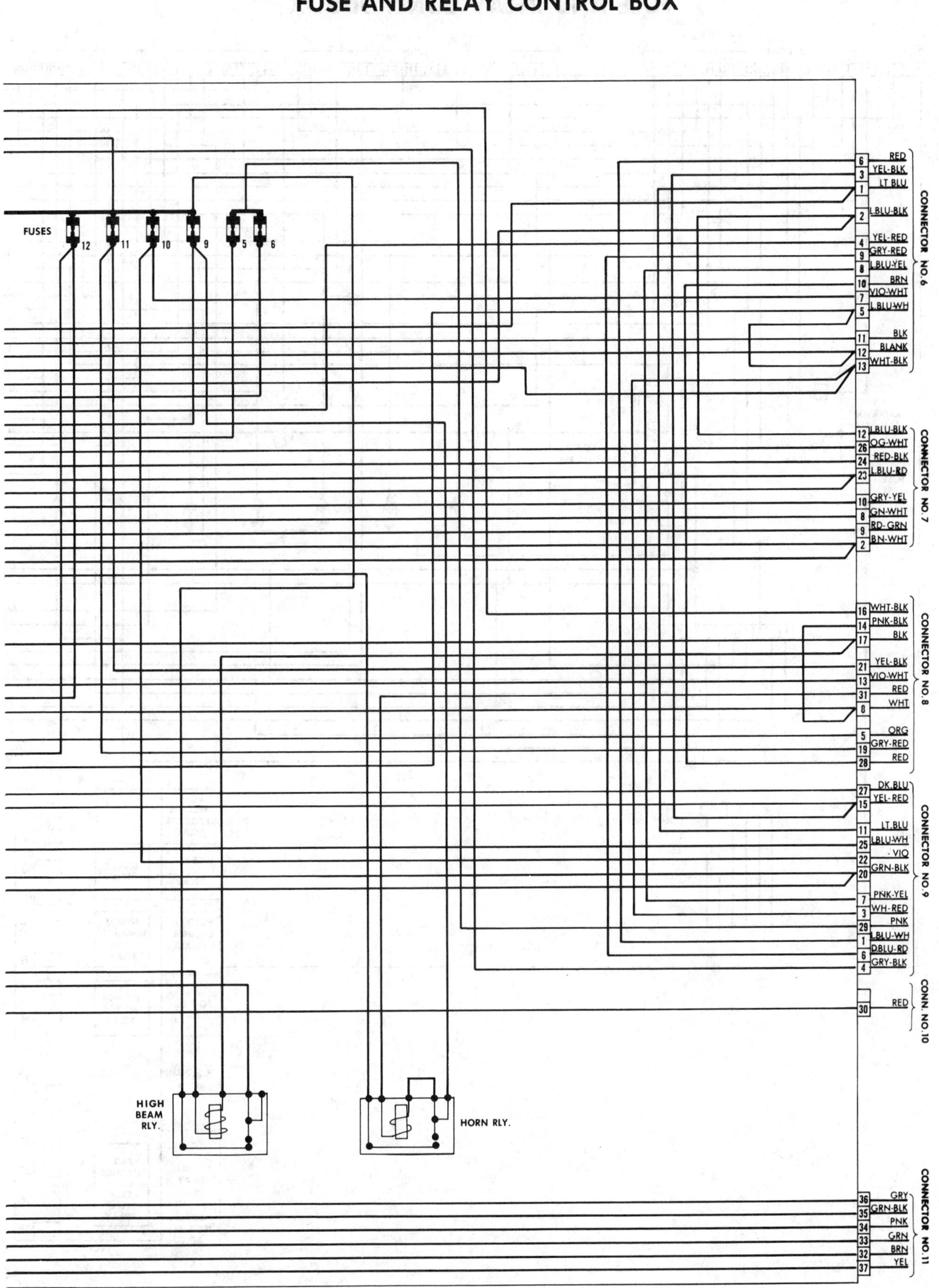

Fuse and Relay Control Box
Fiat 131

FUSE AND RELAY CONTROL BOX

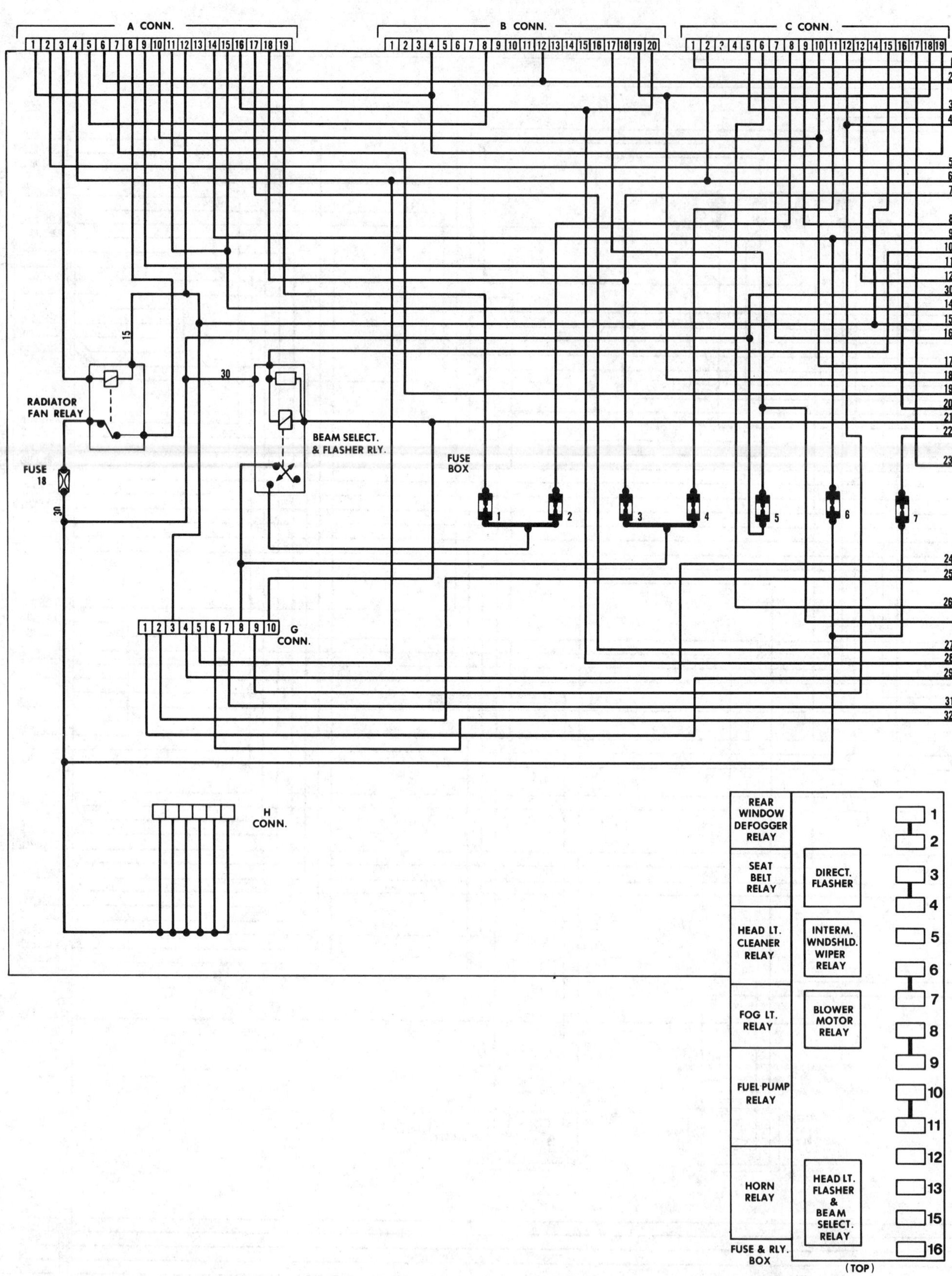

Fuse and Relay Control Box
Porsche 924

FUSE AND RELAY CONTROL BOX

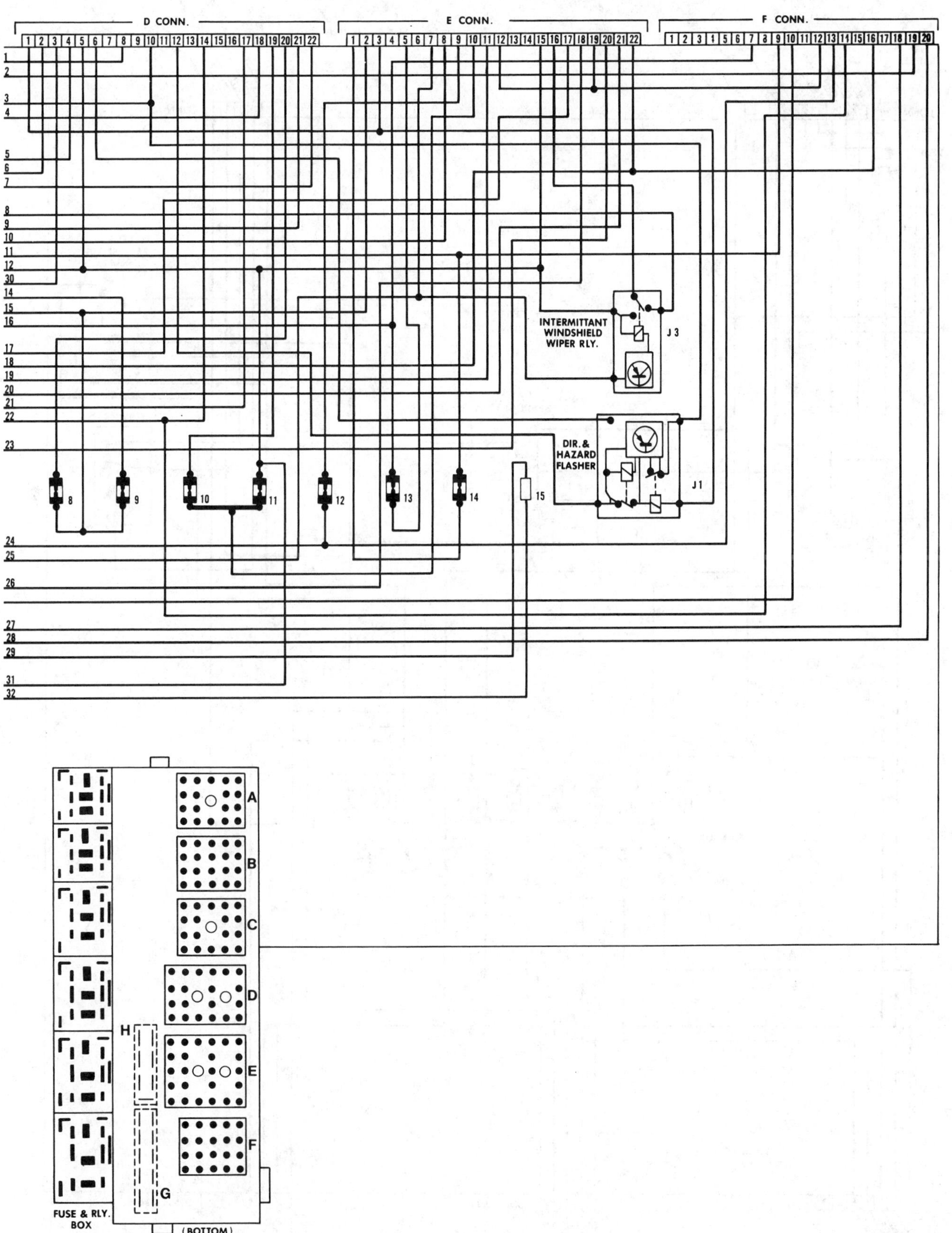

Fuse and Relay Control Box
Porsche 924

FUSE AND RELAY CONTROL BOX

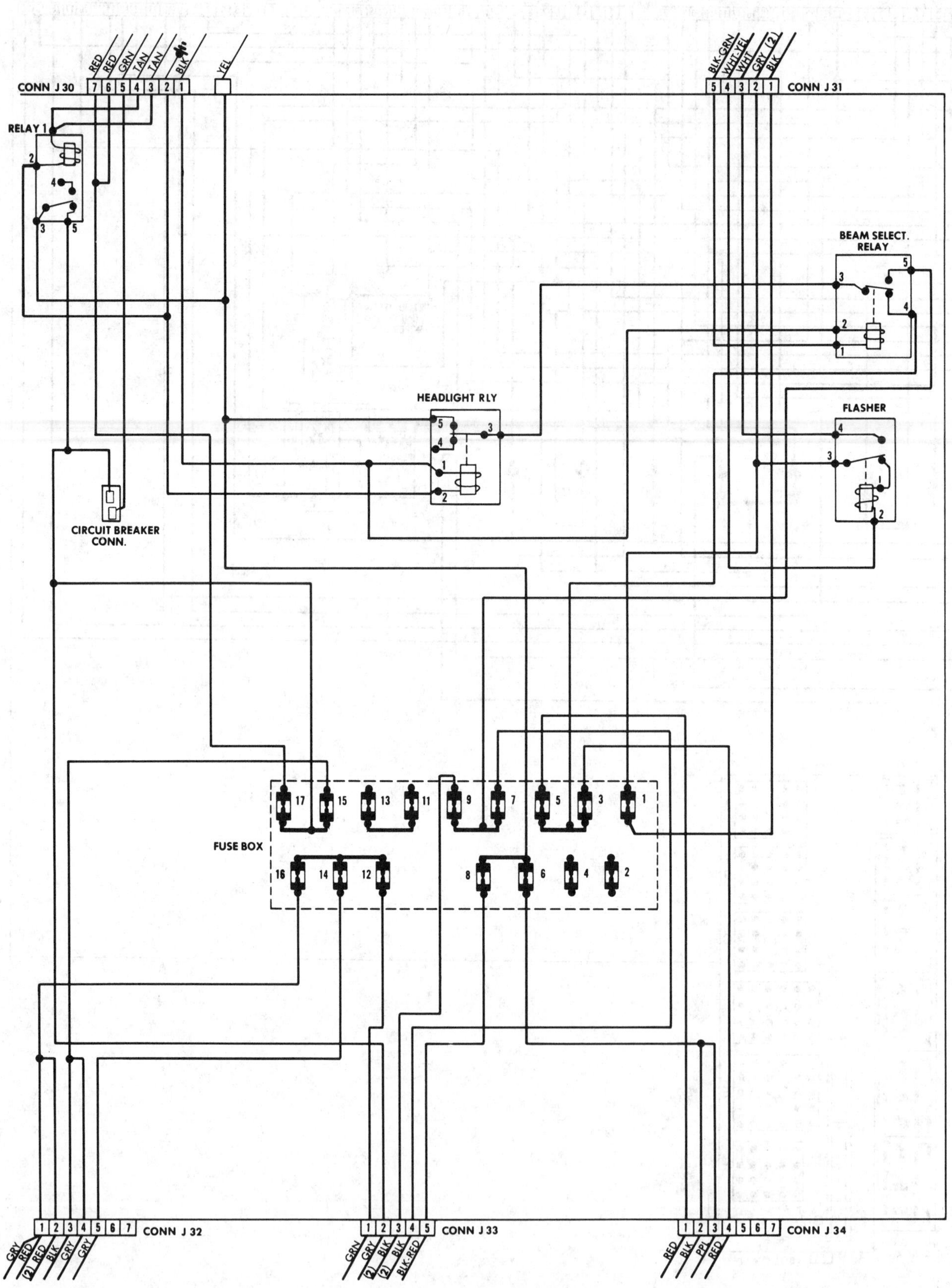

Fuse and Relay Control Box (Renault R-17 Gordini)

FUSE AND RELAY CONTROL BOX (Cont.)

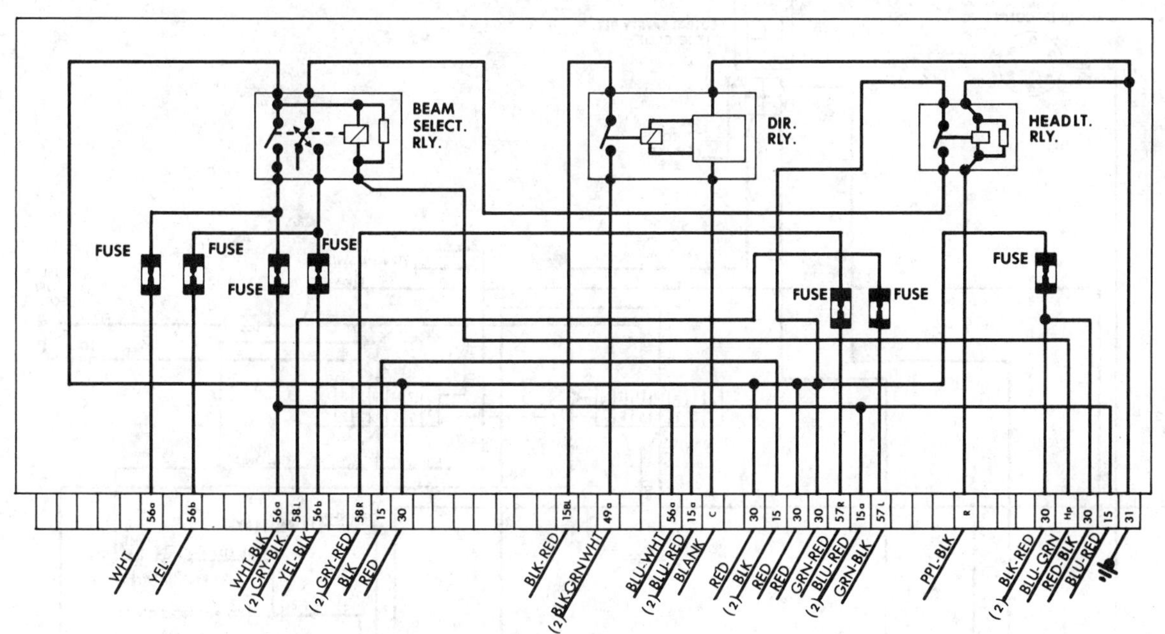

Fuse and Relay Control Box
(Audi 100LS)

HEATER AND AIR CONDITIONING SYSTEM

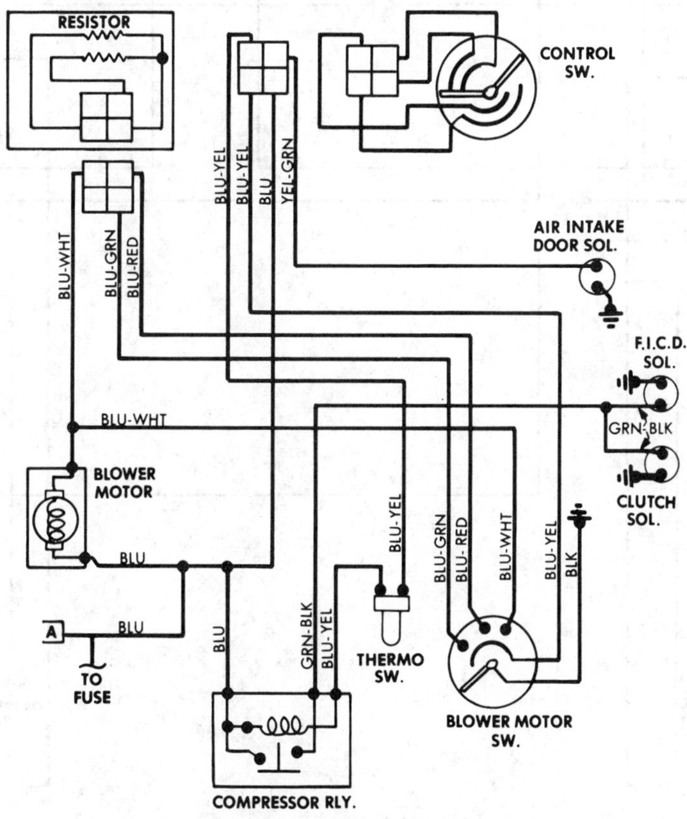

Heater and Air Conditioning System
(Datsun 810)

AUTOMATIC TRANSMISSION SYSTEM

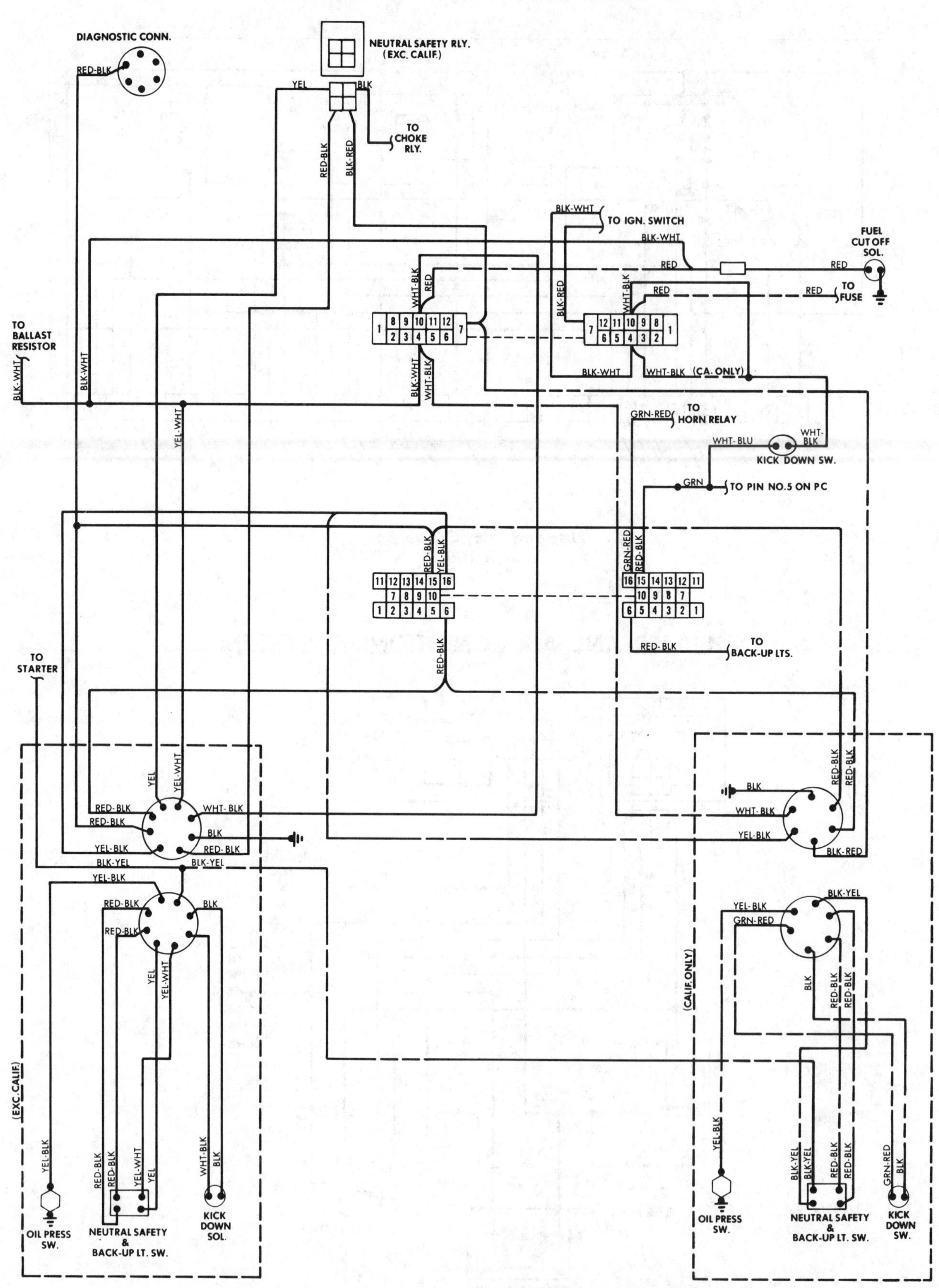

Automatic Transmission System (Datsun 200SX)

ELECTRO SENSOR COMPUTER SYSTEM

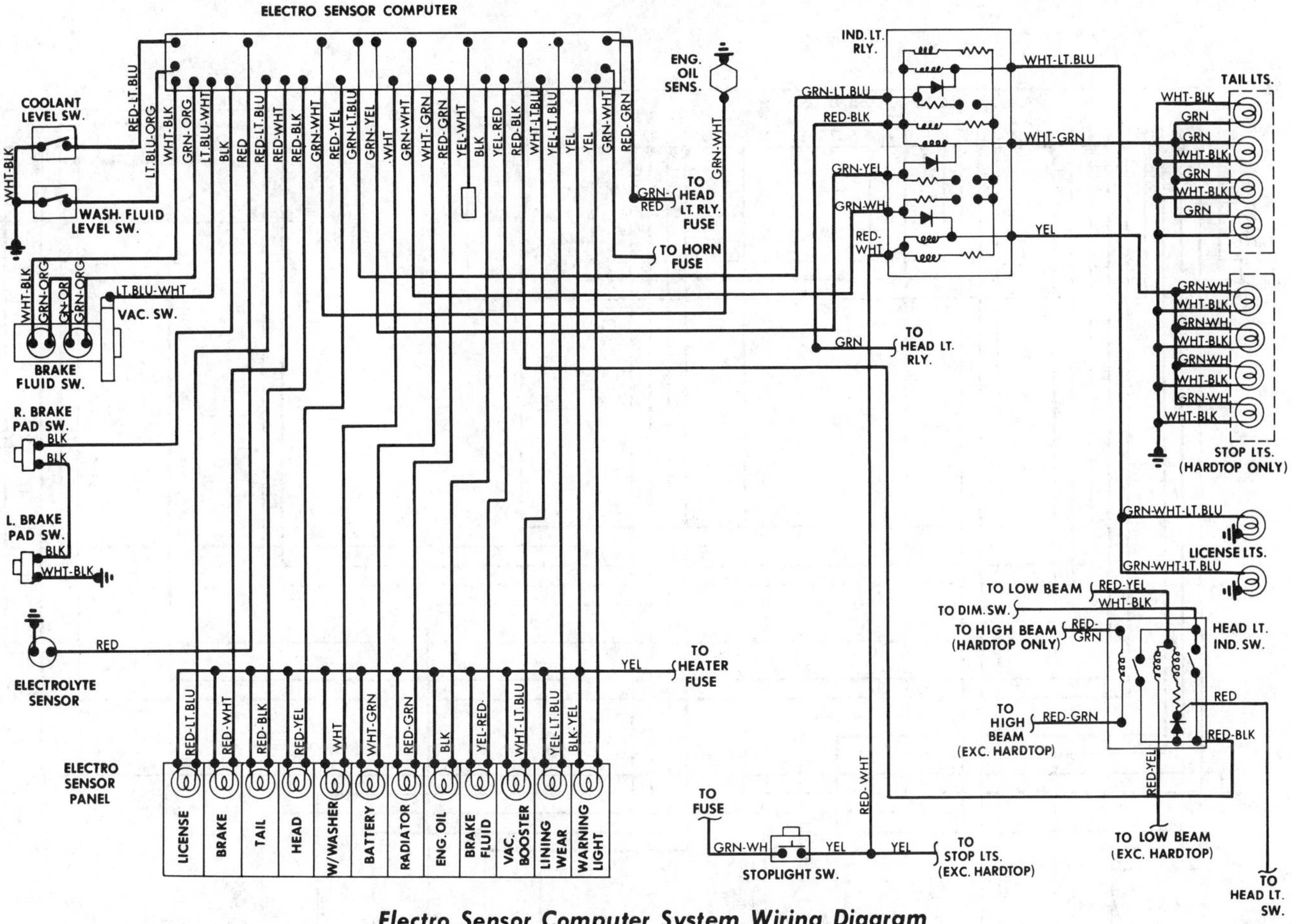

ELECTRO SENSOR COMPUTER

RED-LT.BLU, LT.BLU-ORG, WHT-BLK, LT.BLU-WHT, GRN-ORG, BLK, RED, RED-LT.BLU, RED-WHT, RED-BLK, GRN-WHT, RED-YEL, GRN-LT.BLU, GRN-YEL, WHT, GRN-WHT, WHT-GRN, RED-GRN, YEL-WHT, BLK, YEL-RED, RED-BLK, WHT-LT.BLU, YEL-LT.BLU, YEL, GRN-WHT, RED-GRN

COOLANT LEVEL SW.

WHT-BLK

WASH. FLUID LEVEL SW.

WHT-BLK, GRN-ORG, GRN-ORG, GRN-ORG

LT.BLU-WHT

VAC. SW.

BRAKE FLUID SW.

R. BRAKE PAD SW.

BLK

BLK

L. BRAKE PAD SW.

BLK

WHT-BLK

RED

ELECTROLYTE SENSOR

ENG. OIL SENS.

GRN-WHT

GRN-RED

TO HEAD LT. RLY. FUSE

TO HORN FUSE

IND. LT. RLY.

GRN-LT.BLU

RED-BLK

GRN-YEL

GRN-WHT

RED-WHT

WHT-LT.BLU

WHT-GRN

YEL

GRN

TO HEAD LT. RLY.

TAIL LTS.

WHT-BLK, GRN, GRN, WHT-BLK, GRN, WHT-BLK, GRN

GRN-WHT, WHT-BLK, GRN-WHT, WHT-BLK, GRN-WHT, WHT-BLK, GRN-WHT, WHT-BLK

STOP LTS. (HARDTOP ONLY)

GRN-WHT-LT.BLU

LICENSE LTS.

GRN-WHT-LT.BLU

TO LOW BEAM

RED-YEL

TO DIM. SW.

WHT-BLK

TO HIGH BEAM (HARDTOP ONLY)

RED-GRN

HEAD LT. IND. SW.

TO HIGH BEAM (EXC. HARDTOP)

RED-GRN

RED

RED-BLK

RED-YEL

TO LOW BEAM (EXC. HARDTOP)

TO HEAD LT. SW.

YEL

TO HEATER FUSE

RED-LT.BLU, RED-WHT, RED-BLK, RED-YEL, WHT, WHT-GRN, RED-GRN, BLK, YEL-RED, WHT-LT.BLU, YEL-LT.BLU, BLK-YEL

ELECTRO SENSOR PANEL

LICENSE, BRAKE, TAIL, HEAD, W/WASHER, BATTERY, RADIATOR, ENG. OIL, BRAKE FLUID, VAC. BOOSTER, LINING WEAR, WARNING LIGHT

RED-WHT

TO FUSE

GRN-WH

YEL

YEL

STOPLIGHT SW.

TO STOP LTS. (EXC. HARDTOP)

Electro Sensor Computer System Wiring Diagram
(Toyota, All Models So Equipped)

DIESEL INJECTION SYSTEM

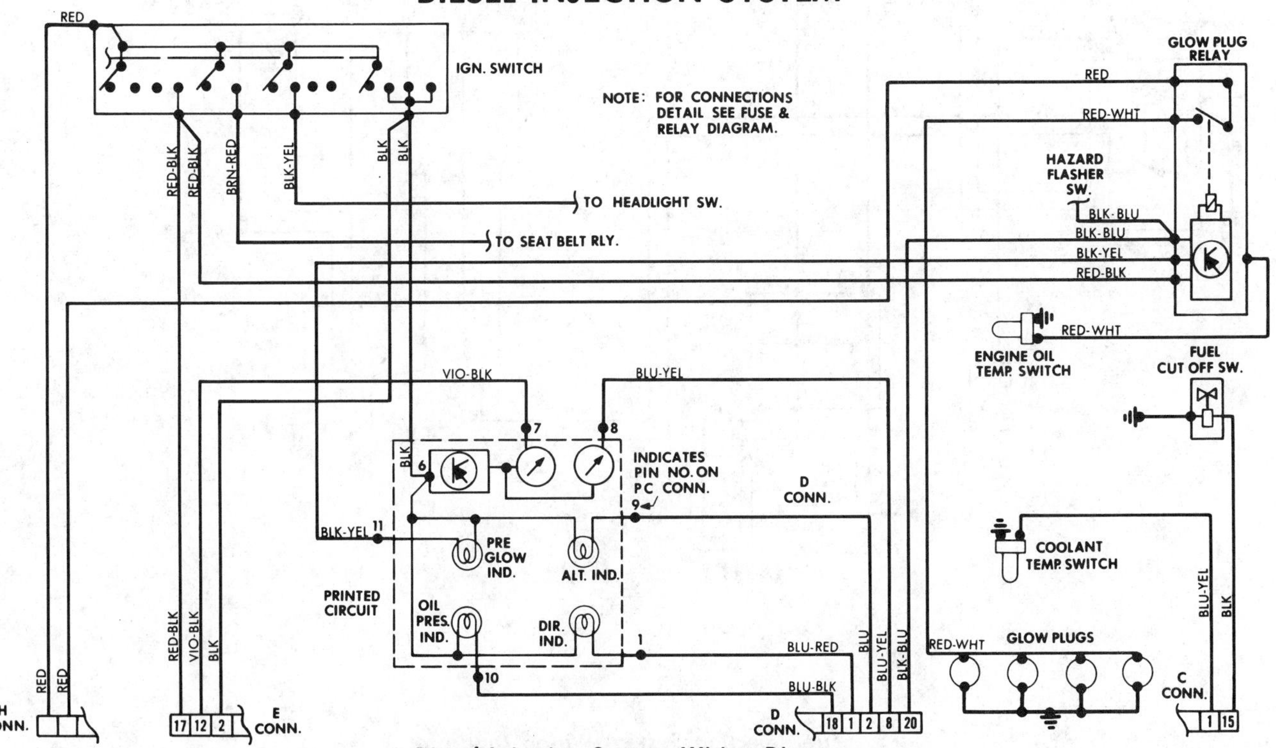

Diesel Injection System Wiring Diagram
(Volkswagen Rabbit Diesel)

FUEL INJECTION SYSTEMS

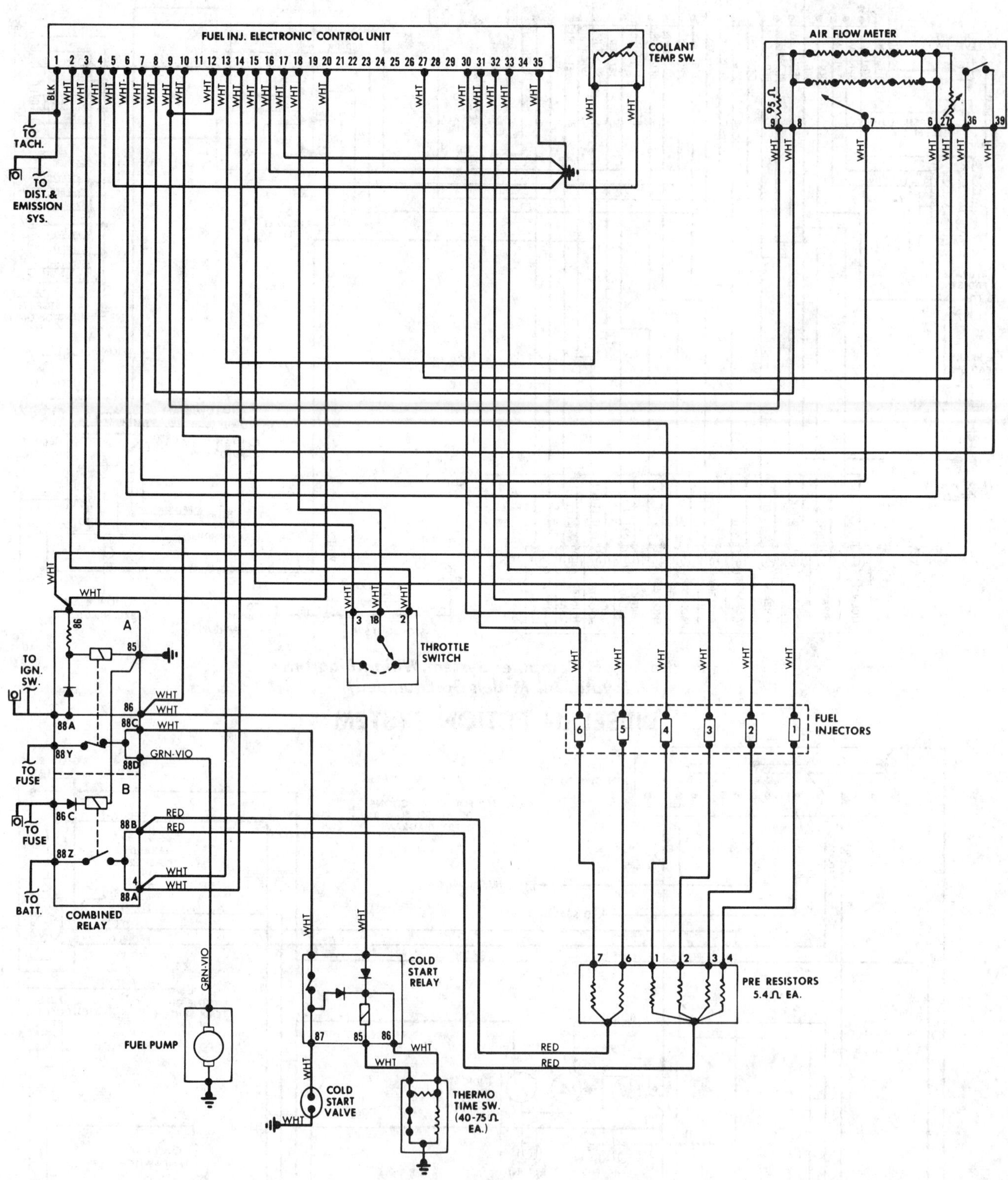

Fuel Injection System Wiring Diagram
(BMW 630 CSi)

FUEL INJECTION SYSTEMS (Cont.)

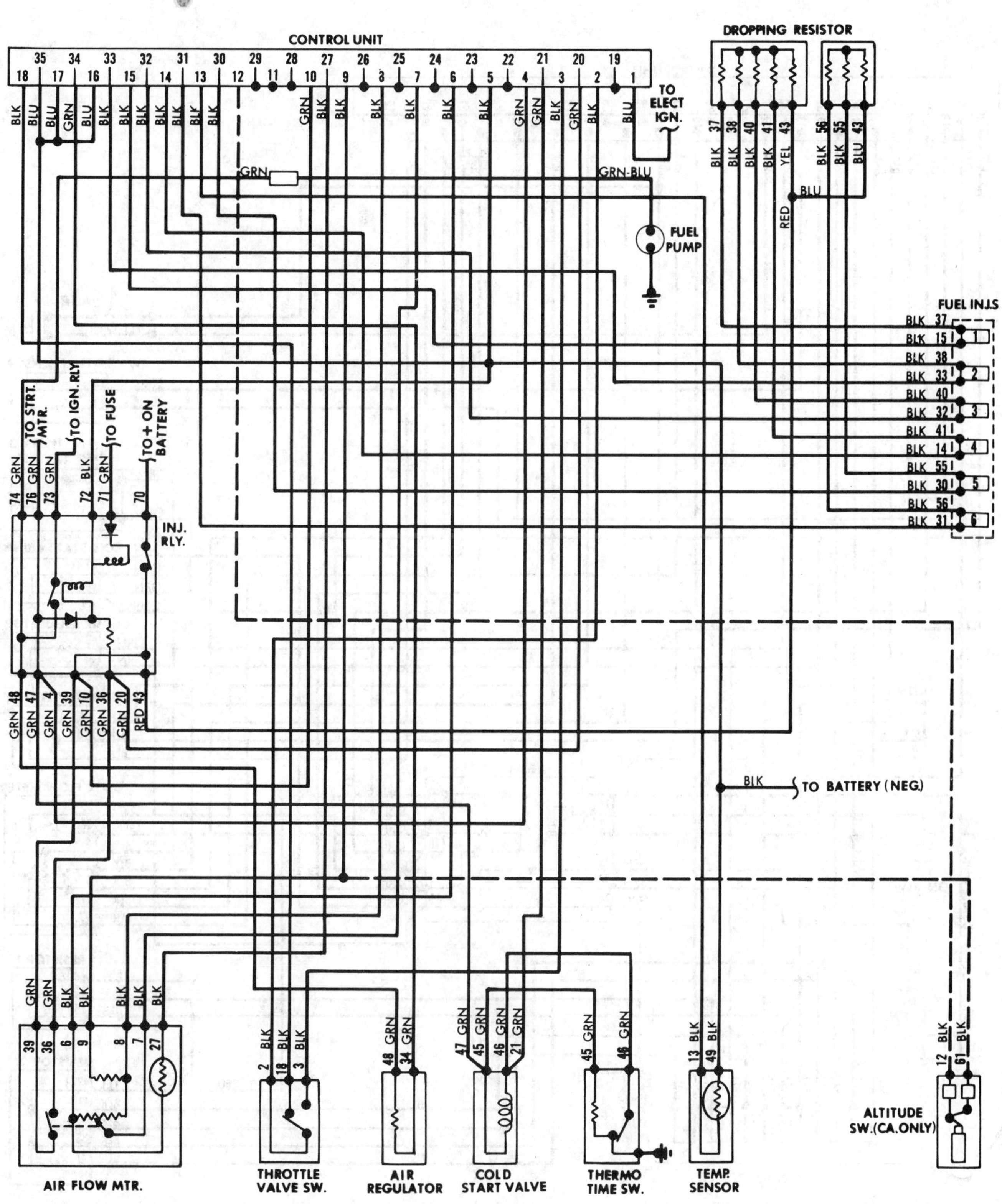

Fuel Injection System Wiring Diagram (Datsun 280Z)

FUEL INJECTION SYSTEMS (Cont.)

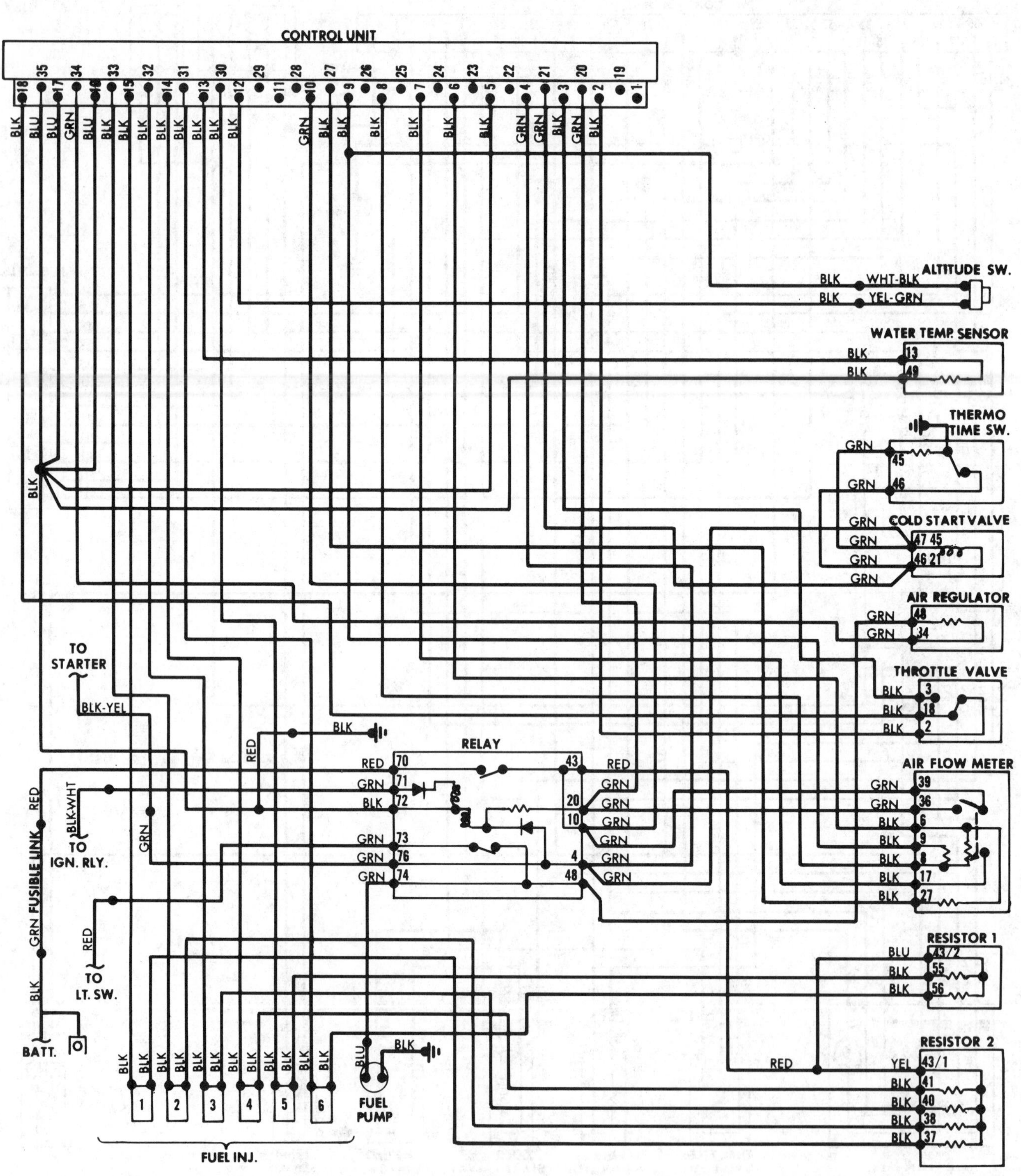

Fuel Injection System Wiring Diagram
(Datsun 810)

FUEL INJECTION SYSTEMS (Cont.)

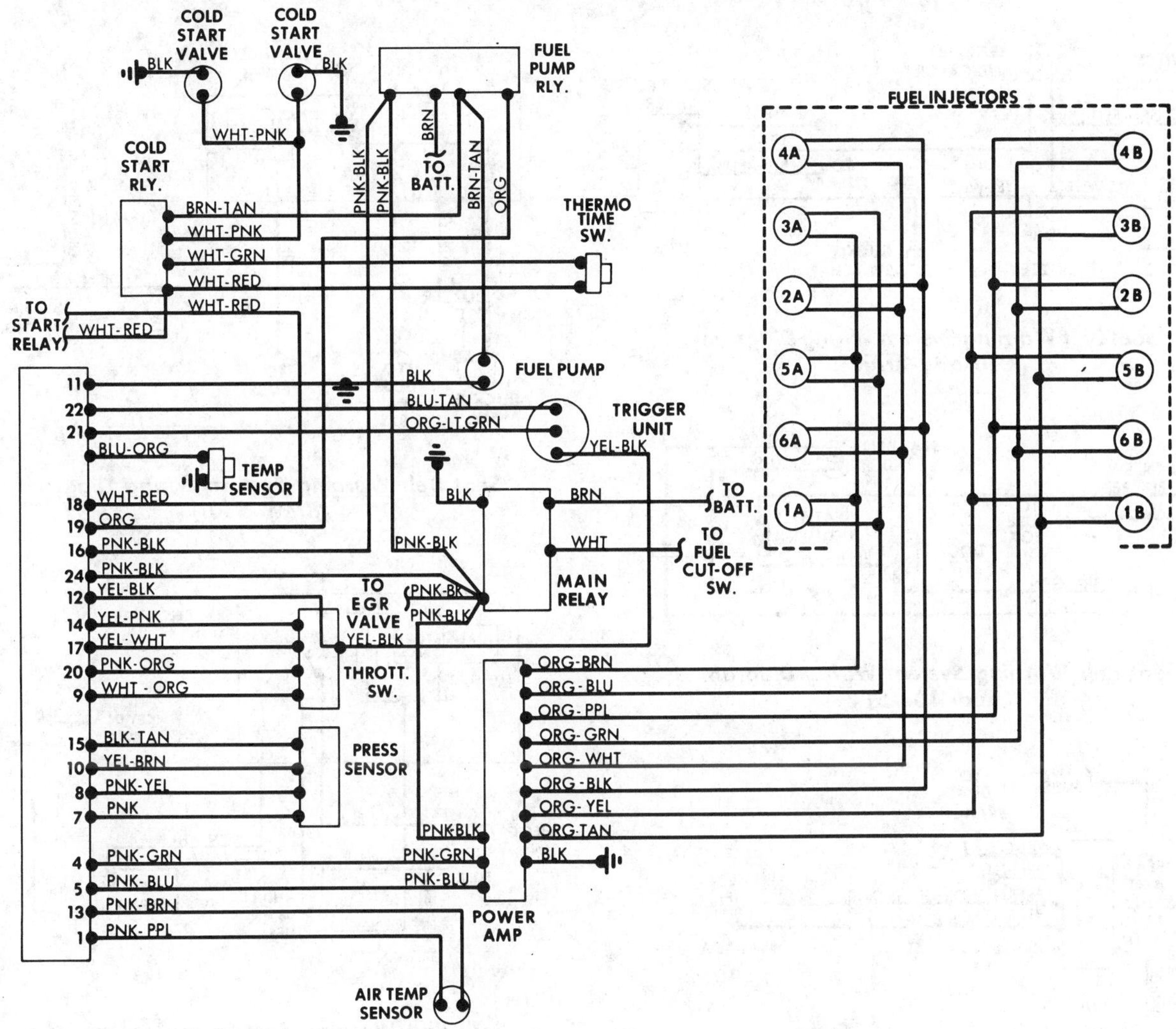

COLD START VALVE
COLD START VALVE
BLK
BLK
FUEL PUMP RLY.
WHT-PNK
COLD START RLY.
PNK-BLK
PNK-BLK
BRN
TO BATT.
BRN-TAN
ORG
BRN-TAN
WHT-PNK
WHT-GRN
WHT-RED
WHT-RED
THERMO TIME SW.
TO START RELAY
WHT-RED
FUEL INJECTORS
4A
3A
2A
5A
6A
1A
4B
3B
2B
5B
6B
1B
11
22
21
BLK
FUEL PUMP
BLU-TAN
ORG-LT.GRN
TRIGGER UNIT
YEL-BLK
BLU-ORG
TEMP SENSOR
18
WHT-RED
19
ORG
16
PNK-BLK
24
PNK-BLK
12
YEL-BLK
14
YEL-PNK
17
YEL-WHT
20
PNK-ORG
9
WHT - ORG
BLK
BRN
TO BATT.
PNK-BLK
WHT
TO FUEL CUT-OFF SW.
MAIN RELAY
TO EGR VALVE
PNK-BK
PNK-BLK
YEL-BLK
THROTT. SW.
15
BLK-TAN
10
YEL-BRN
8
PNK-YEL
7
PNK
PRESS SENSOR
ORG-BRN
ORG-BLU
ORG-PPL
ORG-GRN
ORG-WHT
ORG-BLK
ORG-YEL
ORG-TAN
BLK
PNK-BLK
4
PNK-GRN
PNK-GRN
5
PNK-BLU
PNK-BLU
13
PNK-BRN
1
PNK-PPL
POWER AMP
AIR TEMP SENSOR

Fuel Injection System Wiring Diagram (Jaguar V12)

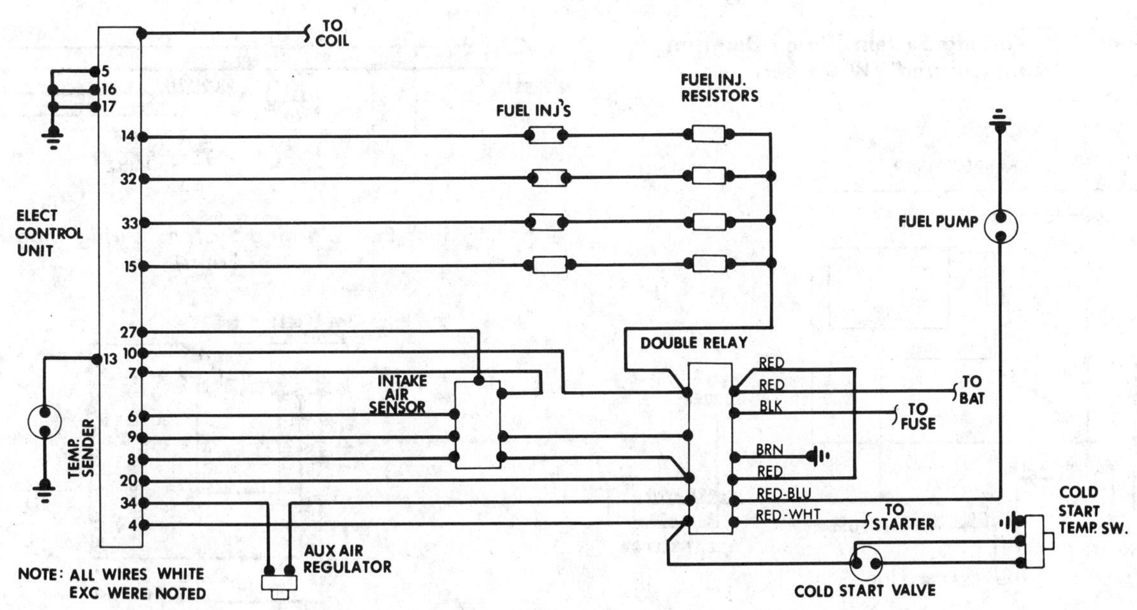

TO COIL
5
16
17
14
32
33
15
FUEL INJ'S
FUEL INJ. RESISTORS
ELECT CONTROL UNIT
FUEL PUMP
27
10
13
7
DOUBLE RELAY
INTAKE AIR SENSOR
RED
RED
BLK
TO BAT
TO FUSE
6
9
8
20
34
4
TEMP. SENDER
BRN
RED
RED-BLU
RED-WHT
TO STARTER
COLD START TEMP. SW.
AUX AIR REGULATOR
COLD START VALVE
NOTE: ALL WIRES WHITE EXC WERE NOTED

Fuel Injection System Wiring Diagram (Volkswagen Type 1 & 2)

SEAT BELT WARNING SYSTEMS

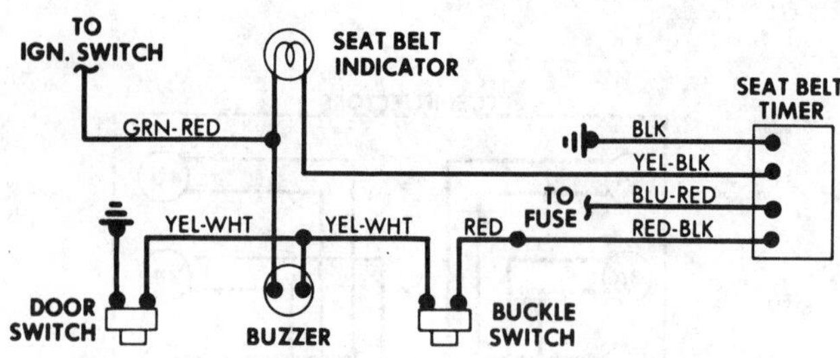

Seat Belt Warning System Wiring Diagram (Colt and Arrow)

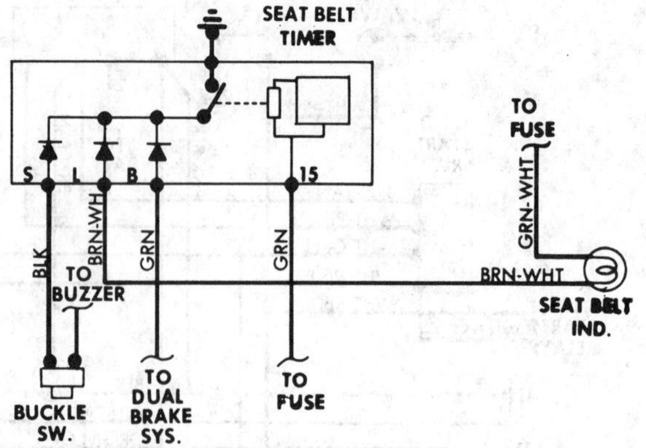

Seat Belt Warning System Wiring Diagram (BMW 530i)

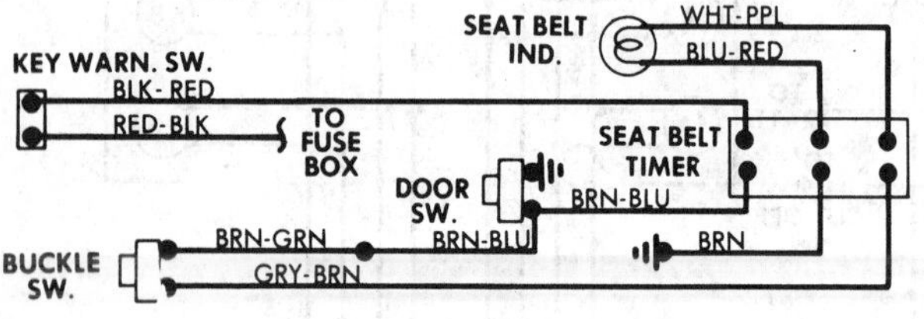

Seat Belt Warning System Wiring Diagram (Audi 100LS)

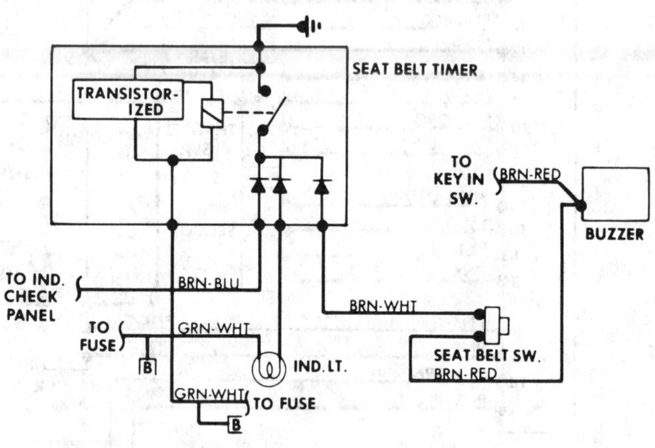

Seat Belt Warning System Wiring Diagram (BMW 630CSi)

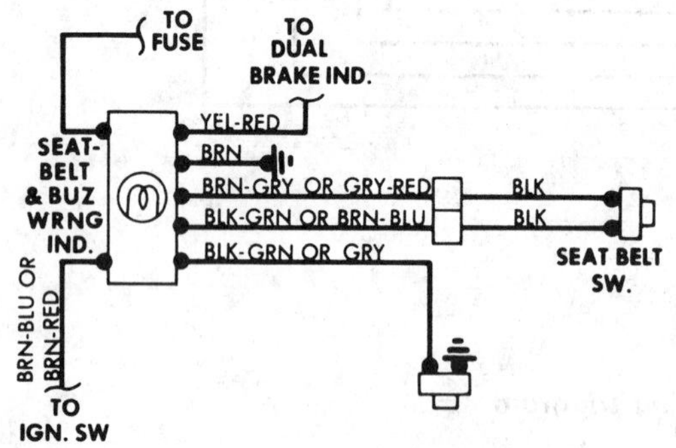

Seat Belt Warning System Wiring Diagram (Audi Fox and VW Dasher)

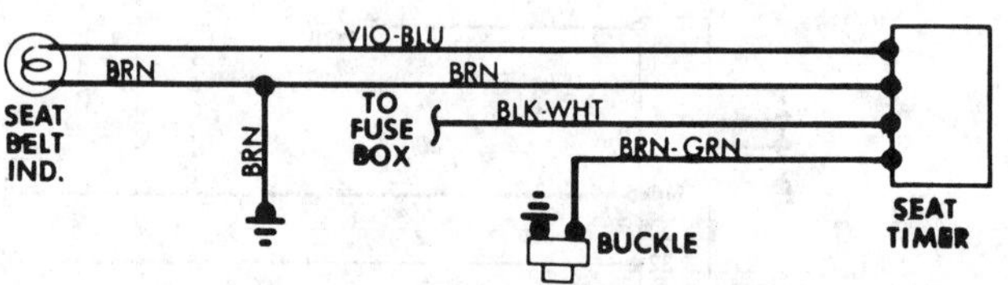

Seat Belt Warning System Wiring Diagram (Capri)

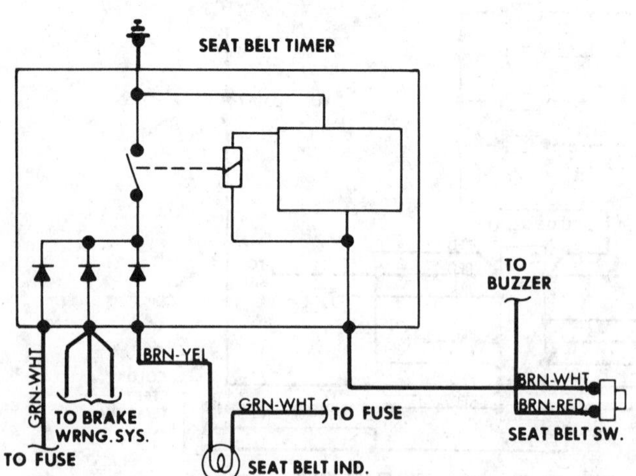

Seat Belt Warning System Wiring Diagram (BMW 320i)

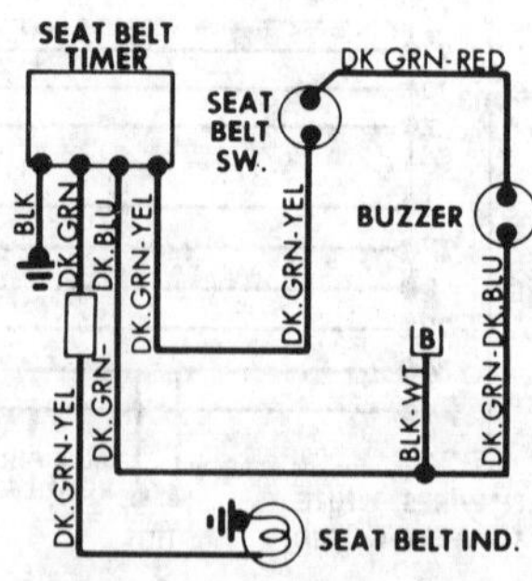

Seat Belt Warning System Wiring Diagram (Courier)

SEAT BELT WARNING SYSTEMS (Cont.)

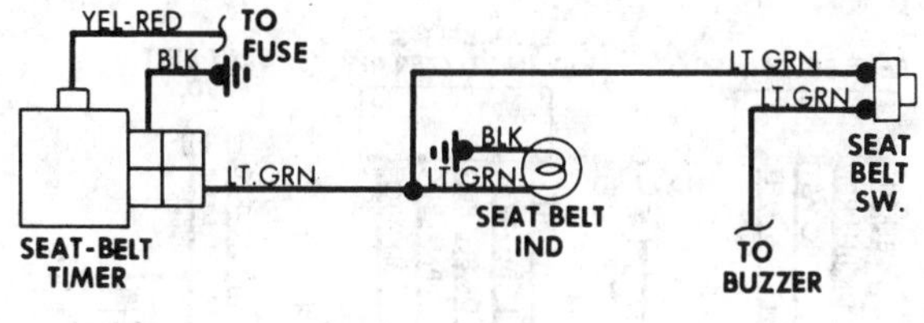

Seat Belt Warning System Wiring Diagram (Datsun F10)

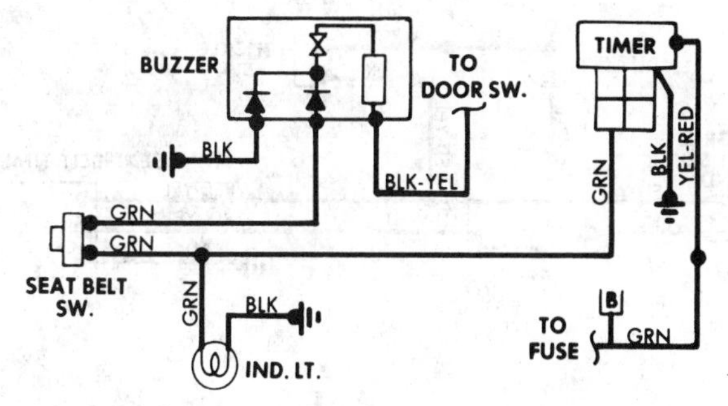

Seat Belt Warning System Wiring Diagram (Datsun 280Z)

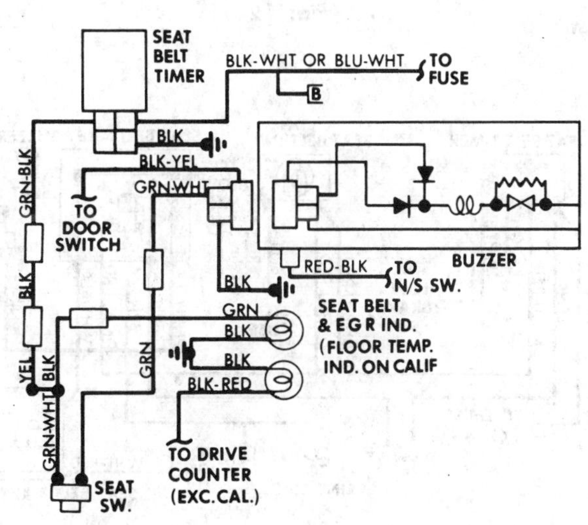

Seat Belt Warning System Wiring Diagram (Datsun B210)

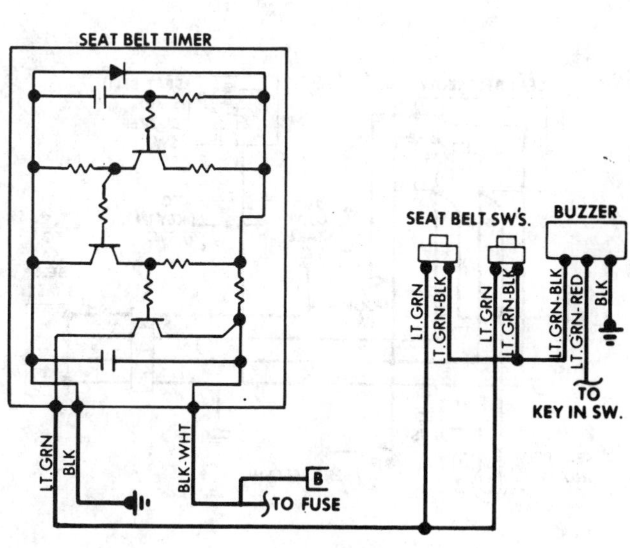

Seat Belt Warning System Wiring Diagram (Datsun 710)

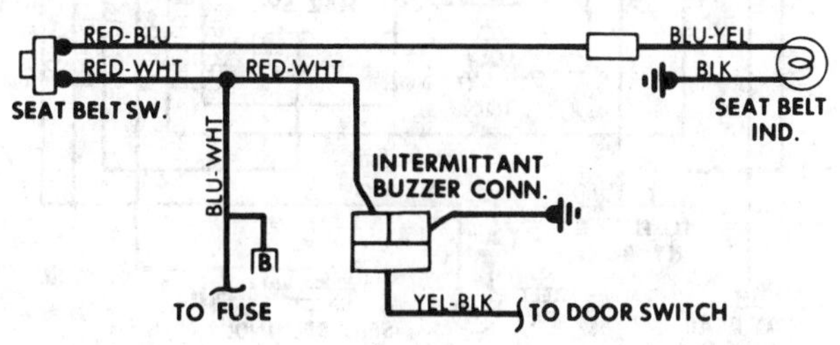

Seat Belt Warning System Wiring Diagram (Datsun 200SX)

Seat Belt Warning System Wiring Diagram (Datsun 810)

SEAT BELT WARNING SYSTEMS (Cont.)

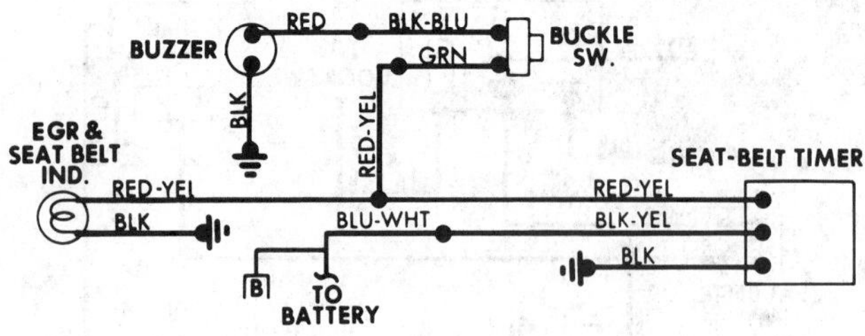

Seat Belt Warning System Wiring Diagram (Datsun 620 Pickup)

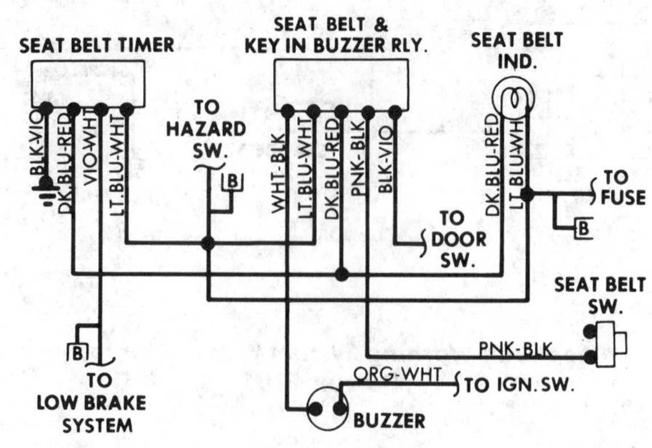

Seat Belt Warning System Wiring Diagram (Fiat 124)

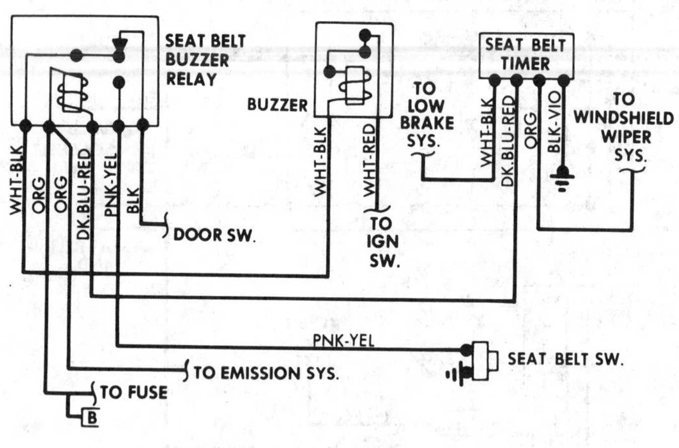

Seat Belt Warning System Wiring Diagram (Fiat X1/9)

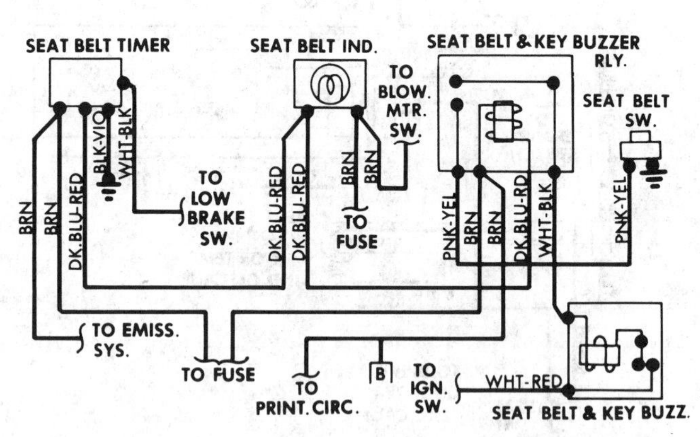

Seat Belt Warning System Wiring Diagram (Fiat 128)

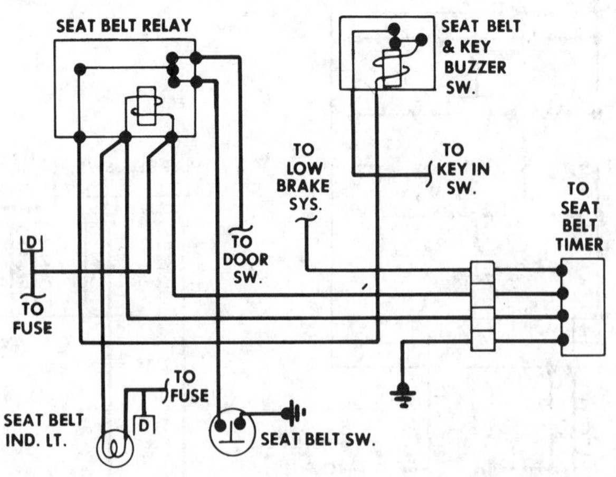

Seat Belt Warning System Wiring Diagram (Fiat 3P)

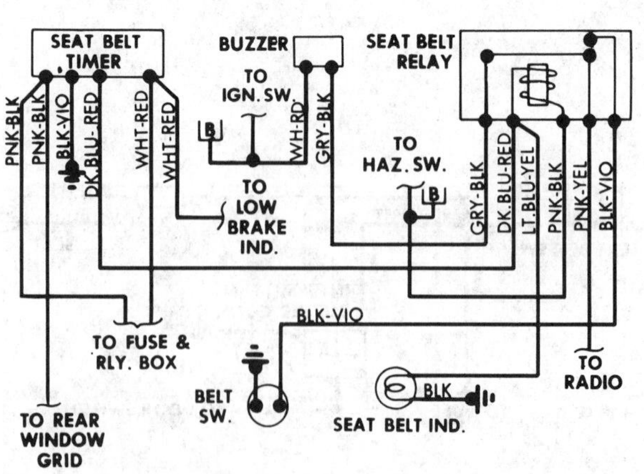

Seat Belt Warning System Wiring Diagram (Fiat 131)

SEAT BELT WARNING SYSTEMS (Cont.)

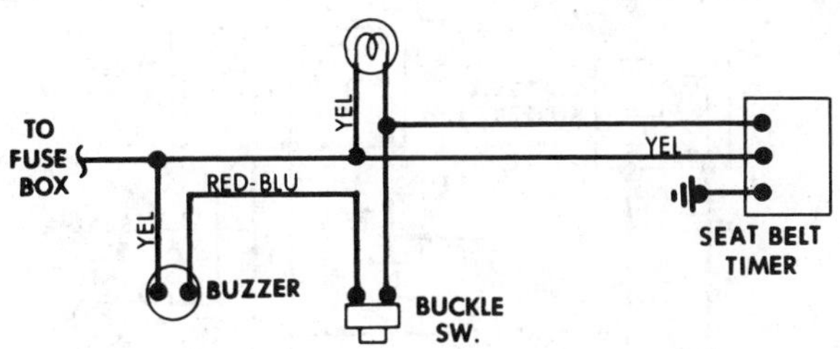

Seat Belt Warning System Wiring Diagram (Honda)

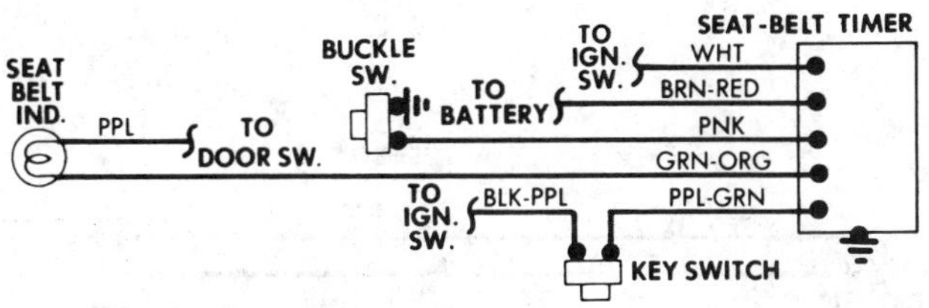

Seat Belt Warning System Wiring Diagram (Jaguar)

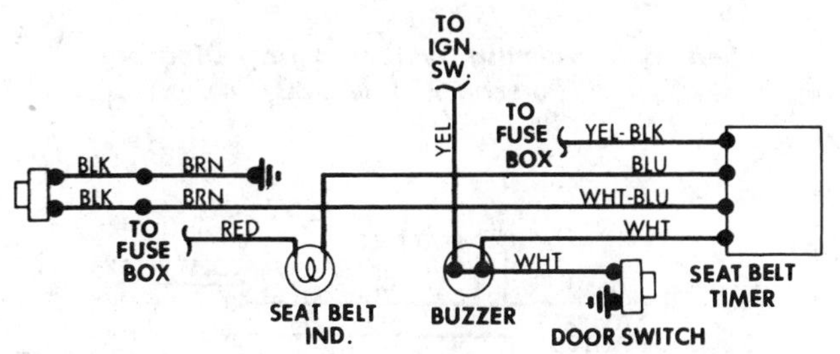

Seat Belt Warning System Wiring Diagram (Lancia)

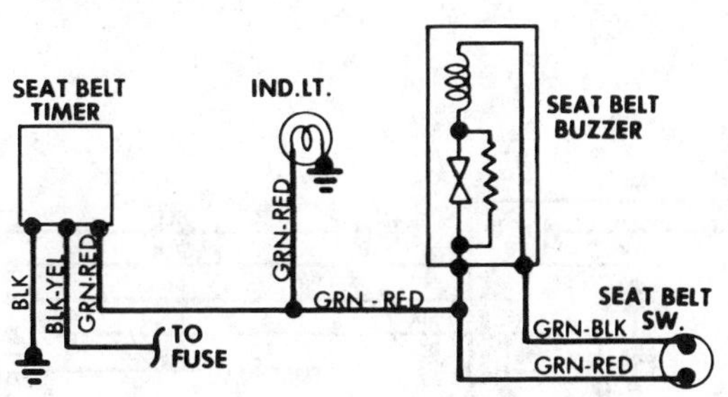

Seat Belt Warning System Wiring Diagram (LUV)

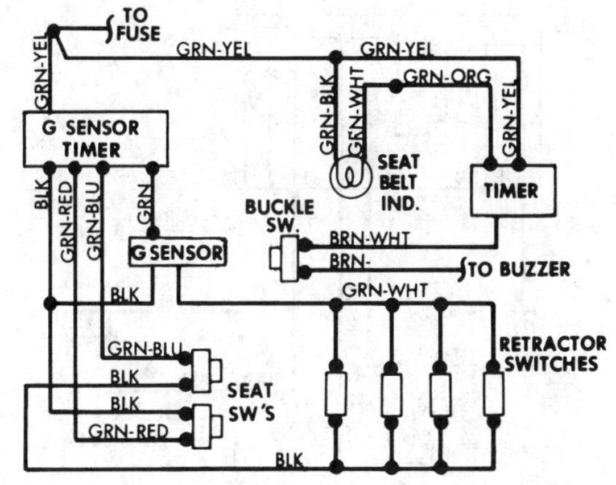

Seat Belt Warning System Wiring Diagram (Mazda 808)

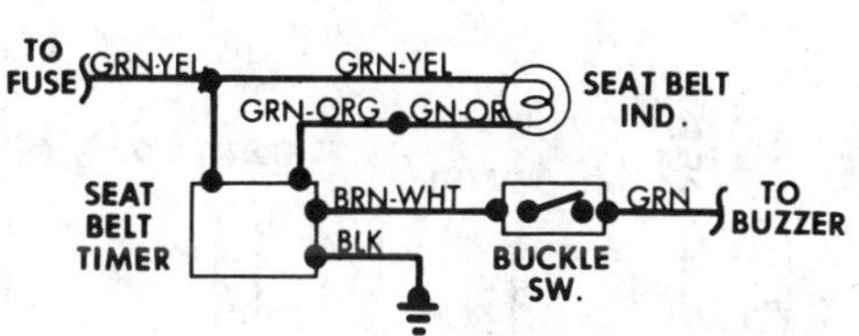

Seat Belt Warning System Wiring Diagram (Mazda RX3SP and GLC)

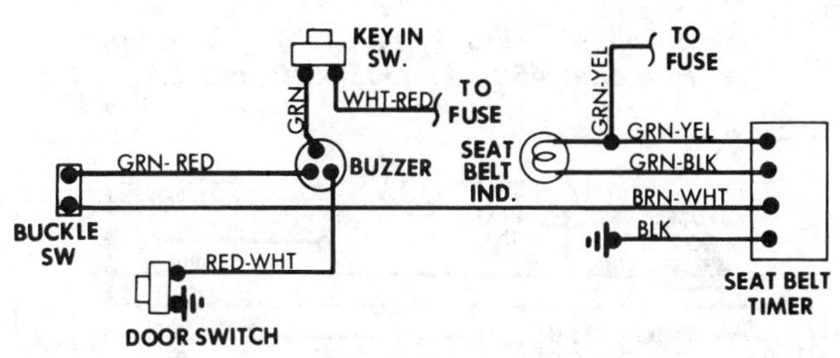

Seat Belt Warning System Wiring Diagram (Mazda Cosmo)

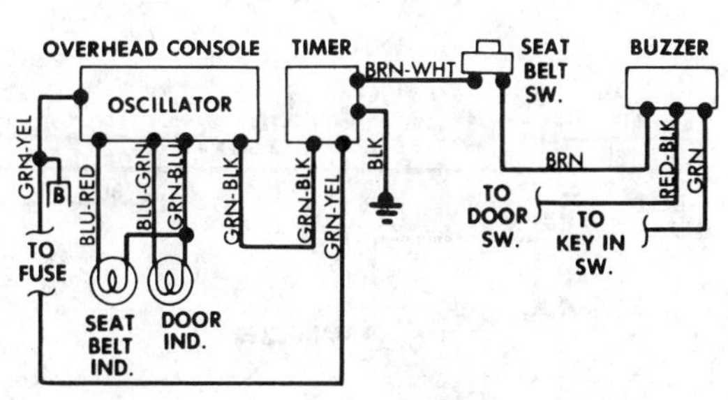

Seat Belt Warning System Wiring Diagram (Mazda RX4)

SEAT BELT WARNING SYSTEMS (Cont.)

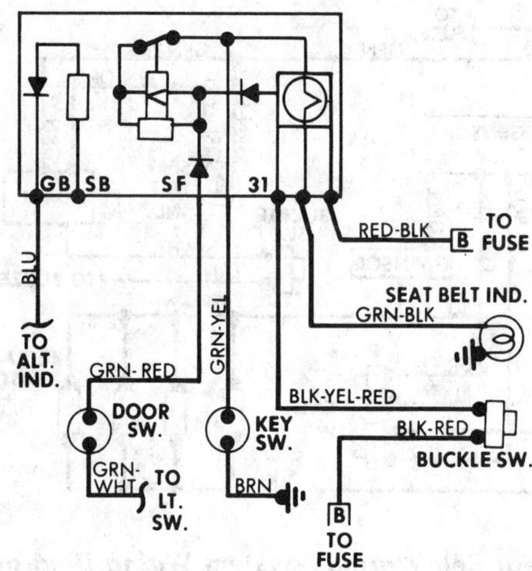

Seat Belt Warning System Wiring Diagram (Mercedes 280SE, 230, 240D and 300D)

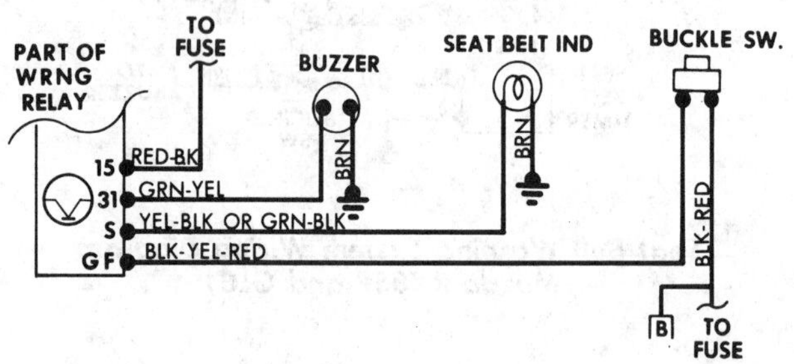

Seat Belt Warning System Wiring Diagram (Mercedes 450SEL, 450SL-SLC and 6.9)

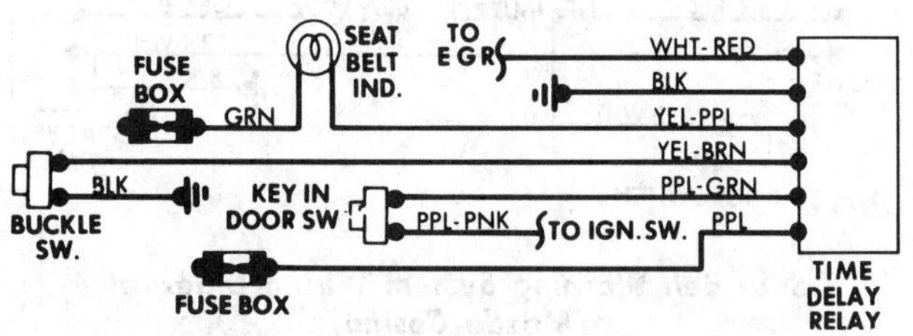

Seat Belt Warning System Wiring Diagram (MG Midget)

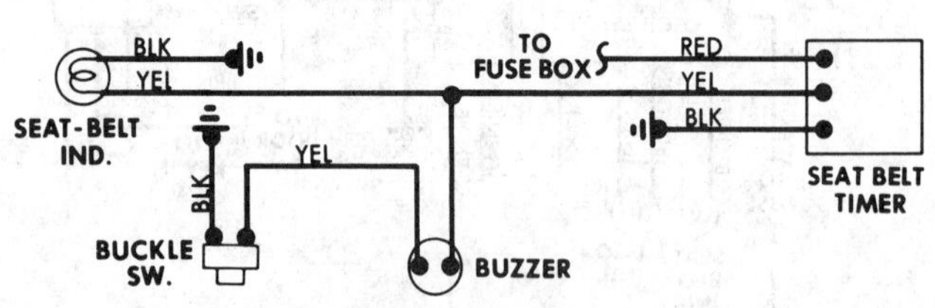

Seat Belt Warning System Wiring Diagram (Opel)

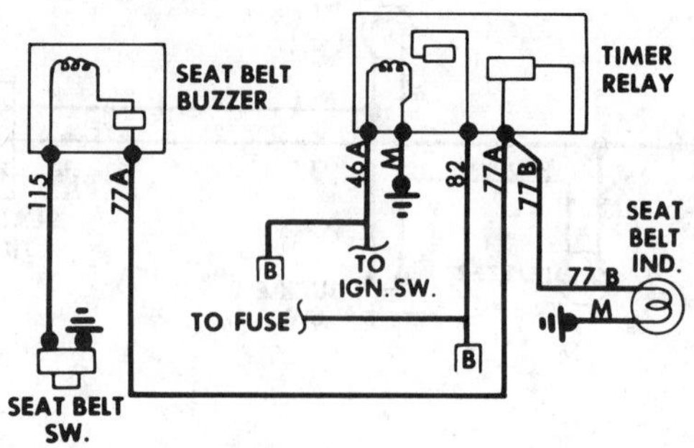

Seat Belt Warning System Wiring Diagram (Peugeot 604)

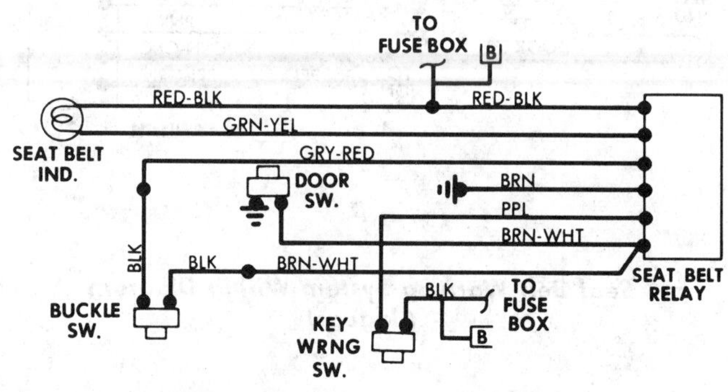

Seat Belt Warning System Wiring Diagram (Porsche 911 & 930)

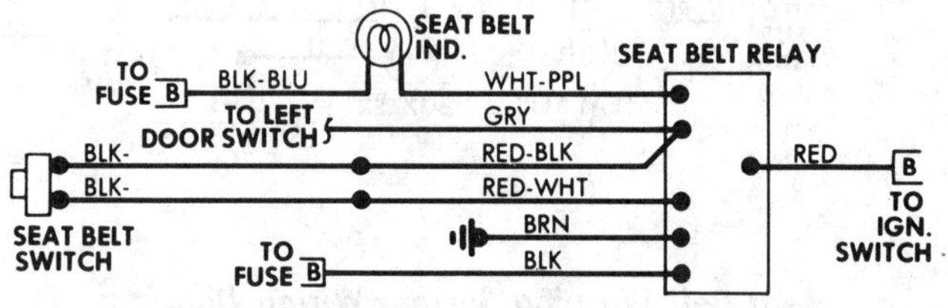

Seat Belt Warning System Wiring Diagram (Porsche 924)

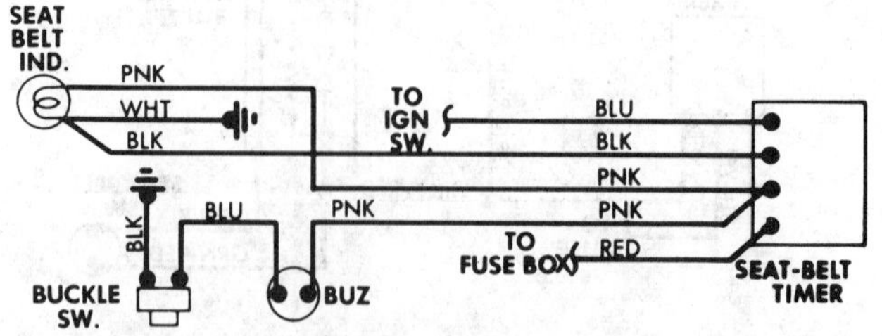

Seat Belt Warning System Wiring Diagram (Renault R-5)

SEAT BELT WARNING SYSTEMS (Cont.)

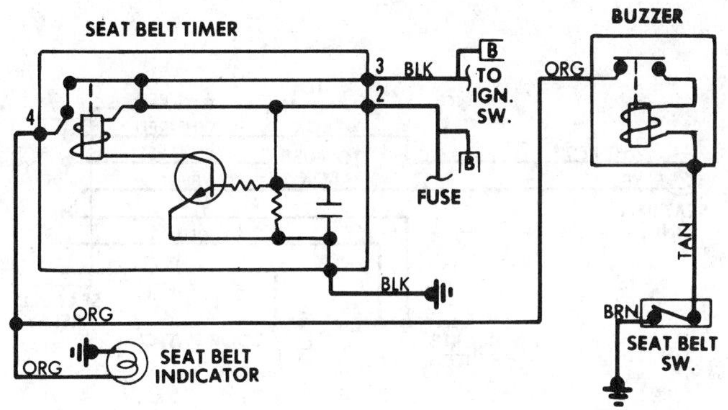

Seat Belt Warning System Wiring Diagram (Renault Gordini)

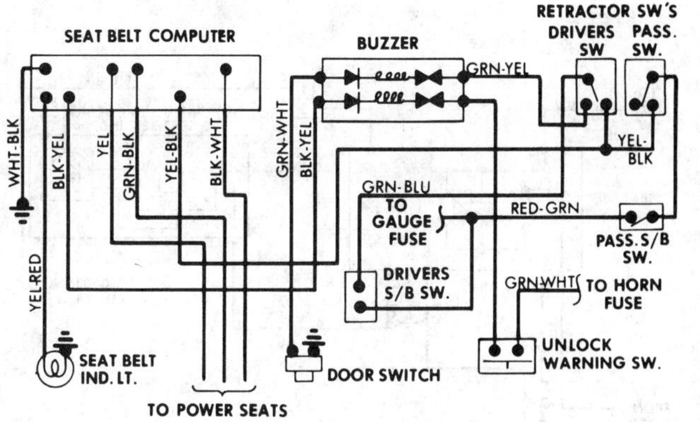

Seat Belt Warning System Wiring Diagram (Toyota Corolla)

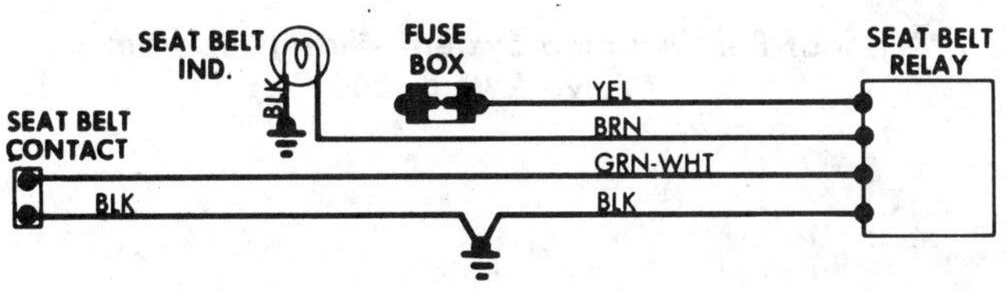

Seat Belt Warning System Wiring Diagram (Saab 99)

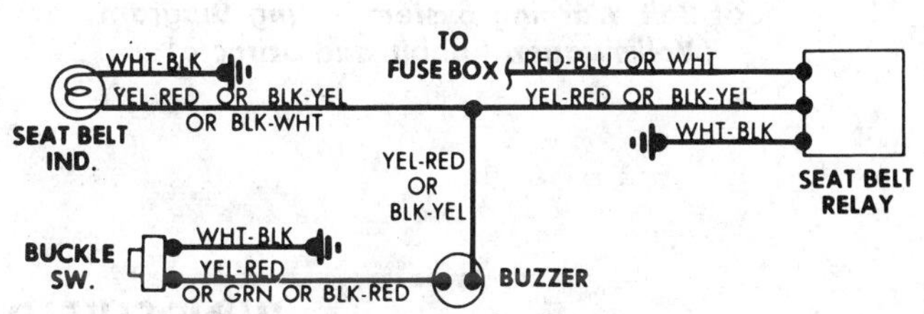

Seat Belt Warning System Wiring Diagram (Toyota Corona)

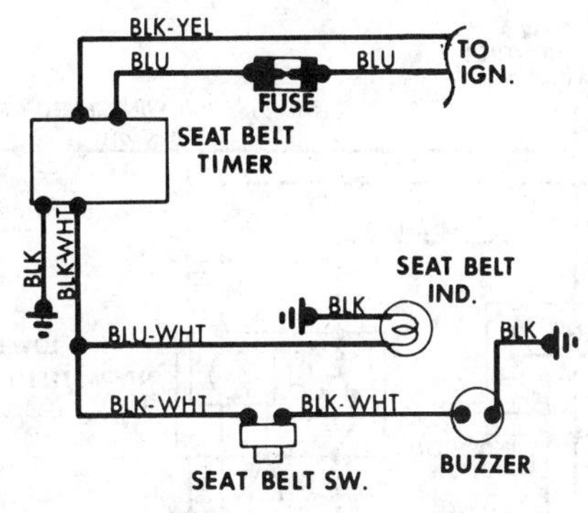

Seat Belt Warning System Wiring Diagram (Subaru)

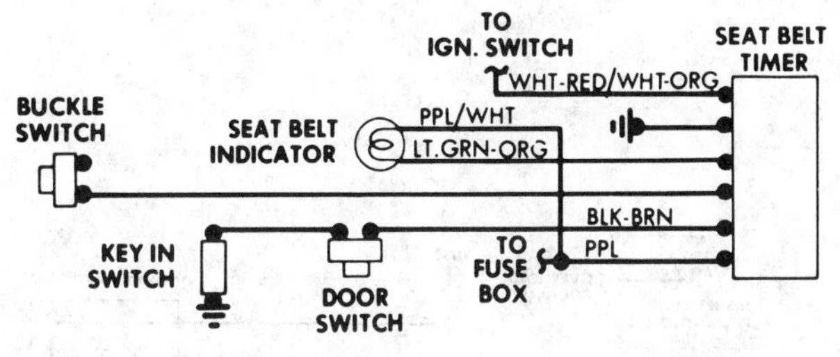

Seat Belt Warning System Wiring Diagram (Triumph TR7 & Spitfire)

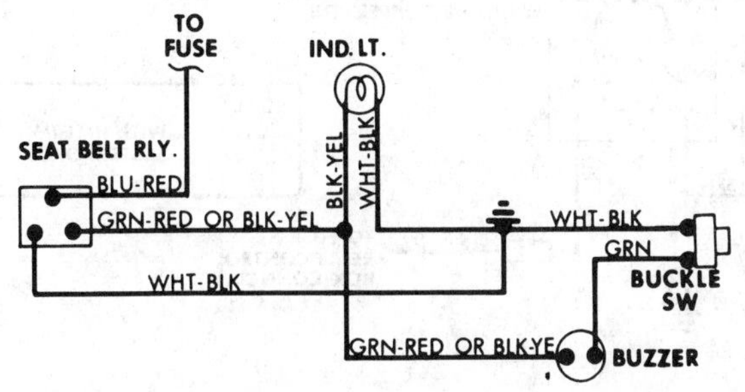

Seat Belt Warning System Wiring Diagram (Toyota Celica and Land Cruiser FJ40)

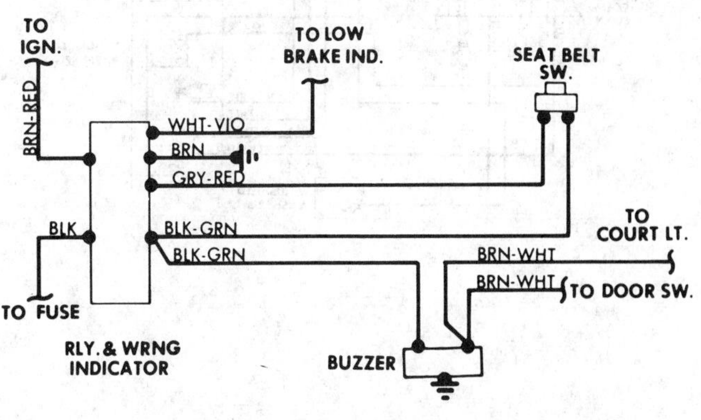

Seat Belt Warning System Wiring Diagram (Volkswagen Type 1)

SEAT BELT WARNING SYSTEMS (Cont.)

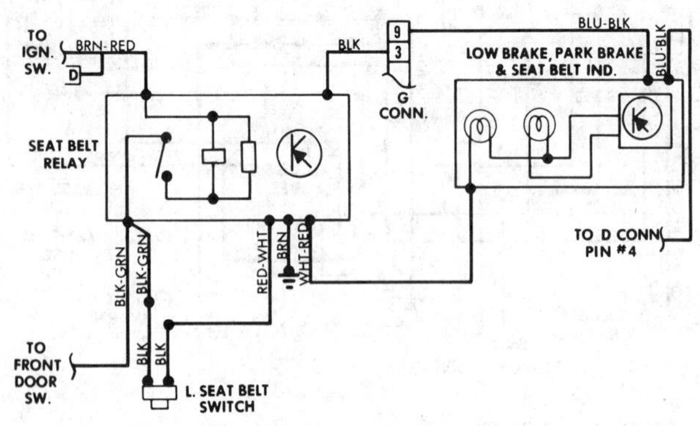

Seat Belt Warning System Wiring Diagram (Volkswagen Rabbit and Scirocco)

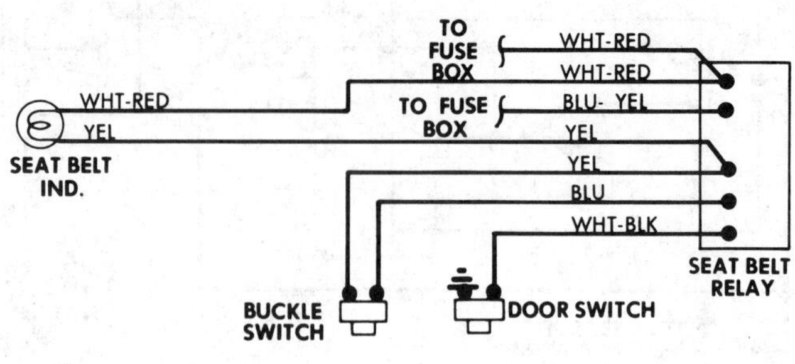

Seat Belt Warning System Wiring Diagram (Volvo 240 & 260)

WINDSHIELD WIPER SYSTEMS

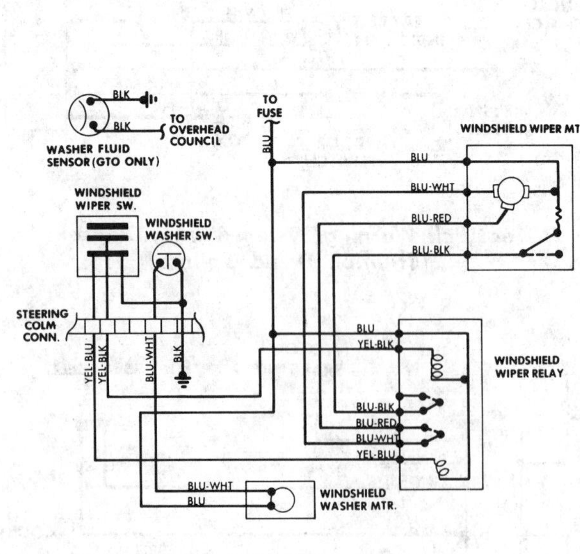

Windshield Wiper System Wiring Diagram (Arrow and Colt)

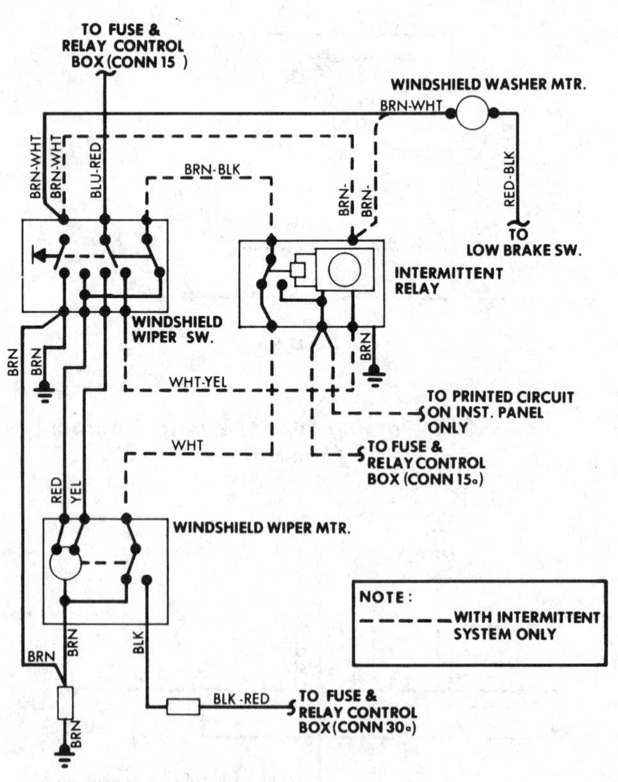

Windshield Wiper System Wiring Diagram (Audi 100LS)

WINDSHIELD WIPER SYSTEMS (Cont.)

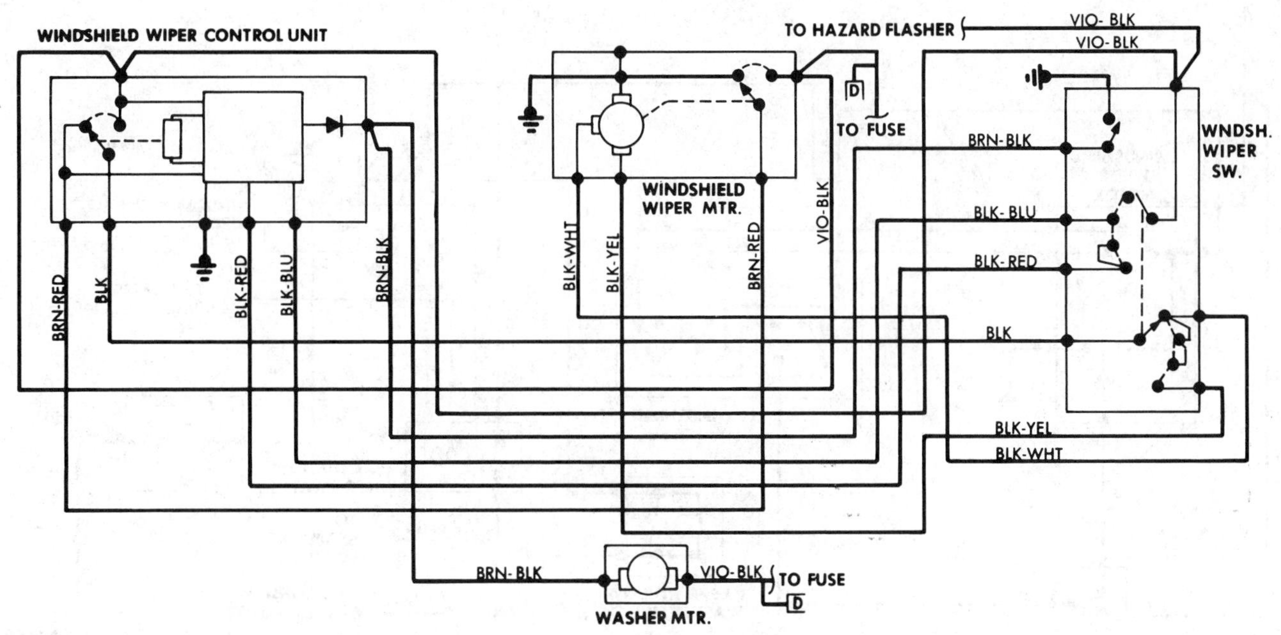

Windhield Wiper System Wiring Diagram (BMW 320i)

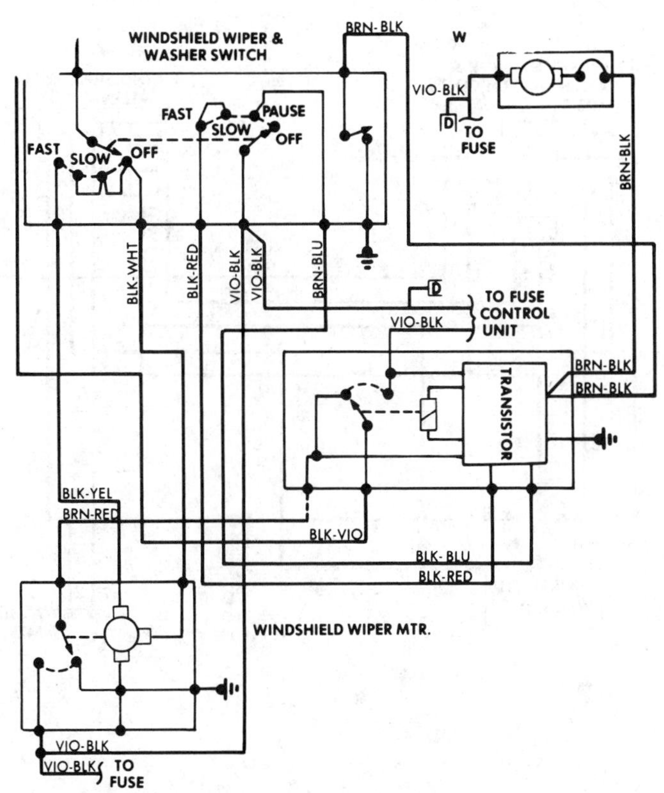

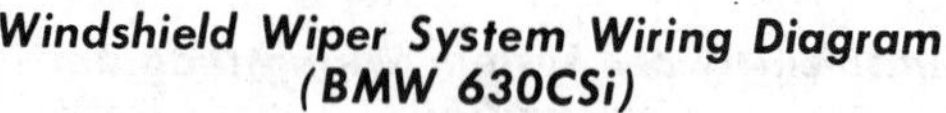

Windshield Wiper System Wiring Diagram (BMW 630CSi)

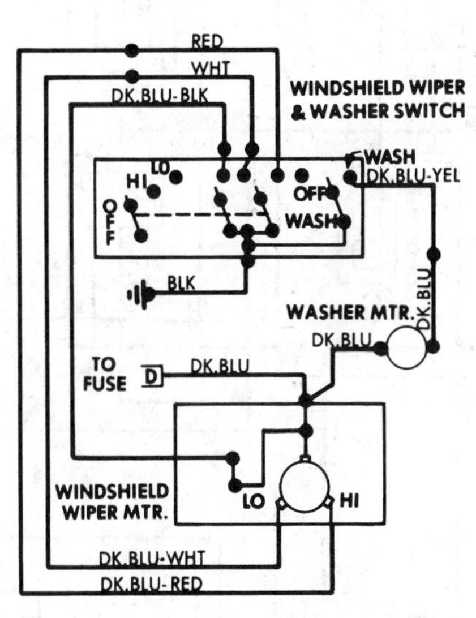

Windshield Wiper System Wiring Diagram (Courier)

WINDSHIELD WIPER SYSTEMS (Cont.)

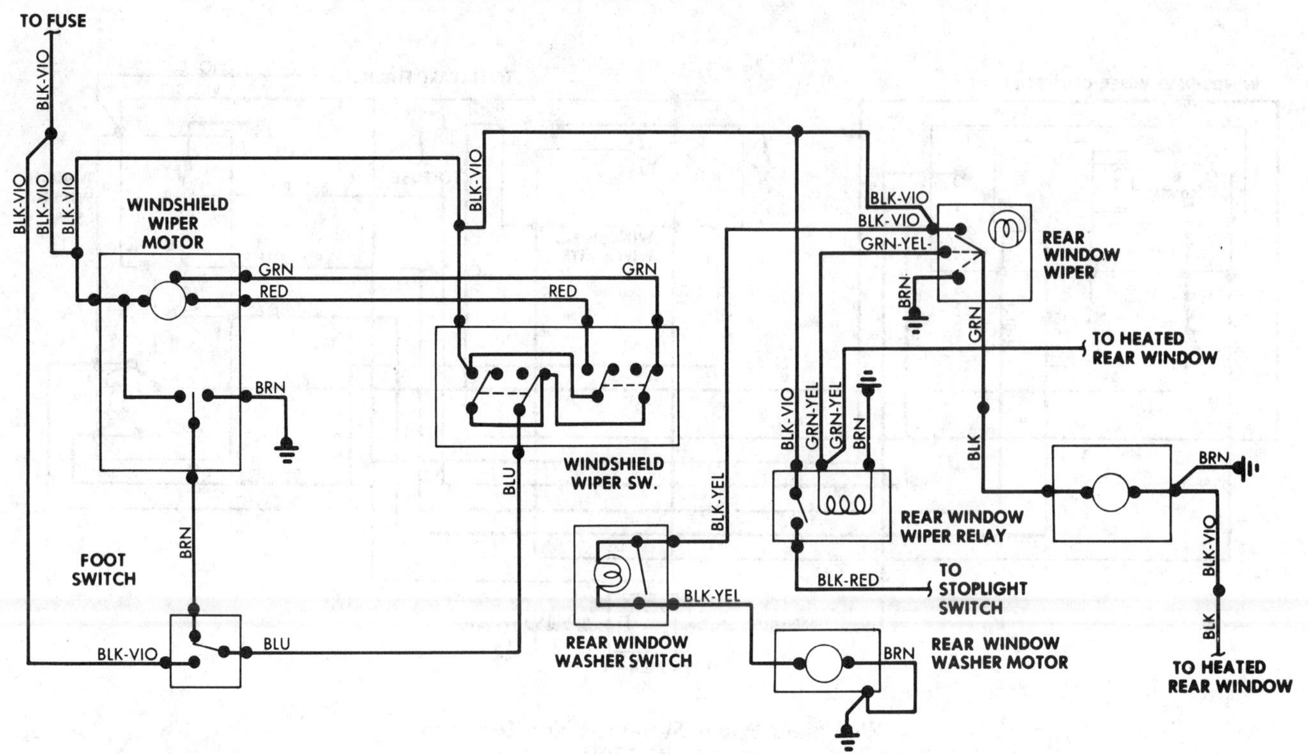

Windshield Wiper System Wiring Diagram (Capri)

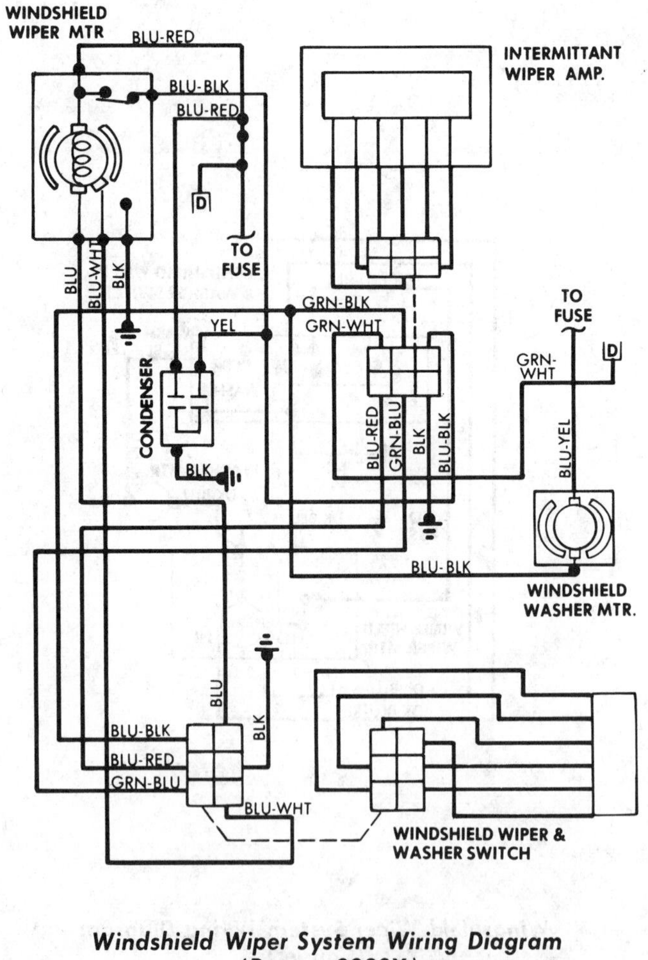

WINDSHIELD WIPER MTR
BLU-RED
BLU-BLK
INTERMITTANT WIPER AMP.
D
TO FUSE
BLU
BLU-WHT
BLK
GRN-BLK
GRN-WHT
YEL
CONDENSER
BLU-RED
GRN-BLU
BLU-BLK
GRN-WHT
BLU-YEL
WINDSHIELD WASHER MTR.
BLU-WHT
WINDSHIELD WIPER & WASHER SWITCH

Windshield Wiper System Wiring Diagram (Datsun 200SX)

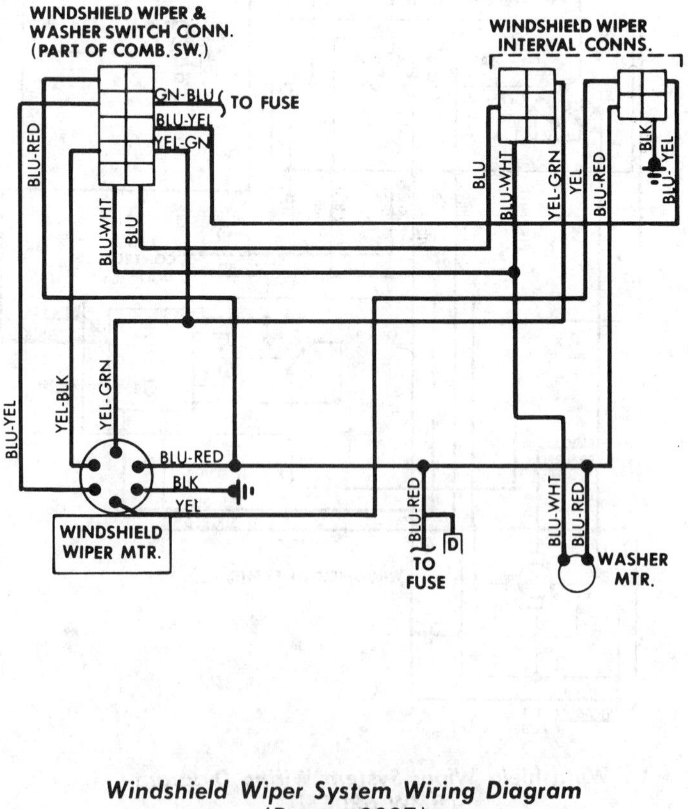

WINDSHIELD WIPER & WASHER SWITCH CONN. (PART OF COMB. SW.)
GN-BLU
BLU-YEL
YEL-GN
TO FUSE
WINDSHIELD WIPER INTERVAL CONNS.
BLU-RED
BLU-WHT
BLU
YEL-GRN
YEL
BLK
BLU-YEL
YEL-BLK
YEL-GRN
WINDSHIELD WIPER MTR.
D
TO FUSE
WASHER MTR.

Windshield Wiper System Wiring Diagram (Datsun 280Z)

WINDSHIELD WIPER SYSTEMS (Cont.)

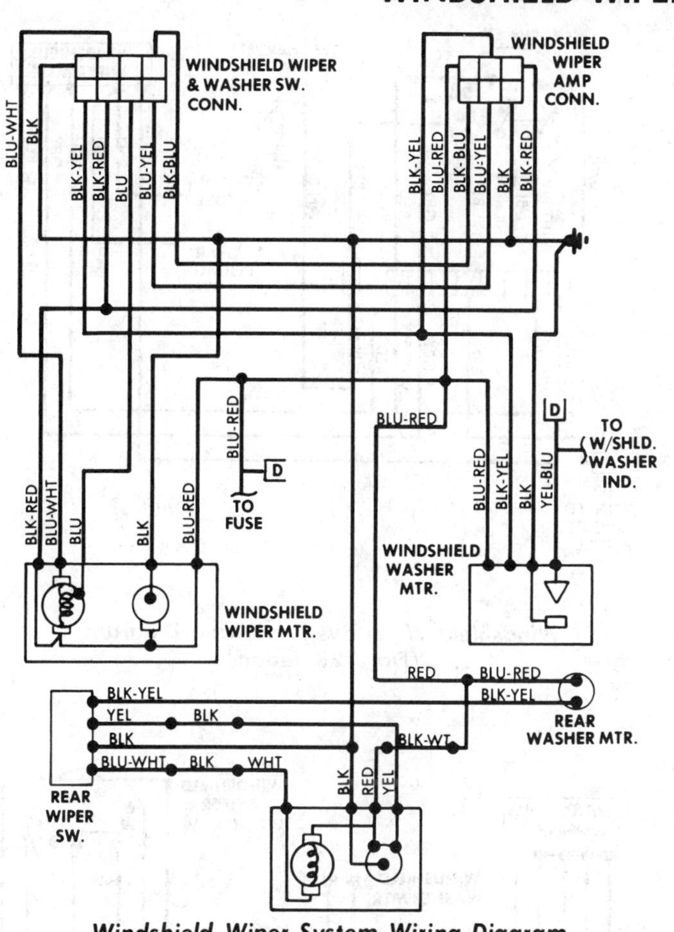

Windshield Wiper System Wiring Diagram (Datsun 810)

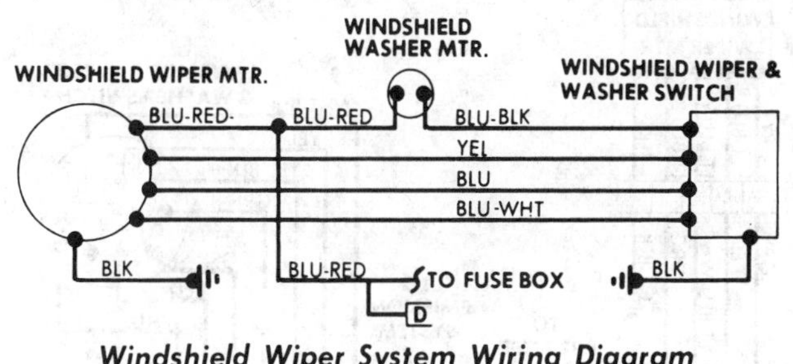

Windshield Wiper System Wiring Diagram (Datsun Pickup)

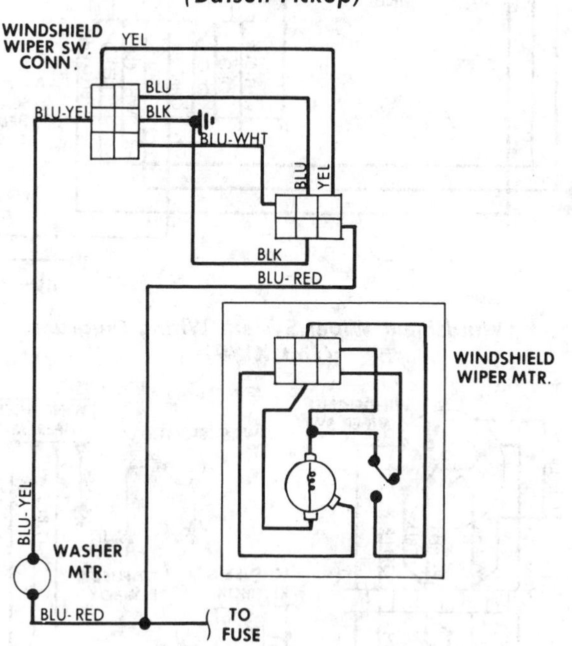

Windshield Wiper System Wiring Diagram (Datsun F10)

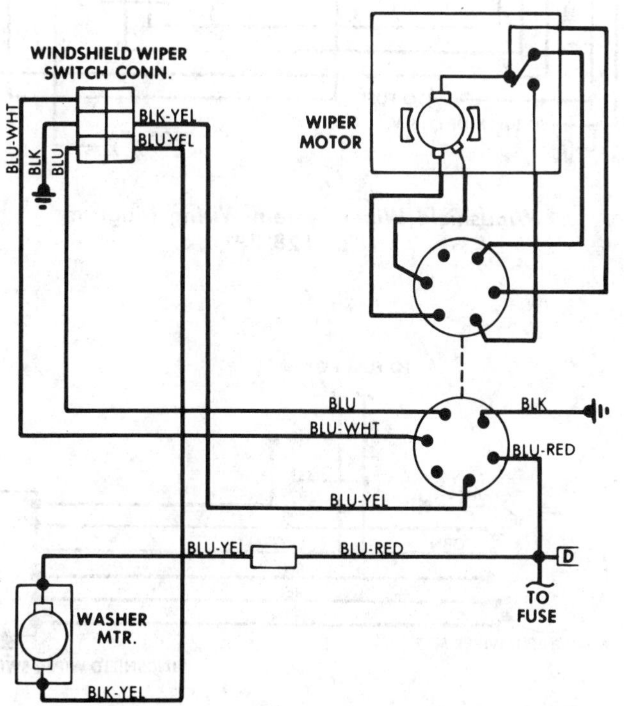

Windshield Wiper System Wiring Diagram (Datsun B210)

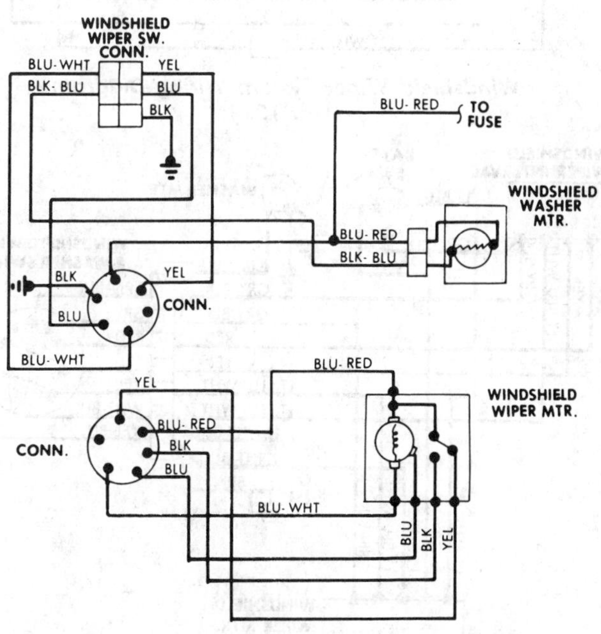

Windshield Wiper System Wiring Diagram (Datsun 710)

WINDSHIELD WIPER SYSTEMS (Cont.)

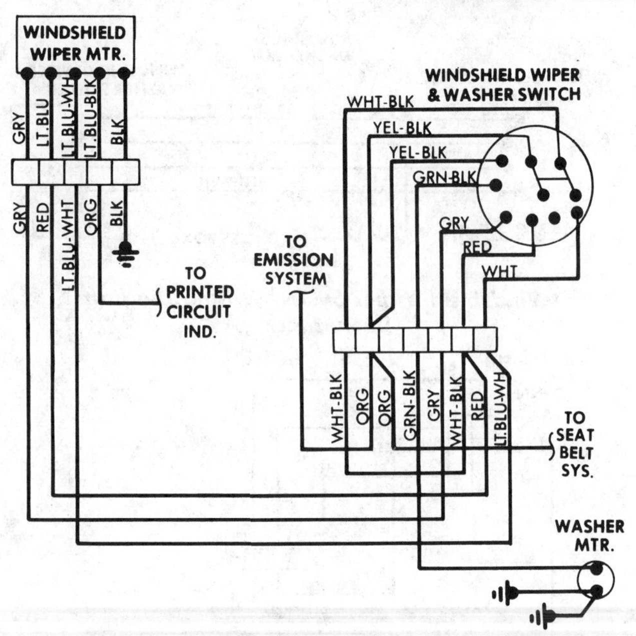

Windshield Wiper System Wiring Diagram (Fiat X1/9)

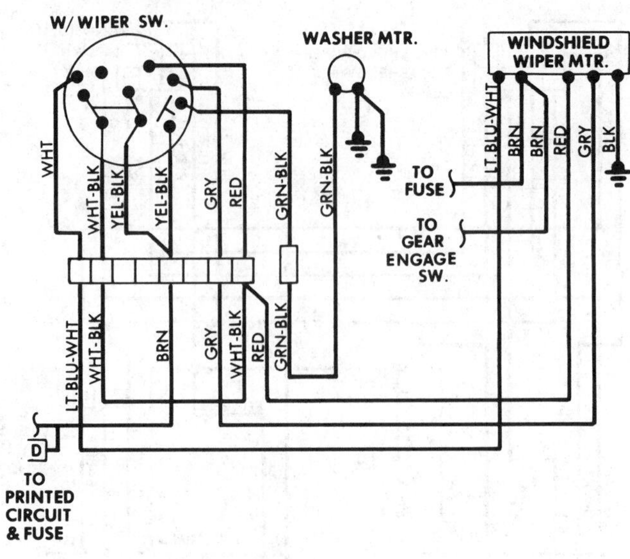

Windshield Wiper System Wiring Diagram (Fiat 128 Sedan)

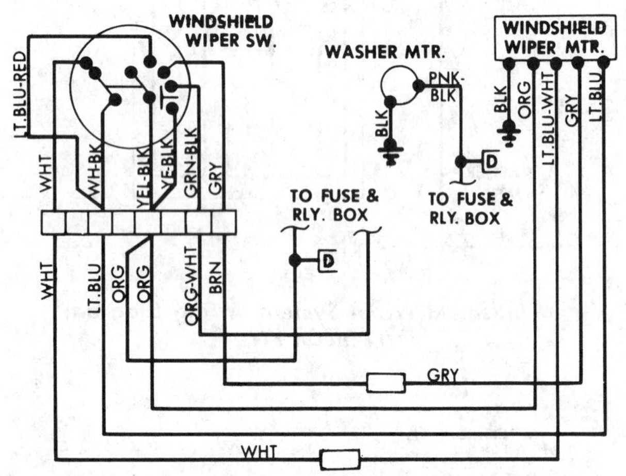

Windshield Wiper System Wiring Diagram (Fiat 131)

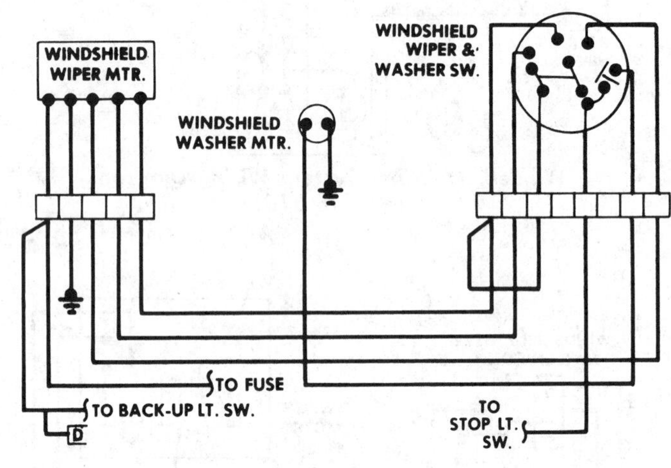

Windshield Wiper System Wiring Diagram (Fiat 128 3P)

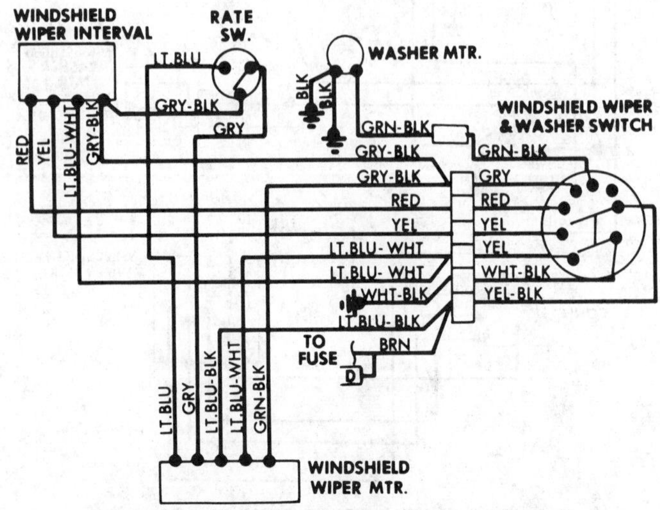

Windshield Wiper System Wiring Diagram (Fiat 124)

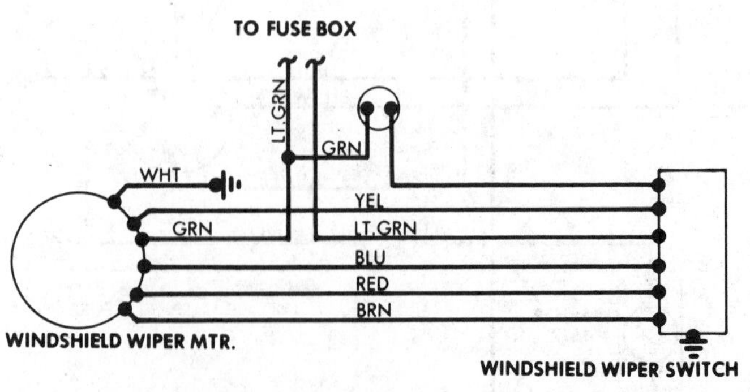

Windshield Wiper System Wiring Diagram (Jaguar)

WINDSHIELD WIPER SYSTEMS (Cont.)

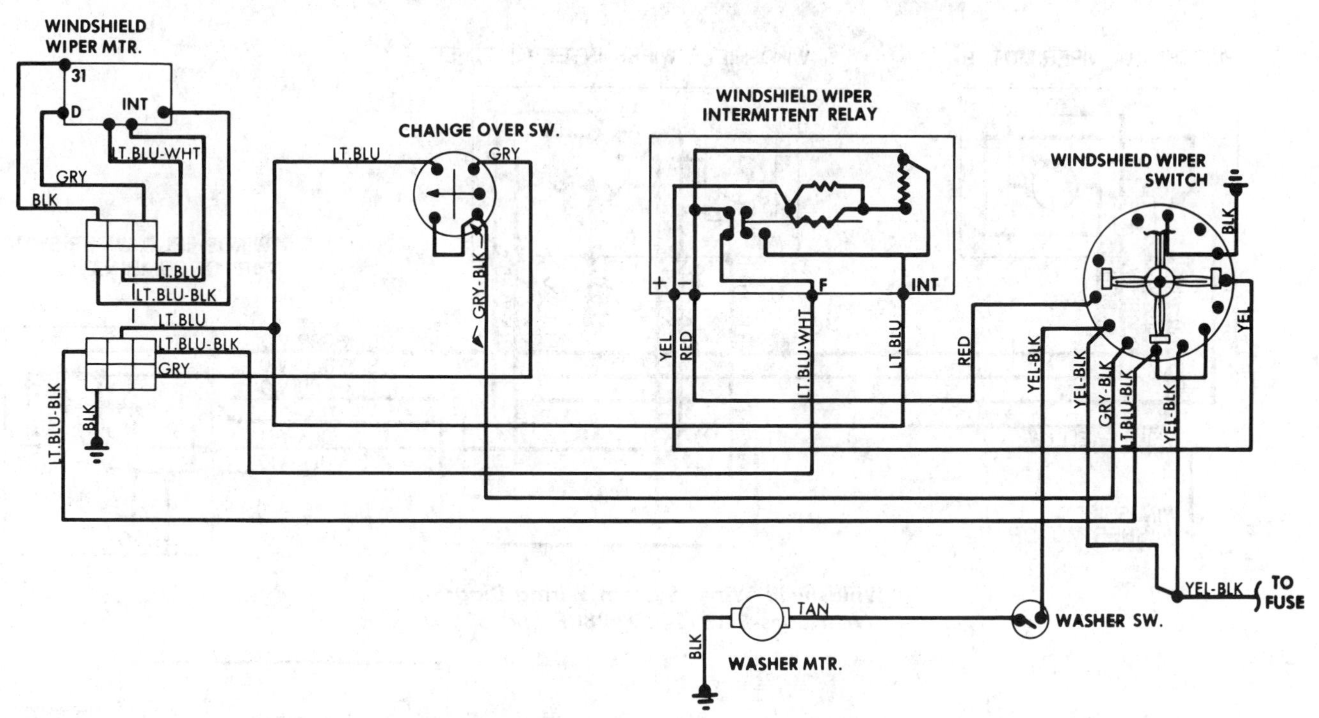

Windshield Wiper System Wiring Diagram
(Lancia)

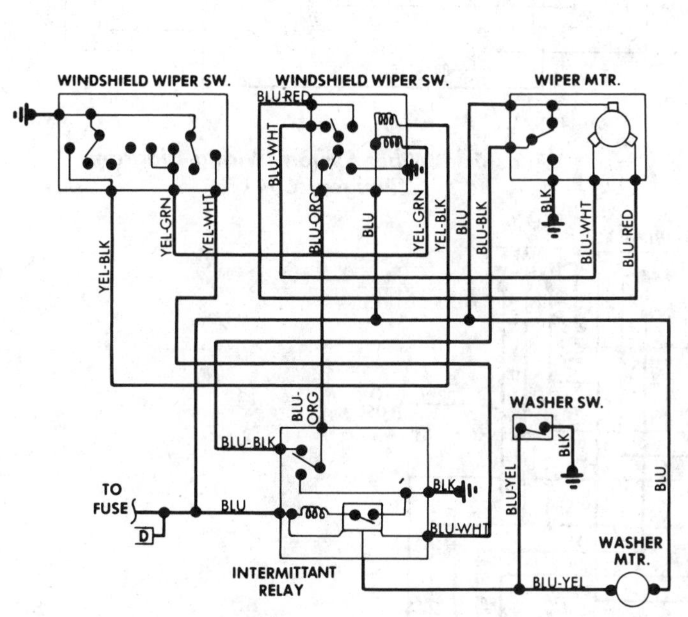

Windshield Wiper System Wiring Diagram
(Mazda RX-4)

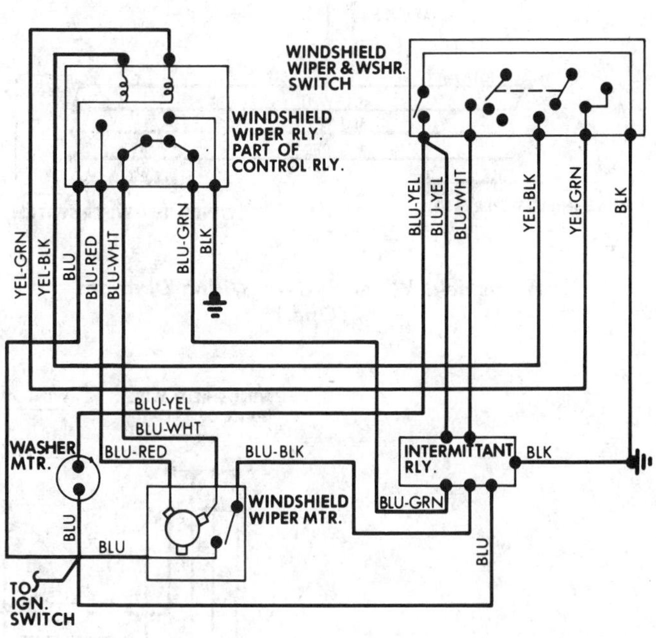

Windshield Wiper System Wiring Diagram
(Mazda Cosmo)

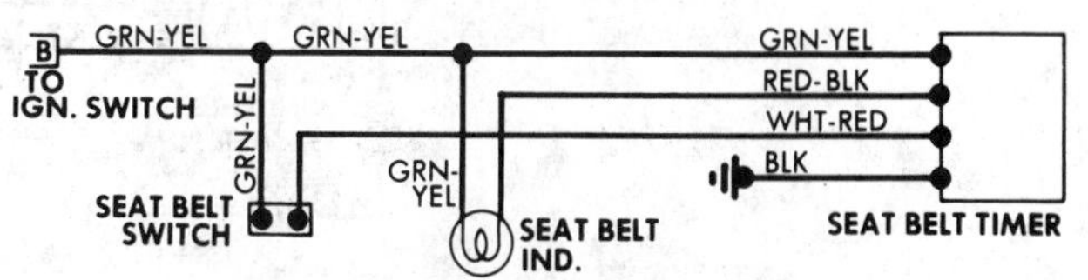

Windshield Wiper System Wiring Diagram
(Mazda Pickup)

WINDSHIELD WIPER SYSTEMS (Cont.)

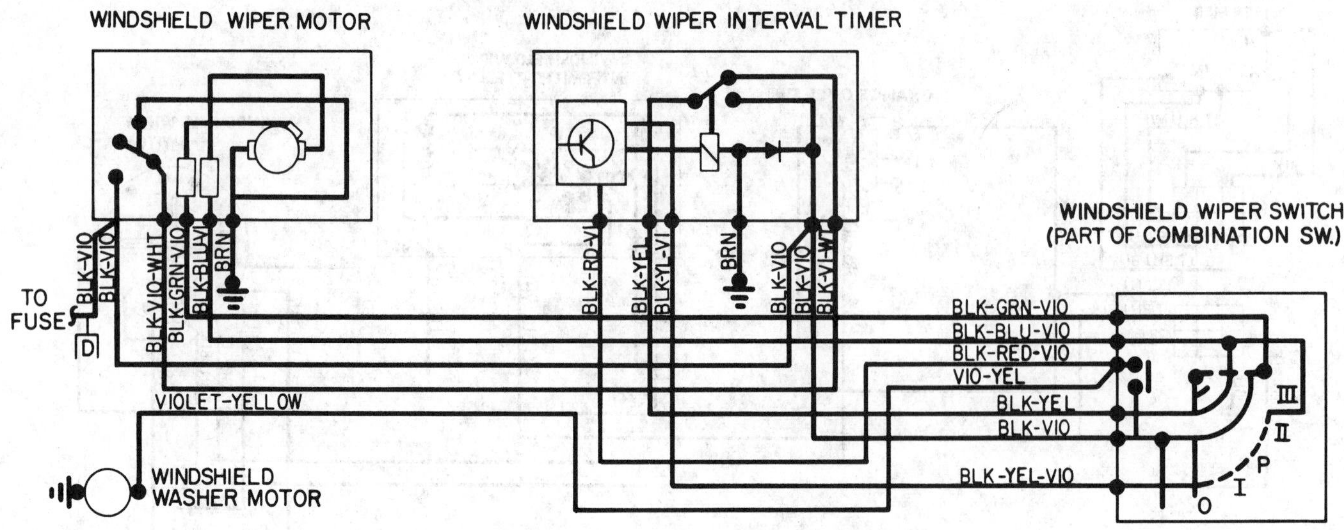

Windshield Wiper System Wiring Diagram (Mercedes-Benz 240D, 280E and 300D)

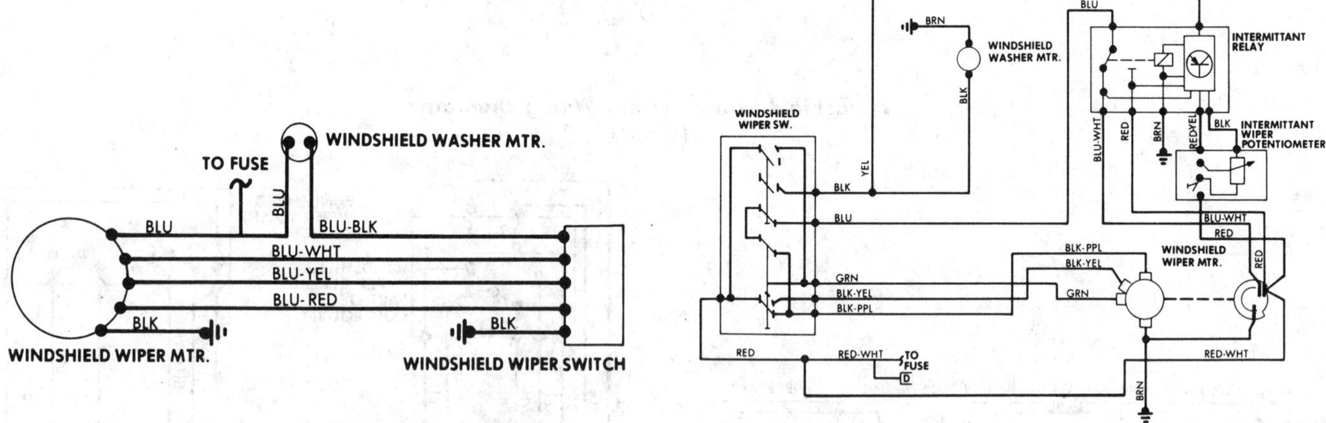

Windshield Wiper System Wiring Diagram (Opel)

Windshield Wiper System Wiring Diagram (Peugeot 604)

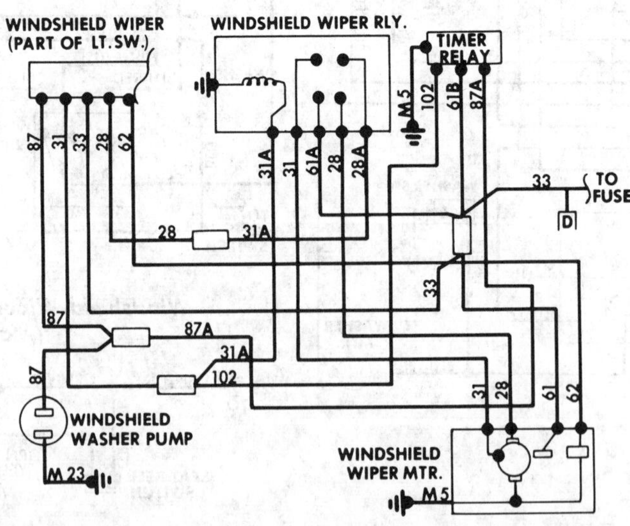

Windshield Wiper System Wiring Diagram (911S and Turbo Carrera)

WINDSHIELD WIPER SYSTEMS (Cont.)

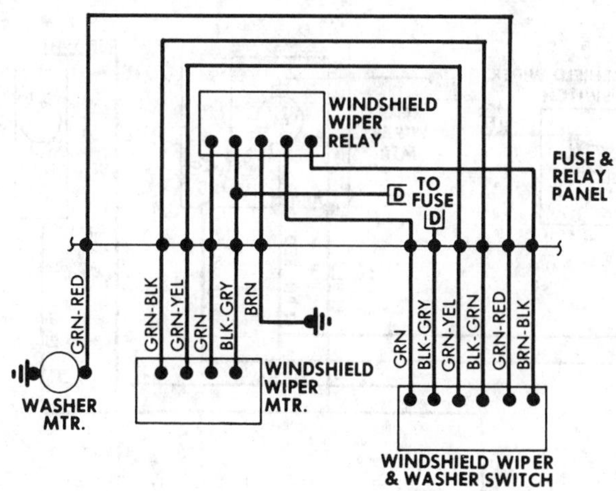

Windshield Wiper System Wiring Diagram (Porsche 924)

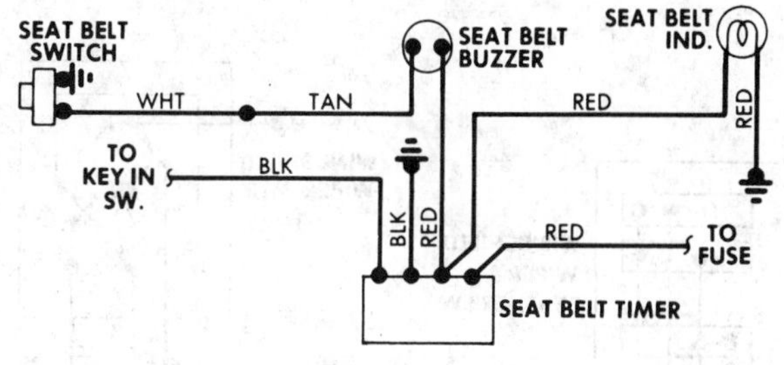

Windshield Wiper System Wiring Diagram (Renault R-12)

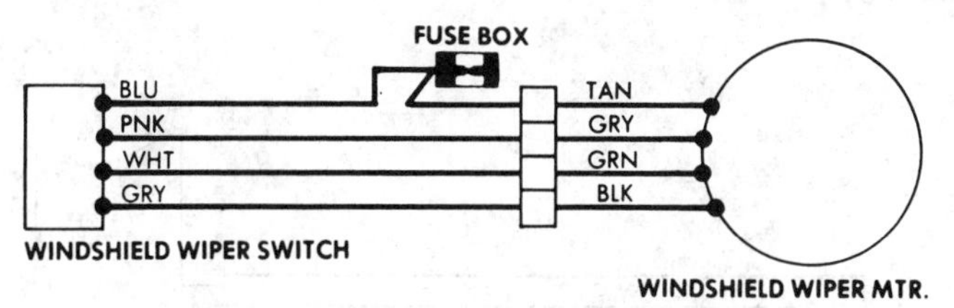

Windshield Wiper System Wiring Diagram (Renault R-5)

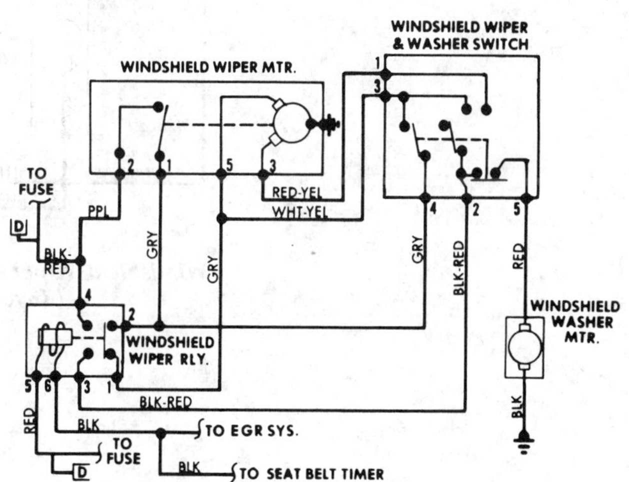

Windshield Wiper System Wiring Diagram (Renault Gordini)

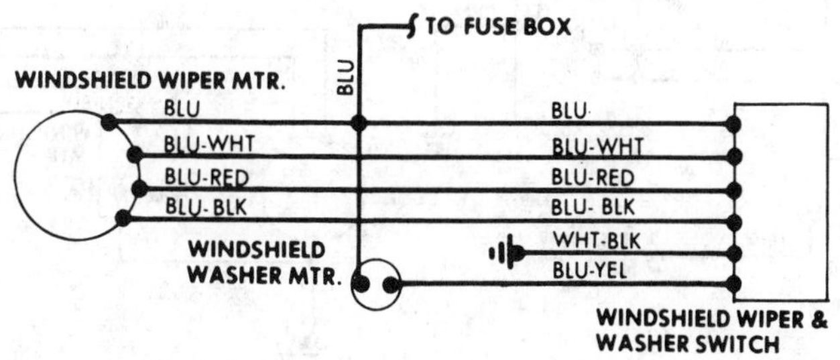

Windshield Wiper System Wiring Diagram (Toyota Celica)

WINDSHIELD WIPER SYSTEMS (Cont.)

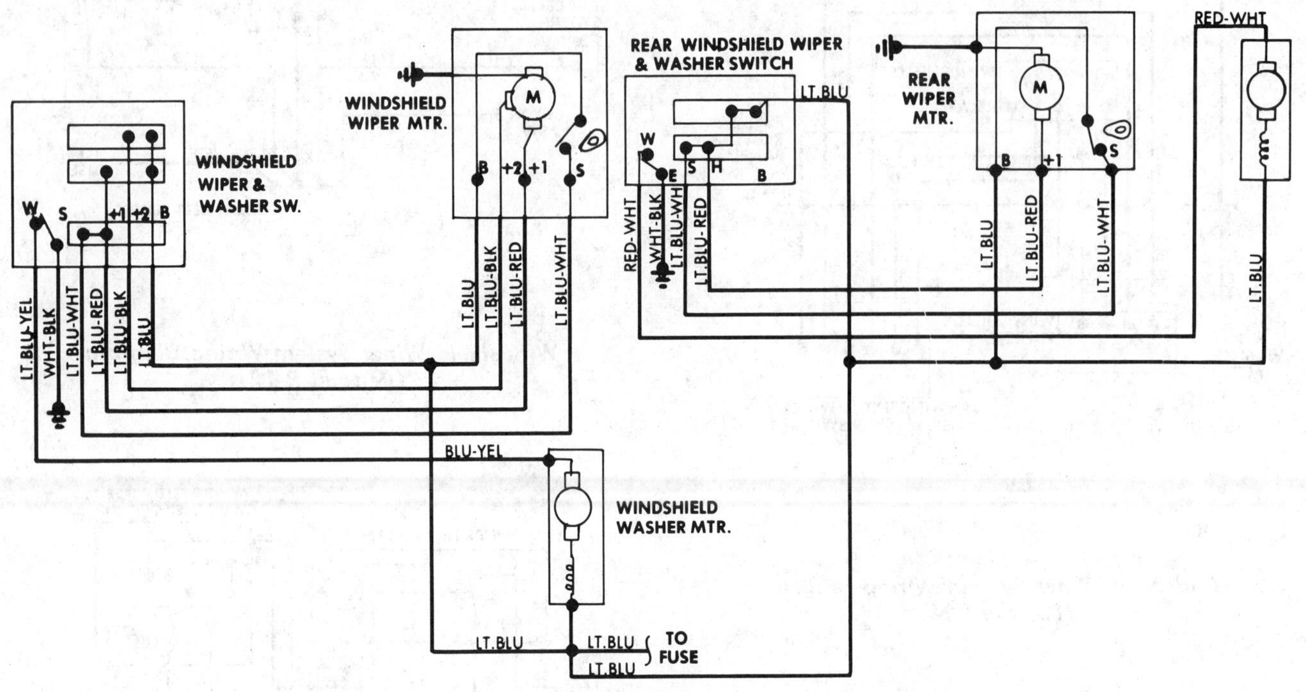

Windshield Wiper System Wiring Diagram
(Toyota Corona)

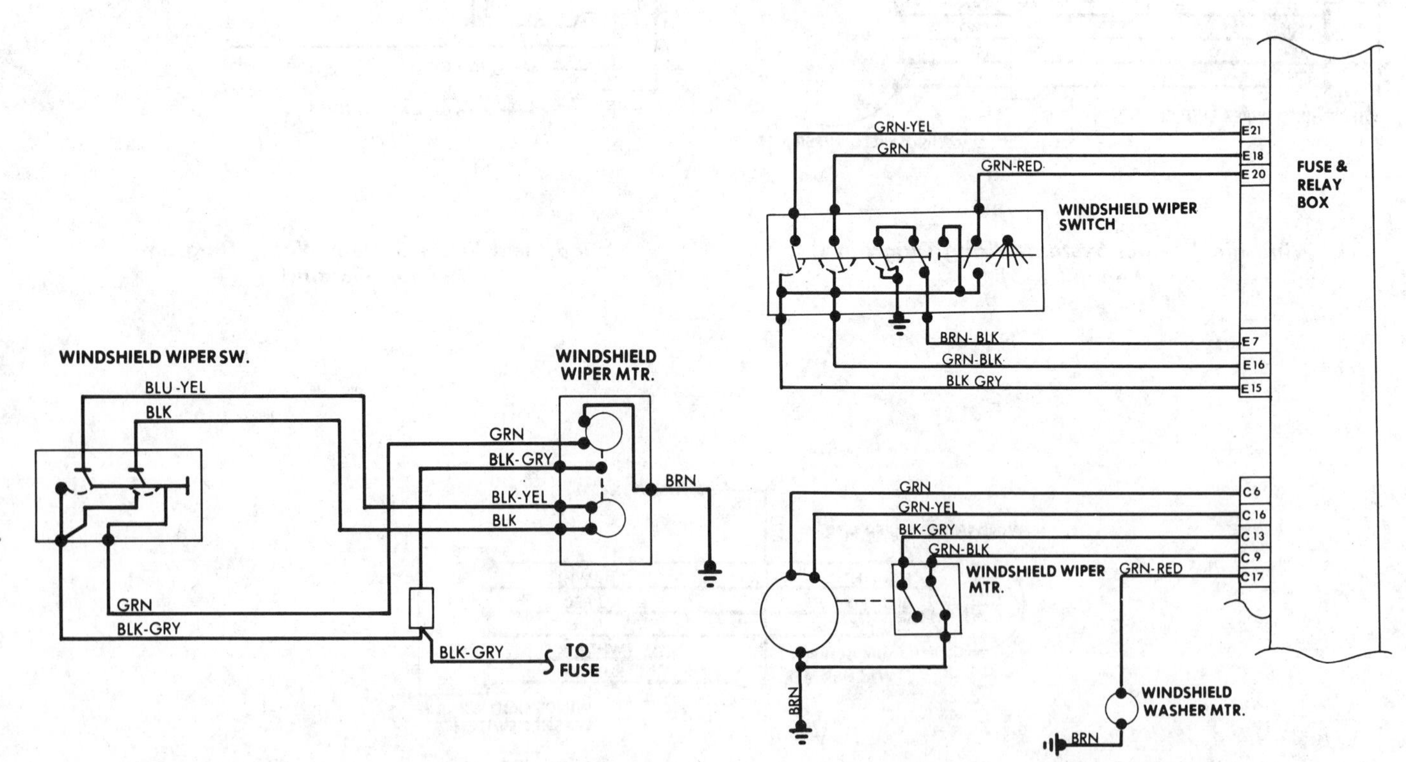

Windshield Wiper System Wiring Diagram
(Volkswagen Type 1 and 2)

Windshield Wiper System Wiring Diagram
(Volkswagen Rabbit and Scirocco)

ARROW

FUSE BLOCK

Fuse block is located on the wall cover to the left of the drivers seat and contains 10 fuses and three spare fuses. Circuits protected are as follows:

① — 15 Amp. Cigar Lighter, Radio, Horn.
② — 15 Amp. Windshield Wiper/Washer.
③ — 10 Amp. Headlights (Upper).
④ — 10 Amp. Headlights (Lower).
⑤ — 5 Amp. Dome & Instrument Lights.
⑥ — 15 Amp. Stop & Hazard Lights.
⑦ — 15 Amp. Rear Window Defogger.
⑧ — 15 Amp. Heater.
⑨ — 15 Amp. Turn Signals, Back-Up Lights, Voltage Regulator
⑩ — 15 Amp. Tail & Parking Lights.

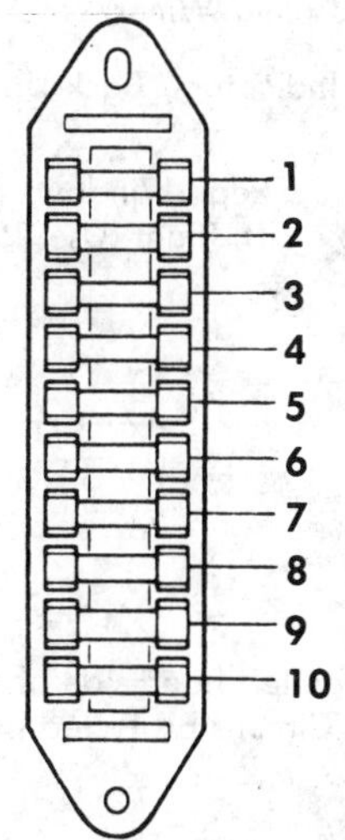

Fig. 1 Arrow Hardtop & Station Wagon Fuse Block (Colt Same)

AUDI

FUSE BLOCK

Fox — Fuse block is located on left behind dashboard bin attached to the steering column. It contains 15 fuses arranged horizontally. Circuits protected by the fuses are, from left to right:

① — 8 Amp. Low Beam Left.
② — 8 Amp. Low Beam Right.
③ — 8 Amp. High Beam Left, High Beam Warning Light.
④ — 8 Amp. High Beam Right.
⑤ — 16 Amp. Rear Window Defogger.
⑥ — 8 Amp. Stop Lights, Hazard Flasher.
⑦ — 8 Amp. Cig. Lighter, Radio, Clock, Interior Light.
⑧ — 8 Amp. Fuel & Temperature Gauge, Warning Lights, Turn Signals, Wiper/Washer (Automatic).
⑨ — 8 Amp. Back-Up Lights, Shift Console Light.
⑩ — 16 Amp. Fresh Air Fan, Rear Window Defogger, Voltmeter.
⑪ — 8 Amp. Horn, Windshield Wiper/Washer.
⑫ — 8 Amp. License Plate Light.
⑬ — 8 Amp. Tail, Parking & Side Marker Lights (Right).
⑭ — 8 Amp. Tail, Parking & Side Marker Lights (Left)
⑮ — 16 Amp. Radiator Fan.

100 Models — Fuse Block is mounted in front of passenger compartment next to clutch pedal. Block contains 10 fuses, mounted horizontally. Circuits protected by the fuses are, from left to right:

① — 8 Amp. Turn Signals and Emergency Flasher.
② — 16 Amp. Windshield Washer, Fan Motor, Horn, Gauges, Oil Pressure Warning Light and Back-Up Lights.
③ — 16 Amp. Windshield Wiper Motor, Cigarette Lighter, Clock and Stop, Instrument, License Plate, Glove Compartment and Interior Lights.
④ — 8 Amp. Right Hand Tail Light.
⑤ — 8 Amp. Left Hand High Beam.
⑥ — 8 Amp. Right Hand High Beam and High Beam Indicator.
⑦ — 8 Amp. Left Hand Low Beam.
⑧ — 8 Amp. Right Hand Low Beam.
⑨ — 8 Amp. Left Hand Tail Light.
⑩ — 8 Amp. Rear Window Defogger, Radiator Fan Motor, Clock.

BMW

FUSE BLOCK

320i Models — Fuse block is located in a damp-proof case in the engine compartment above the wheel arch on the left side. Circuits protected by the fuses are listed on the fuse block cover

530i & 630CSi — Fuse block is located in engine compartment near battery. Circuits protected are listed on fuse block cover.

① — 16 Amp. Headlight Main Beam, Main Beam Telltale Light.
② — 8 Amp. Headlight Low Beam (Right).
③ — 8 Amp. Headlight Low Beam (Left).
④ — 8Amp. Right Rear Parking & Side Lights, License Plate Light, Instrument Lighting, Fog Lamp Relay, Engine Compartment Lighting.
⑤ — 8 Amp. Left Rear Parking & Side Lights.
⑥ — 8Amp. Combined Relay L-Jetronic, Cold Start Valve, Electric Fuel Delivery Pump.
⑧ — Blank.
⑨ — 16 Amp. Cigar Lighter, Automatic Radio Antenna.
⑩ — 8 Amp. Hazard Warning Flashers, Clock, Glove Box Light, Interior Light, Luggage Compartment Light.

BMW (Cont.)

⑪ — 16 Amp. Windshield Wiper/Washer, Stop Lights.

⑫ — 8 Amp. Turn Indicators, Back-Up Lights, Horn Relay, Radio

⑬ — 16 Amp. Heated Rear Window, Electric Sliding Roof, Electric Window Lift, Right (Use 25 Amp. Fuse for Window Lift).

⑭ — 25 Amp. Heater Blower, Electric Window Lift, Left. Air Conditioning.

⑮ — 8 Amp. Fog Light, Right.

⑯ — 8 Amp. Fog Light, Left.

⑰ — 25 Amp. Electrical Auxiliary Fan (Automatic Model).

CAPRI II

FUSE BLOCK

Fuse block is located on left hand side of engine compartment and contains 7 fuses. Circuits protected by the fuses are, from left to right:

1 — 8 Amp. Cigarette Lighter, Clock, Interior Light, Hazard Flasher.
2 — 8 Amp. License Plate Light, Instrument Lights, Map Light.
3 — 8 Amp. Right Tail, Parking and Side Marker Lights.
4 — 8 Amp. Left Tail, Parking and Side Marker Lights.
5 — 8 Amp. Horn, Heater Blower.
6 — 16 Amp. Front and Rear Wiper Motors, Back-Up Light, Instrument Lights.
7 — 8 Amp. Turn Signals, Stop Lights.

NOTE — *Four additional 16 Amp. fuses are located on the bottom of the headlight relay to protect headlight circuits. Relay is located near fuse block. One additional 16 Amp. fuse is located inside the plastic cover of the heated backlight relay. Relay is located under dash below ash tray.*

COLT

FUSE BLOCK

Fuse block Is located on the wall cover to the left of the drivers seat and contains 14 fuses and three spare fuses. Circuits protected are as follows:

① — 10 Amp. Right High Beam.
② — 10 Amp. Left High Beam.
③ — 10 Amp. Taillights.
④ — 5 Amp. Parking Lights
⑤ — 15 Amp. Rear Window Defogger.
⑥ — 10 Amp. Back-Up Lights.
⑦ — 10 Amp. Turn Signals, Volt. Regulator.
⑧ — 10 Amp. Right Low Beam.
⑨ — 10 Amp. Left Low Beam.
⑩ — 15 Amp. Cig. Lighter, Radio, Horn.
⑪ — 10 Amp. Windshield Wiper/Washer.
⑫ — 15 Amp. Heater.
⑬ — 15 Amp. Hazard Warning Flashers.
⑭ — 5 Amp. Dome Light.

FUSIBLE LINK

All Models — Fusible link is located in wire between battery and alternator near battery terminal. Purpose of fusible link is to protect the power and charging circuits from excessive current.

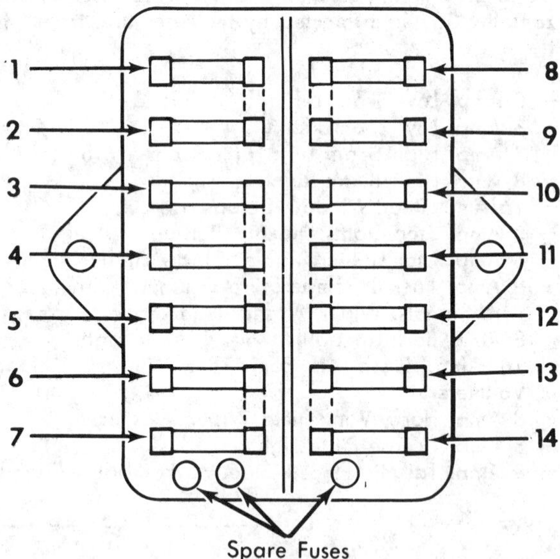

Fig. 2 Dodge Colt Hatchback Fuse Block (Arrow the Same)

COURIER

FUSE BLOCK

Fuse block is located on left side of engine compartment near the windshield. Block contains nine fuses. Circuits protected by the fuses are, front to rear:

① — 15Amp. Horn, Stop Lights, Hazard Warning Flasher, Interior Light, Cigar Lighter.
② — 15 Amp. Hood & Glove Box Light, Electric Rear Window Defroster.
③ — 15 Amp. Headlights (High Beam).

COURIER (Cont.)

④ — 15 Amp. Headlights (Low Beam).
⑤ — 10 Amp. Tail, License, Front Parking, Front Side Marker, Instrument Lights.
⑥ — 10 Amp. Windshield Wipers/Washers.
⑦ — 15 Amp. Heater/Defroster Blower Motor, Radio.
⑧ — 10 Amp. Front & Rear Turn Signal Lights, Fasten Seat Belt, Oil Pressure & Brake Warning Lights, Fuel Gauge, Temperature Gauge, Back-Up Lights.
⑨ — 15 Amp. Engine.

DATSUN

FUSE BLOCK

200SX — Fuse block is located under instrument panel, left of steering column and contains eight fuses. Circuits protected are as follows:

① — 10 Amp. Gauges, Flasher, Back-Up Lights.
② — 15 Amp. Windshield Wiper/Washer, Heater.
③ — 15 Amp. Stop Light, Hazard Warning Lights, Horn.
④ — 15 Amp. Cigar Lighter, Clock, Dome Light.
⑤ — 15 Amp. Seat Belt Warning.
⑥ — 10 Amp. Headlights.
⑦ — 10 Amp. Tail, Parking & Interior Lights.
⑧ — 20 Amp. Radio, Rear Window Defogger.

B210 — Fuse block is located under instrument panel to left ot steering column and contains 8 fuses. Circuits protected are as follows:

1 — 10 Amp. Kickdown Switch, Neutral Safety Switch, Turn Signals, Back-Up Lights, Gauges, Warning Lights, Tachometer.
2 — 15 Amp. Windshield Wiper/Washer, Heater.
3 — 15 Amp. Hazard Warning System, Stop Lights, Horn.
4 — 15 Amp. Interior Light, Theft Protection System, Cigarette Lighter.
5 — 10 Amp. EGR and Catalyist Warning System.
6 — 15 Amp. Headlights.
7 — 10 Amp. Parking, Tail, Side Marker and Instrument Lights.
8 — 20 Amp. Rear Window Defogger, Radio.

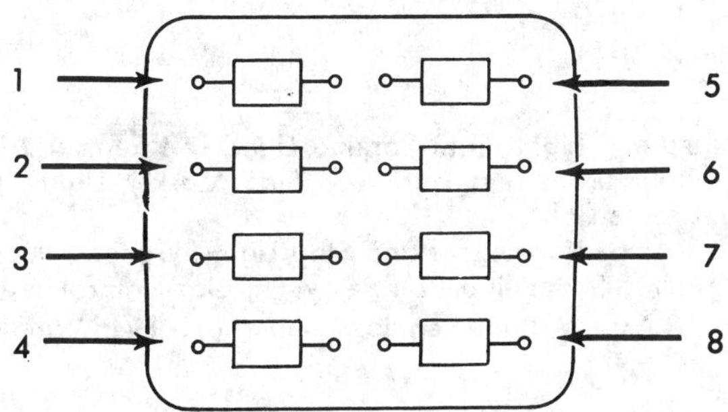

Fig. 3 Datsun B210 Fuse Block

710 — Fuse block is located under the instrument panel and contains 10 fuses. Circuits protected are as follows:

1 — 10 Amp. Turn Signals, Back-Up Lights.
2 — 5 Amp. Warning Lights, Gauges.
3 — 20 Amp. Heater, Radio.
4 — 10 Amp. Windshield Wiper/Washer.
5 — 10 Amp. Left Headlight.
6 — 20 Amp. Side Marker, Tail and License Lights, Instrument and Control Illumination Lights.
7 — 10 Amp. Hazard Warning System, Interior Lights, Theft Protection System.
8 — 10 Amp. Clock, Cigarette Lighter.
9 — 20 Amp. Stop Lights, Horn.
10 — 10 Amp. Right Headlight.

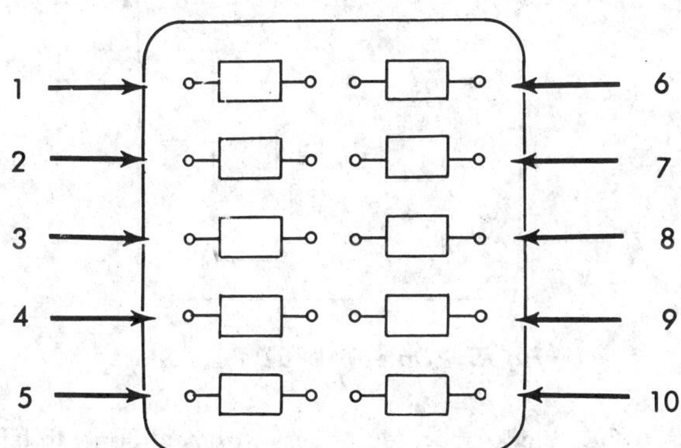

Fig. 4 Datsun 710 Fuse Block

810 — Fuse block is located under the instrument panel on the right kick panel and contains 11 fuses. Circuits protected are as follows:

① — 20 Amp. Rear Window Defogger.
② — 10 Amp. Flasher.
③ — 5 Amp. Solenoid
④ — 20 Amp. Air Conditioning
⑤ — 10 Amp. Windshield Wiper/Washer
⑥ — 10 Amp. Headlights (Left).
⑦ — 10 Amp. Side Marker & Tail Lights
⑧ — 10 Amp. Dome Light.
⑨ — 10 Amp. Common
⑩ — 20 Amp. Stop Lights, Horn.
⑪ — 10 Amp. Headlights (Right).

280Z — Fuse block is located on right side kick panel and contains 14 fuses. Circuits protected are as follows:

① — 10 Amp. Right Headlight.
② — 10 Amp. Left Headlight.
③ — 10 Amp. Flashers.
④ — 10 Amp. Gauges.
⑤ — 20 Amp. Air Conditioner.
⑥ — 15 Amp. Windshield Wiper/Washer.

DATSUN (Cont.)

⑦ — 10 Amp. Radio.
⑧ — 15 Amp. Parking & Tail Lights.
⑨ — 10 Amp. Interior Lights.
⑩ — 10 Amp. Cigar Lighter, Clock, Map Light.
⑪ — 15 Amp. Horn, Stop Lights.
⑫ — 10 Amp. Hazard Warning Lights.
⑬ — 20 Amp. Rear Window Defogger.
⑭ — 1 Amp. Catalyst Warning Light.

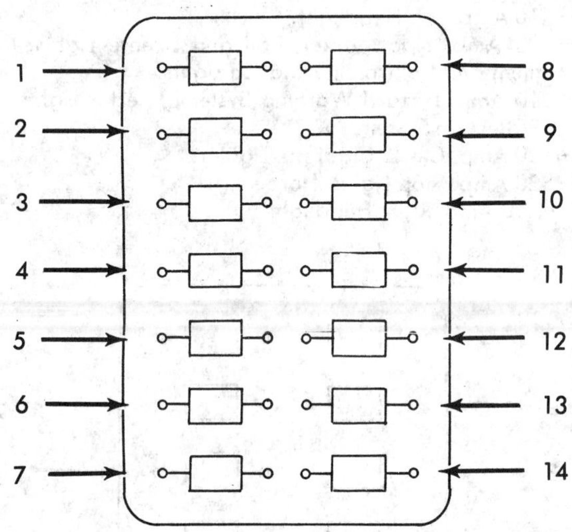

Fig. 5 Datsun 280Z Fuse Block

F10 — Fuse block is located under instrument panel to left of steering column and contains eight fuses. Circuits protected are as follows:

① — 15 Amp. Headlights.
② — 10 Amp. Taillights.
③ — 15 Amp. Horn, Stop Lights, Hazard Warning Lights.
④ — 15 Amp. Fan Motor.
⑤ — 20 Amp. Rear Window Defogger, Cig. Lighter, Clock.
⑥ — 15 Amp. Windshield Wiper/Washer, Heater, Radio.
⑦ — 10 Amp. Cooling Fan, Gauges, Turn Signals.
⑧ — 10 Amp. Auto. Choke, EGR Solenoid, Throttle Opener.

Pickup — Fuse block is located under instrument panel to the left of steering column and contains six fuses. Circuits protected are as follows:

1 — 10 Amp. Heater, Emission Control.
2 — 15 Amp. Windshield Wiper/Washer, Heater Blower.
3 — 10 Amp. Back-Up, Warning and Turn Signal Lights, Gauges, Kickdown Switch, Voltage Regulator.
4 — 10 Amp. Side Marker, Tail, License, Engine Compartment, Instrument and Control Illumination Lights.
5 — 15 Amp. Headlights.
6 — 15 Amp. Hazard Warning System, Horn, Stop Lights.

Pickup — In addition, pickup models have fusible links protecting the interior lights, cigarette lighter and clock.

FUSIBLE LINK

All Models — Fusible link is located in wire between battery and alternator near the battery. Its purpose is to protect the alternator and related circuits.

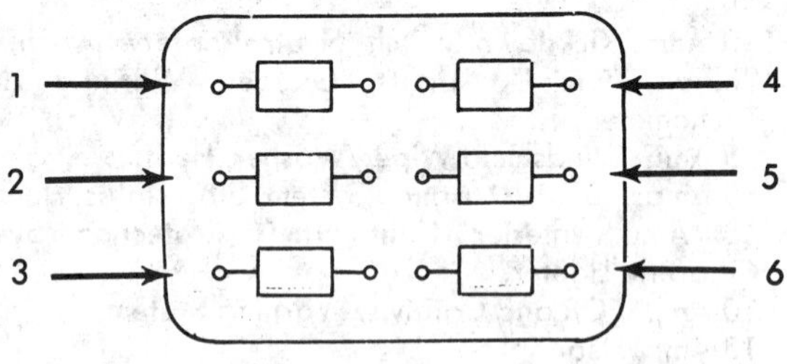

Fig. 6 Datsun Pickup Fuse Block

FIAT

FUSE BLOCK

124 Sport Spider — Fuse block is located under instrument panel to left of steering column. Block contains 10 fuses. Circuits protected by the fuses are as follows:

1 — 25 Amp. Electropneumatic Horns, Engine Fan Motor.
2 — 8 Amp. Windshield Wiper/Washer, Heater Fan Motor.
3 — 8 Amp. Left Headlight High Beam, High Beam Indicator.
4 — 8 Amp. Right Headlight High Beam.

5 — 8 Amp. Right Headlight Low Beam.
6 — 8 Amp. Left Headlight Low Beam.

7 — 8 Amp. Left Front Parking Light, Parking Light and Tail Light Indicator, Right Rear Tail Light, Left Front and Right Rear Side Marker Lights, Left License Plate Light, Cigar Lighter Illumination, Instrument Cluster Lights, Hazard Warning Signal Switch Light, Control Knob Illumination.

8 — 8 Amp. Right Front Parking Light, Left Rear Tail Light, Right Front and Left Rear Side Marker Lights, Right License Light.
9 — 8 Amp. Turn Signal and Stop Lights, Gauges, Warning Lights, Seat Belt Buzzer Relay, Emission Control System.
10 — 8 Amp. Voltage Regulator, Alternator Field Winding.

NOTE — *One 8 Amp. fuse and one 16 Amp. fuse are in separate holders near the fuse block. The 8 Amp. fuse protects Fuel Pump and Relay. The 16 Amp. fuse protects Cigar Lighter, Clock, Courtesy Light, Hazard Warning Light and Remove Key and Fasten Seat Belt Buzzer.*

128 (Except 3P Coupe) — Fuse block is located under instrument panel to left of steering column and contains eight fuses. Two additional fuses, in separate holders, protect Fuel Pump and Relay (8 Amp.) and Rear Window Defogger (16 Amp.). Fuses in block protect the following circuits:

FIAT (Cont.)

1 — 8 Amp. Gauges, Warning Lights, Turn Signals, Stop Lights, Back-Up Lights, Heater, Windshield Wiper, Seat Belt Buzzer Relay, Emission Control System
2 — 16 Amp. Interior Lights, Horns, Engine Fan Motor, Hazard Warning Flasher, Remove Key & Seat Belt Buzzer.
3 — 8 Amp. Left Headlight High Beam and High Beam Indicator.
4 — 8 Amp. Right Headlight High Beam.
5 — 8 Amp. Left Headlight Low Beam.
6 — 8 Amp. Right Headlight Low Beam.
7 — 8 Amp. Left Front Parking and Side Marker Lights, Parking and Tail Lights, Right Tail and Side Marker Lights, and Left License Plate Light.
8 — 8 Amp. Right Parking and Side Marker Lights, Left Rear Tail and Side Marker Lights, Right Side License Plate Light, Instrument Cluster Lights, Hazard Warning Flashers, Instrument Control Knob Illumination.

128 3P Coupe — Fuse block is located under instrument panel to left of steering column and contains 10 fuses. One additional fuse in separate holder, protects Fuel Pump and Relay (8 Amp). Fuses in block protect the following circuits:

1 — 8 Amp. Stop and Back-Up Lights, Windshield Wiper/Washer, Diverter Valve Relay.
2 — 8 Amp. Gauges, Indicator Lights, Turn Signals, Heater Blower, Key and Seat Belt Buzzer Relay, Diverter Solenoid Valve.
3 — 8 Amp. Left Headlight High Beam and High Beam Indicator.
4 — 8 Amp. Right Headlight High Beam.
5 — 8 Amp. Left Headlight Low Beam.
6 — 8 Amp. Right Headlight Low Beam.
7 — 8 Amp. Left Front Parking and Side Marker Lights, Parking and Tail Lights Indicator, Right Rear Tail and Side Marker Lights, Left License Plate Light.
8 — 8 Amp. Right Front Parking and Side Marker Lights, Left Rear Tail and Side Marker Lights, Right License Plate Light, Instrument Lights, Heater Control Illumination Light, Hazard Warning Flashers.
9 — 16 Amp. Horn Relay, Engine Fan Motor, Courtesy Light.
10 — 16 Amp. Cigar Lighter, Remove Key/Fasten Seat Belts Buzzer.

X1/9 — Fuse block is located under instrument panel to left of steering column. Fuse block contains 12 fuses. Fuses in block protect the following circuits:

1 — 8 Amp. Gauges, Indicator Lights, Turn Signals, Stop Lights, Back-Up Lights, Heater Blower, Windshield Wiper/Washer, Seat Belt & Key Buzzer System.
2 — 8 Amp. Headlight Motors, Carburetor Fan Relay, Courtesy Light, Key/Seat Belt Buzzer.
3 — 8 Amp. Left Headlight High Beam and High Beam Indicator.
4 — 8 Amp. Right Headlight High Beam.
5 — 8 Amp. Left Headlight Low Beam.
6 — 8 Amp. Right Headlight Low Beam.
7 — 8 Amp. Left Front Parking and Side Marker Lights, Parking and Tail Lights Indicator, Right Rear Tail and Side Marker Lights, Left License Light, Control and Instrument Illumination Lights.
8 — 8 Amp. Right Front Parking and Side Marker Lights, Left Rear Tail and Side Marker Lights, Right License Plate Light.
9 — 16 Amp. Hazard Warning Flashers and Indicator, Cigarette Lighter, Rear Window Defogger.
10 — 16 Amp. Engine Fan, Horn and Relay.
11 — 3 Amp. Headlight Concealing Relay.
12 — 3 Amp. Headlight Raising Relay.

131 — Fuse block is located under glove compartment and contains one row of 12 fuses and another row of two fuses. Fuses in block protect the following circuits:

① — 8 Amp. Stop & Back-Up Lights, Warning Indicators, Gauges, Heater Fan Motor, Electronic Tachometer; Rear Window, Air Conditioner, Starter Inhibitor Switch & Fasten Seat Belt Relays.
② — 10 Amp. Windshield Wiper/Washer
③ — 10 Amp. Left Tail & Right Front Parking Lights, Right Front & Left Side Marker Lights.
④ — 8 Amp. Left Front Parking & Right Tail Lights, Left Front & Right Side Marker Lights, License Plate Lights, Instrument Lights.
⑤ — 8 Amp. Left Outboard Headlight (Low Beam).
⑥ — 8 Amp. Right Outboard Headlight (Low Beam).
⑦ — 16 Amp. Inboard Headlights (High Beam)
⑧ — 16 Amp. Outboard Headlights (High Beam), High Beam Indicator.
⑨ — Horn, Horn Relay Winding, Engine Fan Motor.
⑩ — 16 Amp. Clock, Courtesy Lights, Cigar Lighter, Radio Antenna Motor (When Installed).
⑪ — 16 Amp. Rear Window Defogger, Hazard Warning System.
⑫ — 16 Amp. Air Conditioner Compressor & Evaporator Fan & Condenser Motor.
⑬ — 16 Amp. Remove Key Buzzer
⑭ — Spare Fuse.

HONDA

FUSE BLOCK

Civic & Civic CVCC— Fuse block is located on right side kick panel. Block contains eight fuses. Circuits protected are, from top to bottom:

① — 10 Amp. Voltage Regulator.
② — 10 Amp. Windshield Wiper/Washer.
③ — 10 Amp. Turn Signals, Back-Up Lights, Fuel Gauge.
④ — 15 Amp. Heater, Radio, Rear Window Defogger.
⑤ — 15 Amp. Hazard Warning Light, Horn, Stop Lights.
⑥ — 10 Amp. Cig. Lighter, Clock, Interior Lights.
⑦ — 15 Amp. Taillights, License Light, Instrument Lights.
⑧ — 15 Amp. Headlights.

HONDA (Cont.)

Accord — Fuse block is located under the dashboard on drivers side. Block contains 10 fuses. Circuits protected are, from top to bottom:

① — 10 Amp. Windshield Wiper/Washer.
② — 10 Amp. Voltage Regulator, Fuel Pump.
③ — 10 Amp. Turn Signals, Back-Up Lights, Fuel Gauge.
④ — 15 Amp. Headlight High Beam.
⑤ — 15 Amp. Headlight Low Beam.
⑥ — 15 Amp. Taillights, Instrument Lights
⑦ — 10 Amp. Cig. Lighter, Clock Interior Lights.
⑧ — 15 Amp. Hazard Warning Lights, Horn, Stop Lights.
⑨ — 15 Amp. Heater.
⑩ — 15 Amp. Radio, Rear Window Defroster.

IN-LINE FUSES

One large 55 Amp. in-line fuse is installed in main battery cable to prevent damage to main wiring harness. Fuse is located in engine compartment near battery.

JAGUAR

FUSE BLOCK

XJ6 Models — Fuse block is located behind instrument panel. Access to fuses is obtained by turning access panel retaining pin counterclockwise until it unlocks. Panel will then drop slightly and bottom edge may be lifted clear of opening. Circuits protected are as follows:

1 — 20 Amp. Fog Lights.
2 — 15 Amp. Hazard Warning System.
3 — 35 Amp. Map and Interior Lights, Cigarette Lighter, Clock, Electric Aerial.
4 — 15 Amp. Back-Up Lights, Gauges.
5 — 15 Amp. Turn Signals.
6 — 35 Amp. Stop Lights, Battery Cooling, Horn Relay, Windshield Washer.
7 — 15 Amp. Instrument Lights.
8 — 15 Amp. Left Side Marker and Tail Lights.
9 — 15 Amp. Right Side Marker and Tail Lights.
10 — 50 Amp. A/C and Heater Relay.
11 — 50 Amp. A/C Control System and Compressor Clutch, Windshield Wipers.
12 — 35 Amp. Rear Window Defogger.

IN-LINE FUSES

Head Lights — High beam is protected by a 25 Amp. in-line fuse and low beam is governed by a 10 amp in-line fuse.

Horn Relay — Circuit is protected by a 17 Amp. in-line fuse.

LANCIA

FUSE BLOCK

Fuse block is fitted to the engine compartment and is provided with a pressure tight cover. Block contains 11 fuses. Circuits protected are as follows:

① — 8 Amp. Right Front & Left Rear Side Marker Lights, Side Lights Tell-Tale, Instrument Lights, License Plate Light (Right).
② — 8 Amp. Engine Compartment Light, Left Front & Right Rear Side Marker Lights, License Plate Light (Left), Cigar Lighter, Wipe-Speed Change-Over Switch, Hazard Switch.
③ — 8 Amp. Left Low Beam.
④ — 8 Amp. Right Low Beam.
⑤ — 8 Amp. Left High Beam.
⑥ — 8 Amp. Right High Beam, High Beam Indicator Light.
⑦ — 8 Amp. Stop Lights.
⑧ — 16 Amp. Back-Up Light, Windshield Wiper/Washer, Air Conditioner Booster Fan, Coolant Radiator Motor Driven Fan, Emission Control Switches.
⑨ — 16 Amp. Turn Indicator, Radio, Electric Antenna Motor, Electric Window Lift, Rear Window Defogger, Cigar Lighter, Air Horns Electro-Compressor, Indicator Lights Instrument Lights.
⑩ — 8 Amp. Front & Rear Dome Lights, Clock, Plug-In Socket, Buzzer.
⑪ — 25 Amp. Air Horns, Electro-Compressor, Cigar Lighter, Rear Window Defogger, Air Conditioner Booster Fan Motor.

IN-LINE FUSES

In-line fuses protect electric window lifts (25 Amp.), hazard warning signal (16 Amp.), engine coolant motor driven fan (16 Amp.), air conditioner system (25 Amp.) and electric fuel pump (16 Amp.).

LUV

FUSE BLOCK

Fuse block is installed in engine compartment on left inner fender panel near firewall and contains 11 fuses with fuse applications listed on cover. Fuse applications are as follows:

1 — 15 Amp. Lighting Switch.
2 — 15 Amp. Tail and Instrument Lights.
3 — 15 Amp. Turn Signals, Stop Lights, Horn.
4 — 15 Amp. Interior Light, A/C.
5 — 15 Amp. Heater, Back-Up Lights.
6 — 15 Amp. Fuel Pump, Emission Control.
7 — 15 Amp. Windshield Wiper/Washer, Cigarette Lighter, Radio.
8 — 10 Amp. Right High Beam Headlight.
9 — 10 Amp. Left High Beam Headlight.
10 — 10 Amp. Right Low Beam Headlight.
11 — 10 Amp. Left Low Beam Headlight.

MAZDA

Cosmo, RX-3SP, RX-4 & 808 – Fuse block is located just below the glove box and contains 11 fuses. Circuits protected are as follows:

① – 20 Amps. Instrument Panel, Parking, Side Marker, Tail & License Plate lights.
② – 10 Amp. Right Headlight (Low Beam).
③ – 10 Amp. Left Headlight (Low Beam).
④ – 10 Amp. Right Headlight (High Beam), High Beam Indicator Light.
⑤ – 10 Amp. Left Headlight (High Beam).
⑥ – 15 Amp. Clock, Cigar Lighter, Glove Box Light, Trunk Compartment, Step & Interior Lights, Ignition Reminder Switch.
⑦ – 20 Amp. Horn, Stop Lights, Hazard Warning Flasher.
⑧ – 20 Amp. Air Conditioner, Rear Window Defogger.
⑨ – 10 Amp. Indicator Lights, Gauges, Turn Signal Lights, Tachometer.
⑩ – 20 Amp. Heat Hazard Warning Light, Ignition Coil, Fuel Pump, Choke Switch, Ignition Relay, Emission Control Devices.
⑪ – 15 Amp. Regulator, Kick Down Solenoid Switch, EGR Warning Light.

GLC – The fuse block is located under the instrument panel and contains 10 fuses. Circuits protected are as follows:

① – 15 Amp. Horn, Stop & Turn Signal Lights.
② – 15 Amp. Interior Light, Cigar Lighter, Clock, Key Reminder Buzzer.
③ – 15 Amp. Tail & License Lights, Parking & Side Marker Lights, Instrument Kights.
④ – Not Used.
⑤ – Not Used.
⑥ – 10 Amp. Rear Window Defogger.
⑦ – 10 Amp. Windshield Wiper/Washer, Rear Window Wiper/Washer
⑧ – 15 Amp. Heater, Remote Control Hatchback Release.
⑨ – 10 Amp. Back-Up Lights, Kickdown Switch, Warning Lights, Gauges, Seat Belt Warning Light, Turn Signal Indicator.
⑩ – 10 Amp. Hazard Warning Lights, Choke Switch, Regulator

Pickup – Fuse block is located in left rear corner of engine compartment and contains six fuses. Circuits protected by fuses in block are as follows:

① – 15 Amp. Ignition Coil, Fuel Pump, Ignition Relay, Kickdown Solenoid Switch.
② – 10 Amp. Regulator, Kickdown Relay.
③ – 10 Amp. Warning Lights, Gauges, Back-Up & Turn Signal Lights, Tachometer.
④ – 15 Amp. Horn, Stop Lights, Hazard Warning Switch.
⑤ – 10 Amp. Interior Light, Cigar Lighter.
⑥ – 15 Amp. Instrument Panel, Parking, Side Marker Tail & License Plate Lights.

IN-LINE FUSES

A fuse block containing large in-line fuses is installed in engine compartment near battery. Fuse amperage and circuits protected is printed on fuse block cover.

MERCEDES-BENZ

FUSE BLOCK

All (Exc. 450 SL & SLC) – Main fuse block is located under hood on left inner fender panel. Fuse capacities and circuits protected are marked on fuse block cover.

450 SL & SLC – Main fuse block is located on right side kick panel. Fuse capacities and circuits protected are marked on fuse block cover.

IN-LINE FUSES

Additional fuses for optional equipment and/or standard extras such as sliding sun roof, heated rear window, radio, automatic antenna, electric windows and air conditioning are located in engine compartment.

MG

FUSE BLOCK

Fuse block is located on right hand side of engine compartment. Fuse block contains four 35 Amp. fuses and two spares. Circuits protected are, from top to bottom:

① – 35 Amp. One Parking Light, One Tail Light, One License Plate Light, One Front & Rear Side Marker Light.
② – 35 Amp. One Parking Light, One Tail Light, One Licence Plate Light, One Front & Rear Side Marker Light.
③ – 35 Amp. Turn Signal Indicator, Stop Lights, Back-Up Lights, Seat Belt & Brake Warning Lights.
④ – 35 Amp. Horn, Interior & Luggage Compartment Lights, Headlight Flasher, Cigar Lighter.

IN-LINE FUSES

Auxiliary Equipment – A 35 Amp. in-line fuse located above fuse block (MG Midget) or below fuse block (MGB) protects Windshield Wipers/Washer, Heater Blower Motor, and Radio.

Fan Thermostat – A 35 Amp. in-line fuse protects the fan thermostat circuit.

Hazard Warning – A 35 Amp. in-line fuse located behind Hazard Warning Switch protects Warning Lights.

Radio – A separate additional in-line fuse protects Radio.

OPEL

FUSE BLOCK

Fuse block is located on the right side kick panel. Block contains 13 fuse positions and four spare fuses. Circuits protected are as follows:

① — 15 Amp. Headlights Upper Beam.
② — 15 Amp. Windshield Wiper/Washer, Radio.
③ — 15 Amp. Horn, Turn Signals.
④ — 15 Amp. Rear Window Defogger.
⑤ — 15 Amp. Cig. Lighter, Interior Light.
⑥ — 15 Amp. Air Conditioning.
⑦ — 15 Spare Circuit.
⑧ — 10 Amp. Headlights Low Beam.
⑨ — 10 Amp. Fuel Pump, Emission Control System.
⑩ — 10 Amp. Ign. Coil, Volt. Regulator, Instrument Lights.
⑪ — 15 Amp. Heater, Back-Up Lights.
⑫ — 15 Amp. Lighting Switch.
⑬ — 15 Amp. Taillights.

FUSIBLE LINKS

Fusible links and in-line fuses are utilized throughout the wiring system to prevent short circuits. Main fusible link is located near the battery.

PEUGEOT

FUSE BLOCK

604 — Fuse block is located on the left side of vehicle behind door and under instrument panel. Fuse block contains nine fuses. Circuits protected are, from left to right:

NOTE — *Fuse amperage is identified by color code only. Green is 10 Amp. and Brown is 16 Amp.*

① — Cigar Lighter, Horns, Dome Lights, Clock, Emergency Flasher, Key Warning Buzzer.
② — Stop & Back-Up Lights, Neutral Safety Switch, Gauges, Warning Lights, Seat Belt & Turn Signal Indicators.
③ — Rear Window Defogger, Map Reading Light, Accessories, Dash Indicators.
④ — Air Conditioner Blower, Sun Roof, Catalyst Warning Light, Windshield Wiper/Washer, EGR Warning Light, Blower Motor Thermocontact.
⑤ — Front & Rear Parking Lights, Side Marker Lights, Instrument Lights, High Beam & Parking Light Indicator.
⑥ — Blower Motor & Air Conditioner Compressor Relays.
⑦ — Front & Rear Windows (Right).
⑧ — Front & Rear Windows (Left).
⑨ — Rear Window Lockout.

PORSCHE

FUSE BLOCK

924 Models — Fuse block is located under instrument panel to left of steering column and contains 15 fuses. Circuits protected are, from left to right:

① — 8 Amp. Left Headlight (Low Beam)
② — 8 Amp. Right Headlight (Low Beam).
③ — 8 Amp. Left Headlight (High Beam).
④ — 8 Amp. Right Headlight (High Beam).
⑤ — 16 Amp. Additional Headlights.
⑥ — 8 Amp. Interior Lights, Retractable Headlights.
⑦ — 8 Amp. Emergency Flashers.
⑧ — 8 Amp. Turn Signal Indicator, Brake Warning Light.
⑨ — 8 Amp. Horn, Back-Up Lights, Rear Window Wiper.
⑩ — 8 Amp. Fresh Air Blower.
⑪ — 8 Amp. Windshield Wipers.
⑫ — 8 Amp. License Plate & Luggage Compartment Lights.
⑬ — 8 Amp. Side Marker Light (Right)
⑭ — 8 Amp. Side Marker Light (Left).
⑮ — 16 Amp. Fan, Fog Lights.

911S & Carrera Models — Main fuse block is located inside luggage compartment on left side and contains 21 fuses. An additional fuse block is located in engine compartment on left side under regulator cover. Secondary fuse block protects Sportomatic and Fan Relay (5 Amp.), Heater Fan (25 Amp.) and Rear Window Defogger (25 Amp.). Main fuse block protects the following circuits, from front to rear:

1 — 16 Amp. Fog Lights.

2 — 5 Amp. License Plate & Control Lights, Fog Light Relay.

3 — 5 Amp. Right Front and Rear Parking Lights.

4 — 5 Amp. Left Front and Rear Parking Lights.
5 — 8 Amp. Right Headlight Low Beam.
6 — 8 Amp. Left Headlight Low Beam.
7 — 8 Amp. Right Headlight High Beam.
8 — 8 Amp. Left Headlight High Beam, High Beam Indicator.
9 — 5 Amp. Right Front Flasher Light.
10 — 5 Amp. Left Front Flasher Light.

11 — 16 Amp. Flasher Relay, Brake and Back-Up Lights.

12 — 25 Amp. Rear Window Defroster Relay, Fresh Air Blower, Rear Window Defroster Control Light.

13 — 25 Amp. Windshield Wiper/Washer, Air Conditioner.
14 — 25 Amp. Electric Sunroof, Rear Window Wiper.
15 — 16 Amp. Cigar Lighter, Blower Switch Control Light.

16 — 25 Amp. Power Windows.
17 — 16 Amp. Emergency Flasher.
18 — 5 Amp. Interior, Glove Compartment, and Luggage Compartment Lighting, Clock.

19 — 16 Amp. Headlight Washer.
20 — 25 Amp. Blower for Air Conditioner.
21 — 25 Amp. Fuel Pump.

RENAULT

FUSE BLOCK

R-5 – Fuse block is located under the dashboard and to the right of the steering column. Circuits protected are, from left to right:

① – 8 Amp. Windshield Wiper.
② – 8 Amp. Cig. Lighter, Interior Lights.
③ – 5 Amp. Turn Signals.
④ – 8 Amp. Heater Motor.
⑤ – 15 Amp. Rear Window Defogger, Back-Up Lights.
⑥ – 5 Amp. Solenoids.

R-12 – Fuse block is located inside glove compartment and contains six fuses. Circuits protected are, from top to bottom:

1 – 5 Amp. Flasher Unit.
2 – 8 Amp. Heated Rear Window (Defroster).
3 & 4 – 8 Amp. Circuits Independent Of Ignition Switch.
5 – 8 Amp. Circuits Dependent On Ignition Switch.
6 – 5 Amp. Automatic Transmission.

R-17 – Fuse block is located under instrument panel, below speedometer and contains 10 fuses. Circuits protected are, left to right:

1 – 15 Amp. (Yellow) Instrument Panel, Stop and Back-Up Lights, Rear Window Defroster.
2 – 5 Amp. (Green) Automatic Transmission.
3 – 5 Amp. (Green) Flasher Unit.
4 – 8 Amp. (Blue) Heating/Ventilation Fan Motor.
5 – 15 Amp. (Yellow) Left Electric Window.
6 – 15 Amp. (Yellow) Right Electric Window.
7 – 8 Amp. (Blue) Windshield Wipers.
8 – Spare.
9 – 8 Amp. (Blue) Electronic Injection.
10 – 8 Amp. (Blue) Interior and Trunk Light, Cigar Lighter, Clock.

SAAB

FUSE BLOCK

99 Models – Electrical system is protected by 12 fuses. Fuse block is mounted on the right wheel housing in the engine compartment. All parts of the system are fused except the headlights and the ignition system. A label by the fuse box shows which fuses protect which circuits.

SUBARU

FUSE BLOCK

Fuse block is located on the right side of inner fender panel under hood and contains eight fuses. Fuses protect circuits as indicated, from right to left:

1 – 25 Amp. Lighting Switch.
2 – 20 Amp. Key Warning Buzzer System, Interior Light, Clock, Hazard Warning Flasher, Stop Lights, Turn Signals, Cigarette Lighter.
3 – 30 Amp. Ignition Switch, Horn.
4 – 20 Amp. Radio, Heater, Windshield Wiper/Washer.
5 – 10 Amp. Front Combination, Tail, Side Marker, License and Instrument Lights.
6 – 15 Amp. Back-Up Light, Turn Signal Flasher, Turn Signal Lights, Cooling Fan Motor.
7 – 15 Amp. Headlight Low Beam.
8 – 15 Amp. Headlight High Beam.

TOYOTA

FUSE BLOCK

Corona – Fuse block is located on left side of drivers compartment under instrument panel. Circuits protected are:

1 – 5 Amp. Radio, Tape Player.
2 – 10 Amp. Cigar Lighter, Door Warning Light.
3 – 15 Amp. Light Control Relay, Parking, Side Marker, Instrument Panel, Tail, and License Plate Lights.
4 – 15 Amp. Horn, Hazard Warning Lights, Stop Lights, Seat Belt Warning Light and Buzzer.
5 – 10 Amp. Interior Lights.
6 – 15 Amp. Spare Terminal.
7 – 15 Amp. Windshield Wiper/Washer.
8 – 10 Amp. Ignition Coil.
9 – 15 Amp. Turn Signal Lights, Regulator, Main Relay.
10 – 15 Amp. Heater Blower, Gauges, Back-up Lights, Brake Warning Lights.
11 – 15 Amp. Rear Window Defogger.

Celica – Fuse block is located on left side of drivers compartment under instrument panel. Circuits protected are:

① – 15 Amp. Front Parking Lights, Front & Rear Side Marker Lights, Tail, License, Glove Box & Instrument Lights.

TOYOTA (Cont.)

② — 20 Amp. Stop Lights, Hazard Warning Lights, Horn, Key Warning Buzzer.
③ — 15 Amp. Cigar Lighter, Clock; Interior, Door Courtesy & Luggage Compartment Lights
④ — 20 Amp. Heater/Air Conditioner Blower Motor, Seat Belt Warning Light & Buzzer, Back-Up Lights, Meter & Gauges.
⑤ — 15 Amp. Rear Window Defogger.
⑥ — 15 Amp. Turn Signal Lights, Windshield Wiper/Washer
⑦ — 15 Amp. Main Relay, Regulator IG Terminal.
⑧ — 15 Amp. Radio & Tape Player.

Corolla — Fuse block is located on left side of drivers compartment under instrument panel. Circuits protected are:

1 — 15 Amp. Horn, Hazard Warning System, Stop Lights, Seat Belt Warning System, Key Warning Buzzer, Stop Light Bulb Failure Warning Light.
2 — 15 Amp. Parking, Side Marker, Instrument Panel, Ashtray, Control Illumination, Tail and License Lights.
3 — 15 Amp. Cigarette Lighter, Interior Lights, Clock, Spot Light.
4 — 15 Amp. Radio, Stereo Tape Player.
5 — 15 Amp. Heater.
6 — 15 Amp. Turn Signals, Windshield Wiper/Washer.
7 — 15 Amp. Voltage Regulator, Emission Control System, Fuel Pump.
8 — 15 Amp. Rear Window Defogger, Back-Up Lights, Tachometer.

Pickup — Fuse block is located on left side of drivers compartment under instrument panel. Circuits protected are:

1 — 15 Amp. Instrument Panel, Parking, Side Marker, Tail, and License Plate Lights.
2 — 20 Amp. Horns,Stop Lights.
3 — 20 Amp. Cigar Lighter, Interior Lights, Coolant Temperature Warning Light, Hazard Warning Lights.
4 — 20 Amp. Radio, Windshield Wipers and Washer.
5 — 20 Amp. Heater Blower, Gauges, Back-Up Lights.
6 — 15 Amp. Alternator Regulator, Turn Signal Lights.
7 — 15 Amp. Ignition Coil, Emission Control System, Fuel Pump
8 — 20 Amp. Spare.

Land Cruiser — Fuse block is mounted under dash to left of steering column (Station Wagon Models) or on left hand kick panel (All exc. Station Wagon Models). Fuse block contains 8 fuses. Circuits protected are, from end of block labeled "TOP":

1 — 15 Amp. Instrument, Parking, Side Marker, Tail and License Plate Lights.
2 — 20 Amp. Stop Lights, Horn and Hazard Warning System.
3 — 20 Amp. Cigarette Lighter, Interior Lights and Inspection Light Socket.
4 — 20 Amp. Radio, Windshield Wiper and Washer Motors.
5 — 20 Amp. Back-Up Lights, Heater and Gauges.
6 — 15 Amp. Turn Signal Lights.
7 — 15 Amp. Ignition Coil, Emission Control System, Voltage Regulator, Fuel Cut Solenoid.
8 — 20 Amp. Headlights.

FUSIBLE LINKS

All Models — A fusible link is located in main battery feed wire near the battery. Protects all circuits except for starter motor.

TRIUMPH

FUSE BLOCK

Spitfire — Fuse block is mounted on left hand side of firewall in engine compartment, adjacent to clutch master cylinder. Block contains three 35 Amp. fuses. Circuits protected are as follows:

1 — Fuse fed by white wire protects Windshield Wipers, Fuel and Temperature Indicator, Stop, Reverse and Turn Signal Lights, Seat Belt Warning System.
2 — Fuse fed by red-green wire protects Parking, Side Marker, Tail, Instrument Panel, and License Plate Lights.
3 — Fuse fed by brown wire protects Dimmer Switch, Key Warning Buzzer, Courtesy Light, Horn, Hazard Warning System.

TR7 — Fuse block is located on a relay plate and is accessible after removal of cover panel at front of glovebox. Block contains four 35 Amp. fuses. Circuits protected are as follows:

① — 35 Amp. Air Conditioner.
② — 35 Amp. Cigar Lighter, Horn, Clock, Hazard Warning System, Courtesy Light.
③ — 35 Amp. Back-Up Lights, Heater, Windshield Wiper/Washer, Stop Lights, Turn Signals, Air Conditioner Control System.
④ — 35 Amp. Interior Lights, Parking & Side Marker Lights, Tail Lights.

VOLKSWAGEN

FUSE BLOCK

Type 1 (Beetle) — Fuse block is located under instrument panel in approximatelythe center of the vehicle and contains 12 fuses. Additional in-line fuses are located and protect circuits as follows: An 8 Amp. fuse located in engine compartment above ignition coil, protects the Back-Up Lights. An 8 Amp. fuse located underneath the rear seat, left side, protects the Rear Window Defogger. A 16 Amp. fuse located in front luggage compartment near the heater, protects the Auxiliary Heater. Fuse block circuits protected are, from left to right:

① — 8 Amp. Left Tail Light.
② — 8 Amp. Right Tail Light, Parking & Side Marker Lights, License Plate Light.

VOLKSWAGEN (Cont.)

③ – 8 Amp. Left Low Beam.
④ – 8 Amp. Right Low Beam.
⑤ – 8 Amp. Left High Beam, High Beam Warning Light.
⑥ – 8 Amp. Right High Beam.
⑦ – 8 Amp. Not Used.
⑧ – 8 Amp. Emergency Flasher.
⑨ – 16 Amp. Interior Light.
⑩ – 16 Amp. Windshield Wiper, Fresh Air Fan, Rear Window Defogger.
⑪ – 8 Amp. Safety Belt Warning System, Stop Lights, Brake Warning Light, Horn.
⑫ – 8 Amp. Turn Signals, Gauges, Warning Lights, Emission System (EGR).

Type 2 (Transporter) – Fuse block is located under instrument panel on right side of steering column. Fuse block contains 12 fuses. Two additional in-line fuses are used as follows: An 8 Amp. fuse, located in engine compartment near ignition coil on manual transmission models, protects the Back-Up Lights. A 16 Amp. fuse, located in engine compartment near blower motor protects the Warm Air Blower. Fuses in block protect the following circuits, left to right:

① – 8 Amp. Left Tail Light, Left Rear Marker Light.
② – 8 Amp. Right Tail Light, Parking Lights, License Plate Light, Right Rear Side Marker Light, Front Side Marker Lights.
③ – 8 Amp. Left Low Beam.
④ – 8 Amp. Right Low Beam.
⑤ – 8 Amp. Left High Beam, High Beam Indicator.
⑥ – 8 Amp. Right High Beam.
⑦ – 8 Amp. Accessories.
⑧ – 8 Amp. Emergency Flasher, Interior Lights.
⑨ – 16 Amp. Accessories.
⑩ – 16 Amp. Windshield Wipers, Rear Window Defogger
⑪ – 8 Amp. Horn, Stop Lights, Brake Warning Light.
⑫ – 8 Amp. Turn Signals Warning Lights, Back-Up Lights.

Rabbit & Scirocco – Fuse block is located under instrument panel on left side of vehicle and contains 15 fuses in one centralized unit. Two additional in-line fuses are used as follows: An 8 Amp. fuse located above fuse block, protects Rear Window Wiper. A 16 Amp. fuse located above fuse block, protects Electric Fuel Pump. Circuits protected by fuses in block are:

① – 8 Amp. Left Headlight Low Beam.
② – 8 Amp. Right Headlight Low Beam.
③ – 8 Amp. Left Headlight High Beam and Indicator.
④ – 8 Amp. Right Headlight High Beam.
⑤ – 16 Amp. Rear Window Defogger.
⑥ – 8 Amp. Stop Lights, Hazard Warning Flasher.
⑦ – 8 Amp. Interior Lights, Cigar Lighter.
⑧ – 8 Amp. Turn Signal System.
⑨ – 8 Amp. Back-Up Lights, Horn.
⑩ – 16 Amp. Fresh Air Fan.
⑪ – 8 Amp. Windshield Wipers, Rear Window Defogger.
⑫ – 8 Amp. Luggage Compartment & License Plate Lights.
⑬ – 8 Amp. Right Parking, Tail & Side Marker Lights.
⑭ – 8 Amp. Left Parking, Tail & Side Marker Lights
⑮ – 16 Amp. Radiator Fan.

Dasher – Fuse block is located on the left side behind the dashboard bin and contains 15 fuses. One additional fuse is located above fuse No. 7. A 16 Amp. fuse protects the Fuel Pump Relay. Circuits protected by fuses in the block are, from left to right:

① – 8 Amp. Left Low Beam.
② – 8 Amp. Right Low Beam.
③ – 8 Amp. Left High Beam & Warning Light.
④ – 8 Amp. Right High Beam.
⑤ – 16 Amp. Rear Window Defogger.
⑥ – 8 Amp. Stop Lights, Hazard Warning Flasher.
⑦ – 8 Amp. Cigar Lighter, Clock, Radio, Interior Light.
⑧ – 8 Amp. Gauges, Warning Lights, Turn Signal Indicator.
⑨ – 8 Amp. Back-Up Lights, Shift Console Light.
⑩ – 16 Amp. Fresh Air Fan, Rear Window Defogger (Switch Current)
⑪ – 8 Amp. Horn, Windshield Wiper/Washer.
⑫ – 8 Amp. License Plate Light.
⑬ – 8 Amp. Right Tail, Parking & Side Marker Lights.
⑭ – 8 Amp. Left Tail, Parking & Side Marker Lights.
⑮ – 16 Amp. Radiator Fan.

VOLVO

FUSE BLOCK

240 Series – Fuse block is located in front of front left door pillar. Circuits protected are, from top to bottom:

① – 8 Amp. Cigar Lighter, Rear Window Wiper/Washer.
② – 16 Amp. Windshield Wiper/Washer, Heater Fan, Horn
③ – 16 Amp. Rear Window Defogger, Overdrive.
④ – 8 Amp. Glove Compartment Light, Back-Up Lights, Air Conditioner.
⑤ – 8 Amp. Instrument and Warning Lights, Turn Signals, Relay (Fuel Injection System), Seat Belt Warning.
⑥ – 8 Amp. Hazard Warning Lights, Engine Compartment Light.
⑦ – 8 Amp. Clock, Fuel Pump.
⑧ – 8 Amp. Stop Lights, Interior Light.
⑨ – 8 Amp. Buzzer Ignition Switch.
⑩ – Spare.
⑪ – 8 Amp. Left Parking & Side Marker Lights, Rear Fog Lights.
⑫ – 8 Amp. Right Parking & Side Marker Lights, Instrument Panel Lights; Seat Belt, Ash Tray & Shift Positions Lights.

260 Series – Fuse block is located in front of front left door pillar and contains 12 fuses. Circuits protected are, from top to bottom:

① – 8 Amp. Cigar Lighter, Rear Window Wiper/Washer.
② – 16 Amp. Windshield Wiper/Washer, Heater Fan, Horn.
③ – 16 Amp. Rear Window Defogger, Overdrive.
④ – 8 Amp. Glove Compartment Light, Back-Up Lights, Heated Seat, Air Conditioner, Window Lift.
⑤ – 8 Amp. Instrument & Warning Lights, Relay (Fuel Injection System), Seat Belt Warning.
⑥ – 8 Amp. Hazard Warning Light, Engine Compartment & Trunk Lights.
⑦ – 16 Amp. Clock, Fuel Pump.
⑧ – 8 Amp. Stop Lights, Interior Light.
⑨ – 8 Amp. Buzzer Ignition Switch.
⑩ – 16 Amp. Window Lift.
⑪ – 8 Amp. Left Parking & Side Marker Lights, Left License Plate Light.
⑫ – 8 Amp. Right Parking & Side Marker Lights, Right License Plate Light, Instrument, Seat Belt, Ash Tray & Shift Position Lights.

Section 5
ENGINES

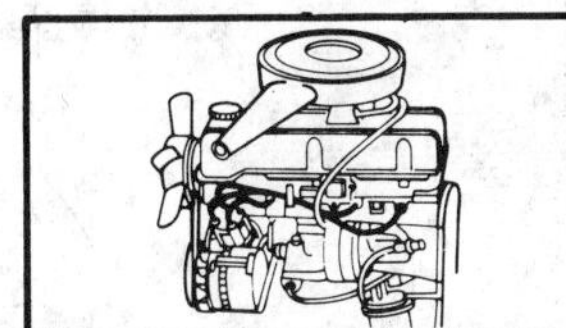

Contents

NOTE — ALSO SEE GENERAL INDEX.

1600 & 2000 cc 4 CYLINDER

ENGINE CODING

ENGINE IDENTIFICATION

Engine model code number is stamped on the left side of the engine block just below the starter. Engine serial number is stamped on right side of block on a flat just forward of the manifold. Numbers are decoded as follows:

Application In. (cc)	Model Code
97.5 (1600)	4G32
121.7 (2000)	4G52

ENGINE & CYLINDER HEAD

ENGINE

1) Drain cooling system, remove battery, disconnect ground strap, wiring from ignition coil, vacuum control solenoid valve, fuel cut-off solenoid valve, generator, starter, transmission switch, back-up light switch, water temperature gauge and oil pressure switch.

2) Remove air cleaner and disconnect attaching hoses. Disconnect accelerator linkage and heater hoses. Unbolt and separate exhaust pipe from manifold. Disconnect pipe mounting bracket at transmission.

3) Disconnect hose between fuel filter and fuel pump return pipe. Remove radiator and radiator shroud. If equipped with automatic transmission, remove oil cooler pipe and tie rod when removing radiator.

4) Remove console box, then detach control lever assembly from transmission. Remove hood. Disconnect speedometer cable and back-up light switch wiring from transmission. Disconnect clutch cable from shift lever and then disconnect cable from its bracket (if equipped with manual transmission). Drain transmission. If equipped with transmission dynamic vibration damper, remove damper, remove locking bolts for attaching flange yoke at rear of propeller shaft, then draw shaft out of transmission.

5) Support transmission on a suitable jack and remove front and rear mount bolts. Remove rear engine support bracket. Attach suitable lifting device to front and rear engine hangers. Lift engine-transmission assembly obliquely upward and out of engine compartment. **NOTE** — *Keep transmission lower than engine when removing.*

INTAKE MANIFOLD

Removal & Installation — Drain cooling system, remove air cleaner assembly, water outlet hose, heater hoses, accelerator linkage and choke cable. Disconnect vacuum line, fuel line, water hose on carburetor side, and wiring for water temperature gauge. Remove carburetor, and then remove intake manifold. To install, reverse removal procedure and tighten all nuts and bolts.

CYLINDER HEAD

Removal — 1) Remove rocker arm cover. Turn crankshaft until No. 1 piston is at top of its compression stroke. **NOTE** — *If dowel pin at forward end of camshaft is at position shown in illustration when crankshaft pulley notch is aligned with timing mark "T" at front of timing chain case, then No. 1 piston is at TDC.*

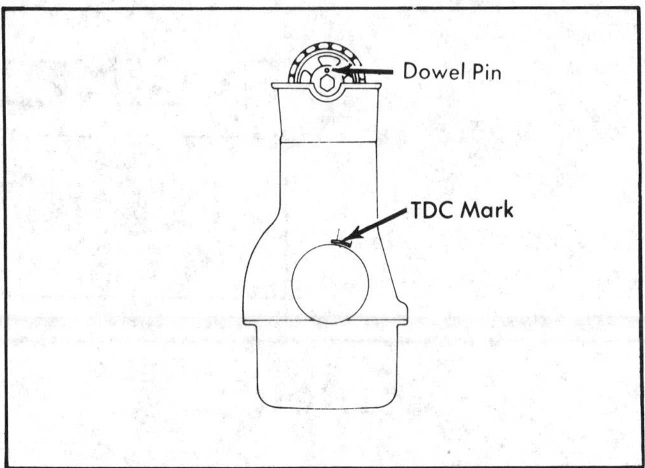

Fig. 1 Setting No. 1 Piston at TDC

2) Draw a mating mark in white paint on timing chain in line with mating mark on camshaft sprocket. Remove camshaft sprocket. Unscrew cylinder head bolts and nuts according to illustrated loosening sequence. **CAUTION** — *Loosen head bolts in two or three stages in order to prevent head warping.* Note dowel locator pins when removing head, and take care not to damage pins or twist chain when lifting off head.

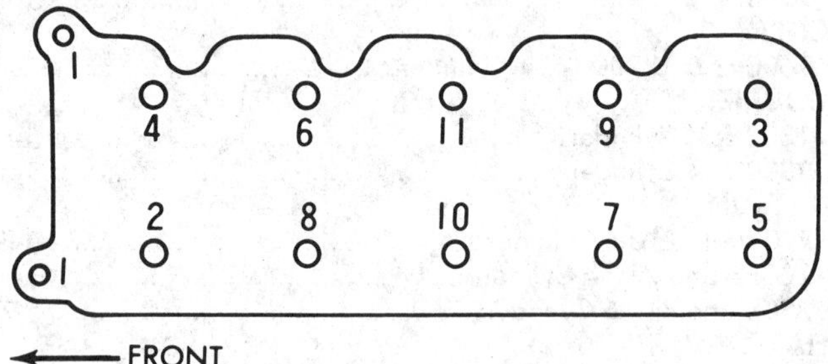

Fig. 2 Cylinder Head Loosening Sequence (1600 & 2000 cc)

Installation — 1) To install, reverse removal procedure, noting the following: Apply sealant to points at which cylinder head gasket will rest over junction of front cover chain case and cylinder block.

2) Tighten cylinder head bolts in sequence shown and in three or four stages. Install camshaft sprocket onto camshaft while pulling upward. If installation is difficult, slacken chain tensioner as required. Turn crankshaft back about 90°. Tighten sprocket lock bolt. Adjust valve clearance.

1600 & 2000 cc 4 CYLINDER (Cont.)

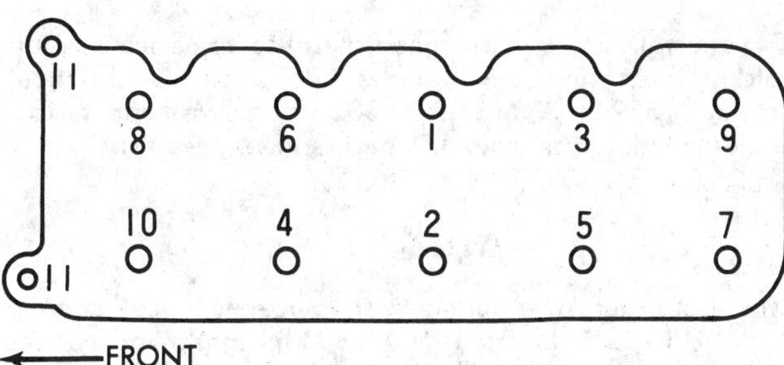

Fig. 3 Cylinder Head Tightening Sequence (1600 & 2000 cc)

Removal; 1600 with Counterbalance Shaft – 1) Turn crankshaft until No. 1 piston is at top of compression stroke, (notch on crankshaft pulley is in alignment with "T" position on timing indicator). Remove bolts in upper timing belt cover. Draw mating mark on timing belt in alignment with mark on camshaft sprocket.

2) Remove camshaft sprocket, with timing belt attached, from camshaft. A holder provided on the timing belt lower front cover holds the sprocket in position. Remove upper under cover. Remove head bolts in reverse of tightening sequence. Head bolts should be loosened in two or three stages to prevent cylinder head warpage.

Installation; 1600 with Counterbalance Shaft – 1) To install, reverse removal procedure. Dowel pins are provided at front and rear of cylinder block. Do not slide cylinder head when installing. Pull camshaft sprocket upward while installing.

2) If camshaft sprocket is hard to lift and cannot be easily fitted into spacers, insert a screwdriver into the top hole of sprocket, set the end of the screw driver under the ridge portion of the upper under cover and pry sprocket up.

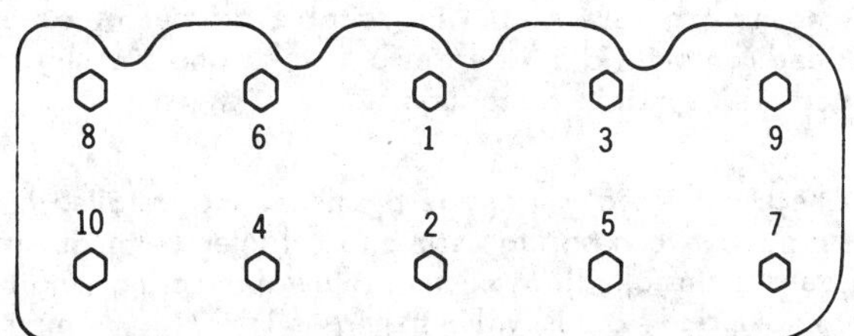

Fig. 4 Cylinder Head Tightening Sequence (1600 cc with Counterbalance Shaft)

VALVES

VALVE ARRANGEMENT

Intake – Left side.
Exhaust – Right side.

ROCKER ARM & CAMSHAFT ASSEMBLY

Removal – Remove camshaft bearing cap nuts. Holding assembly by front and rear caps, lift rocker arm shaft off head. Disassemble individual components, keeping rocker arms and corresponding components in proper sequence for reassembly. Remove camshaft from cylinder head.

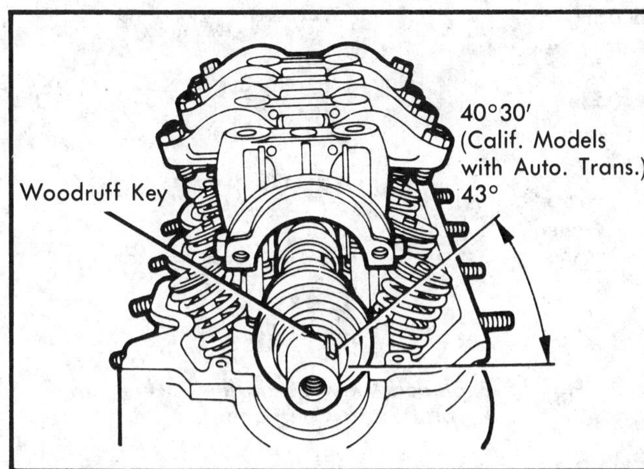

Fig. 5 Camshaft Woodruff Key Position

NOTE – *On 1600 cc with counterbalance shaft, distributor drive is at front of camshaft. Camshaft woodruff key must be positioned at a 40° 30' angle to valve cover gasket surface (Fig. 5).*

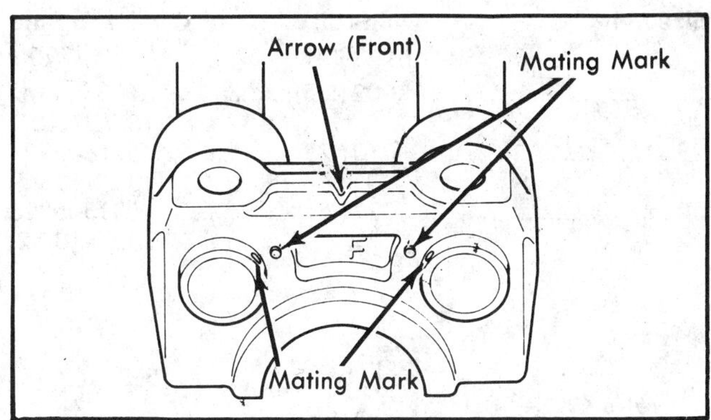

Fig. 6 Location of Rocker Shaft Mating Marks

Installation – 1) Install camshaft on head after completing servicing described within this article. See *Camshaft*. Install caps, rocker arms, springs, and wave washers onto both rocker arm shafts. **NOTE** – *The front bearing cap has embossed mating mark on front side, which should be aligned with indent marks on front end of rocker arm shafts. Each cap also has arrow which marks direction of installation (front).* Ensure all parts are returned to original positions. On 1600 cc models, right side rocker arm shaft has eight oil holes and left side has four. On 2000 cc models, right side has 12 oil holes and left side has 4.

2) Install assembled rocker arm shaft assemblies to cylinder head. Be sure that dowel pin is directly on top of camshaft. Tighten caps in following order: 3, 2, 4, front, and rear. **NOTE** – *No. 4 and front caps are to be tightened together with the valve cover bracket.*

1600 & 2000 cc 4 CYLINDER (Cont.)

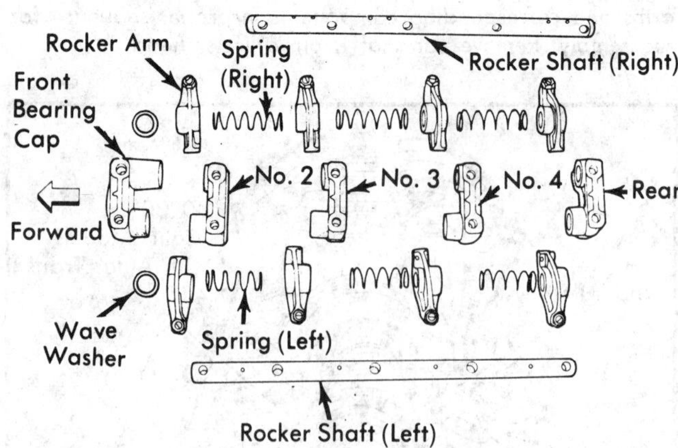

Fig. 7 Exploded View of Engine Rocker Arm and Shaft Components

VALVE GUIDE SERVICING

1) Check valve stem-to-guide clearance, and if clearance exceeds service limits as listed in table, replace valve guide with next oversize component. Guides are available in the following oversizes:

Valve Guide Oversizes

Size Mark	Guide Size In. (mm)	Cyl. Head Bore In. (mm)
5	.002 (.05)	.5138-.5145 (13.05-13.07)
25	.010 (.25)	.5216-.5224 (13.25-13.27)
50	.020 (.51)	.5315-.5323 (13.50-13.52)

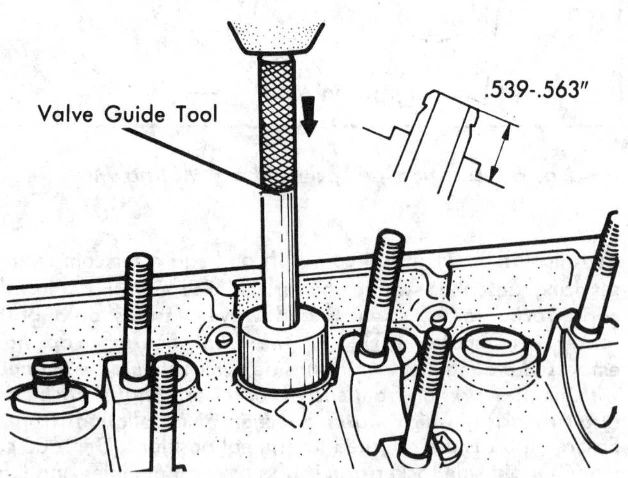

Fig. 8 Valve Guide Installation and Height

2) Heat cylinder head to approximately 480°F (249°C), and then use a suitable valve guide tool to drive out each guide toward the combustion chamber. Ream guide bore in cylinder head to specified size (after head has cooled to room temperature).

3) To install new guides, reheat head to same temperature, quickly insert and drive guides into head. Guide should protrude .539-.563" (13.69-14.30 mm) above head surface, as illustrated. Check guide I.D. and ream as necessary.

VALVE STEM OIL SEALS

After installing valve spring seat, place stem seal on valve guide. Using suitable tool (MD998005), lightly hammer seal into proper position (see illustration). When installing, use care not to twist seal. Do not reuse old seals.

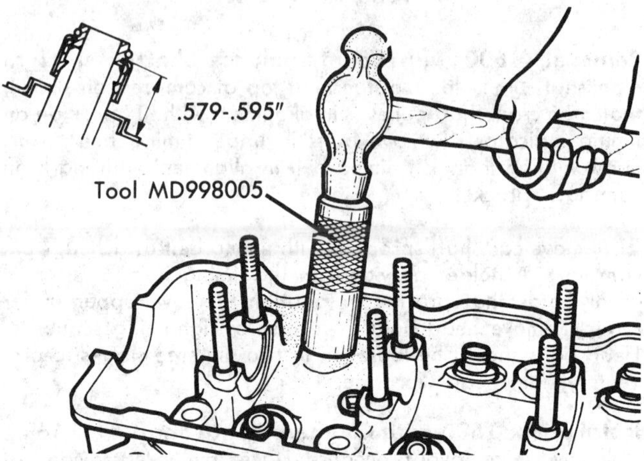

Fig. 9 Valve Stem Oil Seal Installation and Height

VALVE SEAT SERVICING

1) Check valve seat for damage or wear. Replace or rework seat, as necessary. If reworking seat, check valve guide first. Make proper replacement, if required, then check seat for necessary corrections.

2) Recondition valve seat with suitable grinder or cutter to specified contact width. After rework, valve and seat should be lapped with suitable compound.

3) Check valve seat shrinkage by measuring installed height of spring between spring seat and retainer (with all spring components installed). Maximum allowable spring length for both intake and exhaust valve springs is 1.590 (40.39 mm).

4) Remove valve seat by thinning down with a suitable cutter, then machine seat bore to proper size for replacement seat. Heat head to approximately 480°F (250°C) and press in oversize seat. Replacement seats are available in .012" (.305 mm) and .024" (.610 mm) oversizes, marked "30" and "60" respectively.

VALVE SPRING

1) With camshaft removed, install spring compressor, remove retainer lock, retainer and spring. Keep components in proper order for reassembly.

2) Install valve spring with enamel identification mark toward rocker arm. Compress spring, making sure spring compressor does not interfere with stem seal. Install retainer and lock.

1600 & 2000 cc 4 CYLINDER (Cont.)

VALVE SPRING INSTALLED HEIGHT

1) Check free length and tension of each valve spring. If beyond specifications, replace spring. Using a square, check each spring for proper squareness (1.5° or less). Replace spring if excessively out of square.

2) Measure installed height of spring between spring seat and retainer, with spring seat, retainer and retainer lock installed.

VALVE CLEARANCE ADJUSTMENT

1) Ensure timing marks on camshaft sprocket and chain are aligned. With head assembly installed, temporarily adjust valves (sequence for adjustment; 1-3-4-2), according to following procedure: At compression stroke TDC, for cylinder being adjusted, loosen rocker arm nuts, then, turning adjusting screw, adjust valve clearance to specifications.

2) After completion of engine assembly, run engine until coolant temperature is 176°F, then readjust valves.

NOTE — *Torque head bolts, with engine warm, prior to final valve clearance adjustment; otherwise, clearance will change if head bolts are torqued last.*

Valve Clearance

Application	Cold In. (mm)	Hot In. (mm)
Intake	.003 (.08)	.006 (.15)
Exhaust	.007 (.18)	.010 (.25)

PISTONS, PINS & RINGS

PISTON & CONNECTING ROD ASSEMBLY

Removal — Remove cylinder head and oil pan. Check to ensure connecting rods and rod caps are marked to aid in assembling components to their original position. Remove carbon ridge from cylinder bores. Remove connecting rod caps. Remove connecting rod and piston assembly through top of cylinder block.

Installation — To reinstall, lubricate all internal surfaces with engine oil before installation. Make sure front mark on piston head faces front of engine. Use a ring compressor to compress rings (without changing their position) and install piston and connecting rod assembly in to cylinder block in their original position. Tap lightly on piston dome with wooden handle tool while guiding connecting rod onto crankshaft. Install rod cap onto proper piston and connecting rod assembly. Tighten attaching bolts. Install cylinder head and oil pan.

FITTING PISTONS

1) After checking block for distortion (not to exceed .002"-.05 mm), cracks, scratches or other abnormalities, measure bores at three levels. If any bore distortion exceeds .008" .20 mm from standard bore size, refinish all cylinders and install oversize pistons.

Oversize Pistons

Application	Size Mark	Diam. In. (mm)
1600 cc		
.010" OS	0.25	3.0374 (77.15)
.020" OS	0.50	3.0472 (77.40)
.030" OS	0.75	3.0571 (77.65)
.039" OS	1.00	3.0669 (77.90)
2000 cc		
.010" OS	0.25	3.3163 (84.23)
.020" OS	0.50	3.3262 (84.49)
.030" OS	0.75	3.3360 (84.73)
.039" os	1.00	3.3464 (85.00)

2) Check outside diameter of piston by measuring at a point .079" (2 mm) from bottom of skirt and at 90° to pin bore. Determine amount of cylinder reboring required to meet specified clearance.

3) To prevent distortion due to the high temperature of the cutting process, this operation should be done in stages and in sequence of 2-4-1-3 or 3-1-4-2. Hone bore to finish size, using a honing angle of 30-45°. Ensure piston-to-cylinder clearance is within specification.

PISTON PINS

Check piston pin-to-bore fit; pin should press in smoothly by hand (at room temperature). When assembling, apply engine oil to outside of pin and to piston pin bore, position rod to piston ("FRONT" mark upward), align pin with pressing tool, and press pin into piston and rod.

PISTON RINGS

Measure piston ring side and end clearance for all pistons and replace rings as necessary. When replacing a ring without correcting the cylinder bore, check ring end gap at lower part of cylinder that is less worn. When replacing a ring, be sure to use one of the same size. Install rings on piston with end gaps staggered at 120° intervals, but make sure no ring gap is in line with thrust face of pin bore. Also be sure the manufacturer's marks are facing upward when rings are installed.

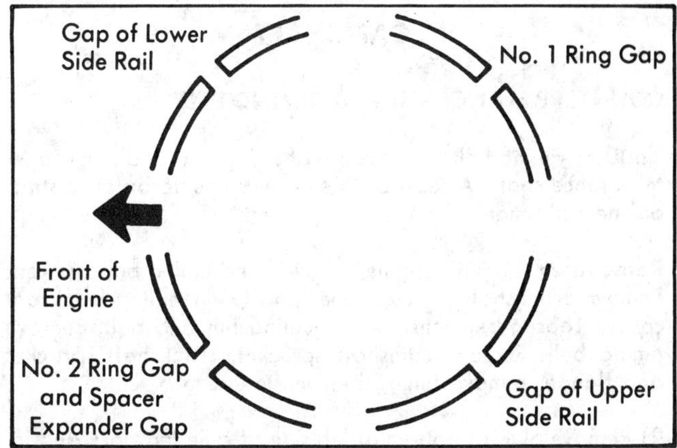

Fig. 10 Piston Ring Gap Positions

1600 & 2000 cc 4 CYLINDER (Cont.)

NOTE — *Ensure oil ring gap is opposite the expander joint. The following ring sizes are available:*

Piston Ring Sizes

Ring Size	**Size Mark**
1600 & 2000 cc	
Standard	No Mark
.010" (.25 mm) OS.	25
.020" (.50 mm) OS.	50
.030" (.75 mm) OS.	75
.039" (1.00 mm) OS.	100

CRANKSHAFT MAIN & CONNECTING ROD BEARINGS

MAIN & CONNECTING ROD BEARINGS

1) Inspect each bearing for peeling, melting, seizure or improper contact. Replace defective bearings. Measure outside diameter of crankshaft and connecting rod journals to determine if out-of-round or tapered.

2) Cut Plastigage to same length as width of bearing. Place it parallel with journal (not over oil holes). Install crankshaft bearings and caps, tightening to specifications. Always install caps with arrow facing forward.

NOTE — *Do not turn crankshaft with Plastigage installed.*

3) Remove main bearing cap from crankshaft and measure Plastigage at widest part (using scale on Plastigage package). Repeat procedure for connecting rod bearings. If clearance exceeds limits, bearing should be replaced or undersize bearing installed. Undersize bearings are available in .010" (.25 mm), .020" (.50 mm), and .030" (.75 mm) undersizes.

THRUST BEARING

With crankshaft bearing caps installed, check thrust clearance (end play) by inserting feeler gauge between center main bearing and crankshaft thrust face. If clearance exceeds specified limits, replace center main bearing.

CAMSHAFT

COUNTERBALANCE SHAFT & TIMING BELT

1600 — Timing belt drives camshaft, oil pump and (left) counterbalance shaft. A separate belt drives counterbalance shaft on the right side.

Removal — **1)** With engine removed and timing belt marked. Remove crankshaft pulley, upper and lower timing belt front covers. Loosen belt tensioner mounting nut and bolt. Remove timing belt. Remove camshaft sprocket, crankshaft sprocket and flange, remove timing belt tensioner.

2) Remove plug at bottom of left side of cylinder block and insert a screwdriver, to keep left counterbalance shaft in position. Remove crankshaft sprocket and counterbalance shaft sprocket from right side. Remove timing belt covers from right side. Remove water pump and cylinder head assembly. Remove oil pan and oil pick-up screen. Remove oil pump cover.

3) Insert screwdriver throuqh pluq hole in cylinder block, to hold counterbalance shaft. Loosen oil pump driven gear bolt. Remove front case with left counterbalance shaft attached. Remove right counterbalance shaft from cylinder block.

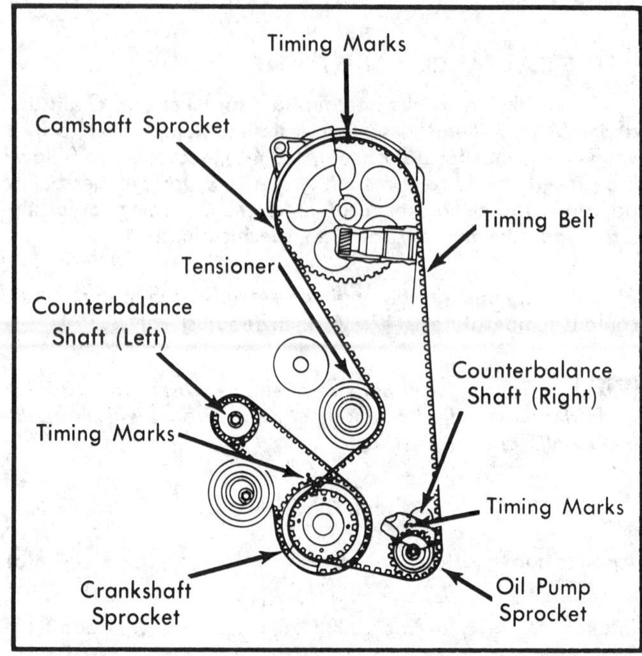

Fig. 11 Counterbalance Shaft and Timing Belts (1600 cc)

Installation — **1)** To install, reverse removal procedure. Check to ensure that all timing marks are in alignment. To adjust tension on right side. Lift tensioner toward belt; tighten nut and bolt. Make sure that the shaft of the tensioner does not rotate in the same direction as the bolt tightens. Correct adjustment is obtained when belt deflects .20-.27" (5-7 mm) with finger pressure.

2) To adjust counterbalance shaft and timing belt, start with timing belt installed on crankshaft sprocket, oil pump sprocket and camshaft sprocket, making sure that all timing marks are in alignment. With tensioner installed, lightly push up toward mounting nut, to make sure that timing belt comes into complete mesh with camshaft sprocket. Tighten mounting nut and bolt (tighten nut first).

3) Turn crankshaft through a complete rotation in normal direction. (Make sure that crankshaft is turned smoothly and in the correct direction.) Loosen tensioner mounting nut and bolt. At this time, the loose side of the belt will be given tension. Tighten nut and bolt (nut first).

COUNTERBALANCE SHAFT & CHAIN

NOTE — *The counterbalance shafts on 2000 cc models are driven by the crankshaft via chains. The left counterbalance shaft rotates in the same direction as the crankshaft. The right*

1600 & 2000 cc 4 CYLINDER (Cont.)

counterbalance shaft, is driven by the oil pump and rotates in the opposite direction.

Removal – With engine removed and placed upside down, remove oil pan and screen. Remove crankshaft pulley, flywheel and timing chain case. Remove chain guides A, B and C *(See Fig. 9)*. Remove sprocket B locking bolts. Remove crankshaft sprocket B, counterbalance shaft sprocket B and chain B.

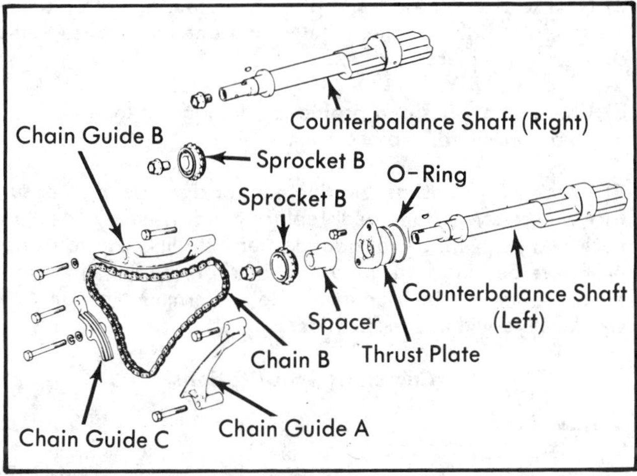

Fig. 12 Exploded View of Counterbalance Shaft (2000 cc)

Installation – To install reverse removal procedure. To adjust tension of chain B, tighten chain guide A mounting bolt. Tighten chain guide C mounting bolt. Shake right and left B sprockets to collect slack at point P *(See Fig. 10)*. Adjust position of chain guide C so when chain is pulled in direction of arrow Y, clearance between chain guide B and links of chain B will be .04-.14" (1.0-3.6 mm). Tighten bolts securely. Install chain case and gasket.

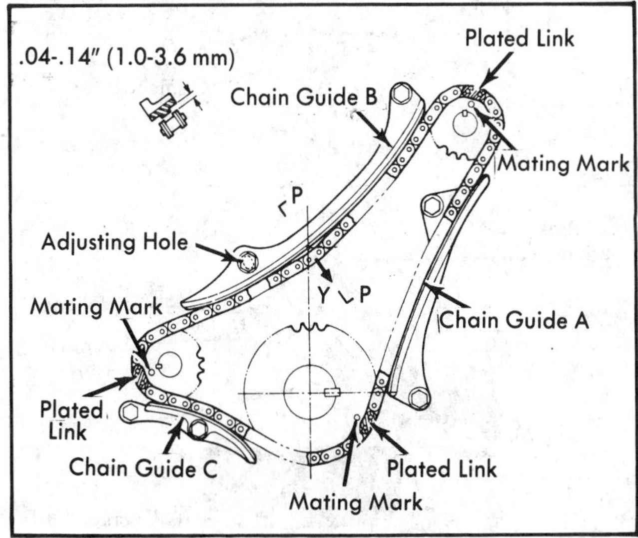

Fig. 13 Adjusting Tension of Counterbalance Shaft (2000 cc)

COUNTERBALANCE SHAFTS

Removal & Installation, 2000 cc – 1) With balancer and timing chain removed, proceed as follows: Remove oil pump mounting bolts. Remove bolt locking oil pump driven gear and right counterbalance shaft. Withdraw right counterbalance shaft from cylinder block.

NOTE – *If bolt locking oil pump driven gear and counterbalance shaft is hard to loosen, remove oil pump and counterbalance shaft as an assembly. Then remove lock bolt to disassemble.*

2) Remove thrust plate supporting front of left counterbalance shaft. (Thrust plate is removed by threading bolts into plate holes at same time). Withdraw counterbalance shaft from cylinder block. To install, reverse removal procedure.

1600 cc with Counterbalance Shaft – Oil pump is gear type. It also serves as a source to drive counterbalance shaft.

Removal – With timing belt removed, remove oil pump sprocket and remove plug at bottom of left side of cylinder block. Insert a screwdriver in hole to keep counterbalance shaft in position. Remove upper and lower timing belt under covers. Remove oil pan and oil screen, remove oil pump cover and assembly.

Inspection – Check entire body for cracks and abnormal wear. Check cover for cracks or wear, replace if badly worn. When bearing replacement is necessary, replace oil pump body assembly.

Installation – Reverse removal procedure, checking all alignment marks (*Fig. 14*).

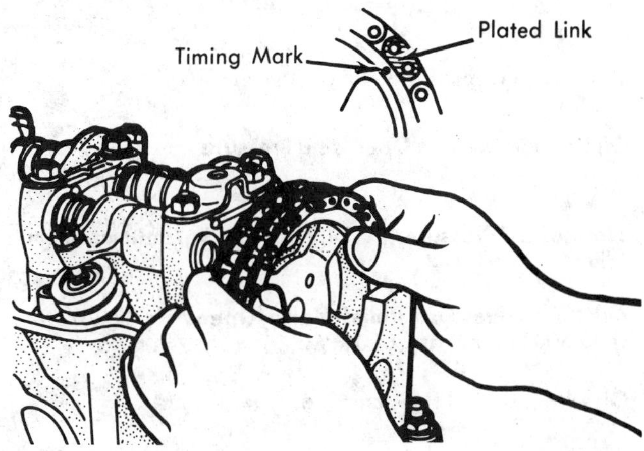

Fig. 14 Camshaft Sprocket Alignment and Installation

TIMING CHAIN & BELT

1600 & 2000 cc Timing Chain Removal – With timing case front covers removed and piston of No. 1 cylinder at TDC, remove crankshaft and camshaft sprockets. Depress timing chain tensioner, while removing timing chain. Remove camshaft sprocket holder and timing chain guides.

Installation – To install, reverse removal procedure ensuring

1600 & 2000 cc 4 CYLINDER (Cont.)

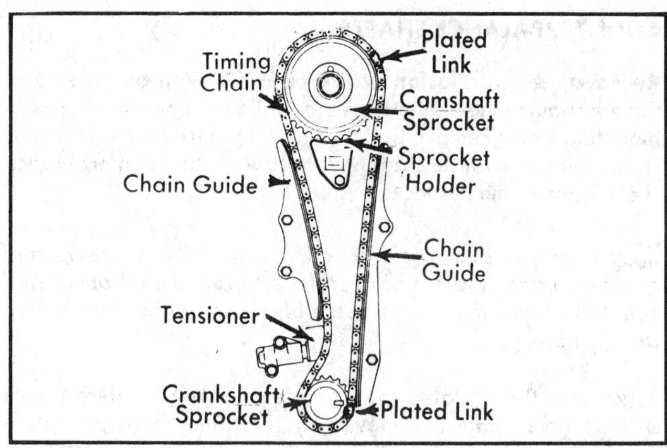

Fig. 15 Timing Chain Alignment and Installation

that chrome plated links of timing chain are in alignment with mating marks (punch marks) of crankshaft and camshaft sprockets.

1600 cc Timing Belt Removal – With timing case covers removed and piston of No. 1 cylinder at TDC, loosen tensioner mounting nut and bolt. Move tensioner to release pressure from timing belt. Tighten nut and bolt to hold tensioner in position and remove timing belt.

Installation – 1) Align all timing marks (*Fig. 14*). Install timing belt. Loosen belt tensioner. Lightly push tensioner toward mounting nut to ensure that belt and sprocket come into complete mesh. Tighten tensioner mounting nut and bolt.

2) Turn crankshaft through a complete rotation, (do not turn in reverse direction, do not push or shake belt). Loosen tensioner nut and bolt; belt will be at correct tension. Tighten tensioner mounting nut and bolt (tighten nut first). Reinstall remaining components.

CAMSHAFT

1) With camshaft removed from vehicle, first visually check camshaft for any obvious defects. Attach a dial gauge to No. 2 or No. 3 journal. Turn camshaft one complete revolution and read the total gauge measurement. Divide this amount in half to determine amount of camshaft bend.

2) Next, check camshaft end play by measuring with a feeler gauge (camshaft installed) between front bearing cap and camshaft end piece.

3) Check cam lobes and profile for damage. If lobe height is less than specified, replace camshaft.

4) Check each camshaft bearing cap for damage. If inner surface is excessively damaged, replace head assembly. Measure each cap I.D. with a dial gauge after installing cap to its appropriate bearing half. Measure camshaft journal diameters, then use these measurements to determine if camshaft clearance is within specifications.

Camshaft Specifications

Application	1600 cc	2000 cc
End Play	.002-.006" (.05-.15mm)	.004-.008" (.1-.2mm)
Bend	.0008" (.02mm)	.0008" (.02mm)
Height	①.020" (0.5mm)	①.020" (0.5mm)

① – Minus

ENGINE OILING

Crankcase Capacity – 4.5 quarts

Oil Pressure Switch Operating Pressure – 2.8-5.7 psi (20-40 kg/cm²)

Normal Oil Pressure – 14.2 psi (99.8 kg/cm²), minimum, at idle.

Oil Pump Pressure Relief Valve Opens – 56.9-71.1 psi (400-500 kg/cm²) at 2,000 RPM.

Oil Filter – Full-flow, cartridge type.

ENGINE OILING SYSTEM

1600 cc – Lubrication system is force-feed type, using a trochoid type pump. The pump body is integral with timing chain case.

2000 cc – Oil pump is gear type and also serves as a source to turn counterbalance shaft.

OIL PUMP

Removal, 1600 cc – Remove splash shield from under body. Remove oil filter, remove oil pump cover bolts. Remove rotor and assembly with cover. Check inner and outer rotors, if worn beyond specification, replace.

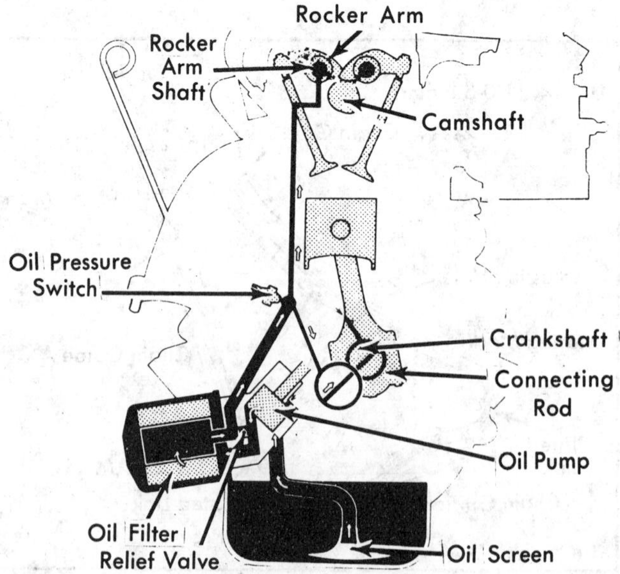

Fig. 16 Cutaway View of Engine Oiling System

1600 & 2000 cc 4 CYLINDER (Cont.)

ENGINE OILING (Cont.)

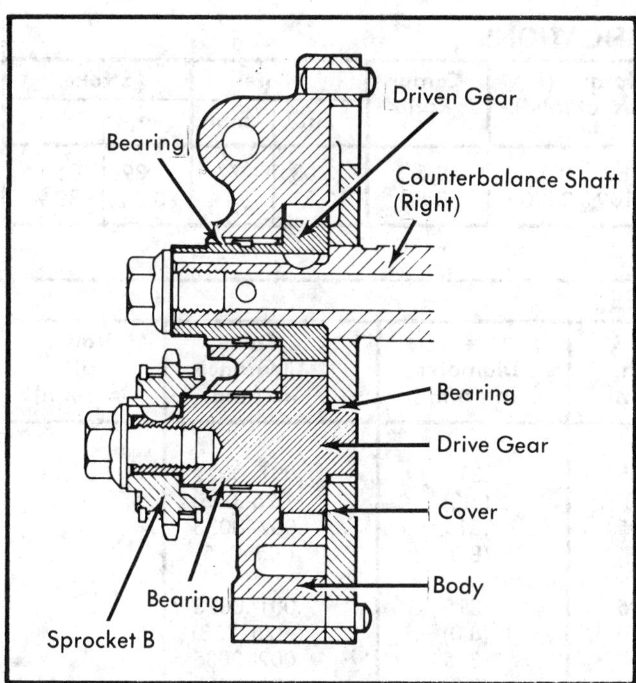

Fig. 17 Cutaway View of Oil Pump

Installation – Reverse removal procedure.

Removal, 2000 cc – Drain engine oil. Remove oil pan and gasket (discard gasket). Remove bolt locking oil pump drive gear and right counterbalance shaft. Remove oil pump mounting bolts. Withdraw oil pump from cylinder block.

Inspection – Check entire body for cracks and excessive wear. Check gears for ridge wear. Check oil holes and passages for clogging. Check cover for ridge wear. Replace all worn parts. Measure all clearances as shown in *Fig. 14*.

CAUTION – *Prior to installation, fill oil pump with a sufficient amount of engine oil through delivery port.*

Installation – **NOTE** – *Make sure keyway of oil pump driven gear fits woodruff key at end of counterbalance shaft, and does not go out of keyway.* After installing pump into block, firmly tighten oil pump mounting bolts. Tighten counterbalance shaft and driven gear mounting bolt.

Oil Pump Specifications

Application	Clearance In. (mm)
1600 cc Trochoid Type	
Inner-to-Outer Rotor	.0047 (.12)
Rotor-to-Cover End Play	.0008-.0039 (.02-.1)
Outer Rotor-to-Chain Case	.0039-.0063 (.1-.16)
1600 & 2000 cc Gear Type	
Gear Teeth-to-Housing	.0041-.0059 (.1-.15)
Gear End Play	.0024-.0047 (.06-.12)
Gear-to-Bearing	.0008-.0018 (.02-.046)
Drive Gear (Rear)-to-Bearing	.0017-.0026 (.044-.066)

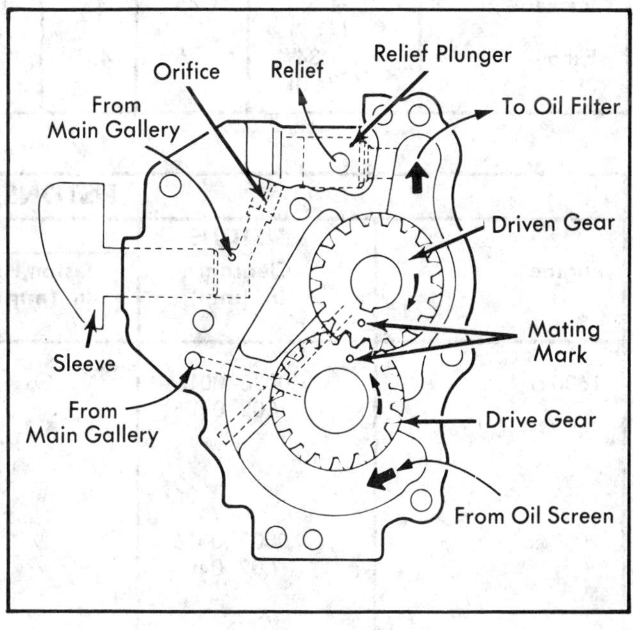

Fig. 18 Mating Marks of Oil Pump Gears

ENGINE COOLING

Thermostat – 180°F (82°C)

Radiator Cap – 13 psi (91.4 kg/cm²)

Cooling System Capacity
1600 cc – 7.7 qts. (7.3 liters)
2000 cc – 9.5 qts. (9 liters)

WATER PUMP

Drain coolant, loosen hoses from pump and loosen alternator. Remove fan, pulley, and fan belt. Remove water pump bolts. To install, reverse removal procedure.

1600 & 2000 cc 4 CYLINDER (Cont.)

ENGINE SPECIFICATION

GENERAL SPECIFICATIONS

Year	Displ. cu. ins.	Displ. cc	Carburetor	HP at RPM	Torque (Ft. Lbs. at RPM)	Compr. Ratio	Bore in.	Bore mm	Stroke in.	Stroke mm
1977	97.5 121.7	1600 2000	2-Bbl. 2-Bbl.	83@5500 96@5500	89@3500 109@3500	8.5:1 8.5:1	3.03 3.31	77 84.1	3.39 3.54	86.1 89.9

VALVES

Engine & Valve	Head Diam. In. (mm)	Face Angle	Seat Angle	Seat Width In. (mm)	Stem Diameter In. (mm)	Stem Clearance In. (mm)	Valve Lift In. (mm)
1600 cc							
Intake	1.50 (38.1)	45°	45°	.035-.051 (.9-1.3)	.315 (8.0)	.001-.0022 (.025-.055)	.....
Exhaust	1.22 (31.0)	45°	45°	.035-.051 (.9-1.3)	.315 (8.0)	.002-.0033 (.05-.085)	.....
2000 cc							
Intake	1.65 (41.9)	45°	45°	.035-.051 (.9-1.3)	.315 (8.0)	.001-.0023 (.025-.058)	.....
Exhaust	1.34 (34.0)	45°	45°	.....	.315 (8.0)	.002-.0035 (.05-.088)	.....

PISTONS, PINS, RINGS

Engine	PISTONS Clearance In. (mm)	PINS Piston Fit In. (mm)	PINS Rod Fit In. (mm)	RINGS Rings	RINGS End Gap In. (mm)	RINGS Side Clearance In. (mm)
1600 cc	.0008-.0016 (.02-.04)	①	Press Fit	No. 1	.008-.016 (.2-.4)	.0012-.0028 (.03-.07)
				No. 2	.008-.020 (.2-.4)	.0008-.0024 (.02-.06)
				No. 3	.008-.020 (.2-.4)	.0008-.0024 (.02-.06)
2000 cc	.0008-.0016 (.02-.04)	①	Press Fit	No. 1	.0098-.0177 (.25-.45)	.0024-.0039 (.06-.10)
				No. 2	.0078-.0359 (.2-.9)	.0008-.0024 (.02-.06)
				No. 3	.0078-.0359 (.2-.9)	.0008-.0024 (.02-.06)

①— Thumb press fit without rod installed

CRANKSHAFT MAIN & CONNECTING ROD BEARINGS

Engine	MAIN BEARINGS Journal Diam. In. (mm)	MAIN BEARINGS Clearance In. (mm)	MAIN BEARINGS Thrust Bearing	MAIN BEARINGS Crankshaft End Play In. (mm)	CONNECTING ROD BEARINGS Journal Diam. In. (mm)	CONNECTING ROD BEARINGS Clearance In. (mm)	CONNECTING ROD BEARINGS Side Play In. (mm)
1600 cc	2.244 (57)	.0008-.0028 (.02-.07)	No. 3	.002-.007 (.05-.18)	1.772 (45)	.0004-.0028 (.01-.06)	.004-.01 (.1-.25)
2000 cc	2.598 (66)	.0008-.0028 (.02-.07)	No. 3	.002-.007 (.05-.18)	2.087 (53)	.0008-.0028 (.01-.06)	.004-.01 (.1-.25)

1600 & 2000 cc 4 CYLINDER (Cont.)

ENGINE SPECIFICATIONS (Cont.)

CAMSHAFT			
Engine	Journal Diam. In. (mm)	Clearance In. (mm)	Lobe Lift In. (mm)
1600 & 2000 cc	1.339 (34)	.002-.0035 (.05-.09)	....

① — Wear limit

VALVE SPRINGS			
Engine	Free Length In. (mm)	PRESSURE Lbs. @ In. (kg @ mm)	
		Valve Closed	Valve Open
1600 cc	1.823 (46.3)	61.7@1.469 (27.9@37.3)	.....
2000 cc	1.869 (47.5)	61@1.59 (27.6@40.4)	.....

TIGHTENING SPECIFICATIONS	
Application	**Ft. Lbs. (mkg)**
Camshaft Bearing Cap	13-14 (59-73)
Camshaft Sprocket	
1600 cc	44-57 (59-78)
2000 cc	37-43 (49-58)
Cylinder Head Bolts (Cold)	
1600 cc	51-54 (69-73)
2000 cc	65-72 (89-98)
Main Bearing Caps	
1600 cc	37-39 (49-53)
2000 cc	55-61 (74-83)
Connecting Rod Caps	
1600 cc	24-25 (32-34)
2000 cc	33-34 (45-47)
Crank Pulley	
1600 cc	44-50 (59-68)
1600 cc w/Counterbalance Shaft	7.5-8.5 (10-11)
2000 cc	80-94 (108-127)
Flywheel-to-Crankshaft	94-101 (128-137)
Drive Plate-to-Crankshaft	84-90 (113-122)

100LS 4 CYLINDER

ENGINE CODING

ENGINE IDENTIFICATION

Engine number is die stamped on left side of engine block at clutch housing. Engine serial number is preceded by two letters which identify the engine as follows:

Application	Engine Code
Manual Trans.	①YR
Automatic Trans.	YD

① — Code for California Man. Trans. is YC.

ENGINE, CYLINDER HEAD & MANIFOLDS

ENGINE

NOTE — *Engine and transmission assembly are removed together. A hoist, with block-and-tackle and a pit, or suitable frame-contact hoist is necessary for removal operation.*

1) Remove engine hood (only if working with block-and-tackle equipment). Remove apron below front bumper. Disconnect battery. Detach breather hose at air cleaner, remove air cleaner assembly and cover intake opening.

2) Set heater controls at "WARM", remove radiator cap, unscrew plug at bottom of radiator, and drain coolant. **NOTE** — *To ensure complete draining of coolant, remove breather screw located in heater inlet hose at firewall.* Disconnect all coolant lines between radiator, heater, and engine.

3) Detach fuel hose from fuel pump. Disconnect servo brake unit vacuum hose (if equipped) from intake manifold. Unscrew speedometer cable from transmission. Disconnect clutch cable at mount, and gearshift mechanism connections at transmission.

4) Detach accelerator linkage at fuel injection, mount, and connecting rod. Remove throttle shaft. Separate brake line at retaining clip on body. To prevent fluid from escaping, brace or otherwise support brake pedal in full up position.

5) Remove guard plate for right engine mount. Disconnect all electrical wiring from engine and transmission, including the following: ignition leads, idle cutoff valve (if installed), thermostat, four-pole plug of regulator, oil pressure switch, starter connections, back-up light switch, fuel injection system, and all ground leads.

6) Remove the radiator. Unscrew fan support and remove fan and stop pad (on front crossmember). **NOTE** — *This operation is only necessary if a frame contact type hoist or a pit is being used of which the opening is not large enough to permit lowering the engine and transmission with the fan attached.*

7) Loosen and remove front exhaust pipe at exhaust manifold and primary muffler. Unscrew driveshaft flange at brake discs (note presence of thin insulator between flange and disc). Turn driveshaft flange in direction of wheel slightly, then fasten driveshafts to upper control arms with wire. Remove front stabilizer bar.

8) Position block and tackle or frame-contact equipment to engine and lift the assembly until pressure is released from engine and transmission mounts. Remove rear crossmember. Unscrew retaining nut from right engine mount (when engine is lowered note location of washers and sleeve on right mount).

9) Unscrew retaining nut of left mount without disturbing position of counter nut on upper side of frame bracket. Carefully lower engine and transmission assembly from vehicle.

10) To install assembly, reverse removal procedure noting the following: Engine mounts are not to be fully tightened until rear crossmember has been installed and engine alignment and height have been set such that the fan stop may be tightened to its mounting holes without strain.

NOTE — *If alternator is replaced on removed engine, ensure mounting nut faces forward. If nut faces starter, alternator removal will not be possible with engine in vehicle.*

EXHAUST MANIFOLD

1) With exhaust pipe and air cleaner removed from manifold, unbolt exhaust manifold heat shroud.

2) Unscrew eight mounting nuts and remove exhaust manifold.

NOTE — *When installing, ensure notches in gaskets face downward and beaded edge toward outside.*

INTAKE MANIFOLD

1) After loosening hose clamps, remove coolant hose from between thermostat and intake manifold. Remove vacuum lines from fuel injection system.

2) Disconnect fuel line at fuel pump and air breather hose from manifold. From underside of manifold, remove manifold support bolt. Unbolt and remove intake manifold.

NOTE — *When installing, reverse removal procedure, and use new gaskets and seals.*

CYLINDER HEAD

1) Remove alternator and bracket, distributor cap, and spark plug wires.

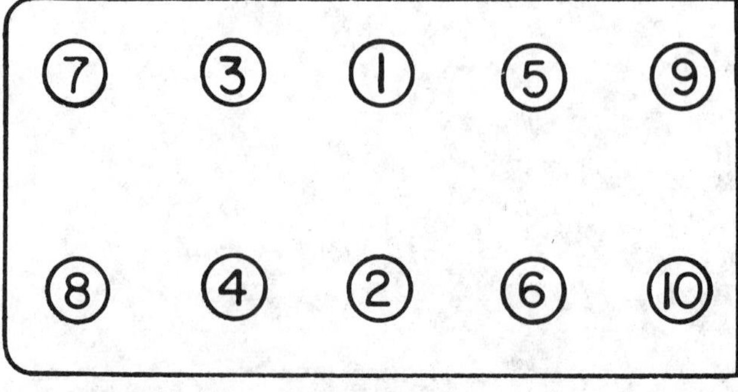

Fig. 1 Audi 100 Cylinder Head Tightening Sequence

100LS 4 CYLINDER (Cont.)

2) Remove cylinder head cover.

3) Unscrew oil filter and oil pressure switch. Remove both manifolds as previously described. Detach thermostat housing.

4) Remove breather line from water pump and head by unbolting flange on head and metal coupler on pump.

5) Detach water pump, fuel pump, and distributor. Loosen all rocker arm nuts until arms move freely.

6) Unscrew cylinder head mounting bolts in sequence shown in illustration. Remove cylinder head. To install, reverse removal procedure.

NOTE — *After installation of new cylinder head, do not drive vehicle at top speed for approximately 150 miles, to prevent scoring cylinder surface.*

VALVES

VALVE ARRANGEMENT

I-E-I-E-I-E-I-E (front to rear).

VALVE GUIDE SERVICING

1) Heat cylinder head in oil bath or oven to approximately 248°F (120°C). Using a suitable tool, drive valve guide(s) out, working from underside of head.

2) Allow head to cool, slowly, to room temperature. Using a suitable measuring device, check guide bore. Interference fit of new guide must be .0003-.0004" (.007-.010 mm). Select suitable replacement guide(s) and insert lock clip in groove of new guide(s).

3) Apply small amount of grease to bore in cylinder, then reheat head to 248°F (120°C). Using valve guide driver (having first undercooled guide, if possible), drive new guide into head until its lock washer is well seated.

4) After head has cooled to room temperature, check fit of guide(s) by lightly striking with hammer and drift. Ream guide to correct clearance.

VALVE STEM OIL SEALS

After removing rocker arm assemblies, as previously described, valve stem seals may be pried off, using two screwdrivers. Then, remove intake valve spring discs and exhaust valve spring Rotocaps. Ensure all parts are kept in proper order for reassembly.

VALVE SEAT INSERTS

1) Set up special seat turning tool (F 4, or equivalent), as shown in illustration. Place tool vertically and position cutter on center of cylindrical side of seat insert.

2) Attach suitable crank-turn cutter until groove is cut large enough to take up claws of extractor, as in illustration.

3) Heat cylinder head in oil bath or oven to approximately 248°F (120°C). Remove nut from cutter, then turn hex head of tool screw until claws are firmly in place. Position extractor

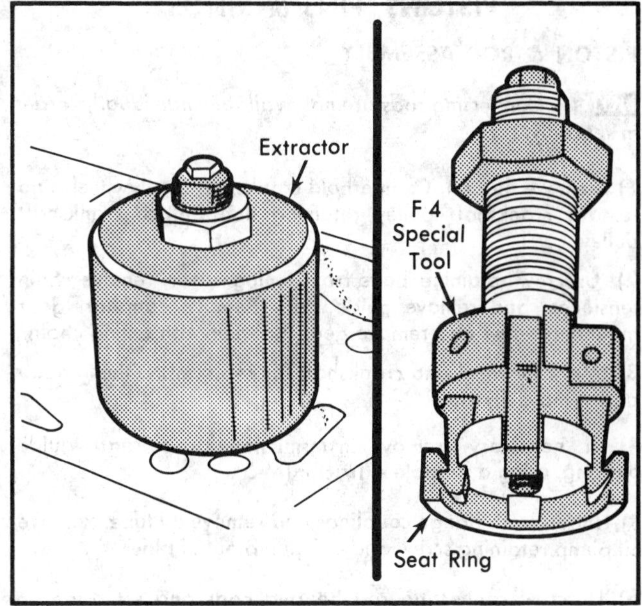

Fig. 2 Using Valve Seat Removal Tool

portion of tool as shown; replace and turn nut until seat is extracted. **NOTE** — *It will be necessary to counterhold head of screw while turning nut.*

4) When selecting replacement seat inserts, note that intake inserts have an inside diameter of 1.3" (33 mm) and a 15° chamfer. Exhaust valve seat inserts have no chamfer and an inside diameter of 1.18" (30 mm).

5) Reheat cylinder head to temperature specified, chill insert, and drive into head (up to stops).

ROCKER ARM ASSEMBLY

Unscrew adjusting nuts and remove rocker arms with rocker balls. Mount suitable valve spring tool to appropriate rocker arm mounting screw and depress valve springs. Remove valve spring retainers and release springs. Remove outer and inner springs, placing them in order for reassembly (keep all rocker arms, balls, and retainers with their respective springs).

VALVE CLEARANCE ADJUSTMENT

1) Allow engine to reach normal operating temperature. Remove air cleaner, cylinder head cover, spark plugs, and distributor cap, as necessary.

2) Jack up one front wheel and place transmission in 4th gear. Turn raised wheel until No. 1 piston is at TDC of compression stroke, with valves of No. 4 cylinder overlapped. Both valves of No. 1 cylinder should be closed.

3) Adjust valves in firing order: 1-3-4-2. Turn adjusting nut on each rocker arm until appropriate clearance is reached:

Valve Tappet Clearance At 176°F (80°C)

Application	Clearance
Intake	.006" (.15 mm)
Exhaust	.016" (.40 mm)

100LS 4 CYLINDER (Cont.)

PISTONS, PINS & RINGS

PISTON & ROD ASSEMBLY

NOTE – *Connecting rods are not available individually, order in sets only.*

1) Remove oil pan. Counterhold crankshaft (at flywheel) and remove crankshaft pulley retaining nut. Detach crankshaft pulley.

2) Unscrew retaining bolts from timing cover, remove chain tensioner, and remove guide strip. Remove camshaft gear mounting screw and remove gear together with timing chain.

3) Mark flywheel and crankshaft for reassembly, then unbolt and remove flywheel.

4) If necessary, remove transmission drive shaft guide bearing, using a suitable extractor (M-5).

5) Unbolt both flange couplings and remove oil tube. Remove oil pump retaining screw and pull pump out of block.

6) Unscrew connecting rod bearing caps and set aside, in exact order, for reinstallation. Push the rod and piston assemblies out toward cylinder head side, keeping assemblies in exact order for reinstallation.

PISTON PIN REPLACEMENT

1) Remove circlip. Heat piston and pin assembly to approximately 140°F (60°C). Using suitable driver, remove pin from piston and rod.

2) Measure pin diameter and rod bushing wear. If measurements exceed specifications, replace components.

3) Replace pin using same procedure as for removal. Lock pin in place with snap ring.

FITTING PISTONS

NOTE – *Cylinder sizes of new, as well as exchange, engines are die stamped on starter end of block just below cylinder head.*

1) Measure cylinder bores at three levels (top, middle, and bottom), then repeat procedure 90° to first measurements. If amount of wear is greater than .003" (.08 mm) from specifications listed in table, rebore cylinder and install oversize pistons.

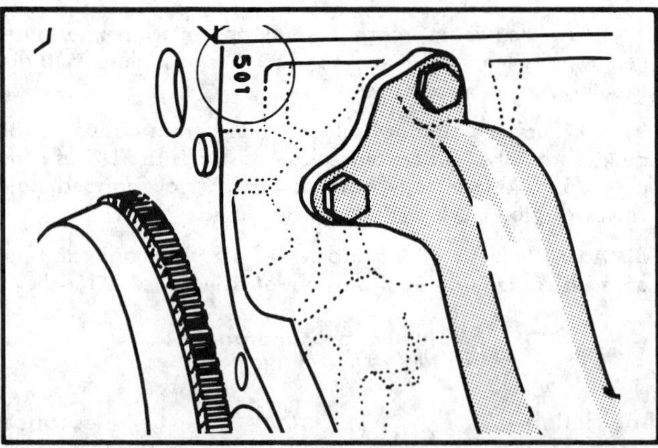

Fig. 3 View Showing Location of Cylinder Size Mark

2) If reusing pistons, measure OD approximately 0.63" (16 mm) from bottom of piston and at 90° to pin bore. Piston wear which exceeds .0016" (.04 mm) beyond specification necessitates replacement.

3) Check piston ring side clearance and end gap. Replace rings which exceed specifications. Install rings with side marked "Top" facing up. Space end gaps so that rings are staggered and not parallel with block centerline.

4) Check piston pins as previously described. Check connecting rod bushings. Inside diameter of bushing should be .945" (24 mm) in order to provide proper clearance for piston pin in rod bushing. If replacing connecting rod bushing, new bushing must be a press fit in connecting rod with .0011-.0035" (.029-.090 mm) interference fit.

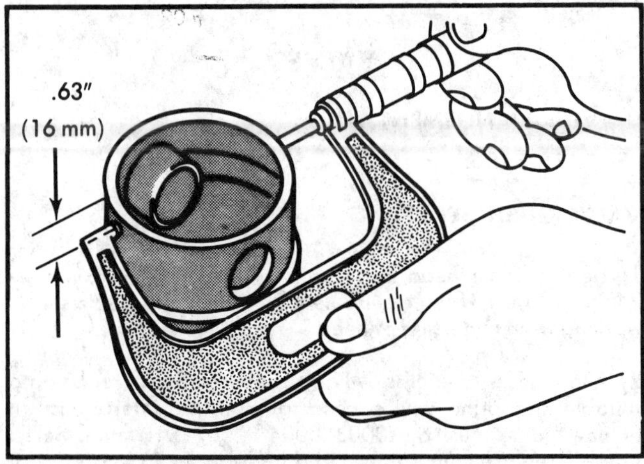

Fig. 4 Correct Procedure to Measure Piston Diameter

5) Apply thin coat of oil to cylinder surfaces. Slide piston and rod assembly into proper bores (with ring compressor attached), with arrow mark, on top edge of piston, facing forward.

6) Position connecting rod bearings, install new rod cap nuts and bolts and torque to specifications.

Standard Pistons & Cylinder Diameter

Piston Dia. ①	Cyl. Dia. ①	Stamp Code
3.3062 (83.98)	3.3074 (84.01)	401
3.3066 (83.99)	3.3078 (84.02)	402
3.3070 (84.00)	3.3082 (84.03)	403

Oversize Pistons & Cylinder Diameter

Piston Dia. ①	Cyl. Dia. ①	Stamp Code
3.3161 (84.23)	3.3173 (84.26)	426
3.3165 (84.24)	3.3177 (84.27)	427
3.3169 (84.25)	3.3181 (84.28)	428
3.3259 (84.48)	3.3271 (84.51)	451
3.3263 (84.49)	3.3275 (84.52)	452
3.3267 (84.50)	3.3279 (84.53)	453
3.3456 (84.98)	3.3468 (85.01)	501
3.3460 (84.99)	3.3472 (85.02)	502
3.3464 (85.00)	3.3476 (85.03)	503

① – Measurements are In. (mm).

100LS 4 CYLINDER (Cont.)

CRANKSHAFT MAIN & CONNECTING ROD BEARINGS

NOTE — *Short blocks, received under exchange program have Woodruff Key on pulley end of crankshaft. Pulley and spacer must be grooved, .197" (5mm) wide and .141" (3.5mm) deep.*

CRANKSHAFT

1) Remove oil pan and front pulley. Remove timing cover and camshaft sprocket (with timing chain), *see procedures in Timing Chain Replacement.*

2) Mark relative position of flywheel to crankshaft, then unbolt and remove flywheel. If necessary, use extractor to draw out transmission drive shaft guide bearing.

3) Disconnect oil line at oil pump and block. Unscrew oil pump retaining bolt and pull pump out of block.

4) Unscrew connecting rod bearing caps, remove bearings from rods, and push out piston assemblies. **NOTE** — *Keep all parts in proper sequence for reinstallation.*

5) Unscrew main bearing cap screws and carefully remove caps with bearings. Lift out crankshaft and extract rear oil seal. Set crankshaft aside, taking care to protect the sealing ring surface.

6) When reinstalling crankshaft gear, heat gear to approximately 140°F (60°C) and slide it onto crankshaft. Fit Woodruff key into position. *See Main Bearing Service concerning bearing replacement and/or fit.*

CAUTION — *Number four main bearing cap has a weaker dowel pin boss on one side. If during assembly this boss is broken, entire engine block must be replaced. Main bearing caps are matched to specific block and cannot be interchanged.*

MAIN BEARING SERVICE

1) Remove main bearings from block by pressing to one side with fingertips.

2) Clean bearing faces and connecting rod journals. Place Plastigage axially on the journal. Install rod cap in position and tighten bolts to specifications. **NOTE** — *Do not turn crankshaft during this operation.*

3) Remove rod cap and measure width of Plastigage with scale provided. Corresponding number on scale represents bearing clearance. Repeat procedure for other connecting rod journals. Replace bearings and rework journals as necessary.

4) Install main bearing caps, with bearings, to block (crankshaft not installed). Tighten cap bolts to specifications. Insert suitable gauge and determine wear on main bearings. Procedure may be repeated for connecting rod bearings.

5) Bearings are available in three undersizes, in increments of .010" (.25 mm).

6) Install crankshaft to block and repeat Plastigage method to determine main bearing clearance. If main bearing replacement is required, replace entire set (five bearings).

ENGINE FRONT COVER & OIL SEAL

If front oil seal leakage is determined, seal may be replaced without removing timing cover, as follows:

1) Remove crankshaft pulley. Carefully pry out seal using screwdriver.

2) Apply suitable lubricant to lips of new seal and outer edge of seal. Place seal in position with open end facing engine. Using suitable tool (SM-3, or equivalent), press in seal.

3) If timing cover is removed, press new seal into position from inside, until seal rests against stop.

REAR MAIN BEARING OIL SEAL SERVICE

1) To install rear main bearing oil seal, place seal on suitable seal installer (10.3) and slide it on crankshaft by hand with sealing lip facing crankshaft.

2) Insert two flywheel mounting bolts through assembly ring. Tighten bolts until seal reaches stop. Remove assembly ring.

CAMSHAFT

CAMSHAFT

1) With crankshaft and piston assemblies removed, as previously described, unscrew oil pressure valve from inside block.

2) Unscrew camshaft guide flange mounting screws and remove flange from front of block.

3) Screw handle (or other suitable device) into camshaft and remove by carefully pulling upward (block in vertical position).

4) When installing new, or exchange, camshaft, apply Molykote to bearing and cam surfaces to improve run-in process.

CAMSHAFT END THRUST

1) Install camshaft and sprocket. Tighten stretch screw until sprocket rests against flange of camshaft. Check camshaft for ease of operation.

2) Check camshaft end play with a dial indicator. Maximum permissible slop is .004" (.10 mm). If limit is exceeded, install new camshaft flange.

TIMING CHAIN REPLACEMENT

1) Unscrew timing cover mounting bolts and remove cover. Bend open lockplate and unscrew hydraulic chain tensioner plug, insert screwdriver, or similar tool and turn plunger to the left, to prevent plunger from springing out.

2) Unscrew chain tensioner and guide rail. Remove camshaft sprocket together with timing chain.

3) Use replacement chain with straight links (do not use indented links). Place chain on gear with aligning marks in proper position, *see Valve Timing.*

4) Place base plate of tensioner in position and install tensioner, with plunger. Torque holding screws to specifications.

5) Unlock plunger with screwdriver, by turning left. Check to ensure free movement of plunger. Continue turning counterclockwise, as necessary, as spring and automatic adjuster are built into plunger.

100LS 4 CYLINDER (Cont.)

6) Screw in plunger plug with lockplate. Torque plug to specification.

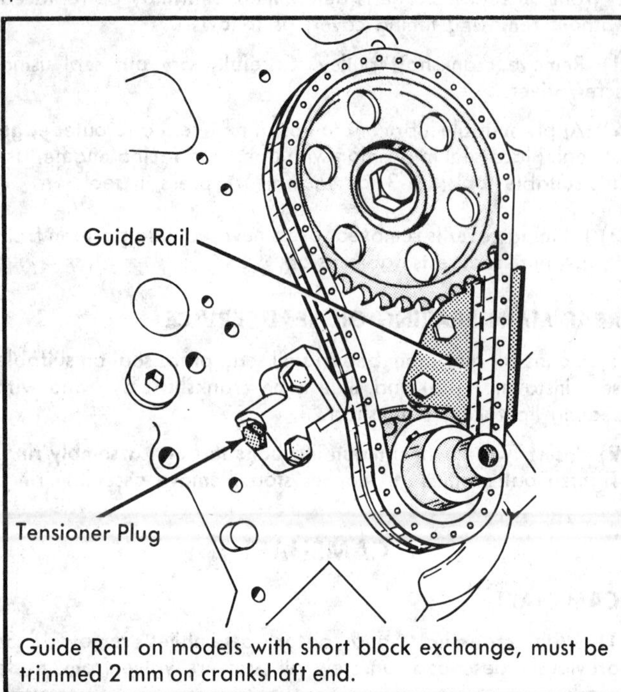

Guide Rail on models with short block exchange, must be trimmed 2 mm on crankshaft end.

Fig. 5 View Showing Timing Chain Assembly

VALVE TIMING

1) Remove camshaft sprocket mounting bolt, as it is necessary to remove sprocket when installing chain.

2) Turn camshaft sprocket until punched tooth is in exact alignment with notch in guide rail, as illustrated.

3) Carefully remove camshaft sprocket; when doing so, do not turn camshaft.

4) Turn crankshaft until No. 1 cylinder is at TDC of compression stroke. Place chain over gear and position camshaft sprocket in timing chain such that it is possible to slide sprocket onto camshaft with marks in alignment.

5) Torque camshaft sprocket stretch screw to specification.

6) Replace chain tensioner, as described previously.

7) Recheck No. 1 piston at TDC, of compression stroke, and ensure proper valve overlap on No. 4 cylinder.

8) Set valves of No. 1 cylinder **without clearance**, or turn adjusting nut until valves are slightly raised.

9) Place dial indicator with slight pretension on intake valve. Set gauge at "ZERO". Continue turning crankshaft clockwise until gauge shows a valve stroke of .039" (1 mm).

10) Timing is correct if timing mark of front pulley shows approximately 6°BTDC. If timing as checked on No. 1 cylinder is within specifications, gap of all valves may be adjusted without checking timing at other cylinders.

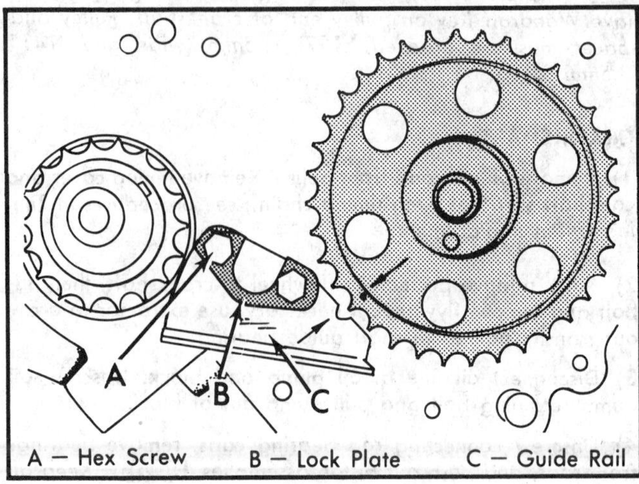

A — Hex Screw B — Lock Plate C — Guide Rail

Fig. 6 Correct Procedure to Align Camshaft Sprocket

ENGINE OILING

ENGINE OILING SYSTEM

Engine lubrication is accomplished through forced oil circulation. Oil is sucked out of oil pan through pump, fed through a pressure line to oil filter, then into main channels. Rocker lever bearings are lubed from center camshaft bearing, fed through vertical bore in block.

Crankcase Capacity — 4.8 qts.

Oil Filter — Replaceable spin-on type.

Normal Oil Pressure — 14 psi minimum; 85 psi maximum.

ENGINE COOLING

WATER PUMP

NOTE — *Manufacturer does not recommend overhaul of water pump. If damage or wear is suspected, replace pump.*

Remove fan belt(s) and drain coolant. Remove alternator pulley, detach hoses from water pump, and remove thermostat. Unscrew water pump pulley retaining nut while counterholding pulley, then pry pulley off. Unscrew all mounting bolts and remove pump mounting plate and water pump. To install, reverse removal procedure.

Thermostat — 180°F (82°C) summer; 189°F (87°C) winter.

Cooling System Capacity — 8 qts. (7.5 liters).

ENGINE SPECIFICATIONS

GENERAL SPECIFICATIONS										
Year	Displ.		Carburetor	HP at RPM	Torque (Ft. Lbs. at RPM)	Compr. Ratio	Bore		Stroke	
	cu. ins.	cc					in.	mm	in.	mm
1977	114	1871	Fuel Inj.	92 @ 5500	106.3 @ 3300	8.0:1	3.31	84	3.32	84.4

100LS 4 CYLINDER (Cont.)

ENGINE SPECIFICATIONS (Cont.)

VALVES

Engine & Valve	Head Diam. In. (mm)	Face Angle	Seat Angle	Seat Width In. (mm)	Stem Diameter In. (mm)	Stem Clearance In. (mm)	Valve Lift In. (mm)
100LS							
Intake	1.496 (38.0)	45°	45°	.087-.118 (2.2-3.0)	.353 (8.97)	.001 (.03)	.....
Exhaust	1.299 (33.0)	45°	45°	.087-.118 (2.2-3.0)	.352 (8.95)	.002 (.05)	.....

PISTONS, PINS, RINGS

Engine	PISTONS	PINS		RINGS		
	Clearance In. (mm)	Piston Fit In. (mm)	Rod Fit In. (mm)	Rings	End Gap In. (mm)	Side Clearance In. (mm)
100LS	.012 (.3)	.0005-.0009 (.013-.023)	Press Fit	All	.039 (1.0)	.006 (.15)

CRANKSHAFT MAIN & CONNECTING ROD BEARINGS

Engine	MAIN BEARINGS				CONNECTING ROD BEARINGS		
	Journal Diam. In. (mm)	Clearance In. (mm)	Thrust Bearing	Crankshaft End Play In. (mm)	Journal Diam. In. (mm)	Clearance In. (mm)	Side Play In. (mm)
100LS	2.520 (64)	.0016-.0039 (.040-.10)	No. 4	.0028-.0075 (.07-.19)	1.886 (47.9)	.0012-.0031 (.03-.08)	.004-.009 (.11-.23)

VALVE TIMING

Engine	INTAKE		EXHAUST	
	Open (BTDC)	Close (ABDC)	Open (BBDC)	Close (ATDC)
100LS	5°	37°	39°	3°

TIGHTENING SPECIFICATIONS

Application	Ft. Lbs. (mkg)
Manifolds-to-Head	17.5 (2.4)
Intake Manifold Support	14.5 (2.0)
Oil Line (Pump-to-Block)	7 (1.0)
Rocker Adjusting Nuts	11-36 (1.5-5.0)
Heater Flange-to-Head	14.5 (2.0)
Camshaft Guide Flange	18 (2.5)
Timing Chain Guide Rail	9 (1.2)
Rocker Studs	①72 (10)
No. 5 Main Bearing Cap	24 (3.2)
Other Main Bearing Caps (In Steps)	58 (8.0)
Engine Mount-to-Block	30 (4.2)
Engine Mount-to-Carrier	43 (6.0)
Oil Pump-to-Block	14.5 (2.0)
Connecting Rod Caps	25-31 (3.5-4.3)
Crankshaft Pulley	130-180 (18-25)
Head Bolts (In Steps)	
Step 1	29 (4.0)
Step 2	43 (6.0)
Step 3	58 (8.0)
Step 4 (Engine Warm)	65 (9.0)
Timing Cover	7 (1.0)
Oil Pan	
8mm Bolts	11 (1.5)
6mm Bolts	6 (0.8)

① — Maximum torque.

FOX 4 CYLINDER

ENGINE CODING

ENGINE IDENTIFICATION

Engine number is stamped on distributor side of engine block, just above the fuel pump. Number prefix indicates engine/transmission application as follows:

Application	Engine Code
1.6 Liter Calif.	YG
1.6 Liter Fed.	YK,YH
Man. Trans.	XK
Auto. Trans.	ET

ENGINE & CYLINDER HEAD

ENGINE

NOTE — *Leave all fuel injection lines connected to components.*

1) Disconnect battery ground cable. Loosen clutch adjusting nut and remove clutch cable. Disconnect electrical plug connector and pressure regulator lines. Remove vacuum hoses, ignition and emission control systems from intake manifold. Remove cold start valve, pull out injectors and remove accelerator cable.

2) Disconnect electrical wires at: ignition coil, fan motor, radiator thermo switch, alternator and oil pressure switch. Drain and remove radiator and radiator grille. Remove starter and exhaust pipe nuts.

3) On vehicles with air conditioning, remove intake air duct, radiator, radiator grille and cooling fan. Remove condenser (do not loosen or remove air conditioner hoses) and hang up with wire. Remove air filter, intake air distributor, ERG valve, horn and compressor.

4) Remove front engine mount and lower mounting bolts at engine block. Remove flywheel guard. On automatic transmission vehicles, remove torque converter cover and torque to drive plate bolts. Support transmission with floor jack or stand.

5) Using suitable engine sling (tool No. US1105) lift engine and transmission, until transmission housing contacts steering drive. Adjust jack or stand to make contact with transmission. Remove upper mounting bolts at engine block. Pry engine and transmission apart and remove intermediate plate.

6) On manual transmission vehicles, engine must be turned and lifted, to prevent damage to transmission main shaft, clutch and body. On automatic transmissions models lift engine straight out. Secure torque converter with suitable tool (tool No. 32-200).

Installation — To install engine, reverse removal procedure. Check that torque converter is fully seated on one-way clutch, and can be easily turned by hand. Check that all engine mounts are free of strain, realign if necessary.

CYLINDER HEAD

Removal & Installation — **1)** Disconnect battery ground cable. Drain coolant system and disconnect hoses which are connected to cylinder head. Disconnect exhaust pipe and electrical wires. Disengage accelerator linkage and disconnect at holder. Loosen alternator tensioner and remove camshaft drive belt and "V" belt.

2) Loosen head bolts in reverse of tightening sequence *(See Fig. 1)*. To install, place head gasket with word "top" facing cylinder head. Position cylinder head on gasket and install bolts. Tighten bolts, in steps, in sequence shown in *Fig. 1*. Reinstall remaining components and retime camshaft. Retighten head bolts after 1000 miles.

NOTE — *On some models 11 mm cylinder head bolts with 12 mm polygon socket heads have been installed in place of 10 mm hexagon socket head bolts. Torque new head bolts to 55 ft lb (7.5 mkg), then tighten ¼ turn more. New head bolts do not have to be retorqued after 1000 miles.*

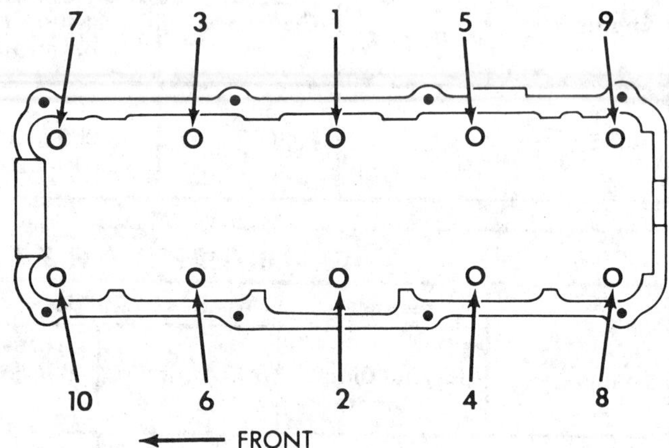

Fig. 1 Cylinder Head Tightening Sequence

VALVES

VALVE ARRANGEMENT

E-I-E-I-I-E-I-E (front to rear).

VALVE GUIDE SERVICING

1) Before taking measurements, clean valve guides with a cleaning broach. To measure, attach a suitable device with a dial indicator (VW 689/1) to mounting surface of cylinder head. Insert a new valve into valve guide until stem is flush with end of guide. Rock valve against dial indicator and check amount of guide-to-stem clearance. Maximum valve rock should not exceed .039" (1.0 mm) for intake valves, and .051" (1.3 mm) for exhaust valves.

2) Use suitable press and adaptor (10-206) to remove and install valve guides. Press worn guides out from combustion chamber side. Coat new guide with oil and press into cold cylinder head from camshaft side. Do not use more than 1 Ton of pressure or guide shoulder may break. Ream guide by hand to proper size.

VALVE STEM OIL SEALS

NOTE — *Valve stem seal, may be removed with cylinder head installed on vehicle.*

FOX 4 CYLINDER (Cont.)

1) With camshaft removed, remove spark plug, turn crankshaft until piston is at BTC. Install pressure hose (tool No. VW 653) in spark plug hole and apply constant pressure.

2) Remove valve spring with valve spring compressure (tool No. VW 541). Remove valve stem seal with suitable tool (No. 10-218). To install use suitable tool (No. 10-218), slide plastic sleeve on valve stem, lubricate seal and push carefully on valve guide.

VALVE SPRINGS

With tappets removed, install suitable valve spring compressor (Tool No. 10-210). Compress springs and remove valve keepers and collar. Lift out valve springs. To install, reverse removal procedure.

MECHANICAL VALVE LIFTER ASSEMBLY

With camshaft and tappet discs removed, lift out tappets. Inspect for wear or damage, replace as necessary. Oil tappet lightly and replace in original position.

VALVE CLEARANCE ADJUSTMENT

1) Adjust valve clearances in firing number order (1-3-4-2). Rotate camshaft until number four cylinder valves overlap and measure number one cylinder valve clearances. Clearance is measured with engine warm. With a feeler gauge, measure clearance of each cylinder in turn and note clearance. If clearance is within .002" (.05 mm) of specifications, no adjustment is necessary.

2) Determine thickness of tappet disc installed. Using tappet clearance previously noted, calculate required thickness of disc needed to achieve proper tappet clearance. Tappet discs are available in .0019" (.05 mm) increments, from .1181" (3.0 mm) to .1673" (4.25 mm). Thickness is stamped on bottom side of tappet disc.

3) Special tools (tool No. VW 546 and US 4476) are required to remove tappet clearance discs. Rotate camshaft so cams of one cylinder overlap and cams of cylinder to be changed no longer rest on tappets. Rotate tappet until openings are at 90° angles to camshaft. Install tool No. VW 546 to depress tappets. Using tool No. US 4476, grasp tappet disc through opening in side of tappet and rotate out from under camshaft. Install proper disc and remove tool No. VW 546. Repeat procedure until all tappets are adjusted.

Valve Clearances

Application	In. (mm)
Intake	
Hot	.008-.012 (.20-.30)
Cold	.006-.010 (.15-.25)
Exhaust	
Hot	.016-.020 (.41-.51)
Cold	.014-.018 (.36-.46)

NOTE — *Cold settings are given for reference as initial settings to be used during engine rework. Final adjustments are to be made with engine warm. After head repairs, recheck valve clearance adjustment after 600 miles.*

PISTONS, PINS & RINGS

OIL PAN

Drain engine oil. Attach a suitable lifting device to engine, and apply supporting tension to engine. Remove auxiliary bolts (alternately), then remove left and right engine mounts. Unscrew oil pan bolts and remove pan. When installing, gasket is installed dry, and oil pan bolts are to be tightened in a criss-cross pattern.

PISTON & ROD ASSEMBLY

1) Before removing connecting rods, mark rod and cap for proper reinstallation. Remove rod bolts and caps and carefully push piston and rod assembly out top of cylinder.

2) On reassembly of piston and rod assemblies, cast bosses on rod and cap, as well as locating projections of bearing inserts face toward intermediate shaft. All connecting rods must be of same weight class. Weight class numbers are stamped on bottom of connecting rod caps. Using a suitable ring compresser, install piston and rod assemblies with arrow on crown of piston facing forward.

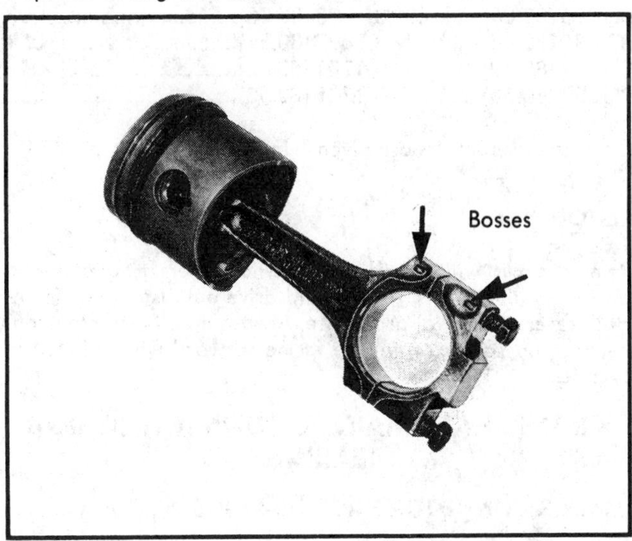

Fig. 2 Location of Connecting Rod Bosses

FITTING PISTONS

1) Measure cylinder at three points: .39" (10 mm) from top and bottom, and at center of cylinder bore. Take measurements in line with thrust face and at 90° to thrust face.

2) Measure pistons at .63" (16 mm) from bottom of piston skirt (measuring at 90° to pin bore). Combining this measurement with measurement of corresponding cylinder bore, if piston-to-cylinder clearance exceeds .003" (.08 mm), oversize pistons must be installed.

3) Place piston rings squarely in top of cylinder bore (above ring ridge) and measure end gap; replace as necessary. Measure ring side clearance; replace rings and/or pistons if clearance exceeds .005" (.13 mm). Install rings on piston with end gaps 120° offset to each other (start with oil ring gap facing directly to rear). Ensure stamped word "TOP" on rings is facing upward.

FOX 4 CYLINDER (Cont.)

NOTE – *Engine blocks are stamp coded above water pump as to size of pistons installed.*

Standard Pistons & Cylinder Dia.
(1588 cc Engine)

Piston Dia. ①	Cyl. Dia. ①	Stamp Code
3.1291 (79.48)	3.1303 (79.51)	951
3.1295 (79.49)	3.1307 (79.52)	952
3.1299 (79.50)	3.1311 (79.53)	953

① – Measurements are given in In. (mm).

Oversize Pistons & Cylinder Dia.
(1588 cc Engine)

Piston Dia. ①	Cyl. Dia. ①	Stamp Code
3.1390 (79.73)	3.1402 (79.76)	976
3.1394 (79.74)	3.1406 (79.77)	977
3.1398 (79.75)	3.1409 (79.78)	978
3.1488 (79.98)	3.1500 (80.01)	001
3.1492 (79.99)	3.1504 (80.02)	002
3.1496 (80.00)	3.1508 (80.03)	003
3.1685 (80.48)	3.1697 (80.51)	051
3.1689 (80.49)	3.1701 (80.52)	052
3.1693 (80.50)	3.1705 (80.53)	053

① – Measurements are given in In. (mm).

PISTON PINS

Remove circlip with a pair of needle-nose pliers. Heat piston to approximately 140°F (60°C) and drive out piston pin. To install, reverse removal procedure. Always install piston on connecting rod so arrow will be facing forward when placed in cylinder.

CRANKSHAFT MAIN & CONNECTING ROD BEARINGS

MAIN & CONNECTING ROD BEARINGS

1) Push crankshaft toward one end and measure crankshaft end play at No. 3 (thrust) bearing. Main bearing caps are stamp-numbered "1" to "5" (front to rear) and must return to original positions upon reassembly. Measure end play of connecting rods. Remove rod and main bearing caps and check bearing clearance, using Plastigage method.

2) Measure crankshaft journals with a micrometer to determine if crankshaft is out-of-round. Maximum ovality permissible is .0012" (.03 mm). Install main inserts with bearing half having oil groove into block. Lubricate bearings and install caps.

Crankshaft Journal Diameters

Size	Main Bearing①	Connecting Rod①
Std.	2.124(53.95)	1.809(45.95)
1st US	2.114(53.70)	1.799(45.70)
2nd US	2.104(53.45)	1.789(45.45)
3rd US	2.094(53.20)	1.779(45.20)

① – Diameters given in In.(mm).

REAR MAIN BEARING OIL SEAL

Rear main bearing oil seal may be replaced with engine in vehicle, if transmission and flywheel are removed. Carefully pry oil seal from crankcase. Install suitable tool (Tool No. 10-205) on crankshaft. Slide seal over tool, by hand, as far as possible. Then remove tool. Press seal in, up to stop, with suitable tool (Tool No. 10-220), by tightening both bolts alternately.

INTERMEDIATE SHAFT OIL SEAL

Press seal out of flange. Using suitable tool (Tool No. 10-203), press new seal into flange until it is flush.

FRONT MAIN BEARING OIL SEAL

1) Front main bearing oil seal may be replaced with engine in vehicle. Remove license plate, radiator grille and camshaft belt guard. Rotate crankshaft to TDC. Use a screwdriver to lock crankshaft from turning (through opening in transmission case). Remove pulley bolt. Loosen camshaft belt tensioner and alternator adjuster. Remove both belts.

2) Pry seal out of flange using suitable tool (Tool No. 10-219). Do not place tool between seal and crankshaft, rather inner edge of support ring by cutting dust lip with sharp edge of tool. Using suitable tool (Tool No. 10-203), place seal over guide sleeve of tool. Press seal in until it is flush with flange. To install remaining components, reverse removal procedure and check valve timing.

CAMSHAFT

TIMING BELT

1) Remove radiator grille. Loosen alternator mounting bolts and remove "V" belt. Remove camshaft belt guard. Loosen mounting nut of camshaft belt tensioner arm and remove tension from belt. Slide belt forward off camshaft sprocket.

2) Install new belt and adjust tensioner arm until belt can be turned 90° with thumb and index finger at a point midway between camshaft sprocket and intermediate sprocket. Check valve timing.

CAMSHAFT

1) Bolt tool No. 10-200 to cylinder head. Tighten spindle until bracket of tool rests on camshaft. Remove camshaft bearing bolts and caps. Remove tension from tool spindle. Remove tool and camshaft.

2) To install camshaft, reverse removal procedure beginning with number five bearing first, as it controls end play of camshaft. Bearing caps are numbered one through five and must be installed in proper order.

VALVE TIMING

Turn camshaft sprocket until punch mark on rear of camshaft sprocket is in alignment with rocker cover gasket on left side of engine. Turn crankshaft pulley and intermediate shaft sprocket until notch on pulley is aligned with punch mark on in-

FOX 4 CYLINDER (Cont.)

termediate shaft sprocket. Slide camshaft belt in place and adjust tension as previously described.

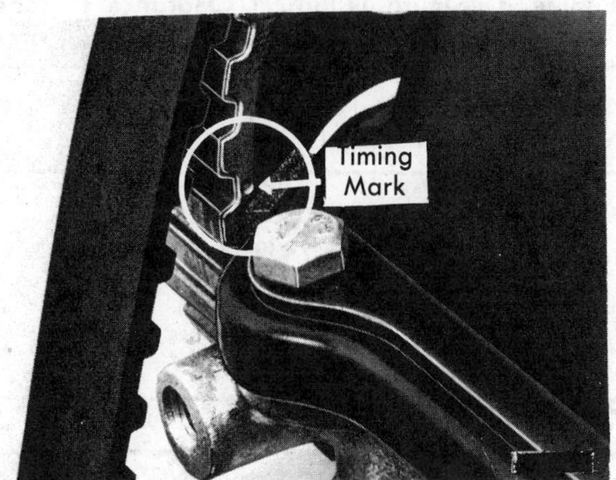

Fig. 3 Location of Camshaft Timing Marks

ENGINE OILING

Crankcase Capacity — 3.15 qts. (2.98 liters).

Oil Filter — Replaceable spin-on type.

Normal Oil Pressure — 28 psi at 2000 RPM; 99.5 psi at 5000 RPM.

ENGINE OILING SYSTEM

Oiling system is a pressure feed system. A gear type oil pump lifts oil from oil pan and pressure feeds it to crankshaft journals, camshaft bearings and intermediate shaft. Other parts of system receive oil mist or splash for lubrication.

OIL PUMP

Remove oil pan and two oil pump mounting bolts. Pull pump straight down and out of engine. Remove two pump cover bolts and separate cover from pump body. Ensure that oil pump gear backlash is .002-.008" (.05-.20 mm). Check that rotor end clearance is not more than .006" (.15 mm). Remove pump drive shaft and gears. Bend up metal edges and remove filter screen. To assemble, reverse disassembly procedure.

ENGINE COOLING

Cooling System Capacity
Without expansion chamber — 6½ qts.
With expansion chamber — 7qts.

Thermostat

Opens at — 176° F (80° C)

Radiator Cap — 14 psi.

WATER PUMP

1) Drain coolant and remove alternator. Remove camshaft belt guard, hose clamps and pump hoses. Remove water pump mounting bolts and lift out pump by turning slightly.

2) Remove pulley and pump body mounting screws. Separate pump assembly from housing. To reassemble, reverse diassembly procedure using new gasket and pump-to-block seal.

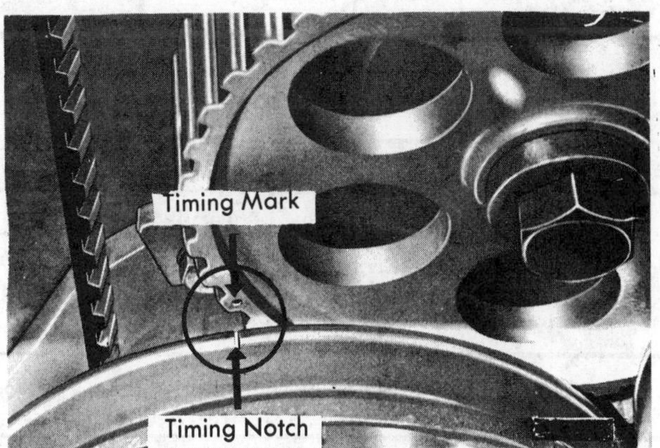

Fig. 4 Location of Crankshaft & Intermediate Shaft Timing Marks

GENERAL SPECIFICATIONS

Year	Displ.		Carburetor	HP at RPM	Torque (Ft. Lbs. at RPM)	Compr. Ratio	Bore		Stroke	
	cu. ins.	cc					in.	mm	in.	mm
1977	97	1588	Fuel Inj.	①78@5500	.....	8.0:1	3.13	79.5	3.15	80.0

①Calif. — 76 HP.

VALVES

Engine & Valve	Head Diam. In. (mm)	Face Angle	Seat Angle	Seat Width In. (mm)	Stem Diameter In. (mm)	Stem Clearance In. (mm)	Valve Lift In. (mm)
1588 cc							
Intake	1.338 (34)	45°	45°	.....	.314 (7.97)	.....	.....
Exhaust	1.220 (31)	45°	45°	.....	.313 (7.95)	.....	.....

FOX 4 CYLINDER (Cont.)

VALVE SPRINGS

Engine	Free Length In. (mm)	PRESSURE Lbs. @ In. (kg @ mm)	
		Valve Closed	Valve Open
1588 cc Inner	.....	.....	46-51@.72 (21-23@18.3)
Outer	.....	.....	96-106@.92 (44-48@22.3)

CAMSHAFT

Engine	Journal Diam. In. (mm)	Clearance In. (mm)	Lobe Lift In. (mm)
1588 cc	1.021-1.022 (25.9-26.0)	①	②

① — Axial Play: .0018-.0046" (.048-.118 mm).
Wear Limit: .006" (.15 mm).
Radial Play: .0015-.0024" (.04-.06 mm).
② — Base-to-lobe: 1.901" (48.3 mm).

PISTONS, PINS, RINGS

Engine	PISTONS	PINS		RINGS		
	Clearance In. (mm)	Piston Fit In. (mm)	Rod Fit In. (mm)	Rings	End Gap In. (mm)	Side Clearance In. (mm)
1588 cc	.0012 (.031)	①	.0004-.0008 (.010-.020)	Comp.	.012-.017 (.30-.43)	.0008-.002 (.02-.05)
				Oil	.010-.016 (.25-.40)	.0008-.002 (.02-.05)

① — Push fit at 140° F (60° C).

CRANKSHAFT MAIN & CONNECTING ROD BEARINGS

Engine	MAIN BEARINGS				CONNECTING ROD BEARINGS		
	Journal Diam. In. (mm)	Clearance In. (mm)	Thrust Bearing	Crankshaft End Play In. (mm)	Journal Diam. In. (mm)	Clearance In. (mm)	Side Play In. (mm)
1588 cc	2.124 (53.95)	.001-.003 (.028-.088)	No. 3	.003-.007 (.07-.17)	1.809 (45.95)	.001-.003 (.028-.088)	.015 (.40)

VALVE TIMING

Engine	INTAKE		EXHAUST	
	Open (BTDC)	Close (ALDC)	Open (BLDC)	Close (ATDC)
1588 cc	7°	43°	47°	3°

TIGHTENING SPECIFICATIONS

Application	Ft. Lbs. (mkg)
Head Bolts (In Steps)	
Cold	54 (7.5)
Warm	62 (8.5)
Main Bearing Caps	47 (6.5)
Connecting Rod Caps	32 (4.0)
Flywheel	43-50 (6.0-7.0)
Intermediate Shaft Sprocket	58 (8.0)
Crankshaft Pulley	58 (8.0)
Oil Pan Bolts	6 (0.8)
Exhaust Manifold	17 (2.3)
Intake Manifold	18 (2.5)
Camshaft Bearing Caps	15 (2.0)
Camshaft Sprocket	58 (8.0)
Oil Pressure Switch	9 (1.3)

320i 4 CYLINDER

ENGINE CODING

ENGINE IDENTIFICATION

Identification number is located on tag attached to engine crankcase. First six digits of code are used to identify engine.

ENGINE & CYLINDER HEAD

ENGINE

NOTE – *The "A" behind model number is for automatic transmission models.*

Removal – **1)** On 320i models, remove all mounting bolts accessible from above. Remove exhaust support and exhaust pipe at manifold. Remove drive shaft at transmission, remove center bearing. Remove drive shaft at center journal. Remove speedometer cable, disconnect back-up light switch.

2) Remove center console from transmission, remove circlip and washer, pull out selector rod. Remove clutch slave cylinder, support transmission with jack or stand. Remove crossmember and remaining transmission mounting bolts. Remove transmission towards rear of vehicle.

3) On 320i A, remove accelerator cable. Remove all mounting bolts accessible from above. Remove oil filler neck and drain oil. Remove exhaust support and exhaust pipe at manifold. Remove speedometer drive cable. Remove drive shaft at transmission, remove center bearing and remove drive shaft at center journal. Remove selector rod at selector lever.

4) Remove drive plate bolts from torque converter. Remove transmission oil cooler lines, support transmission with jack or stand. Remove crossmember at body, remove remaining transmission mounting bolts. Remove transmission and torque converter from vehicle.

5) Remove radiator and cowl, disconnect battery, disconnect wires to injection valves, marking location for reassembly. Remove fuel lines and hoses to pressure converter. Disconnect wires from distributor and central electrical plug, remove harness from holders on wheelhouse.

6) Install engine sling (tool No. 11 0 000). Remove left engine mount, and upper engine damper. Remove right engine mount, remove engine from vehicle.

Installation – Reverse removal procedure, making sure torque converter is positioned correctly before installing.

CYLINDER HEAD

Removal – **1)** Pull off breather tube, then pull hose with connector out of tube. Dismantle air cleaner assembly. Disconnect ground lead from battery. Drain cooling system. Loosen clamp screw and pull out choke cable.

2) Remove wires to injection valves (mark for reassembly). Remove pressure converter hoses, water hoses at cylinder head and crankcase hoses at throttle housing and thermo valve (marking for reassembly). Remove upper timing case cover, disconnect plug connectors and ignition coil wires. Remove distributor cap and pull plugs off cold start valve, auxiliary air valve and timing valve. Disconnect oil pressure switch wire.

3) Set piston of No. 1 cylinder at TDC, (rotor points to notch in distributor housing, indicator points to notch in pulley). Remove timing chain tensioner and timing chain sprocket. Remove exhaust pipe at manifold and holder to transmission. Remove cylinder head bolts in reverse sequence of tightening, remove cylinder head.

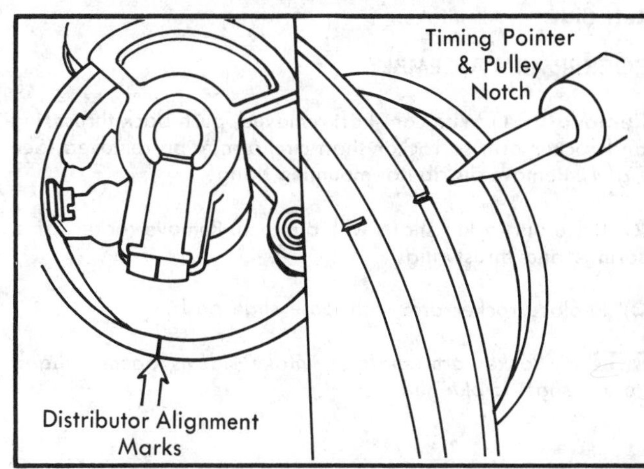

Fig. 1 Correct Procedure to Set No. 1 Piston at TDC

Installation – Ensure installation guides extend .197" (5 mm) beyond cylinder head mounting surface. Also be sure there is no oil in blind holes, or head bolts will not be able to exert required holding force on head. Replace cylinder head and components in reverse of removal procedure, tightening head bolts, in a series of steps, according to sequence illustrated (with engine at normal operating temperature).

NOTE – *Retorque cylinder head bolts after 600 miles (1000 km).*

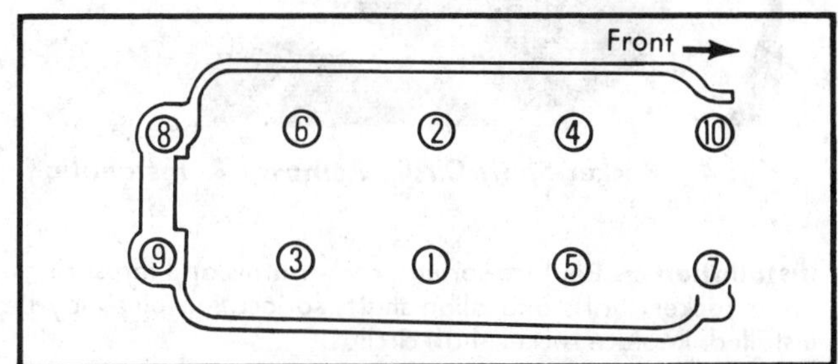

Fig. 2 Cylinder Head Tightening Sequence

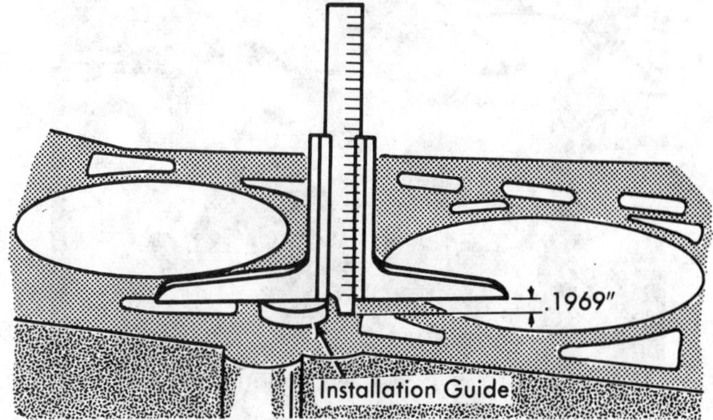

Fig. 3 Correct Procedure to Measure Cylinder Head Installation Guide

320i 4 CYLINDER (Cont.)

VALVES

VALVE ARRANGEMENT

Right Side – All exhaust.

Left Side – All intake.

ROCKER ARM ASSEMBLY

Removal – **1**) With camshaft removed, push back thrust ring and rocker arm so rocker shaft circlip may be removed *(See Fig. 4)*. Remove distributor mounting flange.

2) Drive out rocker shafts with a punch. Remove rocker arms, springs and thrust rings.

3) Replace rocker arm with loose slide pads.

NOTE – *Rocker arm shaft on intake side is open. Exhaust rocker shaft is plugged.*

Fig. 4 Rocker Shaft Circlip Removal & Installation

Installation – Replace springs, rocker arms and thrust rings. Insert rocker shafts and align shafts so locating pins may be installed. Replace rocker shaft circlips.

Fig. 5 View Showing Rear Exhaust Rocker Shaft Plugs

VALVE SPRING SERVICE

Remove valve keepers and collar. Check spring for wear or fatigue. Replace worn springs with green marked springs only. Install spring, collar and keepers.

VALVE GUIDE SERVICE

1) Check valve guide for wear. If replacement is necessary, press out guide toward combustion chamber. Measure guide bore in cylinder head. If bore exceeds .5512" (14 mm), ream head and install oversize guide.

2) Heat cylinder head to 428-482°F (220-250°C) and press in new guide from top side until tapered groove end protrudes .591" (15 mm) above surface. Ream guide to obtain specified clearance. Valve guides are available in the following sizes (O.D. measurements given):

Valve Guide Sizes

Application	Guide O.D. In. (mm)
Standard	.5532 (14.05)
1st Oversize	.5551 (14.10)
2nd Oversize	.5590 (14.20)
3rd Oversize	.5630 (14.30)

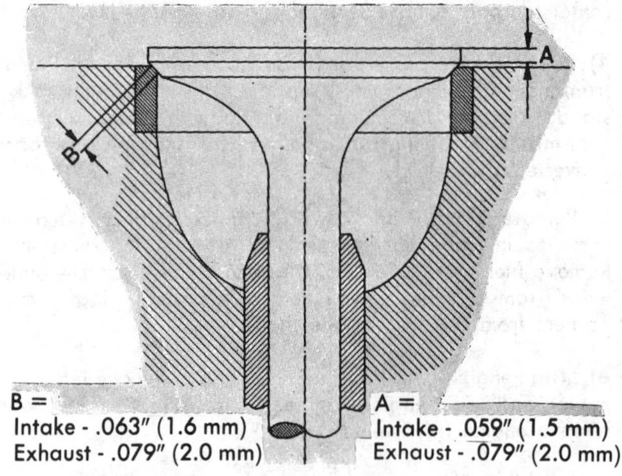

Fig. 6 Checking Valve Head & Seat Thickness

VALVE SEAT SERVICE

Refer to illustration and note minimum valve seat and valve head thicknesses. If either specification is not met, replace necessary component. When replacing valve seat, remove old seat by turning out with suitable cutting tool. Drill out bore to appropriate oversize: note valve seat oversize to be used and rebore head allowing for shrink-fit of replacement seat. When installing new seat, heat head to approximately 392°F (200°C) and chill valve seat to approximately –94°F

320i 4 CYLINDER (Cont.)

(−70°C). Replacement seats are available in the following oversizes:

Replacement Valve Seat Rings

Application	Measurement In. (mm)
Intake	
1st Oversize	1.864 (47.35)
2nd Oversize	1.872 (47.55)
Exhaust	
1st Oversize	1.589 (40.35)
2nd Oversize	1.596 (40.55)

VALVE CLEARANCE ADJUSTMENT

Adjust valves in firing order sequence (1-3-4-2) with No. 1 cylinder at TDC of compression stroke. Using a feeler gauge between rocker eccentric and valve stem, set clearance to .008-.010" (.20-.25 mm) with engine hot or to .006-.008" (.15-.20 mm) with engine cold. Loosen nut of rocker eccentric, insert a rod in eccentric hole and rotate until proper clearance is obtained *(See Fig. 7)*.

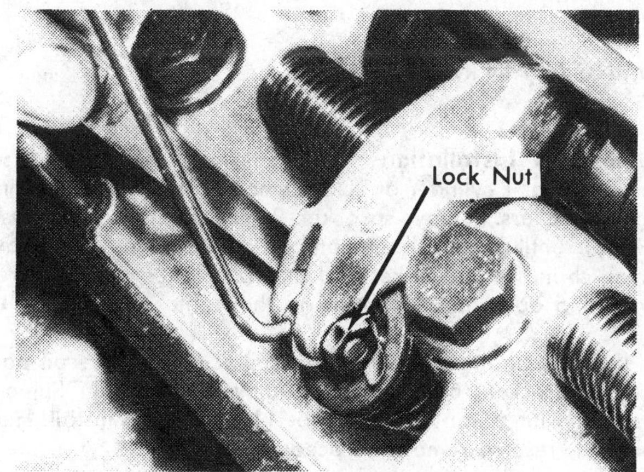

Fig. 7 Correct Procedure to Perform Tappet Adjustment

PISTONS, PINS & RINGS

OIL PAN

With engine installed, remove bolts securing steering to front axle carrier, move steering out of way. Drain oil, remove bolts securing oil pan, swing pan down. Turn crankshaft and remove oil pan. Coat crankcase ends where timing cover and rear main bearing cover join crankcase with sealing compound before reassembly.

PISTON & ROD ASSEMBLY

Removal – After removing oil pan and cylinder head, rotate crankshaft to TDC of piston and rod assembly to be removed. Unscrew connecting rod cap nuts and push assembly out top of engine. Replace worn or damaged parts as necessary, according to appropriate service procedure indicated in this article.

Installation – Place rings on piston with marking "TOP" facing upward and ring end gaps 180° apart. Install piston with arrow facing forward and oil hole in wrist pin end of connecting rod facing timing chain. Ensure connecting rod and bearing cap numbers match, with No. 1 rod nearest the timing chain.

CONNECTING ROD BUSHING

1) Remove circlips and push out wrist pin. Check for wear in piston and connecting rod. If rod bushing is worn, press out old bushing and press in new bushing with ends 90° to oil hole.

2) Wrist pins come in two diameters, white coded wrist pin with "W" stamped on piston crown or black coded wrist pin with "S" stamped on piston crown.

3) Drill oil holes in bushing and ream bushing diameter to specifications. Piston pin should be a light push fit through connecting rod bushing.

FITTING PISTONS

Piston crowns are marked with arrow for direction of installation and a "+", "–" or no sign to show weight classification. All pistons should have same weight mark. Measure piston and cylinder diameter to determine clearance (see specifications). Measure piston diameter at 90° to wrist pin bore near bottom of piston skirt, see following table for distance from bottom of piston.

Piston Measuring Location

Piston	In. (mm)
Mahle	.622 (15.8 mm)
KS	.923 (23.45 mm)

Piston Sizes

Application (Grade)	Diameter In. (mm)
Standard	3.5027 (88.97)
Intermediate	3.5059 (89.05)
No. 1 Oversize	3.5126 (89.22)
No. 2 Oversize	3.5224 (89.47)

CRANKSHAFT MAIN & CONNECTING ROD BEARINGS

MAIN BEARING SERVICE

Plastigage method is used to determine connecting rod and main bearing journal clearances. Standard or undersize crankshafts are marked red or blue. Color coded inserts must agree with crankshaft color code *(See Figures 8 & 9)*. The following table shows color code and undersizes available:

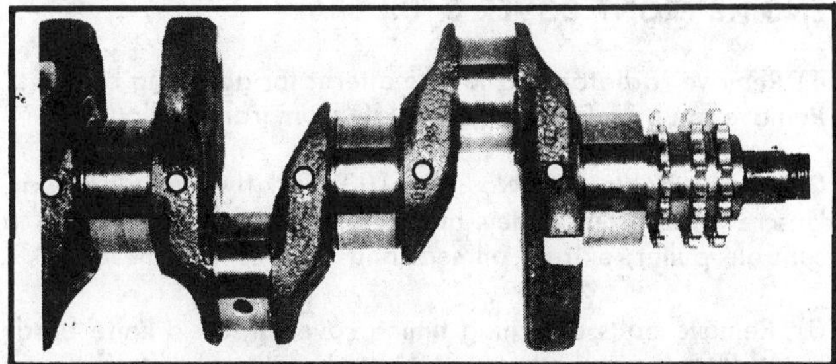

Fig. 8 View Showing Original Crankshaft Marks

320i 4 CYLINDER (Cont.)

Main Bearing Journal

Application	In. (mm)
Original	2.165 (55.0)
1st Stage	2.156 (54.75)
2nd Stage	2.146 (54.50)
3rd Stage	2.136 (54.25)

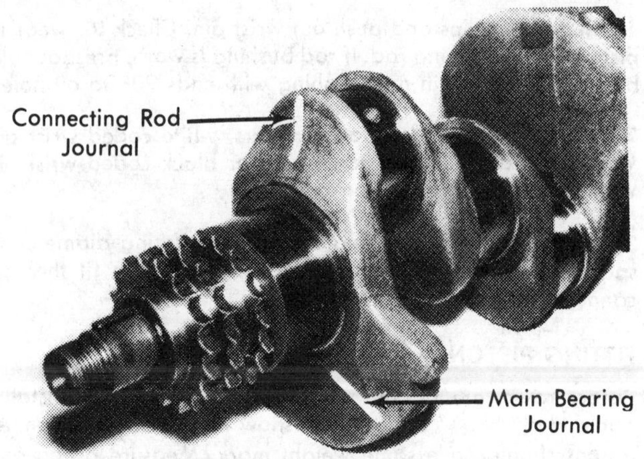

Fig. 9 View Showing Undersize Crankshaft Marks

Connecting Rod Journal

Application	In. (mm)
Original	1.889 (48.0)
1st Stage	1.879 (47.75)
2nd Stage	1.870 (47.50)
3rd Stage	1.860 (47.25)

THRUST BEARING ALIGNMENT

Attach a dial indicator to crankcase with shaft touching flywheel. Move flywheel in and out to determine endplay of crankshaft. If endplay is excessive, replace center main bearing inserts.

REAR MAIN BEARING OIL SEAL SERVICE

With flywheel removed, unscrew six attaching bolts from rear crankshaft seal holder. Carefully run a knife blade between seal holder and oil pan gasket to break seal. Remove seal holder and press out old seal, press in new seal. Coat oil pan gasket at either side with sealing compound and replace seal holder.

CAMSHAFT

ENGINE FRONT COVER & OIL SEAL

1) Remove radiator and loosen alternator adjusting brackets. Remove fan belt. Detach cover plate from transmission.

2) Using suitable tool (No. 11 2 100), lock flywheel ring gear. Unscrew nut from pulley hub and remove pulley. Using a suitable puller, extract oil seal and replace with new seal.

3) Remove bolts attaching timing cover. Insert a knife blade between cover and oil pan gasket to break seal. Lift off timing cover. To install, reverse removal procedures.

CAMSHAFT

Removal – 1) With cylinder head removed, loosen clamping screw and pull out distributor. Attach head assembly to a suitable holding tool (No. 11 1 040). Remove oil line and cold start valve.

2) Adjust valve clearance to maximum possible. Attach a suitable compression frame to preload the rocker assembly . Check end play between guide plate and camshaft. Remove guide plate and carefully withdraw camshaft.

Installation – 1) When replacing camshaft, note the following: After guide plate has been installed, it must be possible to easily rotate the camshaft. Make sure that notch in flange aligns with cast tab on cylinder head. Adjust valve clearances, note position of oil pipe sealing rings.

2) When replacing distributor, turn rotor counterclockwise by about 1.4" (3.5 mm) from notch in distributor housing, bring distributor drive into mesh with camshaft drive. Ensure vacuum advance has been located in original position. Adjust ignition timing.

TIMING CHAIN REPLACEMENT

Removal & Installation – 1) Remove distributor cap, set piston of No. 1 cylinder at TDC. Remove upper and lower timing case covers. Remove sprocket. Remove circlip and unscrew pivot pin until guide rail rests on cylinder head gasket. Remove timing chain from sprocket and crankshaft. Remove guide rail by pulling down and swinging to the right.

2) If timing chain sprockets need replacing. Remove oil pan, remove sprocket from oil pump. Remove timing chain. Remove sprocket with suitable puller (No. 11 2 000). To install: Heat sprocket, reverse removal procedure.

VALVE TIMING

Rotate engine to TDC of No. 1 piston. Position camshaft so that timing mark on camshaft flange is straight up and locating pin hole is straight down. Without moving crankshaft or camshaft, install camshaft sprocket so that it engages locating pin hole in camshaft flange.

TIMING CHAIN TENSIONER SERVICE

NOTE – *Chain tensioner is correct if chain gives under slight thumb pressure.*

1) Unscrew tensioner plug and remove piston and spring.

CAUTION – *Tensioner plug is under high spring pressure, use care when removing plug.*

2) Press piston out of sleeve. Remove ball bearing and perforated disc. Clean all parts thoroughly.

320i 4 CYLINDER (Cont.)

3) Reassemble sleeve, perforated disc, ball bearing and piston, making sure perforated disc does not block bleed slots *(See Fig. 10).*

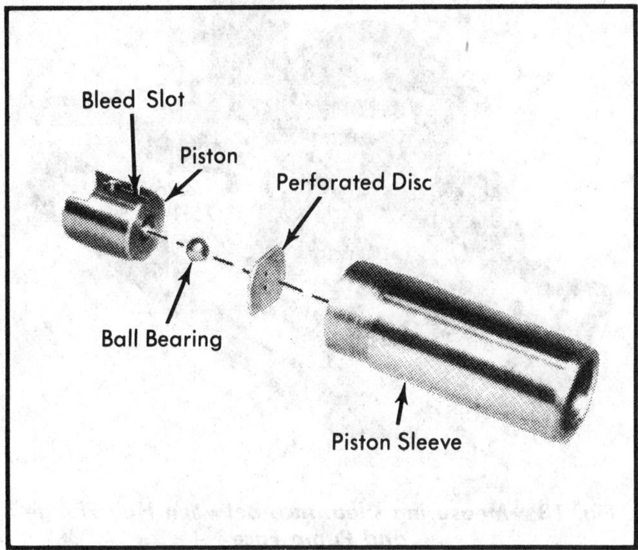

Fig. 10 Exploded View of Chain Tensioner Piston Assembly

4) Install piston in tensioner body. Place spring with tapered end facing tensioner plug. Screw tensioner plug slightly into tensioner body. Fill oil pocket with engine oil and move tensioner rail back and forth until oil comes out around plug threads. Tighten tensioner plug.

ENGINE OILING

ENGINE OILING SYSTEM

A chain driven rotor type oil pump pressure feeds oil to a full-flow oil filter. From oil filter, oil is circulated through passages to all moving parts of the engine.

Crankcase Capacity – 4.5 qts. (4.25 liters) with filter
Oil Filter – Full-Flow
Oil Pressure – 57psi@4000RPM
Pressure Regulator Valve – Non-adjustable

OIL PUMP

1) Remove oil pan and oil pump sprocket. Remove bolts attaching pump pick-up. Remove two bolts mounting pump to crankcase and lift out pump.

2) Unscrew union and remove spring and plunger from pump body. Remove pick-up tube and cover from pump body.

3) Measure clearance between outer rotor-to-pump body, rotor-to-rotor and rotor face-to-pump body flange (see specifications).

4) Using suitable puller, remove drive flange from rotor shaft. Press drive flange on new rotor shaft to a distance of 1.68" (42.7 mm) between flange and rotor face *(See Fig. 11).*

5) To install, reverse removal procedure, noting the following if replacing a gear-type pump with a rotor-type pump: Install a 46-link drive chain, and adjust chain tension so that chain can be depressed with light thumb pressure. Compensating plates are available for insertion between block and pump mounting if chain tension cannot be correctly set. Change upper section of oil filter mounting as rotor-type pump requires larger pressure relief valve opening.

Fig. 11 Measuring Distance Between Flange and Rotor Face

NOTE – *When installing compensating plate between oil pump and crankcase make sure oil hole is in proper position.*

Oil Pump Specifications

Application	Measurement In. (mm)
Rotor-to-Housing	.0014-.0043 (.04-.11)
Inner-to-Outer Rotor	.0047-.0079 (.12-.20)
Cover-to-Rotor	.0039-.0059 (.10-.15)
Press. Relief Spring (Free Length)	2.68 (68.1)

ENGINE COOLING

Thermostat – Opens at 176°F (80°C).
Cooling System Capacity – 7.4 qts. (7 liters)

WATER PUMP

1) Loosen alternator bracket. Remove fan and drive belt. Loosen hose clamps and remove water pump.

2) Using a suitable puller, remove fan hub from impeller shaft. Extract circlip and spacer ring from front of pump.

3) Press impeller off shaft and pump bearing out of housing. Drive friction seal out of housing and lift out cover ring.

320i 4 CYLINDER (Cont.)

4) Replace any worn or damaged parts. Using suitable tool, press impeller onto shaft until there is clearance of .031-.047" (.79-1.2 mm) between impeller and pump face.

5) Press fan hub onto pump shaft until a distance of 2.96-2.97" (75.1-75.5 mm) exists between hub flange and pump face *(See Fig. 16)*. To install, reverse removal procedure.

Fig. 12 Measuring Clearance Between Water Pump Impeller and Pump Face

Fig. 13 Measuring Clearance Between Hub Flange and Pump Face

ENGINE SPECIFICATIONS

GENERAL SPECIFICATIONS

Year	Displ. cu. ins.	Displ. cc	Carburetor	HP at RPM	Torque (Ft. Lbs. at RPM)	Compr. Ratio	Bore in.	Bore mm	Stroke in.	Stroke mm
1977	121.4	1990	Fuel Inj.	①110@5800	②112@3750	8.1:1	3.504	89	3.150	80

① – Calif. 105@5800
② – Calif. 108.5@3750

VALVES

Engine & Valve	Head Diam. In. (mm)	Face Angle	Seat Angle	Seat Width In. (mm)	Stem Diameter In. (mm)	Stem Clearance In. (mm)	Valve Lift In. (mm)
320i							
Intake	1.805 (45.84)	45° 30′	46°	.059-.083 (1.50-2.10)	.3134-.3139 (7.960-7.975)	.0010-.0020 (.025-.055)	.....
Exhaust	1.490 (37.84)	45° 30′	46°	.061-.081 (1.55-2.05)	.3129-.3134 (7.945-7.960)	.0015-.0030 (.040-.070)	.....

VALVE SPRINGS

Engine	Free Length In. (mm)	PRESSURE Lbs. @ In. (kg @ mm) Valve Closed	PRESSURE Lbs. @ In. (kg @ mm) Valve Open
320i	1.712 (43.5)	64@1.48 (29@37.6)	154@1.12 (70@28.5)

VALVE TIMING

Engine	INTAKE Open (BTDC)	INTAKE Close (ALDC)	EXHAUST Open (BLDC)	EXHAUST Close (ATDC)
320i	18°	66°	66°	18°

320i 4 CYLINDER (Cont.)

ENGINE SPECIFICATIONS (Cont.)

PISTONS, PINS, RINGS						
	PISTONS	PINS		RINGS		
Engine	Clearance In. (mm)	Piston Fit In. (mm)	Rod Fit In. (mm)	Rings	End Gap In. (mm)	Side Clearance In. (mm)
320i	.0018 (.045)	①.0008-.0024 (.002-.006)	.0001-.0004	No.1	①0118-.0177 (.30-.45)	.0024-.0036 (.06-.092)
				No.2	.008-.016 (.20-.40)	②.0016-.0028 (.040-.072)
				No.3	.010-.020 (.25-.50)	②.0012-.0024 (.030-.062)

① — Mahle Pistons — .0004-.0020 (.001-.005)
② — Mahle Pistons No. 2 .0012-.0024 (.030-.062)
No. 3 .0008-.0020 (.020-.052)

CRANKSHAFT MAIN & CONNECTING ROD BEARINGS							
	MAIN BEARINGS				CONNECTING ROD BEARINGS		
Engine	Journal Diam. In. (mm)	Clearance In. (mm)	Thrust Bearing	Crankshaft End Play In. (mm)	Journal Diam. In. (mm)	Clearance In. (mm)	Side Play In. (mm)
320i							
Red	2.165 (55.0)	.0004-.0008 (.010-.020)	Center	.0033-.0068 (.085-.174)	1.8878-1.8885 (47.95-47.966)	.0009-.0027 (.023-.069)	.....
Blue	2.165 (55.0)	.0008-.0011 (.020-.029)			1.8878-1.8885 (47.95-47.96)	.0009-.0027 (.023-.069)	

CAMSHAFT			
Engine	Journal Diam. In. (mm)	Clearance In. (mm)	Lobe Lift In. (mm)
2002 ①			
No. 1	1.3764-1.3772 (34.96-34.98)	.0013-.0029 (.033-.074)	.2764 (7.02)
No. 2	1.6520-1.6528 (41.96-41.98)	.0013-.0029 (.033-.074)	.2764 (7.02)
No. 3	1.6913-1.6921 (42.96-42.98)	.0013-.0029 (.033-.074)	.2764 (7.02)

① — End play is .0008-.005" (.020-.127 mm).

TIGHTENING SPECIFICATIONS

Application	Ft. Lbs. (mkg)
Cylinder Head Studs ①	
Step 1	25-33 (3.5-4.5)
Step 2	43-47 (6.0-6.5)
Step 3	49-52 (6.8-7.2)
Main Bearing Caps	42-46 (5.8-6.3)
Connecting Rod Bolts	38-41 (5.2-5.7)
Flywheel-to-Crankshaft ②	76-83 (10.5-11.5)
Rocker Arm Lock Bolts	7-8 (0.9-1.1)
Oil Pan Bolts	7-8 (0.9-1.1)
Camshaft Oiler (Hollow Bolt)	8-9 (1.1-1.3)
Crankshaft Pulley	101-108 (14-15)
Fuel Pump	7-10 (1.0-1.4)
Timing Cover	7-18 (0.9-2.5)

① — With engine at normal operating temperature.
② — Coat bolts with Loctite.

530i & 630CSi 6 CYL. ENGINES

ENGINE CODING

ENGINE IDENTIFICATION

Engine serial number is same as chassis serial number. Engine serial number is stamped in crankcase above starter.

ENGINE, CYLINDER HEAD & MANIFOLDS

ENGINE

1) Remove hood and disconnect battery ground cable. Remove radiator and air cleaner with fuel injection air volume control unit. Disconnect distributor vacuum line and wires from ignition coil. Disconnect fuel feed hose at fuel filter, hose at charcoal filter and vacuum hoses from brake booster. Disconnect all remaining fuel and coolant hoses.

2) Remove engine ground cable. Remove distributor cap and secondary wiring. Disconnect plug from fuel injection control unit and pull harness into engine compartment. Remove all remaining electrical connections.

3) Disconnect wires from starter and alternator. Disconnect accelerator linkage. Remove nuts from engine mounts. Remove protective cover from under engine. Remove power steering pump (if equipped). Attach a hoist to lifting holes at front and rear of engine.

4) Remove transmission. *See Manual Transmission Removal and Automatic Transmission Removal.* On Manual Transmission models, push back rubber boot on slave cylinder, remove circlip and pull slave cylinder out toward front. Disconnect exhaust pipes at front and rear manifolds.

5) Remove throw-out bearing lever and bearing from clutch housing. Raise engine and swing out to right to remove. To install, reverse removal procedure. Install drive pulley in correct position and lubricate contact surfaces of throw-out bearing lever with Molykote Longterm 2 paste.

MANUAL TRANSMISSION

1) Pull up boot from shift lever, remove circlip and pull shift lever up and out. Remove exhaust pipe support bracket. Disconnect drive shaft at transmission, loosen threaded coupling of drive shaft at rear of center support bearing.

2) Remove center support bearing and pull drive shaft from transmission. Remove speedometer cable and disconnect back-up light switch connection. Disconnect transmission from clutch housing. Support front of engine, remove transmission crossmember and transmission.

3) To install, reverse removal procedure. When installing drive shaft, push center support bearing rearward .08" (2 mm) and tighten nuts.

AUTOMATIC TRANSMISSION

1) Disconnect accelerator cable from reverse lever and drain transmission. Remove oil filler tube and plug opening. Remove exhaust system and disconnect lines to transmission. Disconnect wire harness to transmission.

2) Rotate torque converter and remove four bolts securing converter to drive plate. Disconnect shift rod from lever. Disconnect drive shaft coupling at rear of transmission and loosen threaded coupling at rear of center support bearing.

3) Remove center support bearing and pull drive shaft down and out to remove. Disconnect speedometer cable and back-up light connection. Remove transmission crossmember, allowing engine oil pan to rest on front axle crossmember.

4) Place a jack under transmission and remove ground strap. Separate transmission from engine, making sure torque converter stays in housing in transmission. Remove transmission.

5) To install, reverse removal procedure. When installing, make sure center support of torque converter is below edge of transmission. Push center support bearing rearward .08" (2 mm) and tighten nuts. Adjust accelerator cable lever.

INTAKE MANIFOLD

Remove all hoses and lines from manifold. Remove EGR valve and bellows to air volume meter. Remove electrical connector from throttle switch. Detach manifold from supports and bend back supports slightly. Remove intake manifold. To install, reverse removal procedure and replace all gaskets.

CYLINDER HEAD

1) Remove air cleaner, spark plug wire tube and valve cover. Disconnect battery ground cable and drain cooling system. Disconnect fuel line at fuel pump and accelerator linkage.

2) Disconnect all fuel and vacuum lines, along with all wiring from injection system and cylinder head. Disconnect accelerator linkage.

3) Remove upper front cover. *See Engine Front Cover & Oil Seal.* Bend back lock tabs and remove camshaft sprocket bolts and sprocket. Remove timing chain tensioner plug, spring and piston. Disconnect water hoses at base of intake manifolds.

4) Disconnect exhaust pipes. Remove cylinder head bolts and install aligning pins to keep rocker arm shafts from moving. Remove cylinder head.

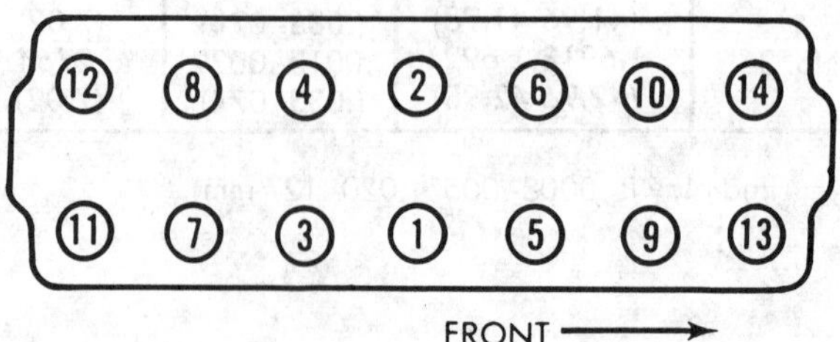

Fig. 1 Cylinder Head Tightening Sequence

5) To install, reverse removal procedure. Thoroughly clean mating surfaces and install a new gasket with sealer. Tighten bolts to specifications in sequence shown in illustration.

530i & 630CSi 6 CYL. ENGINES (Cont.)

6) Install camshaft sprocket and timing chain in correct position. See *Timing Chain Replacement*. Install valve cover and tighten nuts to specification.

7) After installation is complete and engine has run for a short time, shut off and allow to cool to approximately 100°F (38°C). Retighten cylinder head bolts to specification in same sequence.

VALVES

VALVE ARRANGEMENT

Left Side – Intake valves.
Right Side – Exhaust valves.

ROCKER ARM ASSEMBLY

1) Remove camshaft. See *Camshaft Removal*. Push rocker arms and thrust rings against springs and remove circlips from front rocker arm shafts.

2) Remove two countersunk rocker arm shaft locking bolts next to number one bearing bore of camshaft. Install a suitable removing tool (No. 11 3 060) in shaft and pull out of cylinder head. Remove rocker arms, thrust rings, springs and disc.

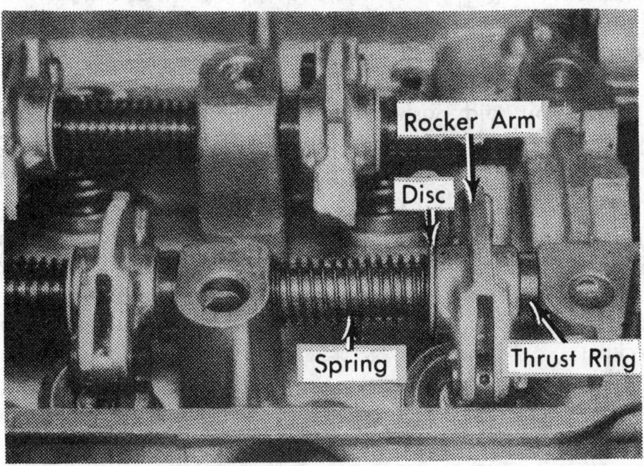

Fig. 2 Installed View of Rocker Arm Assembly

3) Check rocker arm shaft for wear. If diameter is less than .6083" (15.45 mm), replace rocker arm shaft. Check cam follower on rocker arms. If loose, replace rocker arms.

4) Install spring, disc, rocker arm and thrust ring. Install rocker arm shafts and adjust so that recesses in shafts are aligned with cylinder head bolt holes in cylinder head.

5) To disassemble rear rocker arm assemblies, remove rear cover on cylinder head. Use same procedure for rear shafts as used for front. Install self sealing discs on bolts for rear cover plate and use Cabritol sealer on plate gasket.

VALVE GUIDE SERVICING

1) With valve removed, check inside diameter of valve guide. If size exceeds specifications, drive guide out through combustion chamber with a suitable driver (No. 11 1 100).

2) Check size of valve guide bore in cylinder head. If size exceeds .5519" (14.018 mm), an oversize guide must be installed. If guide or bore condition warrant, the following sizes of guides are available for service replacement: .5551" (14.10 mm), .5591" (14.20 mm), and .5630" (14.30 mm).

3) Guides require a .0013-.0027" (.033-.069 mm) press fit in cylinder head, with head heated to 428-482°F (220-250°C). Ream head bores according to guide size being installed.

4) Using suitable driver (No. 11 1 120), drive guide into cylinder head from top until top of guide protrudes .591" (15.0 mm). Ream valve guide until correct clearance with valve is obtained.

VALVE STEM OIL SEALS

A rubber umbrella type oil seal is installed on valve stem before valve spring is installed.

VALVE SPRING

1) With rocker arms and shaft removed, compress valve spring with a suitable valve spring conpressor (No. 11 1 600). Remove valve keepers, release spring compressor and remove spring and retainer.

2) Check valve spring free length, and if less than specified, replace spring. Also check spring pressure in a suitable tester. Spring compressed length and pressure should be as indicated in table.

3) Install spring with green or white paint stripe end (tight coil end) against cylinder head. To install, reverse removal procedure.

VALVE CLEARANCE ADJUSTMENT

Remove valve cover and rotate engine until piston of valves being adjusted is at TDC of compression stroke. Loosen nut on rocker arm and rotate adjustment cam until correct clearance is obtained. Check or adjust valve clearance with engine hot. Valve clearance for both intake and exhaust valves is .012-.014" (.30-.35 mm).

Fig. 3 Procedure to Adjust Valve Tappet Clearance

530i & 630CSi 6 CYL. ENGINES (Cont.)

PISTONS, PINS & RINGS

OIL PAN

1) Remove protective cover from under engine, drain oil and remove front suspension stabilizer. Loosen alternator and remove belt.

2) Remove power steering pump (if equipped) but do not disconnect hoses. Remove bolt securing power steering pump bracket to side of oil pan.

3) Loosen bearing block until oil pan can be removed. Detach support bracket above slave cylinder from crankcase. Rotate crankshaft until No. 6 connecting rod is above oil pan mating surface of crankcase.

4) Remove oil pan retaining bolts, lower front of oil pan, turn rear of pan towards support bracket and remove oil pan. To install, reverse removal procedure. Clean mating surfaces and apply Atmosit Sealer to junctions of crankcase and timing cover, and flywheel end cover.

PISTON & ROD ASSEMBLY

1) With cylinder head and oil pan removed, remove connecting rod cap. Push piston and rod assembly up and out through top of motor.

2) To install, insert bearing halves in rod and rod cap. Position rings so that ring gaps are approximately 180° apart from each other.

3) Compress piston rings and install piston in cylinder with arrow toward front of engine. Push piston into cylinder and make sure bearings are properly seated against crankshaft journal.

4) Match numbers on rod and rod cap and install on same side. Tighten nuts to specifications.

Fig. 4 View Showing Connecting Rod Cap Installation

PISTON PIN REPLACEMENT

1) With piston and rod assembly removed, remove circlips from piston pin hole in piston. Drive out piston pin and separate piston from connecting rod. Thoroughly clean and inspect rod and piston.

2) Piston pins are manufactured in two classes. Pin class is designated by color code on pin or a letter stamped in pin. A corresponding letter is stamped in piston. Pin-to-piston clearance is same for each class of pin, but pin-to-rod clearance varies depending on class of pin. See *Specifications*.

Piston Pin Class Designation

Application	Pin Diameter In. (mm)
White or "W"	.8660-.8661 (21.997-22.000)
Black or "S"	.8659-.8660 (21.994-21.997)

3) Classes of pins and pistons must not be interchanged. If piston or pin is replaced, it must be replaced with one of a corresponding class and weight. Weight classification is designated by a "+" or a "-" stamped in top of piston.

4) Check pin-to-piston clearance, if clearance exceeds that specified and pin is not worn, replace piston. Check pin-to-rod clearance, if clearance exceeds that specified, depending on pin class, new bushing must be installed.

5) Press out old bushing and install new one with split in bushing rotated 90° from oil hole in connecting rod. Drill through oil hole in connecting rod. Ream bushing to specified clearance with piston pin.

6) If connecting rod is replaced, replace with rod which is within 4 grams of rod being replaced. Position piston on connecting rod with arrow on piston facing in same direction as oil hole in connecting rod. Lubricate and install piston pin and circlips.

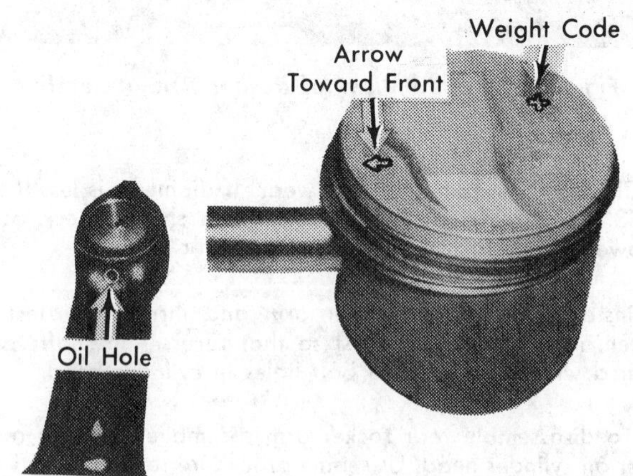

Fig. 5 Piston & Connecting Rod Assembly & Markings

FITTING PISTONS

1) With piston removed and disassembled from connecting rod, measure diameter of piston. Measure with micrometer

530i & 630CSi 6 CYL. ENGINES (Cont.)

positioned 90° from pin hole and at a point measured from bottom of piston skirt (*Distance "A", see Fig. 7*). **NOTE** — *Distance "A" depends on piston manufacturer, see table below.*

Application	Manufacture	Distance "A"
530i	Mahle	.807" (20.5 mm)
530i	KS	1.033" (26.25 mm)
630i	Mahle	0.630" (16.00 mm)
630i	KS	0.947" (24.05 mm)

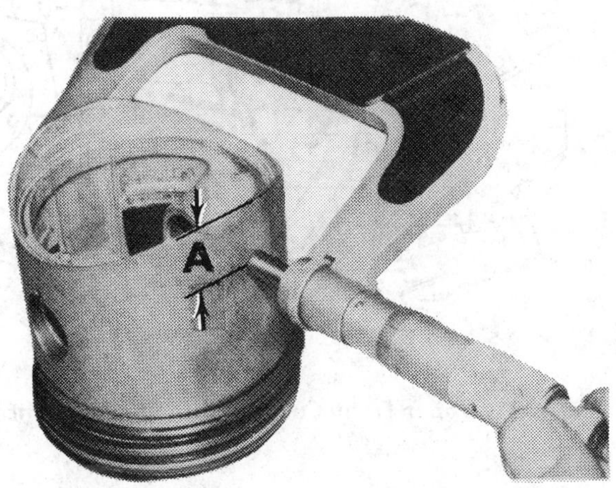

Fig. 6 View Showing Correct Procedure to Measure Piston Diameter

2) Measure inside diameter of bore in crankcase. If clearance exceeds specification, crankcase must be bored for next oversize piston. Pistons are available in .010" (.25 mm) and .020" (.50 mm) oversize.

3) Check piston ring side clearance and end gap. If new rings are installed, install with word "TOP" stamped in ring toward top of piston.

CRANKSHAFT MAIN & CONNECTING ROD BEARINGS

MAIN & CONNECTING ROD BEARING SERVICE

1) With engine removed, remove clutch, flywheel, cylinder head, oil pan and timing chain. *See Timing Chain Replacement.* Remove rear main bearing oil seal mount.

2) Remove pistons and connecting rods. Remove main bearing caps and lift out crankshaft. Thoroughly clean and inspect crankshaft. Blow out oil passages with compressed air.

3) Main bearings journals are manufactured in two standard sizes. Sizes are designated by a colored dot on crankshaft balance weight next to individual journal (see illustration). Color code designation is given is specifications.

4) Check main and connecting rod bearing clearance using the Plastigage method. If bearing clearance is more than specified, crankshaft must be ground to next undersize. Bearings for undersize crankshafts are available in .010" (.25 mm), .020" (.50 mm) and .030" (.75 mm) undersizes.

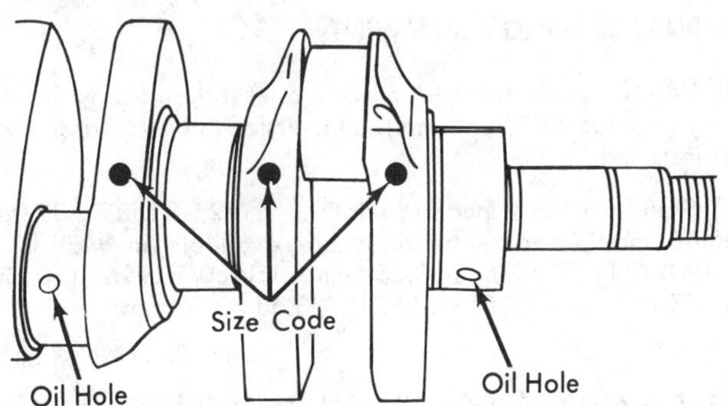

Fig. 7 Crankshaft Color Code Markings

5) Install bearing halves in crankcase and bearing caps. Lubricate crankshaft bearing journals and install crankshaft in crankcase.

6) Install bearing caps with numbers on caps running from one through six in order from front to rear. Install caps with bearing locks on same side as bearing locks in crankcase.

7) Tighten caps to specifications. Check crankshaft endplay. See *Thrust Bearing Alignment.* To install remaining components, reverse removal procedure.

NOTE — *Ground crankshafts are marked with painted stripes (See Fig. 8).*

Fig. 8 View Showing Crankshaft Undersize Markings

Crankshaft Journal Sizes

	In. (mm)
Connecting Rod	**In. (mm)**
Standard	1.888-1.889 (47.97-47.99)
1 paint stripe	1.852-1.853 (47.72-47.74)
2 paint stripes	1.851-1.852 (47.48-47.49)
3 paint stripes	1.850-1.851 (47.22-47.24)
Main Bearings Red Code	**In. (mm)**
Standard	2.361-2.362 (59.98-59.99)
1 paint stripe	2.324-2.325 (59.73-59.74)
2 paint stripes	2.323-2.324 (59.48-59.49)
3 paint stripes	2.322-2.323 (59.23-59.24)
Main Bearings Blue Code	**In. (mm)**
Standard	2.361-2.362 (59.98-59.99)
1 paint stripe	2.324-2.325 (59.72-59.73)
2 paint stripes	2.323-2.324 (59.47-59.48)
3 paint stripes	2.322-2.323 (59.22-59.23)

530i & 630CSi 6 CYL. ENGINES (Cont.)

THRUST BEARING ALIGNMENT

1) With flywheel installed, check crankshaft end play. If end play exceeds .007" (.18 mm), an oversize thrust bearing must be installed.

2) Standard thrust bearing width is 1.1823-1.1835" (30.03-30.06 mm) Oversize bearings are available in widths of 1.1902-1.1913" (30.23-30.26 mm), 1.1980-1.1996" (30.43-30.47 mm) and 1.2059-1.2071" (30.63-30.66 mm).

REAR MAIN BEARING OIL SEAL REPLACEMENT

NOTE – *To replace rear main bearing oil seal in vehicle, transmission must be removed.*

1) Remove clutch and flywheel and drain engine oil. Remove bolts securing oil pan to rear main bearing oil seal mount.

2) Pry oil pan down at area around seal mount, taking care not to damage gasket. Remove bolts securing seal mount to crankcase and remove mount.

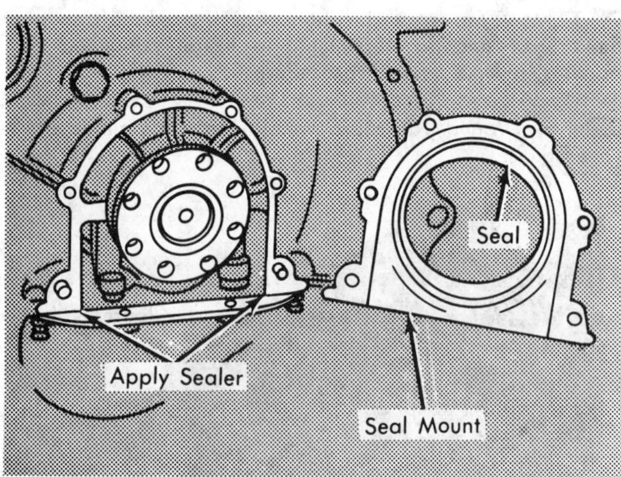

Fig. 9 Installing Rear Main Bearing Oil Seal

3) Pry out old seal and install new one making sure it is fully seated in mount. Apply Atmosit sealer to junction of oil pan and seal mount. To install mount, reverse removal procedure.

ENGINE FRONT COVER AND OIL SEAL

Upper Front Engine Cover – 1) Remove distributor cap and valve cover. Remove thermostat housing and thermostat. Rotate crankshaft untill number one cylinder is at TDC of compression stroke. Distributor rotor should point at notch in distributor.

2) Remove timing cover bolts, push rotor in clockwise direction and remove cover with distributor drive. Pull distributor drive out of front cover.

3) To install, thoroughly clean mounting surfaces and use new gasket with sealer. Install distributor drive in camshaft. Rotate rotor counterclockwise approximately 1.38" (35.05 mm) from notch in distributor housing, and install cover.

4) Lightly tighten bolts one and two (see illustration), then tighten remaining bolts to specification in sequence shown in illustration. Tighten bolts one and two to specification. To install remaining components, reverse removal procedure.

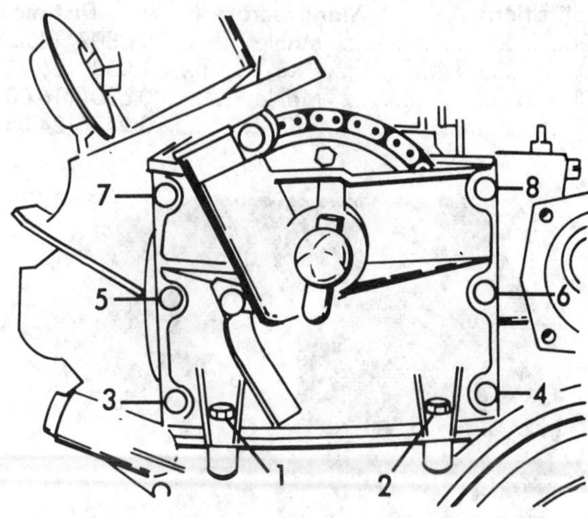

Fig. 10 Upper Front Cover Tightening Sequence

Lower Front Engine Cover – 1) Remove upper front engine cover as previously outlined. Remove timing chain tensioner piston, fan clutch and crankshaft pulley. Remove lower front engine cover.

2) Replace oil seal. To install cover, reverse removal procedure. Thoroughly clean mating surfaces and use new gasket with sealer. Tighten bolts to specification.

NOTE – *Oil seal can be replaced without removing lower front engine cover.*

3) Remove protective cover from under engine. Remove alternator drive belt. Place a piece of cardboard in front of crankshaft pulley, against radiator.

4) Remove crankshaft pulley nut and remove pulley. Pry out old seal and install new one. If sealing portion of pulley has a groove worn in it, install seal so that sealing edge does not run in groove.

CAMSHAFT

CAMSHAFT

1) Remove cylinder head as previously outlined. Remove fuel pump and fuel pump push rod. Remove oil distribution pipe. With camshaft still positioned at TDC for number one cylinder, open intake valve clearance on No. 2 and No. 4 cylinders.

2) Attach a suitable pressure frane (No.11 1 060) to cylinder head to open all valves. Remove bolts securing camshaft thrust plate to cylinder head and carefully withdraw camshaft.

3) Install camshaft in cylinder head and tighten down thrust plate. Set cylinder six to overlap and release pressure plate. The tapped hole in sprocket flange must align with cast protrusion in cylinder head (see illustration). Check camshaft endplay.

530i & 630CSi 6 CYL. ENGINES (Cont.)

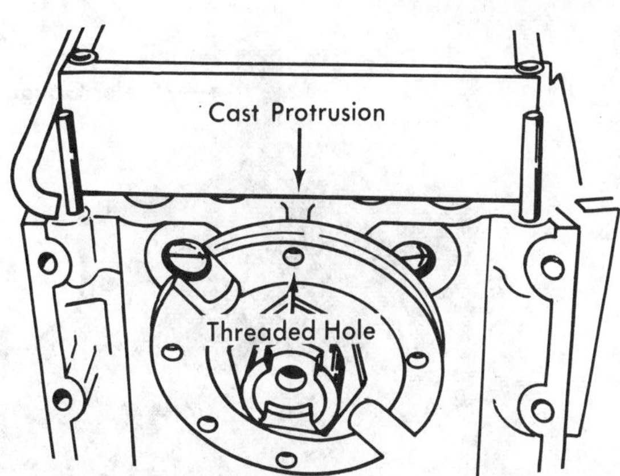

Fig. 11 View Showing Proper Camshaft Alignment

4) Install oil pipe, making sure seals are installed above and below pipe at points where it is bolted to head. Oil pipe must be installed, so oil holes spray between rocker arms and cams of intake and exhaust valves.

5) To install remaining components, reverse removal procedure.

CAMSHAFT ENDPLAY

Check camshaft endplay with a feeler gauge. If endplay exceeds .001-.007" (.03-.18 mm), replace camshaft thrust plate.

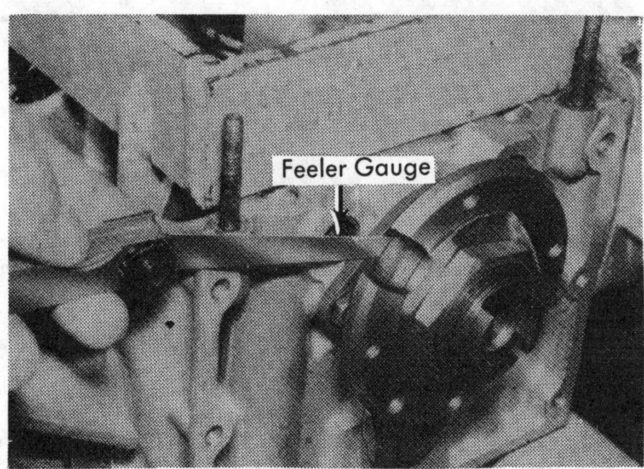

Fig. 12 Using Feeler Gauge to Check Camshaft End Play

TIMING CHAIN REPLACEMENT

1) Rotate crankshaft until number one cylinder is at TDC of compression stroke. Rotor should point to notch in distributor. Remove front engine covers as previously outlined. Mark front side of timing chain for installation.

2) Bend over lock tabs and remove camshaft sprocket with timing chain. If mileage of vehicle exceeds 30,000 miles, replace timing chain. Replace sprockets if worn or damaged.

3) To replace crankshaft sprocket, remove oil pan, oil pump sprocket and chain. Remove Woodruff key and "O" ring and pull off crankshaft sprocket with a suitable puller (No. 11 1 200). To install, reverse removal procedure. Adjust oil pump chain tension.

4) To install timing chain, reverse removal procedure, making sure number one cylinder is at TDC of compression stroke. Line up tapped hole in sprocket hub with cast protrusion in cylinder head and install timing chain and sprocket.

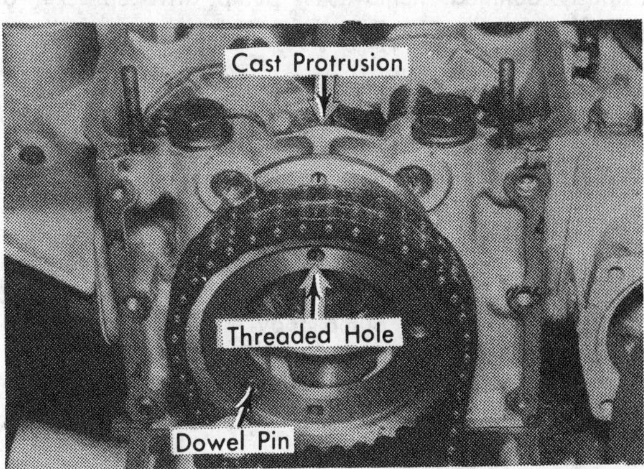

Fig. 13 Correct Alignment for Timing Chain Installation

TIMING CHAIN TENSIONER

1) Remove tensioner plug, spring and piston. Check length of spring and piston assembly. Length of spring should be 6.122" (155.5 mm). Piston assembly length should be 2.441" (62.0 mm)

2) Check piston with compressed air to see if air vent slots (see illustration) are plugged. Clean slots if air does not pass through. When assembling piston, do not block air vents with disc.

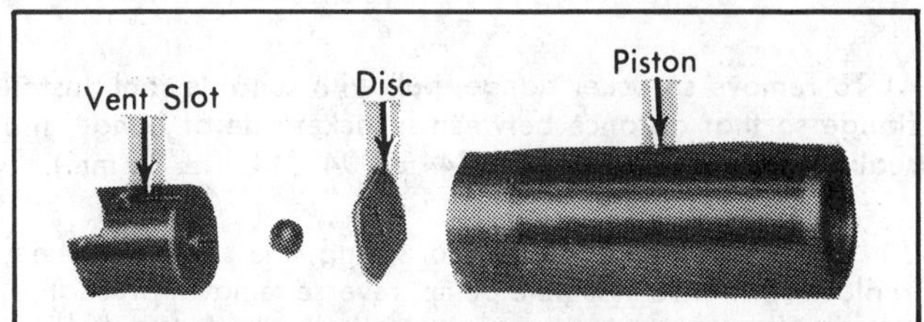

Fig. 14 Exploded View of Timing Chain Tensioner Piston

3) Install piston, spring with conical end toward plug and slightly tighten plug. Fill oil well full of oil and remove valve cover to vent air from piston. Move tensioning rail back and forth untill oil comes out at plug. Tighten plug and reverse removal procedure to install remaining components.

ENGINE OILING

ENGINE OILING SYSTEM

Full pressure oil system, utilizing a chain driven Eaton rotor type oil pump, a full flow oil filter and a pressure regulator valve.

Crankcase Capacity – 6 qts.

Oil Filter – Full-flow, paper element type.

Normal Oil Pressure – 26-29 psi (18-20 kg/cm^2) at idle and 72.5 psi (51 kg/cm^2) at full speed.

Pressure Regulator Valve – Mounted in oil pump. See *Oil Pump Removal.*

530i & 630CSi 6 CYL. ENGINES (Cont.)

OIL PUMP

1) Remove oil pan, front engine covers and timing chain as previously outlined. Remove oil pump drive sprocket and chain. Remove oil pump.

2) Remove pressure regulator plug, spring and piston. Remove pump cover and thoroughly clean and inspect all components. Check clearance between inner and outer rotors. If clearance exceeds maximum specified, replace rotors.

3) Check clearance between outer rotor and pump body and clearance between rotor sealing face and mating surface of pump body and pump cover. If either clearance exceeds maximum specified, replace pump body.

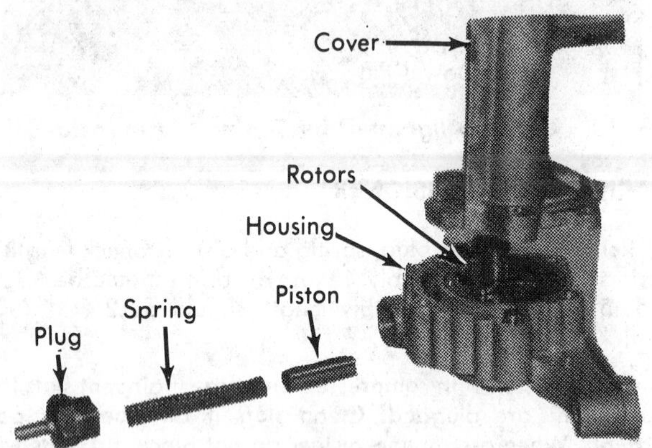

Fig. 15 View of Oil Pump Assembly

4) To remove sprocket flange, pull with suitable tool. Install flange so that distance between sprocket side of flange and sealing side of inner rotor is 1.744±.004" (44.30±.10 mm).

5) Check free length of regulator spring, if less than specified, replace spring. To assemble pump, reverse removal procedure. Attach oil pump to crankcase and install sprocket and chain. Chain should slightly depress when pushed in with thumb.

6) If chain depresses more than recommended, remove pump and install shims between pump and crankcase mounting points. Make sure oil holes line up on front shim. Rear shim must be same thickness as front. To install remaining components, reverse removal procedure.

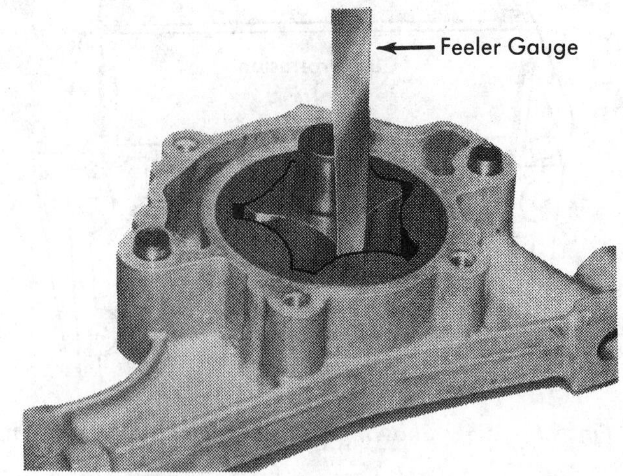

Fig. 16 Using Feeler Gauge to Check Rotor Clearance

Oil Pump Specifications	
Application	**Measurement In. (mm)**
Rotor-to-Rotor Clearance	.0047-.0118 (.12-.30)
Rotor-to-Housing Clearance	.0029-.0049 (.07-.13)
Sealing Face-to-Housing Clearance	.002-.0036" (.05-.09)
Regulator Spring Free Length	2.677 (67.99)

ENGINE COOLING

WATER PUMP

Remove clutch fan, pulley, side bar and connecting hose. Remove water pump. To install, reverse removal procedure. Use new gaskets and sealer.

Thermostat – Opens at 183°F (84°C) on man. trans. models or at 176°F (80°C) on auto. trans. models.

Cooling System Capacity – 12.7 qts.

ENGINE SPECIFICATIONS

GENERAL SPECIFICATIONS

Year	Displ. cu. ins.	Displ. cc	Carburetor	HP at RPM	Torque (Ft. Lbs. at RPM)	Compr. Ratio	Bore in.	Bore mm	Stroke in.	Stroke mm
1977	182	2985	Fuel Inj.	175@5500	188@4500	8.1:1	3.504	89	3.150	80

530i & 630CSi 6 CYL. ENGINES (Cont.)

ENGINE SPECIFICATIONS (Cont.)

VALVES							
Engine & Valve	Head Diam. In. (mm)	Face Angle	Seat Angle	Seat Width In. (mm)	Stem Diameter In. (mm)	Stem Clearance In. (mm)	Valve Lift In. (mm)
2985 cc							
Intake	1.811 (46.0)	45°	46°	.063-.079 (1.6-2.0)	.3135-.3149 (7.963-7.998)	.0010-.0022 (.025-.055)	.....
Exhaust	1.496 (38.0)	45°	46°	.079-.095 (2.0-2.4)	.3128-.3135 (7.945-7.963)	.0016-.0028 (.040-.070)	.....

VALVE SPRINGS			
Engine	Free Length In. (mm)	PRESSURE Lbs. @ In. (kg @ mm)	
		Valve Closed	Valve Open
2985 cc	①1.712 (43.5)	64±2.6@1.480 (29±1.2@37.6)	.....

① — Some springs are 1.811" (46.0 mm), depending on spring manufacturer.

② — On models with automatic transmission; 154±6 lbs.@1.122" (70±2.8 kg@28.5 mm).

PISTONS, PINS, RINGS						
Engine	PISTONS	PINS		RINGS		
	Clearance In. (mm)	Piston Fit In. (mm)	Rod Fit In. (mm)	Rings	End Gap In. (mm)	Side Clearance In. (mm)
2985 cc	.0016-.0018 (.040-.045)	.0000-.0002 (.001-.005)	①.0002-.0005 (.005-.013)	No. 1	.012-.020 (.30-.50)	③.002-.004 (.06-.09)
			②.0003-.0006 (.008-.016)	No. 2	.008-.016 (.20-.40)	③.001-.002 (.03-.06)
				Oil	.010-.016 (.25-.40)	③.0008-.002 (.02-.05)

① — White color code.

② — Black color code.

③ — Mahle specifications shown; For KS, No. 1 .002-.004" (.06-.09 mm), No. 2 .002-.003" (.04-.07 mm), Oil .001-.002 (.03-.06 mm). For Alkan, No. 1 .003-.004" (.07-.10 mm), No. 2 .001-.002" (.03-.06 mm), Oil .001-.002" (.03-.06 mm).

CRANKSHAFT MAIN & CONNECTING ROD BEARINGS							
Engine	MAIN BEARINGS				CONNECTING ROD BEARINGS		
	Journal Diam. In. (mm)	Clearance In. (mm)	Thrust Bearing	Crankshaft End Play In. (mm)	Journal Diam. In. (mm)	Clearance In. (mm)	Side Play In. (mm)
2985 cc							
Red Code	2.3614-2.3618 (59.98-59.99)	.0012-.0028 (.030-.070)	No. 4	.0033-.0069 (.085-.174)	1.8888-1.8894 (47.975-47.991)	.0009-.0027 (.023-.069)	.....
Blue Code	2.3610-2.3614 (59.97-59.98)	.0012-.0027 (.030-.068)					

530i & 630CSi 6 CYL. ENGINES (Cont.)

ENGINE SPECIFICATIONS (Cont.)

CAMSHAFT			
Engine	Journal Diam. In. (mm)	Clearance In. (mm)	Lobe Lift In. (mm)
2985 cc			
No. 1	1.3764-1.3770 (34.96-34.98)	.0013-.003 (.034-.075)	.2802 (7.12)
No. 2	1.7304-1.7310 (43.95-43.97)		
No. 3	1.7704-1.7710 (44.97-44.98)		
No. 4	1.8094-1.8100 (45.96-45.97)		

VALVE TIMING				
	INTAKE		EXHAUST	
Engine	Open (BTDC)	Close (ALDC)	Open (BLDC)	Close (ATDC)
2985 cc①	14°	54°	54°	14°
2985 cc②	26°	66°	66°	26°

① — With .020" (.51 mm) clearance between heel of camshaft and rocker pad.

② — With .015" (.38 mm) clearance between heel of camshaft and rocker pad.

TIGHTENING SPECIFICATIONS

Application	Ft. Lbs. (mkg)
Cyliner Head Bolts ①	
1st Stage	25-32 (3.5-4.4)
2nd Stage	43-47 (6.0-6.5)
3rd Stage	49-52 (6.8-7.2)
Main Bearing Bolts	42-46 (5.8-6.4)
Rod Cap Nuts	38-41 (5.3-5.7)
Camshaft Thrust Plate	101-108 (14.0-15.0)
Upper Front Engine Cover	7-8 (0.9-1.1)
Lower Front Engine Cover	7-8 (0.9-1.1)
Oil Pan Bolts	7-8 (0.9-1.1)
Timing Chain Tensioner Plug	22-29 (3.0-4.0)
Rocker Arm Clamp Bolt	6.5-8.0 (0.8-1.1)
Flywheel Bolts ②	72-84 (10.0-11.6)
Crankshaft Pulley Nut	
Flat Nut	173-188 (24.0-26.0)
Shoulder Nut	318-333 (44.0-46.0)
Regulator Valve Plug (Oil Pump)	18-22 (2.5-3.0)
Camshaft Oil Pipe Hollow Bolt	8-9.5 (1.1-1.3)

① — With engine at normal operating temperature.

② — Coat threads with Loctite.

2300 cc 4 CYLINDER

ENGINE CODING

ENGINE IDENTIFICATION

The second series of digits of vehicle identification number, located on a plate riveted to top of right fender apron, indicates engine type.

Engine	Code
2300 cc	YA

ENGINE, CYLINDER HEAD & MANIFOLDS

ENGINE

Capri – **1)** Disconnect battery cables. Disconnect all hoses and connections to air cleaner assembly while noting positions to aid in reassembly, then remove air cleaner assembly. Mark hood hinge locations, then remove hood. Raise vehicle on a hoist and remove engine shield. Drain cooling system and crankcase.

2) Remove starter. Remove converter bolt access plug and three converter-to-flywheel bolts. Remove flywheel or converter housing cover and lower housing attaching bolts. Disconnect exhaust pipe from exhaust manifold. Disconnect transmission cooler lines from radiator on models with automatic transmission.

3) Remove engine mount nuts. Disconnect and plug fuel lines at fuel pump. Remove power steering pump pulley and lower power steering-to-bracket bolt. Lower vehicle. Remove fan shroud, radiator hoses, and radiator. Disconnect heater and vacuum hoses at engine. Disconnect power brake hose and oil pressure line.

4) Disconnect kickdown cable. Disconnect accelerator cable retaining clip at ball stud, then pull lightly on cable while depressing tangs one at a time on bracket clip and remove throttle cable. Disconnect idle solenoid. Disconnect water temperature wire, vacuum amplifier, alternator wires, and ground wire.

5) Disconnect vacuum hose and coil wire from distributor. Remove alternator adjusting arm bolt, power steering pump-to-bracket bolts and remove pump. Disconnect choke wire. Support transmission and housing with a floor jack, then remove housing-to-engine attaching bolts. Attach lifting hoist to engine, and carefully lift engine from vehicle.

Courier – **1)** Remove hood, marking location of hinges. Disconnect battery, drain cooling system. Remove air cleaner and heat stove assembly. Disconnect radiator hoses at radiator. Remove radiator and shroud. Disconnect thermactor hoses at pump. Disconnect heater hoses, choke cable and accelerator linkage. Disconnect brake vacuum booster hose and vacuum amplifier.

2) Remove alternator and bracket, and move out of the way. Disconnect fuel line at carburetor. Raise vehicle and drain crankcase. Disconnect exhaust pipe from manifold and remove exhaust pipe hanger. Remove right engine mount bracket. Remove lower transmission-to-engine attaching bolts. Lower vehicle, support transmission with a jack and remove remaining transmission-to-engine attaching bolts.

3) Install a suitable engine lifting sling, to engine lifting hooks. Remove clutch slave cylinder from transmission. Pull engine forward until it clears transmission shaft. Lift engine from vehicle.

INTAKE MANIFOLD

Removal & Installation – Remove air cleaner and disconnect fuel line from carburetor. Disconnect distributor and crankcase ventilation hoses at intake manifold. Disconnect carburetor linkage from carburetor. Remove nuts and bolts, then remove intake manifold and carburetor as an assembly from engine. To install, reverse removal procedure while noting the following: Use a new gasket upon installation. Tighten manifold nuts and bolts, in two steps, using sequence as shown in illustration.

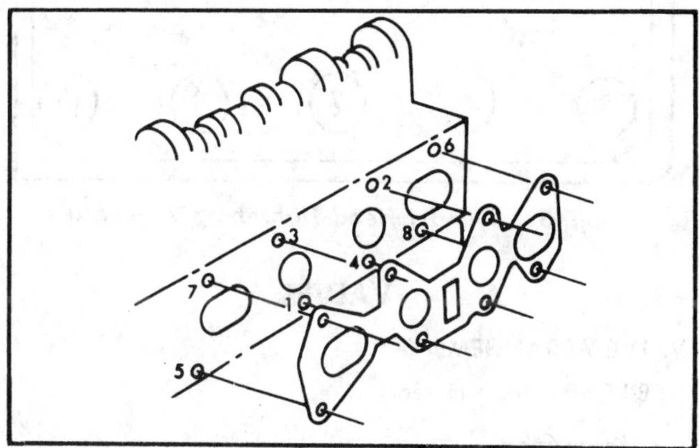

Fig. 1 Intake Manifold Tightening Sequence

EXHAUST MANIFOLD

Removal & Installation – Remove air cleaner and two attaching nuts from top of exhaust manifold shroud. Remove attaching nuts from muffler inlet pipe and manifold, then remove exhaust manifold. To install, apply a light film of graphite grease on exhaust manifold and install manifold. Tighten nuts to specification in sequence shown in illustration.

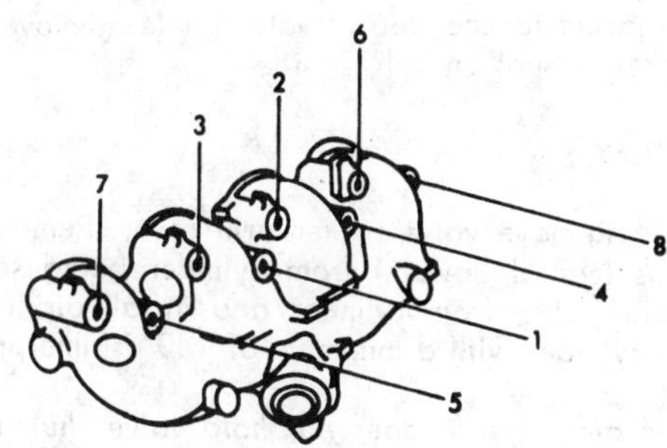

Fig. 2 Exhaust Manifold Tightening Sequence

CYLINDER HEAD

Removal – Drain cooling system, remove air cleaner and rocker arm cover. Remove exhaust manifold. Remove intake manifold and carburetor as an assembly. Disconnect spark plug wires from plugs. Remove all drive belts, fan, and pulley. Remove crankshaft pulley attaching bolt and crankshaft pulley. Remove camshaft drive belt cover, loosen drive belt

2300 cc 4 CYLINDER (Cont.)

tensioner and remove belt. Remove water outlet elbow from cylinder head. Remove timing belt inner cover-to-cylinder head attaching bolt. Remove cylinder head bolts, then remove cylinder head and camshaft as an assembly.

Installation – Clean gasket material from cylinder head and block. Install new gasket on block. Place cylinder head assembly on block and install head bolts. Tighten bolts, in two steps, using sequence shown in illustration. Reverse removal procedure for remaining components and adjust timing belt tension.

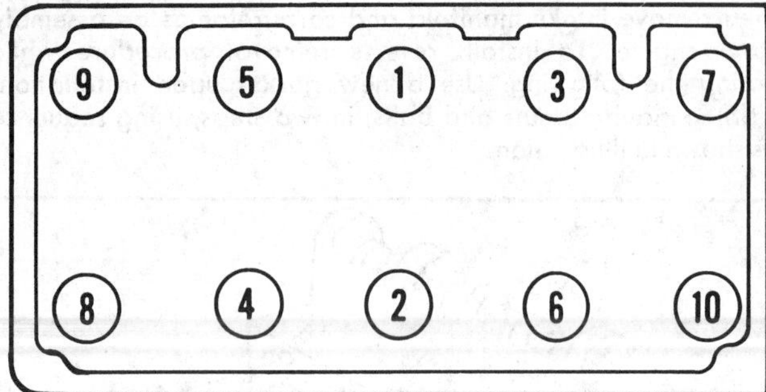

Fig. 3 Cylinder Head Tightening Sequence

VALVES

VALVE ARRANGEMENT

E-I-E-I-E-I-E-I (front to rear).

VALVE GUIDES

If valve guides become worn they may be reamed to install a new valve with oversize stem. When going from a standard size stem to oversize, always use reamers in sequence to obtain final desired bore. The valve seat must be refaced after a guide has been reamed, and a suitable tool used to break sharp corner (ID) of guide.

VALVE STEM OIL SEALS

With valve in head, place plastic installation cap over end of valve stem. Start stem seal carefully over cap and push seal down until jacket touches top of valve guide. Remove plastic cap and bottom seal on valve guide.

VALVE SPRINGS

Removal – Remove valve rocker arm cover. Remove both rocker arms (cam followers) from cylinder being serviced. Remove spark plug from cylinder and install air line and adapter to cylinder with a minimum of 140 psi line pressure.

NOTE – *If air pressure does not hold valve shut, remove cylinder head for inspection.* Use a suitable tool to compress valve spring, then remove retainer locks. Remove tool, spring retainer, spring, and valve stem seal. **CAUTION** – *DO NOT remove air pressure.*

Installation – Install NEW valve stem oil seal, valve spring and retainer. Compress spring and install retainer locks. **CAUTION** – *Do not compress spring more than necessary to install locks.* Remove compressor tool, turn off air and remove adapter. Apply Lubriplate to all contact surfaces of rocker arms and install in position. **CAUTION** – *Make sure that the affected lash adjuster has been collapsed and released before rotating camshaft.*

VALVE SPRING INSTALLED HEIGHT

Measure assembled height of valve spring from surface of the spring pad to underside of spring retainer. If height is not within specifications, install .030" (.76 mm) spacer(s) between spring and pad to obtain recommended height. DO NOT install spacers unless necessary, as excess use of spacers will result in overstressing valve springs and overloading camshaft lobe.

Spring Height Specifications

Engine	Installed Height
2300 cc	1.531"(38.89 mm)

HYDRAULIC LASH ADJUSTER ASSEMBLY

Two types of hydraulic lash adjusters are used in 2300 cc engines. Clean and inspect all parts of assembly. Replace the entire assembly if plunger is not free in body. Assemble lifter assembly and check for freeness of operation by pressing down on the cap. Lifters may also be checked with a hydraulic tester to check leakdown rate.

HYDRAULIC LASH ADJUSTMENT

Position camshaft so high point of cam lobe is facing away from valve to be checked (valve closed). Remove coil spring holding cam follower arm to lash adjuster. Use special tool (T74P-6565-B) to slowly apply pressure to cam follower until lash adjuster is completely collapsed. Hold in this position and check clearance between follower and cam. If not within specifications, inspect cam follower, valve spring installed height, and cam.

Lash Adjustment Specifications

Application	Clearance In.(mm)
Intake (Cold)	.008 (.20)
Exhaust (Cold)	.010 (.25)

PISTONS, PINS & RINGS

OIL PAN

Removal – Remove dipstick and flywheel housing cover, then drain crankcase. Disconnect steering coupling from rack and pinion and unbolt rack and pinion from crossmember; move assembly forward for clearance. Withdraw oil pan mounting bolts and maneuver pan from vehicle.

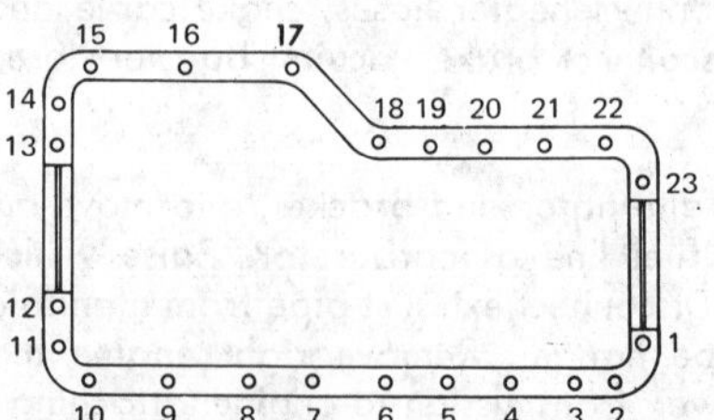

Fig. 4 Oil Pan Tightening Sequence

2300 cc 4 CYLINDER (Cont.)

Installation – To install oil pan, reverse removal procedure refering to tightening sequence illustration.

PISTON & ROD ASSEMBLY

Removal – Remove cylinder head, oil pan, and oil pump. Remove ridge at top of cylinder bores using a ridge reamer before removing pistons from block. **NOTE** – *Keep tops of pistons covered during this procedure.* Rotate crankshaft and inspect connecting rods and rod caps for cylinder identification. Identify them if necessary. Remove rod cap and push each piston and rod assembly out top of cylinder bore. **NOTE** – *Be careful not to nick crankshaft journals.* Install rod caps on mating rods.

Installation – Oil piston rings and cylinder walls with light engine oil. Install ring compressor on piston, then insert rod and piston assembly into cylinder bore and guide rod over crankshaft journal. **NOTE** – *Notch on piston head should point towards front of engine.* Tap piston into cylinder bore using a wooden handle, install rod cap and tighten nuts in two steps. Repeat procedure for each piston assembly.

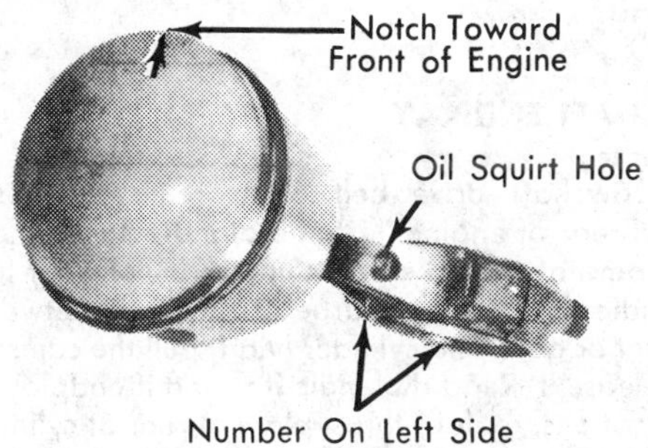

Fig. 5 Piston & Rod Assembly Installation Features

FITTING PISTONS

1) Check piston to cylinder bore clearance by measuring the piston and cylinder bore diameters. Measure outer diameter of piston at centerline of piston pin bore and at 90° to pin bore axis. Measure the diameter of each cylinder bore at the top, middle and bottom, with the gauge placed at right angles and parallel to the centerline of the engine.

2) Standard size pistons are color coded; red, blue or have .003" OS stamped on the dome. Select the piston to assure the proper clearance. When the bore diameter is in the lower one third of specified range, a red piston should be used. When the bore diameter is in the middle one third a blue piston should be used. When the bore diameter is in the upper one third, the .003" OS piston should be used.

3) If no piston can be fitted, refinish the cylinder to provide proper clearance. When a piston has been fitted, mark it for assembly in the cylinder to which it has been fitted.

Piston Code	Diameter In. (mm)
Red	3.7780-3.7786 (95.961-95.976)
Blue	3.7792-3.7798 (95.991-96.006)
.003" OS.	3.7804-3.7831 (96.022-96.037)

Cylinder Bore Range . 3.7795-3.7831" (95.999-96.090mm)
Piston-to-Bore Clearance .. .0014-.0022" (.0355-.0558mm)

PISTON PINS

Removal – Remove bearing inserts from connecting rod and cap. Mark pistons and pins to assure assembly with same rod. Press piston pin from piston and connecting rod.

Installation – Apply light coat of engine oil to all parts. Assemble piston to connecting rod with oil squirt hole (in connecting rod) and notch (on piston head) positioned as shown in illustration. Start piston pin in piston and connecting rod, then press pin through piston and connecting rod until pin is centered in piston.

CRANKSHAFT MAIN & CONNECTING ROD BEARINGS

MAIN & CONNECTING ROD BEARINGS

NOTE – *Following procedures are with oil pan and oil pump removed.*

Connecting Rod Bearings – After ensuring rod caps are marked for cylinder identification, remove rod caps. Use Plastigage method to check for proper bearing clearance. If not within specifications, new bearings must be installed. New bearings are available in .001" (.025 mm) and .002" (.051 mm) undersizes. Selective fitting is required on each connecting rod. A standard bearing may be used in combination with either undersize bearing. **NOTE** – *Always replace bearings in pairs. Never use a new bearing in combination with a used bearing.* Coat bearing surfaces with oil, install rod cap and tighten nuts.

Main Bearings – 1) Position jack under counterweight adjoining bearing being checked so weight of crankshaft will not compress Plastigage and provide an erroneous reading. With all bearing caps (other than one being checked) tight, check clearances using Plastigage method.

2) If clearances are excessive, a .001" (.025 mm) or .002" (.051 mm) undersize bearing may be used in combination with a standard bearing. If .002" (.051 mm) undersize bearings are used on more than one journal, they must be positioned in cylinder block rather than bearing cap. **NOTE** – *Always replace bearings in pairs. Never use a new bearing in combination with a used bearing.* If standard and .002" (.051 mm) undersize combination do not bring bearing clearance within specified limits, crankshaft will have to be refinished and undersized bearings installed.

3) Remove all upper main bearings by inserting suitable tool in oil hole of crankshaft journal and rotating crankshaft clockwise to roll bearing from engine. Oil new upper bearing and insert plain (unnotched) end between crankshaft and indented (or notched) side of block. Rotate bearing into place. Install all main bearing caps with arrows pointing to front of engine.

REAR MAIN BEARING OIL SEAL

Removal & Installation – 1) Split lip type seal is provided for service replacement. Remove oil pan and oil pump. Loosen

2300 cc 4 CYLINDER (Cont.)

all main bearing cap bolts, allowing crankshaft to drop (not more than 1/32") and remove rear main bearing cap. Remove oil seal from cap and clean oil seal groove. Remove upper seal half from block using seal removal tool or small metal screw in end of seal. **CAUTION** — *Extreme care should be taken not to scratch or mar crankshaft seal surface.*

2) Dip new split lip type seal halves in clean engine oil. Carefully install upper seal into its groove with undercut side of seal toward front of engine, by rotating it on seal journal of crankshaft until approximately 3/8" protrudes below parting surface. **CAUTION** — *Be sure no rubber has been shaved from outside diameter of seal.* Tighten remaining bearing caps. Install lower seal in rear main bearing cap with undercut side of seal toward front of engine.

3) Allow seal to protrude approximately 3/8" above parting surface to mate with upper seal. **NOTE** — *Locating tab must face rear of engine.* Apply suitable sealer to rear main bearing cap mating surfaces, taking care not to permit sealer on seal, install main bearing cap and tighten bolts.

FRONT CRANKSHAFT OIL SEAL REPLACEMENT

Removal & Installation — Remove alternator drive belt and crankshaft pulley. Remove camshaft drive belt. See *Camshaft Drive Belt Replacement.* Slide camshaft drive belt sprocket and belt off crankshaft. **NOTE** — *It may be necessary to utilize a puller to withdraw sprocket.* Fit a suitable tool (T71P-6150-A) over end of crankshaft and remove seal. To install new seal, reverse removal procedure.

NOTE — *Cylinder front cover and auxiliary shaft seals are replaced using procedure outlined above.*

Fig. 6 Removing Front Crankshaft Oil Seal

CAMSHAFT

CAMSHAFT DRIVE BELT

Removal & Installation — See *Camshaft Timing.*

CAMSHAFT

Removal — With cylinder head removed from engine, remove rocker arms. **NOTE** — *Keep rocker arms in order for reinstallation in original position.* Remove camshaft sprocket attaching bolt. Slide sprocket and belt guide plate from camshaft. Remove camshaft thrust plate from rear of cylinder head and carefully slide camshaft out rear of cylinder block.

Installation — Oil camshaft with engine oil and apply Lubriplate to valve stem tips. Oil rocker arms and carefully install camshaft in cylinder head. Install thrust plate, bolts and tighten. Check camshaft endplay and replace thrust plate if endplay is not within specifications. **NOTE** — *Use new camshaft attaching bolt or use new Teflon tape on threads of old bolt.*

CAMSHAFT BEARINGS

Removal & Installation — Use suitable tool (71P-6250A) to remove and install bearings. **NOTE** — *Lube hole in bearing must be aligned with oil hole in journal.*

CAMSHAFT LOBE LIFT

Measure distance between major and minor diameters of each cam lobe with a micrometer. Difference in readings is lobe lift. If readings vary or do not meet specifications, replace camshaft.

CAMSHAFT ENDPLAY

With camshaft drive belt cover removed, push camshaft toward rear of engine. Install dial indicator so indicator point is on camshaft sprocket attaching screw or gear hub and zero dial indicator. Using a large screwdriver between camshaft sprocket or gear and cylinder head, pull the camshaft forward and release it. Read dial indicator and if endplay is not within specifications, replace thrust plate at rear of cylinder head.

CAMSHAFT TIMING

Checking Timing — Remove access plug from belt cover and position crankshaft to TDC by aligning pointer on cover with "O" mark on crankshaft damper. **CAUTION** — *Turn engine in direction of normal rotation only.* Look through access hole and check that timing mark on camshaft drive sprocket is aligned with pointer on inner belt cover. Remove distributor cap and check that rotor is facing number one position on cap.

Adjusting Timing — **1)** If timing is incorrect or it is necessary to remove belt, remove timing belt outer cover and loosen belt tensioner adjustment screw. Position tension adjusting tool on tension spring roll pin and release belt tensioner. Tighten adjustment screw to hold tensioner in released position. Remove crankshaft damper, belt guide and drive belt.

2) Position crankshaft sprocket and camshaft sprocket as shown in illustration. Remove distributor cap and set rotor to No. 1 firing position by turning auxiliary shaft. Install drive belt over crankshaft sprocket and then counterclockwise over auxiliary and camshaft sprockets. Align belt fore and aft on sprockets.

3) Loosen tensioner adjustment screw and allow tensioner to move against drive belt. Remove spark plugs and rotate crankshaft two complete turns in direction of normal rotation to remove slack from belt. Tighten tensioner adjustment and pivot bolts. Recheck timing mark alignment.

2300 cc 4 CYLINDER (Cont.)

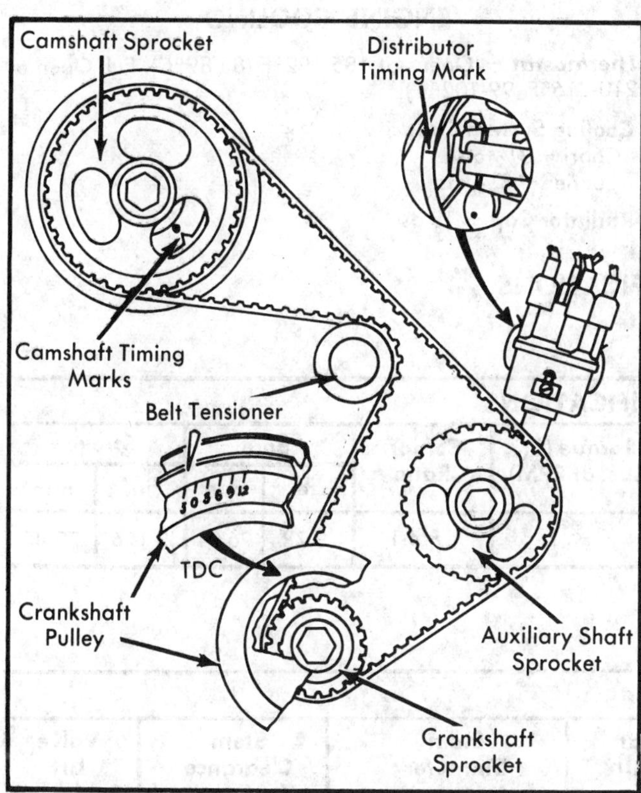

Fig. 7 Location of Timing Marks

AUXILIARY SHAFT

Removal – Remove drive belt cover, drive belt and auxiliary sprocket retaining bolt and washer. Slide sprocket from auxiliary shaft. Remove distributor, fuel pump and auxiliary shaft cover. Remove thrust plate and carefully remove shaft from cylinder block. Remove bearing from block, if worn or damaged, using suitable tool.

Installation – Align oil holes in bearing with those in block and drive bearing into place using a suitable tool. Oil shaft with engine oil and slide into cylinder block. CAUTION – *Do not allow gear and fuel pump eccentric to touch bearing surfaces during installation.* Install thrust plate, gasket and shaft cover, fuel pump, distributor and sprocket. Install and adjust drive belt. Install drive belt cover.

ENGINE OILING

ENGINE OILING SYSTEM

Oiling system is force feed type using a full flow oil filter. Oil enters main oil gallery from oil filter and flows to main bearings and camshaft bearings. Connecting rod bearings are supplied from front and rear main bearings via inclined main oil gallery. Distributor shaft receives oil from passage drilled in auxiliary shaft. Cams and cam follower arms are passages. A squirt hole in each rod bearing end supplies oil to piston thrust side of cylinder. Auxiliary shaft is connected with supplied from camshaft bearings and valve lash adjusters are oiled from drilled oil passages in cylinder head.

Crankcase Capacity – 4 qts. with filter change

Oil Filter Type – Full flow.

Normal Oil Pressure (Hot) – 40-60 psi at 2000 RPM.

Pressure Regulator Valve – In pump body. Not adjustable.

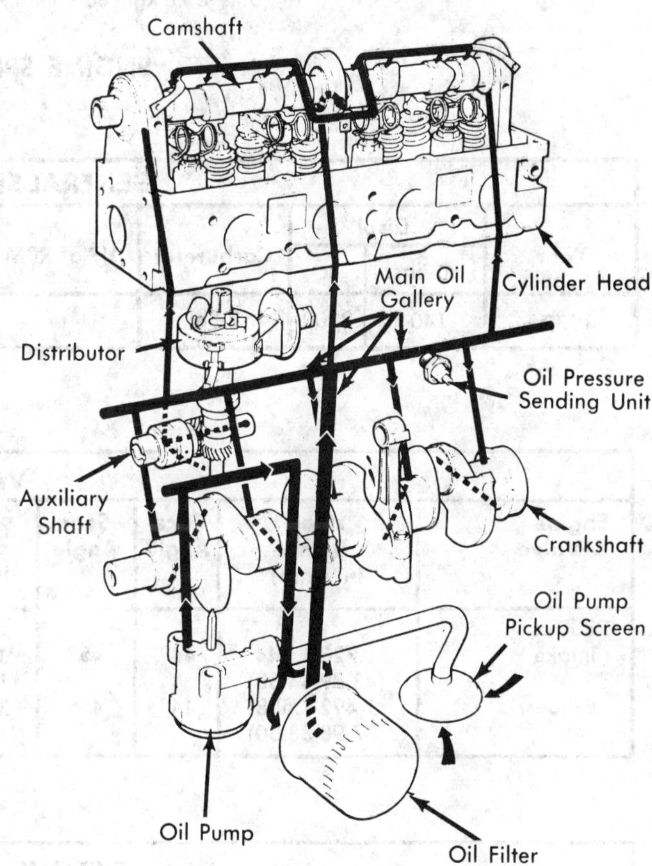

Fig. 8 Engine Oiling System

OIL PUMP

NOTE – *Remove oil pump and cover. Check clearances and if not within specifications, replace oil pump. Do not disassemble oil pump.*

Removal – Remove oil pan and separate pick-up tube and screen from body of pump. Remove oil pump attaching bolts. Remove three cover attaching screws and remove cover.

Oil Pump Specifications

Application	Clearance In.(mm)
Drive Shaft-to-Housing	.0015-.0029(.038-.074)
Rotor Assembly End Clearance	.001-.004(.025-.101)
Outer Rotor-to-Housing	.001-.007(.025-.178)
Relief Valve-to-Bore	.0015-.0029(.038-.074)

2300 cc 4 CYLINDER (Cont.)

Installation – Clean and check pump clearances. Install pump cover and attaching screws. Position a new gasket and oil inlet tube on pump and install attaching bolts.

Relief Valve Spring
Tension .... 7.54-8.33 lbs @1.53" (3.42-3.78 kg@38.9 mm)

ENGINE COOLING

Thermostat – Opens at 185-192°F (85-89°C). Full Open at 210-216°F (99-102°C).

Cooling System Capacity
Capri – 7½ qts.
Courier – 8½ qts.

Radiator Cap – 13 psi.

ENGINE SPECIFICATIONS

GENERAL SPECIFICATIONS

Year	Displ. cu. ins.	Displ. cc	Carburetor	HP at RPM	Torque (Ft. Lbs. at RPM)	Compr. Ratio	Bore in.	Bore mm	Stroke in.	Stroke mm
1977	140	2300	2-Bbl.	.....	.....	8.4:1	3.78	96.01	3.126	79.40

VALVES

Engine & Valve	Head Diam. In. (mm)	Face Angle	Seat Angle	Seat Width In. (mm)	Stem Diameter In. (mm)	Stem Clearance In. (mm)	Valve Lift In. (mm)
2300 cc							
Intake	1.728-1.744 (43.89-44.30)	44°	45°	.060-.090 (1.52-2.29)	.3416-.3423 (8.68-8.69)	.0010-.0027 (.025-.069)	.3997 (10.15)
Exhaust	1.492-1.508 (37.90-38.30)	44°	45°	.070-.090 (1.78-2.29)	.3411-.3418 (8.66-8.68)	.0015-.0032 (.038-.081)	.3997 (10.15)

PISTONS, PINS, RINGS

Engine	PISTONS Clearance In. (mm)	PINS Piston Fit In. (mm)	PINS Rod Fit In. (mm)	RINGS Rings	RINGS End Gap In. (mm)	RINGS Side Clearance In. (mm)
2300 cc	.0014-.0022 (.035-.056)	.0002-.0004 (.005-.010)	①	Comp.	.010-.020 (.25-.51)	.002-.004 (.051-.102)
				Oil	.015-.055 (.38-1.40)	Snug

① – Interference Fit.

CRANKSHAFT MAIN & CONNECTING ROD BEARINGS

Engine	MAIN BEARINGS Journal Diam. In. (mm)	MAIN BEARINGS Clearance In. (mm)	MAIN BEARINGS Thrust Bearing	MAIN BEARINGS Crankshaft End Play In. (mm)	CONNECTING ROD BEARINGS Journal Diam. In. (mm)	CONNECTING ROD BEARINGS Clearance In. (mm)	CONNECTING ROD BEARINGS Side Play In. (mm)
2300 cc	2.3982-2.3990 (60.91-60.93)	.0008-.0026 (.020-.066)	No. 3	.004-.008 (.10-.20)	2.0464-2.0472 (51.979-51.999)	.0008-.0015 (.020-.038)	.0035-.0105 (.089-.267)

2300 cc 4 CYLINDER (Cont.)

ENGINE SPECIFICATIONS (Cont.)

VALVE SPRINGS			
Engine	Free Length In. (mm)	PRESSURE Lbs. @ In. (kg @ mm)	
		Valve Closed	Valve Open
2300 cc	1.824 (46.3)	71-79@1.56 (32-36@39.6)	180-198@1.16 (82-90@29.5)

CAMSHAFT			
Engine	Journal Diam. In. (mm)	Clearance In. (mm)	Lobe Lift In. (mm)
2300 cc	1.7713-1.7720 (44.991-45.009)	① .001-.003 (.025-.076)	.2437 (6.19)

① — Endplay is .001-.007" (.025-.178 mm).

TIGHTENING SPECIFICATIONS	
Application	Ft. Lbs.(mkg)
Auxiliary Shaft Gear	28-40(3.9-5.5)
Auxiliary Shaft Thrust Plate	6-9(.8-1.2)
Belt Tensioner Pivot	28-40(3.9-5.5)
Belt Tensioner Adjuster	14-21(1.9-2.9)
Camshaft Gear	50-71(6.9-8)
Camshaft Thrust Plate	6-9(.8-1.2)
Connecting Rod	
Step 1	25-30(3.5-4.1)
Step 2	30-36(4.1-5.0)
Crankshaft Pulley	80-114(11.1-15.8)
Cylinder Head	
Step 1	60(8.3)
Step 2	80-90(11.1-12.4)
Exhaust Manifold-to-Cylinder Head	16-23(2.2-3.2)
Flywheel-to-Crankshaft	54-64(7.5-8.8)
Front Cover	6-9(.8-1.2)
Intake Manifold-to-Cylinder Head	14-21(1.9-2.9)
Main Bearing Cap	
Step 1	60(8.3)
Step 2	80-90(11.1-12.4)
Oil Pan-to-Block	
M6 Bolts	7-9(1.0-1.2)
M8 Bolts	11-13(1.5-1.8)
Rocker Arm Cover	4-7(.6-1.0)
Timing Belt Cover	6-9(.8-1.2)
Water Pump-to-Cylinder Block	14-21(1.9-2.9)

2800 cc V6

ENGINE CODING

ENGINE IDENTIFICATION

The second series of digits of vehicle identification plate, located on top of right front fender apron, indicates engine type.

Application	Engine Code
2800 cc	PX

ENGINE, CYLINDER HEAD & MANIFOLDS

ENGINE

1) Disconnect battery cables. Disconnect all hoses and connections to air cleaner assembly while noting positions to aid in reassembly, then remove air cleaner assembly. Mark hood hinge locations, then remove hood. Raise vehicle on a hoist. Drain cooling system and crankcase.

2) Remove lower radiator hose and starter. Remove converter bolt access plug and three converter-to-flywheel bolts. Disconnect exhaust pipes from exhaust manifold. Remove converter housing-to-engine attaching bolts. Remove engine mount nuts.

3) Disconnect transmission cooler lines from radiator on models with automatic transmission. Disconnect and plug fuel lines at fuel pump. Loosen power steering pump idler, then remove power steering pump from bracket and position to one side. Disconnect oil pressure line and lower vehicle.

4) Remove downshift rod. Remove clutch linkage on models with manual transmission. Remove upper radiator hose, fan shroud, and radiator. Disconnect heater hoses at engine, remove hose retainer at rocker arm cover, and position hoses to one side.

5) Disconnect distributor vacuum line, connector and coil wire. Disconnect transmission vacuum line at intake manifold, and power brake vacuum hose. Disconnect accelerator cable retaining clip at ball stud, then pull lightly on cable while depressing tangs one at a time on bracket clip and remove throttle cable.

6) Disconnect rear ground wire and alternator connectors. Position a floor jack to support transmission. Attach lifting hoist to engine, and carefully lift engine from vehicle.

INTAKE MANIFOLD

Removal – 1) Remove air cleaner, disconnect battery negative cable, and throttle cables. Drain cooling system, disconnect hose from water outlet-to-radiator, and hoses and line from water outlet-to-water pump. Remove distributor cap and spark plug wires as an assembly.

2) Disconnect distributor wire and distributor vacuum line. Mark location of rotor and distributor housing, then remove distributor. Remove fuel line and filter between fuel pump and carburetor, then remove rocker arm covers. Remove intake manifold nuts and bolts, then remove intake manifold assembly.

Installation – Apply sealing compound to joining surfaces and position gasket on block. Tab on right bank cylinder head gasket must fit into cutout of manifold gasket. Install sealing compound to retaining bolt bosses on intake manifold. Install manifold on cylinder block. Install bolts and nuts, then tighten in sequence as shown in illustration. Install remaining components in reverse of removal procedure.

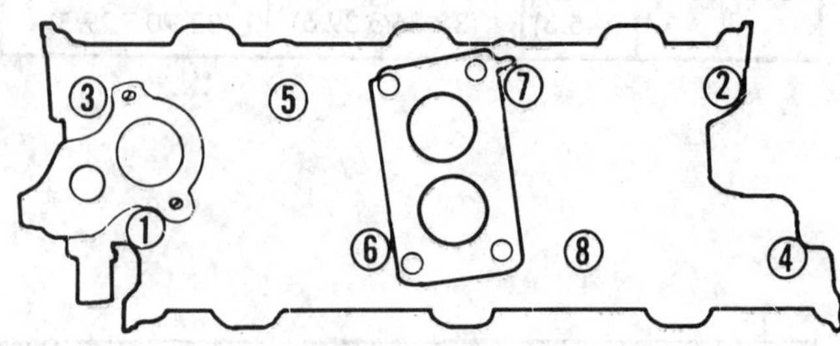

Fig. 1 Intake Manifold Tightening Sequence

CYLINDER HEAD

Removal – Remove intake manifold. Disconnect carburetor linkage and remove carburetor. Remove rocker arm shaft by loosening two bolts at a time. Remove oil baffles. Remove push rods while keeping in correct order for reinstallation into original position. Remove exhaust manifold. Remove cylinder head bolts and lift cylinder head from block.

Installation – Clean old gasket material from cylinder head and block. Install new cylinder head gaskets on block ensuring that "TOP" and "FRONT" markings on gasket are properly positioned. Position cylinder heads on block, install bolts and tighten in sequence as shown in illustration. Install remaining components in reverse of removal procedure.

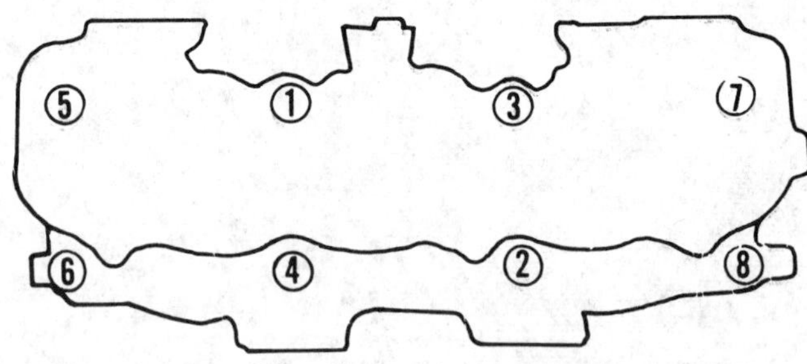

Fig. 2 Cylinder Head Tightening Sequence

VALVES

VALVE ARRANGEMENT

I-E-E-I-E-I (Left Side Front-to-Rear).

I-E-I-E-E-I (Right Side Front-to-Rear).

2800 cc V6 (Cont.)

VALVE GUIDES

Worn valve guides can be reamed to .008" (.203 mm), .016" (.406 mm), or .032" (.813 mm) oversizes. When going from standard size valve to an oversize, always use reamers in sequence. After reaming, break sharp corner (ID) at top of valve guide. When valve guides are reamed, valve seats must be refaced to maintain proper valve seal.

VALVE STEM OIL SEALS

Cup or umbrella type seals used on all valves. Install seals with cup side down.

VALVE SPRINGS

Removal – Remove valve rocker arm cover. Remove rocker arm shaft and both push rods of cylinder to be serviced. Remove spark plug from cylinder and install air line and adapter to cylinder. **NOTE** – *If air pressure does not hold valve shut, remove cylinder head for inspection.* Use a suitable tool to compress valve, then remove retainer locks. Remove tool, spring retainer, spring, and valve stem seal. **CAUTION** – *DO NOT remove air pressure.*

Installation – Install NEW valve stem oil seal, valve spring and retainer. Compress spring and install retainer locks. **CAUTION** – *Do not compress spring more than necessary to install locks.* Remove compressor tool, turn off air and remove adapter. Install remaining components in reverse of removal procedure.

VALVE SPRING INSTALLED HEIGHT

Install valve springs with open spaced coils away from head. Measure distance between cylinder head spring pad and valve spring retainer. Install spacers if necessary to bring spring to proper specifications. **CAUTION** – *Excess spacers will result in possible spring breakage and camshaft lobe wear.*

Spring Height Specifications

Application	Installed Height In. (mm)
All	1.578-1.609 (40.08-40.86)

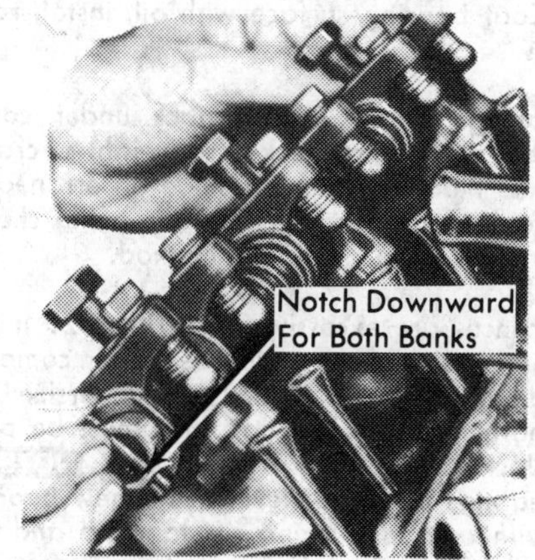

Fig. 3 Rocker Arm Assembly Alignment

ROCKER ARM ASSEMBLY OVERHAUL

Disassembly – With rocker arm cover removed, remove rocker arm shaft stand bolts and lift off rocker arm assembly. Using a drift, drive lock sleeve (pin) out of rocker. Remove spring washers, rocker arms, springs and rocker shaft supports.

Assembly – Fit shaft supports, springs, rocker arms and spring washers. Install new drive lock sleeve (pin). Rocker arm shaft must be fitted to cylinder head with oil holes facing down toward head. Position notch on front of rocker shaft downward (see illustration).

VALVE CLEARANCE ADJUSTMENT

Preliminary (Cold) Adjustment – 1) Before adjusting valves, torque rocker arm stand bolts to specifications.

2) Adjust valves at TDC on compression stroke in firing order sequence (1-4-2-5-3-6).

3) Rotate crankshaft clockwise, (viewed from front), until number one piston is at TDC. Using a step-type feeler gauge (go and no go), adjust intake to .014" and exhaust to .016".

4) Adjust remaining valves by rotating crankshaft a 1/3 of a turn for each cylinder until all valves have been adjusted. Two complete revolutions will adjust all valves.

Final (Hot) Adjustment – 1) Run engine until normal operating temperature is reached.

2) Using a step-type feeler gauge and engine at idle, adjust intake and exhaust valves to .014" intake and .016" exhaust.

PISTONS, PINS & RINGS

OIL PAN

Removal – Remove oil level dipstick and bolts attaching fan shroud to radiator. Position shroud over fan. Disconnect battery ground cable. Loosen alternator bracket and adjusting bolts. Raise vehicle, drain crankcase, remove splash shield, and starter. Remove engine front support nuts, raise engine, then place wood blocks between front supports and chassis. Remove clutch or converter housing cover, then withdraw oil pan bolts and oil pan.

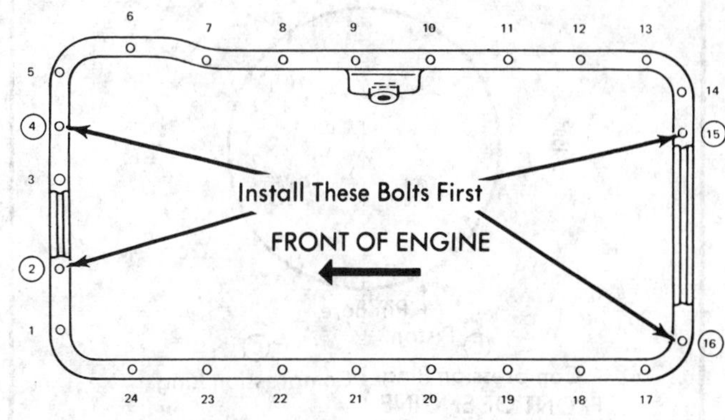

Fig. 4 Oil Pan Tightening Sequence

2800 cc V6 (Cont.)

Installation – Using a suitable sealing compound, coat contact surfaces and place two piece gasket on face of block. Position front and rear oil pan seals in place with tabs of seals lapping over oil pan gasket. Position oil pan on block and tighten bolts as shown in illustration.

PISTON & ROD ASSEMBLY

NOTE – *New pistons must be installed in same cylinders for which they were fitted and used pistons in same cylinder from which they were removed.*

Removal – With cylinder head and oil pan removed, use a suitable ridge cutter to remove any ridge or deposits on upper end of cylinder bore. **NOTE** – *Piston must be at bottom of stroke and covered with cloth to collect cuttings.* Inspect connecting rods and caps for cylinder identification and mark as necessary. Remove rod cap and push piston and rod assembly out top of cylinder block taking care not to nick crankshaft journal or cylinder wall.

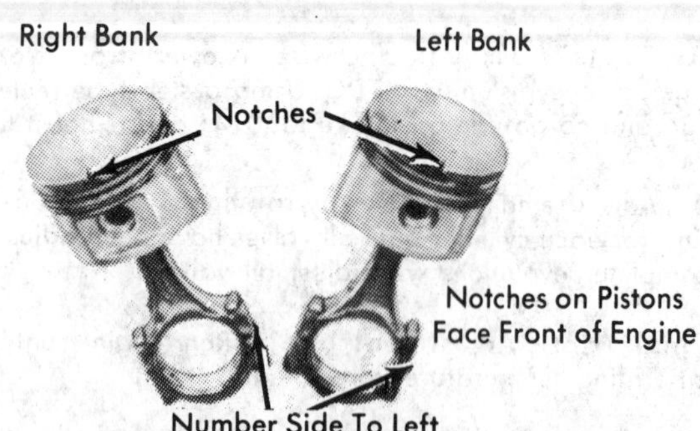

Fig. 5 Piston & Rod Assembly Installation Features

Installation – Lightly coat cylinder bores, pistons and rings with engine oil. Ensure that ring gaps are properly spaced (see illustration) and install ring compressor on piston. Install each piston and rod assembly (with notch on piston head facing front of engine) in its respective bore and guide connecting rod onto crankshaft journal while tapping piston head with hammer handle to seat connecting rod against crankshaft. Install rod caps and tighten.

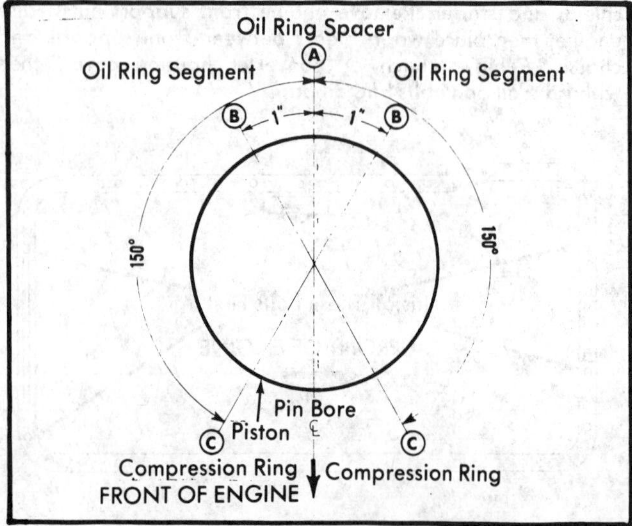

Fig. 6 Spacing of Piston Ring Gaps

FITTING PISTONS

Check piston to cylinder bore clearance by measuring piston and bore diameters. Measure OD of piston at centerline of piston pin bore and at 90° to pin bore axis. Refer to specifications for correct clearance. Oversize pistons are available in .020" and .040" oversizes.

PISTON PIN REPLACEMENT

Piston pin bore and OD of piston pin must be within specifications. Remove old pin using an arbor press and suitable piston support and driver tool. Assemble piston to rod with notches on piston facing forward. Rod numbers face to left side of engine.

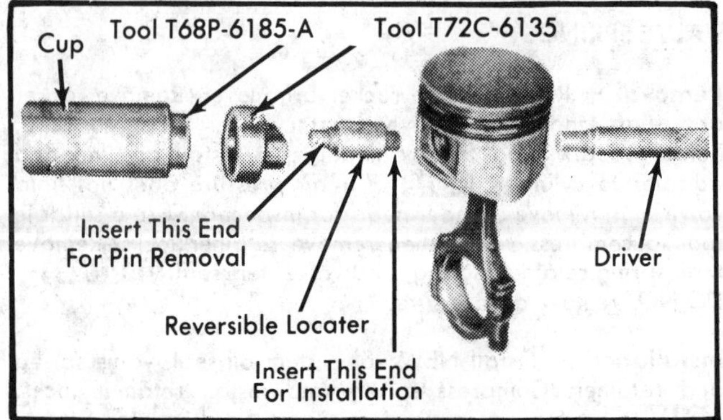

Fig. 7 Piston Pin Installation Tools

CRANKSHAFT MAIN & CONNECTING ROD BEARINGS

MAIN & CONNECTING ROD BEARINGS

NOTE – *Following procedures are with oil pan and oil pump removed.*

Connecting Rod Bearings – After ensuring rod caps are marked for cylinder identification, remove rod caps. Use Plastigage method to check for proper bearing clearance. If not within specifications, new bearings must be installed. New bearings are available in .001" (.025 mm) and .002" (.051 mm) undersizes. Selective fitting is required on each connecting rod. A standard bearing may be used in combination with either undersize bearing. **NOTE** – *Always replace bearings in pairs. Never use a new bearing in combination with a used bearing.* Coat bearing surface with oil, install rod cap and tighten nuts.

Main Bearings – **1)** Position jack under counterweight adjoining bearing being checked so weight of crankshaft will not compress Plastigage and provide an erroneous reading. With all bearing caps (other than one being checked) tight, check clearances using Plastigage method.

2) If clearances are excessive, a .001" (.025 mm) or .002" (.051 mm) undersize bearing may be used in combination with a standard bearing. If .002" (.051 mm) undersize bearings are used on more than one journal, they must be positioned in cylinder block rather than bearing cap. **NOTE** – *Always replace bearings in pairs. Never use a new bearing in combination with a used bearing.* If standard and .002" (.051 mm) undersize combination do not bring bearing clearance within specified limits, crankshaft will have to be refinished and undersized bearings installed.

2800 cc V6 (Cont.)

3) Remove all upper main bearings (except rear main) by inserting suitable tool in oil hole of crankshaft journal and rotating crankshaft clockwise to roll bearing from engine. Oil new upper bearing and insert plain (unnotched) end between crankshaft and indented (or notched) side of block. Rotate bearing into place. Install all main bearing caps with arrows pointing to front of engine. **NOTE** — *If rear main bearing is to be replaced, engine must be removed from vehicle.*

THRUST BEARING ALIGNMENT

Install all bearing caps except thrust bearing cap and tighten. Install thrust bearing cap with bolts finger tight. Pry crankshaft to front of engine and hold forward while prying thrust bearing cap to rear. Hold crankshaft forward and tighten bolts on thrust bearing cap. Check crankshaft endplay.

REAR MAIN BEARING OIL SEAL

Removal — Remove transmission, clutch pressure plate and disc (if equipped), flywheel, flywheel housing and rear plate. Remove old seal using two sheet metal screws (see illustration) while taking care not to damage oil sealing surface.

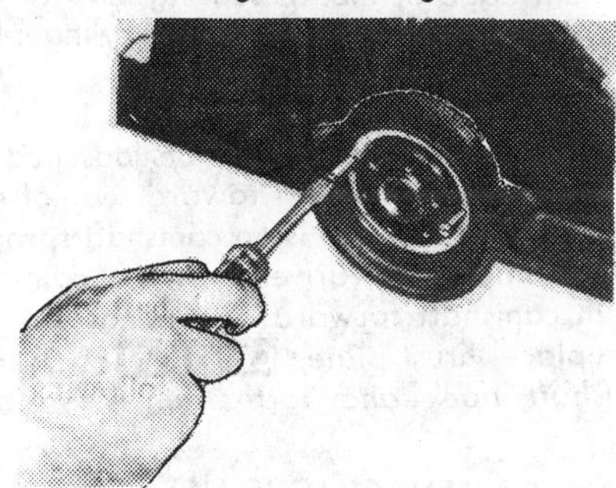

Fig. 8 Using Metal Screws to Remove Crankshaft Rear Oil Seal

Installation — Coat seal-to-cylinder block surface of oil seal with oil. Coat seal contact surface of oil seal and crankshaft with Lubriplate. Start seal in recess and install with suitable tool (T72C-6165). Drive seal into position until firmly seated.

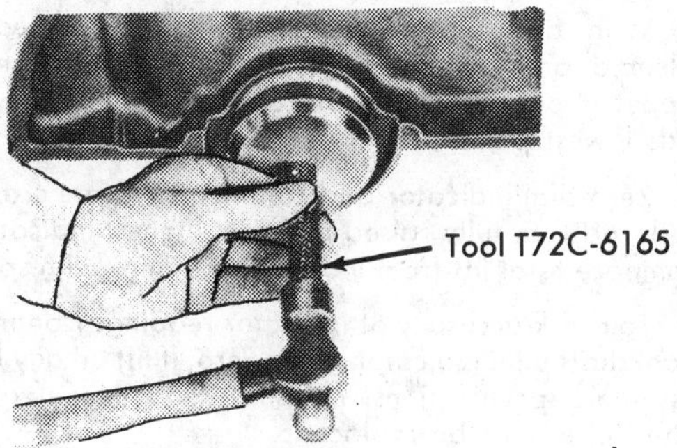

Fig. 9 Installing Crankshaft Rear Oil Seal

ENGINE FRONT COVER

Removal — Remove oil pan, radiator, alternator, drive belts, water pump, and water hoses. Remove drive belt pulley and if necessary, remove guide sleeves from block. Remove front cover attaching bolts. Tap cover with a plastic hammer to break seal and remove cover.

Installation — Apply sealing compound to gasket surfaces on cylinder block and both sides of gasket. Position gasket and front cover, then install retaining bolts. Fit new seal rings to guide sleeve and insert guides in block with chamfered end toward front cover. Apply sealer to front cover and place gasket on cover. Using suitable alignment tool (T74P-6019) to center cover, then install and tighten bolts.

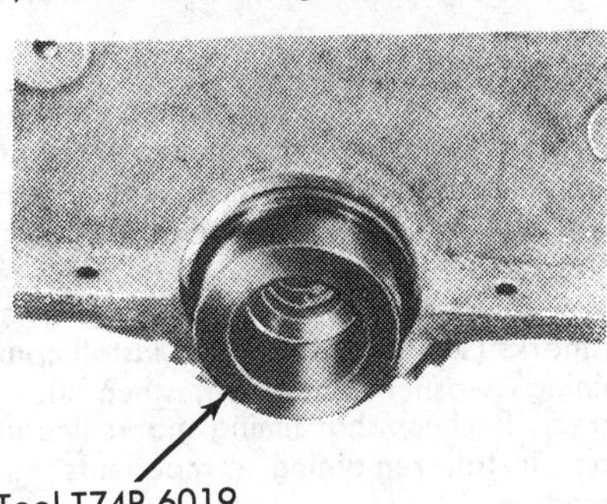

Fig. 10 Using Tool to Align Engine Front Cover

FRONT COVER OIL SEAL

Removal & Installation — Remove radiator and crankshaft pulley. Using a suitable pulling tool (as shown in illustration), remove front cover oil seal. To install a new seal, coat seal with Lubriplate and slide installing tool (T74P-6700) and seal onto crankshaft. Seat seal until tool bottoms out on front cover. Reinstall crankshaft pulley, radiator and adjust drive belt.

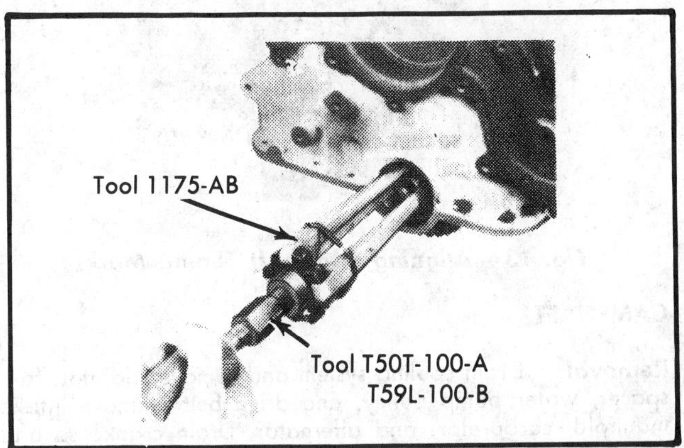

Fig. 11 Removing Front Oil Seal

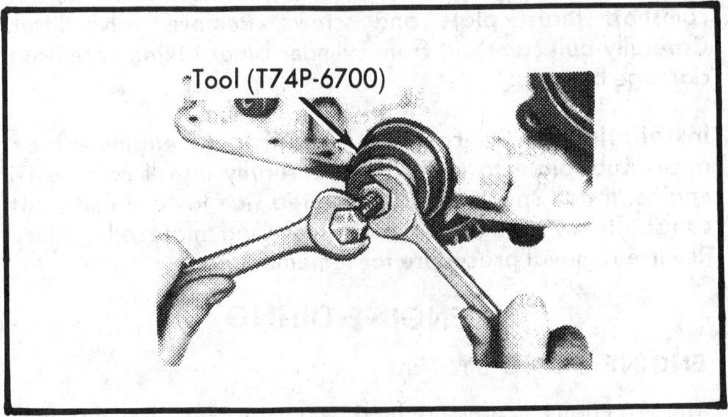

Fig. 12 Installing Front Oil Seal

2800 cc V6 (Cont.)

CAMSHAFT

TIMING GEARS

Using a dial indicator, check that backlash between camshaft gear and crankshaft gear is .006-.010" (.15-.25 mm). If backlash exceeds specifications, replace both gears as follows:

Removal – Drain cooling system and crankcase. Remove radiator, oil pan, front cover and water pump. Remove camshaft gear retaining bolt and slide gear off camshaft. Use a suitable gear puller and remove crankshaft gear.

Installation – Turn camshaft and crankshaft as necessary to align timing marks (see illustration) and install camshaft gear. Install retaining washer and bolt, then tighten. Install crankshaft gear. Recheck that timing marks line up as shown in illustration. Install remaining components in reverse of removal procedure.

Fig. 13 Aligning Camshaft Timing Marks

CAMSHAFT

Removal – Drain cooling system and remove radiator, fan, spacer, water pump pulley, and drive belt. Remove intake manifold, carburetor, and alternator. Drain crankcase and remove rocker arm and shaft assemblies. Remove push rods and mark for installation in original position. Remove oil pan, crankshaft pulley, front cover, and camshaft gear. Remove camshaft thrust plate and screws. Remove valve lifters. Carefully pull camshaft from cylinder block taking care not to damage bearings.

Installation – Oil camshaft journals with engine oil and apply Lubriplate to cam lobes. Carefully install camshaft in engine. Install spacer ring (chamfered side toward camshaft), camshaft key and thrust plate (covering main oil gallery). Reverse removal procedure for remaining parts.

ENGINE OILING

ENGINE OILING SYSTEM

The V-6 engine is pressure feed by a rotor type oil pump, which filters all oil through a full flow filter before entering engine. An oil gallery supplies oil to crankshaft main bearings, from there through slanted passages in crankshaft to connecting rod journals. Connecting rod big ends have a squirt hole which sprays oil on thrust side of cylinder bores. Oil from the oil gallery also feeds camshaft main bearings, which have grooves 180° of their circumference. From these grooves passages lead to distributor drive gear and rocker arm shafts.

Crankcase Capacity – 4.5 quarts. Add .5 quart with filter change.

Oil Filter – Full flow type.

CAMSHAFT BEARINGS

Removal – With engine removed from vehicle, remove flywheel, camshaft and rear bearing bore plug. Use suitable collet and back-up nut assembled on expanding mandrel to remove bearings.

Installation – Position new bearings at bearing bores and press into place using correct size expanding collet being sure to center pulling plate and puller screw to avoid damage to bearing. Align oil holes in cylinder block when bearings are installed. Front edge of No. 1 bearing must be installed .040-.060" (1.0-1.5 mm) below front face of cylinder block.

CAMSHAFT END THRUST

Rocker arm shaft assembly must be loosened sufficiently to free camshaft. Push camshaft toward rear of engine and install dial indicator so point is on camshaft sprocket bolt. Zero indicator. Position screwdriver between camshaft gear and block, pull camshaft forward and release. If endplay is excessive, replace thrust plate. **CAUTION** – *Do not attempt to pry camshaft back and forth with valve train load on camshaft.*

CHECKING CAMSHAFT LOBE LIFT

Check lift of each camshaft lobe in consecutive order as follows:

1) Remove rocker arm shaft assemblies, making sure each push rod is in valve lifter socket. Install a dial indicator so that ball socket adapter of indicator rests on the end of push rod and in same plane as push rod movement.

2) With an auxiliary starter switch connected to starter solenoid and ignition switch "OFF", bump crankshaft until tappet is on base circle of camshaft lobe. This will be push rods lowest point.

3) Zero dial indicator and continue to rotate crankshaft until push rod is in fully raised position (highest indicator reading). Compare total lift from indicator readings with specifications.

4) To check accuracy of indicator readings, continue to rotate crankshaft until indicator reads zero. If lift on any lobe is .005" less than specifications, camshaft and tappet operating on worn lobe must be replaced.

Normal Oil Pressure – 40-55 psi @ 2000 RPM.

Pressure Regulator Valve – Non-adjustable.

OIL PUMP

Disassembly – Remove pick-up tube and screen assembly from pump housing. Remove cover and lift out two-piece rotor assembly. Drill a small hole and insert self-threading sheet metal screw into oil pressure relief valve plug and remove plug. Remove spring and valve.

2800 cc V6 (Cont.)

Reassembly — Clean, inspect (see specifications) and oil all parts. Install relief valve, spring and new plug in oil pump housing. Install plug with flat side pointing out and spread plug in housing using a drift. Install inner and outer rotors and shaft assembly in housing with dot reference marks up. Install cover and pick-up tube assembly.

Oil Pump Specifications

Clearance	Specification In.(mm)
Outer Race-to-Housing	.006-.012(.15-.30)
Rotor Endplay	.0011-.0041(.028-.104)
Shaft-to-Housing	.0014-.0029(.036-.074)
Relief Valve-to-Bore	.0015-.0030(.038-.076)

Relief Valve Spring Pressure — 13.6-14.7 Lbs. @ 1.39" (6.17-6.67 kg @ 35.3 mm).

Cooling System Capacity — 8.5 quarts.

Pressure Radiator Cap — Opens at 13 psi.

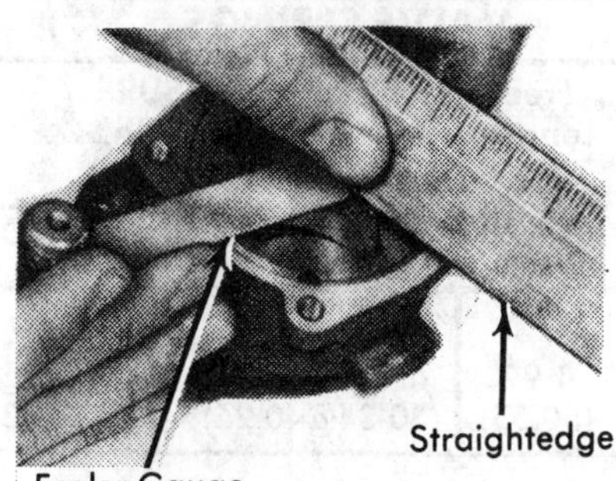

Fig. 14 Measuring Oil Pump Rotor End Play

ENGINE COOLING

WATER PUMP

Removal — Drain cooling system. Remove lower radiator hose, and heater return hose. Loosen alternator mounting bolts and remove drive belt. Disconnect fan shroud from radiator and position behind fan. Remove fan, pulley and shroud. Remove attaching bolts, water pump, water inlet housing and thermostat from front cover.

Installation — Apply sealer to both sides of a new gasket and position gasket on water pump. Position water pump on front cover with two bolts finger tight. Install new water inlet housing gasket, with sealer on both sides, to water pump. Install thermostat, rubber gasket, and water inlet housing. Install and tighten remaining water pump attaching bolts while noting different length bolts. Reinstall, fan, pulley, shroud, drive belt and hoses. Fill cooling system.

Thermostat — Starts to Open at 185-192°F (85-89°C). Fully Open at 210-216°F (99-102°C).

TIGHTENING SPECIFICATIONS

Application	Ft. Lbs.(mkg)
Camshaft Gear	32-36(4.4-5.0)
Camshaft Thrust Plate	12-15(1.7-2.1)
Connecting Rod Bearing Cap	21-25(2.9-3.5)
Crankshaft Damper	92-103(12.7-14.2)
Crankshaft Pulley-to-Damper	18-25(2.5-3.5)
Cylinder Head	
Step One	29-40(4.0-5.5)
Step Two	40-51(5.5-7.1)
Step Three	65-80(9.0-11.1)
Exhaust Manifold	16-23(2.2-3.2)
Flywheel	47-51(6.5-7.1)
Front Cover	12-15(1.7-2.1)
Intake Manifold	
Step One	3-6(.4-.8)
Step Two	6-11(.8-1.5)
Step Three	11-16(1.5-2.2)
Step Four	15-18(2.1-2.5)
Main Bearing Cap	65-75(9.0-10.4)
Oil Pan	5-7(.7-1.0)
Oil Pump	12-15(1.7-2.1)
Rocker Arm Cover	3-5(.4-.7)
Rocker Shaft Supports	43-49(5.9-6.8)
Water Pump	7-9(1.0-1.2)

ENGINE SPECIFICATIONS

GENERAL SPECIFICATIONS

Year	Displ.		Carburetor	HP at RPM	Torque (Ft. Lbs. at RPM)	Compr. Ratio	Bore		Stroke	
	cu. ins.	cc					in.	mm	in.	mm
1977	170	2800	2-Bbl.	.....	.....	8.2-1	3.66	92.964	2.79	70.866

2800 cc V6 (Cont.)

ENGINE SPECIFICATIONS (Cont.)

VALVE SPRINGS			
Engine	Free Length In. (mm)	PRESSURE Lbs. @ In. (kg @ mm)	
		Valve Closed	Valve Open
2800 cc All	1.99 (50.55)	67-75@1.585 (30-34@40.26)	144-156@1.222 (65-71@31.04)

CAMSHAFT			
Engine	Journal Diam. In. (mm)	Clearance In. (mm) ①	Lobe Lift In. (mm)
2800 cc Front	1.6497-1.6505 (41.902-41.923)	.001-.0026 (.025-.066)	.2555 (6.49)
No. 2	1.6347-1.6355 (41.521-41.542)		
No. 3	1.6197-1.6205 (41.140-41.161)		
Rear	1.6065-1.6073 (40.805-40.825)		

① — Endplay is .0008-.0040" (.02-.10 mm).

VALVES							
Engine & Valve	Head Diam. In. (mm)	Face Angle	Seat Angle	Seat Width In. (mm)	Stem Diameter In. (mm)	Stem Clearance In. (mm)	Valve Lift In. (mm)
2800 cc Intake	1.570 (39.88)	44°	45°	.050-.079 (1.3-2.0)	.3158-.3167 (8.02-8.04)	.0008-.0025 (.02-.06)	.373 (9.47)
Exhaust	1.269 (32.23)	44°	45°	.050-.079 (1.3-2.0)	.3149-.3156 (8.00-8.02)	.0018-.0035 (.046-.089)	.373 (9.47)

CRANKSHAFT MAIN & CONNECTING ROD BEARINGS							
Engine	MAIN BEARINGS				CONNECTING ROD BEARINGS		
	Journal Diam. In. (mm)	Clearance In. (mm)	Thrust Bearing	Crankshaft End Play In. (mm)	Journal Diam. In. (mm)	Clearance In. (mm)	Side Play In. (mm)
2800 cc All	2.2433-2.2441 (56.980-57.000)	0005-.0019 (.013-.048)	No. 3	.004-.008 (.10-.20)	2.1252-2.1260 (53.980-54.000)	.0005-.0022 (.012-.056)	.004-.011 (.10-.28)

PISTONS, PINS, RINGS						
Engine	PISTONS	PINS		RINGS		
	Clearance In. (mm)	Piston Fit In. (mm)	Rod Fit In. (mm)	Rings	End Gap In. (mm)	Side Clearance In. (mm)
2800 cc	.0011-.0019 (028-.048)	.0003-.0006 (.008-.015)	①	Comp.	.015-.023 (.381-.584)	.0020-.0033 (.051-.084)
				Oil	.015-.055 (.381-.584)	Snug

① — Interference Fit.

1800 cc 4 CYLINDER

ENGINE CODING

ENGINE IDENTIFICATION

Vehicle engine information is stamped on a plate riveted to body at right rear of engine compartment.

Application	Engine Code
All Models	VB

ENGINE, CYLINDER HEAD & MANIFOLDS

ENGINE

1) Remove hood and drain cooling system. Remove air cleaner assembly. Disconnect upper radiator hose at engine and lower hose at radiator. Unbolt and remove radiator.

2) Disconnect accelerator linkage and fuel line at carburetor. Disconnect linkage from intake manifold, cable at air by-pass valve, choke cable, battery cables, coil wires at distributor and coil lead wires.

3) Remove fan, loosen alternator retaining bolts and remove alternator belt. If equipped with Thermactor (air pump), remove mounting bolts and pump drive belt. Remove alternator bracket and adjusting arm bolts and position alternator out of the way. Pull Thermactor hoses off pump, remove bracket and position pump aside. Disconnect heater hoses from intake manifold and Thermactor air hose from by-pass valve.

4) Disconnect lead wire and boot from oil pressure sending unit, battery cable from block and wires from starter solenoid. Raise vehicle and drain oil. Remove splash shield and separate exhaust pipe from manifold. Remove clutch housing and bottom starter bolts.

5) Lower vehicle, remove upper starter bolts and withdraw starter. Place a floor stand under transmission. Connect a lifting sling to engine hanger brackets. Disconnect engine mounts and pull engine forward until clear of transmission shaft. Lift engine from vehicle. To install, reverse removal procedures.

INTAKE MANIFOLD

Removal – 1) Drain cooling system. Remove air cleaner assembly and accelerator linkage. Disconnect choke cable and fuel line at carburetor.

2) Disconnect Thermactor hoses (if equipped), crankcase ventilation hose, heater return hose and by-pass hose. Remove attaching nuts and lift manifold, with carburetor, off studs.

Installation – To install, reverse removal procedure while noting the following: Clean all gasket surfaces and install a new gasket. Install intake manifold and tighten attaching bolts working from the center of manifold towards each end. Fill cooling system when all components are installed.

CYLINDER HEAD

Removal – 1) Drain cooling system. Remove hood and air cleaner assembly. Disconnect lead wire and vacuum line from distributor. Rotate crankshaft until number one cylinder is at TDC of compression stroke. Remove plug wires and cap from distributor as an assembly. Remove distributor and rocker arm cover.

2) Raise vehicle and disconnect exhaust pipe from manifold. Lower vehicle and remove accelerator linkage. Disconnect temperature sending wire, throttle cable at air by-pass valve, choke cable and fuel line from carburetor.

3) Disconnect Thermactor hoses (if equipped), heater return hose at intake manifold, by-pass hose, water pump hose, and upper radiator hose at engine. Disconnect lead wire from slow fuel valve. Remove intake manifold bracket and lower front cylinder head bolt.

4) Remove nut, washer and distributor gear from camshaft, then remove nut, washer and camshaft sprocket. Remove cylinder head bolts. Remove rocker arm assembly and camshaft. Lift head assembly off of engine block. Relieve tension from timing chain by removing tensioner cover and loosening tensioner attaching bolts.

Installation – To install, reverse removal procedure while noting the following: Clean all gasket surfaces and use new gaskets upon installation. Install cylinder head and tighten bolts to specifications in sequence as shown in illustration.

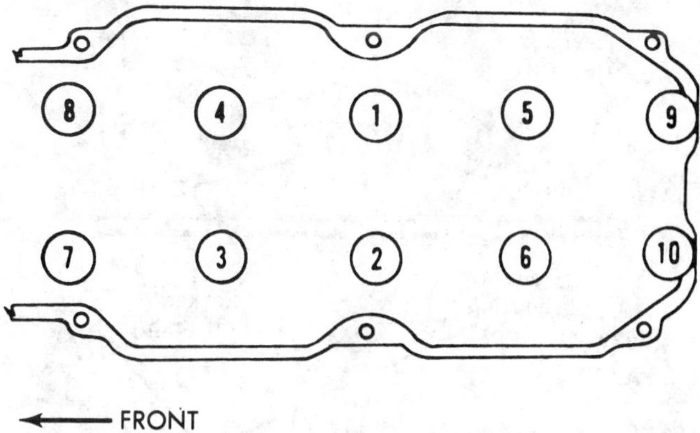

Fig. 1 Cylinder Head Tightening Sequence

VALVES

VALVE ARRANGEMENT

Intake – Left side.
Exhaust – Right side.

VALVE GUIDE SERVICING

Check guides for wear or damage, replace as necessary. With valves removed, using suitable tool (T72J-6510), drive valve guides out top of cylinder head. Install new guides, making sure exhaust and intake guides are in proper locations. Drive guide in until ring around guide touches head.

VALVE STEM OIL SEALS

With valves and springs removed, pull oil seals off valve guides using suitable tools (T72J-6571 and T59L-100-B). Install new seals on valve guides with large diameter hole facing cylinder head.

1800 cc 4 CYLINDER (Cont.)

VALVE SPRINGS

Removal – With cylinder head removed from engine proceed as follows: Compress valve springs and remove retainer locks. Release springs and remove spring retainers, springs, and valves. **NOTE** – *Identify all valve components for installation into original positions. Exhaust and intake retainers must be installed in original position to prevent premature valve failure.*

Installation – Lubricate valves, valve stems and valve guide with engine oil. Apply Lubriplate to valve tips. Install new valve oil seals on valve guides and install valves in guide from which it was removed. Install valve springs and retainer. Compress springs and install retainer locks. Release springs and install cylinder head.

VALVE SPRING INSTALLED HEIGHT

Check valve spring pressure at specified height, replace if not within specifications. Measure free length of spring, if not within three percent, replace spring. Using a square, check that spring is not more than 1/16" out-of-square.

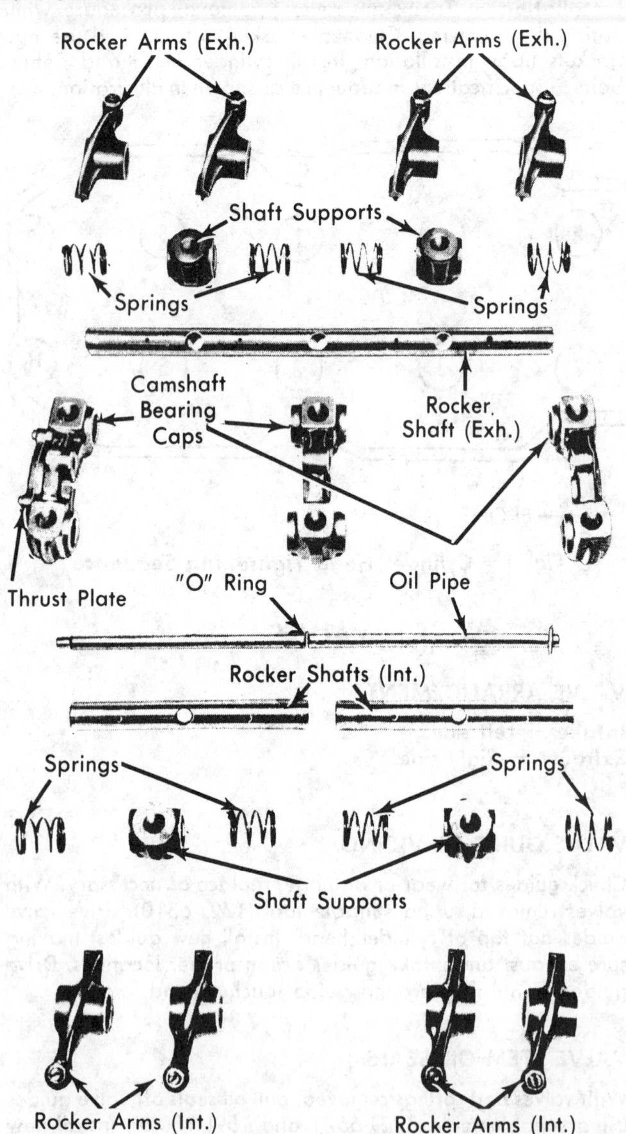

Fig. 2 Exploded View of Rocker Arm & Shaft Assembly

ROCKER ARM ASSEMBLY

1) Remove front bearing cap from rocker shafts. Slide rocker arms, springs, supports and bearing caps (with oil pipe) off both shafts, keeping parts in order for reassembly.

2) Remove oil pipe from bearing caps. Remove camshaft thrust plate from front bearing cap, if necessary. Prior to reassembly, lubricate arms and shafts with heavy (MS) motor oil. When installing shafts in intake side, ensure ends with longer length between oil hole and tip are turned inward, toward each other. Make sure "O" ring on oil pipe is centered in middle bearing cap passage.

VALVE CLEARANCE ADJUSTMENT

1) With engine at normal operating temperature, rotate crankshaft until number one piston is at TDC of compression stroke. Check clearance with feeler gauge at either camshaft or valve.

2) Clearance must be .012" (.305 mm). If not within specifications, loosen adjusting screw lock nut and turn adjusting screw with feeler gauge in place. Hold screw in position and tighten lock nut. Adjust valves in firing order sequence; 1-3-4-2.

PISTONS, PINS & RINGS

OIL PAN

Removal – Raise vehicle on hoist and remove front splash shield. Drain crankcase, remove clutch release cylinder attaching nuts and position cylinder to one side. Remove the engine rear brace attaching bolts and loosen bolts on left side. Disconnect emission line from oil pan. Remove oil pan attaching nuts and bolts, and lower oil pan onto crossmember. Remove oil pump pick-up tube, and remove oil pan from vehicle.

Installation – To install, reverse removal procedure while noting the following: Clean all gasket surfaces and use new gaskets upon installation. Ensure that oil pump pick-up tube and screen are clean before installing.

PISTON & ROD ASSEMBLY

Removal – 1) With cylinder head and oil pan removed, remove oil pump. Rotate crankshaft until piston to be removed is at bottom of travel. Place a cloth on piston to collect cuttings, then using a ridge reamer, remove any ridge or deposits from upper end of cylinder. **NOTE** – *Do not cut into ring travel area in excess of 1/32".*

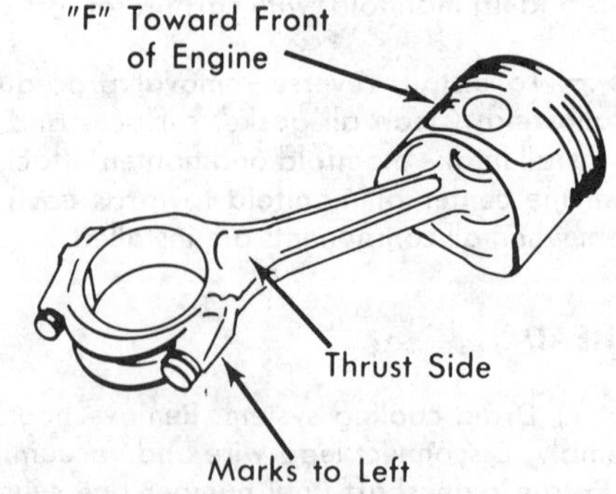

Fig. 3 Piston & Rod Assembly Installation Features

1800 cc 4 CYLINDER (Cont.)

2) Make sure connecting rod caps are marked so they may be replaced in their original positions, then remove rod caps. Push piston and rod assembly out top of cylinder. Take care not to damage bearing journal.

Installation — Oil piston rings, pistons and cylinder walls with engine oil. With rings properly spaced, install ring compressor onto piston. Install piston and rod assembly into its original bore. Make sure connecting rod marks are facing left side of engine and "F" mark on piston is facing forward (see illustration). Install rod caps and tighten rod bolts.

FITTING PISTONS

1) Determine piston-to-cylinder bore clearance. Check cylinder for out-of-round or taper. Fit new pistons if necessary. Pistons are available in .010", .020", .030" and .040" oversizes.

2) Place rings in cylinder near bottom of bore and measure end gaps. Place rings on piston and measure side clearance. If high steps have developed on lower back side of ring lands replace piston.

3) Place rings on piston with end gaps 120° apart so that no gap is located on thrust face or piston pin bore. Using suitable ring compressor, install piston in proper bore with "F" marking facing forward.

PISTON PINS

Piston pins are removed using an arbor press, pilots and driver. Measure pin and connecting rod diameters to ensure proper fit.

Fig. 4 Measuring Piston Ring Gap

CRANKSHAFT MAIN & CONNECTING ROD BEARINGS

MAIN & CONNECTING ROD BEARINGS

1) Inspect each bearing for scored, chipped or worn surface and replace if condition exists. If copper base is visible through bearing overlay, replacement is not necessary, if within specifications.

2) When installing new bearings, fit bearings to minimum specified clearance. Use Plastigage method to determine bearing clearances. Inserts are available in .010", .020" and .030" undersizes.

THRUST BEARING ALIGNMENT

Push crankshaft to one side to take up end play. Insert a feeler gauge between thrust washers and crankshaft. Replace thrust washers if measurement is not within specifications. Install new thrust washers with oil groove facing crankshaft thrust side.

REAR MAIN BEARING OIL SEAL

NOTE — *If rear main bearing seal replacement is only operation being performed, it can be done in vehicle; however if it is being replaced in conjunction with rear main bearing, engine must be removed.*

Remove transmission and clutch assembly. Using an awl, punch two holes in seal and install sheet metal screws. Using a pair of levers, pry out old seal. Press in new seal, reinstall clutch and transmission.

ENGINE FRONT COVER

Removal — 1) Remove hood and drain cooling system. Disconnect upper radiator hose at engine and lower hose at radiator. Remove radiator, drive belts, crankshaft pulley, and water pump. Remove cylinder head to front cover bolt. Raise vehicle and remove front splash shield.

2) Disconnect emission line from oil pan. Remove oil pan. Lower vehicle, remove alternator bracket to block bolts and position alternator to one side. Remove thermactor pump to block bolts and position to one side. Remove steel tube bolts and tube from front of engine. Remove attaching bolts for front cover and remove front cover.

Installation — To install engine front cover, reverse removal procedure.

FRONT COVER OIL SEAL

Drain cooling system, disconnect radiator hoses and remove radiator. Loosen alternator and Thermactor attaching bolts (if equipped). Remove drive belts. Remove crankshaft pulley, then pull seal from shaft, using suitable tool (T72J-6700). Install new seal using suitable tool (T72J-6700-A). Reverse removal procedures for remaining components.

TIMING CHAIN

Removal — 1) Remove cylinder head and front cover. Remove oil pump gear attaching nut, oil pump-to-block attaching bolts and loosen gear on the pump. Remove oil pump, gear and oil pump chain.

2) Remove timing chain tensioner and loosen timing chain guide strip screws. Remove oil slinger. Remove outer gear (for oil pump chain) from crankshaft. Remove timing chain and crankshaft gear.

Installation — 1) Position crankshaft inner sprocket into timing chain, then install sprocket and chain onto crankshaft. Install oil pump with gear onto cylinder block. Install oil pump chain and outer sprocket to crankshaft while positioning chain onto oil pump gear. Install timing chain tensioner. See *Timing*

1800 cc 4 CYLINDER (Cont.)

Chain Tensioner. Do not release snubber spring tension. Install cylinder head and camshaft to cylinder block.

NOTE — *Do not install rocker arm assembly at this time.*

2) Obtain correct timing chain alignment referring to *Timing Chain Alignment* illustration and using the following procedure: Rotate crankshaft to TDC of compression stroke on number one cylinder. This will place crankshaft with keyway facing straight up. Position camshaft with keyway facing straight up. Timing chain must now be positioned on camshaft sprocket so single plated link is aligned with timing mark on right-hand side of camshaft sprocket at rocker arm cover joint face, while facing engine. The two plate links on timing chain must straddle timing mark on BDC of crankshaft sprocket.

3) Install rocker arm shaft assembly, cylinder head bolts, and tighten all bolts to specifications. Adjust timing chain tension. See *Timing Chain Tension*. Release tensioner snubber and install front cover. Install remaining components in reverse of removal procedure and adjust valve clearance.

TIMING CHAIN TENSION

1) Remove crankshaft pulley and water pump. Remove cover from tensioner. Rotate crankshaft slightly in direction of engine rotation. Lift release on tensioner and compress snubber spring fully. Install wedge in tensioner so it will not release.

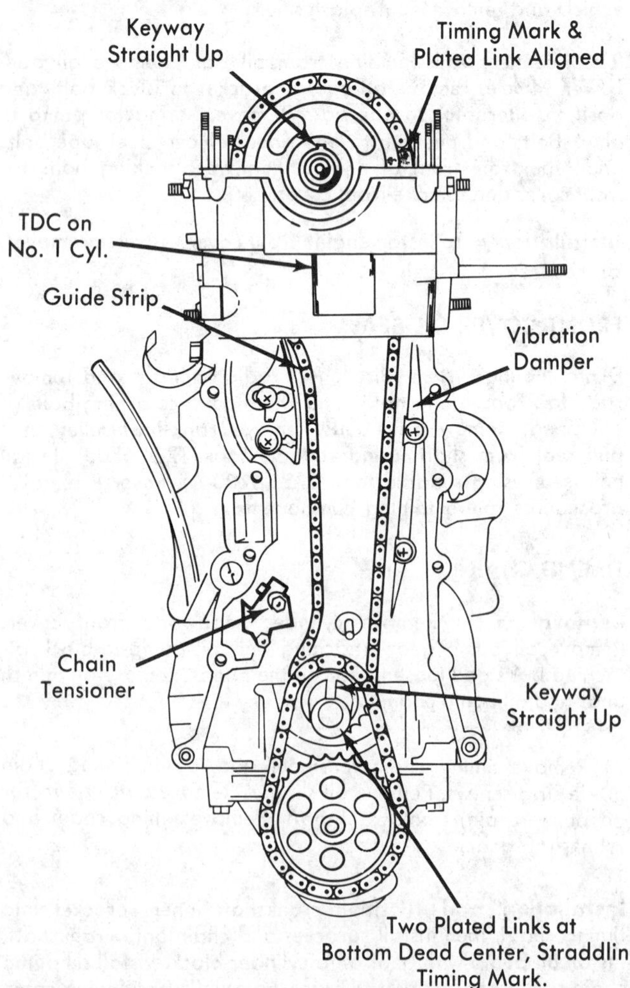

Fig. 5 Timing Chain & Sprocket Alignment

2) Remove two access plugs and aluminum washers from holes in timing chain cover and side of head. Loosen guide strip attaching screws. Press top of strip with lever inserted through access hole in head.

3) Tighten guide strip attaching screws with screwdriver inserted through hole in cover. Remove wedge from tensioner, allowing snubber to take up chain slack.

4) Install access plugs and aluminum washers to their respective holes. Replace chain tensioner cover and gasket. Install water pump and crankshaft pulley. Tighten bolts and adjust belt tension.

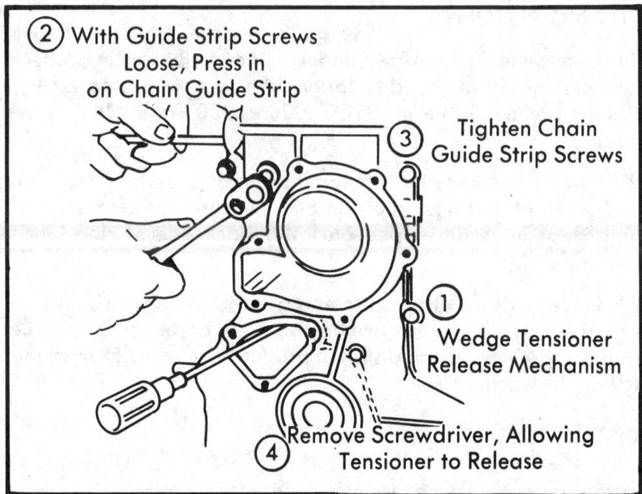

Fig. 6 Adjusting Timing Chain Tension

OIL PUMP CHAIN

Check oil pump chain for excessive deflection as shown in illustration. If deflection is more than .157" (3.97 mm), install adjusting shims between cylinder block and oil pump body.

Fig. 7 Measuring Oil Pump Chain Deflection

CAMSHAFT

CAMSHAFT

Removal — 1) Remove hood and water pump. Disconnect vacuum line and lead wire from distributor. Rotate crankshaft

1800 cc 4 CYLINDER (Cont.)

to position number one cylinder on TDC of compression stroke. Remove plug wires and distributor cap as an assembly, then remove distributor from engine. Remove rocker arm cover.

2) Remove crankshaft pulley, then remove cover from timing chain tensioner. Lift release on tensioner and compress snubber spring fully. Wedge a screwdriver in the tensioner to keep spring compressed. Remove cylinder head bolts and rocker arm assembly.

3) Remove nut, washer, and distributor gear from camshaft. Remove camshaft gear attaching nut and washer. Carefully remove camshaft from gear and engine block. **NOTE** — *Do not remove camshaft gear from timing chain and ensure that gear teeth-to-chain relationship is not disturbed.*

Installation — To install, reverse removal procedure while noting the following: When installing camshaft to gear take care not to disturb gear-to-chain relationship. Adjust timing chain tension. Check camshaft end play. Adjust valve clearance.

CAMSHAFT BEARINGS

Remove camshaft and inspect bearings for wear or damage. Use Plastigage method to determine clearance. Replace bearings which do not meet specifications.

CAMSHAFT END THRUST

Check camshaft end play with a feeler gauge inserted between thrust plate and camshaft flange. End play should be checked at time of overhaul, before gear and sprocket are replaced.

CAM LOBE LIFT

Remove rocker arm cover. Measure distance between major and minor diameters (see illustration) of each lobe with a Vernier caliper. Difference between diameters of each cam is lobe lift. If lobe lift loss exceeds .008" (.20 mm), replace camshaft. Check lift of each lobe in consecutive order and note each reading.

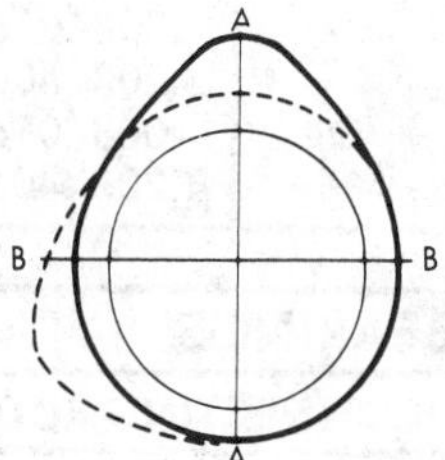

Fig. 8 Measuring Camshaft Base Circle and Lobe Lift

VALVE TIMING

Rotate crankshaft and camshaft until keyways are straight up. Place timing chain on camshaft sprocket so single plated link is aligned with timing mark on right-hand side of camshaft sprocket at rocker arm cover joint face, while facing engine. The two plate links on timing chain must straddle timing mark on BDC of crankshaft sprocket. Crankshaft in this position will be TDC of number one cylinder.

ENGINE OILING

Crankcase Capacity — 4 qts. (Add 1 qt. with filter change).
Oil Filter — Disposable type.
Oil Pressure — 50-64 psi @ 3000 RPM; 4.25 psi @ idle.

ENGINE OIL SYSTEM

Rotor type oil pump is chain driven by crankshaft. Timing chain is lubricated by oil jet in cylinder block and oil holes in slipper head of adjuster. Oil holes in large end of connecting rods align with oil holes in crankshaft to lubricate pistons and components.

OIL PUMP

1) Remove oil inlet tube from pump. Remove and discard gaskets. Remove cover, withdraw inner rotor and shaft assembly. Remove outer race. Remove cotter pin from body, pull cap out of chamber, and take out spring and plunger.

2) Assemble in reverse order. Rotor, shaft and outer race are serviced as an assembly. If one component is damaged, replace all three. Install new cotter pin and gasket. Prime pump with oil before installing unit in block.

Oil Pump Specifications

Application	Clearance In. (mm)
Lobe-to-Lobe	.002-.006 (.051-.152)
Rotor End Clearance	.002-.004 (.051-.102)
Outer Rotor-to-Housing	.006-.010 (.152-.254)

ENGINE COOLING

Thermostat — Begins to open at 180°F; fully open 203°F.

Cooling System Capacity — 7½ qts. (includes heater).

Radiator Cap — 13 psi.

WATER PUMP

Remove hood and drain cooling system. Remove lower hose from water pump, disconnect upper radiator hose at engine and lower hose at radiator. Remove radiator from vehicle. Loosen alternator and Thermactor pump (if equipped). Remove drive belt(s), fan, and pulley. Remove crankshaft pulley. Remove water pump. To install, reverse removal procedure.

1800 cc 4 CYLINDER (Cont.)

ENGINE SPECIFICATIONS

GENERAL SPECIFICATIONS

Year	Displ. cu. ins.	Displ. cc	Carburetor	HP at RPM	Torque (Ft. Lbs. at RPM)	Compr. Ratio	Bore in.	Bore mm	Stroke in.	Stroke mm
1977	109.6	1796	2-Bbl.	....	....	8.6-1	3.07	78	3.70	94

VALVES

Engine & Valve	Head Diam. In. (mm)	Face Angle	Seat Angle	Seat Width In. (mm)	Stem Diameter In. (mm)	Stem Clearance In. (mm)	Valve Lift In. (mm)
1796 cc							
Int.	1.6496-1.6575 (41.90-42.10)	45°	45°	.055 (1.397)	.3161-.3167 (8.029-8.044)	.0007-.0021 (.017-.053)	.....
Exh.	1.2953-1.3031 (32.90-33.09)	45°	45°	.055 (1.397)	.3159-.3167 (8.024-8.044)	.0007-.0023 (.017-.058)	.....

VALVE SPRINGS

Engine	Free Length In. (mm)	PRESSURE Lbs. @ In. (kg @ mm) Valve Closed	Valve Open
1796 cc			
Inner	1.438 (36.52)	16.3@1.30 (7.4@33.0)	.....
Outer	1.469 (37.31)	26.8@1.36 (12.2@34.5)	.....

VALVE TIMING

Engine	INTAKE Open (BTDC)	INTAKE Close (ALDC)	EXHAUST Open (BLDC)	EXHAUST Close (ATDC)
1796 cc	13°	57°	62°	8°

PISTONS, PINS, RINGS

Engine	PISTONS Clearance In. (mm)	PINS Piston Fit In. (mm)	PINS Rod Fit In. (mm)	RINGS Rings	RINGS End Gap In. (mm)	RINGS Side Clearance In. (mm)
1796 cc	.0022-.0028 (.056-.071)	.0002-.0006 (.005-.015)	.0004-.0012 (.010-.030)	1	.008-.016 (.203-.406)	.0014-.0028 (.036-.071)
				2	.008-.016 (.203-.406)	.0012-.0025 (.030-.064)
				Oil	.008-.016 (.203-.406)	.0012-.0024 (.030-.061)

CRANKSHAFT MAIN & CONNECTING ROD BEARINGS

Engine	MAIN BEARINGS Journal Diam. In. (mm)	MAIN BEARINGS Clearance In. (mm)	MAIN BEARINGS Thrust Bearing	MAIN BEARINGS Crankshaft End Play In. (mm)	CONNECTING ROD BEARINGS Journal Diam. In. (mm)	CONNECTING ROD BEARINGS Clearance In. (mm)	CONNECTING ROD BEARINGS Side Play In. (mm)
1796 cc	2.4779-2.4785 (62.93-62.95)	① .0005-.0015 (.013-.038) ② .0012-.0024 (.030-.061)	5	.003-.01 (.076-.254)	2.0842-2.0848 (52.938-52.954)	① .001-.0011 (.025-.028) ② .001-.003 (.025-.076)	.004-.008 (.102-.203)

① — Desired.
② — Allowable.

1800 cc 4 CYLINDER (Cont.)

ENGINE SPECIFICATIONS (Cont.)

CAMSHAFT			
Engine	Journal Diam. In. (mm)	Clearance In. (mm) ①	Lobe Lift In. (mm)
1796 cc			
Front	1.7695-1.7701 (44.945-44.960)	.0007-.0027 (.018-.069)	②
Center	1.7691-1.7697 (44.935-44.950)	.0011-.0031 (.028-.079)	②
Rear	1.7695-1.7701 (44.945-44.960)	.0007-.0027 (.018-.069)	②

① — End play is .001-.007" (.025-.178 mm).
② — See Cam Lobe Lift procedure.

TIGHTENING SPECIFICATIONS	
Application	Ft. Lbs.(mkg)
Main Bearing Caps	60-65(8.3-9.0)
Connecting Rod Caps	30-33(4.1-4.6)
Cylinder Head	
Cold	63-68(8.7-9.4)
Hot	69-73(9.5-10.1)
Oil Pan	5-9(.7-1.2)
Flywheel	112-118(15.5-16.3)
Distributor Drive Gear	57(7.9)
Oil Pump-to-Block	13-20(1.8-2.8)
Camshaft Sprocket	51-64(7.1-8.8)
Rocker Arm Cover	1-2(.1-.3)
Oil Pump Sprocket	22-26(3.0-3.6)
Intake Manifold	14-19(1.9-2.6)
Exhaust Manifold	16-21(2.2-2.9)

B210 & F10 4 CYLINDER

ENGINE CODING

ENGINE IDENTIFICATION

Engine serial and code number is stamped on right rear side of cylinder block, below mating surface of cylinder head and cylinder block. First three digits are engine code.

Application	Code
1397 cc	A14

ENGINE, CYLINDER HEAD & MANIFOLDS

ENGINE

NOTE – *Manufacturer recommends that engine and transmission be removed as an assembly.*

1) Disconnect battery ground and fusible link. Mark hood hinge location and remove hood. Drain coolant from radiator and engine. Remove radiator shroud, disconnect upper and lower hoses and remove radiator.

2) Drain engine oil, then disconnect all electrical wiring and vacuum hoses from engine and transmission. Disconnect fuel line at fuel pump.

3) Remove air cleaner and disconnect accelerator control wire. Disconnect hoses from air conditioning compressor, air pump hoses, carbon canister hoses, altitude compensator hoses (Calif. models), emergency air relief valve hoses (Calif. only), vacuum hoses, and heater hoses.

4) Disconnect hydraulic lines and remove clutch slave cylinder on vehicles with manual transmission. Disconnect speedometer cable at transmission. Disconnect selector range lever (automatic transmissions) or gear shift control lever (manual transmissions).

5) On F10 models disconnect right and left drive shafts from differential side flange. Remove radius link support, securing bolt. Disconnect front mounting insulators from sub-frame. Remove bolts securing rear mounting insulator to transmission case.

6) Disconnect exhaust pipe from exhaust manifold. On models with catalytic converter, remove sensor harness protector and two front pipe clamps. Secure exhaust pipe to body frame to prevent from falling. Remove propeller shaft and plug extension housing to prevent oil leakage. **NOTE** – *Mark propeller shaft and flange so installation will be in the original position.*

7) Support transmission using a floor jack. Remove rear engine mount-to-body bolts. Support engine using suitable hoist and sling assembly, then remove front mounting brackets-to-engine mount attaching bolts. Remove engine and transmission as an assembly.

INTAKE & EXHAUST MANIFOLDS

Removal & Installation – 1) Remove air cleaner and disconnect accelerator cable and choke cable. Disconnect and plug fuel line at carburetor. Disconnect exhaust pipe at exhaust manifold.

2) Remove nuts retaining intake and exhaust manifold to cylinder head and remove intake and exhaust manifold as an assembly. Remove gasket and thoroughly clean mating surfaces. Remove bolts and separate intake and exhaust manifold. To install, reverse removal procedure and use new gasket. Tighten nuts and bolts to specifications.

CYLINDER HEAD

Removal – Remove manifold assembly as previously outlined. Remove rocker arm cover, rocker arm assembly, and push rods. Remove cylinder head retaining bolts and remove cylinder head.

Installation – Thoroughly clean mating surfaces. Use new gasket with no sealer and install cylinder head. Install cylinder head retaining bolts. **NOTE** – *One cylinder head bolt is smaller diameter and has a hollow head. Install this bolt on right side center of cylinder head.* Tighten cylinder head bolts in two or three steps to specifications in sequence as shown in illustration. Reverse removal procedure to install remaining components. Adjust valve clearance.

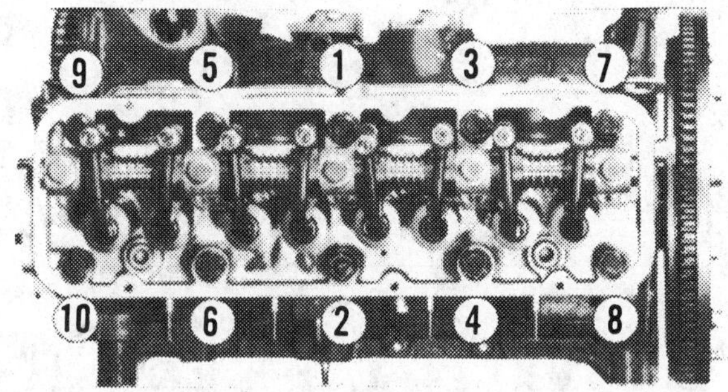

Fig. 1 Tightening Sequence for Cylinder Head

VALVES

VALVE ARRANGEMENT

E-I-I-E-E-I-I-E (front to rear).

VALVE GUIDE SERVICING

Check valve stem-to-guide clearance. If clearance is more than .0039" (.1 mm) and valve stem is not worn, valve guide must be replaced. Replace valve guide using the following procedure.

Fig. 2 Installation of Valve Guides

B210 & F10 4 CYLINDER (Cont.)

1) Using suitable tool (ST11320000), remove guide from cylinder head. Ream guide hole in cylinder head to .4803-.4807" (12.19-12.21 mm) to install replacement guide.

2) Heat cylinder head to approximately 302-392°F (150-200°C). Install guide using same driver as used for removal. Ream valve stem bore in guide to .3150-.3156" (8.00-8.015 mm) using a suitable reamer (ST110320000). Reface valve seat surface.

VALVE STEM OIL SEALS

An oil seal is installed on all valve stems inside valve spring. Install seal with large end over valve guide.

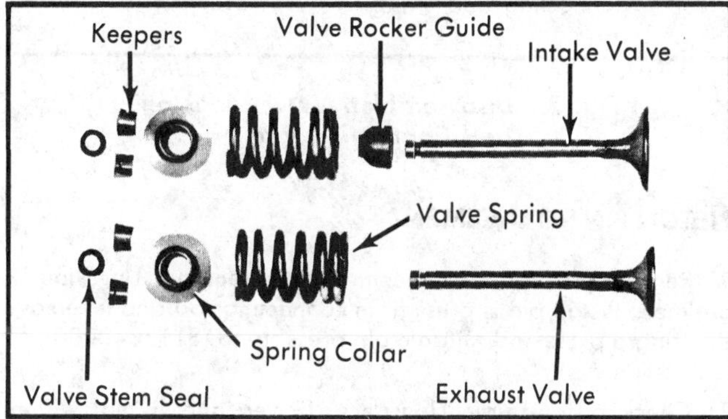

Fig. 3 Disassembled View of Valve Assemblies

VALVE SPRINGS

Removal – With cylinder head removed, compress valve spring using a suitable valve spring compressor (ST12070000) and remove valve keepers. Release spring compressor and remove spring retainer and spring.

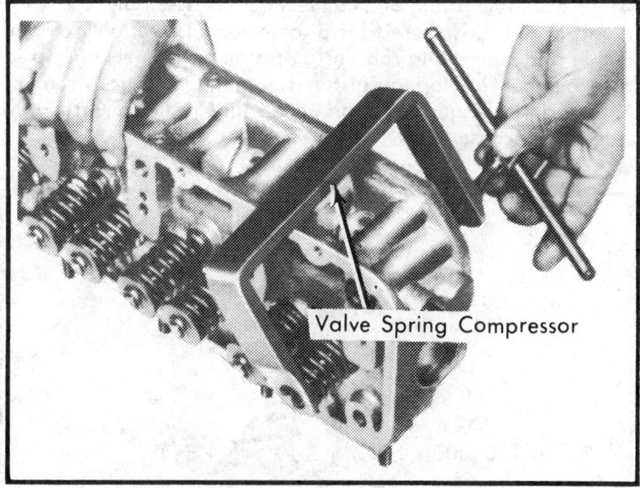

Fig. 4 Removing the Valve Spring

Installation – Install valve spring with white painted end toward cylinder head. Install valve spring retainer. Compress valve spring using removal tool and install valve keepers. **NOTE** – *Make sure valve is properly seated on spring seat.*

VALVE SPRING INSTALLED HEIGHT

Valve spring must be square within 1/16". Valve spring installed height is 1.52" (38.7 mm). Check valve spring by applying specified load and measuring spring height. If spring height and pressure, or squareness does not meet specifications, replace spring.

ROCKER ARM ASSEMBLY

1) Remove valve cover and remove bolts securing rocker arm assembly to cylinder head. Remove rocker arm assembly.

2) Slide off support stands, rocker arms and springs. Thoroughly clean and inspect all components for signs of wear or seizure. Measure rocker arm-to-shaft clearance. Standard clearance is .0008-.0021" (.020-.054 mm). Replace as necessary.

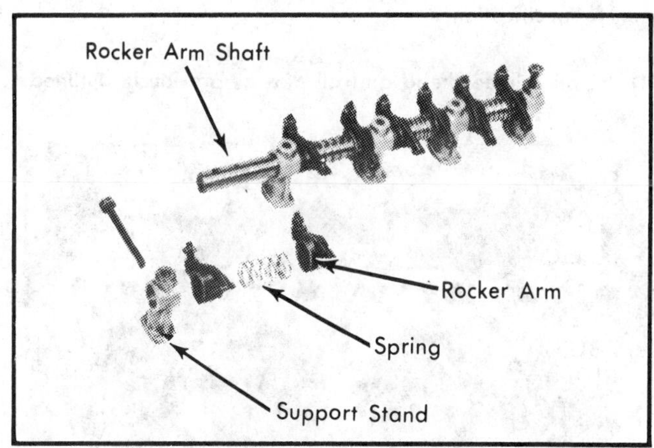

Fig. 5 Rocker Arm Assembly Components

3) If valve contact surface of rocker arm is worn, resurface using a suitable grinder.

4) Reverse disassembly and removal procedures to assemble and install rocker arm assembly. Tighten bolts to specifications and adjust valve clearance.

VALVE TAPPET SERVICE

Check valve tappet for signs of wear or seizure. Check clearance between valve tappet and tappet bore in crankcase. If clearance is more than .0059" (.15 mm), replace valve tappet. Standard clearance is .0008-.0020" (.02-.05 mm).

VALVE CLEARANCE ADJUSTMENT

Rotate engine until piston of valves being adjusted is at TDC of compression stroke. Adjust both intake and exhaust valves to .010" (.25 mm) with engine cold. With engine hot, readjust valve clearance on both intake and exhaust valves to .014" (.35 mm).

B210 & F10 4 CYLINDER (Cont.)

PISTONS, PINS & RINGS

PISTON & ROD ASSEMBLY

1) Remove cylinder head and oil pan. Remove nuts from connecting rod and remove connecting rod cap with bearing half. Push piston and connecting rod assembly with bearing half up and out through top of crankcase.

2) To install piston and connecting rod assembly, thoroughly oil rings, piston and cylinder wall. Make sure ring gaps are situated approximately 180° apart and not on thrust side of piston. Make sure bearing halves are properly seated in connecting rod and cap.

3) Install a ring compressor and compress rings. Install piston in cylinder with number on top of piston toward front of engine. With piston installed in cylinder, and connecting rod and bearings seated against crankshaft journal, install rod cap with numbers on the same side as connecting rod. Tighten nuts to specification.

4) Install cylinder head and oil pan as previously outlined.

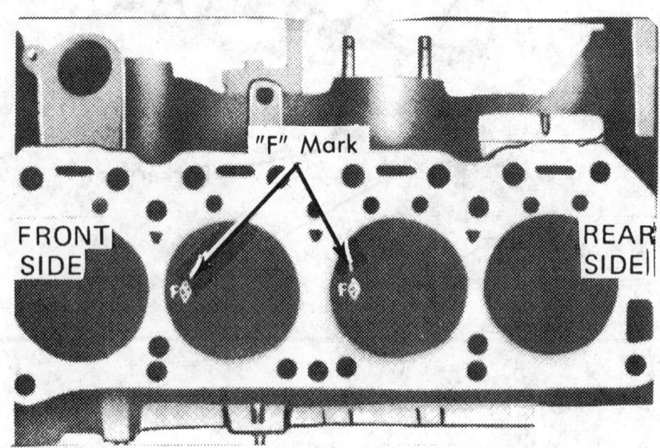

Fig. 6 Correct Installed Piston Position

FITTING PISTONS

1) Check piston-to-cylinder clearance with a feeler gauge and spring tension gauge. With a .0016" (.04 mm) feeler gauge installed between piston and cylinder wall, a force of 1.1-3.3 lbs. (.5-1.5 kg) measured on spring tension gauge, should be needed to extract feeler gauge.

2) Measure piston diameter at top of skirt 90° to piston pin axis. Measure cylinder bore halfway down cylinder and 90° to crankshaft center line. Pistons and rings are available in standard and two oversizes.

Piston Specifications

Application In.(mm)	Piston Size In.(mm)
Std.	2.9908-2.9927(75.967-756.017)
.020(.50) O/S	3.0105-3.0124(76.467-76.517)
.040(1.0) O/S	3.0301-3.0321(76.967-77.017)

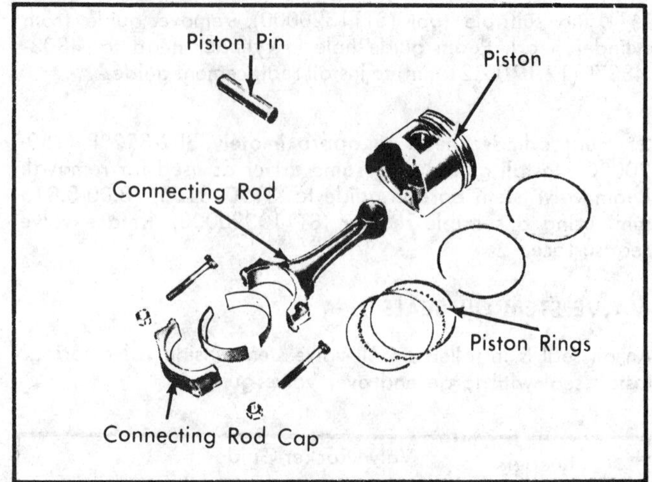

Fig. 7 Disassembled Veiw of Piston and Connecting Rod

PISTON PIN REPLACEMENT

1) Remove piston and connecting rod assembly as previously outlined. Piston pin is press fit in connecting rod and is removed using a press and suitable pin press stand (ST13040000).

2) Check piston-to-pin clearance. If clearance is not within specifications, replace both piston and piston pin. Piston pin should push fit through piston by hand with both piston and pin at room temperature.

3) Piston pin should be press fit into connecting rod. If interference fit is not within specifications, replace connecting rod or piston pin as necessary. If connecting rod is replaced, insure that new rod is within .176 ounces (5 grams) of defective connecting rod.

4) To assemble piston and connecting rod assembly, use same mandral and driver used for disassembly. Thoroughly oil pin, piston and connecting rod. Install piston on connecting rod so that number on top of piston is pointing toward front of engine and oil squirt hole on connecting rod is toward right side of crankcase.

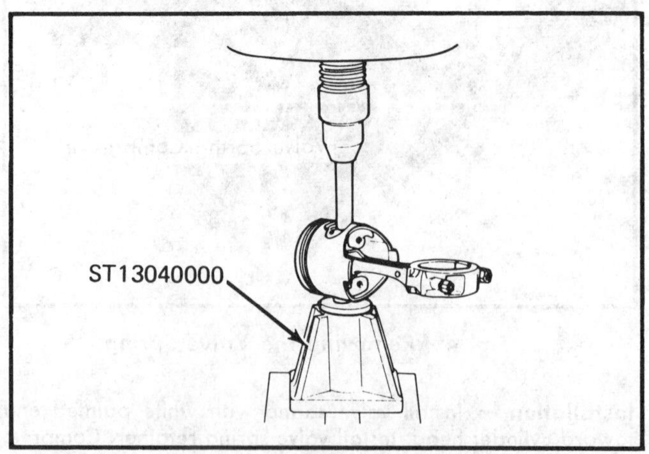

Fig. 8 Removing and Installing Piston Pin

B210 & F10 4 CYLINDER (Cont.)

CRANKSHAFT MAIN & CONNECTING ROD BEARINGS

MAIN & CONNECTING ROD BEARINGS

Removal – With engine removed from vehicle, remove cylinder head, oil pan, and piston and connecting rod assemblies. Remove alternator and engine mounting bracket from left side. Remove water pump, crankshaft pulley, and timing chain cover. Remove oil thrower and chain tensioner. Remove camshaft sprocket bolt, and remove both sprockets and timing chain as an assembly. Remove clutch and flywheel. Loosen main bearing cap bolts in two or three steps, then remove caps. Remove rear oil seal and carefully lift out crankshaft.

Inspection – 1) Thoroughly clean and inspect crankshaft. Blow out oil passages with compressed air. Check crankshaft for runout on center main bearing journal. If runout is more than .002" (.05 mm), crankshaft is bent and must be replaced.

2) Check all main and connecting rod bearings using Plastigage method. Check main and connecting rod journals for out-of-round or taper. If more than .0012" (.03 mm), crankshaft must be ground to next undersize. Main and connecting rod journals may be ground to the undersizes indicated in tables.

Main Bearing Journals

Application In. (mm)	Diameter In. (mm)
Std.	1.9666-1.9671 (49.951-49.964)
.001 (.02)	1.9665-1.9670 (49.949-49.962)
.01 (.25)	1.9567-1.9572 (49.701-49.714)
.02 (.50)	1.9469-1.9474 (49.451-49.464)
.03 (.75)	1.9370-1.9376 (49.201-49.214)
.04 (1.0)	1.9272-1.9277 (48.951-48.964)

Connecting Rod Journals

Application In. (mm)	Diameter In. (mm)
Std.	1.7701-1.7706 (44.961-44.974)
.003 (.08)	1.7670-1.7675 (44.881-44.894)
.005 (.12)	1.7654-1.7659 (44.841-44.854)
.01 (.25)	1.7603-1.7608 (44.711-44.724)
.02 (.50)	1.7504-1.7509 (44.461-44.474)
.03 (.75)	1.7406-1.7411 (44.211-44.224)
.04 (1.0)	1.7307-1.7313 (43.961-43.974)

Installation – 1) Install main bearing halves to engine block ensuring that all bearings are on correct journal. Bearings for journal No. 1 and No. 5 are the same. Bearings for journals No. 2 and No. 4 are the same. Journal No. 3 requires the thrust bearing. Upper and lower bearings are not interchangeable except for journals No. 2 and No. 4.

2) Apply oil to main bearing surface and install crankshaft. Install main bearing caps with arrow pointing toward front of engine. **NOTE** – *Apply sealer to main bearing caps at point where cap contacts cylinder block.* Tighten main bearing caps, in two or three steps, starting at center bearing and working outwards. Ensure crankshaft rotates smoothly.

3) Check crankshaft end play. *See Thrust Bearing Alignment.* Install timing chain in correct position with crankshaft and camshaft sprockets. Install rear oil seal. Install clutch and flywheel. Install oil thrower and chain tensioner. Install timing chain cover, crankshaft pulley, and water pump. Install alternator and engine mounting bracket. Install piston and connecting rod assemblies, oil pan, and cylinder head.

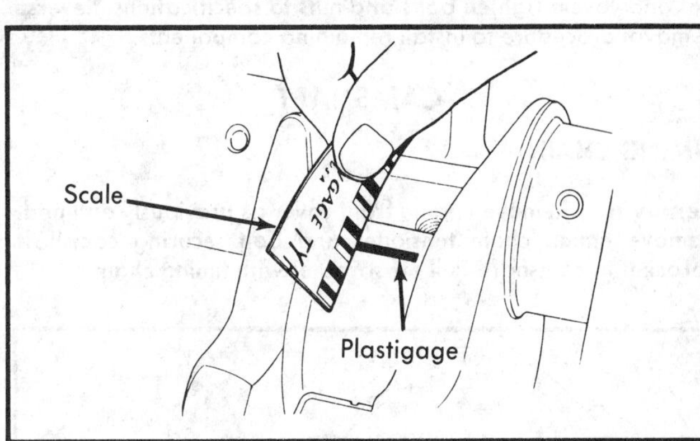

Fig. 9 Checking Bearings with Plastigage Method

THRUST BEARING ALIGNMENT

Thrust bearing is installed on No. 3 main bearing journal. Check crankshaft end play by inserting a feeler gauge between flange of thrust bearing and crankshaft. End play should be .002-.006" (.05-.15 mm).

Fig. 10 Checking Crankshaft End Play

REAR MAIN BEARING OIL SEAL SERVICE

Apply sealer to corners of crankcase that holds rear main bearing cap. Apply light grease to sealing edge on seal and install seal. Install rear main bearing cap and tighten bolts to specifications.

Fig. 11 Installing Rear Main Bearing Oil Seal

B210 & F10 4 CYLINDER (Cont.)

ENGINE FRONT COVER & OIL SEAL

Removal & Installation – Remove drive belt, fan, and water pump pulley. Remove water pump and crankshaft pulley. Remove oil pan and front cover. Replace seal in front cover whenever cover is removed. Thoroughly clean mating surfaces and apply sealer to both sides of gasket. Install gasket and cover. Tighten bolts and nuts to specifications. Reverse removal procedure to install remaining components.

CAMSHAFT

TIMING CHAIN

Removal – Remove engine front cover as previously outlined. Remove timing chain tensioner and bolt securing camshaft sprocket to camshaft. Pull off sprocket with timing chain.

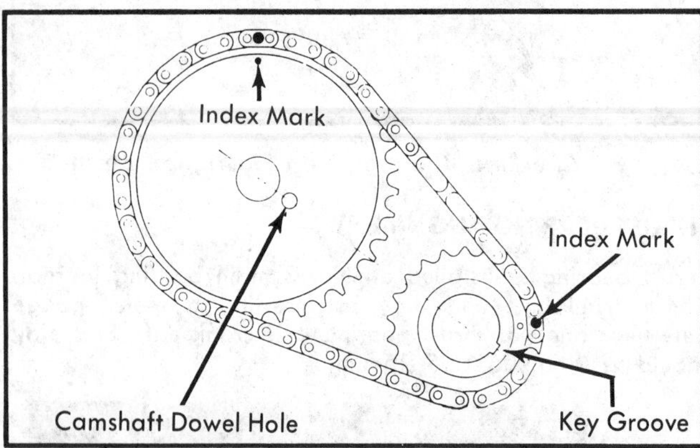

Fig. 12 Correct Alignment for Timing Chain Installation.

Installation – Install timing chain and camshaft sprocket with markings correctly aligned as shown in illustration. Oil sprocket teeth and chain with engine oil. Install and tighten camshaft sprocket bolt. Install chain tensioner and tighten attaching bolts. Check dimension "L" of tensioner, and if over .591" (15 mm), replace chain tensioner. Install oil thrower in front of camshaft sprocket. Install timing chain cover.

CAMSHAFT

Removal – Remove engine front cover, and valve train components as previously outlined. Remove fuel pump and oil pump with filter. Remove timing chain tensioner and remove timing chain with sprockets. Remove two bolts from camshaft lock plate and carefully pull camshaft from engine block.

Inspection – Thoroughly clean and inspect camshaft for wear or scoring. Check runout of camshaft using a dial indicator on center bearing journal. If runout exceeds .002" (.05 mm), replace camshaft. Check journal diameter, and if diameter is more than .0039" (.10 mm) from standard, camshaft journals must be ground to next undersize. Bearings are available in standard and three undersizes.

Installation – Coat camshaft with light coat of engine oil and carefully install camshaft into engine. Install camshaft lock plate with word "LOWER" at bottom. Install valve train components. Install timing chain with sprockets and timing chain tensioner. Install engine front cover. Install fuel pump and oil pump.

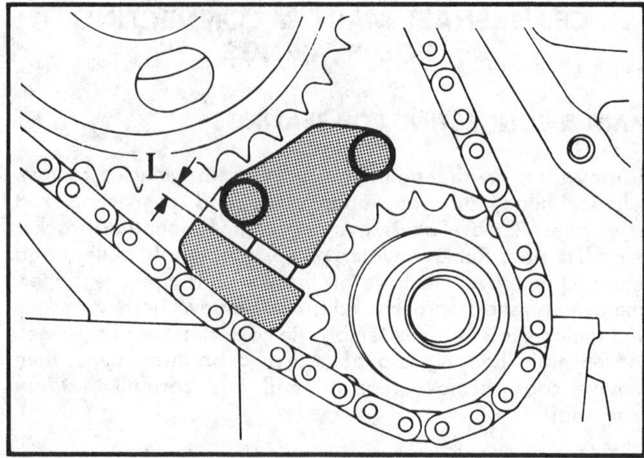

Fig. 13 Checking the Timing Chain Tensioner

CAMSHAFT BEARING REPLACEMENT

1) With camshaft removed, check journal diameter and bearing inside diameter. If journal measurement is within tolerance and clearance between camshaft journals and bearings exceeds .0059" (.15 mm), bearings must be replaced.

2) Remove and install appropriate bearings in crankcase using a suitable driver (ST16110000). Make sure oil holes in bearings align with oil holes in crankcase. Bearings must be line bored after installation. Install taper plug in crankcase using sealer. Install camshaft as previously outlined.

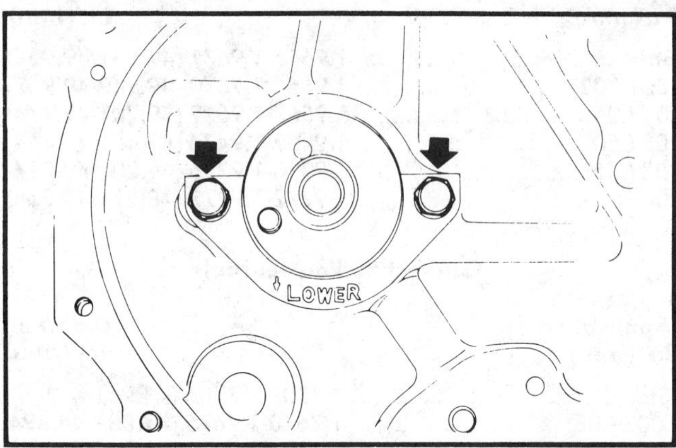

Fig. 14 Correct Camshaft Lock Plate Installation

CAMSHAFT END THRUST

Check camshaft end thrust with camshaft, lock plate, and camshaft sprocket in position by using a dial indicator on camshaft sprocket bolt. If end play exceeds .0039" (.10 mm), replace lock plate.

ENGINE OILING

Crankcase Capacity – 3⅞ quarts (with filter).

Oil Filter – Full-flow, replaceable element.

Oil Pressure – More than 11 psi (.8 kg/cm²) at idle; 54-74 psi (3.8-5.2 kg/cm²) at 3000 RPM.

Pressure Relief Valve – Nonadjustable, located in oil pump cover.

B210 & F10 4 CYLINDER (Cont.)

ENGINE OILING SYSTEM

Oil is circulated through engine by pressure provided by a trochoid rotor type pump. Oil pump is mounted on side of crankcase and driven by camshaft. Oil is drawn from oil pan by oil pump and into full flow oil filter mounted under oil pump. Oil is then pumped into main oil gallery of crankcase where it is distributed to crankshaft journals, timing chain tensioner and squirter that lubricates timing chain. Oil is circulated from crankshaft main bearing journals to camshaft journals and from center camshaft journal to rocker arm shaft to lubricate rocker arms and valves. Cylinder walls and piston pins are lubricated by oil squirted from squirt hole in connecting rod.

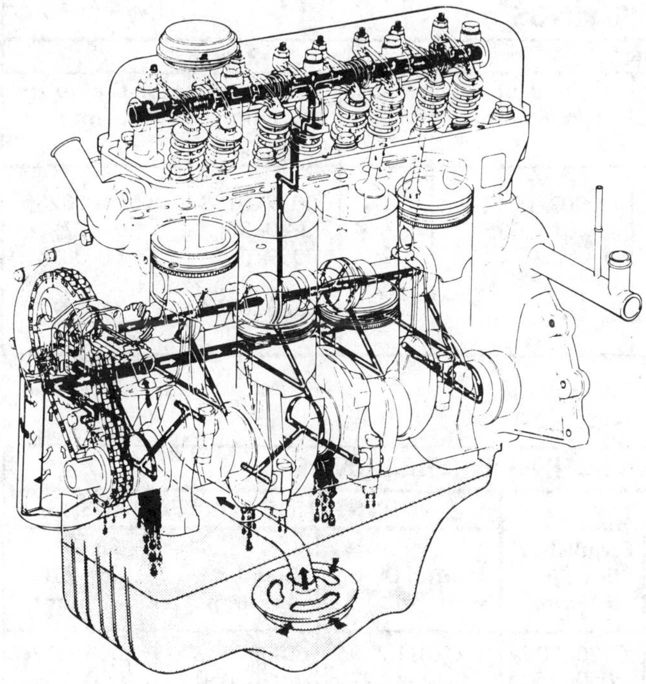

Fig. 15 Engine Oiling System

OIL PUMP

Remove pump cover from pump body. Slide outer rotor from pump body. Remove pressure regulator plug, washer, shim, spring, and valve. Thoroughly clean and inspect all components for wear or scoring. Check side and tip clearance between rotors. Check clearance between outer rotor and pump body. If clearances are excessive, replace components as necessary.

Oil Pump Specifications

Application	In. (mm)
Rotor-to-Rotor Side Clearance	.002-.0047 (.05-.12)
Rotor-to-Tip Clearance	.0016-.0047 (.04-.12)
Rotor-to-Pump Body	.0059-.0083 (.15-.21)
Regulator Valve Spring	
Free Length	1.71 (43.49)
Pressure Length	1.19 (30.3)

ENGINE COOLING

WATER PUMP

Removal & Installation – Drain cooling system and remove fan belt. Remove fan shroud, fan blade, spacer and pulley (or torque coupling). Remove water pump assembly and gasket from front cover. To install, reverse removal procedure.

Thermostat – Opens at 177-183°F.

Cooling System Capacity

B210 Automatic Transmission – 6 quarts
B210 Manual Transmission – 6¼ quarts
F10 – 7 quarts

Radiator Cap – 9 psi.

ENGINE SPECIFICATIONS

GENERAL SPECIFICATIONS

Year	Displ. cu. ins.	Displ. cc	Carburetor	HP at RPM	Torque (Ft. Lbs. at RPM)	Compr. Ratio	Bore in.	Bore mm	Stroke in.	Stroke mm
1977	85.24	1397	1 x 2-Bbl.	.....	.....	8.5-1	2.99	76	3.03	77

VALVES

Engine & Valve	Head Diam. In. (mm)	Face Angle	Seat Angle	Seat Width In. (mm)	Stem Diameter In. (mm)	Stem Clearance In. (mm)	Valve Lift In. (mm)
All							
Int.	1.46 (37)	45.5°	45°	.0512 (1.3)	.3138-.3144 (7.970-7.985)	.0006-.0018 (.015-.045)	.3114 (7.91)
Exh.	1.18 (30)	45.5°	45°	.0709 (1.8)	.3128-.3134 (7.945-7.960)	.0016-.0028 (.040-.070)	.3236 (8.22)

B210 & F10 4 CYLINDER (Cont.)

ENGINE SPECIFICATIONS (Cont.)

VALVE SPRINGS			
Engine	Free Length In. (mm)	PRESSURE Lbs. @ In. (kg @ mm)	
		Valve Closed	Valve Open
All	1.831 (46.5)	52.7 @ 1.52 (23.9 @ 38.7)	129 @ 1.189 (58.5 @ 30.2)

VALVE TIMING				
	INTAKE		EXHAUST	
Engine	Open (BTDC)	Close (ALDC)	Open (BLDC)	Close (ATDC)
All	14°	54°	56°	20°

PISTONS, PINS, RINGS						
	PISTONS	PINS		RINGS		
Engine	Clearance In. (mm)	Piston Fit In. (mm)	Rod Fit In. (mm)	Rings	End Gap In. (mm)	Side Clearance In. (mm)
All	.0009-.0017 (.023-.043)	.0003-.0005 (.008-.012)	.0007-.0014① (.017-.035)	1	.0079-.0138 (.20-.35)	.0016-.0028 (.04-.07)
				2	.0059-.0118 (.15-.30)	.0011-.0024 (.03-.06)
				Oil	.0118-.0354 (.30-.90)	snug snug

① — Interference fit.

CRANKSHAFT MAIN & CONNECTING ROD BEARINGS							
	MAIN BEARINGS				CONNECTING ROD BEARINGS		
Engine	Journal Diam. In. (mm)	Clearance In. (mm)	Thrust Bearing	Crankshaft End Play In. (mm)	Journal Diam. In. (mm)	Clearance In. (mm)	Side Play In. (mm)
All	1.9666-1.9671 (49.95-49.96)	.0008-.0024 (.020-.062)	No. 3	.0020-.0059 (.050-.150)	1.7701-1.7706 (44.96-44.97)	.0008-.0020 (.020-.050)	.008-.012 (.20-.30)

CAMSHAFT			
Engine	Journal Diam. In. (mm)	Clearance In. (mm)	Lobe Lift In. (mm)
All No. 1	1.7237-1.7242 (43.78-43.80)	.0015-.0024 (.037-.060)	Int. .222 (5.65)
2	1.7041-1.7046 (43.28-43.30)	.0011-.0020 (.027-.050)	Exh. .233 (5.92)
3	1.6844-1.6849 (42.78-42.80)	.0016-.0025 (.040-.063)	
4	1.6647-1.6652 (42.28-42.30)	.0011-.0020 (.029-.050)	
5	1.6224-1.6229 (41.21-41.22)	.0015-.0024 (.037-.060)	

TIGHTENING SPECIFICATIONS	
Application	Ft. Lbs. (mkg)
Cylinder Head	51-54 (7.0-7.5)
Connecting Rod	23-27 (3.2-3.8)
Main Bearing Caps	36-43 (5.0-6.0)
Camshaft Sprocket	29-35 (4.0-4.8)
Camshaft Lock Plate	3-4 (0.4-0.5)
Timing Chain Tensioner	4.3-5.8 (0.6-0.8)
Front Cover	3.6-5.1 (.5-.7)
Oil Pan	2.9-4.3 (.4-.6)
Oil Pump	6.5-10.1 (.9-1.4)
Rocker Arm Shaft	14-18 (2.0-2.5)
Manifolds	10.8-14.5(1.5-2.0)
Crankshaft Pulley	108-145(15-20)
Flywheel	54-61(7.5-8.5)
Oil Strainer	6.5-10(.9-1.4)
Engine Mounts	14-18(1.9-2.5)
Water Pump	6.5-10.0(.9-1.4)

200SX, PICKUP & 710 4 CYLINDER

ENGINE CODING

ENGINE IDENTIFICATION

Engine number is stamped on right rear side of cylinder block at cylinder head contact surface. The number is preceded by engine model L20B.

ENGINE, CYLINDER HEAD & MANIFOLD

ENGINE

NOTE – *It is recommended that engine and transmission be removed as a unit. Engine can then be separated from transmission.*

Model 620 (Pickup) – **1)** Mark alignment on hood and hood hinges, then remove hood. Remove all hoses to air cleaner, remove air cleaner. Disconnect battery ground cable.

2) Remove canister hoses to intake manifold and vacuum gallery. Remove air pump-to-air pump air cleaner hose. Drain cooling system and crankcase. Remove radiator hoses and transmission oil cooler lines. Remove radiator and shroud. Disconnect heater hoses and engine ground cable.

3) Disconnect wires to following components: Accelerator wire at carburetor, oil pressure switch, auto choke heater, vacuum control solenoid, coil lead, distributor, thermal transmitter, anti-dieseling solenoid, alternator, starter, and back-up lamp switch.

4) Disconnect power brake unit vacuum hose at intake manifold. Disconnect speedometer cable from rear extension housing. On manual transmissions, remove floor cover, detach rubber boot, remove "E" ring and control lever pin from transmission striking rod guide, remove lever. On automatic transmissions remove screws to disconnect control knob from lever, remove selector rod, range lever and control lever assembly with bracket.

5) On models with air conditioning, remove flexible hose support, remove four compressor bolts, move compressor to battery support. Remove hoses to fast idle control device solenoid valve, remove fast idle control device actuator.

6) Remove attaching screws, disconnect clutch operating cylinder and flexible tube as an assembly. Disconnect exhaust pipe from exhaust manifold. Disconnect center bearing bracket from crossmenber and propeller shaft from flange at rear axle. Remove propeller shaft and plug rear end of transmission to prevent oil leakage.

7) Attach a lifting hoist to engine and remove front mount bolts at support. Support transmission with a floor jack and loosen two rear mounting bolts. Remove rear mount to side member bolts, remove rear mount. Remove steering idler arm and push down cross rod. Pull engine forward and carefully remove engine and transmission as an assembly.

Model 200SX, 710 – **1)** Mark alignment marks on hood and hood hinges, remove hood. Disconnect battery ground cable. Drain cooling system and crankcase. Disconnect transmission oil cooler lines and remove splash board on automatic transmission models.

2) Remove all hoses to air cleaner, remove air cleaner. Disconnect fuel pump hoses and carbon canister hose. Disconnect air pump-to-air pump air cleaner hose. Disconnect coil wire, ground cable from engine, distributor terminal wires at top of radiator, and starting motor "E" terminal wire, ("B" terminal on 710 models).

3) Disconnect power unit hose at intake manifold. Disconnect air conditioner vacuum hose from intake manifold. Remove fast idle control device from bracket. Loosen drive belts, remove compressor mounting bolts. Remove compressor from engine.

4) Remove accelerator linkage from carburetor. Disconnect heater hoses, remove radiator hoses, shroud, grille and radiator. On manual transmission models, detach rubber boot, remove nut from shift lever, remove shift lever. On automatic transmissions, disconnect joint between control lever and selector rod.

5) Disconnect speedometer cable from extension housing. Remove clutch operating cylinder from clutch housing. On California models, remove heat shield insulators on front exhaust pipe and catalytic converter, then separate front exhaust pipe from converter. All other models, disconnect front pipe from rear pipe.

6) Remove front exhaust pipe mounting and separate pipe from exhaust manifold. Disconnect center bearing bracket from crossmember and propeller shaft from flange at rear axle. Remove propeller shaft and plug end of transmission to prevent oil leakage. Support transmission with a floor jack.

7) Remove rear engine mounts and connect a lifting hoist to engine. Remove front engine mounts. Pull engine forward and carefully remove engine and transmission as an assembly.

CYLINDER HEAD

Removal – **1)** Drain cooling system. Remove air cleaner after disconnecting hoses and ducts. Disconnect spark plug wires from spark plugs and valve cover. Disconnect fuel hose from carburetor and remove fuel pump. Remove PCV hose and anti-backfire valve-to-EGR passage hose. Disconnect vacuum hoses and linkage to carburetor, then remove carburetor.

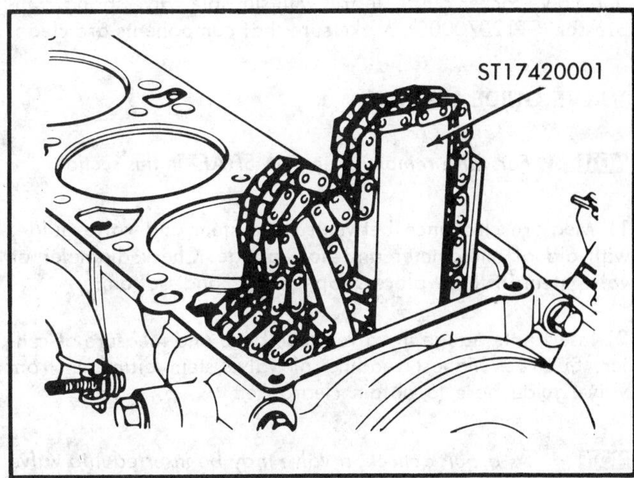

Fig. 1 Holding Timing Chain with Special Support Tool

200SX, PICKUP & 710 4 CYLINDER (Cont.)

2) Disconnect all hoses and vacuum lines from intake manifold to cylinder head or block. Remove intake and exhaust manifold as an assembly. Remove rocker cover and fuel pump drive cam. Turn crankshaft so No. 1 piston is at TDC on compression stroke . Paint alignment marks on timing chain and camshaft sprocket to aid in installation. Remove camshaft sprocket, and use suitable retainer tool (ST17420001) to support timing chain as shown in *Fig.1* Remove cylinder head attaching bolts and remove cylinder head.

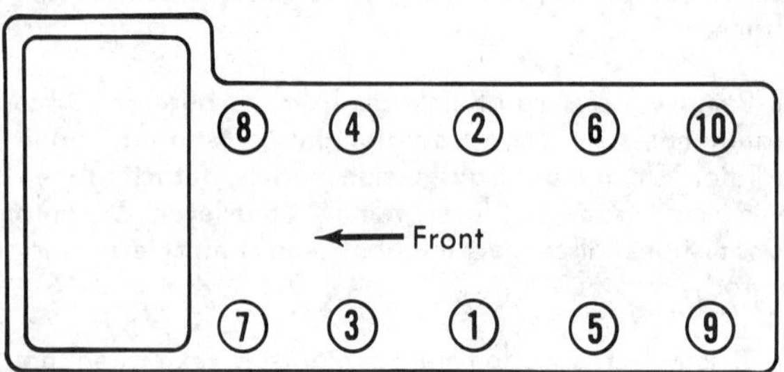

Fig. 2 Cylinder Head Tightening Sequence

VALVES

VALVE ARRANGEMENT

E-I-I-E-E-I-I-E (front to rear)

NOTE — *Camshaft MUST be removed to take out valves. See Camshaft Removal & Installation in this Section.*

VALVES

Removal — With camshaft removed. Remove valves using suitable valve spring compressor (ST12070000). Take care not to lose valve spring, seat, oil seal, valve collet, and rocker guide. Check each valve for worn, damaged or deformed heads or stems.

Installation — Install oil seal on valve guide. Assemble order, valve, inner and outer valve spring, spring retainer, valve collet and valve rocker guide. Install with suitable valve spring compressor (ST12070000). Make sure that components are clean.

VALVE GUIDE SERVICE

NOTE — *For valve removal, see CAMSHAFT in this section.*

1) Measure clearance between valve stem and valve guide, with aid of micrometer and hole gauge. Check diameter of valve stem in three places: top, center, and bottom.

2) Insert hole gauge in valve guide bore and measure at center. Subtract highest reading of valve stem diameter from valve guide bore to obtain clearance.

NOTE — *As a quick check, a valve may be inserted into valve guide and moved either left or right, (parallel with rocker arm). If tip moves .0079" or more, clearance is beyond maximum limit, of .0039".*

VALVE SEAT INSERTS

1) Check valve seats for pitting at valve contact surface. Valve seat inserts of .0197" oversize are available if necessary. To remove old inserts machine should be set so that boring cannot continue beyond bottom face of insert recess in cylinder head.

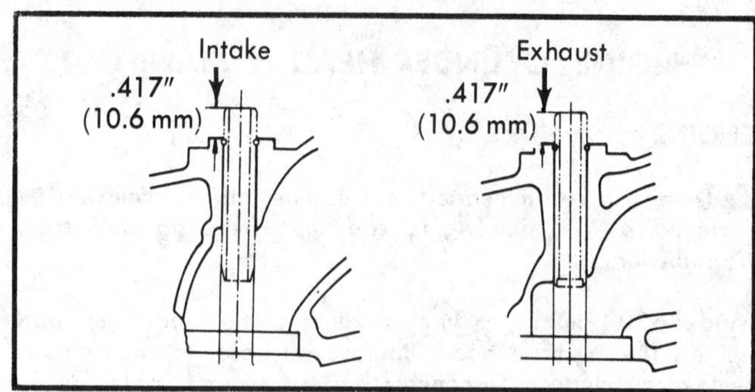

Fig. 3 Intake & Exhaust Valve Guides

2) Machine cylinder head recess diameter to concentric circles to valve guide center so that insert will have correct fit. Heat cylinder head to 302-392° F and install insert making sure that it beds on bottom face of recess.

3) Valve seats should be cut or ground to correct face angle and seat width and to head diameter of valve to be installed.

VALVE SPRING INSTALLED HEIGHT

With valves closed, inner spring should have a height of 1.378" (35.0 mm) and outer spring should have a height of 1.575" (40.0 mm). See specification for pressure with valves opened or closed.

VALVE ADJUSTMENT

Loosen pivot locking nut and turn pivot screw until specified clearance is obtained with engine cold. Tighten pivot locking nut after adjustment and recheck clearance. Warm up engine. With engine stopped, measure valve clearance and reset to hot clearances if necessary.

Valve Adjustment Specifications

Valve	Hot	Cold
Intake	.010" (.25 mm)	.008" (.20 mm)
Exhaust	.012" (.30 mm)	.010" (.25 mm)

PISTONS, PINS & RINGS

PISTON & ROD ASSEMBLY

Removal — Remove connecting rod nuts and bearing caps. Push piston and rod assembly out top of cylinder, using care not to damage any bearing surface. Retain all components in proper order for reassembly.

200SX, PICKUP & 710 4 CYLINDER (Cont.)

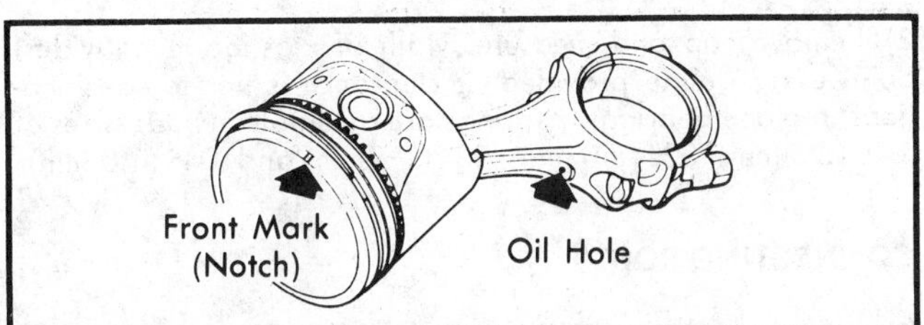

Fig. 4 Piston & Rod Assembly Installation Features

Installation – Reassemble piston and rod so that oil hole in connecting rod is facing right side of engine and notch on top of piston is facing forward. Install connecting rod on original journal with rod and cap marks on same side. Tighten connecting rod nuts and check rod side play.

FITTING PISTONS

1) Measure cylinder bores for wear or taper at top, bottom and middle on thrust face and at 90° to thrust face. If excessive wear is found rebore cylinder and install oversize pistons. Oversize pistons are available as shown in table.

2) When boring cylinders, use cylinder order of 2-4-1-3 to prevent heat distortion. After honing cylinder to final fit, check piston fit using spring tension pull scale. A force of .44-3.31 lbs. (.2-1.5 kg.) should be obtained extracting a .0016" (.04 mm) feeler gauge.

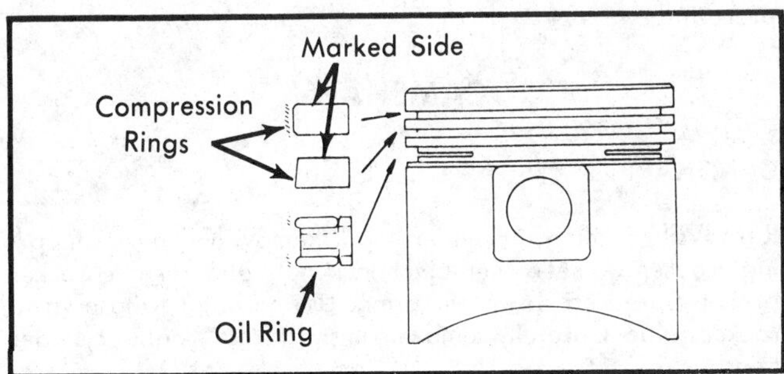

Fig. 5 Installation Order of Piston Rings

3) Measure piston ring end gap and side clearance and replace as necessary. Install rings on pistons with end gaps 180° apart and so no end gap is in line with thrust face. Install rings with top mark facing upward.

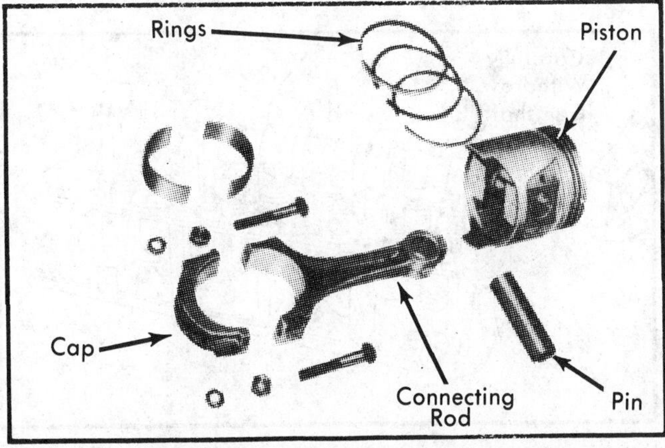

Fig. 6 Exploded View of Piston and Rod Assy.

NOTE – *If only piston ring is to be replaced, measure gap at bottom of bore. Oversize rings are available in .020" (1.00 mm).*

PISTON PINS

Pin must be a tight press fit in connecting rod, pressing force is from one to one and a half tons. When pressing pin into connecting rod, oil pin and press pin so that oil jet of connecting rod large end is directed toward right side of cylinder block.

Piston Specifications

Application In. (mm)	Piston Size In. (mm)
Standard	3.3459-3.3478 (84.985-85.035)
.020 (.50) OS	3.3648-3.3667 (85.465-85.515)
.040 (1.00) OS	3.3844-3.3864 (85.965-86.015)

CRANKSHAFT MAIN & CONNECTING ROD BEARINGS

CRANKSHAFT

Removal – With engine removed from vehicle, remove cylinder head and oil pan. Remove flywheel and rear plate. Remove oil strainer, oil pump and drive spindle. Remove front cover, chain tensioner, chain slack side guide, and timing chain. Remove oil thrower, crankcase worm gear, and timing drive sprocket. Remove piston and rod assemblies. Remove main bearing caps using suitable puller (KV101041SO) to remove center and rear main bearing caps.

NOTE – *Keep all main bearing caps in order to aid in reassembly. Remove rear oil seal, remove crankshaft.*

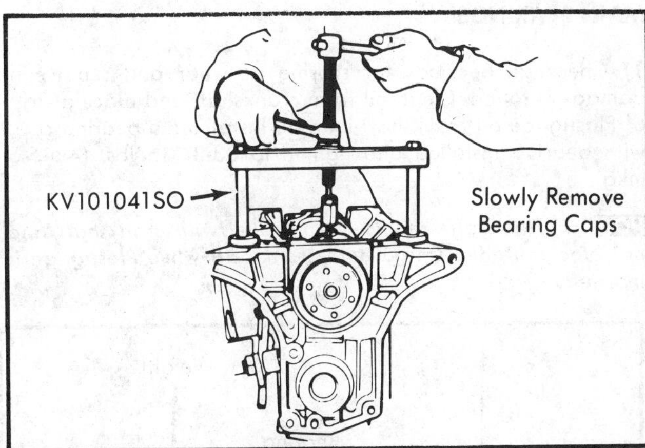

Fig. 7 Rear Main Bearing Cap Removal

Inspection – Check all crankshaft journals for scoring, wear or cracks. Taper and out-of-round on all journals must not exceed .001" (.025 mm). Check crankshaft for bend using dial indicator at center journal of crankshaft. If bend exceeds .004" (.10 mm), which is one-half of indicator reading, replace crankshaft. Check main driveshaft pilot bearing at rear of crankshaft for wear or damage and replace if necessary.

200SX, PICKUP & 710 4 CYLINDER (Cont.)

Installation – 1) Install main bearing halves to engine block ensuring that all bearings are on correct journal. Journal No. 3 requires a thrust bearing. Bearing for No. 1 is the same as for journal No. 5 except that an oil hole is provided in No. 1. Upper and lower bearings are interchangeable.

2) Apply oil to main bearing surface and install crankshaft. Install main bearing caps with arrow pointing toward front of engine. Shift crankshaft toward front of engine, tighten main bearing caps, in two or three steps, starting at center bearing and working outwards. Ensure crankshaft rotates smoothly.

NOTE – *Apply sealer to rear main bearing cap at point where cap contacts cylinder block.*

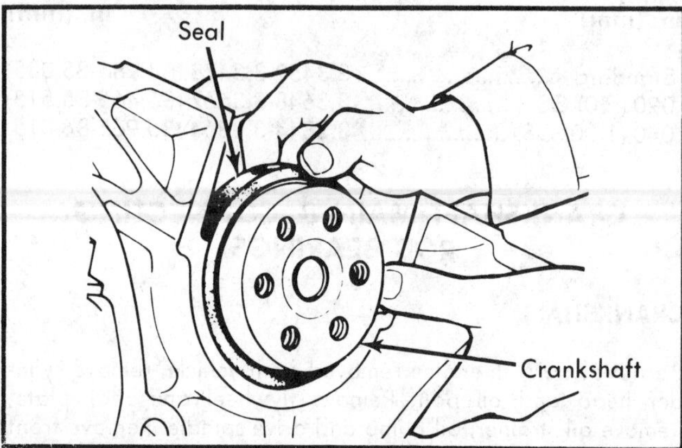

Fig. 8 Rear Oil Seal Removal

3) Check crankshaft end play, and if not within specifications replace center thrust bearing. Install side seals in rear main bearing cap, after applying sealer to seals. Install rear oil seal. Install rear end plate and flywheel. Install piston and rod assemblies. Install remaining components in reverse of removal procedure

MAIN BEARINGS

1) Check all bearings for scoring or wear and replace if damage is found. Clean oil from crankshaft and place a strip of Plastigage on crankshaft journal. Install main bearing cap, with bearing installed and tighten to 33-34 ft. lbs. (4.5-5.5 mkg).

NOTE – *Plastigage should run parallel with crankshaft and not block oil hole. Do not turn crankshaft while Plastigage is inserted.*

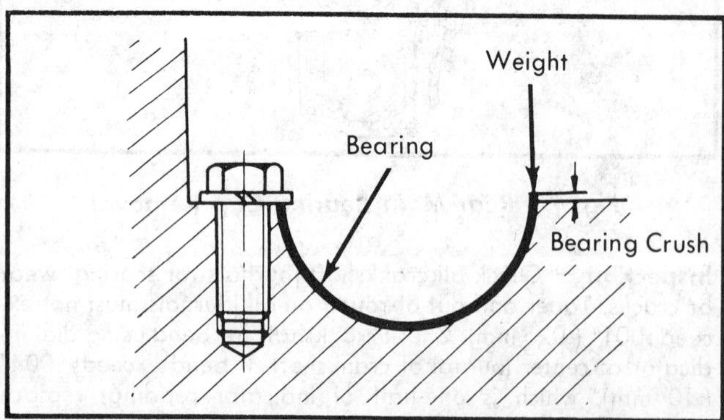

Fig. 9 Measuring Bearing Crush in Cylinder Block

2) Remove cap and measure width of Plastigage at widest point using gauge provided. If clearance is not to specifications, replace bearings. Bearings are available in undersizes of .01" (.25 mm) .02" (.50 mm) .03" (.75 mm) and .04" (1.0 mm).

CONNECTING RODS

Check connecting rod bearings in same manner as main bearings using Plastigage. Tighten connecting rod caps to 33-40 ft. lbs. (4.5-5.5 mkg) Bearings are available in undersizes of .0024" (.06 mm), .005" (.12 mm), .01" (.25 mm), .02" (.50 mm), .03" (.75 mm) and .04" (1.0 mm). Check bearing crush of connecting rod bearings in same manner as for main bearings. Clearance must be .0006-.0018" (.015-.045 mm).

ENGINE FRONT COVER

Removal – Drain cooling system, disconnect hoses and remove radiator. Remove all drive belts, fan blade and pulley. Disconnect all wiring and connections to thermostat housing and remove housing. Remove crankshaft pulley and water pump. Remove spark plug wires from plugs. mark position of distributor base to engine and position of rotor to distributor. Disconnect distributor wires from coil and remove distributor. Remove oil pump with drive spindle. Remove front cover attaching bolts and front cover.

Installation – To install engine front cover, reverse removal procedure

CAMSHAFT

CAMSHAFT

Removal – Remove cylinder head. Remove valve rocker spring. Loosen valve rocker pivot lock nuts and remove rocker arms by pressing down on spring. Use care not to lose valve rocker guide. Carefully remove camshaft from front of cylinder head.

Installation – Carefully install camshaft into cylinder head taking care not to damage bearing. Install camshaft locating plate with oblong groove of plate, facing front of cylinder head. Install camshaft sprocket and tighten attaching bolts. Install remaining components in reverse of removal procedure and tighten all nuts and bolts.

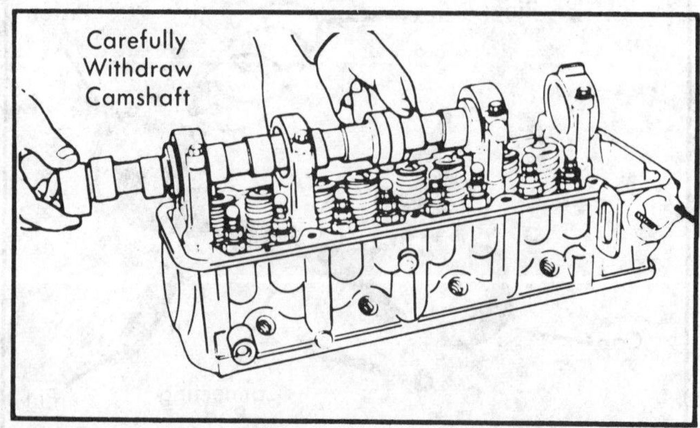

Fig. 10 Withdrawing Camshaft from Cylinder Head

200SX, PICKUP & 710 4 CYLINDER (Cont.)

CAMSHAFT BEARINGS

Measure inner diameter of camshaft bearing and outer diameter of camshaft journal. If wear or damage is excessive, replace cylinder head assembly.

NOTE – *Do not remove camshaft bearings. If bearings are removed, bearing centers will be out of alignment and proper reassembly will be difficult without center boring.*

TIMING CHAIN & GEARS

Remove engine front cover and camshaft drive sprocket and fuel pump cam. Remove timing chain, tensioner and chain guide. Remove oil thrower, crankshaft worm gear and crankshaft chain drive gear. To install, reverse removal procedure.

NOTE – *When Installing timing chain, camshaft key points upward. Set timing chain so that mating marks align with crankshaft and camshaft sprockets There are 44 chain links between the two timing marks.*

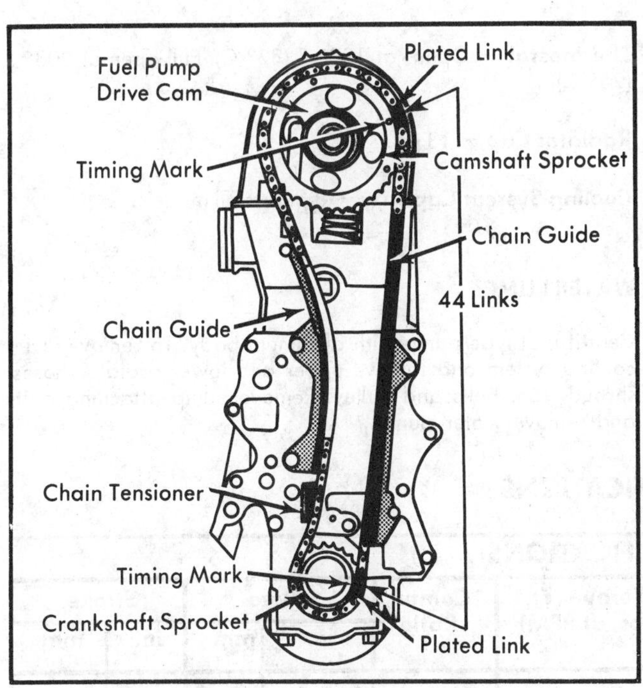

Fig. 11 Timing Chain & Sprocket Alignment

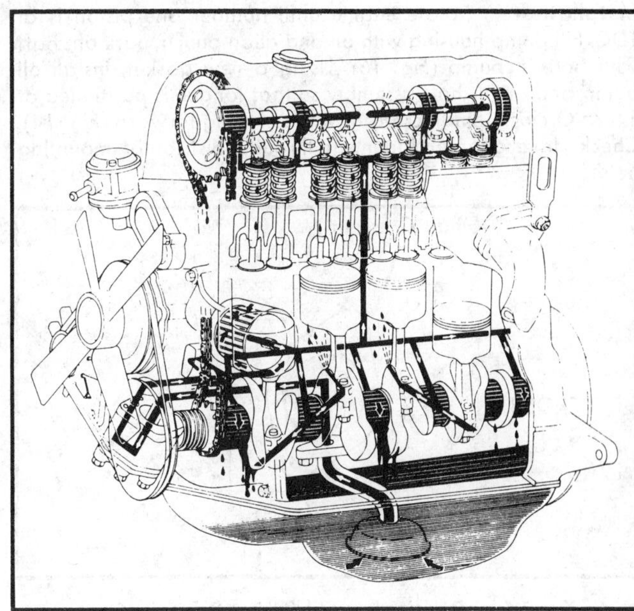

Fig. 12 Cutaway View of Engine Oiling System

ENGINE OILING SYSTEM

Oil drawn from pan passes through screen to oil pump and is delivered to oil filter and to main oil gallery. Main oil gallery supplies oil to crankshaft main bearings and drilled passages in crankshaft. Oil sprayed from jet holes on connecting rods lubricates cylinders and piston pins. Oil from main gallery lubricates chain tensioner and timing chain. Center hole in crankshaft, center bearing feeds camshaft bearings on cylinder head. Valve rocker mechanism is lubricated through oil gallery in camshaft and through a small channel at base circle portion of each cam. Rocker arms and valves are lubricated intermittently through small holes or oil pipe.

ENGINE OILING

Crankcase Capacity – 4.5 Quarts with filter change.

Oil Filter – Full-flow, disposable cartridge.

Oil Pressure – 11-40 psi. (.8-2.8 kg/cm²) at idle, 50-70 psi. (3.5-5.0 kg/cm²) at maximum.

Pressure Relief Valve – Non-adjustable.

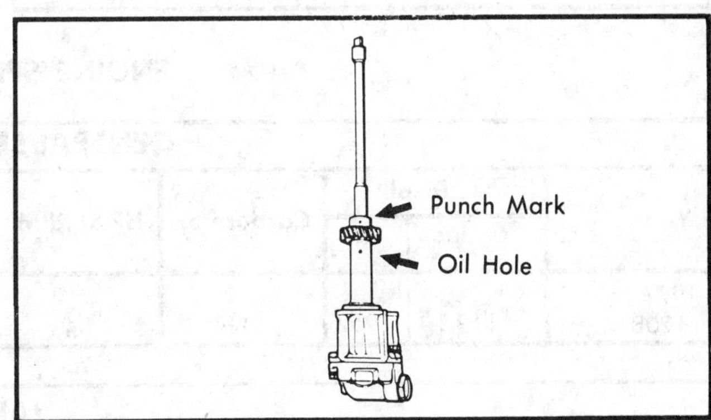

Fig. 13 Aligning Oil Pump Timing Marks

OIL PUMP

Removal – Pump assembly is installed at bottom of front cover, by four bolts. Pump is driven by distributor, drive shaft is rotor type. Remove distributor, drain engine oil, remove splash and stabilizer. Remove oil pump body together with drive shaft.

200SX, PICKUP & 710 4 CYLINDER (Cont.)

Installation – Rotate engine until number one piston is at TDC. Fill pump housing with oil and align punch mark on shaft with hole in pump (*Fig. 13*). Using a new gasket, install oil pump and drive shaft assembly so that tongue is positioned at 11:25 O'clock. Small crescent will be facing forward (*Fig. 14*). Check drive gear engagement through distributor mounting hole.

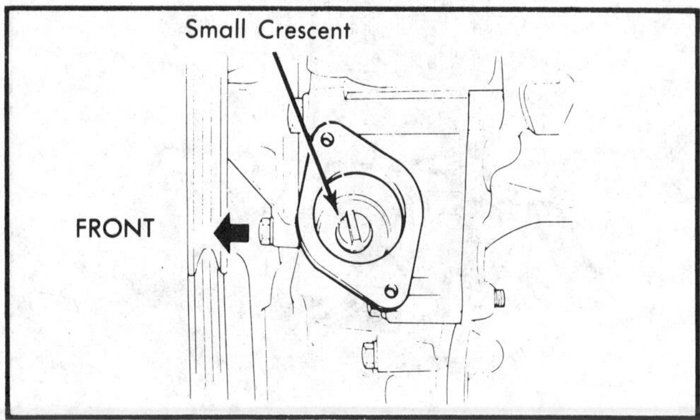

Fig. 14 Positioning Oil Pump Drive in Engine

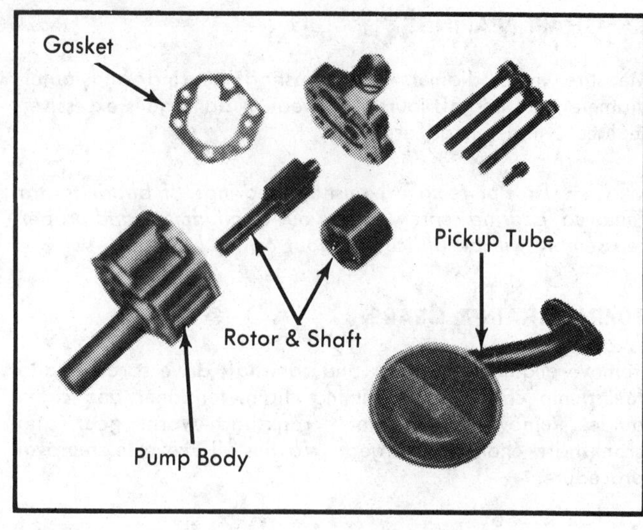

Fig. 15 Exploded View of Oil Pump & Pickup Tube

Inspection – Remove cover from oil pump body, remove gears. Wash parts with cleaning solvent, inspect for wear or damage. Make sure clearances are to specification. Pump is serviced as an assembly only. Replace pump if any part is worn or damaged.

Oil Pump Specifications

Application	① Clearance In. (mm)
Rotor Side Clearance (Rotor to Bottom Cover)	0.20 (0.0079)
Rotor Tip Clearance	0.20 (0.0079)
Outer Rotor to Body	0.5 (0.0197)

① – Wear limit specifications given.

ENGINE COOLING

Thermostat – Opens at 180° F (82° C). Full open at 203° F (95° C).

Radiator Cap – 13 psi.

Cooling System Capacity – 8 quarts all models.

WATER PUMP

Centrifugal type pump with aluminum body. To remove drain cooling system and remove upper and lower radiator hoses, shroud, fan, belts and pulley. Remove pump attaching bolts and remove water pump.

ENGINE SPECIFICATIONS

GENERAL SPECIFICATIONS

Year	Displ.		Carburetor	HP at RPM	Torque (Ft. Lbs. at RPM)	Compr. Ratio	Bore		Stroke	
	cu. ins.	cc					in.	mm	in.	mm
1977 L20B	119.1	1952	1-2Bbl.	.....	.....	8.5-1	3.35	85	3.39	86

VALVES

Engine & Valve	Head Diam. In. (mm)	Face Angle	Seat Angle	Seat Width In. (mm)	Stem Diameter In. (mm)	Stem Clearance In. (mm)	Valve Lift In. (mm)
L20B							
Intake	1.654-1.661 (42.0-42.2)	45°	45°	.0551-.0630 (1.4-1.6)	.3136-.3142 (7.965-7.980)	.0008-.0021 (.020-.053)	.413 (10.5)
Exhaust	1.378-1.386 (.35.0-35.2)	45°	45°	.0709-.0866 (1.8-2.2)	.3128-.3134 (7.945-7.960)	.0016-.0029 (.040-.073)	.413 (10.5)

200SX, PICKUP & 710 4 CYLINDER (Cont.)

ENGINE SPECIFICATIONS (Cont.)

PISTONS, PINS, RINGS

Engine	PISTONS	PINS		RINGS		
	Clearance In. (mm)	Piston Fit In. (mm)	①Rod Fit In. (mm)	Rings	End Gap In. (mm)	Side Clearance In. (mm)
L20B	.0010-.0018 (.025-.045)	.0001-.0006 (.003-.015)	.0006-.0013 (.015-.033)	No. 1	.010-.016 (.25-.40)	.0016-.0029 (.040-.073)
				No. 2	.012-.020 (.30-.50)	.0012-.0028 (.030-.070)
				Oil	.012-.035 (.30-.90)	.....

① — Interference fit.

CRANKSHAFT MAIN & CONNECTING ROD BEARINGS

Engine	MAIN BEARINGS				CONNECTING ROD BEARINGS		
	Journal Diam. In. (mm)	Clearance In. (mm)	Thrust Bearing	Crankshaft End Play In. (mm)	Journal Diam. In. (mm)	Clearance In. (mm)	Side Play In. (mm)
L20B	2.3599-2.3604 (59.942-59.955)	.0008-.0024 (.020-.062)	No. 3	.002-.007 (.05-.18)	1.9670-1.9675 (49.961-49.974)	.001-.002 (.025-.055)	.0079-.0118 (.20-.30)

VALVE SPRINGS

Engine	①Free Length In. (mm)	PRESSURE Lbs. @ In. (kg @ mm)	
		Valve Closed	Valve Open
Inner	1.766 (44.85)	27.1@1.378 (12.3@35)	56.2@.965 (25.5@24.5)
Outer	1.968 (49.98)	47@1.575 (21.3@40)	108@1.161 (49@29.5)

① — If valve spring is out-of-square more than .063" (1.6 mm) replace spring.

CAMSHAFT

Engine	Journal Diam. In. (mm)	①Clearance In. (mm)	Lobe Lift In. (mm)
L20B	1.8877-1.8883 (47.948-47.963)	.0015-.0026 (.038-.067)	.276 (7.0)

① — End play is .003-.015" (.08-.38 mm).

TIGHTENING SPECIFICATIONS

Application	Ft. Lbs. (mkg)
Cylinder Head	
Step One	29 (4.0)
Step Two	43 (6.0)
Step Three	47-61 (6.5-8.4)
Connecting Rods	33-40 (4.6-5.5)
Flywheel	101-116 (14-16)
Main Bearings	33-40 (4.6-5.5)
Camshaft Sprocket	86-116 (12-16)
Oil Pan	4-7 (.6-.9)
Crankshaft Pulley	86-116 (12-16)
Manifolds	9-12 (1.2-1.7)
Rocker Pivot Lock Nuts	36-43 (5-6)

810 & 280Z 6 CYLINDER

ENGINE CODING

ENGINE IDENTIFICATION

Engine serial number is stamped on right rear side of cylinder block where cylinder head contacts block. Number is preceeded by engine model designation, L28 (280Z), L24 (810).

ENGINE & CYLINDER HEAD

ENGINE

NOTE – *It is recommended that engine and transmission be removed as a unit. Engine can then be separated from transmission assembly.*

1) Fuel hose pressure must be decreased to zero, before engine removal. Disconnect battery ground cable, ground lead wire (black) from fuel pump, and lead wire from "S" terminal of starter. Remove cold start valve attaching bolts and valve. Connect a ground cable to battery. Place cold start valve in a container, turn ignition switch to "START" position, and release fuel hose pressure.

NOTE – *280Z Disconnect cold start valve harness connector. Using two jumper wires, connect each terminal to the battery, positive and negative terminals. Connect other terminals of jumpers to cold start valve, for two or three seconds.*

2) Scribe alignment marks around hood hinges and remove hood. Drain cooling system and engine crankcase. Disconnect battery cables. Remove radiator hoses. Remove air flow meter and air duct clamps with rubber hoses. Remove air cleaner and disconnect hoses from canister, then remove canister. Disconnect transmission cooler lines (automatic transmission models), and remove radiator and shroud.

3) Disconnect accelerator linkage. Disconnect the wiring to starter, alternator, oil pressure switch, neutral switch, back-up lamp switch, EGR solenoid valve, electric fuel injector, throttle valve switch, cold start valve, air regulator, vacuum cutting solenoid (manual transmission models), and all wiring to thermostat housing.

4) Disconnect wiring to boost controlled deceleration solenoid valve. Disconnect engine ground cable to engine, and high tension cable between coil and distributor. Disconnect wire for block terminal. Disconnect fuel return hose and fuel charge hose, heater hoses, and all vacuum hoses. On models with automatic transmission, disconnect wire to inhibitor switch and downshift solenoid.

5) Remove clutch operating cylinder on models with manual transmission. Disconnect speedometer cable from rear extension housing. Remove center console, "C" ring, and control lever pin from transmission striking rod guide, then remove control lever on models with manual transmission. On models with automatic transmission, disconnect shift control lever.

6) Disconnect exhaust pipe from exhaust manifold. Disconnect exhaust pipe bracket from rear extension housing and tie exhaust pipe out of the way. Mark propeller shaft and pinion flange to aid in reassembly, then remove propeller shaft from vehicle. Plug rear of extension housing to prevent oil leakage. Support transmission with a jack and remove rear engine mount. Use a hoist to raise engine and remove front engine mount attaching bolts. Raise engine and transmission and remove from vehicle as a unit.

CYLINDER HEAD

Removal – **1)** Drain cooling system and disconnect upper radiator hose and heater hoses. Dissipate fuel hose pressure to zero. *See step 1) under Engine Removal.* Remove air regulator and all connecting hoses as an assembly. Remove spark plug wires at plug end. Remove EGR control valve, vacuum switching valve and hoses as an assembly. Remove throttle chamber with dash pot and boost controlled deceleration device.

2) Remove fuel lines, vacuum hoses, and canister purge hose pressure regulator. **NOTE** – *Remove clip attaching fuel inlet hose to injector and take care not to twist or bend fuel inlet hose during removal.* Remove thermostat housing and all attached switches as an assembly. Remove PCV valve hose, sub-heat shield plate, and EGR tube.

3) Remove intake manifold and heat shield plate. Remove exhaust manifold. Remove all drive belts. Remove camshaft sprocket attaching bolt and remove sprocket from timing chain. **NOTE** – *Use special tool ST17420001 to support timing chain so timing marks on crankshaft sprocket and timing chain will remain unchanged to simplify timing mark alignment upon reassembly.* Remove oil pipe. Remove cylinder head attaching bolts working from the ends towards center of cylinder head. Remove cylinder head from engine block.

Installation – With cylinder head and block surface clean, install cylinder head gasket. **NOTE** – *Do not use sealer on gasket or head surfaces.* Install cylinder head and attaching bolts. Tighten cylinder head bolts in three steps using sequence indicated in illustration. Install camshaft sprocket and attaching bolt while making sure timing chain has not moved from its originnal position. Install remaining components in reverse of removal procedure, and tighten all nuts and bolts.

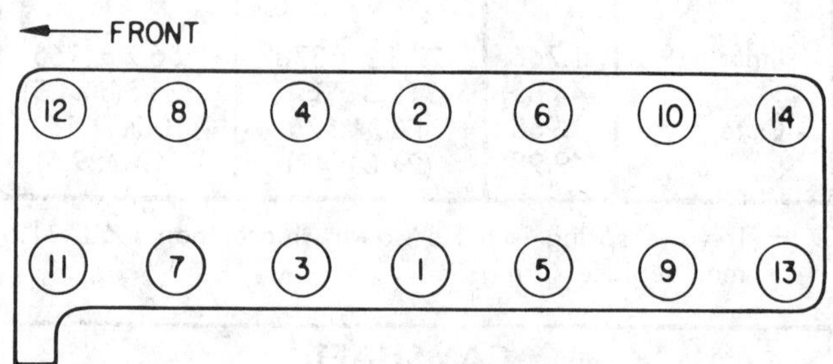

Fig. 1 Cylinder Head Tightening Sequence.

VALVES

VALVE ARRANGEMENT

E-I-I-E-I-E-I-E-I-E-I-I-E (front to rear).

VALVE GUIDES CHECKING

1) Measure clearance between valve stem and valve guide with aid of micrometer and hole gauge. Check diameter of valve stem in three places: top, center and bottom.

810 & 280Z 6 CYLINDER (Cont.)

2) Insert hole gauge in valve guide bore and measure at center. Subtract highest reading of valve stem diameter from valve guide bore to obtain clearance.

NOTE — *As a quick check, a valve may be inserted into valve guide and moved either left or right (parallel with rocker arm). If its tip moves about .0079" or more, the clearance is beyond maximum limit of .0039".*

VALVE GUIDE REPLACEMENT

1) Using a press and drift pin, force worn guide from cylinder head working from combustion cylinder side. Although this procedure may be carried out at room temperature, higher temperatures will aid removal.

2) Ream cylinder head side guide hole to provide interference fit of .0011-.0019" (.027-.049 mm). Press new valve guide into cylinder head so that it will fit smoothly when cylinder head is heated to 302-392°F (150-200°C).

3) Ream bore of valve guides to .3150-.3157" (8.000-8.018 mm). Correct valve seat surface using new valve guide as axis.

VALVE SEAT INSERTS

Check valve seats for pitting at valve contact surface. Valve seat inserts of .020" (.5 mm) oversize are available if necessary.

VALVE STEM OIL SEALS

An oil seal is installed on all intake and exhaust valve stems inside of valve spring.

VALVE SPRINGS

Removal — With cylinder head removed, loosen pivot lock nut and remove rocker arm by pressing valve spring down, taking care not to lose valve rocker guide. Remove camshaft taking care not to damage camshaft bearings and cam lobes. Compress valves and remove valve keepers. Remove compressing tool, then remove spring retainer, inner and outer springs, oil seal and valve spring seat.

Installation — Install spring seat and fit oil seal onto valve guide. Install inner and outer valve springs, spring retainer, valve keepers and rocker guide. **NOTE** — *Outer spring must be installed with painted side toward cylinder head.* Install camshaft to cylinder head. Press valve springs down using a screwdriver and install rocker arms. Install valve rocker springs.

VALVE SPRING INSTALLED HEIGHT

Valve spring must be square within 1/16". Valve spring installed height is 1.38" (35 mm) for inner spring and 1.57" (40 mm) for outer spring. If spring height and pressure, or squareness does not meet specifications, replace spring.

VALVE ADJUSTMENT

Loosen pivot locking nut and turn pivot screw until specified clearance is obtained with engine cold. Tighten pivot locking nut after adjustment and recheck clearance. Warm up engine. With engine stopped, measure valve clearance and reset to hot clearances if necessary.

Valve Adjustment Clearances

Valve	Hot	Cold
Intake	.010"(.25 mm)	.008"(.20 mm)
Exhaust	.012"(.30 mm)	.010"(.25 mm)

PISTONS, PINS & RINGS

PISTON & ROD ASSEMBLY

1) Remove cylinder head and oil pan. Remove nuts from connecting rod and remove connecting rod cap with bearing half. Push piston and connecting rod assembly with bearing half up and out through top of crankcase. **NOTE** — *Keep connecting rod caps with their respective piston and rod assembly as caps are not interchangeable.*

2) To install piston and connecting rod assembly, thoroughly oil rings, piston and cylinder wall. Make sure ring gaps are situated approximately 180° apart and not on thrust side of piston or in line with piston pin. Make sure bearing halves are properly seated in connecting rod and cap.

3) Install a ring compressor and compress rings. Install piston in cylinder with notch mark on piston head toward front of engine. With piston installed in cylinder, and connecting rod and bearings seated against crankshaft journal, install rod caps to their respective piston and rod assembly. Oil jet of connecting rod should face right side of cylinder block. Install cylinder head and oil pan.

FITTING PISTONS

1) Visually inspect cylinder block for cracks or flaws. Using a suitable bore gauge, measure cylinder for out-of-round or taper. If cylinder bore out-of-round or taper exceeds .0006" (.015 mm), refinish cylinder bore. When any one cylinder is bored, all cylinders must be bored.

2) Determine piston oversize according to amount of wear in cylinder (see specifications). By measuring piston at thrust face and adding mean of piston-to-cylinder clearance, finish hone of cylinder may be determined.

3) After honing cylinder to final fit, measure piston-to-cylinder clearance using pull scale and feeler gauge. Extracting force to pull scale should be .44-3.31 lbs. (.2-1.5 kg) using a .0016" (.04 mm) feeler gauge. If cylinder bores are worn beyond limits, undersize cylinder liners are available. Liners should have an interference fit of .0031-.0035" (.08-.09 mm) in cylinder block.

Piston Specifications

Piston Size In. (mm)	Piston Diameter In. (mm)
Standard	3.3852-3.3872(85.985-86.035)
.020 (.50) O/S	3.4041-3.4061(86.465-86.515)
.040 (1.0) O/S	3.4238-3.4258(86.965-87.015)

810 & 280Z 6 CYLINDER (Cont.)

PISTON PINS

Using suitable press and related adaptors, remove piston pin from piston and connecting rod. Measure pin bore diameter in piston and connecting rod. If wear exceeds specifications, replace both piston and pin. Pin must fit piston with light thumb pressure at room temperature. Piston pin is a press fit (interference) in connecting rod. If connecting rod is replaced, insure that new rod is within .247 ounce (7 grams) of the defective connecting rod. Install piston pin to piston and connecting rod so oil hole on connecting rod will face right side of engine and notch on piston head will face forward when assembly is installed.

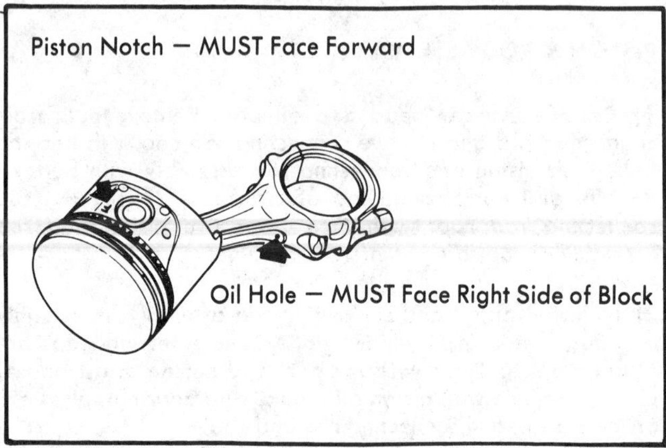

Fig. 2 Piston and Connecting Rod Alignment.

CRANKSHAFT MAIN & CONNECTING ROD BEARINGS

CRANKSHAFT

Removal — With engine removed from vehicle, remove cylinder head and oil pan. Remove flywheel and end plate. Remove oil pump, front cover, chain tensioner and chain guides. Remove timing chain, oil thrower, crankshaft worm gear, and chain drive sprocket. Remove piston and rod assemblies. Remove main bearing caps using a special puller (ST1651S000) to remove center and rear main bearing caps. **NOTE** — *Keep all main bearing caps in order to aid in reassembly*. Remove rear oil seal, then remove crankshaft.

Fig. 3 Rear Main Bearing Cap Removal.

Inspection — Check shaft journals and crankpins for scoring, wear, or cracks. Taper and out-of-round of journals and crankpins must not exceed .0012" (.03 mm). Check crankshaft for bend using a dial indicator at center journal of crankshaft. If bend exceeds .004" (.10 mm), which is one-half of indicator reading, replace crankshaft. Check main drive shaft pilot bearing at rear of crankshaft for wear or damage and replace if necessary.

Installation — **1)** Install main bearing halves to engine block ensuring that all bearings are on correct journal. Journal No. 4 requires a thrust bearing. Bearing for journal No. 1 is the same as for journal No. 7. Upper and lower bearings are not interchangeable.

2) Apply oil to main bearing surface and install crankshaft. Install main bearing caps with arrow pointing toward front of engine. **NOTE** — *Apply sealer to main bearing caps at point where cap contacts cylinder block.* Shift crankshaft toward front of engine, then tighten main bearing caps, in two or three steps, starting at center bearing and working outwards. Ensure crankshaft rotates smoothly.

3) Check crankshaft end play, and if not within specifications, replace center thrust bearing. Install side seals in rear main bearing cap after applying sealer to seals. Install rear oil seal. Install rear end plate and flywheel. Install piston and rod assemblies. Install cylinder head, crankshaft sprocket, worm gear, chain drive sprocket, oil thrower, and timing chain. Install chain guides and tensioner, front cover, oil pump and oil pan. Install remaining components in reverse of removal procedure.

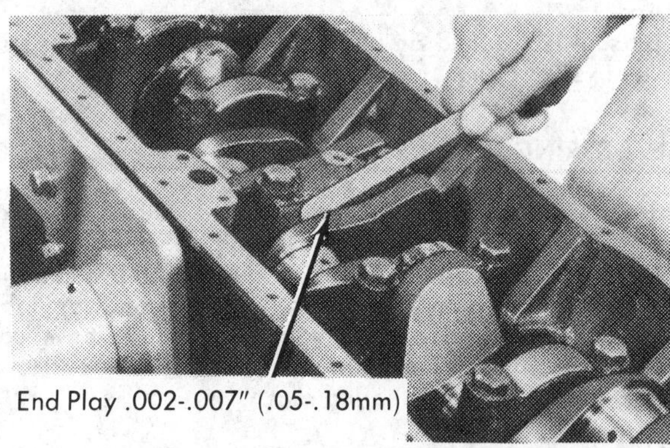

Fig. 4 Measuring End Play at No.4 Main Bearing.

MAIN BEARING CLEARANCE

1) Check all bearings for scoring or wear and replace if damage is found. Clean oil from crankshaft and place a strip of Plastigage on crankshaft journal. **NOTE** — *Plastigage should run parallel with crankshaft journal and should not block oil hole.* Install main bearing cap, with bearing installed, and tighten to 33-40 ft. lbs. (4.5-5.5 mkg). **NOTE** — *Do not turn crankshaft while Plastigage is inserted.*

2) Remove cap and measure width of Plastigage at widest point using gauge provided with Plastigage. If clearance is not to specifications, replace bearings. Bearings are available in undersizes of .01" (.25 mm), .02" (.50 mm), .03" (.75 mm), and .04" (1.0 mm).

810 & 280Z 6 CYLINDER (Cont.)

3) Bearings are manufactured with crush to cause bearing to snug down into bore. To measure, set bearing in cap or cylinder block and lock one side end of bearing. Press other side of bearing until back surface touches bore. Measure bearing crush, as shown in illustration, using a feeler gauge. Measurement must be 0-.0012" (0-.03 mm).

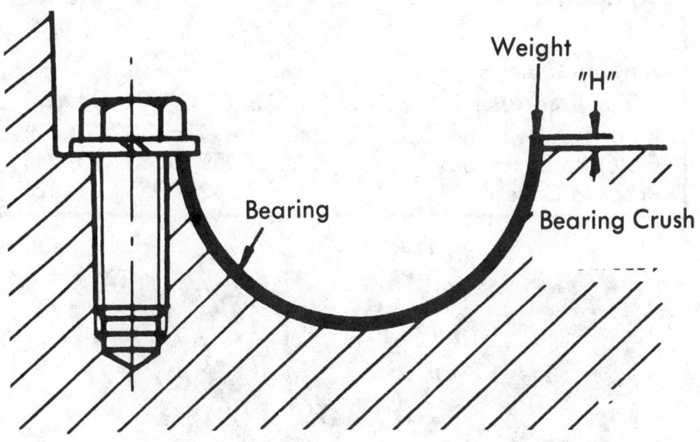

Fig. 5 Measuring Bearing Crush in Cylinder Block.

CONNECTING ROD BEARING CLEARANCE

Check connecting rod bearing clearance in same manner as main bearing clearance using Plastigage. Tighten connecting rod caps to 33-40 ft. lbs. (4.5-5.5 mkg). Bearings are available in undersizes of .0024" (.06 mm), .005" (.12 mm), .01" (.25 mm), .02" (.50 mm), .03" (.75 mm), and .04" (1.0 mm). Check bearing crush of connecting rod bearings in same manner as for main bearings. Clearance must be .0006-.0018" (.015-.045 mm).

ENGINE FRONT COVER

Removal – Drain cooling system, disconnect hoses and remove radiator. Remove all drive belts, fan blade and pulley. Disconnect all wiring and connections to thermostat housing and remove housing. Remove crankshaft pulley and water pump. Remove spark plug wires from plugs, mark position of distributor base to engine and position of rotor to distributor. Disconnect distributor wires from coil and remove distributor. Remove oil pump with its drive spindle. Remove front cover attaching bolts and front cover.

Installation – Apply sealer to four corners of front cover and gasket, then install cover onto cylinder block. Tighten front cover attaching bolts. Install oil pump with drive spindle. Install distributor while aligning matching marks. Reconnect spark plug wires and all distributor connections. Install water pump and crankshaft pulley. Install thermostat housing and reconnect all wiring. Installfan blade and pulley. Install drive belts, radiator, hoses, and fill cooling system.

CAMSHAFT

CAMSHAFT

Removal – Remove cylinder head. Remove valve rocker springs. Loosen valve rocker pivot lock nuts and remove rocker arms by pressing down on spring. Use care not to lose valve rocker guide. Carefully remove camshaft from front of cylinder head.

Fig. 6 Withdrawing Camshaft From Cylinder Head.

Installation – Carefully install camshaft into cylinder head taking care not to damage bearings. Install camshaft locating plate with oblong groove of plate facing front of cylinder head. Install camshaft sprocket and tighten attaching bolt. Install remaining components in reverse of removal procedure, and tighten all nuts and bolts.

CAMSHAFT BEARINGS

NOTE – *Do not remove camshaft bearings. If bearings are removed, bearing centers will be out of alignment and proper reassembly will be difficult without center boring.*

Measure inner diameter of camshaft bearing and outer diameter of camshaft journal. If wear or damage is excessive, replace cylinder head assembly.

TIMING CHAIN

Removal – Remove engine front cover. Remove camshaft drive sprocket, timing chain, tensioner and chain guide. Remove oil thrower, crankshaft worn gear and crankshaft sprocket.

Installation – Install components in reverse of removal procedure while noting the following: When installing timing chain, camshaft sprocket or crankshaft sprocket, make sure camshaft and crankshaft keys point upward. Set timing chain so that its mating marks match marks on crankshaft and camshaft sprockets on right-hand side. There are 42 chain links between the two timing chain marks. Factory setting of camshaft sprocket is number one hole, if chain is excessively stretched use number two or three hole to achieve correct valve timing.

810 & 280Z 6 CYLINDER (Cont.)

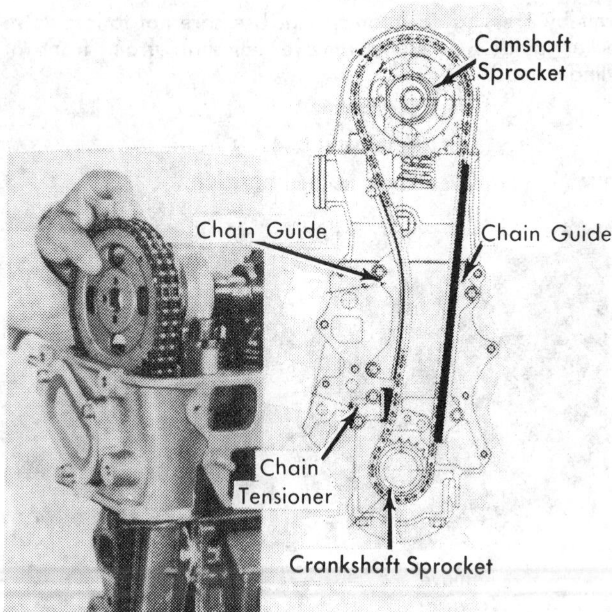

Fig. 7 Timing Chain and Sprocket Installation.

ENGINE OILING

ENGINE OILING SYSTEM

Oil drawn from oil pan passes through a screen to oil pump. Oil is delivered to full flow oil filter and to main oil gallery. Main oil gallery supplies oil to crankshaft main bearings and drilled passages in crankshaft. Oil sprayed from jet holes on connecting rods lubricates cylinders and piston pins. Oil from main gallery lubricates chain tensioner and timing chain. A center oil hole in the crankshaft center bearing feeds camshaft bearings on cylinder head. Valve rocker mechanism is lubricated through oil gallery in camshaft and through a small channel at base circle portion of each cam. Rocker arms and valves are lubricated intermittenly through small holes or oil pipe.

Crankcase Capacity – 5 qts. including filter change.

Oil Filter – Full-flow, with disposable cartridge.

Oil Pressure – 50-57 psi (3.5-4.0 kg/cm²) @ 2000 RPM.

OIL PUMP

Oil pump assembly is installed to bottom of front cover by four bolts. Pump is driven by oil pump drive spindle assembly which is in turn driven by gear on crankshaft. To remove oil pump, first remove distributor. Drain engine oil and remove oil pump body together with drive spindle. To disassemble, proceed as follows:

1) Remove pump cover and gasket. Slide pump rotors from pump body. Remove regulator cap, valve and spring. Clean all components with cleaning solvent, and inspect for wear or damage. Check the clearances indicated in the following table and ensure clearances are to specifications. If components are not to specifications, replace entire pump assembly.

2) Assemble pump in reverse of disassembly while making sure mark dotted on rotors faces oil pump body. Fill pump housing with engine oil before installing to front cover.

Oil Pump Specifications

Application	Clearance In. (mm)
Inner-to-Outer Rotor Side Clearance	.0016-.0032"(.04-.08 mm)
Rotor Tip Clearance	Less Than .0047 (.12)
Outer Rotor-to-Body	.0059-.0083 (.15-.21)
Rotor-to-Cover	.0012-.0051 (.03-.13)

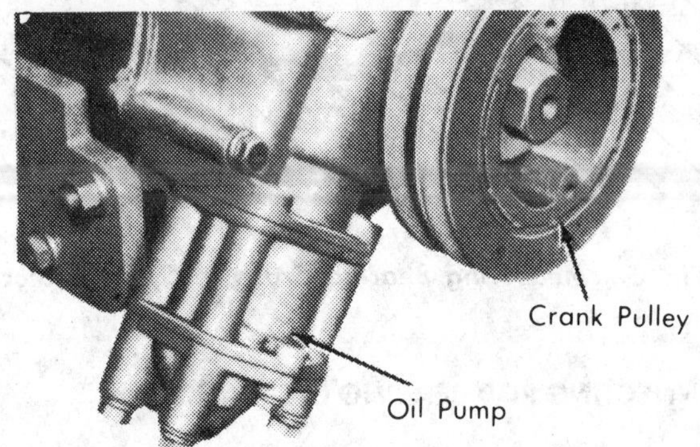

Fig. 8 Location of Oil Pump Assembly.

ENGINE COOLING

WATER PUMP

Centrifugal type pump with aluminum body. To remove, drain cooling system and remove fan shroud. Remove fan belts, fan, and pulley. Remove pump attaching bolts and remove water pump from front cover.

Thermostat – Opens at 180°F (82°C).

Cooling System Capacity – 10 qts.

Radiator Cap – 13 psi.

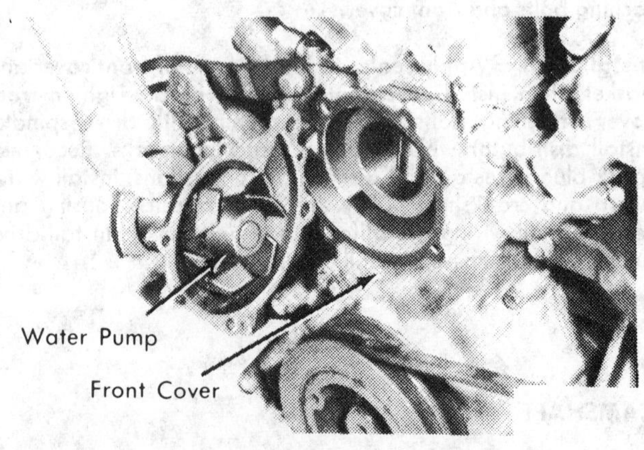

Fig. 9 Installing Water Pump to Front Cover.

810 & 280Z 6 CYLINDER (Cont.)

ENGINE SPECIFICATIONS

GENERAL SPECIFICATIONS										
Year	Displ.		Carburetor	HP at RPM	Torque (Ft. Lbs. at RPM)	Compr. Ratio	Bore		Stroke	
	cu. ins.	cc					in.	mm	in.	mm
1977										
L28	168.0	2753	Fuel Inj.	.....	.....	8.3-1	3.390	86	3.110	79
L24	146.0	2393	Fuel Inj.	.....	.....	8.6-1	3.270	83	2.90	73.7

VALVES							
Engine & Valve	Head Diam. In. (mm)	Face Angle	Seat Angle	Seat Width In. (mm)	Stem Diameter In. (mm)	Stem Clearance In. (mm)	Valve Lift In. (mm)
L28							
Int.	1.73 (44.0)	45.5	45.5	.055-.063 (1.4-1.6)	.3136-.3142 (7.965-7.980)	.0008-.0021 (.020-.053)	.433 (11)
Exh.	1.38 (35.0)	45.5°	45.5°	.071-.087 (1.8-2.2)	.3128-.3134 (7.945-7.960)	.0016-.0029 (.040-.073)	.433 (11)
L24							
Int.	1.64 (42.0)	45.5°	45.5°	.055-.063 (1.4-1.6)	.3136-.3142 (7.965-7.980)	.0008-.0021 (.020-.053)	.394 (10)
Exh.	1.38 (35.0)	45.5°	45.5°	.071-.087 (1.8-2.2)	.3128-.3134 (7.945-7.960)	.0016-.0029 (.040-.073)	.413 (10.5)

VALVE SPRINGS			
Engine	Free Length In. (mm)	PRESSURE Lbs. @ In. (kg @ mm)	
		Valve Closed	Valve Open
L28			
Inner	1.766 (44.85)	27.1@1.378 (12.3@35)	56.2@.965 (25.5@24.5)
Outer	1.968 (49.98)	47@1.575 (21.3@40)	108@1.161 (49@29.5)
L24			
Inner	1.766 (44.85)	27@1.378 (12.3@35)	54.9@.984 (24.9@25)
Outer	1.986 (49.98)	47@1.575 (21.3@40)	105.2@1.181 (47.7@30)

CAMSHAFT			
Engine	Journal Diam. In. (mm)	Clearance In. (mm)	Lobe Lift In. (mm)
L28	1.8878-1.8883 (47.949-47.962)	.0015-.0026 (.038-.067)	In.&Exh. .275 (7.00)
L24	1.8878-1.8883 (47.949-47.962)	.0015-.0026 (.038-.067)	In. .261 (6.65) Exh. .275 (7.00)

810 & 280Z 6 CYLINDER (Cont.)

ENGINE SPECIFICATIONS (Cont.)

PISTONS, PINS, RINGS						
	PISTONS	PINS		RINGS		
Engine	Clearance In. (mm)	Piston Fit In. (mm)	Rod Fit In. (mm)	Rings	End Gap In. (mm)	Side Clearance In. (mm)
L28	.0010-.0018 (.025-.045)	.0002-.0051 (.006-.013)	① .0006-.0013 (.015-.033)	No.1	.0098-.0157 (.25-.40)	.0016-.0029 (.040-.073)
				No.2	.0118-.0197 (.30-.50)	.0012-.0028 (.030-.070)
				Oil	.0118-.0354 (.30-.90)	Snug
L24	.0010-.0018 (.025-.045)	.0002-.0051 (.006-.013)	① .0006-.0013 (.015-.033)	No.1	.0098-.0157 (.25-.40)	.0016-.0029 (.040-.073)
				No.2	.0118-.0197 (.30-.50)	.0012-.0028 (.030-.070)
				Oil	.006-.012 (.15-.30)	Snug

① — Interference fit.

CRANKSHAFT MAIN & CONNECTING ROD BEARINGS							
	MAIN BEARINGS				CONNECTING ROD BEARINGS		
Engine	Journal Diam. In. (mm)	Clearance In. (mm)	Thrust Bearing	Crankshaft End Play In. (mm)	Journal Diam. In. (mm)	Clearance In. (mm)	Side Play In. (mm)
L28&L24	2.1631-2.1636 (54.942-54.955)	.0008-.0028 (.022-.071)	Center	.002-.007① (.05-.18)	1.9670-1.9675 (49.961-49.974)	.0010-.0022 (.025-.056)	.0079-.0118 (.20-.30)

① — Interference fit.

TIGHTENING SPECIFICATIONS

Application	Ft. Lbs.(mkg)
Cylinder Head	
Step One	29(4.0)
Step Two	47(6.5)
Step Three	54-61(7.5-8.5)
Connecting Rod	33-40(4.5-5.5)
Flywheel	94-108(13-15)
Camshaft Gear	94-108(13-15)
Oil Pan	4.3-7.2(.6-1.0)
Oil Pump-to-Front Cover	8-11(1.1-2.1)
Oil Pump Cover	5-7(.7-1.0)
Camshaft Lock Plate	3.6-5.8(.5-.8)
Crankshaft Pulley	94-108(13-15)
Main Bearing Cap	33-40(4.5-5.5)
Front Cover	
6M Bolt	2.9-5.8(.4-.8)
8M Bolt	7.2-11.6(1.0-1.6)
Rocker Pivot Lock Nuts	36-43(5-6)
Intake & Exhaust Manifolds	
8M Bolt	1-13(1.4-1.8)
10M Bolt	29-40(4.0-5.5)

128 & X1/9 4 CYLINDER

ENGINE CODING

ENGINE IDENTIFICATION

Engine identification and serial numbers are stamped in crankcase on flywheel side of engine next to union for radiator hoses. Engine code is stamped above serial number.

Application	Engine Code
128 (Calif.)	128A1.031.6
128 (Federal)	128A1.040.6
X1/9 (Calif.)	128AS.040.5
X1/9 (Federal)	128AS.040.6

ENGINE, CYLINDER HEAD & MANIFOLDS

ENGINE

NOTE – *Engine and transmission are removed as one unit.*

Model 128 – 1) Raise and support vehicle with safety stands. Raise hood and disconnect stay rod. Remove spare tire from engine compartment. Remove lower protective guard. Disconnect both battery cables.

2) Drain complete cooling system. Lower heater lever inside vehicle. Remove radiator cap and supply tank cap. Open drain on bottom of radiator and on inner side of crankcase.

3) Disconnect wires from coil to distributor. Disconnect wires at generator, starter, oil pressure switch and water temperature sending unit. Remove air cleaner housing and cartridge.

4) Disconnect accelerator linkage and choke cable at carburetor. Disconnect fuel inlet line at fuel pump. Disconnect exhaust pipe at exhaust manifold.

5) Remove radiator hoses from union at left side of engine. Remove heater hoses from engine. Remove speedometer cable from transmission. Remove adjustable rod from clutch release lever by removing nut and lock-nut.

6) From underneath vehicle, remove stabilizer bar from body and lower suspension control arms. Remove exhaust pipe support bracket from transmission. Disconnect rod from gear shift control lever.

7) Remove left wheel and tire. Remove left tie-rod nut and separate tie-rod from steering arm using a suitable puller (A.47044). Disconnect shock absorber at lower mount. Remove outer axle nuts from both sides.

8) Remove strut connecting engine to body. Attach a suitable lifting fixture (A.60559) to engine. Connect lifting fixture to a hoist and raise engine slightly. Remove bolt from clamp securing engine to body. Remove engine support crossmember from under engine.

9) Pull shafts of axle joints from bearing housings. Secure axle shafts to differential with wire to prevent working loose from seats. Remove engine and transmission assembly from bottom of vehicle. Separate transmission and differential assembly from engine.

Model X1/9 – 1) Disconnect battery cables and loosen fuel cap to vent fuel tank. Drain complete cooling system. Disconnect hoses from air injection valve and air cleaner, then disconnect fresh air duct from fan. Remove air cleaner assembly with fresh air duct.

2) Disconnect hoses from air pump, then separate heater return hose at coupling joint and heater hose at pump. Disconnect wires from alternators. Remove bolts holding louvered protection panel below carbon trap in rear firewall.

3) Disconnect choke linkage, hoses and wires from carburetor. Disconnect electrical leads from distributor, oil pressure switch, water temperature sending unit and starter.

4) Remove clamp holding fuel lines to firewall and disconnect fuel lines from firewall. Disconnect accelerator cable from support. Remove cooling system expansion tank and disconnect hoses from thermostat. Disconnect clutch master cylinder from transmission and swing out of way.

5) Raise and support vehicle with safety stands. Remove remaining bolt attaching louvered panel in rear firewall, then remove panel. Remove alternator heat shield, engine panels and wheel panels. Drain transmission and differential assembly. Disconnect back-up light and seat belt interlock connectors, then remove clamps to allow wires to come out with engine. Disconnect speedometer cable and gearshift linkage from transmission.

6) Disconnect ground strap at engine, then remove muffler and muffler upper bracket. Remove axle boot retaining bolts and slide boots away from differential.

7) Remove nuts securing hand brake cable brackets to control arms. Remove bolts attaching control arms to body and swing arms down out of brackets. **NOTE** – *Record number of shims at control arm mounting points for installation purpose.* Move control arms away from differential until axles are free of differential.

8) Remove lower crossmember attaching bolts and remove crossmember. From above engine, disconnect reaction arm from bracket on engine, then remove front engine mount through bolt. Remove engine and transmission assembly from bottom of vehicle. Separate transmission and differential from engine.

INTAKE & EXHAUST MANIFOLD

1) Drain cooling system. Remove spare tire from engine compartment. Remove air cleaner and cartridge. Disconnect accelerator linkage and choke cable from carburetor. Remove carburetor pre-heating water hoses.

2) Remove carburetor with guard and gaskets. Remove shroud from intake and exhaust manifold. Remove intake and exhaust manifold from engine.

3) To install, use new gaskets and reverse removal procedure.

128 & X1/9 4 CYLINDER (Cont.)

CYLINDER HEAD

NOTE – *This procedure is with engine in vehicle.*

1) Drain engine cooling system and remove spare tire from engine compartment. Remove air cleaner housing and cartridge. Disconnect spark plug wires at spark plugs.

2) Disconnect accelerator linkage and choke cable at carburetor. Disconnect fuel line at carburetor. Disconnect wire from temperature sending unit.

3) Disconnect heater hose at cylinder head. Disconnect all water hoses at union on left side of engine. Disconnect exhaust pipe from exhaust manifold.

4) Disconnect reaction rod from engine bracket and hose from exhaust shroud. Remove timing cover, then remove alternator and water pump drive belt. Remove air pump drive belt, then loosen nut on tensioner pulley and remove timing belt. Remove cylinder head nuts and bolts, then remove head and manifolds as an assembly.

5) Thoroughly clean gasket surfaces on crankcase and cylinder head. Use new gasket and install with word "Alto" up. Reverse removal procedure to install remaining components. Tighten cylinder head nuts to 69 ft. lbs. (9.5 mkg) in sequence as shown in *Fig. 1*. Make sure timing belt is properly installed.

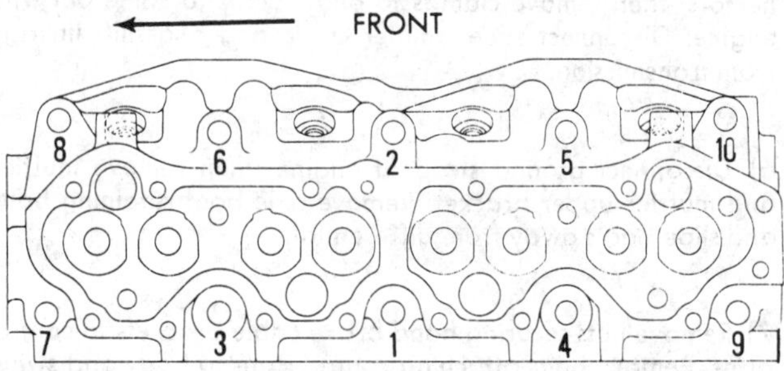

Fig. 1 Cylinder Head Tightening Sequence

VALVES

VALVE ARRANGEMENT

E-I-I-E-E-I-I-E

VALVE GUIDE SERVICING

1) With cylinder head removed and disassembled, check clearance between valve stem and valve guide. If clearance is more than .006", and valve stem is not worn, valve guide must be replaced.

2) Drive guide from cylinder head using a suitable driver (A.60153). Use same driver to install guides with a suitable spacer installed (6A intake and 6S exhaust).

VALVE STEM OIL SEALS

Use new seals when assembling cylinder head. Use a suitable guide (A.60313) to install seals on valve guides.

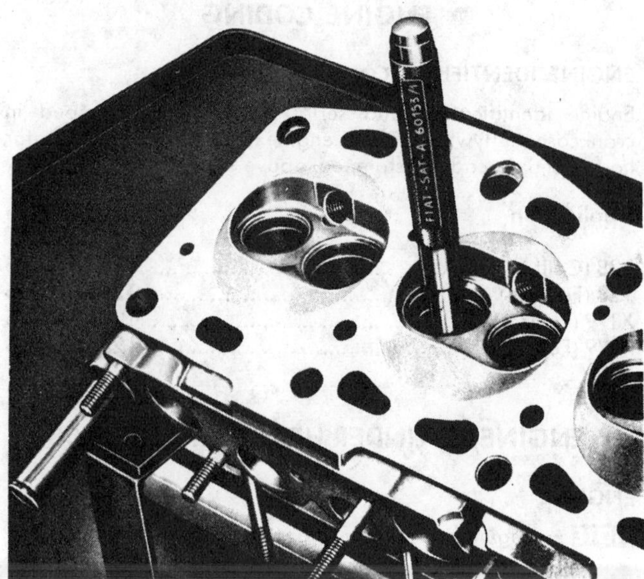

Fig. 2 Using Special Driver to Remove Valve Guide

VALVE SPRING REMOVAL

1) Remove cylinder head as previously outlined. Remove camshaft housing cover, carburetor, intake and exhaust manifolds. Remove camshaft housing with camshaft.

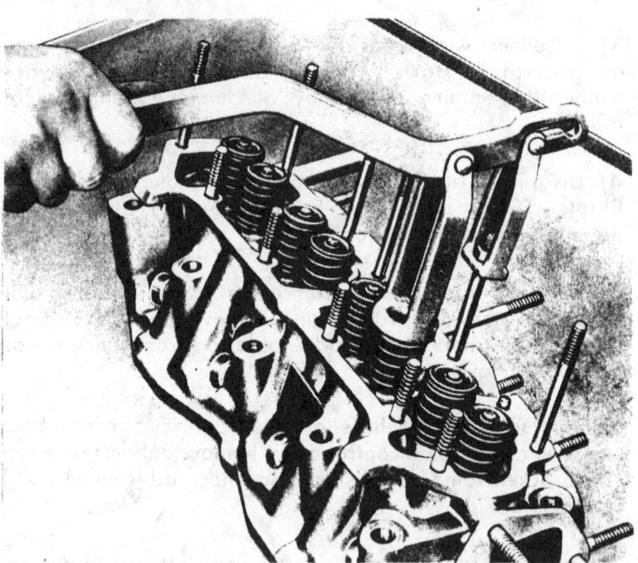

Fig. 3 Using Special Valve Spring Compressor to Remove Valve Springs

2) Using a suitable valve spring compressor (A.60311) compress valve spring. Remove valve keepers and release compressor. Remove spring retainer, inner spring, outer spring, lower spring seat and washer.

3) Inspect valve springs for wear or cracking. Using a suitable spring tester (AP.5049) check inner and outer springs against specifications with specified load applied.

4) To install valve spring, reverse removal procedure. Install cylinder head as previously outlined.

128 & X1/9 4 CYLINDER (Cont.)

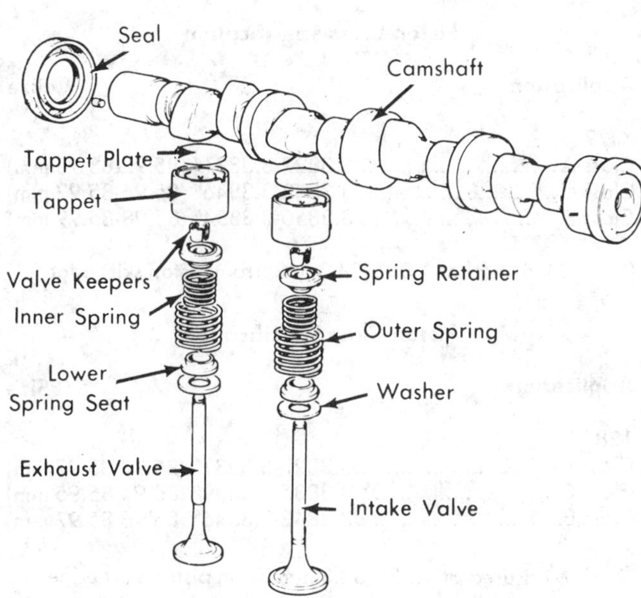

Fig. 4 Expanded View of Valve Train Components

VALVE CLEARANCE ADJUSTMENT

NOTE — *Valve clearance is checked and adjusted with engine cold.*

1) Remove camshaft cover. Rotate engine until lobe on camshaft of valve being checked is pointing straight up. Using a feeler gauge, check clearance between camshaft lobe and valve tappet plate.

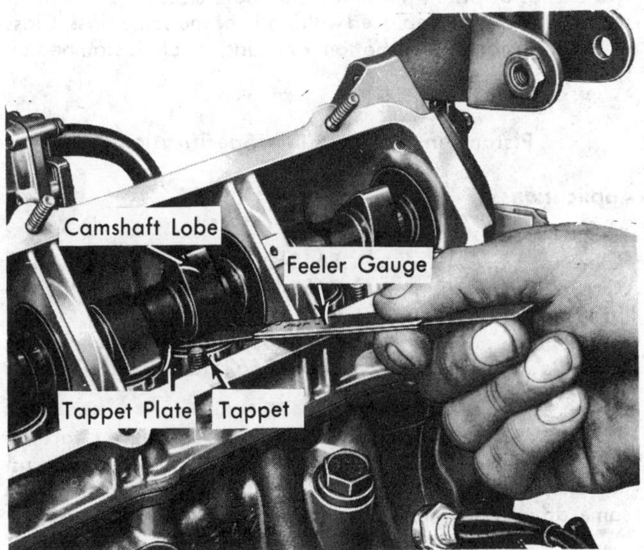

Fig. 5 Showing Where to Make Valve Clearance Check

2) If clearance is not as specified, insert a suitable spring compressor (A.60421) under camshaft to release spring tension against camshaft lobe. Remove tappet plate with a suitable removing tool (A.87001). With plate removed, measure thickness to determine size of plate to be installed.

Valve Clearance Specifications

Application	Intake Valve	Exhaust Valve
All	.012" (.3mm)	.016" (.4mm)

3) Valve tappet plates are available in various thicknesses: .1280-.1850" (3.251-4.699 mm) in increments of .0019" (.048 mm). Plate size is shown on face, install this side toward tappet. Use same procedure on both intake and exhaust valves. Recheck clearance and install camshaft cover.

Fig. 6 Using Special Tool to Remove Valve Tappet Plate

PISTONS, PINS & RINGS

OIL PAN

NOTE — *This procedure is with engine in vehicle.*

1) Attach a suitable engine support (A.70526) to top of engine. Remove protective shields and engine crossmember.

2) Drain oil and remove oil pan retaining screws and oil pan. To install, clean all gasket surfaces, use new gasket and reverse removal procedure.

PISTON & ROD ASSEMBLY

1) Remove oil pan and cylinder head as previously outlined. Remove oil pump. See *Oil Pump*. Remove nuts from connecting rods and remove rod caps. Push piston and rod assembly up and out through top.

2) To install, compress piston rings with a suitable ring compressor. Pistons must be installed with number stamped on connecting rod and rod cap facing away from auxiliary shaft on 128 models and with number facing towards auxiliary shaft on model X1/9.

3) Tighten rod nuts to specifications. Install remaining components as previously outlined.

128 & X1/9 4 CYLINDER (Cont.)

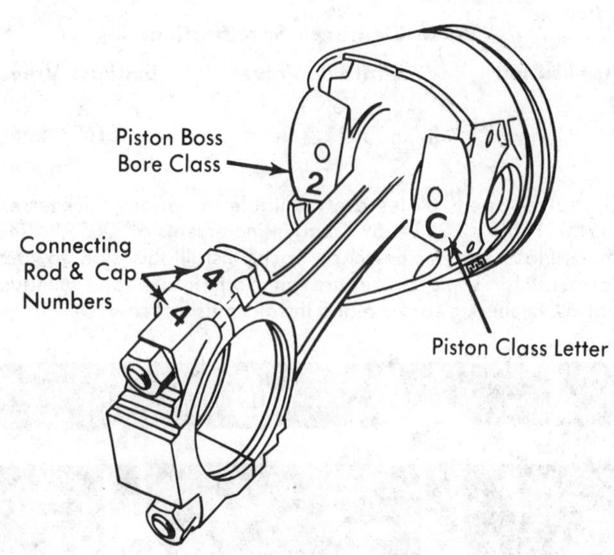

Fig. 7 Piston & Connecting Rod Assembly Showing Identification Class Numbers

FITTING PISTONS

1) With piston and rod assembly removed and disassembled as previously outlined, thoroughly clean piston. Check ring side clearance, side clearance should be no more than .006" (.15mm). Check ring end gap in cylinder against specifications.

2) Check fit of piston in cylinders with rings removed. There should be no more than .006" (.15mm) clearance. Pistons are available in .0079" (.2mm), .0157" (.4mm) and .0236" (.6mm) oversizes. There are three classes of standard size pistons. If piston is replaced, one of the same class must be installed. Class of piston is stamped on bottom of piston.

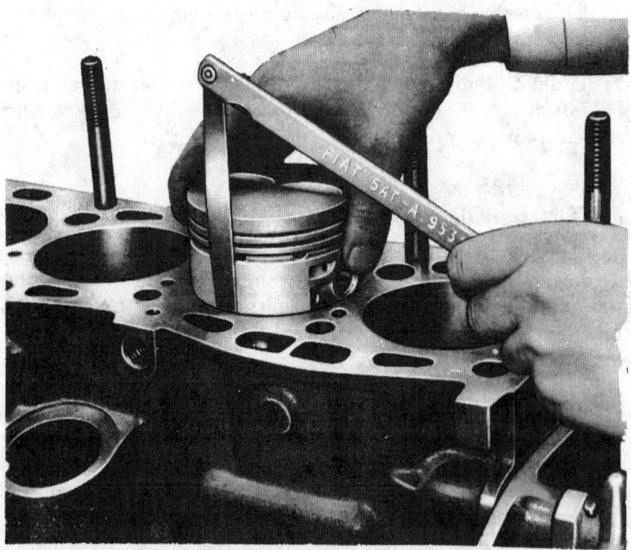

Fig. 8 Using a Feeler Gauge to Check Piston-to-Cylinder Wall Clearance

Piston Class Specification

Application	①Size
X1/9	
Class A	3.3827-3.3831" (85.92-85.93 mm)
Class C	3.3842-3.3846" (85.96-85.97 mm)
Class E	3.3850-3.3854" (85.98-85.99 mm)

① — Measured at 1.35" (34.3 mm) from piston skirt edge.

Piston Class Specification

Application	①Size
128	
Class A	3.3827-3.3831" (85.92-85.93 mm)
Class C	3.3835-3.3839" (85.94-85.95 mm)
Class E	3.3842-3.3846" (85.96-85.97 mm)

① — Measured at 1.35" (34.3 mm) from piston skirt edge.

3) When installing rings, make sure gaps are spaced approximately 120° apart. Assemble piston and connecting rod and install in vehicle as previously outlined.

PISTON PIN REPLACEMENT

1) Remove piston and rod assembly as previously outlined. Remove circlips and drive out piston pin using a suitable driver (A.60251).

2) Check fit of pin in piston. Pin should be push fit in piston and should not fall through under its own weight. There are two classes of piston pin and piston bore sizes. If piston pin is replaced it must be replaced with a pin of the same class. Class of piston is stamped on bottom and class of pin is stamped on face of pin.

Piston Pin & Bore Class Specifications

Application	Size
Piston Pin	
Class 1	.8658-.8659" (21.991-21.994mm)
Class 2	.8659-.8660" (21.994-21.996mm)
Piston Pin Bore	
Class 1	.8660-.8661" (21.996-21.999mm)
Class 2	.8661-.8662" (21.999-22.002mm)

3) Check piston pin clearance in connecting rod. If clearance is more than specified, drive bushing from connecting rod using a suitable driver (A.60054). Install a new bushing with same driver and ream to size with a new piston pin.

4) Piston pin bore in piston is offset .08". Install connecting rod with numbered side on same side as offset. Lubricate piston pin and secure connecting rod big end in a vise. Place piston in proper position with connecting rod and push in piston pin using a sutable driver (A.60251). Install circlips.

5) Install piston and connecting rod assembly as previously outlined.

128 & X1/9 4 CYLINDER (Cont.)

CRANKSHAFT MAIN & CONNECTING ROD BEARINGS

MAIN & CONNECTING ROD BEARING SERVICE

1) Remove engine as previously outlined. Remove cylinder head, oil pan, clutch and flywheel as previously outlined. Remove oil pump. See *Oil Pump.* Remove all sprockets and timing belt. See *Timing Belt Replacement.*

2) Remove cover plates and seals from both ends of engine. Remove all piston and connecting rod assemblies. Remove main bearing caps with lower bearing halves.

3) Remove crankshaft and upper bearing halves. Remove thrust bearings from flywheel end main bearing saddle. Thoroughly clean and inspect crankshaft and crankcase.

4) Check crankshaft journals for out-of-round, if more than .0002", crankshaft must be ground to next undersize. Bearings for undersize crankshafts are available in .010", .020", .030" and .040" undersize.

5) Use the Plastigage method to check main bearing clearances. Install upper bearing halves in crankcase and install crankshaft. Place a piece of Plastigage on journal and install main bearing cap with bearing. Tighten bolts to specifications and then remove main bearing cap.

6) With cap removed, check flattened Plastigage against scale on back of package to determine if clearance is as specified. Check connecting rod bearing clearance using same procedure. If clearance is incorrect, crankshaft must be ground to next undersize and bearings of corresponding undersize installed.

7) With correct clearance obtained, install upper bearing halves in crankcase. Lubricate bearings and install crankshaft. Install main bearing caps with bearings and tighten bolts to specifications. Rotate crankshaft to check for freedom of movement.

8) Check crankshaft endplay. See *Thrust Bearing Alignment.* Install remaining components in reverse of removal order or as previously outlined. Install engine as previously outlined.

Fig. 9 Fitting Crankshaft Thrust Washer to Block

THRUST BEARING ALIGNMENT

1) With crankshaft installed and main bearing caps tightened to specifications. Attach a dial indicator to crankcase with arm against flywheel end of crankshaft. Pry crankshaft back and forth to measure endplay.

2) If endplay is more than .0104", remove flywheel end main bearing cap and install oversize thrust rings. Thrust rings are available in .005" oversize. Install a suitable size thrust ring to obtain correct endplay.

FRONT & REAR MAIN BEARING OIL SEAL SERVICE

1) Front and rear main bearing oil seals are secured in end plates mounted to both ends of crankcase. Both seals should be replaced when crankshaft has been removed.

2) Drive seals from end plates and install new ones. Lubricate sealing lip of seal and use new gaskets when installing end plates.

CAMSHAFT

TIMING BELT REPLACEMENT

NOTE – *This procedure is with engine in vehicle. If a timing belt is loosened or removed to perform repair work, it should always be replaced.*

Removal 128 – 1) Remove right guard and loosen timing chain cover retaining screws, from under vehicle. Remove timing chain cover. Check timing by aligning index marks on top and bottom of camshaft sprocket with index marks on engine mounting and upper case. Index on crankshaft sprocket should be in alignment with index on crankshaft seal case.

2) Put vehicle in low gear and apply hand brake to prevent crankshaft from turning. Remove fan belt, loosen tensioner pulley retaining nut and relieve tension. Remove timing belt.

Installation – Install new belt, making sure belt and sprocket teeth engage correctly. Tighten pulley support nut. Recheck timing. Install remaining components.

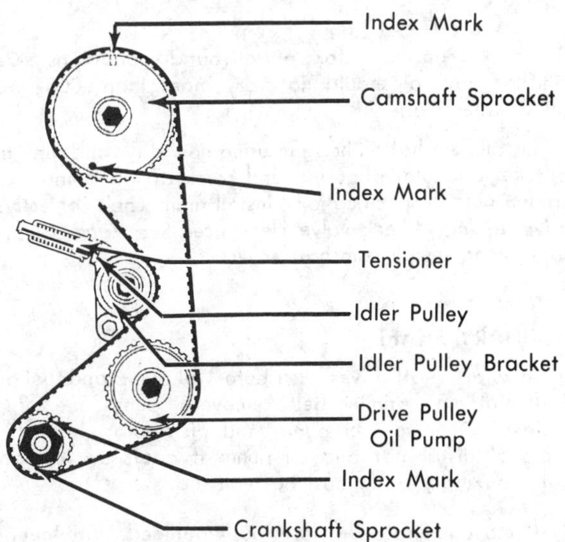

Fig. 10 Front View of Engine Showing Timing Belt Installed

128 & X1/9 4 CYLINDER (Cont.)

Removal X1/9 – 1) Rotate No. 4 cylinder into firing position at top dead center. Position transmission into 4th gear, to prevent crankshaft from turning. Apply parking brake.

NOTE – *If camshaft is turned independently of engine, valves may hit pistons causing engine damage.*

2) Remove right guard from under engine. Remove timing bolts and cover. Loosen alternator and remove alternator/water pump drive belt. Loosen air pump and remove drive belt.

3) Remove valve cover and check that camshaft lobes of No. 4 cylinder are pointing up. Remove distributor. Loosen idler pulley lock nut. Remove timing belt starting at idler pulley.

Installation – 1) Install timing belt making sure that teeth are properly engaged in sprockets. Start installation of timing belt at crankshaft pulley. Release idler pulley lock nut and retighten after tension is on belt.

NOTE – *Never allow engine to rotate backwards, or slack will develop in belt and belt will jump timing.*

2) Rotate engine one-half turn. Loosen idler pulley lock nut to ensure all slack is removed. Retighten lock nut. Rotate engine until No. 4 cylinder is in firing position (cam lobe up). Install remaining components in reverse of removal order.

CAMSHAFT

1) Remove timing belt protective cover and loosen belt tensioner. Remove timing belt from camshaft sprocket and remove sprocket from camshaft. Remove camshaft cover, camshaft and housing. Remove camshaft from housing and thoroughly clean and inspect both.

2) If camshaft housing bores show signs of wear or scoring and are out of round, replace housing. Check camshaft for signs of seizure or scoring. If scoring or seizure marks cannot be removed with a fine abrasive stone, replace camshaft.

3) Check camshaft for out-of-round conditions. Center camshaft journal should not vary more than .008" out-of-round. Check lobe lift.

4) Install camshaft in housing using new drive end seal. Install sprocket and place housing and camshaft on cylinder head. Tighten nuts to specifications. Install timing belt correctly. See *Valve Timing*. Check valve clearance. See *Valve Clearance Adjustment*. Install camshaft cover.

AUXILIARY SHAFT

1) Auxiliary shaft drives; distributor, oil pump and fuel pump. Shaft is driven by timing belt. Remove oil pump. See *Oil Pump Removal*. Remove fuel pump and distributor. Inspect drive gears of distributor and oil pump, if gears are chipped or worn, auxiliary shaft must be replaced.

2) Remove timing belt as previously outlined. With fuel pump, oil pump and distributor removed, remove auxiliary shaft sprocket. Remove lock plate and auxiliary shaft. Thoroughly clean and inspect shaft.

3) Check inner and outer journals of shaft. If journal size is less than specified, replace shaft. Check inside diameter of inner and outer bushings, if more than specified, replace bushings.

4) To replace bushings, drive out of crankcase using a suitable driver (A.60372/1/2 outer journal and A.660372/1 inner journal). Install new bushings using same drivers as used for removal. Make sure oil holes in bushings align with oil holes in crankcase. Ream bushings to specified clearance with shaft using a suitable reamer (A.90365).

5) Install auxiliary shaft and lock plate. Install sprocket and secure with lock plate and screw. Install remaining components as previously outlined or in reverse of removal order.

Auxiliary Shaft Specifications

Application	Size
Auxiliary Shaft	
Outer Journal	1.4013-1.4023" (35.59-35.62mm)
Inner Journal	1.2575-1.2583" (31.94-31.96mm)
Bushings (Reamed)	
Outer Journal	1.4041-1.4049" (35.66-35.68mm)
Inner Journal	1.2598-1.2606" (32.00-32.02mm)
Clearance	
Outer Journal	.0018-.0036" (.046-.091mm)
Inner Journal	.0016-.0031" (.04-.08mm)

VALVE TIMING

1) With timing belt removed, rotate camshaft sprocket until marks on sprocket are in alignment with index marks on engine.

2) Rotate crankshaft sprocket until mark on sprocket aligns with index on end plate. Install timing belt as previously outlined, making sure camshaft or crankshaft are not rotated.

ENGINE OILING

Crankcase Capacity – 4.5 qts. Add ¾ qt. for filter.

Oil Filter – Full flow, mounted on front side of engine.

Normal Oil Pressure – 64-85 psi. with engine @212°F.

Pressure Relief Valve – Mounted in oil pump. See *Oil Pump*.

ENGINE OILING SYSTEM

Oil is circulated through engine by pressure provided by a gear type oil pump. Pump is mounted on bottom of crankcase and driven by the auxiliary shaft. Oil is drawn from oil pan by oil pump and circulated through a full flow oil filter. Oil is then pumped into main oil gallery of crankcase where it is distributed to crankshaft and camshaft. Oil flows through crankshaft to lubricate main and connecting rod bearings. Cylinders, pistons and piston pins are lubricated by oil squirted from hole in connecting rod. Oil flows through camshaft to journals. Oil is squirted from number two and four journal to lubricate valve tappets and valves. Auxiliary shaft is lubricated by oil from main oil gallery. Excess oil flows back into oil pan.

128 & X1/9 4 CYLINDER (Cont.)

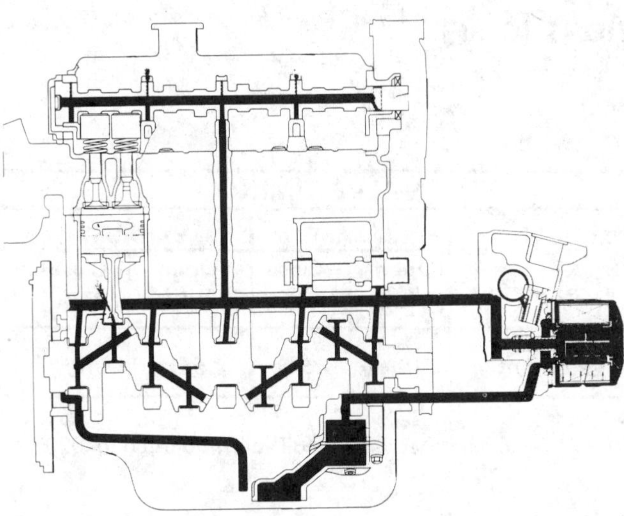

Fig. 11 Diagram Showing Engine Lubrication Flow

OIL PUMP

1) Remove oil pan as previously outlined. Remove retaining screws and slide out oil pump with suction tube.

2) Clamp pump housing in a vise and remove suction pipe with filter screen and relief valve. Remove pump cover and gears. Thoroughly clean all components.

3) Check both gears for excess wear and replace if necessary. Check clearance between gears, if more than .010", replace both gears. Check gear-to-pump housing clearance, if more than .010", replace gears or housing as necessary.

4) Check gear endplay by placing a straight edge on mating surface of pump and inserting a feeler gauge between straight edge and gears. If clearance is more than .006", replace gears or housing as necessary. Check clearance between drive gear shaft and housing, if more than .004", replace gear or housing as necessary.

5) Inspect pressure relief spring for cracking or wear. Inspect valve for wear or scoring. Check spring against specifications. Spring should not collapse below given length under given load. Replace spring if length is less than specified.

6) Assemble oil pump in reverse of disassembly order. To install, reverse removal procedure.

Oil Pump Specifications

Application	Clearance
Gear-to-Gear	.006" (.15mm)
Gear-to-Housing	.004-.007" (.11-.18mm)
Gear Endplay	.0008-.0041" (.02-.11mm)

ENGINE COOLING

Thermostat — Fully open @176-183° F.

Cooling System Capacity
128 — 7.25 qts.
X 1/9 — 11.25 qts

WATER PUMP

1) Remove protective panels from bottom of engine and drain cooling system. Remove alternator and drive belt. Disconnect hoses from water pump, then remove nuts attaching water pipe to pump and disconnect pipe. Remove bolts holding water pump to engine and remove pump.

2) Clean all gasket surfaces and install new gasket. To install, reverse removal procedure and refill cooling system. Run engine and check for leaks.

ENGINE SPECIFICATIONS

GENERAL SPECIFICATIONS

Year	Displ.		Carburetor	HP at RPM	Torque (Ft. Lbs. at RPM)	Compr. Ratio	Bore		Stroke	
	cu. ins.	cc					in.	mm	in.	mm
1977										
128	78.7	1290	1-Bbl.	62@6000	67@4000	8.5-1	3.39	86	2.19	55.5
X1/9	78.7	1290	1-Bbl.	61@5800	76@4000	8.5-1	3.39	86	2.19	55.5

VALVES

Engine & Valve	Head Diam. In. (mm)	Face Angle	Seat Angle	Seat Width In. (mm)	Stem Diameter In. (mm)	Stem Clearance In. (mm)	Valve Lift In. (mm)
1290cc							
Intake	1.4173 (36)	45°	45°	.0787 (2)	.3139-.3146 (7.974-7.992)	.0012-.0026 (.030-.066)	.3839 (9.75)
Exhaust	1.2205 (31)	45°	45°	.0787 (2)	.3139-.3146 (7.974-7.992)	.0012-.0026 (.030-.066)	.3839 (9.75)

128 & X1/9 4 CYLINDER (Cont.)

ENGINE SPECIFICATIONS (Cont.)

VALVE SPRINGS			
Engine	Free Length	PRESSURE (LBS.)	
		Valve Closed	Valve Open
1290 cc			
Inner	1.646 (41.81)	33@1.220 (15@31.00)	62@.846 (28@21.49)
Outer	2.122 (53.90)	86@1.417 (39@36.00)	131@1.043 (60@26.49)

VALVE TIMING				
	INTAKE		EXHAUST	
Engine	Open (BTDC)	Close (ABDC)	Open (BBDC)	Close (ATDC)
1290 cc①	10°	54°	54°	10°

① — Valve timing checked with all valves adjusted to .020".

PISTONS, PINS, RINGS						
	PISTONS	PINS		RINGS		
Engine	Clearance In. (mm)	Piston Fit In. (mm)	Rod Fit In. (mm)	Rings	End Gap In. (mm)	Side Clearance In. (mm)
1290cc	.0020-.0028① (.05-.07)	.0001-.0003 (.002-.008)	.0004-.0006 (.010-.016)	No. 1	.0118-.0177 (.30-.45)	.0018-.0030 (.045-.077)
				No. 2	.0118-.0177 (.30-.45)	.0016-.0028 (.040-.072)
				No. 3	.0098-.0157 (.25-.40)	.0012-.0024 (.030-.062)

① — 128 models .0028-.0035" (.07-.09 mm).

CRANKSHAFT MAIN & CONNECTING ROD BEARINGS							
	MAIN BEARINGS				CONNECTING ROD BEARINGS		
Engine	Journal Diam. In. (mm)	Clearance In. (mm)	Thrust Bearing	Crankshaft End Play In. (mm)	Journal Diam. In. (mm)	Clearance In. (mm)	Side Play In. (mm)
1290cc	1.9994-2.0002 (50.785-50.805)	.0016-.0033 (.040-.085)	①	.0021-.0104 (.055-.265)	1.7913-1.7920 (45.498-45.518)	.0014-.0034 (.036-.086)	....

① — Thrust ring is installed at flywheel end main bearing cap.

CAMSHAFT			
Engine	Journal Diam. In. (mm)	Clearance In. (mm)	Lobe Lift In. (mm)
1290cc			
No. 1	1.1789-1.1795 (29.944-29.960)	.0011-.0028 (.029-.070)	....
No. 2	1.8872-1.8878 (47.935-47.950)	.0012-.0028 (.030-.070)	....
No. 3	1.8951-1.8957 (48.135-48.150)	.0012-.0028 (.030-.070)	....
No. 4	1.9030-1.9035 (48.335-48.350)	.0012-.0028 (.030-.070)	....
No. 5	1.9108-1.9114 (48.535-48.550)	.0012-.0028 (.030-.070)	....

TIGHTENING SPECIFICATIONS	
Application	Ft. Lbs. (mkg)
Cylinder Head Bolts	69 (9.5)
Cylinder Head Nuts	69 (9.5)
Main Bearing Cap Bolts	58 (8.0)
Connecting Rod Cap Bolts	36 (5.0)
Intake and Exhaust Manifold Nuts	22 (3.0)
Camshaft Sprocket Bolt	61 (8.5)
Timing Belt Tensioner Pulley Nut	33 (4.5)
Crankshaft Pulley and Sprocket Nut	101 (14.0)
Flywheel-to-Crankshaft Bolts	61 (8.5)

124 & 131 4 CYLINDER

ENGINE CODING

ENGINE IDENTIFICATION

Engine identification number is stamped in pad above oil filter mount on left side of engine.

Application	Engine Code
124 Spider & 131 Models with Catalytic Converter	132 A1.031.6
124 Spider & 131 Models without Catalytic Converter	132 A1.040.6

ENGINE & CYLINDER HEAD

ENGINE

1) Disconnect battery and all electrical connections to engine. Drain cooling system, remove shroud, all hoses and radiator. Remove air cleaner.

2) Disconnect accelerator rod from carburetor. Remove nuts holding linkage on cam housing cover. Disconnect fuel inlet and return hoses from carburetor.

3) Disconnect power brake unit vacuum line from manifold (if equipped). From inside driver's compartment, press down on gear shift lever and pry out retaining ring with a screwdriver.

4) Remove transmission cover. From under vehicle, disconnect drive shaft from transmission and remove drive shaft safety cross strap. Remove drive shaft center pillow block.

5) Disconnect speedometer drive from transmission. Disconnect back-up light switch cables at transmission (if equipped). Disconnect clutch fork return spring and remove adjusting rod.

6) Remove inspection cover from bottom of clutch housing. Disconnect exhaust pipe support bracket from rear of transmission and remove starter from clutch housing.

7) Position a suitable transmission support to a floor jack and position under transmission. Remove bolts securing transmission to engine and remove rear crossmember.

8) With transmission supported by jack, pull to rear until input shaft clears release bearing. Lower jack when transmission is clear and remove from under vehicle.

9) Remove clutch assembly from flywheel. Attach a suitable lifting fixture to engine, raise slightly and remove nuts securing engine to front motor mounts. Lift engine up and remove.

10) To install engine and transmission, reverse removal procedure. Make sure engine and transmission connect properly.

CYLINDER HEAD

Removal – 1) Disconnect battery, drain cooling system and remove air cleaner. Disconnect water temperature sending unit connection and spark plug wires. Disconnect water hoses.

2) Disconnect accelerator cable from lever on firewall and disconnect accelerator rod from lever on carburetor. Disconnect fuel line and fuel overflow from carburetor. Disconnect power brake vacuum line and starter relay cable. Disconnect all other pipes, hoses and wires to intake manifold and cylinder head.

3) Disconnect exhaust pipe from manifold and remove starter heat shield. Remove timing belt. *See Timing Belt Replacement.* Remove cylinder head retaining bolts and remove cylinder head.

Installation – 1) Before installation of cylinder head, position camshafts so that reference marks on sprockets are aligned with fixed pointers on front of cylinder head.

2) When installing cylinder head, camshafts must not be moved in either direction. Rotate crankshaft and bring pistons number 1 and 4 to TDC.

3) Install two dummy studs in one cylinder head bolt hole at front and rear of engine. Install new cylinder head gasket on block and carefully install cylinder head, making sure any valves in open position do not contact block.

4) Install a few head bolts and tighten manually and remove dummy studs. Install remaining head bolts and tighten to specification in sequence shown in illustration.

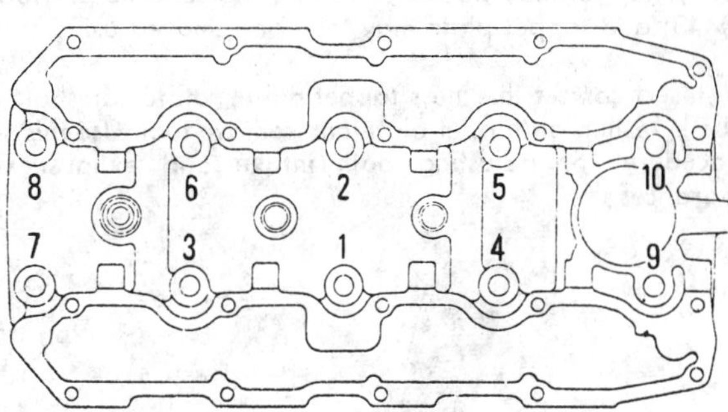

Fig. 1 Cylinder Head Tightening Sequence

VALVES

VALVE ARRANGEMENT

Left Side – All Intake
Right Side – All Exhaust

VALVE GUIDE SERVICING

1) Measure clearance of valve stem in guide with a dial indicator. If clearance exceeds specifications, valve guide must be replaced.

2) Drive guide out of head from combustion chamber side through top of head. Drive new guide in from top of head. Install new guide with snap ring flush against head.

VALVE SPRING REMOVAL

1) With cylinder head removed, remove camshaft carriers with camshafts. Compress valve spring with a spring compressor and remove both valve keepers.

124 & 131 4 CYLINDER (Cont.)

2) Release spring compressor, remove upper spring retainer, inner and outer springs and lower spring retainer. To assemble cylinder head, reverse disassembly procedure.

VALVE CLEARANCE ADJUSTMENT

1) Valve clearance is checked and/or adjusted with engine cold. Intake valve clearance is .018" (.457 mm). Exhaust valve clearance is .020" (.508 mm).

2) To adjust valves, remove camshaft covers from cylinder head. Rotate crankshaft until camshaft lobe of valve being adjusted is pointing away from valve (valve will be closed).

3) Using a feeler gauge, measure valve clearance. If clearance is not as specified, a thicker or thinner tappet plate must be installed to obtain specified clearance.

4) Tappet plates are available in service thicknesses of .128" (3.25 mm) and from .130" to .185" (3.30 mm to 4.70 mm) in increments of .004" (.10 mm).

5) To replace tappet plate, rotate camshaft until valve is fully open. Insert a suitable tappet hold down tool (A 60422) over lobe of valve being adjusted. Rotate camshaft and remove tappet plate by means of scribe through notch in tappet. Alternately, tappet may be pried down using suitable pry tool (A 60443) and tappet plate may then be removed using scribe.

6) Insert correct thickness tappet plate, rotate camshaft until lobe is resting on tappet plate and remove tool. Use this same procedure for adjusting both intake and exhaust valve clearances.

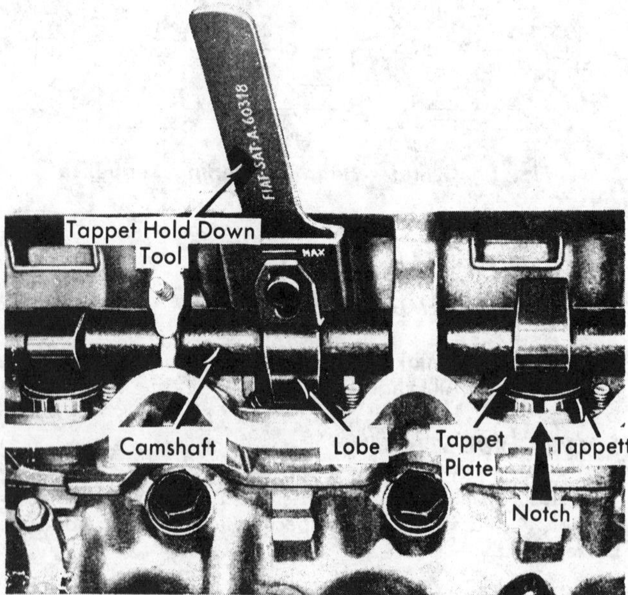

Fig. 2 Correct Procedure to Adjust Valve Clearance

PISTONS, PINS & RINGS

OIL PAN

1) Raise vehicle and drain crankcase. Disconnect front motor mounts and raise engine enough to remove oil pan.

2) To install, clean all mating surfaces thoroughly and install a new gasket with sealer. Reverse removal procedure and tighten bolts to specification.

PISTON & ROD ASSEMBLY

1) When installing piston and rod assembly, thoroughly oil piston pin in piston boss. Make sure ring gaps are spaced approximately 120° apart.

2) Lubricate rings and cylinder bore. Compress rings with a ring compressor and install assembly in cylinder block so that numbers on connecting rod and cap are facing away from auxiliary shaft. Tighten connecting rod nuts to specification.

FITTING PISTONS

1) Standard pistons are manufactured in three size classes and cylinder bores are machined according to piston class. Class of piston and bore is designated by a letter code.

2) Class code of piston is stamped on bottom of piston pin boss. Class of cylinder bore is stamped next to appropriate cylinder on oil pan flange on bottom of cylinder block.

3) Measure piston size at right angle to piston pin and 1.876 (47.65 mm) below piston head. If piston is replaced for any reason, one of the same class must be installed. **NOTE** — *Refer to class designation on cylinder block (see Fig. 4).*

Std. Piston Class Designation & Size

Class	In. (mm)
A	3.3051-3.3055 (83.95-83.96)
C	3.3059-3.3063 (83.97-83.98)
E	3.3066-3.3070 (83.99-84.00)

4) With piston size determined, measure cylinder bore. If clearance exceeds specification, cylinders must be rebored and oversize pistons installed.

Oversize Pistons

Application	Amt. of Oversize In. (mm)
1st Oversize	.0079 (0.2)
2nd Oversize	.0157 (0.4)
3rd Oversize	.0236 (0.6)

NOTE — *If replacement pistons are used, ensure that the four pistons are the same weight within ±.18 oz. (±5g).*

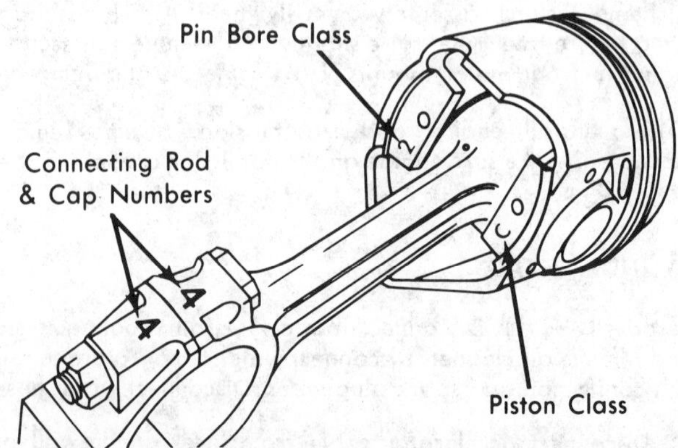

Fig. 3 Piston & Rod Assembly Markings

124 & 131 4 CYLINDER (Cont.)

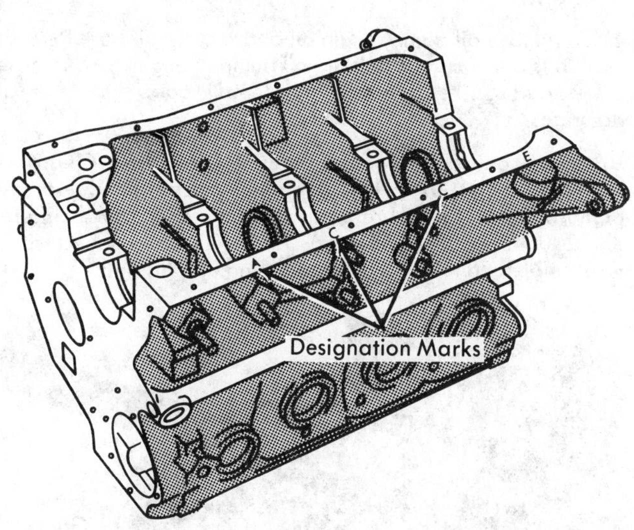

Fig. 4 Piston Bore Class Designation Marks

PISTON PIN REPLACEMENT

1) Remove circlips from piston and push piston pin out of piston and connecting rod. Separate piston from connecting rod.

2) Check clearance of piston pin in piston and connecting rod. If clearance is excessive, piston and connecting rod must be rebored for a .0079" (.2 mm) oversize pin.

3) Bushing in small end of connecting rod is replaceable and requires a .0017-.0040" (.043-.102 mm) interference fit.

4) To assemble piston and rod assembly, position piston on connecting rod with side of piston having offset portion of piston pin bore on same side as connecting rod numbers.

5) Oil piston pin and insert in piston and connecting rod. Install circlips and check piston for freedom of movement on pin. Check alignment.

CRANKSHAFT MAIN & CONNECTING ROD BEARINGS

MAIN & CONNECTING ROD BEARINGS

NOTE – *On late production models, modified main and connecting rod bearings have been installed. New clearances are; Main bearings .0015-.0025" (.032-.067 mm), Connecting rod bearings .0014-.0024" (.031-.065 mm). Modified bearings can be installed in earlier engines, however bearing clearances must meet new specifications.*

1) With crankshaft removed, thoroughly clean and inspect for cracks or scoring on journals. Check all journals for out-of-round condition, using a micrometer. If journal is out-of-round or tapers more than .0002" (.005 mm), crankshaft must be reground for undersize bearings.

2) Bearing-to-journal clearance is checked by the Plastigage method. If clearance exceeds specifications, crankshaft must be ground for undersize bearings.

3) Main and connecting rod bearings are available in .010" (.25 mm), .020" (.51 mm), .030" (.76 mm), and .040" (1.02 mm) undersizes.

CRANKSHAFT END PLAY

1) Mount a dial indicator on front of engine and pry crankshaft back and forth to measure crankshaft end play.

2) If end play exceeds specifications, adjustment may be made by installing new thrust washers to bring end play within specification.

ENGINE FRONT COVER & OIL SEAL

Engine front cover oil seal should be replaced whenever front cover is removed. Make sure new seal is squarely seated in cover. Lubricate seal contact lip before installing cover.

TIMING BELT REPLACEMENT

1) Drain cooling system and remove upper radiator hose. Remove upper section of air duct. Rotate crankshaft until marks on both camshaft sprockets are aligned with fixed pointer on front of engine. Number 4 piston should now be at TDC firing position.

2) Place transmission in fourth gear and apply parking brake to prevent crankshaft from turning. **CAUTION** – *Do not turn crankshaft or camshafts independent of each other as valves may hit pistons.*

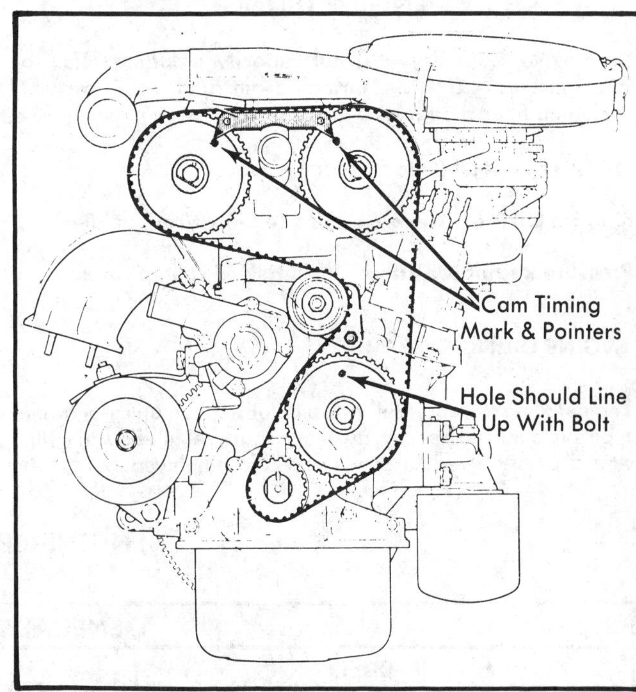

Fig. 5 Camshaft Sprocket Timing Marks

3) Remove lower engine protection plate and all drive belts. Loosen belt idler pulley nut and mounting bracket bolt, release tension on timing belt, tighten pulley nut and bracket bolt and remove belt. **NOTE** – *Anytime tension is relieved from timing belt, it must be replaced.* Install belt making sure not to move

124 & 131 4 CYLINDER (Cont.)

sprockets. Make sure that hole in auxiliary shaft pulley is lined up with tensioner pulley bolt.

4) To adjust timing belt tension loosen belt idler pulley nut and bracket mounting bolt. Spring will adjust tension. Tighten idler pulley nut and bracket bolt. Check belt tension two or three times, rotating crankshaft ½ to ¾ turns between checks.

CAMSHAFT

CAMSHAFT

1) Remove front cover, drive belts, and timing belt. Remove carburetor, intake manifold, distributor, exhaust manifold and cam covers. Remove air pump support bracket and air pump. Remove front cam housing bolts and install special tool (A.60446) to remove camshaft pulleys.

2) Remove camshaft housings and gaskets from crankcase. Remove end plates from housings. Slide camshafts out of housings. To install, reverse removal procedure.

AUXILIARY SHAFT

Auxiliary shaft drives: distributor, oil pump and fuel pump. Shaft is driven by timing belt. Remove oil pump. *See Oil Pump Removal.* Remove fuel pump and distributor. Remove front cover and timing belt. Remove auxiliary shaft sprocket. Remove retainer plate and shaft from crankcase. To install, reverse removal procedure.

ENGINE OILING

Crankcase Capacity – Total capacity including filter, oil lines, etc. is 4.5 qts. Normal drain and refill capacity (including filter change) is 4 qts.

Oil Filter – Full-flow, cartridge type.

Normal Oil Pressure – 64-85 psi (4.5-6 kg/cm²) at idle.

Pressure Regulator Valve – Installed in pump cover.

ENGINE OILING SYSTEM

Engine oiling system is full pressure lubrication utilizing a gear type oil pump driven by auxiliary shaft. A full-flow oil filter and a pressure regulator valve is also employed.

OIL PUMP

1) To remove oil pump, drain oil and remove oil pan. Remove two bolts and washers holding oil pump to engine and remove pump and gasket. Visually inspect all parts for wear or damage.

2) Check gears for tooth-to-housing clearance. Clearance should be .004-.007" (.11-.18 mm). Place straightedge across pump body and measure gear end play. End play should be .0012-.0045" (.031-.116 mm). Replace parts as necessary, reassemble and reinstall oil pump using new gaskets.

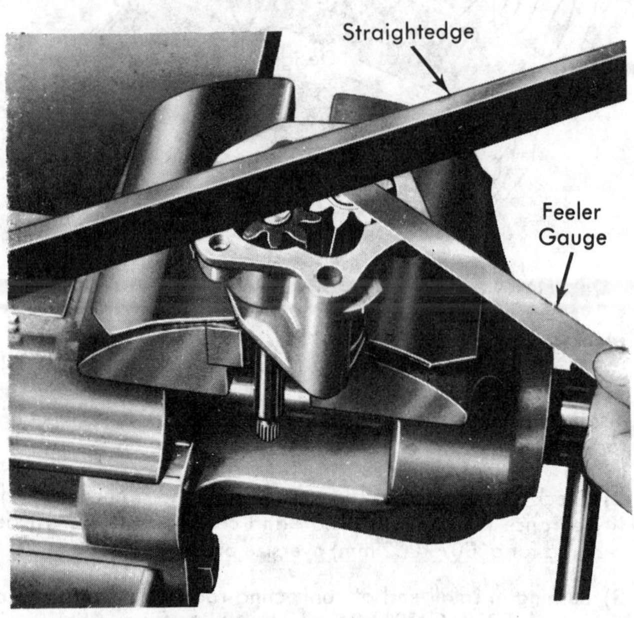

Fig. 6 Checking Oil Pump Gear End Play

ENGINE COOLING

Thermostat Opening Temperature – 178-185°F (81-85°C).

Cooling System Capacity – 8.5 qts.

Radiator Cap – 11psi.

WATER PUMP

To remove water pump, remove alternator and drive belt. Disconnect water hoses from pump and remove three bolts securing pulley on pump. Remove four bolts securing pump to engine and remove pump and gasket. To install, reverse removal procedure and use new gasket.

ENGINE SPECIFICATIONS

GENERAL SPECIFICATIONS

Year	Displ.		Carburetor	HP at RPM	Torque (Ft. Lbs. at RPM)	Compr. Ratio	Bore		Stroke	
	cu. ins.	cc					in.	mm	in.	mm
1977	107.13	1756	1x2-Bbl.	①86@6200	②90@2800	8.0-1	3.31	84	3.12	79.2

① – 83@5800 when equipped with catalytic converter.
② – 86@2800 on 131 models or 89@2800 on 124 models when equipped with catalytic converter.

124 & 131 4 CYLINDER (Cont.)

ENGINE SPECIFICATIONS (Cont.)

VALVES							
Engine & Valve	Head Diam. In. (mm)	Face Angle	Seat Angle	Seat Width In. (mm)	Stem Diameter In. (mm)	Stem Clearance In. (mm)	Valve Lift In. (mm)
1756 cc							
Int.	1.622-1.638 (41.2-41.6)	45°	45°	.079 (2.0)	.3139-.3146 (7.974-7.992)	.0012-.0026 (.030-.066)	.3765 (9.564)
Exh.	1.412-1.435 (35.85-36.45)	45°	45°	.079 (2.0)	.3139-.3146 (7.974-7.992)	.0012-.0026 (.030-.066)	.3765 (9.564)

VALVE SPRINGS			
Engine	Free Length In. (mm)	PRESSURE Lbs. @ In. (kg @ mm)	
		Valve Closed	Valve Open
1756 cc Inner Spring	1.646 (41.8)	33@1.220 (14.9@31)	62@.846 (28.1@21.5)
Outer Spring	2.122 (53.9)	86@1.417 (38.9@36)	131@1.043 (59.5@26.5)

VALVE TIMING				
Engine	INTAKE		EXHAUST	
	Open (BTDC)	Close (ALDC)	Open (BLDC)	Close (ATDC)
1756 cc	5°	53°	53°	5°

PISTONS, PINS, RINGS						
Engine	PISTONS	PINS		RINGS		
	Clearance In. (mm)	Piston Fit In. (mm)	Rod Fit In. (mm)	Rings	End Gap In. (mm)	Side Clearance In. (mm)
1756 cc	.0016-.0024 (.040-.060)	.0001-.0003 (.002-.008)	.0004-.0006 (.010-.016)	No. 1	.0118-.0177 (.30-.45)	.0018-.0030 (.045-.077)
				No. 2	.0078-.0139 (.20-.35)	.0011-.0027 (.030-.070)
				Oil	.0078-.0139 (.20-.35)	.0011-.0024 (.030-.062)

CRANKSHAFT MAIN & CONNECTING ROD BEARINGS							
Engine	MAIN BEARINGS				CONNECTING ROD BEARINGS		
	Journal Diam. In. (mm)	Clearance In. (mm)	Thrust Bearing	Crankshaft End Play In. (mm)	Journal Diam. ① In. (mm)	Clearance ② In. (mm)	Side Play In. (mm)
1756 cc	2.0860-2.0868 (52.99-53.00)	0020-.0037 (.050-.095)	No. 5	.002-.012 (.05-.30)	1.9997-2.0001 (50.79-50.80)	.0018-.0031 (.045-.079)	....

① — Journal diameter is machined in two sizes designated by class codes. Specification given is class "A". Class "B" is smaller by .0004" (.010 mm).

② — Clearance varies according to class of connecting rod journal. Specification given is class "A". Class "B" clearance is larger by .0001" (.002 mm).

124 & 131 4 CYLINDER (Cont.)

ENGINE SPECIFICATIONS (Cont.)

CAMSHAFT			
Engine	Journal Diam. In. (mm)	Clearance In. (mm)	Lobe Lift In. (mm)
1756 cc			
Front	1.1788-1.1795 (29.94-29.96)	.0019-.0035 (.049-.090)	.3824 (9.71)
Middle	1.8013-1.8020 (45.75-45.77)	.0011-.0027 (.029-.070)	.3824 (9.71)
Rear	1.8171-1.8178 (46.15-46.17)	.0011-.0027 (.029-.070)	.3824 (9.71)

TIGHTENING SPECIFICATIONS	
Application	Ft. Lbs. (mkg)
Cylinder Head Bolts	54 (7.5)
Front Main Bearing Cap Bolts	58 (8.0)
Main Bearing Cap Self-Locking Bolts	83 (11.5)
Intake & Exhaust Manifold Nuts	18 (2.5)
Connecting Rod Nuts	36 (5.0)
Flywheel-to-Crankshaft Bolt	62 (8.5)
Camshaft Sprocket Bolt	87 (12)
Tensioner Nut	33 (4.6)

CIVIC 4 CYLINDER

ENGINE CODING

ENGINE IDENTIFICATION

Engine serial number is stamped on a machined surface at rear of engine, near starter. Engine serial number is preceded by engine model number. Model number is EB2.

ENGINE & CYLINDER HEAD

ENGINE

Removal – 1) Disconnect battery ground cable. Remove hood after scribing location marks for reinstallation. Drain radiator and disconnect hoses from engine. Drain lubricant from transmission. Remove air cleaner and air intake pipe.

2) Remove fan shroud. Disconnect hoses from canister fitting being careful not to bend fittings. Disconnect fuel pump inlet line. Disconnect and place out of way the following wires, hoses or cables: Throttle and choke cable from carburetor. Clutch cable from release arm. Ignition coil wires at distributor. Back-up light wires. TCS wires. Alternator harness wires. Water temperature and oil pressure switch wires. Throttle opener hose and carburetor insulator to throttle opener vacuum hose.

3) Remove by-pass valve assembly and bracket. Disconnect heater hoses at firewall. Remove engine torque rod, starter and front wheels. Remove exhaust pipe flange nuts, then lower pipe. Disconnect both lower control arm ball joints.

4) Hold out of way and pull left and right axle drive shafts out of differential case. Drive out gear shift 8 mm pin and disconnect rod at transmission case. Disconnect gear shift extension at the engine not at shift lever. On automatic transmission models only, disconnect shift cable at console then, disconnect cooler lines at transmission.

5) Attach an engine hoist to motor and take up slack allowing load to be lifted from mounts. With engine supported, remove two center mount bracket nuts. Remove left engine mount. Lift engine from vehicle being careful not to allow auxiliary components to bang against vehicle.

Installation – To install engine, reverse removal procedure and note the following: Use new shift rod pin. After installing drive shafts attempt to move inner joint housing in and out of differential housing. If movement is easy, drive shaft end clips should be replaced. When connecting heater hoses, upper hose goes to water pump connecting pipe.

CYLINDER HEAD

NOTE – *To minimize the chances of warping cylinder head, remove head after engine has been allowed to cool.*

Removal – 1) Scribe index marks on hood, then take hood off. Drain coolant from radiator. Remove air cleaner hardware. Disconnect upper radiator hose. Disconnect tubing between canister and idle cut-off valve. Disconnect throttle linkage.

2) Disconnect the following items: heater hoses at intake manifold. Temperature sensor wires. Fuel line to carburetor. Engine torque rod.

3) Remove air pump to exhaust manifold hose. Disconnect exhaust pipe at manifold. Remove valve cover. Remove upper timing belt cover. Bring No. 1 piston to TDC.

4) Loosen timing belt adjusting and pivot bolt, then remove camshaft pulley bolt and remove pulley. Take off fuel pump and take out distributor. Remove the oil pump gear holder and the pump gear and shaft. Loosen bolts evenly and lift off cylinder head.

Installation – To install cylinder head, reverse removal procedure and tighten bolts in sequence shown in *Fig. 1*.

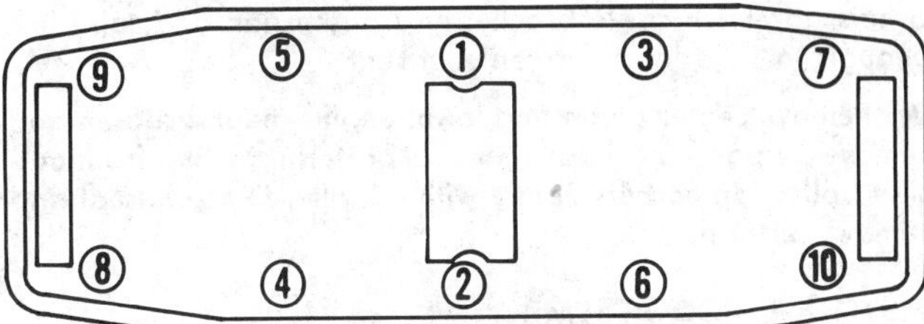

Fig. 1 Cylinder Head Tightening Sequence

VALVES

VALVE ARRANGEMENT

Front Side – All Exhaust
Rear Side – All Intake

ROCKER ARM ASSEMBLY

Removal – Loosen rocker arm shaft bolts in criss-cross pattern starting with end supports. Starting with number four cylinder support, pull out 4 mm pin and remove supports, rocker collars, rocker arms and springs. Retain components in proper order for reassembly.

Installation – When reinstalling rocker arms, place intake rocker arm shaft so that notch faces rear of vehicle and oil holes are on the bottom. Exhaust rocker arm shaft is installed with oil holes facing down and dowel pin hole on left-hand side of engine. After assembly check rocker arms for freedom of movement.

VALVE SPRINGS

Using a suitable valve spring compressor, remove valve keepers, collars and springs. Check valve springs for squareness, they should be within 2° of true. Measure free length of springs. Minimum usable length is 1.614" (41.00 mm) for inner spring and 1.532" (38.91 mm) for outer spring.

VALVE GUIDE SERVICING

Using a suitable drift, drive valve guides out top side of head. Install new guides and ream to provide proper clearance. Install new intake valve guide seals.

VALVE CLEARANCE ADJUSTMENT

1) Rotate engine until number one piston is at TDC on compression stroke, check intake valves of number one and two

CIVIC 4 CYLINDER (Cont.)

cylinders and exhaust valves of number one and three cylinders. Rotate crankshaft 360° and check intake valves of number three and four cylinders and exhaust valves of number two and four cylinders.

2) Loosen lock nut of valve to be adjusted. Insert a feeler gauge between rocker arm and valve stem to measure clearance. Turn adjuster until proper clearance is obtained. This procedure is performed with engine cold, and proper valve clearance is .004-.006" (.10-.16 mm).

PISTONS, PINS & RINGS

OIL PAN

1) Raise front of vehicle and support with floor stands. Attach a hoist to clutch cable bracket on transmission and raise just enough to take load off center mount.

2) Remove center beam and lower engine mount. Loosen and remove oil pan bolts in a criss-cross pattern, starting from outside bolts. Tap corners lightly with a mallet to break seal and remove oil pan.

PISTON & ROD ASSEMBLY

1) With oil pan and cylinder head removed, ream any ridge from top of cylinders. Mark piston and rod assemblies for proper reinstallation. Remove rod caps and push piston and rod assemblies out top of cylinder with a hammer handle.

2) Assemble piston and connecting rod with piston front mark and connecting rod oil jet hole on same side and facing intake manifold. Using a ring compressor, install piston and rod assemblies in proper cylinder.

FITTING PISTONS

Measure cylinder bore for wear and taper. Measure piston diameter, then determine if piston-to-cylinder clearance is within specification. If not, two different oversize pistons (and rings) are available. Oversizes are .010" (.25 mm) and .022" (.55 mm). Oversize pistons are stamped on the crown with a number corresponding to the metric equivalent of oversize. Similarly, oversize rings are also stamped on their top side to correspond to amount to oversize. Match pistons and rings according to these oversize markings.

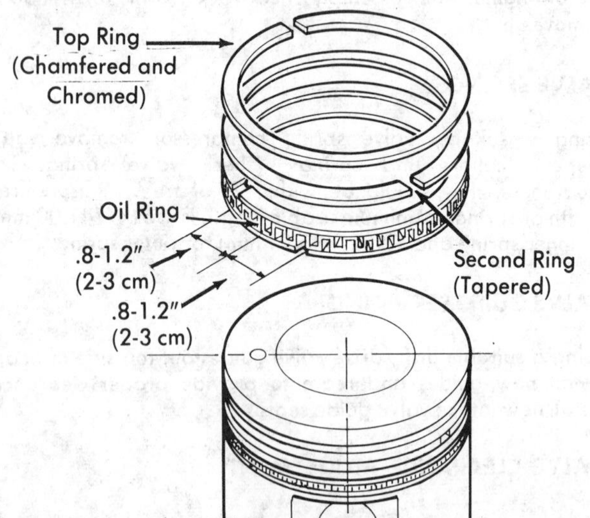

Fig. 2 View of Piston Rings Showing Ring End Gap Locations

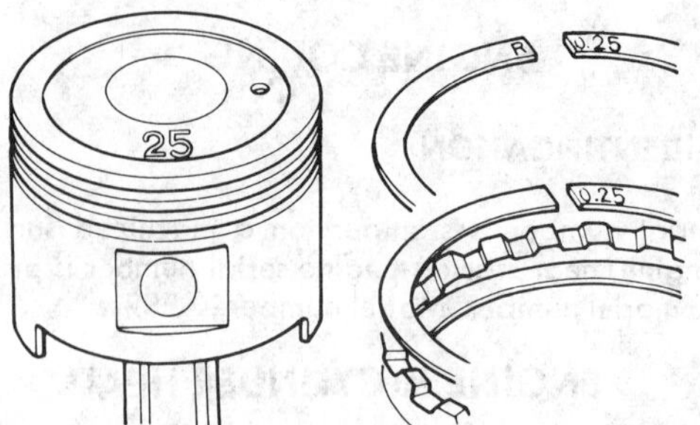

Fig. 3 Showing Piston and Ring Size Stamped on Component

PISTON PINS

Using a press and suitable tool (07973-6340000), press piston pin out of piston and connecting rod. Install new pin by placing pilot through piston and connecting rod. Lightly oil piston pin and place piston, rod, pin and ram on the base. Press in pin until it is centered in connecting rod.

CRANKSHAFT MAIN & CONNECTING ROD BEARINGS

MAIN & CONNECTING ROD BEARINGS

1) Prior to disassembly, mark main and connecting rod bearing caps for reassembly to their original locations. Measure crankshaft for bend, out-of-round or taper. No attempt to regrind crankshaft is to be made as bearing journals are specially heat-treated.

2) Using Plastigage method, determine bearing clearances. If bearing replacement is necessary use following procedure to determine bearing size required.

3) Referring to illustration, note that all **letters** stamped on crankshaft counterweight pads apply to connecting rods and all **numbers** apply to main bearing journals. Both connecting rods and main bearing journals have mating numbers (stamped on connecting rod) or letters (stamped on block) which when paired are used to determine color of bearing insert to be used. *See Engine Specifications*

THRUST BEARING ALIGNMENT

Measure thrust bearing clearance and replace thrust washers if necessary. Install thrust washers with oil grooves facing toward crankshaft.

CAMSHAFT

TIMING BELT

1) Remove water pump drive belt, water pump pulley and crankshaft pulley. Remove upper timing belt cover from cylinder head.

2) Remove lower timing belt cover from engine block. Loosen (do not remove) timing belt adjusting and pivot bolts. Slide belt off pulleys. To install, reverse removal procedure using care not to excessively bend or twist timing belt. Do not expose belt to engine oil as this will cause belt rubber to swell. Install belt in same direction of rotation to prevent premature wear or failure.

CIVIC 4 CYLINDER (Cont.)

CAMSHAFT

1) With cylinder head removed, loosen rocker shaft support bolts in a criss-cross pattern beginning with outside support. Lift rocker shaft assembly from head. Remove camshaft and right-hand seal or tachometer drive body (if equipped).

2) Inspect camshaft and cylinder head bearing surfaces for wear or damage. Check camshaft runout. If runout exceeds .002" (.05 mm), repair or replace as necessary. Measure cam lobe height. If lobes are worn to 1.4245" (36.18 mm) for intake or 1.4193 (36.05 mm) for exhaust, replace camshaft.

3) Oil camshaft bearing journals. Install camshaft and seal or tachometer drive body (if equipped). Loosen rocker arm adjusting screws, and apply silicone seal to mating surfaces on end camshaft supports and cylinder head. Install rocker arm assembly and tighten support bolts in reverse of removal.

VALVE TIMING

Rotate crankshaft pulley until TDC mark is aligned with index mark on timing belt cover. Rotate camshaft pulley until Woodruff key is facing up and timing marks on pulley are parallel with top of cylinder head. Without disturbing pulley position, slide on timing belt. Rotate engine a quarter of a revolution and tighten adjusting bolt, then pivot bolt. Do not apply pressure to timing belt, use only tension of adjusting spring.

Fig. 5 Camshaft Alignment Marks in Position for Installing Camshaft Belt

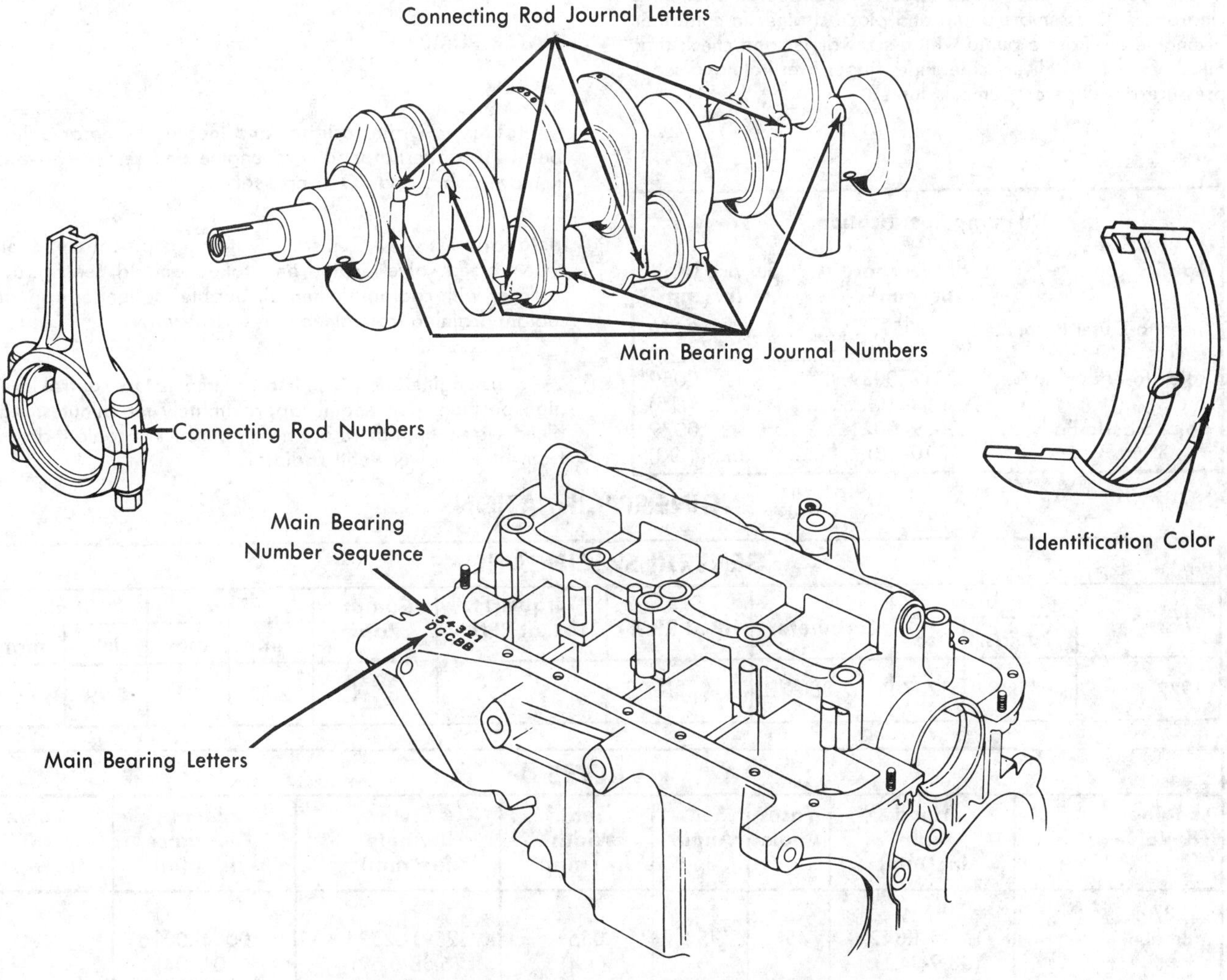

Connecting Rod Journal Letters

Main Bearing Journal Numbers

Connecting Rod Numbers

Identification Color

Main Bearing Number Sequence

Main Bearing Letters

Fig. 4 Crankshaft and Connecting Rod Bearing Identification with Detail for Each Component

CIVIC 4 CYLINDER (Cont.)

ENGINE OILING

Crankcase Capacity – 3.2 qts.
Oil Filter – Disposable with built-in by-pass valve.
Normal Oil Pressure – 48-58 psi, 21 psi minimum at idle.
Pressure Regulator Valve – Non-adjustable.

ENGINE OILING SYSTEM

A trochoid type oil pump draws oil from oil pan and delivers it under pressure through main bearing cradle to main and connecting rod bearings. Oil passes through rods to an oil jet which lubricates pistons and cylinder walls. An oil passage carries oil to camshaft bearings and rocker arms. Oil mist lubricates valve stems.

OIL PUMP

1) Remove oil pan, oil passage block and oil pump assembly. Pull oil relief valve cotter pin and remove seat, spring and valve.

2) Remove two pump body bolts and disassemble pump. Inspect pump for wear or damage. Measure pump operating clearances. Reassemble pump and place strainer in container of engine oil. Rotate pump with a screwdriver and check that oil comes out of delivery side. Place finger over hole and see if pressure develops as pump is turned.

Oil Pump Specifications

Application	Std. Clearance In. (mm)	Service Limit In. (mm)
Inner-to-Outer Rotor	.0059 (.15)	.0079 (.20)
Rotor-to-Body	.0012-.0039 (.03-.10)	.0059 (.15)
Rotor Side-to-Body	.0039-.0071 (.10-.18)	.0079 (.20)

ENGINE COOLING

Thermostat – Opens at 178-183°F (80-84°C).

Thermoswitch – On: 191-197°F (88-92°C); Off: 182-188°F (83-87°C).

Cooling System Capacity – 4.2 qts.

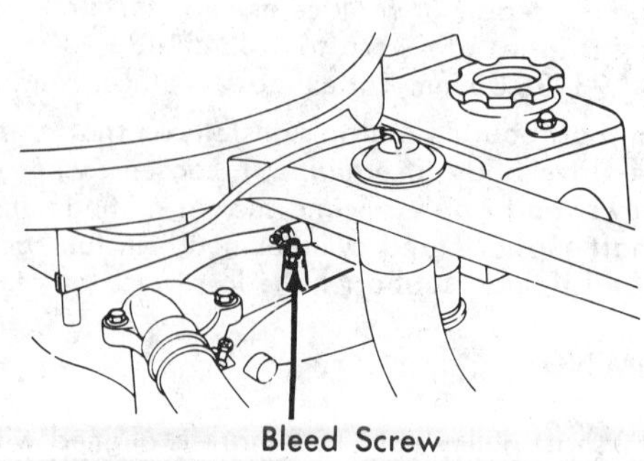

Fig. 6 Coolant Bleed Valve in Intake Manifold

WATER PUMP

Removal – Drain radiator and loosen alternator adjusting bolts. Push alternator toward engine and remove drive belt. Remove pump and "O" ring seal.

Installation – 1) Reinstall water pump. Loosen cooling system bleed valve located on intake manifold, see *Fig. 6*. Fill radiator with coolant. When air bubbles no longer appear in coolant draining from bleed valve, close valve.

2) Start engine and place heater temperature control lever in high position. Run engine approximately ten minutes. Again bleed system until there are no air bubbles in coolant draining from bleed valve. Refill radiator.

ENGINE SPECIFICATIONS

GENERAL SPECIFICATIONS

Year	Displ. cu. ins.	Displ. cc	Carburetor	HP at RPM	Torque (Ft. Lbs. at RPM)	Compr. Ratio	Bore in.	Bore mm	Stroke in.	Stroke mm
1977	75.48	1237	2-Bbl.	....	....	8.1:1	2.83	72	2.99	76

VALVES

Engine & Valve	Head Diam. In. (mm)	Face Angle	Seat Angle	Seat Width In. (mm)	Stem Diameter In. (mm)	Stem Clearance In. (mm)	Valve Lift In. (mm)
1237 cc							
Intake	1.335-1.342 (33.9-34.1)	45°	45°	.0551 (1.4)	.2591-.2594 (6.58-6.59)	.0004-.0016 (.01-.04)	.....
Exhaust	1.177-1.185 (29.9-30.1)	45°	45°	.0551 (1.4)	.2579-.2583 (6.55-6.56)	.0020-.0031 (.05-.08)	.....

CIVIC 4 CYLINDER (Cont.)

ENGINE SPECIFICATIONS (Cont.)

VALVE SPRINGS			
Engine	Free Length In. (mm)	PRESSURE Lbs. @ In. (kg @ mm)	
		Valve Closed	Valve Open
1237 cc			
Intake			
Inner	1.654 (42.0)	19.8-24.2@1.358 (9.0-11.0@34.5)	59.0-67.9@1.024 (26.8-30.8@26.0)
Outer	1.573 (39.95)	16.7-20.6@1.437 (7.6-9.35@36.5)	72.5-83.5@1.094 (32.9-37.9@27.8)
Exhaust			
Inner	1.654 (42.0)	25.8-31.5@1.358 (11.7-14.3@34.5)	40.8-49.6@1.024 (18.5-22.5@26)
Outer	1.573 (39.95)	51.4-62.4@1.437 (23.3-28.3@36.5)	79.4-90.4@1.094 (36.0-41.0@27.8)

CAMSHAFT			
Engine	Journal Diam. In. (mm)	Clearance① In. (mm)	Lobe Lift In. (mm)
1237 cc			
Intake	.....	.0020-.0035 (.05-.09)	.220 (5.6)
Exhaust	....	.0020-.0035 (.05-.09)	.216 (5.5)

① — End play: .0197" (.50 mm) maximum.

VALVE TIMING				
Engine	INTAKE		EXHAUST	
	Open (BTDC)	Close (ALDC)	Open (BLDC)	Close (ATDC)
1237 cc	10°	20°	30°	10°

PISTONS, PINS, RINGS						
Engine	PISTONS	PINS		RINGS		
	Clearance In. (mm)	Piston Fit In. (mm)	Rod Fit In. (mm)	Rings	End Gap In. (mm)	Side Clearance In. (mm)
1237 cc	.0012-.0039 (.03-.10)	.0004-.0008 (.010-.022)	① .0006-.0015 (.016-.039)	No. 1	.008-.016 (.20-.40)	.0008-.0018 (.020-.045)
				No. 2	.008-.016 (.20-.40)	.0008-.0018 (.020-.045)
				Oil	.008-.035 (.20-.90)	.....

① — Interference fit.

Main Bearing Journals				In. (mm)
Crankcase Counterbore Dia. 2.13 (54) / Journal Dia. 1.97 (50)	A 0 to .0002 (0 to .006)	B .0002 to .0005 (.006 to .012)	C .0005 to .0007 (.012 to .018)	D .0007 to .0009 (.018 to .024)
1 0 to −.0002 (0 to −.006)	Red −.0001 to −.0002 (−.002 to −.005)	Pink .00004 to −.0001 (.001 to −.002)	Yellow .0002 to .00004 (.004 to .001)	Green .0003 to .0002 (.007 to .004)
2 −.0002 to −.0005 (−.006 to −.012)	Pink .00004 to −.0001 (.001 to −.002)	Yellow .0002 to .00004 (.004 to .001)	Green .0003 to .0002 (.007 to .004)	Brown .0004 to .0003 (.010 to .007)
3 −.0005 to −.0007 (−.012 to −.018)	Yellow .0002 to .00004 (.004 to .001)	Green .0003 to .0002 (.007 to .004)	Brown .0004 to .0003 (.010 to .007)	Black .0005 to .0004 (.013 to .010)
4 −.0007 to −.0009 (−.018 to −.024)	Green .0003 to .0002 (.007 to .004)	Brown .0004 to .0003 (.010 to .007)	Black .0005 to .0004 (.013 to .010)	Blue .0006 to .0005 (.016 to .013)

CIVIC 4 CYLINDER (Cont.)

ENGINE SPECIFICATIONS (Cont.)

CRANKSHAFT MAIN & CONNECTING ROD BEARINGS							
	MAIN BEARINGS				CONNECTING ROD BEARINGS		
Engine	Journal Diam. In. (mm)	Clearance In. (mm)	Thrust Bearing	Crankshaft End Play In. (mm)	Journal Diam. In. (mm)	Clearance In. (mm)	Side Play In. (mm)
1237 cc	1.969-1.970 (49.9-50.0)	.0009-.0017 (.024-.042)	No. 2	.004-.014 (.10-.35)	1.575-1.576 (39.9-40.0)	.0008-.0015 (.020-.038)	.0059-.0118 (.15-.30)

Connecting Rod Bearing Journals				In. (mm)
Connecting Rod Dia. 1.69 (43) / Crankpin Dia. 1.57 (40)	1 0 to .0002 (0 to .006)	2 .0002 to .0005 (.006 to .012)	3 .0005 to .0007 (.012 to .018)	4 .0007 to .0009 (.018 to .024)
A 0 to −.0002 (0 to −.006)	Red −.0002 to −.0003 (−.005 to −.008)	Pink −.0001 to −.0002 (−.002 to −.005)	Yellow .00004 to −.0001 (.001 to −.002)	Green .0002 to .00004 (.004 to .001)
B −.0002 to −.0005 (−.006 to −.012)	Pink −.0001 to −.0002 (−.002 to −.005)	Yellow .00004 to −.0001 (.001 to −.002)	Green .0002 to .00004 (.004 to .001)	Brown .0003 to .0002 (.007 to .004)
C −.0005 to −.0007 (−.012 to −.018)	Yellow .00004 to −.0001 (.001 to −.002)	Green .0002 to .00004 (.004 to .001)	Brown .0003 to .0002 (.007 to .004)	Black .0004 to .0003 (.010 to .007)
D −.0007 to −.0009 (−.018 to −.024)	Green .0002 to .00004 (.004 to .001)	Brown .0003 to .0002 (.007 to .004)	Black .0004 to .0003 (.010 to .007)	Blue .0005 to .0004 (.013 to .010)

TIGHTENING SPECIFICATIONS

Application	Ft. Lbs. (mkg)
Main Bearing Cap	27-31 (3.7-4.3)
Connecting Rod Cap	18-21 (2.6-3.0)
Camshaft Support	13-16 (1.8-2.4)
Flywheel	34-38 (4.7-5.3)
Cylinder Head Bolts	37-42 (5.1-5.8)
Crankshaft Pulley	34-38 (4.7-5.3)
Timing Belt Pulley	18-25 (2.5-3.5)
Intake & Exhaust Manifolds	13-17 (2.0-2.5)

CIVIC CVCC & ACCORD 4 CYLINDER

ENGINE CODING

ENGINE IDENTIFICATION

Engine serial number is stamped at right, rear of engine. Serial number is preceded by engine model number.

Application	Code
CVCC	
Sedan	ED3-3
Station Wagon	ED4-3
Accord	
Fed.	KA
Calif.	KL
High Alt.	KH

ENGINE & CYLINDER HEAD

ENGINE

Removal – 1) Remove grill to gain access to hood screws and remove hood after scribing location marks for reinstallation. Disconnect battery ground cable from battery and transmission. Completely remove engine torque arm. Disconnect all wiring and vacuum hoses to engine.

2) Drain radiator and disconnect coolant lines. Remove radiator. On automatic transmission models, remove transmission oil cooler lines. Remove starter motor and distributor cap. Disconnect clutch cable from clutch arm. Remove cooling fan housing with fan. Remove emission control box from firewall. Remove complete air cleaner assembly and engine mount heat shield.

3) On Accord models only, remove clutch slave cylinder with hose. Disconnect throttle and choke cables from carburetor. On automatic transmission models only, remove center console and remove shift control from shift lever. Raise front of vehicle and remove both front wheels. Drain crankcase and transmission fluid. Disconnect speedometer cable from transmission complete with drive gear.

4) Remove cotter pin and nut from both lower ball joints. Disengage both ball joints from steering knuckles using driver and collar (07941-6710000). Pry both constant velocity joints out about .5" (12.7 mm) and pull sub-axles out of transmission case. Remove front crossmember and front lower engine mount bolt. On manual transmission models, drive out pin securing shift linkage.

5) Disconnect lower torque arm from transmission. On automatic transmission models, pull shift control cable out of housing. Disconnect exhaust pipe. Attach chain hoist to engine and position lifting hook 7 chain links from left side of engine and 14 links from right side of engine. Raise hoist slightly to place tension on lifting sling. Install a protective shield between engine and radiator.

6) Disconnect nut from rear engine mount and remove complete front engine mount assembly. Remove three bolts from left shock absorber mount assembly and push left engine mount into shock absorber mount bracket as far as it will go. Lift engine and remove from vehicle.

Installation – To install, reverse removal procedure and note following: Use new shift rod pin. Make sure sub-axles bottom in transmission, and spring clip holds sub-axle securely. Arrows on combination lights point outward. Adjust all control cables after installation is completed.

CYLINDER HEAD

NOTE – *To minimize the chances of warping cylinder head, remove head after engine has been allowed to cool.*

Removal – 1) Scribe index marks on hood, then remove hood. Drain radiator and remove complete air cleaner assembly. Disconnect upper radiator hose and all vacuum lines to cylinder head and intake manifold. Disconnect throttle and choke cables.

2) Disconnect all wiring and hoses to intake manifold and cylinder head. Remove engine torque rod. Disconnect exhaust pipe from manifold. Remove valve cover and upper timing belt cover. Rotate engine until number one piston is at top dead center position.

3) Loosen timing belt adjusting and pivot bolt, then remove camshaft pulley bolt and remove pulley. Take off fuel pump and remove distributor. Remove oil pump gear holder and pump gear and shaft. Loosen bolts in reverse of tightening sequence *(See Fig. 1)*, a little at a time and lift off cylinder head.

Installation – To install cylinder head, reverse removal procedure and tighten bolts in sequence shown in *Fig. 1*.

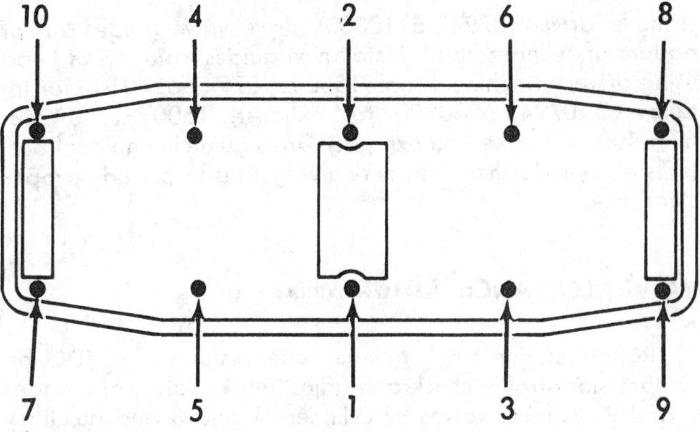

Fig. 1 Cylinder Head Tightening Sequence

VALVES

VALVE ARRANGEMENT

Rear Side – I-E-E-I-I-E-E-I (left to right).
Front Side – All Auxiliary.

ROCKER ARM ASSEMBLY

Removal – Loosen rocker arm shaft support bolts in criss-cross pattern starting with end supports. Pull out roll pins from both end shaft supports and remove supports, rocker collars, rocker arms and springs. Retain components in proper order for reassembly.

CIVIC CVCC & ACCORD 4 CYLINDER (Cont.)

Installation – Measure all rocker arms for arm-to-shaft clearance. If clearance exceeds .0035" (.08 mm), replace rocker shaft and/or arms. Assemble in reverse of disassembly and install rocker arm assembly on engine. Tighten support bolts in a criss-cross pattern starting with center support.

VALVE SPRINGS

Intake & Exhaust Valves – Using valve spring compressor, remove valve keepers, collars and springs. Check valve springs for squareness, free length and tension. Install in reverse of removal procedure, making sure closely wound coils are nearest cylinder head.

Auxiliary Valves – Cut lock nut retainer with a cold chisel and remove. Remove valve holder nut using wrench (07907-6570001). Pull out and remove valve holder assembly complete with valve. Using valve spring compressor, compress spring and remove valve keepers, collars and springs. Remove "O" ring from valve holder. Check valve springs for squareness, free length and tension. Install in reverse of removal procedure using new "O" ring on valve holder. Install lock nut retainer with tab in positioning hole and flatten down retainer on holder nut using driver.

VALVE GUIDE SERVICING

NOTE – *On 1600 cc engines, it may be necessary to heat cylinder head to 300° F (150° C), to remove or install valve guides.*

Using a driver (07942-6110000), drive valve guides out of bottom of cylinder head. Install new guides from top of head using driver attachment tool (1500 cc, 07943-6340100 for intake, or 07943-6340200 for exhaust; 1600 cc, 07943-6710000 for intake and exhaust). Drive guide in until tool bottoms on cylinder head. Ream valve guides to provide proper clearance.

VALVE CLEARANCE ADJUSTMENT

1) Rotate engine until number one piston is at TDC on compression stroke, check and adjust intake valves of cylinder 1 and 2, exhaust valves of cylinders 1 and 3 and auxiliary valves of cylinders 1 and 2. Rotate crankshaft 360° and check and adjust intake valves of cylinder 3 and 4, exhaust valves of cylinders 2 and 4 and auxiliary valves of cylinders 3 and 4.

2) To adjust all valves, loosen lock nut and insert feeler gauge between rocker arm and valve stem. Turn adjuster to obtain proper clearance and tighten lock nut, recheck valve clearance. Specified valve clearance with engine cold (cylinder head less than 100°F (38°C) is .006" (.15 mm) for all valves.

PISTONS, PINS & RINGS

OIL PAN

1) Raise front of vehicle and support with floor stands. Attach a hoist to transmission and raise just enough to take load off center mount.

2) Remove center support and lower engine mount. Loosen and remove oil pan bolts in a criss-cross pattern, starting from outside bolts. Tap corner lightly with a mallet to break seal and remove oil pan. To install, reverse removal procedure.

PISTON & ROD ASSEMBLY

1) With oil pan and cylinder head removed, ream any ridge from top of cylinders. Mark piston and rod assemblies for proper reinstallation. Remove rod caps and push piston and rod assemblies out top of cylinder with a hammer handle.

2) Assemble piston and connecting rod with piston front mark and connecting rod oil jet hole on same side and facing intake manifold. Using a ring compressor, install piston and rod assemblies in proper cylinder.

FITTING PISTONS

1) Measure cylinder bore for taper and out-of-round. If taper exceeds .004" (.1 mm) or out-of-round exceeds .002" (.05 mm), rebore cylinder for oversize pistons. Determine piston-to-cylinder clearance. If not within specifications, rebore cylinder for oversize pistons. An oversize piston of 2.923" (74.25 mm) diameter is available.

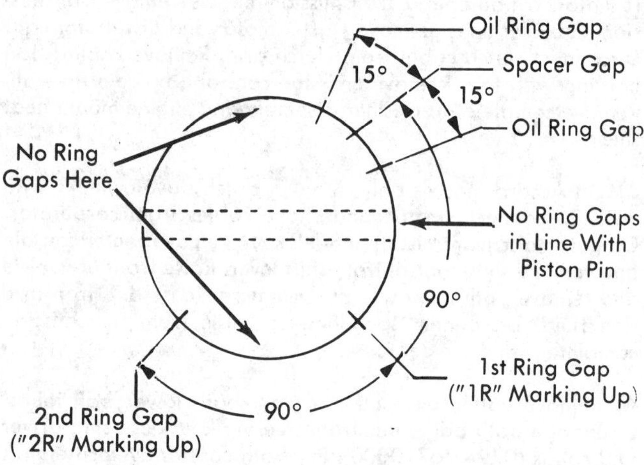

Fig. 2 Piston Ring Installation

2) Install three piece oil ring on piston with end gaps of rails and spacer staggered about 15°. Install top ring about 90° from oil spacer and second ring about 180° from spacer. Make sure no end gaps are in line with piston pin hole or thrust face of piston. Install all rings with markings facing upward.

PISTON PINS

Using a press and piston pin removal tool set (07973-6570000), press piston pin out of piston and connecting rod. Install new pin by placing pilot through piston and connecting rod. Lightly oil piston pin and place piston, rod, pin and ram on press base. Press in pin until centered in connecting rod.

CIVIC CVCC & ACCORD 4 CYLINDER (Cont.)

CRANKSHAFT MAIN & CONNECTING ROD BEARINGS

MAIN & CONNECTING ROD BEARINGS

1) Prior to disassembly, mark main and connecting rod bearings caps for reassembly in their original positions and check crankshaft endplay and connecting rod side play. Remove piston and connecting rod assemblies, remove main bearing caps and remove crankshaft.

2) Measure crankshaft for bend, out-of-round and taper *(See Specifications)*. If any measurement exceeds specifications, crankshaft must be replaced. Do not attempt to regrind crankshaft as bearing journals are specifically heat-treated.

Crankshaft Wear Specifications

Application	Standard In. (mm)	Service Limit In. (mm)
Bend	.0024 (.06)	.0118 (.30)
Taper	.0002 (.005)	.0004 (.010)
Out-Of-Round	.0002 (.005)	.0004 (.010)

3) Using Plastigage method, determine bearing clearances. If bearing replacement is necessary, use following procedure to determine bearing size to use.

4) Referring to *Fig. 3* and *Fig. 4*, note that all **letters** stamped on crankshaft counterweight pads apply to connecting rod journal nearest letter. All **numbers** stamped on crankshaft apply to nearest main bearing journal. Connecting rod caps have numbers stamped on cap and cylinder block has Roman numerals stamped on pad at flywheel end of block.

5) To determine color (size) of bearing insert to use, pair up numbers and/or letters on tables and where the column and row intersect, this will be bearing insert to use. Example: For a main bearing, use "Main Bearing Journals" table. If number stamped on crankshaft is "2" and roman numeral stamped on block for corresponding journal is "III", you would use a "Green" bearing insert

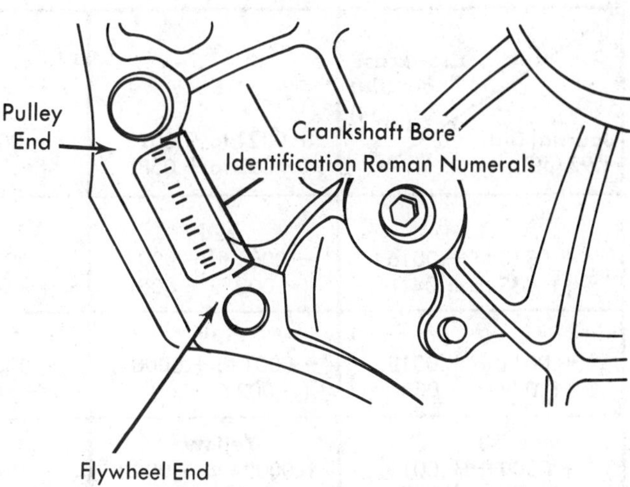

Fig. 3 Crankshaft Identification Locations (All Engines)

THRUST BEARING ALIGNMENT

Measure thrust bearing clearance and replace thrust washers or crankshaft as necessary. Do not change thrust washer thickness either by grinding or shimming. Install thrust washers with oil grooves facing toward crankshaft.

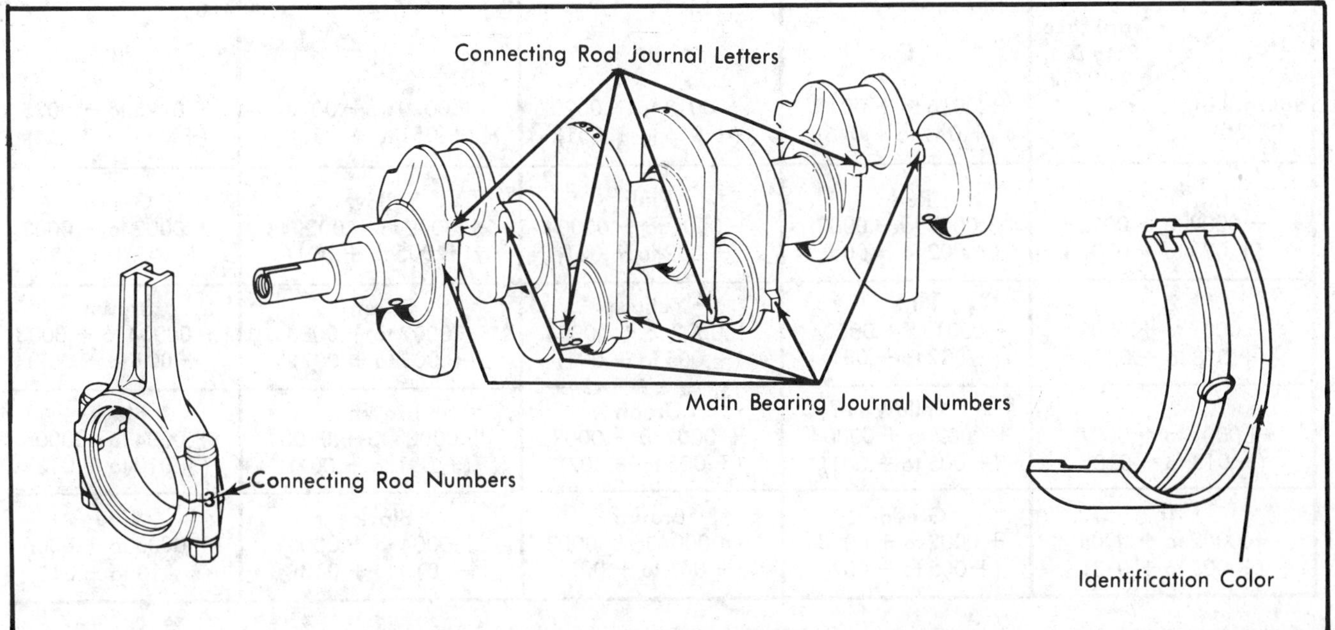

Fig. 4 Connecting Rod Bearing & Cylinder Block Identification Locations

CIVIC CVCC & ACCORD 4 CYLINDER (Cont.)

CVCC 1487cc Main Bearing Journals In. (mm)				
Crankcase Bore Dia. 2.13 (54) / Journal Dia. 1.97 (50)	I +.0021 to +.0023 (+.052 to +.058)	II +.0023 to +.0025 (+.058 to +.064)	III +.0025 to +.0027 (+.064 to +.070)	IIII +.0027 to +.0030 (+.070 to +.076)
1 +.0013 to +.0016 (+.033 to +.041)	Red −.0001 to −.0002 (−.002 to −.005)	Pink −.0001 to +.00004 (−.002 to +.001)	Yellow +.00004 to +.0002 (+.001 to +.005)	Green +.0002 to +.0003 (+.004 to +.007)
2 +.0011 to +.0013 (+.028 to +.033)	Pink −.0001 to +.00004 (−.002 to +.001)	Yellow +.00004 to +.0002 (+.001 to +.025)	Green +.0002 to +.0003 (+.005 to +.007)	Brown +.00004 to +.0003 (+.001 to +.007)
3 +.0009 to +.0011 (+.023 to +.028)	Yellow +.00004 to +.0002 (+.001 to +.005)	Green +.0002 to +.0003 (+.005 to +.007)	Brown +.00004 to +.0003 (+.001 to +.007)	Black +.0004 to +.0005 (+.010 to +.013)
4 +.0006 to +.0009 (+.016 to +.023)	Green +.0002 to +.0003 (+.005 to +.007)	Brown +.00004 to +.0003 (+.001 to +.007)	Black +.0004 to +.0005 (+.010 to +.013)	Blue +.0005 to +.0006 (+.013 to +.016)

Accord 1600cc Main Bearing Journals In. (mm)				
Crankcase Bore Dia. 2.13 (54) / Journal Dia. 1.97 (50)	I +.0016 to +.0018 (+.041 to +.046)	II +.0018 to +.0020 (+.046 to +.051)	III +.0020 to +.0023 (+.051 to +.058)	IIII +.0023 to +.0025 (+.058 to +.064)
1 +.0009 to +.0012 (+.023 to +.030)	Red −.0001 to −.0002 (−.002 to −.005)	Pink −.0001 to +.00004 (−.002 to +.001)	Yellow +.0002 to +.00004 (+.005 to +.001)	Green +.0002 to +.0003 (+.005 to +.007)
2 +.0007 to +.0009 (+.018 to +.023)	Pink −.0001 to +.00004 (−.002 to +.001)	Yellow +.0002 to +.00004 (+.005 to +.001)	Green +.0002 to +.0003 (+.005 to +.007)	Brown +.00004 to +.0003 (+.001 to +.007)
3 +.0005 to +.0007 (+.013 to +.018)	Yellow +.0002 to +.00004 (+.005 to +.001)	Green +.0002 to +.0003 (+.005 to +.007)	Brown +.00004 to +.0003 (+.001 to +.007)	Black +.0004 to +.0005 (+.010 to +.013)
4 +.0002 to +.0005 (+.005 to +.013)	Green +.0002 to +.0003 (+.005 to +.007)	Brown +.00004 to +.0003 (+.001 to +.007)	Black +.0004 to +.0005 (+.010 to +.013)	Blue +.0005 to +.0006 (+.013 to +.015)

CIVIC CVCC & ACCORD 4 CYLINDER (Cont.)

Connecting Rod Bearing Journals In. (mm)				
Connecting Rod Dia. 1.69 (43) / Journal Dia. 1.654 (42)	1 0 to +.0002 (0 to +.006)	2 +.0002 to +.0005 (+.006 to +.012)	3 +.0005 to +.0007 (+.012 to +.018)	4 +.0007 to +.0009 (+.018 to +.024)
A 0 to −.0002 (0 to −.006)	**Red** −.0002 to −.0003 (−.005 to −.008)	**Pink** −.0001 to −.0002 (−.002 to −.005)	**Yellow** −.0001 to +.00004 (−.002 to +.001)	**Green** +.00004 to +.0002 (+.001 to +.004)
B −.0002 to −.0005 (−.006 to −.012)	**Pink** −.0001 to −.0002 (−.002 to −.005)	**Yellow** −.0001 to +.00004 (−.002 to +.001)	**Green** +.00004 to +.0002 (+.001 to +.004)	**Brown** +.0002 to +.0003 (+.004 to +.007)
C −.0005 to −.0007 (−.012 to −.018)	**Yellow** −.0001 to +.00004 (−.002 to +.001)	**Green** +.00004 to +.0002 (+.001 to +.004)	**Brown** +.0002 to +.0003 (+.004 to +.007)	**Black** +.0003 to +.0004 (+.007 to +.010)
D −.0007 to −.0009 (−.018 to −.024)	**Green** +.00004 to +.0002 (+.001 to +.004)	**Brown** +.0002 to +.0003 (+.004 to +.007)	**Black** +.0003 to +.0004 (+.007 to +.010)	**Blue** +.0004 to +.0005 (+.010 to +.013)

CAMSHAFT

Camshaft Lobe Height	
Application	**In. (mm)**
1487 cc	
Intake	1.4966-1.5029 (38.01-38.17)
Exhaust	1.4789-1.4851 (37.56-37.72)
Auxiliary	1.6475-1.6537 (41.85-42.01)
1600 cc	
Intake	1.4856-1.4951 (37.74-37.98)
Exhaust	1.4856-1.4951 (37.74-37.98)
Auxiliary	1.7316-1.7410 (43.98-44.22)

TIMING BELT

1) Remove water pump drive belt, water pump pulley and crankshaft pulley. Remove upper timing belt cover from cylinder head and remove lower timing belt cover from engine block.

2) Loosen, do not remove, timing belt adjusting and pivot bolts. Slide belt off pulleys. To install, reverse removal procedure using care not to excessively bend or twist belt. Do not expose belt to engine oil or grease as this will damage belt. Install belt so same direction of rotation will be maintained to prevent excessive belt wear.

CAMSHAFT

1) Remove rocker arm assembly, then lift out camshaft . Inspect camshaft and cylinder head bearing surfaces for wear or damage. Check camshaft runout. If runout exceeds .004" (.10 mm), replace camshaft. Measure total camshaft lobe height. If total height of lobes is not to specifications, replace camshaft.

2) Oil camshaft bearing journals and install camshaft and seal or tachometer drive body. Apply silicone seal to mating surfaces on end camshaft supports and cylinder head. Install rocker arm assembly and tighten to specifications.

VALVE TIMING

Rotate crankshaft until TDC mark on flywheel or automatic transmission drive plate is aligned with index mark. Rotate camshaft until woodruff key is pointing straight up and timing marks on pulley are parallel with top of cylinder head *(See Fig. 5)*. Without disturbing pulley positions, slide on timing belt and adjust belt tension.

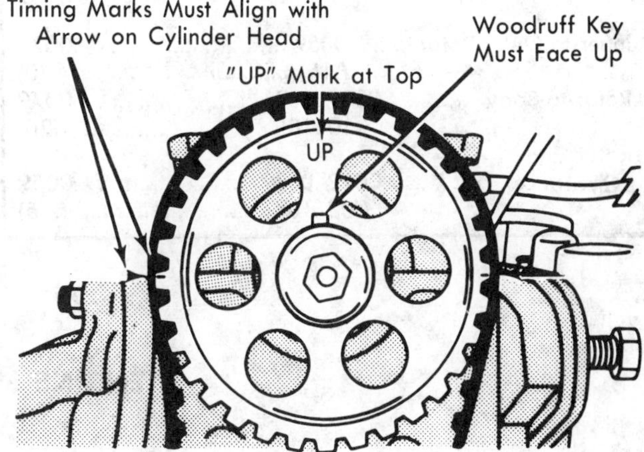

Fig. 5 Camshaft Alignment Marks in Position for Installing Camshaft Belt

TIMING BELT TENSION

Loosen timing belt pivot and adjustment bolts on lower timing belt cover. **NOTE** – *Upper bolt is pivot bolt and lower bolt is adjusting bolt.* Rotate engine a quarter of a turn counterclockwise and tighten adjusting bolt, then tighten pivot bolt. Do not apply pressure to timing belt while adjusting tension.

CIVIC CVCC & ACCORD 4 CYLINDER (Cont.)

ENGINE OILING

ENGINE OILING SYSTEM

A rotor type oil pump draws oil from oil pan and delivers it under pressure through main bearing cradle to main and connecting rod bearings. Oil passes through rods to an oil jet which lubricates pistons and cylinder walls. An oil passage carries oil to camshaft bearings and rocker arms. Oil mist lubricates valve stems.

OIL PUMP

1) Remove oil pan, then oil pump assembly may be removed by removing four long bolts (one bolt under strainer). Pull out relief valve cotter pin and remove seat, spring and valve.

2) Remove two pump body bolts and disassemble pump. Inspect pump for wear or damage. Measure pump operating clearances and relief valve spring free length. Reassemble pump making sure marks on rotors face outward and are adjacent to each other. Place oil pickup in container of oil and operate pump with screwdriver to ensure that it is operating. Place finger over outlet hole and check the pressure is created as pump is turned.

NOTE – *If oil pump driven gear is to be replaced, camshaft must also be replaced.*

Oil Pump Specifications

Application	Standard In. (mm)	Service Limit In. (mm)
Inner-to-Outer Rotor	.0059 (.15)	.0079 (.20)
Rotor-to-Body	.0039-.0071 (.10-.18)	.0079 (.20)
Rotor End Clearance	.0012-.0039 (.03-.10)	.0059 (.15)

Crankcase Capacity – 3.2 qts. (includes filter)

Oil Filter – Disposable with built-in by-pass valve.

Pressure Regulator Valve – Non-adjustable.

1487 cc Normal Oil Pressure – 48-58 psi (3.4-4.2 kg/cm) at 3000 RPM. 20 psi (1.4 kg/cm^2) minimum at idle speed.

1600 cc Normal Oil Pressure – 54-60 psi (3.8-4.2 kg/cm^2) at 3000 RPM. 21 psi (1.5 kg/cm ^{2}) minimum at idle speed.

ENGINE COOLING

Thermostat – Starts to open at 176-183°F (80-84°C) and is fully open at 203°F (95°C).

Thermoswitch – Operates at 191-197°F (88.5-91.5°C).

Cooling System Capacity – 4.2 quarts on 1487 cc, and 5.3 quarts on 1600 cc.

WATER PUMP

Removal – Drain radiator and loosen alternator adjusting bolts. Push alternator toward engine and remove drive belt. Remove water pump and "O" ring seal.

Installation – 1) Reinstall water pump. Loosen cooling system bleed valve located on thermostat housing. Fill radiator with coolant. When air bubbles no longer appear in coolant draining from bleed valve, close valve.

2) Start engine and place heater temperature control lever in high position. Run engine about ten minutes. Again open bleed valve and bleed system until there are no air bubbles in coolant draining from bleed valve. Refill radiator.

ENGINE SPECIFICATIONS

GENERAL SPECIFICATIONS

Year	Displ.		Carburetor	HP at RPM	Torque (Ft. Lbs. at RPM)	Compr. Ratio	Bore		Stroke	
	cu. ins.	cc					in.	mm	in.	mm
1977										
CVCC	90.80	1487	1x3-Bbl.	60@5000	77@3000	7.9:1	2.91	74.0	3.41	86.5
Accord	97.63	1600	1x3-Bbl.	.....	.....	8.0:1	2.91	74.0	3.66	93.0

CIVIC CVCC & ACCORD 4 CYLINDER (Cont.)

ENGINE SPECIFICATIONS (Cont.)

VALVES							
Engine & Valve	Head Diam. In. (mm)	Face Angle	Seat Angle	Seat Width In. (mm)	Stem Diameter In. (mm)	Stem Clearance In. (mm)	Valve Lift In. (mm)
1487 cc							
Intake	1.374-1.382 (34.9-35.1)	46°	46°	.055 (1.4)	.259-.260 (6.58-6.59)	.0004-.0016 (.01-.04)	.....
Exhaust	1.138-1.146 (28.9-29.1)	46°	46°	.055 (1.4)	.258-.259 (6.55-6.56)	.002-.003 (.05-.08)	.....
Auxiliary	.467-.471 (11.85-11.95)	45°	45°	.022 (.56)	.216-.217 (5.48-5.49)	.0008-.002 (.02-.05)	.....
1600 cc							
Intake	1.374-1.382 (34.9-35.1)	46°	46°	.055 (1.4)	.259-.260 (6.58-6.59)	.0008-.002 (.02-.05)	.....
Exhaust	1.098-1.106 (27.9-28.1)	46°	46°	.055 (1.4)	.258-.259 (6.55-6.56)	.002-.003 (.05-.08)	.....
Auxiliary	.469-.476 (11.9-11.10)	45°	45°	.022 (.56)	.216-.217 (5.48-5.49)	.001-.002 (.02-.05)	.....

PISTONS, PINS, RINGS						
	PISTONS	PINS		RINGS		
Engine	Clearance In. (mm)	Piston Fit In. (mm)	Rod Fit In. (mm)	Rings	End Gap In. (mm)	Side Clearance In. (mm)
1487 cc & 1600 cc	.0012 (.03)	.0004-.0009 (.010-.022)	①0-.0007 (0-.019)	No. 1	.008-.016 (.2-.4)	.0008-.0018 (.020-.045)
				No. 2	.008-.016 (.2-.4)	.0008-.0018 (.020-.045)
				Oil	②.008-.035 (.2-.9)	.....

① — Interference fit.

② — .012-.035" (.25-.89 mm) on 1487 cc.

CRANKSHAFT MAIN & CONNECTING ROD BEARINGS							
	MAIN BEARINGS				CONNECTING ROD BEARINGS		
Engine	Journal Diam. In. (mm)	Clearance In. (mm)	Thrust Bearing	Crankshaft End Play In. (mm)	Journal Diam. In. (mm)	Clearance In. (mm)	Side Play In. (mm)
1487 cc & 1600 cc	1.9687-1.9697 (50.006-50.030)	①.0010-.0022 (.026-.055)	No. 4	.0039-.0138 (.10-.35)	1.6526-1.6535 (41.976-42.000)	.0008-.0015 (.020-.038)	.0059-.0118 (.15-.30)

① — .0010-.0017" (.026-.044 mm) on 1600 cc.

CAMSHAFT			
Engine	Journal Diam. In. (mm)	Clearance In. (mm)①	Lobe Lift In. (mm)
1487 cc & 1600 cc	.....	.0020-.0059 (.050-.150)	.....

① — End play is .0020-.0039" (.050-.098 mm).

CIVIC CVCC & ACCORD 4 CYLINDER (Cont.)

ENGINE SPECIFICATIONS (Cont.)

VALVE SPRINGS			
Engine	Free Length In. (mm)	PRESSURE Lbs. @ In. (kg @ mm)	
		Valve Closed	Valve Open
1487 cc			
Intake			
Inner	1.583 (40.2)	12@1.358 (5.5@34.5)	59-68@1.024 (27-31@26)
Outer	1.573 (39.95)	11@1.437 (5@36.5)	72-84@1.094 (33-38@28)
Exhaust			
Inner	2.047 (52.0)	23@1.331 (10.5@33.8)	39-50@.988 (17-22@26)
Outer	2.138 (54.3)	51-62@1.432 (23-28@36)	79-90@1.108 (36-41@28)
Auxiliary	1.146 (29.1)	14-17@.906 (7-8@23)	21-26@.787 (10-12@20)
1600 cc			
Intake			
Inner	1.583 (40.2)	23@1.583 (10.5@34.5)	59-68@1.024 (27-31@26)
Outer	1.573 (39.95)	19@1.437 (9@36.5)	72-84@1.094 (33-38@28)
Exhaust			
Inner	2.047 (52.0)	31.5@1.358 (14.3@34.5)	39-50@1.024 (17-22@26)
Outer	2.118 (54)	60@1.437 (27.2@36.5)	79-90@1.108 (36-41@28)
Auxiliary	1.146 (29.1)	17@.906 (7.6@23.0)	21-26@.787 (10-12@20)

TIGHTENING SPECIFICATIONS

Application	Ft. Lbs. (mkg)
1487cc	
Connecting Rod Bolts	20 (2.7)
Main Bearing Bolts	33 (4.7)
Cylinder Head Bolts	44 (6.0)
Aux. Valve Holder Nut	50 (7.0)
Camshaft Sprocket Bolt	22 (3.0)
Intake/Exhaust Manifold Bolts	16 (2.2)
Rocker Arm Support	
6 mm Bolts	10 (1.4)
8 mm Bolts	16 (2.2)
Lower Torque Arm	5-9 (.7-1.2)
Upper Torque Arm	25-31 (3.5-4.3)
1600 cc	
Connecting Rod Bolts	18-21 (2.5-2.9)
Main Bearing Bolts	30-35 (4.2-4.8)
Cylinder Head Bolts	40-47 (5.5-6.5)
Aux. Valve Holder Nut	47-54 (6.5-7.5)
Camshaft Sprocket Bolt	18-25 (2.5-3.5)
Intake/Exhaust Manifold Bolts	14-17 (2.0-2.4)
Rocker Arm Support	
6 mm Bolts	7-10 (1.0-1.4)
8 mm Bolts	14-17 (2.0-2.4)
Lower Torque Arm	5-9 (.7-1.2)
Upper Torque Arm	25-31 (3.5-4.3

XJ6 4.2 LITER 6 CYLINDER

ENGINE CODING

ENGINE IDENTIFICATION

Engine can be identified by the number stamped on top of cylinder block at rear of engine and on identification plate in engine compartment. The "L" following the engine number denotes low compression engine.

Beginning serial number for two door models is 2J 50001 and starting serial number for four door models is 2T 50001.

ENGINE & CYLINDER HEAD

1) Remove hood. Disconnect battery. If equipped with air conditioning, discharge system and disconnect suction and pressure hoses (immediately cap all openings). Remove inlet and outlet fuel pipes at heat exchanger. Plug inlet pipe. Free inlet pipe of all connections and secure out of way (to valance). Remove screws securing heat exchanger. Secure A/C hoses away from engine. Beneath right fender well, remove receiver-drier retaining screws, then secure receiver-drier and hose away from engine.

2) Remove wing valance stays. Remove air cleaner. Detach and remove radiator. Disconnect coolant hoses to expansion tank. Remove both engine mount-to-bracket nuts. Drain power steering fluid. Disconnect power steering lines. Slacken pump mounting bolts and push pump as close as possible to engine.

3) Pull connectors from alternator. Separate connector plug from engine harness. Disconnect brake vacuum pipe at manifold, and secure pipe out of way. Release pipe clip and pull heater-A/C operating vacuum pipe from non-return valves; secure away from engine. Remove exhaust manifolds.

4) Remove starter cable and solenoid cable. Disconnect heater hoses at firewall connectors. Detach inner and outer throttle cables and secure away from engine. Remove choke cables from carburetors and position out of way. Disconnect hoses from charcoal canister.

5) Remove banjo bolt at clutch master cylinder reservoir, release hose from clip and secure across engine. Position suitable lifting device and attach to rear lifting eye. **NOTE** – *If vehicle is equipped with manual transmission, position vehicle on hoist or blocks to increase ground clearance by approximately one foot.* Remove overdrive switch from gear lever knob, then remove knob from gear lever (if equipped).

6) Remove nut at center of rear gearbox mounting. Unscrew two nuts securing bracket on gearbox. Remove heat shield. Position jack to support mounting plate of transmission, then unscrew four retaining set screws. Lower jack and remove mounting plate (with spring washers and rubber rings).

7) Remove special nuts securing propeller shaft to output flange. Separate gearbox harness at snap connectors (Man. Trans. vehicles). From transmission unit selector lever, remove nut to release ball peg on inner selector cable, and remove setscrew and spring washer securing outer selector cable clamp (Auto. Trans. vehicles). Disconnect speedometer cable from transmission.

8) From front of vehicle, position jack to support assembly beneath transmission oil sump. Support engine on lifting assembly. Carefully lower rear of engine and raise front.

CAUTION – *When maneuvering engine, take care not to damage the air conditioning expansion valve (if equipped).* Withdraw engine forward and upward.

CYLINDER HEAD

Removal – 1) Disconnect battery. Drain cooling system. Remove both wing valance stays (firewall-to-fender support rods), removing pressure line from support rod if equipped with air conditioning. Remove air cleaner. Detach inner and outer throttle cables from abutment and linkage brackets. Separate kickdown cable from linkage and retainers (if equipped with Model 65 Auto. Trans.).

2) If equipped with air conditioning, release inlet and outlet fuel line union nuts at heat exchanger. Plug line. Remove clips securing A/C suction line to engine. Remove screws and lay heat exchanger at left side of engine compartment.

3) Release union nut at EGR "Y" connector. Remove four screws and carefully separate cover from secondary throttle housing. Pull vacuum line from EGR valve. **NOTE** – *Completion of this step will depend upon whether vehicle is equipped with a fixed orifice EGR valve or a variable orifice EGR valve.*

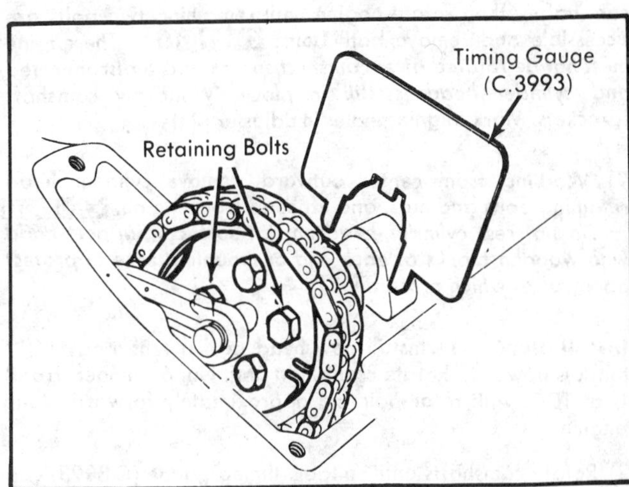

Fig. 1 Retaining Bolts Installed to Hold Camshaft During Cylinder Head Installation

4) Pull anti-deisel system vacuum line "H" fitting from "T" connector at gulp valve. Detach air line from fresh air injection manifold. Remove float chamber and carburetor breather crossover pipes from rubber connectors and plastic clips; lay these to left side of engine compartment.

5) Slacken pipe clip at air injection manifold check valve, then remove air injection pipe. Remove air pump and bracket. Detach setscrew at rear of cylinder block securing EGR system supply line. Unscrew EGR pipe from exhaust manifold adaptor. Remove adaptor.

6) Remove heat shield from exhaust manifold. Remove steering pump drive belt and swing pump away from engine. Detach top hose from radiator. Pull remote header and radiator bleed lines from header tank. Release coolant hose from water pump. Remove secondary throttle heater hose. Note connections and remove all vacuum lines and wires from beneath intake manifold.

XJ6 4.2 LITER 6 CYLINDER (Cont.)

7) Remove exhaust manifolds from cylinder head. Disconnect two camshaft oil lines from rear of head. Remove distributor cap, spark plugs, and plug wires. Unbolt and remove camshaft covers. Detach breather housing from front of head.

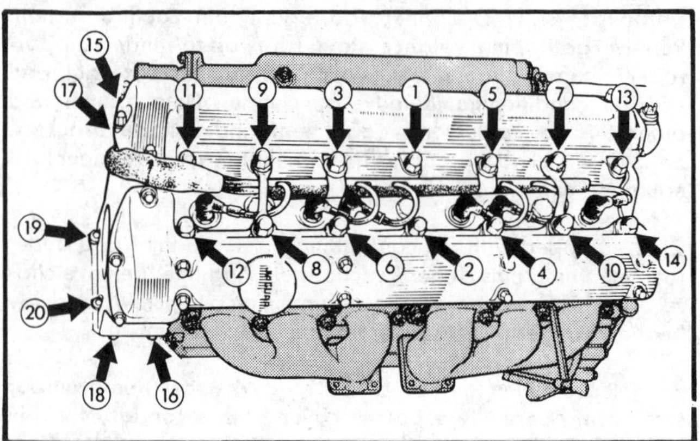

Fig. 2 Jaguar XJ6 Cylinder Head Tightening Sequence

8) Remove camshaft sprocket retaining bolt (from both camshafts), then rotate engine until remaining two bolts are accessible and remove both bolts. **CAUTION** – *The engine must not be rotated after camshaft sprockets are disconnected and cylinder head is still in place.* Withdraw camshaft sprockets. Mark aligning holes in adjuster plates.

9) Working from center outward, remove cylinder head retaining bolts and nuts, and lift head from engine. **CAUTION** – *Do not rest cylinder head on flat surface. Support head with wooden blocks at each end of mounting face to protect open valves which protrude.*

Installation – 1) Install new head gasket (ensuring "TOP" mark is upward). Rotate crankshaft until No. 6 cylinder (front) is at TDC, with rotor pointing approximately forward along engine.

2) Rotate camshafts until suitable timing gauge (C.3993) can be located in front flange slots *(Fig. 1)*. Lower cylinder head into position, attach spark plug wire brackets and lifting brackets to appropriate head studs, then place washers and 14 large domed nuts on stud. Affix nuts and washers at forward end of head, then tighten all nuts *(Fig. 2)*.

3) Locate sprockets on camshaft flanges and ensure both holes in each flange are positioned with aligning holes marked during removal. If necessary, remove circlip and reposition adjuster plate. Make sure engine is not rotated until camshaft sprockets are fully seated and chain installed.

4) Secure each adjuster plate to camshaft, then rotate engine until remaining attachment holes are accessible. Install bolts and bend up lock plate tabs. Set timing chain tension using a suitable adjusting tool (JD2B). Tighten lock nut.

5) Ensure No. 6 (front) cylinder is at TDC and recheck position of camshafts using timing gauge (C.3993). Complete installation by reversing remainder of removal procedures. Recheck ignition timing and perform exhaust emission check.

VALVES

VALVE ARRANGEMENT

Left Side – All exhaust.
Right Side – All intake.

VALVE GUIDE SERVICING

Check valve guide for wear and proper guide-to-valve stem clearance. If guide is worn beyond specifications, replace guide by heating head in boiling water for approximately 30 minutes (or by other suitable method), then drive guide(s) out of head from combustion chamber end. Coat new guide with graphite grease and refit circlip. Reheat head and drive new guide in from top until circlip is seated in groove. **NOTE** – *When installing oversize replacement guides, check O.D. of guide to be used, and if necessary, ream cylinder head bore to obtain proper interference fit.*

Replacement Valve Guides

Application	Size Mark	Dimension In. (mm)
Standard	No Mark	.501-.502 (12.73-12.75)
1st Oversize	1 Groove	.503-.504 (12.78-12.80)
2nd Oversize	2 Grooves	.506-.507 (12.85-12.8)
3rd Oversize	3 Grooves	.511-.512 (12.98-13.00)

VALVE SPRING SERVICING

CAUTION – *Support ends of cylinder head with wooden blocks to prevent damage to valves. Opened valves protrude below face of cylinder head.*

1) Remove camshaft bearing caps, note markings for reassembly. Remove camshaft, tappets and adjusting pads. Retain tappets and pads in proper order for reassembly.

Fig. 3 Using Special Valve Spring Compressor Tool No.JD.6118C to Remove Spring

2) Install suitable spring compressor (Churchill No. JD.6118C) and a block of wood between valve and work table. Compress springs and remove valve keepers. Compare old spring

XJ6 4.2 LITER 6 CYLINDER (Cont.)

with new spring or with specification table. Replace springs as necessary. To install, reverse procedure.

VALVE TAPPET SERVICE

Remove tappets and adjusting pads, keeping components in order. **NOTE** — *Valves are numbered and must be kept in order (if removed). No. 1 is at flywheel end of engine.* Inspect all tappets, guides, and adjusting pads for wear. If tappet guide is to be replaced, bore out old guide until it collapses (taking care not to damage head bore). Ensure head is at room temperature and measure tappet guide bore, then grind replacement guide to obtain a .003" (.076 mm) interference fit. Also grind the same amount from the "lead in" at the bottom end of guide. Heat head and drive in tappet guide, then ream guide to 1.75" (44.5 mm). Replace other necessary parts.

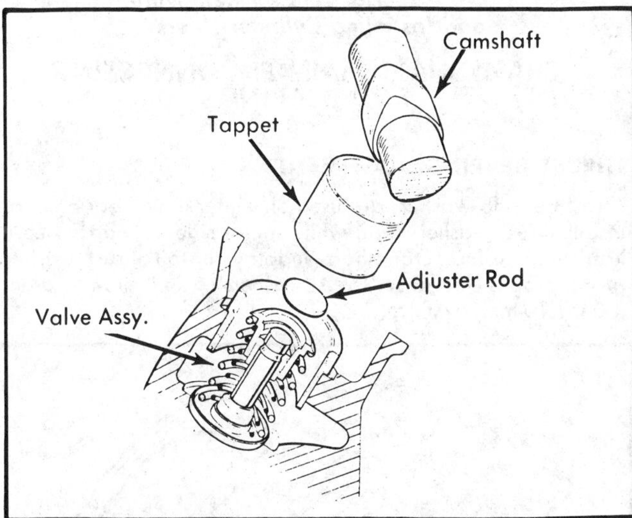

Fig. 4 Expanded View of Valve Tappet Assemblies

VALVE TAPPET CLEARANCE

NOTE — *If checking valve clearances with cylinder head removed, the camshafts must be installed and checked one at a time. It is imperative that this be followed, as position fouling is likely if camshafts are rotated independently while both are installed.*

1) If not already done, remove camshaft covers. Rotate camshaft and record clearance between heel of each cam and its respective tappet. If head is installed, and adjustment is to be made, rotate camshaft and install valve timing gauge (C.3993) before removing final camshaft retaining bolt. If required, disconnect sprockets from camshafts. See *Valve Timing.*

2) Remove camshaft bearing caps and lift off camshaft. Remove each tappet taking note of its location. Remove adjusting pad. Subtract appropriate valve clearance of .012-.014" (.305-.356 mm) from initial clearance measured. Select appropriate adjusting shim which will equal this measurement. Adjusting pads are available in increments of .001" (.03 mm) from .085" (2.16 mm) to .110" (2.79 mm) and are marked with letters from "A" to "Z" respectively.

3) Insert adjusting pads and install tappets. Attach camshafts (using timing gauge if head is installed). Torque camshaft bearing cap nuts, connect camshaft sprockets, and install camshaft covers.

PISTONS, PINS & RINGS

OIL PAN REMOVAL (ENGINE INSTALLED)

1) Remove front suspension components to gain access and suitable clearance. Drain engine oil. Remove nuts securing oil return pipe. Unscrew nuts, bolts, and washers securing transmission oil cooler pipe clips (Auto. Trans.).

2) Remove setscrews and nuts retaining oil pan to block (note location of short screw at right front). Unbolt and remove intake strainer box.

3) When installing, ensure "O" ring is properly positioned on oil return pipe. Lightly coat new oil seal with grease and locate in oil pan groove (DO NOT trim seal ends, press into groove until flush). Lightly coat new pan gasket and install pan. Reverse remaining procedures.

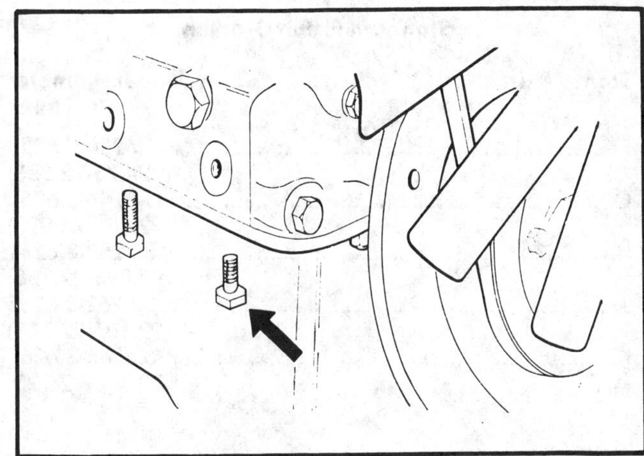

Fig. 5 Position of Short Screw in Oil Pan

PISTON & ROD ASSEMBLY

1) With cylinder head and oil pan removed, unscrew nuts from connecting rod caps, and remove caps, keeping in order for reassembly. **NOTE** — *Rod caps and rods are numbered to correspond to their positions (No. 1 is at flywheel end). Remove connecting rod bolt and withdraw piston and rod assembly out top of cylinder.*

2) If installing original assemblies, ensure they are replaced in original cylinders. If installing new assemblies, stamp-mark assemblies with numbers "1" through "6". Position pistons in cylinders with "FRONT" mark forward.

XJ6 4.2 LITER 6 CYLINDER (Cont.)

PISTON RINGS

After checking ring end gap and side play, install compression rings in top two grooves and oil ring in bottom groove. Both compression rings have tapered peripheries and are marked with "TOP" to ensure correct installation. The top ring is also chrome-plated and cargraph (red) coated; the red coating must NOT be removed. When fitting oil ring, ensure expander ends do not overlap.

PISTON PINS

When removing and replacing piston pins, immerse assembly in hot oil bath (or use other suitable method) to bring piston end of assembly to approximately 230°F (110°C). When installing pins, always use new pin circlips. Note that pins are color coded for grading purposes. Always select proper color pin for replacement.

FITTING PISTONS

Check piston and cylinder bore to determine if proper clearance exists. If necessary to rebore cylinder for installation of oversize piston, note that reboring is not to exceed .030" (.76 mm). Oversize pistons are available in .010", .020", and .030" (.25 mm, .51 mm, and .76 mm) oversizes. If replacing pistons with standard sizes (no reboring), note the following list of piston grades and select replacement piston of same grade. Piston grade is stamped in piston crown and on top face of block adjacent to cylinder.

Standard Piston Grading

Stamp Mark	Cylinder Diameter In. (mm)
F	3.6250-3.6253 (92.075-92.083)
G	3.6254-3.6257 (92.085-92.093)
H	3.6258-3.6261 (92.095-92.103)
J	3.6262-3.6265 (92.106-92.113)
K	3.6266-3.6269 (92.116-92.123)

CYLINDER LINERS

1) Should piston-to-cylinder clearance be excessive and reboring requires more than .030" (.76 mm) to clean up cylinders, new cylinder liners must be installed.

2) Press out the worn liners from below, using a suitable block. Lightly coat outer top half of new liner with a jointing compound, then press in new liner until flush with top of block. Smear more jointing compound around area of liner-to-block mating surface.

3) Bore out liner to correspond with grade of piston to be installed. Following reboring process, the blanking plugs in the main oil gallery should be removed and cylinder block oilways thoroughly cleaned. When dry, coat interior of crankcase with an oil and heat resistant paint.

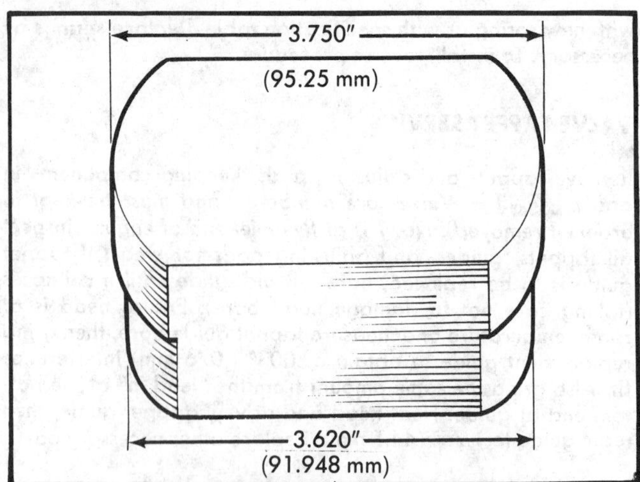

Fig. 6 Special Tool for Removing and Installing Cylinder Liners

CRANKSHAFT MAIN & CONNECTING ROD BEARINGS

THRUST BEARING ALIGNMENT

Thrust bearing washers are used on center main bearing caps. Install thrust washers with white metal side outwards (see illustration). Check crankshaft endplay, install thrust washers giving proper clearance. Thrust washers come in standard and .004" (.10 mm) oversize.

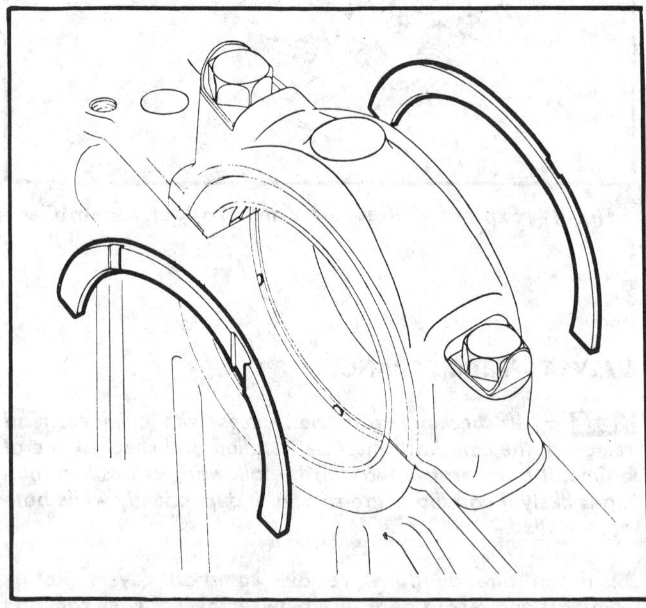

Fig. 7 Position of Thrust Washers on Crankshaft

MAIN BEARING SERVICE

Remove connecting rod and main bearing caps, retaining all parts in exact order for reassembly. Note that all caps are numbered for reassembly reference. When wear or out-of-roundness exceeds .003" (.08 mm), regrind crankshaft and install undersize bearings. Bearings are available in .010", .020", .030", and .040" (.25 mm, .51 mm, .76 mm, and 1.02 mm) undersizes. If regrinding must exceed .040" (1.02 mm), replace crankshaft.

XJ6 4.2 LITER 6 CYLINDER (Cont.)

REAR MAIN BEARING OIL SEAL

NOTE – *The following procedure must be performed before crankshaft is reinstalled.*

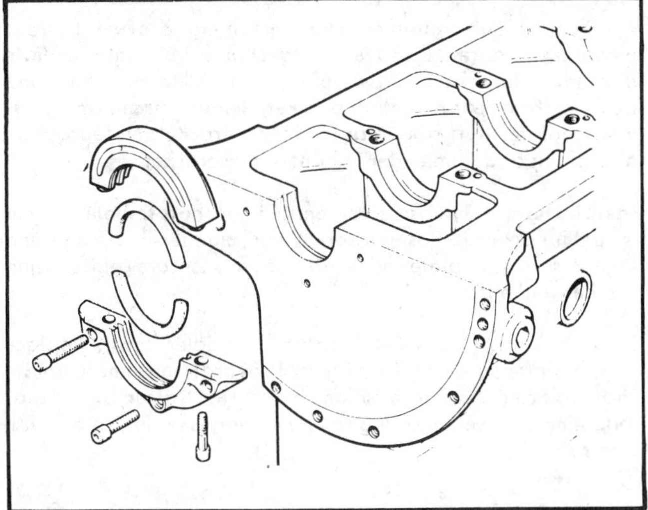

Fig. 8 Expanded View of Crankshaft Rear Oil Seal

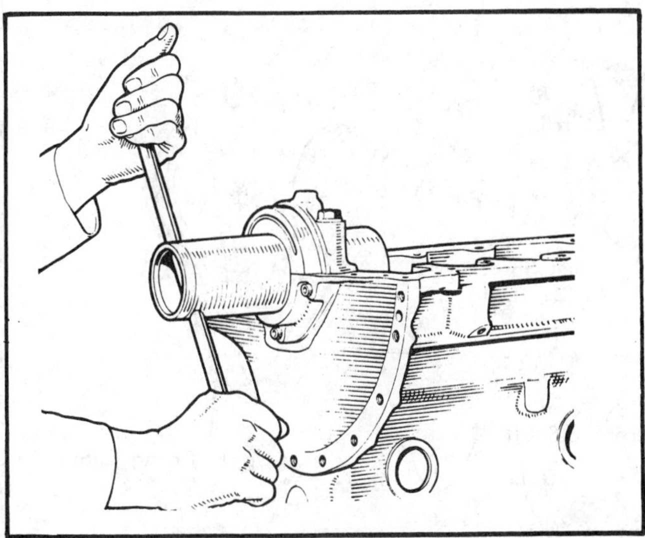

Fig. 9 Using Special Tool to Size Rear Oil Seal

1) Carefully tap new rear oil seal halves into position, then roll seal into housing (with a hammer handle) until ends do not protrude. **NOTE** – *DO NOT cut seal ends.* When both halves are properly in place, secure them with Allen screws.

2) Attach rear main bearing cap without bearings and torque to 72 ft. lbs. (10 mkg). Assemble rear oil seal housing to cylinder block, using three Allen screws. Lightly coat inside surface of oil seal with graphite grease and insert a suitable sizing tool (JD.17B) as shown in illustration. Press tool inward and turn until it is fully seated; this should properly size the oil seal. Remove sizing tool by pulling and twisting in opposite direction. Remove oil seal housing and install crankshaft.

CAMSHAFT

ENGINE FRONT COVER & OIL SEAL

Removal – 1) Remove radiator and fan belt. Mark position of vibration damper for reassembly. Remove pulley. Using a pair of levers, pry damper off of split cone. Remove split cone.

2) Remove oil pan and water pump. Unscrew screws attaching timing cover and slide timing cover and oil seal off of crankshaft.

Installation – 1) Place new seal in groove in timing cover. Using a new gasket and sealing compound, intall timing cover and seal. Reinstall oil pan with a new gasket. Install short screw in front right hand corner of oil pan.

2) Reinstall split cone on crankshaft. Position crankshaft damper to mark, install pulley and torque attaching bolts to specifications. Reinstall remaining components in reverse of removal procedures.

CAMSHAFT

1) After removing necessary components to gain access to camshaft covers, unscrew ten dome head nuts and two cross head screws which retain each camshaft cover. Detach crankcase breather from front of head. Use a suitable tool (JD.2B) to slacken timing chain (rotate tool in clockwise direction).

2) Bend back tabs from camshaft sprockets and remove two top bolts from each camshaft sprocket, then rotate engine to

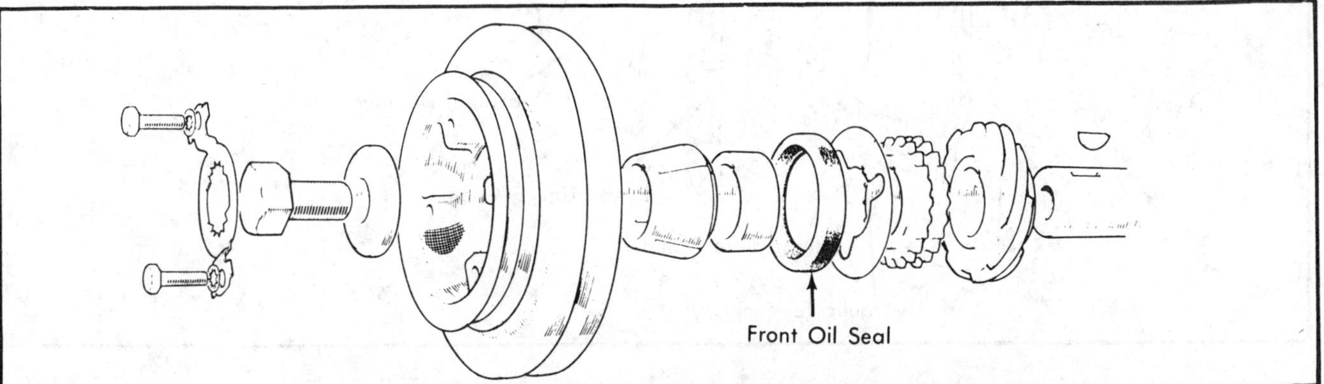

Fig. 10 Exploded View of Crankshaft Damper with Detail of Oil Seal

XJ6 4.2 LITER 6 CYLINDER (Cont.)

gain access to other two screws. Rotate engine further until valve timing gauge (C.3993) can be installed. CAUTION – *Engine is not to be rotated once sprockets are removed from camshafts.* Draw sprockets from camshafts and slide sprockets up support brackets. Mark attachment holes in adjuster plate for reassembly reference. Remove camshaft bearing cap retaining nuts and withdraw camshaft. Keep all components in proper order for reassembly.

TIMING CHAIN REPLACEMENT

Removal – 1) Remove cylinder head, oil pan, water pump, crankcase breather, vibration damper (including cone and Woodruff key), and timing gear cover. Withdraw timing pointer, distance piece, and front oil seal.

2) Remove oil slinger from crankshaft. Unscrew two bottom timing chain tensioner and chain guides retaining screws. Withdraw conical filter behind tensioner. Slacken four setscrews securing top timing chain assembly (do not remove setscrews at this point).

3) Withdraw crankshaft timing sprocket and chain assembly. Be sure to remove spacers, top timing chain damper, and top timing chain retainer. Disengage camshaft sprockets from top chain. Remove nut and serrated washer from idler shaft and withdraw serrated plate, plunger, and spring.

4) Remove nuts retaining front mounting bracket to rear mounting bracket. Remove timing chains from intermediate and idler sprockets. Draw idler shaft, idler sprocket, and bushing from rear mounting bracket. Remove circlip and press intermediate shaft from rear mounting bracket. Note location of bushing and shim under intermediate sprocket.

Installation – 1) Position eccentric idler shaft to hole in front mounting bracket. Position spring and plunger in bracket and locate serrated plate on shaft. Loosely secure plate using washer and nut.

2) Attach idler sprocket (21 teeth) to idler shaft. Replace intermediate sprocket (large gear forward) onto intermediate shaft, placing shim in position. Install shaft assembly in rear mounting bracket, ensuring roll pin engages in slot; retain with circlip.

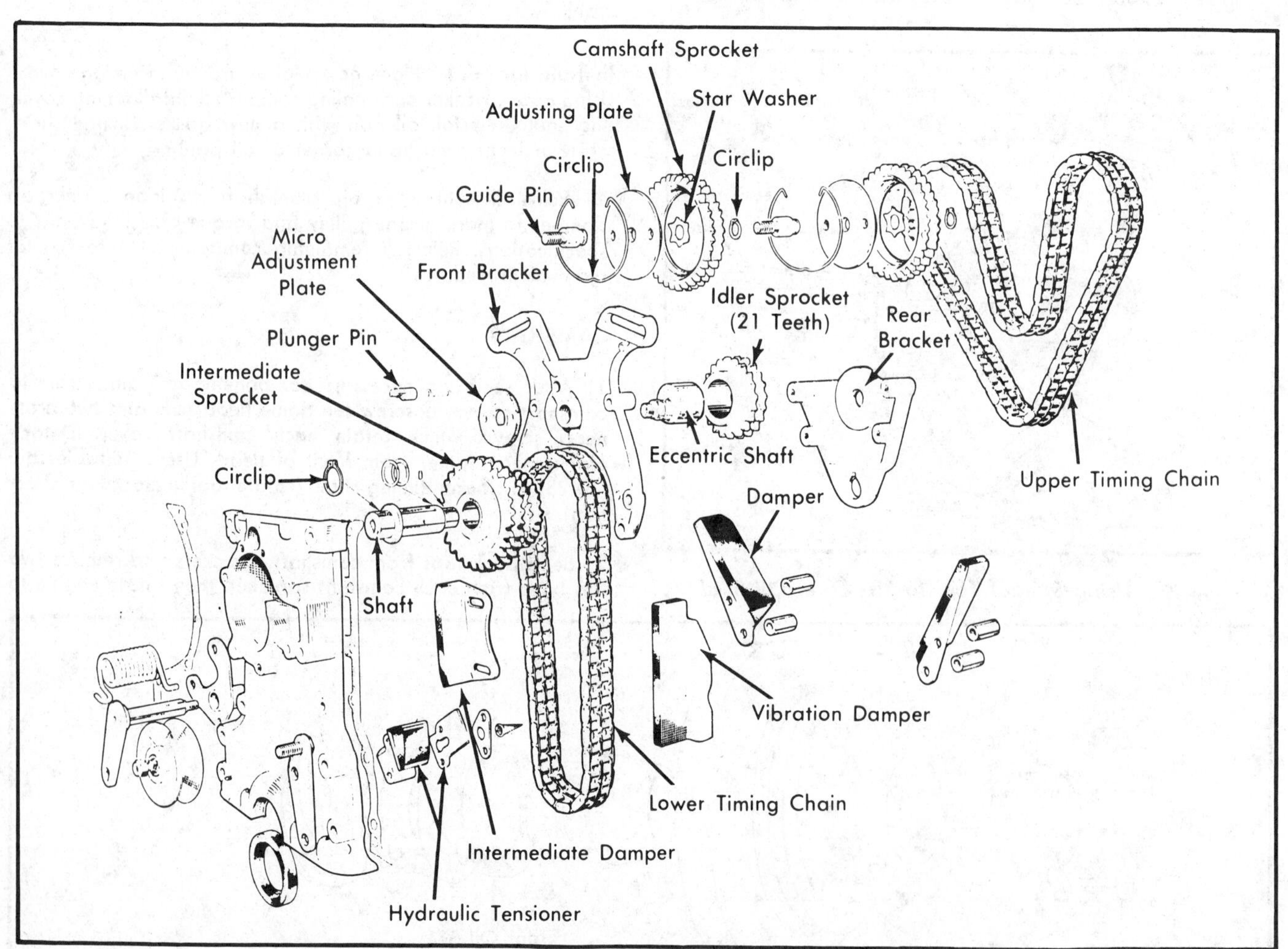

Fig. 11 Exploded View of Timing Gear Assembly

XJ6 4.2 LITER 6 CYLINDER (Cont.)

3) Locate top timing chain (longer) on small intermediate sprocket, and lower timing chain on large sprocket. Loop top chain beneath idler sprocket and secure top mounting bracket to rear bracket.

4) Install four long setscrews and spring washers to front mounting bracket and attach dampers, chain support plate, and spacers to setscrews. Equalize loops of top timing chain and locate camshaft sprockets in loops. Rotate eccentric idler shaft to lift idler sprocket to its highest position between camshaft sprockets.

5) Ensure Woodruff key is positioned in crankshaft. Locate crankshaft sprocket, but do not fully seat at this time. Loop bottom timing chain beneath crankshaft sprocket, then tap sprocket until it is fully seated. Position and secure crankshaft sprocket assembly.

6) Install, but do not tighten, bottom timing chain guides. Insert conical filter into its hole in cylinder block. Screw slipper into tensioner until .125" (3.17 mm) exists between slipper and body. Locate tensioner on shims as necessary to ensure slipper runs central on chain, and secure using two setscrews and lock plate.

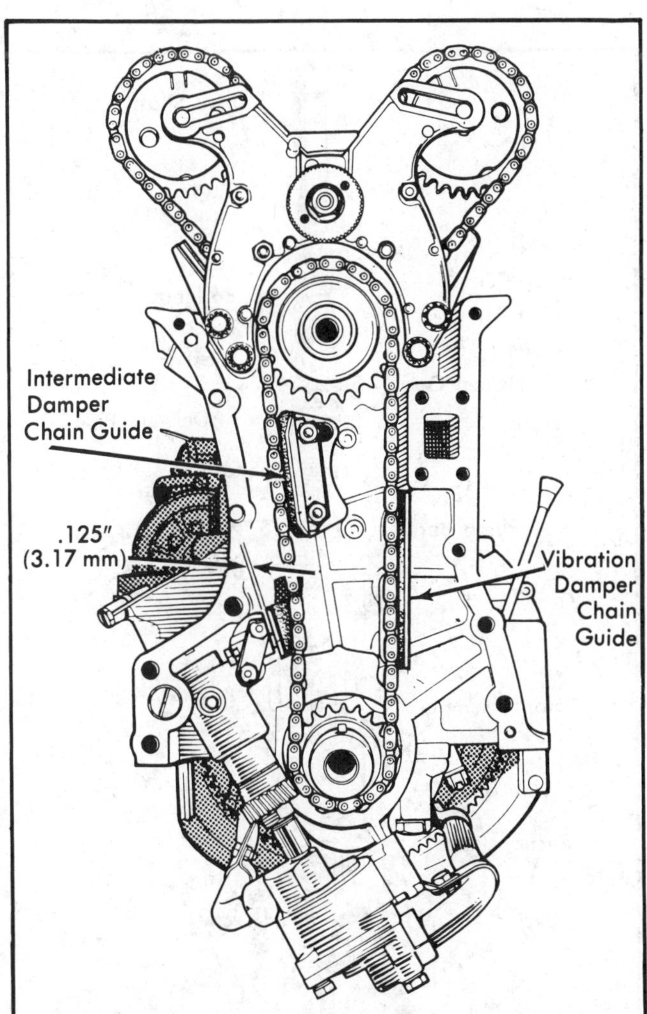

Fig. 12 Lower Timing Chain Adjustment Measurement Point

7) Place slip gauge or spacer card supplied with new tensioner between slipper and body of tensioner to maintain dimension set earlier, then adjust intermediate damper to touch chain. Tighten setscrews and bend up tabs of lock plate. Remove slip gauge and top chain or tensioner slipper to release ratchet. Position oil slinger on crankshaft. Replace timing cover.

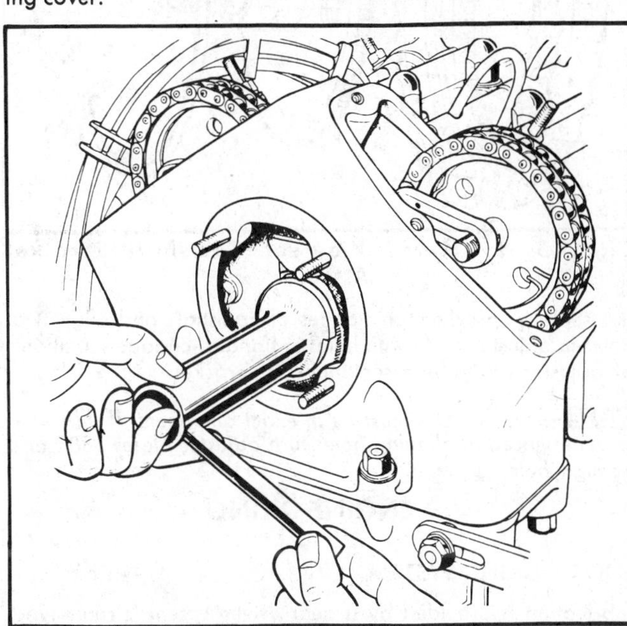

Fig. 13 Making Upper Timing Chain Adjustment

VALVE TIMING

1) Rotate engine so that No. 6 (front) piston is at TDC on compression stroke, and distributor rotor arm points at No. 6 segment. Check that timing chains are properly adjusted. *See Timing Chain Replacement.*

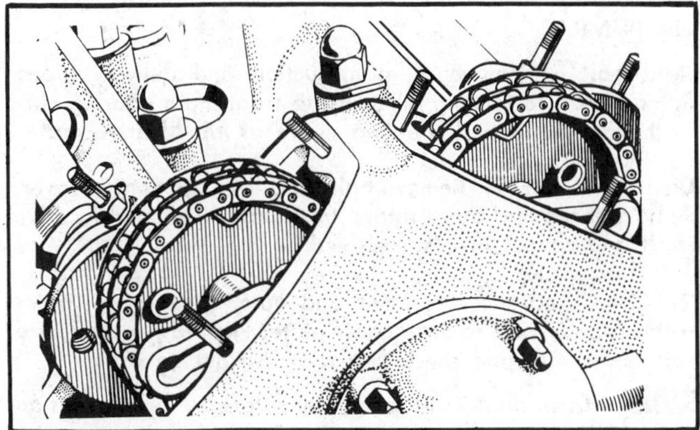

Fig. 14 View Showing Camshaft Sprockets in Disconnected Position

2) Remove lock wire from camshaft sprocket screws. Rotate engine until inaccessible screws can be removed. Return engine to TDC of No. 6 piston and remove remaining screws. Tap camshaft sprockets off camshaft flanges.

3) Accurately position camshafts with valve timing gauge *(Fig. 14)*, and check that TDC marks are in exact alignment. Withdraw circlips from camshaft sprocket assembly and press adjusting plates forward until serrations disengage *(Fig. 14)*.

XJ6 4.2 LITER 6 CYLINDER (Cont.)

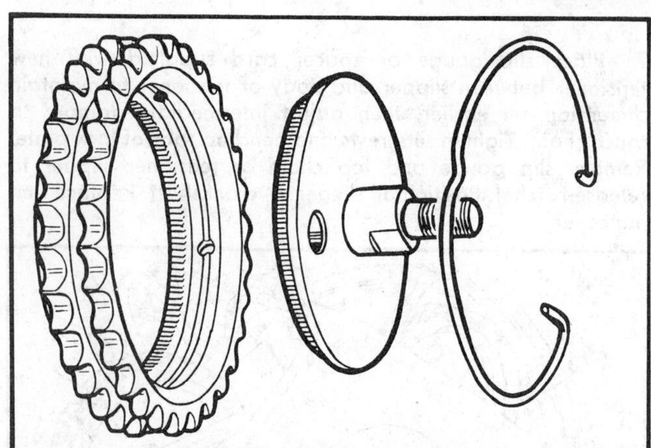

Fig. 15 Expanded View of Camshaft Sprocket Assembly

4) Replace sprockets on flanges of camshaft and align two holes in adjuster plate with holes in flanges. Engage serrations of adjuster plates with serrations in sprocket.

NOTE — *Screw holes must be in exact alignment. If difficulty is experienced in aligning holes turn adjuster plates 180° and realign holes.*

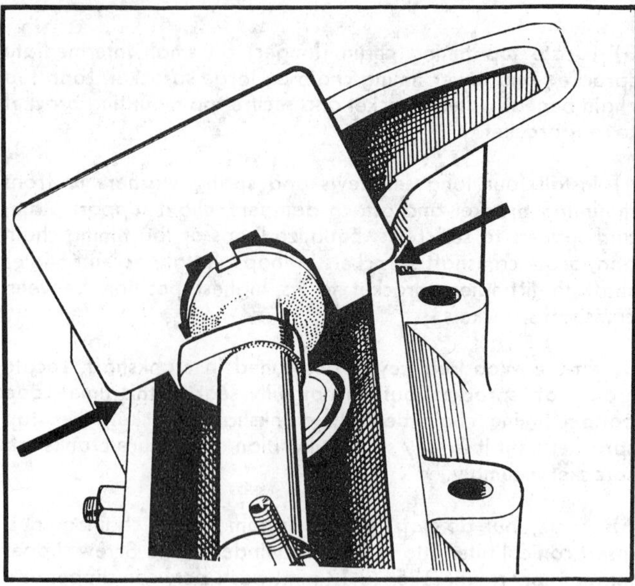

Fig. 16 Valve Timing Guide Inserted in Place

5) Replace circlips in camshaft sprockets. Replace camshaft sprocket screws and lock wire. Recheck valve timing.

ENGINE OILING

ENGINE OILING SYSTEM

Lubrication is provided by a gear driven eccentric rotor type pump. Oil from pump goes through a full-flow oil filter to all moving engine components.

Crankcase Capacity — 7.2 qts.

Oil Filter — Replace every 3,000 miles.

Normal Oil Pressure (Hot) — 40 psi @ 3,000 RPM.

OIL PUMP

Removal — Remove oil pan, suction and delivery pipes. Remove bolts attaching oil pump to front main bearing cap. Withdraw pump and coupling sleeve at top of drive shaft.

Disassembly — 1) Remove bolts and take off bottom cover. Remove inner and outer rotors. Inner rotor is pinned to drive shaft and cannot be disassembled.

2) Check clearances of inner and outer rotor lobes, outer rotor-to-body and rotor-to-cover plate. Place drive shaft in a soft jawed vise and check that rotor is tight on pin.

NOTE — *Drive shaft, inner and outer rotors are supplied as an assembly only.*

Assembly — Reassemble in reverse order of disassembly. Install outer rotor to pump body with chamfered end forward. Use new "O" rings on suction and delivery pipes. To install, reverse removal procedures.

Oil Pump Specifications

Application	Clearance In. (mm)
Inner-to-Outer Rotor	.006 (.15)
Outer Rotor-to-Body	.010 (.25)
Rotor-to-Cover (End Play)	.0025 (.06)

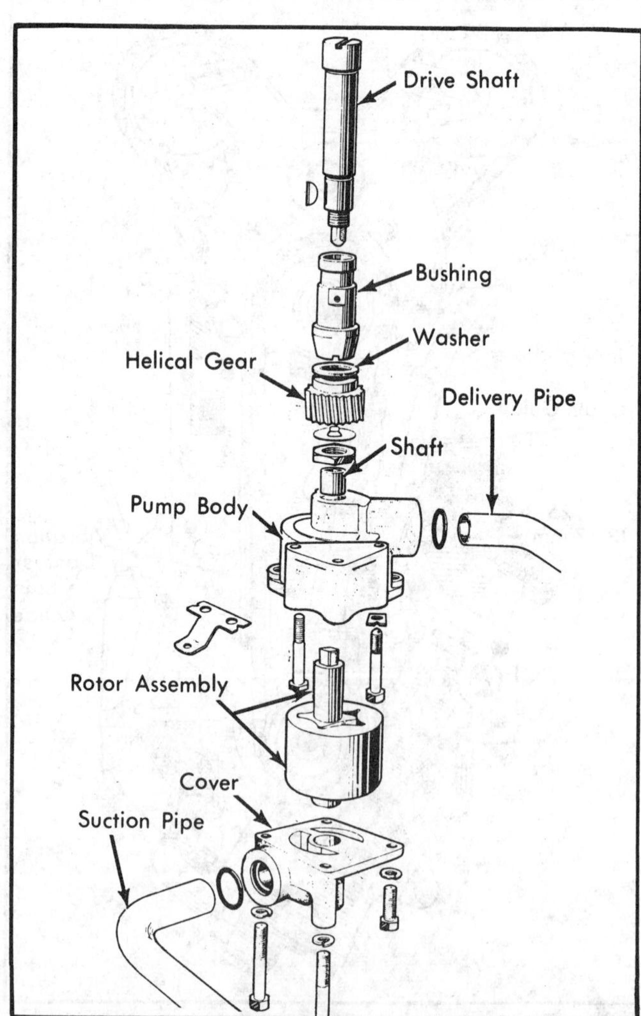

Fig. 17 Exploded View of Jaguar Oil Pump

XJ6 4.2 LITER 6 CYLINDER (Cont.)

ENGINE COOLING

WATER PUMP

Disassembly – 1) Remove water pump and gasket from timing cover. Pull fan hub from shaft with a puller. Loosen lock nut and remove Allen locating screw.

2) Using an arbor press and a tube measuring 1 3/32" O.D. and 31/32" I.D., press shaft and impeller assembly out of pump body. Do not press on shaft or bearing will be damaged.

3) Press shaft from impeller and remove seal and rubber thrower. Spindle and bearing assembly cannot be further disassembled.

4) Clean and inspect all parts for wear or damage. Bearing is sealed and lubricated, therefore do not wash in solvents.

Assembly – 1) Install shaft and bearing assembly into pump body from rear. Align and install locating screw and lock nut. Place rubber thrower in its groove on shaft in front of seal.

2) Coat outside of brass seal housing with suitable water resistant sealer and install into recess in pump housing. Push seal into its housing with carbon face towards rear of pump.

3) Press impeller onto shaft until rear face of impeller is flush with end of shaft. Press fan hub onto shaft until it is flush with end of shaft.

Cooling System Capacity – 19.25 qts.

TIGHTENING SPECIFICATIONS	
Application	**Ft. Lbs. (mkg)**
Cylinder Head Nuts	54 (7.5)
Main Bearing Caps	72 (10)
Connecting Rod Caps	37.5 (5.1)
Flywheel	67 (9.2)
Camshaft Cap	9 (1.2)
Torque Converter	35 (4.8)
Camshaft Cover	5-6 (.7-.8)
Rear Engine Mount-to-Body	
5/16" Bolt	14-18 (1.9-2.5)
3/8" Bolt	27-32 (3.7-4.4)
Front Engine Bracket-to-Beam	14-18 (1.9-2.5)

ENGINE SPECIFICATIONS

GENERAL SPECIFICATIONS										
Year	Displ.		Carburetor	HP at RPM	Torque (Ft. Lbs. at RPM)	Compr. Ratio	Bore		Stroke	
	cu. ins.	cc					in.	mm	in.	mm
1977	258.4	4235	2x1-Bbl.	195 @ 4750	.....	7.5:1	3.625	92.07	4.173	106

VALVES							
Engine & Valve	Head Diam. In. (mm)	Face Angle	Seat Angle	Seat Width In. (mm)	Stem Diameter In. (mm)	Stem Clearance In. (mm)	Valve Lift In. (mm)
4235 cc							
Intake	1.75 (44.45)	45°	45°	.....	.310-.3125 (7.87-7.94)	.001-.004 (.025-.10)	.375 (9.525)
Exhaust	1.625 (41.28)	45°	45°	.....	.310-.3125 (7.87-7.94)	.001-.004 (.025-.10)	.375 (9.525)

CAMSHAFT			
Engine	Journal Diam. In. (mm)	Clearance In. (mm)	Lobe Lift In. (mm)
4235 cc	.9990-.9995 (25.375-25.387)	.0005-.002 (.013-.05)	.....

VALVE TIMING				
	INTAKE		EXHAUST	
Engine	Open (BTDC)	Close (ABDC)	Open (BBDC)	Close (ATDC)
4235cc	15°	57°	57°	15°

XJ6 4.2 LITER 6 CYLINDER (Cont.)

ENGINE SPECIFICATIONS (Cont.)

PISTONS, PINS, RINGS						
	PISTONS	PINS		RINGS		
Engine	Clearance In. (mm)	Piston Fit In. (mm)	Rod Fit In. (mm)	Rings	End Gap In. (mm)	Side Clearance In. (mm)
4235 cc	.0007-.0013 (.018-.033)	① Press Fit	② Push Fit	No. 1	.015-.020 (.38-.51)	.0015-.0035 (.038-.089)
				No. 2	.009-.014 (.23-.35)	.0015-.0035 (.038-.089)
				Oil	.015-.045 (.38-1.14)	③

① — When heated to 230°F (110°C). ② — At room temperature, without piston. ③ — Self-expanding.

CRANKSHAFT MAIN & CONNECTING ROD BEARINGS							
	MAIN BEARINGS				CONNECTING ROD BEARINGS		
Engine	Journal Diam. In. (mm)	Clearance In. (mm)	Thrust Bearing	Crankshaft End Play In. (mm)	Journal Diam. In. (mm)	Clearance In. (mm)	Side Play In. (mm)
4235 cc	2.749-2.750 (69.85-69.86)	.0008-.0025 (.020-.063)	Center	.004-.006 (.10-.15)	2.086-2.0866 (52.98-53.00)	.001-.0027 (.025-.069)	.0058-.0087 (.147-.221)

VALVE SPRINGS			
Engine	Free Length In. (mm)	PRESSURE Lbs. @ In. (kg @ mm)	
		Valve Closed	Valve Open
4235 cc			
Inner	1.734 (44.04)	.....	.....
Outer	2.103 (53.42)	.....	.....

XJS & XJ12 SERIES 2 V12

ENGINE CODING

ENGINE IDENTIFICATION

Engine number is stamped on cylinder block at rear of engine, between cylinder heads. Two compression ratios are used in these engines and are identified by the suffix letter as follows:

Suffix Letter	Comp. Ratio
S	9.0:1
L	7.8:1

ENGINE, CYLINDER HEAD & MANIFOLDS

ENGINE

NOTE — *It is necessary to remove entire power unit (engine and transmission assembly) as an assembly. Engine and transmission may then be separated.*

1) Remove hood and battery. Drain engine and cooling system.

NOTE — *Only qualified air conditioning personnel should loosen or remove air conditioning hoses or fittings to prevent personal injury. All hoses or fittings which are removed should be immediately sealed with clean dry plugs.*

2) On air conditioned models, discharge air conditioning system. Disconnect suction and pressure hoses. Remove pressure and suction unions from rear of compressor and plug openings. Tie hoses back away from engine.

3) Remove fender well straps and air cleaners. Disconnect oil pump-to-cooler lines and remove radiator complete with oil cooler.

4) On air conditioned models, remove compressor delivery hose from vehicle. Tie condenser/evaporator hose back away from engine.

5) Disconnect coolant hoses to remote header tank at engine. Remove nut and lock washer attaching engine mount to engine bracket. Remove oil from power steering reservoir. Disconnect lines from power steering pump.

6) Disconnect connectors from alternator and separate engine harness connector. Remove hose between servo unit and vacuum reservoir. Disconnect clips securing fuel pipes to filter, plug pipes.

7) Disconnect operating line from heater vacuum reservoir non-return valve at manifold stub and heater water valve at valve inlet. Disconnect heater return line from water rail at firewall union. Remove coil and ballast resistor assembly.

8) Disconnect clips securing cold start relay harness from left hand fuel rail and cross over pipe. Remove remaining clips on harness. Remove cover of cold start relay, disconnect cables. Remove harness from engine.

9) Disconnect cable from throttle switch and trigger unit. Remove connectors from kickdown switch. Remove starter cable from firewall terminal.

10) Install suitable engine support tool (MS.53A) into drip channel directly above rear lifting eyes and tighten supporting screws. Disconnect both exhaust pipes at manifolds. Remove front exhaust pipe which is not trapped by steering pinion housing. Lower trapped front pipe and move rear end of pipe toward center line of vehicle. Slide pipe towards front of vehicle and draw flanges down past steering housing.

11) Remove attaching hardware from heat shields. Remove four screws, washers and spacers from engine mounting plate. Place a jack and suitably formed block of wood beneath mounting plate and remove nut attaching rear engine mount.

12) Lower jack and remove mounting plate. Disconnect propeller shaft and speedometer cable. Remove pinch bolt attaching transmission outer selector cable and disconnect inner cable from selector lever at transmission by removing nut and lock washer.

13) Remove ground strap from frame member. Place a jack beneath front suspension crossmember and remove engine support tool. Attach suitable lifting sling to engine eyes.

NOTE — *Chains of engine hoist must be of sufficient length to ensure that distance between lifting eyes and hook of hoist is 34.5" (876 mm) from front eyes to hook and 41" (1041 mm) from rear eyes to hook.*

14) Carefully lift engine with hoist, simultaneously raising jack to keep engine level. Lift only 2-3" (51-76 mm).

CAUTION — *Throughout lift, rear of engine must be kept as high as possible until oil pan is clear of steering housing.*

15) Lift engine level, while observing forward corner of oil pan and steering housing. Apply side pressure to engine until it has been lifted clear of steering assembly and lines. Pull engine from subframe, allowing angle of tilt to increase until drive flange is clear of firewall. Lift engine to clear bumper.

INTAKE MANIFOLD

1) Remove air cleaner and drain cooling system. Depressurize fuel system (remove connector from fuel pump relay switch, crank engine for a few seconds). Remove fuel pipe from overrun valves. Remove hose clip securing pressure regulator return hose from fuel rail.

2) Disconnect manifold pressure hose and electrical connectors from kickdown switch. Disconnect throttle cable from pedestal. Release throttle cross-rod from bell-crank. Disconnect electrical connectors from injectors and cold start injector. Disconnect brake vacuum hose.

3) Remove nuts securing manifold to cylinder head. Remove screws securing air rail clips to manifold ram tubes. Remove EGR valve from throttle housing flange. Remove manifold stud spacers. Remove intake manifold, carefully moving air balance pipe and fuel pipes out of the way.

CYLINDER HEAD

NOTE — *The following procedure may be used for removal of either right or left cylinder head.*

1) Disconnect battery and drain cooling system. Remove right camshaft cover (necessary to remove right hand camshaft cover to remove either right or left cylinder head). Remove rubber grommet from timing cover.

XJS & XJ12 SERIES 2 V12 (Cont.)

2) Rotate engine, using crankshaft damper nut until valve timing gauge (C.3993) can be fitted in slot in camshaft front flange. Insert blade of suitable screwdriver (JD.42-2) through hole and release locking catch on timing chain tensioner. Using suitable tool (JD.42 and support plate JD.42-1 or JD.44) retract timing chain tensioner.

3) If left cylinder head is to be removed, remove left camshaft cover. Disconnect camshaft sprocket from camshaft and attach a suitable retaining tool (Special Tool JD.40).

4) Remove heat shield from exhaust manifold and solenoid heat shield (right-hand head). Loosen screw clamp attaching heater return pipe-to-hose and ease cross pipe forward. Remove clamps attaching manifold coolant bleed pipe to front of cylinder head.

5) Remove camshaft oil feed banjo nut. Remove three nuts holding front of cylinder head to timing cover. Progressively loosen cylinder head nuts working from center outward. Remove cylinder head and place on wood blocks to prevent damage to valves. Discard old gasket.

NOTE – *Do not rotate engine until suitable cylinder liner retaining tools (Special Tool JD.41) have been attached to cylinder head studs.*

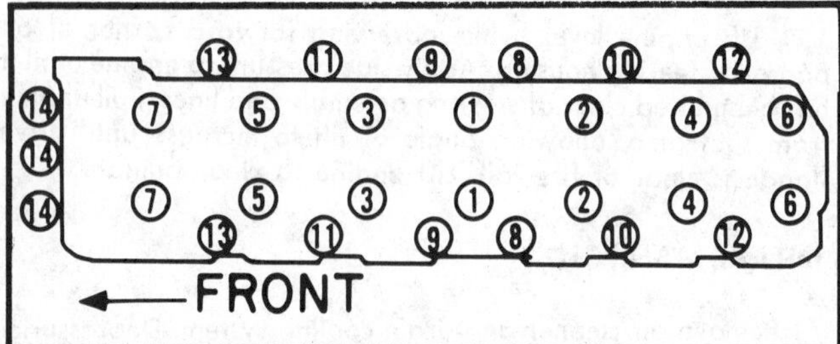

Fig. 1 Cylinder Head Tightening Sequence

CYLINDER HEAD INSTALLATION

1) Attach suitable dial indicator to a cylinder head stud and rotate engine to set No. 1 piston on right bank at TDC. Turn camshaft until valve timing gauge (Special Tool C.3993) can be attached to slot in camshaft front flange. Repeat for camshaft on left cylinder head. Remove cylinder liner retaining tool.

NOTE – *Do not rotate engine until cylinder head(s) are installed.*

2) Install gasket making sure side marked "TOP" is up. Do not use jointing compound or grease. Install right cylinder head and nuts. Tighten nuts to specifications in order shown in illustration.

3) Tighten cylinder head-to-timing cover nuts to specifications. If camshaft and sprocket holes are not in alignment, remove circlip which holds camshaft coupling to sprocket and disengage coupling from splines.

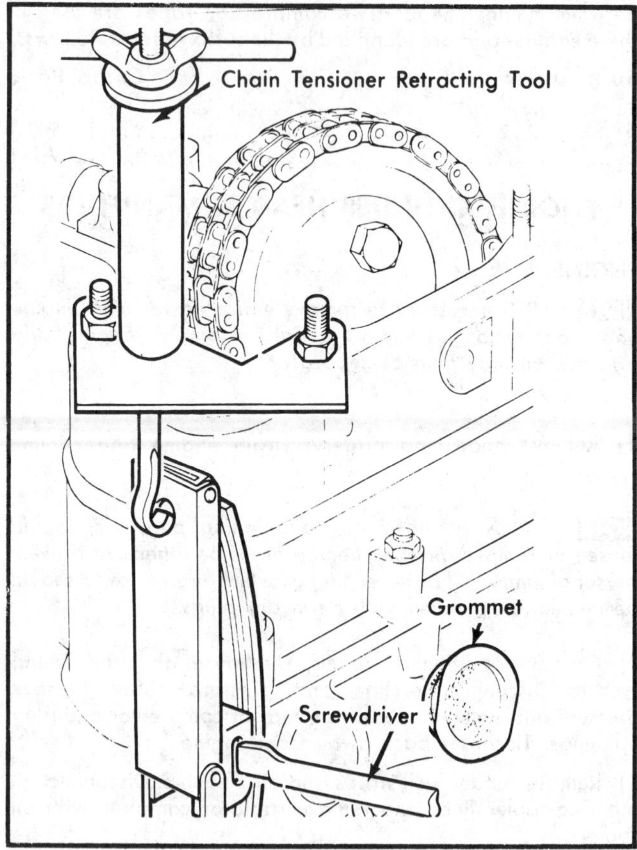

Fig. 2 Correct Procedure to Use Tensioner Retracting Tool

4) Rotate coupling until access to retaining bolt holes can be obtained. Remove sprocket retaining tool (JD.40) and bolt coupling to camshaft.

5) Engage sprocket with coupling, then replace circlip and remove valve timing gauge (C.3993). Repeat procedures as outlined in steps **2)** through **6)** for left cylinder head.

6) Rotate engine until remaining camshaft sprocket retaining bolts can be installed; secure bolts with tab washers. Remove timing chain tensioner retracting tool (Special Tool JD.42 and Support Plate JD.42-1).

7) Insert suitable screwdriver (Special Tool JD.42-2) through hole in timing cover and trip locking catch. Reinstall rubber grommet.

8) Install exhaust pipes, camshaft covers, refill cooling system and reconnect battery.

XJS & XJ12 SERIES 2 V12 (Cont.)

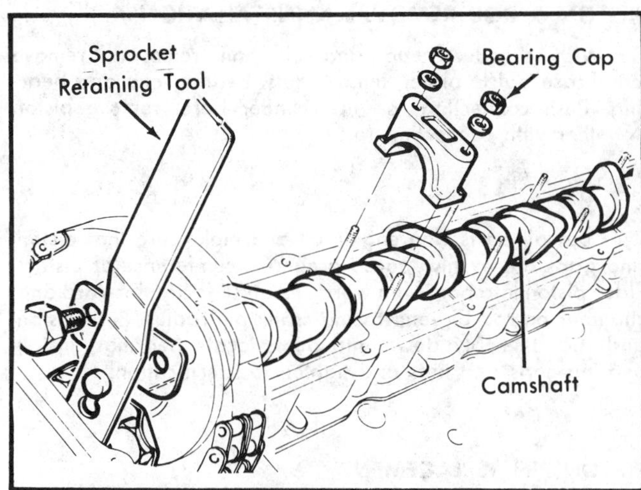

Fig. 3 Correct Procedure to Remove Camshaft

VALVES

VALVE ARRANGMENT

Right Side – E-I-I-E-E-I-I-E-E-I-I-E (front to rear).
Left Side – E-I-I-E-E-I-I-E-E-I-I-E (front to rear).

VALVE GUIDE SERVICING

1) With valves and valve springs removed, check clearance between valve guide and stem. Clearance should be to specification.

2) To replace guides, immerse head in boiling water for 30 minutes. Using piloted drift, drive guide out of head from combustion chamber side. Coat new guide with graphite grease and attach circlip.

3) Heat cylinder head once again and drive guide in from top until circlip is seated in groove.

Replacement Guides

Application	Marking	Size In. (mm)
1st Oversize	2 Grooves	.506-.507 (12.85-12.88)
2nd Oversize	3 Grooves	.511-.512 (12.98-13.00)

4) When new guides are installed, always use next size larger than old guide. Ream guides to obtain proper valve stem clearance.

VALVE STEM OIL SEALS

Install valves and place cylinder head on wooden blocks. Install valve spring seats, intake valve oil seals, springs and collars. Compress springs using suitable tool (Special Tool J.6118B and Adaptor J.6118C-2) and install keepers.

NOTE – *Oil seals used on intake valves only.*

VALVE TAPPET CLEARANCE ADJUSTMENT

1) With intake manifolds and camshaft covers removed, check clearance between each tappet and heel of each cam. Record clearance for each and then subtract appropriate valve clearance from clearances obtained. Select suitable adjusting pads which eaual this new measurement. Corrected clearance should be .012-.014" (.305-.356 mm) with engine cold.

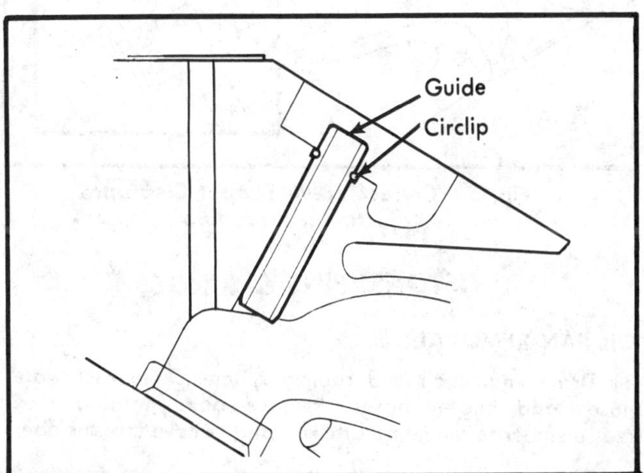

Fig. 4 View Showing Correct Valve Guide Installation

2) To install new adjusting pads, proceed as follows to remove camshaft and tappets: Bend back locking tabs and remove two camshaft sprocket retaining bolts. Rotate engine until access to remaining bolts is obtained. Bend back locking tabs, mark position of camshaft to sprocket, and remove bolts.

3) Using suitable tool (Jaguar Sprocket Retaining Tool JD.40), hold sprocket in place. Lift camshaft out of tappet block. Remove tappets and install adjusting pads.

NOTE – *Do not rotate engine with camshaft disconnected.*

4) Reinstall tappets, camshaft, bearing caps, washers and nuts. Tighten bearing cap nuts evenly and torque to 9 ft. lbs. Recheck clearance, reassemble, replace camshaft cover and manifolds.

NOTE – *Adjusting pads are available in .001" (.03 mm) increment sizes from .085-.110" (2.16-2.79 mm). Pads have a letter stamped on surface which indicates size: "A" through "Z" respectively.*

XJS & XJ12 SERIES 2 V12 (Cont.)

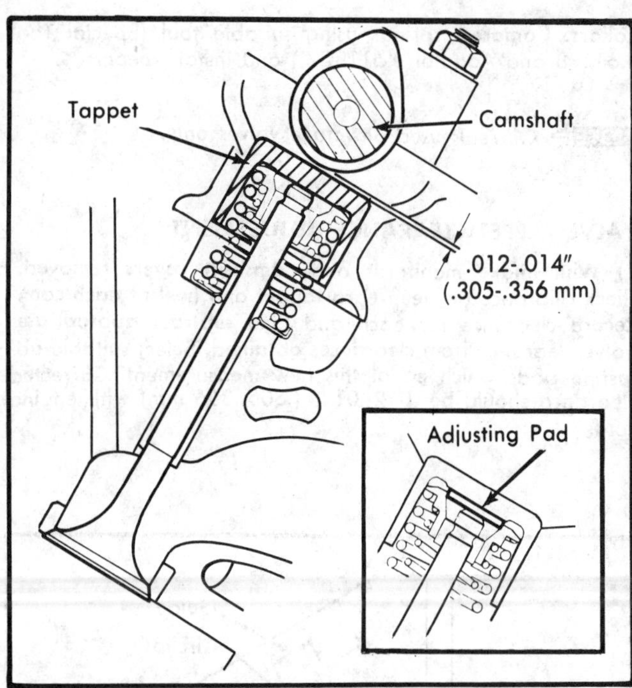

Fig. 5 Correct Valve Tappet Clearance Adjustment Procedure

PISTONS, PINS & RINGS

OIL PAN REMOVAL

1) Drain engine oil and cooling system. Disconnect water hoses and heater hoses. Remove bolts holding front crossmember to mounting brackets and remove crossmember.

2) Remove oil pan bolts and serrated washers. Lower oil pan. Remove and discard "O" ring from oil delivery elbow. To install, reverse removal procedure and use new "O" ring and oil pan gasket.

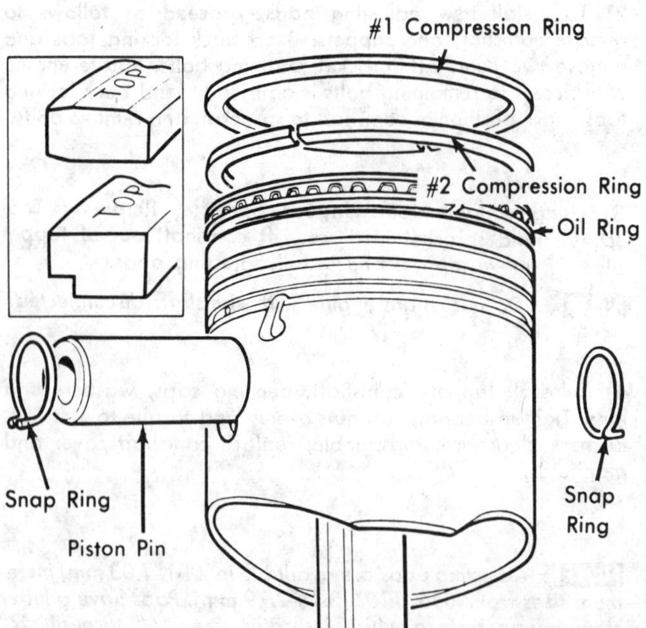

Fig. 6 Exploded View of Piston Assembly

PISTON & ROD REMOVAL & INSTALLATION

1) With cylinder head and oil pan removed, remove crankcase baffle plate. Remove nuts, bearing cap and bearing. Push connecting rod up cylinder bore, remove piston together with connecting rod.

2) Coat all parts with engine oil and make sure that piston ring gaps are evenly spaced around circumference of piston. Place piston into bore with word "FRONT" facing forward and chamber on rod big-end facing crank pin radius. Push piston and rod assembly down into bore, locate bearings, install bearing caps and nuts and tighten to specifications.

PISTON PIN REPLACEMENT

NOTE — *Pistons are supplied complete with pin. As pins and pistons are matched assemblies, it is not permissible to interchange component parts.*

Remove circlip, push pin out of piston. When installing pin, piston should be fitted so the word FRONT faces towards front of engine.

FITTING PISTONS

No oversize pistons are available due to use of wet liner type cylinder sleeves. If liner or piston is damaged or worn, replacement must be of standard size.

NOTE — *Bearings are available in only standard size. Due to extremely hard surface of crankshaft journals, it is not possible to grind crankshafts satisfactory. Crankshafts are available on exchange basis and are supplied complete with matching bearings.*

CRANKSHAFT MAIN & CONNECTING ROD BEARINGS

MAIN BEARING SERVICE

1) With piston and rod assembly removed, remove bolts and locking plate holding flywheel (manual transmission) or drive plate (automatic transmission) to crankshaft.

2) Remove flywheel or drive plate. Remove nut and bolt holding oil suction pipe clamp to bracket and remove suction pipe. Remove small nuts holding main bearing caps. Start from center bearing.

3) Remove pillar nuts and large nuts holding main bearing caps. Start from center. Remove bearing caps and bearing. Slide rear main bearing casting out of cylinder block. Remove and discard seals. Lift crankshaft out of cylinder block, remove upper half of main bearings.

XJS & XJ12 SERIES 2 V12 (Cont.)

CYLINDER LINER REPLACEMENT

NOTE – *If liners are to be replaced after removal, they should be marked and reinstalled in their original bore.*

1) With crankshaft and pistons removed, remove cylinder liner retaining tools (Special Tools JD.41). Position a suitable mandrel between cylinder liner and arbor press.

2) Press out cylinder liners from below. To install, smear liners with Hylomar and slip liners into cylinder block. Remove excessive sealant. Make sure liners are correctly seated and install retaining tools.

NOTE – *If cylinder liners are replaced. New liners must be of the same grade as the old liners.*

Cylinder Liners

Bore Grade	In. (mm)
A-Red	3.543 (89.98)
B-Green	3.544 (90.01)

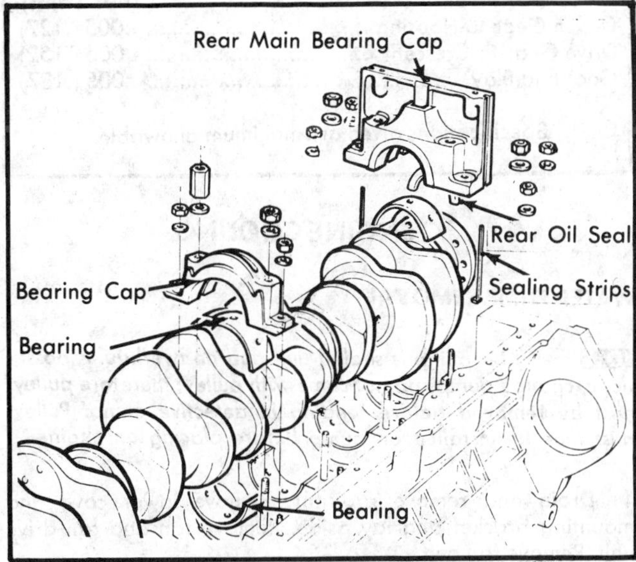

Fig. 7 Exploded View of Main Bearing & Rear Oil Seal Assemblies

REAR MAIN BEARING OIL SEAL SERVICE

1) With crankshaft out of cylinder block and rear main bearing casting removed, install new sealing strips in grooves of rear main bearing casting. Install new rear oil seal. Install bearing casting on cylinder block and tighten nuts. Seat rear oil seal using suitable tool (Special Tool JD.17B & Adaptor JD.17B-1). Remove rear main bearing casting.

2) Coat upper main bearings with oil and install in cylinder block. Smear rear oil seal with Dag Colloidal Graphite. Oil upper main bearings and install in cylinder block, position crankshaft, install bearings in caps and install caps. Tighten to specifications.

THRUST WASHER ALIGNMENT

Measure crankshaft end play. Remove bearing caps and install thrust washer(s) in groove in block; select washers as necessary to bring end play within specifications. Grooved side of washer must face outward.

ENGINE FRONT COVER & OIL SEAL

1) Drain cooling system and remove front sub-frame crossmember complete with expansion tank. Remove both cylinder heads and oil pan. Remove alternator and power steering pump. Remove air injection pump and water pump.

2) Remove bolts holding pulley to damper and remove pulley. Remove crankshaft damper bolt and strike damper sharply with leather mallet. Remove damper and cone.

3) Pry seal out of timing cover and discard. Remove spacer. Smear new oil seal with engine oil and install oil seal in recess. Tap into place using leather mallet. Reinstall spacer and reverse removal procedure.

4) If entire front cover is to be removed, remove alternator and air pump mounting brackets and remove bolt and serrated washers which hold timing cover to cylinder block. Note positions of bolts and dowel bolts. Remove timing cover.

NOTE – *If entire front cover is removed, oil seal may be replaced with front cover removed from engine.*

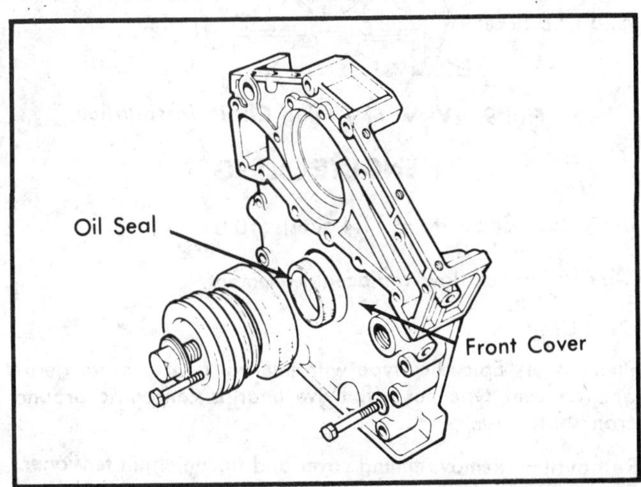

Fig. 8 Detail of Front Cover Oil Seal

CAMSHAFT

CAMSHAFT REMOVAL

1) With camshaft covers removed, bend back locking tabs and remove two camshaft sprocket retaining bolts. Rotate engine until valve timing gauge can be installed in slot in camshaft. Bend back locking tabs and mark relative position of camshaft to sprocket.

2) Remove bolts. Attach sprocket retaining tool (Special Tool JD.40). Do not rotate engine with camshaft disconnected. Progressively loosen camshaft bearing caps nuts starting with center cap and working towards ends. Remove bearing caps, lift camshaft out of tappet block.

XJS & XJ12 SERIES 2 V12 (Cont.)

TIMING CHAIN REMOVAL

With timing cover removed, install suitable tool to retain intermediate shaft (jackshaft). Retaining tool (Special Tool JD.39) available for this purpose. Disconnect timing chain from camshaft and intermediate shaft (jackshaft) sprockets. Remove crankshaft sprocket and chain.

NOTE — *Do not rotate engine with chain removed.*

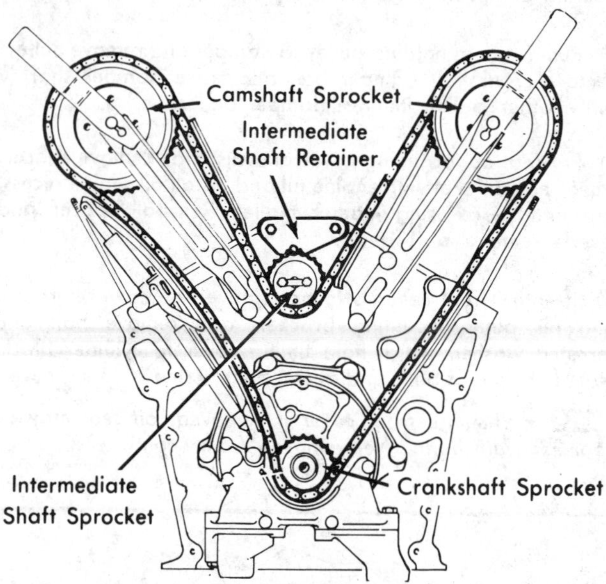

Fig. 9 View of Timing Chain Installation

ENGINE OILING

Crankcase Capacity — 11.4 quarts (10.8 liters).

Oil Filter — Full-flow, replaceable element.

OIL PUMP

Pump is of "Epicyclic" type with internal and external gears and crescent type cut off. Drive gear is concentric around crankshaft nose.

Removal — Remove timing cover and timing chain tensioner. Remove spacer from crankshaft and remove timing chain and sprocket from crankshaft. Remove Woodruff key. To install, reverse removal procedure.

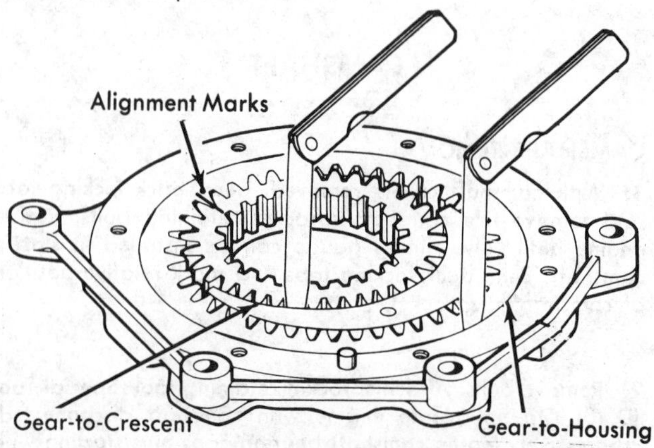

Fig. 10 Correct Procedure to Measure Oil Pump Clearances

Overhaul — 1) Remove eight bolts and lockwashers and remove pump cover from gear housing. Mark drive and driven gear faces to make sure gears are replaced in same position as removed.

2) Remove both gears, and clean thoroughly. Check condition of all gears. Remove burrs with file. Reinstall driven gear and check radial clearance between gear and housing. Checks should not be taken at any of the six radial flats on the gear.

3) Reinstall drive gear and check radial clearance between gear and crescent. Check gear end play by placing straight edge across joint face of housing and measure clearance between straight edge and gear.

4) To reassemble, lubricate all gears with clean oil, check that surfaces are clean, and reverse disassembly procedure.

Oil Pump Specifications

Application	Clearance ①In. (mm)
Driven Gear-to-Housing	.005 (.127)
Drive Gear-to-Crescent	.006 (.152)
Gear End Play	.005 (.127)

① — Specifications given are maximum allowable.

ENGINE COOLING

WATER PUMP REMOVAL

NOTE — *Water pump is sealed unit and no overhaul is possible. Exchange pumps do not come with pulley, therefore pulley must be removed before sending in defective pump. Pulley must then be installed on pump before placing on engine.*

1) Drain and remove radiator. Remove lower cowl and mounting bracket and lay aside. Remove fan and fan drive unit. Remove fan belt.

2) Remove trunnion adjusting bolt and hardware attaching idler pulley housing. Unscrew two studs. Remove air pump and compressor pump belts.

3) Loosen steering pump pivot bolts enough to draw adjustment bolt from special stud. Remove special stud. Remove thermostat switch housing and bottom hose complete as an assembly. Remove crankshaft pulley and damper assembly.

NOTE — *Tap damper with a rawhide mallet to break taper. Do not mislay Woodruff key.*

4) Loosen upper hose clamp on engine cross pipe. Remove screw and washers attaching water pump. Pull pump out and downwards to clear cross pipe hose. To install, reverse removal procedure.

Thermostats — Two thermostats are used. Opening temperature is 174-181F (79-83C).

Cooling System Capacity — 21.5 qts.
Radiator Cap — 13 psi.

XJS & XJ12 SERIES 2 V12 (Cont.)

ENGINE SPECIFICATIONS

GENERAL SPECIFICATIONS										
Year	Displ. cu. ins.	Displ. cc	Carburetor	HP at RPM	Torque (Ft. Lbs. at RPM)	Compr. Ratio	Bore in.	Bore mm	Stroke in.	Stroke mm
1977	326	5343	4x1 Bbl.	.....	.....	① 9.0:1	3.543	90	2.756	70

① — See Engine Identification.

VALVES							
Engine & Valve	Head Diam. In. (mm)	Face Angle	Seat Angle	Seat Width In. (mm)	Stem Diameter In. (mm)	Stem Clearance In. (mm)	Valve Lift In. (mm)
V12							
Intake	① 1.623-1.627 (41.22-41.32)	45°	44.5°	....	.3092-.3093 (7.854-7.856)	.001-.004 (.03-.10)	.375 (9.5)
Exhaust	① 1.358-1.362 (34.50-34.60)	45°	44.5°	....	.3092-.3093 (7.854-7.856)	.001-.004 (.03-.10)	.375 (9.5)

① — XJ-S models; Intake 1.620-1.630″ (41.15-41-40 mm), Exhaust 1.355-1.365″ (34.42-34.67 mm).

VALVE SPRINGS			
Engine	Free Length In. (mm)	PRESSURE Lbs. @ In. (kg @ mm) Valve Closed	Valve Open
V12			
Inner	1.734 (44)	....	....
Outer	2.103 (53.4)	....	....

PISTONS, PINS, RINGS						
Engine	PISTONS Clearance In. (mm)	PINS Piston Fit In. (mm)	PINS Rod Fit In. (mm)	RINGS Rings	RINGS End Gap In. (mm)	RINGS Side Clearance In. (mm)
V12	.0012-.0017 (.03-.04)	Push Fit	.0000-.0002 (.000-.005)	1	.014-.020 (.36-.51)	.0029 (.07)
				2	.010-.015 (.25-.38)	.0034 (.09)
				Oil	.015-.045 (.38-1.14)	① .0055-.0065 (.14-.17)

① — XJ-S models have a self expanding oil ring.

CRANKSHAFT MAIN & CONNECTING ROD BEARINGS							
Engine	MAIN BEARINGS Journal Diam. In. (mm)	MAIN BEARINGS Clearance In. (mm)	MAIN BEARINGS Thrust Bearing	MAIN BEARINGS Crankshaft End Play In. (mm)	CONNECTING ROD BEARINGS Journal Diam. In. (mm)	CONNECTING ROD BEARINGS Clearance In. (mm)	CONNECTING ROD BEARINGS Side Play In. (mm)
V12	3.0007-3.0012 (76.218-76.231)	.0015-.003 (.04-.07)	Center	.004-.006 (.10-.15)	2.2994-2.3000 (58.40-58.42)	.0015-.003 (.04-.07)	.007-.013 (.17-.33)

XJS & XJ 12 SERIES 2 V12 (Cont.)

ENGINE SPECIFICATIONS (Cont.)

CAMSHAFT			
Engine	Journal Diam. In. (mm)	Clearance In. (mm)	Lobe Lift In. (mm)
V12	1.0615-1.0620 (26.96-26.97)	.001-.003 (.03-.07)	....

VALVE TIMING				
	INTAKE		EXHAUST	
Engine	Open (BTDC)	Close (ABDC)	Open (BBDC)	Close (ATDC)
V12	17°	59°	59°	17°

TIGHTENING SPECIFICATIONS	
Application	Ft. Lbs. (mkg)
Cylinder Head	
7/16" Nuts	52 (7.2)
3/8" Nuts	27-28 (3.7-3.9)
Main Bearing Cap	
1/2" Nuts	63 (8.7)
3/8" Nuts	27-28 (3.7-3.9)
Connecting Rod Caps	40-41 (5.5-5.7)
Flywheel	67 (9.3)
Crankshaft Bolt	125-150 (17.3-20.7)
Camshaft Cap Nuts	9 (1.2)
Camshaft Cover Screws	8 (1.1)
Union Block-to-Compressor	10-25 (1.4-3.5)

1800 cc 4 CYLINDER

ENGINE CODING

ENGINE IDENTIFICATION

Engine number is stamped on cylinder block. Further identification data is found below windshield inside engine compartment, on upper left hand side of instrument panel by windshield, and inside door closing areas.

Engine Identification Numbers①

Body Style	Chassis No.	Engine No.
Beta Sedan	828 CB.6	828 A1.040.6
Beta HPE	828 AF.1	828 A1.040.6
Beta Coupe	828 AC.1	828 A1.040.6

① – Engines equipped with catalytic converters are numbered 828 A1.031.6.

ENGINE & CYLINDER HEAD

ENGINE

1) Remove the alternator and slacken front wheel retaining bolts. Raise vehicle and drain coolant from engine and radiator. Take off front wheels and splash guards. Remove all flexible hoses from carburetor and electrical lead from slow-running cut-out switch.

2) Remove low pressure hose for servo-brake, fast idling and diverter valve from induction manifold. Disconnect leads from the distributor and diverter valve thermo-switches.

3) On vehicles with air conditioning, slacken mounting bolts and drop compressor downward. Remove drive belt. Disconnect electric cables from the isobaric valve and compressor ground cable. Remove compressor and position it on its side so oil does not enter conditioner circuit. Remove leads from thermistor and engine oil pressure switch and take off oil filter base.

4) Lift out battery. Remove line from recovery tank, and remove tank. Slide line from diverter valve and disconnect drive belt from air pump. Remove air pump complete with support and line. Detach pipe from air pipe leading to exhaust ducts on the cylinder head. Remove distributor assembly.

5) Unscrew the constant velocity joints from their flanges by the wheel well. Take off support brackets and disconnect the exhaust pipe from the manifold. Remove flywheel guard and bolts holding transmission and engine mounts. Remove the gear front control shaft from the idler lever and selector rod.

6) Detach heater hoses from cylinder head and water pump inlet hose. Remove hoses from radiator. Remove speedometer drive shaft from transmission and cables from 1st and 2nd gear switch, 3rd and 4th gear switch and 5th gear commutator switch. Mark electrical connections for later installation.

7) Disconnect ground wire from transmission and leads from starter motor. Remove clutch release lever return spring. Release the control cable from the clutch release lever and slip the cable sheath from stop bracket.

8) Remove circlip and detach the release lever from the shaft. Remove clutch stop bracket. Remove engine-to-body anchoring rod. Disconnect fan leads and remove the fan from the radiator. Mount brackets (88017363) on cylinder block stud bolts for use in hoisting engine and transmission from vehicle.

9) Mount a hoist above vehicle and attach hook (88017362). Raise engine and transmission and remove from vehicle. Set on support stand (88017364) and attach support (88027068A) to transmission. Remove starter motor and transmission from engine. Lock the crankshaft with locking tool (88013347), and remove the clutch assembly.

10) To install engine, reverse removal procedure. Be sure to tighten constant velocity flange bolts to proper torque. Start engine and check for leaks.

CYLINDER HEAD

1) Disconnect positive battery cable. Drain coolant from radiator and engine. Remove exhaust pipe from manifold. Remove right-hand brace from engine compartment opening and take off air cleaner. Disconnect choke control cable and fuel supply and leak-off hoses from carburetor.

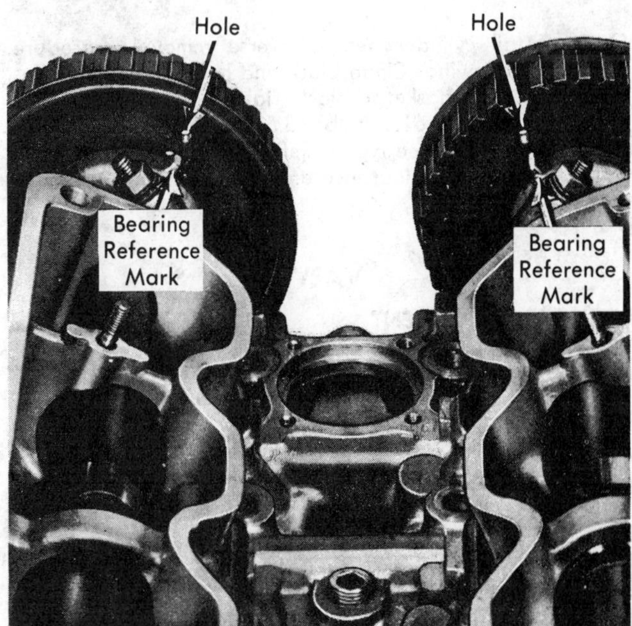

Fig. 1 Camshaft Bearing and Gear Timing Marks

2) Disconnect brake servo unit vacuum hose from intake manifold. Disconnect cables from spark plugs, coolant temperature gauge transmitter and engine overheating warning light switch. Disconnect throttle control rod from carburetor and set it aside. Remove splash guard from right hand wheel well. Remove timing gear cover.

3) Using a spanner wrench (88011321) on crankshaft nut, turn crankshaft in direction of rotation until the camshaft bearing timing marks *(See Fig. 1)* line up with holes in camshaft drive gears. Remove the timing reference pointers fitted bracket. Disconnect coolant outlet pipe from both the cylinder head and rubber hoses.

1800 cc 4 CYLINDER (Cont.)

4) Remove engine-to-body anchoring rod. Lift off engine coolant outlet and inlet pipes. Disconnect heater hose with mounting bracket from cylinder head. Remove alternator upper mounting link.

5) Loosen timing belt stretcher and remove timing belt from gears and stretcher. Remove bolts and lift off cylinder head complete with manifolds.

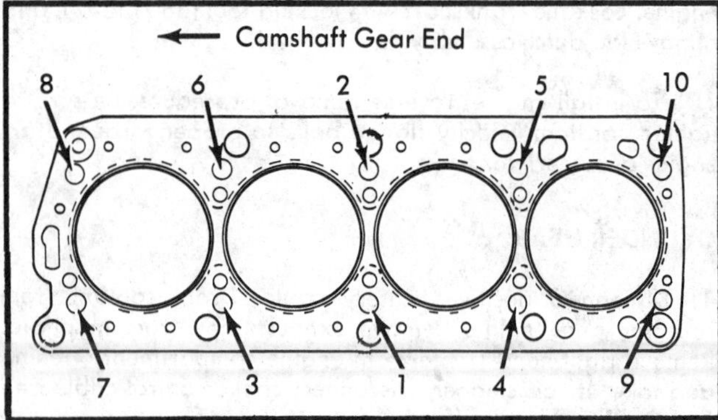

Fig. 2 Cylinder Head Bolt Tightening Sequence

6) To install cylinder heads, reverse removal procedure, noting the following: Clean block and head mating surfaces. Install new head gasket to block. Tighten cylinder head bolts to a final torque of 61.5 ft. lbs. (8.5 mkg) in proper sequence and in two stages. *See Fig. 2.* Refit timing belt and set valve timing. Check valve clearance and install remaining parts in reverse order.

VALVES

VALVE ARRANGEMENT

Intake — Left side (Viewed from flywheel end).
Exhaust — Right side (Viewed from flywheel end).

VALVE SPRINGS

1) Remove cylinder head. Remove both intake and exhaust manifolds and carburetor. Use spring compressor (88012041) to load valve springs. Remove split collets and remove upper collars, inner and outer springs, lower cups and washers.

2) Test springs for proper strength, using a suitable tester (88095021).

VALVE GUIDE SERVICING

1) Visually check inner diameter of valve guides for scoring or signs of seizure. Use gauges (88015018 and 88015019) to measure valve guide bores.

2) If guides need servicing, remove guide seals. Using a remover-installer tool (88012042), remove guides from cylinder head. Check guides to determine class, by measuring external diameter. New valve guides should belong to same class as those removed.

Available Valve Guide Diameters

Measurement	Inches (mm)
Standard Guide O.D.	.590-.591 (14.998-15.016)
1st Oversize Guide O.D.	.591-.592 (15.018-15.036)
2nd Oversize Guide O.D.	.598-.599 (15.198-15.216)

3) Heat cylinder head (manufacturer recommends in an electric furnace) to 212° F (100° C). Install the new guides using the installer tool (88012042) and spacer (88012042B).

NOTE — *Replacement valve guides feature an inner diameter bored to specifications. Reaming may be necessary, however, in isolated cases.*

4) After the cylinder head has cooled, check inner diameter and if necessary ream to proper size. With guides fitted in cylinder head, inner diameter should measure .3158-.3165" (8.022-8.040 mm). Use gauge 88015018 to check for inner diameter of .3153-3157" (8.01-8.02 mm) and 88015019 to check for inner diameter of .3161-.3165" (8.03-8.04 mm).

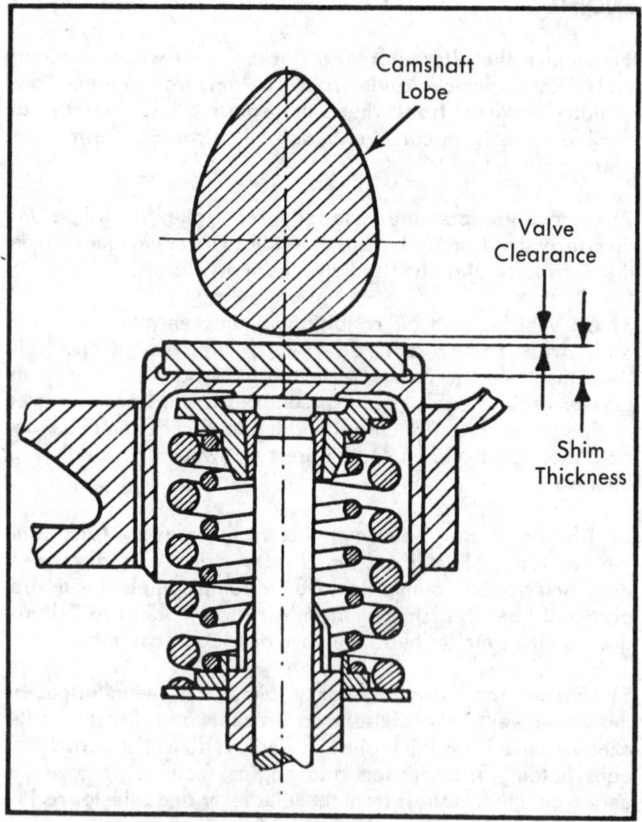

Fig. 3 Measuring Valve Clearance

VALVE CLEARANCE ADJUSTMENT

1) The Lancia 1800 cc engine has two camshafts, one operating directly upon the exhaust valves, the other on the intake valves. No rocker arms or shafts are necessary.

2) Check valve clearance in order of firing sequence (1-3-4-2). Using a spanner wrench (88011321), turn crankshaft so that

1800 cc 4 CYLINDER (Cont.)

cylinder to be checked is in the expansion stroke (cam lobe pointing vertically for that cylinder). *See Fig. 3.*

3) Measure clearance of each valve, using a feeler gauge between the base of the cam lobe and the tappet shim. Make a note of each valve's clearance.

Valve Clearance Specifications

Valve	Inches (mm)
Intake	.0161-.0193 (.41-.49)
Exhaust	.0181-.0213 (.46-.54)

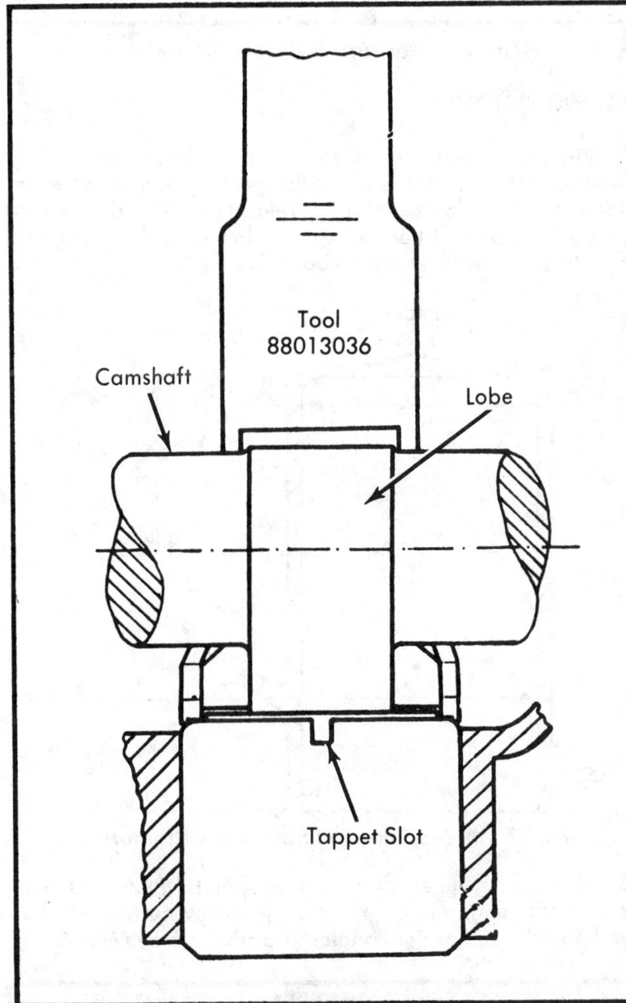

Fig. 4 Adjusting Valve Clearance

4) To adjust valves, turn crankshaft until piston of cylinder to be adjusted is in expansion stroke (cam lobe vertical). Turn tappets so slot *(See Fig. 4)* is toward side of engine. Turn crankshaft further so that valve to be adjusted is fully open. Attach suitable tool (88013036) between camshaft and tappet and secure against housing.

5) Turn the crankshaft (turning camshafts) until camshaft lobe does not depress the tappet any longer, while the tool keeps the tappet locked in the open valve position. Apply air pressure to tappet slot, and remove the adjusting shim *(See Fig. 5)* using pliers (88013038).

6) Measure the thickness of the adjusting shim removed. Add the previously measured valve clearance for valve being adjusted. Subtract from this total the recommended valve clearance. Replace the previously removed adjusting shim with one having the thickness of the difference obtained by your subtraction.

Example:

Measured intake valve clearance	=	.015" (0.38mm)
Add measured shim thickness	=	.142" (3.60mm)
Total of shim thickness and clearance	=	.157" (3.98mm)
Subtract recommended clearance	=	.017" (0.43mm)
Difference is required shim thickness①	=	.140" (3.55mm)

① — Shims for adjusting valve clearance are available in thicknesses ranging from .1280-.1850" (3.25-4.70 mm) in .0020" (.05 mm) increments. Thickness of shim is stamped on its face, and stamped side must be installed facing downward. To be on safe side, always check shim thickness with a micrometer before installing it.

7) Fit the shim in place, using pliers (88013038). Turn crankshaft until camshaft fully depresses the tappet. Remove tool (88013036). When all valves have been set, recheck for proper clearance and reinstall parts previously removed.

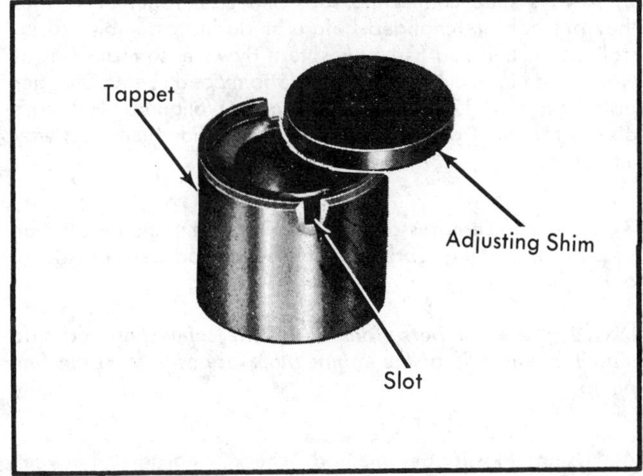

Fig. 5 Removing Adjusting Shims From Tappets

PISTONS, PINS & RINGS

OIL PAN

1) Remove bracket securing exhaust pipe to engine block. Remove right-hand constant velocity joint from drive flange and set drive shaft aside. Remove exhaust pipe from manifold. Take off flywheel guard and remove bolts from right-hand engine mount. Loosen left-hand engine mount.

2) Remove the gear control selector rod from the front control shaft. Drain coolant and oil from engine. Disconnect speedometer drive cable, and remove gear front control shaft from idler lever. Disconnect speedometer drive cable from EGR valve. Remove battery cables and lift out battery.

1800 cc 4 CYLINDER (Cont.)

3) Remove ignition coil and hose clip. Remove clutch control cable support bracket. Disconnect inlet hose from the radiator. Detach anchoring rod from cylinder head and frame. Remove heater hose support bracket from exhaust camshaft housing and remove air cleaner assembly.

4) Remove engine compartment opening right-hand brace. Turn front wheels to full right and remove splash guard from right-hand wheel well. Disconnect outlet hoses from radiator.

5) Attach lifting cable (88017362) to engine and using a hoist, lift engine slowly upward only enough to permit oil pan bolt removal. Then, lift engine further until oil pan can be removed. To install, reverse removal procedures.

PISTON & ROD ASSEMBLY

1) Place engine on stand, remove timing belt, cylinder head and oil pan. Remove oil pump from crankcase. Turn ancillary units drive shaft until the fuel pump control cam points towards the fuel pump itself. Remove connecting rod caps and slide pistons and rods out top of block as an assembly. Inspect connecting rods, bearing shells and crankshaft surfaces for scoring and wear. Check that crankpin surfaces do not show signs of scoring or seizure.

2) Always keep connecting rods and caps together so that they are not interchanged before or during assembly. To install piston and rod assemblies, turn flywheel so crankpins of No. 1 and No. 4 cylinders are at bottom dead center. Stagger piston rings at 120° intervals (gaps not aligned). Lubricate pistons for No. 1 and No. 4 cylinders and slide them part way into bores.

3) Use a ring compressor (88013200) to complete installation of pistons, pushing lubricated connecting rod bearings down onto crankpins.

NOTE – *The numbers stamped on the connecting rod side must face the side of the engine block opposite from the fuel pump.*

4) Using Plastigage method, check clearance between crankpins and bearing shells. To do so, remove oil marks from connecting rod bearing shell. Place a piece of Plastigage lengthwise on crankpin at center of connecting rod cap bearing shell. Lightly grease ends of string to stick it to crankpin.

5) Attach connecting rod cap with bearing shell and torque to 38 ft. lbs. (5.2 mkg). **NOTE** – *Be sure you do not turn crankshaft in process, or Plastigage may be damaged and give incorrect reading.* Remove connecting rod cap and measure width of the flattened Plastigage at its widest point. Use scale stamped on envelope for reading clearance between connecting rod bearing shells and crankpin. Clearance should match specifications.

6) Remove Plastigage from crankpins and lubricate and fit caps of No. 1 and No. 4 connecting rods. Tighten to proper torque. Install piston and rod assemblies in cylinders No. 2 and No. 3 and check for clearance in same manner. When proper, torque connecting rod cap nuts. Reinstall oil pump, oil pan, oil filter base and other parts previously removed.

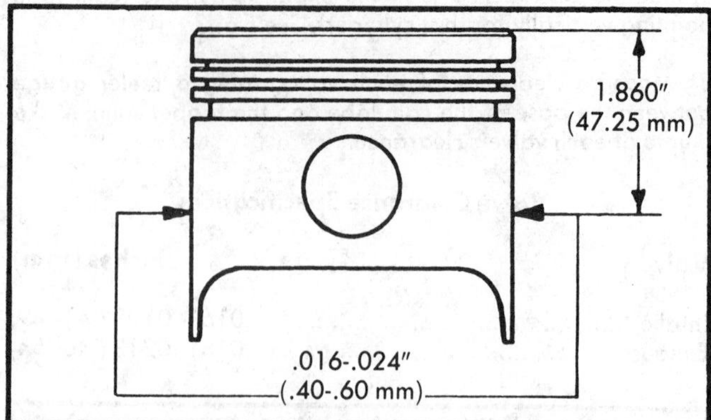

Fig. 6 Measuring Piston Diameter

FITTING PISTONS

1) Visually inspect pistons for signs of seizure or scoring. Remove rings and set aside in proper location for later installation (if not to be replaced). Measure outside diameter of pistons at a point 1.86" (47.25 mm) below piston crown and at right angles with piston pin bore. *See Fig. 6.*

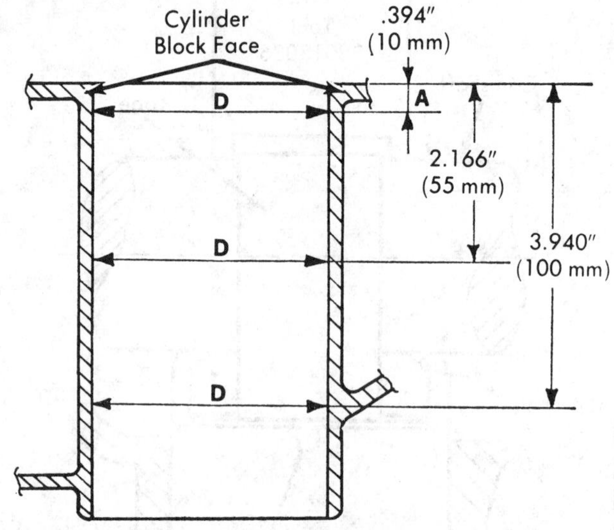

Fig. 7 Measuring Cylinder Bore Diameters

2) Measure cylinder diameters at points .394" (10 mm), 2.166" (55 mm), and 3.94" (100 mm) below surface of block and parallel and at right angles to crankshaft. *See Fig. 7.*

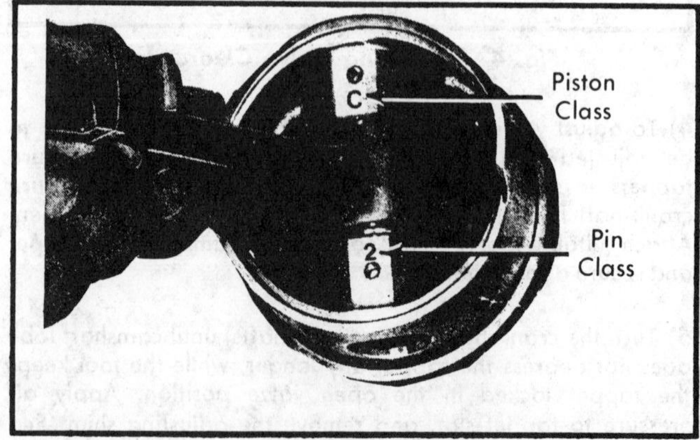

Fig. 8 Identifying Marks for Piston & Pin Classes

1800 cc 4 CYLINDER (Cont.)

3) Subtract the diameter of each piston from the diameter of its cylinder. Clearance should be .0157-.0236" (.40-.60 mm). Pistons, piston pins and bores vary by class as to size. Class identification numbers and letters for pistons and pins are found inside the piston on piston pin bore casting (underneath side of piston). *See Fig. 8.* Cylinder blocks are also stamped as to cylinder bore class.

Piston Sizes Available①

Class	Inches (mm)
Class A	3.3051-3.3055 (83.95-83.96)
Class B	3.3055-3.3059 (83.96-83.97)
Class C	3.3059-3.3063 (83.97-83.98)
Class D	3.3063-3.3067 (83.98-83.99)
Class E	3.3067-3.3070 (83.99-84.00)

① — Standard pistons for Classes A, C, and E and pistons and rings .0078" (.2 mm), .0157" (.4 mm), and .0235" (.6 mm) oversize are furnished for repairs.

Cylinder Bore Classes

Class	Inches (mm)
Class A	3.3070-3.3074 (84.00-84.01)
Class B	3.3074-3.3079 (84.01-84.02)
Class C	3.3079-3.3083 (84.02-84.03)
Class D	3.3083-3.3087 (84.03-84.04)
Class E	3.3087-3.3091 (84.04-84.05)

Piston Pin Sizes①

Class	Inches (mm)
Class 1	.8658-.8659 (21.991-21.994)
Class 2	.8659-.8660 (21.994-21.997)

① — Piston pin bore sizes for each class pin should be .0002" (.005 mm) larger than above pin sizes.

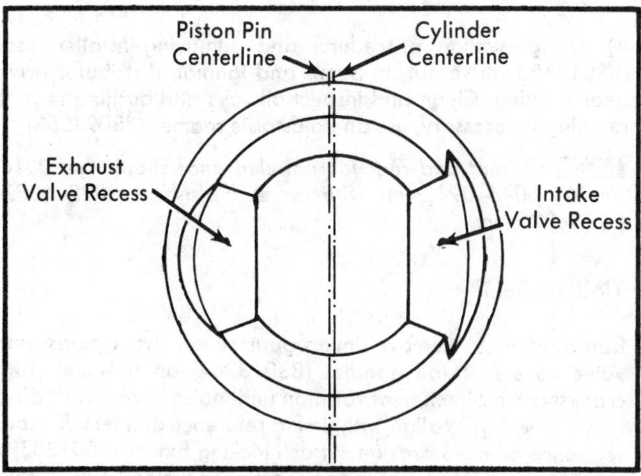

Fig. 9 Piston Crown Viewed From Top

4) When installing pistons on connecting rods, be sure the intake valve recess *(See Fig. 9)* in the piston crown is on the side of the connecting rod with the lubrication hole. Use suitable tool (88012211) to install circlips securing piston pins.

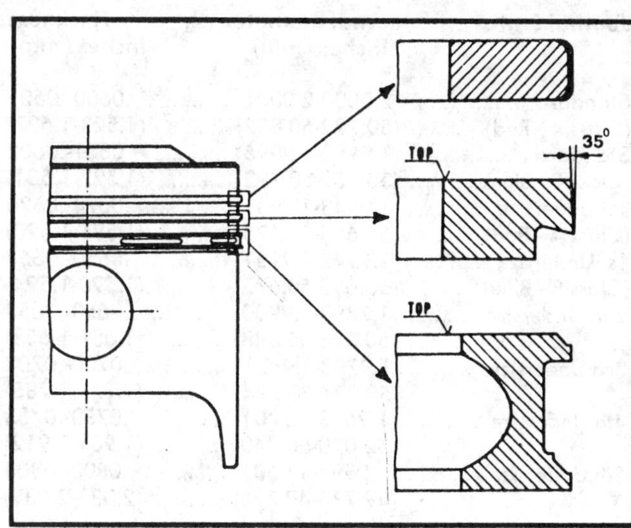

Fig. 10 Installing Rings on Pistons

5) Fit the rings to the piston using pliers (88012202), making sure all "Top" markings are facing upwards and gaps are staggered 120° from each other. *See Fig. 10.*

CRANKSHAFT MAIN & CONNECTING ROD BEARINGS

MAIN & CONNECTING ROD BEARINGS

1) With crankshaft removed, check main journal and connecting rod journal diameters. Oversize bearing shells are available if journals require grinding. Check clearance of both crankpin and main bearing journals, using Plastigage method outlined under *PISTON & ROD ASSEMBLY.*

Main Bearing Shell Thickness

Journal Status	Journal Diameter Inches (mm)	Bearing Shell Thickness Inches (mm)
Standard	2.0860-2.0868	.0718-.0721
	(52.985-53.005)	(1.825-1.831)
1st Undersize	2.0810-2.0818	.0743-.0746
	(52.858-52.878)	(1.888-1.894)
2nd Undersize	2.0760-2.0768	.0769-.0771
	(52.731-52.751)	(1.952-1.958)
3rd Undersize	2.0660-2.0668	.0819-.0821
	(52.477-52.497)	(2.079-2.085)
4th Undersize	2.0560-2.0568	.0869-.0871
	(52.223-52.243)	(2.206-2.212)
5th Undersize	2.0460-2.0468	.0919-.0921
	(51.969-51.989)	(2.333-2.339)

2) When reassembling, be sure to align connecting rod caps and rods so that matching numbers align. When installing main bearing caps, front cap is of different shape and caps are numbered for proper installation.

1800 cc 4 CYLINDER (Cont.)

Crankpin Bearing Shell Thickness

Journal Status	Journal Diameter Inches (mm)	Bearing Shell Thickness Inches (mm)
Standard	2.0000-2.0001	.0600-.0601
(Class A - Red)	(50.792-50.802)	(1.523-1.527)
Standard	1.9993-1.9996	.0601-.0602
(Class B - Blue)	(50.782-50.792)	(1.527-1.531)
1st Undersize	1.9943-1.9951	.0624-.0626
(Class A - Red)	(50.655-50.675)	(1.586-1.590)
1st Undersize	1.9942-1.9951	.0650-.0653
(Class B - Blue)	(50.655-50.675)	(1.590-1.594)
2nd Undersize	1.9893-1.9900	.0650-.0653
	(50.528-50.548)	(1.650-1.658)
3rd Undersize	1.9793-1.9801	.0700-.0703
	(50.274-50.294)	(1.777-1.785)
4th Undersize	1.9693-1.9701	.0750-.0753
	(50.020-50.040)	(1.904-1.912)
5th Undersize	1.9597-1.9605	.0800-.0803
	(49.776-49.796)	(2.031-2.039)

3) Check crankshaft end play. End play is controlled by two half thrust washers in the cap of the rear main journal. Standard width of thrust washers is .0909-.0929" (2.310-2.360 mm). Oversize thrust washers are .0960-.0979" (2.437-2.487 mm) thick.

4) When installing piston on connecting rod, use suitable tool (88012210). The following size connecting rods (bushing inner diameters) are available.

Connecting Rod Bushing Diameters①

Pin Class	Bushing I.D. Inches (mm)
Class 1	.8663-.8664 (22.004-22.007)
Class 2	.8664-.8665 (22.007-22.009)

① — Inner diameters for clearance purposes should be measured with bushing installed in rod.

FRONT OIL SEAL

Fit the crankshaft front oil seal cover on new gasket. Do not tighten bolts. Place new oil seal in cover and using suitable installing tool (88012313), drive oil seal in by screwing the sheave mounting nut to the crankshaft. Remove the tool, fit the timing belt drive gear to the crankshaft and tighten bolts to secure the oil seal cover.

REAR OIL SEAL & FLYWHEEL

Fit the crankshaft rear oil seal cover on new gasket. Position crankshaft with crankpins for No. 1 and No. 4 cylinders at TDC. Fit flywheel so timing mark registers with TDC for crankpins No. 1 and No. 4. Install flywheel mounting bolts. Install flywheel locking tool (88013347) and torque bolts to 61 ft. lbs. (8.5 mkg).

ANCILLARY DRIVE SHAFT

1) Using installing-removing tool (88012455), drive off crankcase-mounted bearings of ancillary drive shaft. *See Fig. 11.* Tool features a front end divided in two sections of different diameters to match each bearing's inner diameter.

2) Clean bearing seats and be sure crankcase oilways are not clogged. Using same tool, install smaller diameter inner bearing into its housing. Then install front bearing. Make sure oilways coincide with those present on crankcase.

3) Ream the bearing inner diameter using suitable reamer (88014325). Clean bearings with compressed air through the oilways.

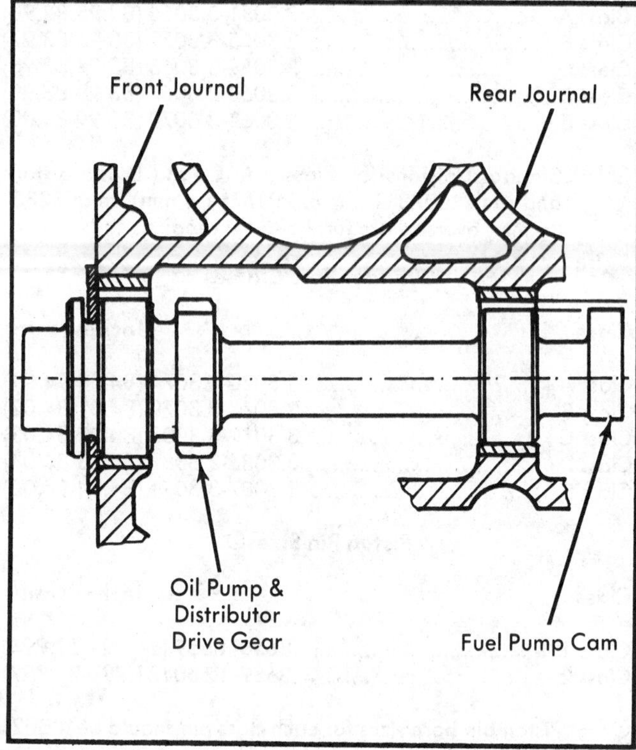

Fig. 11 Ancillary Drive Shaft Components

4) Using similar procedure and removing-installer tool (88012456) drive out oil pump and ignition distributor drive gear bushing. Clean and inspect oilways and bushing seat. If reaming is necessary, use an adjustable reamer (88094053).

NOTE — *Front and rear journal clearance should be .0018-.0036" (.046-.091 mm) with an end play of .0028-.0087" (.070-.220 mm).*

TIMING BELT

Removal — 1) Remove timing gear cover, spark plugs, and valve covers. Install handles (88013344) on flywheel. Turn crankshaft in direction of rotation until holes in camshaft drive gears *(See Fig. 1)* align with timing reference pointers. Remove reference pointers bracket. Attach locking fixture (88013039), by engaging dowel pins in camshaft gear timing holes. Attach fixture to cylinder head.

2) Remove belt stretcher nut and bolt and release tension from belt. Slip belt off gears and install new belt every 25,000 miles. Check belt stretcher spring strength using a suitable tool (80015052). Torque spanner (88091134) set at 10 ft. lbs. (1.4

1800 cc 4 CYLINDER (Cont.)

mkg) must yield when reference marks on tool and spring are aligned.

Installation – 1) Align reference mark on crankshaft pulley with timing mark on fixture (88013039). When both marks correspond exactly, pistons No. 1 and No. 4 will be at TDC. Fixture reference hole should also line up with ancillary drive shaft reference hole. Check alignment by inserting dowel pin.

2) Install timing belt. Unlock the belt stretcher bolt applying pressure to the belt. Tighten bolt and nut to 32.5 ft. lbs. (4.5 mkg). Once tensioning bolt is torqued, remove fixture (88013039). Turn the crankshaft a few times, partially release the belt stretcher and finally relock it properly. Install timing reference pointers bracket.

CAMSHAFT

CAMSHAFTS

1) With timing belt removed, remove camshaft gears. Attach retainer (88013151) to camshaft drive gears and tighten bolt which clamps the two halves of retainer together. Knock down tab of lock plates and partly unscrew gear securing bolts. Lift off retainer and gears with respective bolts and lock plates.

2) Remove rear cover plate from camshaft housing and remove camshaft. Using tool (88012315) remove oil seal. Examine camshaft journals and lobes for signs of seizure or scoring. Check camshaft housing bearings for scoring and excessive wear. Check clearances between journals and bearings. See charts for proper clearance. End play should be .0039-.0077" (.100-.195 mm).

3) When installing camshaft gears, reverse procedure and torque camshaft gear bolts to 87 ft. lbs. (12 mkg).

VALVE TIMING

To check valve timing, turn crankshaft until reference mark on sheave aligns with long mark on timing gear cover. *See Fig. 12.* Check that the two holes in camshaft gears (one in each) are aligned with reference marks on front camshaft bearings. *See Fig. 12.* If adjustment is necessary, use tool (88013039) as instructed under *TIMING BELT.*

ENGINE OILING

Crankcase Capacity – 4.25 qts. (4 ltr) without filter; 5.25 qts. (5 ltr) with filter.

Oil Filter – Full-flow, quick-change. Gauze-type filter in pump strainer.

Normal Oil Pressure – 57-87 psi. (4-6 kg/cm^2) at 6000 RPM at 185°F (85°C).

ENGINE OILING SYSTEM

The gear-type oil pump is driven off the ancillary drive shaft and provides pressure lubrication to all engine parts. A full-flow type oil filter is used along with an oil pressure regulating valve.

OIL PUMP

1) Remove oil pan. Loosen mounting bolts and remove oil pump. Place pump in soft-jawed vise and remove strainer

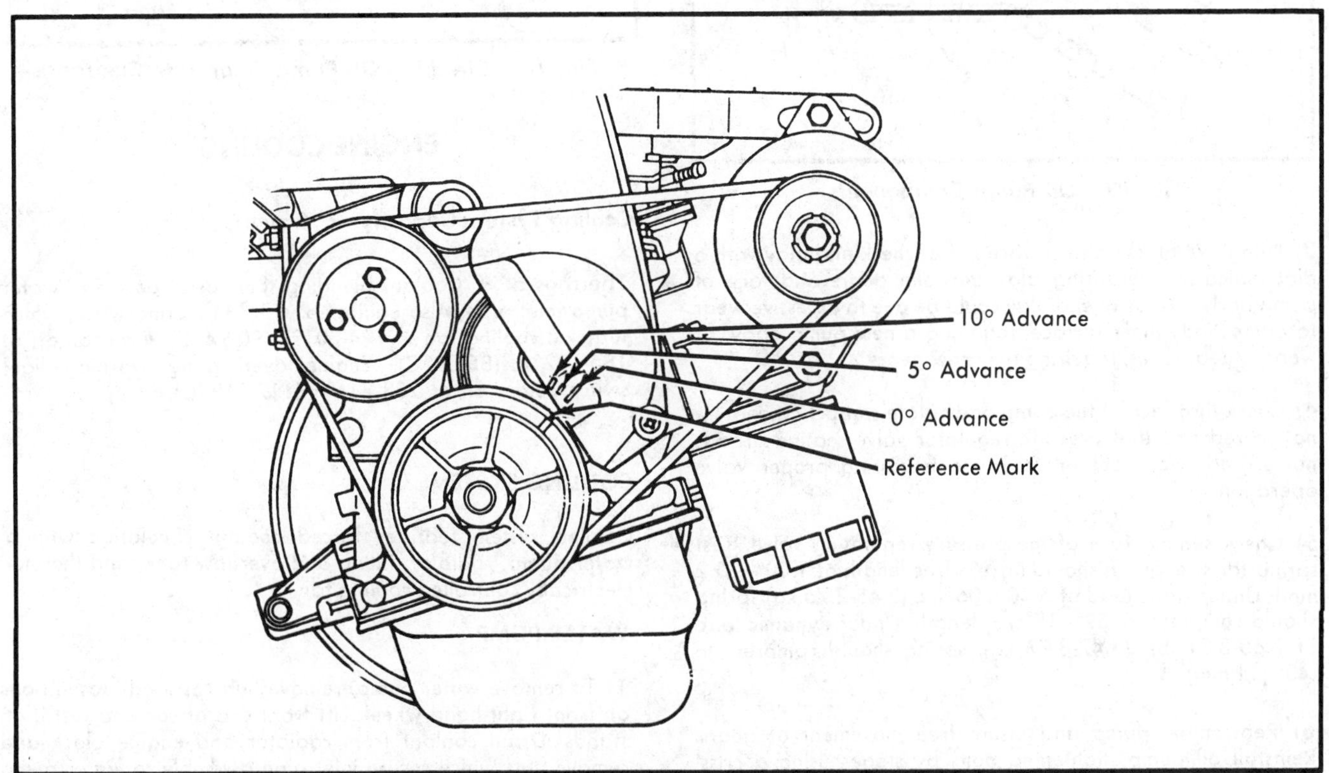

Fig. 12 Valve Timing Reference Marks

1800 cc 4 CYLINDER (Cont.)

assembly. Remove spring, pressure regulating valve and pump body plate.

2) Remove pump from vise and remove gears from pump body. *See Fig. 13.* Inspect gears for scoring or "steps" and replace if necessary. Check side clearance between gears and pump body. *See Fig. 14.* Excessive clearance indicates wear to drive gear shaft in the pump body or between the driven gear and its shaft.

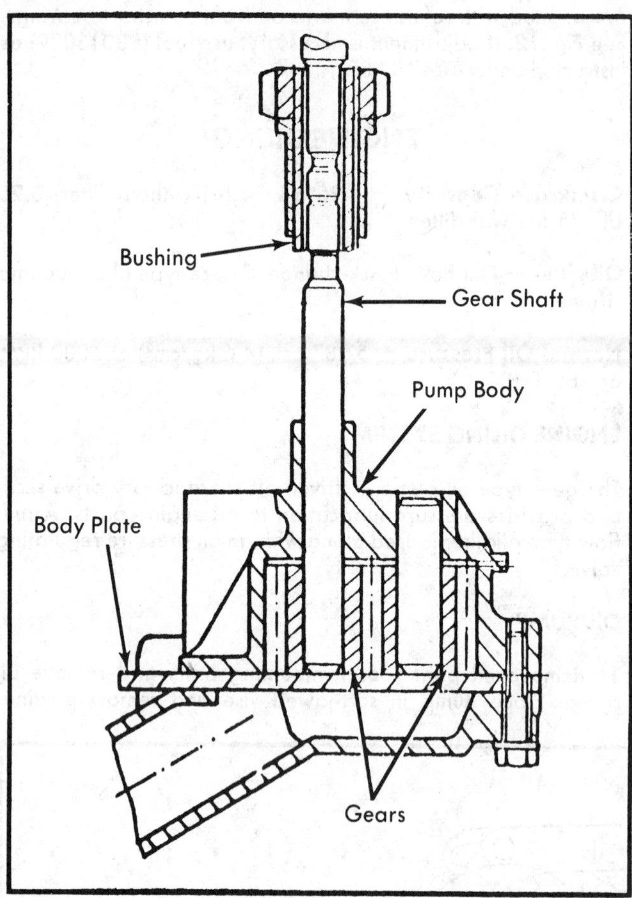

Fig. 13 Oil Pump Components

3) Using "V" blocks and surface plate, check end play with a dial indicator, measuring play between gears and face of pump body. Excessive end play could be due to excessive wear to pump body inner surface, requiring a new pump body, or wear to gear faces, requiring only new gears.

4) Check that face of the pump body plate contacting gears is not scored and that pressure regulator valve seating area is not scored, worn out or otherwise impairing proper valve operation.

5) Check sealing face of the pressure regulating valve. Test spring for strength. It should have a free length of 1.00" (25.2 mm). Under static load of 5.40-6.06 lbs. (2.45-2.75 kg) spring should compress to .59" (15 mm) length. Under dynamic load of 7.65-8.31 lbs. (3.47-3.77 kg), spring should compress to .43" (11 mm).

6) Reassemble pump and insure free movement of gears. Reinstall oil pump, tightening bolts by stages using a criss-cross pattern.

7) Install a new gasket and complete installation of oil pan and parts previously removed. Use tool (88013039) for retiming camshafts and ancillary drive shaft. Lower engine into place on mounting buffers and complete installation.

Oil Pump Specifications

Measurement	Inches (mm)
Drive Shaft Bushing, I.D.	.6305-.6314 (16.016-16.037)
Diameter, Gear Shank	.6287-.6293 (15.970-15.985)
Clearance, Bushing-to-Shaft	.0012-.0026 (.031-.067)
Pump Gear Housing Depth	1.819-1.839 (30.020-30.072)
Pump Gear Thickness	1.1794-1.1807 (29.956-29.989)
Gear End Play	.0012-.0046 (.031-.116)
Clearance, Gear-to-Housing	.0010-.0032 (.026-.080)
Clearance, Gear-to-Gear	.0059 (.15)

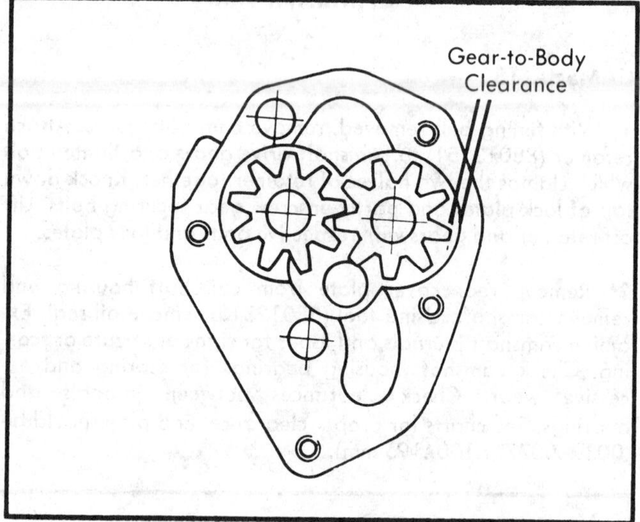

Fig. 14 Checking Oil Pump Gear Side Clearance

ENGINE COOLING

Cooling System Capacity – 9 quarts (8.5 ltr).

Thermostat – Coolant blending thermostat device in water pump inlet pipe. Also equipped with fan thermoswitch, which turns on cooling fan at 194-201°F (90-94°C); turns fan off at 185-192°F (85-89°C). Engine overheating warning light switch comes on at 233-244°F (112-118°C).

COOLING SYSTEM

Cooling system features forced coolant circulation with a water pump, radiator, filling and overflow tank, and thermo-electrically controlled cooling fan.

WATER PUMP

1) To remove water pump, remove hub cap and loosen bolts on front right-hand wheel. Lift front end of car and rest it on stands. Drain coolant from radiator and engine block and remove nuts which secure inlet pipe assembly to water pump (from beneath vehicle).

1800 cc 4 CYLINDER (Cont.)

2) Remove right-hand wheel and engine guard. Loosen retaining bolts on water pump sheave and slacken drive belt. Remove drive sheave. Remove timing gear cover, bolts securing pump inlet pipe to mounting bracket of engine anchoring rod, and inlet pipe from water pump.

3) Remove bolts securing pump to the crankcase and lift off pump. Pump assembly is supplied only as a complete unit and cannot be repaired. When installing new pump, use new seal between pipe and water pump. Fill with coolant and check for leaks.

ENGINE SPECIFICATIONS

GENERAL SPECIFICATIONS

Year	Displ.		Carburetor	HP at RPM ①	Torque (Ft. Lbs. at RPM) ①	Compr. Ratio	Bore		Stroke	
	cu. ins.	cc					in.	mm	in.	mm
1977	107.13	1756	2-Bbl	86@6200	90@2800	8.0-1	3.31	84	3.12	79.2

① — Models with catalytic converters — 83 HP at 5800 RPM; 89 Ft. Lbs. at 3200 PM.

VALVES

Engine & Valve	Head Diam. In. (mm)	Face Angle	Seat Angle	Seat Width In. (mm)	Stem Diameter In. (mm)	Stem Clearance In. (mm)	Valve Lift In. (mm)
1800 cc							
Intake	1.622-1.638 (41.2-41.6)	45°	45°	.083 (2.1)	.314-.315 (7.974-7.992)	.001-.003 (.030-.066)	.....
Exhaust	1.411-.435 (35.85-36.45)	45°	45°	.067 (1.7)	.314-.315 (7.974-7.992)	.001-.003 (.030-.066)	.....

VALVE SPRINGS

Engine	Free Length In. (mm)	PRESSURE Lbs. @ In. (kg @ mm)	
		Valve Closed	Valve Open
1800 cc			
Inner	1.666 (42.32)	31.7-34.0@1.22 (14.4-15.4@31)	59.3-64.6@.85 (269-29.3@21.5)
Outer	2.122 (53.9)	82.5-89.1@1.42 (37.4-40.4@36)	125.7-136.7@1.02 (57-62@26)

CAMSHAFT

Engine	Journal Diam. In. (mm)	Clearance In. (mm)	Lobe Lift In. (mm)
1800 cc			
Front	1.1789-1.1795 (29.944-29.960)	.0019-.0035 (.049-.090)	.....
Center	1.801-1.802 (45.755-45.771)	.0011-.0028 (.029-.070)	.....
Rear	1.8171-1.8178 (46.155-46.171)	.0011-.0028 (.029-.070)	.....

PISTONS, PINS, RINGS

Engine	PISTONS	PINS		RINGS		
	Clearance In. (mm)	Piston Fit In. (mm)	Rod Fit In. (mm)	Rings	End Gap In. (mm)	Side Clearance In. (mm)
1800 cc	.0157-.0236 (.40-.60)	.0001-.0003 (.002-.008)	.0004-.0006 (.010-.016)	No. 1	.012-.018 (.30-.45)	0018-.0030 (.045-.077)
				No. 2	.008-.014 (.20-.35)	.0012-.0028 (.030-.070)
				No. 3 (Oil)	.008-.014 (.20-.35)	.0012-.0024 (.030-.062)

1800 cc 4 CYLINDER (Cont.)

ENGINE SPECIFICATIONS (Cont.)

CRANKSHAFT MAIN & CONNECTING ROD BEARINGS							
	MAIN BEARINGS				CONNECTING ROD BEARINGS		
Engine	Journal Diam. In. (mm)	Clearance In. (mm)	Thrust Bearing	Crankshaft End Play In. (mm)	Journal Diam. In. (mm)	Clearance In. (mm) ①	Side Play In. (mm)
1800 cc	2.086-2.087 (52.985-53.005)	.002-.003 (.050-.094)	Center	.002.012 (.055-.305)	2.000-2.001 (50.792-50.802)	.0016..0030 (.041-.075)	.005-.018 (.127-.457)

① — Dimensions given are for Class A Bearing Shells. With Class B Bearing Shells, clearance would be .0017-.0030" (.043-.077 mm) for crankpin journals of 1.999-2.000" (50.782-50.792 mm).

TIGHTENING SPECIFICATIONS	
Application	Ft. Lbs. (mkg)
Front Main Bearing Cap Nuts	59.3 (8.2)
Other Main Bearing Cap Nuts	83.2 (11.5)
Flywheel Bolts	61.5 (8.5)
Connecting Rod Cap Nuts	37.6 (5.2)
Cylinder Head Bolts	①61.5 (8.5)
Camshaft Housing Nuts	16 (2.2)
Exhaust Pipe Nuts	17.4 (2.4)
Manifold Nuts	18 (2.5)
Crankshaft Nut	181 (25)
Camshaft Gear Bolts	87 (12)
Spark Plugs	27.5 (3.8)
Temperature Gauge Transmitter	36 (5)
Timing Belt Tensioner Nut	32.5 (4.5)

① — Tighten in two stages to final torque setting.

VALVE TIMING				
	INTAKE		EXHAUST	
Engine	Open (BTDC)	Close (ALDC)	Open (BLDC)	Close (ATDC)
1800 cc	5°	53°	53°	5°

LUV PICKUP 4 CYLINDER

ENGINE CODING

ENGINE IDENTIFICATION

Engine number is located in casting on right upper center portion of cylinder head.

ENGINE, CYLINDER HEAD & MANIFOLDS

ENGINE

1) Disconnect battery cables, drain crankcase and cooling system. Disconnect carburetor linkage, all necessary water and fuel hoses, vacuum lines, and electrical leads. Also disconnect exhaust pipe at manifold flange. Remove radiator.

2) Disconnect drive shaft, clutch slave cylinder and speedometer cable. Remove gearshift lever assembly and exhaust pipe bracket. Attach suitable hoist and take up weight of engine. Remove front and rear engine mounts. Carefully pull engine forward adjusting hoist to clear stationary components.

INTAKE & EXHAUST MANIFOLD

1) Remove air cleaner and carburetor. Disconnect PCV valve, power brake vacuum line and exhaust pipe from exhaust manifold. Note for reinstallation position of lifting hanger.

2) Remove nuts, lock washers and flat washers holding manifolds to cylinder head. Slide manifolds off together. Once off, manifolds can be separated by removing exhaust manifold mounting studs. To install, reverse removal procedure.

NOTE – *Torque manifold stud in sequence, working from inner nuts outward.*

CYLINDER HEAD

1) Drain cooling system. Disconnect exhaust pipe from manifold. Disconnect all necessary water hoses, vacuum lines, carburetor linkage, and electrical leads. Remove air cleaner assembly and valve cover. Rotate number four cylinder into firing position. Lock timing chain adjuster by depressing and turning automatic adjuster slide pin 90° clockwise *(See Fig. 6)*.

NOTE – *Do not remove the timing chain from camshaft sprocket.*

2) Remove timing chain sprocket from camshaft. Remove front cover. Using suitable tool (J-24239), remove cylinder head bolts in progressional sequence starting with outer bolts. Remove cylinder head, intake and exhaust manifolds as an assembly. To install, reverse removal procedure.

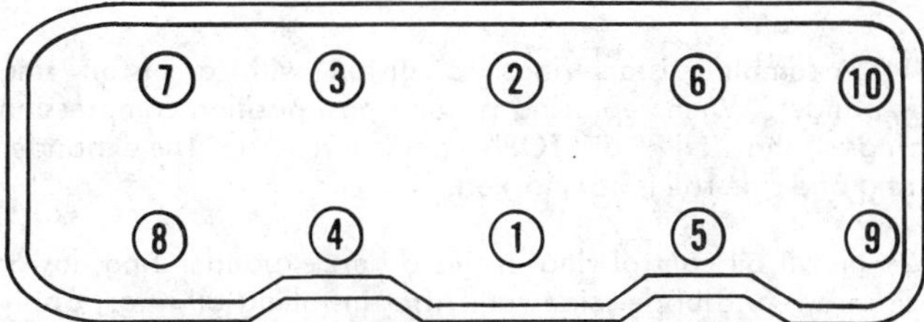

Fig. 1 Cylinder Head Tightening Sequence

VALVES

VALVE ARRANGEMENT

E-I-I-E-E-I-I-E

VALVE GUIDE

Removal & Installation – 1) Inspect inside diameter of valve guide for grooves or uneven wear. Measure inside diameter of valve guides with caliper gauge. Measure diameter of valve stem and compare measured values to determine clearance. If clearance is greater than .008" (.20 mm) for intake, or .010" (.25 mm) for exhaust, replace both valve and valve guide.

2) Drive valve guides toward upper face of cylinder head, using suitable valve guide replacer tool (J-26512). Valve guides cannot be driven downward. Valve guides are held in position by snap rings.

NOTE – *Before installation of valve guide, remove lower spring seat.*

3) To install, apply engine oil to outer circumference of valve guide, and install into position in cylinder head. Holding valve guide installer tool (J-26512-1) and (J-26512-2) against valve guide, drive valve guide into cylinder head until tool bottoms on cylinder head.

NOTE – *Replace valve whenever valve guide is replaced.*

VALVE STEM OIL SEALS

Inspect intake and exhaust valve stem oil seal lips and inner face. Replace valve stem oil seals at time of reassembly, if wear is noticable.

VALVE SPRING REMOVAL

Remove rocker arm shaft and bracket assembly. Remove spark plug, and connect compressed air to cylinder at spark plug opening. Using spring compressor tool (J-26513), compress valve spring and remove retainers, spring, and spring cap. Remove valve stem oil seal and lower spring seat. To install, reverse removal procedure.

VALVE SPRING INSTALLED HEIGHT

Visually check valve springs for damage and replace as necessary. Measure free length of valve springs using suitable calipers and replace if measured value is beyond limit. With a valve spring tester check valve spring tension and compare it with values in chart, replace as necessary.

NOTE – *Install springs with close wound coils next to cylinder head.*

ROCKER ARM ASSEMBLY

1) Loosen rocker shaft bracket nuts in sequence, starting with outer brackets. Remove the spring from the shaft, and then remove rocker arm brackets and arms keeping parts in order for reassembly.

LUV PICKUP 4 CYLINDER (Cont.)

2) Inspect rocker arm shaft for wear damage or excessive runout. If runout is greater than .0156" (.396 mm), replace shaft. Diameter of shaft is .8071" (20.5 mm). Replace shaft if diameter is less than .8012" (20.35 mm).

3) To install, apply engine oil to rocker arm shaft, rocker arms, and valve stems. Install longer shaft on exhaust side and shorter shaft on intake side. Aligning marks on shafts are turned to front side.

4) Assemble brackets and arms to shafts, so cylinder number (on upper face of bracket) is pointed to front of engine. Align No. 1 shaft bracket with mark on the intake and exhaust valve side rocker arm shafts. Place springs between shaft bracket and rocker arm. Punch mark on rocker arm shafts must be turned upward. Tighten shaft bracket nuts.

NOTE – *Hold rocker arm springs with a wrench while torquing nuts, to prevent damage to spring. Torque nuts in sequence, starting with center bracket and working outward.*

VALVE CLEARANCE

With No. 1 or No. 4 cylinder piston at top dead center, loosen lock nut and adjust intake valves to .006" (.15 mm), and exhaust valves to .010" (.25 mm). When valves are correctly adjusted reset lock nut.

Valve Adjustment Sequence

Application	Intake/Cylinder	Exhaust/Cylinder
No. 1 @ TDC	1,2	1,3
No. 4 @ TDC	3,4	2,4

PISTONS, PINS & RINGS

OIL PAN

Raise vehicle. Drain crankcase and remove front splash shield. Remove crossmember. Disconnect relay rod at idler arm and lower relay rod. Remove left hand bell housing brace. Remove oil pan bolts and pan. To install, reverse removal procedure.

PISTON & ROD ASSEMBLY

1) Position cylinder body so flywheel side is down. Using suitable tool, scrape carbon from upper part of cylinder wall.

2) Remove connecting rod bearing cap nuts and bearing cap. Using a wood rod, push piston, together with connecting rod, upward. Removal sequence is 1, 4, 2, & 3. **NOTE** – *Ensure piston and connecting rod are pulled parallel to cylinder wall.*

3) To install piston and rod assembly, position piston so notch mark on crown of piston is facing front of engine. Align cylinder number marks on connecting rods so they will be on right-hand side of front mark on piston.

PISTON PIN

Removal – Using a press and piston pin removal tool set (J-25270), press piston pin out of piston and connecting rod assembly.

NOTE – *Manufacturer recommends replacing with NEW piston pins.*

Installation – Install new pin by placing pilot through piston and connecting rod. Lightly oil piston pin and place piston, rod, pin, and ram on press base. Press in pin until its centered in connecting rod.

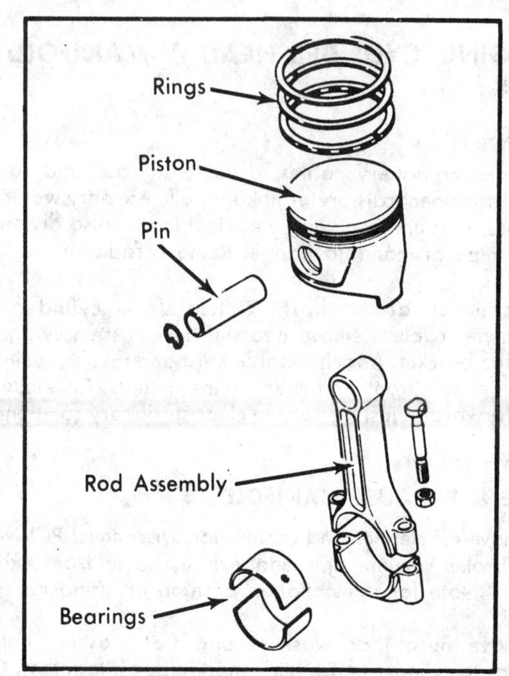

Fig. 2 Exploded View of Piston & Connecting Rod

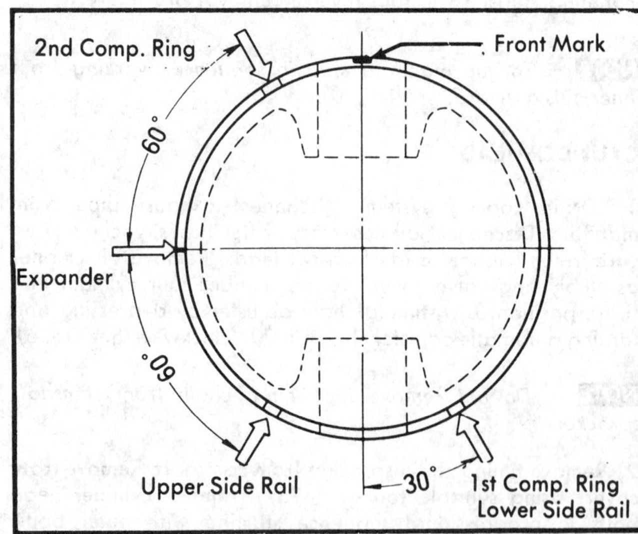

Fig. 3 Position of Piston Rings

PISTON RINGS

1) Assemble piston rings to piston with a piston ring expander. When replacing piston rings, position compression rings so that "NPR" or "TOP" mark is turned up. The expander ring and side rail is not marked.

2) Install oil control ring in this order; expander ring, lower side rail, and upper side rail. After installing all rings, apply clean engine oil to the entire rings. Check that rings turn smoothly in their ring grooves.

LUV PICKUP 4 CYLINDER (Cont.)

FITTING PISTONS

1) Check piston clearance by inserting piston pull-scale with .0018-.0026" feeler gauge, one inch long, into cylinder. Fit piston, crown first, into cylinder so feeler gauge is wedged by piston.

2) Holding piston to prevent side thrust, withdraw gauge with a steady pull on scale. Clearance is correct when gauge reads 1.1-2.2 lbs. **NOTE** — *It is advisable to take several readings.*

3) Measure weight of assembled pistons and compare the values. Ensure values between pistons are within .2 ozs. If value is exceeded, make necessary adjustments by selecting a connecting rod of suitable weight or by grinding.

Piston Class

Piston Size	Piston Grade	Piston Diameter In. (mm)
Standard	A	3.3049-3.3053 (83.944-83.955)
Standard	B	3.3053-3.3057 (83.955-83.965)
Standard	C	3.3057-3.3061 (83.965-83.975)
Standard	D	3.3061-3.3065 (83.975-83.985)

NOTE — *Pistons are available in .020" (0.5mm) and .040" (1.0mm) oversize.*

CRANKSHAFT MAIN & CONNECTING ROD BEARINGS

MAIN & CONNECTING ROD BEARING SERVICE

NOTE — *The following procedure is with engine, cylinder head, timing cover, oil pan, and timing chain removed.*

Connecting Rod Bearings — After ensuring rod caps are marked for cylinder identification, remove rod caps. Use Plastigage method to check for proper clearance. If not within specifications, new bearings must be installed. New bearings are available in standard, .010", and .020".

NOTE — *Always replace bearings in pairs. Never use a new bearing in combination with a used bearing.*

Main Bearings — 1) With all bearing caps (except one being checked) tight, check clearances using Plastigage method. If clearances are excessive, undersized bearings will have to be installed. Remove upper bearings by inserting tool into oil hole of crankshaft and rotating crankshaft clockwise to roll bearing from engine.

2) To check crankshaft out of round place crankshaft on two "V" shaped blocks at No. 1 and No. 5 journals. Hold dial indicator in contact with No. 3 journal and slowly turn crankshaft, recording highest point on journal. Replace crankshaft if bend exceeds .0038" (.097 mm). Standard assembly value is .0012" (.030 mm) or less.

3) To check crankshaft end play, place bearings and crankshaft in crankcase. Install thrust bearing on both sides of No. 3 crankshaft journal. Shift crankshaft endwise and measure clearance between thrust bearing and journal side face. If clearance is greater than .0117" (.297 mm), install oversize thrust bearings. Standard value is .0024-.0094" (.061-.239 mm).

NOTE — *Main bearing caps are installed with marks on bottom of caps facing forward. Number two and three bearing caps can be distinguished by an "A" stamped on caps.*

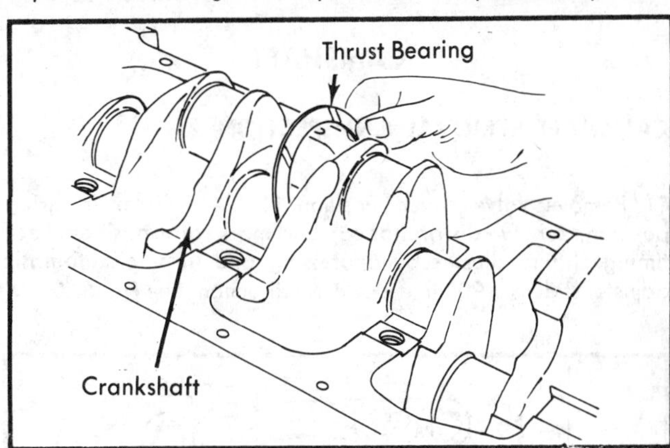

Fig. 4 Installing Thrust Bearing

REAR MAIN OIL SEAL

Removal — Remove oil pan and transmission. Remove clutch (if equipped). Remove starter and flywheel assembly. Remove seal retainer bolts and pry seal out of retainer.

Installation — To install, reverse removal procedure noting the following: Fill clearance between lips of seal with grease, and coat lips of seal with engine oil. Place retainer on flat surface and drive seal into place using suitable seal installer tool (J-22354).

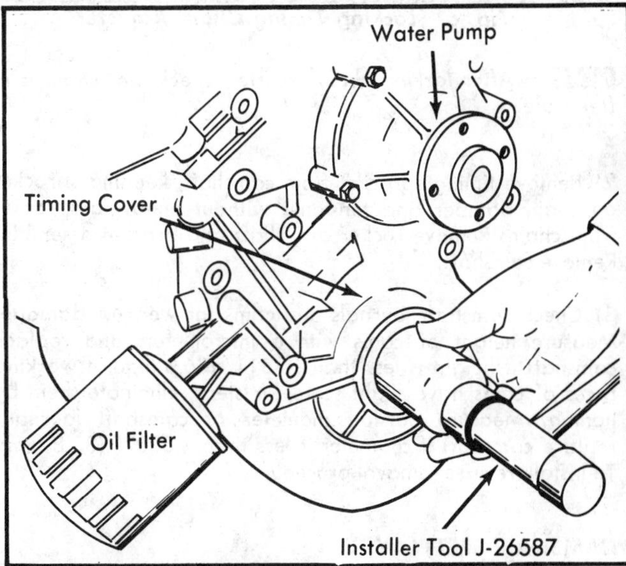

Fig. 5 Installing Timing Cover Oil Seal

FRONT COVER & OIL SEAL

Removal — Remove cylinder head and oil pan as previously outlined. Remove oil pump pickup tube. Remove harmonic balancer and AIR belt. If equipped with air conditioning, remove compressor and mounting brackets. Remove distributor cap (wires attached), then remove distributor. Remove front cover.

LUV PICKUP 4 CYLINDER (Cont.)

Installation – Align oil pump drive gear punch mark with oil filter side of cover. Align center of dowel pin with alignment mark on oil pump case. Rotate No. 1 and 4 cylinders to top dead center. Install front cover by engaging pinion gear with oil pump drive gear on crankshaft *(See Fig. 5)*. Install front cover and reverse removal procedure.

CAMSHAFT

CAMSHAFT REMOVAL & INSPECTION

1) Remove valve cover. Position No. 4 cylinder in firing position. Remove distributor cap and mark rotor position. Lock timing chain adjuster by depressing and turning automatic adjuster slide pin 90° in a clockwise direction. See Fig. 6.

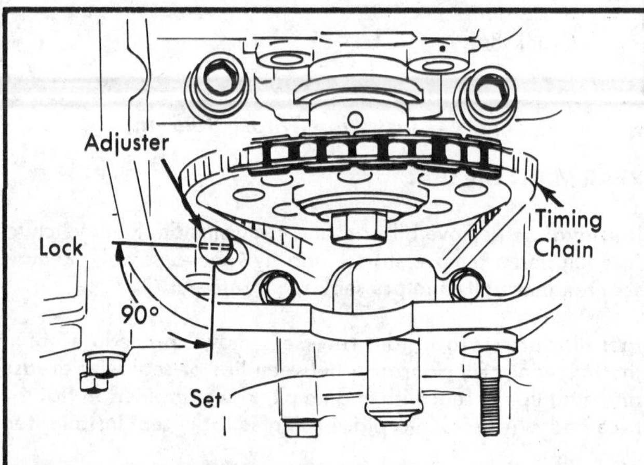

Fig. 6 Locking Timing Chain Adjuster

NOTE – *After locking chain adjuster, check that chain is in free state.*

2) Remove timing sprocket from camshaft, keeping sprocket on chain damper and tensioner without removing sprocket from chain. Remove rocker arm shaft and bracket assembly. Remove camshaft.

3) Check camshaft journals and cams for wear or damage. Measure height of cams with a micrometer, and replace camshaft if height is less than 1.4311" (36.3 mm). If working faces of cams have slight scores or steps, eliminate them by honing. Measure outside diameter of camshaft journals, replace camshaft if diameter is less than 1.3307" (33.8 mm). To install, reverse removal procedure.

CAMSHAFT END PLAY

Measure camshaft end play with thrust plate installed in thrust groove. Replace thrust plate if end play is found to exceed .0078" (.198 mm). Standard end play is .002-.006" (.05-.15 mm).

CAMSHAFT BEARING REPLACEMENT

Camshaft bearings are not replaceable. Camshaft rides in a carrier. If clearance is beyond limits, replace camshaft carrier.

TIMING CHAIN REPLACEMENT

1) Remove front cover as outlined previously. Remove camshaft sprocket and timing chain. All other parts can now be inspected for wear, replace as necessary. If crankshaft sprocket needs replacement, remove with suitable gear puller (J-25031).

2) Install timing sprocket and pinion gear, groove side toward front cover. Align key grooves with key on crankshaft, then drive into position with suitable installing tool (J-26587). Turn crankshaft so that key is turned toward cylinder head side and No. 1 and 4 cylinders are at top dead center.

NOTE – *Keep timing chain engaged with camshaft sprocket until sprocket is installed on camshaft.*

3) Align mark plate on timing chain with mark on crankshaft timing sprocket. Side of chain with mark plate is on front side, and side of chain with most links between mark plates is on chain guide side. Camshaft timing sprocket marked side, faces forward and marks align with timing chain mark plate. Install front cover.

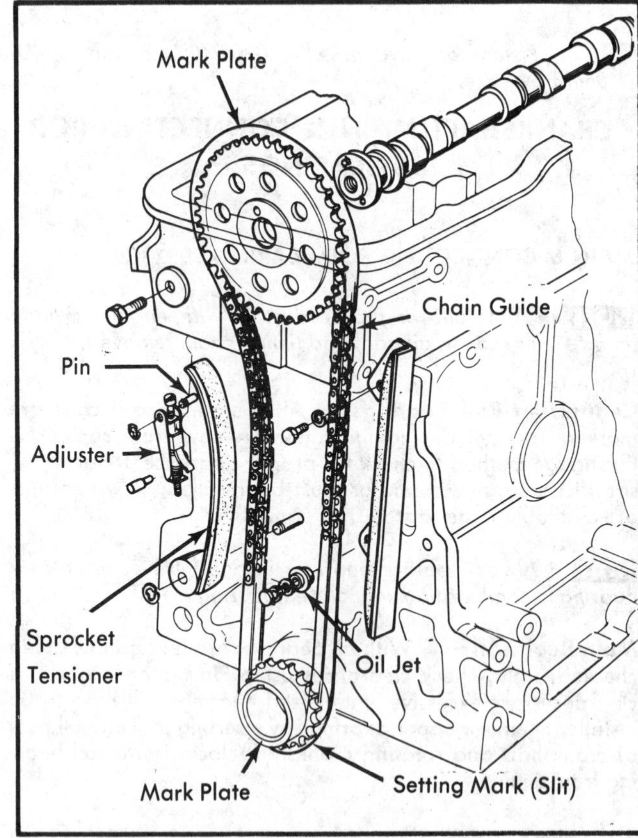

Fig. 7 Camshaft, Timing Chain & Components

ENGINE OILING SYSTEM

Trochoid type oil pump is designed to deliver 3.7 gallons of oil per minute through the engine at a pump speed of 1400 RPM. Lubricating system is designed to deliver oil at a rate of 57 psi.

Crankcase Capacity – 4.7 quarts.

LUV PICKUP 4 CYLINDER (Cont.)

ENGINE OILING

Oil Filter – Full-flow disposable canister type.

Normal Oil Pressure – 57 psi.

Relief Valve – Located on side of cylinder block near oil filter. Opening pressure of relief valve is 57-71 psi.

OIL PUMP

NOTE – *Oil pump can be serviced with engine in or out of vehicle. Procedure given is with engine in vehicle.*

Removal – Remove front cover, distributor, and oil pan as outlined previously. Remove oil pickup tube. Remove oil pump mounting bolts and remove pump assembly.

Inspection – 1) Measure tip clearance with a feeler gauge, between drive rotor and driven rotor. Replace entire pump assembly if clearance is greater than .0079" (.2 mm).

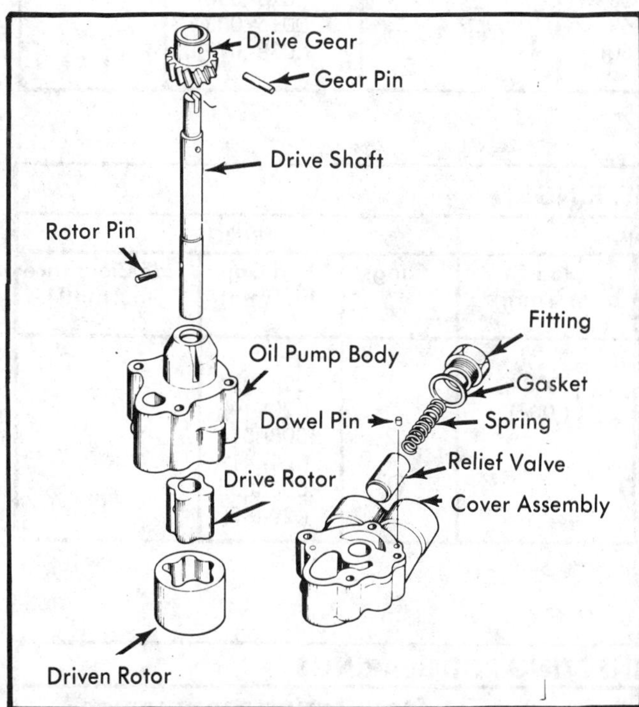

Fig. 8 Exploded View of Oil Pump Assembly

2) Measure clearance between driven rotor and inner wall of pump body. Replace entire pump assembly if clearance is greater than .0098" (.249 mm).

3) Using a square and a feeler gauge, measure clearance between drive rotor, driven rotor, and oil pump cover. Replace entire pump assembly if clearance is greater than .0079" (.2 mm). Inspect all parts wear or damage.

Installation – 1) Align mark on camshaft with mark on No. 1 rocker arm shaft bracket. Align notch on crankshaft pulley with "O" mark on front cover. When the two sets of marks are aligned, No. 4 cylinder is at top dead center on compression stroke.

2) Install driven rotor so that alignment mark aligns with mark on the drive rotor. Engage drive gear with pinion gear on crankshaft so alignment mark is turned rearward and is away from crankshaft by approximately 20° in clockwise rotation *(See Fig. 9).*

3) When oil pump is installed; make sure mark on drive gear is turned to rear side as viewed from the clearance between front cover and cylinder block. Slit at end of shaft must be parallel with front face of cylinder block, and is offset as viewed through distributor fitting hole.

4) Install pump cover by fitting it to the dowel pins, then install mounting bolts. Install relief valve assembly and rubber hose on cover. Reverse removal procedure.

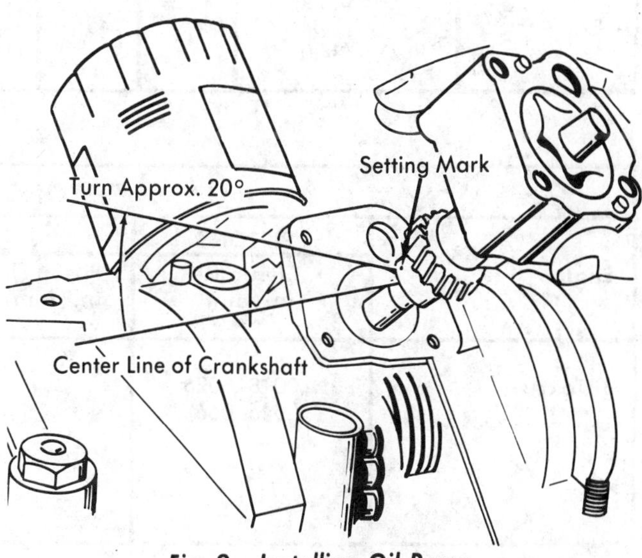

Fig. 9 Installing Oil Pump

ENGINE COOLING

WATER PUMP

Disconnect negative battery cable. Remove lower cover. Drain cooling system. If equipped with air conditioning, remove fan and air pump drive belt. Remove fan, fan pulley, and air pump drive pulley. Remove set plate and pulley. On all other models remove fan nuts and fan. On all models, remove attaching bolts and water pump from vehicle.

Thermostat – opens at 180°F (82°C)

Cooling System Capacity – 6.4 qts.

Pressure Cap – 15 psi.

LUV PICKUP 4 CYLINDER (Cont.)

ENGINE SPECIFICATIONS

GENERAL SPECIFICATIONS

Year	Displ. cu. ins.	Displ. cc	Carburetor	HP at RPM	Torque (Ft. Lbs. at RPM)	Compr. Ratio	Bore in.	Bore mm	Stroke in.	Stroke mm
1977	110.8	1816	1x2-Bbl.	80 @4800	95 @3000	8.5:1	3.31	84	3.23	82

VALVES

Engine & Valve	Head Diam. In. (mm)	Face Angle	Seat Angle	Seat Width In. (mm)	Stem Diameter In. (mm)	Stem Clearance In. (mm)	Valve Lift In. (mm)
1816 cc							
Int.	1.67 (42.4)	45°	45°	.047-.063 (1.19-1.60)	.....	.0009-.0022 (.023-.056)	.....
Exh.	1.34 (34.0)	45°	45°	.047-.063 (1.19-1.60)	.....	.0015-.0031 (.038-.079)	.....

PISTONS, PINS, RINGS

Engine	PISTONS Clearance In. (mm)	PINS Piston Fit In. (mm)	PINS Rod Fit In. (mm)	RINGS Rings	RINGS End Gap In. (mm)	RINGS Side Clearance In. (mm)
1816 cc	.0018-.0026 (.046-.066)	①	.0024 (.061)	1	.008-.016 (.20-.41)	.....
				2	.008-.016 (.20-.41)	.....
				Oil	.008-.035 (.20-.89)	.....

① — Press fit.

CRANKSHAFT MAIN & CONNECTING ROD BEARINGS

Engine	MAIN BEARINGS Journal Diam.	MAIN BEARINGS Clearance	MAIN BEARINGS Thrust Bearing	MAIN BEARINGS Crankshaft End Play	CONNECTING ROD BEARINGS Journal Diam.	CONNECTING ROD BEARINGS Clearance	CONNECTING ROD BEARINGS Side Play
1816 cc	2.205 (56.01)	.0016 (.041)	No. 3	.118 (.3)	1.929 (48.99)	.0020 (.051)	.011 (.28)

CAMSHAFT

Engine	Journal Diam. In. (mm)	Clearance In. (mm)	Lobe Lift In. (mm)
1816 cc	1.3362-1.3370 (33.94-33.96)	.0024 ① (.061)	.....

① — End Play .002-.006" (.05-.15 mm)

VALVE TIMING

Engine	INTAKE Open (BTDC)	INTAKE Close (ALDC)	EXHAUST Open (BLDC)	EXHAUST Close (ATDC)
1816 cc	21°	65°	55°	20°

LUV PICKUP 4 CYLINDER (Cont.)

ENGINE SPECIFICATIONS (Cont.)

VALVE SPRINGS			
Engine	Free Length In. (mm)	PRESSURE Lbs. @ In. (kg @ mm)	
		Valve Closed	Valve Open
1816 cc			
Inner	1.78 (45.2)	21.5 @1.52 (9.7 @38.6)	.....
Outer	1.85 (47.0)	37.0 @1.61 (16.8 @40.9)	.....

TIGHTENING SPECIFICATIONS	
Application	Ft. Lbs. (mkg)
Cylinder Head	
Step 1	61 (8.43)
Step 2	72 (9.95)
Main Bearings	72 (9.95)
Connecting Rod Bearings	33 (9.54)
Flywheel	69 (9.54)
Camshaft Sprocket	58 (8.02)
Rocker Arm Shaft Bracket Nuts	16 (2.21)

808(1300), 808(1600) & GLC

ENGINE CODING

ENGINE IDENTIFICATION

Engine number on the 1586 cc engine is stamped on cylinder block directly behind dipstick. Engine number on the 1272 cc is stamped on right side of block below distributor.

Application	Engine	Code
GLC	1272 cc	TC
808 (1300)	1272 cc	TC
808 (1600)	1586 cc	NA

ENGINE & CYLINDER HEAD

ENGINE

Removal, 1272cc & 1586cc – 1) Remove hood marking hood hinge location. Drain cooling system and crankcase. Remove battery and air cleaner. Disconnect accelerator and choke cable from carburetor. Disconnect fuel lines at fuel pump, (Calif. models, disconnect fuel lines at carburetor and fuel pump).

2) Disconnect wires from temperature sending unit, oil pressure switch, alternator, distributor, reverse lamp switch and starter. Disconnect exhaust pipe from manifold. Remove cover plate from clutch housing. Support transmission with a jack and remove nuts and bolts attaching transmission to engine.

3) Remove engine mount attaching nuts and bolts. Install a lifting sling to engine lifting brackets, attach a lifting hoist and raise slightly. Pull engine forward until clear of clutch shaft. Lift engine from vehicle.

4) Disconnect the EGR pipes from the exhaust manifold and intake manifold (on Calif. vehicles, disconnect the vacuum sensing tube from the intake manifold). Remove the servo diaphragm and vacuum control valve from the intake manifold. Remove the anti-afterburn valve from intake manifold. Remove the exhaust manifold and port liners from cylinder head.

Installation – To install, reverse removal procedure.

NOTE – *Additional engine component disassembly (with engine removed).*

CYLINDER HEAD

Removal – 1) Remove engine lifting brackets from cylinder head. Remove exhaust manifold or thermal reactor along with port liners and gaskets. Disconnect ignition wires at spark plugs and vacuum control tube at distributor. Remove lock nut, then remove distributor from cylinder head.

2) Disconnect hoses and remove air pump with bracket. Remove water pump fan and pulley. Disconnect hose from ventilation valve at intake manifold. Disconnect anti-afterburn valve hose on 808 models. Remove attaching bolts, then remove intake manifold and carburetor as an assembly.

3) Remove rocker arm cover, gasket, and oil seals. Install ring gear brake tool (49 0118 271A) to flywheel to prevent flywheel from rotating. Remove lock nut and washer, then slide distributor drive gear from camshaft. Remove camshaft sprocket lock nut. Remove cylinder head-to-front cover attaching bolt.

4) On 1272 cc 808 models, remove blind cover from timing chain cover and install chain tensioner guide (49 1975 260), to prevent slipper head of tensioner from popping out. Loosen, in steps, cylinder head bolts in the reverse of tightening sequence and then remove bolts. Remove rocker arm assembly. Carefully pull camshaft to rear and remove from sprocket and cylinder head.

5) Remove camshaft sprocket. **CAUTION** – *Timing chain should be lifted up to prevent chain tensioner slipper head from disengaging which will cause difficulty in chain tension adjustment upon reassembly.* Remove camshaft bearings from cylinder head. Remove cylinder head and gasket.

Installation – 1) Install camshaft sprocket to timing chain and position on top of chain guide strip and chain vibration damper. **NOTE** – *Ensure matching marks on chain and sprocket are aligned.* Install new cylinder head gasket, then position cylinder head while aligning dowels.

2) Install camshaft bearings to cylinder head and to bearing caps. Lubricate bearing surfaces with engine oil. Carefully install camshaft to sprocket while aligning keyway and fit journals to respective bearings. Position rocker arm assembly on cylinder head. **NOTE** – *Ensure that the flat surface of ball on each rocker arm is facing down.*

3) Install cylinder head bolts and tighten, in steps, according to sequence shown in *Fig. 1.* Install cylinder head-to-front cover bolt. Install and tighten camshaft lock nut, then bend tab of lock washer. Install distributor drive gear, tighten nut and bend lock washer.

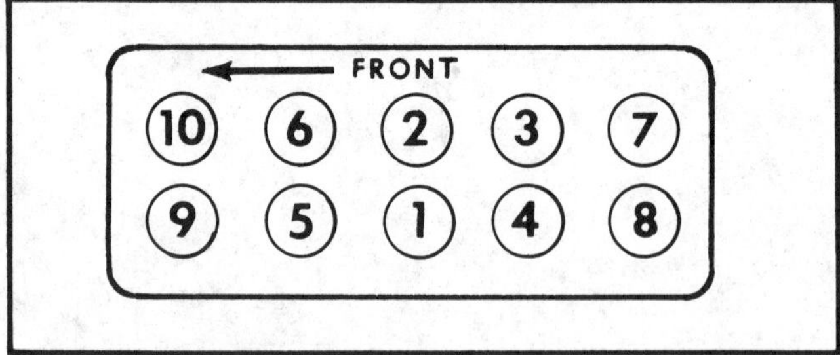

Fig. 1 Tightening Sequence for Cylinder Head

4) Carefully press top of chain guide strip, using a lever, through opening of cylinder head. Tighten guide strip attaching screws. Adjust timing chain tension. See *Timing Chain Adjustment*. Install remaining components in reverse of removal procedure.

VALVES

VALVE ARRANGEMENT

Right Side – All Intake.
Left Side – All Exhaust.

808(1300), 808(1600) & GLC (Cont.)

VALVE GUIDE SERVICING

Remove worn valve guide, using valve guide removal/installation tool and hammer. Install new guide until ring on guide just touches cylinder head. Install new valve seal onto valve guide using a seal pusher tool (42 0223 160B).

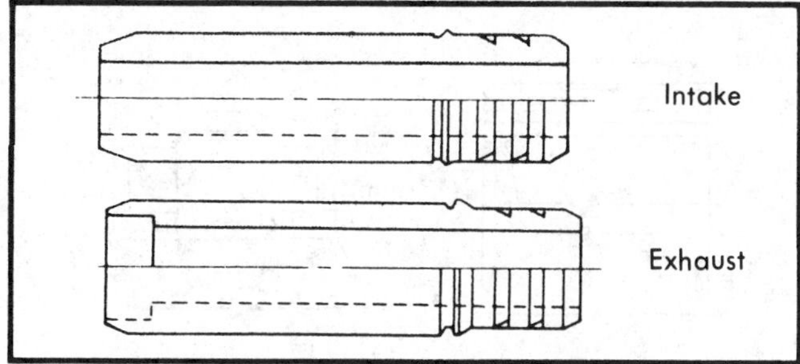

Fig. 2 Valve Guide Assemblies

VALVE SPRING

Remove all carbon from inside combustion chamber. Using a suitable valve spring compressor, compress valve springs and remove taper sleeves, upper spring seat, valve springs and lower spring seat. If necessary, valve can now be removed.

NOTE – *Mark components for reinstallation, as they are disassembled.*

VALVE SPRING INSTALLED HEIGHT

With valve springs removed, inspect for corrosion or damage and replace as necessary. Using suitable valve spring tester, measure free length and fitting pressure.

ROCKER ARM ASSEMBLY

1) With rocker arm assembly removed and disassembled, inspect all components for wear or damage. The standard clearance between rocker arm bore and shaft on 1272 cc is, .0008-.0029" (.020-.074 mm), and on 1586 cc is, .0011-.0032" (.028-.081 mm). If measured clearance is beyond .004" (.102 mm), replace rocker arm or shaft.

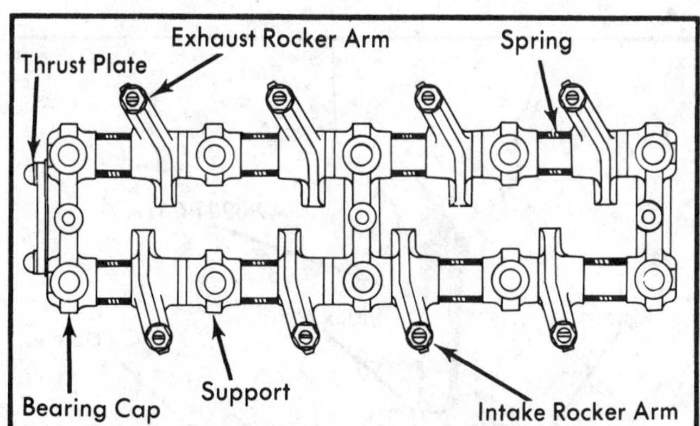

Fig. 3 1272 cc Rocker Arm Assembly

2) Reassemble and install rocker shaft while noting the following: Intake and exhaust rocker arm shaft supports are interchangeable. Intake side uses two rocker shafts. On intake side, end of shaft with longer distance between oil hole and shaft end face each other. Center bearing cap oil hole faces toward intake side.

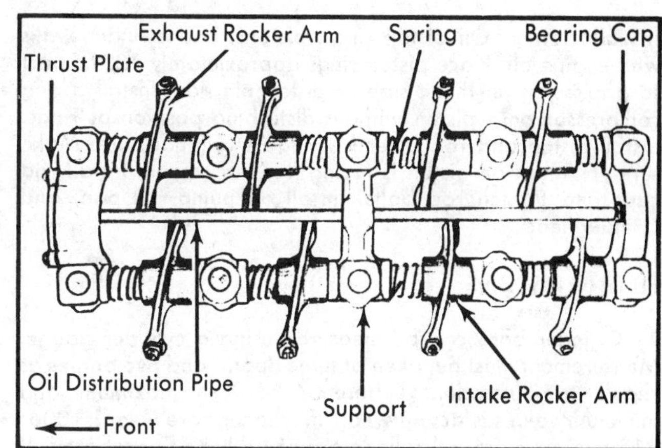

Fig. 4 1586 cc Rocker Arm Assembly

3) When installing the oil distribution pipe make sure the oil ejection hole faces camshaft. After pipe is installed press "O" ring into hole for pipe on center bearing cap. When installing rocker arm assembly make sure flat surface on ball of each rocker arm faces downward. Align dowels and install assembly to cylinder head. Before tightening cylinder head bolts, offset each exhaust rocker arm .040" (1 mm) from valve stem center.

VALVE CLEARANCE ADJUSTMENT

To adjust clearance, loosen lock nut and insert feeler gauge between rocker arm and valve stem. Turn adjusting screw until proper clearance is obtained.

NOTE – *Before adjusting, ensure flat surface of ball on rocker arm is facing downward.*

Valve Clearance Specifications

Application	Intake In.(mm)	Exhaust In.(mm)
1272cc		
Valve side	.010 (.25)	.012 (.30)
Camshaft side	.007 (.18)	.009 (.22)
1586 cc		
Valve side	.012 (.30)	.012 (.30)
Camshaft side	.009 (.22)	.009 (.22)

PISTONS, PINS & RINGS

OIL PAN

Raise vehicle and drain crankcase. Remove under cover and clutch release cylinder bolts, and let cylinder hang. Remove clutch cover plate. Remove oil pan and gasket. To install, reverse removal procedure.

PISTON & ROD ASSEMBLY

Removal – Remove oil pan, cylinder head, and oil pump. Make sure connecting rod caps are marked so they may be replaced in their original positions, then remove rod caps. Push piston and rod assembly out top of cylinder. Take care not to damage bearing journal.

808(1300), 808(1600) & GLC (Cont.)

Installation – Oil piston rings, pistons, and cylinder walls with engine oil. Place piston rings approximately 120° apart so gap is not on thrust side or piston pin side. Install a ring compressor onto piston without disturbing position of rings. Install piston and rod assembly into its original bore. Make sure "F" mark on piston is facing front of engine. Install rod caps and tighten rod bolts. Install oil pump, oil pan, and cylinder head.

FITTING PISTONS

1) Cylinder bore can be measured using a cylinder gauge. Measurement must be taken at three depths and two angles as shown in illustration. Difference between maximum and minimum values is actual wear. If cylinder bore wear is .006" (.15 mm) or more, all cylinders must be honed or rebored. If cylinder is honed or rebored, oversize pistons and rings are available in .010" (.25 mm), .020" (.50 mm), .030" (.75 mm), and .040" (1.00 mm) oversizes.

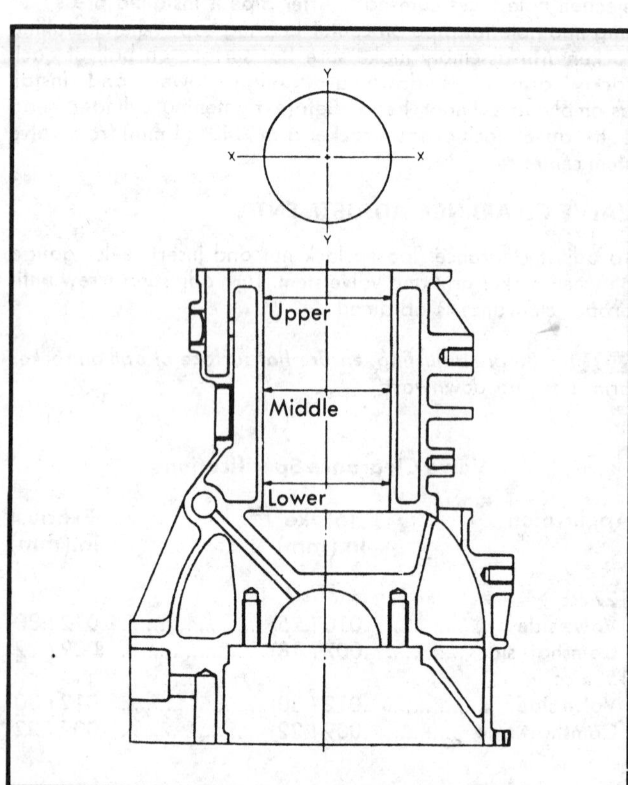

Fig. 5 Points for Measuring Cylinder Bore

Standard Piston Specifications

Application	Diameter In. (mm)
1272 cc	
A	2.8718-2.8726 (72.948-72.956)
B	2.8722-2.8730 (72.959-72.967)
C	2.8590-2.8598 (72.649-72.657)
1586 cc	
A	3.0683-3.0691 (77.935-77.955)
B	3.0705-3.0713 (77.991-78.011)
C	3.0583-3.0591 (77.681-77.701)

2) Carefully inspect pistons and replace those severely damaged due to scoring, scratching or burning. Measure pistons at points A, B & C, as shown in *Fig. 6* using a micrometer. If piston is not within specifications, replace piston and rebore cylinder.

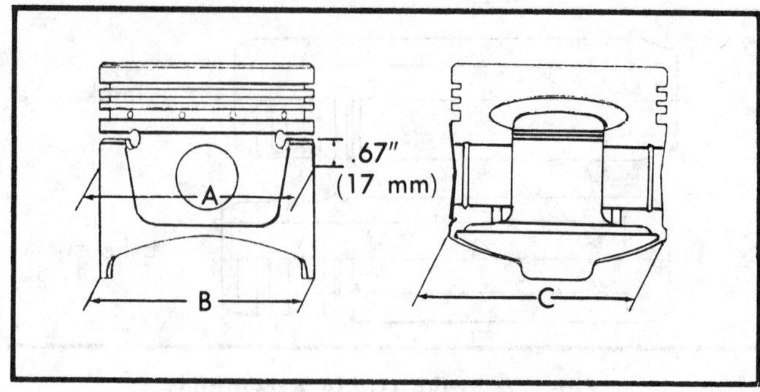

Fig. 6 Points for Measuring Piston

PISTON PIN REPLACEMENT

1) Remove piston pin circlips. Using suitable piston pin removal tool, extract piston pin. If pin is hard to remove, heat piston assembly.

2) Check fit of piston pin in connecting rod bushing. Fit should be .0004-.0012". If tolerance is exceeded, replace bushing.

3) To replace connecting rod bushing, press out worn bushing and install new one; ensure connecting rod and bushing oil holes align. Using suitable tool, finish ream new bushing. Correct fit is hand push, light resistance.

4) Begin reassembly by replacing piston pin circlip. Place connecting rod in piston so oil hole on connecting rod and piston index mark "F" are in relation. See *Fig. 7*. Using suitable piston pin installation tool, seat piston pin. Install second circlip.

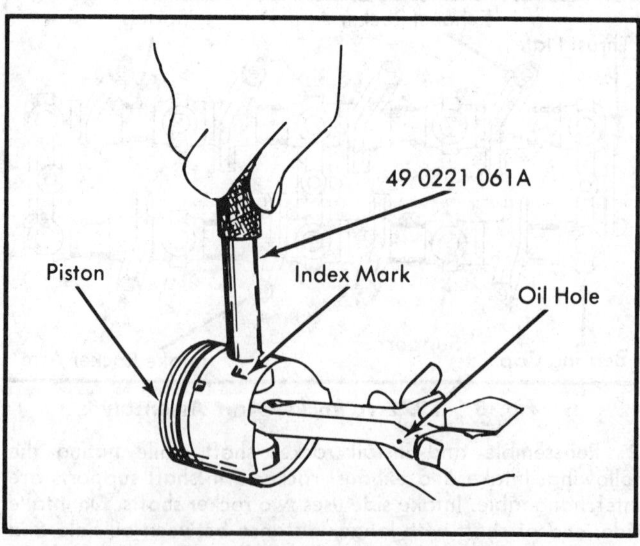

Fig. 7 Installing Piston Pin

808(1300), 808(1600) & GLC (Cont.)

CRANKSHAFT MAIN & CONNECTING ROD BEARINGS

MAIN & CONNECTING ROD BEARINGS

1) Remove engine and oil pan. Check main and connecting rod bearing clearances using Plastigage method. If measured value exceeds correct clearance, bearing must be replaced.

2) Using a micrometer, measure diameter of connecting rod and main bearing journals. If wear is more than .0020" at any journal, crankshaft must be ground to fit .010", .020" or .030" undersize bearings.

3) Using a dial indicator, check crankshaft for out-of-round. Maximum allowable out-of-round is .0012" (.030 mm).

4) Fit five upper main bearings to cylinder block and lower bearings to caps. Install thrust washer halves to cylinder block with oil grooved surface facing crankshaft thrust side. Fit new oil seal at rear of crankshaft. Insert side seals on both sides of rear main bearing cap. Install main bearing caps. No. 1 through No. 4 bearing caps are marked for correct installation, No.5 may or may not be indexed.

5) Insert connecting rod assembly into cylinder as previously described. Fit upper bearing to rod and over crankshaft. Fit lower bearing to rod cap and install cap. Tighten all bolts to specifications. **NOTE** — *Ensure engine is free to turn.*

6) End play is compensated for by thrust washers placed at No. 5 main bearing. Check crankshaft end play using a dial indicator. End play must not exceed .012", if it does thrust washers must be replaced. Thrust washers are available in .010", .020" & .030" oversizes.

CAMSHAFT

CAMSHAFT

NOTE — *Lift timing chain upward to prevent the slipper head of chain tensioner from coming out, and causing difficulty in adjusting the timing chain.*

1) Remove valve cover. Install ring gear brake tool (49 0118 271A) to the flywheel. Remove lock nut and washer, and slide distributor drive gear from camshaft. Remove lock nut from camshaft sprocket.

2) Remove the bolt that attaches timing chain cover to cylinder head. Remove cylinder head bolts in reverse of tightening sequence. Lift out rocker arm assembly. Pull camshaft rearward and remove sprocket. Carefully remove camshaft. If necessary camshaft bearings can be removed at this time.

CAMSHAFT BEARING REPLACEMENT

1) Inspect cam face and journals, ensuring they are not worn or scored. Using a micrometer, measure cam height. Standard cam height is: 1272 cc intake and exhaust is 1.7369" (44.116 mm), and 1586 cc intake is 1.7605" (44.715 mm) and exhaust is 1.7592" (44.682 mm). If measured value differs from standard specification by more than .008" (.20 mm), replace camshaft.

2) Measure diameter of camshaft bearing journals. If wear is more than .002" (.051 mm) above maximum standard diameter, camshaft must be ground to accept .010", .020" or .030" undersize bearings.

3) Inspect camshaft bearing clearances using Plastigage method. If standard clearances are exceeded, replace bearings. If new bearings are properly fitted, correct clearance can be obtained without filing, shimming or scraping.

4) Using a dial indicator, check camshaft out-of-round. Camshaft must not exceed .0012" (.030 mm) out-of-round.

5) Check camshaft end play using a feeler gauge. Standard clearance is .001-.007" (.025-.178 mm). If wear limit of .008" (.20 mm) is exceeded, replace thrust plate.

TIMING CHAIN

Removal — 1) Remove cylinder head and oil pan with engine removed from vehicle. Remove front cover and gaskets, then remove oil thrower from crankshaft. Remove chain tensioner, guide strip, and vibration damper.

2) Remove oil pump sprocket lock nut and washer. Remove crankshaft sprocket, oil pump drive chain, and oil pump sprocket. Remove crankshaft spacer, timing chain and crankshaft sprocket. Remove key and spacer from crankshaft.

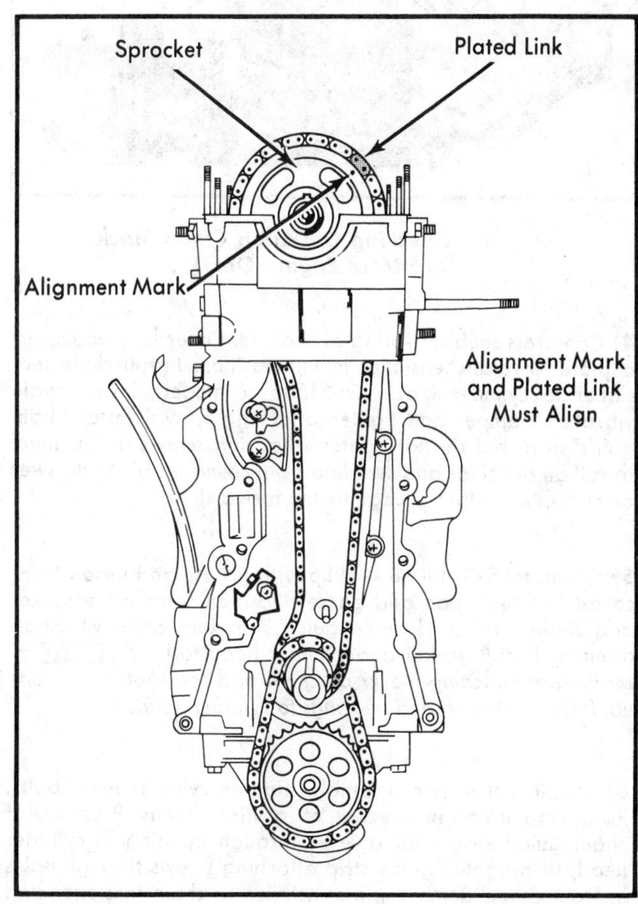

Fig. 8 Alignment Marks of Timing Chain & Sprockets

808(1300), 808(1600) & GLC (Cont.)

Installation – 1) On 1272 cc models, install timing chain guide strip, but do not tighten attaching screws. Install vibration damper. On all models, install spacer and key onto crankshaft. Place timing chain on crankshaft and camshaft sprockets with index marks aligned.

2) Align crankshaft and its sprocket keyway, then fit sprocket onto crankshaft. Install crankshaft spacer. Fit key on oil pump shaft. Install oil pump drive chain onto oil pump and crankshaft sprockets, align keyway and install assembly onto crankshaft and oil pump shafts.

3) On 1272 cc models, tighten oil pump sprocket nut and bend tab of lockwasher. Install oil baffle plate a spacer onto crankshaft. On all other models, check the slack of oil pump drive chain. If slack exceeds .157" (4 mm), install adjusting shims between cylinder block and oil pump body. Tighten oil pump sprocket nut and bend tab of lockwasher.

Fig. 9 Checking Oil Pump Chain Slack (1586 cc Engine Only)

4) Compress snubber spring of chain tensioner fully and insert a plate to retain tensioner in this position. Install chain tensioner to cylinder block. On 1586 cc models, install chain vibration damper and tighten attaching screws. Install chain guide strip, but do not tighten attaching screws at this time. Install oil deflector and seal into front cover. Install oil thrower on crankshaft with the edge facing forward.

5) On all models, fill oil seal lip with grease and install front cover. Install oil pan and gasket. Position camshaft sprocket and chain on top of chain guide strip and chain vibration damper. Install gasket and cylinder head to block. **NOTE** – *Make sure matching marks on chain and sprockets are aligned. Install camshaft and bearings to cylinder head.*

6) Install rocker arm assembly. Tighten cylinder head bolts. Rotate crankshaft in direction of rotation slightly. Press top of chain guide strip with a lever through opening in cylinder head, then tighten guide strip attaching screws through holes in front cover. Remove plate installed in chain tensioner and tensioner will be properly set. Install remaining components in reverse of removal procedure.

ENGINE OILING

ENGINE OILING SYSTEM

Oil is circulated under pressure by a rotor type pump. The pump is mounted on cylinder block inside the oil pan and is driven by crankshaft.

Crankcase Capacity – Approximately 3.2 quarts.

Oil Pressure – 50-64 psi (3.5-4.5 kg/cm²) @ 3000 RPM.

Oil Filter – Full flow cartridge.

Pressure Regulator Valve – Nonadjustable.

OIL PUMP

1) Check clearance between lobes of rotors with a feeler gauge. If clearance exceeds .010", replace both rotors.

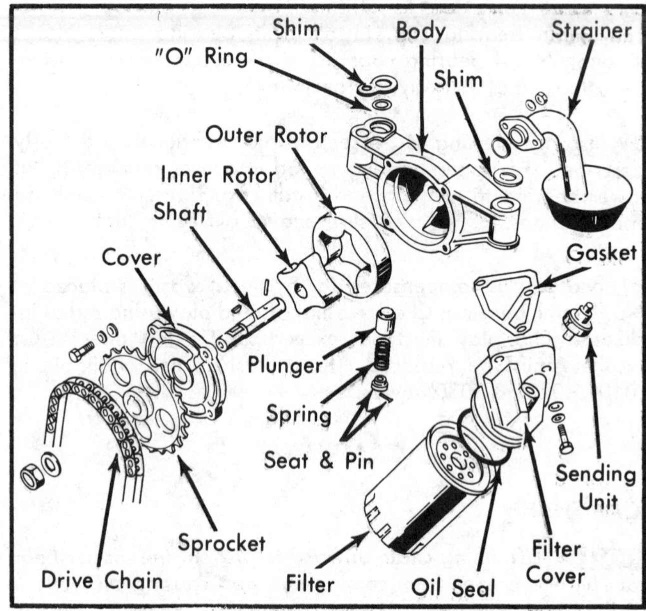

Fig. 10 1586 cc Oil Pump Assembly

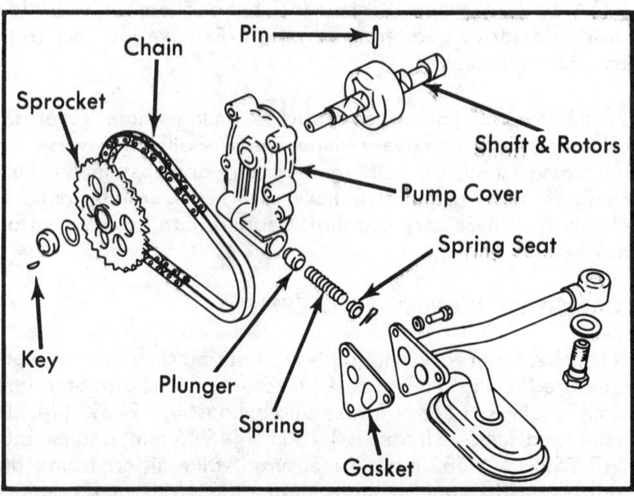

Fig. 11 1272 cc Oil Pump Assembly

808(1300), 808(1600) & GLC (Cont.)

2) Inspect clearance between outer rotor and pump body, using a feeler gauge. Maximum clearance is .012".

3) To check rotor ends, place a straightedge across pump body and measure clearance between rotor and straight edge, using a feeler gauge. Then place straightedge across cover and measure clearance between straight edge and cover.

Oil Pump Specifications

Application	Clearance In. (mm)
Rotor-to-Rotor	.002-.006 (.051-.152)
Rotor-to-Body	.006-.010 (.152-.254)
End Play	.002-.004 (.051-.102)

ENGINE COOLING

WATER PUMP

NOTE — *It may be necessary to remove radiator.*

Remove bolts mounting fan and pulley to water pump. Remove nuts and bolts holding water pump to timing chain cover. Remove alternator bracket and water pump.

Cooling System Capacity — 1272 cc 5.9 qts., 1586 cc 7.9 qts., B1600 models 6.8 qts.

Thermostat — Begins to open at 180°F (82°C) and is fully open at 203°F (95°C).

Radiator Cap — 13 psi.

ENGINE SPECIFICATIONS

GENERAL SPECIFICATIONS

Year	Displ.		Carburetor	HP at RPM	Torque (Ft. Lbs. at RPM)	Compr. Ratio	Bore		Stroke	
	cu. ins.	cc					in.	mm	in.	mm
1977										
808(1300) & GLC	77.6	1272	1x2-Bbl.	.....	.....	9.2:1	2.87	73	2.99	76
808(1600)	96.8	1586	1x2-Bbl.	.....	.....	8.6:1	3.07	78	3.27	83

VALVES

Engine & Valve	Head Diam. In. (mm)	Face Angle	Seat Angle	Seat Width In. (mm)	Stem Diameter In. (mm)	Stem Clearance In. (mm)	Valve Lift In. (mm)
1272 cc							
Intake	1.4173 (35.99)	45°	45°	.055 (1.4)	.314-.317 (7.98-8.05)	.0007-.0021 (.018-.053)	.....
Exhaust	1.2205 (31.00)	45°	45°	.055 (1.4)	.314-.317 (7.98-8.05)	.0007-.0023 (.018-.058)	.....
1586 cc							
Intake	1.6536 (42.00)	45°	45°	.055 (1.4)	.314-.317 (7.98-8.05)	.0007-.0021 (.018-.053)	.....
Exhaust	1.2992 (32.99)	45°	45°	.055 (1.4)	.314-.317 (7.98-8.05)	.0007-.0023 (.018-.058)	.....

① — Specification is ± .0039" (.099 mm).
② — Wear limit is .008" (.20 mm).

PISTONS, PINS, RINGS

Engine	PISTONS	PINS		RINGS		
	Clearance In. (mm)	① Piston Fit In. (mm)	Rod Fit In. (mm)	Rings	End Gap In. (mm)	Side Clearance In. (mm)
1272 cc & 1586 cc	.0021-.0026 (.057-.066)	−.0006 to +.0002 (−.014 to +.005)	.0004-.0012 (.01-.03)	No. 1	.008-.016 (.2-.4)	.0014-.0028 (.035-.070)
				No. 2	.008-.016 (.2-.4)	.0012-.0025 (.030-.064)
				Oil	.008-.016 (.2-.4)	.0012-.0024 (.030-.062)

① — In some instances it may be necessary to heat piston to insert pin.

808(1300), 808(1600) & GLC (Cont.)

ENGINE SPECIFICATIONS (Cont.)

CRANKSHAFT MAIN & CONNECTING ROD BEARINGS							
	MAIN BEARINGS				CONNECTING ROD BEARINGS		
Engine	Journal Diam. In. (mm)	Clearance In. (mm)	Thrust Bearing	Crankshaft End Play In. (mm)	Journal Diam. In. (mm)	Clearance In. (mm)	Side Play In. (mm)
1272 cc	2.4780-2.4786 (62.941-62.956)	.0012-.0024 (.030-.061)	No. 5	.003-.009 (.08-.23)	1.7693-1.7699 (44.940-44.955)	.0011-.0029 (.028-.074)	.004-.008 (.10-.20)
1586 cc	2.4780-2.4786 (62.939-62.954)	.0012-.0024 (.030-.061)	No. 5	.003-.009 (.08-.23)	2.0842-2.0848 (52.939-52.954)	.0011-.0030 (.028-.074)	.004-.008 (.10-.20)

VALVE SPRINGS			
Engine	Free Length In. (mm)	PRESSURE Lbs. @ In. (kg @ mm) Valve Closed	Valve Open
1272 cc			
Inner	1.449 (36.8)	20.9 @ 1.26 (9.5 @ 32.0)	.....
Outer	1.587 (40.3)	43.7 @ 1.319 (19.8 @ 33.5)	.....
1586 cc			
Inner	1.449 (36.8)	20.9 @ 1.26 (9.5 @ 32.0)	.....
Outer	1.469 (37.3)	31.4 @ 1.339 (14.25 @ 34.0)	.....

VALVE TIMING				
	INTAKE		EXHAUST	
Engine	Open (BTDC)	Close (ALDC)	Open (BLDC)	Close (ATDC)
1272	13°	50°	57°	6°
1586 Fed.	13°	54°	57°	10°
1586 Calif.	18°	49°	62	5°

CAMSHAFT			
Engine	Journal Diam. In. (mm)	Clearance In. (mm)①	Lobe Lift In. (mm)
1272 cc			
Front	1.6516-1.6522 (41.950-41.966)	.0014-.0030 (.035-.076)	.....
Center	1.6504-1.6510 (41.920-41.936)	.0026-.0042 (.065-.106)	.....
Rear	1.6516-1.6522 (41.950-41.966)	.0014-.0030 (.035-.076)	.....
1586 cc			
Front	1.7695-1.7701 (44.946-44.961)	.0007-.0027 (.019-.069)	.....
Center	1.7691-1.7697 (44.936-44.951)	.0011-.0031 (.029-.079)	.....
Rear	1.7695-1.7701 (44.946-44.961)	.0007-.0027 (.019-.069)	.....

① — End play is .001-.007" (.025-.178 mm).

TIGHTENING SPECIFICATIONS	
Application	Ft. Lbs. (mkg)
GLC	
Cylinder Head	
Cold	47-51 (6.5-7.0)
Hot	51-54 (7.0-7.5)
Main Bearing Cap	43-47 (6.0-6.5)
Connecting Rod Cap	29-33 (4.0-4.5)
Oil Pump Sprocket	22-25 (3.0-3.5)
Camshaft Sprocket	51-58 (7.0-8.0)
Crankshaft Pulley	80-87 (11.0-12.0)
Distributor Drive Gear	51-58 (7.0-8.0)
Intake Manifold	14-19 (1.9-2.6)
Exhaust Manifold	12-17 (1.6-2.3)
808 (1300 & 1600)	
Cylinder Head	
Cold	56-60 (7.7-8.3)
Hot	69-72 (9.5-10.0)
Main Bearing Cap	61-65 (8.4-9.0)
Connecting Rod Cap	36-40 (5.0-5.5)
Oil Pump Sprocket	22-25 (3.0-3.5)
Camshaft Sprocket	51-58 (7.0-8.0)
Crankshaft Pulley	101-108 (14.0-14.9)
Distributor Drive Gear	51-58 (7.0-8.0)
Intake Manifold	14-19 (1.9-2.6)
Exhaust Manifold	16-21 (2.2-2.9)

RX-3 SP, RX-4, COSMO & PICKUP

ENGINE CODING

ENGINE IDENTIFICATION

Engine identification number is stamped on the front engine housing behind the distributor. Engines are identified with code numbers as follows:

Engine Codes

Application	Code
RX-3	12A
RX-4 & Cosmo	13B

ENGINE REMOVAL

ENGINE REMOVAL

1) Disconnect negative battery cable and drain cooling system and engine oil. Disconnect primary wiring coupler and high tension wires from ignition coils. Disconnect wire at "B" terminal of alternator and remove coupler from rear of alternator. Disconnect coupler from vacuum control valve (manual transmission).

2) Disconnect bullet connector from choke heater lead of carburetor. Remove couplers from water temperature switch,

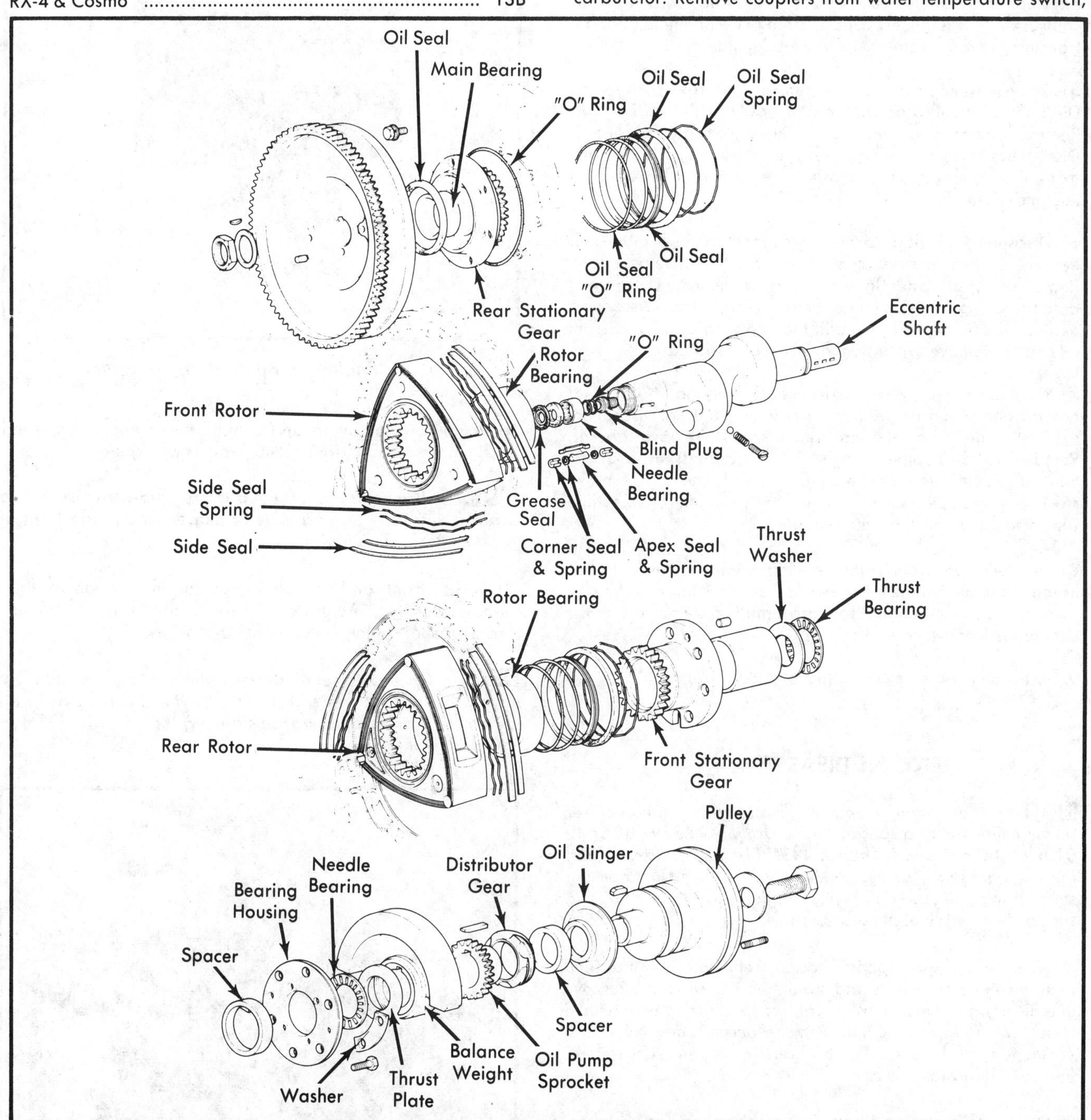

Fig. 1 Exploded View of Rotors & Eccentric Shaft Assembly

vacuum switch (automatic transmission), A/C solenoid valve, and from deceleration control valve.

3) Remove connector from EGR solenoid (California). Disconnect couplers to transmission at rear of engine, from oil thermo sensor (except California), and from oil level sensor lead. Disconnect connector from water temperature gauge unit.

4) Remove positive cable from "B" terminal and ignition switch wire from "S" terminal of starting motor. Disconnect vacuum sensing hose from No. 2 vacuum switch (California). Remove air cleaner assembly. Pull couplers from idle switch and air control valve. Disconnect coupler from richer solenoid (manual transmission) and from power valve solenoid

5) Remove fuel line and fuel return line from carburetor. Disconnect accelerator and choke cables from carburetor. Remove sub-zero starting assist hose (except California). Disconnect vacuum sensing hose from vacuum line (automatic transmission), and vacuum sensing line for power brakes from inlet manifold.

6) Disconnect air hose to heat exchanger at inlet manifold. Remove A/C compressor, cooling fan and fan drive assembly. Remove upper and lower radiator hoses. Disconnect automatic transmission fluid lines at radiator. Disconnect heater hoses from radiator and rear housing and hoses from oil cooler. Remove expansion tank cap and radiator.

7) Remove secondary air line from heat exchanger to thermal reactor and pipe from exchanger to inlet manifold. Disconnect exhaust pipe from thermal reactor and remove gasket. Remove exhaust pipe hanger from transmission bracket. Remove clutch release cylinder from clutch housing. Remove starting motor. Remove transmission-to-engine bolts, while supporting transmission with suitable jack.

8) Remove nuts from right and left engine mounts. Install lifting sling on engine hanger brackets and hoist slightly to take up slack. Pull engine forward until it clears clutch shaft. Lift engine from vehicle.

9) To install engine, reverse removal procedure.

ENGINE DISASSEMBLY

NOTE — *To simplify engine disassembly, manufacturer recommends use of a special engine stand (49 0839 000 or 49 0107 680A) and special hanger (49 1114 005) for supporting the front housing. See Fig. 2* Also note that this front housing support may be used on previous engines (where rear housing support units were previously used).

1) Remove oil hose support bracket from front housing, then mount engine on stand and front housing support. Remove engine hanger bracket from front cover. Disconnect vacuum hoses, air hoses and wiring. Remove deceleration valve and vacuum control valve. Remove air pump and drive belt. Remove alternator and belt.

2) Disconnect metering oil pump connecting rod and oil tubes. Remove inlet manifold and carburetor as an assembly. Remove manifold gasket and "O" rings. Remove thermal reactor (exhaust manifold), distributor, engine mounts and oil filter assembly. Remove eccentric shaft pulley for compressor.

NOTE — *On engines equipped with manual transmission, attach braking tool (49 1881 060) to flywheel. On engines with automatic transmission, attach stopping tool (49 1881 055) to counterweight.*

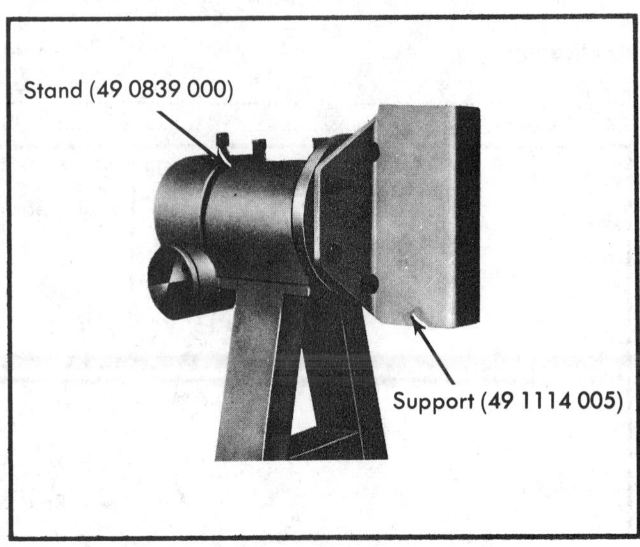

Fig. 2 Engine Stand & Hanger Support

3) Remove water pump and gasket. Invert engine on stand and remove oil pan, gasket and strainer with gasket.

NOTE — *When removing oil pan, pry upward using two screwdrivers, one on each side of oil pan and just in front of tapered corners on flywheel end.*

4) Mark front and rear housings for installation in their original positions. Return engine to upright position. Unscrew eccentric shaft pulley bolt and remove pulley.

NOTE — *On engines equipped with manual transmission, attach braking tool (49 1881 060) to flywheel. On engines with automatic transmission, attach stopping tool (49 1881 055) to counterweight.*

Fig. 3 Removing Sprocket & Chain from Engine

RX-3 SP, RX-4, COSMO & PICKUP (Cont.)

5) Turn engine so that front end is up. Remove front cover with gasket. Remove "O" ring from oil passage on front housing. Slide distributor drive gear off shaft. Remove chain adjuster. Remove oil pump sprocket lock washer and nut. Slide oil pump sprocket and eccentric shaft sprocket and drive chain off shafts simultaneously. *See Fig. 3.* Remove keys from shafts. Slide balance weight, thrust washer and needle bearing off shaft.

6) Remove bearing housing, needle bearing, spacer and thrust plate from shaft. Remove oil pump. Return engine to upright position.

NOTE — *On engines equipped with manual transmission, attach braking tool (49 1881 060) to flywheel. On engines with automatic transmission, attach stopping tool (49 1881 055) to counterweight.*

7) Remove clutch cover assembly and clutch disc. Straighten tab on lock washer and remove flywheel nut using special tool (49 0820 035). Remove the flywheel using puller (49 0823 300A or 49 0839 305A).

8) If equipped with automatic transmission, remove counterweight. To do so, remove drive plate. Straighten tab of lock washer and remove counterweight nut using special tool (49 0820 035). Remove counterweight, using puller (49 0839 305A).

Fig. 4 Loosening Sequence of Tension Bolts

9) Turn rear of engine upward. Loosen tension bolts in sequence shown in *Fig. 4,* doing so in two or three steps. Remove bolts and lift rear housing off shaft. Remove any seals stuck to rotor sliding surface of rear housing, and replace them in original positions. Remove and discard two sealing rubbers and two "O" rings from rear side of rear rotor housing.

10) Attach dowel puller (49 0813 215A). Pull tubular dowels *(See Fig. 5)* from rear rotor housing. Hold housing with hand to prevent it from turning or pulling upward. Lift rear rotor housing away from rotor, being careful not to drop apex seals off rear rotor. Remove and discard two sealing rubbers and two "O" rings from front side of rear rotor housing.

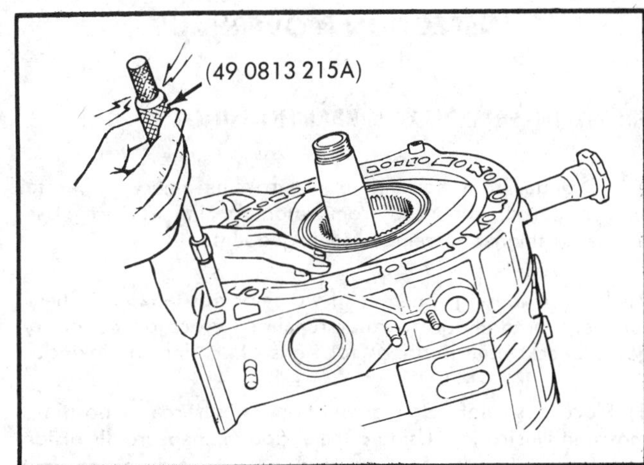

Fig. 5 Extracting Tubular Dowels from Engine

11) Remove side pieces, apex seals and springs from rear rotor and store in order for reassembly. Remove all corner seals, corner seal springs, side seals and side seal springs and store in order for later reassembly.

12) Remove rear rotor from eccentric shaft and place it upside down on a clean sheet of cloth. Remove seals and springs from remaining side of rear rotor and store in order for reassembly.

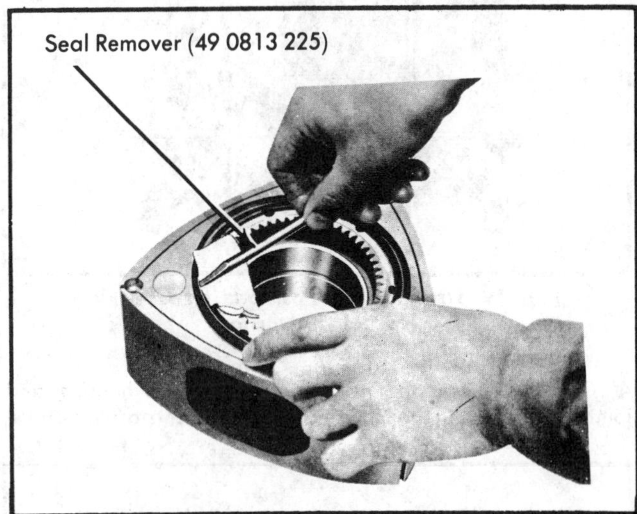

Fig. 6 Prying Oil Seal from Rotor

13) Mark each rotor as to front or rear. Remove oil seals from rear rotor using suitable prying tool (49 0813 225), *Fig. 6,* being careful not to damage oil seal lip.

NOTE — *Do not exert strong force at any one point in removing seal. Mark rear oil seal springs of each rotor to aid in repositioning them upon reassembly.*

14) Holding intermediate housing down by hand, pull tubular dowel from intermediate housing, using dowel puller (49 0813 215A). *See Fig. 5.* Lift intermediate housing from shaft. To do so, hold housing up off front housing, while helper pushes upward on eccentric shaft. Lift out eccentric shaft.

15) Repeat procedures **10)** through **14)** to remove front rotor housing and rotor assembly.

RX-3 SP, RX-4, COSMO & PICKUP (Cont.)

INSPECTION & OVERHAUL

FRONT, INTERMEDIATE & REAR HOUSINGS

1) To clean front housing, use extra fine emery paper to remove carbon deposits from rotor running surface. Use ketone or thinner to remove sealing agent.

2) Inspect housing for signs of water or gas leakage. Check for wear or damage to rotor running surface or stationary gear. Check main bearings for signs of scoring or flaking.

3) Place a straightedge across housing surface in positions shown in illustration. Using a feeler gauge, measure distortion of front housing. Replace or reface housing if distortion limit of .0016" (.04 mm) is exceeded, *(Fig. 7)*.

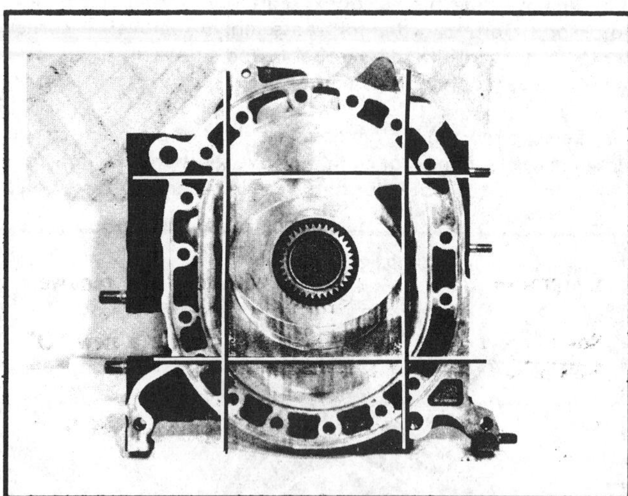

Fig. 7 Straightedge Positions for Checking Housing Distortion

4) Check for wear on rotor sliding surfaces of housing and joint surfaces with rotor housing. Measurements are made using a dial indicator, *Fig. 8*. If wear exceeds .0039" (.10 mm), reface or replace housing.

Fig. 8 Measuring Housing Wear with a Dial Indicator

NOTE – *Side housings (front, intermediate and rear housings) can be reused by grinding them, if the required finish can be maintained.*

5) Measure inner diameter of main bearing and outer diameter of bearing journal on eccentric shaft. Standard clearance is .0016-.0028" (.04-.07 mm). If clearance exceeds .0039" (.10 mm), replace bearing or eccentric shaft.

6) To replace main bearing, remove stationary gear retaining bolts. Drive stationary gear, with bearing, out of housing using a suitable mandrel (49 0813 235).

7) Place stationary gear in a press, use same mandrel and press main bearing out of stationary gear. Install new bearing while aligning tang of bearing with slot of stationary gear. Press bearing into gear until adapter of mandrel just contacts stationary gear flange. Drive stationary gear into housing with same mandrel. Align dowel pin on housing with slot in gear flange, *(Fig. 9)*. Tighten stationary gear retaining bolts.

NOTE – *When installing rear main bearing, check condition of "O" ring and replace if necessary. Apply sealing agent on stationary gear flange prior to installing it on rear housing. Align pin and slot.*

Fig. 9 Stationary Gear Slot & Dowel Alignment

ROTOR HOUSING, INTERMEDIATE HOUSING, & ROTOR

ROTOR HOUSINGS

1) To clean housing, wipe off sealing agent or carbon in rotor running surface with a rag and ketone or thinner. Remove rust deposits in water cooling passages.

2) Inspect for cracks or damage to chromium plated surface. Check for signs of gas or water leakage. Housing must be replaced if any of these conditions exist.

3) Place a straightedge across sealing surface of rotor housing and check for distortion, using a feeler gauge. If distortion exceeds .0016" (.04 mm), replace housing. See *Fig. 10*.

RX-3 SP, RX-4, COSMO & PICKUP (Cont.)

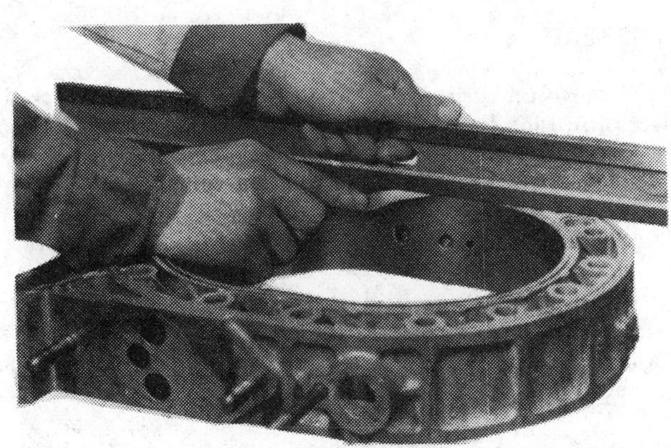

Fig. 10 Measuring Rotor Housing for Distortion

4) Check rotor housing thickness at points A, B, C, and D in *Fig. 11*. If micrometer readings vary between point A and minimum value for B, C, and D by more than .0024" (.06 mm), replace rotor housing.

NOTE – *This excessive clearance would indicate a possibility of gas or water leakage.*

ROTORS

1) Combustion condition of rotor can be determined by analyzing color of combustion area before cleaning. General color of combustion area should be brown.

2) Combustion is correct if leading side area of rotor combustion area is brown and trailing side is a blackish color. Check side surface of rotor for signs of gas leakage.

3) Inspect oil seals and replace if necessary. Remove carbon from rotor with fine emery paper. Remove carbon from seal grooves with a carbon remover. Wash rotor in a cleaning solution and blow dry, with compressed air. Inspect rotor for wear or damage and check internal gear for cracking or chipped teeth.

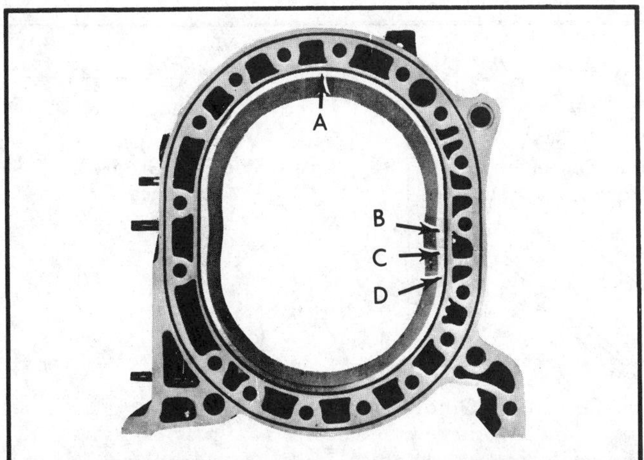

Fig. 11 Rotor Housing Thickness Check Points

4) Measure width of rotor at three points around edge. Subtract maximum rotor width from width of rotor housing at point A, *(Fig. 11)*. Difference should be within .0039-.0083" (.10-.21 mm). If clearance is excessive, replace rotor assembly. If less than specified, internal gear has probably come out. Strike internal gear lightly with plastic hammer and remeasure clearance.

5) Measure inner diameter of rotor bearing and outside diameter of rotor bearing journal on eccentric shaft. Replace rotor bearing if clearance exceeds .0039" (.10 mm). *See Rotor Bearing Replacement*.

OIL SEALS

ROTOR OIL SEAL

With oil seal installed in rotor, measure contact lip width of seal. Seal must be replaced if contact width exceeds .031" (.8 mm). Measure seal protrusion *(See Fig. 12)* and replace seal spring if protrusion is less than .020" (.5 mm).

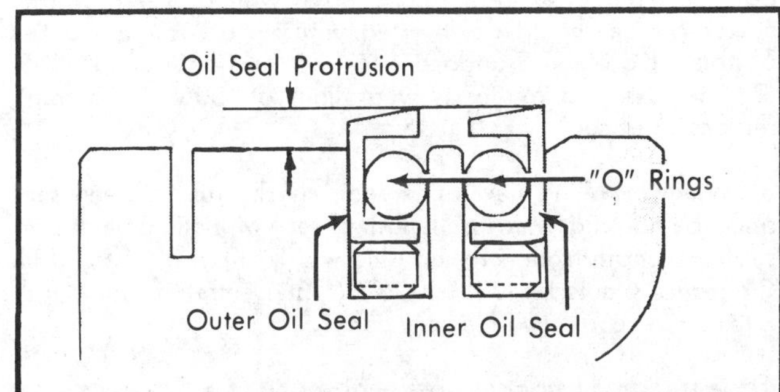

Fig. 12 Measuring Point of Oil Seal Protrusion

ROTOR BEARING REPLACEMENT

Place rotor bearing on support so internal gear is facing downward. Using rotor bearing replacer (49 0813 240) without adapter ring, press bearing out of rotor, *(Fig. 13)*. Clean bearing bore with emery paper if necessary. Place rotor on support with internal gear upward. Place a new rotor bearing so slot in rotor bore is in line with bearing lug. Press new bearing (using tool without adaptor), until bearing is flush with rotor boss.

Fig. 13 Pressing Rotor Bearing from Rotor

RX-3 SP, RX-4, COSMO & PICKUP (Cont.)

APEX SEAL

1) Clean all carbon from apex seal and spring with a cleaning solution (not emery paper). Measure height of apex seal with a micrometer (see illustration). Replace seal if height is less than .275" (7.0 mm).

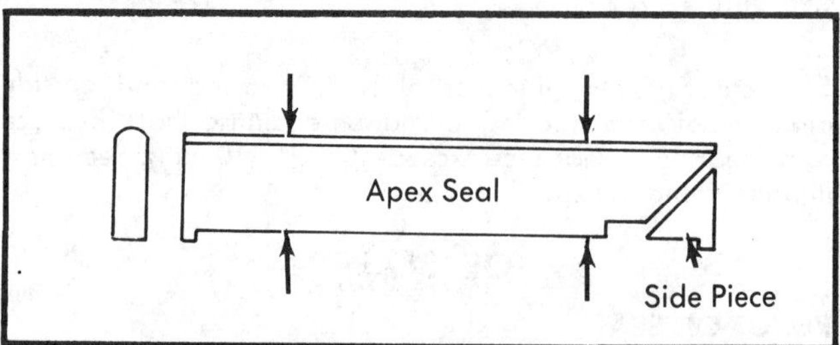

Fig. 14 Measuring Apex Seal Height

2) Check gap between apex seal and groove. To check gap, place apex seal in its respective groove on rotor and measure gap between apex seal and groove with a feeler gauge. Feeler gauge should be inserted until tip of gauge reaches bottom of groove. Standard clearance is .0020-.0035" (.05-.09 mm). If gap exceeeds wear limit of .0059" (.15 mm), replace apex seal.

3) When installing new apex seal, check gap between seal and side housing. Measure length of seal with micrometer and subtract length from rotor housing width at point A, *(Fig. 11)*. Clearance should be .0051-.0067" (.13-.17 mm). If seal length is excessive, correct with emery paper.

4) Be sure free height of apex seal spring *(Fig. 15)*, is at least .22" (5.5 mm) on RX-3 models and .15" (3.8 mm) on other models.

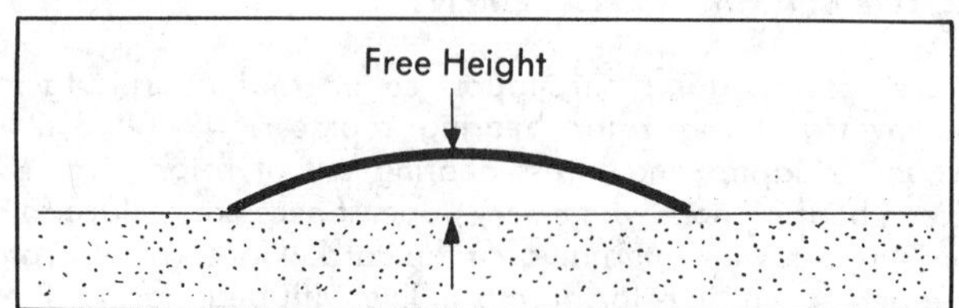

Fig. 15 Measuring Free Height of Apex Seal Spring

SIDE SEAL

1) Remove all carbon from side seal and spring. Check side seal protrusion from rotor surface, and confirm free movement by pressing with finger. Protrusion should be more than .02" (.5 mm). Check gap between side seal and groove with a feeler gauge. Standard gap is .0016-.0028" (.04-.07 mm). If wear limit of .004" (.10 mm) is measured, replace side seal.

2) Check gap between side seal and corner seal with seals installed on rotor. Insert feeler gauge between end of side seal (against rotating direction of rotor) and the corner seal. If gap exceeds .016" (.4 mm), replace side seal.

3) When side seal is replaced, adjust gap between side seal and corner seal by grinding one end of side seal along round shape of corner seal, using a fine file. Make gap .002-.006" (.05-.15 mm).

CORNER SEAL

1) Clean carbon from corner seal. Check corner seal protrusion from rotor surface, and check free movement by pressing with finger. Protrusion should be more than .02" (.5 mm).

2) Check gap between corner seal and seal groove. Gap limit is .0031" (.08 mm). A gap this large indicates uneven wear of corner seal groove caused by dirt entering engine (due to damaged or clogged air cleaner).

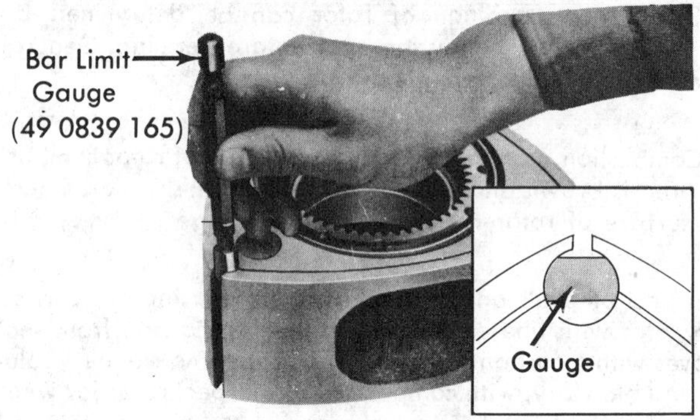

Fig. 17 Checking Corner Seal Groove Measurement

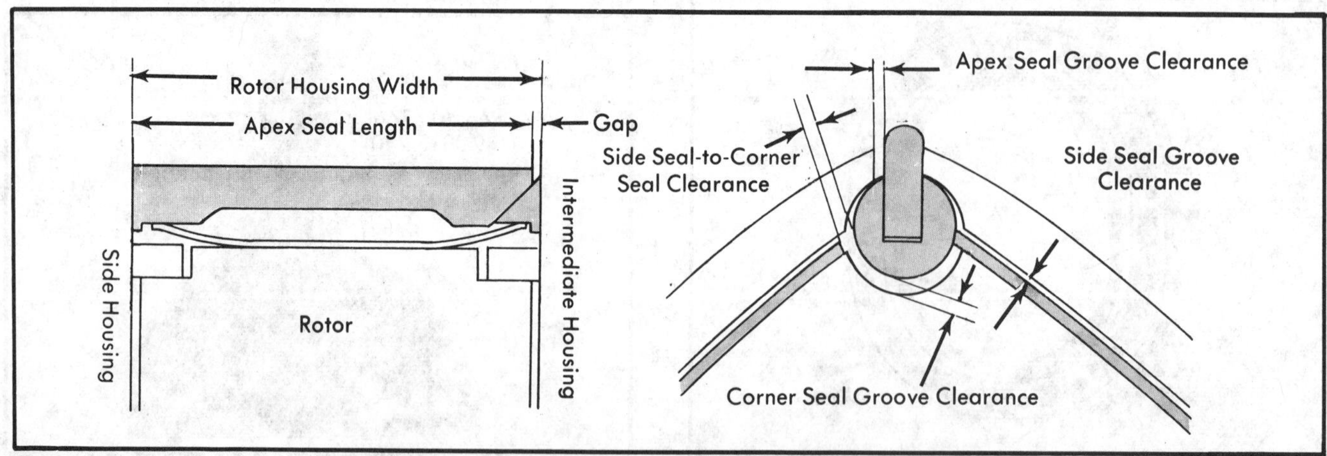

Fig. 16 Measuring Clearance of Apex, Side & Corner Seals

RX-3 SP, RX-4, COSMO & PICKUP (Cont.)

3) Extent of corner seal groove wear is determined by using special Bar Limit Gauge (49 0839 165), and is classified according to the following:

Neither End of Gauge Goes Into Groove – Indicates that gap conforms to specifications.

"Go" End of Gauge Goes Into Groove – Indicates that gap is more than standard, but less than wear limit. In this case replace corner seal, *(Fig. 17)*.

Both Ends of Gauge ("Go" and "No Go") Go in Groove – Indicates gap exceeds wear limit of .0031" (.8 mm). Replace rotor.

ECCENTRIC SHAFT MAIN & ROTOR BEARINGS

ECCENTRIC SHAFT

1) Thoroughly clean eccentric shaft in a suitable cleaning solution and blow out oil passages with compressed air. Inspect shaft for scratching or scoring of bearing journals and possible blocked oil passages.

2) Check rotor bearing clearance by measuring inner diameter of the rotor bearing and outer diameter of the eccentric shaft rotor journal. Clearance should be .0016-.0031" (.04-.08 mm). Replace the bearing if clearance exceeds .0039" (.10 mm). Replace eccentric shaft if journal diameters are under specified limits.

3) Place eccentric shaft in two "V" blocks. Mount a dial indicator and check runout of both ends by rotating shaft slowly. If runout exceeds .0024" (.06 mm), replace shaft.

4) Oil passages in eccentric shaft are sealed by a blind plug in rear of shaft. Inspect plug for possible oil leakage. If leakage is detected, remove plug with an Allen wrench and install new "O" ring. Tighten plug.

5) Inspect needle bearings in end of shaft for wear or damage. Check for spring weakness, stuck, or damaged steel ball at the oil jets. Inspect front needle bearing, bearing housing, and thrust plate for wear or damage. Inspect front and rear oil seals for leaks, replace as necessary.

ENGINE ASSEMBLY

OIL SEALS

1) Place rotor on rubber pad or cloth. Install oil seal springs in their respective grooves on rotors, with each edge of spring fitted in stopper hole. Ensure oil seal springs have been painted in cream or blue color: cream colored springs must be placed on front faces of both rotors and blue springs on rear faces of rotors. When installing, painted side of spring must face oil seal (upward), *Fig. 18*.

2) Insert new "O" ring in each oil seal. Install inner oil seal to each side of rotor as follows: Position oil seal to groove so square edge of spring fits in stopper notch of oil seal. Press into position by using a used inner oil seal so lip of inner oil seal sinks into position approximately .016" (.4 mm) below surface of rotor.

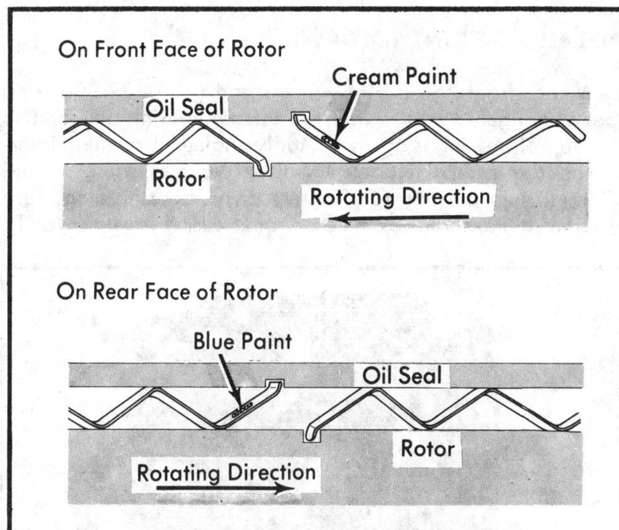

Fig. 18 Installing Oil Seal Spring on Rotor

3) Install outer oil seal so square edge of spring fits in stopper notch of oil seal. Push head of oil seal in position slowly with fingers. **NOTE** – *Take care not to deform lip of oil seal.* Apply sufficient lubricant to each oil seal and groove, and confirm smooth movement of each seal by pressing head of seals. Check oil seal protrusion. *See Rotor Oil Seal Replacement.*

APEX, CORNER & SIDE SEALS

NOTE – *Before installing apex seal, cut the assist piece with a knife to a length of .08-.10" (2.0-2.8 mm). Peel off paper and install assist piece on apex seal, Fig. 19.*

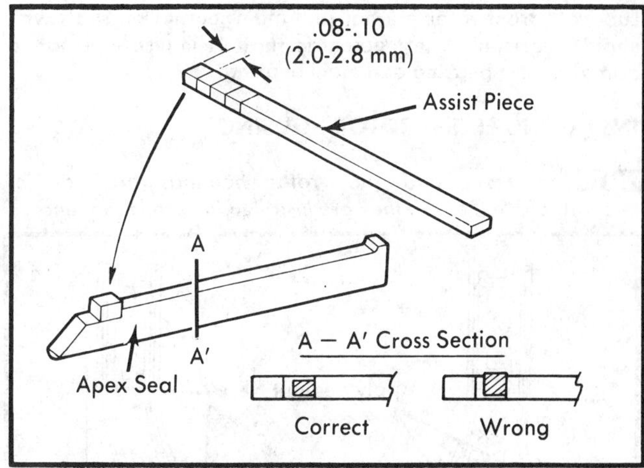

Fig. 19 Installing Assist Piece on Apex Seal

1) Position apex seals, without springs, and side pieces into their respective grooves so that each side piece rests on rear side of each rotor. Place corner seals and springs into their respective grooves, then position side seals and springs in proper grooves.

RX-3 SP, RX-4, COSMO & PICKUP (Cont.)

2) Apply engine lubricant to each spring. Ensure smooth movement of each spring. Check seal protusion, as described previously. Invert rotor and install seals on other side of rotor.

INSTALLING FRONT ROTOR

1) Mount front housing on work stand (49 0839 000) and special hanger (49 1114 005). Turn front housing on stand so that top of housing is upward. Apply engine lubricant to internal gear of rotor. Hold apex seals in place by using the old "O" ring and position rotor assembly on front housing. Turn housing so that sliding surface of front housing faces upward.

Fig. 20 Positioning Rotor Apex for Reassembly

2) Mesh internal gear and stationary gear so that one of the rotor apexes is set to any one of the four positions as illustrated. Remove old "O" ring. *See Fig. 20.*

NOTE — *Take care not to drop corner seals into ports.*

INSTALLING ECCENTRIC SHAFT

Lubricate front rotor journal and main journal on shaft with engine lubricant. Insert eccentric shaft being careful not to damage rotor bearing and main bearing.

INSTALLING FRONT ROTOR HOUSING

NOTE — *Front and rear rotor housings are not interchangeable. Be sure they are installed in correct sequence.*

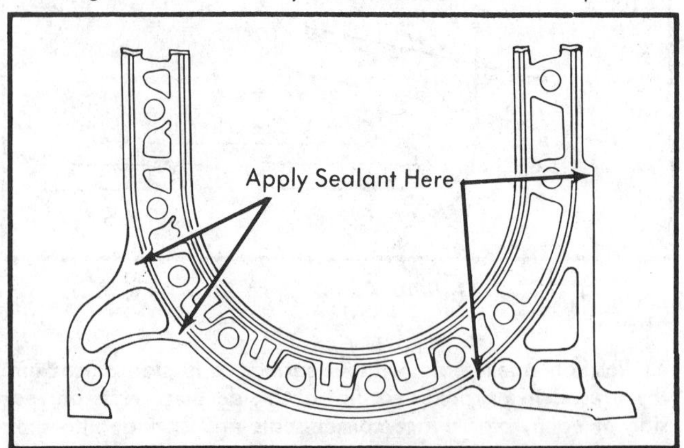

Fig. 21 Applying Sealing Agent to Rotor Assembly

1) Apply sealing agent to front side of front rotor housing in areas shown in *Fig. 21*. Do not use cooling system sealers.

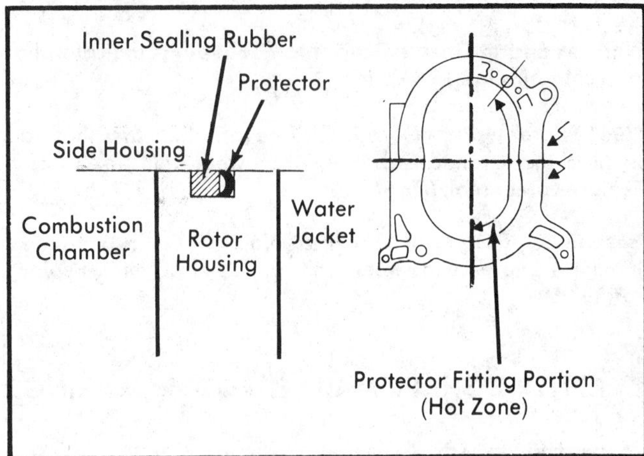

Fig. 22 Installing Protectors for Inner Sealing Rubbers

2) To provide greater durability to sealing rubbers, install a protector behind each inner sealing rubber, (*Fig. 22*). Install new "O" ring, sealing rubbers and protector in front side of rotor housing. Apply a light coating of petroleum jelly to hold them in place.

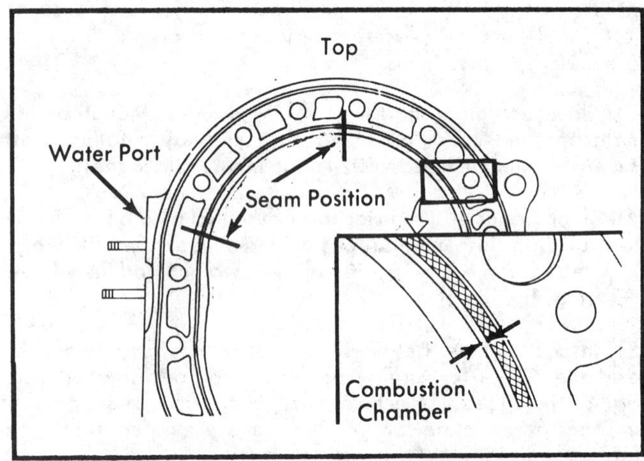

Fig. 23 Positioning Inner Sealing Rubber

NOTE — *Inner sealing rubber is square type. The wider white line of sealing rubber should face toward combustion chamber and seam of rubber should be placed as shown in Fig. 23.* Do not stretch sealing rubbers.

3) Invert front rotor housing, being careful of seals, and install it on front housing. Apply engine lubricant to dowels and insert them through front rotor housing into front housing. Install new "O" rings, sealing rubbers and protector to rear side of front housing.

4) Insert apex seal springs, confirming spring direction, *Fig 16*. Install corner seal springs and corner seals in their respective grooves. Install side seal springs and side seals. Fit side pieces to their original positions. Apply engine oil to all seals. Apply sealant to rear side of front rotor housing in areas shown in *Fig. 21*. Apply engine oil to sliding surfaces of front rotor housing.

RX-3 SP, RX-4, COSMO & PICKUP (Cont.)

INSTALLING INTERMEDIATE HOUSING

Turn front housing and rotor assembly so that top of housing is upward. Pull eccentric shaft outward approximately 1.0" (25 mm), but not more than 1.5" (38 mm). Rotate eccentric shaft until eccentric portion points to 2 o'clock position. Install intermediate housing over eccentric shaft and turn engine so that rear of engine is upward.

INSTALLING REAR ROTOR & HOUSING

Use same procedures up to *Intermediate Housing* when installing rear rotor and rotor housing.

INSTALLING REAR HOUSING

Position engine with rear end upward. Apply sufficient lubricant onto stationary gear and main bearing. Install rear housing onto rear rotor housing, and turn rear rotor slightly to engage rear housing stationary gear with rear rotor internal gear.

TIGHTENING TENSION BOLTS

Place a new sealing washer on each tension bolt and oil threads of each bolt. Refer to illustration and tighten bolts in sequence shown in *Fig. 24*. Tighten bolts in steps until final torque setting of 23-27 ft. lbs. (3.2-3.8 mkg) is reached. After tightening, turn eccentric shaft and make sure rotation is light and smooth.

Fig. 24 Tightening Sequence of Tension Bolts

FLYWHEEL COUNTERWEIGHT INSTALLATION

With Man. Trans. – **1)** Apply lubricant to oil seal in rear housing. Mount flywheel to rear end of eccentric shaft so that key fits into flywheel keyway. Apply sealing agent to both sides of flywheel lock washer, and place washer in position. Fit lock nut by fingers. Hold flywheel with suitable ring gear brake tool (49 1881 060) and tighten lock nut to 289-362 ft. lbs. (40-50 mkg). Bend up lock tabs on washer.

2) Hold clutch disc in position with clutch disc centering tool (49 0813 310). Mount clutch cover and pressure plate assembly on flywheel and align the "0" marks of clutch cover and flywheel. Install 4 standard and 2 reamer bolts finger tight. To avoid distortion of pressure plate cover, tighten bolts in steps, a few turns at a time, until all are tight. Torque bolts to 13-20 ft. lbs. (1.8-2.7 mkg).

With Auto. Trans. – Fit key, lock washer and lock nut on eccentric shaft as described for Man. Trans. vehicles. Hold counterweight with suitable tool (49 1881 055) and tighten lock nut to 289-362 ft. lbs. (40-50 mkg). Bend tab of lock washer and attach drive plate on counterweight.

ECCENTRIC SHAFT END-THRUST ADJUSTMENT

1) Turn engine so front is up. Install thrust plate with chamfer downward, and slide spacer and needle bearing on eccentric shaft. Lubricate shaft and bearings and install bearing housing.

NOTE – *If bearing housing has not been removed, use care that center of needle bearing in bearing housing comes to center of eccentric shaft and that spacer is seated to thrust plate.*

2) Lubricate and install needle bearing, thrust washer, and balance weight on shaft. Install keys in oil pump and eccentric shaft keyways. Place oil pump drive chain on oil pump sprocket and eccentric shaft sprocket, and install sprockets on shafts.

3) Install key in eccentric shaft. Install distributor drive gear, with "F" mark on gear, facing front of engine. Install eccentric shaft pulley on shaft. Use new washer and tighten pulley bolt to 54-69 ft. lbs. (7.5-9.5 mkg).

Fig. 25 Measuring Eccentric Shaft End Play with a Dial Indicator

4) Turn engine so top is upward. Attach a dial indicator on the flywheel or counterweight so it contacts rear housing. Move flywheel or counterweight back and forth. Standard end play is .0016-.0028" (.04-.07 mm). If end play is more than .0035" (.09 mm) grind spacer on surface plate with

RX-3 SP, RX-4, COSMO & PICKUP (Cont.)

emery paper or install thinner spacer. If end play is less than .0016" (.04 mm), install thicker spacer.

5) Oversize spacers are available in four oversizes from .3181" to .3150" (8.08 mm to 8.00 mm) and are identified by stamped letter "X", "Y", "V", and "Z" respectively. When spacer has been installed, recheck end play.

NOTE – *If end play is below specified amount, spacer thickness is too small; if end play is beyond specifications, spacer is too thick.*

6) When end play is within specifications, remove eccentric shaft pulley and proceed with engine assembly.

INSTALLING FRONT COVER & ECCENTRIC SHAFT PULLEY

Turn engine so front is upward. Remove eccentric shaft pulley. Tighten oil pump sprocket nut and bend tab of lock washer. Place chain adjuster in position and tighten attaching nuts. Check that plunger extends .47" (12 mm). *(See Fig. 27).* If measurement is less, replace adjuster or chain. Install new "O" ring on front housing oil passage and install guide plate over chain adjuster. Install front cover and gasket on front housing. Lubricate oil seal in front cover. Install eccentric shaft pulley, using a new washer. Torque to 54-69 ft. lbs. (7.5-9.5 mkg).

INSTALLING OIL STRAINER & OIL PAN

Invert engine so bottom of engine is up. Install oil strainer gasket and strainer on front housing. Cut off excess gaskets along mounting surface of oil pan. Apply sealant to joints of each housing. Place gasket and oil pan in position and torque bolts to 5-7 ft. lbs. (.7-1.0 mkg) evenly.

INSTALLING WATER PUMP

Turn engine upright, position gasket and water pump on front housing and tighten attaching bolts. **NOTE** – *For further information on cooling system components, see Cooling System in this article.*

INSTALLING DISTRIBUTOR

Rotate eccentric shaft until yellow mark (leading timing mark) on pulley aligns with indicator pin on front cover. Align notch on distributor housing with punch mark on driven gear. Insert distributor so that lock bolt is located in center of its slot; then engage distributor gears. Rotate distributor to the right until contact points close. Then, turn left and stop when contact points just begin to separate. Tighten lock nut and install rotor and cap.

INSTALLING EXTERNAL COMPONENTS

Install thermal reactor, inlet manifold with carburetor, alternator and drive belt, air pump and drive belt, oil filter assembly and all other external components. Before removing engine from stand, install engine hanger bracket to front cover.

ENGINE OILING

Crankcase Capacity
RX-3 SP – 5.5 qts. with filter change
RX-4, Cosmo & Pickup – 5.3 qts. without filter change

Oil Filter – Full-flow, disposable cartridge-type filter mounted on rear housing.

Normal Oil Pressure – 14-54 psi at engine idle speed; 64-79 psi at 3000 RPM.

Pressure Regulator Valve – Mounted in rear housing, valve regulates oil pressure at high RPM. Valve opens to release oil pressure. If oil pressure is less than normal, check regulator valve piston for wear and ensure that spring free length is 1.83" (46.4 mm).

ENGINE OILING SYSTEM

Engine oiling system is forced circulation utilizing a two rotor type oil pump. Oil pump is mounted on front housing and is chain driven through eccentric shaft. A full-flow oil filter is mounted on rear housing. An oil metering pump, pressure regulator valve and an oil cooler in radiator are also employed.

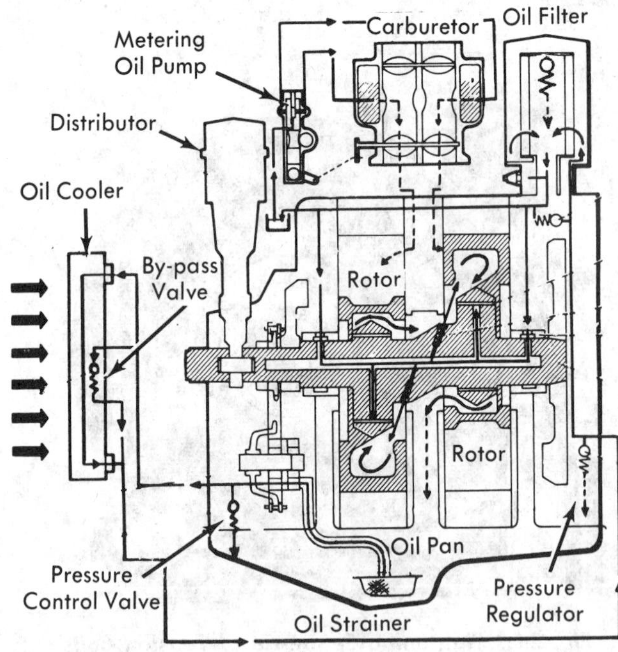

Fig. 26 Cutaway View of Engine Oiling System

OIL PUMP

NOTE – *Oil pump is mounted on front engine housing and must be checked or overhauled with front engine cover removed.*

1) With front engine cover removed, check chain adjuster. If it extends more than .47" (12 mm) from housing, replace chain or adjuster *Fig. 27.*

RX-3 SP, RX-4, COSMO & PICKUP (Cont.)

Fig. 27 Measuring Oil Pump Drive Chain Tensioner Extension

2) With oil pump removed, remove snap ring, rear rotors and key from shaft. Remove middle plate lock screw and middle plate.

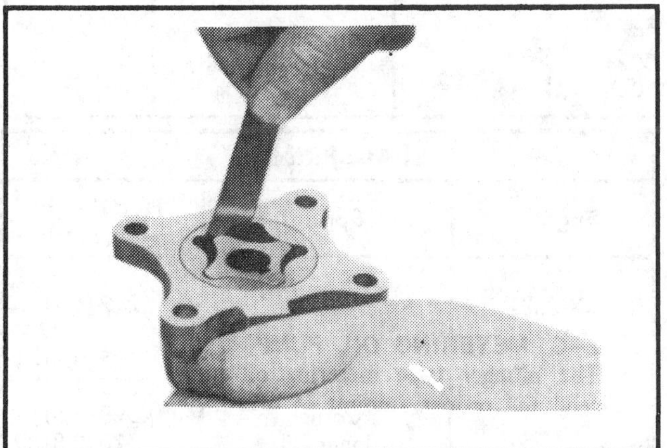

Fig. 28 Measuring Rotor Lobe Clearance

3) Insert a feeler gauge between lobes of inner and outer rotors and check clearance *(Fig. 28)*. If beyond .006" (.15 mm), replace both rotors.

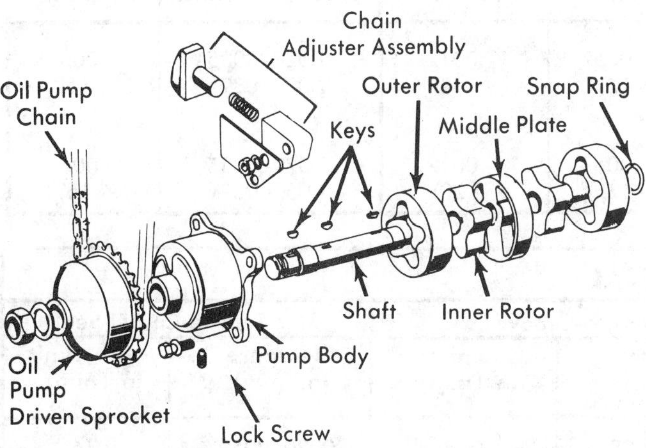

Fig. 29 Exploded View of Oil Pump Assembly

4) Check clearance between outer rotor and pump housing with a feeler gauge. If clearance exceeds .012" (.30 mm), replace rotors or housing.

5) Place a straightedge across pump mounting surface and check rotor end play with a feeler gauge. If beyond .006" (.15 mm), correct pump body or replace rotors.

6) To assemble oil pump, reverse disassembly procedure. Install oil pump and tighten bolts. Install sprockets and chain as previously outlined. *See Eccentric Shaft Endthrust Adjustment.*

METERING OIL PUMP

Metering oil pump regulates amount of oil pumped to float chamber of carburetor. The oil enters combustion chamber with air/fuel mixture to lubricate seals within chamber. Amount of oil increases as engine RPM increases and the control lever on metering pump is actuated by a rod connected to throttle lever. To check amount of oil discharge proceed as follows:

1) Disconnect connecting rod, then disconnect oil lines at carburetor. Start engine and adjust idle to 2000 RPM. Once oil flow from hoses becomes steady, measure volume discharged. Pump should discharge .068-.085 oz. (2.0-2.5 cc) in six minutes.

NOTE — *As carburetor will not be receiving oil during test, add a small amount of clean oil to carburetor to provide proper lubrication during testing.*

2) To adjust oil metering pump, turn the adjusting screw clockwise to increase flow or counterclockwise to decrease flow. One complete turn will change oil discharge flow by .0068 ounces for six minutes of operation. Make sure lock nut of adjustment screw is locked, then recheck metering oil pump discharge rate.

ENGINE COOLING

Thermostat — Wax Pellet Type
RX-3 SP, RX-4 &
Cosmo — 180°F (82°C)
Pickup — 190°F (88°C)

Cooling System Capacity — 10 qts.

Pressure Cap — 13 psi.

WATER PUMP

1) Drain cooling system and remove air cleaner. Remove attaching bolts and drive fan. Loosen water pump pulley bolts. Remove air pump and drive belt.

2) Remove alternator and drive belt. Remove water pump pulley bolts and pulley. Remove water pump attaching nuts and bolts, then remove water pump. To install, reverse removal procedure.

RX-3 SP, RX-4, COSMO & PICKUP (Cont.)

ENGINE SPECIFICATIONS

GENERAL SPECIFICATIONS

Engine	cu. ins.	cc	Carburetor	HP at RPM	Torque (Ft. Lbs. at RPM)	Compr. Ratio	Rotor Housing Width	
							in.	mm
RX-3SP	35	573	4-Bbl.	.....	.....	9.4-1	2.7559	70
RX-4, Cosmo & Pickup	40	654	4-Bbl.	.....	.....	9.2-1	3.150	80

① ROTOR HOUSING, INTERMEDIATE HOUSING & ROTOR

Engine	ROTOR HOUSING		INTERMEDIATE HOUSING		ROTOR		
	Width	Distortion Limit	Width	Distortion Limit	Inside Diameter	Housing-to-Rotor Clearance	Land Protrusion
RX-3SP	2.7559 (70)	.0024 (.06)	.....	.0024 (.06)	.....	.0039-.0083 (.10-.21)	.....
RX-4, Cosmo & Pickup	3.150 (80)	.0024 (.06)	.....	.0024 (.06)	.....	.0039-.0083 (.10-.21)	.....

① — In. (mm)

OIL SEAL

Height In. (mm)	Seal Lip Contact Width	
	Standard In. (mm)	Limit In. (mm)
.220 (5.6)	.008 (.2)	.031 (.8)

① SEAL SPRINGS

Engine	Spring	Free Height In. (mm)
RX-3SP	Apex	.272 (6.9)
RX-4, Cosmo & Pickup	Apex	.185 (4.7)
	Side	.075 (1.9)
	Corner	.098 (2.5)
	Inner Oil	.110 (2.8)
	Outer Oil	.102 (2.6)

① — In. (mm)

① APEX SEAL

Engine	Length	Seal Width	Height	Seal-to-Housing		Seal-to-Rotor	
				Clearance	Wear Limit	Groove Clearance	Wear Limit
RX-3SP	2.750 (69.85)	.118 (3)	.335 (8.5)	.0051-.0067 (.13-.17)	.0012 (.30)	.0020-.0035 (.051-.089)	.006 (.15)
RX-4, Cosmo & Pickup	3.1438 (79.85)	.118 (3)	.335 (8.5)	.0051-.0067 (.13-.17)	.0012 (.30)	.0020-.0035 (.051-.089)	.006 (.15)

① — In. (mm)

SIDE SEAL

Engine	Thickness In. (mm)	Width In. (mm)	Seal-to-Groove		Side Seal-to-Corner Seal	
			Clearance In. (mm)	Limit In. (mm)	Clearance In. (mm)	Limit In. (mm)
All	.039 (1)	.138 (3.5)	.0016-.0028 (.04-.07)	.004 (.10)	.0020-.0059 (.05-.15)	.016 (.40)

RX-3 SP, RX-4, COSMO & PICKUP (Cont.)

ENGINE SPECIFICATIONS (Cont.)

CORNER SEAL						
			Seal-to-Groove		Side Seal-to-Corner Seal	
Engine	Diameter In. (mm)	Width In. (mm)	Clearance In. (mm)	Limit In. (mm)	Clearance In. (mm)	Limit In. (mm)
All	.433 (11)	.276 (7)	.0008-.0019 (.020-.048)	.0031 (.08)	.0020-.0059 (.05-.15)	.016 (.40)

ECCENTRIC SHAFT MAIN & ROTOR BEARINGS					
	MAIN BEARINGS			ROTOR BEARINGS	
Engine	Journal Diameter In. (mm)	Clearance In. (mm)	Eccentric Shaft Endplay In. (mm)	Journal Diameter In. (mm)	Clearance In. (mm)
All	1.6929 (43)	.0016-.0028 (.04-.07)	.0016-.0028 (.04-.07)	2.9134 (74)	.0016-.0031 (.04-.08)

PORT TIMING				
	INTAKE		EXHAUST	
Engine	Open (ATDC)	Close (ABDC)	Open (BBDC)	Close (ATDC)
All	32°	40°	75°	38°

TIGHTENING SPECIFICATIONS	
Application	**Ft. Lbs. (mkg)**
Oil Pump Sprocket	22-25 (3.0-3.5)
Oil Pan	5-7 (0.7-1.0)
Eccentric Shaft Pulley	72-87 (10-12)
Intake Manifold	12-17 (1.6-2.3)
Thermal Reactor	22-40 (3.0-5.5)
Flywheel Lock Nut	289-362 (40-50)
Crankshaft Pulley	72-87 (10-12)
Water Pump	13-20 (1.8-2.7)
Clutch Cover	13-20 (1.8-2.7)

230 4 CYLINDER

ENGINE CODING

ENGINE IDENTIFICATION

Engine code is determined by first six digits of engine identification number, stamped on left side of engine block.

Model	Type	Engine Code
230	123.023	115.954

ENGINE & CYLINDER HEAD

ENGINE

NOTE — *The hood no longer has to be removed, to remove the engine. The hood can be opened to a 90° position and held in place by a locking mechanism located on the left hinge.*

Removal — **1)** Disconnect battery ground cable. Drain cooling system and remove engine oil cooler lines. Remove radiator guard and radiator, disconnect heater hoses.

2) Disconnect all vacuum, fuel and oil lines from engine and transmission. On vehicles with air conditioning, remove compressor from engine and set aside with hoses connected. Disconnect all electrical leads and cables from engine and transmission.

3) Disconnect linkage and choke cable from carburetor, gearshift linkage from transmission, and exhaust pipe from manifold. Loosen steering relay arm and move it downward together with center tie rod and steering shock absorber.

4) Disconnect engine shock absorber from support and exhaust pipe bracket from transmission. Attach suitable lifting sling to engine. Mark position of transmission crossmember in relation to chassis base panel, disconnect rubber mount and remove crossmember.

5) Disconnect speedometer cable from transmission. Disconnect propeller shaft and shaft plate from transmission, loosen clamping nut and slide shaft and plate to the rear. Loosen power steering pump bracket and push reservoir towards engine.

6) Remove front engine mount bolts and front limit stop. Raise engine slightly, tilt it at a 45° angle and lift out engine and transmission assembly. Separate engine from transmission. To install, reverse removal procedure.

CYLINDER HEAD

Removal — **1)** Drain cooling system. Disconnect all water hoses attached to cylinder head. Remove vent line, air cleaner and rocker cover.

2) Disconnect vacuum and fuel line from carburetor. Loosen fuel filter screws and move filter out of way. Disconnect exhaust pipe at manifold.

3) Disconnect spark plug wires from spark plugs and heat sensor from thermostat. Rotate engine until camshaft is in a position to have opened the least amount of valves as possible.

4) Remove top chain guide. Unscrew camshaft sprocket screw. Remove chain tensioner and camshaft sprocket.

5) Loosen and remove head bolts, working from outside toward inside of head. Remove four socket screws at front of head. Lift off head and gasket.

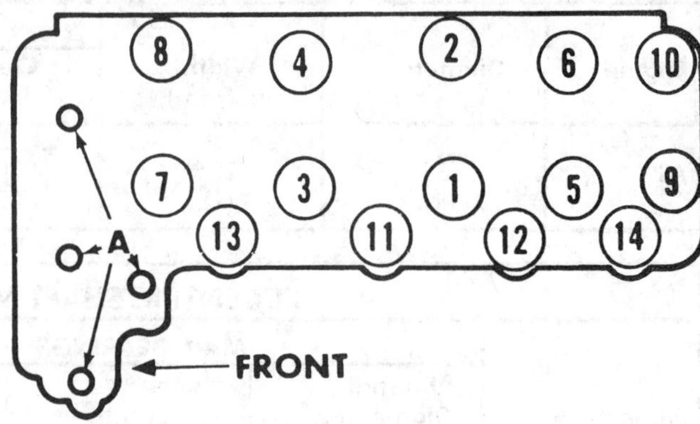

Fig. 1 Cylinder Head Tightening Sequence

Installation — **1)** Rotate engine until No. 1 piston is at TDC on compression stroke. Install head gasket and cylinder head. Torque head bolt in sequence shown in illustration to required specifications.

2) Install four socket head screws at front of cylinder head. Insert Woodruff key in camshaft. Position shim on camshaft to align with mark on first camshaft bearing support.

3) Install camshaft sprocket and chain placing tension on driving side of chain. Use care not to move either camshaft or crankshaft.

4) Check end play of camshaft. See *Camshaft Bearing Replacement*. Install upper chain guide. Using new seal, fill chain tensioner with oil and install in place.

5) Position rocker arm assembly, rotate camshaft until no load is on rocker arms while tightening. Adjust valve lifters with engine cold. See *Valve Clearance Adjustment*.

6) Reinstall remaining components in reverse of removal. Run engine until it has reached 176°F (80°C) and retighten cylinder head bolts, check tappet clearance. (Loosen each head bolt slightly, a bolt at a time, then retorque to specifications).

VALVES

VALVE ARRANGEMENT

E-I-I-E-E-I-I-E (front to rear).

VALVE GUIDE SERVICING

1) Thoroughly clean carbon from guide bore and measure inside diameter. If measurement exceeds .3553" (9.03 mm) on intake guides or .4343" (11.03 mm) on exhaust guides, guide must be replaced.

2) Drive guides out through top of head with a suitable driver. Drive new guides into cylinder head from top until snap ring contacts top of head. Guide bores might require reaming to obtain correct fit with valve stem.

230 4 CYLINDER (Cont.)

3) Valve guides require a .0004-.0012" (.01-.03 mm) press fit in cylinder head. If fit is too loose, two oversize valve guides are available. Size of oversize guides is determined by a color code. Standard guide outside diameter is .5523-.5531" (14.03-14.05 mm) for intake guides and .5917-5925" (15.03-15.05 mm) for exhaust guides.

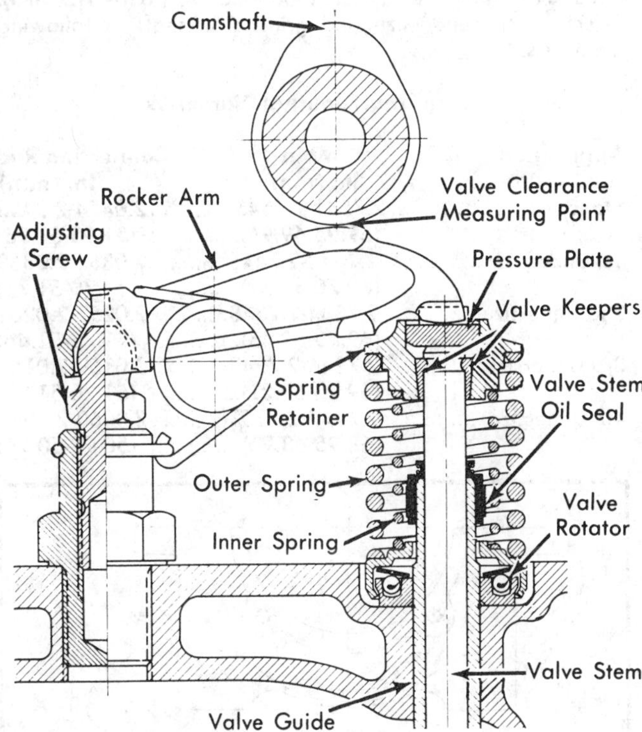

Fig. 2 Sectional View of Valve Train Components

Valve Guide Specifications

Application	In. (mm)
Intake Guide	
Red Code	.5594-.5602 (14.21-14.23)
White Code	.5673-.5681 (14.41-14.43)
Exhaust Guide	
Red Code	.5988-.5996 (15.21-15.23)
White Code	.6066-.6075 (15.41-15.43)

VALVE STEM OIL SEALS

Valve seals are used on both intake and exhaust valves. Seal is teflon-type material utilizing lock ring mounted around seal to secure unit to valve guide. Valve spring must be removed to replace seal.

VALVE SPRING REMOVAL

Compress valve spring with a suitable spring compressor. Remove valve keepers and release spring compressor. Remove upper spring seat, both valve springs and valve rotator. Check spring for wear or fatigue and replace as necessary. To install valve springs, reverse removal procedure.

ROCKER ARM ASSEMBLY

1) Remove valve cover. Remove spring clamp from notch in top of rocker arm and push outward over ball cup of rocker arm. Rotate camshaft until there is no load on rocker arm being removed.

CAUTION — *Rotate engine in correct direction of rotation by cranking collar bolt on crankshaft. Do not rotate by turning bolt on camshaft. If these procedures are not followed, drive chain tensioning rail could be distorted or damaged.*

2) Insert a suitable spring compressor (112 589 08 61 00) between camshaft and valve spring and push valve spring down to relieve pressure from rocker arm. Lift rocker arm off of ball pin and remove.

3) To install rocker arm, reverse removal procedure. Check and, if necessary, adjust valve clearance.

MECHANICAL VALVE LIFTER ADJUSTMENT

1) Valve clearance can be checked or adjusted with engine either cold or warm. Clearance is measured between sliding surface of rocker arm and heel of camshaft. Remove breather line from valve cover and remove valve cover.

2) Rotate engine until camshaft lobe is pointing away from sliding surface of rocker arm to be checked.

CAUTION — *Rotate engine in correct direction of rotation by use of collar bolt on crankshaft. Do not try to turn engine using bolt on camshaft end as drive chain tensioning rail could be distorted or damaged by not following correct procedure.*

3) Measure valve clearance. If clearance is too tight, turn rocker arm adjusting screw clockwise using suitable adjusting wrench (000 589 32 07 00 or equivalent) and a torque wrench. If clearance is excessive, turn adjusting screw counterclockwise.

4) A required torque of 14.5-28.8 ft. lbs. (2-4 mkg) is needed when screwing adjusting screw in or out of cylinder head. If torque is less, adjusting screw, base plate or both must be replaced.

5) If clearance is too small and adjusting screw cannot be screwed into cylinder head any further, a thinner pressure plate must be installed in valve spring retainer. Standard thickness of pressure plate is .177" (4.5 mm). Undersize plates are available .138" (3.5 mm) and .098" (2.5 mm) thick.

Valve Clearance Specifications

Application	Clearance
Intake	
Cold	.004" (.10 mm)
Warm	.006" (.15 mm)
Exhaust	
Cold	.008" (.20 mm)
Warm	.010" (.25 mm)

PISTONS, PINS & RINGS

OIL PAN REMOVAL

Removal & Installation — 1) Drain engine oil. Remove dipstick and guide tube. Take off cover plate from clutch housing. Unbolt oil pan.

230 4 CYLINDER (Cont.)

2) Loosen steering shock absorber and drag link, turn both to one side. Unscrew drag link on intermediate steering and turn aside. Remove oil pan.

3) Clean all surfaces thoroughly. Install new gaskets. Position oil pan in place, tighten bolts, and reinstall all related parts in reverse of removal procedure.

NOTE — *Beginning at the chassis number 018206, two studs are provided at the front to make it easier to center oil pan on crankcase. The oil seal bore on the oil pan is also machined beginning at these same numbers.*

PISTON & ROD ASSEMBLY

Removal — **1)** Remove cylinder head and oil pan. Unscrew connecting rod nuts. Tap rod bolts with a plastic mallet to loosen rod on crankshaft. Push piston and connecting rod assembly out top of cylinder block.

2) Remove piston circlips. Heat piston to 104-140°F and press out piston pins.

Installation — **1)** Heat piston and reinstall piston pin and circlips. Piston and piston pin must be matched.

2) Install connecting rod and cap so cylinder numbers face left side of engine and arrow on piston crown faces forward.

NOTE — *Piston must be installed facing proper direction or damage to the engine will occur.*

3) Connecting rod bolts must be replaced if, after several tightenings, expansion has reached minimum diameter of .2834" (7.2 mm). Normal diameter of connecting rod bolts is .3307" (8.4 mm). Drive out old bolts and insert new bolts using same spline face position.

NOTE — *First tightening after new bolts are installed is 50 ft. lbs. (7 mkg). Subsequent tightenings are 36 ft. lbs. (5 mkg).*

4) Rotate crankshaft until piston is at TDC. Measure distance between top of cylinder block and piston crown. Piston must not recess more than .024-.043" (.6-1.1 mm) below block surface.

FITTING PISTONS

Measure piston and cylinder diameters to determine running clearance. Piston diameter is measured at 90° to piston pin bore near bottom of piston skirt. Install rings with marking "TOP", "F" or "GOE" up.

Piston Specifications

Application	In. (mm)
Standard	3.6902-3.6910 (93.73-93.75)
1st Oversize	3.7059-3.7067 (94.13-94.15)
2nd Oversize	3.7216-3.7224 (94.53-94.55)

PISTON PINS

Removal & Installation — Remove circlips, heat piston to 104-140°F and press out piston pin using suitable tool. Check pin for undue wear or fatigue, replace if necessary. Diameter of piston pin should be 1.0234-1.0236" (25.994-25.999 mm). Heat piston and install piston pin and circlips.

CRANKSHAFT MAIN & CONNECTING ROD BEARINGS

MAIN & CONNECTING ROD BEARINGS

Measure main bearing and connecting rod journals for out-of-round and taper. Out-of-round must not exceed .0002-.0004" (.005-.010 mm) and taper .0004-.0006" (.010-.015 mm). Select proper undersize and grind crankshaft to following diameters:

Crankshaft Journal Diameters

Application	Main In. (mm)	Connecting Rod In. (mm)
Standard	2.7541-2.7545 (69.95-69.96)	2.0454-2.0458 (51.95-51.96)
1st Undersize	2.7442-2.7446 (69.70-69.71)	2.0356-2.0360 (51.70-51.71)
2nd Undersize	2.7344-2.7348 (69.45-69.46)	2.0257-2.0261 (51.45-51.46)
3rd Undersize	2.7246-2.7249 (69.20-69.21)	2.0159-2.0163 (51.20-51.21)
4th Undersize	2.7147-2.7151 (68.95-68.96)	2.0060-2.0064 (50.95-50.96)

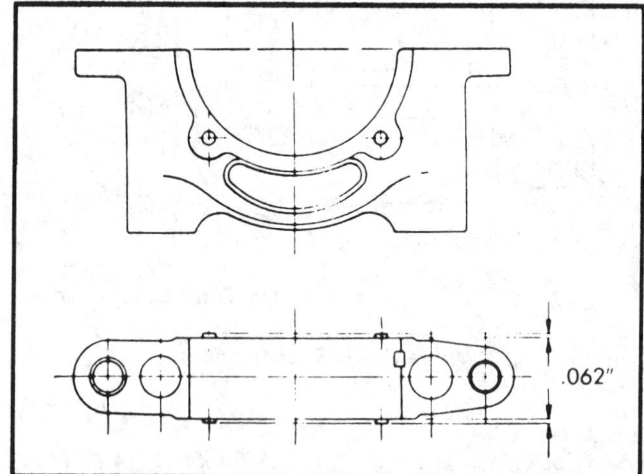

Fig. 3 Detail of Center Main Bearing Cap

THRUST BEARING ALIGNMENT

Center main bearing cap has pin-located thrust washers to adjust crankshaft end play. Measure end play and install thrust washers giving proper end play. Measure pin protusion from main bearing cap to see that it does not exceed .062" (1.6 mm), as illustrated. Standard and oversize thrust washers are available in the following sizes:

Thrust Washer Specifications

Application	In. (mm)
Standard	.078 (1.98)
1st Oversize	.080 (2.03)
2nd Oversize	.082 (2.08)
3rd Oversize	.084 (2.13)
4th Oversize	.086 (2.18)
5th Oversize	.088 (2.23)
6th Oversize	.090 (2.28)
7th Oversize	.092 (2.33)

230 4 CYLINDER (Cont.)

REAR MAIN BEARING OIL SEAL

1) With oil pan and crankshaft removed, insert fabric oil seal in crankcase groove behind rear main bearing. Cut seal so that seal protrudes slightly above parting face.

2) Install other seal half in oil pan groove, coat lubricant on seal halves. Reinstall crankshaft and oil pan. Rotate crankshaft to check tightness of seal, if too tight, remove oil pan and crankshaft, tamp down high spots using suitable tool to roll down material. Reinstall all related parts.

FRONT OIL SEAL

Removal – 1) Remove attaching bolt and crankshaft pulley. Attach a suitable puller and remove counterweight. Remove oil pan.

2) Press out seal ring and remove spacer from crankshaft.

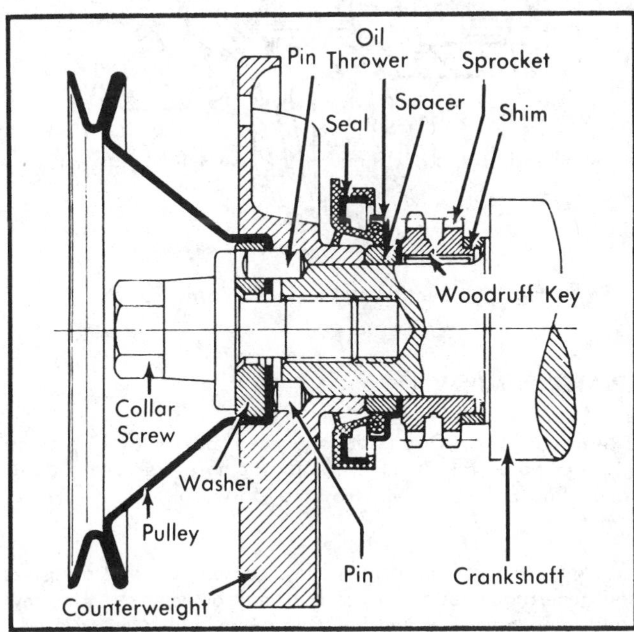

Fig. 4 Sectional View of Crankshaft Front Oil Seal

Installation – 1) Beginning with chassis number 018206, a new seal ring with a 360° shoulder replaced the previous ring with a 180° shoulder. These engines also have the face of the oil seal bore on the oil pan machined, so that the crankcase and oil pan have a flat surface. Rings with the 180° shoulder may still be used in repairing older models.

NOTE – *Radial seal rings with the 360° shoulders must be used in repairing engines with oil pans having the machined oil seal bores.*

2) Lubricate seal lip with oil. Slide oil thrower ring onto crankshaft. Slip radial seal ring onto installation sleeve (130 589 00 61 00) and press seal in until it touches the crankcase face. Install a new hard-chromium plated spacer washer (121 031 04 51) on crankshaft.

3) Replace oil pan. Install remaining components in reverse of removal procedures.

CAMSHAFT

TIMING CHAIN REPLACEMENT

1) Remove rocker cover and disconnect spark plug wires at spark plugs. Remove all four spark plugs to allow engine to turn over freely.

NOTE – *Removal of rocker arm brackets is not imperative, but is recommended in order to avoid damage to valves or pistons, if, while turning engine, chain jumps over camshaft sprocket.*

2) Grind off pins on a link of old chain and remove link. Using a master link, connect new chain to old chain on driving side of old chain.

NOTE – *Install master link facing camshaft side of chain with spring lock closed end facing direction of rotation (see illustration).*

3) Slowly turn engine in direction of rotation, feeding new chain in and old chain out uniformly. After chain threading is complete, join ends of new chain with master link and make sure spring lock closed end is facing direction of rotation. Check that valve timing is correct. See *Valve Timing*. Reverse removal procedures for remaining components.

VALVE TIMING

1) Rotate No. 1 piston to TDC of compression stroke. Align camshaft timing mark with mark on No. 1 camshaft bearing support bracket (see illustration). Install camshaft sprocket.

2) If correct valve timing is not achieved when camshaft sprocket is installed, offset Woodruff keys are available to make timing corrections, see following table:

Offset Woodruff Keys

Offset	Crankshaft Correction
.0275" (.7 mm)	4°
.0354" (.9 mm)	6 1/2°
.0433" (1.1 mm)	8°
.0511" (1.3 mm)	10°

Fig. 5 Camshaft Timing Marks & Timing Chain Master Link

ENGINE OILING

Crankcase Capacity – 5.8 qts. with filter.

Oil Filter – Full-flow, clean main element 3,000 miles. Replace by-pass element 3,000 miles.

230 4 CYLINDER (Cont.)

Normal Oil Pressure – 7.1 psi (.5 kg/cm^2) at idle speed; 42 psi (3.07 kg/cm^2) at 3000 RPM.

Pressure Regulator Valve – Non-adjustable.

ENGINE OILING SYSTEM

Engine lubrication is provided by a gear type oil pump, which force feeds oil through an oil filter to oil gallery. From oil gallery, oil flows to main and connecting rod bearings. Pistons, wrist pins and connecting rod bushings are splash lubricated. A vertical oil passage from oil gallery has a transverse passage which supplies oil to intermediate sprocket shaft and bearings. Another oil passage supplies oil to oil pump drive shaft and helical gear. Vertical passage also supplies oil to No. 1 camshaft bearing. An external oil tube attached to No. 1 camshaft bearing support lubricates other camshaft bearings and rocker arms.

OIL PUMP

Removal – Remove oil pan. Remove two attaching screws and lift out pump.

Disassembly – 1) Remove oil strainer. Unscrew lower pump body, and remove pump gears and shafts. Measure clearances between gear-to-body and gear-to-cover (see specifications).

2) If cast-in bushings in housing are worn, replace complete housing. Worn gears are replaced as an assembly. Assemble upper and lower housing without a gasket. Install strainer with a new gasket. Check that pump turns freely.

Installation – 1) Align drive shaft follower with helical gear and follower faces with respect to one another.

2) Insert oil pump with bracket and tighten mounting screws. Install oil pan.

Oil Pump Specifications

Application	In. (mm)
Gear-to-Body	.0008-.0024 (.02-.06)
Gear-to-Cover	.0020-.0028 (.05-.07)
Backlash	.0020-.0059 (.05-.15)

ENGINE COOLING

Cooling System Capacity – 10.6 qts. with heater.

Thermostat – Wax Pellet Type, opens at 170-179°F (77-81°C).

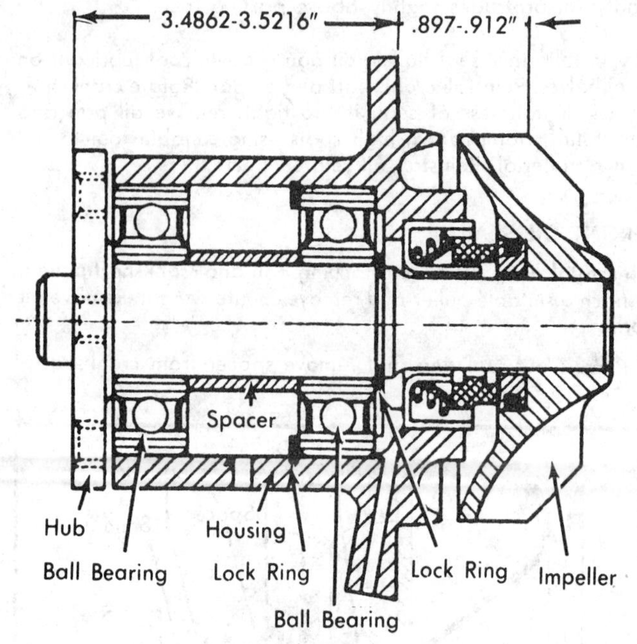

Fig. 6 Sectional View of Water Pump

WATER PUMP

Removal – 1) Drain cooling system below level of pump. Loosen hose clamps on top radiator hose. Remove radiator mounting bolts and push radiator forward.

2) Remove fan from drive pulley. Loosen nuts and adjusters on generator enough so fan belt may be removed. Unscrew and remove venting line between pump and cylinder head.

3) Water pump is a maintenance-free type. When installing pump, check hub-to-flange and impeller-to-flange distance, (see illustration).

ENGINE SPECIFICATIONS

GENERAL SPECIFICATIONS

Year	Displ. cu. ins.	Displ. cc	Carburetor	HP at RPM	Torque (Ft. Lbs. at RPM)	Compr. Ratio	Bore in.	Bore mm	Stroke in.	Stroke mm
1977	140.8	2307	1x1 Bbl.	86@4800	116@3000	8-1	3.69	93.75	3.29	83.6

230 4 CYLINDER (Cont.)

ENGINE SPECIFICATIONS (Cont.)

VALVES							
Engine & Valve	Head Diam. In. (mm)	Face Angle	Seat Angle	Seat Width In. (mm)	Stem Diameter In. (mm)	Stem Clearance In. (mm)	Valve Lift In. (mm)
2307 cc							
Intake	1.846-1.854 (46.9-47.1)	45°	45°	.071-.099 (1.8-2.5)	.352-.353 (8.95-8.97)	.....	.....
Exhaust	1.455-1.467 (36.95-37.25)	45°	45°	.059-.099 (1.5-2.5)	.430-.431 (10.93-10.95)	.....	.....

PISTONS, PINS, RINGS						
	PISTONS	PINS		RINGS		
Engine	Clearance In. (mm)	Piston Fit In. (mm)	Rod Fit In. (mm)	Rings	End Gap In. (mm)	Side Clearance In. (mm)
2307 cc	.0010-.0014 (.025-.035)	.0000-.0001 (.0000-.0025)	.0004-.0009 (.0101-.0228)	No. 1	.014-.022 (.35-.55)	.0024-.0036 (.060-.092)
				No. 2	.014-.022 (.35-.55)	.0015-.0028 (.040-.072)
				No. 3	.010-.016 (.25-.40)	.0012-.0024 (.030-.062)

CRANKSHAFT MAIN & CONNECTING ROD BEARINGS							
	MAIN BEARINGS				CONNECTING ROD BEARINGS		
Engine	Journal Diam. In. (mm)	Clearance In. (mm)	Thrust Bearing	Crankshaft End Play In. (mm)	Journal Diam. In. (mm)	Clearance In. (mm)	Side Play In. (mm)
2307 cc	2.7541-2.7545 (69.95-69.96)	.0012-.0028 (.031-.068)	Center	.004-.009 (.10-.22)	2.045-2.046 (51.94-51.97)	.0012-.0027 (.031-.068)	.005-.010 (.12-.26)

VALVE SPRINGS			
Engine	Free Length In. (mm)	PRESSURE Lbs. @ In. (kg @ mm) Valve Closed	Valve Open
2307 cc			
Inner	1.77 (44.9)	28.2-33.5@1.22 (12.8-15.2@31)	50.3-55.6@.827 (22.8-25.2@21)
Outer	1.97 (50)	79.4@1.54 (36@39)	149.3-168.2@1.18 (67.7-76.3@30)

VALVE TIMING				
	INTAKE		EXHAUST	
Engine	Open (ATDC)	Close (ALDC)	Open (BLDC)	Close (BTDC)
2307 cc	14°	20°	22°	12°

TIGHTENING SPECIFICATIONS	
Application	Ft. Lbs. (mkg)
Cylinder Head Bolts	
10 mm bolts①	
Stage 1	14.5 (2.0)
Stage 2	29 (4.0)
Stage 3	40 (5.5)
12 mm bolts①	
Stage 1	29 (4.0)
Stage 2	51 (7.0)
Stage 3	72 (10)
Connecting Rod Bolts	②29-36 (4.0-5.0)
Main Bearing Cap Bolts	65 (9.0)
Crankshaft Sprocket Bolt	195-239 (27-33)
Oil Pan Bolts	6 (1.1)
Flywheel Bolts	22-29 (3.0-4.0)
Camshaft Bearing Bolts	18 (2.5)
Camshaft Sprocket Bolt	58 (8.0)

① – Final step with engine warm, 10 mm bolts 40 ft lbs. (5.5 mkg), 12 mm bolts 72 ft lbs. (10 mkg).

② – Plus 90-100° rotation.

240D DIESEL 4 CYLINDER

ENGINE CODING

ENGINE IDENTIFICATION

Engine identification number is stamped on left side of cylinder block. First six digits of this number are used for engine identification purposes.

Application	Type	Engine Coding
240D	123.123	616.912

NOTE — *If vehicle is equipped with air conditioning, it is not necessary to disconnect refrigerant hoses. Only detach compressor from its mounting and position compressor and hoses out of way.*

ENGINE CYLINDER HEAD & MANIFOLDS

ENGINE

NOTE — *The hood no longer has to be removed, to remove the engine. The hood can be opened to a 90° position and held in place by a locking mechanism located on the left hinge.*

Removal — 1) Disconnect battery ground cable. Drain cooling system and remove engine oil cooler lines. Remove radiator guard and radiator, disconnect heater hoses.

2) Remove air intake silencer. Disconnect fuel hoses and vacuum hose to power brake. On models with power steering and level control, disconnect and plug oil lines.

3) Disconnect oil pressure gauge hose. Disconnect idle control cable and stop-start cable. Remove accelerator linkage.

4) Disconnect ground cable from engine to chassis and all other electrical leads. Disconnect gearshift linkage and exhaust pipe at manifold.

5) Loosen steering relay arm and move downward together with center tie rod and steering shock absorber. Disconnect hydraulic line from clutch slave cylinder.

6) On Auto. Trans. models, disconnect oil cooler lines between transmission and oil cooler.

7) Disconnect exhaust pipe support bracket at transmission, loosen clamp on exhaust pipe and push downward.

8) Attach suitable lifting sling to engine. Mark position of rear engine crossmember in relation to chassis base panel, disconnect rubber mount at transmission and remove crossmember.

9) Disconnect speedometer cable. Disconnect propeller shaft and shaft plate from transmission. Push propeller shaft to rear after loosening clamping nut.

10) Disconnect plug from automatic transmission.

11) Remove bolts at both front engine mounts. Remove front limit stop. Loosen one screw and move power steering reservoir to one side.

12) Lift out engine at a 45° angle.

Installation — To install, reverse removal procedures.

INTAKE & EXHAUST MANIFOLD

Intake Manifold — Remove air cleaner. Disconnect throttle linkage and bowden cable for idling control on throttle duct. Unscrew vacuum line. Remove attaching nuts and intake manifold from cylinder head.

Exhaust Manifold — Disconnect exhaust pipe from manifold. Remove attaching nuts and lift off exhaust manifold.

CYLINDER HEAD

Removal — 1) Drain cooling system. Disconnect all water hoses attached to cylinder head. Remove vent line, air cleaner and rocker cover.

2) Disconnect vacuum line, injection lines and leakage oil line. Loosen fuel filter screws and move filter out of the way. Remove exhaust pipe from manifold.

3) Disconnect cable to glow plugs and heat sensor from water thermometer. Rotate engine until there is no load on rocker arms and remove rocker arm assembly.

4) Remove top chain guide. Unscrew camshaft sprocket screw. Remove chain tensioner and camshaft sprocket.

5) Loosen and remove head bolts, working from outside toward inside of head. Remove four socket screws at front of head. Lift off head and gasket.

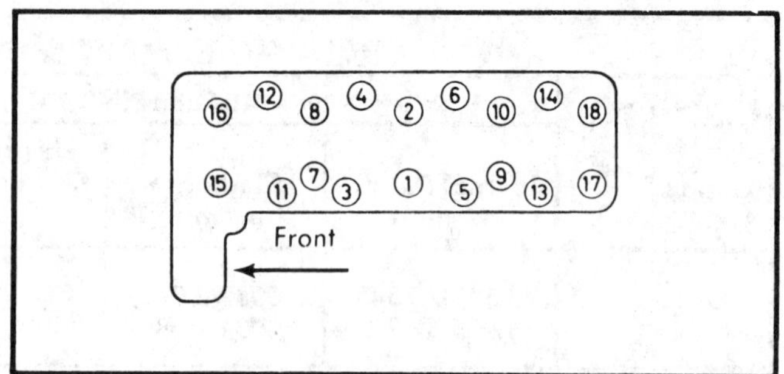

Fig. 1 Cylinder Head Tightening Sequence

Installation — 1) Rotate engine until No. 1 piston is at TDC of compression stroke. Install head gasket and cylinder head, torque head bolts to specifications (see illustration).

2) Install four socket screws in front of head. Connect ground lead for glow plugs to screw under main fuel filter. Insert Woodruff key in camshaft. Place shim on camshaft so mark aligns with mark of first camshaft bearing support.

3) Install camshaft sprocket and chain with tension on driving side of chain, using care not to move camshaft or crankshaft.

4) Check endplay of camshaft. See *Camshaft Bearing Replacement*. Install upper chain guide. Using a new seal, install chain tensioner filled with oil.

5) Install rocker arm assembly, rotating camshaft so there is no load on rocker arms while tightening. Adjust tappets with engine cold. See *Valve Clearance Adjustment*.

6) Reinstall remaining components in reverse of removal. Run engine until it has reached 176°F (80°C) and retighten cylinder head bolts, check tappet clearance. (Loosen each head bolt slightly, a bolt at a time, then retorque to specifications).

240D DIESEL 4 CYLINDER (Cont.)

VALVES

VALVE ARRANGEMENT

E-I-I-E-E-I-I-E (front to rear).

VALVE GUIDE SERVICING

1) Check valve guide bores and ensure they are not less than .3937" (10.00 mm) or larger than .3947" (10.025 mm). Remove all carbon before measuring guides.

2) Using a suitable drift, drive intake guide out toward top of head and exhaust guide toward combustion chamber.

3) Press in new guides from combustion side until specified distance is achieved. See *Fig.* 2. Check guide bores and remove any tight spots.

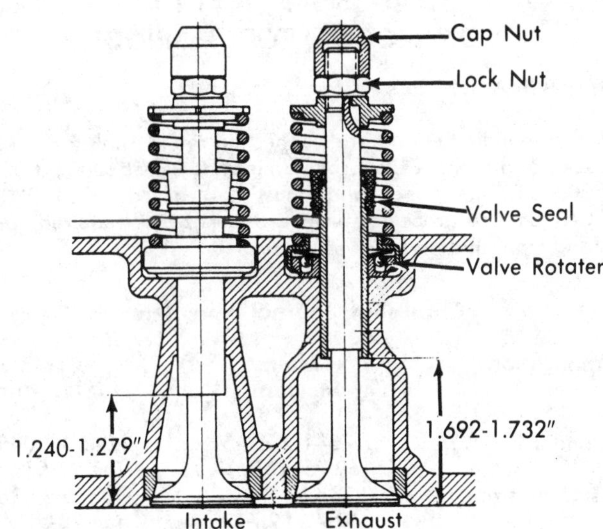

Fig. 2 Installed View of Valve Assemblies

4) Valve guides are available in standard and one oversize (coded red). An interference fit of .0004-.0015" (.010-.040 mm) is used. If guide does not meet specifications, install oversize part. Note that intake guides are 2.40" (60.96 mm) long and exhaust guides are 1.95" (49.53 mm) long.

Valve Guide Specification

Application	Guide O.D. In. (mm)	Cyl. Head Bore In. (mm)
Standard	.5522-.5527	.5511-.5518
	(14.03-14.04)	(14.00-14.02)
Oversize (Red)	.5601-.5605	.5590-.5597
	(14.23-14.24)	(14.20-14.22)

VALVE STEM OIL SEALS

1) Using a spring compressor, unscrew cap nut and lock nut from valve stem. Remove valve collar and spring.

2) Prepare a tool for removing oil seal. See *Fig.* 3. Using oil seal tool, lever oil seal off of guide and stem.

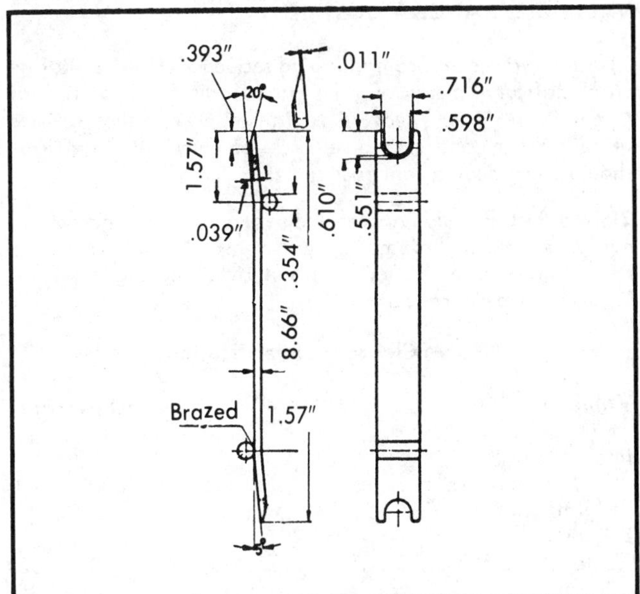

Fig. 3 Valve Stem Oil Seal Tool

3) Place plastic sleeve over threaded end of valve stem. Slide new oil seal in place, using oil seal tool. Install spring and collar. Screw lock nut and cap nut on end of valve stem.

VALVE SPRING

Remove rocker arms. Using a spring compressor, unscrew cap nut and lock nut. Remove valve spring collar and lift out spring. Check spring for wear or fatigue, replace as necessary. To install, reverse removal procedures with close wound coils next to cylinder head.

ROCKER ARM ASSEMBLY

1) Remove air cleaner and tappet cover. Loosen rocker arm bracket bolts, rotate camshaft so there is no load on rocker arms being removed.

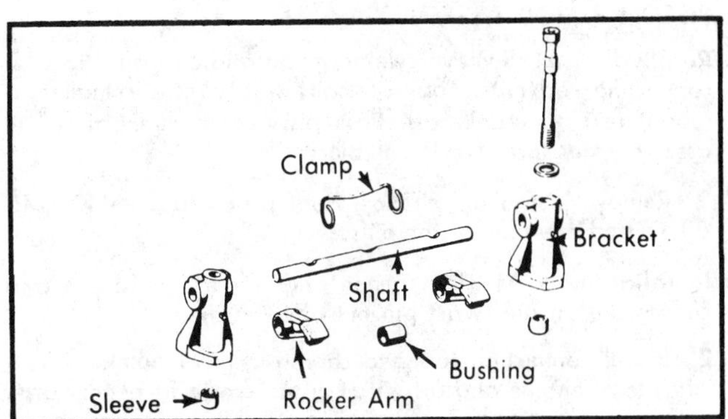

Fig. 4 Detail of Rocker Arm Assembly

2) Slide rocker arm brackets, rocker arms tightening clamp and spacer off of shaft. Inspect all parts for wear. Replace shaft, rocker bushing or rocker bracket if necessary. To install, reverse removal procedures.

240D DIESEL 4 CYLINDER (Cont.)

VALVE CLEARANCE ADJUSTMENT

1) Adjust valves according to firing sequence (1-3-4-2). Rotate crankshaft until piston of valves to be adjusted is at TDC of compression stroke. Measure clearance between slide surface of rocker arm and cam base circle of camshaft. Cam lobe should be vertical to cam base circle.

2) To adjust, fit holding wrench on valve retainer. Loosen cap nut while holding hex nut. Adjust clearance by turning cap nut. After adjustment, lock cap nut by tightening hex nut. Recheck valve clearance:

Valve Clearance Specifications

Valve	Inches (mm)
Intake	
Cold	①.0039 (.10)
Warm	①.0059 (.15)
Exhaust	
Cold	.012 (.30)
Warm	.014 (.35)

① – Add .002" (.05 mm) additional clearance if ambient temperatures are below -4° F (-20° C) for extended periods.

PISTONS, PINS & RINGS

OIL PAN

1) Remove oil pan cover, if equipped. Drain engine oil. Remove dipstick and tube. Detach cover plate from clutch housing. Remove oil pan bolts.

2) Loosen steering shock absorber and drag link and turn to one side. Unscrew drag link on intermediate steering and turn aside. Remove oil pan.

NOTE - *Beginning at chassis number 033886, two studs are provided at the front to make it easier to center oil pan on crankcase. At same time, oil seal bore on the oil pan began to be machined.*

PISTON & ROD ASSEMBLY

Removal – **1)** Remove cylinder head and oil pan. Unscrew connecting rod nuts. Tap rod bolts with a plastic mallet to loosen rod on crankshaft. Push piston and connecting rod assembly out top of cylinder block.

2) Remove piston pin circlips. Heat piston to 104-140° (40-60°C) and press out piston pins.

Installation – **1)** Heat piston and reinstall wrist pin and circlips. Piston and wrist pin must be matched.

2) Install connecting rod and cap so cylinder numbers face left side of engine and arrow on piston crown faces forward.

NOTE – *Piston must be installed facing proper direction or damage to the engine will occur.*

3) Connecting rod bolts are of a special design, having an expansion shank which is used to measure bolt stress. If, after several tightenings, the expansion section of the bolt has reached a minimum diameter of .2834" (7.2 mm), the bolt must be replaced. When new, this shank portion should be .3307" (8.4 mm). When replacing, drive out old bolts and insert new ones into same spline pattern in rod cap. **NOTE** – *First tightening of NEW bolts is to 50.6 ft. lbs. (7.0 mkg); subsequent tightenings should be to 36 ft. lbs. (5.0 mkg).*

4) Rotate crankshaft until piston to be measured is at TDC. Measure distance from top of cylinder block to piston crown. Piston must not protrude more than .035" (.90 mm) nor less than .004" (.10 mm) above block surface.

FITTING PISTONS

Measure piston and cylinder diameters to determine running clearance. Piston diameter is measured at 90° to piston pin bore near bottom of piston skirt. There are two compression rings and one oil ring. Install compression rings with markings "top" or "F" and oil ring with marking "GOE" or "F" facing upward.

CRANKSHAFT MAIN & CONNECTING ROD BEARINGS

MAIN BEARING SERVICE

Measure main bearing and connecting rod journals for out-of-round and taper. Out-of-round must not exceed .0002-.0004" (.005-.010 mm) and taper must not exceed .0004-.0006" (.010-.015 mm). Select proper undersize, if required, and grind crankshaft to following diameters:

Crankshaft Journal Diameters

Application	Main In. (mm)	Con. Rod In. (mm)
Standard	2.7541-2.7545 (69.95-69.96)	2.0454-2.0458 (51.95-51.96)
1st Undersize	2.7442-2.7446 (69.70-69.71)	2.0356-2.0360 (51.70-51.71)
2nd Undersize	2.7344-2.7348 (69.45-69.46)	2.0257-2.0261 (51.45-51.46)
3rd Undersize	2.7246-2.7249 (69.20-69.21)	2.0159-2.0163 (51.20-51.21)
4th Undersize	2.7147-2.7151 (68.95-68.96)	2.0060-2.0064 (50.95-50.96)

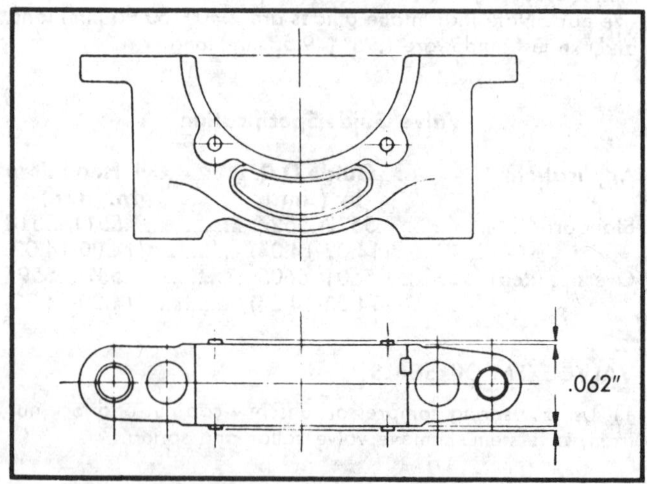

Fig. 5 Detail of Center Main Bearing Cap

240D DIESEL 4 CYLINDER (Cont.)

THRUST BEARING ALIGNMENT

Center main bearing cap has pin located thrust washers to adjust crankshaft end play. Measure end play and install thrust washer(s) required to give proper end play. Measure pin protrusion from main bearing cap to ensure it does not exceed .062" (1.57 mm) as illustrated. Standard and oversize thrust washers are available in the following sizes:

Thrust Washer Thicknesses

Application	In. (mm)
Standard	.078 (1.98)
1st Oversize	.080 (2.03)
2nd Oversize	.082 (2.08)
3rd Oversize	.084 (2.13)
4th Oversize	.086 (2.18)
5th Oversize	.088 (2.23)
6th Oversize	.090 (2.28)
7th Oversize	.092 (2.33)

REAR MAIN BEARING OIL SEAL SERVICE

1) With oil pan and crankshaft removed, insert fabric oil seal in groove in crankcase behind rear main bearing. Cut seal at parting face so that it protrudes slightly above parting face.

2) Install other half in oil pan groove, using tallow on seal halves. Reinstall crankshaft and oil pan. Rotate crankshaft to check tightness of seal. If seal is too tight, remove oil pan and crankshaft and roll down high spots with a hammer handle.

FRONT OIL SEAL

Removal – 1) Remove attaching bolt and crankshaft pulley. Attach a suitable puller and remove counterweight. Remove oil pan.

2) Press out seal ring and remove spacer from crankshaft.

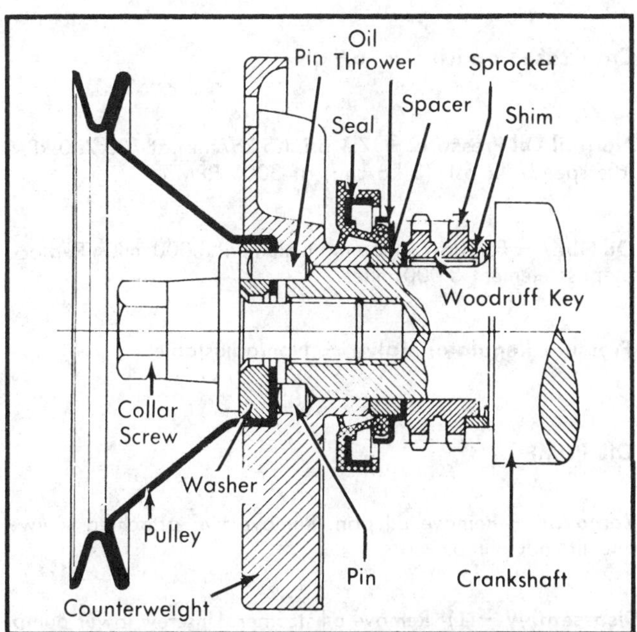

Fig. 6 Sectional View of Crankshaft Front Oil Seal

Installation – 1) Beginning with chassis number 033886, a new seal ring with a 360° shoulder replaced the previous ring with a 180° shoulder. The face of the oil seal bore on the oil pan also became machined, so that the crankcase and oil pan have a flat surface. Rings with the 180° shoulder may still be used in repairing previous models.

NOTE – *Radial seal rings with the 360° shoulders must be used in repairing engines with oil pans having the machined oil seal bore.*

2) Lubricate seal lip with oil. Slide oil thrower ring onto crankshaft. Slip radial seal ring onto installation sleeve (130 589 00 61 00) and press seal in until it touches the crankcase face. Install a new hard-chromium plated spacer washer (615 031 01 51) on crankshaft.

3) Place oil pan on two centering studs at front of crankcase and complete installation, by installing components in reverse of removal procedures.

CAMSHAFT

CAMSHAFT

1) Remove camshaft sprocket and rocker arm assembly. Disconnect external camshaft oiling tube.

2) Remove camshaft bearing supports. Slide camshaft bearing supports off of camshaft. To install, reverse removal procedures.

CAMSHAFT BEARING REPLACEMENT

1) Inspect camshaft bearing journals for wear. If worn, grind bearing journals and fit undersize bearings.

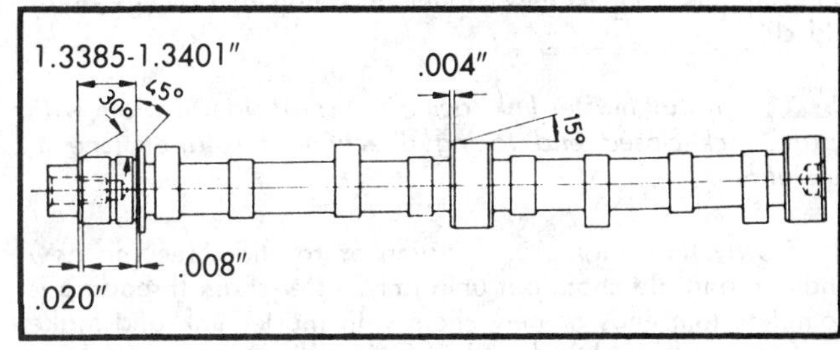

Fig. 7 Detail of Camshaft

2) Bearing on No. 1 journal controls camshaft end play. Width of journal is 1.3385-1.3401" (34.0-34.03 mm). Place bearing on camshaft and install retaining ring. Using a feeler gauge, measure clearance between camshaft flange and bearing. *See Fig. 8.* Lap bearing to proper fit. The following table lists camshaft bearing journal diameters for standard and undersize bearings:

Camshaft Journal Diameters

Application	Journal No. 1 In. (mm)	Journal No. 2 & 3 In. (mm)
Standard	1.3763-1.3769 (34.96-34.97)	1.8290-1.8297 (6.46-46.47)
Intermediate (Grey)	1.3723-1.3730 (34.86-34.87)	1.8251-1.8257 (46.36-46.37)
1st Undersize (Red)	1.3664-1.3671 (34.71-34.72)	1.8192-1.8198 (46.21-46.22)

240D DIESEL 4 CYLINDER (Cont.)

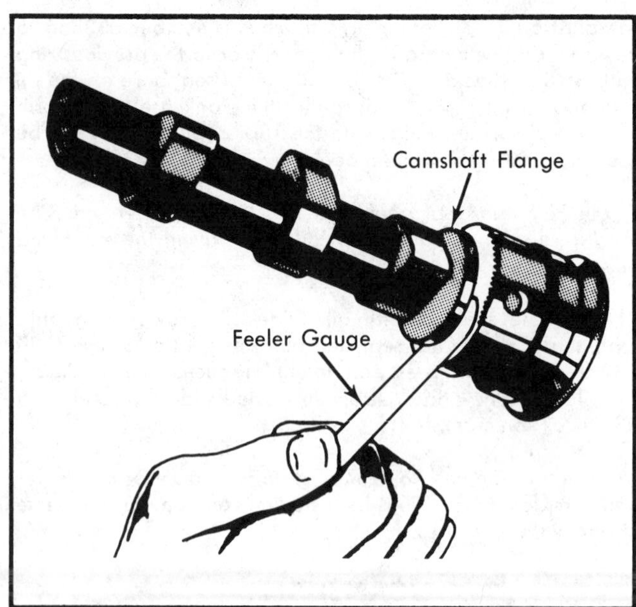

Fig. 8 Measuring Camshaft End Play

TIMING CHAIN REPLACEMENT

1) Remove rocker cover and glow plugs so that engine turns easily. Remove chain tensioner and rocker arm brackets.

NOTE — *Removal of rocker arm brackets is not imperative, but is recommended in order to avoid damage to valves or pistons, if, while turning engine, chain jumps over camshaft sprocket.*

2) Grind off pins on a link of old chain and remove link. Using a master link, connect new chain to old chain on driving side of old chain.

NOTE — *Install master link facing camshaft side of chain with spring lock closed end facing direction of rotation (see illustration).*

3) Slowly turn engine in direction of rotation, feeding new chain in and old chain out uniformly. After chain threading is complete join ends of new chain with master link and make sure spring lock closed end is facing direction of rotation. Check that valve timing is correct. See *Valve Timing*. Reverse removal procedures for remaining components.

VALVE TIMING

1) Rotate No. 1 piston to TDC of compression stroke. Align camshaft timing mark with mark on No. 1 camshaft bearing support bracket (see illustration). Install camshaft sprocket.

2) If correct valve timing is not achieved when camshaft sprocket is installed, offset Woodruff keys are available to make timing corrections, see following table:

Offset Woodruff Keys

Offset	Crankshaft Correction
.0275" (.7 mm)	4°
.0354" (.9 mm)	6 1/2°
.0433" (1.1 mm)	8°
.0511" (1.3 mm)	10°

Fig. 9 Camshaft Timing Marks Location

ENGINE OILING

ENGINE OILING SYSTEM

Engine lubrication is provided by a gear type oil pump, which force feeds oil through an oil filter to oil gallery. From oil gallery, oil flows to main and connecting rod bearings. Pistons, wrist pins and connecting rod bushings are splash lubricated. A vertical oil passage from oil gallery has a transverse passage which supplies oil to intermediate sprocket shaft and bearings. Another oil passage supplies oil to oil pump drive shaft and helical gear. Vertical passage also supplies oil to No. 1 camshaft bearing. An external oil tube attached to No. 1 camshaft bearing support lubricates other camshaft bearings and rocker arms.

Crankcase Capacity — 6.9 qts.

Normal Oil Pressure — 7.1 psi. (.5 kg/cm²) at 700-780 RPM idle speed; 42 psi. (3 kg/cm²) at 3000 RPM.

Oil Filter — Full-flow, clean main element 3,000 miles. Replace by-pass element 3,000 miles.

Pressure Regulator Valve — Non-adjustable.

OIL PUMP

Removal — Remove oil pan. Remove two attaching screws and lift out pump.

Disassembly — **1)** Remove oil strainer. Unscrew lower pump body, and remove pump gears and shafts. Measure clearances between gear-to-body and gear-to-cover (see specifications).

240D DIESEL 4 CYLINDER (Cont.)

2) If cast-in bushings in housing are worn, replace complete housing. Worn gears are replaced as an assembly. Assemble upper and lower housing without a gasket. Install strainer with a new gasket. Check that pump turns freely.

Installation – 1) Align drive shaft follower with helical gear and follower faces with respect to one another.

2) Insert oil pump with bracket and tighten mounting screws. Install oil pan.

Oil Pump Specifications

Application	In. (mm)
Gear-to-Body	.0009-.0022 (.023-.056)
Gear-to-Cover	.0018-.0029 (.046-.074)
Gear Backlash	.0019-.0059 (.048-.15)

ENGINE COOLING

Thermostat – Open at 172-180° F (78-82° C).

Cooling System Capacity – 10.5 qts.

WATER PUMP

Removal – 1) Drain cooling system below level of pump. Loosen hose clamps on top radiator hose. Remove radiator mounting bolts and push radiator forward.

2) Remove fan from drive pulley. Loosen nuts and adjusters on generator enough so fan belt may be removed. Unscrew and remove venting line between pump and cylinder head.

3) Water pump is a maintenance free type. When installing pump, check hub-to-flange and impeller-to-flange distance, (see illustration).

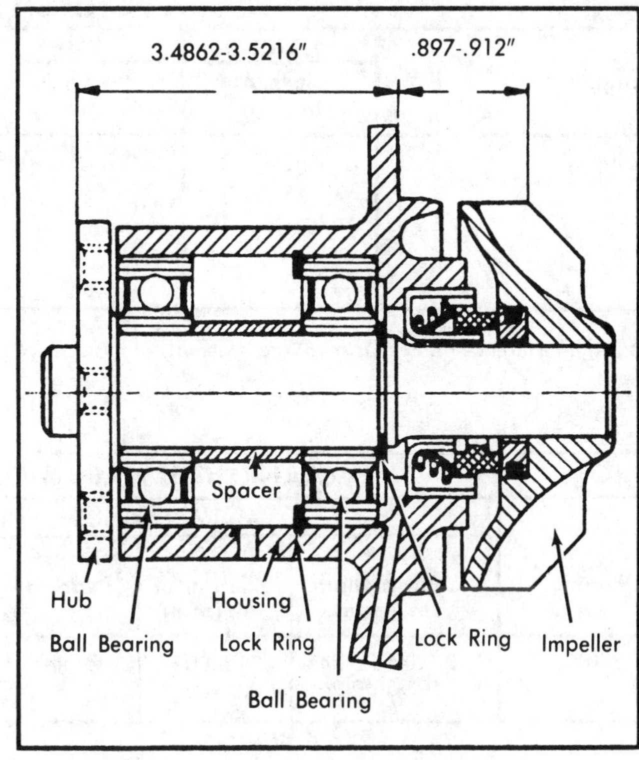

Fig. 10 Sectional View of Water Pump

ENGINE SPECIFICATIONS

GENERAL SPECIFICATIONS

Year	Displ.		Carburetor	HP at RPM	Torque (Ft. Lbs. at RPM)	Compr. Ratio	Bore		Stroke	
	cu. ins.	cc					in.	mm	in.	mm
1977	146.7	2404	Fuel Inj.	62@4200	97@2400	21.0-1	3.58	91	3.64	92.4

VALVES

Engine & Valve	Head Diam. In. (mm)	Face Angle	Seat Angle	Seat Width In. (mm)	Stem Diameter In. (mm)	Stem Clearance In. (mm)	Valve Lift In. (mm)
2404 cc							
Intake	1.563-1.571 (39.70-39.90)	30°	30°	.051-.063 (1.3-1.6)	.3906-.3913 (9.92-9.94)	.0030 (.075)	.....
Exhaust	1.343-1.350 (34.10-34.30)	30°	30°	.098-.114 (2.5-2.9)	.3906-.3913 (9.92-9.94)	.0030 (.075)	.....

240D DIESEL 4 CYLINDER (Cont.)

ENGINE SPECIFICATIONS (Cont.)

PISTONS, PINS, RINGS						
	PISTONS	PINS		RINGS		
Engine	Clearance In. (mm)	Piston Fit In. (mm)	Rod Fit In. (mm)	Rings	End Gap In. (mm)	Side Clearance In. (mm)
2404 cc	.0007-.0015 (.018-.038)	①	Push Fit	No. 1	.0079-.0138 (.20-.35)	.004-.005 (.100-.132)
				No. 2	.0079-.0138 (.20-.35)	.003-.004 (.070-.102)
				No. 3	.0098-.0157 (.25-.40)	.001-.002 (.030-.062)

① — Interference fit. See *Piston & Rod Assembly in this article.*

CRANKSHAFT MAIN & CONNECTING ROD BEARINGS							
	MAIN BEARINGS				CONNECTING ROD BEARINGS		
Engine	Journal Diam. In. (mm)	Clearance In. (mm)	Thrust Bearing	Crankshaft End Play In. (mm)	Journal Diam. In. (mm)	Clearance In. (mm)	Side Play In. (mm)
2404 cc	2.7541-2.7545 (69.95-69.96)	.0012-.0027 (.031-.068)	Center	.0039-.0090 (.10-.22)	2.0454-2.0458 (51.95-51.96)	.0012-.0027 (.031-.068)	.005-.010 (.12-.26)

VALVE SPRINGS			
Engine	Free Length In. (mm)	PRESSURE Lbs. @ In. (kg @ mm)	
		Valve Closed	Valve Open
2404 cc	1.988 (50.5)	58.2@1.512 (26.4@38.41)	116.8@1.177 (53.0@29.9)

VALVE TIMING				
	INTAKE		EXHAUST	
Engine	Open (ATDC)	Close (ALDC)	Open (BLDC)	Close (BTDC)
2404 cc	13.5°	15.5°	19°	17°

CAMSHAFT ①			
Engine	Journal Diam. In. (mm)	Clearance In. (mm)	Lobe Lift In. (mm)
2404 cc			
No. 1	1.3763-1.3769 (34.96-34.97)	.0010-.0026 (.025-.066)	.....
No. 2 & 3	1.8290-1.8297 (46.46-46.47)	.0010-.0026 (.025-.066)	.....

① — End play should be .003-.006" (.070-.149 mm)

TIGHTENING SPECIFICATIONS	
Application	Ft. Lbs. (mkg)
Cylinder Head	
Step 1	29 (4)
Step 2	43 (6)
Step 3①	65 (9)
Camshaft Bearing Caps	18 (2.5)
Glow Plugs	36 (5)
Prechamber in Cyl. Head	108-130 (15-18)
Connecting Rod Caps	29-36 (4-5)
Main Bearing Caps	65 (9)
Crankshaft Front Hex Bolt	195-239 (27-33)
Oil Pan Bolts	8 (1.1)
Camshaft Sprocket Bolt	58 (8)

① — With engine warm.

300D DIESEL 5 CYLINDER

ENGINE CODING

ENGINE IDENTIFICATION

Engine identification number is stamped on left side of cylinder block. First six digits of this number are used for engine identification purposes.

Application	Chassis Type	Engine Code
300D	123.130	617.912

NOTE — *If vehicle is equipped with air conditioning, it is not necessary to disconnect refrigerant hoses. Only detach compressor from its mounting and position compressor and hoses out of way.*

ENGINE & CYLINDER HEAD

ENGINE

NOTE — *The hood no longer has to be removed, to remove the engine. The hood can be opened to a 90° position and held in place by a locking mechanism located on the left hinge.*

Removal — 1) Disconnect battery ground cable. Drain cooling system and remove engine oil cooler lines. Remove radiator guard and radiator, disconnect heater hoses.

2) Remove air intake silencer. Disconnect fuel hoses and vacuum hose to power brake. On models with power steering and level control, disconnect and plug oil lines.

3) Disconnect oil pressure gauge hose. Disconnect idle control cable and stop-start cable. Remove accelerator linkage.

4) Disconnect ground cable from engine to chassis and all other electrical leads. Disconnect gearshift linkage and exhaust pipe at manifold.

5) Loosen steering relay arm and move downward together with center tie rod and steering shock absorber. Disconnect hydraulic line from clutch slave cylinder.

6) On Auto. Trans. models, disconnect oil cooler lines between transmission and oil cooler.

7) Disconnect exhaust pipe support bracket at transmission, loosen clamp on exhaust pipe and push downward.

8) Attach suitable lifting sling to engine. Mark position of rear engine crossmember in relation to chassis base panel, disconnect rubber mount at transmission and remove crossmember.

9) Disconnect speedometer cable. Disconnect propeller shaft and shaft plate from transmission. Push propeller shaft to rear after loosening clamping nut.

10) Disconnect plug from automatic transmission.

11) Remove bolts at both front engine mounts. Remove front limit stop. Loosen one screw and move power steering reservoir to one side.

12) Lift out engine at a 45° angle. To install, reverse removal procedures.

INTAKE & EXHAUST MANIFOLD

Intake Manifold — Remove air cleaner. Disconnect throttle linkage and bowden cable for idling control on throttle duct. Unscrew vacuum line. Remove attaching nuts and intake manifold from cylinder head.

Exhaust Manifold — Disconnect exhaust pipe from manifold. Remove attaching nuts and lift off exhaust manifold.

CYLINDER HEAD

Removal — 1) Drain cooling system. Disconnect all water hoses attached to cylinder head. Remove vent line, air cleaner and rocker cover.

2) Disconnect vacuum line, injection lines and leakage oil line. Loosen fuel filter screws and move filter out of the way. Remove exhaust pipe from manifold.

3) Disconnect cable to glow plugs and heat sensor from water thermometer. Rotate camshaft until there is no load on rocker arms, and remove rocker arm assemblies (rear assembly for three cylinders; front assembly for two).

4) Remove top chain guide. Unscrew camshaft sprocket screw. Remove chain tensioner and camshaft sprocket.

5) Loosen and remove head bolts, working from outside toward inside of head. Remove four socket screws at front of head. Lift off head and gasket.

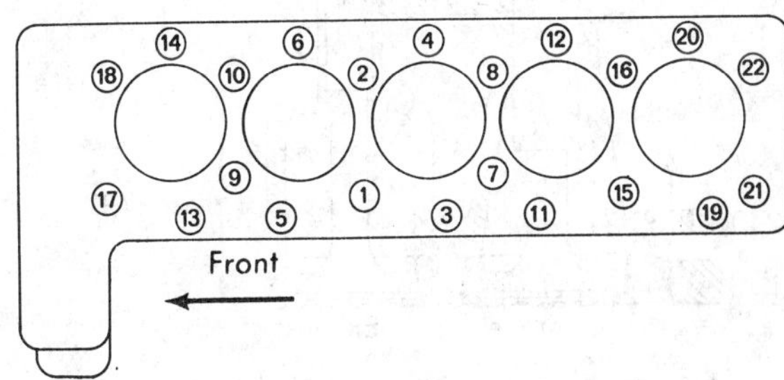

Fig. 1 Cylinder Head Tightening Sequence

Installation — 1) Rotate engine until No. 1 piston is at TDC of compression stroke. Install head gasket and cylinder head, torque head bolts to specifications (see illustration).

2) Install four socket screws in front of head. Connect ground lead for glow plugs to screw under main fuel filter. Insert Woodruff key in camshaft. Place shim on camshaft so mark aligns with mark of first camshaft bearing support.

3) Install camshaft sprocket and chain with tension on driving side of chain, using care not to move camshaft or crankshaft.

4) Check endplay of camshaft. See *Camshaft Bearing Replacement*. Install upper chain guide. Using a new seal, install chain tensioner filled with oil.

5) Install rocker arm assemblies (rear assembly for three cylinders; front for two). Rotate camshaft so there is no load on rocker arms while tightening. Adjust valve clearance with engine cold. See *Valve Clearance Adjustment*.

6) Reinstall remaining components in reverse of removal. Run engine until it has reached 176°F (80°C) and retighten cylinder head bolts, check tappet clearance. (Loosen each head bolt slightly, a bolt at a time, then retorque to specifications).

300D DIESEL 5 CYLINDER (Cont.)

VALVES

VALVE ARRANGEMENT

E-I-I-E-E-I-I-E-E-I (front to rear).

VALVE GUIDE SERVICING

1) Check valve guide bores and ensure they are not less than .3937" (10.00 mm) or larger than .3947" (10.025 mm). Remove all carbon before measuring guides.

2) Using a suitable drift, drive intake guide out toward top of head and exhaust guide toward combustion chamber.

3) Press in new guides from combustion side until specified distance is achieved. See *Fig. 2*. Check guide bores for free movement of valves, and remove any tight spots.

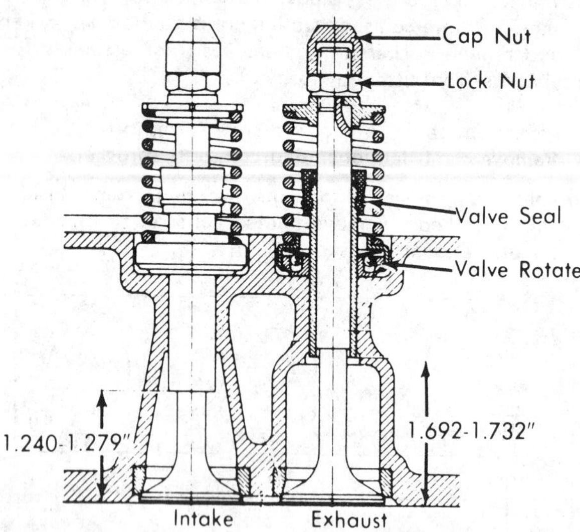

Fig. 2 Installed View of Valve Assemblies

4) Valve guides are available in standard and one oversize (coded red). An interference fit of .0004-.0015" (.010-.040 mm) is used. If guide does not meet specifications, install oversize part. Note that intake guides are 2.40" (60.96 mm) long and exhaust guides are 1.95" (49.53 mm) long.

Valve Guide Specification

Application	Guide O.D. In. (mm)	Cyl. Head Bore In. (mm)
Standard	.5522-.5527	.5511-.5518
	(14.03-14.04)	(14.00-14.02)
Oversize (Red)	.5601-.5605	.5590-.5597
	(14.23-14.24)	(14.20-14.22)

VALVE STEM OIL SEALS

1) Using a spring compressor, unscrew cap nut and lock nut from valve stem. Remove valve collar and spring.

2) Prepare a tool for removing oil seal. See *Fig. 3*. Using oil seal tool, lever oil seal off guide and stem.

3) Place plastic sleeve over threaded end of valve stem. Slide new oil seal in place, using oil seal tool. Install spring and collar. Screw lock nut and cap nut on end of valve stem.

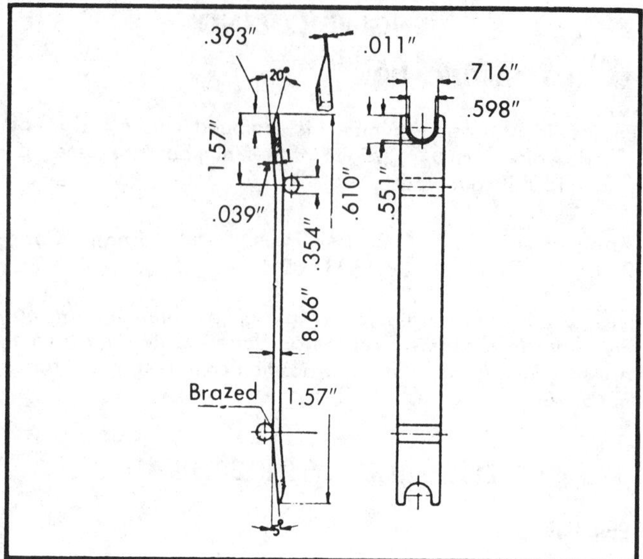

Fig. 3 Valve Stem Oil Seal Tool

Remove rocker arms. Using a spring compressor, unscrew cap nut and lock nut. Remove valve spring collar and lift out spring. Check spring for wear or fatigue, replace as necessary. To install, reverse removal procedures with close wound coils next to cylinder head.

ROCKER ARM ASSEMBLIES

NOTE – *Rocker arms are mounted in two groups. Rear group serves three cylinders; front group, two cylinders.*

1) Remove air cleaner and tappet cover. Loosen rocker arm bracket bolts, rotate camshaft so there is no load on rocker arms being removed.

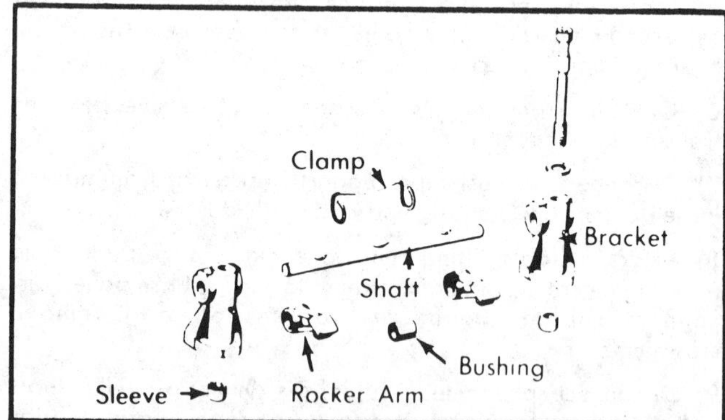

Fig. 4 Detailed View of Front Rocker Arm Assembly

2) Slide rocker arm brackets, rocker arms tightening clamp and spacer off of shaft. Inspect all parts for wear. Replace shaft, rocker bushing or rocker bracket if necessary. To install, reverse removal procedures.

VALVE CLEARANCE ADJUSTMENT

1) Adjust valves according to firing sequence (1-2-4-5-3). Rotate crankshaft until piston of valves to be adjusted is at

300D DIESEL 5 CYLINDER (Cont.)

TDC of compression stroke. Measure clearance between slide surface of rocker arm and cam base circle of camshaft. Cam lobe should be vertical to cam base circle.

2) To adjust, fit holding wrench on valve retainer. Loosen cap nut while holding hex nut. Adjust clearance by turning cap nut. After adjustment, lock the cap nut by tightening hex nut against it. Recheck valve clearance:

Valve Clearance Specifications

Valve	Inches(mm)
Intake	
Cold	①.0039 (.10)
Warm	①.0059 (.15)
Exhaust	
Cold	.012 (.30)
Warm	.014 (.35)

① – Add .002" (.05 mm) additional clearance if ambient temperatures are below -4°F (-20°C) for extended periods.

PISTONS, PINS & RINGS

OIL PAN

NOTE – *Two studs are provided at the front to make it easier to center oil pan on crankcase. Oil seal bore on oil pan is also machined to provide a common flat surface.*

1) Remove oil pan cover, if equipped. Drain engine oil. Remove dipstick and tube. Detach cover plate from clutch housing. Remove oil pan bolts.

2) Loosen steering shock absorber and drag link and turn to one side. Unscrew drag link on intermediate steering and turn aside. Remove oil pan.

PISTON & ROD ASSEMBLY

Removal – **1)** Remove cylinder head and oil pan. Unscrew connecting rod nuts. Tap rod bolts with a plastic mallet to loosen rod on crankshaft. Push piston and connecting rod assembly out top of cylinder block.

2) Remove piston pin circlips. Heat piston to 104-140° (40-60°C) and press out piston pins.

Installation – **1)** Heat piston and reinstall wrist pin and circlips. Piston and wrist pin must be matched.

2) Install connecting rod and cap so cylinder numbers face left side of engine and arrow on piston crown faces forward.

NOTE – *Piston must be installed facing proper direction or damage to the engine will occur.*

3) Connecting rod bolts are of a special design, having an expansion shank which is used to measure bolt stress. If, after several tightenings, the expansion section of the bolt has reached a minimum diameter of .2834" (7.2 mm), the bolt must be replaced. When new, this shank portion should be .3307" (8.4 mm). When replacing, drive out old bolts and insert new ones into same spline pattern in rod cap. **NOTE** – *First tightening of NEW bolts is to 50.6 ft. lbs. (7.0 mkg); subsequent tightenings should be to 36 ft. lbs. (5.0 mkg).*

4) Rotate crankshaft until piston to be measured is at TDC. Measure distance from top of cylinder block to piston crown. Piston must not protrude more than .035" (.90 mm), nor less than .004" (.10 mm) above block surface.

FITTING PISTONS

Measure piston and cylinder diameters to determine running clearance. Piston diameter is measured at 90° to piston pin bore near bottom of piston skirt. There are two compression rings and one oil ring. Install compression rings with marking, "top" or "F", and oil ring with marking, "GOE" or "F", facing upward.

CRANKSHAFT MAIN & CONNECTING ROD BEARINGS

MAIN BEARING SERVICE

NOTE – *The 300D crankshaft has four counterweights and six main bearings.*

Measure main bearing and connecting rod journals for out-of-round and taper. Out-of-round must not exceed .0002-.0004" (.005-.010 mm) and taper must not exceed .0004-.0006" (.010-.015 mm). Select proper undersize, if required, and grind crankshaft to following diameters:

Crankshaft Journal Diameters

Application	Main In. (mm)	Con. Rod In. (mm)
Standard	2.7541-2.7545 (69.95-69.96)	2.0454-2.0458 (51.95-51.96)
1st Undersize	2.7442-2.7446 (69.70-69.71)	2.0356-2.0360 (51.70-51.71)
2nd Undersize	2.7344-2.7348 (69.45-69.46)	2.0257-2.0261 (51.45-51.46)
3rd Undersize	2.7246-2.7249 (69.20-69.21)	2.0159-2.0163 (51.20-51.21)
4th Undersize	2.7147-2.7151 (68.95-68.96)	2.0060-2.0064 (50.95-50.96)

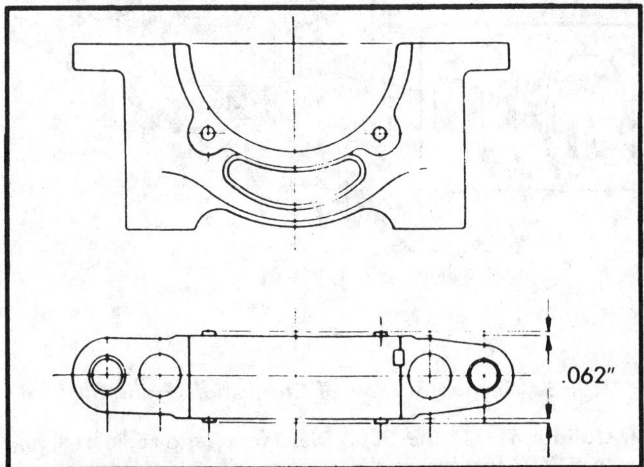

Fig. 5 Detail of Third Main Bearing Cap

300D DIESEL 5 CYLINDER (Cont.)

THRUST BEARING ALIGNMENT

Third main bearing cap has pin located thrust washers to adjust crankshaft end play. Measure end play and install thrust washer(s) required to give proper end play. Measure pin protrusion from main bearing cap to ensure it does not exceed .062" (1.57 mm) as illustrated *(See Fig. 5)*. Standard and oversize thrust washers are available in the following sizes:

Thrust Washer Thicknesses

Application	In. (mm)
Standard	.078 (1.98)
1st Oversize	.080 (2.03)
2nd Oversize	.082 (2.08)
3rd Oversize	.084 (2.13)
4th Oversize	.086 (2.18)
5th Oversize	.088 (2.23)
6th Oversize	.090 (2.28)
7th Oversize	.092 (2.33)

REAR MAIN BEARING OIL SEAL SERVICE

1) With oil pan and crankshaft removed, insert fabric oil seal in groove in crankcase behind rear main bearing. Cut seal at parting face so that it protrudes slightly above parting face.

2) Install other half in oil pan groove, using tallow on seal halves. Reinstall crankshaft and oil pan. Rotate crankshaft to check tightness of seal. If seal is too tight, remove oil pan and crankshaft and roll down high spots with a hammer handle.

FRONT OIL SEAL

Removal — 1) Remove attaching bolt and crankshaft pulley. Attach a suitable puller and remove counterweight. Remove oil pan.

2) Press out seal ring and remove spacer from crankshaft.

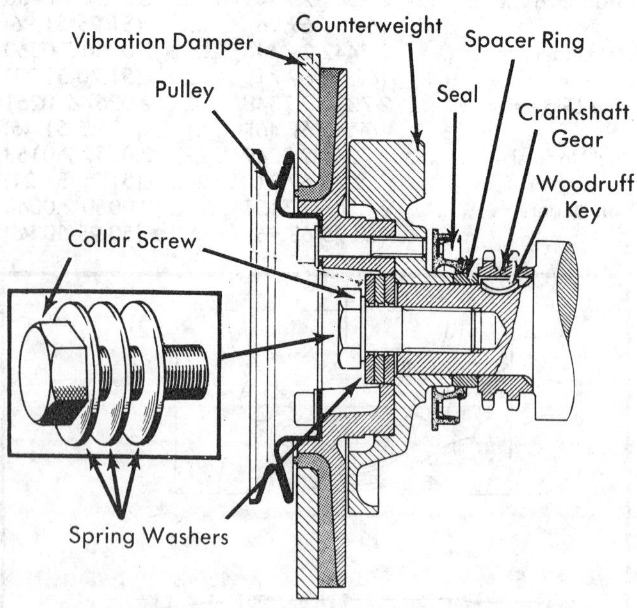

Fig. 6 Sectional View of Crankshaft Front Oil Seal

Installation — 1) The 300D Diesel features a radial seal ring with a 360° shoulder and an oil pan with a machined oil seal bore area. Always use the 360° shouldered seal ring.

2) Lubricate seal lip with oil. Slide oil thrower ring onto crankshaft. Slip radial seal ring onto installation sleeve (130 589 00 61 00) and press seal in until it touches the crankcase face. Install a new hard-chromium plated spacer washer (615 031 01 51) on crankshaft.

3) Place oil pan on two centering studs at front of crankcase and complete installation, by installing components in reverse of removal procedures.

4) When installing vibration damper, use the collar screw (000 961 018 019) with three conical spring washers (127 993 00 26) instead of the collar screw with conical sleeve, used on the 300D models through Chassis No. 000984. See *Fig. 6*.

5) To install collar screw with spring washers on vehicles equipped with the old vibration damper and conical sleeve, either install a new vibration damper (617 030 01 03) or bore out old damper to accept spring washers. See *Fig. 7* for dimensions when reboring damper.

Vibration Damper Boring Dimensions

Location	Inches (mm)
Diameter of Bore	1.922-1.938 (48.8-49.2)
Depth of Bore	.55 (14.0)

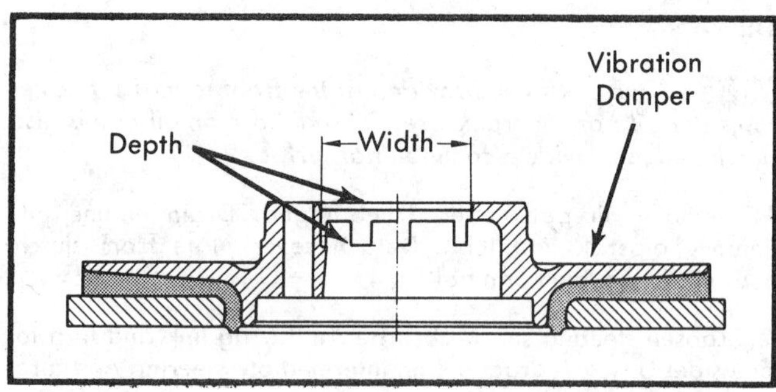

Fig. 7 Instructions for Reboring Vibration Damper

CAMSHAFT

CAMSHAFT

1) Remove camshaft sprocket and rocker arm assemblies. See *Fig. 8*. Disconnect external camshaft oiling tube.

Fig. 8 Rocker Arm Assemblies and Camshaft Bearings

300D DIESEL 5 CYLINDER (Cont.)

2) Remove camshaft bearing supports. Slide bearing supports off of camshaft. To install, reverse removal procedures.

CAMSHAFT BEARING REPLACEMENT

1) Inspect camshaft bearing journals for wear. If worn, grind bearing journals and fit undersize bearings.

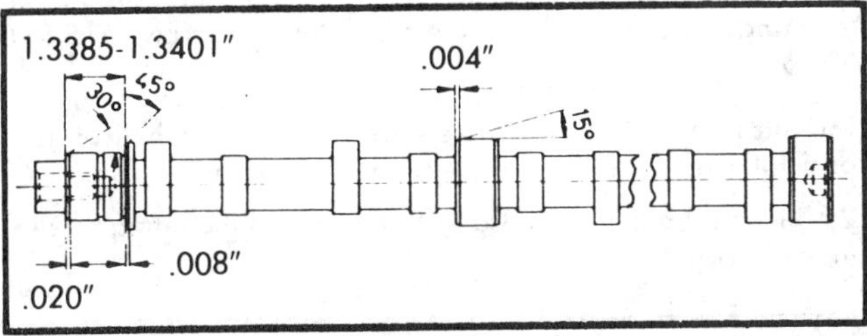

Fig. 9 Detailed View of Camshaft

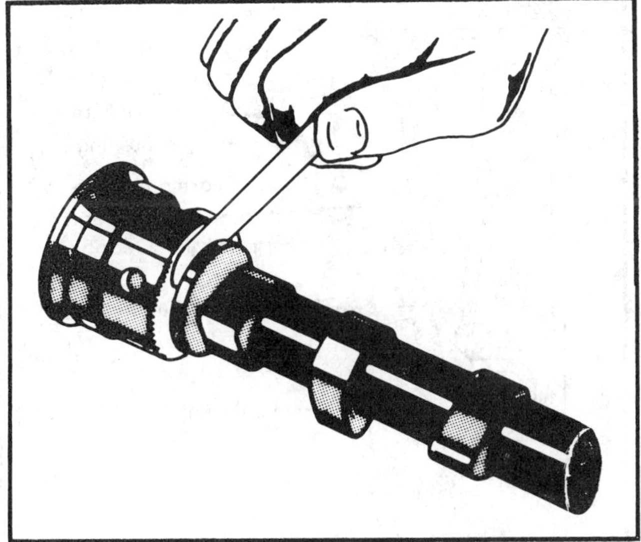

Fig. 10 Measuring Camshaft End Play

2) Bearing on No. 1 journal controls camshaft end play. Width of journal is 1.3385-1.3401" (34.0-34.03 mm). Place bearing on camshaft and install retaining ring. Using a feeler gauge, measure clearance between camshaft flange and bearing (see illustation). Lap bearing to proper fit. The following table lists camshaft bearing journal diameters for standard and undersize bearings:

Camshaft Journal Diameters

Application	Journal No. 1 In. (mm)	Journal No. 2, 3, & 4 In. (mm)
Standard	1.3763-1.3769 (34.96-34.97)	1.8290-1.8297 (6.46-46.47)
Intermediate (Grey)	1.3723-1.3730 (34.86-34.87)	1.8251-1.8257 (46.36-46.37)
1st Undersize (Red)	1.3664-1.3671 (34.71-34.72)	1.8192-1.8198 (46.21-46.22)

TIMING CHAIN REPLACEMENT

1) Remove rocker cover and glow plugs so that engine turns easily. Remove chain tensioner and rocker arm brackets.

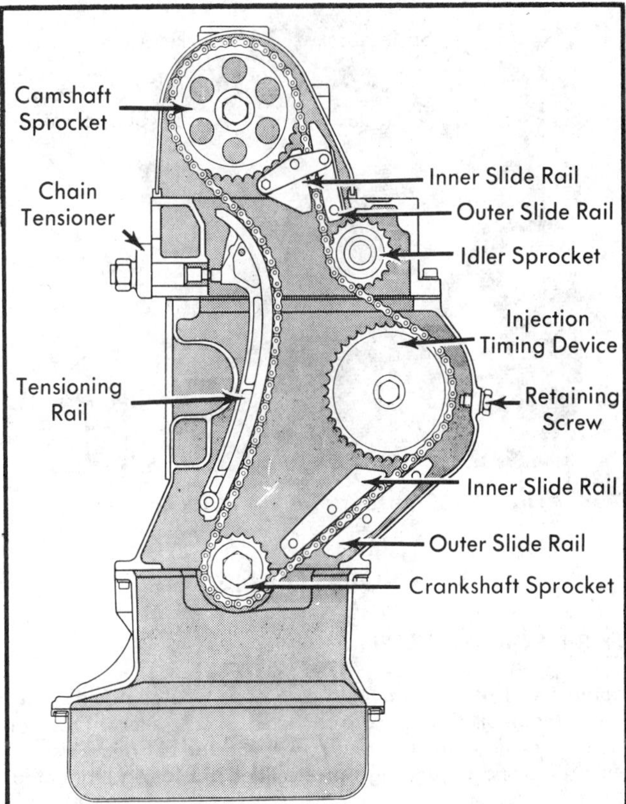

Fig. 11 Timing Chain & Related Components

NOTE — *Removal of rocker arm brackets is not imperative, but is recommended in order to avoid damage to valves or pistons, if, while turning engine, chain jumps over camshaft sprocket.*

2) Grind off pins on a link of old chain and remove link. Using a master link, connect new chain to old chain on driving side of old chain.

NOTE — *Install master link facing camshaft side of chain with spring lock closed end facing direction of rotation (see illustration).*

3) Slowly turn engine in direction of rotation, feeding new chain in and old chain out uniformly. After chain threading is complete join ends of new chain with master link and make sure spring lock closed end is facing direction of rotation. Check that valve timing is correct. See *Valve Timing*. Reverse removal procedures for remaining components.

VALVE TIMING

1) Rotate No. 1 piston to TDC of compression stroke. Align camshaft timing mark with mark on No. 1 camshaft bearing support bracket (see illustration). Install camshaft sprocket.

2) If correct valve timing is not achieved when camshaft sprocket is installed, offset Woodruff keys are available to make timing corrections, see following table:

Offset Woodruff Keys

Offset	Crankshaft Correction
.0275" (.7 mm)	4°
.0354" (.9 mm)	6 1/2°
.0433" (1.1 mm)	8°
.0511" (1.3 mm)	10°

300D DIESEL 5 CYLINDER (Cont.)

Fig. 12 Camshaft Timing Mark Locations

ENGINE OILING

ENGINE OILING SYSTEM

Engine lubrication is provided by a gear type oil pump, which force feeds oil through an oil filter to oil gallery. From oil gallery, oil flows to main and connecting rod bearings. Pistons, wrist pins and connecting rod bushings are splash lubricated.

A vertical oil passage from oil gallery has a transverse passage which supplies oil to intermediate sprocket shaft and bearings. Another oil passage supplies oil to oil pump drive shaft and helical gear. Vertical passage also supplies oil to No. 1 camshaft bearing. An external oil tube attached to No. 1 camshaft bearing support lubricates other camshaft bearings and rocker arms.

Crankcase Capacity – 7.0 quarts (7.95 ltr) with filter.

Oil Filter – Full-flow. Thermostat opens to oil cooler at 203°F (95°C). Clean main element every 3,000 miles. Replace by-pass element every 3,000 miles.

Normal Oil Pressure – 7.1 psi (.5 kg/cm²) at 700-800 RPM; 42 psi (3 kg/cm²) at 3000 RPM.

Pressure Regulator Valve – Non-adjustable.

OIL PUMP

Removal – Remove oil pan. Remove two attaching screws and lift out pump.

NOTE – *Beginning at Chassis No. 31200 (Engine No. 012967), the yellow lock screw (M8) securing the thrust bushing in the oil pump drive was replaced with a black lock screw (M10). To improve the secure positioning of thrust bushing, the black screw (615 990 01 15) should be substituted at the earliest possible opportunity. Tighten lock screw to 11-19 ft. lbs. (1.5-2.5 mkg). See Fig. 13.*

Disassembly – 1) Remove oil strainer. Unscrew lower pump body, and remove pump gears and shafts. Check clearances between gear-to-body and gear-to-cover.

2) If cast-in bushings in housing are worn, replace complete housing. Worn gears are replaced as an assembly. Assemble upper and lower housing without a gasket. Install strainer with a new gasket. Check that pump turns freely.

NOTE – *Beginning at Engine No. 027648, a new thrust bushing (615 180 00 44) with a thicker wall was adapted. The cover disc under the screw plug has been eliminated, and the "O" ring formerly located under the cover disc has been moved down onto the side of the thrust bushing. Parts are not interchangeable. Always use the black locking screw (615 990 01 15).*

Installation – 1) Align drive shaft follower with helical gear and follower faces with respect to one another.

2) Insert oil pump with bracket and tighten mounting screws. Install oil pan.

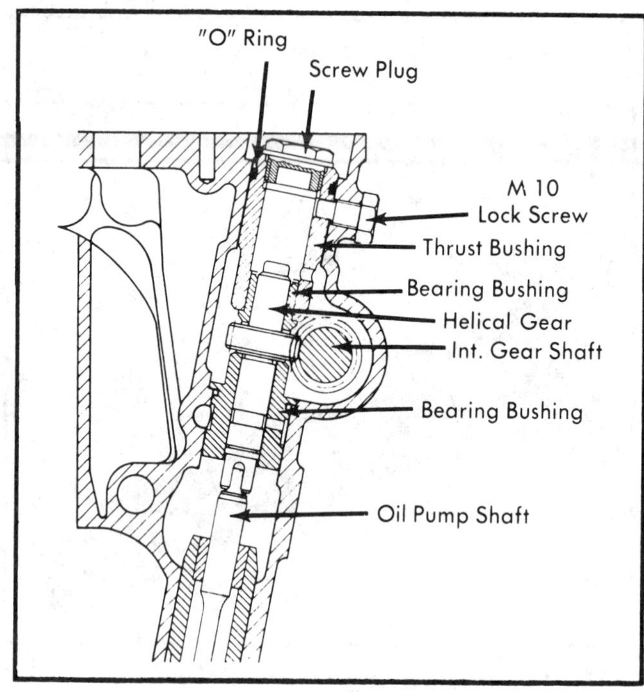

Fig. 13 Location of Thrust Bushing Lock Screw

ENGINE COOLING

Thermostat – Opens at 78-82°F (26-28°C).

Fig. 14 Thermostat Housing Vent Screw

300D DIESEL 5 CYLINDER (Cont.)

Cooling System Capacity — 10.8 quarts (10.2 ltr).

NOTE — *When filling engine with water, vent screw on thermostat housing must be removed until water flows from it. See Fig. 14.*

WATER PUMP

Removal — 1) Drain cooling system below level of pump. Loosen hose clamps on top radiator hose. Remove radiator mounting bolts and push radiator forward.

2) Remove fan from drive pulley. Loosen nuts and adjusters on generator enough so fan belt may be removed. Unscrew and remove venting line between pump and cylinder head.

3) Water pump is a maintenance free type. When installing pump, check hub-to-flange and impeller-to-flange distance. See Fig. 15.

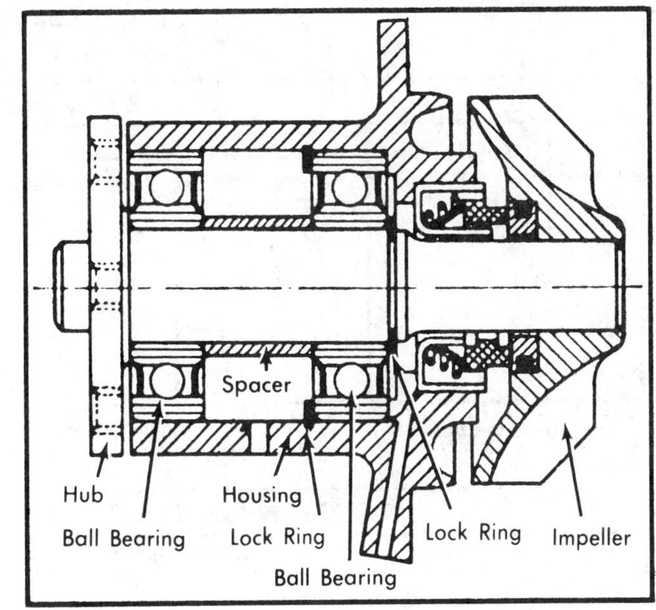

Fig. 15 Sectional View of Water Pump

ENGINE SPECIFICATIONS

GENERAL SPECIFICATIONS

Year	Displ. cu. ins.	Displ. cc	Carburetor	HP at RPM	Torque (Ft. Lbs. at RPM)	Compr. Ratio	Bore in.	Bore mm	Stroke in.	Stroke mm
1977	183.4	3005	Fuel Inj.	77@4000	115@2400	21.0-1	3.58	91	3.64	92.4

VALVES

Engine & Valve	Head Diam. In. (mm)	Face Angle	Seat Angle	Seat Width In. (mm)	Stem Diameter In. (mm)	Stem Clearance In. (mm)	Valve Lift In. (mm)
3005 cc							
Intake	1.563-1.571 (39.70-39.90)	30°	30°	.051-.063 (1.3-1.6)	.3906-.3913 (9.92-9.94)	.0030 (.075)	.....
Exhaust	1.343-1.350 (34.10-34.30)	30°	30°	.098-.114 (2.5-2.9)	.3906-.3913 (9.92-9.94)	.0030 (.075)	.....

VALVE SPRINGS

Engine	Free Length In. (mm)	PRESSURE Lbs. @ In. (kg @ mm) Valve Closed	Valve Open
3005 cc	1.988 (50.5)	58.2@1.512 (26.4@38.41)	116.8@1.177 (53.0@29.9)

CAMSHAFT ①

Engine	Journal Diam. In. (mm)	Clearance In. (mm)	Lobe Lift In. (mm)
3005 cc			
No. 1	1.3763-1.3769 (34.96-34.97)	.0010-.0026 (.025-.066)	.....
No. 2, 3, & 4	1.8290-1.8297 (46.46-46.47)	.0010-.0026 (.025-.066)	.....

① — End play is .003-.006" (.070-.149)

300D DIESEL 5 CYLINDER (Cont.)

ENGINE SPECIFICATIONS (Cont.)

PISTONS, PINS, RINGS

Engine	PISTONS	PINS		RINGS		
	Clearance In. (mm)	Piston Fit In. (mm)	Rod Fit In. (mm)	Rings	End Gap In. (mm)	Side Clearance In. (mm)
3005 cc	.0007-.0015 (.018-.038)	①	Push Fit	No. 1	.0079-.0138 (.20-.35)	.004-.005 (.100-.132)
				No. 2	.0079-.0138 (.20-.35)	.003-.004 (.070-.102)
				No. 3	.0098-.0157 (.25-.40)	.001-.002 (.030-.062)

① — Interference fit. *See Piston & Rod Assembly in this article.*

CRANKSHAFT MAIN & CONNECTING ROD BEARINGS

Engine	MAIN BEARINGS				CONNECTING ROD BEARINGS		
	Journal Diam. In. (mm)	Clearance In. (mm)	Thrust Bearing	Crankshaft End Play In. (mm)	Journal Diam. In. (mm)	Clearance In. (mm)	Side Play In. (mm)
3005 cc	2.7541-2.7545 (69.95-69.96)	.0012-.0029 (.031-.073)	No. 3	.0039-.0090 (.10-.22)	2.0454-2.0458 (51.95-51.96)	.0012-.0029 (.031-.073)	.005-.010 (.12-.26)

VALVE TIMING

Engine	INTAKE		EXHAUST	
	Open (ATDC)	Close (ALDC)	Open (BLDC)	Close (BTDC)
3005 cc	13.5°	15.5°	19°	17°

TIGHTENING SPECIFICATIONS

Application	Ft. Lbs. (mkg)
Cylinder Head	
Step 1	29 (4)
Step 2	43 (6)
Step 3①	65 (9)
Camshaft Bearing Caps	18 (2.5)
Glow Plugs	36 (5)
Prechamber in Cyl. Head	108-130 (15-18)
Connecting Rod Caps	29-36 (4-5)
Main Bearing Caps	65 (9)
Crankshaft Front Hex Bolt	195-239 (27-33)
Oil Pan Bolts	8 (1.1)
Oil Pump Lock Screw (M10)	11-19 (1.5-2.5)
Oil Pump Screw Plug	32-40 (4.5-5.5)
Camshaft Sprocket Bolt	58 (8)

① — After engine is warm, recheck for 65 ft. lbs. (9 mkg) torque.

280 6 CYLINDER

ENGINE CODING

ENGINE IDENTIFICATION

Engine number is stamped on front left side of cylinder block. Engine is a six cylinder double overhead cam type referred to as an M110.

Application	Chassis Type	Engine Coding
280E	123.033	110.984
280SE	116.024	110.985

ENGINE, CYLINDER HEAD & MANIFOLDS

ENGINE

NOTE — *Engine and transmission must be removed as a unit. On 123 series vehicles, engine hood does not have to be removed. The hood can be opened to a 90° position and held in place by a locking mechanism on the left hinge.*

Removal — 1) Remove radiator and fan. On vehicles with level control, remove pump from engine and place aside with hoses connected. On vehicles with air conditioning, remove compressor and set aside with hoses connected.

2) Drain oil supply tank and disconnect power steering hoses from pump. Remove retaining ring from longitudinal accelerator shaft and push toward firewall to remove.

3) Disconnect all water, vacuum, oil and electrical lines leading to engine. Disconnect exhaust pipes from manifold and strut on transmission. Attach suitable lifting sling and remove engine mounting hardware. Lift engine from vehicle at a 45° angle. To install, reverse removal procedures.

INTAKE MANIFOLD

Removal — Partially drain radiator and remove air cleaner. Disconnect electrical wires, water hoses and vacuum lines. Disconnect cold start valve and remove linkage. Remove attaching screws and remove intake manifold.

Installation — To install, reverse removal procedure, using a new gasket.

CYLINDER HEAD

Removal — 1) Drain and remove radiator. Remove air cleaner and valve cover. Remove battery and idler pulley with mounting bracket. Disconnect air conditioning compressor and condenser and place aside with all hoses connected.

2) Remove cover and vacuum pump from front of camshaft housing. Disconnect all electrical leads, water hoses and vacuum lines from cylinder head and manifold.

3) Remove longitudinal regulating linkage and EGR line. Disconnect oil return line at cylinder head. Loosen hose between water pump and thermostat housing. Disconnect bypass line at water pump.

4) Loosen dipstick guide tube at cylinder head and bend slightly to the side. Disconnect exhaust pipes at manifold and transmission. Remove preheater scoop. Using a screwdriver, force out rocker arm tension springs. Using suitable tool (110 589 04 61 00), remove all rocker arms.

5) Rotate crankshaft until both camshaft timing marks are correctly aligned with crankshaft at TDC on firing stroke. Using suitable holding wrench (116 589 01 01 00), remove both camshaft sprocket bolts.

6) Remove upper slide rail and pull out bearing bolts, using suitable puller (115 589 19 33 00). Remove chain tensioner. Push both camshafts toward rear of engine to separate sprockets and camshafts, using suitable tool (110 589 03 33 00). While supporting sprockets, remove spacer ring (intake) and both spacer sleeves in front of camshaft bearings.

7) Remove sealing plug and pull out bearing bolt, using suitable tool (115 589 19 33 00). Lift up timing chain and pull idler sprocket from camshaft housing. Using same puller, remove slide rail bearing pin and slide rail.

8) Loosen head bolts in reverse of tightening order. Remove two 8mm bolts in chain box with a magnet, do not drop washers into timing cover. Pull up timing chain and force tension rail toward center of engine. Using two men, lift cylinder head vertically from cylinder block.

Installation — 1) Place head gasket on cylinder block. Lay two pieces of wood, ½"x1¾"x9½" long, upright between cylinders one and two and flat between cylinders five and six. Mount cylinder head at an inclined position, so that timing chain and tensioner rail can be installed.

2) Lift cylinder head and carefully remove wooden pieces. Lower head, making sure front dowel pin is engaged. Install head bolts and tighten in three stages. Insert 8 mm bolts in chain box using a greased Allen wrench.

NOTE — *After tightening all head bolts, camshaft should be free to turn by hand.*

3) Install lower slide rail and idler sprocket. Place spacer on intake camshaft journal. With engine at TDC, install camshaft sprockets with timing marks aligned, using suitable tool (110 589 03 33 00).

NOTE — *TDC mark on vibration damper is next to dowel pin.*

4) Place spacers in front camshaft bearing of both camshafts. Install camshaft sprockets bolts, but do not tighten. Install upper slide rail and rigid chain tensioner. Using suitable holder tool (116 589 01 01 00), tighten expansion bolts.

NOTE — *If early type camshaft sprocket bolts with two spring washers were installed, replace with new expansion bolts (110 990 02 19) and a single washer (110 990 23 40).*

5) Rotate engine two revolutions and recheck camshaft timing marks. Install swing lever and tensioner springs. Install chain tensioner and adjust valve clearances. Retighten head bolts after engine has been warmed to 176°F (water temperature). Tighten by first loosening head bolts a ¼ of a turn, one at a time and tighten in tightening order. Retighten 8mm bolts in chain box.

6) If complaints are received of excessive oil consumption or blue smoke, replace cylinder head covers and gaskets with new style. Cylinder head cover (110 010 05 30) has extra oil

280 6 CYLINDER (Cont.)

baffles at left front and rear, and a higher oil baffle on front right side. New gasket (110 016 05 21) has "D" shaped holes rather than full round. New head covers and gaskets were used in production beginning with engine number 038726 on the 110.021 engine, and engine number 026766 on the 110.922 engine.

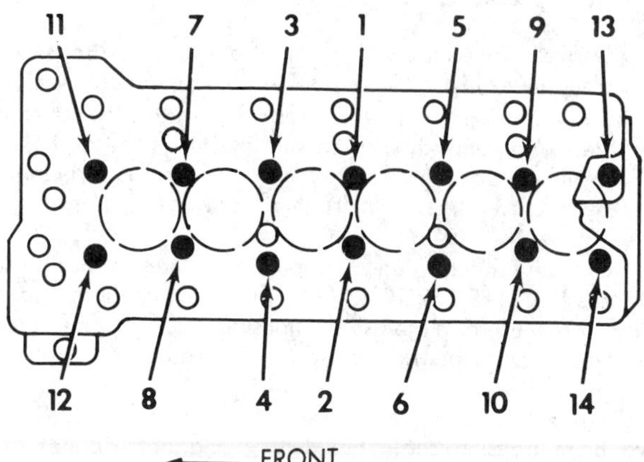

Fig. 1 Cylinder Head Tightening Sequence

VALVES

VALVE ARRANGEMENT

Right Side – All exhaust.
Left Side – All intake.

VALVE GUIDE SERVICING

1) Using a suitable drift, drive valve guide out top of cylinder head. Inspect guide bore in cylinder head, drive new standard guide in until lock ring touches head, if head condition permits.

2) If standard valve guide is not tight in head, ream cylinder head and install oversize valve guide. Heat cylinder head to 194°F and chill valve guide. Drive new guide in until lock ring touches head.

Valve Guide Specifications

Application	Guide O.D. In. (mm)	Head I.D. In. (mm)
Intake		
Std.	.5523-.5331	.5519-.5527
	(14.03-14.05)	(14.02-14.04)
1st O.S. (red)	.5594-.5602	.5590-.5598
	(14.21-14.23)	(14.20-14.22)
2nd O.S. (white)	.5673-.5681	.5669-.5677
	(14.41-14.43)	(14.40-14.42)
Exhaust		
Std.	.5917-.5925	.5913-.5921
	(15.03-15.05)	(15.02-15.04)
1st O.S. (red)	.5988-.5996	.5984-.5992
	(15.21-15.23)	(15.20-15.22)
2nd O.S. (white)	.6066-.6074	.6062-.6070
	(15.41-15.43)	(15.40-15.42)

VALVE STEM OIL SEALS

With valve springs removed, pull off old seal. Place assembly sleeves over intake valve stems and slide new valve stem seal over valve stems. Remove assembly sleeve and force seal over end of valve guide with installation mandrel.

VALVE SPRINGS

1) With camshaft housing removed, place piston on TDC of cylinder from which springs are to be removed. Install a compressed air line to spark plug hole to pressurize valves.

2) Remove valve thrust pieces. Attach suitable holding rail (110 589 00 62 00) to cylinder head. Lightly tap valve collars to loosen keepers. Install suitable spring compressor and press down on springs. Remove valve keepers and release pressure on springs. Remove inner and outer springs and check for wear or fatigue. To install, reverse removal procedures with close wound coils (color coding) next to cylinder head.

ROCKER ARM & STUD ASSEMBLY

1) With a screwdriver, pry out rocker arm tensioner springs. Using crankshaft, rotate engine until heel of cam lobe is next to rocker arm. Using suitable tool (110 589 04 61 00), remove rocker arm.

2) Unscrew threaded bushing with valve adjusting screw. Lubricate threads of adjusting screw with tallow and check that screw has at least 14.5 ft. lbs. of turning torque in bushing.

3) Install threaded bushing and adjusting screw in cylinder head. Lubricate rocker arm and pivot. Using suitable tool (110 589 04 61 00), install rocker arms and tensioner springs. Readjust valve clearances.

CAUTION – *Do not rotate engine by camshaft sprocket bolts. Do not rotate engine in reverse as camshaft sprocket may jump time.*

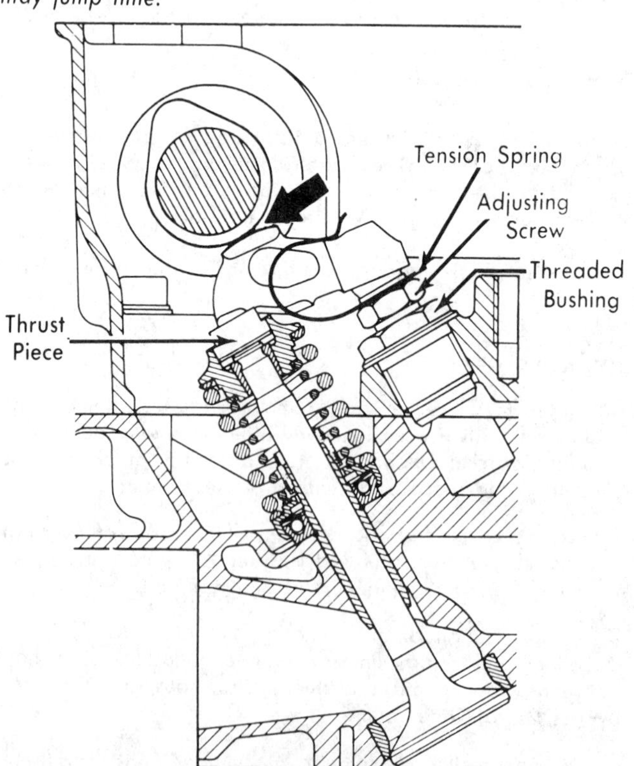

Fig. 2 Sectional View of Rocker Arm and Valve Assembly

280 6 CYLINDER (Cont.)

VALVE CLEARANCE ADJUSTMENT

Rotate crankshaft until heel of camshaft lobe is next to rocker arm. Insert a feeler gauge between camshaft and rocker arm. Turn adjusting screw until proper clearance is achieved.

Valve Clearance

Application	In. (mm)
Intake	
Hot	①.006 (.15)
Cold	①.004 (.10)
Exhaust	
Hot	.012 (.30)
Cold	.010 (.25)

① — Winter Clearance, add .002" (.05mm).

PISTONS, PINS & RINGS

OIL PAN

NOTE — *A two piece oil pan is used. To remove complete oil pan, engine and transmission must be removed (See Engine Removal).*

Removal — Disconnect both front engine mounts. Disconnect engine shock absorbers on right front axle carrier. Attach a lifting sling. Remove front axle, and oil lines from automatic transmission. Loosen oil dipstick guide tube. Drain engine oil and pull off oil return line on oil pan.

Installation — Clean parting surfaces on crankcase and oil pan. Replace rear radial sealing ring in oil pan, working seal into pan with a wooden hammer handle. Cut seal ends so there is .024" protruding. Coat sealing surfaces with sealing compound and install oil pan. To install remaining components, reverse removal procedure.

NOTE — *Beginning at the chassis numbers shown under FRONT COVER OIL SEAL, two studs are provided at the front to make it easier to center oil pan on crankcase. The oil seal bore on the oil pan is also machined beginning at these same numbers.*

PISTON & ROD ASSEMBLY

Removal — With oil pan and cylinder head removed, remove rod caps and push piston and rod assembly out top of cylinder. Remove wrist pin locks and push out wrist pins. Clean and inspect all parts.

Installation — 1) Place piston on connecting rod so that arrow faces forward and recess for bearing insert is facing rear of engine. Install piston and rod assembly in cylinder. Install rod cap with code numbers facing rod numbers.

2) Rod bolts should be checked for minimum diameter with a pair of sharp edged calipers. If diameter is less than .283", replace rod bolts. Tighten rod bolts to 36 ft. lbs. and then tighten an additional 100° of rotation.

FITTING PISTONS

Inspect piston and cylinder for wear or damage. Measure piston clearance, if clearance exceeds .004", bore cylinder and fit new pistons.

Cylinder Bore Specifications

Application	In. (mm)
Standard	3.3858-3.3866 (86.0-86.02)
1st Oversize	3.4055-3.4063 (86.50-86.52)
2nd Oversize	3.4252-3.4260 (87.0-87.02)

CRANKSHAFT MAIN & CONNECTING ROD BEARINGS

MAIN & CONNECTING ROD BEARINGS

1) Remove connecting rod and main bearing caps. Check all bearing journals for wear, taper or out-of-round. The following table gives maximum dimensions which are permissible without repair or new bearings.

Crankshaft Specifications

Application	In. (mm)
Out-of Round	.0002 (.005)
Journal Taper	.0004 (.010)
Journal Flatness	.0006 (.015)
Bearing Bore Out-of-Round	.0004 (.010)
Bearing Bore Taper	.0004 (.010)

2) Bearing inserts for both main and connecting rod journals are color coded. Main bearing inserts with no color are thicker than ones which are blue. Connecting rod inserts with red color are thicker than ones with blue color. Select inserts which will give the mean of clearance range.

Crankshaft Journal Diameters

Application	Main Bearing In. (mm)	Connecting Rod In. (mm)
Std.	2.3602-2.3606 (59.95-59.96)	1.8878-1.8882 (47.95-47.96)
1st U.S.	2.3504-2.3508 (58.70-59.71)	1.8779-1.8783 (47.70-47.71)
2nd U.S.	2.3405-2.3409 (59.45-59.46)	1.8681-1.8685 (47.45-47.46)
3rd U.S.	2.3307-2.3311 (59.20-59.21)	1.8583-1.8587 (47.20-47.21)
4th U.S.	2.3209-2.3213 (58.95-58.96)	1.8484-1.8488 (46.95-46.96)

Bearing Insert Wall Thickness

Application ①	Main Bearing In. (mm)	Connecting Rod In. (mm)
Std.	.1378 (3.50)	.0713 (1.81)
1st U.S.	.1429 (3.63)	.0764 (1.94)
2nd U.S.	.1476 (3.75)	.0811 (2.06)
3rd U.S.	.1528 (3.88)	.0858 (2.18)
4th U.S.	.1575 (4.00)	.0909 (2.31)

① — Number three bearing requires fitting, See *Thrust Bearing Alignment.*

THRUST BEARING ALIGNMENT

Install number three main bearing and measure clearance between bearing and crankshaft sides. If clearance is excessive, install new bearing. New bearings are supplied in oversize widths and must be lapped on non-thrust side to achieve proper clearance. Lap only side away from flywheel.

280 6 CYLINDER (Cont.)

REAR MAIN BEARING OIL SEAL

Press pieces of seal into cylinder block and oil pan with a wooden hammer handle. Cut ends of seal so they protrude .024" above parting surfaces. Reassemble engine and check for oil leaks.

FRONT COVER OIL SEAL

1) Remove pulley, vibration damper and balancing disc. Carefully pry oil seal from cover with a screwdriver. If spacer ring on crankshaft is worn, using suitable puller (115 589 15 33 00), remove and replace ring.

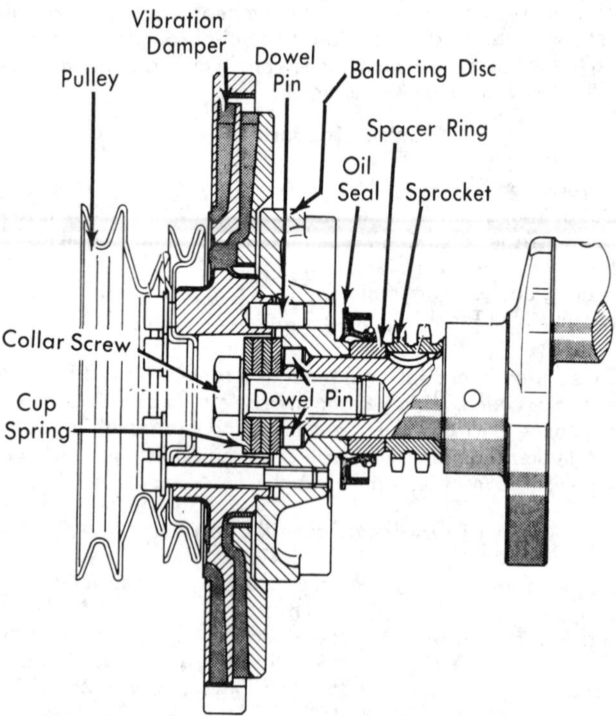

Fig. 3 Cut-Away View of Vibration Damper

2) Slightly lubricate new seal and press into cover, using suitable tool (110 589 07 61 00). Seal must be perfectly square or leaks will occur. Reinstall pulley, vibration damper and balancing disc.

CAMSHAFT

TIMING CHAIN

1) Remove spark plugs and camshaft cover. Remove rocker arm of right-hand exhaust valve. Remove chain tensioner and install a rigid chain tensioner.

2) Cover chain box with a rag, using a chain breaker, separate chain. Join ends of new and old chains together with a master link. Rotate crankshaft in direction of rotation and pull old chain out of engine. Use care that chain does not jump a tooth on sprockets.

3) Join ends of new chain. Rotate crankshaft and check timing marks. Replace rigid chain tensioner with normal chain tensioner. Install rocker arm and adjust valve clearance. Install camshaft cover and spark plugs.

CAMSHAFT & CAMSHAFT HOUSING

Removal – 1) Remove battery and A.I.R. pump. Disconnect air conditioning compressor and set aside with hoses connected. Drain radiator and remove hose between radiator and engine. Remove camshaft cover.

2) Remove camshaft sprocket covers from front of housing. Pry all rocker arm tension springs from rocker arms. Using a suitable tool (110 589 04 61 00), remove all rocker arms.

CAUTION – *Do not turn engine by camshaft bolts. Do not rotate crankshaft in reverse.*

3) Using suitable holding tool (116 589 01 01 00), remove right-hand camshaft sprocket bolt. Set number one piston to TDC on firing stroke with both camshaft timing marks aligned. Remove chain tensioner.

4) Remove slide rail in camshaft housing, using suitable puller (115 589 19 33 00). Remove rear right-hand camshaft cover. Push camshaft to the rear, using suitable tool (110 589 03 33 00), while holding camshaft sprocket in place. Remove sprocket and slide camshaft back in place.

5) Remove head bolts, shown in illustration, in reverse of tightening sequence. Do not remove bolts marked with an "x" in illustration. Remove camshaft housing and camshafts.

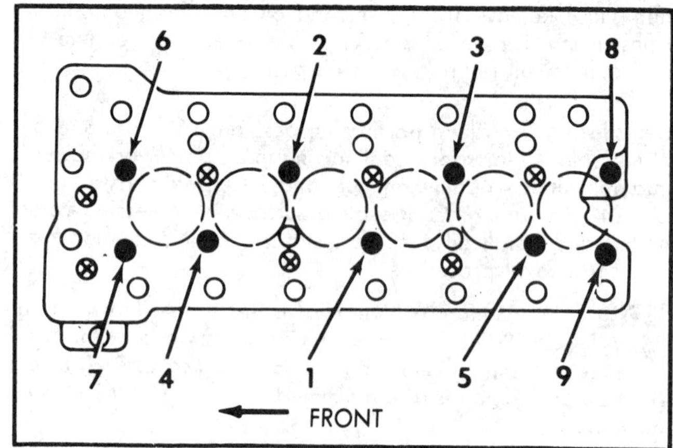

Fig. 4 Camshaft Housing Tightening Sequence

6) Remove left-hand camshaft sprocket in same manner as right-hand sprocket. Remove spacer ring at intake camshaft and slide both camshafts out rear of housing.

Installation – Install steel gasket on cylinder head without sealing compound. Place camshaft housing on head. Oil head bolts and tighten in two steps shown in illustration. One at a time, loosen slightly and retighten five lower head bolts. Tighten 8 mm bolts from center working outward. Install remaining components in reverse of removal procedures.

NOTE – *If early type camshaft sprocket bolts with two spring washers were installed, replace with new expansion bolts (110 990 02 19) and a single washer (110 990 23 40).*

CAMSHAFT BEARINGS

If camshaft bearing journals are worn, damaged or have excessive clearance in camshaft housing bearings, camshaft journals may be ground undersize and a repair housing installed.

280 6 CYLINDER (Cont.)

Front bearing journal *(See "a" in Fig. 6)* is not ground and remains standard. Journal should be fitted with a spacer sleeve. Camshafts do not have to be ground or replaced because of rough surfaces or bearings.

VALVE TIMING

Rotate crankshaft until number one piston is at TDC on firing stroke. Both camshaft timing marks should be aligned with marks on camshaft housing. Offset woodruff keys are available to make corrections to timing. Remember that camshaft sprockets rotate in opposite directions, they rotate toward each other.

NOTE — *Some balance discs have two "O" degree marks. TDC is next to a dowel pin.*

Offset Woodruff Keys

Offset	Part No.	Correction
.0275" (.7 mm)	621 991 04 67	4°
.0354" (.9 mm)	621 991 02 67	6.5°
.0433" (1.1 mm)	621 991 01 67	8°
.0511" (1.3 mm)	621 991 00 67	10°

Fig. 5 Camshaft Timing Marks

ENGINE OILING

Crankcase Capacity — 7 qts. (including filter).

Oil Filter — 1.5 pts. (Full-flow).

Normal Oil Pressure — 7.1 psi (.5 kg/cm²) at 800-900 RPM; 42 psi (3 kg/cm²) at 3000 RPM.

Pressure Regulator Valve — Nonadjustable.

ENGINE OILING SYSTEM

Oil is drawn from the oil pan by a gear type oil pump and pressure fed through a full-flow oil filter to crankshaft main bearings. Passages drilled in crankshaft carry oil to connecting rod bearings. A passageway drilled longitudinally through the connecting rod carries oil from connecting rod bearing to wrist pin bushing. A further passageway carries oil to intermediate shaft, oil pump, and distributor drive gears. This passageway also lubricates camshaft bearings, cam lobes, rocker arms, idler sprocket, and chain tensioner.

OIL PUMP

Remove fuel pump and lower half of oil pan. Remove screws from crankcase and main bearing cap. Pull out oil pump. Disassemble, clean and inspect oil pump. To install, reverse removal procedure.

ENGINE COOLING

Cooling System Capacity — 280E, 10.5 qts. 280SE, 11.5 qts.

Thermostat — Opens at 185-193°F (85-89°C).

WATER PUMP

Drain radiator and disconnect water hoses. Loosen radiator shell and remove radiator. Remove fan and fan clutch (store in upright position). Remove all drive belts. Remove six Allen screws attaching pulley and vibration damper. Withdraw pulley and damper. Remove water pump. To install, reverse removal procedure.

ENGINE SPECIFICATIONS

GENERAL SPECIFICATIONS

Year	Displ.		Carburetor	HP at RPM	Torque (Ft. Lbs. at RPM)	Compr. Ratio	Bore		Stroke	
	cu. ins.	cc					in.	mm	in.	mm
1977	167.6	2746	Fuel Inj.	142@5750①	149@4600②	8.0-1	3.39	86	3.10	78.8

① — Calif. 137@5750 ② — Calif. 142@4600

VALVES

Engine & Valve	Head Diam. In. (mm)	Face Angle	Seat Angle	Seat Width In. (mm)	Stem Diameter In. (mm)	Stem Clearance In. (mm)	Valve Lift In. (mm)
2746 cc							
Intake	1.775-1.783 (45.1-45.3)	45°	45°	.071-.098 (1.8-2.5)	.3524-.3531 (8.95-8.97)	.0019 (.05)	.....
Exhaust	1.4567-1.4645 (37.0-37.2)	45°	45°	.059-.079 (1.5-2.0)	.4307-.4315 (10.94-10.96)	.0023 (.06)	.....

280 6 CYLINDER (Cont.)

ENGINE SPECIFICATIONS (Cont.)

PISTONS, PINS, RINGS						
	PISTONS	PINS		RINGS		
Engine	Clearance In. (mm)	Piston Fit In. (mm)	Rod Fit In. (mm)	Rings	End Gap In. (mm)	Side Clearance In. (mm)
2746 cc	.0010-.0013 (.025-.035)	.00008-.0004 (.002-.011)	.0003-.0007 (.007-.017)	No. 1	.012-.018 (.30-.45)	.0019-.0032 (050-.082)
				No. 2	.012-.018 (.30-.45)	.0011-.0024 (.030-.062)
				No. 3	.010-.016 (.25-.40)	.0004-.0016 (.010-.042)

CAMSHAFT ①			
Engine	Journal Diam. In. (mm)	Clearance In. (mm)	Lobe Lift In. (mm)
2746 cc			
a	.9441-.9445 (23.98-23.99)	.002-.005 (.06-.12)	.....
b	1.9654-1.9661 (49.92-49.94)	.003-.006 (.10-.14)	.....
c	1.9657-1.9665 (49.93-49.95)	.002-.004 (.06-.09)	.....
d	2.0244-2.0252 (51.42-51.44)	.002-.004 (.06-.10)	.....
e	2.0835-2.0842 (52.92-52.94)	.002-.004 (.06-.10)	.....
f	2.1228-2.1236 (53.92-53.94)	.002-.004 (.06-.10)	.....

① — Journal diameters for each journal varies. See illustration below for bearing identification. Dimensions shown are for new camshaft. Journals (except "a") may be ground to accept camshaft housings with repair stages. End play is .002-.005" (.050-.128 mm).

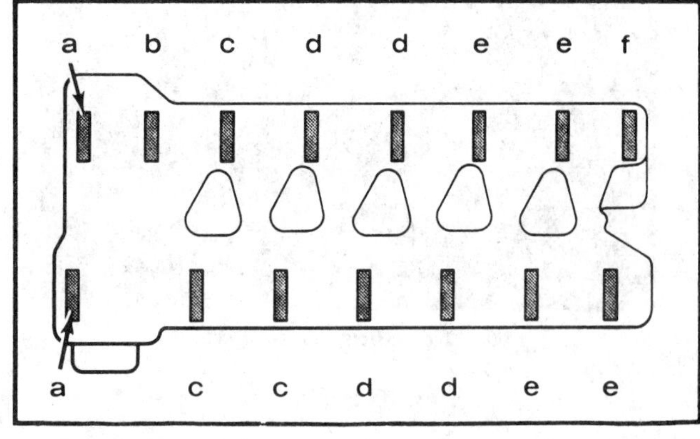

Fig. 6 Camshaft Bearing Identification

CRANKSHAFT MAIN & CONNECTING ROD BEARINGS							
	MAIN BEARINGS				CONNECTING ROD BEARINGS		
Engine	Journal Diam. In. (mm)	Clearance In. (mm)	Thrust Bearing	Crankshaft End Play In. (mm)	Journal Diam. In. (mm)	Clearance In. (mm)	Side Play In. (mm)
2746 cc	2.3602-2.3606 (59.95-59.96)	.001-.003 (.03-.05)	No. 3	.004-.009 (.10-.24)	1.8878-1.8882 (47.95-47.96)	.0005-.0020 (.013-.050)	.004-.009 (.11-.23)

280 6 CYLINDER (Cont.)

ENGINE SPECIFICATIONS (Cont.)

VALVE SPRINGS			
Engine	Free Length In. (mm)	PRESSURE Lbs. @ In. (kg @ mm)	
		Valve Closed	Valve Open
2746 cc			
Inner	1.772 (45)	26.01@1.299 (11.8@33)	50.7@.846 (23@21.5)
Outer	1.949 (49.5)	67.24@1.6535 (30.5@42)	194@1.20 (88@30.5)

VALVE TIMING				
	INTAKE		EXHAUST	
Engine	Open (ATDC)	Close (ALDC)	Open (BLDC)	Close (BTDC)
2746 cc	7°	21°	30°	12°

TIGHTENING SPECIFICATIONS

Application	Ft. Lbs. (mkg)
Main Bearings	58 (8.0)
Connecting Rods	①36 (5.0)
Crankshaft Bolt	289-325 (40-45)
Camshaft Cover	4 (.5)
Cylinder Head Bolts②	
Stage 1	29 (4.0)
Stage 2	51 (7.0)
Stage 3	72 (10)
Camshaft Bolt	72 (10)
Oil Pump	21 (3.0)
Chain Tensioner Nut	36 (5.0)

② – With engine warm, 176°F (80°C) retorque to 72 ft. lbs. (10 mkg).

① – Tighten bolts to 36 ft. lbs. (5 mkg) and then turn bolts an additional 100° of rotation.

4.5 LITER V8

ENGINE CODING

ENGINE IDENTIFICATION

Identification number is located on tag attached to engine crankcase. First six digits of code are used to identify engine, as follows:

Application	Chassis Type	Engine Code
450 SLC	107.024	117.985
450 SL	107.044	117.985
450 SEL	116.033	117.986

ENGINE, CYLINDER HEAD & MANIFOLD

ENGINE

Removal – 1) Disconnect all necessary water hoses, electrical leads (both battery cables), fuel lines, vacuum lines and fuel injection linkage. Remove fan, radiator and air cleaner.

2) Drain power steering reservoir and disconnect hoses. Unbolt air conditioning compressor and position hoses and compressor out of way. **NOTE** – *It is not necessary to discharge the air conditioning system during engine removal if compressor can be moved aside enough to permit engine clearance.*

3) Disconnect fuel injection heating connections, oil pressure gauge, and ground strap. Remove left engine shock mount and loosen right side mount. Disconnect upper left side mount and right side mount from suspension. Disconnect and lower the exhaust system. Disconnect torsion bar and hand brake.

4) Remove tunnel shield and disconnect drive shaft at center bearing. Using suitable jack, support transmission. Remove engine carrier, marking it for reinstallation. Disconnect all linkage extending from transmission. On standard transmission, disconnect hydraulic lines. Attach suitable hoist, remove engine mounting bolts and lift engine from vehicle.

INTAKE MANIFOLD

Drain cooling system and remove air cleaner. Disconnect fuel injection linkage and fuel lines on pressure regulator. Disconnect fuel start valve. Remove ignition valves. Extract intake manifold bolts and lift manifold off in rearward direction. To install, reverse removal procedure.

CYLINDER HEAD

1) Drain cooling system and crankcase. Remove air cleaner and battery. Disconnect cable set for electronic ignition system and fuel injection linkage. Loosen ring line with injection valves and remove.

2) Disconnect and remove intake pipe (manifold). If equipped with automatic transmission, remove fluid filler pipe from its attachment to cylinder head. Remove alternator and bracket. Remove oil pump (high pressure) carrier and distributor.

3) Disconnect exhaust system. Drain power steering reservoir and disconnect both hoses. Remove chain tensioner and valve covers. Mark camshaft gear and chain for reinstallation. Remove upper chain dampers (side rails). Withdraw bolts and remove cylinder head. **NOTE** – *Bottom row of camshaft bearing bolts also secure cylinder head.* Care must be exercised when removing right side cylinder head as chain may not clear. To install, reverse removal procedure.

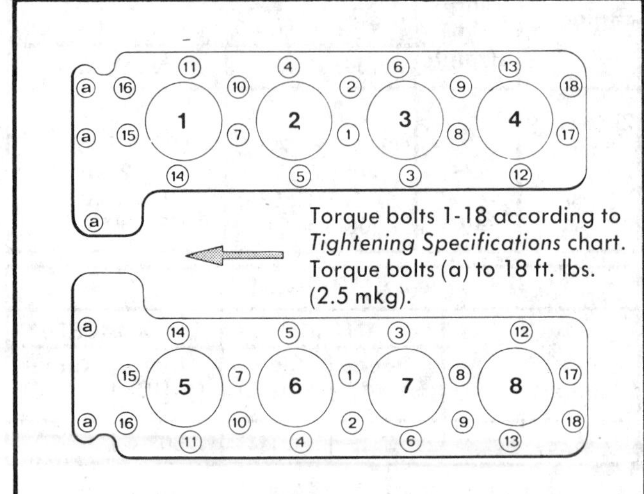

Torque bolts 1-18 according to *Tightening Specifications* chart. Torque bolts (a) to 18 ft. lbs. (2.5 mkg).

Fig. 1 Cylinder Head Tightening Sequence

VALVES

VALVE ARRANGEMENT

Right Bank – E-I-E-I-E-I-I-E (front to rear).
Left Bank – E-I-I-E-I-E-I-E (front to rear).

HYDRAULIC VALVE LIFTERS

1) Hydraulic valve lifters eliminate the need to adjust for valve clearance. *See Fig. 2.* Constant contact of rocker arms with camshaft, valves and lifters not only reduces noise, but also compensates for wear or temperature changes.

2) Oil pressure to operate the lifters is supplied by the oil pump, through a lateral passage in the cylinder head (with connecting bores to each lifter) and an oil passage in the fifth camshaft bearing. The spherical head plunger contains an oil reservoir, which is separated from the pressure chamber by a ball valve. *See Fig. 2.*

3) When engine is stopped and cam lobe exerts pressure on the valve lifter, the plunger can be completely depressed. Oil from pressure chamber flows to reservoir. Turning cam lobe away from rocker arm releases plunger and compression spring pushes it upward until rocker arm rests against cam. Upward plunger movement causes a suction in the pressure chamber, causing oil to flow from reservoir to chamber.

4) The ball valve closes when the cam lobe exerts pressure on rocker arm. Trapped oil in pressure chamber forms a solid hydraulic connection which prevents the plunger from moving fully downward. Leak-off vents permit air and excess oil to escape.

VALVE GUIDE SERVICING

1) With cylinder head removed and suitably supported, clean bores of valve guides. Hard oil carbon deposits can be eliminated with a honing needle.

4.5 LITER V8 (Cont.)

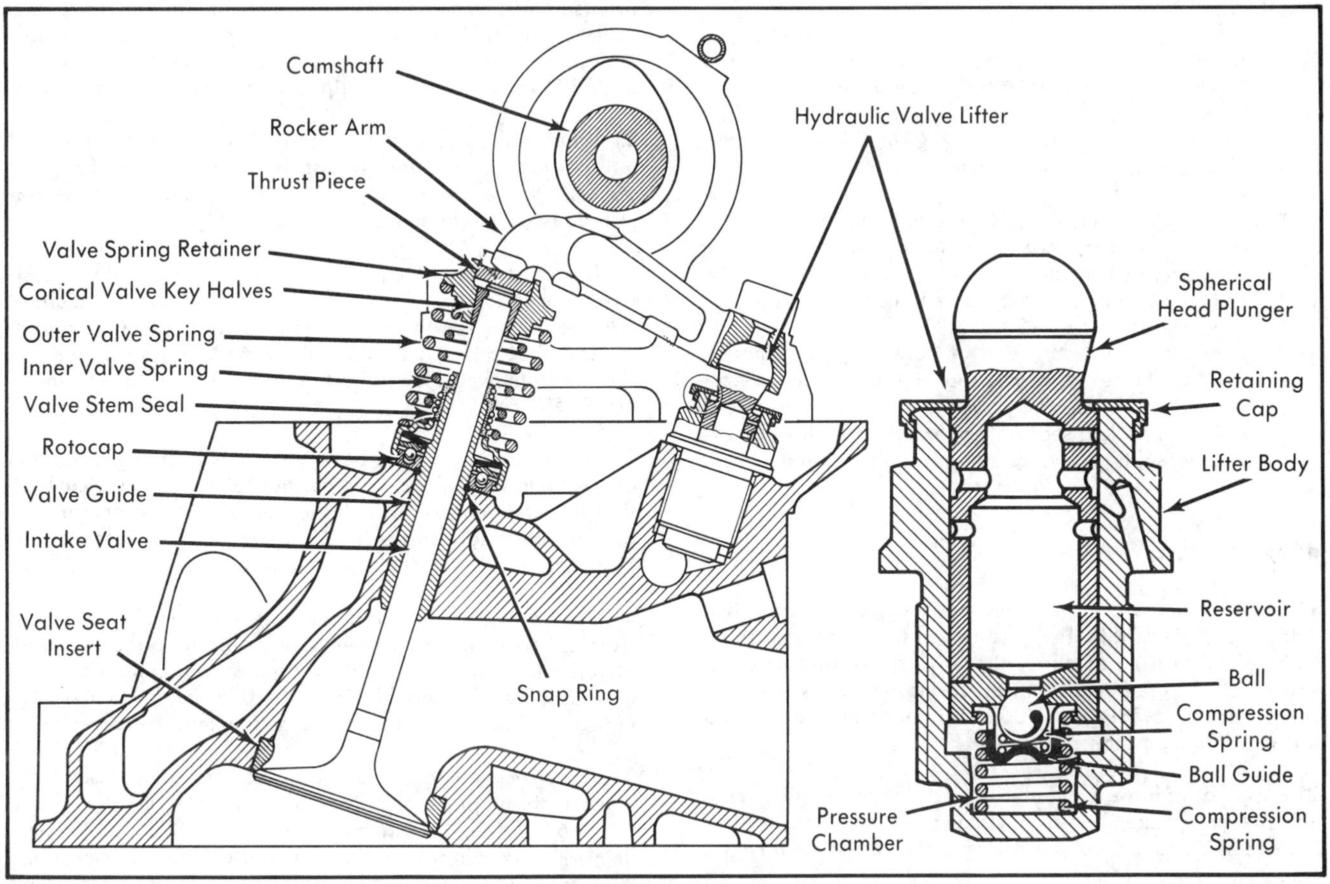

Fig. 2 Cutaway View of Valve System and Lifter

2) Using a suitable plug gauge, inspect valve guides. Inner diameter of new inlet guides should be .354-.355" (9.000-9.015 mm); exhaust guides should be .433-.434" (11.000-11.018 mm). If guide is beyond this tolerance, replace with new guide. *See Fig. 2.*

3) With suitable reamer/installer mandrel, drive worn guide from its bore. Inspect valve guide bore in cylinder head and ream to accept next oversize guide.

NOTE — *Replacement Inlet valve guides are available in overlapping sizes, ranging from .552-.568" (14.014-14.431 mm) outside diameter. Exhaust valve guides are available with outside diameters of .591-.608" (15.014-15.431 mm).*

4) Heat cylinder head to approximately 194° F (90° C) and cool valve guides (if possible). Coat guide bore with oil and, using remover/installer mandrel, seat new guide in bore.

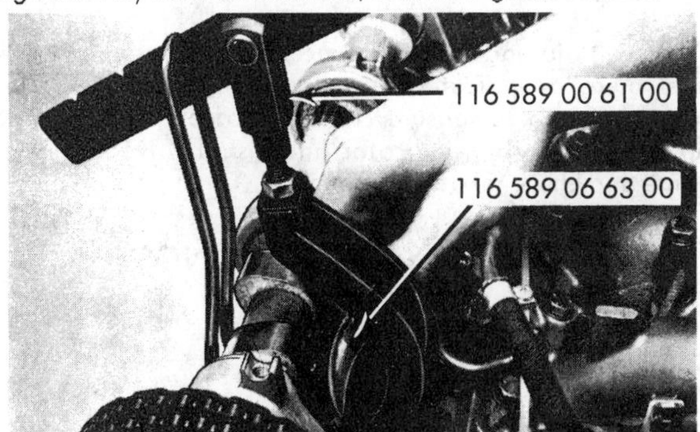

Fig. 3 Removing Conical Valve Key Halves

NOTE — *Be sure snap ring is properly installed. Recheck valve guide clearance and that valve moves freely in guide.*

VALVE STEM SEALS

Removal — Using spring compressor (116 589 00 61 00), remove rocker arms. *See Fig. 3.* Lift out thrust plate, and using special magnet (116 589 06 63 00), remove conical valve key halves. Remove spring retainer, inner and outer valve springs, valve stem seals and rotocaps.

Installation — To install, lubricate valve stem seals. Place assembly sleeve (115 589 10 59 00) on valve and slide seal into place, using assembly tool (116 589 00 43 00). *See Fig. 4.* Install remaining components in reverse order of removal.

Fig. 4 Installing Valve Stem Seal

4.5 LITER V8 (Cont.)

VALVE SEAT RING

1) Check valve guide prior to removing seat ring. See *Valve Guide Servicing*. If seat ring is worn, carefully remove it by machining with a valve seat ring turning tool. Do not machine away entire seat ring. Leave .012-.016" (.3-.4 mm) and remove this portion with a screwdriver or pointed tool.

2) Thoroughly clean the receiving bore and check its diameter. If diameter is within specifications, install a new valve seat ring of the same size. If diameter is not within specification, 1.811-1.812" (46.0-46.02 mm), machine bore to next oversize.

3) To install, heat cylinder head in water to approximately 140° F (60° C). Place pre-cooled seat ring into bore. To position seat ring, lightly tap ring, using a suitable mandrel and hammer. After installing seat ring, peen-lock it at three points. Refinish valve seats. Valve seat runout should not exceed .0011" (.03 mm).

ROCKER ARMS

1) Rocker arms are individually-mounted on the 16 valves, without use of a shaft. They are in constant contact with the camshaft, thrust plates above the valve stems, and hydraulic valve lifters. To remove, compress spring on each valve using compressor (116 589 00 61 00). Mark each arm for installation in original position.

2) Rocker arms have a chamfer behind ball socket (lifter end). This prevents rocker arm from striking retaining cap of lifters in extreme cases. Do not use rocker arms unless they have this chamfer.

3) Whenever camshaft is replaced, new rocker arms must also be installed. Likewise, when new rocker arms are installed, replace the camshaft, as well. When making replacements, check base setting of hydraulic valve lifters.

CHECKING NOISY VALVE LIFTERS

1) Check lifters for noise under no-load conditions (cam lobe pointing upward). On 450SE and 450SEL, turn off ignition and remove fuel pump relay (code 21) from fuse box. Connect starter contact switch to positive battery connection and to pin in contact 1 of plug. On 450SL and 450SLC models, turn off ignition switch, disconnect wire at terminal 16 (red/purple) of 4-prong plug. Connect starter contact switch at terminal 30 (red) and terminal 40 (purple).

2) Try moving rocker arms manually. If they have play, check base setting of hydraulic valve lifter. If setting is within specifications, replace valve lifter.

3) Push downward with a hammer handle on each spherical plunger head (applying pressure to rocker arm above plunger). If plunger drops too fast in comparison to other plungers, replace faulty lifter.

ADJUSTING LIFTERS TO BASE SETTING

NOTE — *Always keep hydraulic valve lifters in an upright position. Rocker arms and valve lifters should always be reinstalled in original locations. When checking and adjusting lifter settings, crank engine for 30 seconds with starter contact switch. To avoid flowing while cranking engine, follow procedure outlined in step **1**), CHECKING NOISY VALVE LIFTERS. Never dissasemble lifters. Replace as a complete unit.*

1) When replacing camshaft or rocker arms or in event of noisy lifters, check and adjust base setting of lifters. To operate properly, the spherical head plunger must be adjusted to a pre-determined setting.

2) To adjust, position cam lobe in the vertical, no-load position. The clearance between the upper edge of plunger cylinder (below socket joint) and the lower edge of the retaining cap should be .028-.075" (.7-1.9 mm). This dimension can change with wear. To adjust, use thinner or thicker thrust pieces. See *Fig. 2*.

3) To measure clearance between points in step **2**), position cam lobe in vertical, no-load position. Mount dial indicator so that its extension fits through the bore of the rocker arm and rests on spherical head plunger. Tighten dial indicator to .08" (2 mm) preload. Adjust dial indicator to zero.

4) Depress valve with spring compressor, removing the load from spherical head plunger. Compression spring will push plunger upward until it rests against retaining cap. This preload dimension should read .028-.075" (.7-1.9 mm) on dial indicator. If outside specifications, setting must be corrected.

5) To correct setting, remove dial indicator and rocker arm. Remove thrust piece and insert measuring thrust piece (100 589 16 63 00), having a thickness of .1870" (4.75 mm). Reinstall rocker arm and dial indicator and repeat measuring process in steps **3**) and **4**). Select correct thrust piece according to measured value:

Thrust Piece Specifications

Measured Value Inches (mm)	Thrust Piece Thickness Inches (mm)
.000-.002 (0-.05)	①.2283 (5.8)
.000-.002 (0-.05)	①.2146 (5.45)
.002-.034 (.06-.87)	.2008 (5.1)
.035-.066 (.88-1.69)	.1870 (4.75)
.067-.099 (1.70-2.51)	.1732 (4.4)
.099-.131 (2.52-3.33)	.1594 (4.05)
Over .131 (3.33)	.1457 (3.7)

① — If measured value is 0-.002" (0-.05 mm), and base setting cannot be obtained with .2146" (5.45 mm) thrust piece, then install .2283" (5.8 mm) thrust piece.

6) Remove dial indicator and rocker arm, and insert selected thrust piece as indicated by measurement and chart. Install rocker arm and remeasure clearance as outlined in steps **3**) and **4**). Remove dial indicator and install valve covers. Start engine and check for valve train noise.

PISTONS, PINS & RINGS

OIL PAN

1) Drain crankcase and disconnect transmission oil cooler (if equipped). Remove air cleaner. Disconnect front torsion bar.

4.5 LITER V8 (Cont.)

2) Disconnect oil damper and place out of way. Remove oil dipstick. Raise front of vehicle and remove cover plate on intermediate flange.

3) On all models equipped with air conditioning, detach coolant compressor and place out of way. **NOTE** — *Do not disconnect coolant lines under pressure.* Loosen oil pan mounting bolts. For access to bolts behind damper align recess. Carefully lower oil pan.

4) When installing oil pan, center on two studs at front of cylinder block, and install remaining bolts.

CRANKSHAFT MAIN & CONNECTING ROD BEARINGS

MAIN & CONNECTING ROD BEARINGS

1) Mount main bearing cap to cylinder block (without bearings in place). Measure inside diameter at three locations. See *Fig. 5.* Be sure cap is properly positioned when taking reading. Offset bearing caps can be moved into center position by lightly tapping them with a plastic hammer.

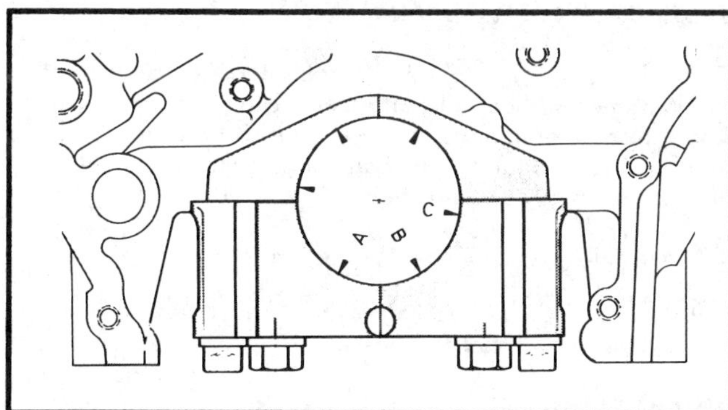

Fig. 5 Location for Measuring Main Bearing Bore Diameter

2) All three measurements should agree. If basic bores exceed specifications and the required overlap of bearing shell halves is not assured, remove .008" (.02 mm) from contact surfaces, using a surface plate.

3) Measure main bearing and connecting rod bearings at front and rear to check for taper. If beyond .0006" (.015 mm), remove excess material from one side of bearing cap, using surface plate.

4 Use proper bearing shells to match measurements obtained. Several overlapping bearing sizes are available. Fit bearing halves into bearing bore and tighten bolts to proper torque. Measure inner diameter of bearings and outer diameter of journals. Difference in measurements should be within bearing clearance specifications. If not, change bearing shell halves.

5) When proper clearance is calculated, clean and oil all parts and install crankshaft. Torque to specifications according to sequence. See *Fig. 6.*

6) With crankshaft properly installed, check for free rotation and for proper end play. Install connecting rods.

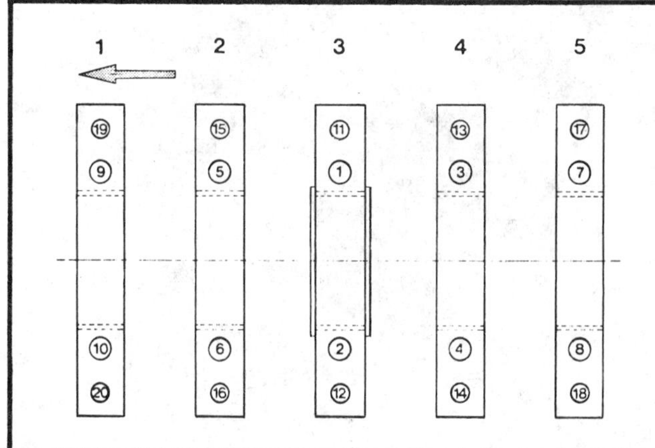

Fig. 6 Crankshaft Main Bearing Tightening Sequence

REAR CRANKSHAFT SEALING RING

1) Remove air cleaner on automatic transmission models only. Disconnect control pressure linkage to transmission. Drain transmission. Disconnect rear torsion bar from mount. **NOTE** — *Level control rod must be disconnected from valve.*

2) Disconnect handbrake linkage. Disconnect from transmission, linkage, vacuum line, speedometer cable and oil filler tube.

3) On manual transmission models only, disconnect hydraulic line and plug openings. Disconnect transmission bell housing and starter, placing it out of way.

4) Remove engine mounts and crossmember after suitably supporting engine. Engine must not tilt downward. Lift out transmission.

5) Remove driven plate or flywheel and intermediate flange. Using two screwdrivers, remove cover and force sealing ring out of cover. To install, use a suitable tool and insert sealing ring. Coat cover with appropriate sealing compound. Reverse removal procedure to install remaining components.

NOTE — *If the rear radial sealing ring causes wear marks on crankshaft bearing, install new sealing ring with the sealing lip offset to the outside.*

Fig. 7 Removing Rear Sealing Ring

4.5 LITER V8 (Cont.)

Fig. 8 Installing Rear Sealing Ring

FRONT CRANKSHAFT SEALING RING

Removal – With engine removed from vehicle. Remove all V-belts, mark hub and crankshaft with paint or chalk. Remove vibration damper, pulley and hub. Remove sealing ring, making sure that crankshaft and receiving bore are not damaged.

Installation – Deburr edge of receiving bore before installing new seal. Lubricate receiving bore and seal lip with oil. Install sealing ring with installation sleeve (110 589 07 61 00). Reassemble remaining components in reverse of removal procedure.

CAMSHAFT

CAMSHAFT REMOVAL

CAUTION – *Never remove both camshafts at the same time.*

1) Remove air cleaner, venturi control valve unit and disconnect vacuum hose to brake unit. Remove valve covers. Remove both camshaft sprocket bolts and spark plugs. Using

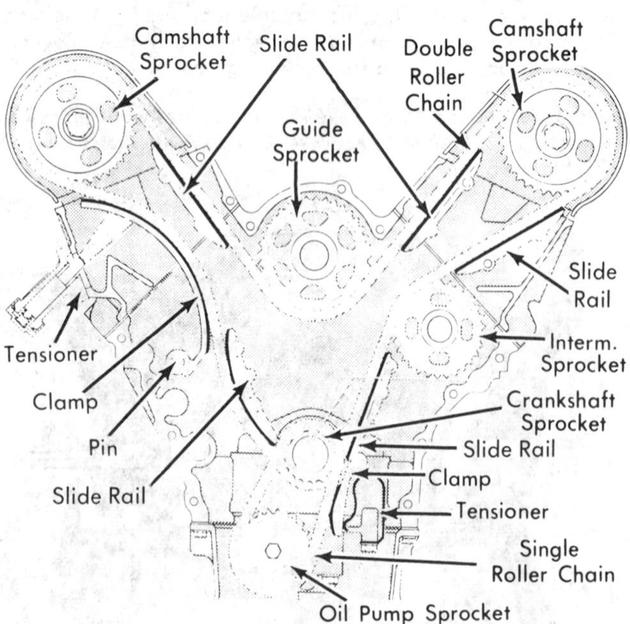

Fig. 9 Timing Chains & Sprockets

suitable tool (116 589 00 61 00), remove rocker arms and mark them for reinstallation in original location.

NOTE – *Whenever rocker arms are replaced, install a new camshaft. Likewise, if a new camshaft is installed, use new rocker arms.*

2) Place No. 1 cylinder at TDC. Ensure timing pointer is at TDC and markings on both compensating washers of camshaft are in alignment with markings on front camshaft bearings.

NOTE – *Fifth camshaft bearing has an oil passage to supply hydraulic valve lifters with oil. Second, third and fourth bearings have two oil pockets.*

3) Connect timing chain and camshaft sprocket with wire so chain does not fall or skip. Drive cam sprocket from camshaft. Remove bearing bracket bolts and lift camshaft off with brackets.

4) To install, lubricate new camshaft and insert into bearing brackets. Position assembly into cylinder head and tighten as required. **NOTE** – *If external lubrication pipe has been removed, replace plastic connectors.* Reverse removal procedure for remaining components.

DISTRIBUTOR DRIVE GEAR

1) With timing and crankshaft chains exposed, disconnect all chain dampers (slide rails) and timing chain tensioner. Remove chain from intermediate sprocket. Pull sprocket forward and remove from bearing in cylinder crankcase by twisting. Remove in an upward direction.

2) To install, reverse removal procedure.

NOTE – *When reinstalling chain, be sure hex bolts on camshaft sprockets are not loosened.*

CHAIN TENSIONER

NOTE – *In all instances chain tensioner is lubricated and connected to oiling circuit.*

450SL & 450SLC – Remove right side valve cover. Extract both mounting bolts and remove chain tensioner. Cable bracket must be held aside.

450SE & 450SEL – Disconnect battery, remove right side valve cover and alternator. Unbolt bracket for right side engine damper from frame. Remove chain tensioner.

VALVE TIMING

1) Measure timing periods on inlet valves of cylinder 1 and 6. Remove hydraulic valve lifters and replace with adjusting screws (116 050 11 20). Adjust each screw so rocker arm just touches the base circle of the cam.

2) Attach a dial indicator so that pointer rests on retainer of intake valve. Preload to .079" (2.007 mm). Turn indicator back to zero.

3) Turn engine in direction of rotation and read dial when gauge reaches 60. Readings should agree with Valve Timing Chart.

4.5 LITER V8 (Cont.)

4) If timing requires correction, install an offset Woodruff Key or new chain. Keys are available in four offsets providing corrections of 4°, 6½°, 8°, and 10°.

5) After checking and adjusting valve timing, reinstall hydraulic lifters and adjust for proper base setting. See *ADJUSTING LIFTERS TO BASE SETTING*.

ENGINE OILING

ENGINE OILING SYSTEM

Lubrication is provided by a gear type oil pump directly driven by crankshaft. Oil is picked up through a strainer from lower portion of oil pan and forced to oil filter through a duct in timing casing. After passing through filter, oil flows to center main duct, to crankshaft and through rod bearings up rods to piston pin bushing. Oil galleries run to cylinder head, valve assemblies and to camshafts. Circuit also includes chain tensioner, ignition and, if applicable, air compressor.

Oil Filter – Disposable cartridge type. Located near front of engine.

Normal Oil Pressure – 7.1 psi@idle; 42.6 psi@3000 RPM.

Over Flow Valve – Valve is located in crankcase and enters into main oil gallery. When filter becomes severely contaminated valve will open and oil will enter in an unfiltered state.

Crankcase Capacity – 8.0 quarts.

ENGINE COOLING

WATER PUMP

Disconnect all necessary water hoses and any remaining components from water pump housing. Remove distributor and all mounting bolts. Remove pump from vehicle. To install, reverse removal procedure.

Thermostat – Located in water pump housing, as shown in illustration. To remove drain cooling system, remove air cleaner, disconnect battery and alternator. Remove housing and thermostat. When installing ensure ball valve is mounted at highest point.

Cooling System Capacity – 15.8 quarts.

Thermostat – Opens at 162-169° F (72-76° C).

Radiator Cap – 13-15 psi.

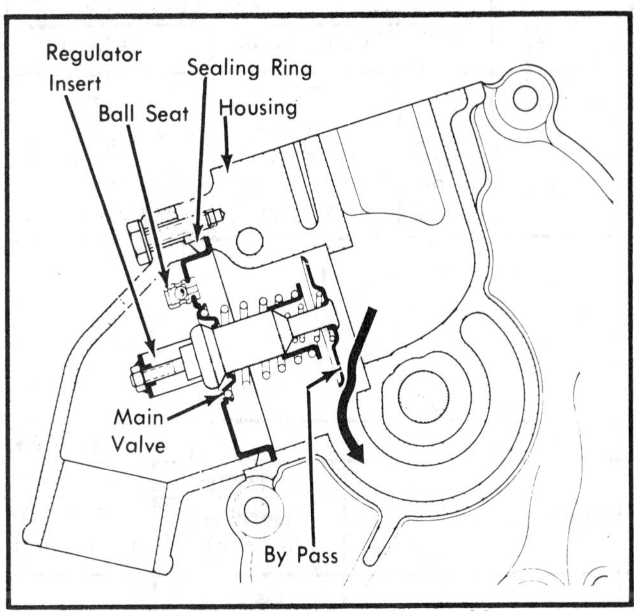

Fig. 10 Water Pump Assembly

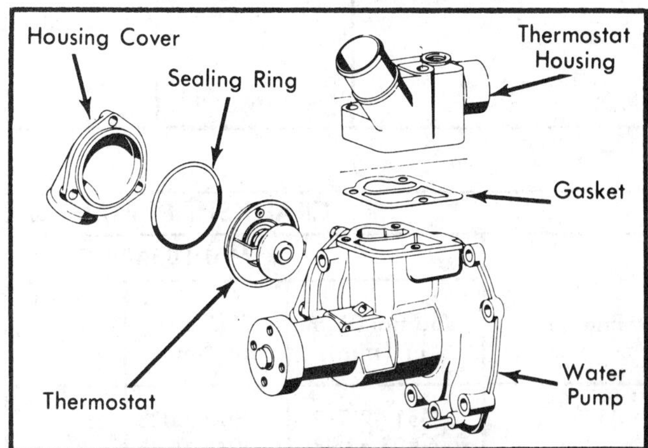

Fig. 11 Water Pump Assembly

GENERAL SPECIFICATIONS

Year	Displ. cu. ins.	Displ. cc	Carburetor	HP at RPM	Torque (Ft. Lbs. at RPM)	Compr. Ratio	Bore in.	Bore mm	Stroke in.	Stroke mm
1977	275.8	4520	Fuel Inj.	180@4750	220@3000	8.1-1	3.62	92	3.35	85

VALVES

Engine & Valve	Head Diam. In. (mm)	Face Angle	Seat Angle	Seat Width In. (mm)	Stem Diameter In. (mm)	Stem Clearance In. (mm)	Valve Lift In. (mm)
Int.	1.7362-1.7440 (44.10-44.30)	45°	45°	.051-.078 (1.3-2.0)	.3523-.3531 (8.95-8.97)	None (Hydraulic Valve Lifters)	.....
Exh.	1.4547-1.4665 (36.95-37.25)	45°	45°	.059-.079 (1.5-2.0)	.4303-.4311 (10.93-10.95)		.....

4.5 LITER V8 (Cont.)

VALVE SPRINGS			
Engine	Free Length In. (mm)	PRESSURE Lbs. @ In. (kg @ mm)	
		Valve Closed	Valve Open
4520 cc			
Inner	1.77 (45)	24.7@1.3 (11.2@33)	50.7@.846 (23@21.5)
Outer	1.95 (49.5)	67.24@1.65 30.5@42)	194@1.2 (88@30.5)

CAMSHAFT ①			
Engine	Journal Diam. In. (mm)	Clearance In. (mm)	Lobe Lift In. (mm)
4520 cc	.....	.0010-.0022 (.025-.057)	.....

① — End play should be .003-.006" (.070-.143 mm).

VALVE TIMING				
	INTAKE		EXHAUST	
Engine	Open ATDC	Close ALDC	Open BLDC	Close BTDC
4520 cc	6.5°	18.5°	23°	8°

PISTONS, PINS, RINGS						
	PISTONS	PINS		RINGS		
Engine	Clearance In. (mm)	Piston Fit In. (mm)	Rod Fit In. (mm)	Rings	End Gap In. (mm)	Side Clearance In. (mm)
4520 cc	.0005-.0015 (.012-.037)	.....	.0002-.0007 (.005-.018)	No. 1	.014-.022 (.35-.55)	.002-.0036 (.050-.092)
				No. 2	.014-.022 (.35-.55)	.0016-.0030 (.040-.082)
				Oil	.010-.016 (.25-.40)	.0012-.0030 (.030-.072)

CRANKSHAFT MAIN & CONNECTING ROD BEARINGS							
	MAIN BEARINGS				CONNECTING ROD BEARINGS		
Engine	Journal Diam. In. (mm)	Clearance In. (mm)	Thrust Bearing	Crankshaft End Play In. (mm)	Journal Diam. In. (mm)	Clearance In. (mm)	Side Play In. (mm)
4520 cc	2.517-2.519 (63.93-63.98)	.0018-.0033 (.045-.084)	.....	.004-.009 (.10-.23)	2.044-2.047 (51.93-52.00)	.0008-.0027 (021-.068)	.009-.015 (.22-.39)

TIGHTENING SPECIFICATIONS

Application	Ft. Lbs. (mkg)
Cylinder Head Bolts	
Cold, First Stage	22 (3)
Cold, Second Stage	36 (5)
Warm, Third Stage	43 (6)
Rocker Cover Bolts	11 (1.5)
Camshaft Bearing Bracket Bolts	36 (5)
Camshaft Sprocket Bolts	72 (10)
Injection Nozzle-to-Injection Valve	7 (1)
Connecting Rod Bolts	①33 (4.5)
Main Bearing Caps	
Large Bolt	72 (10)
Small Bolt	47 (6.5)

Application	Ft.Lbs. (mkg)
Crankshaft Bolt	195-239 (27-33)
Oil Pan	8 (1.1)
Oil Filter-to-Case	29 (4)
Oil Drain Plug	22 (3)
Oil Pressure Relief Valve	29 (4)
Flywheel or Driven Plate	①25 (3.5)
Hydraulic Valve Lifters	36 (5)
Chain Tensioner Nut	80 (11)
Spark Plugs	22 (3)

① — After torque values are achieved, torque an additional 90-100°.

6.9 LITER V8

ENGINE CODING

ENGINE IDENTIFICATION

Engine identification number is located on tag attached to engine crankcase. First six digits of code are used to identify engine.

Application	Chassis Type	Engine Code
6.9 Liter	116.036	100.985

ENGINE & CYLINDER HEAD

ENGINE

NOTE — *Engine and transmission must be removed as a unit.*

Removal — 1) Remove hood, fan, fan shroud and radiator. Remove air cleaner, battery and battery frame. Remove hydraulic lines from hydropneumatic suspension pump. Discharge air-conditioning system.

2) Drain power steering reservoir and remove hoses. Remove all water, vacuum, oil, fuel and electrical lines leading to engine. Remove throttle control shaft.

3) Remove shield between oil pan and reservoir. Remove oil feed and return lines. Remove exhaust pipes and exhaust heat shield. Loosen locknut on drive shaft. Unbolt drive shaft at transmission and push toward the rear. Loosen all connections on transmission. Remove both engine shock absorbers, at frame crossmember.

4) Attach a engine hoist to lifting eyes on engine. Remove rear engine carrier with engine mount. Remove front engine mount. Remove engine and transmission.

Installation — To install reverse removal procedure.

CYLINDER HEAD

NOTE — *Cylinder head can only be removed when engine is cold.*

Removal — 1) Drain cooling system and crankcase. Remove battery, fan and fan shroud. Disconnect hydraulic oil pump lines. Remove alternator and bracket. Remove windshield washer reservoir and bracket. Disconnect injection lines at injector nozzles, and warm-up compensator.

2) Disconnect fuel supply and return from fuel distributor. Disconnect control linkage, remove mixture regulator assembly with lower housing. Remove throttle control shaft. Remove injection nozzles. Remove bracket for oil lines. Disconnect all electrical lines and vacuum lines. Remove intake manifold.

3) Unbolt exhaust pipe at manifold. Remove timing chain tensioner. Remove timing chain guide rails. Mark camshaft sprocket and timing chain. Carefully remove camshaft sprocket, letting timing chain fall down. Remove cylinder head bolts in reverse of tightening sequence. (*Fig. 1*).

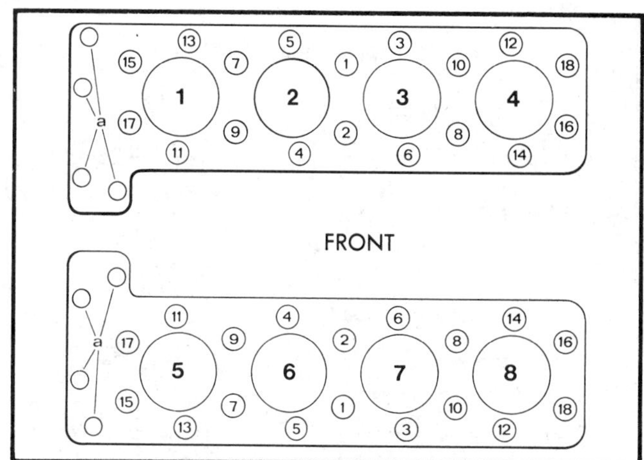

Fig. 1 Cylinder Head Tightening Sequence

NOTE — *To remove cylinder head bolts at rear of left cylinder bank, raise engine at transmission mount. Level adjusting switch must be pulled out to first notch.*

Installation — To install, reverse removal procedure.

NOTE — *Place cylinder head on crankcase and lift, insert new cylinder head gasket.*

VALVES

VALVE GUIDE SERVICING

1) Clean valve guide and remove all hard carbon. Using suitable go no-go plug gauges, check valve guide clearance. Drift out old guide using a suitable drift. Check bore in cylinder head and ream to oversize if necessary.

2) Heat cylinder head to 176-194°F (80-90°C) and chill valve guide. Drive valve guide in until lock ring is seated against cylinder head. Allow cylinder head to cool and check guide fit in head.

VALVE STEM OIL SEALS

Removal — 1) Remove camshaft cover. Remove rocker arm. Rotate engine until both valves are closed and supply compressed air to spark plug hole to hold valves closed.

2) Compress valve springs, using suitable valve spring compressor. Remove valve keepers, collar, springs and valve stem oil seal.

Installation — 1) Install valve stem oil seal. On intake guide, position coil spring at top and clamping strap at bottom. On exhaust, place installation bead on bottom next to valve guide.

2) Install springs, collars and keepers, using a suitable valve spring compressor. Install rocker arm and check tappet clearance. Replace camshaft cover and tighten nuts.

VALVE SPRING

With cylinder head and rocker arms removed, compress valve springs with a suitable valve spring compressor. Remove valve keepers, collar and springs.

6.9 LITER V8 (Cont.)

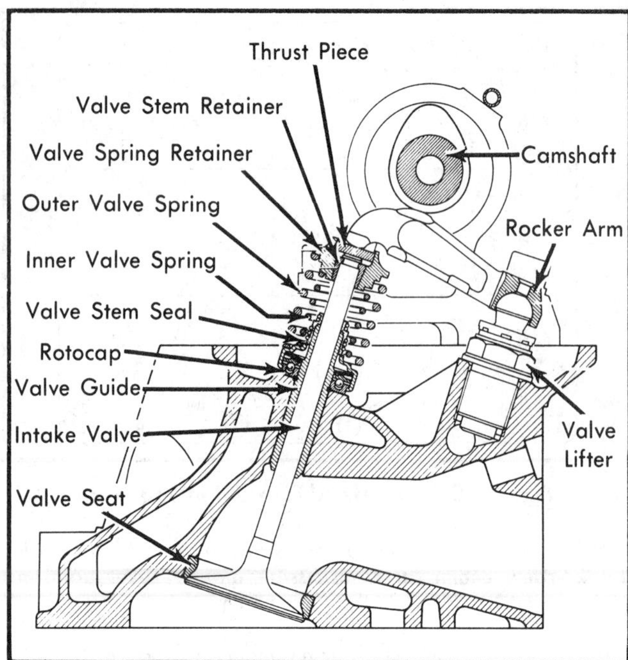

Fig. 2 Valve Assembly

HYDRAULIC VALVE LIFTERS

Removal – Remove camshaft cover and rocker arms. Unscrew hydraulic valve lifters.

Installation – Moisten threads of valve lifter with engine oil and screw into cylinder head. Install rocker arms and camshaft cover. When installing new valve lifters the base setting must be adjusted.

BASE SETTING ADJUSTMENT

NOTE – *With new hydraulic valve lifters installed; crank engine for 30 seconds with remote starter switch, before making adjustment.*

1) Remove load from valve lifter to be checked, by cranking engine until cam lobe points up. Screw in adapter bushing (700 589 05 21) to dial indicator holder. Screw dial indicator holder to one of the studs in the cylinder head.

2) Insert dial indicator extension through bore in rocker arm, making contact with top of valve lifter. Tighten dial indicator to .16" (4mm) preload. Set dial indicator to zero. Push valve spring down with valve spring compressor, to remove load from valve lifter. Check reading on dial indicator, if reading is between .028-.075" (.7-1.9mm) the base setting is correct. If reading is beyond limit, base setting must be corrected.

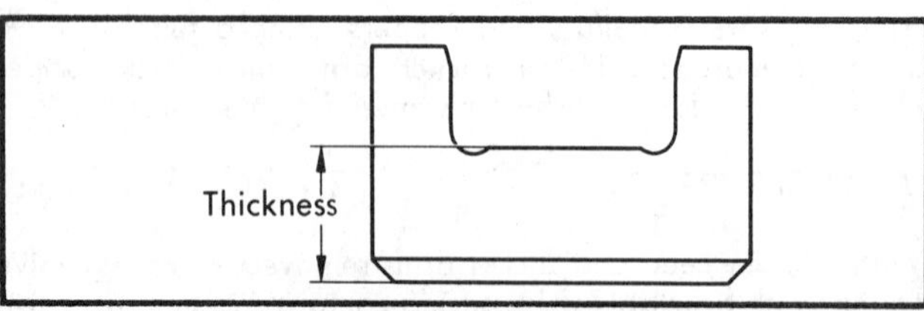

Fig. 3 Thrust Piece

3) To correct base setting, remove rocker arm. Remove thrust piece and insert measuring thrust piece. (*Fig. 3*) Reinstall rocker arm. Repeat measuring procedure outlined in step 2. Use thrust piece according to measured value in table.

Measured Value In. (mm)	Thrust Piece Thickness In. (mm)
0-.002 (0-.05)	.2146/.2283 (5.45/5.8)
.002-.037 (.06-.087)	.2008 (5.1)
.035-.066 (.88-1.69)	.1870 (4.75)
.067-.099 (1.70-2.51)	.1732 (4.4)
.099-.131 (2.52-3.33)	.1594 (4.05)
.131 (above 3.33)	.1457 (3.7)

4) Reinstall remaining components in reverse of removal procedure. Start engine and listen for valve train noises.

Fig. 4 Dial Indicator Installed

ROCKER ARM ASSEMBLY

Removal – Remove battery and camshaft cover. Rotate camshaft (by remote starter switch) until camshaft lobe is pointed up. Using a suitable valve spring compressor (100 589 06 61 00), position compressor between camshaft and valve spring collar, lever valve downward until rocker arm can be removed.

Installation – Reverse removal procedure.

NOTE – *When installing new rocker arms, replace camshaft and check base setting of hydraulic valve lifters.*

PISTONS, PINS & RINGS

OIL PAN

Removal – 1) Remove hood, drain cooling system. Remove upper radiator hose. Drain engine oil. Remove throttle control shaft.

2) Remove transmission oil cooler lines. Remove sheild between oil pan and oil reservoir, remove oil lines from oil pan. Remove two connecting flanges on oil pan and pull them out. Remove oil pan attaching bolts.

6.9 LITER V8 (Cont.)

3) Remove front engine carriers. Remove engine shock absorbers. Raise engine at front lifting eye, until oil pan can be pulled out, in a forward direction.

Installation – To install, reverse removal procedure.

NOTE – *Replace O-ring and rubber seal of connecting flanges. Coat parting surface of oil pan with a sealing compound.*

FITTING PISTONS

Measure pistons and cylinder diameters to determine if pistons or cylinders are worn. Oversize pistons are available.

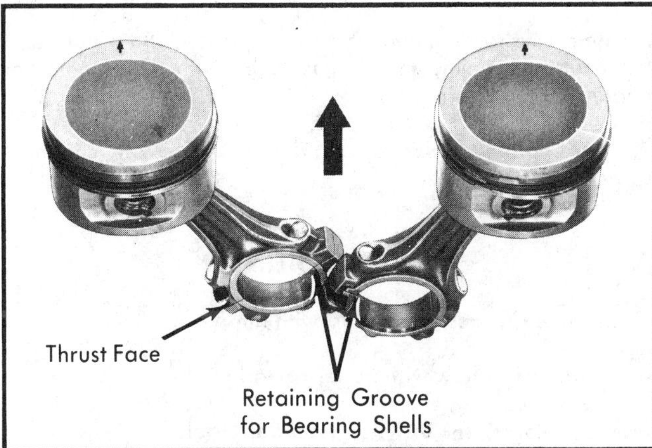

Fig. 5 Piston & Connecting Rod Alignment

PISTON PINS

Piston pin bore is offset from center in the direction of the thrust face side.

CRANKSHAFT MAIN & CONNECTING ROD BEARINGS

MAIN & CONNECTING ROD BEARINGS

Inspect main and connecting rod journals for wear or damage. Maximum wear limit is .02" (.5mm). Regrind crankshaft and install new undersize bearings, if necessary.

REAR MAIN BEARING OIL SEAL

Remove – 1) Remove engine and transmission (See *Engine Removal*). Drain oil, separate transmission from engine. Remove camshaft covers, and camshaft sprocket (See *Camshaft*). Remove oil pan (See *Oil Pan Removal*).

2) Remove front crankcase seal holder. Remove main and connecting rod bearing caps. Mark caps for reassembly. Remove rear bearing seal holder with a suitable tool. Pull double roller chain upward and lift crankshaft. Remove old sealing ring and clean all parts.

Installation – Rubber sealing strip must be installed before fiber seal. Install in reverse of removal procedure.

FRONT MAIN BEARING OIL SEAL

Removal – 1) Remove crankshaft pulley and vibration damper. Remove bolts from seal holder and withdraw seal holder.

2) Remove lock washers on both threaded studs and remove side rail from studs. Support seal holder and drive out seal with suitable tool.

Installation – 1) Heat seal holder and place on suitable support. Press seal in cover. Install side rail over threaded bolts and install lock washers.

2) Coat edges of front cover with sealing compound. Using a wire hook, pull rail outward from seal. Place cover in position on crankcase and remove hook. Install bolts and tighten to specification.

CAMSHAFT

NOTE – *If camshaft is replaced, install new rocker arms. Camshaft code is located at rear of shaft.*

CAMSHAFT

Removal – 1) Place No. 1 piston at TDC of compression stroke. Remove rocker arms. Remove compression spring of the timing chain tensioner by unscrewing plug (See *Fig. 6*).

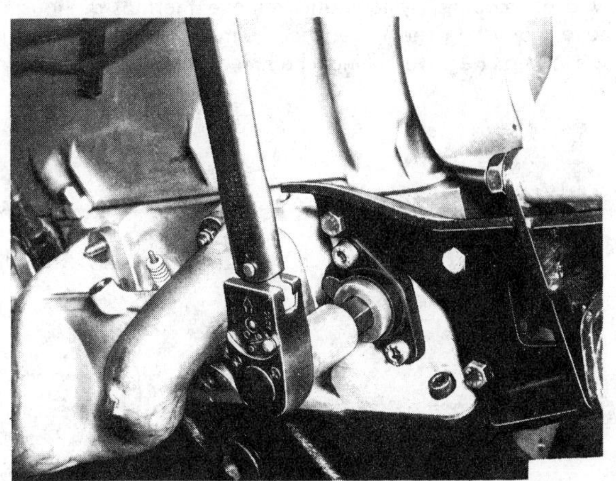

Fig. 6 Timing Chain Tensioner Spring Plug

2) Mark both camshaft sprockets and timing chain. Remove camshaft sprockets and mounting bolts for camshaft bearings. Remove camshafts.

NOTE – *The mounting bolt at the rear of the engine can only be removed by raising left side of the engine.*

Installation – 1) Oil camshaft bearings, mount bearings with camshaft. Tighten mounting bolts (in steps) from the inside to the outside. Camshaft should turn freely.

2) Install compensating washer (V-notch in washer on top of woodruff key). Install camshaft sprockets and timing chain checking alignment of marks. Turn crankshaft one full revolution and place the piston of No. 1 cylinder at TDC of compression stroke.

6.9 LITER V8 (Cont.)

3) With No. 1 piston at TDC the marks on both camshafts must be in alignment (*See Fig. 7*). Install oil pipe. Reverse removal procedure to install remaining components.

Fig. 7 Camshaft Aligning Marks

TIMING CHAIN

Removal – 1) Remove camshaft covers and spark plugs. Partially drain cooling system and remove thermostat housing. Remove requlating shaft, between venturi control unit and injection pump. Remove timing chain tensioner.

2) Brake endless chain and attach new chain with a master link, spring lock facing direction of rotation. Use care not to drop chain down into engine.

Installation – 1) Slowly turn engine in direction of rotation, drawing new chain over sprockets, and pulling old chain from engine. Connect ends of new chain with master link, facing inwards toward camshaft and spring lock facing in direction of rotation.

2) Insert timing chain compression spring and hold in place, put new gasket on plug and screw in place. Check crankshaft in relation to camshaft, to find out if valve timing is correct. Install camshaft covers and spark plugs.

VALVE TIMING

Rotate crankshaft until No. 1 piston is at TDC. Both right and left camshafts timing marks must align with marks on front bearing support (*See Fig. 7*).

NOTE – *Rotate engine by crankshaft, never use camshaft sprocket nuts.*

ENGINE OILING

Crankcase Capacity – 11 qts. with filter

Oil Filter – Full-flow with paper cartridge

Pressure Regulator Valve – Non-adjustable

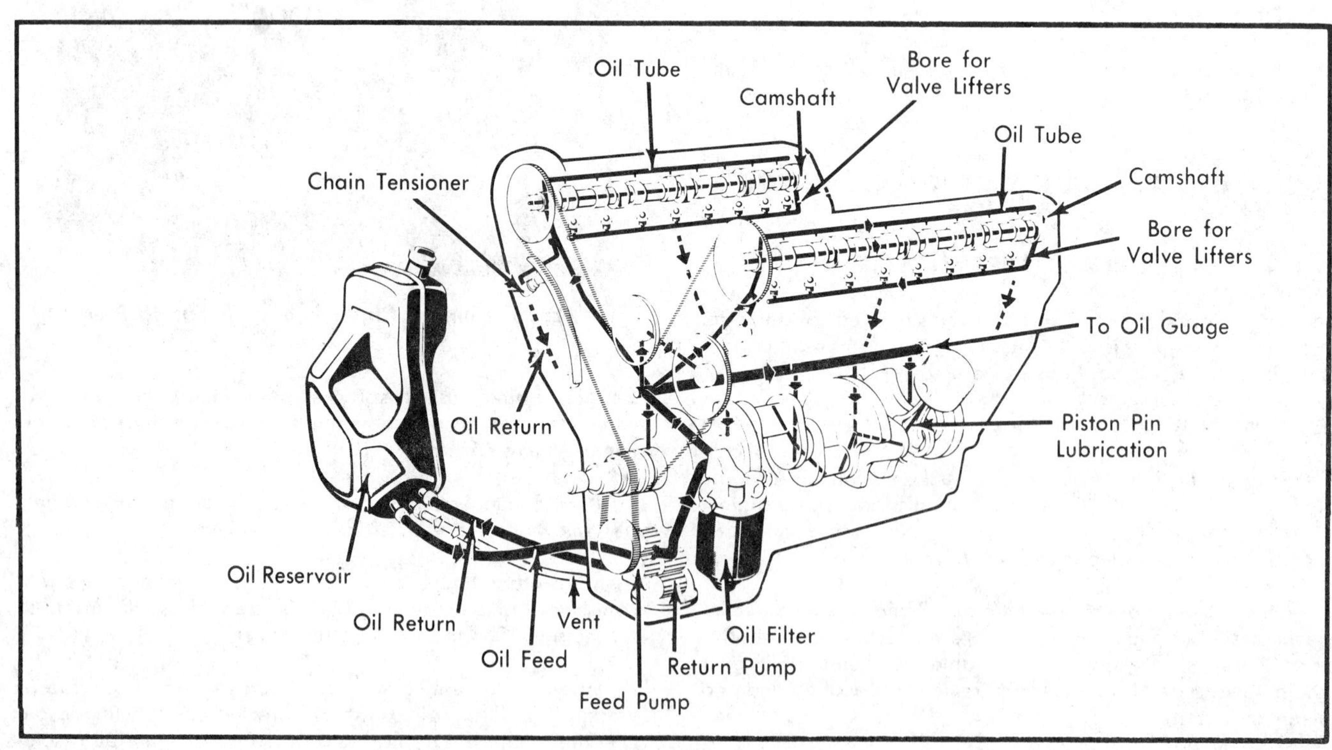

Fig. 8 Engine Oiling System

6.9 LITER V8 (Cont.)

OIL PUMP

A gear type oil pump consisting of a oil feed and oil return pump. The pump is attached to the crankcase and is driven by a duplex roller chain. The oil return pump is larger than the oil feed pump, to limit oil foaming.

ENGINE COOLING SYSTEM

Thermostat – Opens at 189°F (87°C)

Cooling System Capacity – 17 qts.

Radiator Cap – 14 psi

WATER PUMP

Remove bolts and screws attaching bearing housing and water pump housing. With a suitable puller, pull impeller off of pump shaft. Unscrew bolts from cover. Use a long punch inserted in water exhaust bore to release cover (tap lightly with a hammer). Using circlip pliers, take off cover. To reassemble reverse disassembly procedure.

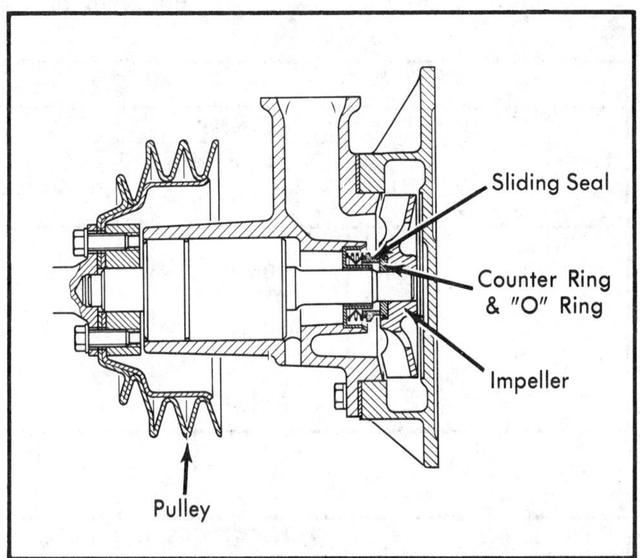

Fig. 9 Water Pump Assembly

ENGINE SPECIFICATION

GENERAL SPECIFICATIONS

Year	Displ. cu. ins.	Displ. cc	Carburetor	HP at RPM	Torque (Ft. Lbs. at RPM)	Compr. Ratio	Bore in.	Bore mm	Stroke in.	Stroke mm
1977	417.1	6834	Fuel Inj.	250@4000	360@2500	8.0:1	4.21	107	3.74	95

VALVES

Engine & Valve	Head Diam. In. (mm)	Face Angle	Seat Angle	Seat Width In. (mm)	Stem Diameter In. (mm)	Stem Clearance In. (mm)	Valve Lift In. (mm)
6834							
Intake	1.736-1.744 (44.10-44.30)	45°	.....	.05-.08 (1.3-2.0)	.3525-.3531 (8.955-8.970)	.....	.....
Exhaust	1.455-1.466 (36.95-37.25)	45°	.....	.06-.08 (1.5-2.0)	.4303-.4311 (10.93-10.95)	.....	.....

VALVE TIMING

Engine	INTAKE Open (BTDC)	INTAKE Close (ALDC)	EXHAUST Open (BLDC)	EXHAUST Close (ATDC)
6834 cc				
Left	4°	14°	26.5°	11.5°
Right	2°	12°	28.5°	13.5°

CAMSHAFT

Engine	Journal Diam. In. (mm)	Clearance In. (mm)	Lobe Lift In. (mm)
6834 cc	.....	.0010-.0022 (.025-.057)	.....

6.9 LITER V8 (Cont.)

ENGINE SPECIFICATION (Cont.)

PISTONS, PINS, RINGS						
	PISTONS	PINS		RINGS		
Engine	Clearance In. (mm)	Piston Fit In. (mm)	Rod Fit In. (mm)	Rings	End Gap In. (mm)	Side Clearance In. (mm)
6834 cc	.0005-.0015 (.012-.037)	.....	.....	No. 1	.014-.022 (.35-.55)	.002-.0036 (.050-.092)
				No. 2	.014-.022 (.35-.55)	.0016-.0032 (.040-.082)
				No. 3	.010-.016 (.25-.40)	.0012-.0028 (.030-.072)

CRANKSHAFT MAIN & CONNECTING ROD BEARINGS							
	MAIN BEARINGS				CONNECTING ROD BEARINGS		
Engine	Journal Diam. In. (mm)	Clearance In. (mm)	Thrust Bearing	Crankshaft End Play In. (mm)	Journal Diam. In. (mm)	Clearance In. (mm)	Side Play In. (mm)
6834 cc	.....	.0016-.0035 (.041-.088)	.....	.004-.009 (.10-.24)	.....	.001-.003 (.030-.068)	.009-.015 (.22-.39)

TIGHTENING SPECIFICATIONS	
Application	**Ft.Lbs (mkg)**
Cylinder Head Bolts	
Stage 1	29 (4.0)
Stage 2	①65 (9.0)
Main Bearing Caps	58 (8.0)
Connecting Rod Caps	36 (5.0)
Flywheel	36 (5.0)
Crankshaft Pulley	290 (30)
Camshaft Bearing	36 (5.0)
Camshaft Sprocket	72 (10)
Chain Tensioner Plug	36 (5.0)
Hydraulic Valve Lifters	36 (5.0)

① — Retorque with warm engine to 65 ft. lbs. (9mkg)

MGB 4 CYLINDER

ENGINE CODING

ENGINE IDENTIFICATION

Engine identification and serial number are stamped on plate secured to right hand side of crankcase.

ENGINE, CYLINDER HEAD & MANIFOLD

ENGINE

1) Disconnect battery cables and remove hood. Drain oil and coolant. Disconnect oil cooler and oil pressure gauges from engine and remove oil cooler mounting bolts. Remove radiator and oil cooler, complete with hoses.

2) Disconnect wiring from generator or alternator, and from distributor. Remove spark plug wires from plugs and remove distributor cap. Disconnect heater hoses and heater control cable.

3) Disconnect water temperature sending unit, disconnect wiring from starter. Disconnect fuel line, choke cables, and remove air cleaners from carburetors. If tachometer is mechanical type, disconnect it.

4) On cars equipped with manual transmission and overdrive, remove gear lever plate, raise rubber boot and remove lever retaining bolts. Remove gear lever. Disconnect wiring from back-up switch and overdrive switch. Disconnect clutch slave cylinder from transmission housing and move it clear of housing.

5) On cars equipped with automatic transmission, disconnect downshift cable from carburetors and disconnect gear lever from transmission. Disconnect wiring from neutral start switch and from back-up switch.

6) Disconnect speedometer cable from transmission and, using engine hoist, take up the weight of engine. Support transmission. Disconnect exhaust pipe from exhaust manifold and release pipe clip from transmission housing. Disconnect and remove propeller shaft. Remove front engine mount bolts.

7) Remove four bolts holding crossmember to frame and remove two bolts holding bottom tie bracket to crossmember. Lower transmission so that it rests on fixed crossmember. Remove rear mounting nuts and remove crossmember.

8) Ease assembly forward until transmission is clear of crossmember, then tilt assembly and lift out of car. Remove transmission from engine if necessary.

Installation – To install engine/transmission assembly, reverse removal procedure.

INTAKE & EXHAUST MANIFOLDS

Removal – Drain cooling system and remove air cleaner. Remove carburetors and disconnect distributor vacuum, brake servo vacuum and anti-run-on valve vacuum hoses at manifold. Remove both EGR and gulp valves. Take off hot air induction tubing. Free heat shield. Disconnect exhaust pipe at manifold. Remove studs mounting manifolds and slide off manifolds.

Installation – Reverse removal procedure using new gasket. Center manifold stud nuts have large washers which hold both intake and exhaust manifolds. Outside nuts have small washers and hold exhaust manifold only.

CYLINDER HEAD

Removal – **1)** Drain cooling system and remove top radiator hose. Remove thermostat housing and thermostat. Remove air cleaners, carburetors and exhaust and intake manifolds. Remove rocker assembly and seven external cylinder head nuts at same time, loosening a turn at a time until all load is released.

2) Disconnect spark plug wires and remove spark plugs. Disconnect heater hose and heater control cable from water valve. Remove water temperature sensor from front of cylinder head and release conductor from its support clip.

3) Loosen clips and disconnect hoses from water pipe on left side of cylinder head. Remove pipe. Remove distributor vacuum line from rear cylinder head stud and remove cylinder head.

Installation – **1)** Thoroughly clean all gasket surfaces and install new gasket. Place cylinder head in position and replace vacuum control line bracket. Install seven cylinder head external nuts finger tight and replace push rods.

2) Replace rocker arm assembly, securing nuts finger tight. Tighten 11 cylinder head nuts a turn at a time in sequence. Tighten four rocker arm assembly nuts and reverse removal procedure for remaining items.

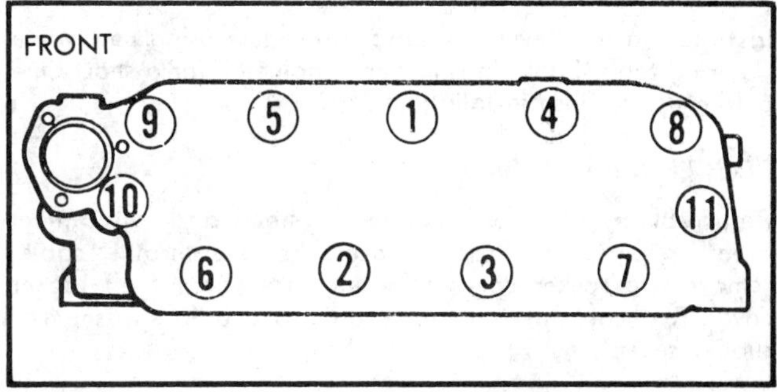

Fig. 1 MGB Cylinder Head Tightening Sequence

VALVES

VALVE ARRANGEMENT

E-I-I-E-E-I-I-E (front-to-rear).

VALVE GUIDE SERVICING

1) Remove cylinder head and valves. Rest cylinder head with machined face downward on a clean surface. Drive valve guide downwards into combustion chamber space with a suitable drift. When installing new guides, they must be driven in from top of cylinder head.

2) Guides must be inserted with end having largest chamfer at top. Guides should be driven into combustion chamber until exhaust valve guides are ⅝" and intake valve guides are ¾" above machined surface of valve spring seating.

MGB 4 CYLINDER (Cont.)

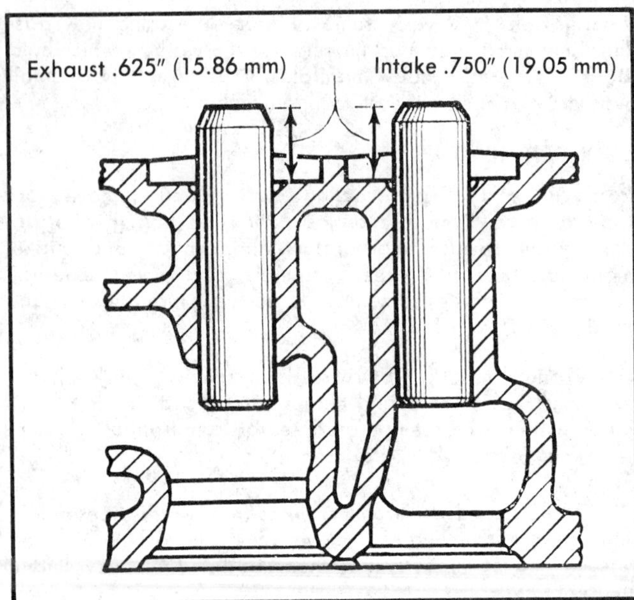

Fig. 2 Cross Sectional View of Installed Valve Guide

VALVE SPRINGS

Removal – Remove cylinder head and rocker arm assembly. Compress springs using suitable tool (18G45). Remove two valve keepers. Release valve springs and remove compressor. Take out valve spring retainer, spring, and bottom retainer. Remove "O" ring seal from groove and remove valve from guide.

Installation – Reverse removal procedure using new valve "O" ring seals. Soak rings in clean engine oil for a short time before use to ease installation.

ROCKER ARM ASSEMBLY

Removal – 1) Drain cooling system and disconnect breather pipe from rocker cover. Remove throttle cable, remove two rocker cover attaching nuts and lift off rocker cover. Take care not to damage cork gasket or lose washers or rubber seals.

2) Notice that under the right rear rocker stud nut there is a locking plate. Unscrew eight rocker shaft bracket nuts and external cylinder head nuts gradually, one turn at a time, until all load is released.

NOTE – *It is important that external cylinder head nuts are loosened at same time to avoid possibility of head distortion and water entering cylinders.*

3) Remove all rocker shaft bracket nuts and remove rocker assembly, complete with brackets and rockers. Remove push rods, arranging them so that they may be replaced in same positions.

Disassembly 1) – Remove set screw locating rocker shaft in rear rocker mounting bracket, then remove cotter pins, flat washers and spring washers. Slide rockers, brackets, and springs off shaft. Make sure to note how components come off so they can be reassembled accurately.

2) Using suitable tool (18G226), place rocker on anvil and drive out worn bushing. Place new bushing on driver and position bushing with butt joint at top of rocker bore and oil groove in bushing at bottom of rocker bore.

3) It is necessary to drill oil holes in bushing to coincide with oilways in rocker. Holes may be drilled either before or after installation.

4) If holes are drilled after installation, remove adjuster screw and use .093" (2.36 mm) drill to extract end plug and to continue oilway through bushing.

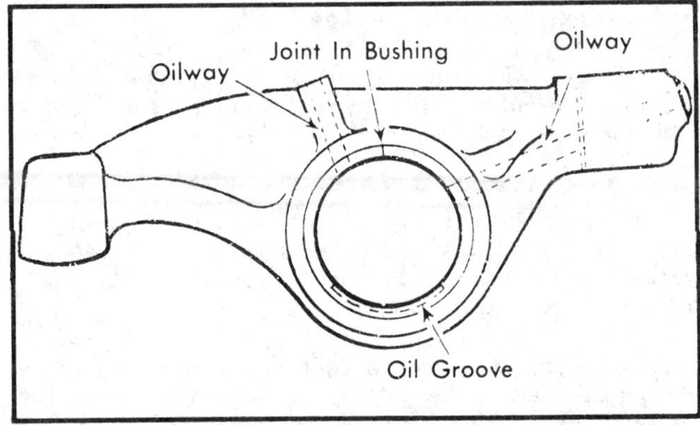

Fig. 3 Rocker Arm Bushing with Detail of Oil Holes

5) Replug end after operation using a rivet and weld rivet into position. Oil hole in top of rocker barrel must continue through the bushing with a No. 47 drill. Finally, burnish ream bushing to .6255-.6260" (15.89-15.90 mm).

Reassembly – Reverse disassembly procedure. Remember to replace rocker shaft locating screw lock plate.

Installation – To install rocker assembly on cylinder head, reverse removal procedure. Make sure cylinder head bolts are retorqued before installing rocker cover.

VALVE CLEARANCE ADJUSTMENT

Remove valve cover and observe opening and closing of valves. To check clearances, turn crankshaft until valves in first column are fully open, then valves in second column may be checked and adjust to .013" (.33 mm). Set clearance with engine warm.

Valves Open	Valves to Adjust
1	8
3	6
5	4
2	7
8	1
6	3
4	5
7	2

MGB 4 CYLINDER (Cont.)

PISTONS, PINS & RINGS

OIL PAN

1) Drain engine oil and drain coolant. Disconnect radiator hoses and remove engine front mounting bolts. Lift engine enough to gain access to front oil pan bolts.

2) Remove all oil pan bolts and remove oil pan from engine. To install, reverse removal procedure using new oil pan gasket.

PISTON & ROD

1) Remove cylinder head and oil pan. Pistons and rods must be removed from top of cylinder block. Unlock and remove big-end bolts and remove bearing caps. Release connecting rods from crankshaft.

2) Remove piston and rod assembly from top of cylinder block and reinstall bearing cap. Big-end bearing caps are offset. Make sure that parts are marked so they may be reassembled in original positions.

PISTON RINGS

1) Place rings in top of cylinder bore. Check ring gaps. Check oil ring to groove clearance. Fit oil control expander. Make sure ends of expander are butting, but not overlapping. Set gaps of rails and expander 90° to each other.

2) Fit stepped compression rings into SECOND groove with face marked "TOP" up. Fit top ring. Place ring gaps 90°to each other away from thrust side of piston.

PISTON PINS

Piston pins are press fit and are fully interchangeable in complete sets with earlier assemblies which have full floating pin. Use suitable tool or press to remove or install pins.

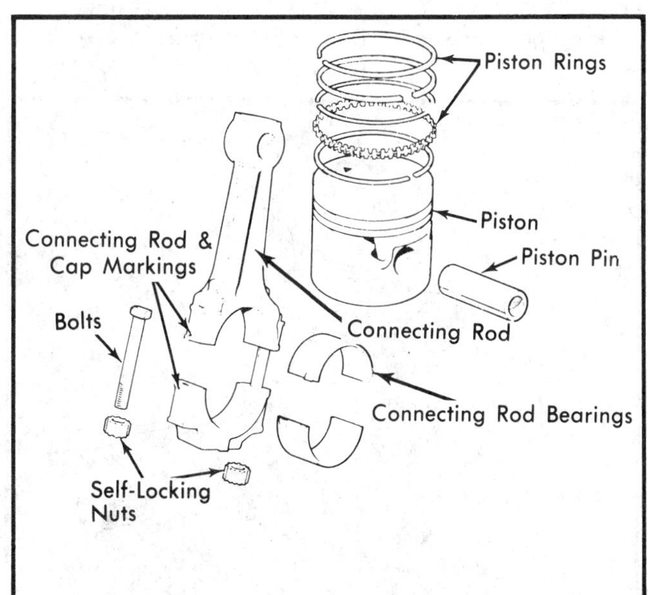

Fig. 4 Exploded View of Piston and Rod Assembly

CRANKSHAFT MAIN & CONNECTING ROD BEARINGS

CRANKSHAFT

Remove engine and remove clutch and flywheel. Remove timing cover, timing wheels and chain. Remove oil pan, oil pump strainer and rear engine mounting plate. Remove big end bearing cap and then take off main bearing caps. Lift crankshaft out of bearings, first marking bearings and bearing caps for correct replacement.

CONNECTING ROD BEARINGS

To remove bearings, bend down locking strips so that bolts may be removed. Remove connecting rod caps and extract bearings. No scraping of bearings is required as bearings are machined to give correct clearance of .001-.0027" (.03-.07 mm).

MAIN BEARINGS

1) Remove engine from car and remove flywheel and clutch, timing chain, oil pan and oil strainer. Remove rear engine mounting plate. Remove two bolts and locking plate holding front main bearing cap to engine front plate. Remove main bearing cap retaining nuts and remove caps and bearings.

2) Bearings are machined to give correct clearance of .001-.0027". When replacing bearings that have been used but are not damaged or worn, make sure that bearing and all surfaces are thoroughly cleaned. Rear main bearing cap horizontal joint surface should be lightly covered with Hylomar Jointing Compound or equivalent before cap is fitted to cylinder block. Tighten bearing cap nuts.

THRUST BEARINGS

A thrust washer is fitted on each side of center main bearing to take crankshaft end thrust. Washers each consist of two semicircular halves, one having a lug located in recess in removable half of bearing and other one being plain.

CAMSHAFT

FRONT COVER & OIL SEAL

Removal – Drain cooling system. Remove radiator. Remove alternator belt and A.I.R. pump belt. Remove fan and pulley from crankshaft. Remove front cover bolts and remove from vehicle. Pry or drive out crankshaft oil seal.

Installation – Dip new oil seal in engine oil. Use installing tool 18G 134 and adapter 18G 134BD to fit seal. Be sure lip of seal is facing inward. Position oil thrower with "F" mark showing. Smear sealing compound on cover and seal. Tighten bolts evenly. Lubricate crankshaft hub and slide pulley on to crankshaft, engaging keyway. Put on new lock nut and tighten bolt.

MGB 4 CYLINDER (Cont.)

TIMING CHAIN & TENSIONER

Removal – Remove front cover. Bend back tensioner lock tabs. Remove tensioner bolts. Pry tensioner out of front plate. Slipper head (piece that rides against chain) is under spring tension. Remove tensioner with back plate. Unlock and remove camshaft nut. Pull off camshaft and crankshaft sprockets with chain.

NOTE – *Crankshaft sprocket has packing washers behind it.*

CAUTION – *Tensioner will almost come apart by itself once head piece has been removed.*

NOTE – *Use care not to lose sprocket packing washers behind crankshaft sprocket. Make sure to replace the same number of washers as removed. To determine correct thickness of washers to be used if new camshaft or crankshaft components have been installed, place straightedge across sides of crankshaft sprocket and measure gap between straightedge and crankshaft sprocket. Select and fit washers as required.*

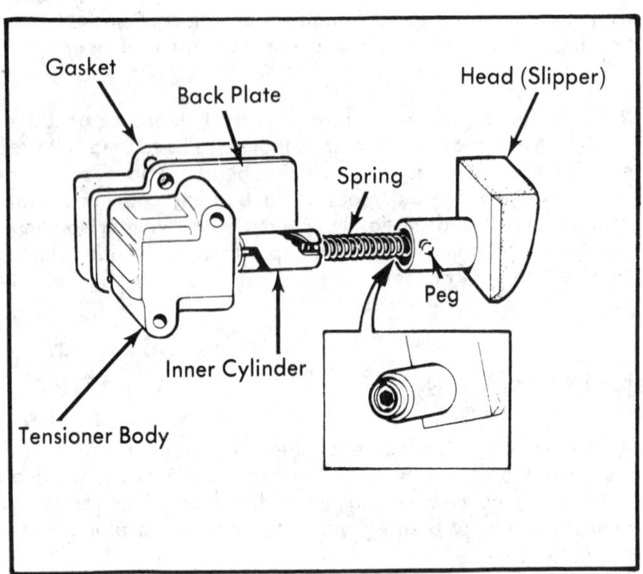

Fig. 5 Exploded View of Timing Chain Tensioner

Installation – **1)** When replacing timing chain and sprockets, set crankshaft keyway at TDC and camshaft keyway at 2 o'clock position. Assemble sprockets to timing chain with index marks in sprockets (if equipped) opposite each other.

2) Keep sprockets in this position and engage crankshaft sprocket keyway with key on crankshaft and rotate camshaft until camshaft sprocket keyway and key are aligned. Push sprockets onto shafts as far as possible and tighten with lock washer and nut. Replace oil thrower with face marked "F" away from engine and replace remaining components.

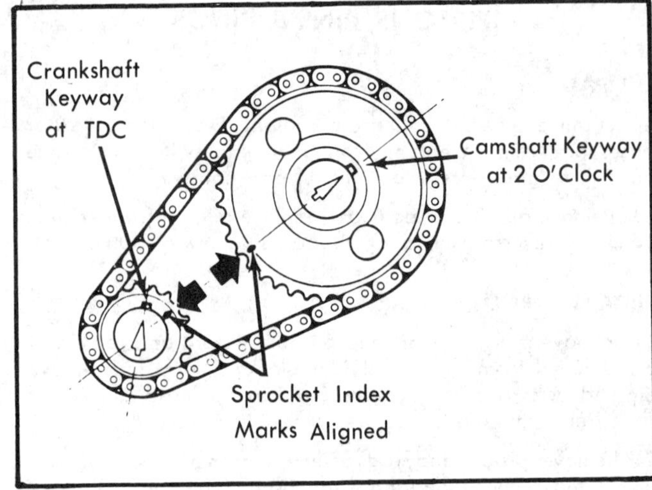

Fig. 6 Camshaft and Crankshaft Sprocket Alignment

CAMSHAFT

1) Disconnect battery and remove intake and exhaust manifolds. Remove push rods and remove tappets. Remove timing cover, timing chain and timing gears.

2) Disconnect distributor vacuum line at distributor and remove two bolts with flat washers which hold distributor to housing. Do not loosen clamping plate bolt or ignition timing will be disturbed. Remove distributor assembly.

3) Remove oil pan, oil pump and oil pump drive shaft. If drive type tachometer is used, disconnect drive and remove nuts and washers and remove drive gear. Remove three set screws and shakeproof washers that hold camshaft locating plate to cylinder block. Remove camshaft.

4) Before reassembly, fix camshaft thrust plate and sprocket to camshaft, then check end play. Specifications should not exceed .003-.007" (.076-.178 mm). Make measurement between retaining plate and thrust face of camshaft front journal.

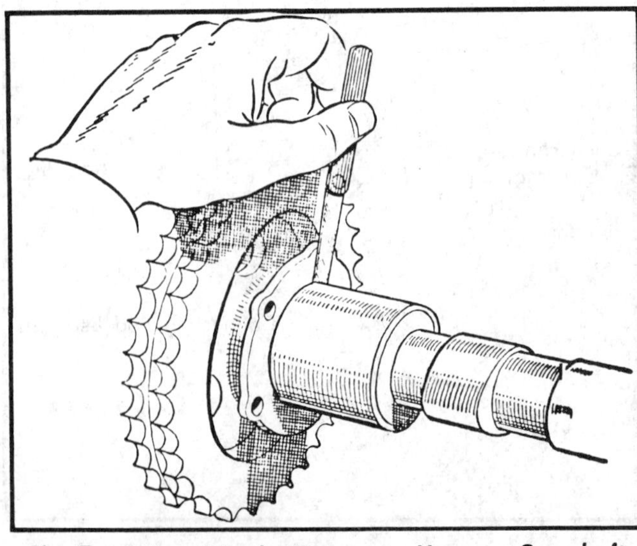

Fig. 7 Using a Feeler Gauge to Measure Camshaft End Play

MGB 4 CYLINDER (Cont.)

CAMSHAFT BEARINGS

NOTE – *Follow manufacturers instructions for proper adapter and washer use on each bearing for removal and installation.*

Removal – Use bearing removal/installation tool 18G 124A and adapters to remove camshaft front bearing. Remove rear bearing in same manner as front bearing, then index tool through front bearing bore to remove center bearing.

NOTE – *Be sure oil holes in new bearings are aligned with lubrication ports in block. The holes must not move once they have been located.*

Installation – Fit new bearings into bore in reverse order of removal. After bearings have been installed, use camshaft bearing bore tool 18G 123A to line bore new bearings.

NOTE – *Cutting edge of boreing tool must be kept dry and free of cuttings at all times.*

VALVE TIMING

1) Set No. 1 cylinder intake valve clearance to .055" with engine cold. Turn crankshaft until valve is about to open. Indicator groove in flange of crankshaft pulley should be opposite longest pointer on indicator bracket beneath crankshaft pulley, indicating TDC.

2) After timing has been checked, valve clearance should be reset. *See Valve Clearance Adjustment.*

ENGINE OILING

Crankcase Capacity – 7¼ pints with filter change.

Oil Filter – Full flow type with disposable cartridge.

Oil Pressure – 10-25 psi (.7-1.7 kg/cm²) @idle: 50-80 psi (3.5-5.6 kg/cm²) @2000 RPM.

ENGINE OILING SYSTEM

Force feed type with rotor type oil pump. A full-flow type oil filter is used. An oil pressure relief valve is used to enable oil to by-pass filter if oil filter becomes blocked.

OIL PUMP

Two bolts hold on oil pump cover and three studs hold pump to crankcase. To remove pump, remove stud nuts and remove pump and drive shaft. To disassemble, proceed as follows:

1) Remove cover, located at base of oil pump by two dowels. Remove outer rotor complete with oil pump shaft. Clean all parts in kerosene and inspect for wear.

2) Rotor end play should be checked as follows: Install rotors in pump body and place straightedge across joint face of pump body. Measure clearance between top face of rotors and underside of straightedge. Clearance should not exceed .005" (.13 mm). If clearance is excessive, remove two cover locating dowels and tap the joint face of pump body.

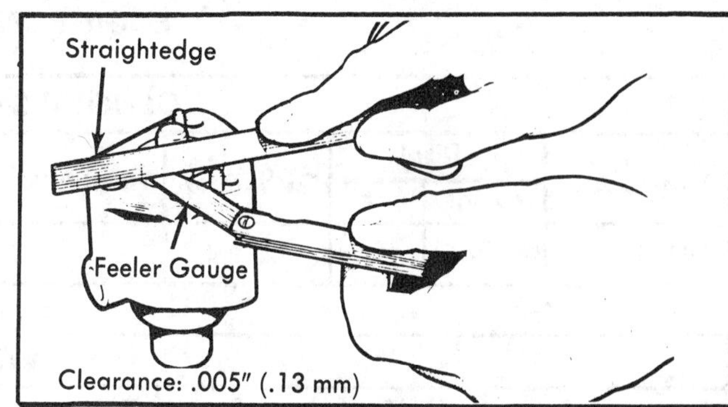

Fig. 8 Measuring Oil Pump Rotor End Play

3) Check clearance between outer rotor and rotor pocket in pump body. If clearance exceeds .010" (.25 mm), pump rotor, pump body, or complete pump assembly should be replaced.

4) Measure clearance of rotor lobes with rotors installed in pump body. If clearance exceeds .006" (.15 mm), rotors must be replaced.

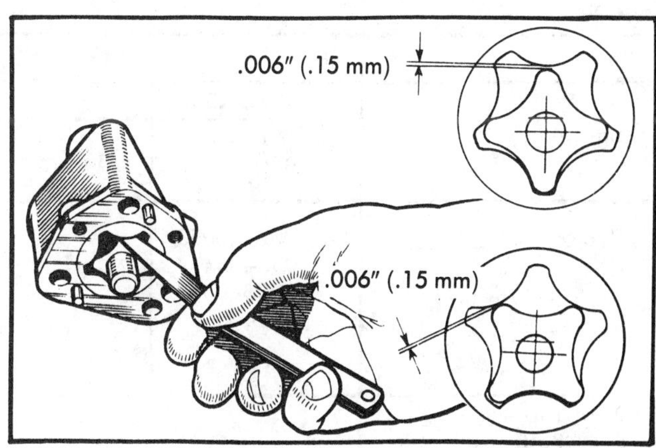

Fig. 9 Measuring Oil Pump Rotor Lobe Clearance

5) Reassemble pump and lubricate all parts with clean engine oil. Make sure outer rotor is installed in pump body with chamfered end at drive end of rotor pocket in pump body.

ENGINE COOLING

Cooling System Capacity – 14.4 pints with heater.

Thermostat – 180°F (82°C) thermostat is standard. A 190 F (88°C) thermostat is available for use in cold climates.

Pressure Cap – Maintains pressure at 15 psi (1.05 kg)

WATER PUMP REPLACEMENT

1) Drain cooling system, remove top and bottom radiator hoses. If oil cooler is installed, disconnect oil cooler lines from both cooler and engine. Remove radiator mounting screws and remove radiator.

2) Remove generator or alternator, unscrew fan and pulley retaining screws and remove fan and pulley. Remove water pump retaining bolts and remove pump. To install, reverse removal procedure.

MGB 4 CYLINDER (Cont.)

ENGINE SPECIFICATIONS

GENERAL SPECIFICATIONS										
Year	Displ.		Carburetor	HP at RPM	Torque (Ft. Lbs. at RPM)	Compr. Ratio	Bore		Stroke	
	cu. ins.	cc					in.	mm	in.	mm
1977	110	1798	2x1-Bbl.	.....	.....	8.0-1	3.16	80.26	3.5	88.9

VALVES							
Engine & Valve	Head Diam. In. (mm)	Face Angle	Seat Angle	Seat Width In. (mm)	Stem Diameter In. (mm)	Stem Clearance In. (mm)	Valve Lift In. (mm)
1798 cc							
Int.	1.500-1.505 (38.1-38.23)	45°	45.5°	...	.3429-.3434 (8.70-8.72)	.0007-.0019 (.02-.05)	.3645 (9.25)
Exh.	1.343-1.348 (34.11-34.23)	45°	45.5°	...	.3423-.3428 (8.69-8.70)	.0013-.0025 (.03-.06)	.3645 (9.25)

PISTONS, PINS, RINGS						
Engine	PISTONS	PINS		RINGS		
	Clearance In. (mm)	Piston Fit In. (mm)	Rod Fit In. (mm)	Rings	End Gap In. (mm)	Side Clearance In. (mm)
1798 cc	① .0021-.0033 (.053-.084) ② .0006-.0012 (.015-.030)	③	Press Fit	No. 1	.012-.022 (.30-.56)	.0015-.0035 (.038-.088)
				No. 2	.012-.022 (.30-.56)	.0015-.0035 (.038-.088)
				Oil	.015-.045 (.38-1.14)	.0016-.0036 (.04-.09)

① — Top.
② — Bottom.
③ — Hand Push Fit at 60°F (15.6°C).

CRANKSHAFT MAIN & CONNECTING ROD BEARINGS							
Engine	MAIN BEARINGS				CONNECTING ROD BEARINGS		
	Journal Diam. In. (mm)	Clearance In. (mm)	Thrust Bearing	Crankshaft End Play In. (mm)	Journal Diam. In. (mm)	Clearance In. (mm)	Side Play In. (mm)
1798 cc	2.1262-2.1270 (54.01-54.02)	.001-.0027 (.03-.07	Center	.004-.005 (.10-.13)	1.8759-1.8764 (47.64-47.66)	.001-.0027 (.03-.07	.....

CAMSHAFT			
Engine	Journal Diam. In. (mm)	Clearance In. (mm)	Lobe Lift In. (mm)
1798 cc			
Front	1.7888-1.7893 (45.42-45.44)	.001-.002 (.025-.051)	.250 (6.35)
Center	1.7288-1.7293 (43.91-43.92)		
Rear	1.6228-1.6233 (41.22-41.23)		

MGB 4 CYLINDER (Cont.)

ENGINE SPECIFICATIONS (Cont.)

VALVE SPRINGS

Engine	Free Length In. (mm)	PRESSURE Lbs. @ In. (kg @ mm)	
		Valve Closed	Valve Open
1798 cc	1.92 (48.8)	.....	.....

VALVE TIMING

Engine	INTAKE		EXHAUST	
	Open (BTDC)	Close (ALDC)	Open (BLDC)	Close (ATDC)
1798 cc	5°	45°	51°	21°

TIGHTENING SPECIFICATIONS

Application	Ft. Lbs. (mkg)
Main Bearing Nuts	70 (9.7)
Flywheel Set Screws	40 (5.5)
Connecting Rod Bolts	31-35 (4.2)
Rocker Bracket Nuts	25 (3.5)
Oil Pump-to-Crankcase	14 (.8)
Oil Pan Bolts	6 (.8)
Side Covers	3-4 (.4-.5)
Timing Cover	
1/4" Screws	6 (.8)
5/16" Screws	14 (1.9)
Rear Plate	
5/16" Screws	20 (2.8)
3/8" Screws	30 (4.1)
Water Pump	17 (2.3)
Thermostat Housing	8 (1.1)
Rocker Cover Nuts	4 (.56)
Manifold Nuts	16 (2.2)
Clutch-to-Flywheel	25-30 (3.5-4.1)
Carburetor Stud Nuts	15 (2.1)
Cylinder Head	45-50 (6.2-6.9)

MIDGET 4 CYLINDER

ENGINE CODING

ENGINE IDENTIFICATION

Engine identification and serial numbers are stamped on crankcase, located on right hand side above generator.

ENGINE, CYLINDER HEAD & MANIFOLD

ENGINE

1) Disconnect battery, remove hood, drain cooling system and remove radiator. Disconnect heater air intake hose. Remove fan, drain engine oil, and disconnect carburetor from manifold.

2) Remove nuts and bolts securing exhaust manifold to exhaust pipe then disconnect running-on control valve vacuum pipe from intake manifold. Disconnect heater hose and heater control valve hose.

3) Disconnect water temperature capillary tube, remove rear rocker cover nut, release support bracket, then disconnect diverter valve hose from check valve. Remove nuts securing manifold and remove manifold. Disconnect electrical leads at alternator.

4) Remove distributor cap and air pump. Disconnect oil pressure gauge tube, engine ground strap, and fuel line. Remove nuts and bolts securing transmission housing and starter motor to engine. Move transmission restraint cable aside then disconnect starter.

5) Place support under transmission then secure suitable lifting device to engine lifting brackets. Remove two nuts securing right and left front engine mounts, raise engine enough to remove bolts from mounts then lift engine from vehicle.

INTAKE & EXHAUST MANIFOLD

Removal – Disconnect battery, remove air cleaner and carburetor. Remove nuts and bolts securing exhaust manifold to exhaust pipe then disconnect running-on control valve vacuum pipe from intake manifold. Disconnect and remove water temperature capillary tube, rear rocker cover nut then release support bracket. Disconnect diverter valve hose from check valve. Remove nuts securing manifold and remove manifold.

Installation – To install intake and exhaust manifold, reverse removal procedure.

CYLINDER HEAD

Removal – 1) Disconnect battery and drain cooling system. Remove air temperature control valve hot air hose, then disconnect distributor vacuum line from carburetor. Disconnect E.G.R. valve and breather pipe from rocker cover. Disconnect fuel line from carburetor.

2) Disconnect carburetor and lay to one side. Unclip distributor vacuum pipe flame-trap and lay aside. Remove temperature sending unit then disconnect capillary tube from intake manifold. Disconnect thermostat housing hose then remove fan guard from radiator. Remove water pump attaching bolts from cylinder head. Disconnect diverter valve hose from check valve and unscrew four air manifold unions from cylinder head.

3) Remove rocker cover nuts, then release support bracket from rear rocker cover stud. Remove air induction manifold, check valve then remove rocker cover. Remove spark plug leads and disconnect exhaust manifold from exhaust pipe. Disconnect the running-on control valve vacuum pipe, heater control valve hose, and heater by-pass hose.

4) Disconnect heater return pipe bracket. Remove rocker shaft assembly. Remove push rods, keeping them in order for reinstallation. Remove cylinder head bolts and lift off cylinder head.

Installation – To install, reverse removal procedure then tighten head nuts gradually in sequence shown in *Fig. 1*.

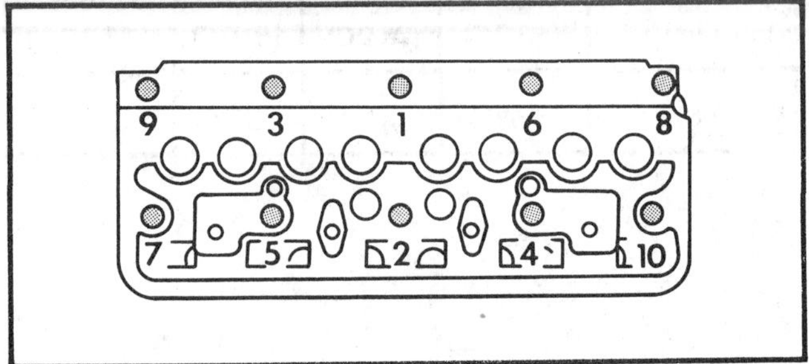

Fig. 1 Midget Cylinder Head Tightening Sequence

VALVES

VALVE ARRANGEMENT

E-I-I-E-E-I-I-E

VALVE GUIDE SERVICING

Removal & Installation – With cylinder head removed, remove valve, spring and retainer. Using suitable tool (60A) and adapter (S 60A-2A), position tool on combustion chamber face of cylinder head, pull replacement guide in driving old guide out. Insure that guide protrusion above cylinder head top face is correct.

ROCKER ARM ASSEMBLY

Removal – Disconnect breather pipe from rocker cover and remove cover. Remove nuts and washers securing rocker arm shaft and remove rocker arm assembly.

Disassembly – Remove cotter key from front end of rocker shaft. Slide off rockers, pedestals, springs and spacers from shaft noting the order for reassembly. Remove screw securing rear pedestal to shaft and remove pedestal and rocker arm.

Reassembly – Reverse disassembly procedure, applying Loctite to rear pedestal locating screw.

MIDGET 4 CYLINDER (Cont.)

Installation – To install rocker arm assembly, reverse removal procedure. Adjust valve clearance.

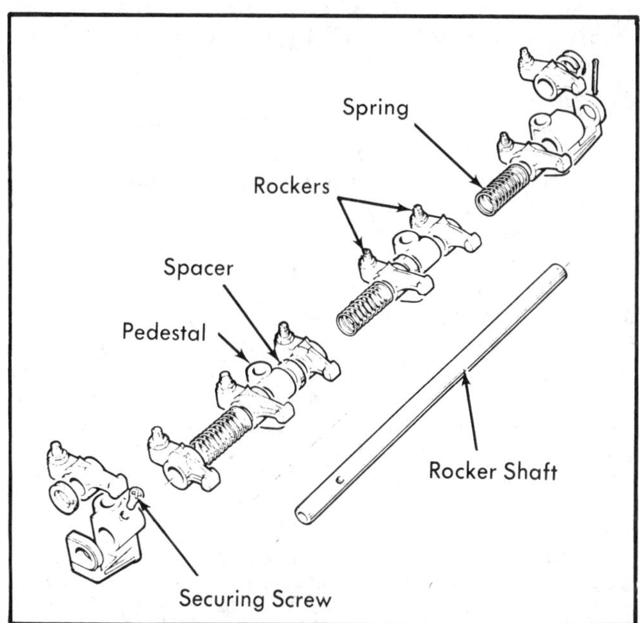

Fig. 2 Disassembled View of Rocker Arm & Shaft

VALVE CLEARANCE ADJUSTMENT

With engine cold, set valve clearance to .010" (.25 mm). To check valve clearance, turn crankshaft until valves in first column are fully open, then valves in the second column may be checked and adjusted as necessary.

Valves Open	Valves to Adjust
1	8
3	6
5	4
2	7
8	1
6	3
4	5
7	2

PISTON, PINS & RINGS

OIL PAN

Drain engine oil, remove oil pan screws and lower oil pan.

PISTON & ROD ASSEMBLY

Removal – Remove cylinder head, drain oil and remove pan. Remove bearing caps and move connecting rods off of crankshaft. Remove piston and rod assembly from cylinder head side of block.

Installation – Lubricate pistons, cylinder bores, and crankshaft with clean oil. Fit pistons and connecting rods to their original bores. Make sure that arrow on piston is pointing towards front of engine and that ring gaps are staggered. To complete installation, reverse removal procedure.

PISTON PINS

Removal & Installation – Piston pin is hand press fit in connecting rod. To remove pin, remove circlips then press out pin. Separate piston from connecting rod. To install, reverse removal procedure and note the following: Install new bushing and ream to proper size. Ensure piston is fitted correctly on connecting rod; arrow on top of piston facing front and cylinder number stamped on connecting rod and cap facing camshaft.

CRANKSHAFT MAIN & CONNECTING ROD BEARINGS

CRANKSHAFT & MAIN BEARING

Removal – 1) Remove engine from vehicle, then remove clutch assembly, and remove flywheel. Remove engine rear adapter plate, water pump and thermostat housing, then remove timing chain and gears. Remove camshaft locating plate and front mounting plate.

2) Remove dipstick, oil pan, crankshaft pulley and drive key. Remove shims if fitted, and two screws securing front sealing block. Remove crankshaft rear oil seal housing. Remove connecting rod and main bearing caps and remove crankshaft.

Installation – 1) Coat pilot bushing with zinc oxide grease and install in crankshaft. Install main bearings, crankshaft, and main bearing caps. Tighten caps to specification. Check crankshaft end play; adjust with selective thrust washers.

2) Install connecting rods, bearings, and caps. Use new bolts and tighten to specification. Install front sealing block using suitable sealing compound, then drive new wedges into slots. Cut protruding edges from wedges. To complete installation, reverse removal procedure.

CAMSHAFT

ENGINE FRONT COVER & OIL SEAL

Removal & Installation – 1) Drain cooling system and remove radiator. Remove air pump and drive belts. Remove water pump and fan as an assembly. Disconnect exhaust pipe from exhaust manifold. Loosen motor mounts and raise engine to allow for removal of crankshaft pulley.

2) Remove front cover, gasket, and oil seal. Remove oil seal from cover. Dip new seal in clean engine oil, and press into front cover using suitable tool (18 G 134) and (18 G 134BM). To complete installation reverse removal procedure.

TIMING CHAIN REPLACEMENT

Removal – Remove engine front cover and oil thrower as previously described. Align timing marks on camshaft and crankshaft sprockets then remove bolts securing camshaft sprocket. Remove camshaft and crankshaft sprockets along with timing chain.

MIDGET 4 CYLINDER (Cont.)

Installation – To install, reverse removal procedure and note the following: Align timing marks and correct any misalignment of timing chain by fitting selective shims behind crankshaft sprocket.

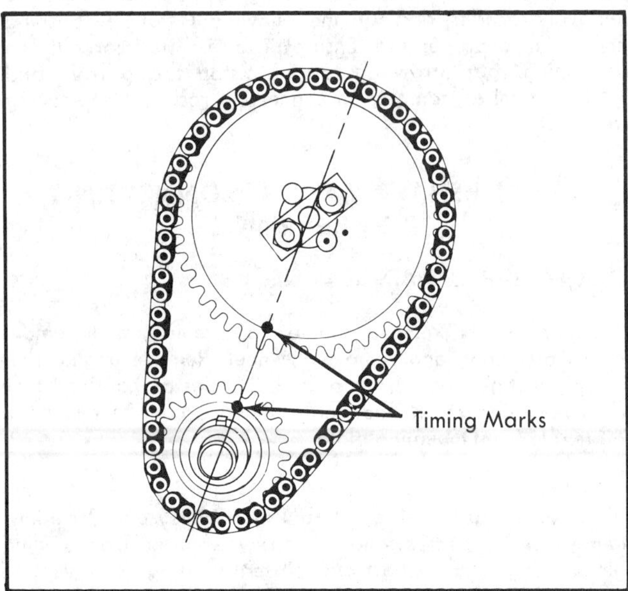

Fig. 3 Timing Chain Sprocket Alignment

CAMSHAFT

Removal – 1) Remove radiator, air pump drive belt and fan belt. Remove thermostat, water pump and fan. Remove crankshaft pulley, and engine front cover. Remove timing chain and gears.

2) Remove bolt securing cam locating plate and remove plate then remove cylinder head. Remove lifters and identify for reassembly. Remove distributor drive shaft and fuel pump. Withdraw camshaft from block.

Installation – To install camshaft, reverse removal procedure and note the following: Check camshaft end play; if end play is excessive, install new locating plate. Standard end play is .0045-.0085" (.120-.216 mm).

VALVE TIMING

1) Adjust valve clearance of number 7 and number 8 valves to .050" (1.27 mm). Rotate crankshaft to bring number 1 piston to TDC on compression stroke. Check that number 1 and 2 valves are fully closed and number 7 and 8 valves have the same clearance.

2) After valve timing has been checked, valve clearance should be set to specification.

ENGINE OILING

Crankcase Capacity – 4.8 qts. including filter.

Oil Filter – Full flow type with disposable cartridge.

Normal Oil Pressure – 40-60 psi; at idle 20 psi.

ENGINE OILING SYSTEM

Force feed system with rotor type oiling pump. A full-flow type oil filter is used. An oil pressure relief valve is used to enable oil to by-pass filter if oil becomes blocked .

OIL PUMP

Removal – Drain crankcase oil and remove oil pan. Loosen oil strainer locknut and unscrew oil strainer from oil pump cover plate. Remove three bolts securing oil pump to crankcase and remove pump.

Disassembly & Inspection – Remove inner rotor and shaft assembly. Remove outer rotor. Clean all components then reinstall rotors in pump body with chamfered edge of outer rotor at driving end of pump body. Place straightedge across face of pump body and check clearance between straightedge and rotors. Clearance should not exceed .0004" (0.1 mm). Check clearance between inner and outer rotors and pump body. Clearance between the inner and outer rotors, measured at the rotor lobes should not exceed .010" (.25 mm). Clearance between outer rotor and pump body should not exceed .008" (0.2 mm). If clearance is excessive at any location, pump should be replaced.

Reassembly – To reassemble, reverse disassembly procedure and ensure that outer rotor is installed in pump body with chamfered end at driving end of pump body.

Installation – To install oil pump, reverse removal procedure.

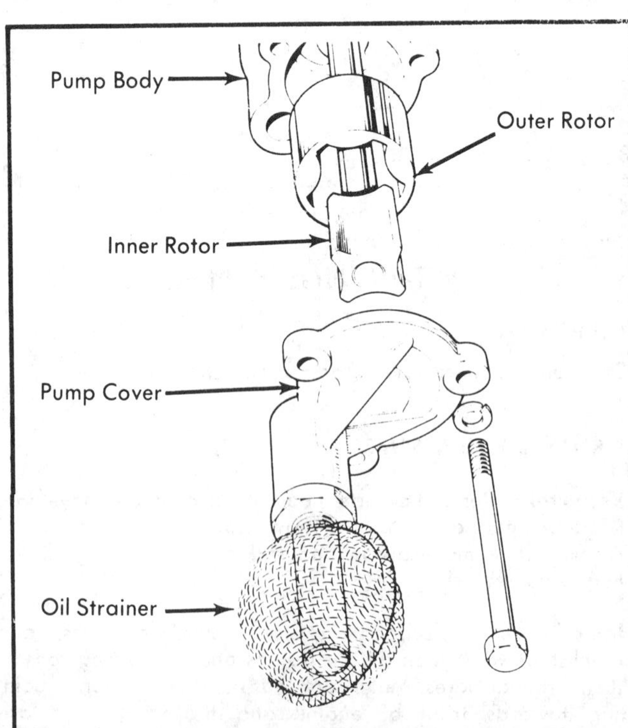

Fig. 4 Engine Oil Pump Disassembled View

MIDGET 4 CYLINDER (Cont.)

ENGINE COOLING

Cooling System Capacity – 4.5 qts.

Thermostat – Opening temperature, 190°F (88°C)

Radiator Cap – 15 psi (1.5 kg)

WATER PUMP

Removal – Remove radiator, loosen alternator adjusting bracket and remove fan belt. Remove nuts and bolts securing fan and remove fan from coupling assembly. Remove nuts securing water pump to thermostat housing and remove water pump, fan coupling, and tolerance ring.

Installation – To install water pump, reverse removal procedure and refill cooling system.

ENGINE SPECIFICATIONS

GENERAL SPECIFICATIONS

Year	Displ.		Carburetor	HP at RPM	Torque (Ft. Lbs. at RPM)	Compr. Ratio	Bore		Stroke	
	cu. ins.	cc					in.	mm	in.	mm
1977	91.0	1493	1x1-Bbl.	.....	.....	7.5-1	2.9	73.7	3.44	87.5

VALVES

Engine & Valve	Head Diam. In. (mm)	Face Angle	Seat Angle	Seat Width In. (mm)	Stem Diameter In. (mm)	Stem Clearance In. (mm)	Valve Lift In. (mm)
1493 cc							
Int.	1.380 (34.99)	45°	45.5°	.....	.3107-.3113 (7.89-7.91)	.0007-.0023 (.02-.06)	.....
Exh.	1.170 (29.71)	45°	45.5°	.....	.3100-.3105 (7.874-7.887)	.0015-.0030 (.04-.07)	.....

PISTONS, PINS, RINGS

Engine	PISTONS	PINS		RINGS		
	Clearance in. (mm)	Piston Fit in. (mm)	Rod Fit in. (mm)	Rings	End Gap in. (mm)	Side Clearance in. (mm)
1493 cc	①.002-.003 (.051-.076) ②.0002-.0016 (.005-.041)	③	④	1	.012-.022 (.305-.559)	.0015-.0035 (.038-.089)
				2	.012-.022 (.305-.559)	.0015-.0035 (.038-.089)
				Oil	.015-.055 (.38-.1.40)	.....

① – At top of skirt.
② – At bottom of skirt.
③ – Hand push fit.
④ – Interference fit.

CRANKSHAFT MAIN & CONNECTING ROD BEARINGS

Engine	MAIN BEARINGS				CONNECTING ROD BEARINGS		
	Journal Diam. In. (mm)	Clearance In. (mm)	Thrust Bearing	Crankshaft End Play In. (mm)	Journal Diam. In. (mm)	Clearance In. (mm)	Side Play In. (mm)
1493 cc	2.3115-2.3120 (58.713-58.725)	.0005-.002 (.013-.050)	Rear	.006-.014 (.15-.36)	1.8750-1.8755 (47.625-47.638)	.001-.003 (.03-.08)	.....

MIDGET 4 CYLINDER (Cont.)

ENGINE SPECIFICATIONS (Cont.)

VALVE SPRINGS			
Engine	Free Length In. (mm)	PRESSURE (LBS.)	
		Valve Closed	Valve Open
1493 cc	1.52 (38.6)	.....	.....

VALVE TIMING				
	INTAKE		EXHAUST	
Engine	Open (BTDC)	Close (ALDC)	Open (BLDC)	Close (ATDC)
1493 cc	18°	58°	58°	18°

CAMSHAFT			
Engine	Journal Diam. in. (mm)	Clearance in. (mm)	Lobe Lift in. (mm)
1493 cc			
No. 1	1.9659-1.9664 (49.93-49.95)	.0016-.0036 (.04-.09)	.....
No. 2	1.9649-1.9654 (49.90-49.92)	.0026-.0046 (.07-.12)	.....
No. 3	1.9659-1.9664 (49.93-49.95)	.0016-.0036 (.04-.09)	.....

TIGHTENING SPECIFICATIONS	
Application	Ft. Lbs. (mkg)
Cylinder Head	46 (6.4)
Connecting Rod Bolt	40-45 (5.5-6.2)
Rocker Shaft	32 (4.4)
Oil Pan	20 (2.8)
Engine Front Cover	
Small Bolt	10 (1.4)
Large Bolt	20 (2.8)
Water Pump	20 (2.8)
Manifold	25 (3.5)
Crankshaft Pulley	150 (20.7)
Rocker Cover	2 (.03)
Main Bearing Cap Bolts	65 (9.0)

1800 cc 4 CYLINDER

ENGINE CODING

ENGINE IDENTIFICATION

Engine number is stamped on a machined pad on right side of cylinder block near the distributor.

ENGINE, CYLINDER HEAD & MANIFOLD

ENGINE

Removal – 1) Remove battery cables and hood. Drain cooling system and crankcase. Remove air cleaner by disconnecting PCV, ECS, AIR and CCS hoses.

2) Disconnect the CCS hot air hose, remove manifold cover and disconnect alternator wiring at connector. Remove exhaust pipe from manifold. Free clutch control cable by turning adjusting nut. Disconnect heater hose at engine and from heater and joint. Disconnect control cable and remove water cock assembly with heater hose. Remove left engine mounting nut and install engine hanger (J-26555) on exhaust manifold stud bolts.

3) Disconnect ground cable from engine, fuel hoses from carburetor and high tension cable from coil. Disconnect vacuum hose at rear of manifold, accelerator control cable from carburetor, and starter motor connections. Disconnect the thermo unit, oil pressure switch, and distributor wiring at connector.

4) Disconnect carburetor solenoid valve lead and automatic choke wiring at connector. Disconnect backup light switch at rear of engine. Disconnect ECS hose from oil pan. Remove right engine mounting nut and stopper plate.

5) Disconnect water hoses from engine and radiator. Remove fan shroud and radiator assembly. Remove gearshift lever assembly. Remove parking brake return spring and disconnect brake cable. Disconnect propeller shaft from transmission.

6) Remove clutch cable heat protector, clutch return spring, and clutch control cable. Remove exhaust pipe bracket from transmission. Remove front side exhaust pipe. Disconnect speedometer cable. Remove four rear engine mounting bolts after lifting engine slightly.

7) Check that all parts have been properly disconnected or removed, and remove engine toward front of vehicle.

Installation – Install all components in reverse order of removal. Check that crankcase and cooling system are refilled. Adjust clutch pedal free play. Check engine for leaks after running at idle. Adjust fan belt tension, distributor breaker point gap, valve clearances, ignition timing and engine idle.

EXHAUST MANIFOLD

Remove air cleaner and hot air hose. Remove manifold cover, EGR pipe and exhaust pipe from manifold, and exhaust manifold from engine. To install, reverse removal procedure, using new gaskets.

INTAKE MANIFOLD

Removal – 1) Drain cooling system completely. Remove air cleaner (*See Engine Removal*).

NOTE – *Incomplete draining will permit coolant to enter cylinders when intake manifold is removed.*

2) Remove the following parts from intake manifold: water top hose, fuel hose, vacuum hose, heater hose (also from connector under instrument panel). Disconnect accelerator control cable and vacuum hose from carburetor. Disconnect automatic choke and solenoid wiring at connectors, PCV hose from cylinder head cover, and EGR pipe from EGR valve. Disconnect AIR vacuum hose from manifold. Remove intake manifold from engine.

Installation – Reverse removal procedure. Use new gaskets and fill cooling system with equal amounts of water and anti-freeze.

CYLINDER HEAD

Removal – 1) Drain cooling system, remove air cleaner, and all parts attached to intake manifold. Remove manifold cover.

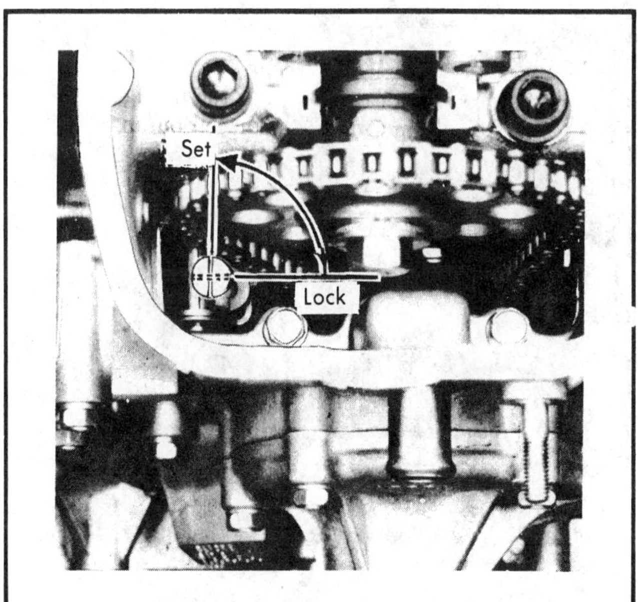

Fig. 1 Locking Timing Chain Adjuster

2) Remove EGR pipe clip from rear of cylinder block, and disconnect exhaust pipe from manifold. Remove cylinder head cover, lock timing chain in place (*See Fig. 1*), and separate sprocket from camshaft. Disconnect air hoses from check valve and AIR pump. Remove air bypass valve and bracket, and remove two bolts securing front cover and cylinder head. Loosen cylinder head bolts in sequence shown in *Fig. 2*. Remove cylinder head with exhaust and intake manifolds.

1800 cc 4 CYLINDER (Cont.)

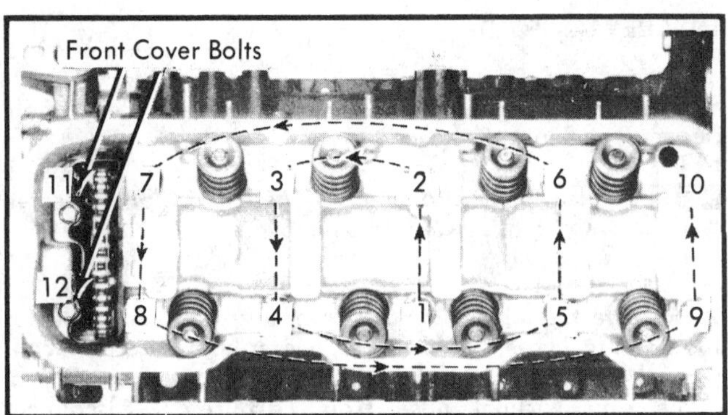

Fig. 2 Cylinder Head Bolt Loosening & Tightening Sequence

NOTE – *Do not separate camshaft timing sprocket from chain. Keep sprocket in chain, and chain between guide and tensioner.*

Installation – 1) Install components in reverse order of removal. Apply a thin coat of liquid gasket evenly on clean block face around sprocket hole. Install a new cylinder head gasket with "TOP" mark up, using dowels for proper alignment. See *Fig. 3*.

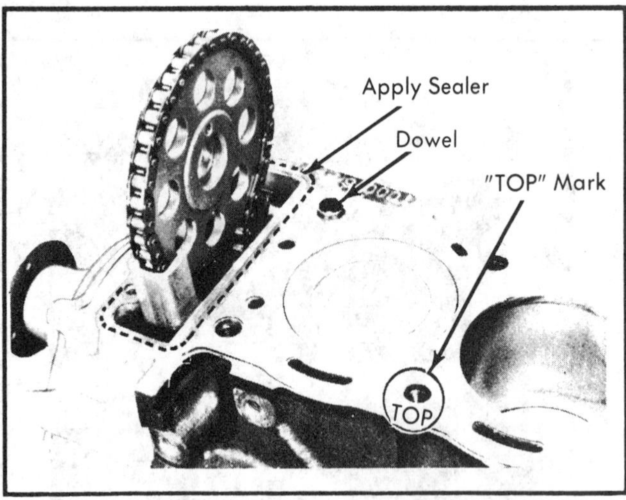

Fig. 3 Installing Liquid Gasket & Head Gasket

2) Align cylinder head over dowels, oil cylinder head bolt threads and install bolts. Install two bolts securing front cover to cylinder head. Tighten cylinder head bolts in sequence (See *Fig. 2*) in two stages. Tighten securely front cover-to-cylinder head bolts.

Cylinder Head Bolt Tightening Specifications

	Ft. Lbs. (mkg)
Step One	61 (8.4)
Step Two	72 (9.9)

VALVES

VALVE ARRANGEMENT

E-I-I-E-E-I-I-E

ROCKER ARM ASSEMBLY & CAMSHAFT

Removal – 1) Remove air cleaner and disconnect accelerator control cable from carburetor. Pull out three clips and high tension cables from head cover. Disconnect AIR vacuum hose and PCV hose. Remove head cover.

2) Align mark on camshaft with mark on No. 1 rocker arm shaft bracket by turning crankshaft, *Fig. 4*. Lock the automatic chain adjuster in free state, by pressing downward on pin while turning it 90 degrees clockwise (See *Fig. 1*).

3) Remove bolt and slip timing sprocket off camshaft. Keep chain on sprocket and support sprocket on chain guide and tensioner. Loosen nuts on rocker arm shaft brackets in stages, starting with the outer brackets. Remove rocker arm assembly and camshaft from cylinder head.

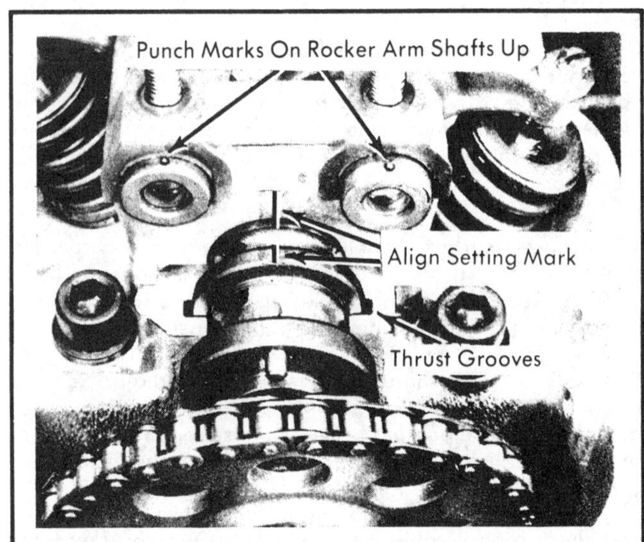

Fig. 4 Installing Camshaft & Rocker Arm Assembly

Installation – 1) Lubricate camshaft and rocker arm assemblies well prior to installation. Install camshaft, aligning thrust grooves, *Fig. 4*. Be sure punch marks on rocker arm shafts are in upward position.

2) Install rocker arm shaft bracket assembly and align camshaft mark with mark on No. 1 rocker arm shaft bracket. See *Fig. 4*. Tighten rocker arm shaft bracket nuts to 16 ft. lbs. (2.2 mkg) torque, while holding rocker arm springs with an adjustable wrench.

3) Align crankshaft pulley groove with TDC mark ("O" mark) on front cover. Be sure No. 4 cylinder (rear) is at TDC. Align sprocket hole with camshaft pin. Install sprocket and tighten bolt to 58 ft. lbs. (8.02 mkg). Set automatic chain adjuster by turning pin 90 degrees counterclockwise *(See Fig. 1)*. Be sure chain is tensioned.

1800 cc 4 CYLINDER (Cont.)

VALVE GUIDE SERVICING

1) Using valve spring compressor (J-26513), remove valve collets, upper seats, and outer and inner springs. Remove seals and lower seat springs. Check stems and guides for wear and clearance. Do not remove guides unless they are to be replaced.

2) To remove guides, use driver (J-26512) to drive guide upward. Drive new guide in until it extends 0.6378" (16.2 mm) above cylinder head, *(See Fig. 5)*. Be sure valve moves freely in guide. Install seals over guides and reassemble.

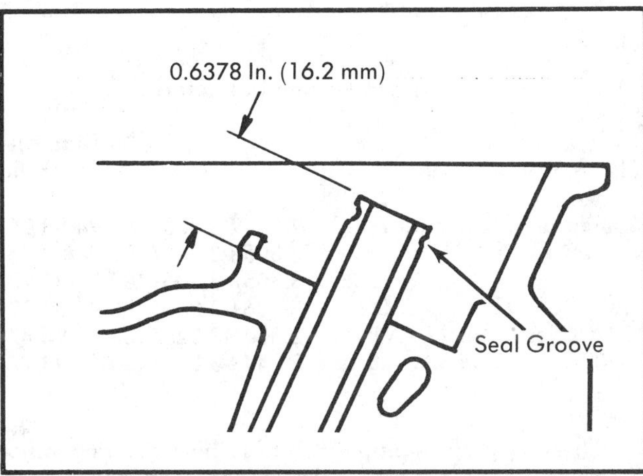

Fig. 5 Installing Valve Guide to Proper Depth

VALVE FACE AND SEAT

1) To replace valve seat insert, weld end of welding rods to several portions of inner face of insert. Allow cylinder head to cool. Apply shock load to welding rods and pull out inserts. Clean insert face area of cylinder head and heat with steam. Chill new insert on dry ice and install in cylinder head.

2) Cut valve seat face with 15°, 45°, and 75°cutters to achieve specified valve seat contact width. Grind valves to an angle of 45° and lap valve and seat to specified width.

VALVE CLEARANCE ADJUSTMENT

1) Check rocker arm shaft bracket nuts for 16 ft. lbs. (2.2 mkg) torque. Bring No. 1 piston (front) to TDC on compression stroke (notched line on crankshaft pulley aligns with "0" mark on front cover). Check clearances of No. 1 and 2 intake valves and No. 1 and 3 exhaust valves.

2) Turn crankshaft one full turn until No. 4 piston (rear) is at TDC on compression stroke, and check clearances of No. 3 and 4 intake valves and No. 2 and 4 exhaust valves.

3) Adjust intake valves to .006"C (.15 mm) and exhaust valves to .010"C (.25 mm).

PISTONS, PINS & RINGS

OIL PAN

Removal – Remove oil pressure switch from block and remove 14 bolts and 6 nuts holding pan to block. Remove dust cover.

Installation – Apply liquid gasket to points shown in *Fig. 6*. Place oil pan gasket on cylinder block, aligning bolt holes. Install and tighten bolts and nuts to 3.6 ft. lbs. (.5 mkg). Check gasket position and install dust cover on the rear plate.

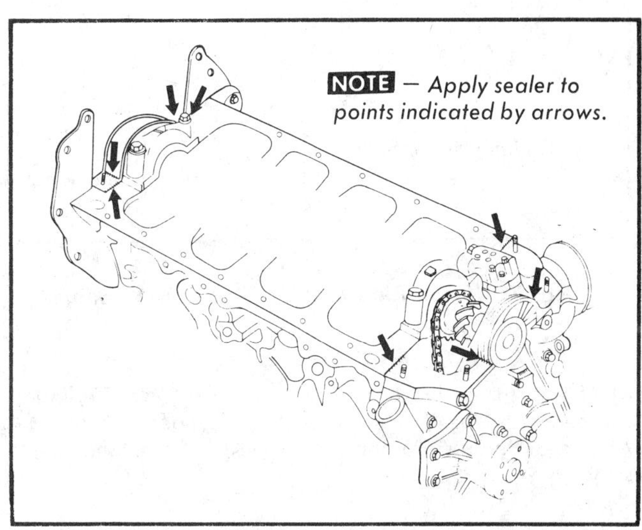

NOTE – Apply sealer to points indicated by arrows.

Fig. 6 Installing Oil Pan & Gasket

PISTON & ROD ASSEMBLY

Removal – Remove cylinder head and oil pan. Remove carbon ridge from cylinder bore. Remove bearing and cap from connecting rod. Remove piston and rod assembly by pushing upward with wooden handle of hammer.

NOTE – *Remove one piston at a time and mark piston, rod, and bearings with their cylinder numbers.*

Installation – 1) Turn crankshaft so that the crankpin of No. 1 cylinder (front) is in uppermost position. Install bearings with tangs inserted in notches in rod and cap. Oil bearing surfaces and outer contact areas of piston and rings.

2) Arrange ring gaps as shown in *Fig. 7*. Mark on head of piston should point toward front of engine. Using ring compressor, push piston head in until connecting rod contacts crankpin. Head of piston should be approximately .016" (.4 mm) below face of block when at TDC.

3) Face of connecting rod with cylinder number mark should be toward starter side of engine. Align number marks on connecting rod cap and rod and torque nuts to 33 ft. lbs. (4.6 mkg).

1800 cc 4 CYLINDER (Cont.)

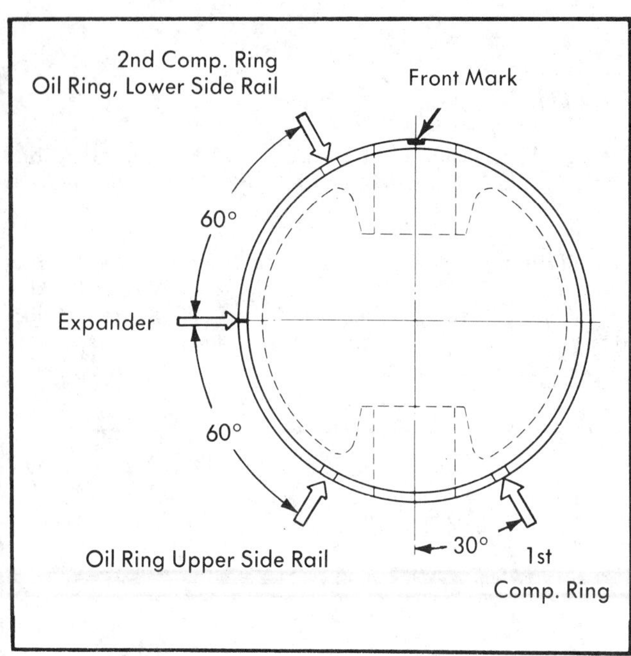

Fig. 7 Piston Ring Position & Piston Marking

4) After piston and rod assembly is installed in No. 1 cylinder, proceed with No. 4, No. 2, and No. 3 cylinders in sequence. After bearing nuts are tightened, check that crankshaft turns smoothly.

PISTON PINS

Do not remove piston from connecting rod unless replacing parts. Always use new piston pin. Check piston pin hole in piston and connecting rod for damage. If pin is to be removed, remove rings and use pin remover (J-25270-45) to press pin from rod. Position piston so that marks on head and notches in connecting rod point upward. Use same position and tool for removal and installation.

FITTING PISTONS

1) Measure cylinder bores .32" (8.1 mm) and 2.76" (70.1 mm) below cylinder block face. Measure both in line and at right angles to crankshaft. If diameter varies more than .0079" (.2 mm), reboring is indicated. Variance of bore diameter after reboring and honing should be less than .0008" (.02 mm).

2) Cylinder bores for various pistons available include:

Cylinder Bore Sizes

Piston Size	Bore Diameter Inches (mm)
Standard	3.3071-3.3087 (84.00-84.04)
.020" Oversize	3.3268-3.3276 (84.50-84.52)
.040" Oversize	3.3465-3.3472 (85.00-85.02)

3) Cylinder blocks are stamped on the upper face to show cylinder bore grade or size:

Cylinder Bore Grades

Bore Size	Bore Grade	Bore Diameter Inches (mm)
Standard	A	3.3071-3.3075 (84.00-84.01)
	B	3.3075-3.3079 (84.01-84.02)
	C	3.3079-3.3083 (84.02-84.03)
	D	3.3083-3.3087 (84.03-84-04)

4) Pistons are also stamped with a grade on their heads to show their diameter at a point 1.575" (40 mm) below piston head and at right angles to piston pin.

Piston Grades and Diameters

Piston Size	Piston Grade	Diameter Inches (mm)
Standard Size	A	3.3049-3.3053 (83.94-83.95)
	B	3.3053-3.3057 (83.95-83.96)
	C	3.3057-3.3061 (83.96-83.97)
	D	3.3061-3.3065 (83.97-83.98)
.020" Oversize	A.B	3.3246-3.3254 (84.44-84.47)
.040" Oversize	A.B	3.3443-3.3451 (84.95-84.97)

5) Check cylinder-to-piston clearance by measuring piston diameter 1.575" (40 mm) below piston head and at right angles with piston pin. Subtract this measurement from cylinder bore diameter, measured 4.724" (120 mm) below face of cylinder block. If clearance is excessive, install oversize pistons.

6) Check end gap and groove clearance. Install rings on pistons using a ring expander. Compression rings should be installed with "NPR" or "TOP" mark turned up. When installing oil control ring, install expander ring, followed by lower side rail and upper side rail. Oil rings are not marked.

7) When all rings are installed, apply engine oil and see that rings move freely in grooves. Weigh piston and rod assemblies. Variation in weight should be less than .42 oz. (12 gms). Adjust gaps as shown in *Fig. 7* and install pistons in block.

CRANKSHAFT MAIN & CONNECTING ROD BEARINGS

MAIN & CONNECTING ROD BEARINGS

Removal – 1) Remove oil pan and pipe from oil pump. Remove crankshaft pulley and front cover assembly. Remove cylinder head, sprockets and timing chain. Remove flywheel assembly, rear plate and oil seal retainer. Remove connecting rod and piston assemblies.

2) Loosen main bearing cap bolts in sequence, beginning with outer bolts. Remove bolts, bearing caps and bearings.

1800 cc 4 CYLINDER (Cont.)

NOTE – *Check each connecting rod and main bearing cap for identification, so that it can be reinstalled in its original location and position.*

3) Lift out crankshaft. Remove thrust bearings and crankshaft bearings from cylinder block.

Inspection – **1)** Using an outside micrometer, measure crankshaft and crankpin journals at front and rear of each journal, *(1 and 2), Fig. 8.* Take both vertical and horizontal measurements (A and B). If wear exceeds .002" (.05 mm), grind crankshaft and install undersize bearings.

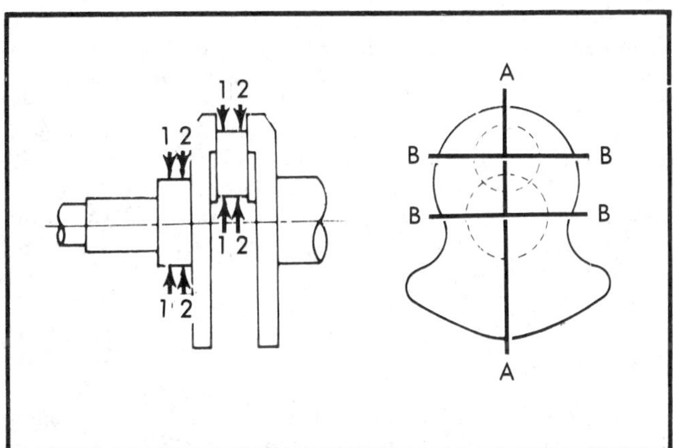

Fig. 8 Measuring Crankshaft & Crankpin Journals

2) Install crankshaft bearings in block and install bearing caps and bolt. Torque to 72 ft. lbs (10 mkg) and measure inside diameter of bearings. Measure inside diameter of connecting rod bearings in same manner, torquing to 33 ft. lbs. (4.6 mkg). Compare outside diameters of journals with inside diameter of bearings to determine oil clearance. Plastigage method may also be used to determine clearance.

3) When installing undersize bearings, grind crankshaft and crankpin journals to match bearing size:

Crankshaft & Crankpin Journal Diameters

Bearing Size	Crankshaft Journal Inches (mm)	Crankpin Journal Inches (mm)
Standard	2.2016-2.2022	1.9262-1.9268
	(55.92-55.94)	(48.92-48.94)
.010" Undersize	2.1917-2.1923	1.9163-1.9169
	(55.67-55.68)	(48.67-48.69)
.020" Undersize	2.1819-2.1825	1.9065-1.9071
	(55.42-55.44)	(48.42-48.44)

4) Check crankshaft end play, and install new thrust bearings on each side of No. 3 journal if excessive.

Installation – **1)** Install bearings in cylinder block and oil generously. Install crankshaft over bearings. Install thrust bearings with oil grooves outward. Clean surfaces and install bearings in caps.

2) Install main bearing caps so cast arrows point toward engine front and numbers on caps and journals align. Tighten bolts in sequence: Cap No. 3, No. 4, No. 2, No. 5, and No. 1. Torque to 72 ft. lbs. (10 mkg). Be sure crankshaft turns easily.

3) Install piston and connecting rod assemblies and other components previously removed.

REAR MAIN BEARING OIL SEAL

Removal – Remove clutch pressure plate assembly. Flatten flywheel bolt lock plates and remove flywheel assembly. Pry off oil seal from retainer.

Installation – Apply grease between lips of oil seal and engine oil to crankshaft. Install oil seal in retainer using setting tool (J-22928-2). Be sure flanged part of oil seal is properly seated on retainer. Reverse removal procedure to complete installation. Use new flywheel bolt lock plates and torque to 69 ft. lbs. (9.5 mkg).

CAMSHAFT

FRONT COVER

Removal – Remove crankshaft pulley, oil filter and distributor from cover. Remove front cover with water pump and oil pump.

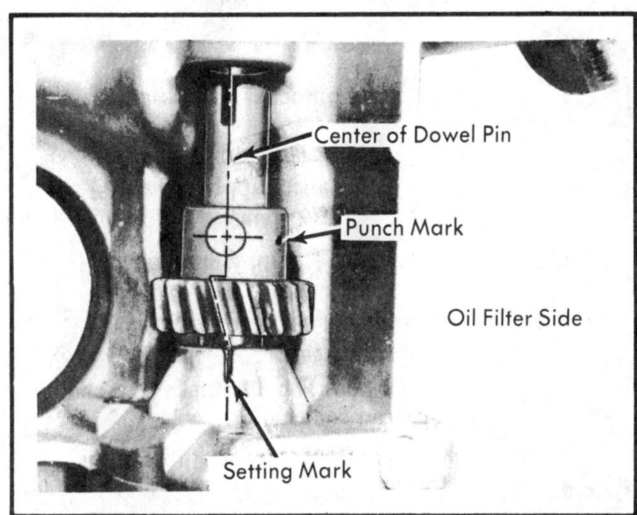

Fig. 9 Aligning Oil Pump in Front Cover

Installation – **1)** Install gasket on block. Be sure oil pump, water pump and oil seal are installed properly. Punch mark on oil pump drive gear face should be turned to oil filter side. Align center of dowel pin with setting mark on oil pump case. See *Fig. 9.*

2) Set No. 1 and No. 4 pistons at TDC. Install cover assembly, engaging pinion gear with oil pump drive gear. Punch mark on oil pump gear should be pointing toward cylinder block. Slot in end of oil pump shaft should be parallel with front of block and offset forward.

1800 cc 4 CYLINDER (Cont.)

FRONT COVER OIL SEAL

Removal & Installation – Remove fan assembly, A/C compressor drive belt, fan belts, crankshaft pulley and pulley boss. Pry out oil seal. To install, fill space between oil seal lips with bearing grease and use setting tool (J-26587). Install crankshaft pulley and torque bolt to 87 ft. lbs. (12 mkg).

TIMING CHAIN

1) To install, turn crankshaft so key points to cylinder head (piston for No. 1 and 4 cylinders at TDC). Place timing chain on crankshaft sprocket, so that mark plate on chain faces forward and aligns with sprocket timing mark.

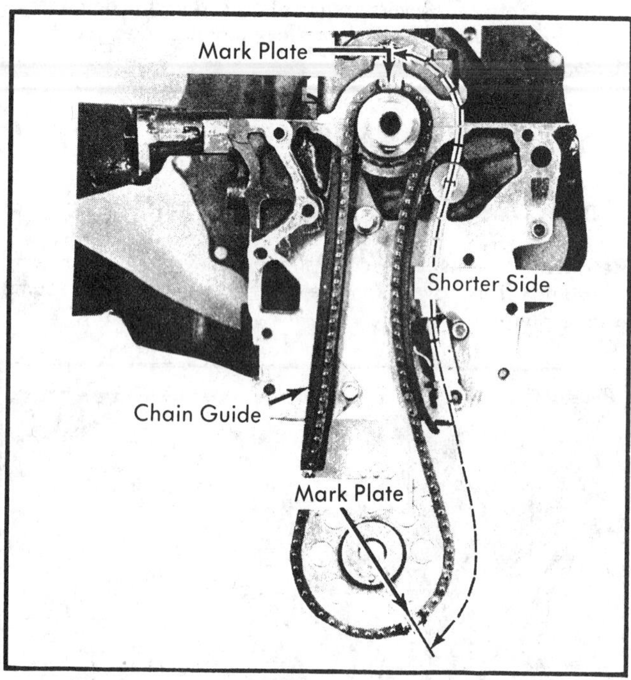

Fig. 10 ***Installing Timing Chain on Sprockets***

NOTE – *Chain has two mark plates. Be sure side of chain with most links between mark plates is toward chain guide side.*

2) Place camshaft timing sprocket in chain so that mark plate on chain aligns with triangular mark on camshaft sprocket. Install camshaft sprocket on camshaft as instructed under *Rocker Arm Assembly & Camshaft*.

VALVE TIMING

Valve timing will be correct if chain is properly installed and if camshaft is installed as instructed under *Rocker Arm Assembly & Camshaft*.

ENGINE OILING

Crankcase Capacity – 5 quarts.

Relief Valve – A relief valve built into oil pump cover bypasses oil to oil pan at 57-71 psi.

Oil Filter – Full-flow type, disposable cartridge. Filter has built-in bypass valve to permit engine oiling in event filter becomes restricted.

ENGINE OILING SYSTEM

A trochoid type pump feeds oil under pressure through the full-flow filter into the oil gallery, which supplies oil to crankshaft journals through drilled passages and ports. Oil is fed to crankpins, piston rings and pins as well as cylinder bore. Pressurized oil is also delivered through the No. 3 crankshaft oil port into the cylinder head to rocker arms, rocker arm shafts and camshaft. Timing chain and sprockets are lubricated by oil fed through No. 1 crankshaft journal to the oil jet on chain guide. Oil splashed by crankshaft lubricates cylinder walls.

OIL PUMP

Removal – 1) Remove engine from vehicle. Remove cylinder head cover, distributor assembly, engine stiffeners and oil pan. Remove oil pipe from pump and remove pump assembly. Remove rubber hose and relief valve assembly.

2) Inspect parts for wear and for clearance between drive rotor and driven rotor and between driven rotor and pump body. Check pump cover gear end clearance and clearance between drive shaft and pump cover hole.

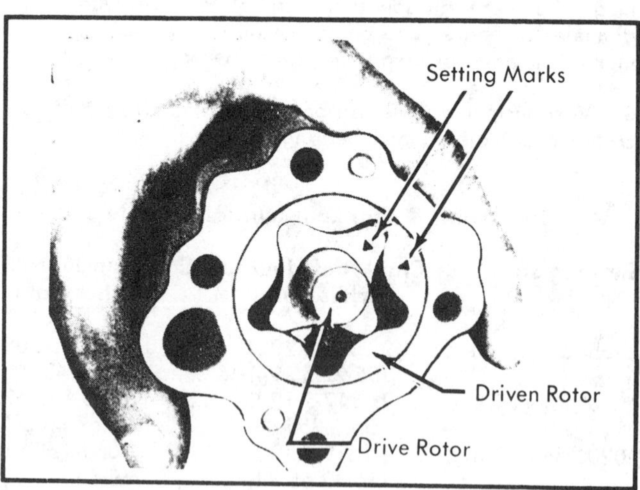

Fig. 11 ***Aligning Rotor Timing Marks***

Installation – 1) Align timing marks on camshaft and rocker arm shaft support. Align notched line on crankshaft pulley with "0" mark on front cover (piston in No. 4 cylinder at TDC on compression stroke).

1800 cc 4 CYLINDER (Cont.)

2) Install driven rotor so timing marks align with drive rotor, *Fig 11*. Install oil pump, engaging drive gear with crankshaft pinion gear. Setting mark on drive gear should be rearward and approximately 20 degrees clockwise from crankshaft centerline. *(See Fig. 12).*

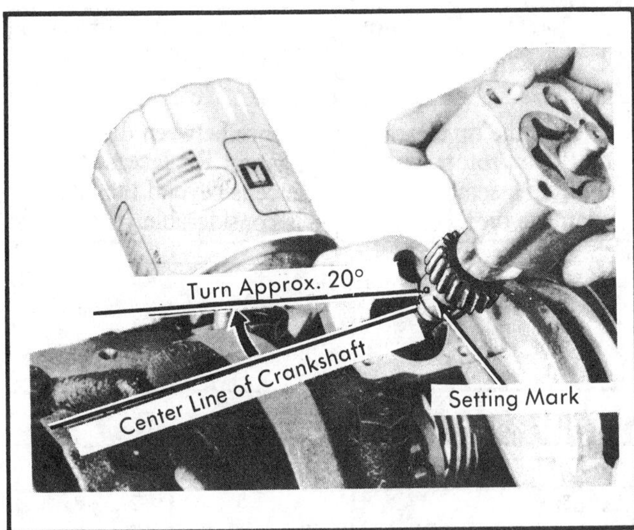

Fig. 12 Installing Oil Pump

3) After installation, check that setting mark is rearward (in clearance between front cover and block). Check that slot in end of pump drive shaft is parallel with front cylinder block face and offset forward, when viewed through distributor hole.

4) Install oil pump cover on dowels, install bolts, relief valve assembly, rubber hose and oil pipe assembly. Install parts previously removed.

Oil Pump Specifications

Measurement Point	Inches (mm)
Drive Rotor-to-Driven Rotor	.0005-.0059 (.012-.150)
Driven Rotor-to-Pump Body	.0063-.0087 (.160-.220)
Rotors-to-Pump Body	.0012-.0035 (.030-.088)
Drive Shaft-to-Pump Cover Hole	.0028-.0043 (.071-.109)

ENGINE COOLING

Thermostat – Wax pellet-type. Begins to open at 177-182° F (81-83° C); fully open at 203° F (95° C).

Cooling System Capacity – 6.8 quarts.

WATER PUMP

Removal – Disconnect battery ground cable, remove radiator shroud and drain coolant from radiator. Remove drive belts. Remove cooling fan and pulley. Remove water pump from front cover.

Installation – If pump body is cracked, water is leaking from seal unit, bearing is noisy or has play, or impellers or front cover assembly are cracked or corroded, replace entire pump. Install new pump by reversing removal procedure.

ENGINE SPECIFICATIONS

GENERAL SPECIFICATIONS

Year	Displ.		Carburetor	HP at RPM	Torque (Ft. Lbs. at RPM)	Compr. Ratio	Bore		Stroke	
	cu. ins.	cc					in.	mm	in.	mm
1977	110.8	1800	2-Bbl	.....	95@3000	8.5-1	3.31	84.1	3.23	82.0

VALVES

Engine & Valve	Head Diam. In. (mm)	Face Angle	Seat Angle	Seat Width In. (mm)	Stem Diameter In. (mm)	Stem Clearance In. (mm)	Valve Lift In. (mm)
1800 cc Intake	.....	45°	①45°	.0472-.0630 (1.20-1.60)	.315 (8.0)	.0009-.0022 (.022-.056)	.....
Exhaust	.....	45°	①45°	.0472-.0630 (1.20-1.60)	.315 (8.0)	.0015-.0031 (.038-.079)	.....

① – Grind seat to obtain proper width.

1800 cc 4 CYLINDER (Cont.)

ENGINE SPECIFICATIONS (Cont.)

PISTONS, PINS, RINGS						
Engine	PISTONS	PINS		RINGS		
	Clearance In. (mm) ①	Piston Fit In. (mm)	Rod Fit In. (mm)	Rings	End Gap In. (mm) ②	Side Clearance In. (mm)
1800 cc	.0018-.0026 (.046-.066)	Push Fit	Press Fit	No. 1 & 2	.008-.016 (.203-.406)	.0010-.0024 (.025-.061)
				Oil	.008-.035 (.203-.890)	.0008 (.020)

①– Piston diameter measured 1.575" (40 mm) below piston head and at right angles to piston pin.

② – End gap is measured with ring in cylinder.

CRANKSHAFT MAIN & CONNECTING ROD BEARINGS							
Engine	MAIN BEARINGS				CONNECTING ROD BEARINGS		
	Journal Diam. In. (mm)	Clearance In. (mm)	Thrust Bearing	Crankshaft End Play In. (mm)	Journal Diam. In. (mm)	Clearance In. (mm)	Side Play In. (mm)
1800 cc	2.2016-2.2022 (55.92-55.94)	.0008-.0025 (.020-.063)	No. 3	.0024-.0094 (.061-.239)	1.9262-1.9268 (48.93-48.94)	.0007-.0030 (.018-.076)	.0079-.0130 (.201-.330)

VALVE SPRINGS			
Engine	Free Length In. (mm)	PRESSURE Lbs. @ In. (kg @ mm)	
		Valve Closed	Valve Open
1800 cc			
Outer	1.8465 (46.9)	.....	32.2-37@1.614 (14.6-16.8@41.0)
Inner	1.7835 (45.3)	.....	18.7-21.5@1.516 (8.5-9.8@38.5)

CAMSHAFT			
Engine	Journal Diam. In. (mm)	Clearance ① In. (mm)	Lobe Lift In. (mm)
1800 cc	1.3362-1.3370 (33.94-33.96)	.0016-.0035 (.041-.089)	.....

① – End play is .0020-.0059" (.051-.150 mm).

TIGHTENING SPECIFICATIONS

Application	Ft. Lbs. (mkg)
Cylinder Head Cover Bolts	3.6 (.50)
Cylinder Head Bolts	72 (9.95)
Oil Pan Bolts	3.6 (.50)
Crankshaft Bearing Cap Bolts	72 (9.95)
Connecting Rod Bearing Cap Bolts	33 (4.56)
Rocker Arm Shaft Bracket Nuts	16 (2.21)
Timing Sprocket Bolt	58 (8.02)
Crankshaft Pulley Bolt	87 (12.03)
Flywheel Bolts	69 (9.45)

504 GASOLINE 4 CYLINDER

ENGINE CODING

ENGINE IDENTIFICATION

Engine serial number is stamped on left side engine mounting face and is also located on the identification plate attached to right inner fender panel.

Engine identification number is stamped on camshaft tunnel. The first letter and five digits designate production number. The last letter is an identification letter and is decoded as follows:

Application	Transmission	Engine Code
XN1 Engine	Manual	UA
XN1 Engine	Automatic	XA

ENGINE & CYLINDER HEAD

ENGINE

1) Remove battery, battery tray and hood. Remove radiator, ignition coil, starter, and windshield bottle. Disconnect heater hoses, fuel feed lines, carburetor controls, vacuum lines and electrical wiring. On automatic transmission models, drain transmission and disconnect transmission dip stick bracket from cylinder head.

2) Remove air cleaner. Lower steering rack housing. Disengage exhaust pipe from manifold. Remove flywheel covering and clutch housing bolts. Attach a suitable hoist to engine and take up weight.

3) Remove four bolts attaching engine mounts to crossmember. **NOTE** – *Ensure left hand brake line is against crossmember*. Raise engine until transmission meets tunnel. Suitably support transmission.

4) On automatic transmission models, remove four bolts connecting converter to flywheel. **NOTE** - *Never remove engine with converter, converter must remain attached to transmission*. Lift engine from compartment. To install engine, reverse removal procedure.

CYLINDER HEAD

Removal – 1) Drain cooling system. Remove air cleaner and support, carburetor and linkage. Remove distributor cap and wires, and remove spark plugs. Remove upper radiator hose and water pump drive belt. Disconnect alternator bracket from cylinder head.

2) Disconnect heater hose from water pump and hose bracket from cylinder head. Disconnect oil supply line at rear of head. Disconnect remaining electrical leads and water hoses. Remove exhaust pipe from manifold.

3) Remove spark plug tube seals and their cups. Remove two cylinder head bolts from position number eight and nine and replace with guide studs. Remove remaining cylinder head bolts and remove rocker arm assembly. Remove push rods and place in order for proper installation.

4) Remove the forward guide stud (number eight) and pivot cylinder head on remaining guide to loosen cylinder head from gasket. **CAUTION** – *Cylinder head gasket sticks to cylinder head, cylinder block and liners. No attempt must be made to lift cylinder head until it has been loosened, otherwise liner seats will be loosened and liner gaskets damaged.*

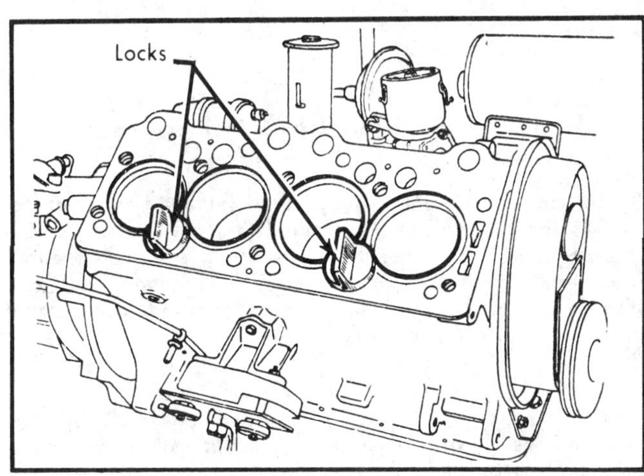

Fig. 1 Cylinder Liner Locks Installed in Position

5) Lift cylinder head to remove. Remove gasket and remaining guide stud. Install suitable liner clamps to prevent any movement of cylinder liners.

Installation – 1) Remove liner locks and ensure inner flats of liners are parallel on liners 1-2 and 3-4. Install cylinder head guide studs. Install new gasket dry with word "DESSUS" facing up. Place cylinder head in position and replace push rods.

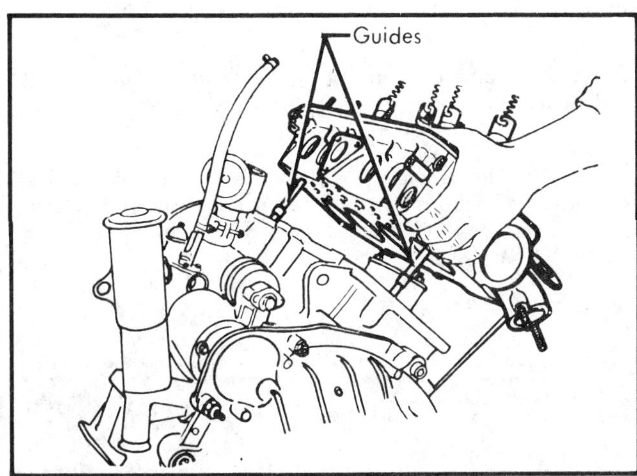

Fig. 2 Fitting Cylinder Head to Engine Block

2) Replace rocker arm assembly on studs, do not tighten nuts. Lubricate cylinder head bolts and install in position, tightening slightly. Tighten cylinder head bolts in sequence to 36 ft. lbs. (5 mkg), then tighten rocker arm assembly nuts to 11 ft. lbs. (1.5 mkg).

504 GASOLINE 4 CYLINDER (Cont.)

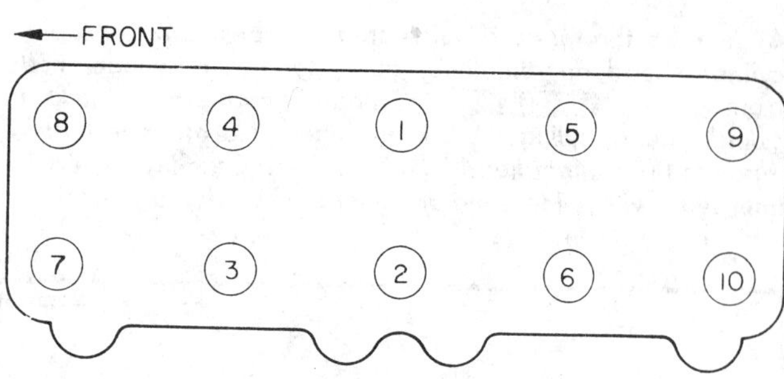

Fig. 3 Cylinder Head Bolt Tightening Sequence

3) Loosen number one cylinder head bolt and retighten to 14.5 ft. lbs. (2 mkg), then continue to tighten the bolt for an additional 90° (one quarter turn). Using same procedure, loosen and tighten remaining head bolts in sequence. **NOTE** — *If in doubt about the tightening of any one bolt, loosen completely and repeat all above operations.*

4) Adjust valves to .006" (.15) for intake and .012" (.30) for exhaust. See *Valve Clearance Adjustment*. After 600 miles, adjust valves to standard clearances.

5) **NOTE** — *Cylinder head bolts MUST be retightened after 600 miles.* To retighten cylinder head bolts, loosen bolt number one completely and retighten according to instructions outlined previously. Follow this same procedure for remaining bolts, working in sequence. Retighten rocker arm assembly nuts.

SPARK PLUG TUBE REPLACEMENT

1) With cylinder head supported, screw in plugs without springs, to prevent dirt from dropping into cylinder.

2) Using suitable extractor or hammer, remove tubes. **NOTE** — *If tubes are removed they can not be reused.*

3) To install tubes, smear suitable sealing compound on tubes and insert them so plug caps are facing as shown in illustration. When tube is fully seated it will protrude 2.835" (72 mm) upward from cylinder head.

Fig. 4 Position of Spark Plug Tubes for Installation

VALVES

VALVE ARRANGEMENT

Left Side — Intake valves.
Right Side — Exhaust valves.

NOTE — Cylinders and valves are numbered with number one at flywheel end.

VALVE SPRING REPLACEMENT

Intake Valve — Turn crankshaft in direction of engine rotation and position where exhaust valve just begins to open. Slide rocker arm off intake valve then bring piston to TDC of compression stroke. Using suitable spring compressor, compress spring and remove keepers, spring retainer and spring.

Exhaust Valve — 1) Remove spark plug from cylinder requiring attention. Rotate crankshaft in direction of engine rotation and bring intake valve to fully closed position. Slide rocker arm off exhaust valve.

2) Insert suitable hinged tool (0 0136) into spark plug hole and bring piston to TDC without forcing as tool is between piston and valve. Using suitable spring compressor, compress spring and remove keepers, spring retainer and spring.

VALVE CLEARANCE ADJUSTMENT

NOTE — *Engine must be allowed to cool at least six hours before adjusting valves.*

Rotate engine until exhaust valve number one is fully opened, then adjust intake valve number three and exhaust valve number four. Rotate engine one half turn until next number valve is fully opened and adjust corresponding valves. See *table*. Continue until all valves have been adjusted.

Valve Adjustment Sequence

Valve Open	Adjust Valves
E 1	I 3 & E 4
E 3	I 4 & E 2
E 4	I 2 & E 1
E 2	I 1 & E 3

Valve Clearance Adjustment

Application	Intake In. (mm)	Exhaust In. (mm)
All Models	①.004 (.10)	.010 (.25)

① — Set No. 1 and No. 4 Intake to .008" (.20 mm).

504 GASOLINE 4 CYLINDER (Cont.)

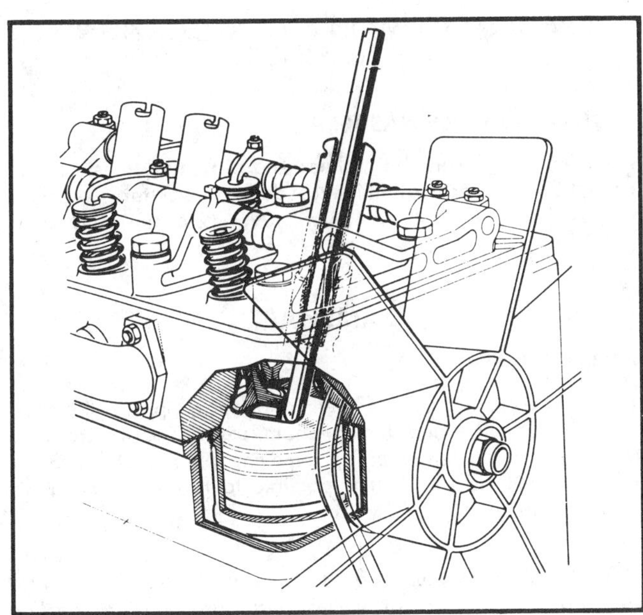

Fig. 5 Removing Valve Spring with Valve Held in Place

PISTONS, PINS & RINGS

PISTON & ROD ASSEMBLY

NOTE — *If liners and pistons are to be replaced, engine must be removed.*

1) Drain crankcase. With engine suitably supported on an engine stand, remove intake and exhaust manifolds. Remove all auxiliary equipment to point shown in *Fig. 6*.

Fig. 6 View of Engine with Auxiliary Equipment Removed

2) Remove cylinder head. See *Cylinder Head Removal*. Remove camshaft hydraulic lifters, keeping them in original order. Remove distributor support drive shaft.

3) Remove oil pan and oil pump. Extract timing cover. Remove bearing caps noting order. Remove pistons and connecting rods. Mark rod assemblies 1-4.

4) To install, fit piston ring clamp on piston. Insert piston and rod assembly, without twisting it. Ensure index arrow is facing front of engine.

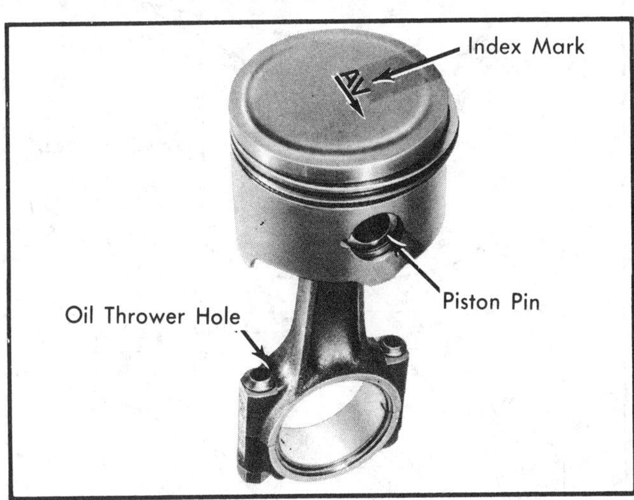

Fig. 7 Piston and Rod Assembly with Index Marks Noted

5) Push piston down cylinder and guide connecting rod with bearing over crankshaft journal. Install bearing cap and tighten to specifications.

FITTING CYLINDER LINERS

1) Before installing, liners must be dirt free. Insert liners, without base gaskets, with flats on shoulder of liners 1-2 and 3-4 parallel.

NOTE — *Do not alter piston/liner pairings.*

2) Place a suitable dial gauge and support on block face. Synchronize dial at 0 and 5. Check each liner at four different points, noting the highest reading.

3) The maximum allowable difference between two diametrically opposed points must be less than .003" (0.07 mm). If specification is exceeded, it may be necessary to change position of liners. **NOTE** — *Suitably mark liners.*

4) Select a base gasket for each liner which will give a protrusion of approximately .004" (0.11 mm). **NOTE** — *Only use one gasket on each liner.*

5) Fit gasket on liner. Engage gasket inner tabs in liner grooves (see illustration). Position tab with reference mark at right angles to flat. Position liners with outer tabs in position as shown in illustration.

6) Fit suitable liner compressor tools (8.0128) to block, seat liners and ensure protrusion is correct. **NOTE** — *Difference in protrusion of adjoining cylinders must not exceed .016" (.04 mm).*

504 GASOLINE 4 CYLINDER (Cont.)

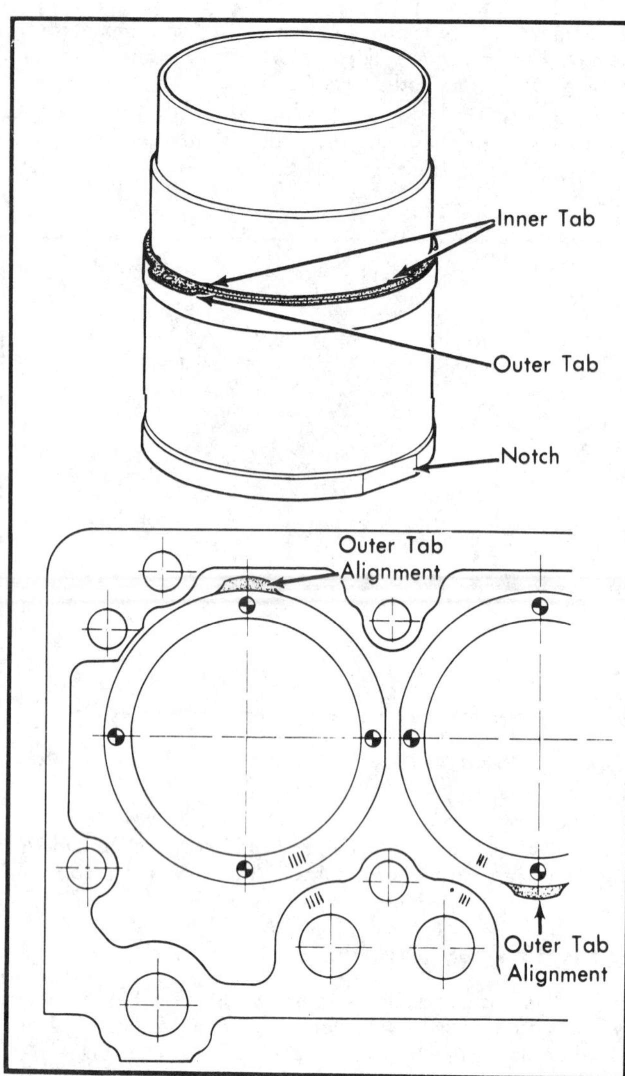

Fig. 8 Fitting Cylinder Liner Gasket to Liner

PISTON PIN REPLACEMENT

Fit piston to rod so that index mark "AV" is at right angles to oil thrower. Insert piston pin, it may be necessary to heat piston to install pin. Install snap rings.

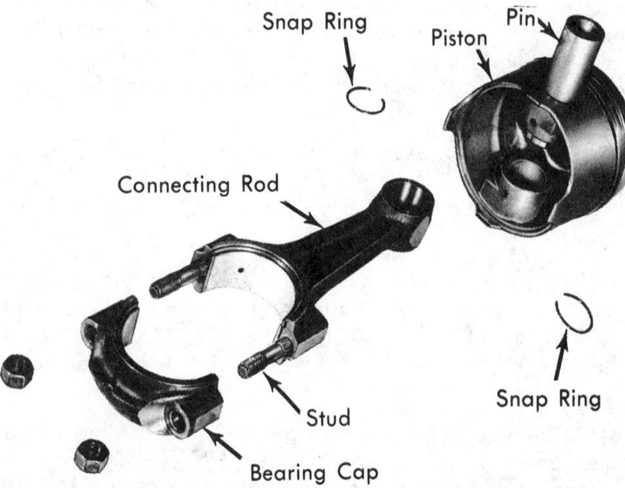

Fig. 9 Exploded View of Piston and Connecting Rod

CRANKSHAFT MAIN & CONNECTING ROD BEARINGS

THRUST BEARING WASHERS

After installing crankshaft, check end play. Play must not exceed .008". If specification is exceeded, oversize thrust washers are available in .094" (2.40mm), .096" (2.45mm) and .098" (2.50mm).

CAMSHAFT

TIMING CHAIN

1) Remove radiator, fan belt and spark plugs. Remove crankshaft pulley and timing chain cover (see illustration). Disengage chain tensioner by removing plug and turn 3mm Allen wrench clockwise. It is possible to further disassemble chain tensioners.

NOTE – *Position camshaft as shown in illustration to avoid any possible contact of valves and pistons when rotating crankshaft with timing chain removed.*

2) Remove camshaft sprocket, timing chain, crankshaft sprocket and Woodruff key.

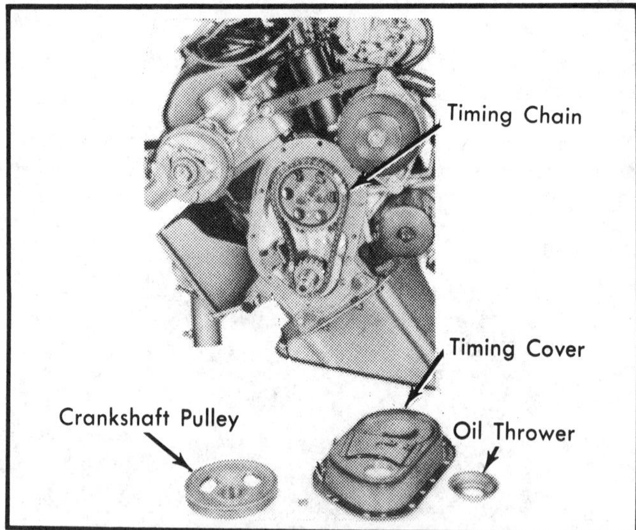

Fig. 10 Timing Cover Removed with Related Components

3) Begin installation by holding crankshaft in original position and installing Woodruff key and sprocket. Position camshaft and then crankshaft as shown in illustration.

4) Install timing chain first on camshaft sprocket, then on crankshaft sprocket. Ensure timing marks are in correct alignment. Fit camshaft with a new washer and tighten bolts. Bend up tabs.

5) Engage chain tensioner by adjusting Allen wrench in a clockwise manner. Install a new tab washer on plug and bend tab. Withdraw tool after installing tensioner.

504 GASOLINE 4 CYLINDER (Cont.)

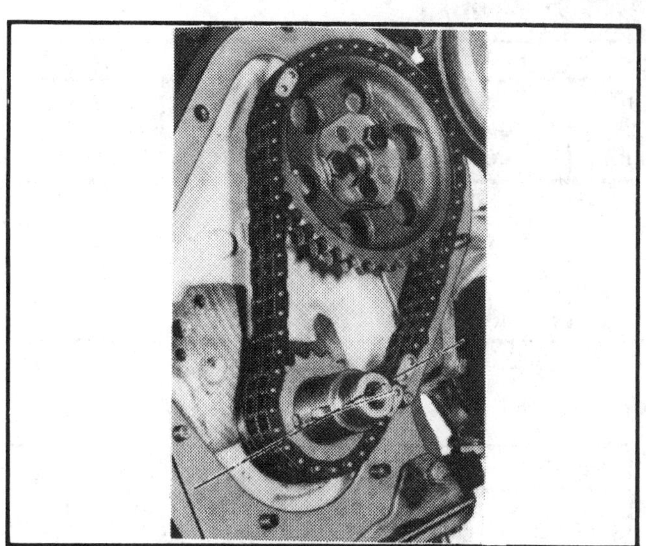

Fig. 11 Correct Position of Crankshaft for Chain Installation

Fig. 12 Proper Alignment of Camshaft and Crankshaft

6) Install thrust washers, if necessary, oil slinger cap, and timing chain cover. Center timing chain cover with suitable tool (0128). Fit crankshaft pulley.

ENGINE OILING

ENGINE OILING SYSTEM

A high output, gear type oil pump is mounted to engine block lower surface and is operated by camshaft.

Crankcase Capacity – Approximately 4.2 qts.

Oil Filter – Full-flow cartridge type.

Normal Oil Pressure – 28-51 psi at idle; 44-67 psi at 4000 RPM.

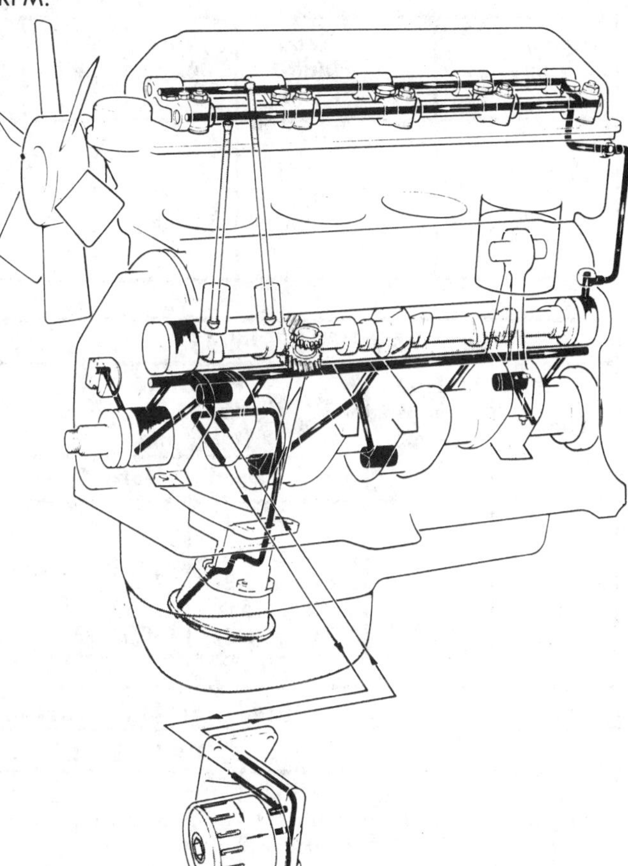

Fig. 13 Sectional View of Peugeot Engine Oiling Circuit with Detail of Components Lubricated

ENGINE COOLING

Thermostat – Opens at 165°F (73.9°C).

Cooling System Capacity – Approximately 8.25 qts.

WATER PUMP

1) Remove radiator, top hose, and fan belt. Disconnect heater hose from pump and the self-disengaging fan brush holder. Remove water pump.

2) To install, reverse removal procedures noting the following: clean contact surfaces before installing new gasket.

SELF-DISENGAGING FAN

Driven by water pump shaft and controlled by a thermal contact-breaker. Fan engages at 183-194°F (84-90°C) and disengages at 169-180°F (76-82°C).

ENGINE SPECIFICATIONS

GENERAL SPECIFICATIONS

Year	Displ. cu. ins.	Displ. cc	Carburetor	HP at RPM	Torque (Ft. Lbs. at RPM)	Compr. Ratio	Bore in.	Bore mm	Stroke in.	Stroke mm
1977	120.2	1970	2x1-Bbl.	.....	.....	8.0-1	3.464	88	3.189	81

504 GASOLINE 4 CYLINDER (Cont.)

ENGINE SPECIFICATIONS (Cont.)

VALVES							
Engine & Valve	Head Diam. In. (mm)	Face Angle	Seat Angle	Seat Width In. (mm)	Stem Diameter In. (mm)	Stem Clearance In. (mm)	Valve Lift In. (mm)
1970 cc							
Int.	1.673 (42.49)	...	30°	...	.3157 (8.019)	...	...
Exh.	1.398 (35.51)	45°	45°	...	.3150 (8.001)	...	...

VALVE SPRINGS			
Engine	Free Length In. (mm)	PRESSURE Lbs. @ In. (kg @ mm)	
		Valve Closed	Valve Open
1970 cc			
Outer	...	137@1.213 (62.1@30.8)	35@1.566 (15.9@39.8)
Inner	...	69@1.055 (31.3@26.8)	18@1.409 (8.16@35.7)

VALVE TIMING				
	INTAKE		EXHAUST	
Engine	Open (ATDC)	Close (ALDC)	Open (BLDC)	Close (ATDC)
1970 cc	2°	39°	30°	8° 30′

CRANKSHAFT MAIN & CONNECTING ROD BEARINGS							
	MAIN BEARINGS				CONNECTING ROD BEARINGS		
Engine	Journal Diam. In. (mm)	Clearance In. (mm)	Thrust Bearing	Crankshaft End Play In. (mm)	Journal Diam. In. (mm)	Clearance In. (mm)	Side Play In. (mm)
1970 cc							
No. 1 (Rear)	2.1616-2.1646 (54.905-54.980)	...	Rear	.003-.008 (.08-.20)	2.1123-2.1131 (53.652-53.673)	.0006-.003 (.016-.076)	.....
No. 2	2.2102-2.2112 (56.140-56.165)						
No. 3	2.2509-2.2515 (57.174-57.189)						
No. 4	2.3050-2.3060 (58.548-58.573)						
No. 5 (Front)	2.3386-2.3392 (59.401-59.416)						

TIGHTENING SPECIFICATIONS

Application	Ft. Lbs. (mkg)
Cylinder Head	See Text
Crankshaft Main Bearing Bolts	54 (7.5)
Connecting Rod Nuts	29 (4.0)
Camshaft Retaining Plate Bolts	12 (1.7)
Camshaft Sprocket Bolts	16 (2.25)
Crankshaft Pulley Bolt	123 (17)
Oil Pan Bolts	7 (1.0)
Flywheel-to-Crankshaft Bolts	49 (6.75)
Engine-to-Clutch Housing	16 (2.25)
Oil Pump Mounting Bolts	7 (1.0)

NOTE – *Piston-to-liner clearance should be .002-.003" (.051-.076 mm).*

NOTE – *Piston pin is a press fit in piston.*

504 DIESEL 4 CYLINDER

ENGINE CODING

ENGINE IDENTIFICATION

Engine number is stamped on left side of engine block just below cylinder head. XD 90 engine numbers are 9000001 and up.

ENGINE & CYLINDER HEAD

ENGINE

1) Remove hood, battery and battery tray. Remove radiator expansion tank, air filter and intake pipe on vacuum pump. Disconnect upper and lower radiator hoses, and upper and lower radiator mountings. Disconnect fan wiring and remove fan and radiator.

2) Disconnect injector pump controls, fuel inlet and fuel outlet lines. Remove heater hose return line. Disconnect starter, oil pressure switch, pre-heat circuit and thermistor wiring. Remove starter.

3) Disconnect alternator wiring and air conditioner hose from cylinder head. Disconnect exhaust pipe at manifold and remove right engine support nut. From left side of engine; disconnect clutch housing sealing plates, upper clutch housing-to-block bolt and left engine support nut.

4) Disconnect exhaust pipe support bracket from transmission. Remove right clutch housing cover plate. Install suitable engine lifting device and raise engine until transmission contacts tunnel. Support transmission.

5) Remove two lower clutch housing-to-block bolts. Carefully move engine forward to clear transmission shaft and lift up to remove from vehicle. When replacing engine, install and tighten all clutch housing-to-block bolts before removing transmission support.

CYLINDER HEAD

CAUTION – *Cylinder head bolts must not be loosened while engine is warm.*

Removal – 1) Drain cooling system. Remove air filter, hose to expansion tank and upper radiator hose. Remove vacuum hose, vacuum pump and belt, idler puller, and water pump belt.

2) Disconnect air conditioner line, and rocker shaft oil line union (located over center intake manifold port). Disconnect exhaust pipe at manifold. Disconnect injector feed lines and remove return lines. Disconnect pre-heat electrical connections at cylinder head.

3) Remove rocker arm cover and rocker arm assembly. **NOTE** – *Do not lose washer (seal) at oil inlet-to-cylinder head connection.* Remove push rods, taking care not to disturb tappets, and set aside in original order for proper installation.

4) Remove one bolt at each end of cylinder head and replace with suitable guide stands. Remove injection holders and injectors. Remove remaining head bolts and remove cylinder head. **CAUTION** – *Do not disturb cylinder liner seating when lifting cylinder head. If gasket adheres to cylinder head, remove one guide stud and rotate head to free from gasket.* Install cylinder liner locks.

Installation – 1) Install new gasket dry with large crimped side facing cylinder block. Place cylinder head over guides and install bolts. Note that eight shorter bolts are installed on injector side, seven medium length bolts on manifold side and remaining long bolts in center. Special ground connecting bolt is installed in No. 19 position.

2) Tighten cylinder head bolts in first step to 29 ft. lbs. (4 mkg) in sequence shown in illustration. In second step, tighten in sequence to 51 ft. lbs. (7 mkg). One bolt at a time in sequence, loosen one quarter turn and retighten to 51 ft. lbs. (7 mkg). Install rocker arm assembly. See *Rocker Arm Assembly*. **NOTE** – *Do not forget the washer (seal) at oil inlet-to-cylinder head connection.*

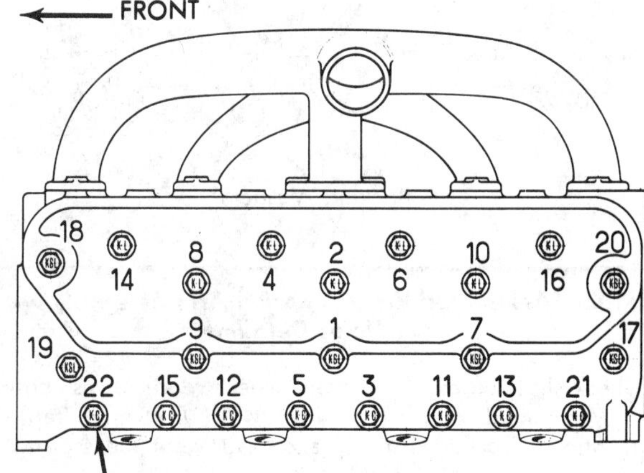

Fig. 1 Cylinder Head Bolt Tightening Sequence

3) Adjust valves to .010" (.25 mm) for intake and .014" (.35 mm) for exhaust. See *Valve Clearance Adjustment*. After 600 miles, adjust valves to standard clearances.

4) **NOTE** – *Cylinder head bolts MUST be retightened after 30 miles and again after 600 miles.* To retighten cylinder head bolts, loosen in sequence, each bolt one quarter turn, then retighten to 51 ft. lbs. (7 mkg). This procedure must be done two times.

VALVES

VALVE ARRANGEMENT

I-E-E-I-I-E-E-I (Front to Rear).

NOTE – *Cylinders and valves are numbered with number one at flywheel end.*

504 DIESEL 4 CYLINDER (Cont.)

VALVE DEPTH

After cylinder head has been resurfaced or valve seats ground or replaced, depth of valve face beneath cylinder head surface must be checked. Measure depth with dial gauge. Depth must be .030-.045" (.75-1.15 mm). If too shallow, regrind valve seats. If too deep, replace valves and/or valve seats.

ROCKER ARM ASSEMBLY

1) To remove rocker arm assembly, remove rocker arm cover and remove rocker shaft support bolts. Lift rocker arm assembly noting oil line union sealing washer. **NOTE** — *Do not omit oil union washer (seal) when installing rocker arm assembly.*

2) To disassemble rocker arm assembly, remove end shaft supports and remove rocker arms, supports, springs and washers. Remove locating screw on lubrication fitting, then remove shaft.

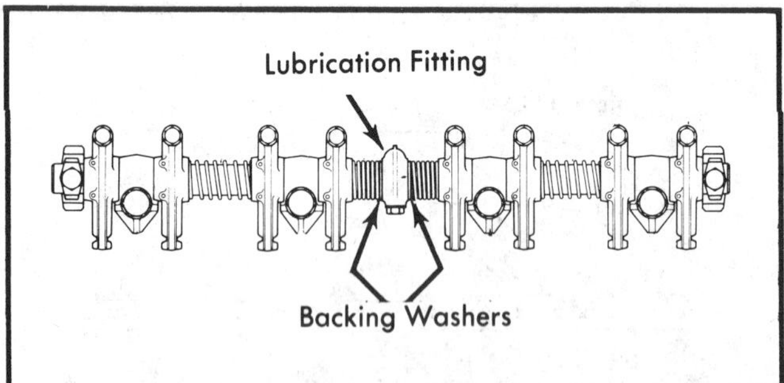

Fig. 2 Assembled View of Rocker Arm Assembly with Oil Holes Detailed

3) Check shaft diameter at areas where rocker arms contact shaft. Minimum diameter of shaft is .746" (18.95 mm). Replace shaft and/or rocker arms if excessive wear or scoring is evident.

4) To assemble rocker arm assembly, slide rocker shaft into lubrication fitting noting that oil holes in shaft are on same side as screw hole in fitting. Line up screw hole in shaft with threaded hole in fitting and install locating screw and copper washer.

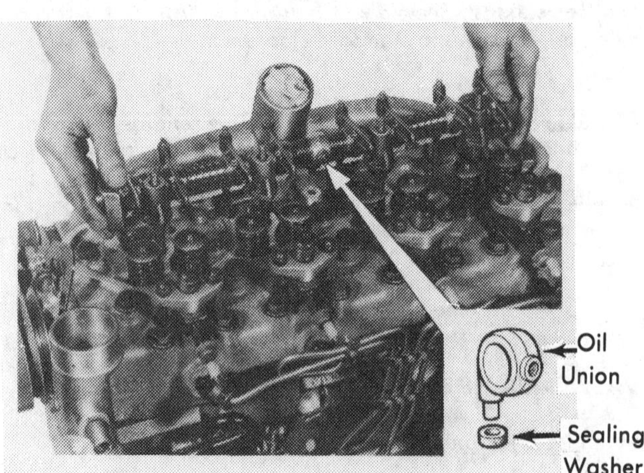

Fig. 3 Installing Rocker Arm Assembly to Cylinder Head

5) Lubricate rocker shaft and install washers, springs, rocker arms and rocker supports. Install shims .004" (.10 mm) thick between outer rocker arms and end supports, then install oil union washer (seal).

6) Install rocker shaft assembly on cylinder head and tighten shaft support bolts. After all bolts are tightened, remove shims and check that all rocker arms operate smoothly.

VALVE CLEARANCE ADJUSTMENT

NOTE — *Engine must be allowed to cool at least six hours before adjusting valves.*

Rotate engine until exhaust valve number one is fully opened, then adjust intake valve number three and exhaust number four. Rotate engine one half turn until next number valve is fully opened and adjust corresponding valves. *See table.* Continue until all valves have been adjusted.

Valve Adjustment Sequence

Valve Open	Adjust Valves
E 1	I 3 & E 4
E 3	I 4 & E 2
E 4	I 2 & E 1
E 2	I 1 & E 3

Valve Clearance Adjustment

Application ①	Intake In. (mm)	Exhaust In. (mm)
New Head Gasket	.010 (.25)	.014 (.35)
Standard Adjustment	.006 (.15)	.010 (.25)

① — Adjust valves to standard adjustment 600 miles after installing new head gasket and retightening cylinder head bolts.

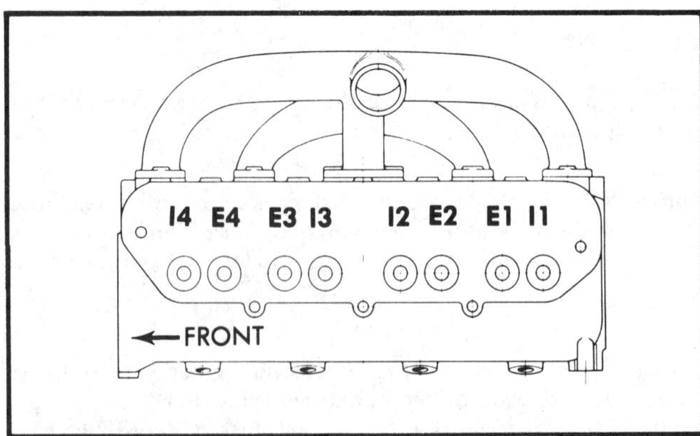

Fig. 4 View of Intake and Exhaust Valve Arrangement

COMBUSTION (SWIRL) CHAMBERS

Removal — Remove cylinder head from vehicle and remove injectors, injector studs, rocker arms, rocker arm mounting

504 DIESEL 4 CYLINDER (Cont.)

studs, manifolds and glow plugs. Using suitable drift (see illustration) carefully drive swirl chambers down and out of cylinder head. **CAUTION** — *Tap drift lightly so as not to damage the inner face of chamber.*

CAUTION — *If the swirl chamber twists and/or sticks in its bore, turn head over, tap chamber back into place with soft mallet, and start over again.*

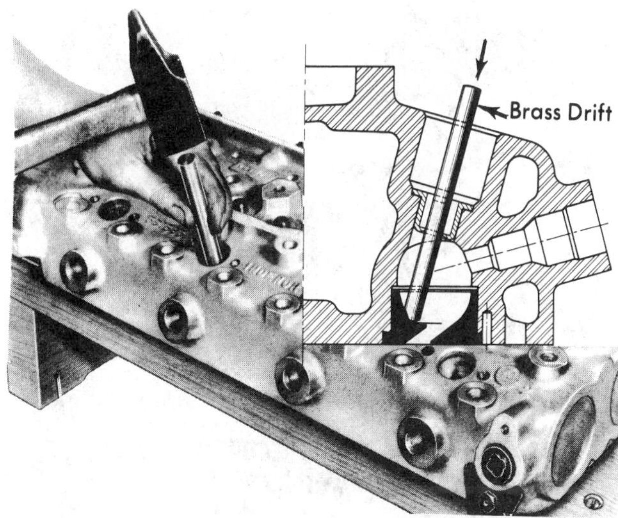

Fig. 5 Removing Combustion Chamber with Hammer and Drift

Inspection — 1) Inspect swirl chambers for distortion and cracks. Small cracks around the gas outlet are acceptable and do not effect engine operation. Replace all doubtful chambers. Measure thickness of shoulder and overall height of chamber.

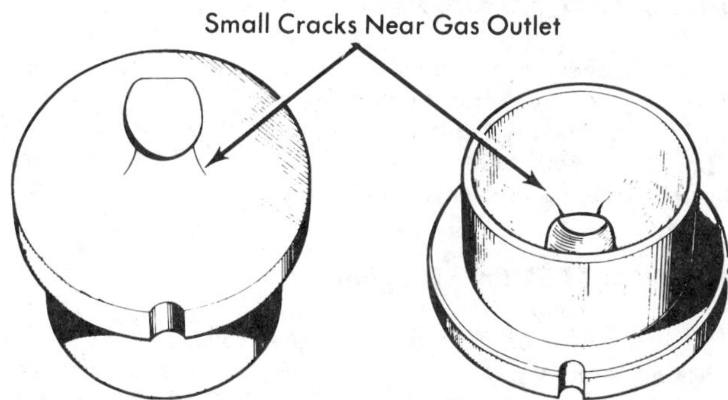

Fig. 6 View Showing Acceptable Cracks in Combustion Chamber

2) Place suitable truing punch (0.0139) over chamber bore in cylinder head, making sure dowel pin in punch is correctly located in head. Tap truing punch to make sure shoulder surface of bore is parallel with cylinder head. Slightly chamfer the edges of the chamber bore.

3) Measure depth of bore and depth to shoulder. Swirl chamber should protrude from cylinder head surface .000-.001" (.00-.03 mm) and clearance from swirl chamber to bottom of chamber bore should be .004-.020" (.10-.50 mm). To adjust clearances, chamber may be machined on shoulder surface and on bottom surface. Never machine face of chamber.

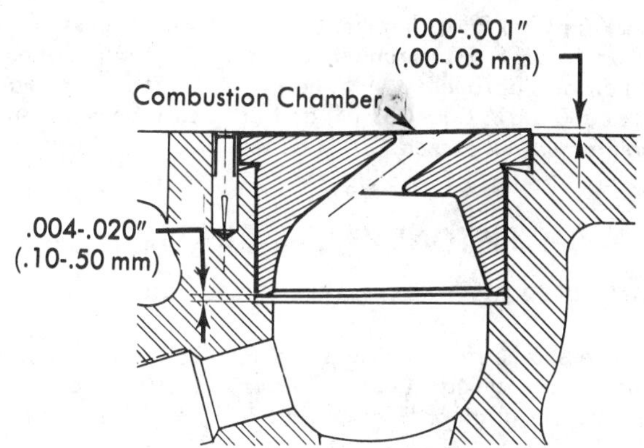

Fig. 7 Cross-Sectional Showing Combustion Chamber Clearance and Protrusion

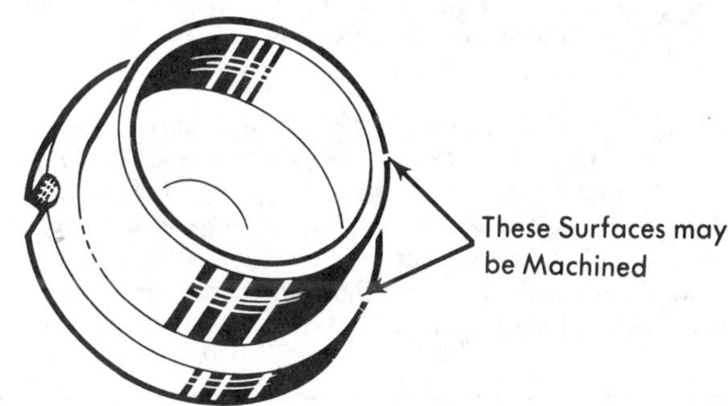

Fig. 8 Combustion (Swirl) Chamber with Detail of Machinable Surfaces

Installation — 1) Insert new wedge pins into the cylinder head and using chamfered drift, drive pins .028" (.7 mm) below cylinder head surface. Carefully insert the swirl chambers in the original bores and lightly tap into place with soft mallet.

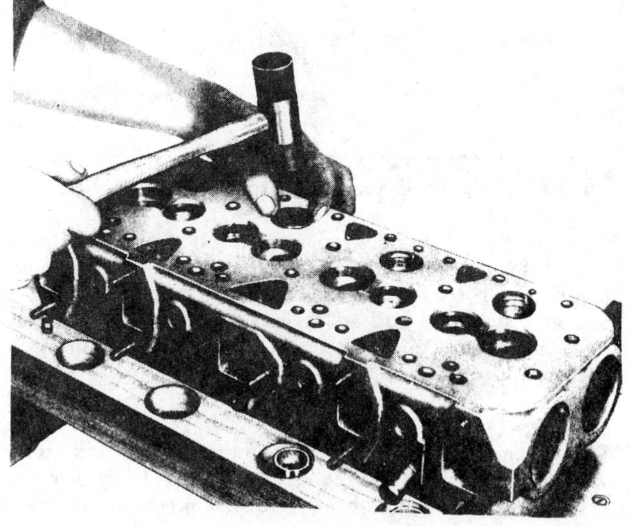

Fig. 9 Installing Combustion (Swirl) Chambers

504 DIESEL 4 CYLINDER (Cont.)

2) Check for tight fit. If chamber is loose, chamber recess must be bored for oversize chamber. Using a dial gauge, check protrusion and parallelism with the cylinder head. Protrusion must be .000-.001" (.00-.03 mm) and difference between any two points must not exceed .001" (.03 mm).

PISTONS, PINS & RINGS

PISTON, LINER & ROD ASSEMBLY

1) Remove engine from vehicle and drain oil. Remove oil pan, oil pump and cylinder head. Mark connecting rods for replacement in original location and remove connecting rod caps.

2) Push pistons up through top of cylinder block and replace connecting rod caps so they do not become mixed. Using suitable cylinder liner puller (0.0101), remove liners. Remove piston pin circlip and remove piston pin.

3) **NOTE** — *Cylinder liners, pistons, piston pins and rings are matched at factory and must not be intermixed.* Remove new pistons from liners and clean all parts thoroughly with trichlorethylene. Do not remove piston rings to clean pistons. Make sure all protective coating has been removed from ring grooves. Blow with compressed air and check that piston rings move freely in their grooves.

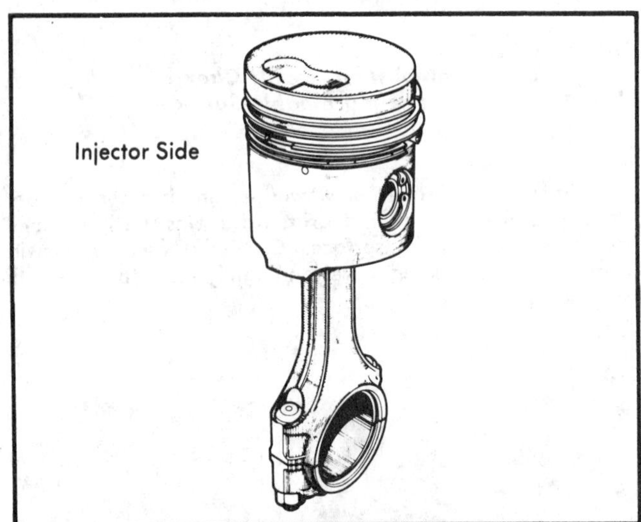

Fig. 10 Assembled View of Piston and Connecting Rod

4) Check fit of piston pin in connecting rod small end bushing. Ream bushing if too tight and replace bushing if too loose. Remove circlip from piston and partially remove piston pin. Position piston and rod so cavity on piston and reference marks on rod are on same side. Lubricate pin and install in piston. Replace circlip.

5) Install liners in cylinder block without gaskets and secure with liner locks. Using dial gauge, ensure that liners protrude .001-.003" (.03-.07 mm) above surface. It may be necessary to change positions of liners to obtain correct protrusion. Suitably mark liners, remove liner locks, remove liners and replace them using gaskets. Replace liner locks.

6) Lubricate pistons, liners and bearings. Using suitable ring compressor, install piston in its respective cylinder liner with cavity in piston facing injector side of engine. Install new rod cap nuts and bolts.

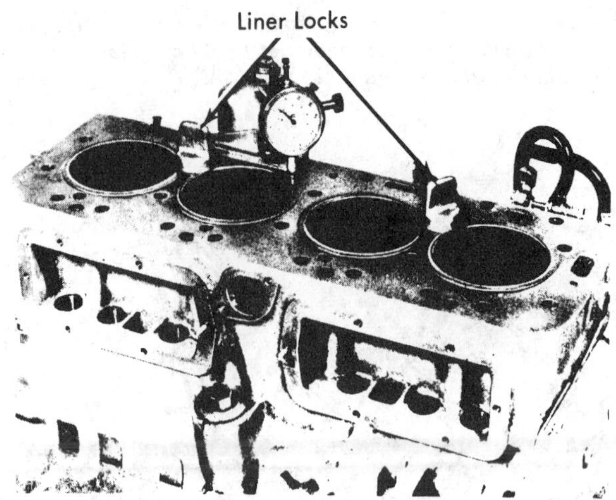

Fig. 11 Measuring Liner Protrusion

CRANKSHAFT MAIN & CONNECTING ROD BEARINGS

MAIN BEARINGS

Bearing caps are installed with the reference mark on injector side. Main bearing cap number two (as numbered from flywheel end) and number four are nearly identical. Bearing cap number two can be identified by letter after the part number.

THRUST BEARING ALIGNMENT

Thrust washers are located on both sides of center main bearing. Measure end play and replace washers as required. Thrust washers are available in standard thickness .091-.092" (2.30-2.33 mm) and oversize .098-.100" (2.50-2.53 mm). Install washers with oil grooves toward crankshaft.

REAR MAIN BEARING OIL SEAL

1) Crankshaft must be removed to replace oil seal. Work seal packing manually into cylinder block and into bearing cap grooves. Place seal forming mandrel (8.0110) onto packing and form packing into groove by tapping mandrel with a hammer.

2) Make sure packing is correctly seated in its groove without being crushed (see illustration). Cut seal packing clean flush with mating surface and follow same procedure for bearing cap.

3) Place side seals in grooves of bearing cap and hold seals into place with suitable shim tool (8.0110 CZ & 8.0110 BZ). Lubricate shims and bring into place in cylinder block, tapping down with hammer handle. Install and tighten bearing cap bolts and check that bearing cap has seated properly. Trim side seals with knife so that they protrude .002" (.05 mm) above lower crankcase mating surface.

504 DIESEL 4 CYLINDER (Cont.)

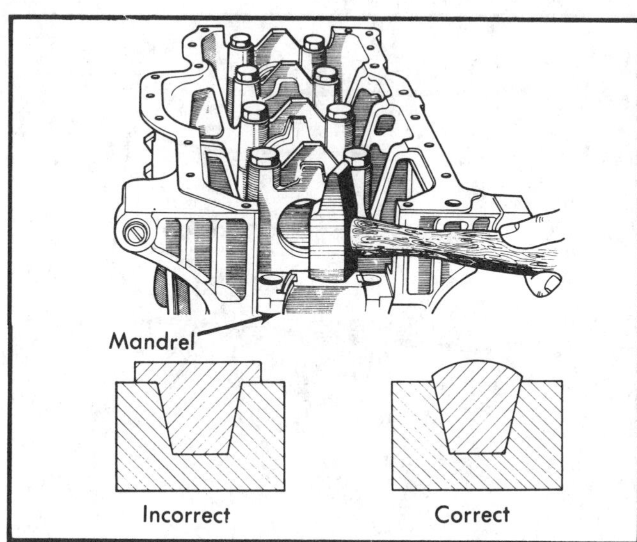

Fig. 12 Using a Mandrel and Mallet to Install Upper Rear Main Oil Seal

CAMSHAFT

TIMING CHAIN

Removal – With engine removed, remove oil pan and front engine cover. Remove plug from timing chain tensioner and release chain tensioner by inserting 3 mm Allen wrench, turning clockwise. Loosen idler gear fastening nut and move idler gear to slack position by turning eccentric. Remove bolts from injection pump gear and remove gear and timing chain.

Installation – 1) Check end play of injection pump support bearing. End play should be .002-.037" (.05-.94 mm). If engine front plate has been removed, lock countersunk screw with two punch marks. Position crankshaft gear timing mark down and camshaft gear mark at 11:00 position (see illustration).

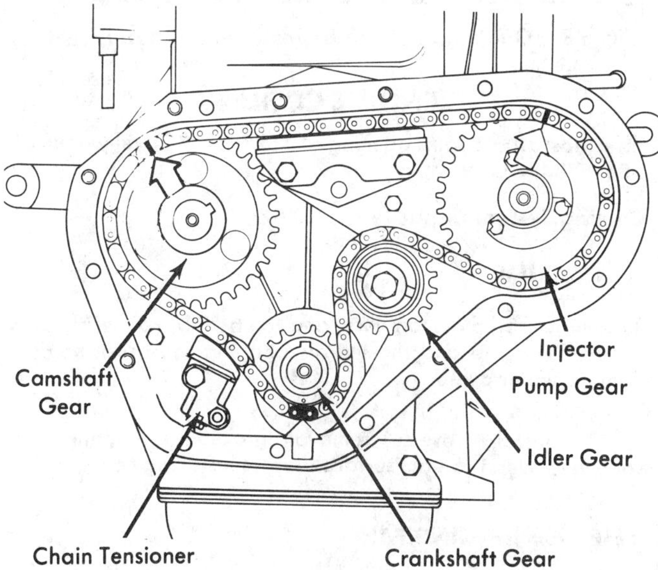

Fig. 13 Timing Chain Installed to Illustrate Timing Mark Alignments

2) Install chain on injection pump gear aligning line on link with mark on gear. Install chain with pump gear onto camshaft and crankshaft sprockets, taking care to align copper link on chain with timing mark on crankshaft gear and link marked with line aligned with the line on camshaft gear. Install locating dowel in injection pump gear.

3) Adjust the idler gear eccentric by rotating eccentric counterclockwise until clearance between tensioner head and body is .020-.040" (.50-1.00 mm). Tighten idler gear fastening nut, then adjust tensioner by turning Allen wrench to right until tensioner head is pushing on chain. Install and lock tensioner plug.

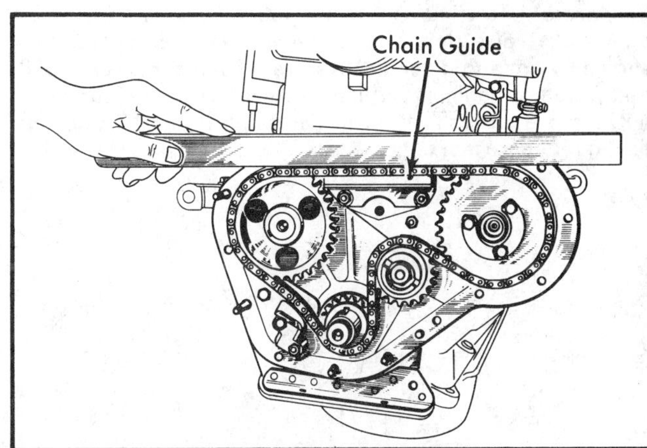

Fig. 14 Using a Straightedge to Adjust Timing Chain Guide

4) Place a straight edge across top of timing chain between camshaft gear and pump gear. Adjust timing chain guide up against chain, then tighten nuts.

CAMSHAFT

Removal – With timing chain removed, remove camshaft thrust plate bolts, gaining access through holes in camshaft gear. Carefully pull camshaft from cylinder block.

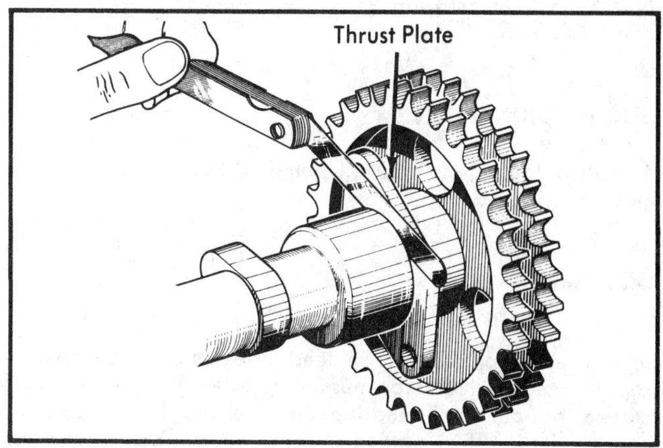

Fig. 15 Measuring Thrust Plate Clearance

504 DIESEL 4 CYLINDER (Cont.)

Installation – If gear was removed from camshaft, heat camshaft gear in well heated oil. Install thrust plate on camshaft, then install shaft key and press gear into place, leaving clearance of .002-.006" (.05-.15 mm) between thrust plate and gear hub. Install camshaft in block and tighten thrust plate bolts. Check camshaft end play, a specification of .002-.006" (.05-.015 mm) should be obtained.

VALVE TIMING

1) With all valve components assembled and cylinder head installed, remove injectors or glow plugs to relieve compression. Adjust valves to correct clearance. See *Valve Clearance Adjustment*.

2) Place a .016" (.40 mm) feeler gauge between rocker arm and intake valve stem of each cylinder in succession. Rotate engine by hand to determine if there is contact between valve and piston at beginning of intake valve opening. If contact is felt, replace crankshaft timing gear with a gear having one timing reference mark.

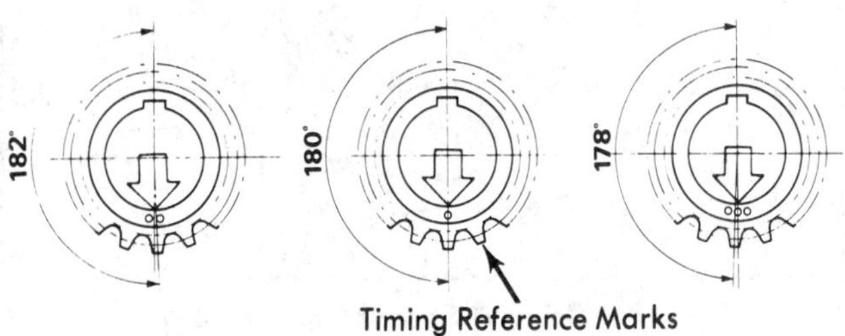

Fig. 16 Showing Different Combinations of Timing Gear Reference Marks

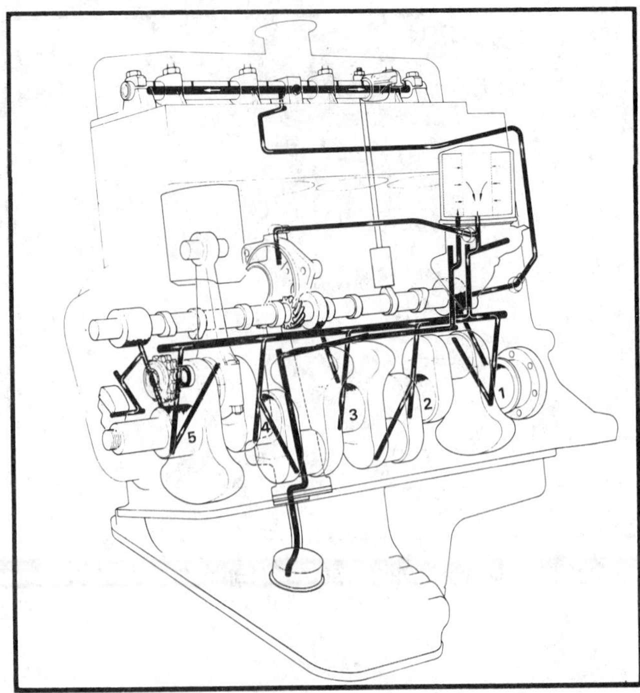

Fig. 17 View of Engine Oiling Circuit for Diesel Models

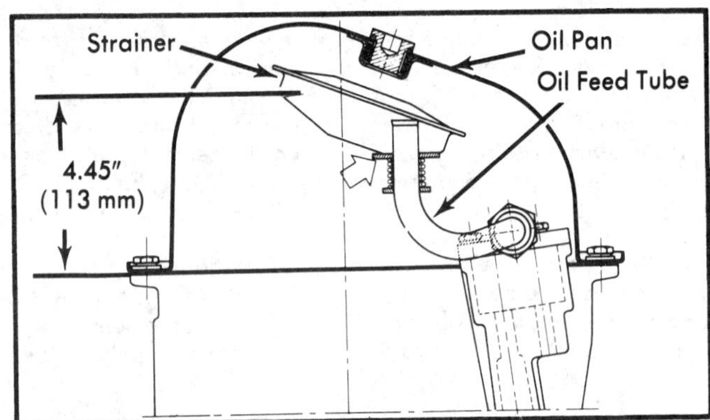

Fig. 18 Oil Pump Feed Tube Installation (Pan Inverted)

ENGINE OILING

Crankcase Capacity – 5.29 qt.
Oil Filter – Full flow cartridge type.
Pressure Regulator Valve – Located in oil pump.
Normal Oil Pressure – Minimum at idle, 22 psi; at 4000 RPM, 42-58 psi.

ENGINE OILING SYSTEM

A high output, gear type oil pump, driven by camshaft, is mounted in oil pan.

OIL PUMP

Whenever the oil pump or oil feed tube has been removed or repositioned, oil feed tube must be adjusted. With oil pump installed, bottom of oil feed tube must extend 4.45" (113 mm) below cylinder block mating surface. After adjusting, oil feed tube, install strainer ensuring thrust washer is under spring tension.

ENGINE COOLING

Thermostat – Begins opening at 162°F (72°C), fully open at 184°F (84°C).

Cooling System Capacity – 10.57 qt.

WATER PUMP

1) Remove radiator, top hose, and fan belt. Disconnect heater hose from pump and the self-disengaging fan brush holder. Remove water pump.

2) To install, reverse removal procedures, noting the following: clean contact surfaces before installing new gasket.

SELF-DISENGAGING FAN

Driven by water pump shaft and controlled by a thermal contact-breaker. Fan engages at 178-182°F (81-83°C) and disengages at 151-158°F (66.5-70°C).

504 DIESEL 4 CYLINDER (Cont.)

ENGINE SPECIFICATIONS

GENERAL SPECIFICATIONS

Year	Displ. cu. ins.	Displ. cc	Carburetor	HP at RPM	Torque (Ft. Lbs. at RPM)	Compr. Ratio	Bore in.	Bore mm	Stroke in.	Stroke mm
1977	128.8	2112	Fuel Inj.	...	...	22.2-1	3.543	90	3.267	83

VALVES

Engine & Valve	Head Diam. In. (mm)	Face Angle	Seat Angle	Seat Width In. (mm)	Stem Diameter In. (mm)	Stem Clearance In. (mm)	Valve Lift In. (mm)
2112 cc							
Int.	1.594 (40.5)	45°	45°	...	.3339-.3346 (8.48-8.50)	.0015 (.04)	.243 (6.173)
Exh.	1.319 (33.5)	45°	45°	...	.3339-.3346 (8.48-8.50)	.0015 (.04)	.243 (6.173)

PISTONS, PINS, RINGS

Engine	PISTONS Clearance In. (mm)	PINS Piston Fit In. (mm)	PINS Rod Fit In. (mm)	RINGS Rings	RINGS End Gap In. (mm)	RINGS Side Clearance In. (mm)
2112 cc	① .0039-.0047 (.10-.12) ② .0035-.0043 (.09-.11)	Press Fit	...	No. 1	.014-.022 (.36-.56)	.....
				No. 2	.014-.022 (.36-.56)	.....
				No. 3	.014-.022 (.36-.56)	.....
				Oil	....	.....

① — Pistons with one notch. ② — Pistons with two notches.

CRANKSHAFT MAIN & CONNECTING ROD BEARINGS

Engine	MAIN BEARINGS Journal Diam. In. (mm)	MAIN BEARINGS Clearance In. (mm)	MAIN BEARINGS Thrust Bearing	MAIN BEARINGS Crankshaft End Play In. (mm)	CONNECTING ROD BEARINGS Journal Diam. In. (mm)	CONNECTING ROD BEARINGS Clearance In. (mm)	CONNECTING ROD BEARINGS Side Play In. (mm)
2112 cc	2.1653-2.1657 (54.999-55.009)	.002-.004 (.05-.10)	...	.003-.011 (.08-.28)	1.9685 (50.000)	.002-.004 (.05-.10)	.....

VALVE SPRINGS

Engine	Free Length In. (mm)	PRESSURE Lbs. @ In. (kg @ mm) Valve Closed	PRESSURE Lbs. @ In. (kg @ mm) Valve Open
2112 cc	1.614 (41.0)	16.75 @ .... (7.6 @ ....)	34.8 @ .... (15.8 @ ....)

TIGHTENING SPECIFICATIONS

Application	Ft. Lbs. (mkg)
Cylinder Head	See Text
Clutch Housing-to-Block	42 (6.0)
Rocker Arm Supports	
End Supports	14 (2.0)
Center Supports	36 (5.0)
Connecting Rod Caps	42 (6.0)
Main Bearing Caps	72 (10)
Timing Chain Idler Gear	36 (5.0)
Crankshaft Pulley	151 (21)
Flywheel Bolts	42 (5.75)
Glow Plugs	33 (4.5)
Manifolds	11 (1.5)
Injector Flanges	14 (2.0)

604 GASOLINE V6

ENGINE CODING

ENGINE IDENTIFICATION

Engine serial number is stamped on a plate fastened to the left side of the engine block near the flywheel. The engine is coded ZM (carburetor) with additional coding of A1 for manual transmission and A3 with automatic transmission.

ENGINE & CYLINDER HEADS

ENGINE REMOVAL

1) Remove hood, carburetor air cleaner and ducting. Drain automatic transmission (if equipped) and cooling system. Disconnect and remove battery.

2) Disconnect electrical leads to air conditioning system and electric fan. Disconnect radiator hoses, heater hoses, and on automatic transmission vehicles only, coolant hoses. On all vehicles, remove fan shroud and radiator. Remove air conditioning condenser and compressor mounting bolts and swing these units clear to the right side.

NOTE — *Do NOT disconnect any air conditioning system hoses or pressure connections.*

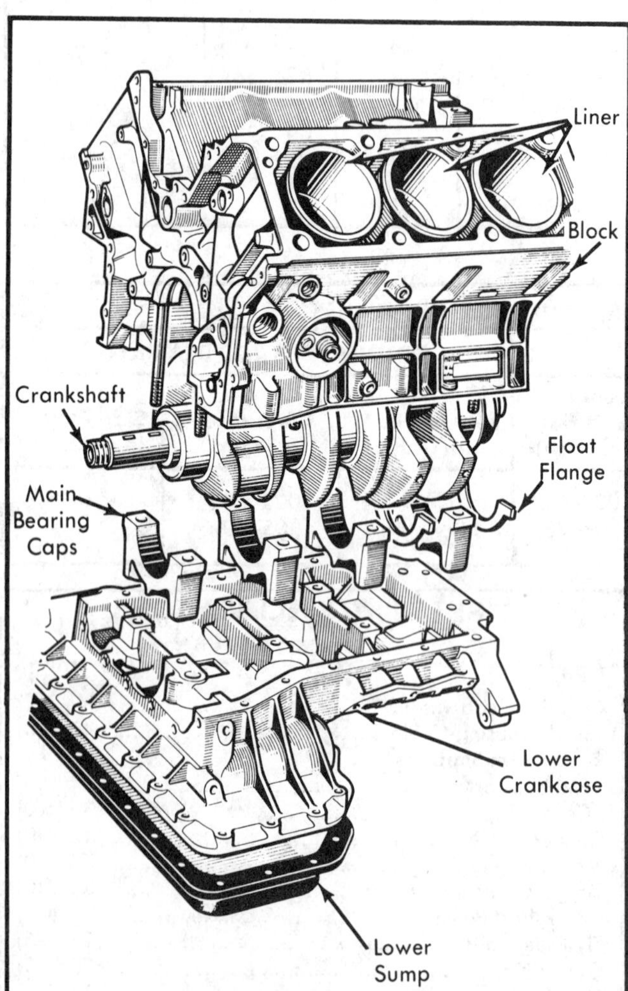

Fig. 1 Exploded View of Peugeot V6 Engine

3) Disconnect rear heater hose, fuel lines, vacuum lines, throttle linkage and electrical connections. Remove upper bolts from clutch housing or torque converter. On automatic transmission models, remove filler pipe. Remove front exhaust pipe connections and engine mounting bolts.

4) Remove muffler and exhaust pipe brackets and heat deflector. Remove starter mounting bolts and clutch housing or converter cover plates. Remove power steering mounting bolts but do NOT disconnect lines. With suitable sling (8.0135) and hoist, lift engine until transmission is about 3/8" below tunnel. Remove steering pump and hang to one side.

5) Fit propeller shaft tube support between muffler and body and tighten to support tube slightly. Remove steering coupling clamp bolt and replace rear steering rack bolts with slightly longer bolts. Remove front crossmember securing bolts and loosen rear bolts about 3/8" to lower the cross member.

6) On automatic transmission models, disconnect starter ring gear flange plate from torque converter. On all models, remove two lower housing securing bolts. Remove engine towards front. Use caution to avoid damaging power steering and automatic transmission cooling tubes. On automatic transmission models, hold torque converter in position. To install, reverse removal procedure.

CYLINDER HEADS

1) Drain cooling system and remove engine hood. Remove air cleaner and ducts. Remove battery. Remove intake manifold and plug intake ports in cylinder heads. Remove insulating plate and hose connecting water pump and cylinder heads. Remove hose between heads.

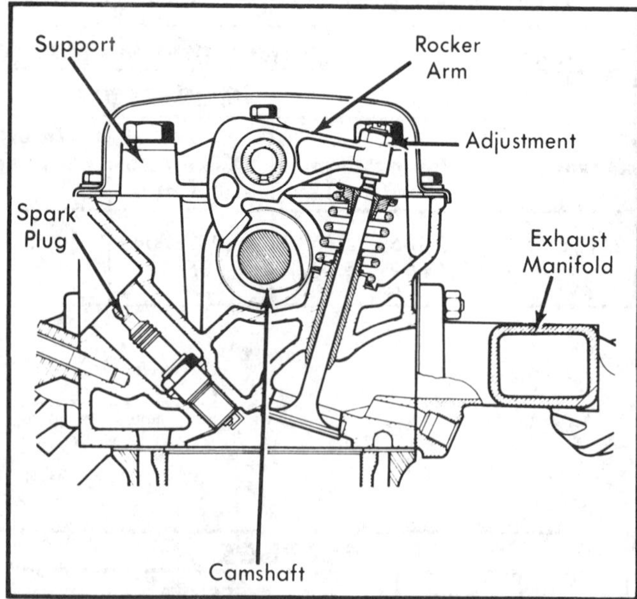

Fig. 2 Sectional View of Cylinder Head

2) To remove left head, lower the cross member and remove fuel pump. Loosen positive battery lead and remove ground cable. To remove right head, remove distributor, coil and filler well for automatic transmission (if equipped). For either head, loosen front muffler mounting and remove exhaust pipe clamp

604 GASOLINE V6 (Cont.)

under manifold. For left head, remove bolt from flexible steering coupler, then lower crossmember by about 3/8".

3) Remove rocker arm cover and camshaft rear cover plate. Remove camshaft sprocket bolt access plug and position sprocket with drive stud or timing mark at top. Lock crankshaft in this position and loosen camshaft sprocket bolt. Place camshaft sprocket support (8.0134 M) on front of timing gear casing and tighten mounting bolts finger tight. Attach sprocket to support through one of the holes in the sprocket web by means of bolt and nut tightened to no more than 11 ft. lbs. (1.5 mkg).

4) Remove all eight cylinder head bolts. On left head, vacuum servo prevents full removal of rearmost two bolts. Lift these as far as they will go and fasten them together with a rubber band. On each head, remove four bolts securing timing gear casing. Remove heads by inserting two "L" shaped rods into cylinder head bolt holes and jiggling until free. Lift off cylinder head-rocker arm assembly.

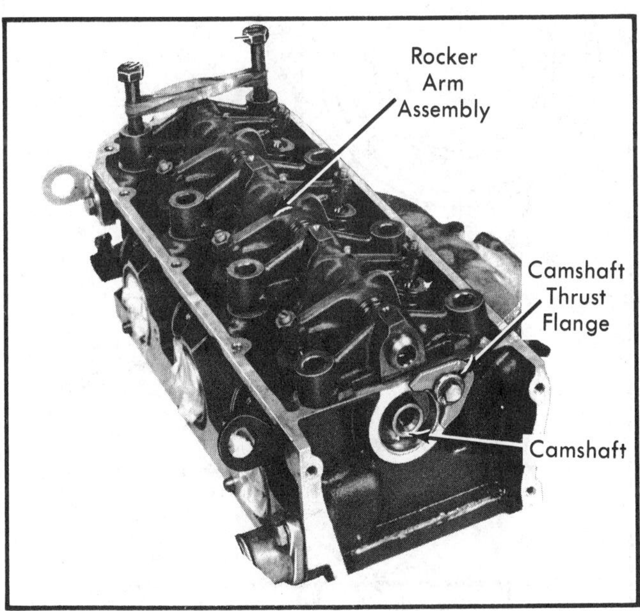

Fig. 3 Left Cylinder Head with Rear Bolts

NOTE — *Timing chain tension must not be released. If accidently released, timing cover must be removed in order to reposition chain tensioner. Retaining bars should be installed to prevent cylinder liner movement.*

Installation — 1) Insert a pin punch in each of the holes under the locating dowels and insert new dowels. Remove liner retaining bars and fit a new head gasket (dry) on block. Place cylinder head-rocker arm assembly into position carefully and hand tighten the four timing gear case bolts.

2) Carefully align keyways and insert camshaft into sprocket. Raise rocker arms and turn sprocket bolt until camshaft has entered sprocket fully, then tighten lightly. Install but do not tighten oiled cylinder head bolts in position. Remove camshaft sprocket support. Install camshaft thrust flange into camshaft flange and tighten bolts.

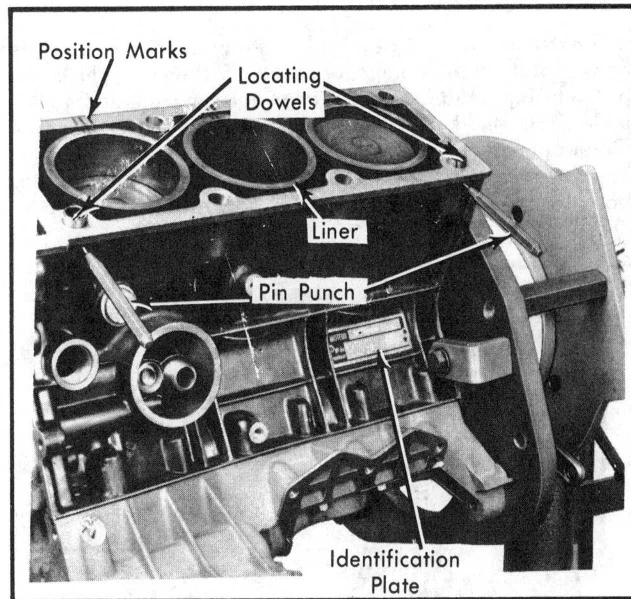

Fig. 4 Positioning Locating Dowels

3) Hold crankshaft and tighten camshaft sprocket bolt. Initially tighten cylinder head bolts in order shown to 43 ft. lbs. (6 mkg), then loosen individually and retighten 14 ft. lbs. (2 mkg). Tighten each bolt in sequence an additional 90° (one quarter turn) to final position.

NOTE — *Due to the position of the brake servo, the two rear bolts on the left head (inserted in head prior to installation) will require special attention. If in doubt about proper tension on any bolt, it must be fully loosened and the tightening procedures repeated.*

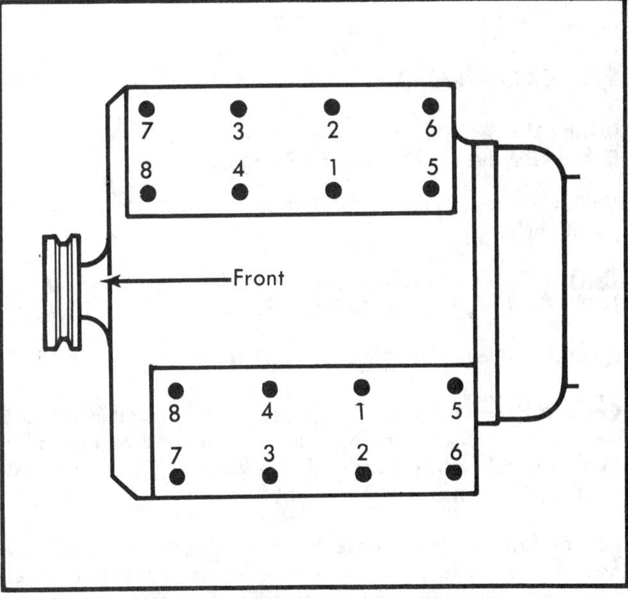

Fig. 5 Cylinder Head Tightening Sequence

604 GASOLINE V6 (Cont.)

4) Tighten access plug, gear case and rear bearing cover plate bolts. Rotate crankshaft to bring No. 5 (center, right bank) piston to Top Dead Center and align notch in crankshaft pulley under "10" mark on timing plate. With vacuum advance diaphragm to rear and unmarked rotor arm to front of engine, install distributor. Align marks on rotor arm and distributor body (4 o'clock position) and snug down securing clamp.

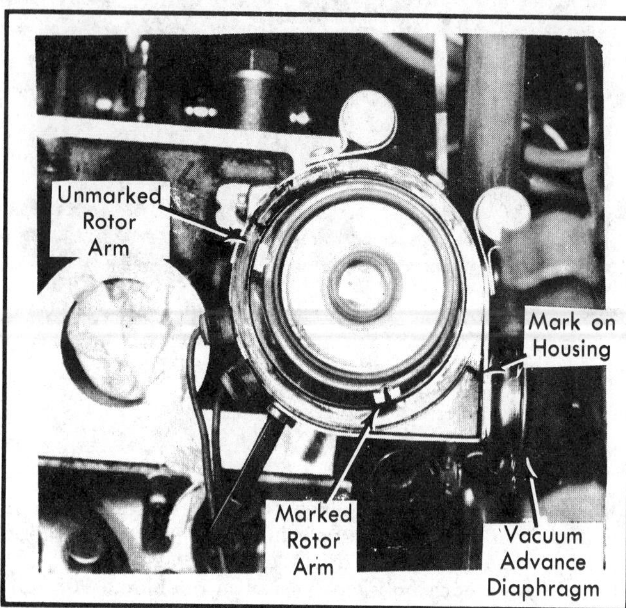

Fig. 6 Installing Distributor

5) Complete installation in reverse order of removal. Final torquing of head should be done after engine has been warmed up at 2000 RPM for 12 minutes, followed by 1 hour for cooling.

VALVES

VALVE ARRANGEMENT

Intake Valves – Inboard side of heads.
Exhaust Valves – Outboard side of heads.

Valves are removed and refitted in the usual way using conventional tools.

NOTE – *Cylinders are numbered from left bank flywheel end 1, 2 and 3; right bank 4, 5 and 6.*

CAMSHAFT AND ROCKER ARM ASSEMBLIES

Camshaft – Remove thrust flange from front of head and rear bearing cover plate. Camshaft is removed and installed from rear of head. Left camshaft has fuel pump drive cam and right camshaft has distributor drive pinion.

Rocker Arms – Mark rocker arms for left or right head. Disassemble, keeping parts in same order as removed. Replace parts as necessary and reassemble in reverse order of disassembly.

NOTE – *Left and right rocker arm assemblies are identical, however, circlip end is at front of left head and to rear on right head. Flat end of boss on support must face toward circlip.*

VALVE CLEARANCE ADJUSTMENT

1) Engine must be cold. Rotate crankshaft so that number 1 cylinder is at TDC on firing stroke (rotor mark lined up with mark on distributor; notch on pulley under "0" on timing plate). Adjust number 1, 2 and 4 intake; number 1, 3 and 6 exhaust clearance.

2) Rotate crankshaft one full revolution so that mark on rotor arm is 180° from mark on distributor housing and notch in pulley is again under "0" mark on timing plate. Adjust number 3, 5 and 6 intake; number 2, 4 and 5 exhaust clearance.

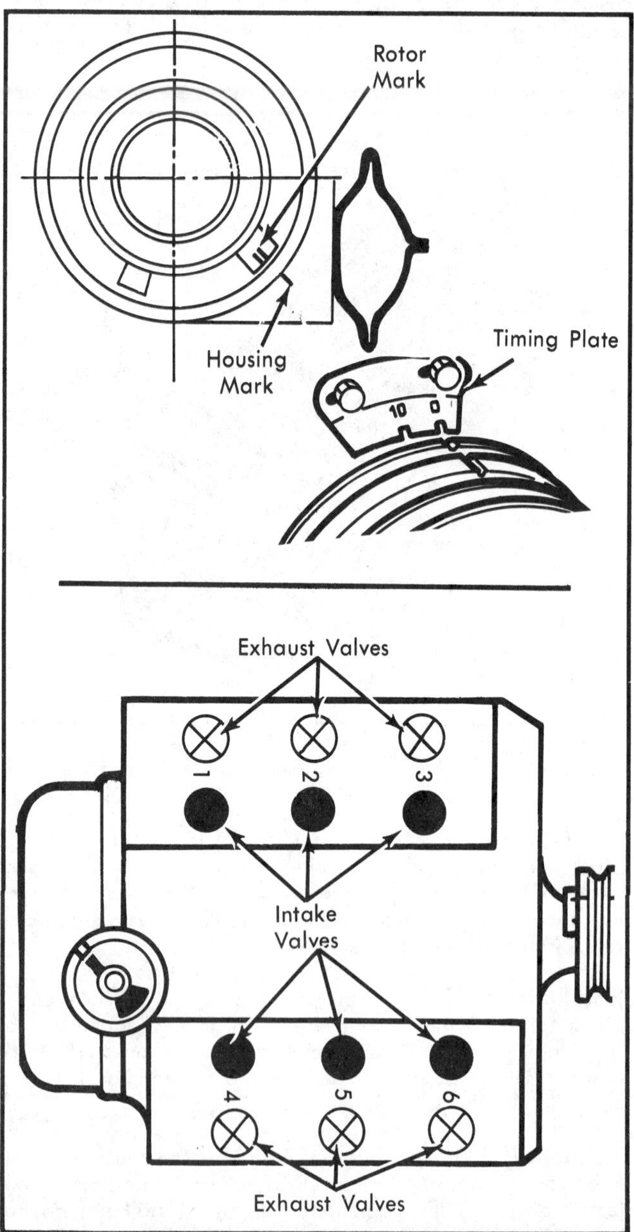

Fig. 7 First Adjusting Position for Setting Valves

604 GASOLINE V6 (Cont.)

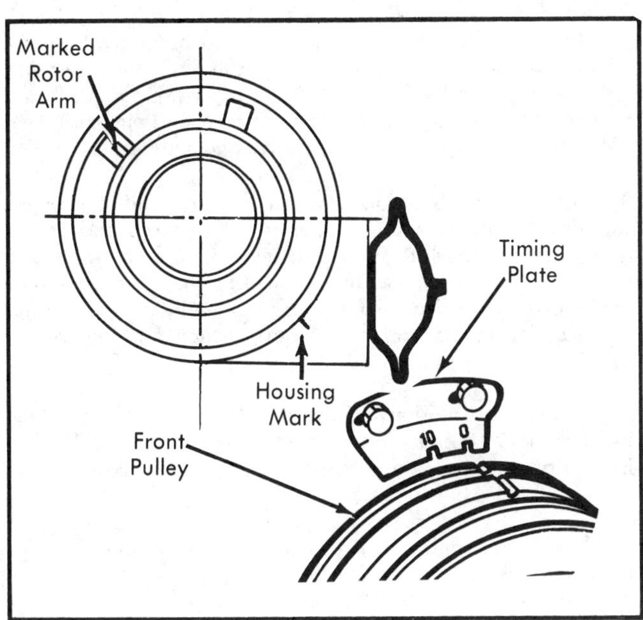

Fig. 8 Second Adjusting Position for Setting Valves

Valve Clearance Adjustment

Valve	In. (mm)
Intake	.004 (.10)
Exhaust	.010 (.25)

PISTONS, PINS & RINGS

PISTON & ROD ASSEMBLY

NOTE — *To accomplish further engine repairs, engine must be removed from car and placed on suitable stand.*

1) Remove cylinder heads, sump and lower crank case. Mark positions of components to ensure proper placement for reassembly. Remove connecting rod cap nuts and bearing caps. Slide protective tubing over rod bolts and remove piston and liner assembly individually.

NOTE — *Piston/rod assemblies must be kept with their respective liners. If piston is removed from rod, it will be necessary to install both a new liner and a new piston.*

2) Match piston and liner. Mount piston and rod assembly with bearing end in soft jawed vise. Arrow on piston top should point away from installer so that when liner is installed, arrow will be in 12 o'clock and notches on liner will be in 3 o'clock positions. Lubricate piston/ring assembly and apply suitable ring compressor. Push liner down over piston assembly without turning until ring compressor is free.

3) Slide protective tubing over connecting rod bolts, then insert piston/liner assemblies in block starting with number one. Finger tighten connecting rod nuts until all assemblies are installed, then tighten to specifications. See *Fitting Cylinder Liners*.

FITTING CYLINDER LINERS

1) Prior to fitting or installing liners, block and liners must be absolutely clean to assure proper fit. Liners will have one, two or three machined marks on top of outboard edge corresponding to "A", "B" or "C" marked on top of piston. For final assembly, liners must project above cylinder block gasket face by .006-.009" (.16-.23 mm).

NOTE — *Liner/piston assemblies must all be of the same category (I-A, II-B or III-C) when installed in any given engine. Do not attempt to install liners with different markings in the same engine.*

2) Place liner in position without its seal and place measuring plate (8.0132) over liner with smooth side up. Place dial indicator in support on plate and take a reading at four points around top of liner. Difference should not exceed .0008" (.02 mm).

3) Measure liner projection through the three elongated holes in plate by placing plunger against block. Difference should not exceed .002" (.05 mm). To determine lower liner seal thickness, subtract largest of readings from .0091" (.23 mm).

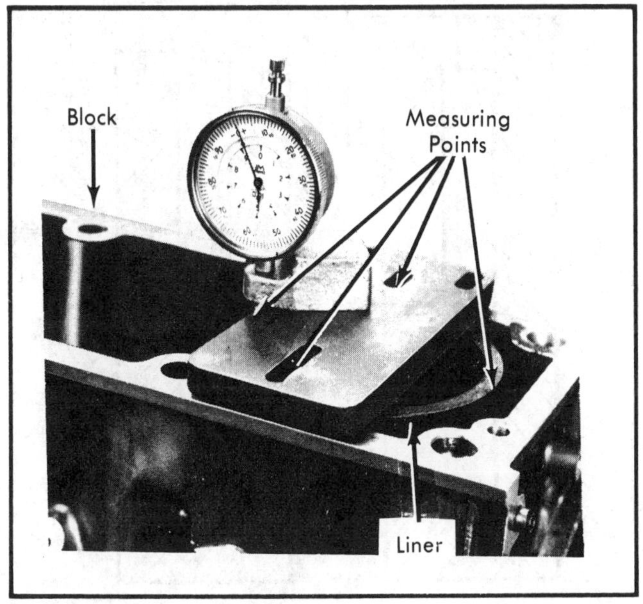

Fig. 9 Measuring Liner Projection

Example:

First reading	.0039" (.10 mm)
Second reading	.0032" (.08 mm)
Third reading	.0035" (.09 mm)

Subtract largest reading .0039" (.10 mm) from .0091" (.23 mm). Result .0052" (.13 mm) indicates thickness of lower liner seal.

604 GASOLINE V6 (Cont.)

Liner Seal Thickness

Tab Color	Thickness – In. (mm)
Blue	.0034 (.087)
White	.0040 (.102)
Red	.0048 (.122)
Yellow	.0057 (.147)

4) Fit identical seals to liners with color tab marking toward top. Place liners in block so that tabs are visible and not trapped under adjacent liner. Repeat measurement as outlined in steps **2)** and **3)** with seal installed while holdingplate down to flatten out seal. Check that height differences between liners does not exceed .0016" (.04 mm).

NOTE – *It is possible to adjust height differences on new liners by rotating them.*

5) In case liner or liners project too far, select thinner seal and repeat measurement. Mark the order and positions of liners on top of liner and edge of block. Match piston & rod assemblies with liners and proceed as in *Piston & Rod Assembly*.

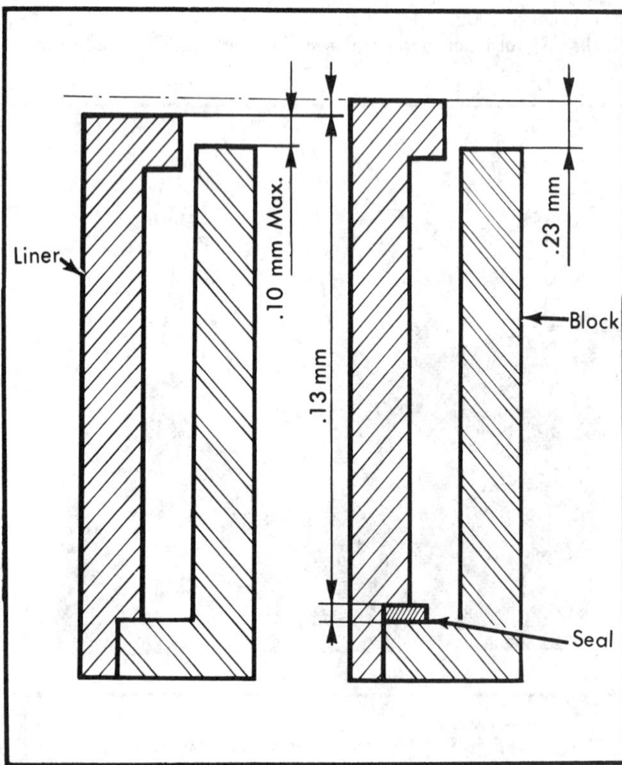

Fig. 10 Cylinder Liner and Seal

PISTON PIN REPLACEMENT

1) Remove old wrist pin with drift (8.0134) and press. Discard old piston and inspect rod for overheating or galling. In order to satisfactorily assemble piston, Pin and rod, wrist pin end of rod must be heated on hot plate.

NOTE – *In order to properly install wrist pins, special tool sets 8.0134 and 8.0139 are required. The success of the operation depends on the speed with which it is carried out.*

2) Arrange left (1, 2 & 3) rods with pistons and matched wrist pins for assembly. Install pistons with arrow head and DT mark upward in special tool and fit connecting rod thrust washer (F4) with number 1-2-3 up on tool. Place wrist pin on drift and tighten cone end finger tight. Immerse cone and pin in oil, then place rod inside piston to locate pin and washer.

3) With pin, drift and cone inserted in piston and rod, adjust support with thrust washer under center of large end of rod and tighten support. Remove drift and rod, then heat pin end of rods until resin core solder will melt on them. Collar end of rods must point downward on washer, then insert pin by hand until cone contacts base. Wait ten seconds and repeat for other rods.

4) Turn support washer over so that figure 4-5-6 is up, then arrange RIGHT side rods with collar pointing UPWARD. Repeat procedures used in Steps **2)** & **3)**. Mark all assemblies for installation with felt tip pen.

NOTE – *Pistons and pins are marked for wrist pin size. See following table:*

Mark on Piston	Wrist Pin Color
①	Blue
②	White
③	Red

CRANKSHAFT MAIN & CONNECTING ROD BEARINGS

MAIN BEARINGS

1) Remove crankshaft and measure main bearing shells. Measure journals for size and maximum run out of .0012" (.03 mm). Clean out all oil passages, keyways and screw threads on crankshaft. Oil bearing shells and place in block with oil holes lined up with passages in block. Shells with groove go in block while those without are placed in bearing caps.

2) Place copper-plated faces of lower end float flanges against shoulders on crankshaft rear bearing area. Fit both front and rear bearing caps so that raised boss is on timing gear side.

3) Place spacers (part of tool set 8.0134) on front and rear bearing caps and tighten nuts to 22 ft. lbs. (3 mkg). Loosen nuts and check crankshaft end play with dial indicator. Play should be .003-.011" (.07-.27 mm). If not within specifications, replace float flanges. Float flanges are available in the following sizes: .0905", .0945", .0965" and .0985" (2.3, 2.4, 2.45 and 2.5 mm).

4) Use same procedures to fit connecting rod bearings as for main bearings. See *PISTON & ROD ASSEMBLY*.

FITTING LOWER CRANKCASE

Remove main bearing spacers from caps. Assure that boss on main bearing caps is on timing gear (front) side. Locating sleeve and new "O" ring must be in position on oil pump. Coat joint face of block with sealing compound and install lower crankcase, all fastenings finger tight. Tighten all main bearing caps to 22 ft. lbs. (3 mkg) in order illustrated. Further angle tighten caps one quarter turn (90°) in order shown. Install anti-emulsion plate, strainer and sump with new cork gasket.

604 GASOLINE V6 (Cont.)

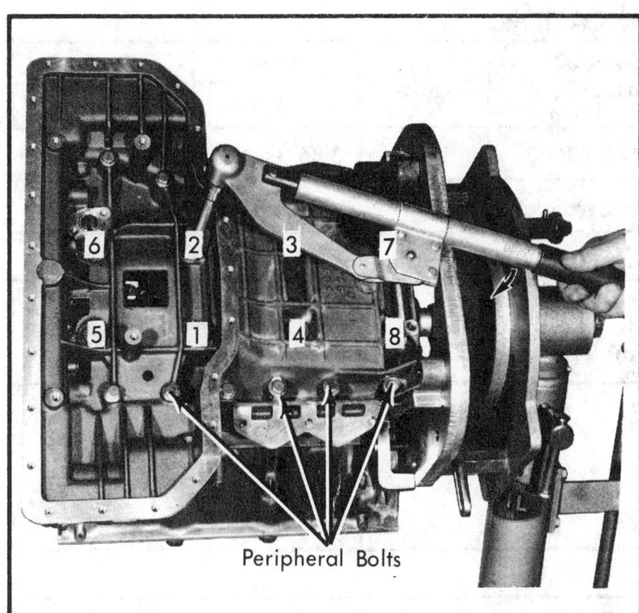

Fig. 11 Main Bearing Tightening Sequence

CAMSHAFT

TIMING GEAR COVER

NOTE — *Timing gear and cover repair work may be accomplished with engine installed or removed from vehicle.*

Removal — **1**) Rotate crankshaft so that notch in pulley is absolutely in line with the 10° mark on timing plate and lock flywheel in place with clamping tool. Drain engine oil and cooling system. Disconnect battery and all hose connections to radiator.

2) Remove and set aside the following: Air filter and ducting, radiator and struts, fan and casing, drive belts, power steering pump and support, crankshaft pulley, rocker arm covers, timing gear cover bolts and timing cover. Oil pump, chain tensioners and timing gears are now accessible.

Installation — To install, reverse removal procedure and note the following: Gasket faces and gaskets must be clean and dry. Timing plate 10° mark must be directly in line with pulley notch. Adhere to all torque specifications.

CHAINS & SPROCKETS

Removal — With timing case cover off, plug ports to crankcase unless crankcase is to be removed. Remove oil pump sprockets, drive chain, spacer, key and oil pump. Release chain tensioners. Mark position of camshaft drive chains if they are to be reused. Remove right camshaft sprocket and chain first, then left side. Remove chain tensioners and drive sprocket.

Installation — **1**) Reinstall filters in front of block. Lock chain tensioner plungers in retracted position, then install tensioners. Install tensioner strips and fixed pads.

2) With keyway at top of crankshaft, insert key and install sprocket with position mark visible from outside. Turn crankshaft so that keyway is aligned to left cylinder bank and camshaft centerline. Place chain over left camshaft sprocket with mark on sprocket between marks on chain. Fit chain over drive sprocket with mark on link in line with position mark on sprocket.

3) Rotate crankshaft clockwise to bring mark on drive sprocket in line with bottom oil pump mounting hole. Align marks on chain and sprockets as in Step **2**) and tighten camshaft bolts. Unlock tensioners and allow to extend without assisting their movement. Tighten in position.

4) Fit spacer, key and oil pump drive sprocket on crankshaft. Install oil pump, sprocket and chain. Install cover as in *TIMING GEAR COVER* section.

TIMING PLATE ADJUSTMENT

With intake manifold removed, rotate engine so that number 1 piston is approaching TDC on the firing stroke. Remove hex head plug near front of left bank of engine. Insert gauge rod to rest against crankshaft counterbalance weight. Turn crankshaft SLOWLY until rod enters slot and locks crankshaft. Check that notch in pulley is aligned with "0" on timing plate. If not, readjust plate and tighten in position.

ENGINE OILING

ENGINE OILING SYSTEM

Positive displacement gear type pump is located at lower left side of engine under timimg case cover. Pump is chain-driven from crankshaft. Oil is picked up through a screen and tube in lower sump, filtered through a 10 to 15 micron type filter and pressure fed through the oil gallery and passages to main and connecting rod bearings.

NOTE — *A 5 to 8 micron filter with red inscriptions is fitted to new or service exchange engines. It is also furnished with piston and liner sets. This filter must be replaced with a Purflux LS 410 (10 to 15 micron) at the 1,000 km inspection.*

Crankcase Capacity — 6.3 qts. (6 liters).

Normal Oil Pressure — 29 psi @900 RPM, 64 psi @4,000 RPM.

ENGINE COOLING

ENGINE COOLING SYSTEM

Pressurized system uses viscus drive type fan. An additional electric fan is used on vehicles equipped with automatic transmission.

Cooling System Capacity — 11 qts. (10 .3 liters).

WATER PUMP

1) Remove intake manifold as in *CYLINDER HEADS* and disconnect hoses at pump. Remove water pump-alternator drive belt and water pump securing bolts. Remove bolts securing water casings to block and remove water pump-casing assembly.

2) Install new "O" rings using sealing compound at water casing connections. Reinstall water pump and casing, then continue assembly in reverse order of disassembly.

604 GASOLINE V6 (Cont.)

GENERAL SPECIFICATIONS

Year	Displ. cu. ins.	Displ. cc	Carburetor	HP at RPM	Torque (Ft. Lbs. at RPM)	Compr. Ratio	Bore in.	Bore mm	Stroke in.	Stroke mm
1977	163.2	2664	①	133@5750	147@3500	8.2-1	3.46	88	2.87	73

①Solex 34 TBIA Single-barrel Primary; Solex 35 CEEI Two-barrel Secondary.

VALVES

Engine & Valve	Head Diam. In. (mm)	Face Angle	Seat Angle	Seat Width In. (mm)	Stem Diameter In. (mm)	Stem Clearance In. (mm)	Valve Lift In. (mm)
Gasoline V6							
Intake	1.73 (44)	①	①	①	①	①	①
Exhaust	1.45 (37)						

① — Information not available from manufacturer at this time.

CRANKSHAFT MAIN & CONNECTING ROD BEARINGS

Engine	MAIN BEARINGS Journal Diam. In. (mm)	Clearance In. (mm)	Thrust Bearing	Crankshaft End Play In. (mm)	CONNECTING ROD BEARINGS Journal Diam. In. (mm)	Clearance In. (mm)	Side Play In. (mm)
Gas. V6	2.7597-2.7604 (70.043-70.062)	①	Rear	.0028-.0106 (.07-.27)	2.0593-2.0600 52.267-52.286	①	①

① — Information not available from manufacturer at this time.

VALVE SPRINGS

Engine	Free Length In. (mm)	PRESSURE Lbs. @ In. (kg @ mm) Valve Closed	Valve Open
Gas V6	①	①	①

① — Information not available from manufacturer at this time.

VALVE TIMING

Engine	INTAKE Open (BTDC)	INTAKE Close (ALDC)	EXHAUST Open (BLDC)	EXHAUST Close (ATDC)
Gas. V6				
Left Bank	9°	45°	45°	9°
Right Bank	7°	43°	43°	7°

TIGHTENING SPECIFICATIONS

Application	Ft. Lbs. (mkg)
Cylinder Head	See Text
Main Bearing Caps	See Text
Connecting Rod Nuts	34 (4.75)
Crankcase Peripheral Bolts	13 (1.75)
Lower Sump	9 (1.3)
Baffle Plate & Strainer	9 (1.3)
Flywheel Bolts	33 (4.5)
Camshaft Thrust Flange	9 (1.3)
Exhaust Manifold Nuts	13 (1.75)
Intake Manifold Bolts	9 (1.3)
Oil Pump Mounting Bolts	9 (1.3)
Oil Pump Sprocket Bolts	5 (.6)
Timing Cover Bolts	9 (1.3)
Crankshaft Pulley	123 (17)
Water Pump Mounting Bolts	13 (1.75)
Water Casing Bolts	9 (1.3)
Bell Housing Bolts	29 (4)

911 S & TURBO CARRERA 6 CYLINDER

ENGINE CODING

ENGINE IDENTIFICATION

Engine identification number is die stamped on blower fan support near oil temperature sensor. Second digit of number identifies engines as follows:

Application	Engine Code
911 S	2
Turbo Carrera	8

ENGINE & CYLINDER HEAD

ENGINE

1) Place vehicle on jack stands. Disconnect negative battery cable. Remove air cleaner. Loosen engine block vent hose at engine and plug vent cover hole. If equipped with air conditioning, detach compressor at console but leave hoses attached.

NOTE — *Air conditioning system is under pressure, DO NOT disconnect hoses until pressure is released.*

2) Remove relay plate cover and disconnect the engine wires at; relay plate, adapter plug, relay plate socket, and ignition control unit. Remove fuel hoses at filter and return line. Disconnect accelerator linkage.

3) Remove rear center tunnel cover in passenger compartment. Remove rubber boot in tunnel by pulling forward over the selector rod. Loosen shift rod coupling and pull coupling off of transmission inner shift rod.

4) Disconnect speedometer sensor wires in tunnel. Remove rubber plug with wire plug. Drain crankcase and plug hoses on engine and oil tank. Remove heater hoses at exchangers. Remove rear stabilizer.

5) Disconnect ground strap at body and battery wires at starter. Disconnect accelerator linkage from pedal and clutch cable from transmission. Loosen drive shaft flange socket head screws at transmission.

CAUTION — *Be careful when jacking assembly upward not to damage the secondary air injection pipes.*

6) Place a suitable jack under engine/transmission assembly and apply a little upward pressure to relieve tension on motor mounts. Remove transmission and engine mount bolts. Lower engine/transmission assembly out of vehicle.

CAUTION — *Do not move vehicle unless drive shafts are suspended horizontally, to prevent damage to dust covers.*

Installation — Reverse removal procedure and note the following: Do not clamp heater hoses, slide them onto the exchangers just before the engine/transmission assembly is in final installation position.

CYLINDER HEAD

Removal — 1) With fuel injection system removed, remove distributor cap and spark plug wires. Remove all cool air ducts and cover shrouds.

2) Remove air ducts connecting air blower outlets and heat exchanger inlets, together with cover shrouds. Remove rear engine mount (transverse leaf spring) from holder.

3) Remove fuel pump and hoses. Remove exhaust pipes and engine mounting bracket. Remove blower pulley and drive belt.

4) Loosen both screws of band strap which attaches alternator to blower housing. Pull blower housing rearward. Disconnect alternator cables and remove blower housing with alternator.

5) Remove heat exchanger using suitable wrenches (No. P 205 & P 217). Disconnect camshaft oil lines between crankcase and chain housing covers. Remove covers.

6) Remove chain tensioner, pivot lever and chain sprocket as an assembly. Remove camshaft sprocket nuts using suitable tools (No. P 202 & P 203). Withdraw sprocket dowel pin, using suitable tool (No. P 212).

7) With a screwdriver lift spring retainers from groove and remove chain guides. Remove camshaft sprockets and flanges. Pry Woodruff keys from camshafts.

NOTE — *Each cylinder has a separate cylinder head. If camshaft housing is removed, any single head may be removed. If camshaft housing is left attached to cylinder heads, cylinder heads and camshaft housing may be removed as an assembly.*

8) To remove a single head, rotate camshaft to take load off of rocker arm shaft to be removed. Loosen rocker arm shafts and push out shafts. Remove camshaft housing.

9) Using a suitable tool (No. P 119), remove cylinder head nuts and lift off cylinder head.

NOTE — *Mark cylinder heads, cylinders and camshaft housings so they will be reassembled in their original positions.*

10) To remove all three cylinder heads and camshaft housing as an assembly, evenly loosen and unscrew cylinder head nuts using suitable tool (No. P 119).

911 S & TURBO CARRERA 6 CYLINDER (Cont.)

Installation – 1) Place cylinder head gaskets on cylinders with perforated side of steel insert facing cylinder. Install cylinder heads and oil return tubes at same time. Coat oil return tubes with engine oil for easier installation. Lightly tighten cylinder head nuts.

2) Install cool air shrouds and attach with clamps. Thinly coat camshaft housing gasket with gasket compound. Slide camshaft housing onto mounting studs. Tighten camshaft housing nuts down a few turns to ensure gasket seal. Install Allen screws in proper location and tighten camshaft housing in a crosswise pattern.

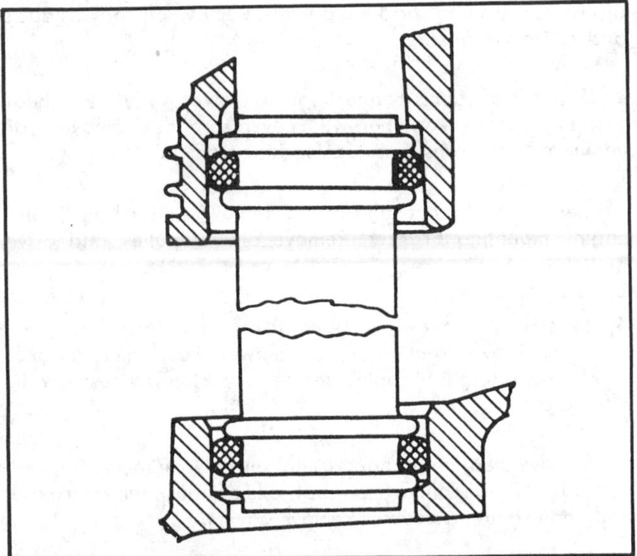

Fig. 1 Cylinder Head Oil Return Tube Installation

NOTE – Camshaft housings are interchangeable, but camshafts are not. Camshafts must be positioned on their proper side; see Fig. 4.

3) Tighten cylinder head nuts in a crosswise pattern, checking that camshaft does not bind in housing. If camshaft binds, loosen cylinder head nuts and tighten in a different sequence. With cylinder head nuts tight, camshaft must be free to rotate.

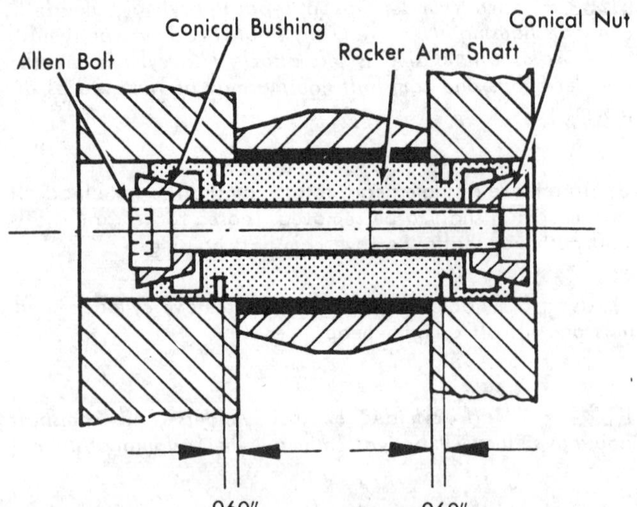

Fig. 2 Cross Sectional View of Rocker Arm Shaft Assembly

4) Install rocker arms and shafts. Install rocker arm shaft with approximately .060" (1.52 mm) clearance between shaft grooves and mounting face; see *Fig. 2*. Tighten Allen bolts to 13 ft. lbs. (1.8 mkg), using suitable tools (P 210 & P 211).

5) Install gasket, "O" ring, sealing flange, thrust plate, spacer, Woodruff key and camshaft sprocket flange as shown in *Fig. 3*. No provision is made to adjust camshaft end play, if sealing flange is worn, replace it.

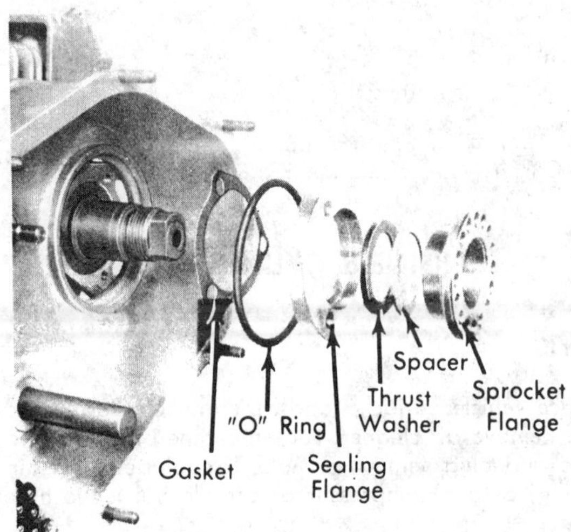

Fig. 3 Assembling Components to Install Camshaft Sprocket Flange and Sprocket

6) Install camshaft sprockets. Check chain alignment; see *Fig. 11*.

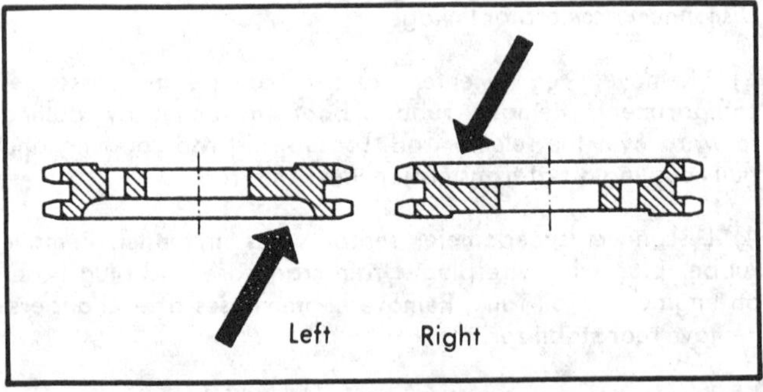

Fig. 4 Camshaft Sprocket Position (Viewed from Blower End of Engine)

7) Install heat exchanger before chain tensioner. Slide chain guides on mounting studs. With a screwdriver lift retaining spring and slide chain guide into place. Install chain tension pivot lever and sprocket. Check that oil holes in pivot stud face upward.

8) Fill and bleed chain tensioners, depress chain tensioners and install. Left chain tensioner may be positioned in only as far as to let camshaft nut to be installed after valve timing. See *Valve Timing*.

9) Install chain housing covers and camshaft oil lines. Reverse removal procedures for remaining components.

911 S & TURBO CARRERA 6 CYLINDER (Cont.)

VALVES

VALVE ARRANGEMENT

All upper valves are intake.

All lower valves are exhaust.

VALVE GUIDE SERVICING

1) Drill out valve guide with a .433" (11 mm) drill from camshaft side of head. Drift out remaining valve guide into combustion chamber.

2) Using a hole gauge, measure guide bore in cylinder head. Turn oversize guide in a lathe until O.D. gives an interference fit of .0012-.0024" (.030-.061 mm).

3) Press valve guide into head from camshaft side until a measurement of .5196" (13.2 mm) is reached. *(See Fig. 5).* Use suitable grease as a lubricant when pressing in valve guides. Bore or ream valve guide I.D. to .3543-.3549" (8.99-9.01 mm).

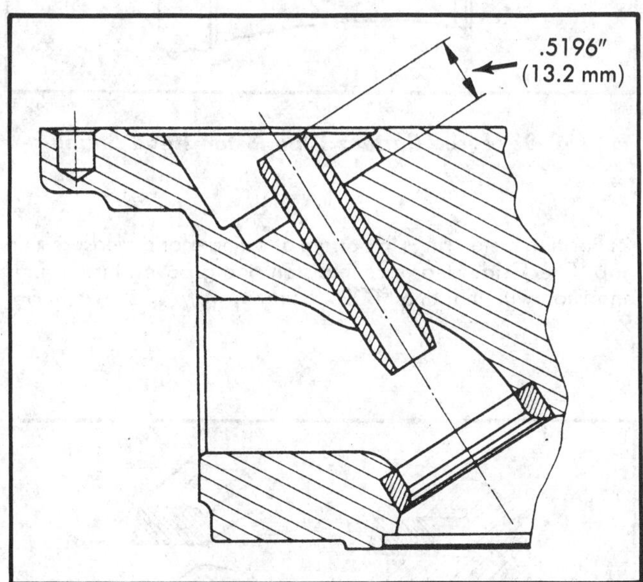

Fig. 5 ***Cross Sectional View of Valve Guide for Replacement***

VALVE STEM OIL SEALS

1) Using a suitable spring compressor, remove valve keepers. Withdraw collar and springs. Remove valve stem oil seal from end of valve guide.

2) Slide a new oil seal over valve stem, using care not to damage seal as it passes over keeper grooves. Force seal over end of valve guide. Reverse removal procedure for springs, collar and keepers.

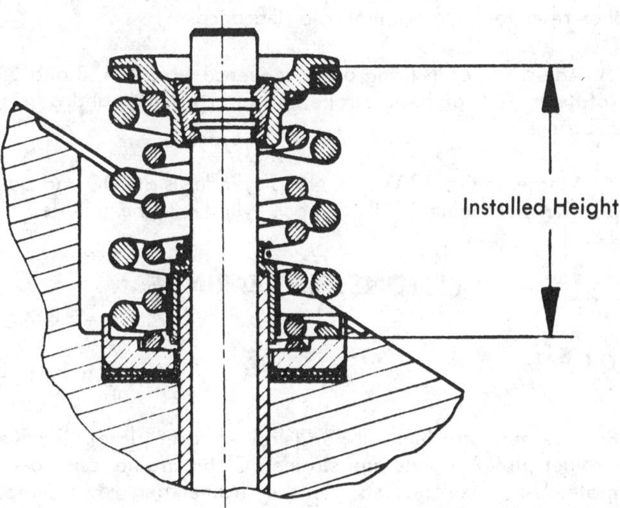

Fig. 6 ***Arrows Indicate Measurement Location Points for Valve Spring Installed Height***

VALVE SPRING SERVICING

1) Using a suitable spring compressor, remove valve keepers and collar. Check springs for wear or fatigue, replace as necessary.

2) Install outer sping with closely wound coils next to cylinder head. Measure installed height of springs; add or remove spacers under valve spring to attain specified installed height.

ROCKER ARM ASSEMBLY

1) Using an Allen wrench, loosen rocker arm shaft bolt. Slide rocker shaft out of cylinder head and remove arm.

2) Check rocker arm shaft and rocker bushing for wear.

Rocker Arm Specifications (In.)

Application	Diameter	Wear Limit
Rocker Arm Bushing	.7090-.7094	.7106
Rocker Arm Shaft	.7080-.7084	.7074
Rocker Arm Width	1.015-1.019	1.011
Housing Width	1.023-1.029	1.033

3) Install rocker arm shaft. Center rocker arm shaft in housing; see *Fig.* 2. Tighten rocker arm Allen bolt.

NOTE — *Install outside rocker arm shafts with Allen bolt facing either cylinder two or five.*

VALVE CLEARANCE ADJUSTMENT

1) Valve clearance should be set to .004" (.10 mm) with engine cold. If valves or seats have been reground, set

911 S & TURBO CARRERA 6 CYLINDER (Cont.)

clearances to .010" (.25 mm), run engine for one-half hour, then reset valves to original cold clearance.

2) Adjust valves in firing order sequence 1, 6, 2, 4, 3 and 5. Rotate to TDC of firing stroke on No. 1 cylinder and adjust clearance.

3) Rotate engine 120° until No. 6 cylinder is at TDC and adjust. Rotate engine 120° for each cylinder to be adjusted.

PISTONS, PINS & RINGS

OIL PAN

Remove nuts attaching oil pan (strainer cover plate). Remove strainer plate, gaskets and strainer. Clean strainer and cover plate. Using new gaskets, replace strainer and cover plate, making sure oil strainer hole slides over pickup tube.

PISTON ASSEMBLY

NOTE — *Connecting rods are not removed from crankshaft until crankcases are separated and crankshaft has been removed. Therefore pistons are removed with connecting rods still attached to crankshaft.*

Mark piston and cylinder for proper relocation upon reassembly. Remove cylinders. Extract piston pin circlip, heat piston to approximately 176°F (80°C), and press out pin. Clean and inspect piston, rings, and pin for each cylinder. **NOTE** — *See measurement procedures in Fitting Pistons.* Replace parts as necessary.

FITTING PISTONS

The Turbo Carrera model incorporates a light alloy (forged aluminum and leaded) piston. The piston top surface is flat, and the marking on piston must face the flywheel as the piston pin is offset by .016" (.4 mm) from piston center.

The 911 S model pistons top cavity must face the exhaust valve for installation. In order to prevent possible "unbalanced" weights and sizes, manufacturer suggests that cylinders and pistons of same type and make be constant throughout the engine.

1) Measure cylinder for wear and out-of-round. Cylinders are marked according to size (see Piston & Cylinder Specifications table). Measure cylinder diameter at 1.18" (30 mm) below the top edge of cylinder.

2) Take one measurement in line with thrust face and another at 90° to this measurement. Cylinder is worn if diameter measurement is more than .004" (0.1 mm) beyond diameter specification. If difference in the two measurements is more than .0016" (.04 mm), then cylinder has exceeded its ovality limit.

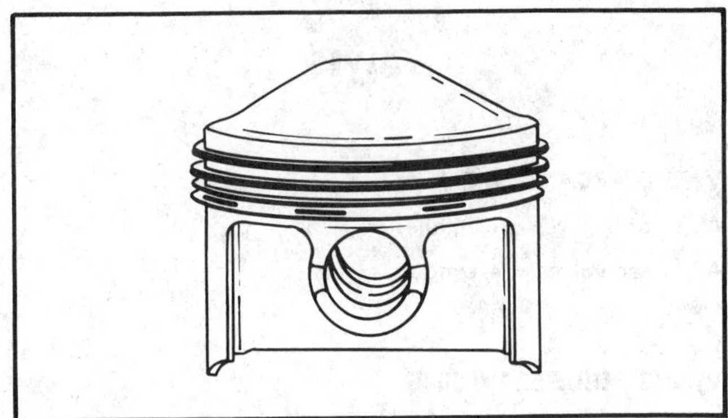

Fig. 7 911 S Model Type Piston Head Shape

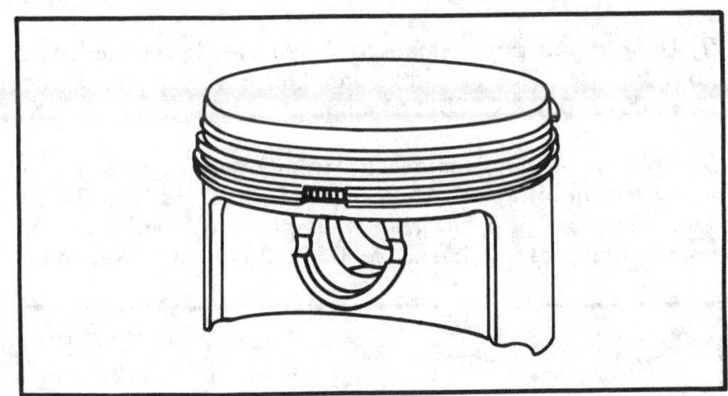

Fig. 8 Turbo Carrera Type Piston Head Shape

3) Position piston rings in bottom of cylinder and measure ring gap. Check side clearance in piston ring grooves. Install rings on piston with marking "TOP" facing upward as shown in *Fig. 9*.

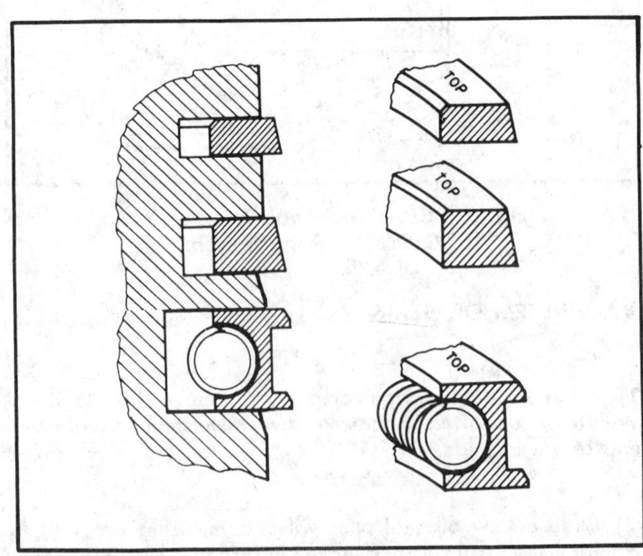

Fig. 9 Sectional View of Piston Ring Installation

911 S & TURBO CARRERA 6 CYLINDER (Cont.)

Piston & Cylinder Specifications (ALL STANDARD SIZES)

Application & Marking	Piston Diam. In. (mm)	Cylinder Diam. In. (mm)
911 S		
0	3.5419-3.5423	3.5433-3.5436
	(89.965-89.975)	(90.000-90.010)
1	3.5423-3.5427	3.5436-3.5440
	(89.975-89.985)	(90.010-90.020)
2	3.5427-3.5431	3.5440-3.5444
	(89.985-89.995)	(90.020-90.030)
Turbo Carrera		
0	3.7375-3.7380	3.7401-3.7405
	(94.933-94.947)	(95.000-95.010)
1	3.7379-3.7384	3.7405-3.7409
	(94.943-94.957)	(95.010-95.020)
2	3.7382-3.7388	3.7409-3.7413
	(94.953-94.967)	(95.020-95.030)

CRANKSHAFT MAIN & CONNECTING ROD BEARINGS

MAIN BEARING SERVICE

1) Separate crankcase halves. Lift out crankshaft and connecting rods. Place crankshaft on a suitable stand and remove connecting rods.

NOTE — *Replace connecting bolts whenever rods are disassembled. Connecting rod bolts are stretch bolts and should never be reused.*

2) Inspect crankshaft and connecting rods for wear, damage or out-of-true. Crankshaft main journals one through seven and all connecting rod journals have the same diameter. Replace bearings or fit undersize bearings as required.

3) Main bearing number eight is a special bearing with an external "O" ring and internal oil seal. A steel dowel pressed in crankcase is used to locate number eight bearing and prevent it from turning. Use care when installing bearing that dowel engages hole and not groove in bearing.

THRUST BEARING ALIGNMENT

Check end play at No. 1 main bearing. Width of No. 1 bearing is 1.1024-1.1044" (28.0-28.05 mm). Maximum wear limit is .011" (.28 mm) beyond specifications. Replace main bearing or crankshaft if excessive wear is present.

MAIN BEARING OIL SEALS (BLOWER END)

Remove belt pulley. Using a screwdriver, pry out old seal. Coat new seal with oil and press in place using suitable tool (No. P 216).

MAIN BEARING OIL SEAL SERVICE (FLYWHEEL END)

Remove flywheel. With a chisel or drift, displace oil seal. With a screwdriver pry out seal. Coat outer seal edges with sealing compound and press into crankcase until seal is flush with face of crankcase, using suitable tool (P 215).

INTERMEDIATE SHAFT BEARING SERVICE

With crankcase halves separated, lift out intermediate shaft and bearings. Inspect shaft and bearings for wear or damage. Replace shaft and bearings as necessary. No undersize bearings are available.

CAMSHAFT

TIMING CHAIN

Remove timing chain housing covers. Remove chain tensioner and chain tensioner sprocket. Remove timing chains. Install

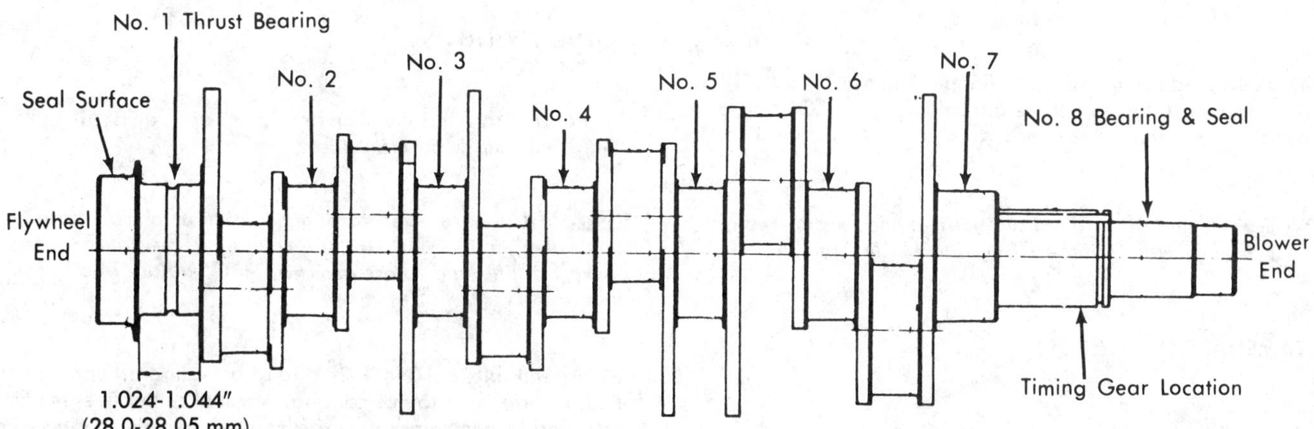

Fig. 10 Side View of Crankshaft with Detail of Bearing Locations

911 S & TURBO CARRERA 6 CYLINDER (Cont.)

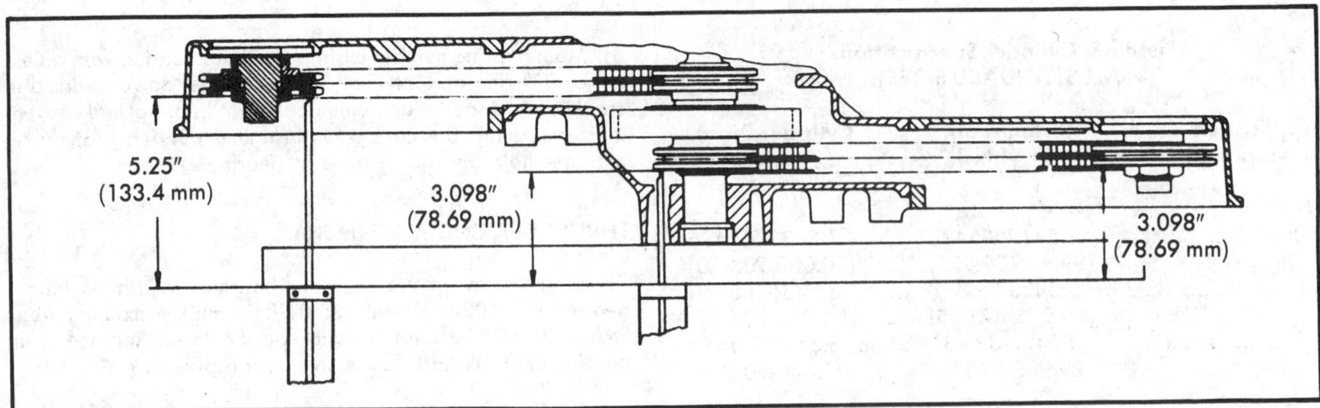

Fig. 11 Top View Showing Timing Chain Alignment

new timing chains. Reverse removal procedure to reassemble. Check valve timing and chain alignment; *see Fig. 11 & 13.*

CAMSHAFT

1) Remove rocker covers and rocker arm assemblies. Disconnect exhaust muffler. Remove oil hose from crankcase to chain housing cover. Remove chain tensioner and chain tensioner sprocket.

2) On 911S models, remove belt pulley from left camshaft. Remove bearing and chain housing covers. With a puller, remove ball bearing from camshaft.

3) Unscrew nuts attaching camshaft sprocket, using suitable tools (No. P 202 & P 203). Using suitable tool (No. P 212), remove dowel pin from camshaft sprocket.

4) Pull sprocket and sprocket flange. Remove Woodruff key from camshaft. Remove three attaching screws, "O" ring and withdraw camshafts rearward.

NOTE – *Camshafts are not symmetrical and must be replaced on side they were removed from during disassembly.*

CAMSHAFT END THRUST

With a dial indicator measure camshaft end play. If end play is excessive replace aluminum thrust washer located behind camshaft sprocket flange.

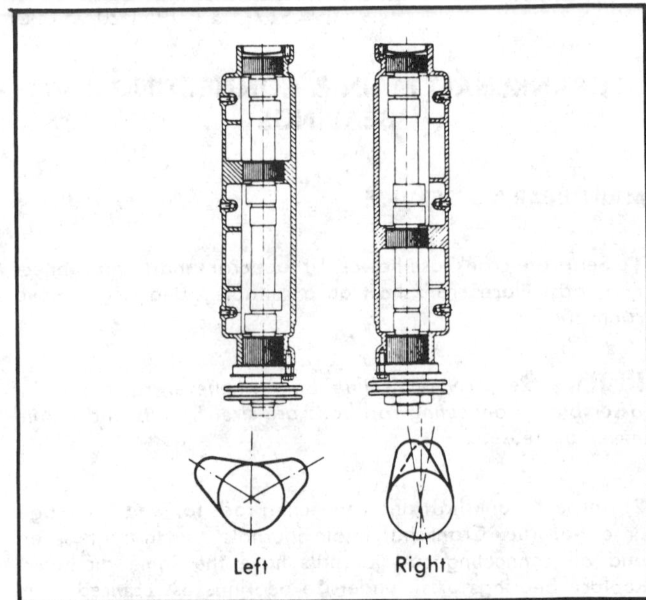

Fig. 12 Camshaft and Housing Location (Viewed from Blower End of Engine)

VALVE TIMING

1) Rotate crankshaft until mark "Z 1" on crankshaft pulley aligns with mark on crankcase.

NOTE – *Use care when rotating crankshaft or camshafts so that valve and piston do not collide. If resistance is felt, backoff a little and rotate camshaft until you are free to continue.*

2) Use suitable tool (No. P 202) to rotate camshaft until dot on end of shaft is on top of camshaft vertical center line *(see Fig. 13).* Find hole in camshaft sprocket which exactly lines-up with camshaft flange and insert dowel pin. Install lock washer and nut.

911 S & TURBO CARRERA 6 CYLINDER (Cont.)

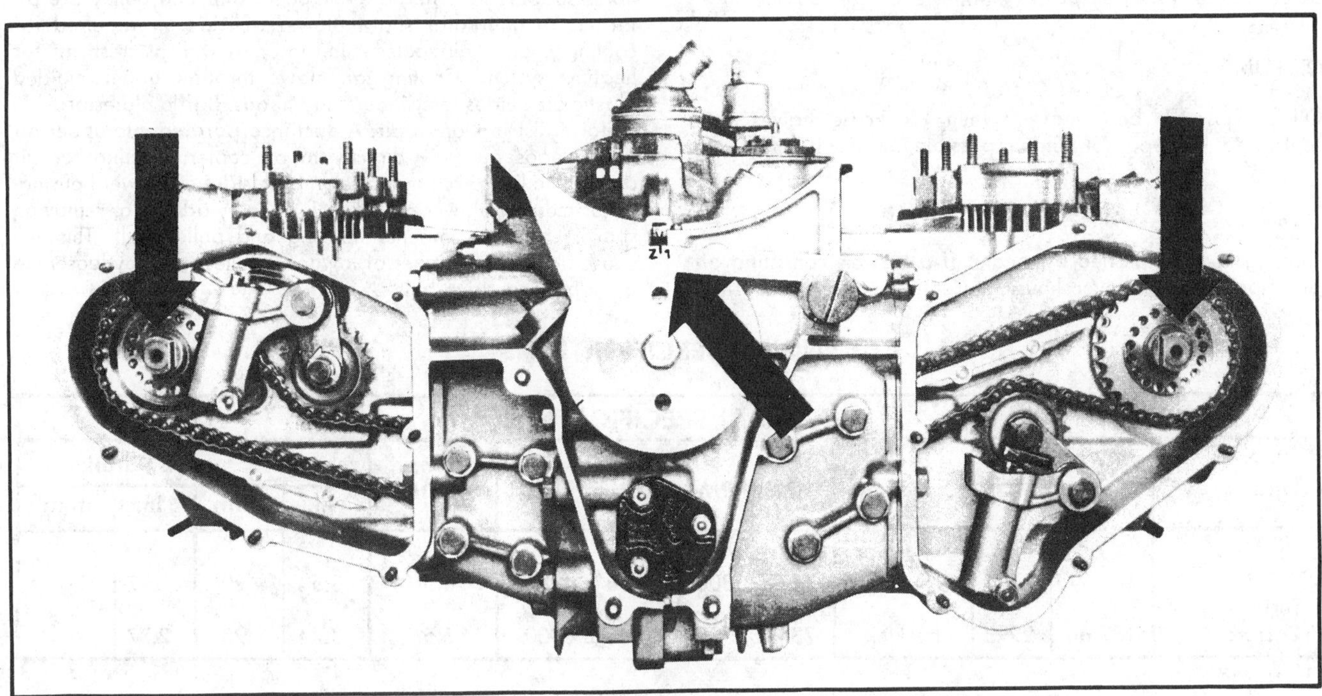

Fig. 13 Head on View of Engine Showing Valve Timing Marks

3) Adjust cylinder No. 1 intake valve clearance to .04" (1 mm). Install a dial indicator with pressure foot resting squarely on valve spring collar. Preload dial indicator to .4" (10 mm) to provide for valve movement.

4) Using a screwdriver, depress chain tensioner on side to be measured and block it with piece of metal. Rotate crankshaft 360° until "Z 1" (TDC) mark is aligned with mark on crankcase. Read dial indicator and compare with measurement given in *Intake Valve Lift Table*.

5) If correct valve opening measurement is not achieved, loosen camshaft nut, remove dowel pin and rotate camshaft until valve is open correct amount. Locate holes which align exactly and install dowel pin. Make sure crankshaft remains on TDC. Rotate crankshaft two complete revoulutions and recheck valve lift, repeat timing procedure if necessary. Repeat procedure on No. 4 cylinder for other side of engine.

Intake Valve Lift

Application	In. (mm)
911 S & Turbo Carrera	.016-.023 (.40-.60)

ENGINE OILING

Oil Capacity – 911 S is 11.6 quarts. Turbo Carrera is 13.7 quarts. Specifications given are total capacities.

Oil Filter – Disposable canister type.

Normal Oil Pressure – 911 S is 73 psi and Carrera is 60 psi @5500 RPM with oil temperature at 175°F.

Pressure Relief Valve – Non-adjustable.

ENGINE OILING SYSTEM

Lubrication is dry sump type. Two independent oil pumps provided for pressure and suction in system. Pressure pump takes oil from an externally mounted oil tank and forces oil to individual oil passages for all main bearings. From main bearings a drilled passage in crankshaft carries oil to connecting rod bearings. Another passage leads to front bearing of intermediate shaft. A passage in intermediate shaft takes oil to rear bearing of shaft.

Camshaft oiling is accomplished by external oil lines leading to camshaft housings. Camshaft housings contain aluminum tubes with holes; three holes of .12" (3.0 mm) diameter carry oil to lubricate camshaft. Six holes of .04" (1.0 mm) diameter splash oil on camshaft lobes. Remaining three holes allow oil to splash against intake valve cover in such a manner that it will drip on rocker arms and valve stems.

Suction pump takes oil from engine sump through a strainer and forces it through oil filter to oil tank. Oil collected in lower part of camshaft housing is returned to crankcase by oil return pipes. Suction pump then returns oil to oil tank. A tube in oil tank carries oil to base of oil tank and filter. The turbo charger is lubricated from a branch off of oil pressure indicator or oil temperature indicator.

Oil pressure regulation is controlled by means of four separate valves. A thermostatically controlled valve directs oil directly to engine when temperature is below 176°F. When temperature is above 176°F, oil flows through oil cooler and then to main bearings. A pressure relief and safety valve located in right crankcase half opens if oil pressure rises above 76.9-99.6 psi and oil is passed directly into crankcase. A safety valve is mounted in left crankcase half immediately after oil pump. It operates in event of a defective pressure relief valve to prevent damage to oil cooler or oil lines. As a safety measure, by-pass valves are built into filter base and filter body. If oil pressure

911 S & TURBO CARRERA 6 CYLINDER (Cont.)

exceeds 28.4 psi, oil by-passes oil filter and flows directly into oil tank.

OIL PUMP

Oil pump may be removed when crankcase halves are separated. No repair of pump is possible, replace if defective.

ENGINE COOLING

Cooling is accomplished by means of a blower, consisting of an impeller and blower housing. Center of blower housing holds support for alternator. Impeller and belt pulley are attached to alternator shaft. Blower delivers air required for cooling engine, oil cooler, alternator as well as fresh air for heating system. Cooling air flows through upper molded plastic air guides to cylinders and heads. Baffle plates provide uniform distribution of air. A duct incorporated into upper air guide leads air flow directly to oil cooler. Ducting for air delivery to heat exchangers is on both sides of blower housing. Adjustment of blower drive belt is done by adding or removing spacers between impeller housing and pulley half. This will cause belt to ride higher of lower on pulley, thereby loosening or tightening drive belt.

ENGINE SPECIFICATIONS

GENERAL SPECIFICATIONS

Year	Displ.		Carburetor	HP at RPM	Torque (Ft. Lbs. at RPM)	Compr. Ratio	Bore		Stroke	
	cu. ins.	cc					in.	mm	in.	mm
1977										
911 S	163.97	2687	Fuel Inj.	157 @5800	168 @4000	8.5:1	3.54	90	2.77	70.4
Turbo Carrera	182.64	2993	Fuel Inj.	234 @5500	245 @4000	6.5:1	3.74	95	2.77	70.4

VALVES

Engine & Valve	Head Diam. In. (mm)	Face Angle	Seat Angle	Seat Width In. (mm)	Stem Diameter In. (mm)	Stem Clearance In. (mm)	Valve Lift In. (mm)
2687 cc							
Intake	1.80-1.81 (45.7-46.0)	45°	45°	.055-.062 (1.4-1.6)	.3526 (8.96)	.....	.....
Exhaust	1.57-1.58 (39.9-40.1)	45°	45°	.055-.062 (1.4-1.6)	.3518 (8.94)	.....	.....
2993 cc							
Intake	1.93-1.94 (49.0-49.3)	25°	45°	.055-.062 (1.4-1.6)	.3526 (8.96)	.....	.....
Exhaust	1.63-1.64 (41.4-41.6)	30°	45°	.055-.062 (1.4-1.6)	.3518 (8.94)	.....	.....

PISTONS, PINS, RINGS

Engine	PISTONS	PINS		RINGS		
	Clearance In. (mm)	Piston Fit In. (mm)	Rod Fit In. (mm)	Rings	End Gap In. (mm)	Side Clearance In. (mm)
2687 cc	.0010-.0018 (.025-.045)	Press Fit	.0007-.0015 (.018-.038)	No. 1	.008-.016 (.20-.40)	.003-.004 (.07-.10)
				No. 2	.006-.014 (.15-.35)	.003-.004 (.07-.10)
				Oil	.006-.014 (.15-.35)	.0008-.002 (.02-.05)
2993 cc	.0020-.0030 (.053-.077)	Press Fit	.0007-.0015 (.018-.038)	No. 1	.004-.008 (.10-.20)	.003-.004 (.07-.10)
				No. 2	.004-.008 (.10-.20)	.001-.003 (.04-.07)
				Oil	.006-.012 (.15-.30)	.0008-.002 (.02-.05)

911 S & TURBO CARRERA 6 CYLINDER (Cont.)

ENGINE SPECIFICATIONS (Cont.)

CRANKSHAFT MAIN & CONNECTING ROD BEARINGS

Engine	MAIN BEARINGS				CONNECTING ROD BEARINGS		
	Journal Diam. In. (mm)	Clearance In. (mm)	Thrust Bearing	Crankshaft End Play In. (mm)	Journal Diam. In. (mm)	Clearance In. (mm)	Side Play In. (mm)
All Engines							
Jrnls 1-7	2.2429-2.2436 (56.97-56.99)	.0003-.0028 (.008-.07)	No. 1	.0043-.0076 (.11-.19)	2.0460-2.0468 (51.97-51.99)	.0011-.0034 (.028-.086)	.....
Jrnl 8	1.219-1.220 (30.96-30.99)	.004 (.10)					

VALVE SPRINGS

Engine	Free Length In. (mm)	①PRESSURE Lbs. @ In. (kg @ mm)	
		Valve Closed	Valve Open
2687 cc			
Intake	.....	1.378 (35)	.....
Exhaust	.....	1.398 (35.5)	....
2993 cc			
Intake	.....	1.319 (33.5)	.....
Exhaust	.....	1.319 (33.5)	.....

① – Measurement given is spring installed height; no pressure specification provided. See *Valve Spring Servicing*.

VALVE TIMING

Engine	INTAKE		EXHAUST	
	Open (BTDC)	Close (ALDC)	Open (BLDC)	Close (ATDC)
2687 cc	6°	50°	24°	2°
2993 cc	3°	37°	29°	3°

TIGHTENING SPECIFICATIONS

Application	Ft. Lbs. (mkg)
Crankcase Joining Bolts	25 (3.5)
Camshaft Housing	18 (2.5)
Main Bearing Caps	25 (3.5)
Flywheel	108 (15)
Connecting Rod Caps	40 (5.5)
Cylinder Head	24 (3.3)
Camshaft Nut	101 (14)
Rocker Arm Shafts	13 (1.8)

924 4 CYLINDER

ENGINE CODING

ENGINE IDENTIFICATION

Engine number is located on left side of crankcase next to the clutch housing. Engine number is coded as follows:

Engine Code Number

Application	1977 Codes	1977½ Codes
924 Federal	XH	XG
924 Calif.	XF	XE

ENGINE, CYLINDER HEAD

ENGINE

Removal – **1**) Disconnect battery cable and remove engine protection plate. Scribe hood at hinges and remove hood. Drain cooling system, remove hoses and expansion tank. Remove fan motors with shroud and alternator cooling hose.

NOTE – *Remove A/C compressor without disconnecting hoses and lay aside.*

2) Disconnect all wiring, hoses, lines, linkage and brackets from engine. Disconnect exhaust pipe at manifold. Support drive line at front brace with wooden block. *See Fig. 1.*

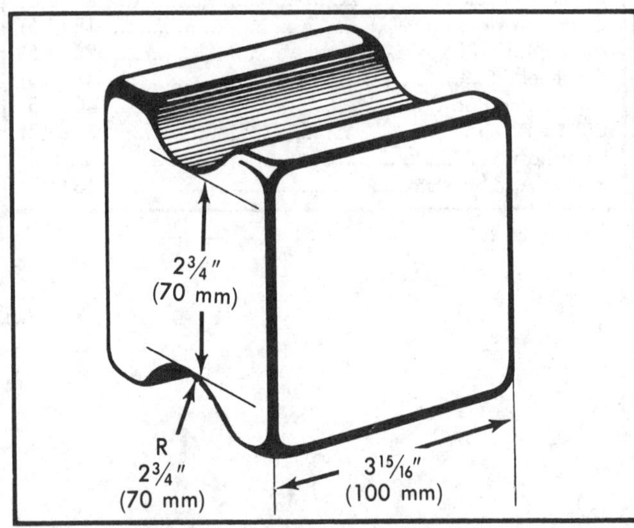

Fig. 1 Drive Line Support Block

3) Disconnect universal joint at steering rack. Disconnect stabilizer bar at frame on both sides and remove crossmember. Attach hoist and lift engine slightly. Remove bellhousing bolts and engine mounts. On vehicles equipped with automatic transmissions, remove bolts from metal/rubber damper. Lift engine carefully and turn at same time.

Installation – To install engine, reverse removal procedure.

CYLINDER HEAD

Removal & Installation – **1**) Disconnect battery ground strap and drain cooling system. Remove hoses and wiring connected to cylinder head. Remove exhaust pipe at manifold and remove camshaft timing belt and "V" belt.

2) Remove cylinder head cover and head bolts in sequence. To install, reverse removal procedures.

NOTE – *Retorque head bolts after 1000 miles (1600 km). Loosen bolts in sequence and retorque to 86 ft. lbs. (12 mkg).*

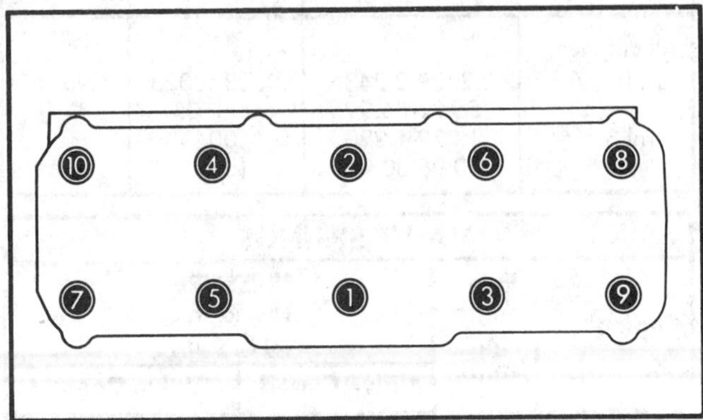

Fig. 2 Cylinder Head Tightening Sequence

VALVES

VALVE ARRANGEMENT

I-E-I-E-I-E-I-E (Front to rear).

VALVE GUIDE SERVICING

NOTE – *At present, there is no procedure for valve guide replacement.*

Measure amount of clearance between valve and valve guide (rock). If wear is excessive, head must be replaced. Intake valve guide maximum clearance is .032" (0.8 mm). Exhaust valve guide maximum clearance is .039" (1.0 mm).

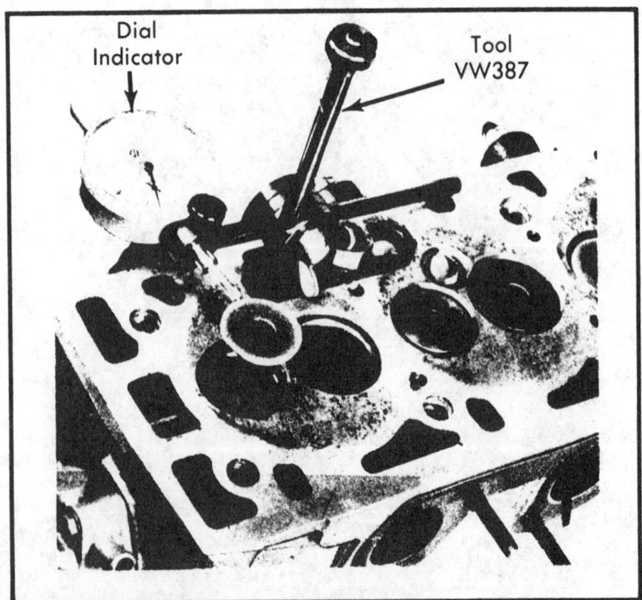

Fig. 3 Measuring Valve Guide Clearance

924 4 CYLINDER (Cont.)

VALVE STEM OIL SEALS

NOTE – *Valve stem oil seal may be replaced with cylinder head installed.*

Remove spark plug on cylinder being serviced, install air hose and adapter to maintain constant pressure in cylinder. Remove camshaft, tappets, valve stem keepers and valve spring. Remove oil seal and discard. To install, reverse removal procedures while noting the following; Be sure plastic sleeve is installed prior to seal installation. Place sleeve on valve stem, lubricate seal and install onto valve stem.

MECHANICAL VALVE LIFTERS

With camshaft removed, lift out tappet and inspect for wear or damage. Oil tappets lightly and replace in original position.

VALVE CLEARANCE ADJUSTMENT

1) Remove cylinder head cover and turn crankshaft until cam lobes of cylinder to be adjusted are pointing upward. Check valve clearance with feeler gauge between tappet and lobe.

Fig. 4 Valve Adjustment

2) Basic valve clearance with engine cold (when reconditioning engine) is .004" (.10 mm) for intake valve and .016" (.40 mm) for exhaust valve. Valve clearance should be checked with engine warmed to 176°F (80°C) oil temperature. Intake valve clearance is .008" (.20 mm) and exhaust clearance is .018" (.45 mm).

3) Adjust clearance by turning screw mounted in tappet with adjusting tool US 8005. Adjustment must be in complete turns only. One turn of screw changes clearance by .002" (.05 mm). After adjusting valve, be sure edge of tappet is in line with green area of tool.

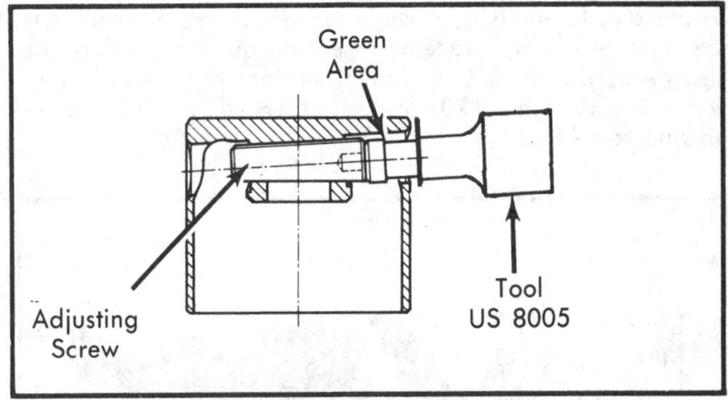

Fig. 5 Valve Lifter Adjustment

PISTONS, PINS & RINGS

OIL PAN

Drain engine oil and loosen left engine mount slightly. Disconnect steering at crossmember and remove crossmember. Remove oil pan bolts and lower oil pan. To install, reverse removal procedure and tighten pan bolts to specifications.

PISTONS & ROD ASSEMBLY

1) Before removing connecting rods, mark rod and cap for installation in original position. Remove rod caps and carefully push piston and rod assembly out top of block.

2) On reassembly of piston and rod assembly, cast bosses on rod and cap must face pulley end of engine. Code numbers must be on same side. Using a suitable ring compressor, install piston and rod assembly with arrow on crown of piston facing front of engine.

FITTING PISTONS

1) Measure cylinder bore .39" (9.9 mm) down from top and up same distance from bottom, also in the center. Take two measurements, one in line with crankshaft and again 90° to crankshaft.

2) Measure piston .63" (16 mm) from bottom of skirt 90° to pin bore. Combine measurements with those taken from cylinder bore. If piston-to-cylinder measurement exceeds .0016" (.04 mm), oversized pistons must be installed.

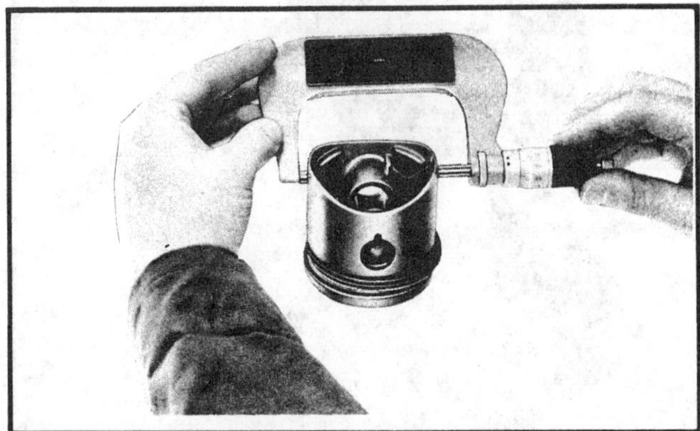

Fig. 6 Measuring Piston Skirt

924 4 CYLINDER (Cont.)

3) Place piston rings squarely in cylinder bore approximately .59" (15 mm) from surface and measure ring gap. If ring side clearance exceeds .039" (1.0 mm), replace rings. Install rings with end gaps offset 120° to each other. Be sure "TOP" mark on ring faces up.

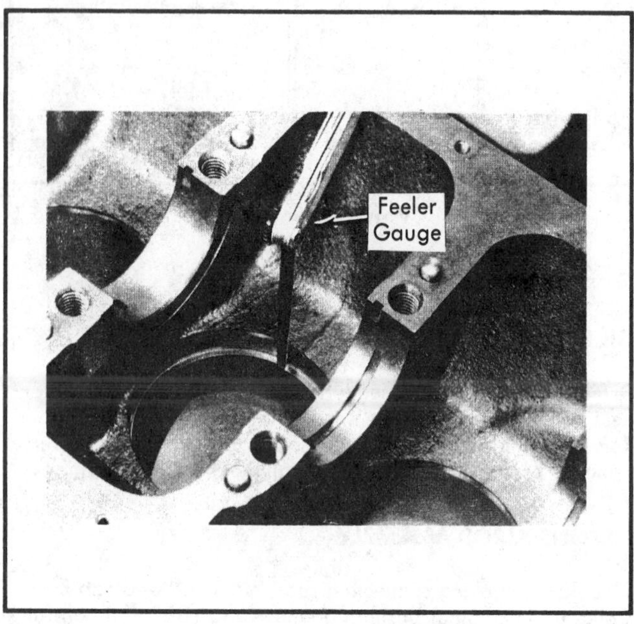

Fig. 7 Measuring Ring Gap

PISTON PINS

Remove circlip and using piston pin remover VW 207c, remove pins. To install, reverse removal procedure.

NOTE — *If pin is hard to install, heat piston to about 65°F (60°C).*

Fig. 8 Piston Pin Removal

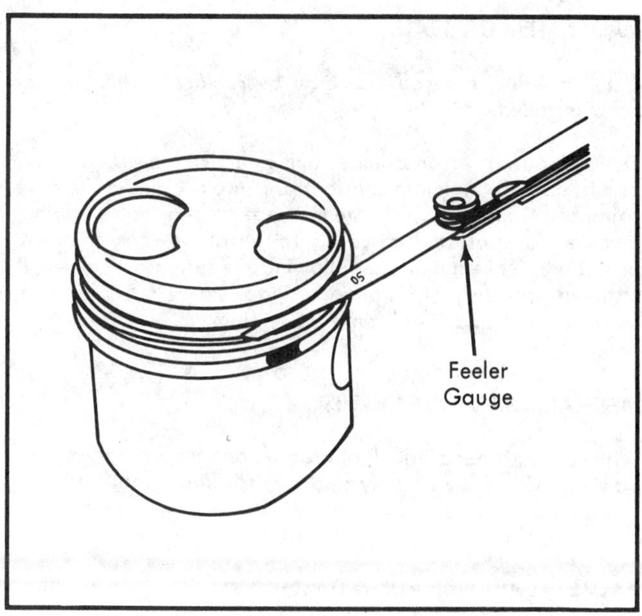

Fig. 9 Piston Ring Side Clearance

CRANKSHAFT MAIN & CONNECTING ROD BEARINGS

MAIN & CONNECTING ROD BEARINGS

1) Push crankshaft toward one end and measure end play at No. 3 thrust bearing. Be sure main bearing caps are marked for reinstallation. Measure connecting rod side play. Remove rod and main bearing caps and check bearing clearance using Plastigage method.

Fig. 10 Measuring Crankshaft End Play

2) Install plain bearing shell into bearing cap. Place grooved shell in block. Do not mix shells. Lubricate bearings and install caps.

924 4 CYLINDER (Cont.)

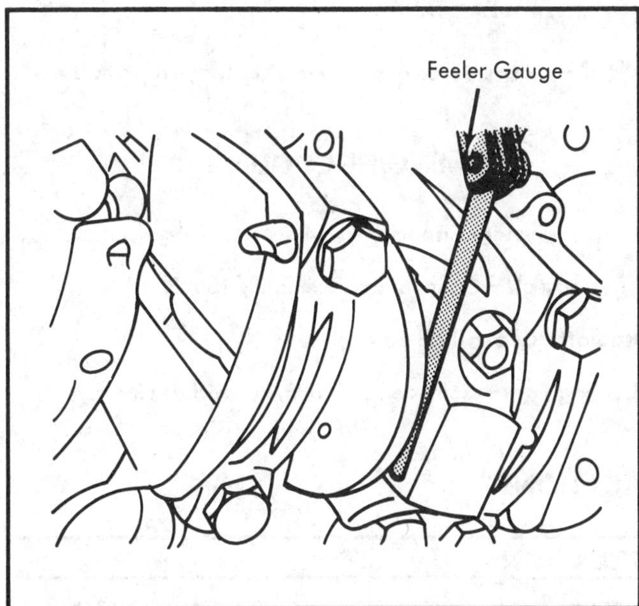

Fig. 11 Measuring Connecting Rod Side Clearance

NOTE — *On No. 5. bearing, coat mating surface of bearing with sealing compound.*

CAMSHAFT

FRONT MAIN BEARING OIL SEAL

Remove pulley bolt and using oil seal removing tool 10-221 (or equivalent), pry oil seal out of oil pump. Use installing tool 2033 to install new seal.

TIMING BELT

Remove belt cover and loosen drive belt tensioner. Remove crankshaft pulley and drive belt pulley. Remove drive belt. To install, reverse removal procedure.

NOTE — *Belt must be tightened until belt can be turned 90° with thumb and index finger at a point midway between crankshaft and camshaft.*

1) Remove "V" belt and toothed belt from engine. Remove cylinder head cover and camshaft lubrication tube. Remove distributor and distributor drive.

NOTE — *Reinstall nuts handtight after tube has been removed.*

2) Remove bearing caps 1, 3 and 5 then carefully, in a crosswise pattern, release bearing caps on 2 and 4.

3) To install camshaft, reverse removal procedure and note the following; Place camshaft into position and install caps 2 and 4 again using a crosswise pattern. Install caps 1, 3 and 5 and tighten all nuts to specifications. Loosen nuts 2 and 4 to install lubrication tube.

NOTE — *Make sure that bore is not off center when installing caps. Position caps to check correct position.*

VALVE TIMING

1) Set dot on camshaft sprocket in line with pointer on cylinder head cover. Notch on crankshaft pulley must be in line with adjusting lug on oil pump housing.

Fig. 12 Camshaft Sprocket Alignment

NOTE — *It is also possible to work with TDC mark on flywheel.*

2) Adjust valves as previously outlined. Use timing light to check ignition and valve timing.

ENGINE OILING

Crankcase Capacity — 4.7 qts. Add approximately 1 pt. with filter.

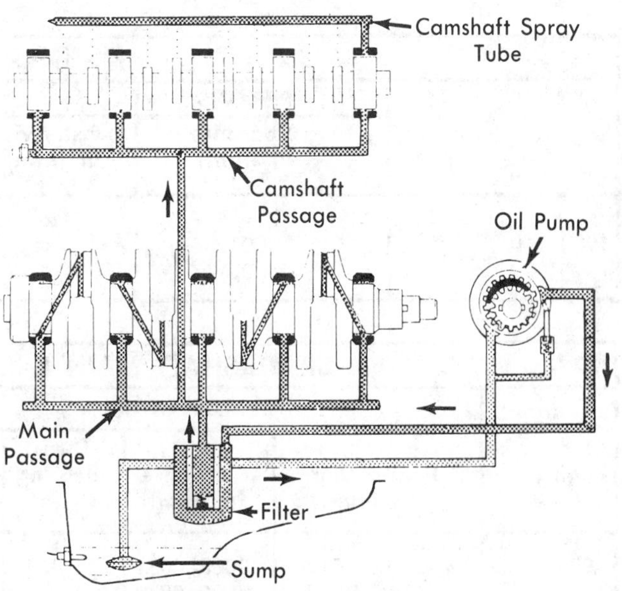

Fig. 13 Engine Oiling System

924 4 CYLINDER (Cont.)

Oil Filter — Spin-on type. Change at first oil change and every other one thereafter.

Oil Pressure — 73-101@5000 RPM.

ENGINE OILING SYSTEM

The engine oiling system is full pressure with rotary (sickle) type pump. Oil is picked up by pump through strainer and suction tube. Oil passes through pump and pressure control valve to oil filter and main oil channels. It is then distributed to main bearings, connecting rods and crankshaft. Camshaft lubrication is provided by spray tube at No. 1 cam bearing. Oil pressure switch is located at end of camshaft lubrication passage. A temperature sensor is located in oil pan.

OIL PUMP

Oil pump is sickle type gear driven directly by crankshaft.

ENGINE COOLING

Cooling System Capacity — 7.4 qts.

Thermostat — Opens at approximately 180°F.

Radiator Cap — 12.8-16.4 psi.

Cooling Fan — Comes on at 198°F, goes off at 189°F.

ENGINE SPECIFICATIONS

GENERAL SPECIFICATIONS

Year	Displ.		Carburetor	HP at RPM	Torque (Ft. Lbs. at RPM)	Compr. Ratio	Bore		Stroke	
	cu. ins.	cc					in.	mm	in.	mm
1977	121	1984	Fuel Inj.	95@5500	109@3000	8.0-1	3.41	86.5	3.32	84.4
1977½	121	1984	Fuel Inj.	110@5750	111@3500	8.5-1	3.41	86.5	3.32	84.4

VALVES

Engine & Valve	Head Diam. In. (mm)	Face Angle	Seat Angle	Seat Width In. (mm)	Stem Diameter In. (mm)	Stem Clearance In. (mm)	Valve Lift In. (mm)
All							
Int.	①1.496 (38)	45°	45°	.087-.118 (2.2-3.0)	.3532 (8.97)	.0157 (0.4)	.....
Exh.	1.299 (33)	45°	45°	.087-.118 (2.2-3.0)	.3524 (8.95)	.020 (0.5)	.....

① — 1977½ Head Diameter 1.575" (40 mm).

PISTONS, PINS, RINGS

Engine	PISTONS	PINS		RINGS		
	Clearance In. (mm)	Piston Fit In. (mm)	Rod Fit In. (mm)	Rings	End Gap In. (mm)	Side Clearance In. (mm)
1984 cc	.0012 (.03)	.....	.0004-.0008 (.01-.02)	.....	.012-.020 (.3-.5)	.0016-.0028 (.04-.07)

CRANKSHAFT MAIN & CONNECTING ROD BEARINGS

Engine	MAIN BEARINGS				CONNECTING ROD BEARINGS		
	Journal Diam. In. (mm)	Clearance In. (mm)	Thrust Bearing	Crankshaft End Play In. (mm)	Journal Diam. In. (mm)	Clearance In. (mm)	Side Play In. (mm)
1984 cc	2.518-2.519 (63.95-63.97)	.0008-.0031 (.02-.08)	3	.0020-.0012 (.05-.08)	1.888-1.889 (47.95-47.97)	.0008-.003 (.02-.07)	.004-.007 (.1-.19)

924 4 CYLINDER (Cont.)

ENGINE SPECIFICATIONS (Cont.)

CAMSHAFT			
Engine	Journal Diam. In. (mm)	Clearance In. (mm)	Lobe Lift In. (mm)
1984 cc	1.0236-1.0245 (26.00-26.02)	.002-.006 (.06-.061)	.....

VALVE TIMING				
	INTAKE		EXHAUST	
Engine	Open (BTDC)	Close (ALDC)	Open (BLDC)	Close (ATDC)
1984 cc	5°	37°	43°	7°
①	4°	44°	44°	4°

① – 1977½.

TIGHTENING SPECIFICATIONS	
Application	Ft. Lbs. (mkg)
Cylinder Head Bolts	①
Cold	72 (10)
Warm	86 (12)
Main Bearing Caps	58 (8)
No 5 Allen Head Bolt	47 (6.5)
Connecting Rod Nuts	43 (6)
Flywheel	65 (9)
Crankshaft Pulley	180 (25)
Oil Pan Bolts	
(M 6)	6 (.8)
(M 8)	11 (1.5)
Exhaust Manifold	18 (2.5)
Intake Manifold	17 (2.4)
Camshaft Bearing Caps	13-18 (1.8-2.5)

① – Bolts must be retorqued after 1000 miles (1600 Km). Loosen bolts in sequence about 30° and retorque to 86 ft. lbs. (12 mkg).

R-5 4 CYLINDER

ENGINE IDENTIFICATION

Type of vehicle and engine number is marked on a number plate riveted to the left rear side of the engine block. Plate is located just below cylinder head mating surface. First five digits indicate engine type.

Engine Identification

Application	Engine Code
R-5 (1228)	810-28

ENGINE, CYLINDER HEAD & MANIFOLDS

ENGINE

NOTE — *Engine and transaxle are removed as an assembly.*

Removal — **1)** Remove battery. Drain coolant from engine and radiator. Drain oil. Take out grille. Remove hood and inner fender support. Remove air cleaner.

2) Disconnect all electrical leads, control cables, vacuum lines and coolant hoses that might interfere with engine removal. Mark each item as it is disconnected. Remove transaxle cover.

3) Remove exhaust pipe flange. Remove radiator mounting nuts. Lift out radiator, cooling fan, and expansion tank. Disconnect steering shaft at flexible coupling. Do not lose rubber bushing.

4) Remove front wheels and place calipers out of way. Disconnect tie rods at rack. Use suitable tool and separate upper ball joints. Remove steering gear box. Be sure to index steering box shims.

5) Remove air pump complete with bracket. Remove top transaxle bolts on bell housing. Attach hydraulic hoist to engine. Remove nuts from engine mounts. Remove shift rod support bolts.

6) Disconnect clutch cable. Remove front transaxle mounting bracket. Slide transaxle to left, then to right to free axle drive shafts. Remove engine assembly from vehicle.

Installation — To install, reverse removal procedure and note: Grease transaxle input shaft and axle drive shafts. Do not damage oil seals on axle drive shafts. Make sure axle drive shafts fully seat. Adjust clutch. Refit steering rubber bushing. Bleed cooling system.

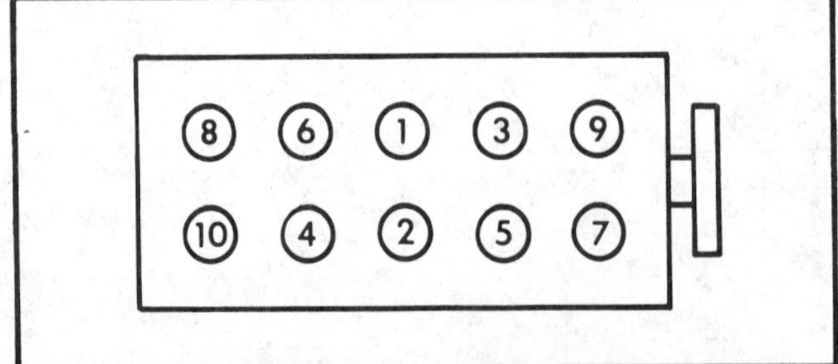

Fig. 1 Cylinder Head Tightening Sequence

INTAKE/EXHAUST MANIFOLD

Removal — Disconnect battery. Remove air filter hose. Disconnect and plug carburetor heating hose. Disconnect choke, accelerator, fuel lines and vacuum lines. Take off carburetor. Separate exhaust pipe. Remove manifold nuts and starter heat shield. Pull manifold from engine.

NOTE — *It may be necessary to remove nut on left engine mount and tilt engine to right to gain enough clearance for removal.*

Installation — To install, reverse removal procedure and replace all gaskets.

CYLINDER HEAD

Removal — **1)** Disconnect battery. Drain cooling system. Remove air cleaner. Disconnect all hoses, vacuum lines, wires, and cables from cylinder head. Loosen air pump and take off belt. Disconnect exhaust pipe at manifold.

2) Disconnect hood lock control cable, place out of way. Take off valve cover. Remove cylinder head bolts; only loosen bolt next to distributor ½ turn. Tap head until free. Remove bolt and head.

Installation — To install cylinder head, reverse removal procedure and note: Make sure new head gasket is installed with "HAUT-TOP" facing up.

VALVES

VALVE ARRANGEMENT

E-I-I-E-E-I-I-E

VALVE GUIDE SERVICING

1) Measure worn guide and replace with nearest oversize. Standard valve guide diameter is .433" (11 mm). First oversize is .437" (11.10 mm) and is identified by one groove mark. Second oversize is .443" (11.25 mm) and is identified by two groove marks.

2) Ream valve guide hole in head to accept new guide. Size of reamer must be equal to outside diameter of new valve guide. To install new guide, lightly lubricate with oil. Fit guide to press with chamfer facing out. Seat guide completely in head. Finish ream valve guide bore to accept valve.

VALVE SPRINGS

Removal, Cylinder Head Installed — Remove valve cover. Remove spark plug of cylinder requiring work. Loosen rocker arm as far as possible and remove push rod. Fit valve retaining tool in spark plug hole. Compress valve spring. Remove keepers, top cup, spring, and base washer. Check spring at free length and under a load.

Installation — Reverse removal procedure and note: Make sure valve spring is installed with closest coil spacing toward cylinder head.

R-5 4 CYLINDER (Cont.)

ROCKER SHAFT

After cleaning rocker shaft components, remove clips and take off springs, rocker arms, and support bearings. End plugs are press fit and cannot be removed. For correct reassembly sequence refer to *Fig. 2*.

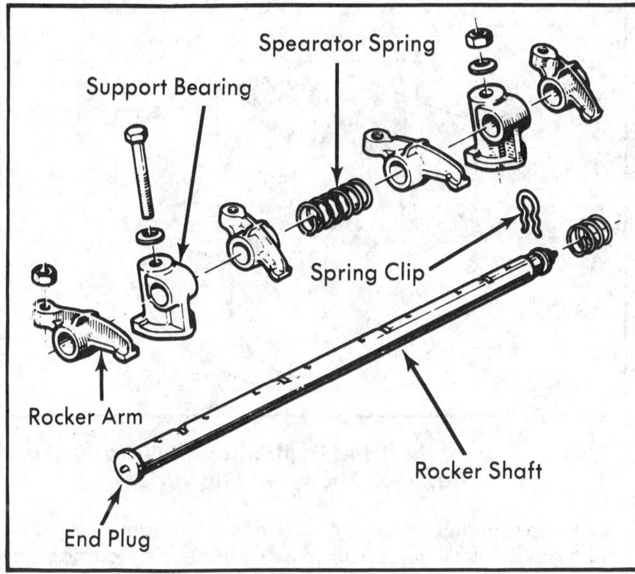

Fig. 2 Rocker Arm Assembly. Illustration Shows Detail of Rocker Shaft Reassembly Sequence

VALVE CLEARANCE

Set intake valve clearance (cold) to .006" (.15 mm) and exhaust valve clearance (cold) to .008" (.25 mm). Use table for valve adjusting sequence.

Valve Adjusting Sequence

Valve Open	Valve to Adjust
No. 1 Exhaust	No 3 Int. & No. 4 Exh.
No. 3 Exhaust	No. 4 Int. & No. 2 Exh.
No. 4 Exhaust	No. 2 Int. & No. 1 Exh.
No. 2 Exhaust	No. 1 Int & No. 3 Exh.

PISTONS, PINS & RINGS

OIL PAN

Removal – 1) Drain oil. Remove sway bar "U" brackets and pull bar down. Remove lower transaxle metal cover. Remove transaxle bolts that mount through gear shift bracket. Clutch protective cover must be removed.

2) Place a jack under front of transaxle to support it. Remove front pad. Raise transaxle front. Remove mounting bolts and tilt pan toward back of vehicle. Rotate crankshaft to provide clearance. Clean gasket surfaces.

Installation – To install, reverse removal procedure and note: Apply gasket sealer to rubber gaskets. Make sure pan side gaskets overlap bearing gaskets.

CYLINDER LINERS

Removal – 1) Disconnect battery. Drain cooling system and oil pan. Remove air cleaner, cylinder head, oil pan, and oil pump. Fit liner clamp on head.

2) Index connecting rods and bearing caps. Remove connecting rod caps and bearings. Remove liner clamp and liner-piston-rod assembly.

NOTE – *Before installing pistons in liners, protrusion of liner above cylinder block must be measured without seal.*

Installation – 1) Check liner protrusion with special tools (Mot. 252 and 251). *See Fig. 3.* Make measurement at two points. Subtract the larger measurement from .005" (.12 mm) to determine correct seal thickness.

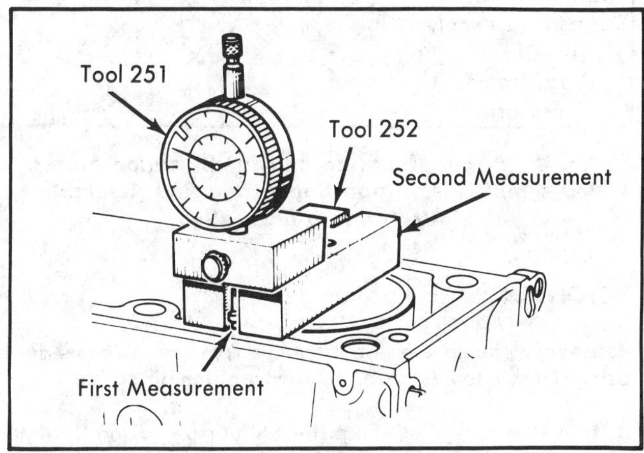

Fig. 3 Using Special Tool Mot. 251 and 252 to Check Cylinder Liner Protrusion. Make Sure Measurement is Made in TWO Places.

2) Seals are available in .003" (.08 mm), .004" (.10 mm), and .005" (.12 mm). Each liner may require a different seal thickness. Fit seal, install liner assembly and recheck measurement.

3) Lubricate bearings and replace connecting rod caps. Place liner-piston-connecting rod assemblies into block. Make sure No. 1 is at clutch end. Number on connecting rod bearing end is on opposite side of camshaft. Arrow on piston must face flywheel. Reverse removal procedure for remaining components.

PISTON & ROD ASSEMBLY

Removal – Remove piston and rod assembly from block with cylinder liners. See *Cylinder Liners*. Remove piston out bottom of liner. Take off rings, piston pin, and connecting rod. See *Piston Pins*.

R-5 4 CYLINDER (Cont.)

Installation – Fit piston pin. Fit rings. Piston rings are pre-gapped. Assemble with "o" mark or "Top" facing up. Lubricate connecting rod assemblies with oil and fit to liner. Make sure machined side of connecting rod bearing is parallel with flat edge on liner top.

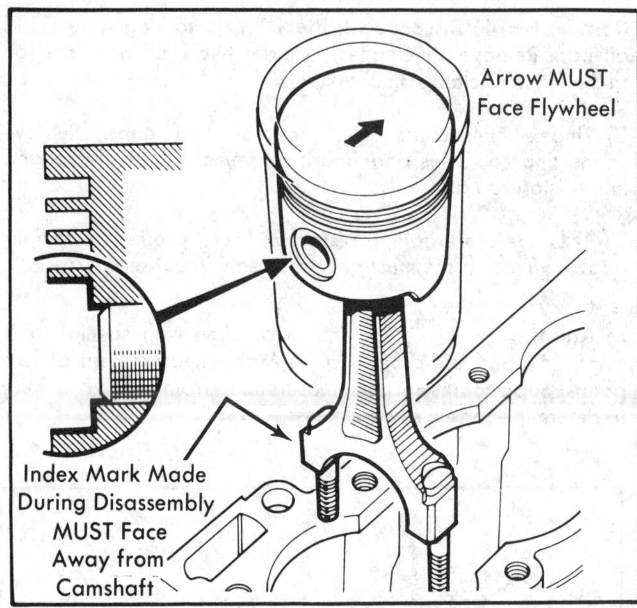

Fig. 4 Piston Mounting and Identification Marks. Reassemble Piston and Connecting Rod Assemblies According to Illustration

PISTON PIN

Removal – Remove piston assembly from liner. Remove rings. Using suitable tool (Mot. 574), extract piston pin.

Installation – **1)** Position piston with arrow facing flywheel. Index mark made during removal on connecting rod must face away from camshaft.

2) Heat connecting rod to 482° F (250° C). Slide new piston over installing mandrel and screw in locating plug (part of tool kit Mot. 574). Lightly oil piston pin. Push mandrel, pin guide, and pin assembly through piston by hand, until piston pin makes contact with rod. This procedure will automatically center and correctly space pin.

CRANKSHAFT MAIN & CONNECTING ROD BEARINGS

MAIN BEARING SERVICE

1) Remove cylinder head and oil pan. Invert engine. Remove connecting rod bearing caps. Mark position of main bearing to block. Remove main bearing caps. Remove crankshaft, upper main bearings, and thrust washers.

2) Use a micrometer and measure crankshaft journals. If any main bearing journal is worn beyond 2.148" (54.55 mm) or any connecting rod journal beyond 1.721" (43.71 mm), crankshaft must be reground and fitted with oversize bearings.

NOTE – *Connecting rod journals are roll hardened. Make sure roll hardening remains intact over a 140° section facing rotational centerline of crankshaft.*

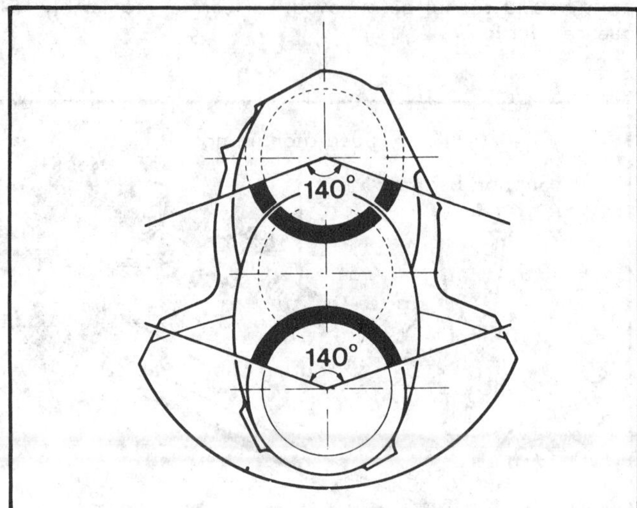

Fig. 5 Crankshaft MUST Maintain Roll Hardened Surfaces as Shown in Illustration

3) Fit upper main bearings. Nos. 1 and 3 are same. Nos. 2, 4, and 5 have two oil holes. Lubricate main bearing journals and fit crankshaft into position. Fit thrust washers, white metal toward crankshaft. Fit bearing to main bearing caps (those with no oil holes). Fit caps being sure to align with previously made reference marks.

4) Fit upper connecting rod bearings and slide over crankshaft. Fit lower half of bearing in cap, then tighten cap. Make sure crankshaft is free to turn.

5) Use a dial indicator and check crankshaft end play. Crankshaft should not have more than .002-.009" (.05-.23 mm) end play. Replace thrust washers if end play is beyond specification.

REAR MAIN BEARING OIL SEAL

With New Crankshaft – Fit new seal to tool Mot. 259-01 (or equivalent). Lubricate outer seal lip. Install seal in original position, seating it until tool lip just contacts cylinder block.

With Original Crankshaft – Offset new seal approximately ⅛" (3 mm) to position seal so it does not rest in same place original seal did. Drive seal into place with tool Mot 259-01 (or equivalent). Seal is seated when tool edge just touches block. Remove tool, insert ⅛" thick spacer, and repeat seating process. This will correctly seat seal into position.

CAMSHAFT

TIMING CHAIN

Removal – With engine removed and suitably supported, remove timing cover and chain tensioner. *NOTE – Tensioner does not have to be removed, it can be wired out of way.* Remove camshaft sprocket lock bolt. Use puller (B. Vi. 28) and remove camshaft sprocket with timing chain. Chain will come off without disturbing crankshaft sprocket.

R-5 4 CYLINDER (Cont.)

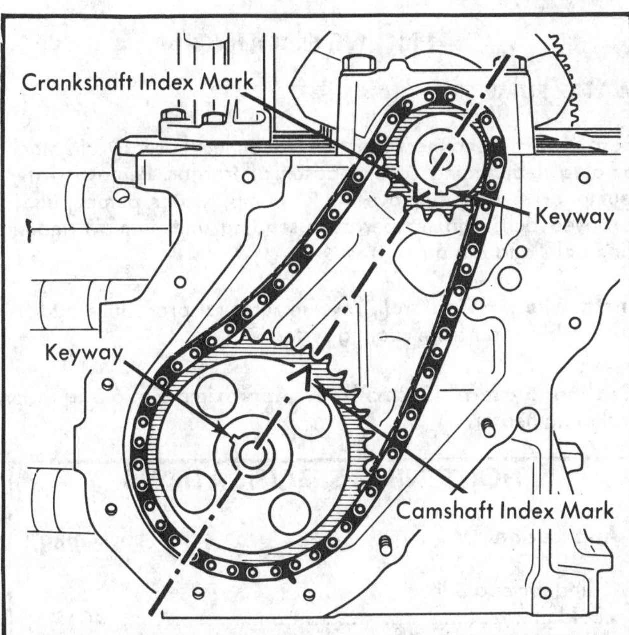

Fig. 6 Installing Timing Chain Keeping Camshaft and Crankshaft Reference Marks Properly Aligned. Also, Note Positions of Crankshaft and Camshaft Keyways. Illustration Does Not Show Timing Chain Tensioner, See Figure 7

Installation – 1) Position chain on camshaft sprocket. Align camshaft reference mark with one on crankshaft. Note position of of camshaft and crankshaft keyway shown in *Fig. 6*. Using a small Allen wrench, activate tensioner mechanism.

2) Refit chain tensioner with thrust plate. Tighten mounting bolts and release load on automatic wear compensator tensioner. Release load by pressing down on bottom of tensioner body. Install new timing chain tensioner.

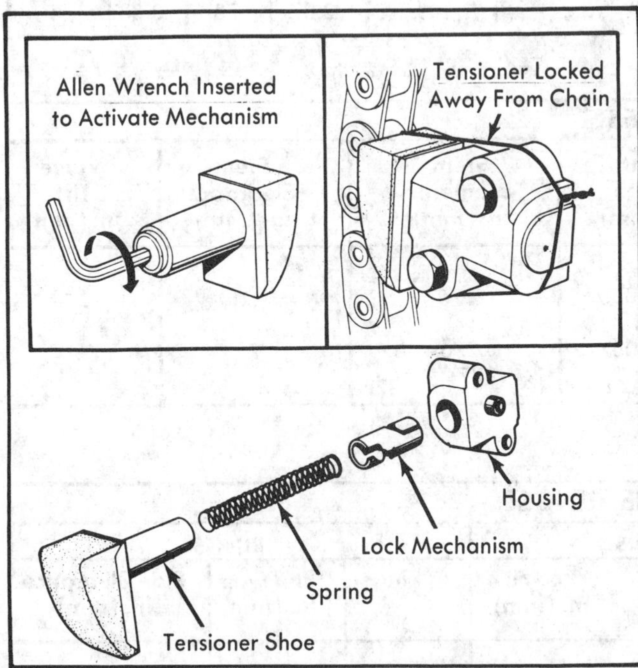

Fig. 7 Sequence of Automotive Wear Compensator Timing Chain Tensioner

CAMSHAFT

Removal – Remove engine and suitably support on stand. Remove cylinder head, distributor drive gear, oil pan, timing chain cover, and timing chain. Work through access slots in camshaft sprocket and remove two flange bolts. Carefully slide camshaft from engine.

Installation – Check clearance between camshaft sprocket and flange. Clearance must not exceed .002-.005" (.05-.12 mm). Lubricate camshaft journals and lobes, then refit camshaft. Install flange and tighten. Refit sprocket and tighten mounting bolt. Make sure all camshaft and crankshaft alignment marks are matched. See *Fig. 6*. Reverse removal procedure for remaining components.

CAMSHAFT OIL SEAL

NOTE – *Camshaft oil seal can be changed without removing engine.*

Removal – Remove air cleaner, air pump, pump support, and drive belt. Remove serrated pulley from camshaft. Insert tool Mot. 500-01 (or equivalent) until lip of oil seal slips over shoulder of tool. Push tool sleeve in. Tighten tool bolt clockwise until seal is removed.

Installation – Slip sleeve of tool over end of camshaft to spread lip of seal. Lubricate seal and slide over sleeve. Using oil seal inserting tool (part of tool Mot. 500-01), press seal inward until it just touches block. Remove sleeve. Screw threaded rod into camshaft with nut and washer at rod end. Tighten nut until tool just meets clutch housing. Replace remaining components in reverse of removal procedure.

ENGINE OILING

Crankcase Capacity – 3¼ quarts without filter change. 3½ quarts with filter change.

Oil Filter – Disposable canister type.

Normal Oil Pressure – 10 psi at idle speed. 50 psi at 4000 RPM.

OIL PUMP

Removal – Drain oil. Remove oil pan. Take out three bolts mounting oil pump and remove pump.

Disassembly – Remove four pump cover bolts. Remove cover slowly; relief valve is under spring tension. Remove driven gear, drive gear, and drive gear shaft.

Inspection – Examine splines on drive shaft. Check ball seat for damage. Check pressure relief spring for fatigue. Check clearance between gears and body. Replace gears if clearance exceeds .008" (.2 mm).

Reassembly – Reverse disassembly procedure.

Installation – Install pump, do not use gasket between oil pump and block. Tighten mounting bolts.

R-5 4 CYLINDER (Cont.)

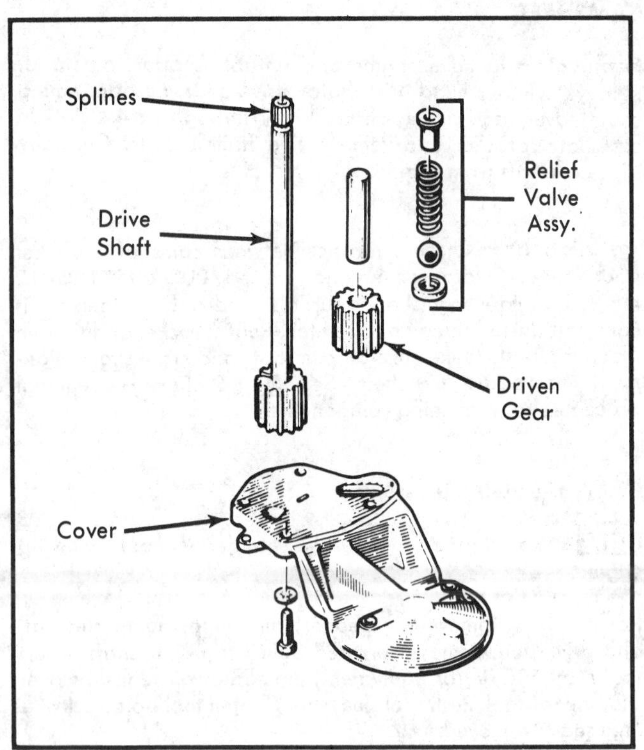

Fig. 8 Exploded View of Oil Pump Assembly

ENGINE COOLING

WATER PUMP

Removal – Disconnect battery. Disconnect hoses. Drain block at plug near timing cover. Loosen alternator. Remove water pump drive belt. Remove A.I.R. pump, water pump pulley, grooved belt, and temperature sending unit. Remove mounting bolts and tap pump free.

Installation – To install, reverse removal procedure and be sure to bleed air from cooling system.

Cooling System Capacity – Approximately 6.5 quarts, including heater.

TIGHTENING SPECIFICATIONS	
Application	**Ft. Lbs. (mkg)**
Cylinder Head Bolts	
Cold	40 (5.5)
Hot (After cooling 50 minutes)	45 (6.2)
Connecting Rods	35 (4.8)
Main Bearings	40-50 (5.5-6.9)
Manifolds	10 (1.4)
Rocker Arm Shaft	10-15 (1.4-2.1)
Timing Sprocket-to-Camshaft	20 (2.8)

ENGINE SPECIFICATIONS

GENERAL SPECIFICATIONS

Year	Displ.		Carburetor	HP at RPM	Torque (Ft. Lbs. at RPM)	Compr. Ratio	Bore		Stroke	
	cu. ins.	cc					in.	mm	in.	mm
1977	78.66	1289	1x2-Bbl.	.....	.....	8.5-1	2.87	73	3.03	77

VALVES

Engine & Valve	Head Diam. In. (mm)	Face Angle	Seat Angle	Seat Width In. (mm)	Stem Diameter In. (mm)	Stem Clearance In. (mm)	Valve Lift In. (mm)
1289							
Int.	1.319 (33.g)	45°	45°	.043-.055 (1.1-1.4)	.276 (7)	.....	.....
Exh.	1.193 (30.3)	45°	45°	.055-.067 (1.4-1.7)	.276 (7)	.....	.....

PISTONS, PINS, RINGS

Engine	PISTONS	PINS		RINGS		
	Clearance In. (mm)	Piston Fit In. (mm)	Rod Fit In. (mm)	Rings	End Gap In. (mm)	Side Clearance In. (mm)
1289	.....	Free Fit	Press Fit	.....	①	.....

① – Pre-set gap; do not alter.

R-5 4 CYLINDER (Cont.)

ENGINE SPECIFICATIONS (Cont.)

CRANKSHAFT MAIN & CONNECTING ROD BEARINGS							
	MAIN BEARINGS				CONNECTING ROD BEARINGS		
Engine	Journal Diam. In. (mm)	Clearance In. (mm)	Thrust Bearing	Crankshaft End Play In. (mm)	Journal Diam. In. (mm)	Clearance In. (mm)	Side Play In. (mm)
1289	2.157 (54.80)	.....	No. 3	.002-.009 (.05-.23)	1.731 (43.96)	.....	.012-.022 (.31-.57)

CAMSHAFT			
Engine	Journal Diam. In. (mm)	Clearance In. (mm)	Lobe Lift In. (mm)
1289	.....	①	.....

① — End play .002-.005" (.05-.122 mm).

VALVE TIMING				
	INTAKE		EXHAUST	
Engine	Open (BTDC)	Close (ALDC)	Open (BLDC)	Close (ATDC)
1289	22°	62°	65°	25°

VALVE SPRINGS			
Engine	Free Length In. (mm)	PRESSURE Lbs. @ In. (kg @ mm)	
		Valve Closed	Valve Open
1289	1.65 (42)	.....	80@1.0 (36@25)

R-12 & R-17 4 CYLINDER

ENGINE CODING

ENGINE IDENTIFICATION

Engine number and type are given on a plate which is riveted to left side of engine block. Number is located just below cylinder head mating surface. First five digits indicate engine type.

Engine Codes

Application	Engine Code
R-12	
Man. Trans.	843-10
Auto. Trans.	843-11
R-17GTL	843-16
R-17 Gordini	843-13

ENGINE, CYLINDER HEAD & MANIFOLDS

ENGINE

1) Disconnect battery, remove hood and drain cooling system. Disconnect all water hoses, electrical leads, vacuum lines and fuel lines. Remove radiator, starter, camshaft pulley and drive belt.

2) Remove top engine-transmission mounting bolt(s). Remove tensioner, fan belt, crankshaft pulley, fuel inlet line, and fan. Disconnect exhaust pipe from manifold and transmission crossmember. Remove clutch shield.

3) Attach suitable hoist (Mot. 477) and take up engine weight. From left and right side, remove engine side mounts and bracket.

4) Raise engine until top of transmission just meets underside of steering crossmember. Suitably support transmission and remove two bottom engine-transmission assembly bolts. Remove engine from vehicle. To install, reverse removal procedure.

INTAKE MANIFOLD

Disconnect battery and drain cooling system. Remove air filter and throttle linkage. Disconnect all necessary hoses, lines and electrical wires. Remove manifold nuts and remove manifold. To install, reverse removal procedure.

CYLINDER HEAD

Removal – 1) Disconnect battery, drain cooling system and remove air filter. Disconnect all necessary water hoses, electrical wires and cable linkage. Remove distributor, alternator (with drive belt) and valve cover.

2) Remove water pump drive belt. Disconnect exhaust pipe at manifold and place out of way. Remove rubber rings and cups from spark plug tubes.

3) Loosen rocker arm adjusting screws and remove push rods. Remove cylinder head bolts and remove rocker arm assembly. Loosen cylinder head by tapping with a plastic hammer to rotate cylinder head in counterclockwise direction.

NOTE – *If cylinder head is stuck, it will be necessary to pivot head on locating dowel on distributor side.*

4) Lift cylinder head slightly and remove tappets, keeping them in order. Remove cylinder head. Install liner clamps to prevent any movement of liners.

Installation – 1) Remove liner clamp. Make sure all cylinder head bolt holes in block are free of excess oil so torque will not be affected. Check cylinder liner protrusion. See *Cylinder Liners*. New cylinder head gasket must be installed DRY.

2) Install locating studs. If proper equipment is not available for alignment, use hole just back of timing chain. Distributor gear alignment is dependent on correct cylinder head installation.

3) Install tappets in cylinder head and place head into position. Tap lightly to hold in place. Place rocker arm assembly in position and remove locating studs (if used). Install lubricated head bolts. Adjust valves. Install remaining components in reverse of removal procedure.

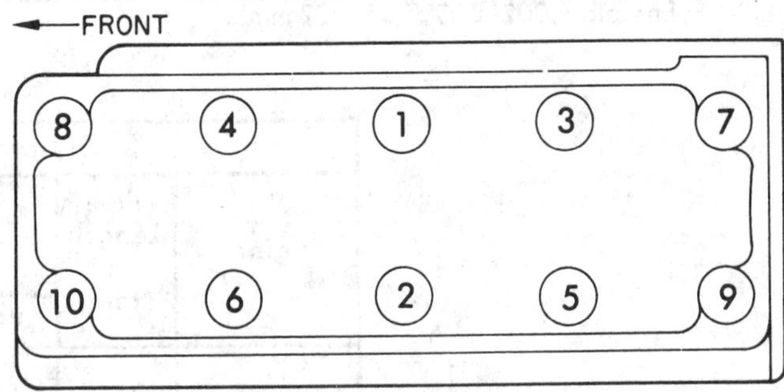

Fig. 1 Cylinder Head Tightening Sequence

VALVES

VALVE ARRANGEMENT (R-17)

Right Side - All Exhaust
Left Side - All Intake

VALVE ARRANGEMENT (R-12)

E-I-I-E-E-I-I-E

VALVE GUIDE SERVICING

1) Remove cylinder head and place on suitable support. **NOTE** – *Valve guide angles is 20° for both intake and exhaust valves.*

2) Measure worn guide and replace with the nearest oversize. Standard valve guide diameter is .512" (13 mm). First oversize guide is .516" (13.10 mm) and is identified by one index mark. The second oversize guide is .522" (13.25 mm) and is identified by two index marks.

3) Turn cylinder head over, and using suitable reamer, ream bore in head to accept new guide. Lubricate new valve guide and install with chamfer facing outward. Using suitable reamer, ream valve guide bore. **NOTE** – *After replacing valve guide, ream corresponding valve seat.*

R-12 & R-17 4 CYLINDER (Cont.)

VALVE SPRINGS

Cylinder Head Installed – **1)** Disconnect battery and remove valve cover. Bring piston to TDC and remove push rod corresponding to spring requiring maintenance.

2) Using suitable tool (Mot.382), compress valve spring and remove retainer, top cup, and spring. Spring can now be further checked. To install, reverse removal procedure.

NOTE – *Valve springs must be fitted with larger coil spacing toward cylinder head.*

Cylinder Head Removed – Using suitable tool (U43P), compress valve spring and remove keepers, top cups, springs and base washers. To install, reverse removal procedure.

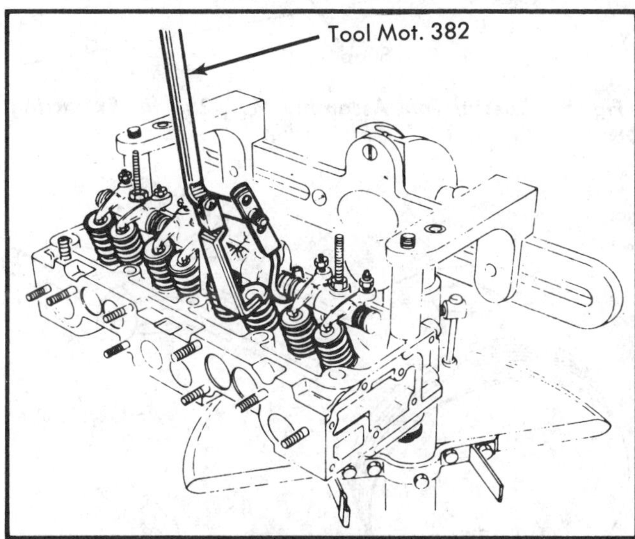

Fig. 2 How to Position Valve Spring Removal Tool on Cylinder Head

ROCKER ARM ASSEMBLY

After disassembling, cleaning, and inspecting rocker shaft components, ensure they are properly reassembled (see illustration). Correct order is: rocker shaft bracket, rocker arm, spring, and rocker arm. Align rocker shaft with oil holes facing push rod side. Bracket holes must line up with holes in rocker shaft.

VALVE TAPPET SERVICE

1) With tappets removed, thoroughly clean tappets and tappet bores in cylinder head. Check clearance between tappets and cylinder head bores.

2) If clearance is excessive, tappet bores must be reamed for oversize tappets. Tappets are available in .008" (.20 mm) oversize. Ream tappet bores to .480" (12.2 mm) if installing new tappets.

VALVE CLEARANCE

With engine cold adjust intake valve clearance to .008" (.2 mm) and exhaust valve clearance to .010" (.25 mm) on all models except Gordini. Adjust intake valve to .010" (.25 mm) and exhaust valve to .012" (.3 mm) on Gordini models.

PISTONS, PINS & RINGS

OIL PAN REMOVAL

Raise vehicle and drain crankcase. Extract oil pan bolts and ease pan from its position. It may be necessary to remove clutch shield. To install, reverse removal procedure.

NOTE – *Ensure oil pan contact surface is scraped clean before installing new gasket.*

CYLINDER LINERS

Removal – **1)** Disconnect battery and drain cooling system and oil pan. Remove cylinder head and install liner clamps. See *Cylinder Head*. Remove oil pan and oil pump.

2) Mark connecting rods on cam side, number one at clutch end. Remove connecting rod caps and bearings. Remove liner clamp and remove liner-piston-rod assembly.

NOTE – *Before installing pistons in liners, protrusion of liner above cylinder block gasket face must be measured.*

Fig. 3 Showing Cylinder Liners Installed in Block

Installation – **1)** Protrusion should be .004-.067" (.10-.170 mm) when checked without "O" ring seal. Various size seals are available to correct protrusion height (if necessary).

2) Install piston and rod assembly in liner. See *Piston & Rod Assembly*. Install piston-rod-liner assembly into cylinder block. **NOTE** – *Number one is at clutch end, arrow points to flywheel and number on connecting rod is on cam side.*

3) Lubricate bearings and replace connecting rod caps. Replace remaining components in reverse of removal taking care not to disturb liner bottom seals.

PISTON & ROD ASSEMBLY

Removal – Piston and connecting rods are removed from cylinder block with cylinder liners. See *Cylinder Liners*. Remove piston through bottom of liner and remove rings, piston pin and connecting rod. See *Piston Pins*.

R-12 & R-17 4 CYLINDER (Cont.)

Installation – 1) Replace connecting rod and piston pin.

NOTE – *Piston must be assembled with arrow on piston pointing downward. Number stamped on connecting rod journal must face right with top of piston toward installer.*

2) Replace piston rings spacing gaps 120° apart. See *Fitting Pistons*. Using suitable ring compressor (Mot.442) push piston through bottom of cylinder liner with flat on side of liner parallel with sides of connecting rod.

FITTING PISTONS

Pistons, rings and liners are matched sets and must never be interchanged. All piston ring clearances and gaps are preset and must not be altered. See *Piston and Rod Assembly*.

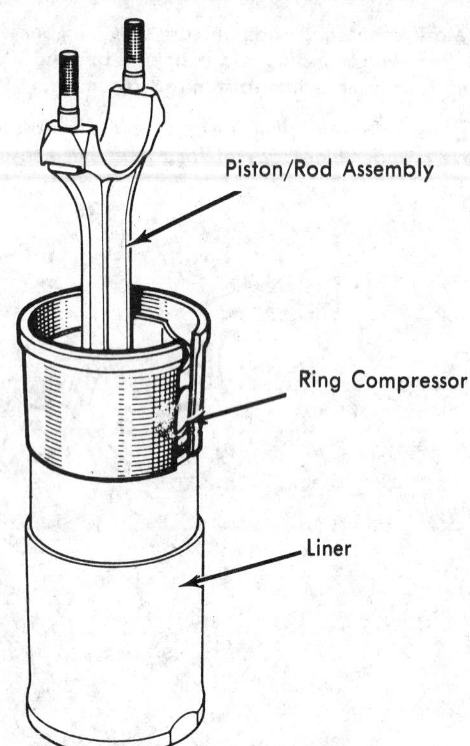

Fig. 4 Inserting Piston into Liner Using Ring Compressor

PISTON PIN REPLACEMENT

1) After removing Piston assembly from liner, remove rings. Using suitable tool (Mot. 255) shown in *Fig. 5* piston can be removed. Extract pin with appropriate adaptors.

2) Check connecting rod for wear or damage. Before preparing new piston, ensure pin is a running fit in piston.

3) Heat connecting rod in water to boiling point or in an oven to 482°F.

4) Slide new piston over installing mandrel and screw locating plug into place. Apply Molykote M 55 to piston pin. Push mandrel pin guide pin assembly through piston, by hand, until piston pin makes contact with connecting rod. Ensure piston and connecting rod are being fitted correctly (see illustration). Place assembly under hydraulic press and carefully seat pin into position.

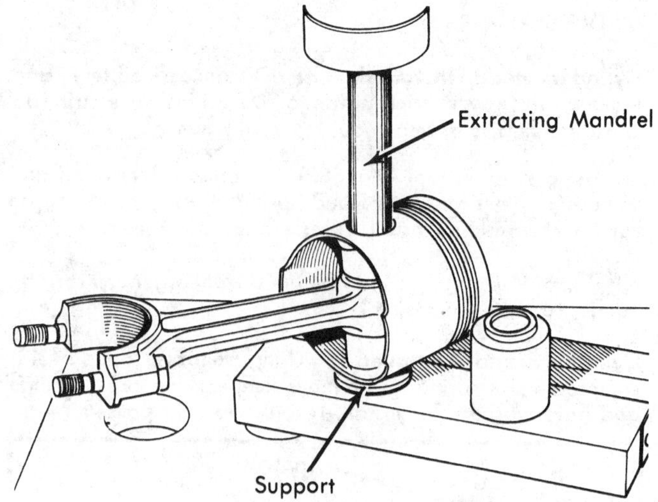

Fig. 5 Special Tool Assembly Mot. 255 for Extracting Piston Pin

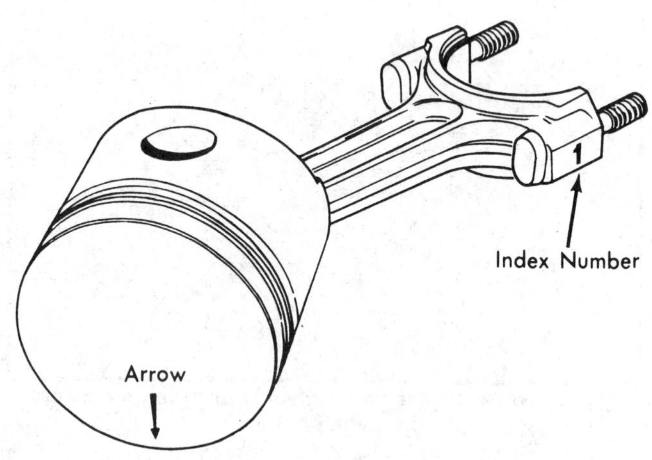

Fig. 6 Piston and Connecting Rod Assembly with Detail of Index Markings

CRANKSHAFT MAIN & CONNECTING ROD BEARINGS

MAIN BEARING SERVICE

1) With cylinder head and oil pan removed, invert engine so crankshaft is exposed. Remove connecting rod bearing caps. Mark position of main bearing caps to cylinder block. Remove all except front main bearing cap.

2) Push up front main bearing by lightly tapping on lower corners. Remove seal and bearing.

3) Remove crankshaft, bearings, and thrust washers. With crankshaft removed, pilot bearing can be replaced.

4) Check crankshaft, connecting rod bearings, and main bearings for wear. If crankshaft diameter is found out of tolerance, it may be ground to fit .010" undersize main and connecting rod bearings.

NOTE – *Crankshaft and connecting rod journals are roll hardened.*

R-12 & R-17 4 CYLINDER (Cont.)

5) Fit upper main bearings (those with oil holes). Lubricate main bearing journals and fit crankshaft into positon. Fit thrust washers, white metal toward crankshaft. Fit bearings to main bearing caps. Numbers 2, 3, 4, and 5 do not have oil holes. Fit main bearings caps into position aligned with previously made reference marks. Carefully install No. 1 main bearing cap and seals. **NOTE** – *Correct fit is imperative.*

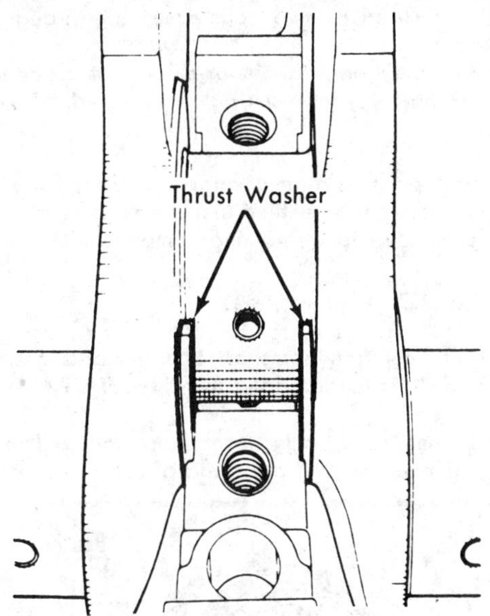

Fig. 7 Crankshaft Thrust Washers in Fitted Position

6) Fit upper connecting rod bearings and rod over crankshaft. Install rod caps and tighten to specification.

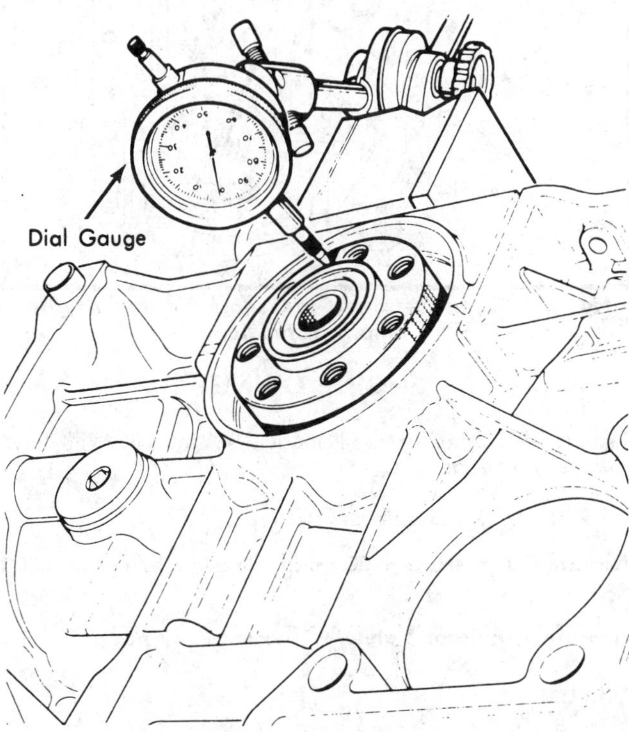

Fig. 8 Using a Dial Gauge to Measure Crankshaft End Play

7) Using a dial gauge, check crankshaft end play. Float must not exceed .009" (.23 mm). If correct end play is not obtained, replace thrust washers. Thrust washers are available in standard and two oversizes.

REAR MAIN BEARING OIL SEAL

NOTE – *Because lip of seal is extremely delicate, exercise caution.*

Fit seal on suitable tool (Mot.259-01) and lubricate outside. Install seal by lightly tapping shaft of installer tool. Seal is fully seated when tool just touches crankshaft.

REAR MAIN OIL SEAL

Engine Installed – 1) Loosen fan belt, unlock and unscrew pulley mounting bolt. Remove pulley and extract oil seal.

2) To install seal, fit oil seal over suitable tool (Mot. 525), align seal, and screw bolt in until tool just meets timing chain cover. Reverse removal procedure for remaining components.

CAMSHAFT

NOTE – *Camshaft specifications not available at time of publication.*

TIMING CHAIN

Removal – 1) With engine removed and suitably supported, remove timing cover and timing chain tensioner. Remove camshaft sprocket retaining bolts, washer and thrust ring.

2) Remove chain damper and camshaft securing bolts. Withdraw crankshaft sprocket and chain, using suitable puller (Mot.49), while easing camshaft forward. **NOTE** – *It is not necessary to completely remove camshaft to remove chain.*

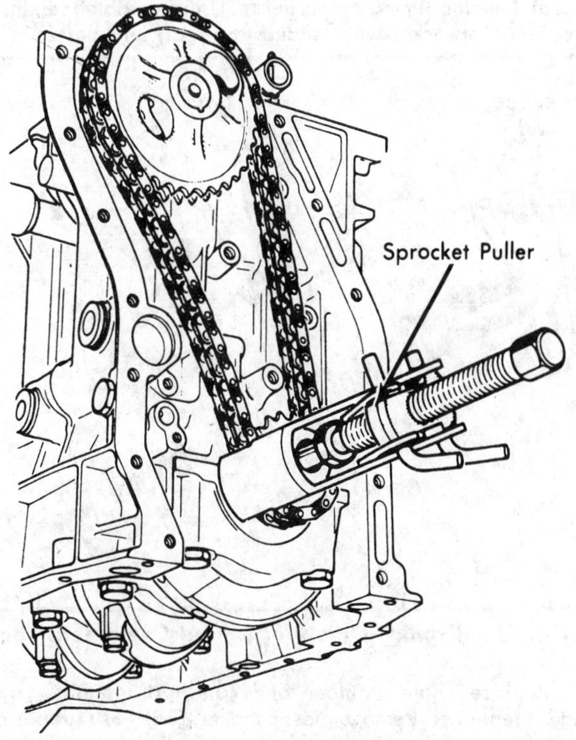

Fig. 9 Using Puller to Remove Crankshaft Sprocket

R-12 & R-17 4 CYLINDER (Cont.)

Installation – 1) Position chain on camshaft sprocket. Align camshaft sprocket timing mark with centers of crankshaft and camshaft. Turn crankshaft, bringing key upward.

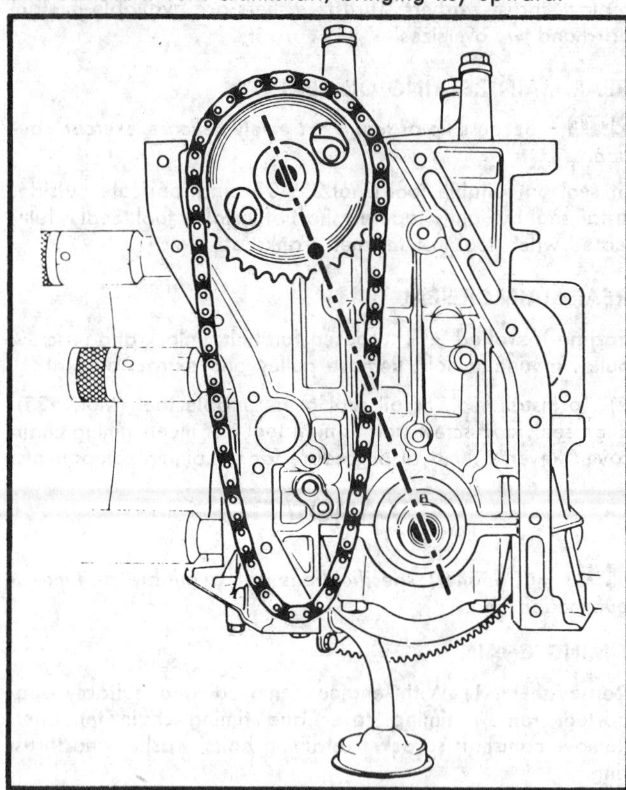

Fig. 10 Camshaft Sprocket Alignment Before Timing Chain Installation

2) Fit crankshaft sprocket on chain (timing mark facing outward), keeping timing marks in line. Using suitable tool, install crankshaft sprocket while sliding camshaft into place.

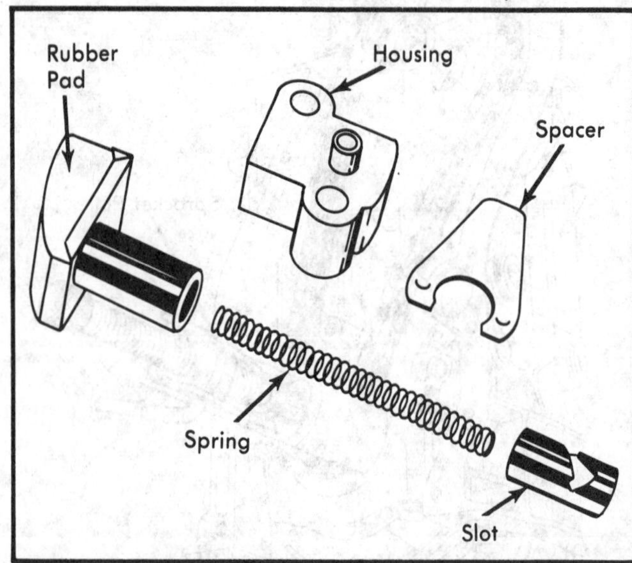

Fig. 11 Exploded View of Timing Chain Tensioner

3) Replace chain damper and camshaft mounting bolts. Adjust tensioner. Remove plastic spacer (red). Push rubber pad until it contacts housing. Lock pin is now disengaged from slot in retainer. Place rubber pad under spring tensioner.

CAMSHAFT REMOVAL

1) Remove and suitably support engine. Remove (in order) cylinder head, distributor drive gear, oil pan, timing chain cover, camshaft rear bearing, timing chain and camshaft. Camshaft is secured by two bolts accessible through pulley.

NOTE – *Camshaft and distributor drive gear are replaced as a set. Camshaft sprocket must be replaced at each disassembly.*

2) To install, position a new flange key. Using suitable press, fit sprocket, taking load behind first camshaft bearing. Reverse removal procedure for remaining components.

VALVE TIMING

Ensure crankshaft and camshaft timing marks are aligned. Check timing chain tension adjustment, see *Fig. 12*.

NOTE – *When chain is in normal position, a line passing through timing marks will not quite bisect camshaft.*

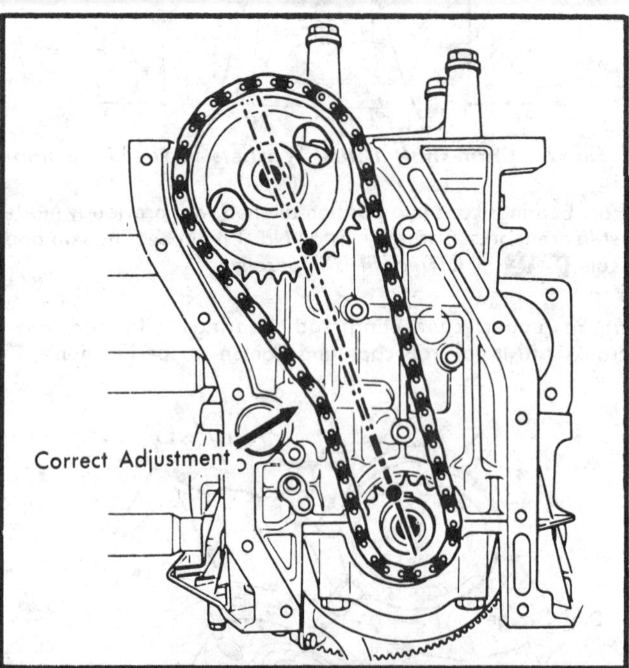

Fig. 12 Camshaft and Crankshaft Alignment with Chain Installed

ENGINE OILING

Crankcase Capacity – All models, 4.2 quarts. With filter change, 4.5 quarts.

Oil Filter – Disposable canister type.

Normal Oil Pressure – 30 psi at idle and 60-70 psi at 4000 RPM.

Pressure Regulator Valve – Located in oil pump.

OIL PUMP

1) With engine and oil pan removed, oil pump can be disassembled. Remove cotter pin retaining relief valve, and lift out cup, spring, spring guide, and piston.

R-12 & R-17 4 CYLINDER (Cont.)

ENGINE OILING (Cont.)

2) Clean all parts and inspect relief valve assembly. Check inner and outer rotors for damage.

3) Measure tip clearance in both positions shown in *Fig. 13*. Clearance in "POSITION 1" must be .002-.012" (.05-.30 mm) and .001-.006" (.03-.15 mm) in "POSITION 2". If either tolerance is exceeded, rotors must be changed.

4) To reassemble, fit piston, spring guide, spring, and cup in position. Install retaining cotter pin, strainer flange seal, strainer and lock tab. Tighten all bolts.

NOTE — *It is possible to remove oil pump cover and rotor without removing engine.*

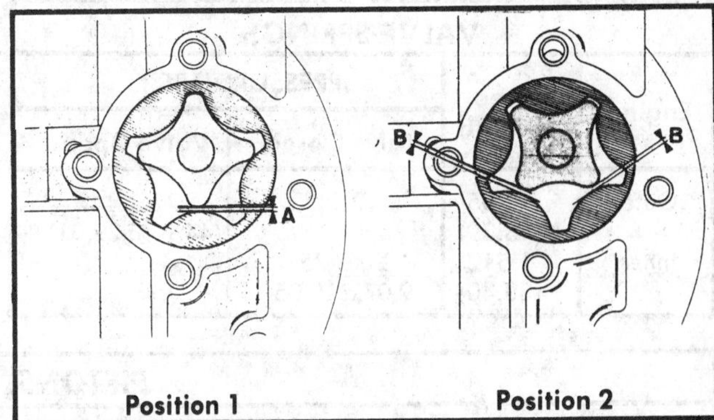

Fig. 13 Measurement Points of Oil Pump Rotor Clearance

ENGINE COOLING

Cooling System Capacity — R-12, 9½ quarts. R-17GTL, 7 quarts. Gordini, 8 quarts.

WATER PUMP

Disconnect battery and drain cooling system. Remove water pump and alternator drive belts. Remove all necessary water hoses. Remove both water pump and camshaft pulleys. Remove water pump. To install, reverse removal procedure.

NOTE — *If water pump is hard to free, tap it with a plastic hammer.*

COOLING SYSTEM REFILL & BLEEDING

1) Open bleed screws located on carburetor (R-12 models) or on engine block and in upper radiator hose. Clamp radiator hose between block and bleeder valve. Make sure hose is shut off as close to water pump as possible.

2) Run engine at about 1500 RPM (fast idle). When air bubbles stop, close bleeder valves. Fill radiator and replace cap. Run engine until thermostat has fully opened. Check expansion bottle after engine has cooled. Change expansion valve if coolant has passed through valve.

ENGINE SPECIFICATIONS

GENERAL SPECIFICATIONS

Year	Displ.		Carburetor	HP at RPM	Torque (Ft. Lbs. at RPM)	Compr. Ratio	Bore		Stroke	
	cu. ins.	cc					in.	mm	in.	mm
1977	100.5	1647	1x2-Bbl. ①	...	...	9.5-1	3.110	79	3.307	84

① — Fuel injection is used on Gordini models.

VALVES

Engine & Valve	Head Diam. In. (mm)	Face Angle	Seat Angle	Seat Width In. (mm)	Stem Diameter In. (mm)	Stem Clearance In. (mm)	Valve Lift In. (mm)
843							
Int.	1.378 (35.00)	45°	45°	.051-.063 (1.30-1.60)	.315 (8.00)	.....	.....
Exh.	1.220 (30.99)	45°	45°	.067-.079 (1.70-2.01)	.315 (8.00)	.....	.....

R-12 & R-17 4 CYLINDER (Cont.)

ENGINE SPECIFICATIONS (Cont.)

VALVE SPRINGS			
Engine	Free Length	PRESSURE (LBS.)	
		Valve Closed	Valve Open
Outer	1.905 (48.39)	...	99@1.142 (44.91@29.01)
Inner	1.512 (38.40)	20@.75 9.07@19.05	...

VALVE TIMING				
Engine	INTAKE		EXHAUST	
	Open (BTDC)	Close (ALDC)	Open (BLDC)	Close (ATDC)
843	10°	42°	46°	10°

PISTONS, PINS, RINGS						
Engine	PISTONS	PINS		RINGS		
	Clearance In. (mm)	Piston Fit In. (mm)	Rod Fit In. (mm)	Rings	End Gap In. (mm)	Side Clearance In. (mm)
All	.....	Free Fit	Press Fit	.....	①	.....

① — Pre-set gap, do not alter.

CRANKSHAFT MAIN & CONNECTING ROD BEARINGS							
Engine	MAIN BEARINGS				CONNECTING ROD BEARINGS		
	Journal Diam. In. (mm)	Clearance In. (mm)	Thrust Bearing	Crankshaft End Play In. (mm)	Journal Diam. In. (mm)	Clearance In. (mm)	Side Play In. (mm)
843	2.158 (54.81)	.....	No. 3	.002-.009 (.05-.23)	1.89 (48.0)	.....	.012-.022 (.32-.56)

TIGHTENING SPECIFICATIONS

Application	Ft. Lbs. (mkg)
Cylinder Head	
Step 1	30 (4.15)
Step 2	50-55 (6.91-7.60)
Step 3	① 55-60 (7.60-8.30)
Main Bearings	45 (6.22)
Intake & Exhaust Manifolds	25 (3.46)
Connecting Rods	30 (4.5)
Crankshaft Bolt	45-50 (6.22-6.91)
Camshaft Sprocket	15 (2.07)
Rocker Shaft Nuts	15-20 (2.07-2.77)
Flywheel	36 (5.0)

① — After engine has been run for at least 10 min. and been allowed to cool for 50 min.

99 – 4 CYLINDER

ENGINE CODING

ENGINE IDENTIFICATION

Engine number is stamped on block and is located near the summer setting on air cleaner.

Engine Identification

Application	① Engine Code
Federal	
Man. Trans.	B20-P06
Auto. Trans.	B20-P03
Calif.	
Man. Trans.	B20-P04
Auto. Trans.	B20-P05

① – Engine code number is followed by a six digit serial number.

ENGINE & CYLINDER HEAD

ENGINE

NOTE – *It is not recommended to remove engine without transmission. Remove engine and transmission as an assembly.*

1) Remove hood attaching bolts and lift off hood. Disconnect battery cables. Unclamp and remove battery. Drain coolant from radiator, engine block and heater core by opening all petcocks.

2) Disconnect vacuum hoses from power assist cylinder and pressure sensor. Disconnect fuel lines from injector tubes. Disconnect EGR system.

3) Disconnect electrical wires from following components: Ignition coil, ballast resistor, temperature sender, radiator fan, thermostat, wipers, headlights, and automatic transmission. Disconnect fuel injection cables.

4) Disconnect electrical leads from the following: Fuel injection distributor, injectors, air cleaner, throttle valve switch at temperature sensor, and temperature switch below intake manifold.

5) Remove air cleaner with hoses. Disconnect throttle cable at driver bracket. Disconnect hoses at thermostat, radiator, water pump and valve at heater core.

6) Remove four screws from front panel. Remove headlight frames and headlights. Disconnect hood lock cable at firewall and wheel housing. Remove front panel, lifting forward and upward.

7) On Man. Trans., remove clutch slave cylinder and hang it out of the way.

8) On Auto. Trans., remove heat shield on exhaust manifold at exhaust manifold and exhaust pipe.

9) On all models, remove exhaust pipe from manifold. Disconnect ground strap at transmission. Raise front of vehicle and place blocks under chassis.

10) On Man. Trans., place transmission in neutral. Knock out front taper pin from gear shift rod. Pull rubber bellows free of groove in gear selector rod, if so equipped. Separate gear selector rod and arm.

11) On Auto. Trans., remove screw for gear selector wire at transmission. Move gear selector lever to position No. 1 and pull outer cable housing back. Using Saab tool 8790388 (or equivalent) on wire, turn tool a small amount and pull out wire.

12) Disconnect speedometer cable from transmission. Remove nuts from engine mounts. Unclamp larger clamps around rubber bellows on inner universal joints. Attach suitable lifting sling to engine.

NOTE – *On models with top mounted alternator, remove alternator and attach rear lifting sling cable to alternator bracket.*

13) Remove attaching hardware from lower end piece of control arm on right-hand side. Turn steering wheel to left and raise engine slightly. Move engine to right and withdraw left universal joint, then move it to left and remove right universal joint.

14) Raise engine to gain access to starter and alternator, disconnect cables. Lift engine clear of vehicle and place on an engine stand. To install, reverse removal procedures.

CYLINDER HEAD

Removal – 1) Disconnect battery cables. Drain coolant (including block). Disconnect throttle cable at housing. Disconnect electrical lead from temperature sender. Remove brake vacuum hose from intake manifold.

2) Disconnect and plug fuel lines from fuel distributor. Disconnect all necessary coolant hoses. Separate exhaust pipe from manifold. Take off ignition wires and cap. Thread a nut on center stud of camshaft sprocket. Clamp stud against mounting plate.

NOTE – *Make sure nut is securely tightened so center stud will not move.*

3) Unbolt retaining bolts from camshaft sprocket. Separate sprocket from camshaft plate. Let sprocket hang in mounting plate by center stud. Remove cylinder head bolts. Support rear of engine. Remove engine mount bolt from head. Take out screws at transmission cover. Remove head.

Installation – To install reverse removal procedures and note the following: Make sure camshaft and bearing cap index marks are aligned. Align flywheel mark with mark on cylinder block. Set ignition with No. 1 piston at TDC. Retorque head bolts after engine has run and allowed to cool.

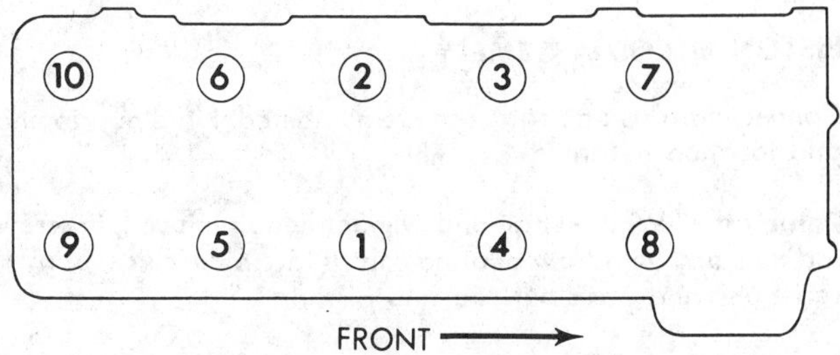

Fig. 1 Cylinder Head Tightening Sequence

99 – 4 CYLINDER (Cont.)

VALVES

VALVE ARRANGEMENT

E-I-I-E-E-I-I-E (front to rear).

VALVE GUIDE SERVICING

1) Check valve guide and valve stem for wear or damage. Using tool 8390437 (or equivalent), withdraw valve guide from camshaft side of head.

2) Install guide from cylinder side of head, using valve guide removal/installation tool 8390437 and adapters. Ream guide to standard size, using a suitable reamer. Check valve seat for true, reface if necessary.

VALVE SPRINGS

1) With cylinder head removed, remove camshaft bearing caps and camshaft.

2) Using a magnet, lift out cam followers along with adjusting pallets and retain in proper order for reassembly.

3) With spring compressor, depress spring and remove valve keepers. Release spring and valve collar.

4) Replace spring and reverse removal procedure.

VALVE CLEARANCE ADJUSTMENT

1) With valve cover removed, rotate engine until valve to be adjusted or checked has heel of cam opposite cam follower. Measure clearance with feeler gauge. If clearance is not within specifications, intake .006-.012" (.152-.305 mm) and .014-.020" (.356-.508 mm) for exhaust, a direct measurement will be required.

2) Install valve measuring tool 8391450 and dial indicator. Measure clearance of all valves and note reading. Proceed to adjust any valve which does not come within the following limits: .008-.010" (.20-.25 mm) intake and .016-.018" (.40-.45 mm) exhaust.

3) Remove camshaft, cam followers and adjusting pallets of any valve needing adjustment.

4) Measure pallet thickness and add noted valve clearance to arrive at total clearance. Subtract proper valve clearance from total clearance to determine needed pallet thickness.

5) Install new adjusting pallets and recheck valve clearance.

PISTONS, PINS & RINGS

PISTON & ROD ASSEMBLY

Connecting rods and rod caps are numbered. Note positioning and location before disassembly.

Removal – With oil pan and cylinder head removed, unscrew rod nuts and withdraw bearing caps. Place plastic sleeves over rod bolts and push out rod and piston.

Installation – Use a ring compressor over piston and fit piston to bore. Make sure notch in piston faces engine/transmission. Install rod cap in position and tighten bolts.

PISTON PIN REPLACEMENT

Piston pins are retained by circlips. Remove circlips and press out piston pins. Check pins and bearings for wear or damage, replace if necessary.

FITTING PISTONS

1) To fit pistons to cylinder bores, use a feeler gauge .500" (12.7 mm) wide and .0005-.0016" (.014-.040 mm) thick. Oil cylinder lightly and insert piston without rings.

2) Attach feeler gauge to a spring scale. Insert feeler gauge between piston and cylinder wall at right angles to piston pin. When feeler gauge can be pulled out of cylinder with a force of 1.8-2.6 lbs. (.816-1.18 kg), piston clearance has been determined.

3) Repeat test at several different depths in cylinder bore. Graded standard and non-graded oversize pistons are available.

Piston Specifications

Application	Diameter In. (mm)
Std. (AB)	3.5425-3.5427 (89.980-89.986)
Std. (C)	3.5433-3.5437 (89.999-90.010)
1st Oversize	3.5619-3.5625 (90.472-90.487)
2nd Oversize	3.5816-3.5822 (90.972-90.987)

4) Check piston rings for end gap and side clearance, using an inverted piston to position ring in bore. On worn bores, measure at lower end of bore.

5) Install rings on piston, making sure gaps of compression rings are 180° apart with lower compression ring mark "TOP" facing up. On three piece oil ring make sure ends are staggered.

CRANKSHAFT MAIN & CONNECTING ROD BEARINGS

MAIN BEARING SERVICE

1) Remove connecting rods and main bearing caps. Measure journals with a micrometer. Out-of-round should not exceed .002" (.051 mm). If crankshaft is near or over stated limit of wear, regrind journals and fit undersize bearings.

2) Using "V" blocks and a dial indicator check crankshaft for bend. If bend exceeds .002" (.051 mm), replace or repair crankshaft.

3) Using Plastigage method, check main bearing and connecting rod bearing journals. If clearance is found excessive, combine suitable undersize bearings to correct clearance. Undersize bearings are available in various thicknesses.

99 – 4 CYLINDER (Cont.)

THRUST BEARING ALIGNMENT

Center main bearing is thrust bearing. Check crankshaft endplay. If it exceeds specifications, replace thrust washers with oil grooves facing crankshaft.

CAMSHAFT

FRONT OIL SEAL SERVICE

NOTE – *Seal may be replaced with engine in vehicle if clutch and flywheel are removed.*

Remove seal ring with a screwdriver. Oil ring surface before installing. Fit new seal with spring ring facing crankshaft.

TIMING COVER & OIL SEAL

Remove pulley using a puller. Pry out old seal. Grease seal with silicone. Install new seal.

CAMSHAFT

Removal – 1) Remove camshaft cover and gaskets. Rotate crankshaft until number one piston is at TDC of compression stroke.

2) Remove camshaft sprocket by screwing a nut onto center stud of camshaft sprocket and clamp center stud against mounting bracket.

CAUTION – *Tighten nut securely, so sprocket and chain can not move. Otherwise chain tensioner will tighten chain, and tensioner can not be reset without lifting engine out of vehicle.*

3) Bend back locks and remove attaching screws from camshaft sprocket. Separate sprocket from camshaft plate until it hangs free with bracket.

4) Remove camshaft bearing caps. Lift off camshaft, inspect camshaft and bearings for wear or damage.

Fig. 2 ***Camshaft Timing Marks***

5) Replace camshaft bearings and caps, then tighten cap nuts. Align camshaft timing mark with mark on cylinder head as shown in *Fig. 3*.

6) Install camshaft sprocket on camshaft. Unscrew nut from center stud on camshaft sprocket and lock both attaching screws. Replace camshaft cover and gaskets.

CAUTION – *Nut on camshaft sprocket center stud must not on any account be unscrewed before sprocket is tightly screwed to camshaft.*

VALVE TIMING & CHAIN REPLACEMENT

Removal – 1) Remove timing cover and camshaft cover. Separate camshaft from camshaft sprocket. *See Camshaft Removal.*

2) Mount pinion sprocket on crankshaft. Align "O" degree mark on flywheel with mark on cylinder block. *See Fig. 3.*

3) Remove chain guides, oil thrower ring and pull sprocket off crankshaft, using a suitable puller.

4) Remove idler shaft keeper plate and withdraw idler shaft.

Installation – 1) Reinstall idler shaft. Install keeper plate and attaching bolts. Position idler sprocket so marked line is horizontal.

2) Mount pinion sprocket on crankshaft. Align "O" degree mark on flywheel with mark on cylinder block (see illustration).

Fig. 3 ***Aligning "O" Degree Mark on Flywheel with Mark on Cylinder Block.***

3) Align camshaft mark with mark on cylinder head. Install straight chain guide with long screw in bottom hole.

4) Loosely mount curved chain guide with short screw in hole nearest idler shaft.

5) Place camshaft chain over camshaft sprocket and mounting bracket. Lower chain and sprocket past camshaft flange until center stud of sprocket is lined up with camshaft.

6) Rotate camshaft sprocket until screw holes match threaded holes in camshaft flange.

7) Place timing chain over crankshaft and idler sprockets so chain will be in a straight line between camshaft and crankshaft as shown in *Fig. 4*. Do not change any of the sprocket settings while installing chain.

99 – 4 CYLINDER (Cont.)

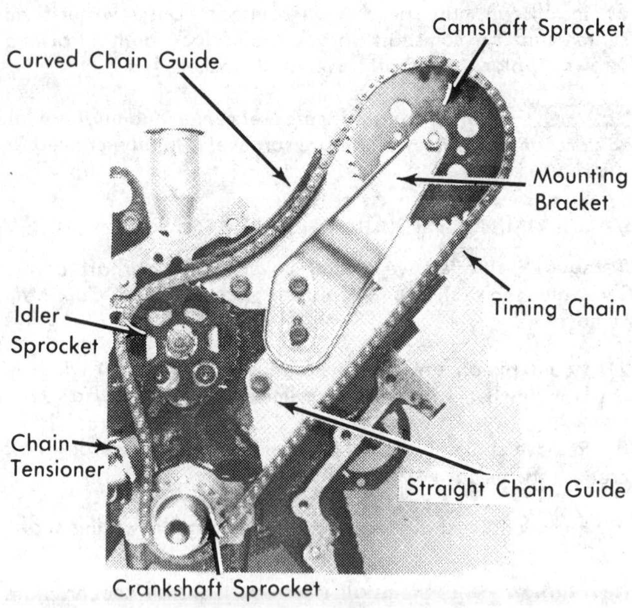

Fig. 4 Front View of Timing Chain Installed and Tightened

8) Guide center stud of camshaft sprocket into camshaft. Install locking plate and one screw. Install screws for chain guides and camshaft sprocket mounting bracket.

9) Rotate crankshaft one revolution. Install and tighten camshaft sprocket screws. Lock screws with locking plate. Check timing marks to see they are properly aligned.

10) Install chain tensioner as follows: Relieve spring pressure on tensioner by turning clamping sleever clockwise to mounting position. Fit a spacer on neck of tensioner and push neck into body of tensioner.

11) Mount chain tensioner and guide plate on block. Remove spacer. Press curved chain guide against chain to stretch it and push tensioner neck into housing. Adjust to leave a clearance of 0.02" (0.5 mm) between housing and tensioner neck, then tighten chain guide. Rotate crankshaft one full turn and check that tensioner has not less than 0.02" (0.5 mm) and not more than 0.06" (1.5 mm) of clearance. Remove nut from camshaft center stud. Reinstall remaining components in reverse order of disassembly.

ENGINE OILING

Crankcase Capacity – 4.0 qts. including filter.

Oil Filter – Full-flow type.

Normal Oil Pressure – 43 psi (3.0 kg/cm^2) @2000 RPM.

Pressure Regulator Valve – Non-adjustable, opens at 57-71 psi (4.0-5.0 kg/cm^2).

ENGINE OILING SYSTEM

Oil pressure is generated by a dual-rotor pump driven from idler shaft. Pump is located on outside of engine. Oil is forced through a full-flow filter and oil channels to various lubrication points. Each connecting rod bearing has a separate oil passage from main bearings.

OIL PUMP

Removal – 1) Remove four screws attaching pump to engine. Withdraw pump and "0" ring from engine. Remove two screws attaching pump cover to housing. Remove rotors and "O" ring from housing.

2) Pull cotter pin from cover and remove plug, "O" ring, spring and pressure relief valve piston. Using a straightedge and feeler gauge, measure clearance between rotors and housing face. If clearance exceeds .002-.0035" (0.05-0.09 mm), use fine emery paper to resurface housing or sides of rotors.

Installation – 1) Clean and oil all parts. Install outer rotor with chamfered edge inward facing toward drive shaft. Install valve piston, spring plug, "O" ring and cotter pin in pump cover.

2) Place "O" ring in pump housing groove. Install cover and tighten screws. Rotate pump up until drive shaft engages in engine. Slide pump up against engine and install four attaching bolts.

ENGINE COOLING

Cooling System Capacity – 8.5 quarts.

Thermostat – Thermostat begins to open at approximately 190°F (88°C).

Radiator Cap – Radiator pressure cap opens at approximately 14.2 psi.

WATER PUMP

Removal – 1) Drain coolant. Disconnect battery. Remove intake manifold. Remove alternator. Remove bolt mounting bracket to pump cover. Unbolt rear engine mounts. Raise rear of engine. Remove bolt mounting alternator bracket to transmission cover. Loosen lower bolt and twist bracket away from engine. Remove last two bolts from cover and remove.

2) Position special tool 8392441 (or equivalent) over water pump and fit two bolts (DO NOT TIGHTEN). Turn tool counterclockwise so peg engages a fin on impeller. Loosen center impeller nut (left hand threads). Remove water pump. DO NOT tap out with hammer.

Installation – To install, reverse removal procedure and note: It may be necessary to use sleeve 8392490 (or equivalent) to seat bearing housing.

99 – 4 CYLINDER (Cont.)

ENGINE SPECIFICATIONS

GENERAL SPECIFICATIONS

Year	Displ. cu. ins.	Displ. cc	Carburetor	HP at RPM	Torque (Ft. Lbs. at RPM)	Compr. Ratio	Bore in.	Bore mm	Stroke in.	Stroke mm
1977	121	1985	Fuel Inj.	.....	.....	8.7-1	3.543	90	3.071	78

VALVES

Engine & Valve	Head Diam. In. (mm)	Face Angle	Seat Angle	Seat Width In. (mm)	Stem Diameter In. (mm)	Stem Clearance In. (mm)	Valve Lift In. (mm)
1985 cc							
Int.	1.654 (42.9)	44.5°	45°	.004-.008 (1-2)	.313-.314 (7.960-7.975)	0.02 (0.5)	.....
Exh.	1.398 (35.5)	44.5°	45°	.004-.008 (1-2)	.313-.314 (7.955-7.980)	0.02 (0.05)	.....

PISTONS, PINS, RINGS

Engine	PISTONS Clearance In. (mm)	PINS Piston Fit In. (mm)	PINS Rod Fit In. (mm)	RINGS Rings	RINGS End Gap In. (mm)	RINGS Side Clearance In. (mm)
1985 cc	.0006-.0016 (.014-.040)	.0002-.0006 (.005-.014)	①	No. 1	.014-.021 (.35-.55)	.002-.003 (.050-.082)
				No. 2	.012-.018 (.30-.45)	.0016-.003 (.040-.072)
				Oil	.015-.055 (.38-1.40)	.....

① — Interference fit.

CRANKSHAFT MAIN & CONNECTING ROD BEARINGS

Engine	MAIN BEARINGS Journal Diam. In. (mm)	Clearance In. (mm)	Thrust Bearing	Crankshaft End Play In. (mm)	CONNECTING ROD BEARINGS Journal Diam. In. (mm)	Clearance In. (mm)	Side Play In. (mm)
1985 cc	2.283-2.284 (57.981-58.000)	.001-.002 (.026-.062)	Center	.003-.0011 (0.08-0.28)	2.047 (51.981-52.000)	.001-.002 (.026-.062)	.....

VALVE SPRINGS

Engine	Free Length In. (mm)	PRESSURE Lbs. @ In. (kg @ mm) Valve Closed	Valve Open
1985 cc	1.700 (43.1)	.....	170-183@1.161 (77.1-83.0@29.5)

VALVE TIMING

Engine	INTAKE ① Open (BTDC)	INTAKE ① Close (ALDC)	EXHAUST ② Open (BLDC)	EXHAUST ② Close (ATDC)
1985cc	10°	54°	46°	18°

① — With .014" (.35 mm) valve clearance.
② — With .022 (.55 mm) valve clearance.

99 - 4 CYLINDER (Cont.)

ENGINE SPECIFICATIONS (Cont.)

CAMSHAFT			
Engine	Journal Diam. In. (mm)	Clearance In. (mm) ①	Lobe Lift In. (mm)
1985 cc	1.139 (28.94)	.....	Int. .421 (10.7) Exh. .433 (11.0)

① — End play is .003-.010" (.08-.25 mm)

TIGHTENING SPECIFICATIONS

Application	Ft. Lbs. (mkg)
Main Bearings	79 (10.9)
Rod Bearings	40 (5.5)
Camshaft Bearing Caps	13 (1.8)
Camshaft Cover	1 (.14)
Crankshaft Pulley	137 (19.00)
Rear Crankshaft Seal	14 (1.9)
Cylinder Head	
Step One	43 (6.0)
Step Two	69 (9.5)
Flywheel	43 (6.0)
Water Pump Impeller	11 (1.5)
Oil Pump	13 (1.8)
Idler Shaft Plate	14 (1.9)
Idler Sprocket	18 (2.5)
Camshaft Sprocket	14 (1.9)
Intake Manifold	13 (1.8)
Exhaust Manifold	14 (1.9)
Thermostat Housing	13 (1.8)

1600 4 CYLINDER

ENGINE CODING

ENGINE IDENTIFICATION

Engine number is stamped on a machined pad near distributor. See table below for engine codes.

Engine Codes

Application	Calif.	Federal
1600 cc		
4-Speed	EA71AF2	EA71AF EA71AF3
4-Speed, 4WD	EA71EF2	EA71EF EA71EF3
5-Speed	EA71AP2	EA71AP EA71AP3
Auto. Trans.	EA71AT5	EA71AT4 EA71AT6

ENGINE

ENGINE

NOTE — *It is possible to remove engine with transmission fitted. Removal procedure given is with transmission remaining in vehicle.*

Removal — 1) Disconnect battery cable. Remove spare wheel from engine compartment. Remove air cleaner assembly.

2) Disconnect fuel line from fuel pump intake, allow fuel to drain into a suitable container. Drain radiator and engine block. Disconnect radiator hoses at engine.

3) Disconnect all wiring to engine and accessories. On 4-WD models remove engine fan from pulley. On Automatic Transmission models disconnect oil cooler pipes.

4) Remove two upper radiator bolts and lift out radiator. Remove nuts on each end of engine-to-firewall strut and remove strut by moving to rear to clear engine hanger. Remove starter from transmission housing.

5) Remove all control cables and vacuum hoses from engine. On Automatic Transmission models disconnect torque converter from engine by rotating crankshaft to remove four bolts through timing hole. Use care that bolts do not drop into housing.

6) Remove engine-to-transmission bolts and nuts and disconnect exhaust pipe. Remove bolts securing front engine mounts-to-engine. Slightly hoist engine with chain hoist attached to front to rear hangers and separate engine from transmission.

7) When separating engine from transmission, ensure that torque converter remains with transmission (Automatic Transmission only). Also, it may be helpful to slightly jack up transmission during removal procedure. Remove engine completly and place on engine stand.

Installation — To install, reverse removal procedure and tighten all bolts and nuts. Adjust all controls and fill engine with suitable coolant.

ENGINE DISASSEMBLY

NOTE — *Remove engine, place on engine stand (399814300X2 or equivalent). Remove starter and proceed as follows:*

1) Separate engine from transmission, if necessary. On automatic transmission only, make sure converter remains on transmission. Drain oil and coolant. Make sure liquid does not run over clutch cover. On manual transmission models, remove clutch cover and disc.

2) Remove silencer with tapered sleeve. Remove fan and pulley. Remove intake manifold assembly with carburetors, vacuum control valve and modulator. Remove EGR valve, thermostat and sending unit. Remove air cleaner, distributor, EGR pipe and air suction system.

3) Remove oil filter duct. 4WD models have a bracket. Use a puller and remove crankshaft pulley. Remove oil pump and filter as an assembly. Remove water pump with hoses and tubes attached.

4) Turn engine over on stand and remove oil pan, crankcase, gasket and transmission cover (if necessary). Remove oil strainer and brackets. Remove either flywheel or converter drive plate. Take off flywheel housing.

5) Remove spark plugs and valve cover. Remove rocker assembly and push rods. Remove cylinder head bolts in sequence See *Fig. 1*. Remove cylinder head and gasket. Use Allen wrench and remove crankcase plug.

6) Position pistons at bottom dead center and remove circlip with long nosed pliars. Access to No. 1 and No. 2 pins is through front crankcase plug holes. Access to No. 3 and No. 4 pins is through rear service holes. Remove pins and pistons, marking for reassembly.

7) Work through hole in camshaft gear and straighten lockwasher, then remove nut. Remove nuts and washers and separate cases. Use valve lifter clips (899804100 or equivalent), to prevent upper crankcase lifters from falling off.

NOTE — *Pull camshaft to rear for crankcase clearance.*

8) Remove oil seal. Lift out crankshaft, distributor gear, and connecting rods. Keep crankshaft bearings in order for reassembly. Remove camshaft and gear. Remove oil pressure switch and valve lifters.

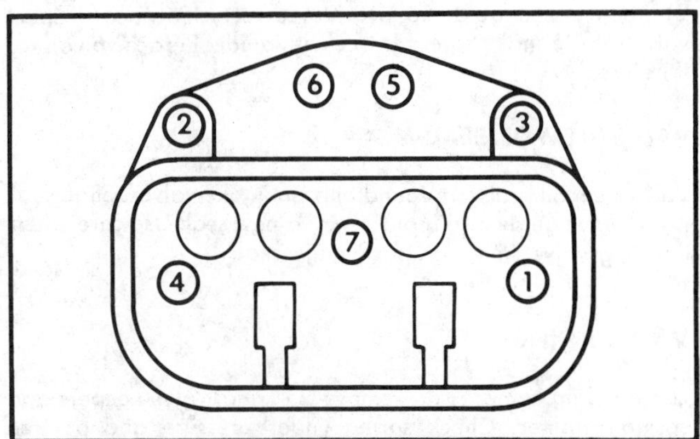

Fig. 1 Cylinder Head Loosening Sequence

1600 4 CYLINDER (Cont.)

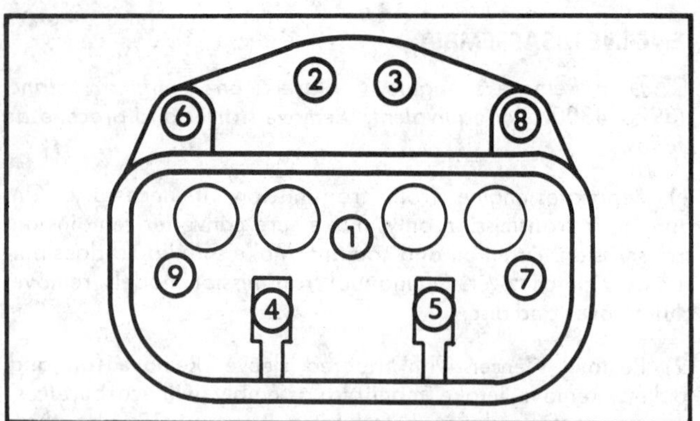

Fig. 2 Cylinder Head Tightening Sequence

VALVES

VALVE ARRANGEMENT

I-E-E-I (both banks, front to rear).

VALVE GUIDE SERVICING

1) Check valve guide for wear or damage. Replace defective guides by using a drift and driving out guide through top of head. Press in new guide from top of head until correct projection of guide above head is achieved. See *Fig. 3*.

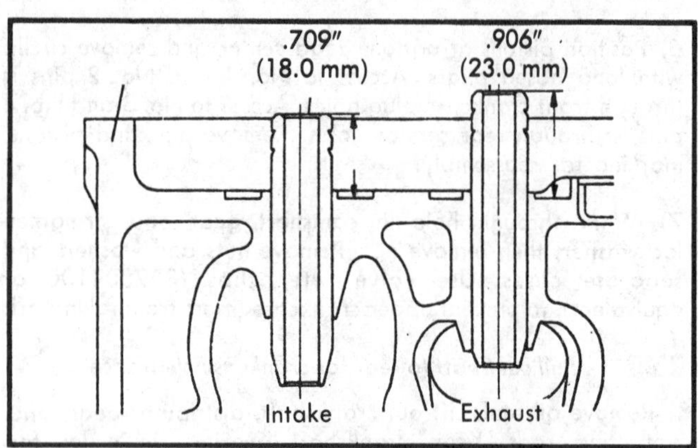

Fig. 3 Correct Valve Guide Projection

2) Ream valve guide to provide correct clearance. Inspect valve seat to make sure it is true with guide. Reface valve seat if necessary.

VALVE STEM OIL SEALS

Valve stem oil seals are found only on intake valves. Slide seal off of valve guide and replace with a new seal. Use care when inserting valve stem not to damage seal.

VALVE SPRING

Use a spring compressor, remove "O" ring, valve keepers and spring retainer. Check spring under pressure and at free length. Replace if necessary. Install spring with wide spaced coils (paint mark) facing valve spring retainer.

ROCKER ARM ASSEMBLY

Check rocker shaft, rocker arm and bushing for wear or damage. Replace any worn parts. Press in new bushing and ream until a clearance of .0006-.002" (.016-.052 mm) is achieved between bushing and shaft.

VALVE TAPPET SERVICE

Remove lifters from crankcase. Inspect tappet for wear or clogged oil hole. Replace lifter if lifter-to-crankcase clearance exceeds .004" (.100 mm). Standard lifter clearance is .0012-.0028" (.030-.072 mm).

VALVE CLEARANCE ADJUSTMENT

With engine cold, rotate engine to TDC of firing stroke. Insert feeler gauge between rocker arm and valve stem. Clearances should be as follows:

Application	Intake In. (mm)	Exhaust In. (mm)
1600	.009-.011 (.23-.27)	.013-.015 (.33-.37)

PISTON, PINS & RINGS

FITTING PISTONS

1) Measure piston bore .028" (7 mm) from top of cylinder in line with crankshaft and again 90° from centerline of crankshaft. Make same measurements 1.48" (37 mm) from top and 2.64" (67 mm) from top of cylinder bore.

2) Measure piston at bottom of skirt 90° from piston pin hole. Measurements should be performed at temperature of 68°F (20°C).

3) Check piston ring end gap and side clearance. Check gap at bottom of cylinder bore. Fit piston rings with "R" or "N" facing up.

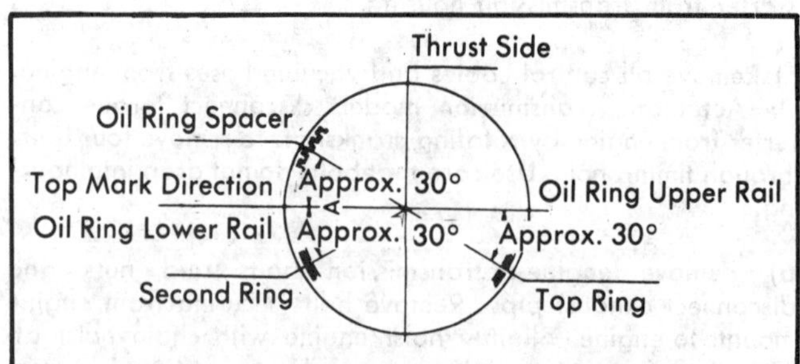

Fig. 4 Piston Ring Gap Position

PISTON PIN

Check piston pin for damage, cracks, wear or distortion. Check connecting rod bushing for wear. If pin or bushing are worn beyond specification, replace bushing in connecting rod and ream to fit standard pin. Piston pin is a thumb push fit at 68°F.

1600 4 CYLINDER (Cont.)

CRANKSHAFT MAIN & CONNECTING ROD BEARINGS

MAIN & CONNECTING ROD BEARINGS

1) Check connecting rod side play with a feeler gauge. If side play exceeds specifications, replace connecting rod.

2) Use Plastigage method to measure both connecting rod and main bearing clearances. Connecting rod bearing inserts are available in standard and .5 mm (.020") and .25 mm (.010") undersizes. Main bearing inserts are available in standard and .3 mm (.012"). .5 mm (.020") and .25 mm (.010") undersizes.

3) Check crankshaft for bend by placing front and rear main journals on "V" blocks and fitting a dial indicator on center journal. Correct or replace crankshaft if bend exceeds .0014" (.035 mm).

REAR MAIN BEARING OIL SEAL SERVICE

Seal is replaced when crankcase halves are split. After crankcase halves have been reassembled, install new seal.

CAMSHAFT

ENGINE FRONT COVER OIL SEAL

With front cover removed drive out old seal. Install new seal using suitable tool (899064110) with or without front cover on engine.

CAMSHAFT

1) Camshaft may be removed when crankcase has been split. Check for wear or damage, replace camshaft if necessary. Using a dial indicator, check that bend does not exceed .002" (.051 mm).

2) Measure end play, if it exceeds .0018-.0045" (.045-.115 mm), remove cam gear and replace thrust plate. Measure camshaft lobe height. If wear exceeds .012" (.3 mm), replace camshaft.

3) Measure camshaft gear runout with dial indicator. Replace camshaft gear if runout exceeds .010" (.25 mm). Measure backlash between camshaft gear and crankshaft gear, if backlash exceeds .006" (.015 mm), replace camshaft gear. Standard value of backlash is .0008-.0020" (.020-.050 mm).

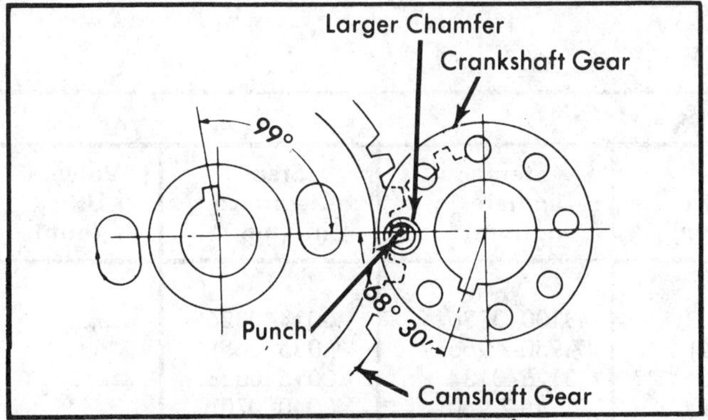

Fig. 5 Valve Timing Marks

VALVE TIMING

With crankcase halves split, install crankshaft and camshaft so punch mark on camshaft gear is visible through chamfered hole in crankshaft gear.

ENGINE OILING

Crankcase Capacity – 3.8 quarts with filter change.

Oil Filter – Full-flow.

Normal Oil Pressure – 35 psi (2.5 kg/cm²) @500 RPM: 57 psi (4.0 kg/cm²) @2500 RPM.

Pressure Regulator Valve – Non-adjustable, opens at 57-64 psi (4.0-4.5 kg/cm²).

ENGINE OILING SYSTEM

Oil is pressure fed by a camshaft driven trochoid type oil pump. Pump incorporates an oil relief and by-pass valve in its body. Oil pump is located externally on engine. Oil from pump passes from main oil gallery to journals of camshaft and crankshaft. From there, oil goes to main bearings, pistons pin bearings and cylinder walls. Oil passes through valve lifters and push rods to oil rocker arms.

OIL PUMP

Removal – Remove four attaching bolts and pull pump and filter forward. Remove oil filter from pump.

Disassembly – 1) Remove screws, lift cover and rotor from pump body. Remove "O" ring. Remove by-pass spring and ball. Unscrew plug and remove washers, spring and pressure relief valve.

2) Measure rotor-to-rotor and outer rotor-to-body clearance, replace any component which exceeds wear limits. Measure rotor side clearance.

3) Inspect relief valve spring, valve and pump body for wear or damage.

NOTE – *Make sure oil pump shaft is aligned with slot in camshaft when reassembling.*

Reassembly – Reassemble in reverse order, using all new gaskets and "O" rings.

Installation – Install oil filter on pump. Using rearward movement reinstall oil pump and four attaching bolts.

Oil Pump Specifications

Application	Std. Clearance In. (mm)
Inner-to-Outer Rotor	.0008-.005 (.02-.12)
Outer Rotor-to-Body	.006-.008 (.15-.21)
Rotor Side Clearance	.002-.005
Relief Valve Spring Free Length	1.85 (47.1)

1600 4 CYLINDER (Cont.)

ENGINE COOLING

THERMOSTAT

Thermostat – Begins to open at 190°F (88°C) and is fully open at approximately 212°F (100°C).

Coolant Capacity – All models approximately 6.3 quarts.

WATER PUMP

Removal – Drain coolant and disconnect main radiator outlet hose. Remove drive belt and attaching bolts, remove water pump.

Disassembly – 1) Remove four screws attaching cover plate and gasket. Remove pulley and locking clip.

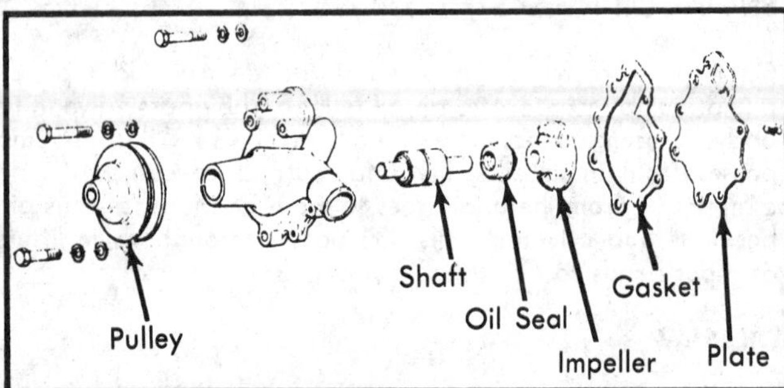

Fig. 6 Exploded View of Water Pump

2) Withdraw shaft, impeller and mechanical seal from pump body. Press pump shaft from impeller.

Reassembly – 1) Using an arbor press, press pump shaft into pump body until locking clip may be installed. Apply sealing compound to edge of mechanical seal and in housing with carbon ring facing toward impeller.

2) Press impeller onto shaft until impeller-to-body clearance is .020-.028" (.5-.7 mm). Support impeller side of pump shaft and press on pulley until distance between center of pulley groove and rear face of pump housing is 2.34-2.37" (59.5-60.1 mm).

Installation – Install water pump together with slotted clip, water pipe, and water by-pass pipe as a unit. Gradually tighten bolts alternately and evenly in several steps to prevent leakage. The clamps for the water hose should be positioned low to prevent interference with the EGR pipe.

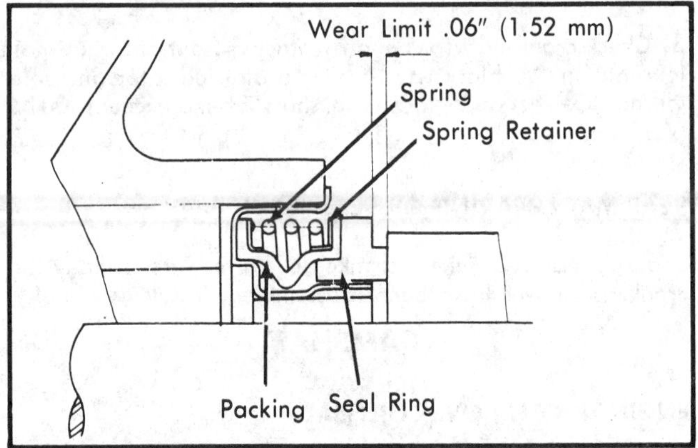

Fig. 7 Detail of Water Pump Seal

ELECTRIC COOLING FAN

All models are equipped with an electric cooling fan motor. 4WD models use a combination of electric fan, engine drive fan and forced cooling (water cooling). All other models utilize electric fan and forced cooling (water cooling).

ENGINE SPECIFICATIONS

GENERAL SPECIFICATIONS

Year	Displ.		Carburetor	HP at RPM	Torque (Ft. Lbs. at RPM)	Compr. Ratio	Bore		Stroke	
	cu. ins.	cc					in.	mm	in.	mm
1977	97	1595	2-Bbl.	67@5200	81@2400	8.5-1	3.62	92	2.36	60

VALVES

Engine & Valve	Head Diam. In. (mm)	Face Angle	Seat Angle	Seat Width In. (mm)	Stem Diameter In. (mm)	Stem Clearance In. (mm)	Valve Lift In. (mm)
1600 cc							
Int.	.....	45°	45°	.040 (1.02)	.3130-.3136 (7.950-7.965)	.0014-.0026 (.035-.065)	.....
Exh.	.....	45°	45°	.055 (1.39)	.3128-.3134 (7.945-7.960)	.0016-.0028 (.040-.070)	.....

1600 4 CYLINDER (Cont.)

ENGINE SPECIFICATIONS (Cont.)

PISTONS, PINS, RINGS						
	PISTONS	PINS		RINGS		
Engine	Clearance In. (mm)	Piston Fit In. (mm)	Rod Fit In. (mm)	Rings	End Gap In. (mm)	Side Clearance In. (mm)
1600 cc	.0004-.0016 (.010-.040)	.00004-.00067 (.001-.017)	.0002-.0016 (.005-.040)	No.1	.012-.020 (0.3-0.5)	.0016-.0031 (.04-.08)
				No.2	.012-.020 (0.3-0.5)	.0012-.0028 (.03-.07)
				No.3	.012-.035 (0.3-0.9)	.....

CRANKSHAFT MAIN & CONNECTING ROD BEARINGS							
	MAIN BEARINGS				CONNECTING ROD BEARINGS		
Engine	Journal Diam.	Clearance	Thrust Bearing	Crankshaft End Play	Journal Diam.	Clearance	Side Play
1600 cc Front & Rear	1.9667-1.9673 (49.955-49.970)	.0004-.0016 (.010-.040)	Center	.0016-.0054 (.040-.137)	1.7715-1.7720 (44.995-45.010)	.0008-.0025 (.020-.064)	.0028-.013 (.07-.33)
Center	1.9671-1.9677 (49.965-49.980)	.0-.0008 (.0-.020)					

VALVE SPRINGS			
Engine	Free Length In. (mm)	PRESSURE Lbs. @ In. (kg @ mm)	
		Valve Closed	Valve Open
1600 cc Inner	1.92 (48.7)	19.7-22.6@1.46 (8.93-10.3@37)	43.1-49.5@1.10 (19.5-22.5@28)
Outer	1.90 (48.2)	40.0-46.0@1.54 (18.1-21.0@39)	91.1-104.7@1.22 (41.3-44.5@31)

CAMSHAFT			
Engine	Journal Diam. In. (mm)	Clearance In. (mm)	Lobe Lift In. (mm)
1600 cc Front & Center	1.0218-1.0226 (25.954-25.975)	.0010-.0025 (.025-.064)	.....
Rear	1.4155-1.4163 (35.954-35.975)	.0010-.0025 (.025-.064)	

TIGHTENING SPECIFICATIONS

Application	Ft. Lbs. (mkg)
Cylinder Head Step 1	14 (2.0)
Step 2	25-29 (3.5-4.0)
Step 3	37-43 (5.1-5.9)
Connecting Rod Nuts	29-31 (4.0-4.3)
Crankshaft Pulley	39-42 (5.4-5.8)
Flywheel Housing	17-20 (2.3-2.7)
Crankcase Plug	51 (7.0)
Crankcase Halves 10 mm Bolts	29-35 (4.0-4.8)
8 mm Bolts	17-20 (2.3-2.7)
6 mm Bolts	3.3-4 (.45-.55)
Intake Manifold	13-16 (1.8-2.2)
Rocker Arm Cover	2.2-2.9 (.30-.40)
Flywheel	30-33 (.42-4.6)
Rocker Arms	37-43 (5.1-5.9)
Oil Pan	3.3-4.0 (.45-.55)

3K-C 4 CYLINDER

ENGINE CODING

ENGINE IDENTIFICATION

Engine serial number and code is stamped in pad on left side of crankcase behind dipstick. First series of digits is engine code.

Application	Code
1166cc Engine (1200 Model)	3K-C

ENGINE, CYLINDER HEAD & MANIFOLDS

ENGINE

NOTE – *Engine and transmission are removed as one unit.*

1) Drain cooling system and disconnect cable from battery to starter. Remove hood support, hinges and hood. Remove right hand headlight rim and radiator grille.

2) Remove hood lock from lock base and remove base with brace. Disconnect electrical connections at horns and remove horns. Remove air cleaner and windshield washer reservoir.

3) Loosen clamps and remove radiator hoses and radiator. Disconnect accelerator cable at bracket and throttle lever on carburetor. Disconnect choke cable from carburetor.

4) Disconnect water hose from bracket on valve cover and disconnect hoses from water pump and water valve. Disconnect cable from water valve.

5) Disconnect electrical wiring harness connector. Remove exhaust pipe from exhaust manifold. Remove left hand front engine mount nut. Disconnect fuel line at fuel pump.

6) Disconnect electrical connections at water temperature sending unit, oil pressure switch, and back-up light switch. Disconnect battery ground cable from crankcase.

7) Remove right hand engine mount nut. Pull out "E" clip from clutch cable at firewall and disconnect clutch cable at lever. Remove coil wire and wire from distributor to coil.

8) Remove carpet from center of floor in drivers compartment. Remove shift lever boot and cap boot. Remove gear shift lever using a suitable tool (09305-12010).

9) Raise rear of vehicle and support with safety stands. Remove drive shaft and insert a suitable plug (09325-12010) in rear of transmission to prevent loss of oil.

10) Remove exhaust pipe support bracket from transmission tail housing. Disconnect speedometer cable at transmission and remove transmission mount bolt from crossmember.

11) Support transmission and remove crossmember. Connect a suitable hoist to engine hangers. Lift engine and transmission assembly up and out toward front of vehicle.

12) To install engine and transmission assembly, reverse removal procedure. With engine installed, adjust clutch pedal freeplay and adjust hood for closing if necessary.

INTAKE MANIFOLD

NOTE – *Intake and exhaust manifold are removed as an assembly.*

1) Remove air cleaner and disconnect choke cable and accelerator cable at carburetor. Disconnect exhaust pipe at exhaust manifold.

2) Disconnect fuel line and vacuum lines from carburetor and remove carburetor. Remove manifold retaining nuts and remove manifolds.

3) To install, reverse removal procedure. Clean mating surfaces, use new gaskets and tighten manifold retaining nuts to specification.

CYLINDER HEAD

1) Drain cooling system and remove air cleaner. Disconnect accelerator cable from support on valve cover and throttle lever. Disconnect choke cable from carburetor.

2) Disconnect water hose bracket from valve cover. Disconnect water hoses from water pump and water control valve. Disconnect cable from water control valve.

3) Disconnect ventilation tube from valve cover. Remove valve cover and bolts securing rocker arm assembly to cylinder head. Remove rocker arm assembly and push rods.

4) Remove upper radiator hose and spark plug wires. Remove windshield washer reservoir. Remove exhaust pipe at exhaust manifold. Remove cylinder head bolts in sequence taking two or three steps and remove cylinder head.

5) To install, reverse removal procedure. Clean mating surfaces and use new gasket. Install gasket with correct side up. Tighten bolts to specification in sequence shown in *Fig. 2*. Adjust valve clearance.

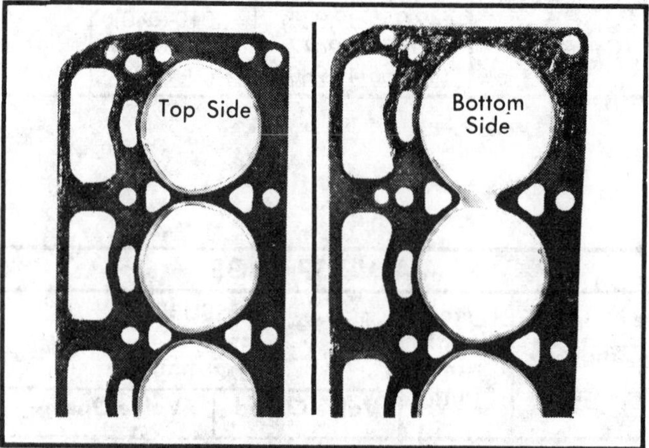

Fig. 1 Cylinder Head Gasket Installation

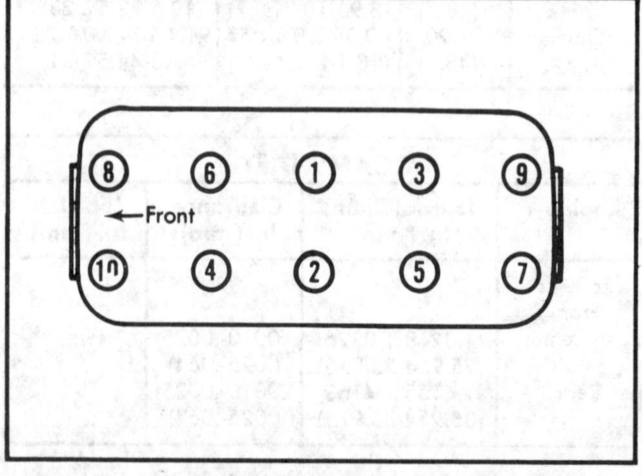

Fig. 2 Cylinder Head Tightening Sequence

3K-C 4 CYLINDER (Cont.)

VALVES

VALVE ARRANGEMENT

E-I-I-E-E-I-I-E

VALVE GUIDE SERVICING

1) Check clearance between valve stem and valve guide. If clearance exceeds .004" (intake) and .005" (exhaust), replace valve guide.

2) To replace valve guide, break off upper portion of guide with a punch and hammer. Drive remaining portion of guide down and out through combustion chamber with a suitable driver (09201-10010).

NOTE — *Cylinder head should be heated to 212-266°F before removal of valve guide.*

3) Install snap ring on valve guide and install valve guide from top using a suitable driver (09201-10010). Drive in guide until snap ring contacts surface of cylinder head.

4) With valve guide installed correctly, ream to appropriate clearance with a reamer.

VALVE STEM OIL SEALS

An "O" ring type seal is installed on end of valve stem above valve keepers after cylinder head is assembled.

VALVE SPRING REMOVAL

1) Remove cylinder head as previously outlined. Compress valve spring with a valve spring compressor and remove valve keepers. Release spring compressor and remove spring retainer, spring cover, spring and spring seat.

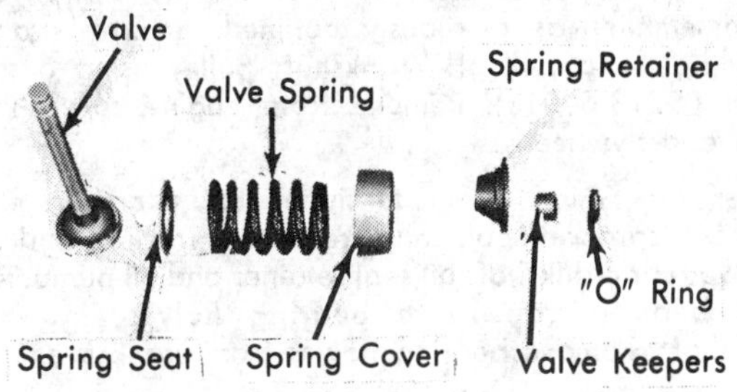

Fig. 3 View of Valve Assembly

2) To assemble, reverse disassembly procedure. After cylinder head is assembled, install "O" ring on valve stem above keepers.

VALVE SPRING INSTALLED HEIGHT

1) With valve spring removed, check length under specified load (see specifications) in a spring tester. Check valve spring free length, if less than 1.83", replace spring.

2) Check valve spring squareness with a steel square. If spring is out of square more than .063" (1.6 mm), replace spring.

ROCKER ARM ASSEMBLY

1) Remove valve cover and rocker arm assembly retaining bolts. Remove rocker arm assembly. Remove retaining clips from both ends of rocker arm shaft. Remove conical springs, rocker arms, springs and support stands.

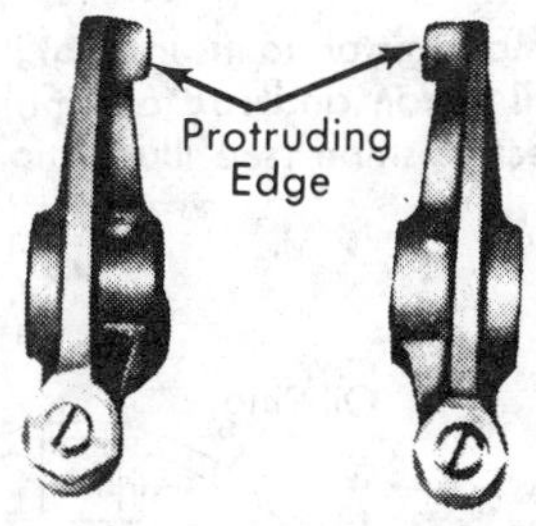

Fig. 4 View of Rocker Arm Assembly

2) Thoroughly clean and inspect all components. Check rocker arm-to-shaft clearance. If clearance exceeds .003", replace rocker arms or shafts as necessary. Reface valve end of rocker arm if worn. Lubricate all components before assembly.

3) Assemble rocker arm assembly in reverse of removal order. There are two types of rocker arms used, install rocker arm so that protruding side of valve end of rocker arm faces support stand. Install rocker stand so that when rocker assembly is installed, "F" mark on rocker stand faces front of engine.

4) To install rocker arm assembly, reverse removal procedure. Install rocker arm assembly so that "F" mark on support stand faces front of engine. Tighten retaining bolts to specifications and adjust valve clearance.

VALVE TAPPET SERVICE

1) Check clearance between valve tappet and tappet bore in crankcase. If clearance exceeds .004", replace tappet with oversize tappet and ream bore in crankcase to appropriate clearance.

2) Oversize tappet available is .002" over standard. Crankcase must be reamed .002" over standard or until correct clearance is obtained. Correct clearance is .0006-.0011".

VALVE CLEARANCE ADJUSTMENT

1) Valve clearance is adjusted with engine cold. Rotate engine until piston of valves being adjusted is at TDC on compression stroke.

2) Adjust valve clearances with engine hot to .008" (intake) and .012" (exhaust).

PISTONS, PINS & RINGS

OIL PAN

NOTE — Engine must be removed to remove oil pan.

1) Remove engine as previously outlined. Drain oil from oil pan and remove oil pan retaining nuts and bolts. Remove oil pan.

2) Clean mating surfaces. Apply sealer to new gasket and install gasket and oil pan. Tighten retaining nuts and screws to specifications. Install engine as previously outlined.

PISTON & ROD ASSEMBLY

1) Remove engine as previously outlined. Remove cylinder head and oil pan as previously outlined. Remove connecting rod cap with bearing half and push piston and connecting rod assembly up and out through top of engine. Mark connecting rod cap to insure that it is installed on same rod and in same position.

3K-C 4 CYLINDER (Cont.)

2) Mark piston to insure that it is installed in same cylinder. To install piston and rod assembly, make sure ring gaps are in correct position (see illustration). Coat piston and rings with oil.

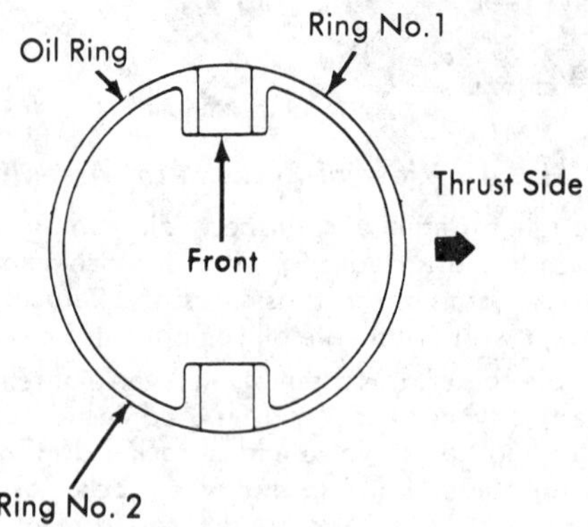

Fig. 5 Piston Ring Gap Arrangement

3) Compress piston rings with a ring compressor and install piston and rod assembly in crankcase with notch in piston facing front of engine. Make sure bearings are properly seated in connecting rod and cap and apply oil to crankshaft journal.

4) Make sure bearing in connecting rod is properly seated against crankshaft journal. Install connecting rod cap in correct position and tighten nuts to specifications. Install cylinder head, oil pan and engine as previously outlined.

PISTON PIN REPLACEMENT

1) Remove circlips from pin hole in piston, heat piston to approximately 158-176°F and drive out piston pin. Make sure piston, pin and connecting rod are marked for assembly with each other.

2) Thoroughly clean and inspect all components. Piston pin should push fit through piston with piston heated to approximately 158-176°F. If pin falls through piston or fit is to loose, replace piston and pin.

3) Check piston pin-to-connecting rod clearance, if more than .002", bushing must be replaced. Press bushing out and install new bushing using a press and a suitable driver (09222-30010). With new bushing installed, ream to correct clearance with piston pin.

4) Thoroughly lubricate all components before assembly. Position piston on connecting rod with notch in piston facing in same direction as mark on lower part of connecting rod (see illustration). Heat piston to 158-176°F and install piston pin and circlips.

FITTING PISTONS

1) Check size of cylinder bore in crankcase, if size is more than .008" over standard, cylinders must be bored to next oversize piston. Pistons and rings are available in .010", .020" and .030" oversize.

2) Check fit of piston in cylinder with a feeler gauge and a spring tension gauge. A .002" or .003" feeler gauge should require 2.2-5.5 lbs., measured on spring tension gauge, to withdraw feeler gauge from between piston and cylinder bore.

3) Check piston rings for wear or damage and replace as necessary. Check piston ring gap in cylinders and piston ring side clearance in pistons (see specifications). Install rings on pistons with marks on rings up and make sure ring grooves in pistons are clean.

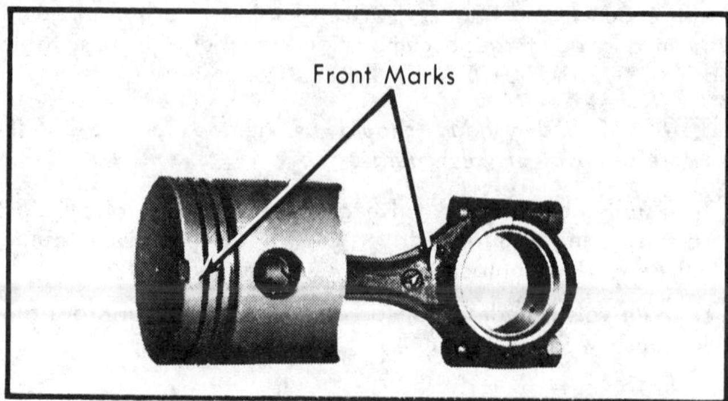

Fig. 6 Piston & Rod Assembly Markings

CRANKSHAFT MAIN & CONNECTING ROD BEARINGS

MAIN & CONNECTING ROD BEARING SERVICE

1) Remove engine as previously outlined. Remove piston and rod assemblies as previously outlined. Remove crankshaft pulley bolt and pull off crankshaft pulley using a suitable puller (09213-60013). Remove front engine cover. Remove clutch and flywheel.

2) Remove timing chain tensioner and damper. Remove camshaft sprocket bolt and remove sprocket and chain. Remove rear crankshaft oil seal retainer and oil pump. Remove main bearing caps with bearing halves and remove crankshaft. Remove bearing halves from crankcase.

3) Thoroughly clean and inspect crankshaft. Blow out all oil passages with compressed air. Check crankshaft for runout by checking center main bearing journal with a dial indicator. If crankshaft is bent more than .0012", replace or repair crankshaft.

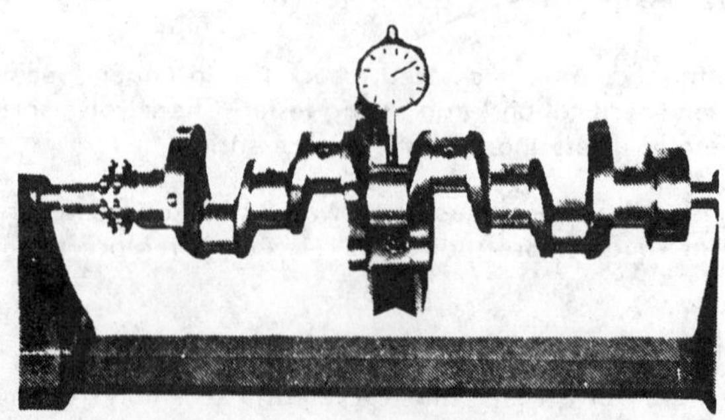

Fig. 7 Checking Crankshaft Runout

3K-C 4 CYLINDER (Cont.)

4) Check main and connecting rod bearing journals with a micrometer. If journals are more than .0003" out-of-round or undersize, crankshaft must be ground to next undersize. Undersize main and connecting rod bearings for ground crankshafts are available in .010", .020" and .030" undersizes.

5) Main and connecting rod bearing clearance is checked by the Plastigage method. To check connecting rod bearing clearance, make sure bearing halves and crankshaft journal are thoroughly clean. Place a piece of Plastigage wire on journal being checked. Install connecting rod cap on connecting rod and tighten nuts to specifications.

6) Remove connecting rod cap and check flattened wire against scale on back of Plastigage package to determine clearance. Main bearing clearance is checked in same manner. If rod bearing clearance is more than standard, a .002" undersize bearing is available. If clearance with this bearing will still exceed standard clearance, crankshaft must be ground to next undersize. The limit of bearing clearance on both main and rod bearings is .004".

7) Install bearing halves in crankcase and in main bearing caps. Lubricate bearings and install crankshaft. Install main bearing caps with arrows pointing toward front of engine. Main bearing caps are numbered one through five and must be installed in that order from front to rear.

8) Tighten bolts to specifications and check crankshaft for freedom of movement. Check crankshaft endplay. See *Thrust Bearing Alignment*. Install rear main bearing oil seal. See *Rear Main Bearing Oil Seal Installation*. Install timing chain in correct position. See *Timing Chain Replacement*. Install remaining components in reverse of removal order. Install engine as previously outlined.

THRUST BEARING ALIGNMENT

Check crankshaft end play with number three main bearing cap and original thrust washers installed. Pry crankshaft back and forth and measure distance moved with a feeler gauge. If end play is more than .012", a thicker thrust washer must be installed. Thrust washers are available in .005" and .010" oversize. Install thrust washers with grooves toward crankshaft.

REAR MAIN BEARING OIL SEAL SERVICE

NOTE – *This procedure is with engine in vehicle.*

1) From inside drivers compartment, remove shift lever boot and cap boot. Remove shift lever using a suitable remover (09305-12010).

Fig. 8 Rear Main Bearing Oil Seal Installation.

2) Raise rear of vehicle and support with safety stands. Disconnect clutch cable from fork. Remove drive shaft and install a sutiable plug (09325-12010) in rear of transmission to prevent loss of oil.

3) Disconnect exhaust pipe support bracket from transmission. Disconnect speedometer cable at transmission. Place a jack under transmission and remove crossmember.

4) Remove mounting bolts from starter, stiffener plate and transmission. Pull transmission back until shaft clears clutch and remove transmission.

5) Remove clutch and flywheel. Remove oil seal retainer and remove oil seal. To install oil seal in retainer, drive in using a suitable driver (09250-10011 set "A").

CAMSHAFT

ENGINE FRONT COVER & OIL SEAL

NOTE – *This procedure is with engine in vehicle.*

1) Drain cooling system and oil pan. Remove air cleaner, hood lock and hood lock base with brace. Disconnect upper and lower radiator hoses and remove radiator.

2) Remove water pump and generator drive belt. Remove crankshaft pulley bolt and pull off pulley with a suitable puller (09213-60013). Remove cover under engine.

3) Remove left and right hand engine mounting nuts. Disconnect exhaust pipe from manifold. Raise front of engine slightly. Front oil seal can be removed now using a suitable puller (09308-10010), or front engine cover can now be removed and seal replaced.

4) If seal is removed with cover still attached to engine, drive in new seal using a suitable driver (09223-22010). To remove cover, remove bolts securing cover to oil pan and remove cover from engine.

5) With cover removed, pry seal out and drive in new seal using a suitable driver (09223-22010). To install cover, clean mating surfaces, use new gasket and sealer and tighten bolts to specifiactions. Reverse removal procedure to install remaining components.

6) To install oil seal retainer, thoroughly clean mating surfaces and use new gasket. Tighten bolts to specifications. Reverse removal procedure to install remaining components.

TIMING CHAIN REPLACEMENT

1) With timing chain installed on engine, attach a spring tension gauge to chain and pull out on chain with a pressure of 22 lbs. and check distance between chain tensioner plunger and tensioner body.

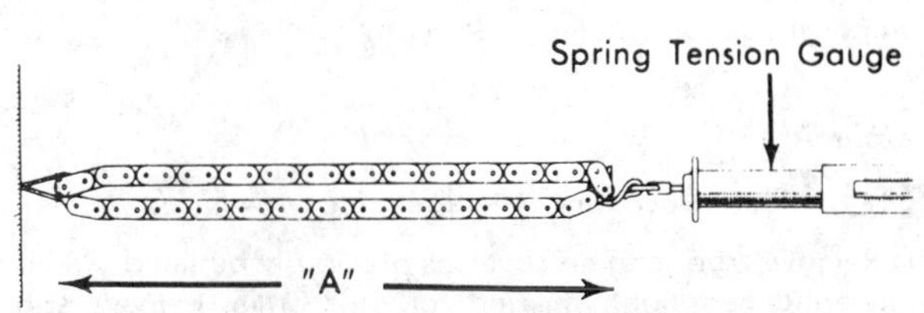

Fig. 9 Timing Chain Checking

3K-C 4 CYLINDER (Cont.)

2) If clearance exceeds .532", chain and sprockets must be removed and checked. Remove camshaft sprocket bolt and remove sprocket and chain. Pull crankshaft sprocket from crankshaft.

3) Secure one link of timing chain and attach spring tension gauge to opposite end (see illustration). With 11 lbs. tension applied to chain, distance "A" should be no more than 10.7". Replace chain if distance is more.

4) Place timing chain on crankshaft sprocket and measure diameter, if less than 2.34", replace sprocket. Measure camshaft sprocket in same manner, if less than 4.48", replace camshaft sprocket.

5) To correctly install sprockets and timing chain, install crankshaft sprocket with "O" mark in line with dowel pin on camshaft (see illustration). Place timing chain on sprocket with mark on chain aligned with mark on sprocket.

6) Align camshaft sprocket "O" mark with mark on timing chain and install camshaft sprocket on camshaft. Tighten camshaft sprocket bolt to specification. Install chain tensioner and vibration damper. Install timing chain cover as previously outlined.

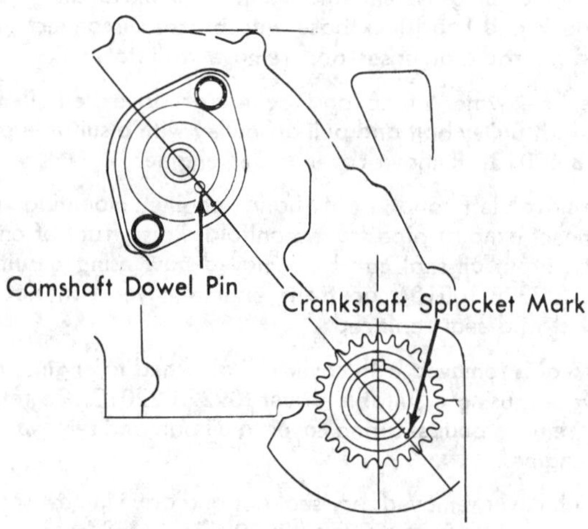

Fig. 10 Timing Chain & Sprocket Installation

TIMING CHAIN TENSIONER & DAMPER

1) Inspect surfaces of tensioner plunger and bore of tensioner body. To test clearance, lubricate plunger and insert it into plunger body. Cover two oil passages with fingers and pull plunger about half way out. Vacuum strong enough to return plunger should be felt.

2) Measure thickness of tensioner head and chain damper wall. Head should be minimum .47" (12 mm) and chain damper should be minimum .28" (7 mm).

CAMSHAFT

NOTE — *This procedure is with engine in vehicle.*

1) Remove front engine cover as previously outlined. Remove right hand headlight rim and radiator grille. Remove spark plugs.

2) Disconnect accelerator cable and choke cable at carburetor. Remove ventilation tube from valve cover and remove valve cover.

3) Loosen valve adjusting screws on rocker arms and remove push rods. Mark or position push rods so that they are installed in same valve tappet. Remove valve tappets and mark or position them to make sure they are installed in same bore in crankcase.

4) Disconnect primary wire and vacuum line from distributor, then remove distributor. Disconnect fuel lines at fuel pump and remove fuel pump.

5) Remove timing chain tensioner. Remove camshaft sprocket and timing chain. Remove camshaft thrust plate and remove camshaft taking care not to damage camshaft lobes or bearings.

6) Check camshaft for runout by checking second bearing journal. If runout exceeds .0012", repair camshaft. Check bearing journals for out-of-round or taper, if more than .001", grind camshaft journals to next undersize and install appropriate bearings in crankcase. See *Camshaft Bearing Replacement*.

7) Check camshaft end thrust. See *Camshaft End Thrust*. To install camshaft reverse removal procedure. Install timing chain correctly. See *Timing Chain Replacement*. Install engine front cover as previously outlined.

CAMSHAFT BEARING REPLACEMENT

NOTE — *Engine must be removed and disassembled to replace camshaft bearings.*

1) With engine removed and disassembled, check clearance between camshaft and bearings. If clearance exceeds .004", bearings should be replaced.

2) If camshaft journals are worn excessively, camshaft journals must be ground to next undersize and appropriate bearing installed. Camshaft bearings are available in .005" and 010" undersize.

3) To replace cam bearings, remove expansion plug from rear of engine. Remove old bearings and install new ones of appropriate size using a suitable bearing replacement tool (09215-22010). Align oil holes in bearings with holes in crankcase.

CAMSHAFT END THRUST

Check clearance between thrust plate and first bearing journal, if clearance exceeds .012", replace thrust plate.

CAM LOBE LIFT

Total height of camshaft lobe is 1.436-1.440" (intake) and 1.432-1.436" (exhaust). Check total lobe height, if less than 1.424" (intake) and 1.420" (exhaust), replace camshaft.

3K-C 4 CYLINDER (Cont.)

ENGINE OILING

Crankcase Capacity – Approximately 3.7 qts. (3.5 ltr) with filter.

Oil Filter – Full flow, mounted on outside of crankcase next to distributor.

Normal Oil Pressure – With engine at 212°F, 28.4 psi @ 300 RPM, 42.6 psi @ 3000 RPM.

Pressure Regulator Valve – Mounted in oil pump. *See Oil Pump.*

ENGINE OILING SYSTEM

Oil is circulated through engine by pressure provided by a trochoid rotor type oil pump. Pump is mounted on bottom of crankcase and driven by camshaft via distributor drive. Oil is drawn from oil pan and circulated through a full flow oil filter into main oil gallery. Oil is then distributed to main and connecting rod bearing journals and camshaft bearing journals. Cylinders and piston pins are lubricated by oil squirting from hole in connecting rod. Oil is supplied to timing chain by oil from timing chain tensioner. Oil flows from number two cam bearing journal to rocker arm shaft to lubricate rocker arms. Excess oil from rocker arm shaft lubricates valves and valve stems.

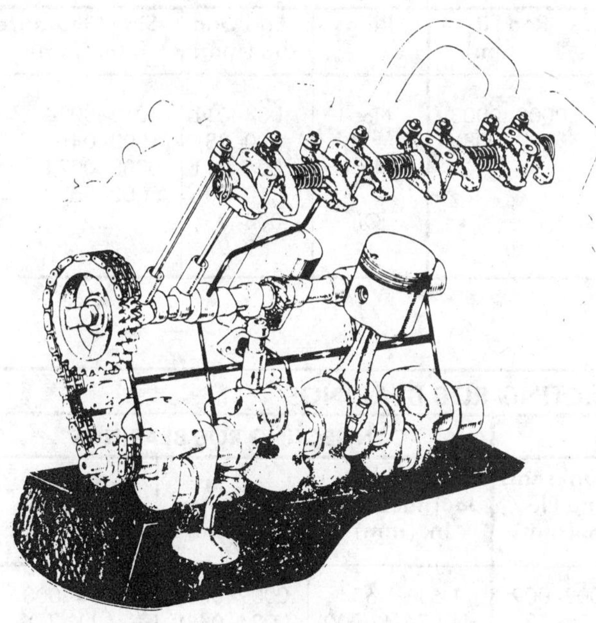

Fig. 11 Engine Oiling System

OIL PUMP

1) Remove oil pan as previously outlined and remove oil pump. Remove oil strainer, pump cover and pressure regulator plug from side of pump body. Remove spring, piston and rotors from pump body.

2) Thoroughly clean and inspect all components. Check rotor tip clearance, if more than .0079", replace rotors. Check clearance between drive rotor and cover. Place a straight edge on mating surface of pump body and insert a feeler gauge between straight edge and drive rotor. If clearance exceeds .0059", replace cover, pump body or rotors.

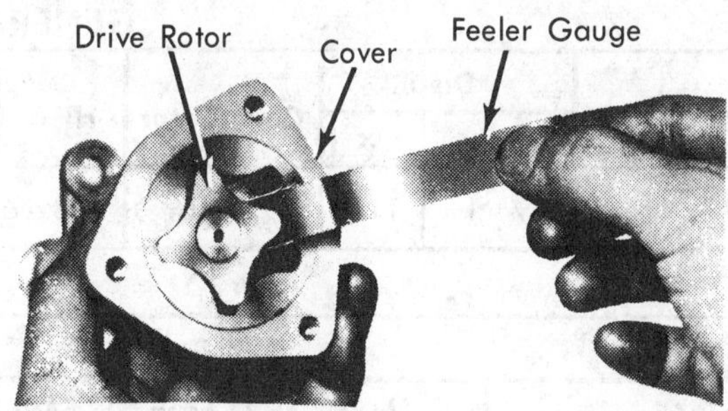

Fig. 12 Oil Pump Tip Clearance Checking

3) Check clearance between outer rotor and pump body with a feeler gauge. If clearance exceed .0079", replace pump body or rotors. Check pressure regulator spring and piston for wear or signs of seizure. Replace as necessary.

4) To assemble pump, reverse disassembly procedure. Install rotors with punch marks to cover. With pump assembled, submerge in clean motor oil and rotate drive shaft to check flow of oil from outlet port. To install pump, reverse removal procedure and install oil pan as previously outlined.

Oil Pump Specifications

Application	In. (mm)
Rotor Tip Clearance	.002-.006 (.04-.16)
	Limit .008 (.2)
Rotor Side Clearance	.001-.004 (.03-.09)
	Limit .006 (.15)
Rotor-to-Body Clearance	.004-.006 (.10-.16)
	Limit .008 (.2)

ENGINE COOLING

WATER PUMP

1) Drain cooling system and remove radiator. Remove water pump drive belt. Remove fan and fan pulley. Remove water pump.

2) To install, clean mating surfaces, use new gasket and reverse removal procedure.

Thermostat – Starts opening at 177°F and is fully open at 203°F.

Cooling System Capacity – 5 qts.

3K-C 4 CYLINDER (Cont.)

ENGINE SPECIFICATIONS

GENERAL SPECIFICATIONS

Year	Displ.		Carburetor	HP at RPM	Torque (Ft. Lbs. at RPM)	Compr. Ratio	Bore		Stroke	
	cu. ins.	cc					in.	mm	in.	mm
1977	71.1	1166	2-Bbl.	73@6000	74.2@3800	9.0-1	2.953	75	2.598	66

VALVES

Engine & Valve	Head Diam. In. (mm)	Face Angle	Seat Angle	Seat Width In. (mm)	Stem Diameter In. (mm)	Stem Clearance In. (mm)	Valve Lift In. (mm)
3K-C							
Intake	.....	45°	45°	.047-.063 (1.2-1.6)	.3136-.3140 (7.965-7.975)	.0014-.0026 (.035-.065)	.....
Exhaust	.....	45°	45°	.047-.063 (1.2-1.6)	.3134-.3140 (7.960-7.975)	.0014-.0028 (.040-.071)	.....

PISTONS, PINS, RINGS

Engine	PISTONS	PINS		RINGS		
	Clearance In. (mm)	Piston Fit In. (mm)	Rod Fit In. (mm)	Rings	End Gap In. (mm)	Side Clearance In. (mm)
3K-C	.001-.002 (.03-.05)	①	.0002-.0003 (.004-.008)	No. 1	.004-.011 (.10-.28)	.0012-.0028 (.03-.04)
				No. 2	.004-.011 (.10-.28)	.0008-.0024 (.02-.06)
				Oil.	.008-.035 (.2-.9)	.....

① — Push fit with piston and pin heated to 158-175°F.

CRANKSHAFT MAIN & CONNECTING ROD BEARINGS

Engine	MAIN BEARINGS				CONNECTING ROD BEARINGS		
	Journal Diam. In. (mm)	Clearance In. (mm)	Thrust Bearing	Crankshaft End Play In. (mm)	Journal Diam. In. (mm)	Clearance In. (mm)	Side Play In. (mm)
3K-C	1.968-1.969 (49.976-50.000)	.0006-.0016 (.016-.040)	No. 3	.002-.009 (.04-.22)	1.653-1.654 (41.976-42.000)	.0009-.0019 (.024-.048)	.004-.008 (.11-.21)

VALVE TIMING

Engine	INTAKE		EXHAUST	
	Open (BTDC)	Close (ABDC)	Open (BBDC)	Close (ATDC)
3K-C	16°	50°	50°	16°

VALVE SPRINGS

Engine	Free Length In. (mm)	PRESSURE Lbs. @ In. (kg @ mm)	
		Valve Closed	Valve Open
3K-C	1.831 (46.5)	70.1@1.512 (31.8@38.4)	.....

3K-C 4 CYLINDER

ENGINE SPECIFICATIONS (Cont.)

CAMSHAFT			
Engine	Journal Diam. In. (mm)	Clearance In. (mm)	Lobe Lift In. (mm)
3K-C		.001-.003 (.03-.07)	Int. .225 (5.72) Exh. .237 (6.02)
Journal			
No. 1	1.701-1.702 (43.21-43.23)		
No. 2	1.691-1.692 (42.96-42.98)		
No. 3	1.681-1.682 (42.71-42.73)		
No. 4	1.671-1.672 (42.46-42.48)		

TIGHTENING SPECIFICATIONS	
Application	Ft. Lbs. (mkg)
Cylinder Head Bolts	39-48 (5.4-6.6)
Manifold Nuts	14-22 (2.0-3.0)
Main Bearing Cap Bolts	39-48 (5.4-6.6)
Connecting Rod Cap Nuts	29-38 (4.0-5.2)
Oil Pan Bolts	2-3(.3-.4)
Camshaft Thrust Plate Bolts	4-7 (.6-.9)
Camshaft Sprocket Bolt	39-48 (5.4-6.6)
Crankshaft Pulley Bolt	33-40 (4.5-6.5)
Flywheel Bolts	39-48 (5.4-6.6)

2T-C 4 CYLINDER

ENGINE CODING

ENGINE IDENTIFICATION

Engine can be identified by first group of numbers and letters in engine serial number. Engine serial number is located on left side of cylinder block behind dipstick. Engine codes are as follows:

Engine Identification

Application	Code
Corolla	2T-C

ENGINE, CYLINDER HEAD & MANIFOLD

ENGINE

1) Disconnect battery and drain cooling system. Remove hood support from body, scribe alignment marks on hood and hinges, and remove hood. Remove right headlight door and remove radiator grille, lower grille moulding, radiator baffle (if equipped), hood lock base, and lock brace.

2) On vehicles with automatic transmission, disconnect oil hoses from radiator. On all vehicles, remove radiator hoses and radiator. Disconnect heater hoses from engine and disconnect water temperature gauge wiring.

3) Remove air cleaner, accelerator torque rod, bond cable and clutch hose bracket. Disconnect right front engine mount. Remove distributor wiring, fuel hose, and disconnect exhaust pipe from manifold. Disconnect left front engine mount.

4) Remove shift lever from inside of vehicle and jack up rear end of vehicle and support on stands. Remove exhaust pipe support bracket, propeller shaft, and disconnect speedometer cable. Remove engine rear support member and lightly support transmission with jack and remove engine rear support.

5) With suitable engine hoist, lift up engine, remove jack and move engine to front and remove from vehicle. To install, reverse removal procedure.

INTAKE MANIFOLD

Removal – Drain cooling system, remove air cleaner and carburetor. Disconnect water hose under manifold. Disconnect ventilation hose from manifold, remove manifold bolts and remove manifold.

Installation – Clean all mating surfaces and use new gaskets. Reverse removal procedure to complete installation.

CYLINDER HEAD

1) Drain cooling system and remove air cleaner assembly. Disconnect radiator hoses, heater hoses, and water temperature sending unit wiring.

2) Remove carburetor torque rod and disconnect choke stove pipe and intake pipe. Disconnect PCV valve hose at intake manifold. Disconnect fuel line and vacuum hose at carburetor.

3) Remove clutch flexible hose bracket at cylinder head and jack up vehicle. Remove exhaust pipe clamp No. 1 and disconnect exhaust manifold from cylinder head.

4) Remove cylinder head bolts in sequence, taking two or three steps. Remove rocker arm assembly and push rods. Remove cylinder head with intake manifold attached. To install, reverse removal procedure.

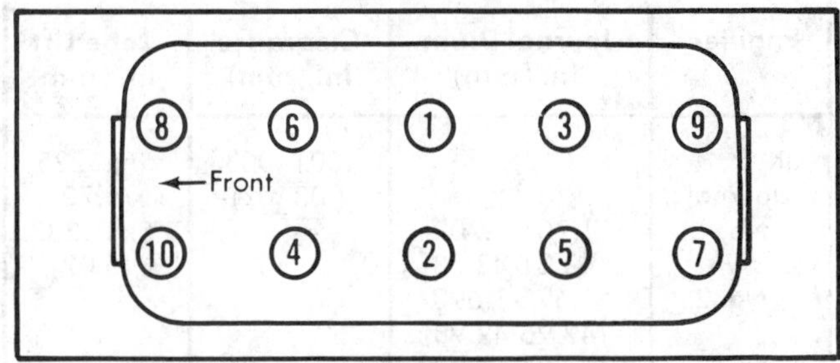

Fig. 1 Cylinder Head Tightening Sequence

VALVES

VALVE ARRANGEMENT

Right Side – All intake.
Left Side – All exhaust.

VALVE GUIDE SERVICING

NOTE – *Manufacturer recommends using new valve guides whenever valves are replaced.*

1) Measure clearance between valve stem and valve guide bushing. If clearance is greater than .003" (.08 mm) for intake or .004" (.10 mm) for exhaust, replace valve and/or guide bushing.

2) Using suitable tool (brass drift), break off top of valve guide. Heat cylinder head to 176-212°F (80-100°C). Using suitable drift (09201-60010), drive out guide bushing toward combustion chamber.

3) Drive in new guide bushing in same direction it was removed. Valve guide should protrude .67" (17 mm) above cylinder head for both intake and exhaust. If necessary, finish bore of valve guide with reamer, to achieve proper clearance.

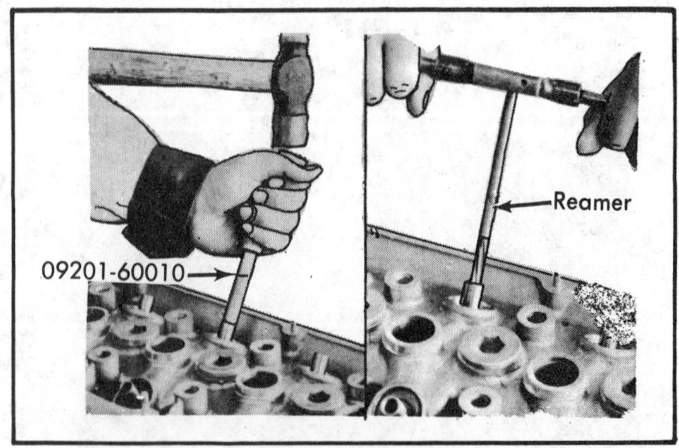

Fig. 2 Removing Valve Guide Bushing and Reaming to Proper Clearance

2T-C 4 CYLINDER (Cont.)

VALVE STEM OIL SEALS

Cup type oil seals are used on all valves. Do not use old seals when valves have been removed. To install, lubricate valve stem and insert in cylinder head. Again lubricate valve stem and carefully push oil seal over valve guide. **NOTE** — *Do not push down on top of seal, use pressure on seal sides only.*

VALVE SPRING FREE LENGTH & INSTALLED HEIGHT

Check all valve springs for correct free length, load length and squareness. Spring squareness should be within .075" (1.9 mm). When installed, valve spring height should be 1.484" (37.7 mm).

ROCKER ARM ASSEMBLY

NOTE — *There are three kinds of valve rocker shaft supports and two kinds of valve rocker shafts and rocker arms. Do not mix them up.*

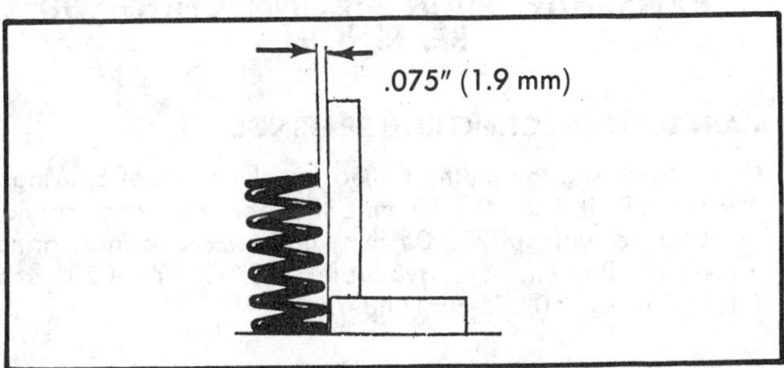

Fig. 3 Using a Straightedge to Check Valve Spring Squareness Limit

Remove cylinder head and remove rocker assembly. To disassemble, remove retainer springs, valve rocker support No. 1, compression springs, valve rocker arms for intake valves, valve rocker arms for exhaust valves and rocker supports No. 3 and No. 2. Clearance between rocker arms and shaft should be .001-.002" (.02-.04 mm). Rocker arm shaft for exhaust valves can be identified by oil hole in end of shaft.

NOTE — *Mark all parts to reassemble in order. Place washer between rocker arm and support number three (center).*

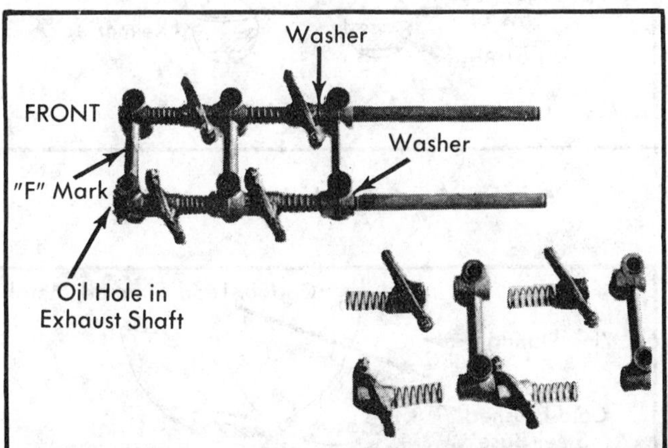

Fig. 4 Partially Disassembled View of Rocker Arm Assembly

VALVE LIFTERS

Inspect lifters and check clearance in bore. If clearance exceeds .004" (.10 mm), select oversize lifter and ream lifter bore to obtain clearance of .001-.002" (.02-.05 mm).

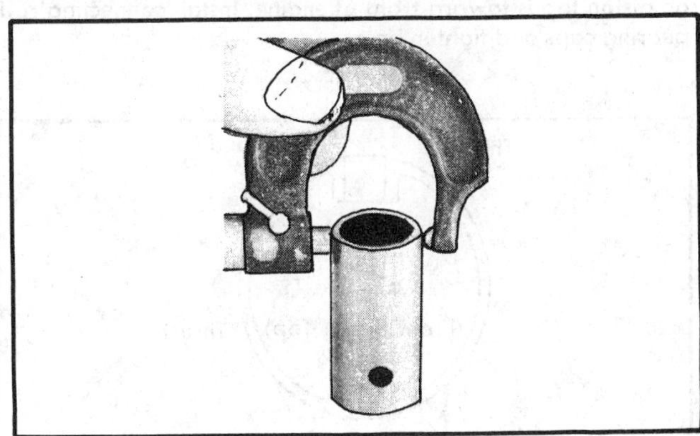

Fig. 5 Measurement Point for Valve Lifter

VALVE CLEARANCE ADJUSTMENT

With number one cylinder at TDC of compression stroke, adjust intake valves of cylinders number one and two, and exhaust valves of cylinders number one and three. Turn crankshaft one complete turn, and adjust intake valves number three and four, and exhaust valves number two and four.

Valve Clearance Adjustment

Valve	Hot In. (mm)
Intake	.008 (.20)
Exhaust	.013 (.33)

PISTONS, PINS & RINGS

OIL PAN

1) Disconnect left and right engine front mounts. Jack up vehicle and support on stands. Remove engine front undercover and right hand stiffener plate. Remove stabilizer bar and oil pan bolts.

2) Place jack under clutch housing and raise slightly taking care not to pull lower radiator hose. Lower oil pan and remove oil pump bolts. Pull oil pan and oil pump forward and outward.

NOTE — *Apply liquid sealer to four corners of oil pan gasket.*

PISTON & ROD ASSEMBLY

Removal — Drain engine coolant system and crankcase. Remove cylinder head, oil pan and oil pump. Remove connecting rod caps and using a wood bar or hammer handle, drive out pistons through top of cylinder block.

2T-C 4 CYLINDER (Cont.)

Installation – Install piston rings on piston with ring gaps spaced and positioned as shown in *Fig. 6.* Code letter and number on ring outside surface should face up. Lubricate piston, crankshaft and cylinder. Using suitable piston ring compressor, insert pistons in cylinders, making sure that notch on piston top is toward front of engine. Install connecting rod bearing caps and tighten bolts.

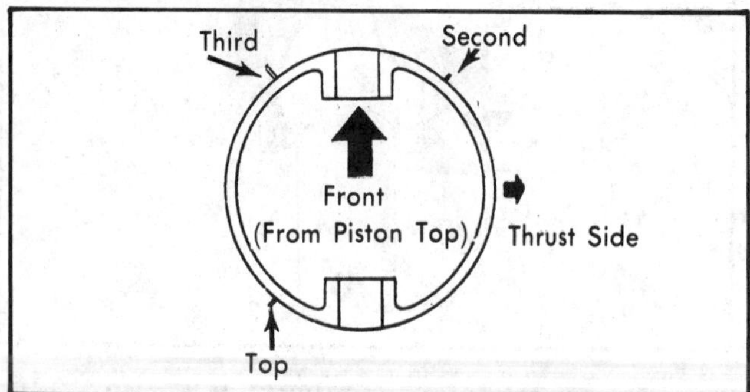

Fig. 6 Installed Position of Piston Rings

NOTE – *Keep pistons arranged so that they will be replaced in the correct bores.*

FITTING PISTONS

1) With piston pin removed and pistons at 68°F, measure diameter of pistons 7/16" (11 mm) below lowest ring groove in direction of thrust. Pistons are available .010", .020", .030" and .040" (.25, .50, .75 and 1.00 mm) oversizes.

2) Measure cylinders at top, center and bottom of bore in two directions. If wear exceeds .008" (.20 mm) on any one cylinder, rebore all cylinders for oversize pistons.

3) Insert piston rings into cylinders and measure end gap at lower part of cylinder where wear is smallest. Measure clearance between ring and ring groove.

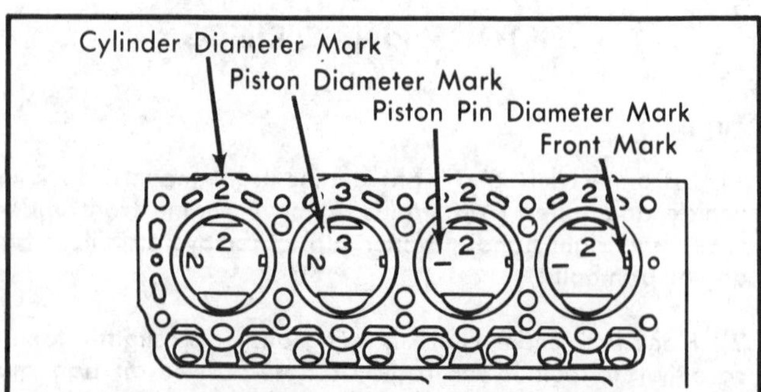

Fig. 7 Diagram Showing Necessary Piston and Cylinder Index Marks

PISTON PIN REPLACEMENT

Using suitable tool and press, press out pin from connecting rod and piston assembly. When installing connecting rod to piston, position so that notch at piston top will be on same side as mark on rod center.

Fig. 8 Using a Press to Remove and Install Piston Pin

CRANKSHAFT MAIN & CONNECTING ROD BEARINGS

MAIN & CONNECTING ROD BEARINGS

1) Using Plastigage method, measure clearance of bearings. Clearance limit is .004" (.10 mm). If proper clearance cannot be obtained with .002" (.05 mm) undersize bearings, grind crankshaft. Bearings are available .002", .010", .020" and .030" (.05, .25, .50, .75 mm) undersizes.

2) Crankshaft bend limit is .001" (.03 mm). Oval and taper wear limit is .0004" (.01 mm). If limits are exceeded, crankshaft must be ground for undersize bearings.

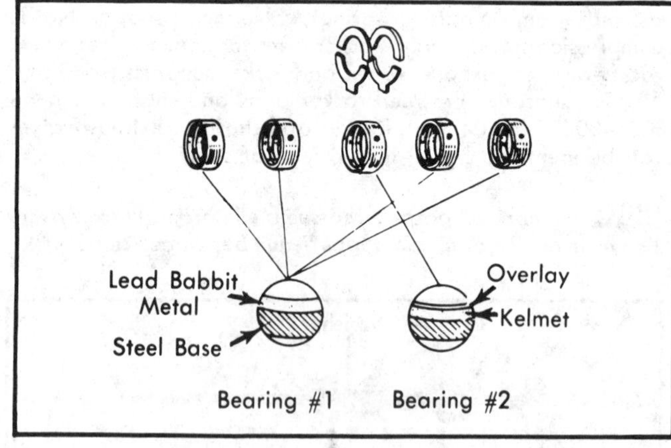

Fig. 9 Crankshaft Bearings

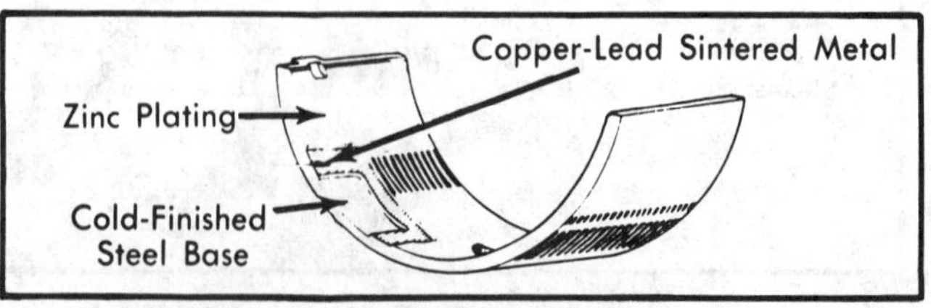

Fig. 10 Connecting Rod Bearings

2T-C 4 CYLINDER (Cont.)

THRUST BEARING ALIGNMENT

Measure crankshaft end play at center bearing. If end play exceeds limit of .012" (.30 mm), install replacement thrust bearings. Bearings are available in standard and oversizes of .005" and .010" (.125 and .25 mm). **NOTE** — *Oil groove on bearing faces toward center.*

REAR MAIN BEARING OIL SEAL

Remove oil seal retainer and drive out old oil seal. Apply grease to seal inner lip and take care not to damage this surface. Using suitable tool (09250-10011), drive new seal into place. Replace oil seal retainer with new gasket.

ENGINE FRONT COVER

1) Jack up vehicle and remove headlamp door and radiator grille. Remove grille lower molding, hood lock base and lock brace. Remove radiator grille and radiator upper baffle. Drain cooling system, disconnect hoses and remove radiator.

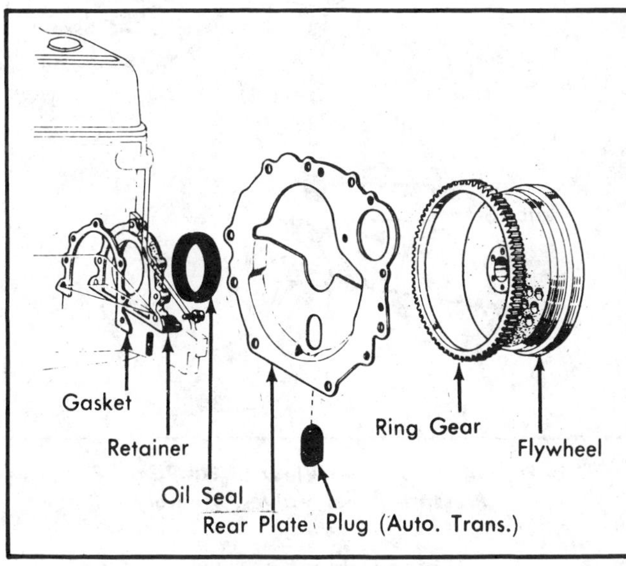

Fig. 11 Oil Seal with Related Components

2) If equipped with Auto. Trans., remove oil cooler hose from radiator. Remove fan belt and water pump assembly. Remove crankshaft pulley. Drain engine oil and remove engine undercover. Remove right hand stiffener plate, and remove oil pan bolts.

3) Timing chain cover may now be removed. To install, reverse removal procedure and tighten components to specifications.

CAMSHAFT

FRONT COVER OIL SEAL

Special Tool 09308-10010 is recommended to pull out oil seal. To install, drive new oil seal into recess in timing cover by using Special Tool 09223-22010.

Fig. 12 Using Special Tool to Install Oil Seal in Front Cover

TIMING CHAIN AND GEAR INSTALLATION

1) After camshaft has been replaced, rotate crankshaft so that key is pointing up with pistons No. 1 and No. 4 at TDC. Turn camshaft and position key so that it lines up with timing mark in thrust plate.

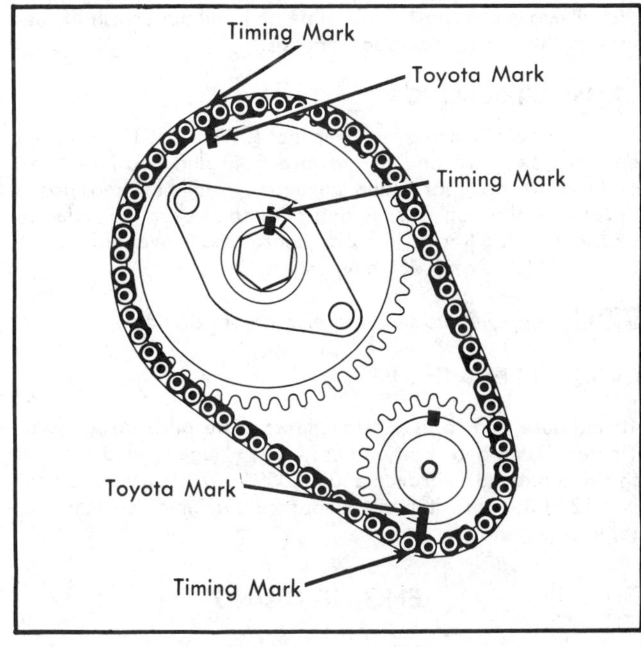

Fig. 13 Timing Chain and Timing Sprocket Marks

2) Assemble crankshaft timing gear and camshaft timing gear to chain so that Toyota marks on each gear line up with chain timing marks. Install gears and chain onto crankshaft and camshaft. Install chain tensioner, chain damper and timing cover.

3) Inspect camshaft for bending and wear. Maximum bend limit is .0012" (.03 mm).

TIMING CHAIN TENSIONER & DAMPER

1) Inspect surfaces of tensioner plunger and bore of tensioner body. To test clearance, lubricate plunger and insert it into

2T-C 4 CYLINDER (Cont.)

plunger body. Cover two oil passages with fingers and pull plunger. Vacuum strong enough to return plunger should be felt.

2) Measure thickness of tensioner head and chain damper wall. Head should be minimum .492" (12.5 mm) and chain damper should be minimum .20" (5.0 mm).

3) To measure chain deflection, pull chain tensioner head with spring scale at 22 lbs. (10 kg). Clearance between tensioner head and body must not exceed .532" (13.5 mm). If limit is exceeded, replace chain, gear or tensioner plunger.

NOTE — *Chain tensioner must be filled with oil after replacing tensioner or timing chain.*

CAMSHAFT

1) Remove timing chain cover. *See Timing Chain Cover Removal.* Remove cam timing gear bolt and timing chain tensioner. Remove timing chain and gears, from camshaft and crankshaft, as a unit. Remove cylinder head, distributor and fuel pump.

2) Remove shift lever and support transmission lightly on jack and remove engine rear support member. Then carefully lower jack. Remove camshaft thrust plate and pull out camshaft, being careful not to damage bearings.

CAMSHAFT BEARINGS

Using suitable bearing remover tool (09215-25010), pull out bearings one, two and five toward front and bearings three and four toward rear. Using same tool, install new bearings in order one through five, taking care to line up oil holes in bearings with oil holes in block. Bearings are available .005" and .010" (.125 and .250 mm) undersize.

NOTE — *Apply liquid sealer to plug at rear of block.*

CAMSHAFT END THRUST

To measure end thrust, install thrust plate and timing gear. Tighten timing gear bolt and use feeler gauge to measure end thrust. Standard clearance is .003-.009" (.07-.22 mm) and limit is .012" (.30 mm). If thrust clearance maximum is exceeded, replace camshaft.

ENGINE OILING

Crankcase Capacity — 4.6 qts. includes filter.

Oil Filter — Full flow type with integral relief valve.

Normal Oil Pressure — 28 psi (2 kg/cm^2) at idle; 43 psi (3 kg/cm^2) running (minimum values).

Oil Pressure Regulator Valve — Begins to open at 51-63 psi (3.6-4.4 kg/cm^2).

OIL PUMP

Oil pan must be removed to gain access to oil pump. If oil pump assembly is tight, tap it out lightly from distributor side. Both drive and driven rotors have punch marks on upper side of rotors, which should be matched when assembling oil pump.

Oil Pump Specifications

Application	In. (mm)
Rotor Tip Clearance	.002-.006 (.04-.16) Limit .010 (.25)
Rotor Side Clearance	.001-.004 (.03-.09) Limit .006 (.15)
Rotor-to-Body Clearance	.004-.006 (.10-.16) Limit .010 (.25)

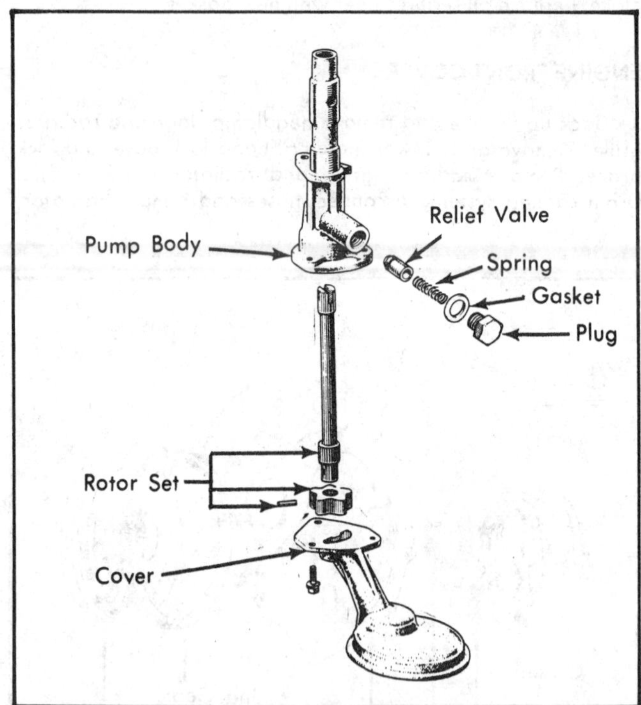

Fig. 14 Exploded View of Oil Pump & Pressure Relief Valve Assembly

ENGINE COOLING

Thermostat — Wax pellet type thermostat with opening temperature of 187-194°F (80-90°C). Fully opened at 212°F (100°C).

Coolant Capacity — Approximately 8 qts.

WATER PUMP

Drain cooling system, remove radiator hoses and by-pass and heater hoses. Remove fan belt. Remove attaching bolts and remove water pump. Separate fan and pulley. To install, reverse removal procedure.

COOLANT DRAINING

Whenever the coolant is drained the following procedure is mandatory: Fill radiator to top, loosen coolant temperature sending unit, and back it out enough to bleed trapped air from cylinder head. When all air has been vented, coolant level in radiator will drop. Be sure that engine is not started during this procedure. Check coolant level.

2T-C 4 CYLINDER (Cont.)

ENGINE SPECIFICATIONS

GENERAL SPECIFICATIONS										
Year	Displ.		Carburetor	HP at RPM	Torque (Ft. Lbs. at RPM)	Compr. Ratio	Bore		Stroke	
	cu. ins.	cc					in.	mm	in.	mm
1977	96.9	1588	1x2-Bbl.	88@6000	91@3800	8.5:1	3.35	85	2.76	70

VALVES							
Engine & Valve	Head Diam. In. (mm)	Face Angle	Seat Angle	Seat Width In. (mm)	Stem Diameter In. (mm)	Stem Clearance In. (mm)	Valve Lift In. (mm)
2T-C							
Intake	1.61 (41)	45°	45°	.055 (1.4)	.3137-.3143 (7.97-7.99)	.0010-.0024 (.025-.061)	.....
Exhaust	1.42 (36)	45°	45°	.055 (1.4)	.3135-.3141 (7.96-7.98)	.0012-.0026 (.030-.066)	.....

PISTONS, PINS, RINGS						
Engine	PISTONS	PINS		RINGS		
	Clearance In. (mm)	Piston Fit In. (mm)	Rod Fit In. (mm)	Rings	End Gap In. (mm)	Side Clearance In. (mm)
2T-C	.002-.003 (.05-.07)	Press Fit	Press Fit	No. 1	.008-.016 (.20-.40)	.0008-.0024 (.02-.06)
				No. 2	.004-.012 (.10-.30)	.002-.0022 (.05-.055)
				Oil	.008-.020 (.20-.51)	.....

CRANKSHAFT MAIN & CONNECTING ROD BEARINGS							
Engine	MAIN BEARINGS				CONNECTING ROD BEARINGS		
	Journal Diam. In. (mm)	Clearance In. (mm)	Thrust Bearing	Crankshaft End Play In. (mm)	Journal Diam. In. (mm)	Clearance In. (mm)	Side Play In. (mm)
2T-C	2.282-2.284 (57.976-58.000)	.0009-.0019 (.024-.048)	Center	.003-.007 (.07-.18)	1.8888-1.8898 (47.976-48.000)	.0009-.0019 (.024-.048)	.006-.010 (.16-.26)

2T-C 4 CYLINDER (Cont.)

ENGINE SPECIFICATIONS (Cont.)

TIGHTENING SPECIFICATIONS	
Application	**Ft. Lbs. (mkg)**
Cylinder Head Bolts	61.5-68.7 (8.5-9.5)
Rocker Arm Support	52-64 (7.2-8.8)
Manifold Bolts	7-12 (1.0-2.0)
Camshaft Thrust Plate	7-12 (1.0-2.0)
Timing Gear Bolt	51-80 (7.0-11.0)
Crankshaft Pulley Bolt	29-43 (4.0-6.0)
Connecting Rod Cap Bolts	29-36 (4.0-5.0)
Main Bearing Cap Bolts	52-64 (7.2-8.8)
Flywheel Bolts	42-43 (5.8-6.0)
Oil Pan Bolts	2-3 (.3-.4)
Radiator Thermo Switch	22-29 (3.0-4.0)

CAMSHAFT			
Engine	**Journal Diam. In. (mm)**	**Clearance In. (mm)**	**Lobe Lift In. (mm)**
2T-C			Int.
No. 1	1.829-1.830 (46.46-46.48)	.0010-.0026 (.025-.066)	.252 (6.39)
No. 2	1.819-1.820 (46.21-46.23)		Exh. .258 (6.55)
No. 3	1.809-1.810 (45.96-45.98)		
No. 4	1.800-1.801 (45.71-45.73)		
No. 5	1.790-1.791 (45.46-45.48)		

VALVE SPRINGS			
Engine	**Free Length In. (mm)**	**PRESSURE (LBS.) Lbs. @ In. (kg @ mm)**	
		Valve Closed	**Valve Open**
2T-C	1.657 (42.1)	58.4@1.484 (26.3@37.7)	.....

20R 4 CYLINDER

ENGINE CODING

ENGINE IDENTIFICATION

Engine serial number is stamped on left side of cylinder block, behind the alternator. Last group of numerals and letters designates engine type.

Application	Engine Code
2189 cc.	20R

ENGINE & CYLINDER HEAD

ENGINE

1) Drain coolant and engine oil. Disconnect battery cables. If equipped with auto. trans., drain fluid. Unscrew hinge bolts and remove hood.

2) Remove air cleaner and disconnect heater hoses, fuel lines and all engine wiring. Disconnect flexible cable to carburetor and remove bracket holding cable to cylinder head cover. Disconnect vacuum hoses to emission control and mark them for reinstallation. Make sure to disconnect throttle retard hose connection at base of carburetor.

3) Disconnect vacuum line for brake booster at intake manifold. If equipped with air conditioning, disconnect lines at compressor. Disconnect plug-in for electric clutch.

4) Remove baffle between radiator and front suspension to gain access to lower radiator hose and auto. trans. hoses. Remove radiator and auto. trans. cooler hoses. Remove fan shrouds and grille, radiator baffle, and radiator. Remove condenser lines and condenser.

5) Remove hood lock support. Disconnect clutch hose bracket (if equipped). Remove front engine mount attaching bolts. Engine will rest on mounts.

6) Disconnect exhaust pipe from exhaust manifold and disconnect support bracket from side of transmission. Remove clutch cylinder (if equipped). Remove support bracket for parking brake equalizer.

7) Disconnect speedometer drive cable, transmission linkage and driveshaft. Remove rear engine support after placing jack under engine and removing engine mounting bolts and crossmember. Engine will rest on jack. Remove engine using engine hoist. To install, reverse removal procedure.

CYLINDER HEAD

1) Disconnect battery and exhaust pipe and drain coolant. Remove air cleaner and cover carburetor. Remove all hoses and linkages to intake manifold, carburetor and cylinder head. Remove spark plug wires and distributor. Remove valve cover and set number one piston to TDC on compression stroke.

2) Paint mating marks on camshaft sprocket and timing chain. Remove rubber half circle seal, distributor drive seal and cam sprocket retaining bolt and remove sprocket from camshaft, allowing sprocket and chain to rest in cylinder head. Remove chain cover bolt, then remove cylinder head bolts in reverse of tightening sequence *(See Fig. 1)*.

3) Pry equally on front and rear of rocker arm assembly and remove same. Lift off cylinder head using care to clear locating dowels. Do not pry between cylinder head and block. To install, reverse removal procedure and note the following: Apply liquid sealer at two front corners of block. Make sure valve timing and clearance is correctly set. Tighten cylinder head bolts in three steps to specified torque and in sequence indicated *(See Fig. 1)*. Set ignition timing statically at 8°BTDC, then reset with timing light.

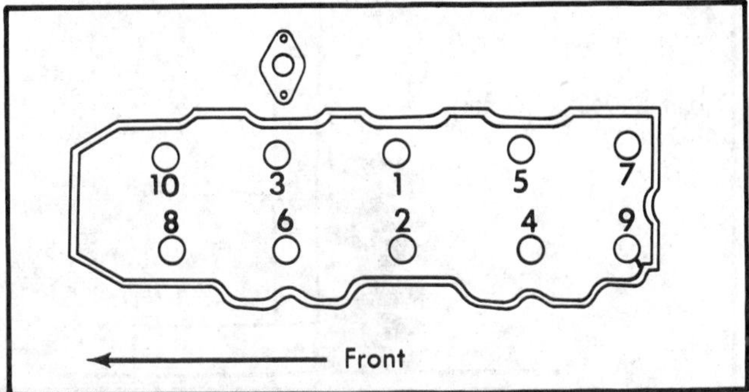

Fig. 1 Cylinder Head Tightening Sequence

VALVES

VALVE ARRANGEMENT

Left Side – All exhaust.

Right Side – All intake.

VALVE GUIDE SERVICING

1) Measure clearance between valve stem and guide. If clearance exceeds specifications, valve guides must be replaced. If valve guide being replaced has a snap ring installed, break guide using brass punch and hammer. Using driver tool (09201-60011), drive old guide down through combustion chamber.

NOTE – *Only replacement valve guides have snap rings.*

2) Drive in new valve guide from top of head until snap ring contacts cylinder head. Guide should have .75" (19 mm) protrusion above cylinder head. Ream new valve guide to provide proper stem clearance.

VALVE STEM OIL SEALS

1) Using a suitable spring compressor, remove valve keepers. Withdraw spring retainer and springs. Remove valve stem oil seal from end of valve guide.

20R 4 CYLINDER (Cont.)

2) Slide a new oil seal over valve stem, using care not to damage seal as it passes over keeper grooves. Force seal over end of valve guide. Reverse removal procedure for remaining components.

VALVE SPRING INSTALLED HEIGHT

1) With valve spring removed, check length under specified load in a spring tester. Check valve spring free length, if less than specified, replace spring.

2) Check valve spring squareness with a steel square. If spring is out of square more than specified, replace spring.

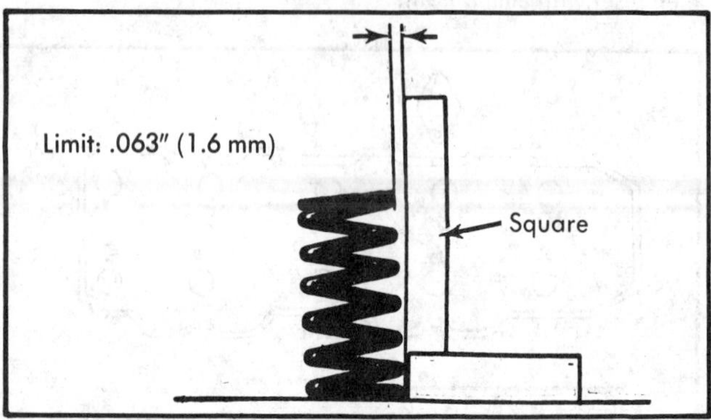

Fig. 2 Checking Valve Spring Squareness

ROCKER ARM ASSEMBLY

If rocker arms appear loose, disassemble rocker arm assembly and measure rocker arm-to-shaft clearance. Clearance should be .0004-.0020″ (.01-.05 mm). If clearance is greater than specifications, replace rocker arm and/or shafts. Reassemble in reverse of disassembly noting that all rocker arms are identical but that all rocker stands are different *(See Fig. 3)*.

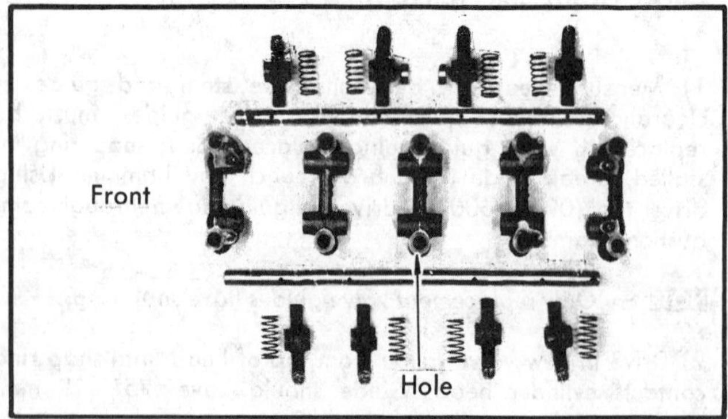

Fig. 3 Disassembled View of Rocker Arm Assembly

VALVE CLEARANCE ADJUSTMENT

Set No. 1 piston to TDC compression stroke. Sprocket timing mark should be slightly left of top. Valve clearance is measured between valve stem and rocker arm. Adjust intake valves 1 & 2 to .008″ (.2 mm) and exhaust valves 1 & 3 to .012″ (.3 mm). Rotate crankshaft one complete revolution and align timing marks at pulley. Adjust intake valves 3 & 4 to .008″ (.2 mm) and exhaust valves 2 & 4 to .012″ (.3 mm).

PISTONS, PINS & RINGS

OIL PAN

NOTE – *No on-car removal procedure available.*

NOTE – *Apply liquid sealer to four corners of oil pan gasket where front cover and rear seal retainer join cylinder block.*

PISTON & ROD ASSEMBLY

Removal – Remove connecting rod caps and remove bearings. Push piston and rod assembly up through cylinder head side. Mark all components with cylinder numbers for correct reassembly.

Installation – Apply oil to piston and piston rings. Install compression rings so stamped code on ring faces upward. Position piston ring gaps as shown in *Fig. 4*. Using suitable ring compressor, install piston and rod assembly in cylinder. Make sure indent on piston faces forward.

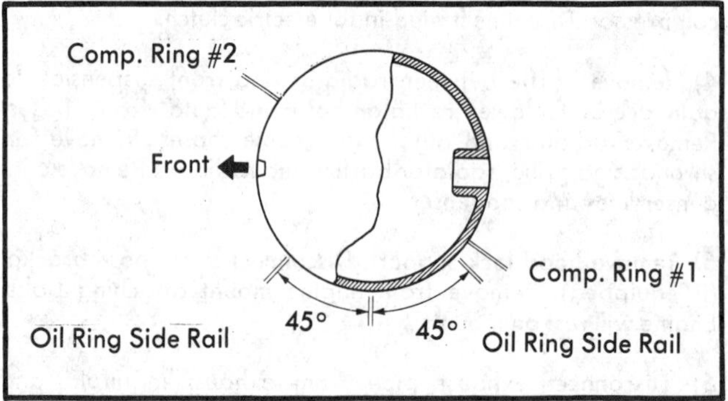

Fig. 4 Correct Piston Ring Gap Arrangement

FITTING PISTONS

1) Measure clearance of piston in cylinder. When measuring piston diameter, measure 90° to pin bore .83″ (21 mm) from piston skirt. If clearance exceeds specifications, cylinders must be bored for oversize piston.

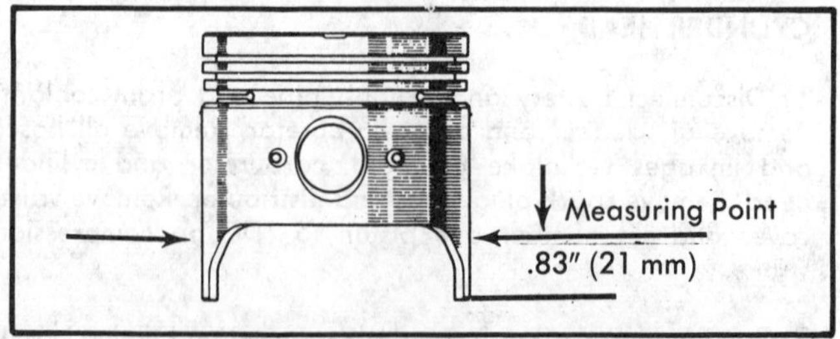

Fig. 5 Piston Diameter Measuring Point

20R 4 CYLINDER (Cont.)

2) Measure piston ring end gaps in cylinder. If cylinder has not been bored, check gap with ring in lowest part of cylinder. Check clearance of piston ring in ring groove.

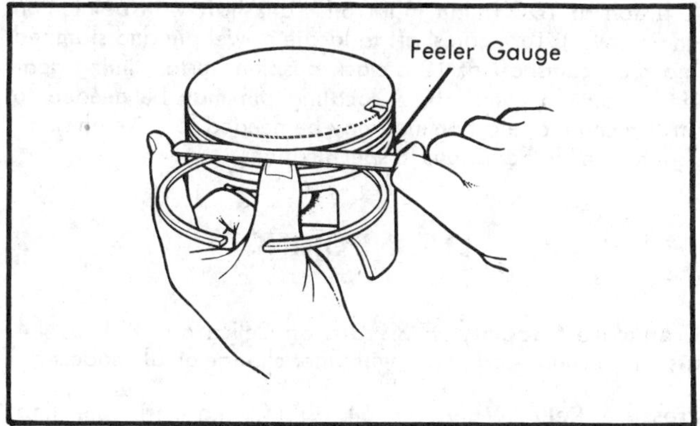

Fig. 6 Measuring Ring Groove Clearance

PISTON PINS

Removal – Heat piston to 176°F (80°C) and push piston pin out of piston and connecting rod. Piston pin should push through connecting rod with thumb pressure when rod is at 68°F (20°C). If pin is too loose in rod, press out bushing from connecting rod using press tool (09222-30010). Install and hone new bushing. **NOTE** – *Piston and pin are a matched set.*

Installation – Heat piston to 176°F (80°C) and position piston and connecting rod so mark on rod and indent on piston crown face same direction. Push piston pin into piston and rod assembly.

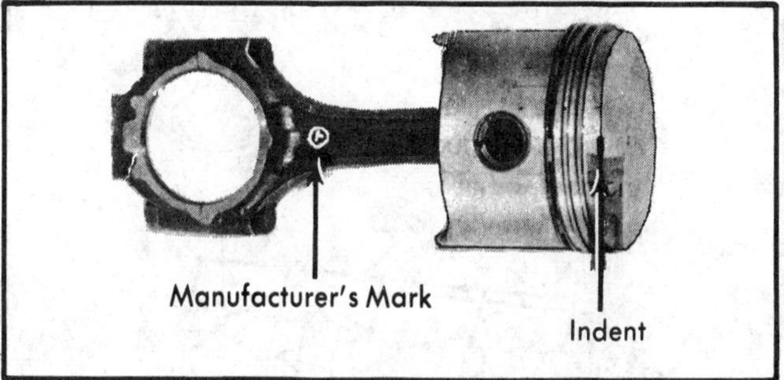

Fig. 7 Correct Alignment of Piston & Rod Assembly

CRANKSHAFT MAIN & CONNECTING ROD BEARINGS

MAIN & CONNECTING ROD BEARINGS

1) Measure crankshaft runout at center bearing journal. If runout exceeds .004" (.1 mm), replace crankshaft. Inspect all journals for wear or scoring. Check for out-of-round or taper. If crankshaft is worn excessively, grind journals for undersize bearings.

2) Measure bearing clearances using Plastigage method. If clearance exceeds specifications, grind journals for undersize bearings. Both main and connecting rod bearings are available .010" (.25 mm) undersize.

THRUST BEARING ALIGNMENT

Check crankshaft thrust clearance at thrust bearing using a feeler gauge. If end play exceeds limit of .012" (.3 mm), replace thrust washers. Thrust washers are available in two oversizes, .005" (.13 mm) and .010" (.25 mm).

REAR MAIN BEARING OIL SEAL

With rear main bearing oil seal retainer removed, pry out old seal. Using suitable tool (09223-41010) drive oil seal in place. After installing new seal, coat seal lip lightly with multi-purpose grease.

Fig. 8 Installed View of Rear Seal & Retainer

CAMSHAFT

ENGINE FRONT COVER OIL SEAL

With engine front cover removed, pry out old seal toward front side. Using suitable tool (09223-50010), drive seal into place. After installing new seal, coat seal lip lightly with multi-purpose grease.

TIMING CHAIN

Removal – 1) Remove cylinder head and oil pan. Remove radiator, drive belts, air pump and alternator bracket. Remove crankshaft pulley and timing chain cover assembly.

2) Remove chain from damper sprocket and remove cam sprocket and chain. Using puller (09213-36010), remove both oil pump drive and chain sprocket. Check chain, sprockets, tensioner and chain dampers for wear and replace as necessary.

Installation – 1) Turn crankshaft until shaft key is at TDC and slide sprocket over key. Position chain with chromed link over sprocket and aligned with mark on sprocket *(See Fig. 9)*.

20R 4 CYLINDER (Cont.)

Fig. 9 Aligning Crankshaft Sprocket & Timing Chain

2) Install cam sprocket in chain so that timing mark on sprocket is located between two chromed links on chain (See *Fig. 10*). Slide oil pump drive spline over crankshaft key. Install new timing cover gasket after first cleaning mounting surface. Turn cam sprocket counterclockwise to remove slack from chain and install timing chain cover.

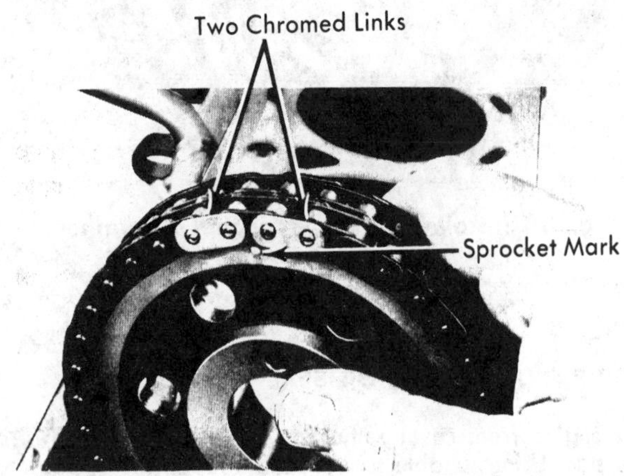

Fig. 10 Aligning Camshaft Sprocket & Timing Chain

3) Continue installation in reverse of removal procedure and set cam timing as follows: With engine at number one cylinder TDC on compression stroke, position camshaft so that dowel on sprocket flange is at 12 o'clock position. Complete reassembly procedure.

CAMSHAFT

With cylinder head and rocker arm assembly removed, remove camshaft bearing caps and lift out camshaft. Camshaft bearing clearance may be checked using Plastigage method. If clearance exceeds specifications, replace cylinder head and/or camshaft. To install, reverse removal procedure. Install bearing caps in numbered order with arrows pointing toward the front. Adjust valve timing.

VALVE TIMING

Valve timing is determined by the relationship between the camshaft and the crankshaft. Turn crankshaft to position No. 1 piston at TDC (align mark on crankshaft with pointer on chain cover). Turn camshaft to locate dowel pin and stamped mark on camshaft at 12 o'clock position. Install timing gear and chain on camshaft. A locating pin may be needed to stretch chain and a hammer may be needed to drive on gear. Tighten timing gear bolts to specifications.

ENGINE OILING

Crankcase Capacity – 3.9 qts. on Celica and Pickup, 4.4 qts. on Corona. Add .9 qts. with filter change on all models.

Pressure Relief Valve – 64 psi (4.5 kg/cm²) operating pressure.

Oil Filter – Full-flow type with paper elements. Located at right side of engine.

ENGINE OILING SYSTEM

Forced feed oiling system utilizing a gear and crescent type oil pump driven from front of crankshaft. Oil from oil pan is pumped through a full flow oil filter and then to oil galleries in cylinder block. Oil is fed to crankshaft bearings, timing chain assembly, camshaft and rocker arm assembly.

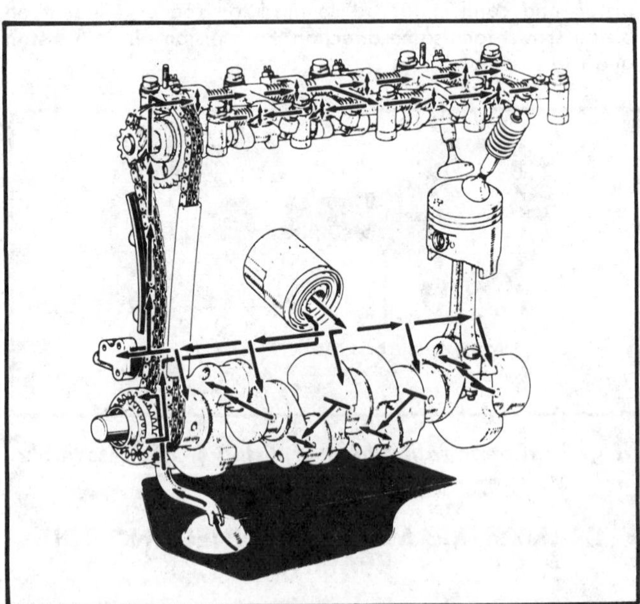

Fig. 11 Engine Oiling System

OIL PUMP

1) Remove oil pan and strainer. Remove drive belts and crankshaft pulley. Unbolt and remove oil pump assembly. Remove oil pump drive spline from crankshaft and "O" ring

20R 4 CYLINDER (Cont.)

from engine block. Remove relief valve plug, spring and piston from pump body. Remove driven and drive gear from pump body.

2) Inspect pump visually for wear or damage and replace parts as necessary. Place gears in pump body and with feeler gauges measure clearance between driven gear and pump body, driven gear-to-crescent tip clearance, drive gear-to-crescent tip clearance. Measure end clearance by placing straight edge across pump body and measuring clearance between gears and straightedge. To reassemble and install, reverse disassembly and removal procedure.

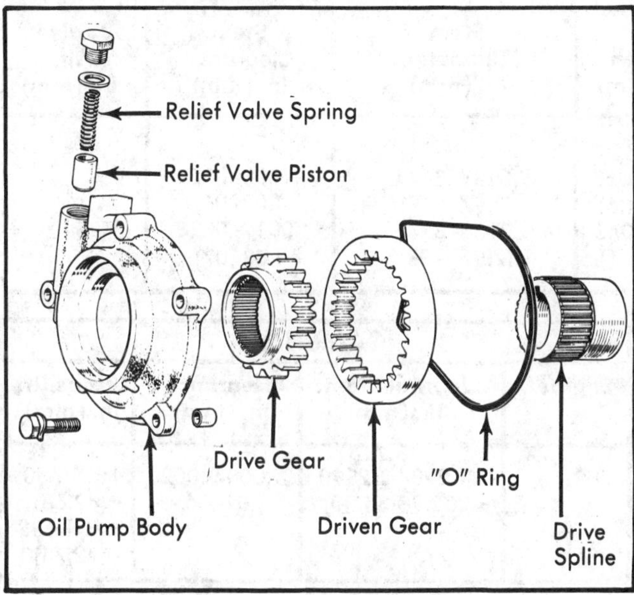

Fig. 12 Exploded View of Oil Pump

Oil Pump Specifications

Application	In. (mm)
Driven Gear-to-Pump Body	.0024-.0059 (.06-.15)
Driven Gear-to-Crescent	.0059-.0083 (.15-.21)
Drive Gear-to-Crescent	.0087-.0098 (.22-.25)
End Clearance	.0012-.0034 (.03-.09)

ENGINE COOLING

Thermostat – Starts to open at 187-194°F (86-90°C) and is fully open at 212°F (100°C).

Cooling System Capacity – 8.5 qts. (including heater).

Radiator Cap – 13 psi (.9 kg/cm²).

WATER PUMP

Loosen fan belt and remove fluid coupling assembly, water pump pully and fan belt. Remove fan from fluid coupling. Remove water pump assembly. To install, reverse removal procedure and use a new gasket.

ENGINE SPECIFICATIONS

GENERAL SPECIFICATIONS

Year	Displ.		Carburetor	HP at RPM	Torque (Ft. Lbs. at RPM)	Compr. Ratio	Bore		Stroke	
	cu. ins.	cc					in.	mm	in.	mm
1977	133.6	2189	1x2-Bbl.	①96@4800	120@2800	8.4-1	3.48	88.5	3.50	89.0

① – Horsepower is 90@4800 RPM on California models.

PISTONS, PINS, RINGS

Engine	PISTONS	PINS		RINGS		
	Clearance In. (mm)	Piston Fit In. (mm)	Rod Fit In. (mm)	Rings	End Gap In. (mm)	Side Clearance In. (mm)
20R	.0012-.0020 (.03-.05)	Press Fit ①	.0002-.0004 (.005-.011) ②	No. 1	.004-.012 (.10-.30)	.008 (.2)
				No. 2	.004-.12 (.10-.30)	.008 (.2)
				Oil	.....	.....

① – Push fit with piston heated to 176°F (80°C).

② – Push fit with piston at room temperature.

20R 4 CYLINDER (Cont.)

ENGINE SPECIFICATIONS (Cont.)

CRANKSHAFT MAIN & CONNECTING ROD BEARINGS							
	MAIN BEARINGS				CONNECTING ROD BEARINGS		
Engine	Journal Diam. In. (mm)	Clearance In. (mm)	Thrust Bearing	Crankshaft End Play In. (mm)	Journal Diam. In. (mm)	Clearance In. (mm)	Side Play In. (mm)
20R	2.3614-2.3622 (59.98-60.00)	.0010-.0022 (.025-.055)	Center	.0008-.0079 (.02-.20)	2.0862-2.0866 (52.99-53.00)	.0010-.0022 (.03-.06)	.0063-.0102 (.16-.26)

VALVES							
Engine & Valve	Head Diam. In. (mm)	Face Angle	Seat Angle	Seat Width In. (mm)	Stem Diameter In. (mm)	Stem Clearance In. (mm)	Valve Lift In. (mm)
20R							
Intake	.....	45°	45°	.047-.063 (1.2-1.6)	.3138-.3144 (7.97-7.99)	.0008-.0024 (.02-.06)	.....
Exhaust	.....	45°	45°	.047-.063 (1.2-1.6)	.3136-.3142 (7.97-7.98)	.0012-.0028 (.03-.07)	.....

VALVE SPRINGS			
Engine	Free Length In. (mm)	PRESSURE Lbs. @ In. (kg @ mm)	
		Valve Closed	Valve Open
20R	1.79 (45.4)	55@1.594 (25.0@40.5)	.....

CAMSHAFT			
Engine	Journal Diam. In. (mm)	Clearance In. (mm)	①Lobe Lift In. (mm)
20R	1.2984-1.2990 (32.98-33.00)	②.0004-.0020 (.01-.05)	Int. 1.680 (42.68) Exh. 1.682 (42.74)

① — Total Lobe Height.
② — End play is .0031-.0071" (.08-.18 mm)

TIGHTENING SPECIFICATIONS	
Application	Ft. Lbs. (mkg)
Cylinder Head Bolts	52-64 (7.2-8.8)
Main Bearing Cap Bolts	69-83 (9.5-11.5)
Connecting Rod Cap Bolts	39-48 (5.4-6.6)
Camshaft Bearing Cap Bolts	12-17 (1.7-2.3)
Timing Chain Cover	7-12 (1.0-1.6)
Crankshaft Pulley Bolt	80-94 (11-13)
Camshaft Sprocket Bolt	51-65 (7.0-9.0)
Intake Manifold	11-15 (1.5-2.1)
Exhaust Manifold	29-36 (4.0-5.0)
Oil Pan	2-3 C.3-.4)
Flywheel Bolts	61-69 (8.5-9.5)

2F 6 CYLINDER

ENGINE CODING

ENGINE IDENTIFICATION

Engine number is stamped on right side of cylinder block above starter motor. First two digits indicate engine type.

Application	Engine Code
4230 cc	2F

ENGINE, CYLINDER HEAD & MANIFOLD

ENGINE

1) Disconnect battery and drain cooling system. Remove hood, radiator grille and hood lock support rod. Disconnect hood lock from radiator support and remove radiator support. Disconnect heater and radiator hoses and remove radiator.

2) Disconnect all necessary wiring and fuel lines. Remove fuel filter assembly and air cleaner. Disconnect rod end of high and low shift rod from shift link lever. Disconnect throttle rod, choke rod, and accelerator rod from carburetor.

3) Remove vacuum hose connection on intake manifold and remove check valve of transfer front drive controller. Disconnect exhaust pipe from manifold and parking brake cable from intermediate lever. Disconnect front propeller shaft from transfer output front shaft flange.

4) Remove engine and transmission undercovers. Disconnect high and low shift rod from transfer high and low shift inner lever. Remove high and low shift link lever and high and low shift rod. Remove clutch release cylinder assembly from engine mount rear bracket.

5) Loosen clamp screws and disconnect vacuum hoses from transfer diaphragm cylinder. Remove front drive indicator switch and disconnect speedometer drive cable from transmission. Disconnect rear propeller shaft from transmission.

6) Disconnect gear shifting rod and gear selecting rod from gear shift outer lever and gear select outer lever. Remove nuts at front and rear engine mounts. Using suitable hoist, move engine up and forward to remove. To install, reverse removal procedure.

INTAKE & EXHAUST MANIFOLDS

Removal – 1) Disconnect battery and remove air cleaner. Disconnect throttle rod, choke rod, accelerator wire, vacuum line, and fuel line from carburetor.

2) Disconnect magnetic valve wire from ignition coil terminal and remove carburetor assembly. Disconnect exhaust pipe from exhaust manifold. Remove manifold nuts, manifolds and gaskets.

Installation – Thoroughly clean all gasket surfaces and install new gaskets. Install manifold assembly and gradually tighten bolts working from center out. Install remaining components in reverse of removal procedure.

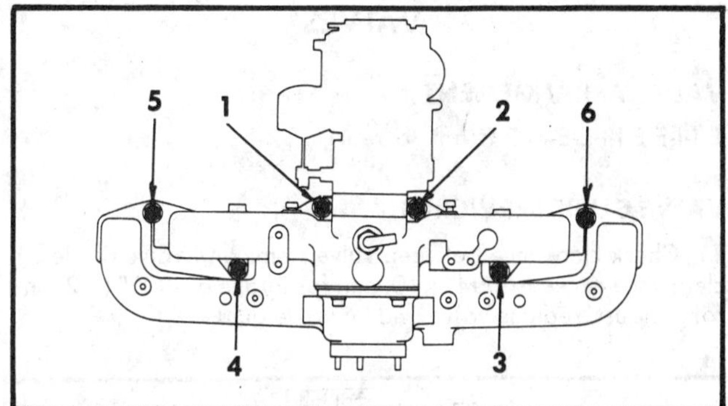

Fig. 1 Manifold Tightening Sequence

CYLINDER HEAD

Removal – 1) Disconnect battery, drain cooling system and remove air cleaner. Remove intake and exhaust manifolds. See *Intake & Exhaust Manifolds*. Remove bolts attaching oil filler tube to rocker arm cover and remove rocker arm cover.

2) Disconnect all necessary wiring, radiator and heater hoses. Remove ignition coil from cylinder head. Remove rocker arm assembly support retaining nuts and bolts and remove rocker arm assembly.

3) Remove push rods and keep in order for proper installation. Loosen cylinder head bolts gradually in sequence shown and remove cylinder head.

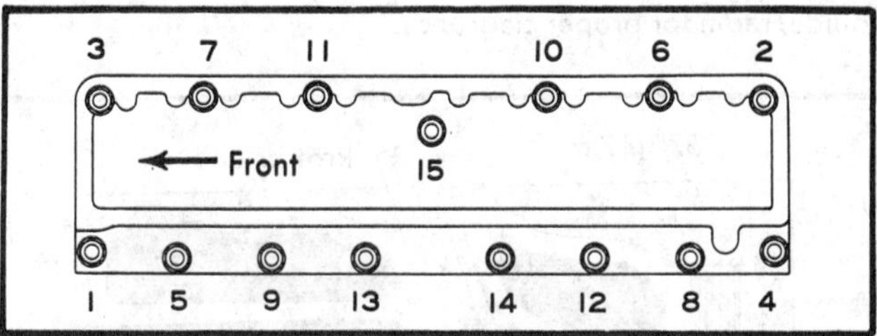

Fig. 2 Cylinder Head Loosening Sequence

Installation – Clean all gasket surfaces and install new gasket. Install cylinder head and tighten bolts gradually in sequence shown. Reverse removal procedure for remaining components.

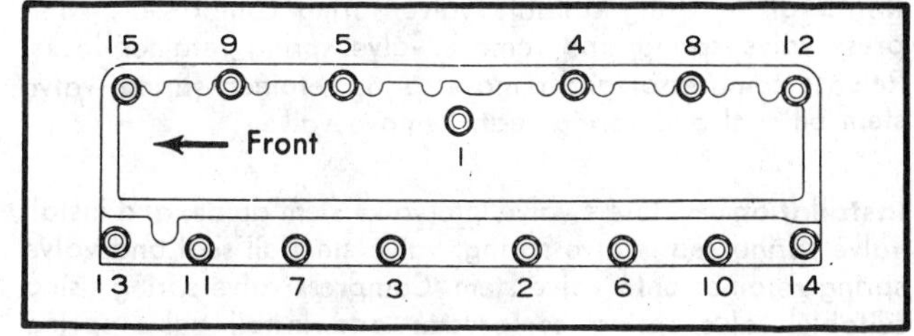

Fig. 3 Cylinder Head Tightening Sequence

2F 6 CYLINDER (Cont.)

VALVES

VALVE ARRANGEMENT

E-I-I-E-E-I-I-E-E-I-I-E (front to rear).

VALVE GUIDE SERVICING

1) Check clearance between valve stems and valve guides. If clearance exceeds .004" (.10 mm) for intake or .005" (.12 mm) for exhaust, replace valve and/or valve guide.

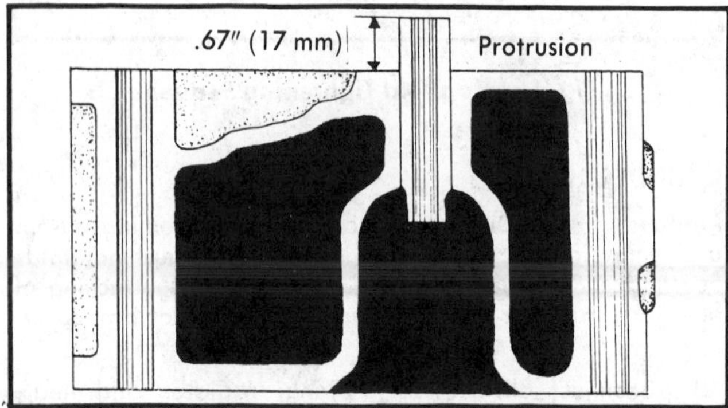

Fig. 4 Intake Valve Guide Installation

2) To replace valve guide, drive guide toward combustion chamber using suitable driver (09201-60011). Using same tool, install new guide from top of cylinder head. Valve guide should extend .67" (17 mm) from top of cylinder head *(See Fig. 4 & 5)*. Intake valve guide length is 2.13" (54 mm) and exhaust guide is 2.32" (59 mm) long. After installing new guide, ream for proper clearance.

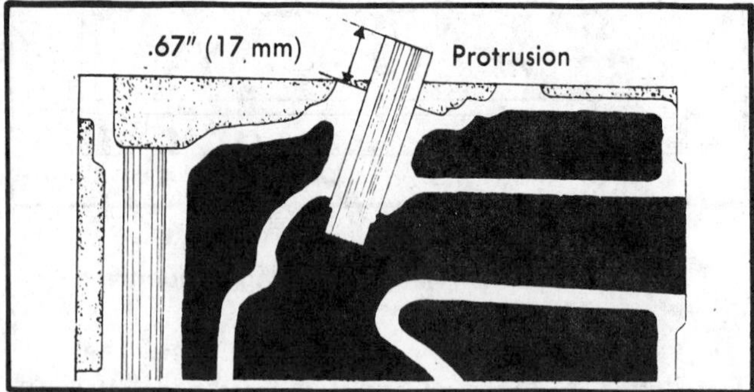

Fig. 5 Exhaust Valve Guide Installation

VALVE SPRINGS

Removal – Using suitable valve spring compressor, compress valve spring and remove valve spring retainer locks. Release compressor and remove spring retainer, spring, valve stem oil seal and spring seat. Remove valve.

Installation – Insert valve into valve stem guide, and install valve spring seat, valve spring, valve stem oil seal and valve spring retainer onto valve stem. Compress valve spring using suitable valve spring compressor and install valve spring retainer locks. Make sure retainer locks seat properly in valve stem groove.

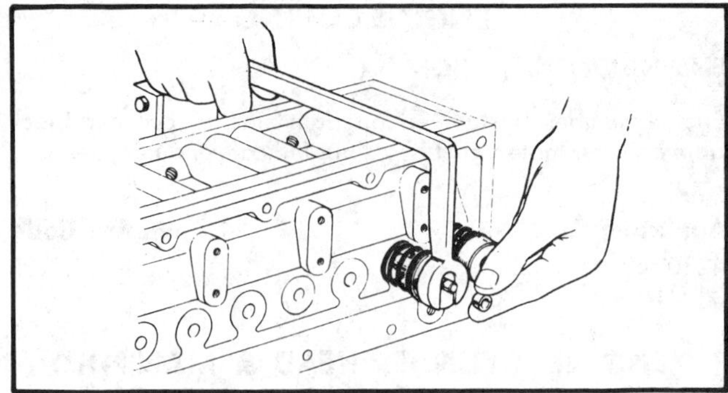

Fig. 6 Removing Valve Springs

VALVE SPRING INSTALLED HEIGHT

After assembling valve, check installed height of valve spring by measuring from spring seat to point where spring contacts oil shield or spacer. Installed height of both intake and exhaust valve springs should be 1.693" (43.0 mm). Check squareness of springs by placing spring on flat surface next to steel square. Squareness should be within .071" (1.8 mm).

ROCKER ARM ASSEMBLY

1) Check rocker arms and shaft for damage or wear. If clearance is excessive, replace bushing and ream to provide a clearance of .0007-.0015" (.017-.037 mm). When replacing bushing make sure oil hole in bushing lines up with oil hole in rocker arm.

2) Install rocker arms, springs and rocker shaft supports onto valve rocker shaft, then install valve rocker shaft lock springs. **NOTE** – *There are two types of rocker arms and two types of rocker supports. Rocker support with oil hole is installed in the fourth position. Boss of rocker supports should face forward.*

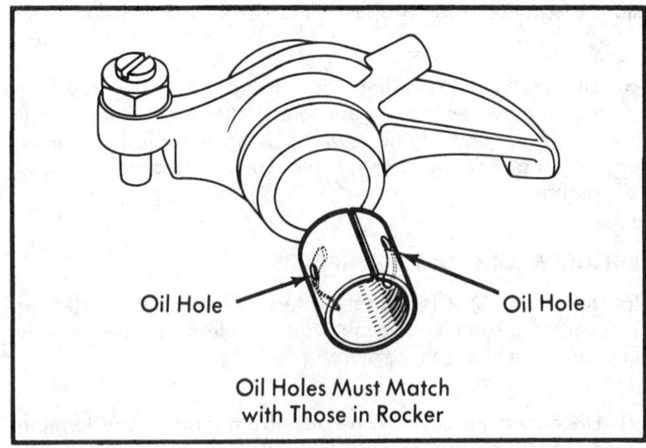

Fig. 7 Rocker Shaft Bushing Alignment

VALVE CLEARANCE ADJUSTMENT

1) Set No. 1 piston at TDC of compression stroke and align timing mark with pointer. Adjust valves 1,2,3,5,7 and 9 (as numbered from front).

2F 6 CYLINDER (Cont.)

2) Rotate crankshaft one complete turn and again align timing mark with pointer. Adjust remaining valves 4,6,8,10,11 and 12.

Valve Clearance Specifications

Valve	Clearance (Hot) In. (mm)
Intake	.008 (.20)
Exhaust	.014 (.35)

PISTONS, PINS & RINGS

OIL PAN

Removal – Remove engine undercovers, and remove flywheel side and undercover. Remove front propeller shaft. Drain oil, remove oil pan attaching bolts and oil pan.

Installation – Thoroughly clean all gasket mating surfaces. Apply liquid sealer onto both oil pan gasket surfaces, install oil pan and tighten bolts. Reverse removal procedure for remaining components.

PISTON & ROD ASSEMBLY

Removal – With cylinder head and oil pan removed, remove connecting rod caps and remove bearings. Push piston and rod assembly up through cylinder block. Mark all components with cylinder numbers for correct reassembly.

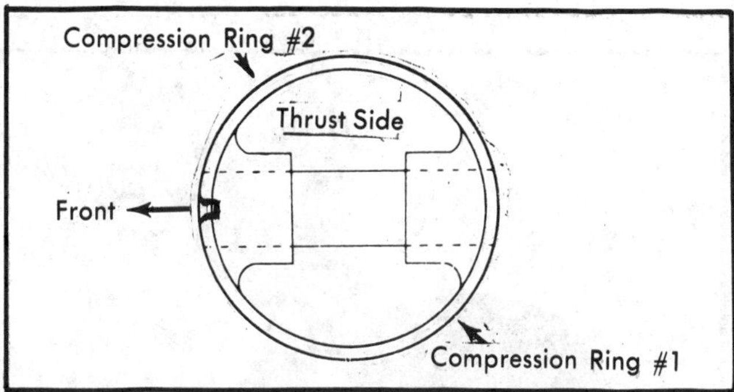

Fig. 8 Piston Ring Gap Spacing

Installation – **1)** Apply oil to piston and rings. Position ring gaps as shown in *Fig. 8.* Use a ring compressor and install piston assemblies through top of cylinder. Notch on piston MUST face FORWARD and index mark (symbol) on connecting rod MUST face REAR.

2) Replace connecting rod bearings and connecting rod caps. Tighten connecting rod bearing cap nuts. Rotate crankshaft to make sure bearings are not too tight.

FITTING PISTONS

1) Measure cylinder bores and pistons to be fitted. Measure piston with micrometer at bottom of skirt at right angles to piston pin. If clearance exceeds specifications, replace piston.

2) If cylinder bore is worn or tapered beyond specifications, cylinder must be bored and oversize pistons installed. Oversize pistons are available in .020" .040" and .060" (.50, 1.00 and 1.50 mm).

Cylinder Bore Specifications

Application	Wear Limits
Bore Wear Limit	.008" (.2 mm)
Taper	.0008" (.02 mm)
Difference Between Cylinders	.002" (.05 mm)

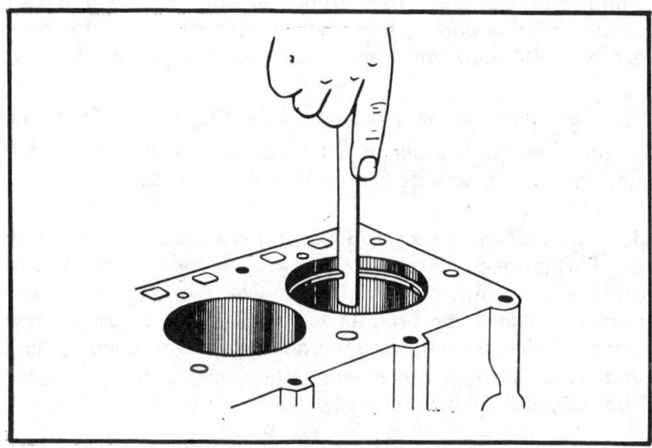

Fig. 9 Measuring Piston Ring Gap

3) Use .001-.002" (.03-.05 mm) feeler gauge with pull scale to check clearance of oversize pistons. Force of 2.2-5.5 lbs. (1.0-2.5 kg) must not be exceeded when pulling feeler gauge from cylinder.

4) Measure piston ring gaps in cylinder. If cylinder has not been bored, check gap with ring in lowest part of cylinder. Check clearance of piston ring in ring groove. Always install rings with marks facing upward.

PISTON PINS

Removal – Remove piston pin bolt and push out piston pin from piston and connecting rod. Mark all parts for correct reassembly.

Fig. 10 Piston and Rod Assembly

2F 6 CYLINDER (Cont.)

Installation – Position piston and connecting rod so that when notch on top of piston faces forward, oil hole in connecting rod faces camshaft side. Push pin into assembly and center pin in piston. Center connecting rod between piston pin bosses and tighten piston pin bolt.

CRANKSHAFT MAIN & CONNECTING ROD BEARING

MAIN & CONNECTING ROD BEARINGS

1) Thoroughly clean crankshaft and blow out oil passages with compressed air. Check crankshaft for runout with a dial indicator on second or third main bearing journal. If runout exceeds .004" (.10 mm), straighten or replace crankshaft.

2) Check main and connecting rod bearing journals for taper or out-of-round. If taper or out-of-round exceeds .0004" (.01 mm), crankshaft must be ground to next undersize.

3) Main and connecting rod bearing clearance is checked by the Plastigage method. If clearance exceeds specifications, replace bearings. If crankshaft wear is excessive and clearance cannot be brought to specifications by use of new standard size bearings, crankshaft must be reground to next undersize. Bearings are available in .002", .010", and .020" (.05, .25, and .50 mm) undersize.

NOTE – *All main bearing configurations are different.*

4) Make sure oil hole in No. 1 and No. 4 main bearing is installed toward block. Arrow on connecting rod cap MUST face FRONT.

THRUST BEARING

Check crankshaft end play at No. 3 main bearing. If clearance exceeds .012" (.3 mm), replace crankshaft bearings.

REAR MAIN BEARING OIL SEAL

To install oil seal without disassembling crankshaft, pry out oil seal with a screwdriver. Use crankshaft rear oil seal replacer tool (Tool 09223-60010) to drive new oil seal into place.

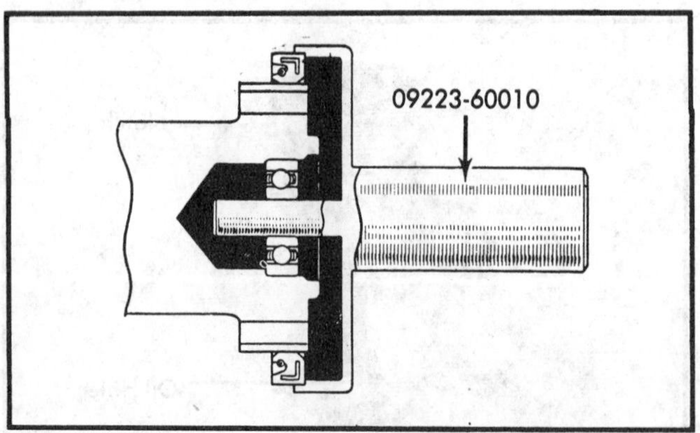

Fig. 11 Rear Oil Seal Installation

CAMSHAFT

ENGINE FRONT COVER

1) Drain cooling system and remove upper and lower radiator hoses. Remove bolts holding radiator to radiator support. Remove radiator upward using care not to damage radiator.

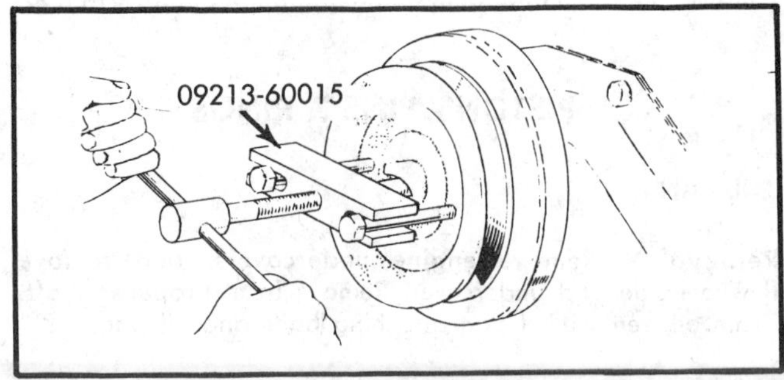

Fig. 12 Crankshaft Pulley Removal

2) Remove fan belt. Remove crankshaft pulley using suitable puller (09213-60015). Remove bolts and remove timinq gear cover and gasket. To install, reverse removal procedure.

FRONT COVER OIL SEAL

Pry old oil seal out using screwdriver. Install new oil seal so that open end of seal is towards inside of timing gear cover. Drive seal in place with suitable tool (09515-35010).

Fig. 13 Front Oil Seal Installation

CAMSHAFT

Remove timing gear cover and gasket. Slide out oil slinger from crankshaft. Remove two bolts retaining camshaft thrust plate onto cylinder block by working through holes in camshaft timing gear. Remove camshaft by pulling out through front of block. Use care not to damage camshaft bearings or journals. To install, reverse removal procedure and set valve timing.

NOTE – *Ensure timing gear oil nozzle is positioned to direct oil onto timing gears. Stake into place with a punch.*

2F 6 CYLINDER (Cont.)

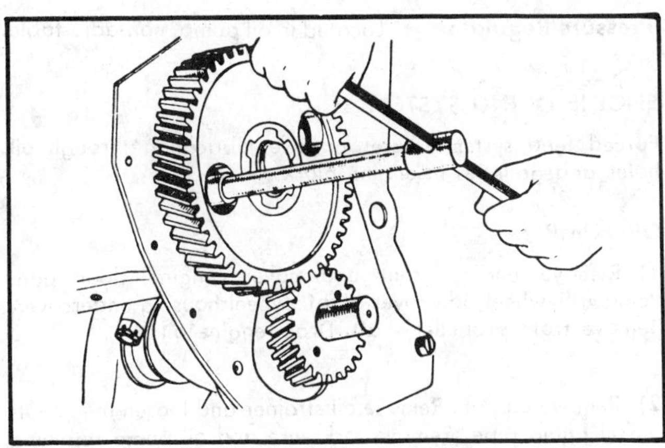

Fig. 14 Removing Camshaft Thrust Plate Bolts

CAM LOBE HEIGHT

Measure height of cam lobe. If wear exceeds specification limit, replace camshaft. Intake lobe limit, 1.496" (38 mm); Exhaust lobe limit, 1.492" (37.9 mm).

CAMSHAFT BEARING

1) Inspect camshaft for runout. If runout exceeds .0059" (.15 mm), replace camshaft. Inspect camshaft journals and bearings for wear or damage. If clearance exceeds specifications, replace camshaft bearings and/or regrind camshaft. Bearings are available in standard .010" and .020" (.25 and .50 mm) oversizes.

2) Drive out camshaft rear expansion plug from cylinder block. Remove front and No. 2 bearing using Camshaft Bearing Remover (Tool 09215-60010). Place front and second bearing adapters against rear of respective bearing, and place replacer against front part of cylinder block.

3) Insert replacer shaft into the three parts, and screw in retainer nut onto replacer shaft. Hold slotted part of shaft with wrench to prevent shaft from turning. By screwing in retainer nut with another wrench, the front and No. 1 bearing will be pulled out to the front.

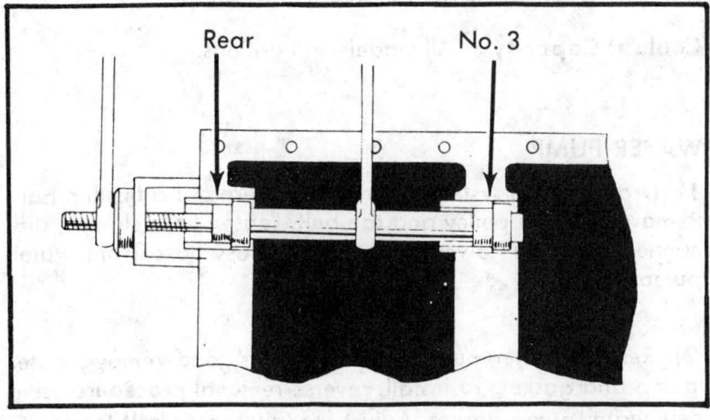

Fig. 15 Measuring Camshaft End Thrust

4) Remove No. 3 and rear bearing towards rear of block using tool in same manner as for front and No. 3 bearing. When installing new bearings, make sure that oil holes of bearing match up with oil holes in cylinder block.

5) When new bearings have been installed, measure to obtain proper clearance. Only a very light cut is required to ream bearings to proper size. Coat rear expansion plug with sealer and reinstall plug in block.

CAMSHAFT END THRUST

Measure end thrust with feeler gauge. Thrust should be .0035-.0059" (.09-.15 mm). If thrust exceeds .008" (.2 mm), replace camshaft thrust plate.

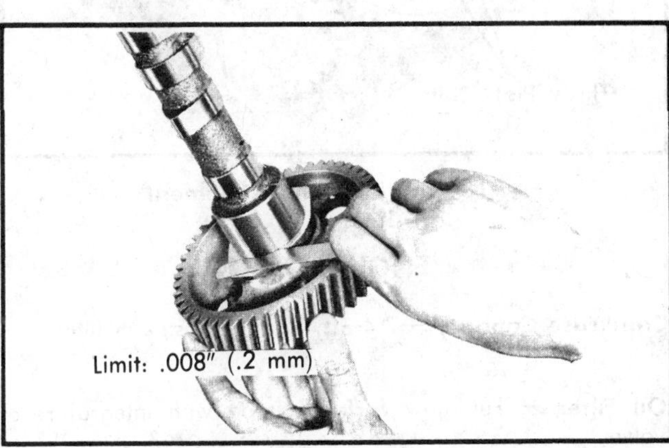

Fig. 16 View Showing Typical Camshaft Bearing Removal (No. 3 & Rear Shown)

CRANKSHAFT TIMING GEAR

Remove pulley key from crankshaft. Using suitable puller (09213-60015), pull off crankshaft gear. To reinstall, drive on gear using suitable driver (09214-60010). Make sure timing mark on gear faces outward.

VALVE TIMING

1) With crankshaft timing gear installed on crankshaft, oil camshaft journals and bearings and insert camshaft. Align mating mark on camshaft timing gear with mark on crankshaft timing gear and push camshaft into position.
timing gear and push camshaft into position. No. 6 cylinder should be at TDC, compression stroke. If oil nozzle was removed, refit with oil hole facing down (toward gears).

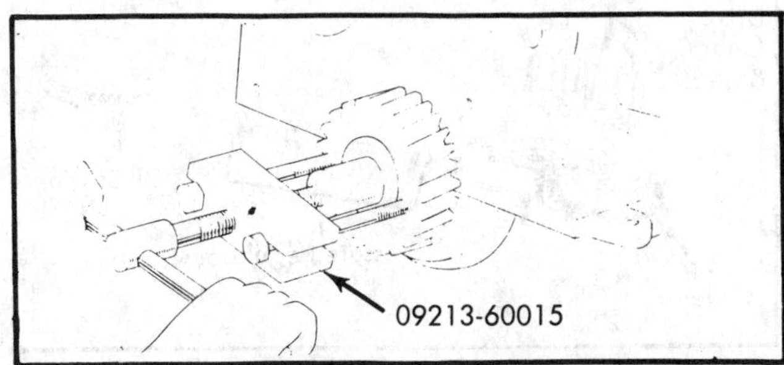

Fig. 17 Crankshaft Timing Gear Removal

2F 6 CYLINDER (Cont.)

2) Tighten camshaft thrust plate retaining bolts to specifications. Check that timing gear backlash does not exceed .008" (.2 mm). Standard backlash is .0020-.0051" (.05-.13 mm). If backlash exceeds specifications, replace both camshaft and crankshaft gears.

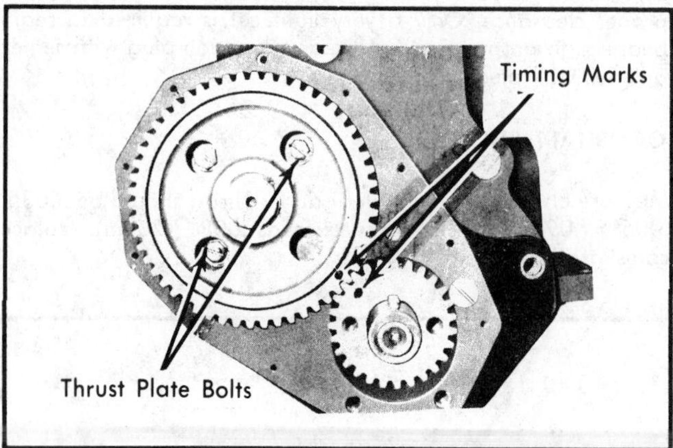

Fig. 18 Timing Mark Alignment

ENGINE OILING

Crankcase Capacity – 7.4 qts. Add 1.0 qts. with filter.

Oil Filter – Full flow cartridge type with integral relief valve.

Normal Oil Pressure – Pressure maintained at 50-64 psi (3.5-4.5 kg/cm²) by safety valve in oil pressure regulator.

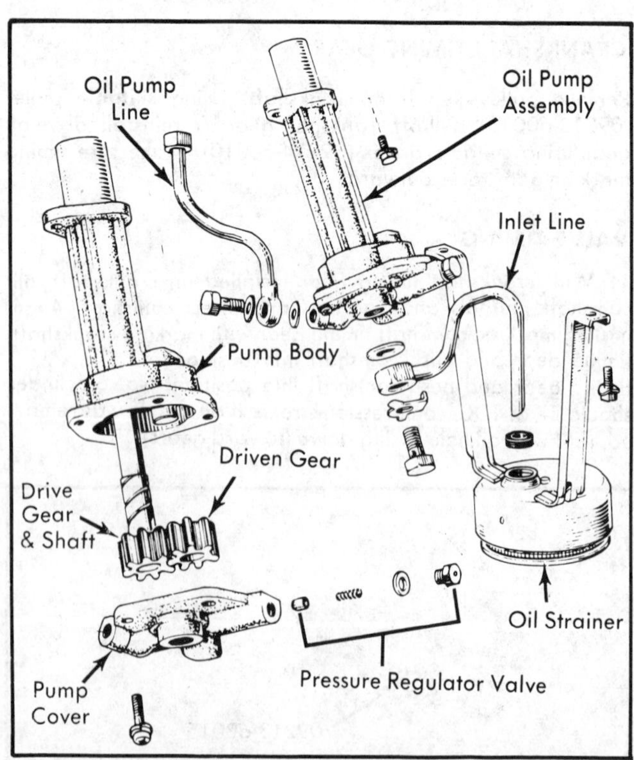

Fig. 19 Exploded View of Oil Pump Assembly

Pressure Regulator – Located in oil pump, non-adjustable.

ENGINE OILING SYSTEM

Forced feed system insures positive lubrication through oil holes and galleries in engine block.

OIL PUMP

1) Remove engine front undercover, engine floor pan. Remove flywheel side cover and flywheel housing undercover. Remove front propeller shaft. Drain engine oil.

2) Remove oil pan. Remove oil strainer and loosen union nuts on oil pump pipe. Remove lock wire and oil pump retaining bolt and remove oil pump and pipe.

3) Straighten union bolt lock washer and remove union bolt, lock washer, gasket, and oil pump inlet pipe from oil pump cover. Remove cover and slide out oil pump driven gear and oil pump drive gear together with oil pump shaft.

4) Inspect gears and housing and check clearance between gear tip and pump body. Measure gear backlash. Place straightedge across pump housing and measure clearance between gear side and straightedge. Place straight edge across pump cover and measure wear. If any parts show wear exceeding specifications or other damage, replace parts as necessary.

Oil Pump Specifications

Application	Standard In. (mm)	Wear Limit In. (mm)
Gear-to-Housing Clearance	.0012-.0043 (.03-.11)	.008 (.2)
Gear Backlash	.0020-.0028 (.05-.07)	.0374 (.95)
Gear Side Clearance	.0012-.0035 (.03-.09)	.0059 (.15)
Cover Wear		.0059 (.15)

ENGINE COOLING

Thermostat – Wax pellet type. Begins to open at 180°F (82°C) and is fully opened at 203°F (95°C).

Coolant Capacity – All models, 4.5 gallons.

WATER PUMP

1) Drain cooling system and remove alternator adjusting bar. Remove fan, fan pulley and fan belt. Loosen hose clamps, disconnect radiator lower hose and by-pass hose from water pump.

2) Remove water pump retaining bolts, and remove water pump and gasket. To install, reverse removal procedure using new water pump gasket. Adjust fan/alternator belt tension to provide .5-.6" (13-15 mm) deflection and fan/air pump belt to provide .3-.4" (7-10 mm) deflection.

2F 6 CYLINDER (Cont.)

ENGINE SPECIFICATIONS

GENERAL SPECIFICATIONS										
Year	Displ.		Carburetor	HP at RPM	Torque (Ft. Lbs. at RPM)	Compr. Ratio	Bore		Stroke	
	cu. ins.	cc					in.	mm	in.	mm
1977	257.9	4230	1x2-Bbl.	....	....	7.8-1	3.70	94	4.00	101.6

VALVES							
Engine & Valve	Head Diam. In. (mm)	Face Angle	Seat Angle	Seat Width In. (mm)	Stem Diameter In. (mm)	Stem Clearance In. (mm)	Valve Lift In. (mm)
2F Engine							
Intake	1.81 (46.0)	45°	45°	.055 (1.4)	.3138-.3144 (7.970-7.985)	.0012-.0024 (.03-.06)	.....
Exhaust	1.48 (37.5)	45°	45°	.067 (1.7)	.3134-.3140 (7.960-7.975)	.0016-.0028 (.04-.07)	.....

PISTONS, PINS, RINGS						
Engine	PISTONS	PINS		RINGS		
	Clearance In. (mm)	Piston Fit In. (mm)	Rod Fit In. (mm)	Rings	End Gap In. (mm)	Side Clearance In. (mm)
2F Engine	.0012-.0020 (.03-.05)	.0003-.0005 (.008-.012)	①	No. 1	.008-.016 (.20-.40)	.0012-.0024 (.03-.06)
				No. 2	.008-.016 (.20-.40)	.0008-.0024 (.02-.06)
				Oil	.....	.....

① — No clearance.

CRANKSHAFT MAIN & CONNECTING ROD BEARINGS							
Engine	MAIN BEARINGS				CONNECTING ROD BEARINGS		
	Journal Diam. In. (mm)	Clearance In. (mm)	Thrust Bearing	Crankshaft End Play In. (mm)	Journal Diam. In. (mm)	Clearance In. (mm)	Side Play In. (mm)
2F Engine							
No. 1	2.6367-2.6376 (66.972-66.996)	.0008-.0017 (.020-.044)	No. 3	.002-.006 (.06-.16)	2.1252-2.1260 (53.98-54.00)	.0008-.0024 (.020-.060)	.004-.009 (.11-.23)
No. 2	2.6957-2.6967 (68.472-68.496)						
No. 3	2.7548-2.7557 (69.972-69.996)						
No. 4	2.8139-2.8148 (71.472-71.496)						

2F 6 CYLINDER (Cont.)

ENGINE SPECIFICATIONS (Cont.)

VALVE SPRINGS			
Engine	Free Length In. (mm)	PRESSURE (LBS.) Lbs. @ In. (kg @ mm)	
		Valve Closed	Valve Open
2F Engine	2.028 (51.5)	71.7@1.693 (32.5@43.0)	.....

CAMSHAFT			
Engine	Journal Diam. In. (mm)	Clearance In. (mm)	Lobe Lift In. (mm)
2F Engine			
No. 1	1.8880-1.8888 (47.955-47.975)	.001-.003 (.025-.075)	.....
No. 2	1.8289-1.8297 (46.455-46.475)		
No. 3	1.7699-1.7707 (44.955-44.975)		
No. 4	1.7108-1.7116 (43.455-43.475)		

TIGHTENING SPECIFICATIONS

Application	Ft. Lbs. (mkg)
Cylinder Head	83-98 (11.5-13.5)
Piston Pin Bolt	39-51 (5.4-7.0)
Connecting Rod Bearing Caps	35-55 (4.8-7.6)
Crankshaft Main Bearing Caps	
Front, No. 2 & No. 3	90-108 (12.5-15)
Rear	76-94 (10.5-13)
Camshaft Thrust Plate Bolts	7-12 (1.0-1.6)
Manifold Nuts	28-37 (3.5-5.1)
Flywheel Bolts	59-62 (8.1-8.5)
Crankshaft Pulley	116-145 (16-20)

SPITFIRE 4 CYLINDER

ENGINE CODING

ENGINE IDENTIFICATION

Engine number is stamped on a machined flange on left side of cylinder block. Number can be broken down as follows:

FM1234UCE

1st & 2nd Digits – Model range.
3rd through 6th Digits – Sequence build number.
7th Digit – USA market.
8th Digit – Calif. market (Catalytic Converter).
9th Digit – Engine unit.

ENGINE, CYLINDER HEAD & MANIFOLD

ENGINE

Removal – 1) Disconnect battery. Drain coolant and engine oil. Remove hood. Remove air cleaner and disconnect emission control lines. From exhaust manifold, separate converter or pipe.

2) Disconnect all necessary water hoses, carburetor throttle linkage, and engine electrical leads. Disconnect and plug fuel lines.

3) Raise vehicle and place on safety stands. Separate exhaust pipe from bracket at transmission, then pull pipe downward past chassis. Take off restraint cable. Remove lower bell housing nuts and bolts. Place jack or stand under bell housing.

4) Lower vehicle to ground. Attach hoist to engine. Remove remaining bell housing bolts, then take out starter. Remove motor mount bolts. Remove engine with hoist.

Installation – Reverse removal procedures to install engine.

INTAKE MANIFOLD

1) Remove air cleaner and disconnect fuel line. Disconnect hose to rocker cover. Unhook throttle return spring. Disconnect and remove throttle cable. Disconnect choke cable, ignition vacuum line and water hoses.

2) Unscrew manifold bolts connecting intake to exhaust manifold. Remove manifold-to-engine bolts and lift out manifold assembly.

CYLINDER HEAD

Removal – 1) Disconnect battery. Drain coolant. Disconnect emission control hoses and vacuum lines; mark for reinstallation. Loosen alternator belt. Disconnect heater hoses. Disconnect fuel evaporation hoses. Separate throttle linkage from carburetor. Remove valve cover. Disconnect heater return line.

2) Remove heat shield from between carburetor and air cleaner. Disconnect exhaust at manifold flange. Remove water pump. Remove rocker arm assembly. Take out push rods. Disconnect fuel line and remove cylinder head.

NOTE – *It may be necessary to remove intake and exhaust manifolds.*

Installation – Note following during installation. Make sure "TOP" tag on rear of gasket faces up.

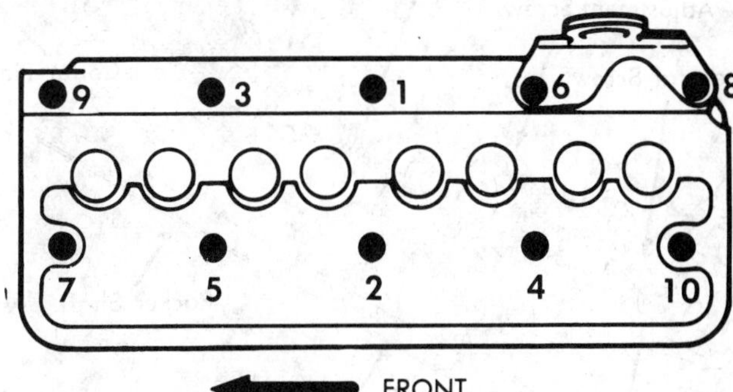

Fig. 1 Cylinder Head Tightening Sequence

VALVES

VALVE ARRANGEMENT

E-I-I-E-E-I-I-E (front to rear).

VALVE GUIDE SERVICING

1) Inspect valve guide wear by inserting a new valve, lifting it slightly off its seat, and rocking sideways. Movement of valve head across seat should not exceed .020" (.51 mm).

2) If replacement is required, use valve guide removal tool 60A and adapters to remove and replace valve guide. Guide protrusion above top face of cylinder head must be between .749-.751" (19.02-19.08 mm).

VALVE SPRINGS

Using suitable valve spring compressor, remove valve retainers. Withdraw collars and valves. Check valve springs for cracks, distortion and load length. When any one spring is defective, it is advisable to replace all springs.

NOTE – *Valve springs can be removed with cylinder head installed in vehicle. Apply air pressure to spark plug hole of spring (valve) to be removed. Air pressure will prevent valve from dropping.*

ROCKER ARM ASSEMBLY

Remove rocker arm cover. Progressively and evenly remove rocker arm pedestal nuts. Lift off rocker arm assembly. Pull cotter pin from front end of rocker shaft. Slide rockers, pedestals, springs and spacers from shaft, noting order for reassembly. Remove screw locating rear pedestal to shaft. Inspect and replace excessively worn parts. To install, reverse removal procedure making sure rear pedestal screw correctly engages rocker shaft.

VALVE TAPPETS

Check valve tappets for chips, score marks, ridges or excessive wear. Replace as necessary and ensure tappets are free to slide and rotate.

SPITFIRE 4 CYLINDER (Cont.)

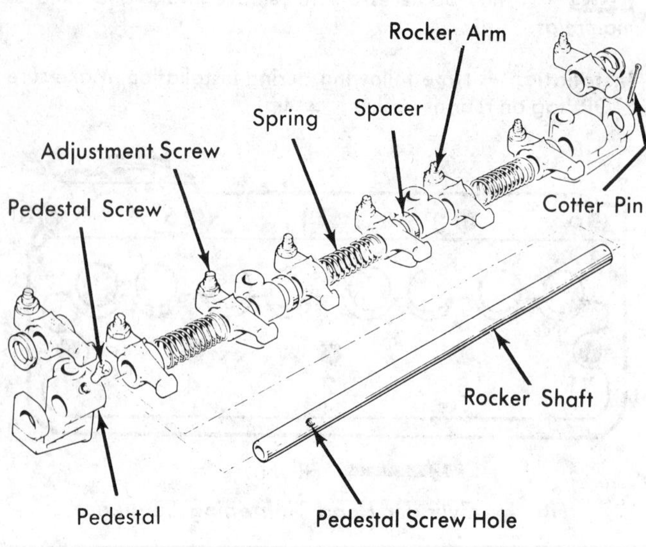

Fig. 2 Detailed View of Rocker Arm Assembly

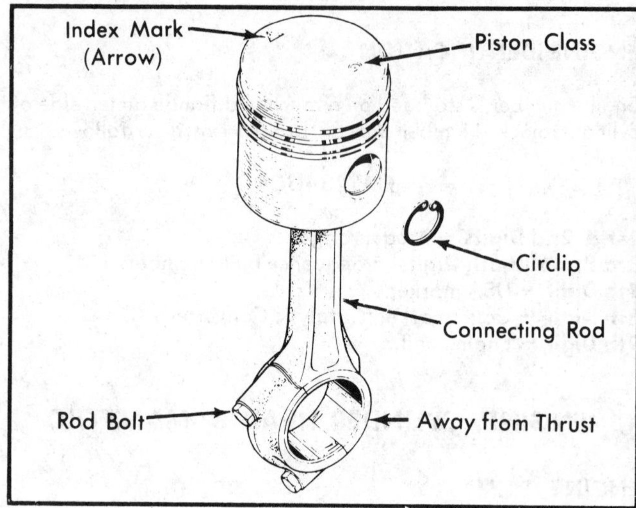

Fig. 3 Assembled View of Piston and Connecting Rod

VALVE CLEARANCE ADJUSTMENT

Disconnect battery, then remove rocker cover and spark plugs. Make necessary adjustment in sequence as indicated in chart below. Turning adjustment screw clockwise will decrease clearance, and turning screw counterclockwise will increase clearance. Proper clearance for intake and exhaust valves is .010" (.25 mm).

Valves Open①	Valves to Adjust
No. 8 & 6	No. 1 & 3
No. 4 & 7	No. 5 & 2
No. 1 & 3	No. 8 & 6
No. 5 & 2	No. 4 & 7

① – Counting from front.

PISTONS, PINS & RINGS

OIL PAN

Removal – Drain oil pan (Calif. models have a bolt with a banjo and two washers instead of the regular sump plug). Remove the 16 bolts mounting oil pan to engine. Drop out oil pan and remove gasket.

Installation – Clean mating surfaces. Lightly coat both sides of gasket with grease or sealer. Refit pan. Make sure longer bolts are fitted to rear of pan.

PISTON & ROD ASSEMBLY

1) Disconnect battery ground cable and drain engine oil. Remove oil pan and cylinder head as previously described.

2) Remove pickup strainer and bring No. 1 & No. 4 connecting rods to accessible position. Index bearing caps and connecting rods.

3) Remove connecting rod bolts and withdraw bearing caps. Push pistons and connecting rods upward, withdrawing them out top of cylinder. Attach bearing cap to respective connecting rod.

4) To install, position No. 1 and No. 4 connecting rods at bottom dead center. Lube journals and connecting rod assemblies with engine oil. Insert connecting rod assembly into cylinder. Make sure arrow on piston head faces engine FRONT. Stagger piston rings away from thrust side of piston. Make sure connecting rod bearing is away from thrust side of cylinder bore.

5) Fit upper bearing and pull connecting rod over crankshaft. Install lower bearing cap and torque bolts to specifications.

PISTON PIN REPLACEMENT

1) Remove circlips from pistons and extract piston pin. Separate piston from connecting rod. Inspect connecting rod bushing for wear and replace if necessary.

2) Using suitable press, remove worn bushing and install replacement. Ensure oil hole in new bushing is aligned with hole in connecting rod. Ream bushing to fit piston pin. Piston pin diameter is .8123-.8125" (20.63-20.64 mm) and is a thumb push fit at 68°F (20°C).

FITTING PISTONS

1) Measure piston across skirt. Check piston for scoring or cracks. Measure cylinder bore and determine if clearance is excessive.

2) Two grades of standard pistons are used; F and G. Identification mark is on piston head and block. One oversize piston is available; .001" (.025 mm). It will be necessary to hone cylinder to insert oversize piston.

3) Install expanding ring in bottom groove of piston with end butting, but not overlapping. Work from bottom of piston and fit bottom rail. Fit top rail into position going over head of piston. Install middle ring with "TOP" facing up. Put on upper compression ring. Stagger rings.

SPITFIRE 4 CYLINDER (Cont.)

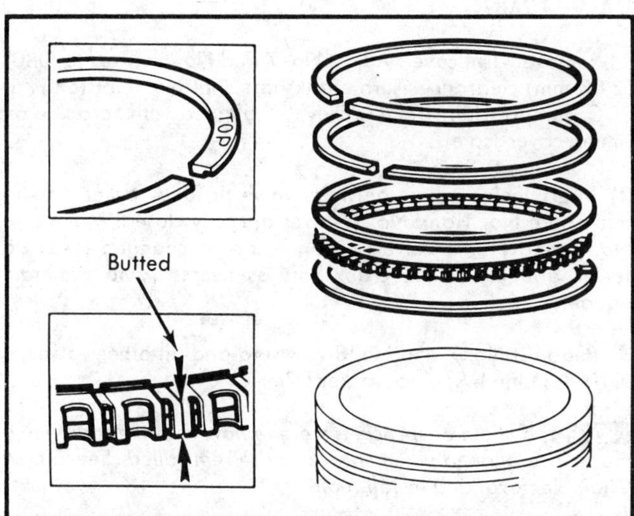

Fig. 4 Order and Detail of Piston Ring Installation

CRANKSHAFT MAIN & CONNECTING ROD BEARINGS

MAIN & CONNECTING ROD BEARINGS

1) Remove engine, cylinder head and oil pan. Remove main and rod bearing caps. Slightly push up connecting rod assembly but do not dislodge it from cylinder. Remove upper connecting rod bearings.

2) Remove crankshaft and upper main bearings. Remove thrust washers from rear main bearing. Examine all bearing journals and determine if regrinding is necessary.

3) Examine each bearing and replace as required. Bearings are available in .010", .020", and .030" (.25, .51, and .76 mm) undersizes. Any undersize crankshaft which is installed or has been installed in service should have a size marking stamped in which corresponds to similar marking on bearings.

4) To install main and connecting rod bearings, reverse removal procedure, noting the following: bend over locking tabs, if equipped.

CRANKSHAFT END PLAY

NOTE – *End play can be adjusted with engine installed in vehicle. Procedure given is with engine removed. Difference occurs as to where dial indicator is mounted.*

Use a dial indicator and set it up as shown in *Fig. 5*. Measure end play by prying against crankshaft and reading dial indicator. Obtained value must lie within specifications. If end play is exceeded, fit oversize thrust washers to rear main bearing.

REAR MAIN BEARING OIL SEAL

1) Remove rear transmission adaptor plate. Remove two bolts attaching oil pan to seal housing and seven bolts attaching seal housing to crankcase. Remove seal housing and press out old seal.

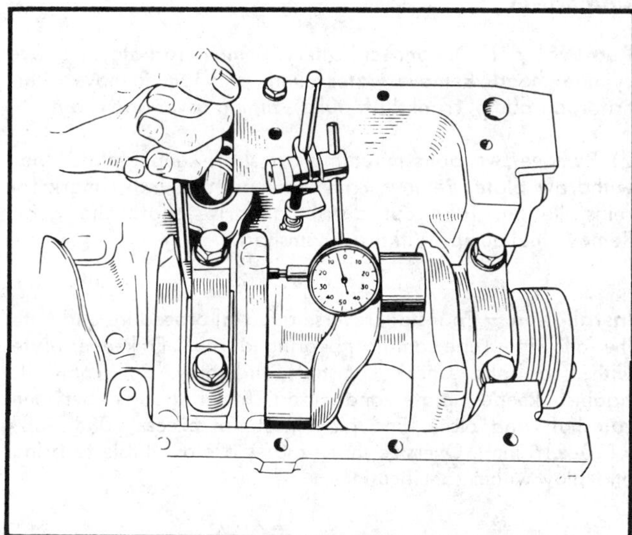

Fig. 5 Using Dial Indicator to Check Crankshaft End Play

2) Coat O.D. of seal with grease and press seal into housing with lip facing crankshaft. Install a new gasket coated with sealing compound. Carefully install seal housing with a plain copper washer on top bolt.

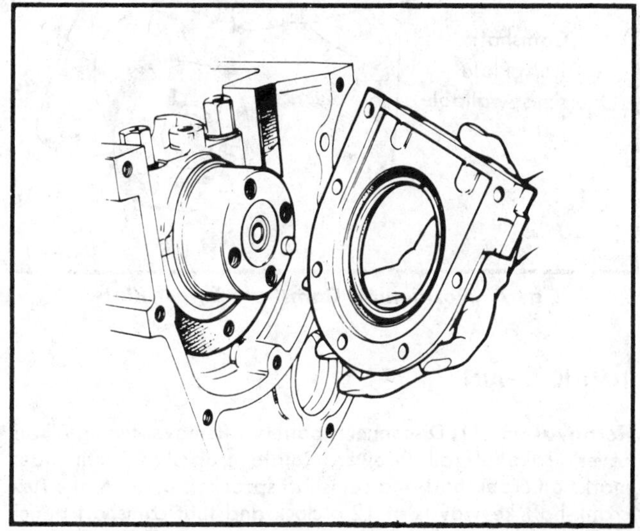

Fig. 6 Fitting Rear Main Bearing Seal Housing into Place

CAMSHAFT

ENGINE FRONT COVER & OIL SEAL

Removal – Remove radiator. Remove left side inner fender panel. Remove air pump, alternator, fan, and crankshaft pulley. Remove air pump/alternator brackets, adjusting links and spacer. Take out timing cover mounting hardware. Loosen and remove cover. Press out old seal. Refit new seal with open side facing engine.

Installation – Note for installation that chain tensioner is inside cover. To facilitate cover installation, use a short piece of welding rod bent 90° to hold tensioner off chain.

SPITFIRE 4 CYLINDER (Cont.)

CAMSHAFT

Removal – 1) Disconnect battery. Remove radiator. Remove cylinder head. Remove water pump and fan. Remove alternator, air pump, crankshaft pulley, timing cover and chain.

2) Remove two bolts mounting camshaft keeper plate, then withdraw plate. Remove cam followers and index mark for reinstallation. Take out distributor drive shaft and gear. Remove fuel pump. Withdraw camshaft.

Installation – To install, reverse removal procedure and note the following: Lube camshaft bearing journals. Fit keeper plate with two bolts. Check camshaft end play. Pull camshaft against keeper plate and insert feeler gauge between camshaft and plate. End play must not exceed .004-.008" (.110-.216 mm). Oversize thrust plates are available to bring end play within specifications.

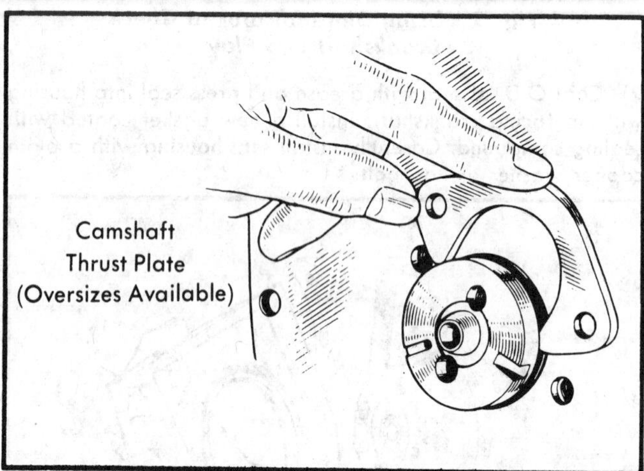

Fig. 7 Positioning Camshaft Thrust Plate

TIMING CHAIN

Removal – 1) Disconnect battery. Remove timing chain cover. Take off oil thrower. Rotate crankshaft until index marks on crankshaft and camshaft sprockets align. Make sure crankshaft keyway is at 12 o'clock and that camshaft punch mark aligns with crankshaft keyway.

2) Bend back camshaft nut lock tabs and remove bolts mounting camshaft sprocket to camshaft. Remove camshaft sprocket and timing chain.

NOTE – *DO NOT rotate camshaft or crankshaft while chain is off sprockets.*

Installation – 1) Remove crankshaft key. Refit both sprockets. Check alignment with straightedge. Install selective fit shims to crankshaft if misalignment occurs. Install key.

2) Fit chain to sprockets. Install sprocket, keep index marks aligned. Slightly secure camshaft sprocket. Measure chain deflection along slack run of chain. 3/8" (9.53 mm) slack should not be exceeded. Reverse removal procedure for remaining components.

VALVE TIMING

1) Remove valve cover. Adjust No. 7 and No. 8 valves to .080" (2.03 mm) clearance. Turn crankshaft until No. 1 piston is at TDC, compression stroke (pulley "V" aligned with zero line on timing cover scale).

2) Insert feeler gauge between valve tip and rocker pad to make sure No. 1 and No. 2 valves are fully closed. Make sure No. 7 and No. 8 valve clearances are unchanged (use two feeler gauges). Move crankshaft as necessary to maintain equality.

3) Readjust No. 7 and No. 8 valves to and all other valves to .010" (.25 mm). Replace rocker cover.

NOTE – *If chain or sprockets were removed, make sure timing marks are aligned when sprockets are reinstalled. See Timing Chain Removal and Installation.*

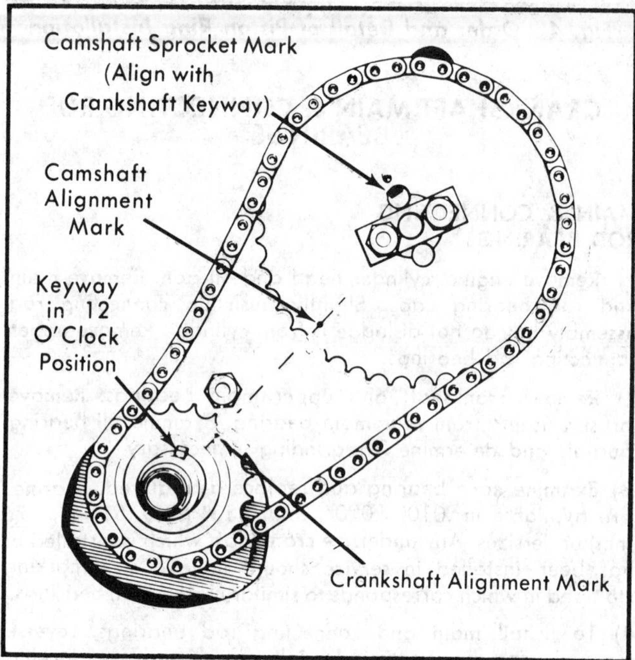

Fig. 8 Camshaft and Crankshaft Alignment Marks

ENGINE OILING

ENGINE OILING SYSTEM

Oil is drawn from engine by a rotor type pump which discharges via a nonadjustable relief valve to a full-flow filter. Cylinder bores, pistons and piston pins are splash lubricated all other components are oiled through drilled passages.

Crankcase Capacity (Drain and Refill) – 4.2 quarts.

Oil Filter – Disposable canister type.

Oil Pressure Relief Valve – Located in cylinder block beneath oil filter. Check relief valve spring free length; it should be 1.53" (38.8 mm).

SPITFIRE 4 CYLINDER (Cont.)

OIL PUMP

1) Remove oil pan previously described. Remove three bolts securing oil pump to crankcase. Lift from vehicle and place in a vise.

2) Place a straightedge across pump body, then use a feeler gauge to check clearance between rotor face and straight edge; it should be .004" (.10 mm).

3) Check clearance between inner rotor and outer rotor. Clearance must not exceed .010" (.25 mm).

4) Check clearance between outer rotor and body; it must not exceed .008" (.20 mm).

5) Check cover plate for scoring, and test on a surface plate for distortion. Examine pump spindle bearing surface in body for excessive wear.

6) Reassembly oil pump installing any new parts as necessary to satisfy specifications. To install oil pump, reverse removal procedure.

ENGINE COOLING

Cooling System Capacity – 4.8 qts.

WATER PUMP

Drain cooling system. Remove radiator hoses, then unbolt and remove radiator. Detach fan belt. Unscrew three nuts securing water pump flange to thermostat and pump housing. Withdraw water pump. Remove fan. To install, reverse procedure.

ENGINE SPECIFICATIONS

GENERAL SPECIFICATIONS

Year	Displ.		Carburetor	HP at RPM	Torque (Ft. Lbs. at RPM)	Compr. Ratio	Bore		Stroke	
	cu. ins.	cc					in.	mm	in.	mm
1977	91	1493	1x1-Bbl.	....	....	9.0-1①	2.90	73.7	3.44	87.5

① – Federal; 7.5-1 California.

VALVES In. (mm)

Engine & Valve	Head Diam.	Face Angle	Seat Angle	Seat Width	Stem Diameter	Stem Clearance	Valve Lift
1493 cc							
Intake	1.375-1.385 (34.97-35.01)	45°	45°	.248-.250① (6.29-6.35)	.3107-3113 (8.05-8.12)	.0008-.0023 (.020-.060)	...
Exhaust	1.168-1.172 (29.66-29.76)	45°	45°	.248-.250① (6.29-6.35)	.3100-.3105 (7.874-7.887)	.0015-.0030 (.038-.076)	...

① – With catalytic converter .258-.260" (31.95-31.00 mm).

PISTONS, PINS, RINGS In. (mm)

Engine	PISTONS	PINS		RINGS		
	Clearance	Piston Fit	Rod Fit	Rings	End Gap	Side Clearance
1493 cc	.002-.003 (.05-.07)	Push Fit	Push Fit	No. 1 & 2	.012-.022 (.30-.55)	.002-.0025 (.051-.063)
				Oil	①	.0025-.0035 (.063-.088)

① – Ends butt.

SPITFIRE 4 CYLINDER (Cont.)

ENGINE SPECIFICATIONS (Cont.)

CRANKSHAFT MAIN & CONNECTING ROD BEARINGS

Engine	MAIN BEARINGS				CONNECTING ROD BEARINGS		
	Journal Diam. In. (mm)	Clearance In. (mm)	Thrust Bearing	Crankshaft End Play In. (mm)	Journal Diam. In. (mm)	Clearance In. (mm)	Side Play In. (mm)
1493 cc	2.3115-2.3120 (58.713-58.725)	...	Rear	.004-.008 (.10-.20)	1.8750-1.8755 (47.625-47.638)	....	....

VALVE SPRINGS

Engine	Free Length In. (mm)	PRESSURE Lbs. @ In. (kg @ mm)	
		Valve Closed	Valve Open
1493 cc	1.52 (38.6)	...@1.342 ...@(34.1)	20 @ .875 (2.8 @ 22.2)

VALVE TIMING

Engine	INTAKE		EXHAUST	
	Open (BTDC)	Close (ABDC)	Open (BBDC)	Close (ATDC)
1493cc	18°	58°	58°	18°

CAMSHAFT In. (mm)

Engine	Journal Diam.	Clearance	Lobe Lift
1493 cc	1.9659-1.9664① (49.934-49.947)	...	...

① — Intermediate Journal 1.9649-1.9654" (49.908-49.921).

TIGHTENING SPECIFICATIONS

Application	Ft. Lbs. (mkg)
Connecting Rod Bolts	
Color Dyed	45 (6.2)
Phosphated	46 (6.4)
Sprocket-to-Camshaft	24 (3.3)
Crankshaft Pulley Nut	150 (20.7)
Cylinder Head Bolts	46 (6.4)
Flywheel-to-Crankshaft	
Cadmium Plated Bolt	40 (5.5)
Parkarised Bolt	45 (6.2)
Intake-to-Exhaust Manifold	14 (1.9)
Manifold-to-Head	25 (3.5)
Main Bearing Cap Bolts	65 (9.0)
Oil Pan Bolts	20 (2.8)
Oil Seal Block Screw	14 (1.9)
Rocker Cover-to-Head	2 (0.3)
Rocker Shaft-to-Head	34 (4.7)
Rear Crankshaft Seal	20 (2.8)
Spark Plugs	20 (2.8)
Timing Cover-to-Front Plate	
⅜" Screw	10 (1.4)
⅞" Screw	20 (2.8)
Stud	16 (2.2)
Bolt	20 (2.8)
Water Pump-to-Head	20 (2.8)

TRIUMPH TR7 4 CYLINDER

ENGINE CODING

ENGINE IDENTIFICATION

Engine number is stamped on cylinder head and may be seen by looking down between intake manifold branches.

CL1234UE

1st & 2nd Digits – Model range.

3rd, 4th, 5th & 6th Digits – Serial number.

7th Digit – "U" denotes USA specification engine.

8th Digit – "E" denotes engine unit.

ENGINE, CYLINDER HEAD & MANIFOLD

ENGINE

1) Disconnect battery and bottom radiator hose, allow coolant to drain. Remove hood, radiator, air cleaner duct and air cleaner hot air hose. Disconnect heater hoses at firewall and brake booster vacuum hose at intake manifold. Disconnect vapor canister hoses from canister, cooling system expansion hose from thermostat housing and vacuum hose from intake manifold to anti-runon valve.

2) Disconnect all electrical leads to engine, fuel line at carburetor(s), choke cable from rear carburetor and throttle cable from throttle linkage. Remove gearshift lever by first removing shift boot, then releasing bayonet cap securing lever to transmission extension. Raise front and rear of vehicle and place on stands. Disconnect propeller shaft from transmission.

3) Disconnect wiring from transmission and remove exhaust downpipe from manifold. Disconnect speedometer cable and remove clutch slave cylinder. Remove complete engine torque strap assembly and disconnect wiring from starter motor. Release wiring harness from clutch housing clips. Remove clutch housing bolts necessary to remove clips and release clutch hydraulic pipe.

4) Remove engine ground strap and hood lock from firewall. Relieve pressure from air conditioning system (if equipped) and disconnect hoses from compressor. Using a lifting sling with a 23" (58.4 cm) leg to rear lift eye and a 18" (45.7 cm) leg to front eye, raise hoist to remove weight of engine.

5) Disconnect right side engine mount and remove five bolts securing rear crossmember to body. Raise rear of vehicle. Hoist engine and remove left side engine mount. Continue raising engine and work it away from vehicle. To install, reverse removal procedure.

INTAKE MANIFOLD

Disconnect battery and drain cooling system, including cylinder block. Remove ducts and air cleaner. Disconnect all hoses, wiring and control cables from manifold and carburetor(s). Remove distributor cap and six manifold bolts. Lift out manifold complete with carburetor(s). To install manifold, reverse removal procedure.

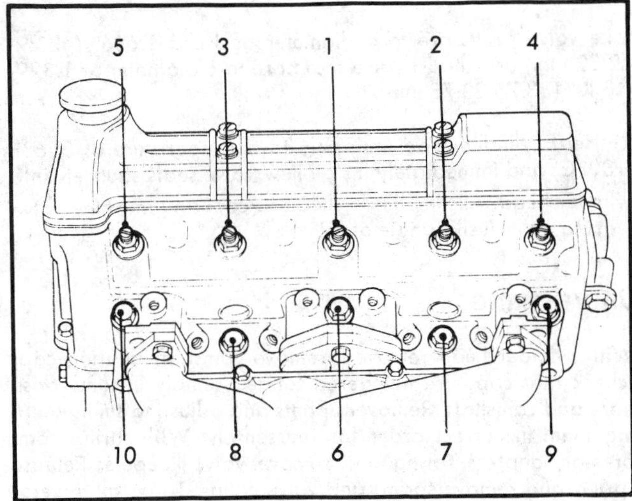

Fig. 1 Cylinder Head Tightening Sequence

CYLINDER HEAD

1) Remove intake manifold as previously described. Remove camshaft cover and semi-circular grommet to gain access to camshaft sprocket nut. Crank engine until camshaft sprocket bottom bolt is accessible and remove bottom bolt. Anchor camshaft sprocket to support bracket. Crank engine so that timing mark on camshaft flange is in line with groove in camshaft front bearing cap and distributor rotor points to manifold rear attachment bolt hole in cylinder head.

2) Unlock and remove top sprocket retaining bolt. Disconnect air hose from air injection check valve and disconnect water pipe from thermostat housing. Disconnect exhaust pipe from manifold. Remove the two cylinder head to timing cover nuts and bolts and loosen cylinder head nuts and bolts in reverse of tightening sequence (See *Fig. 1*). Remove cylinder head complete with exhaust manifold. To install, reverse removal procedure and tighten bolts to specifications in sequence shown in *Fig. 1*.

VALVES

VALVE ARRANGEMENT

E-I-I-E-E-I-I-E (front to rear).

VALVE GUIDE SERVICING

1) Inspect valve guide wear by inserting a new valve, lifting it slightly from its seat, and rocking sideways. Movement of valve head across seat should not exceed .020" (.508 mm).

2) If replacement is required, use valve guide removal and installation tool S-60A and adapters to remove and replace valve guide. After guides are installed, ream out guide using a .3130" (7.95 mm) reamer.

VALVE SEAT INSERT SERVICING

1) If valve seat inserts are too badly damaged to be refaced, replace inserts as follows: Machine-out existing inserts taking care not to damage insert bores in cylinder head. Machine in-

TRIUMPH TR7 4 CYLINDER (Cont.)

take valve seat bore to a diameter of 1.665-1.666" (42.29-42.32 mm) or exhaust valve seat bore to a diameter of 1.329-1.330" (33.75-33.78 mm).

2) Heat cylinder head uniformly to a temperature of 356°F (180°C) and immediately install new valve seats squarely into cylinder head. Allow cylinder head to cool and machine valve seats to an inclusive angle of 89°.

VALVE SPRINGS

With cylinder head removed, remove camshaft bearing caps (check that caps are numbered for reassembly in same position) and camshaft. Remove tappets and adjusting shims keeping them in correct order for reassembly. With spring compressor, depress spring and remove valve keepers. Release spring and remove spring and valve collar. To install, reverse removal procedure.

VALVE CLEARANCE ADJUSTMENT

NOTE – *This operation may be performed with cylinder head on the bench. When on the bench, turn camshaft using a wrench on hexagon at rear of camshaft.*

1) Disconnect battery and remove camshaft cover if cylinder head is installed on engine. Loosen camshaft bearing caps and retighten to specifications. Rotate camshaft or engine and check and record clearance of each valve using a feeler gauge between cam heel and tappet. Maximum clearance exists when cam is vertical to cylinder head.

2) If all clearances are correct, adjustment procedure is completed. If any clearances are incorrect, proceed as follows: Remove camshaft and withdraw each tappet and adjusting shim where clearance requires adjustment, keeping tappets and shims in sequence.

3) Measure shim thickness and add measured valve clearance to arrive at total clearance. Subtract proper valve clearance from total clearance to determine needed shim thickness. Install tappets with correct shims then install camshaft. Recheck valve clearance and install camshaft cover.

Application	Valve Clearance
Intake	.008" (.2 mm)
Exhaust	.018" (.5 mm)

PISTONS, PINS & RINGS

OIL PAN

1) Disconnect battery and remove fresh air duct and fan shroud. Raise vehicle and drain engine oil. Remove two bolts securing coupling plate on bottom of oil pan to clutch housing. Remove engine torque strap assembly. Support front of engine using hoist or jack. **NOTE** – *A bracket, made of angle iron, may be fabricated to bolt into lower timing cover bolt holes. Engine may then be supported by a jack via the fabricated bracket.*

2) Remove two engine right side mounting bolts, then remove left side engine mounting to sub-frame nut. Remove oil pan nuts and bolts. Raise engine sufficiently to enable oil pan, complete with left side engine mounting and cross-member to be removed. To install, reverse removal procedure.

PISTON & ROD ASSEMBLY

Connecting rods and rod caps are numbered. Note positioning and location before disassembly.

Removal – With oil pan and cylinder head removed, unscrew rod nuts and withdraw bearing caps. Place protective sleeves over rod bolts and push out rod and piston. Rotate crankshaft as necessary to gain access to piston and rod assemblies.

Installation – 1) Stager piston ring gaps, lubricate pistons and rings and, using a ring compressor, place piston in cylinder bore ensuring that raised flat portion of piston crown is towards right side of engine.

NOTE – *Some pistons may have arrows stamped on both sides of skirt, on the piston pin bore side, to indicate direction of pin off-set. Ensure that these arrows point to right side of engine also. Alternatively some pistons may have an arrow on the crown. These piston assemblies must be installed with arrow pointing to front of engine.*

2) Install bearing halves in connecting rod and cap and pull connecting rod onto crankpins. Install bearing caps to their respective numbered connecting rod making sure the bearing keeper recesses in connecting rods and caps are on the same side. Install new nuts and tighten.

PISTON PIN REPLACEMENT

1) Remove circlips from pistons and extract piston pin. Separate piston from connecting rod. Inspect connecting rod bushing for wear and replace if necessary.

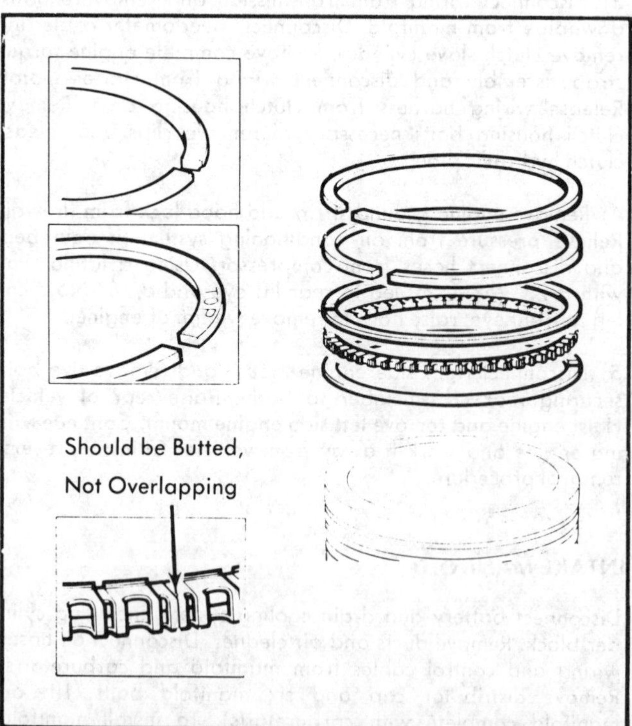

Fig. 2 View Showing Correct Piston Ring Installation

TRIUMPH TR7 4 CYLINDER (Cont.)

2) Using a press, remove worn bushing and install replacement. Ensure oil hole in new bushing is aligned with hole in connecting rod. Ream bushing to fit piston pin. Piston pin diameter is .9374-.9376" (23.810-23.815 mm).

FITTING PISTONS

Inspect and measure cylinder for wear or taper. Measure piston diameter and determine if clearance is correct. Install expanding ring in bottom groove of piston with ends butting but not overlapping. From bottom of piston install bottom rail and from top, upper rail. Install middle ring with word "TOP" facing upward *(see Fig. 2)*. Install upper compression ring and stagger ring gaps.

NOTE – *Oversize rings are available in .010 and .020" (.254 and .508 mm) oversizes.*

CRANKSHAFT MAIN & CONNECTING ROD BEARINGS

MAIN & CONNECTING ROD BEARINGS

1) Remove engine and separate engine and transmission. Remove clutch, flywheel, engine rear adapter plate, oil pan and dipstick. Remove rear main bearing oil seal, timing chain cover, oil pickup screen and oil slinger. Remove crankshaft sprocket, drive key and shims.

2) Remove connecting rod bearing caps and slightly push up connecting rod assembly but do not dislodge it from cylinder. Remove upper and lower connecting rod bearings and install protectors over connecting rod bolts. Remove timing chain and main bearing caps. Lift out crankshaft. Remove pilot bushing, upper and lower main bearing inserts and thrust washers.

3) Examine all bearing journals and determine if regrinding is necessary. When regrinding crankshaft, do not grind journal diameter to less than specified minimum diameter. Examine each bearing half and replace any damaged bearings. Bearings are available in various oversizes. To install, reverse removal procedure making sure that grooves in thrust washers face outward.

Minimum Crankshaft Regrind Diameters

Application	In. (mm)
Main Journal	2.0860-2.0865 (52.984-52.997)
Connecting Rod	1.7100-1.7105 (43.434-43.447)

CRANKSHAFT END PLAY

Using a feeler gauge or dial indicator, measure crankshaft end play by levering crankshaft back and forth. Value must be within specifications. If not, thrust washers are available in various oversizes.

REAR MAIN BEARING OIL SEAL

1) Disconnect battery and remove transmission, clutch and flywheel. Remove two rear oil pan bolts, loosen two right side rear and one left side rear oil pan bolts. Remove six bolts securing rear main bearing oil seal housing to crankcase. Press oil seal out of housing.

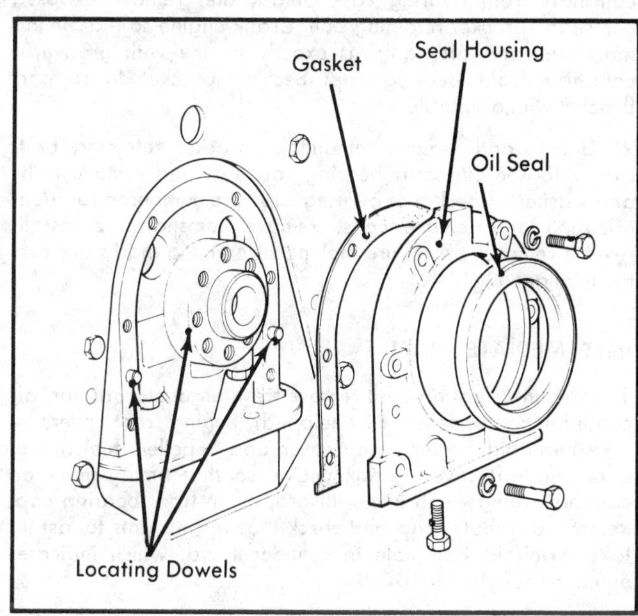

Fig. 3 Exploded View of Rear Main Bearing Oil Seal

2) Lubricate outer diameter of new seal and press it squarely into housing with lip facing crankshaft. Clean gasket area and install new gasket using sealing compound. Lubricate crankshaft and carefully ease seal housing into position on two dowels. Install six retaining bolts noting that two lower bolts are longer. Evenly tighten bolts then install two pan bolts removed previously. Tighten all oil pan bolts and continue assembly in reverse of disassembly.

CAMSHAFT

ENGINE FRONT COVER & OIL SEAL

1) Disconnect battery and remove crankshaft pulleys after first loosening drive belts and removing cooling fan. Remove alternator and mounting brackets. Remove air pump and bracket, and diverter valve and bracket. Remove air conditioning compressor strut (if equipped).

2) Remove two bolts and nuts securing front cover to cylinder head. Remove four bolts securing compressor to engine and three compressor adjusting bolts (if equipped). Remove two front oil pan bolts. Remove front cover center attachment bolt and bottom left side bolt. Remove front cover and gaskets and pry out old seal.

3) Dip new seal in engine oil and with lip facing inward, tap in squarely into front cover until flush with cover. Install front cover on engine in reverse of removal procedure using new gaskets. **NOTE** – *Front oil seal may be replaced with front cover installed by first removing crankshaft pulleys and prying out old seal.*

TRIUMPH TR7 4 CYLINDER (Cont.)

CAMSHAFT

1) Disconnect battery and remove camshaft cover. Crank engine until camshaft timing mark is 180° from groove in camshaft front bearing cap. Unlock and remove exposed camshaft sprocket retaining bolt. Crank engine so that timing mark on camshaft flange is exactly in line with groove in camshaft front bearing cap. Secure sprocket to support bracket with a suitable nut.

2) Unlock and remove remaining sprocket retaining bolt. Evenly loosen camshaft bearing cap nuts and remove bolts and washers. Check that bearing caps are numbered for identification and remove caps. Remove camshaft. To install, reverse removal procedure making sure timing marks are correctly aligned.

INTERMEDIATE SHAFT

1) Disconnect battery and remove fresh air duct, radiator, air conditioning condenser (if equipped), engine front cover, intake manifold, water pump cover and impeller, fuel pump, and camshaft cover. Crank engine so that timing mark on camshaft flange is in line with groove on front bearing cap. Remove distributor cap and check that rotor points to last intake manifold bolt hole in cylinder head, which indicates number one cylinder TDC.

2) Remove the distributor, hydraulic chain tensioner and adjustable timing chain guide. Remove two Allen head screws and withdraw intermediate shaft keeper plate. Lift timing chain clear of sprocket and pull out intermediate shaft (complete with sprocket). Clamp intermediate shaft in a vise and remove sprocket retaining bolt, tab washer and sprocket. To install, reverse removal procedure, making sure valve timing is set correctly and adjusting timing chain tension.

TIMING CHAIN

1) Remove engine front cover, camshaft cover and distributor cap. Disconnect camshaft sprocket as described under *Camshaft Removal*. Make sure that camshaft timing marks are aligned when engine is TDC, No. 1 cylinder compression stroke. Remove hydraulic chain tensioner and guide plate.

2) Remove locking bolt from adjustable chain guide and common bolt securing adjustable guide and camshaft sprocket support bracket. Remove adjustable guide. Remove bolt securing camshaft support bracket and fixed guide while holding camshaft sprocket. Remove fixed guide and release chain from intermediate shaft and camshaft sprockets. Remove (upward) camshaft sprocket and bracket along with timing chain. To install, reverse removal procedure and check valve and intermediate shaft timing.

3) Set chain tension as follows: Insert a .100" (2.54 mm) feeler gauge between chain slipper and tensioner body *(see Fig. 4)*. Loosen three chain guide retainer bolts and press down on timing chain guide between camshaft and intermediate shaft sprockets until feeler gauge is a sliding fit. Hold guide in this position and tighten adjustable guide bolt first, then two remaining bolts. Remove feeler gauge and continue reassembly.

VALVE TIMING

Crank engine until timing mark on crankshaft pulley coincides with zero mark on front cover scale. At this time, distributor rotor should point to rear bolt securing intake manifold to cylinder head and timing mark on camshaft flange is in line with groove in camshaft front bearing cap. To adjust timing it is necessary to remove timing chain.

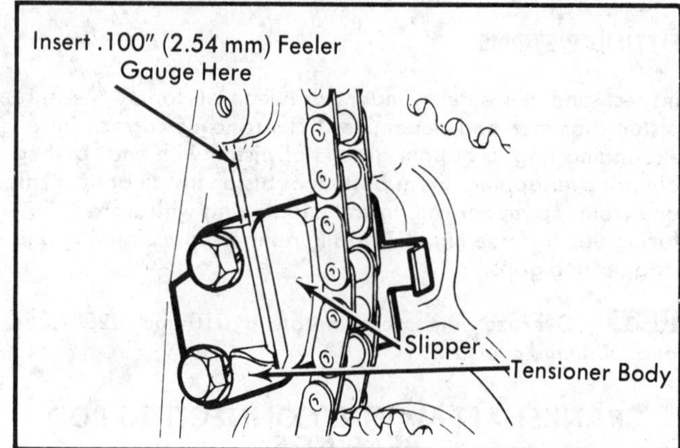

Fig. 4 Adjusting Timing Chain Tension

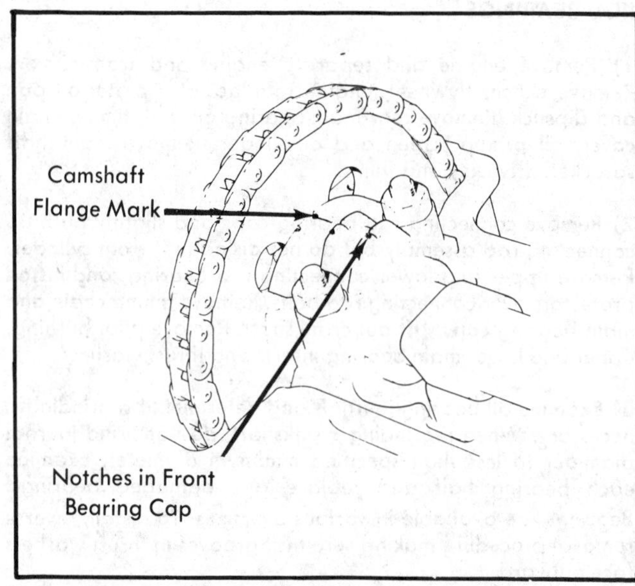

Fig. 5 Alignment of Camshaft Timing

ENGINE OILING

ENGINE OILING SYSTEM

Oil is drawn from engine by a rotor type pump which discharges via a nonadjustable relief valve to a full-flow filter. Cylinder bores, pistons and piston pins are splash lubricated. All other components are oiled through drilled passages.

Crankcase Capacity — 9.5 pts. (including filter).

Oil Filter — Full-flow, paper element type filter.

Oil Pressure Relief Valve — Nonadjustable.

TRIUMPH TR7 4 CYLINDER (Cont.)

OIL PUMP

1) Disconnect battery and raise vehicle. Remove two bolts securing clutch slave cylinder to clutch housing. **NOTE** — *Use care when removing slave cylinder that clutch release mechanism doesn't become dislodged. If mechanism does dislodge, transmission will have to be removed to repair it.* Remove clutch slave cylinder with hydraulic pipe and move out of way.

2) Remove clutch housing nut and bolt, then remove four oil pump retaining bolts and washers. Remove pump from engine complete with hexagonal drive shaft. Remove "O" ring. To disassemble pump, first remove drive shaft. Remove two screws and lift off pump cover from body. Remove pump rotors and "O" ring. Remove cotter pin from pump body and pull out relief valve plug, spring and valve. Remove "O" ring from relief valve plug.

3) Clean all components and install rotors in pump body, ensuring that chamfered edge of outer rotor is at driving end of rotor pocket. Place a straight edge across pump body and with a feeler gauge check clearance between rotor and straight edge. This clearance should be .004" (.1 mm)

4) With a feeler gauge, check clearance between outer rotor and pump body. Clearance must not exceed .008" (.2 mm). Now check the clearance between the inner and outer rotors with a feeler gauge. This clearance must not exceed .010" (.25 mm).

5) Reassemble and install oil pump in reverse of disassembly, using new "O" rings and making sure large end of relief valve is installed inward so spring will engage small end of valve.

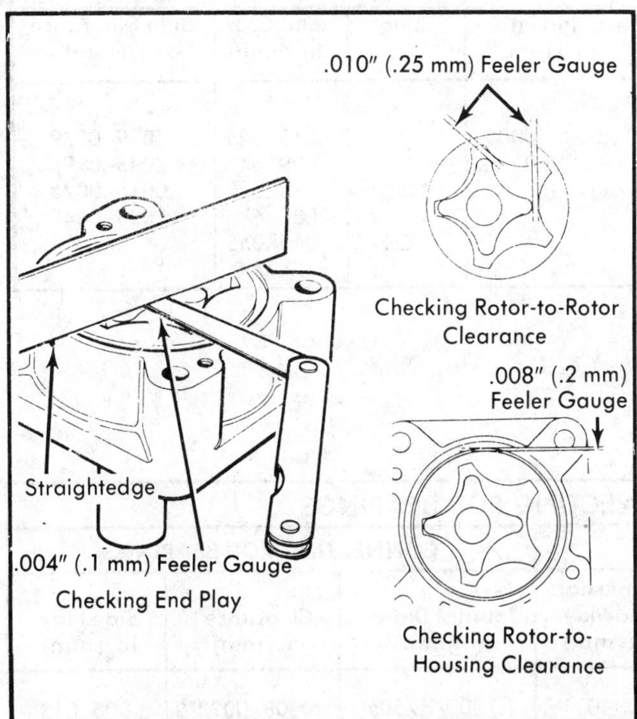

Fig. 6 View Showing Oil Pump Checking Points

ENGINE COOLING

WATER PUMP

1) Disconnect battery and remove intake manifold. Disconnect hoses from water pump cover and remove three bolts securing pump cover to engine. Lift off cover and gaskets. Turn impeller center bolt clockwise until either water pump is released from intermediate shaft drive gear and can be removed, or center bolt is removed. If center bolt comes out, use impact tool (4235A) and adapter (S4235A/10) to remove pump.

2) To overhaul pump, remove center bolt if not previously removed. Use a drift and support tool to remove impeller from shaft. Invert pump assembly (drive gear up) and drift shaft from housing. Remove "O" ring, graphite seal, water slinger, oil seal and circlip from pump shaft. Again invert shaft and drift shaft from bearing. Remove oil slinger. Remove "O" rings from housing.

3) To assemble, reverse disassembly procedure using new seals and "O" rings and noting the following: Make sure oil slinger dish is towards gear. Flat face of oil seal should face bearing. Dish of water slinger should be towards bearing. Install graphite seal with flat face towards bearing.

4) Place pump in housing ensuring that pump and jackshaft gear, mesh correctly and that pump is properly seated. **CAUTION** — *Use of force or impact to seat pump will damage pump.* Ensure gasket surfaces are clean and temporarily install pump cover. Using feeler gauges, check that gap between pump cover and engine is equal, equalize gap by adjusting bolts.

5) Select water pump cover gaskets to equal the gap noted in step **4)** plus .010-.020" (.25-.5 mm) to provide running clearance. Remove pump cover, install selected gaskets, reinstall cover and tighten bolts to specifications. Complete installation in reverse of removal procedure.

Thermostat — Begins to open at about 180°F (82°C).

Cooling System Capacity — 15.5 pts. (including heater).

Radiator Cap — 15 psi (1.05 kg/cm²).

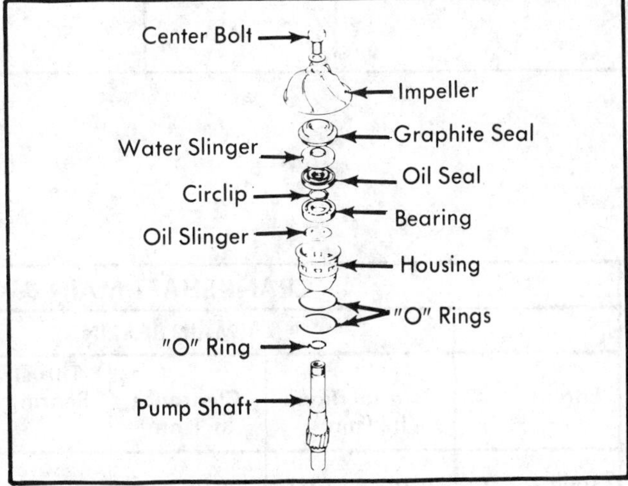

Fig. 7 Exploded View of Water Pump Assembly

TR7 4 CYLINDER (Cont.)

ENGINE SPECIFICATIONS

GENERAL SPECIFICATIONS										
Year	Displ.		Carburetor	HP at RPM	Torque (Ft. Lbs. at RPM)	Compr. Ratio	Bore		Stroke	
	cu. ins.	cc					in.	mm	in.	mm
1977	122	1998	①2x1-Bbl.	.....	.....	8.0-1	3.56	90.3	3.07	78.0

① — 1x1-Bbl. if equipped with catalytic converter.

VALVES							
Engine & Valve	Head Diam. In. (mm)	Face Angle	Seat Angle	Seat Width In. (mm)	Stem Diameter In. (mm)	Stem Clearance In. (mm)	Valve Lift In. (mm)
1998 cc							
Intake	1.560 (39.62)	45°	44.5°	.....	.3103-.3113 (7.881-7.907)	.0017-.0023 (.043-.058)	.....
Exhaust	1.280 (32.51)	45°	44.5°	.....	.3098-.3106 (7.87-7.89)	.0014-.0030 (.035-.076)	.....

PISTONS, PINS, RINGS						
Engine	PISTONS	PINS		RINGS		
	Clearance In. (mm)	Piston Fit In. (mm)	Rod Fit In. (mm)	Rings	End Gap In. (mm)	Side Clearance In. (mm)
1998 cc	.0005-.0015 (.013-.038)	0-.0004 (0-.010)	.0001-.0006 (.003-.015)	No. 1	.015-.025 (.39-.64)	.0019-.0039 (.048-.099)
				No. 2	.015-.025 (.39-.64)	.0015-.0025 (.038-.064)
				Oil	.015-.055 (.39-1.40)	.....

CRANKSHAFT MAIN & CONNECTING ROD BEARINGS							
Engine	MAIN BEARINGS				CONNECTING ROD BEARINGS		
	Journal Diam. In. (mm)	Clearance In. (mm)	Thrust Bearing	Crankshaft End Play In. (mm)	Journal Diam. In. (mm)	Clearance In. (mm)	Side Play In. (mm)
1998 cc	2.1260-2.1265 (54.000-54.013)	.0012-.0022 (.030-.055)	Center	.003-.011 (.08-.28)	1.7500-1.7505 (44.450-44.463)	.0008-.0023 (.020-.058)	.006-.013 (.15-.33)

TRIUMPH TR7 4 CYLINDER (Cont.)

ENGINE SPECIFICATIONS (Cont.)

VALVE SPRINGS			
Engine	Free Length In. (mm)	PRESSURE Lbs. @ In. (kg @ mm)	
		Valve Closed	Valve Open
1998 cc	1.60 (40.64)	.....	.....

VALVE TIMING				
Engine	INTAKE		EXHAUST	
	Open (BTDC)	Close (ALDC)	Open (BLDC)	Close (ATDC)
1998 cc	16°	56°	56°	16°

TIGHTENING SPECIFICATIONS	
Application	Ft. Lbs. (mkg)
Main Bearing Caps	50-65 (6.9-.0)
Camshaft Sprocket Bolt	7-10 (1.0-1.4)
Camshaft Bearing Caps	10-14 (1.4-1.9)
Connecting Rod Bolt	40-45 (5.5-6.2)
Crankshaft Pulley Bolt	90-120 (12.5-16.5)
Cylinder Head Bolts	45-55 (6.2-7.6)
Flywheel-to-Crankshaft	40-45 (5.5-6.2)
Jackshaft Sprocket Bolt	30-38 (4.1-5.3)
Timing Chain Tensioner-to-Block	6.9 (0.9)
Timing Chain Support Brackets & Guides	15-20 (2.1-2.8)

TYPE 1 1600 cc 4 CYLINDER

ENGINE CODING

ENGINE IDENTIFICATION

Engine identification is determined by first digits of serial number. Engine serial number is stamped on crankcase under generator support flange

Application	Engine Code
Type 1	
Fuel Injected	AJ

ENGINE, CYLINDER HEAD & MANIOLD

ENGINE

Removal – 1) Remove air cleaner. Drain oil. Disconnect hoses between fan housing and heat exchangers. Disconnect battery ground, coil wires, alternator, and oil pressure switch.

2) Disconnect fuel injection wiring harness from coil, injectors, crankcase, temperature sensors, air intake distributor and other related parts. Make sure to index mark each wire for reinstallation.

3) From under vehicle, disconnect starter electrical wires. Disconnect fuel line from pressure regulator and plug hose. Unhook back-up lights.

4) Disconnect throttle cable. Remove small cover plates over preheater pipe connections. On models equipped with automatic stick shift, disconnect lead and vacuum hose from control valve. Disconnect transmission lines and plug. Disconnect heater control cables. Disconnect heater ducting at front of heat exchangers.

5) On models equipped with automatic stick shift, remove four converter to drive plate bolts. Remove nuts from lower engine mounting studs. Place a jack under engine and raise until squarely seated against crankcase. Remove left side upper mounting bolt and right side nut and bolt. Slide engine rearward until clear. Lower jack and continue to pull engine to rear.

NOTE – *After engine has been removed, install a retainer to bell housing to keep torque converter in place.*

Installation – To install, reverse removal procedure and note: Lubricate transmission input shaft and clutch release bearing. Also, lightly lubricate starter (Bosch only) drive bushing with multi-purpose grease. Adjust clutch free play. Make sure ignition timing and accelerator control linkage are properly adjusted.

INTAKE MANIFOLD

Removal – 1) Remove fan housing. Disconnect preheating pipes at flanges. Remove injectors, intake air sensor and air intake distributor from crankcase.

2) Remove nuts holding manifold. Disconnect all air and vacuum hoses from air intake distributor. Be sure to index each item for reinstallation.

3) Disconnect exhaust line from EGR valve by removing mounting nuts. Lift off manifold with intake air distributor.

Installation – To install, reverse removal procedure and replace gaskets where necessary.

CYLINDER HEAD

NOTE – *Engine must be removed from vehicle, and manifolds removed, before removing cylinder heads. If cylinders are not to be removed, use retaining device to keep cylinders from pulling free.*

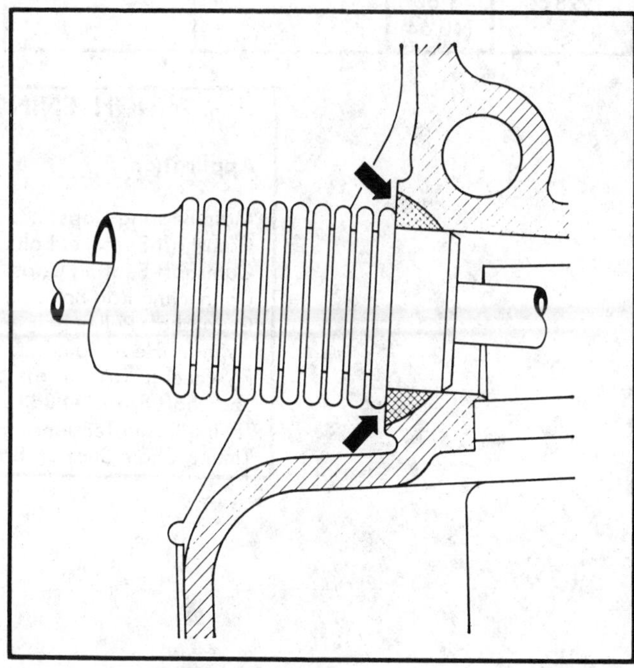

Fig. 1 Push Rod Tube Installation with Detail of Seal Fit

Removal – 1) Remove engine and intake manifold as previously outlined. Remove muffler and heat exchangers. Disconnect spark plug wires at spark plugs. Remove deflector cover plates from under cylinder cover plates and remove cylinder cover plates.

2) On fuel injected engines remove lower left side warm air duct. Remove bolt securing thermostat to bracket and unscrew thermostat from control rod. Disconnect rod from control lever at top.

3) Remove rocker arm cover with gasket and remove rocker arm assemblies. Remove push rods, keeping in order for reassembly. Loosen cylinder head nuts gradually working in sequence from outside toward center and remove cylinder head.

Installation – 1) Install new seals on pushrod tubes. Install cylinder head with new cylinder seals and position pushrod tubes with seams facing upward. Push head onto cylinders to hold pushrod tubes.

2) Install cylinder head washers and nuts to studs and tighten just enough to hold head and pushrod tubes in place. Uniformly tighten nuts in sequence shown in illustration "A" to 7 ft. lbs., then tighten in sequence shown in illustration "B" to required torque. Reverse removal procedure for remaining components. Adjust valves.

TYPE 1 1600 cc 4 CYLINDER (Cont.)

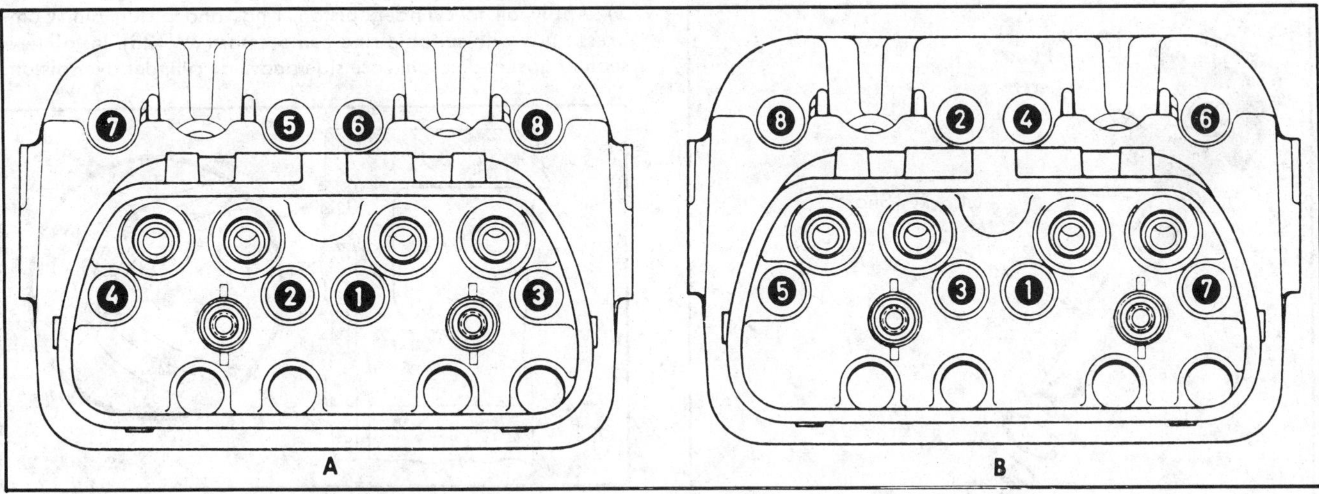

Fig. 2 Step One and Two for Cylinder Head Tightening Sequence — Volkswagen 1600 cc

VALVES

VALVE ARRANGEMENT

E-I-I-E (front to rear), both banks.

VALVE GUIDE SERVICING

1) Place valve in valve guide with stem flush with end of guide. With dial indicator, measure valve rock at valve head. If rock exceeds .031" replace valve guide or valve. Valve guide with inside machined shoulder is exhaust.

2) To replace valve guide, drill guide with shouldered drill to depth of 1½-2" using slow speed drill. Drive guides down through cylinder head with suitable tool. Drive oversize guide from top of cylinder head using press. Pressure required should be 2000-4000 lbs. Ream guides to proper fit.

VALVE STEM OIL SEALS

Coat valve stems with molybdenum-disulfide paste and insert in cylinder head. Slide valve stem seal ring over valve stem and install spring, retainer and keeper.

VALVE SPRINGS

NOTE — *Valve spring may be removed with cylinder head installed. Apply constant air pressure (minimum 85 psi) to cylinder through spark plug hole to hold valve in place while compressing spring.*

Removal — Remove cylinder head cover and rocker arm shaft. Install suitable valve spring compressor tool (VW311H with cylinder head removed, VW653/2 with cylinder head installed). Compress spring retainer and spring and remove valve keepers. Release compressor and remove spring retainer and spring.

Installation — Install valve, valve spring, valve stem seal ring and spring retainer.

NOTE — *Install spring with closely spaced coils against cylinder head.*

2) Compress spring with suitable compressor and install valve keepers.

ROCKER ARM ASSEMBLY

1) Remove valve cover. Remove nuts from rocker arm studs and remove rocker arm assembly. Remove clips from end of shaft and remove washers, rocker arms and shaft supports.

2) Inspect shaft, supports and rocker arms for wear. Inspect sides of rocker arms and supports for wear. Smooth sides with emery paper before installing if worn.

3) To assemble reverse removal procedure. Install new seals on rocker arm studs, and reverse removal procedure to install. Adjust valve clearance.

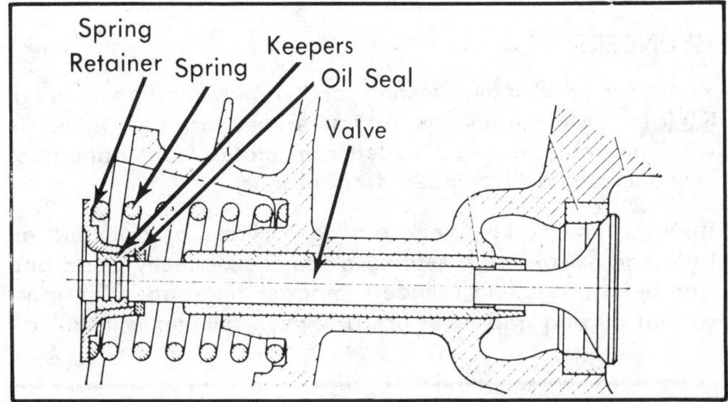

Fig. 3 Sectional View of Valve with Related Parts

VALVE CLEARANCE ADJUSTMENT

Perform adjustment with engine cold. Turn crankshaft until No. 1 cylinder is at TDC position and distributor rotor points to No. 1 cylinder position. Loosen lock-nut and adjust rocker arm adjusting screw until valve clearance is .006". Check clearance between adjusting screw and valve stem of both valves. Tighten lock nut. Turn crankshaft 90° while noting rotor travel. Adjust valves of Nos. 2, 3 and 4 in turn.

TYPE 1 1600 cc 4 CYLINDER (Cont.)

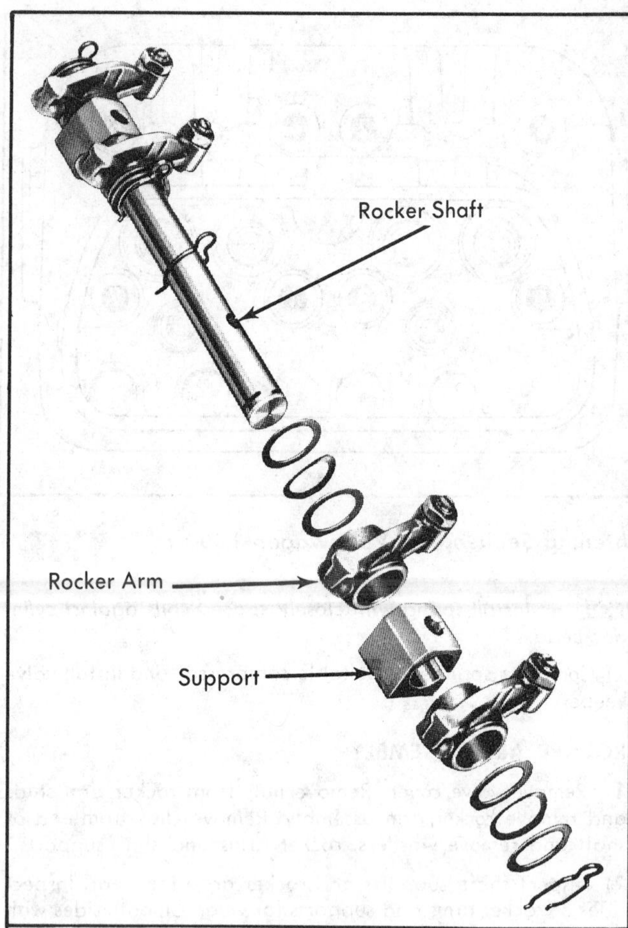

Fig. 4 Expanded View of 1600 cc Rocker Arm Assembly

PISTONS, PINS & RINGS

CYLINDERS

Removal – Remove engine and remove cylinder head. **NOTE** – *Mark cylinders to insure they are reinstalled in original position.* Remove deflector plates from bottom of cylinders and pull cylinders from pistons.

Installation – 1) Check seating surfaces of cylinders on both ends. Make sure seating areas are perfectly clean and true before installing cylinders. Stagger ring gaps 90° apart so that oil ring gap faces upward when cylinder is installed.

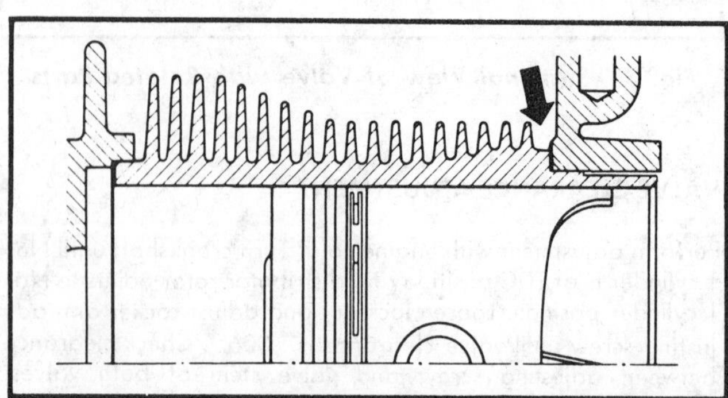

Fig. 5 Shows Correct Position of Cylinder Seal

2) Apply oil to cylinder, piston, rings and piston pin. Compress rings with suitable ring compressor (VW123). Install new sealing gasket on crankcase side and slide cylinder over piston.

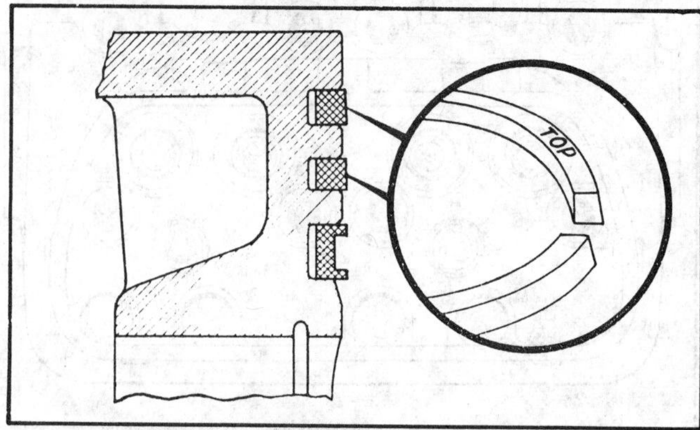

Fig. 6 Installation of Compression Rings 1 and 2

3) Make sure studs do not contact cooling fins when cylinder is completely seated against crankcase. Install cylinder deflector plates and remaining components in reverse of removal.

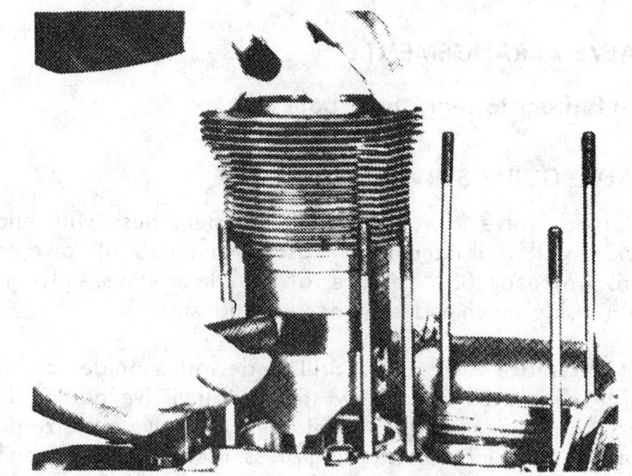

Fig. 7 Cylinder Installation

FITTING PISTONS

1) With piston and cylinder removed, measure clearance between piston and cylinder. Check piston size at bottom of skirt and 90° to piston pin. Check cylinder size at several points throughout cylinder, using largest reading to determine clearance.

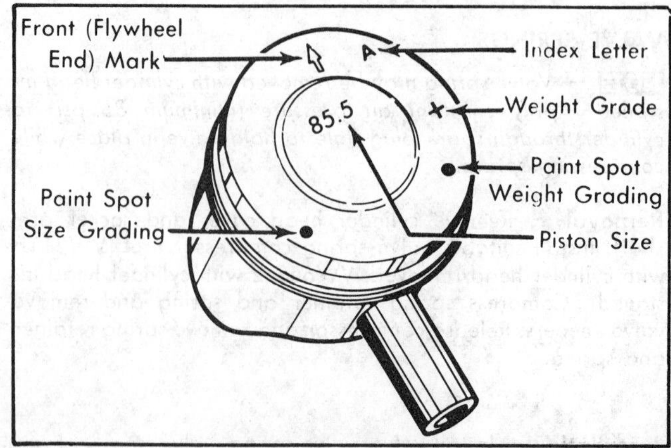

Fig. 8 Top View of Piston with Detail of Piston Markings

TYPE 1 1600 cc 4 CYLINDER (Cont.)

2) If clearance exceeds .008" (.20 mm) replace piston and cylinder as a set. New piston must be of same weight grade as original or within 10 g of original piston weight. Piston size, weight and installation position are marked on top of piston.

NOTE — *Piston alone may be replaced with one of matching size. Only pistons of same size and weight grade should be installed in same engine.*

3) New piston rings are size graded to match piston-cylinder sets. Measure ring gap with ring installed approximately ¼" from bottom of cylinder.

Fig. 9 Using a Feeler Gauge to Measure Ring Gap

4) Install rings on piston and measure ring side clearance using feeler gauge. If clearance exceeds .005" (.12 mm) on top ring or .004" (.10 mm) on second or oil ring, piston must be replaced.

PISTON PINS

Removal — Remove cylinders and mark pistons before removing for proper installation. Using suitable pliers (VW122b), remove piston pin circlips and push piston pin out of piston using suitable tool (VW207).

Installation — 1) Check fit of pin in piston. Piston pin should be light push fit with piston 68-167°F. If pin is too loose, both pin and piston must be replaced. Check clearance of pin in rod. If clearance exceeds .0016" (.04 mm) replace piston pin and rod bushing. See Piston Pin Bushing Replacement.

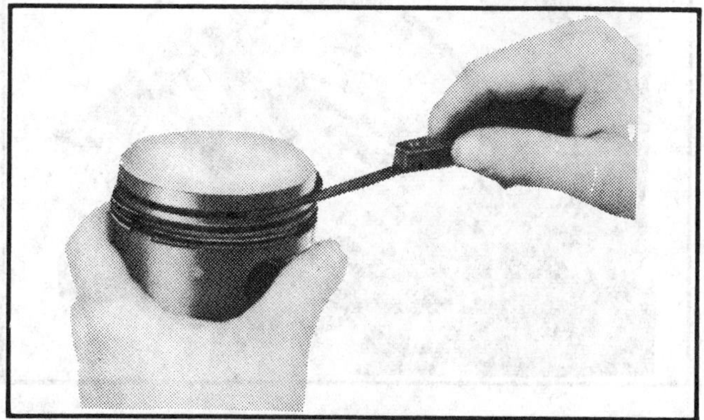

Fig. 10 Using a Feeler Gauge to Measure Ring Clearance

2) Install one circlip in piston on side facing flywheel. Position piston on connecting rod and push piston pin through piston. Replace remaining circlip. **NOTE** — *Piston may be heated to ease pin installation.* Replace remaining components in reverse of removal.

PISTON PIN BUSHING REPLACEMENT

1) At normal temperature, piston pin should push fit in connecting rod. If side clearance is felt with a new pin installed, bushing must be replaced and reamed to correct fit with a new piston pin.

2) Press bushing out using a suitable mandrel and components. Install new bushing using same procedure and tools used for removal.

3) Drill through oil holes in connecting rod. Use handreamer to fit pin into bushing. Bushing should be free of chatter marks when reaming is completed. Piston pin should push fit into bushing without oil. Clearance must be .0004-.0008" (.01-.02 mm).

CRANKSHAFT MAIN & CONNECTING ROD BEARINGS

CRANKCASE DISASSEMBLY

NOTE — *Crankcase must be taken apart to replace connecting rods, connecting rod bearings and main bearings. It is also necessary to disassemble crankcase to remove crankshaft, camshaft and camshaft bearings.*

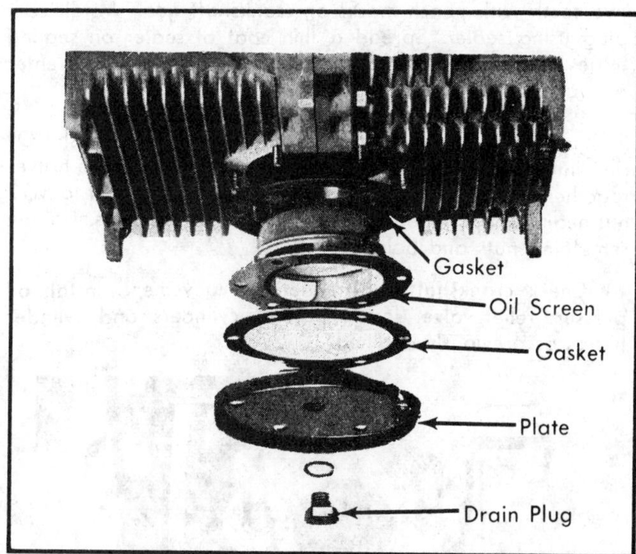

Fig. 11 Bottom View Showing Oil Strainer and Components

1) Remove engine from vehicle and remove cylinder heads, cylinders and pistons as previously outlined. Remove flywheel or drive plate, distributor, fuel pump, distributor drive, distributor drive washer and oil cooler.

2) Remove front pulley nut and remove pulley using suitable puller (VW203). Remove generator support housing and metal shroud from front of engine.

TYPE 1 1600 cc 4 CYLINDER (Cont.)

3) On all models remove oil pump cover and pull oil pump from crankcase using a suitable puller (VW201). Remove retaining plate and screen from bottom of motor. Remove nuts and bolts securing crankcase halves and separate.

CAUTION – *Use a rubber hammer to separate crankcase halves, do not insert any kind of tool between sealing edges.*

4) Remove camshaft and crankshaft. Remove crankshaft oil seal and cam plug. Remove number two bearing halves from both sides of crankcase and remove bearing dowel pins. Remove cam bearings if equipped. Remove oil pressure relief valve.

CRANKCASE ASSEMBLY

1) Thoroughly clean and inspect crankcase halves for wear or cracking. Assemble empty crankcase halves and tighten nuts to specifications. Measure crankshaft bearing bores with an inside micrometer. Specified diameter for bearing bores 1 through 3 is 2.1641-2.1649" (54.97-54.99 mm). Diameter for number 4 bearing bore is 1.5740-1.5748" (40.00-40.01 mm).

2) Flush out all oil passages and blow out with compressed air. Make sure oil suction tube and all studs are tight in crankcase halves.

3) Insert valve tappets and crankshaft bearing dowel pins. Install camshaft bearings if equipped. Install No. 2 bearing halves. Install crankshaft and connecting rod assembly, making sure bearings line up with dowel pins.

4) Install camshaft with "O" on cam gear centered between two teeth with punch marks on crankshaft gear. Install cam plug using sealer. Spread a thin coat of sealer on sealing edges of crankcase halves, making sure sealer does not enter oil passages.

5) Install "O" ring on large crankcase studs and push "O" ring into beveled portion of crankcase. Join crankcase halves together and lightly tighten nuts. Tighten M8 nut next to M12 nut near number 1 bearing then tighten all M12 nuts. Tighten remaining nuts and bolts.

6) Check crankshaft for freedom of movement. Install oil pressure relief valve. install pistons, cylinders and cylinder heads as previously outlined.

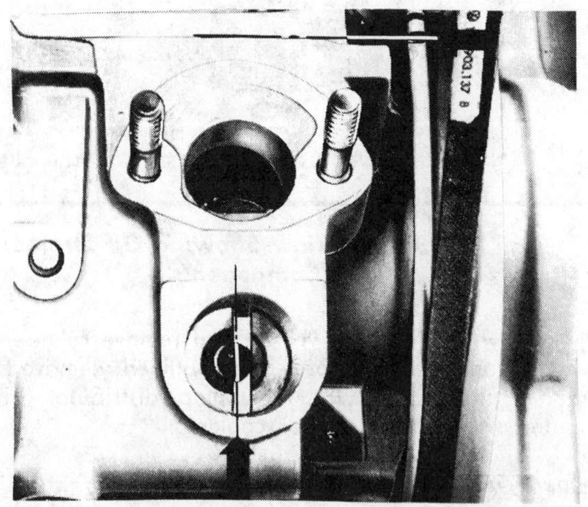

Fig. 12 1600 cc Distributor Drive Installation

7) On all models install all components except distributor and distributor drive in reverse of removal order. Set engine on number one firing position. Place distributor drive washer on a long screwdriver. Insert screwdriver into bottom of distributor hole, drop washer and center in bottom of hole with screwdriver.

8) Insert distributor drive with slot at 90° with crankshaft and small segment of slot toward pulley.

MAIN & CONNECTING ROD BEARING SERVICE

1) Split crankcase and remove crankshaft and connecting rod assembly as previously outlined. Attach crankshaft to a suitable holding fixture (VW310A).

2) Remove Woodruff key, oil thrower and number 4 bearing. Remove connecting rods and bearings. Remove snapring from end of crankshaft.

3) Press distributor drive gear, spacer and crankshaft gear from crankshaft. Remove number 3 bearing. Thoroughly clean crankshaft and blow out all oil passages with compressed air.

4) Check crankshaft for runout, maximum runout is .0011". Check crankshaft journals for out-of-round, maximum out-of-round is .0011". If excessive out-of-round conditions exist, crankshaft must be ground to next undersize.

5) Bearings for undersize crankshafts are available in .010, .020 and .030" undersize. Connecting rod bearing journals are also available in same undersizes.

6) Clean and inspect connecting rods. If bushing has been determined to be worn excessively, install new bushing. *See Piston Pin and Piston Pin Bushing Replacement.* Check connecting rod for twist and bending.

7) If connecting rod is replaced, make sure there is no more than 10 grams difference in weight between new and old connecting rods.

Fig. 13 Using a Feeler Gauge to Check Connecting Rod Side Clearance

TYPE 1 1600 cc 4 CYLINDER (Cont.)

8) Main bearing clearance is checked by the Plastigage method. Place a piece of Plastigage wire across crankshaft journal. Install bearings on crankshaft and install crankshaft in empty crankcase halves. Bolt crankcase together at specified torque. Do not turn crankshaft. Separate crankcase and remove crankshaft. Remove bearings and compare flattened wire to scale on Plastigage package. Compare to specified clearance.

9) If clearance is more than specified, crankshaft can be ground to .010", .020" and .030" undersize. Replacement bearings of appropriate size must be used. This same procedure is used when determining connecting rod bearing clearance.

10) Install bearing halves in rod and rod cap. Install on crankshaft with numbers on rod and rod cap together and with forged mark on rod up when crankshaft is installed. Tighten rod bolts or nuts to specifications. Check rod side clearance.

11) Oil and install number 3 bearing on crankshaft with dowel pin hole toward flywheel. Press on crank gear, spacer and distributor drive gear. Install snap ring. Oil and install number 4 bearing with groove toward oil thrower. Install oil thrower and Woodruff key.

12) Oil and install number 1 bearing and install crankshaft in crankcase as previously outlined.

THRUST BEARING ALIGNMENT

1) Crankshaft endplay must be adjusted with crankshaft oil seal removed. Install two shims, flywheel gasket (paper or metal) and flywheel.

Fig. 14 Checking Crankshaft End Play with Dial Gauge

2) Correct end play is .0028-.0051" and must not exceed .006". Mount dial indicator to crankcase so back and forth movement of crankshaft can be determined. Rock crankshaft back and forth and determine thickness of third shim.

3) Install third shim, oil seal, and flywheel with gasket. Recheck end play. Following shim sizes are available:

Millimeter Marking (Etched in Shim)	Inch Equivalent
0.24 mm	.0094"
0.30 mm	.0118"
0.32 mm	.0126"
0.34 mm	.0133"
0.36 mm	.0142"

MAIN BEARING OIL SEAL SERVICE

1) Remove flywheel and pry out old seal. Clean recess in crankcase and coat with a thin film of sealer.

2) Install a new seal using a suitable installer (VW240D). Make sure seal is squarely seated in recess.

Fig. 15 Crankshaft Oil Seal Installation with Special Tool

3) Lubricate contact surface or seal and install flywheel. Tighten flywheel retaining nut to specification.

CAMSHAFT

CAMSHAFT

1) Split crankcase and remove camshaft as previously outlined. Clean camshaft and inspect riveted joint between camshaft and gear.

2) Inspect camshaft lobes and bearing journals for excessive wear. Maximum wear for bearing journals is .0015". Check camshaft runout on number 2 bearing journal. Maximum runout is .0016".

3) Check backlash between camshaft and crankshaft gears. Correct backlash is 0-.002". If backlash is incorrect, camshafts with different pitch radius are available. Pitch radius is stamped on inner face of gear.

Fig. 16 Correct Position of Camshaft Timing Gear

TYPE 1 1600 cc 4 CYLINDER (Cont.)

CAMSHAFT END THRUST

Camshaft end play is checked with camshaft installed in crankcase half. Measure back and forth movement of camshaft with a dial indicator. If end play exceeds .0062", replace camshaft or camshaft bearings. Correct end play is .0016-.0051".

VALVE TIMING

Install camshaft with "O" stamped in tooth on outside of camshaft gear between two teeth with punch marks on crankshaft gear.

ENGINE OILING

Oil Capacity – 2.6 qts.

Normal Oil Pressure – 28 psi at 2500 RPM

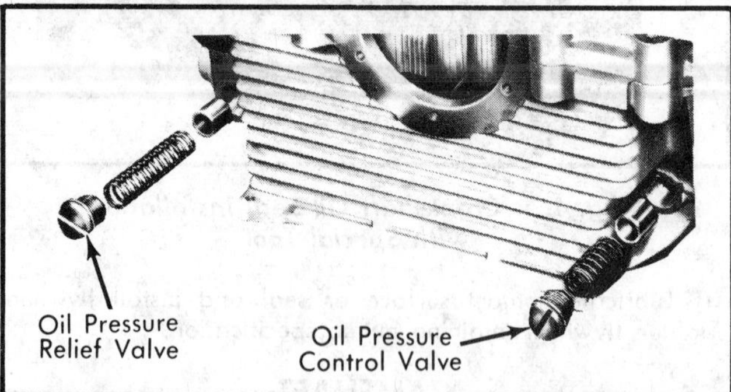

Fig. 17 Oil Pressure Regulator Valves Location

Pressure Regulator Valves – Oil pressure relief valve, used to protect oil cooler from excessive pressure, is located in crankcase to rear of oil pan. Oil pressure control valve, used to control oil pressure to bearings, is located in crankcase forward of oil pan. Oil pressure relief spring should have length of 1.73" at 12.3-16.0 lbs. load. Oil pressure control spring should have length of .795" at 6.8-8.4 lbs. load.

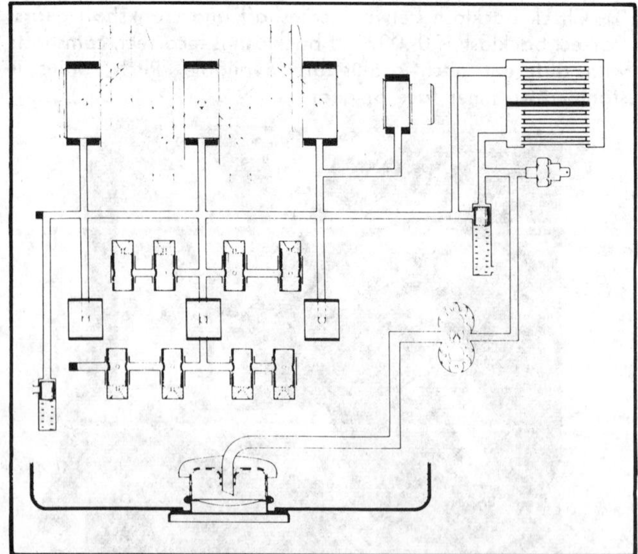

Fig. 18 Engine Lubrication Circulation Diagram

ENGINE OILING SYSTEM

Full pressure lubrication system with gear type oil pump. Oil pump is mounted at front of engine and driven by the camshaft. Oil is pumped through oil cooler into oil passages. Crankshaft main and connecting rod journals oil through cross drilled holes in crankshaft. Oil is pumped to camshaft through oil passages that also lubricate valve tappets. Oil flows through tappets and into push rods to lubricate rocker arms and shafts. Valves and valve stems are lubricated by splash oil. Excess oil flows back into crankcase through push rod tubes. Cylinder walls, pistons and piston pins are oiled by splash oil.

OIL PUMP REPLACEMENT

W/Man. Trans. – 1) Remove crankshaft pulley and metal shroud from behind pulley.

2) Remove oil pump cover and gears. Pull pump housing from crankcase using a suitable puller (VW201). Check gear backlash and endplay.

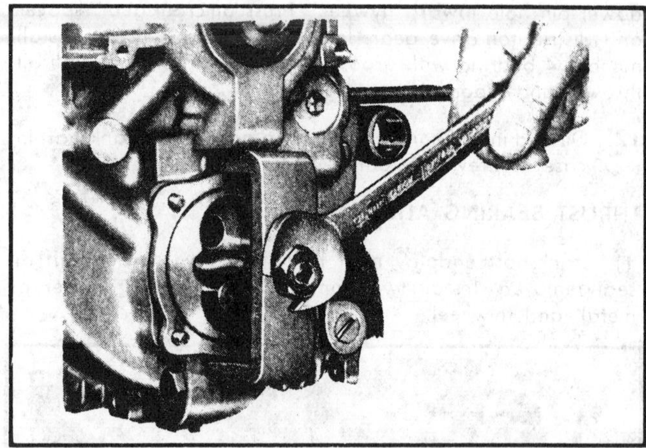

Fig. 19 Removing Oil Pump with Puller Tool

3) Inspect pump body mating surfaces for wear or damage. Install pump body and gasket (without sealer) in crankcase. Insert a suitable pilot in housing in place of gear.

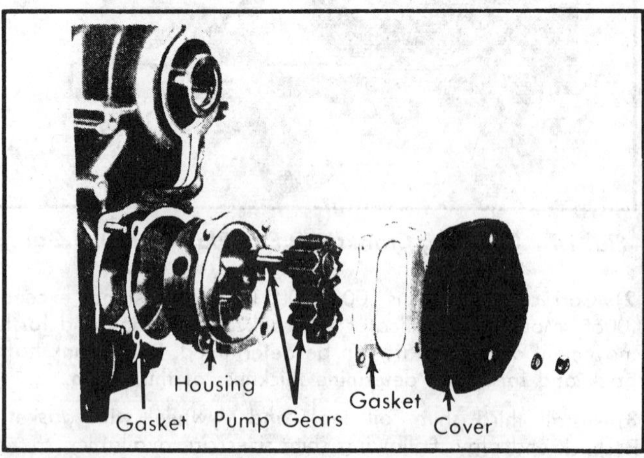

Fig. 20 View of Partially Disassembled Oil Pump

4) Rotate crankshaft 360° twice to center pump body with slot in camshaft. Remove pilot and install gears. Inspect cover and machine flat if necessary. Use new gasket (without sealer) and install cover. Tighten bolts and install remaining components as previously outlined.

TYPE 1 1600 cc 4 CYLINDER (Cont.)

W/Auto Stick Shift – Apply same procedures as outlined above, noting the following: Remove Woodruff keys to avoid damage to intermediate plate seals. If intermediate plate or front cover are damaged, replace complete oil pump.

Oil Pump Specifications

Application	Measurement
Gear Backlash	0-.008" (0-.20 mm)
End Play Without Gasket (Max.)	.004" (.10 mm)

ENGINE COOLING

COOLING SYSTEM

Engine is cooled by a radial fan mounted on end of generator and inside of upright shroud. Fan draws air in through large hole in fan shroud. Air is then directed over finned cylinders and cylinder heads by deflector plates. A thermostat is mounted under cylinders number one and two. Thermostat operates by opening and closing deflector plates in fan shroud.

AIR DUCTS, FAN HOUSING & CONTROL FLAPS

Partical Removal – 1) Remove alternator drive belt. Remove air cleaner and intake air sensor. Remove accelerator cable from guide tube. Remove alternator mounting bracket. Disconnect ignition cables, any hoses, air ducts, or wires that might prevent fan housing upward movement.

2) Remove oil cooler cover bolt and bolt holding fan housing to oil cooler flange. Take off cover and air duct. Remove screws from each end of fan housing. Remove thermostat. Pry off spring clip, separate connecting link from left control flap. Raise fan housing and remove intake manifold and alternator.

NOTE – *For complete removal of components, continue with remaining procedures. It is easier to remove remaining components with engine removed.*

3) Remove fresh air to heat exchangers distributing hoses. Remove crankshaft pulley cover plate and preheater rear cover plates. Free lower air ducting from crankcase and heat exchangers.

4) Slide alternator mounting bracket off support stand. Remove fan housing screws, lift up fan housing and remove. Both control flaps can be removed by unhooking return spring and removing mounting screws in lower part of fan housing.

Installation – To install components, reverse removal procedure.

ENGINE SPECIFICATIONS

GENERAL SPECIFICATIONS

Year	Displ. cu. ins.	Displ. cc	Carburetor	HP at RPM	Torque (Ft. Lbs. at RPM)	Compr. Ratio	Bore in.	Bore mm	Stroke in.	Stroke mm
1977										
Type 1										
AH	96.9	1584	Fuel Inj	46@4000	72@2000	7.3-1	3.36	85.5	2.72	69
AK	96.9	1584	Fuel Inj	46@4000	72@2000	7.3-1	3.36	85.5	2.72	69

VALVES

Engine & Valve	Head Diam. In. (mm)	Face Angle	Seat Angle	Seat Width In. (mm)	Stem Diameter In. (mm)	Stem Clearance In. (mm)	Valve Lift In. (mm)
1600 cc							
Int.	1.40 (35.6)	44°	45°	.051-.063 (1.3-1.6)	.3126-.3130 (7.94-7.95)	.009-.011 (.23-.27)	.....
Exh.	1.26 ①(32.1)	45°	45°	.067-.079 (1.70-2.00)	.3114-.3118 ②(7.91-7.92)	.009-.011 (.23-.27)	.....

① – Carburetor engines. Fuel injection engines 1.19" (30.2 mm).

② – Carburetor engines. Fuel injection engines .3508-.3512" (8.91-8.92 mm)

TYPE 1 1600 cc 4 CYLINDER (Cont.)

ENGINE SPECIFICATIONS (Cont.)

PISTONS, PINS, RINGS						
	PISTONS	PINS		RINGS		
Engine	Clearance In. (mm)	Piston Fit In. (mm)	Rod Fit In. (mm)	Rings	End Gap In. (mm)	Side Clearance In. (mm)
1600 cc	.0016-.0024 (.041-.061)	①	.0004-.0008 (.010-.020)	1	.012-.018 (.20-.45)	.0028-.0039 (.07-.10)
				2	.012-.018 (.30-.45)	.0020-.0028 (.05-.07)
				3	.010-.016 (.25-.40)	.0012-.0020 (.030-.050)

① — Push fit with piston heated to approximately 176°F.

CRANKSHAFT MAIN & CONNECTING ROD BEARINGS							
	MAIN BEARINGS				CONNECTING ROD BEARINGS		
Engine	Journal Diam. In. (mm)	Clearance In. (mm)	Thrust Bearing	Crankshaft End Play In. (mm)	Journal Diam. In. (mm)	Clearance In. (mm)	Side Play In. (mm)
1600 cc							
Journal No. 1	2.1641-2.1649 (54.97-54.99)	.0016-.004 (.04-.10)	No. 1	.003-.005 (.069-.131)	2.1646-2.1654 (54.98-55.00)	.0008-.0028 (.02-.07)	.004-.016 (.10-.40)
2	2.1641-2.1649 (54.97-54.99)	.001-.0035 (.03-.09)					
3	2.1641-2.1649 (54.97-54.99)	.0016-.004 (.04-.10)					
4	1.5740-1.5748 (39.98-40.00)	.002-.004 (.05-.10)					

VALVE SPRINGS			
Engine	Free Length In. (mm)	PRESSURE Lbs. @ In. (kg @ mm)	
		Valve Closed	Valve Open
1600 cc Int. & Exh.	.....	117-135@1.22 (53-61@31.0)	.....

CAMSHAFT			
Engine	Journal Diam. In. (mm)	Clearance In. (mm)	Lobe Lift In. (mm)
1600 cc	.9839-.9843 (24.99-25.00)	.0008-.002 (.02-.05)	....

TIGHTENING SPECIFICATIONS

Application	Ft. Lbs. (mkg)
Cylinder Head	23 (3.2)
Connecting Rod	22-25 (3.0-3.5)
Crankcase Halves (8 mm)	14 (2.0)
Crankcase Halves (12 mm)	18 (2.5)
Rocker Shaft-to-Cylinder Head	14-18 (2.0-2.5)
Oil Pump-to-Crankcase	14 (2.0)
Oil Drain Plug	25 (3.5)
Oil Strainer-to-Crankcase	5 (.7)
Flywheel-to-Crankshaft	253 (35.0)
Clutch-to-Flywheel	18 (2.5)
Converter-to-Driveplate	18 (2.5)
Engine-to-Transmission	22 (3.0)
Generator Pulley	40-47 (5.5-6.5)
Crankshaft Pulley	29-36 (4.0-5.0)
Fan Nut	40-47 (5.5-6.5)

TYPE 2 2000 cc 4 CYLINDER

ENGINE CODING

ENGINE IDENTIFICATION

Engine code number is stamped on crankcase below breather, near coil. First two digits of cast number are engine code.

Engine Identification

Application	Engine Code
Type 2	GD

ENGINE, CYLINDER HEAD & MANIFOLD

ENGINE

Removal – 1) Remove air cleaner. Disconnect battery. Disconnect electrical wiring from the following components: distributor, regulator, oil pressure sending unit, and transmission switch. Make sure to tag each wire for reinstallation. Disconnect back-up light lead at in-line fuse. Fuse is located near coil. Disconnect wire from temperature sensor, if equipped.

2) Disconnect fuel injection wiring harness from coil, injectors, intake air distributors, crankcase, temperature sensors. Disconnect evaporation canister hoses. Remove coil. Remove ducting between warm air blower and heat exchanger. Disconnect accelerator cable from lever on throttle valve shaft.

3) Remove oil filler neck and dipstick. Remove rear side engine cover plates. On automatic transmission models, remove transmission filler pipe by rotating counterclockwise. Also, disconnect vacuum line from intake air distributor. On automatic transmission models, remove converter bolts through opening in lower left side of bell housing. Disconnect starter electrical wires.

4) Disconnect heater control cables. Remove ducting connecting heat exchangers with inside of vehicle. Remove both upper engine to transmission mounting bolts. Place a support (VW785) under transmission. Pull accelerator from guide tube. Disconnect fuel line from pressure regulator and plug opening. Remove both lower engine to transmission mounting bolts.

5) Place a floor jack (or equivalent) under engine. Raise jack until engine is just supported. Remove bolts mounting engine brackets to frame. Slide engine assembly slightly to rear to free input shaft. Lower engine to floor.

NOTE – *On vehicles equipped with automatic transmissions, install strap across converter to prevent torque converter from sliding off support tube.*

Installation – To install, reverse removal procedure and note following: When lining up engine and transmission, place transmission in gear, set parking brake and hand turn crankshaft until splines line up. Make sure rubber seal between engine cover and body is properly positioned. Lubricate clutch release bearing, transmission drive shaft and starter drive bushing (Bosch starters).

INTAKE MANIFOLD

Removal – 1) Fuel injection manifold can be removed with engine in vehicle. Remove air cleaner, hoses, and pressure switch.

2) Disconnect wires on fuel injectors and remove two screws. Pull injectors off with plate and retainer. Make sure locating bushings are removed from manifold. Disconnect hoses on injectors and remove.

3) Remove intake manifold cover plate. Remove nuts and washers securing manifold to cylinder heads. Lift up on manifold and pull from tubes on air distributor.

Installation – To install manifold, reverse removal procedure and note the following: Use new gaskets and tighten intake manifold mounting nuts uniformly. Make sure gray protective cap on injector is to rear and cap is to front.

CYLINDER HEAD

NOTE – *Engine must be removed from vehicle and manifolds removed, before removing cylinder heads. If cylinders are not to be removed, use retaining device to keep cylinders from pulling free.*

Removal – 1) Remove rocker arm cover and gasket. Remove rocker arm shaft retaining nuts, loosening gradually one at a time to relieve spring tension evenly. Remove rocker arm assemblies.

2) Remove push rods, keeping in order for reassembly. Loosen cylinder head nuts gradually working in sequence from outside toward center.

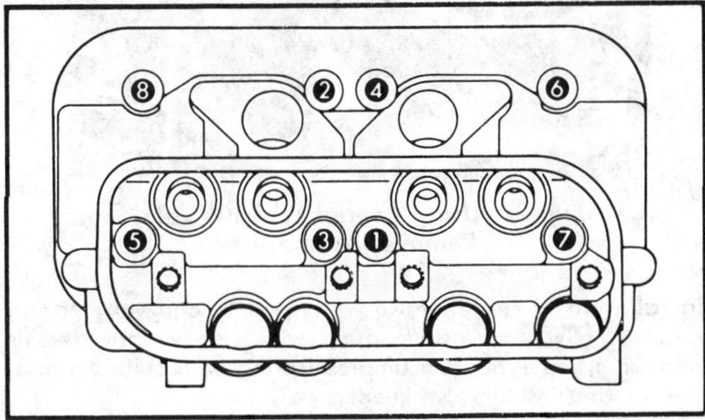

Fig. 1 2000 cc Engine, Cylinder Head Bolt Tightening Sequence

Installation – Install new seal on push rod tubes. Install cylinder head with new gasket over studs. Loosely attach head nuts and washers. Torque cylinder head according to sequence shown in *Fig. 1*. Install push rod tube in place by sliding through top of cylinder head. Reverse removal procedure for remaining components.

VALVES

VALVE ARRANGEMENT

E-I-I-E (both banks)

TYPE 2 2000 cc 4 CYLINDER (Cont.)

VALVE GUIDE SERVICING

1) Place valve in valve guide with stem flush with end of guide. With dial indicator, measure valve rock at valve head. If rock exceeds .047" (1.2 mm), replace valve guide or valve. Valve guide with inside machined shoulder is exhaust.

2) To replace valve guide, drill guide with shouldered drill to depth of 1⁹⁄₁₆ - 1⁶¹⁄₆₄" using slow speed drill. Drive guides down through cylinder head with suitable tool. Drive oversize guide from top of cylinder head using press. Pressure required should be 1000-2000 lbs. Ream guides to proper fit.

VALVE SPRINGS

NOTE — *Valve spring may be removed with cylinder head installed. Apply constant air pressure (minimum 85 psi) to cylinder through spark plug hole to hold valve in place while compressing spring.*

Removal — Remove cylinder head cover and rocker arm shaft. Install suitable valve spring compressor tool (VW311s with cylinder head removed, VW653/2 with cylinder head installed). Compress spring retainer and spring and remove valve keepers. Release compressor and remove spring retainer and spring.

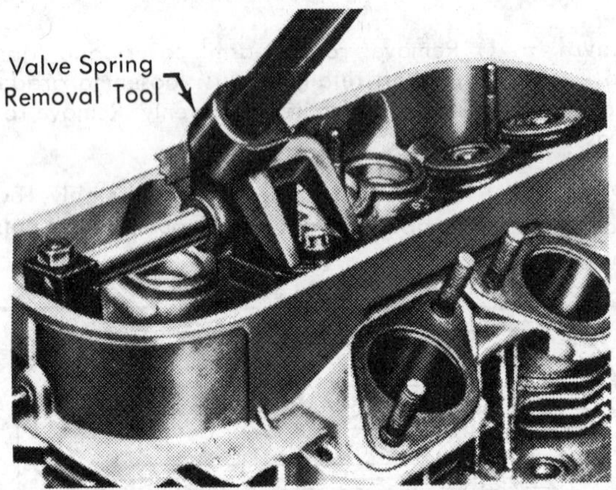

Fig. 2 Using Special Tool VW311s to Remove Valve Spring

Installation — Install valve, valve spring, and valve spring retainer. **NOTE** — *Install spring with closely spaced coils against cylinder head.* Compress spring with suitable compressor and install valve keepers.

ROCKER ARM ASSEMBLY

Removal — Disengage wire valve cover clip. Remove valve cover. Remove 4 rocker shaft retaining nuts. Each side has two separate shafts. Make sure mounting nuts are gradually and evenly loosened until spring tension is relieved.

Inspection — Check rocker arms and shafts for wear. If inside diameter of rocker arm is worn more than .789" (20.0 mm), replace rocker arm. If diameter of rocker shaft is worn to less than .783" (19.9 mm), replace rocker shaft.

Installation — To install, reverse removal procedure and note: Make sure push rod tube retaining wire is reinstalled. Adjust valve clearance.

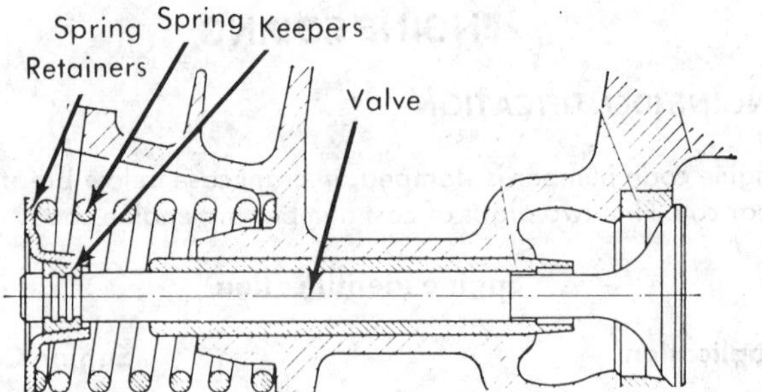

Fig. 3 Sectional View of Valve with Related Parts

VALVE CLEARANCE ADJUSTMENT

Perform adjustment with engine cold. Turn crankshaft until No. 1 cylinder is at TDC position and distributor rotor points to No. 1 cylinder position. Loosen lock nut and adjust rocker arm adjusting screw until valve clearance is .006" . Check clearance between adjusting screw and valve stem of both valves. Tighten lock nut. Turn crankshaft 90° while noting rotor travel. Adjust valves of Nos. 2, 3 and 4 in turn.

PISTONS, PINS & RINGS

CYLINDERS

Removal — Remove engine and remove cylinder head. **NOTE** — *Mark cylinders to insure they are reinstalled in original position.* Remove deflector plates from bottom of cylinders and pull cylinders from pistons.

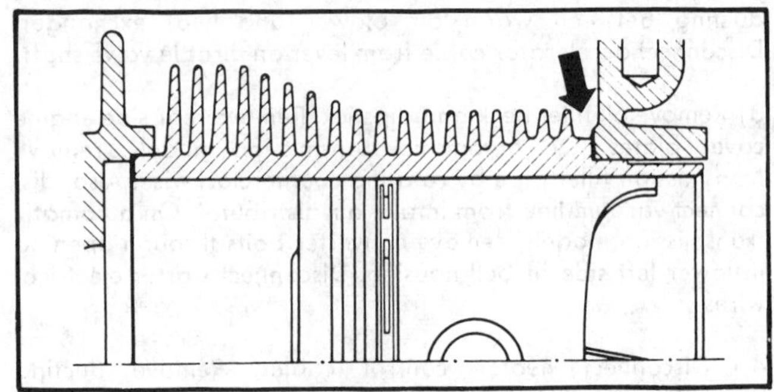

Fig. 4 Location and Seating of Cylinder Seal

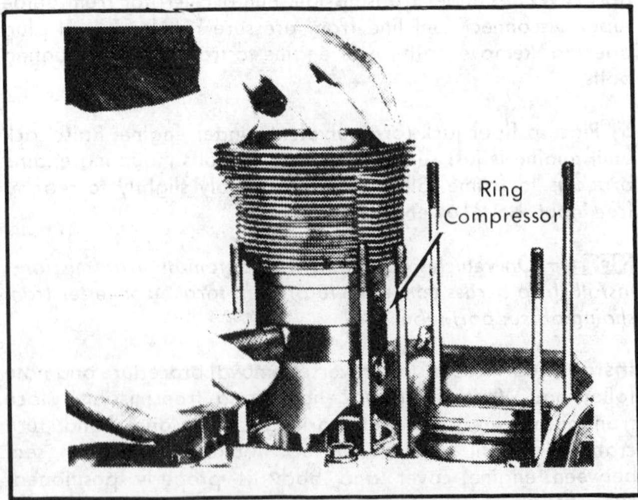

Fig. 5 Installing Cylinder Assembly into Case

TYPE 2 2000 cc 4 CYLINDER (Cont.)

Installation – 1) Check seating surfaces of cylinders on both ends. Make sure seating areas are perfectly clean and true before installing cylinders. Stagger ring gaps 90° apart so that oil ring gap faces upward when cylinder is installed.

2) Apply oil to cylinder, piston, rings and piston pin. Compress rings with suitable ring compressor (VW123). Install new sealing gasket on crankcase side and slide cylinder over piston.

3) Make sure studs do not contact cooling fins when cylinder is completely seated against crankcase. Install cylinder deflector plates and remaining components in reverse of removal.

FITTING PISTONS

1) With piston and cylinder removed, measure clearance between piston and cylinder. Check piston size at bottom of skirt and 90° to piston pin. Check cylinder size at several points throughout cylinder, using largest reading to determine clearance.

2) If clearance exceeds .008" (.20 mm), replace piston and cylinder as a set. New piston must be of same weight grade as original or within 10 g of original piston weight. Piston size, weight and installation position are marked on top of piston *(See Fig. 6)*. Piston and cylinders are available in two oversizes .020" and .040".

NOTE – *Piston alone may be replaced with one of matching size. Only pistons of same size and weight grade should be installed in same engine.*

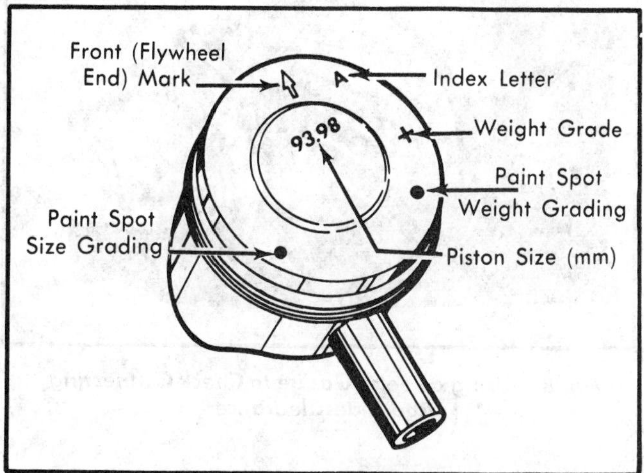

Fig. 6 Top View of Piston with Detail of Piston Markings

3) New piston rings are size graded to match piston/cylinder sets. Measure ring gap with ring installed approximately 3/16" in cylinder. If ring end gap exceeds .035" (.90 mm) for compression rings or .037" (.95 mm) for oil scraper, replace.

4) Install rings on piston and measure ring side clearance using feeler gauge. If clearance exceeds .005" (.12 mm) on top ring or .004" (.10 mm) on second or oil ring, piston must be replaced.

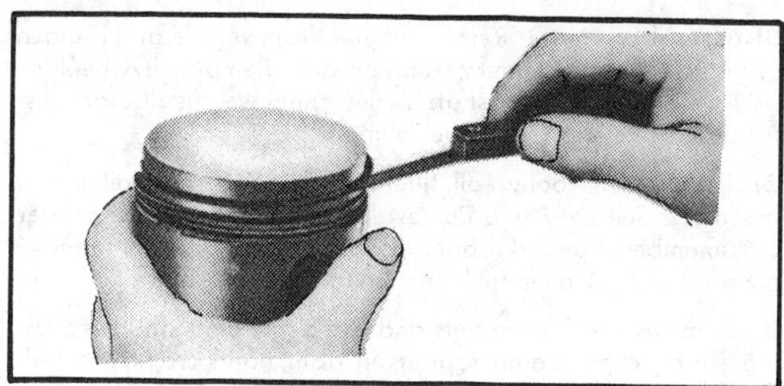

Fig. 7 Measuring Piston Ring Side Clearance with Feeler Gauge

PISTON PINS

Removal – Remove cylinders and mark pistons before removing for proper installation. Using suitable pliers (VW122b), remove piston pin circlips and push piston pin out of piston.

Installation – 1) Check fit of pin in piston. Piston pin should be light push fit with piston at 68-167°F. If pin is too loose, both pin and piston must be replaced. Check clearance of pin in rod. It clearance exceeds .0016" (.041 mm), replace piston pin and rod bushing. *See Piston Pin Bushing Replacement.*

NOTE – *During manufacturing some pistons were made with oversize bores. Oversize pins are supplied for these pistons and are identified by a green paint spot. No attempt should be made to compensate pin or bushing wear with oversize pin.*

2) Install one circlip in piston on side facing flywheel. Position piston on connecting rod and push piston pin through piston. Replace remaining circlip. **NOTE** – *Piston may be heated to ease pin installation.* Replace remaining components in reverse of removal.

PISTON PIN BUSHING REPLACEMENT

1) At normal temperature, piston pin should push fit in connecting rod. If side clearance is felt with a new pin installed, bushing must be replaced and reamed to correct fit with a new piston pin.

2) Press bushing out using a suitable mandrel and components (VW402, 409, 421 and 416B). Install new bushing using same procedure and tools as used for removal.

3) Drill through oil holes in connecting rod. Ream bushing to provide a .0004-.0012" (.01-.03 mm) clearance. Bushing should be free of chatter marks when reaming is completed. Piston pin should be a push fit into bushing without oil.

CRANKSHAFT MAIN & CONNECTING ROD BEARINGS

CRANKCASE

Crankcase must be taken apart to replace connecting rods, connecting rod bearings and main bearings. It is also necessary to disassemble crankcase to remove crankshaft, camshaft, and camshaft bearings.

TYPE 2 2000 cc 4 CYLINDER (Cont.)

Disassembly – 1) Remove engine from vehicle and remove cylinder heads, cylinders, and pistons. Remove flywheel or drive plate, and crankshaft pulley. Remove distributor, distributor drive shaft and fuel pump.

2) Remove oil cooler, oil filter and bracket, and oil pump assembly. *See Oil Pump Removal.* Remove rear engine carrier crossmember, bonded rubber mountings, and fan hub. Remove oil pan and oil filler pipe mounting bracket bolt.

3) Remove six 10 mm nuts and five 8 mm bolts and nuts. Using spring clips, clamp tappets in right hand crankcase half and lift off right hand crankcase half. **CAUTION** – *Never use sharp tool to pry crankcase halves apart. Smallest scratches will cause oil leak. Use rubber hammer to loosen crankcase halves.*

Assembly – 1) Thoroughly clean and inspect both crankcase halves. Remove old sealing compound from mating surfaces and from all bolts, studs and washers. Blow out oil passages with compressed air. Check studs for tightness and check oil suction pipe for tightness.

2) Install crankshaft with connecting rods, in left side crankcase half, making sure dowel pins are properly seated in bearings. Install camshaft. *See Camshaft Installation.* Install camshaft plug using liquid sealer all around plug. Spread liquid sealer over mating surfaces of crankcase halves.

3) Using spring clips, clamp tappets in right hand half of crankcase and join crankcase halves. Coat main bearing bolt heads (10 mm) with sealer and install in crankcase. **NOTE** – *Install plastic dampers (part No. 021 101 107) on shank of main bearing bolts whether or not originally equipped.*

4) Coat the sealing nuts for main bearing bolts with sealer and install nuts with sealing rings outward. Tighten main bearing nuts and bolts and hand turn crankshaft to check for free movement. Coat bolt heads and nuts of 8 mm bolts with sealer, then install and tighten.

5) Check crankshaft end play. *See Thrust Bearing Alignment.* Install new crankshaft oil seals. *See Front Crankshaft Oil Seal Replacement and Rear Crankshaft Oil Seal Replacement.* Install remaining components in reverse of removal procedure.

MAIN & CONNECTING ROD BEARING SERVICE

1) With crankshaft and connecting rod assembly removed, remove snap ring securing distributor drive gear and crankshaft gear to crankshaft. Remove distributor drive gear and crankshaft gear by pressing or using a suitable mandrel (VW457). Remove number three bearing. Remove connecting rods.

2) Thoroughly clean and inspect crankshaft. Blow out oil passages with compressed air. Check runout of crankshaft, if runout is more than .0008" (.020 mm), regrind crankshaft to next undersize.

3) Check crankshaft journals for wear, if journals are worn more than .0012" (.030 mm), regrind crankshaft to next undersize. Main and connecting rod bearings are available in .010", .020" and .030" undersize.

4) Lubricate and install number three bearing. Heat crankshaft to approximately 176°F in an oil bath and install crankshaft and distributor drive gears using suitable drivers (VW427, VW428 and VW415a). Install snap ring.

5) Using Plastigage method, check main and connecting rod bearings. If main bearing clearance on Nos. 1 and 3 exceeds .007" (.18 mm), .0067" (.17 mm) on No. 2, or .0075" (.19 mm) on No. 3; replace bearing. If clearance on any connecting rod bearing exceeds .007" (.15 mm), replace bearing.

6) Install Nos. 1, 3, and 4 main bearings on crankshaft. *See Step 4 for No. 3 main bearing installation.* Install lower bearing half of No. 2 bearing in crankcase. Make sure bearing engages hole in bearing half. Turn bearings on crankshaft to align oil holes. Install connecting rod bearing halves in rod cap and rod. Fit to crankshaft with numbers on rod and cap on same side. Forged mark on connecting rod must face up when crankshaft is installed.

7) Check connecting rod side play with feeler gauge. If side play exceeds .0275" (.70 mm), replace connecting rod. Install crankshaft and connecting rod assembly as previously outlined. Check crankshaft end play. *See Thrust Bearing Alignment.*

Fig. 8 Using a Feeler Gauge to Check Connecting Rod Side Clearance

THRUST BEARING ALIGNMENT

NOTE – *Crankshaft end play is checked with engine assembled.*

1) Install flywheel with two shims, but do not install crankshaft oil seal. Attach dial indicator to crankcase and measure back and forth movement of crankshaft.

2) Calculate necessary thickness of third shim. Install third shim and recheck end play. Thickness of shim is etched on face of shim, always use three shims to obtain correct end play.

TYPE 2 2000 cc 4 CYLINDER (Cont.)

Fig. 9 Using a Dial Indicator to Check Crankshaft End Play

Thrust Bearing Shims

MM Markings On Shim	Inch Equivalent
.24 mm	.0094"
.30 mm	.0118"
.32 mm	.0126"
.34 mm	.0134"
.36 mm	.0142"
.38 mm	.0150"

3) With correct shim thickness determined, install crankshaft oil seal. *See Front Crankshaft Oil Seal.* Install flywheel, tighten bolts as required, and recheck crankshaft end play.

CAMSHAFT

FRONT CRANKSHAFT OIL SEAL

1) Remove flywheel and pry out crankshaft oil seal. Make sure seal seat in crankcase is clean. If necessary, chamfer edges of seal seat.

2) Press seal into crankcase, using a suitable seal installer (VW191). Make sure seal is seated in bottom of crankcase. Lubricate sealing edge of seal, install flywheel, and tighten bolts.

REAR CRANKSHAFT OIL SEAL

1) Remove cooling blower impeller from rear of engine. Remove impeller hub, using a suitable puller (VW185).

2) Pry out old seal and thoroughly clean seal seat in crankcase. Chamfer edges of seal seat, if necessary. Press new seal into crankcase, using a suitable seal installer (VW190). Make sure seal is seated in bottom of crankcase. Lubricate sealing edge of seal and install cooling blower impeller.

DISTRIBUTOR DRIVE INSTALLATION

When crankcase has been assembled, and remaining components installed, distributor drive must be installed. Rotate crankshaft until No. 1 piston is at TDC, compression stroke. Align timing mark on pulley with 0° mark on ignition timing scale. Insert distributor drive with slot at a 12° angle to center line of engine. Small segment of slot must face toward outside of vehicle *(See Fig. 10).*

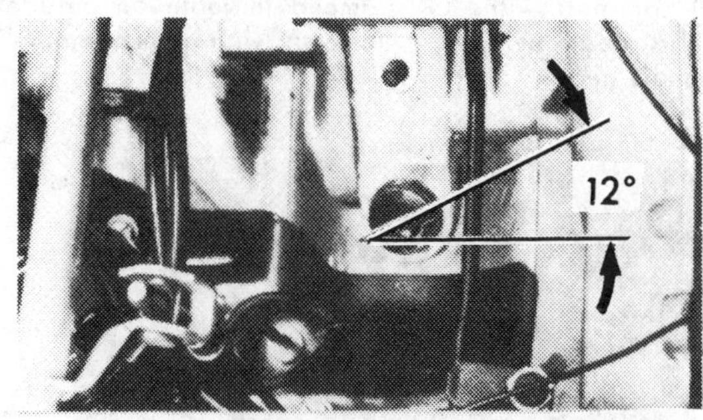

Fig. 10 Engine Distributor Drive Installation Position

CAMSHAFT INSTALLATION

1) With camshaft removed, check riveting of camshaft gear to camshaft. Check camshaft for runout, if runout exceeds .0016" (.041 mm), replace camshaft.

2) Check gear backlash with camshaft and crankshaft installed in crankcase half. Correct backlash is .002" (.05 mm). Gears have correct fit when crankshaft is rotated backwards and camshaft does not try to lift out of bearings.

Fig. 11 Measuring Camshaft End Play with a Dial Indicator

3) If camshaft rises out of bearings, teeth on camshaft gear have the wrong pitch radius for crankshaft gear. Camshafts with gears that have various pitch radii are available. Pitch radius is stamped on back of gear facing number three bearing journal of camshaft.

4) Install camshaft with "O" stamped in tooth on outside of camshaft gear between two teeth with punch marks on crankshaft gear. Assemble crankcase halves as previously outlined *(See Fig. 12).*

CAMSHAFT END PLAY

Camshaft end play is checked with camshaft installed in crankcase half. Measure back and forth movement of

TYPE 2 2000 cc 4 CYLINDER (Cont.)

camshaft with a dial indicator. If end play exceeds .006" (.16 mm), replace camshaft or bearings.

VALVE TIMING

Install camshaft with "O" stamped in tooth on outside of camshaft gear between two teeth with punch marks on crankshaft gear.

Fig. 12 Position of Camshaft Timing Gear

ENGINE OILING

Oil Capacity – 3.15 qts. Add .5 qt. with filter change.

Oil Pressure – 28 psi at 2000 RPM with engine at 176°F.

Oil Filter – Full flow oil filter.

Pressure Regulator Valves – Oil pressure relief valve, used to protect oil cooler from excessive pressure, is located in crankcase under oil filter. Oil pressure control valve, used to control oil pressure to bearings, is located in crankcase below oil breather. Oil pressure relief spring should have length of 1.75" (44.5 mm) at 14 lbs. (2.0 mkg) load. Oil pressure control valve spring should have length of .813" (20.6 mm) at 16 lbs. (2.2 mkg) load.

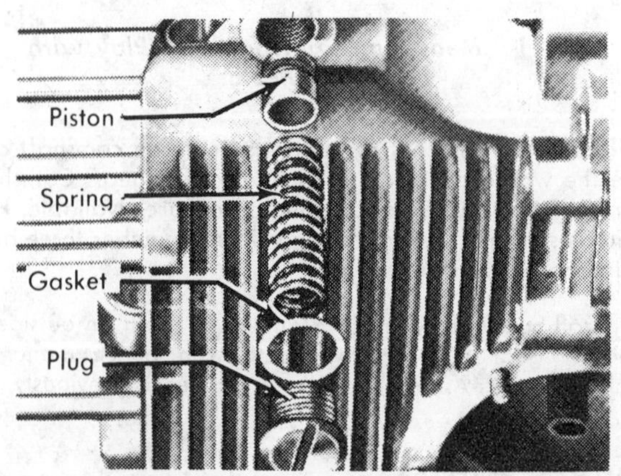

Fig. 13 Expanded View of Relief Valve Components

ENGINE OILING SYSTEM

Full pressure lubrication system utilizing a gear-type oil pump and installed in rear of engine and driven by camshaft. Oil is pumped through oil filter, oil cooler and into main oil passages in crankcase. Crankshaft main and connecting rod journals are oiled through cross-drilled oil passages in the crankcase. Oil is pumped to camshaft through oil passages that also lubricate valve tappets. Oil flows through push rods to lubricate rocker arms and shafts. Valve stems are lubricated by splash oil from rocker arms. Excess oil flows back into crankcase through push rod tubes. Cylinder walls and piston pins are lubricated by splash oil.

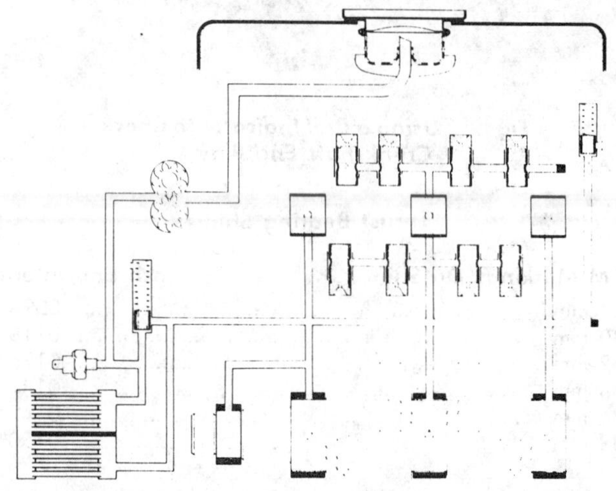

Fig. 14 Distribution of Oil for Engine Lubrication

OIL COOLER

To remove oil cooler, remove cooling air fan housing, three 6 mm nuts with washers attaching oil cooler to rear of crankcase, and bolts attaching oil cooler support strap. Remove support strap and oil cooler as unit. Always use new rubber seals when installing oil cooler.

OIL PUMP

Removal – Remove engine. Remove 4 nuts holding oil pump. Using puller VW803 (or equivalent) as shown in *Fig. 15*, pry oil pump out of crankcase.

Inspection – Check housing for excessive wear, mainly in gear seating portions. Measure gear backlash for wear. Backlash must not exceed .008" (.20 mm). Replace bearing plate if scored.

Installation – Hand turn oil pump drive shaft until fully engaged in camshaft. Rotate crankshaft two revolutions. Pump plate should now be aligned with camshaft. Refit new gasket and reverse removal procedure for remaining components.

TYPE 2 2000 cc 4 CYLINDER (Cont.)

Fig. 15 Using Special Tool (Puller) to Remove Oil Pump

ENGINE COOLING

Thermostat – At 185-194°F (85-90°C), thermostat must have a length of 1.811" (46 mm).

COOLING SYSTEM

Engine is cooled by a radial blower mounted to rear end of crankshaft. Blower draws air through opening in blower shroud at rear of engine. Blower shroud is two-piece unit, mounted around blower and attached to crankcase. As air is drawn in, it is directed over finned cylinders and cylinder heads by deflector plates. A thermostat is mounted under No. 1 and No. 2 cylinders and actuates flaps mounted in shroud to control volume of air directed in deflector plates. As engine warms up, thermostat opens flaps completely to allow total flow of air.

BLOWER SHROUD REMOVAL

1) Remove engine as previously outlined. Remove air injection pump, belt, and adjusting bracket. Remove extension shaft with pulley, ignition timing scale, fan with crankshaft pulley and alternator belt.

2) Disconnect cooling air control cable from control flap shaft. Pull rubber elbow for alternator out of front half of blower shroud. Remove four nuts attaching blower shroud to crankcase and pull assembly to rear and off engine. To install, reverse removal procedure. Adjust air flap control cable by pushing flaps into closed position and tighten cable.

3) Disconnect flap actuating cable from control shaft. Remove nuts securing shroud to crankcase and remove both halves of blower shroud.

4) To install, reverse removal procedure. Adjust air flap control by pushing flaps into closed position and tighten cable control. Attach elbow for cooling alternator to fan shroud front half.

5) Install drive belt and tighten alternator into proper belt tensioning position (maximum 0.6" deflection). Install cover plates and engine as previously outlined.

ENGINE SPECIFICATIONS

GENERAL SPECIFICATIONS

Year	Displ.		Carburetor	HP at RPM	Torque (Ft. Lbs. at RPM)	Compr. Ratio	Bore		Stroke	
	cu. ins.	cc					in.	mm	in.	mm
1977	120	1970	Fuel Injection	.....	.....	7.3-1	3.70	94	2.795	71

VALVES

Engine & Valve	Head Diam. In. (mm)	Face Angle	Seat Angle	Seat Width In. (mm)	Stem Diameter In. (mm)	Stem Clearance In. (mm)	Valve Lift In. (mm)
2000 cc							
Int.	1.476 (37.5)	29.5	30°	.071-.087 (1.80-2.21)	.3125-.3129 (7.936-7.948)	.018 (.46)	.....
Exh.	1.299 (33.0)	45°	45°	.079-.098 (2.01-2.49)	.3508-.3512 (8.910-8.920)	.014 (.35)	.....

VALVE SPRINGS

Engine	Free Length In. (mm)	PRESSURE Lbs. @ In. (kg @ mm)	
		Valve Closed	Valve Open
2000 cc Int. & Exh.	.....	168-186@1.14 (76.20-84.37@28.96)	.....

CAMSHAFT

Engine	Journal Diam. In. (mm)	Clearance In. (mm)	Lobe Lift In. (mm)
2000 cc	.9839-.9843 (24.991-25.001)	.0008-.0020 (.020-.051)	.....

TYPE 2 2000 cc 4 CYLINDER (Cont.)

ENGINE SPECIFICATIONS (Cont.)

PISTONS, PINS, RINGS						
	PISTONS	PINS		RINGS		
Engine	Clearance In. (mm)	Piston Fit In. (mm)	Rod Fit In. (mm)	Rings	End Gap In. (mm)	Side Clearance In. (mm)
2000 cc	.0016-.0024 (.04-.06)	①	.0004-.0012 (.010-.030)	1	.014-.021 (.35-.55)	.002-.003 (.06-.09)
				2	.014-.021 (.35-.55)	.0016-.0028 (.04-.07)
				3	.010-.016 (.25-.40)	.0008-.0019 (.02-.05)

① — Push fit with light thumb pressure.

CRANKSHAFT MAIN & CONNECTING ROD BEARINGS							
	MAIN BEARINGS				CONNECTING ROD BEARINGS		
Engine	Journal Diam. In. (mm)	Clearance In. (mm)	Thrust Bearing	Crankshaft End Play In. (mm)	Journal Diam. In. (mm)	Clearance In. (mm)	Side Play In. (mm)
2000 cc No. 1	2.3609-2.3617 (59.967-59.987)	.0016-.0039 (.041-.099)	No. 1	.0027-.0050 (.069-.127)	1.9677-1.9685 (49.98-50.00)	.0008-.0027 (.020-.069)	.004-.016 (.10-.41)
2	2.3609-2.3617 (59.967-59.987)	.0012-.0035 (.030-.089)					
3	2.3609-2.3617 (59.967-59.987)	.0016-.0039 (.041-.099)					
4	1.5739-1.5748 (39.977-40.025)	.0020-.0039 (.051-.099)					

TIGHTENING SPECIFICATIONS

Application	Ft. Lbs. (mkg)
Connecting Rod Nut	24 (3.32)
Crankcase Half Nuts (8 mm)	14 (1.94)
Crankcase Half Sealing Nuts (10 mm)	25 (3.46)
Cylinder Head Nuts	21 (3.0)
Rocker Shaft-to-Cylinder Head Nuts	10 (1.4)
Heat Exchanger-to-Cylinder Head	16 (2.21)
Oil Pan-to-Crankcase Nuts	9 (1.24)
Drive Plate-to-Crankshaft	65 (8.99)
Hub-to-Crankshaft Bolt	23 (3.18)
Fan-to-Hub	14 (1.94)
Extension Shaft & Pulley-to-Fan	14 (1.94)
Engine-to-Transmission	22 (3.04)
Oil Pump-to-Crankcase	14 (1.94)
Oil Cooler-to-Crankcase	14 (1.94)
Flywheel-to-Crankshaft	80 (11.06)
Clutch-to-Flywheel	14 (1.94)
Torque Converter-to-Driveplate	29 (4.0)

RABBIT (GASOLINE), SCIROCCO & DASHER 4 CYLINDER

ENGINE CODING

ENGINE IDENTIFICATION

Engine identification number is stamped on left side of engine block near ignition distributor.

Engine Codes

Application	Code
Rabbit/Scirocco	
Man. Trans.	EE
Auto. Trans	EF
Dasher	
Man. Trans.	YG
Auto. Trans.	YH

ENGINE, CYLINDER HEAD & MANIFOLDS

ENGINE

NOTE — *On Rabbit and Scirocco models only, engine and transaxle must be removed as an assembly.*

Removal, Rabbit & Scirocco with Man. Trans. — 1) Disconnect battery ground cable. Drain coolant and remove radiator with air ducts and fan. If equipped with A/C, remove compressor and condenser and set aside without disconnecting hoses.

2) Remove fuel injectors from manifold tubes of intake distributor. Disconnect all fuel lines except injector lines from fuel distributor. Remove injection control unit, air ducting and air cleaner.

3) Disconnect electrical wiring from the following: Ignition coil, oil pressure switch, distributor, temperature sending unit, alternator, fuel injection, starter and transmission.

4) Disconnect coolant hoses, accelerator cable, speedometer cable and clutch cable. Remove engine/transaxle front mount. Remove right side headlight cap.

5) Disconnect axle drive shafts and support with wire. Disconnect exhaust pipe from manifold and remove exhaust pipe support. Remove transmission rear mount and ground strap from body to transmission. Remove gear shift linkage.

6) Attach hoist to mount, cast at rear of cylinder head and lower alternator mount in front of engine. Disconnect engine carrier from body and remove left transmission mount. Lift engine and transmission out of vehicle.

7) Using suitable wrench (US 4463), remove TDC sensor (part of analysis system) from clutch housing. To separate transaxle from engine, turn flywheel until mark on flywheel aligns with mark on clutch housing. Remove drive shaft flange cover plate. Then, remove engine-to-transaxle bolts.

Installation — To install engine/transaxle assembly, reverse removal procedure and note the following: When attaching engine to transaxle, align recess (window) in flywheel level with drive shaft flange. Lift assembly into vehicle. Loosely install right engine mount bolt and loosely attach left transaxle mount to transaxle. Align assembly and loosely attach remaining mounts. Tighten mounts.

NOTE — *Mounts must be properly aligned and free of tension before tightening.*

Removal, Rabbit & Scirocco with Auto. Trans. — 1) Disconnect battery. Drain coolant and remove radiator with air ducts and fan. If equipped with A/C, remove compressor and condenser and set aside without disconnecting hoses. Remove fuel injectors form manifold tubes of intake distributor. Disconnect all fuel lines except injector lines from fuel distributor.

2) Remove mixture control unit, air cleaner, and intake air duct. Disconnect fuel return line. Disconnect electrical plug from control pressure regulator. Disconnect throttle housing assembly. Disconnect all engine electrical wires. Make sure wire plug at auxiliary air regulator is disconnected.

3) Disconnect speedometer cable. Disconnect selector lever cable at transaxle. Disconnect throttle cable ball socket from lever and unhook accelerator cable from lever. On Scirocco models, remove right side headlight cap.

4) Disconnect axle drive shafts and support with wire. Disconnect exhaust pipe at manifold flange. Remove engine/transaxle rear mount. Remove cover from engine end of clutch housing. Remove torque converter from drive plate.

5) Fit engine hoist to eyes on cylinder head and slightly raise engine. Remove alternator if necessary. Remove front and left transaxle mounts. Remove right engine mount. Engine is free for removal.

6) Separate engine and transaxle. Make sure drive plate pulls cleanly away from converter and does not move cover off support.

Installation — To install engine/transaxle assembly, reverse removal procedure and note the following: After lifting assembly into vehicle, loosely install right engine mount bolt and loosely attach left transaxle mount to transaxle. Align assembly and loosely attach remaining mounts. Tighten mounts.

NOTE — *Mounts must be properly aligned and free of tension before tightening.*

Removal, Dasher — 1) Disconnect battery. Drain oil. Remove air cleaner. Disconnect clutch operating lever. Disengage cable housing from bracket on engine mount. Disconnect fuel inlet hose and plug.

2) Remove fuse block mounting screws and bend open wiring harness clip. Tie fuel hose, clutch cable and fuse block out of way. Disconnect heater control cable. Remove front engine mount and mount support.

3) Disconnect coil and any engine electrical items that might hinder engine removal. Disconnect all wires from fuel injection components. If equipped with A/C, remove compressor and condenser and set aside without disconnecting hoses. Drain coolant. Remove radiator.

RABBIT (GASOLINE), SCIROCCO & DASHER 4 CYLINDER (Cont.)

4) Work under vehicle and disconnect electrical wires from starter. Remove starter. Disconnect exhaust pipe at manifold. Remove converter bolts through hole left by starter removal. Remove lower bolts that mount engine to transaxle.

5) Attach engine hoist. Raise engine until assembly hits steering rack housing. Support transaxle. Remove upper bolts mounting engine to transaxle. Pry engine from transaxle. Remove intermediate plate. Make sure torque converter is supported.

Installation – To install engine, reverse removal procedure. Make sure all fluid levels are correct. Adjust any cables removed.

CYLINDER HEAD & MANIFOLDS

Removal – **1)** Disconnect duct connecting throttle valve housing with mixture control unit. Drain coolant. Remove camshaft drive belt.

NOTE – *Some California models are equipped with A.I.R. which must be disconnected.*

2) Disconnect exhaust pipe. Remove nuts and bolts that hold exhaust manifold and intake manifold (air intake distributor) to head. Remove manifolds. Remove upper alternator bolt and adjusting bracket. Disconnect all coolant hoses and temperature gauge wire. Remove spark plugs.

3) Remove valve cover. Remove head bolts. Start at either end and work toward center. If head is stuck, insert block of wood in each outboard exhaust port and pry head free.

Installation – To install, reverse removal procedure and note the following: Make sure head gasket is positioned with "OBEN" mark facing up. Tighten head bolts in sequence and steps shown.

NOTE – *Late 1977 models are equipped with polygon head cylinder head bolts. Cold torque is 55 ft. lbs. plus ¼ turn beyond that figure.*

Cylinder Head Tightening Steps

Application	Ft. Lbs. (mkg)
Step One	22 (3.0)
Step Two	43 (6.0)
Step Three	54 (7.5)
Cylinder Head Hot Torque	61 (8.5)

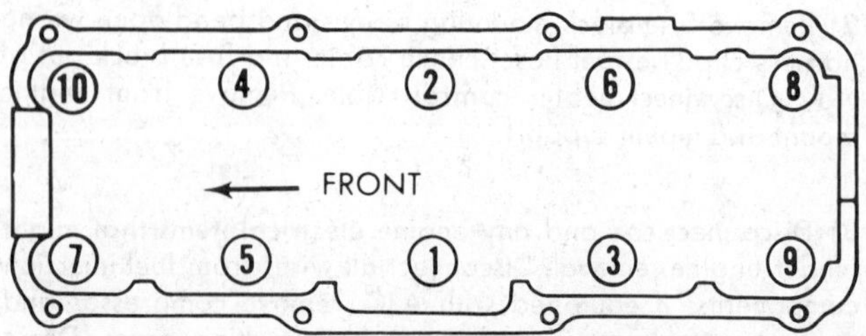

Fig. 1 Cylinder Head Tightening Sequence

Valves

VALVE ARRANGEMENT

E-I-E-I-I-E-I-E (front to rear).

VALVE GUIDE SERVICING

1) Clean valve guides before making measurements. To measure guide, attach a suitable mounting device with a dial gauge (VW689/1) to mounting surface of cylinder head. Insert a new valve until end of stem is flush with end of valve guide.

2) Rock valve head against dial indicator and check amount of rock recorded. Maximum allowable rock is .039" (1 mm) for intake valves and .051" (1.3 mm) for exhaust valves. Proper valve guide diameter is .315"-.316" (8.01-8.04 mm).

3) Use a press and suitable adaptor (10-206) to remove and install valve guides. To remove guides, press out from combustion chamber side of head.

CAUTION Do not use more than one ton pressure once guide shoulder is seated or shoulder may break.

4) Coat new valve guides with engine oil. Press new guides into cold head from camshaft side. Make sure shoulder of guide firmly meets with top of cylinder head.

VALVE STEM OIL SEALS

With tappet, adjuster pad, keepers, springs, and spring seats removed, extract valve stem oil seal. When installing new seal, first position protective plastic sleeve on valve stem, lubricate seal, and use a suitable mandrel (10-204) to push seal onto valve guide.

VALVE SPRINGS

Removal – Remove camshaft and cam followers (tappets). Remove cylinder head from engine. Using suitable spring compressor (VW541), compress spring enough to remove split keeper. Release tool. Take out retainer and valve springs.

Installation – Check springs on spring tester and inspect for cracks or distortion. Reverse removal procedure and note the following: Lower edge of valve spring retainer should be chamfered to prevent valve stem scoring. If necessary, grind a chamfer using stone or other suitable tool. When installing the springs, make sure closely spaced coils of outer springs are against spring seats.

VALVE CLEARANCE ADJUSTMENT

1) Adjust valves with engine at normal operating temperature. Clearance adjustments are to be checked and made according to firing order sequence (1-3-4-2). Rotate crankshaft until No. 4 cylinder valves overlap, then measure valve clearances of No. 1 cylinder.

2) If adjustment is necessary, use special tools 10-208 (disc removal tool) and VW546 (tappet depressing tool) to remove and install adjusting discs. Rotate camshaft until cam lobes no longer rest on adjusting discs of cylinder to be adjusted. Turn

RABBIT (GASOLINE), SCIROCCO & DASHER 4 CYLINDER (Cont.)

tappet until notches are at 90° to camshaft. Insert tool VW546 and depress tappet. Using tool 10-208, grasp tappet disc and rotate it out from under camshaft.

3) Thickness is stamped on bottom side of dics. Using clearance measurement, determine thickness of adjusting disc necessary to bring valve clearances within specifications. Discs are available in .0019" (.05 mm) increments from .1181" (3.0 mm) to .1673" (4.25 mm). Reverse removal procedure to install proper disc. Repeat procedure as required for remaining valves.

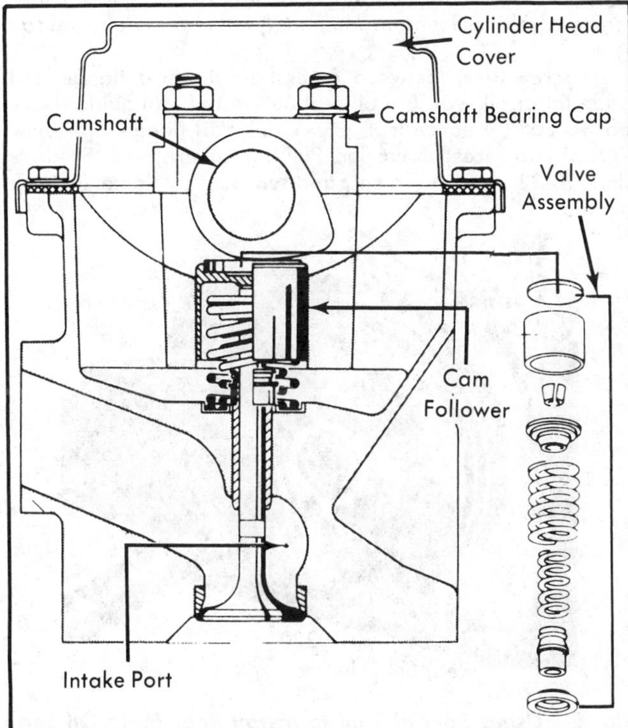

Fig. 2 Assembled View of Valve and Camshaft

Valve Clearance Specifications

Application	In. (mm)
Intake	
Hot	.008-.012 (.20-.30)
Cold	.006-.010 (.15-.25)
Exhaust	
Hot	.016-.020 (.40-.50)
Cold	.014-.018 (.35-.45)

NOTE – *Cold settings are given for reference as initial settings to be used during cylinder head rework. Final adjustments are to be made with engine at normal operating temperature. After head repairs, recheck valve clearances after 600 miles.*

PISTONS, PINS & RINGS

OIL PAN

Removal – Drain oil. Remove nuts mounting engine mounts on subframe. Remove four bolts holding subframe to body. Pull subframe downward to separate engine mounts and body. Remove pan.

Installation – To install, reverse removal procedure. Make sure gasket surfaces are clean before installing new gaskets.

PISTON & ROD ASSEMBLY

NOTE – Piston and rod assemblies can be removed with engine in vehicle. Manufacturer recommends engine removal for extensive overhaul work.

Removal – Mark cylinder number on crown of each piston. If necessary, mark arrows pointing toward front of block on piston crowns. Remove rod cap bolts and force piston out top of cylinder. Use wooden hammer handle for this operation. Mark connecting rods and bearing caps for proper reinstallation.

NOTE – *If a ridge at top of cylinder prevents piston removal, use a ridge reamer to cut down the ridge. DO NOT force piston out of cylinder.*

Installation – Turn crankshaft so No. 1 journal is at BDC. Install piston connecting rod assembly until ring compressor contacts block. Use a wood handle to push piston into cylinder. Install No. 4 Piston and rod assembly. Ensure tabs on bearing halves engage notch in rod and cap. Install and tighten caps on rods 1 and 4. Turn crankshaft 180° and install No. 2 and 3 rod assemblies and rod caps.

PISTON PINS

Removal – Use needle-nosed pliers to remove pin circlips. Press out pin and remove piston from rod. For installation purposes, note direction piston is fitted to rod.

Installation – 1) Check pin fit in each piston. Piston pin must be a thumb-push fit in piston. If correct fit is not obtained, replace both pin and piston.

2) Check pin fit in connecting rod. Wear limit is .0015" (.04 mm). Rebush connecting rod and hone bushing to obtain correct clearance.

FITTING PISTONS

1) Measure cylinder at three points: .39" (10 mm) from top and bottom, and at center of bore. Take measurements in line with thrust face and also at 90° to thrust face. Cylinder wear limit is .0028" (.07 mm) beyond standard dimensions; if this is exceeded, rebore cylinder and install oversize pistons.

2) Measure pistons at .63" (16 mm) from bottom of piston skirt (measuring 90° to pin bore). Combining this measurement with measurement of corresponding cylinder bore, note piston-to-cylinder clearance. If this exceeds .0028" (.07 mm), oversize pistons must be installed.

3) Place piston rings squarely in top of cylinder bore (above ring ridge) and measure end gap. Measure ring side clearance. Install rings on piston with end gaps 120° offset to each other (start with oil ring gap directly to the rear). Ensure stamp mark "TOP" on rings is facing upward.

RABBIT (GASOLINE), SCIROCCO & DASHER 4 CYLINDER (Cont.)

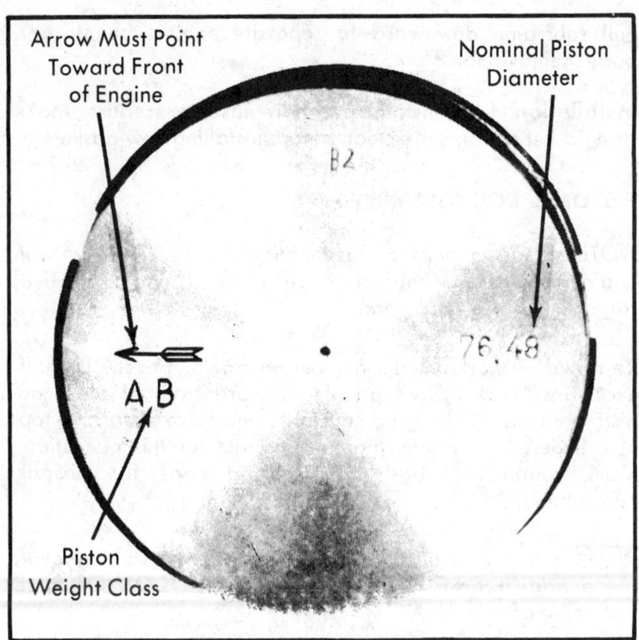

Fig. 3 Codes Stamped on Piston Head

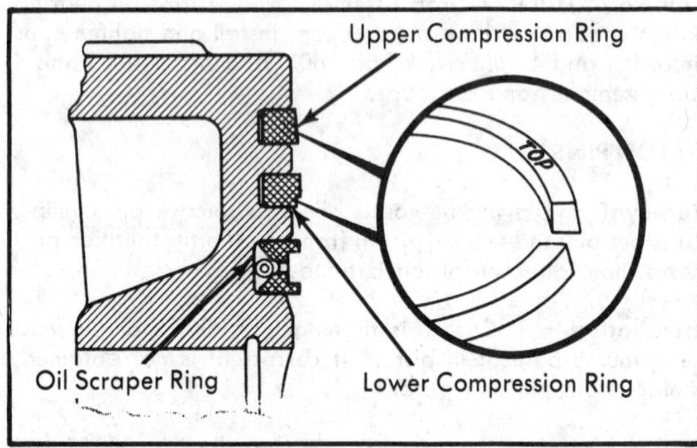

Fig. 4 Piston Ring Installation – Word TOP Must Face Piston Crown

CRANKSHAFT MAIN & CONNECTING ROD BEARINGS

MAIN & CONNECTING ROD BEARINGS

1) Push crankshaft toward one end and measure crankshaft end play at No. 3 (thrust) bearing. Main bearing caps are stamped "1" to "5" (front to rear), and must be returned to original positions upon reassembly. Measure end play (side play) of connecting rods. Remove all bearing caps and check bearing clearance using Plastigage method.

2) Measure crankshaft journals with a micrometer to determine if crankshaft is out-of-round. Maximum ovality permissible is .0012" (.03 mm). Install main inserts with bearing half having oil groove into block. Lubricate bearings and install caps.

Crankshaft Journal Diameters

Size	Main Bearing In. (mm)	Con. Rod Bearing In. (mm)
Standard	2.126 (54.00)	1.81 (46.00)
1st US	2.116 (53.75)	1.80 (45.75)
2nd US	2.106 (53.50)	1.79 (45.50)
3rd US	2.096 (53.25)	1.78 (45.25)

REAR MAIN BEARING OIL SEAL

NOTE – *Rear main bearing oil seal may be replaced with engine in vehicle. Transmission and flywheel must be removed.*

Insert screwdriver between crankshaft flywheel flange and inside lip of oil seal. Pry oil seal out. Install seal guide sleeve tool 10-205 (or equivalent) over crankshaft flange. Start new oil seal into recess in carrier. Pull out guide sleeve. Fit drive plate 10-220 (or equivalent) and seat seal by tightening bolt in plate.

Fig. 5 Using Special Tool to Install Rear Main Oil Seal

FRONT MAIN BEARING OIL SEAL AND INTERMEDIATE SHAFT OIL SEAL

Remove camshaft belt. Remove crankshaft sprocket. Pry seal from seal carrier, being careful not to damage carrier. Use tool 10-219 (or equivalent) to remove seal *(Fig. 6)*. Using suitable tool (10-203), press in new seal until flush with seal carrier. If tool 10-203 was used, remove it and use aluminum part of tool (or equivalent) to press seal in until recessed .080" (2 mm) from front of seal carrier.

NOTE – *Same procedure applies to intermediate shaft oil seal except: Remove intermediate shaft sprocket. Only press new seal in until flush with seal carrier.*

CAMSHAFT

TIMING BELT

NOTE – *Sprockets DO NOT have to be removed to replace camshaft drive belt.*

Removal – Remove A.I.R. pump belt and alternator belt. Remove water pump pulley. Remove camshaft belt cover. Loosen camshaft drive belt tensioner lock nut. Turn adjuster counterclockwise to release tension on belt. Work belt off sprockets.

RABBIT (GASOLINE), SCIROCCO & DASHER 4 CYLINDER (Cont.)

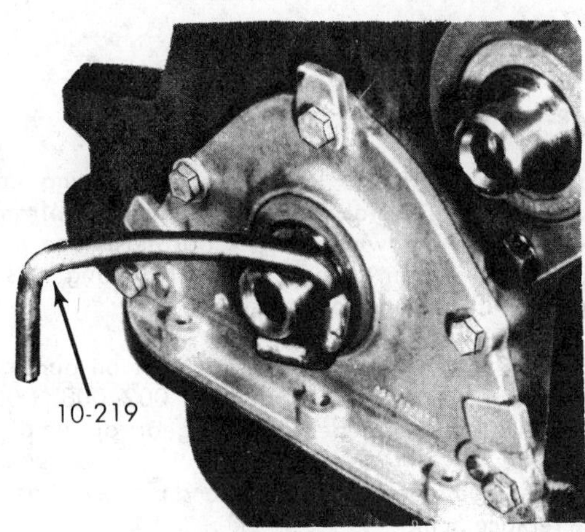

Fig. 6 Using Special Tool to Remove Front Oil Seal

Installation – 1) Rotate camshaft sprocket until index mark (punch mark) on camshaft sprocket is lined up with top surface of valve cover mounting flange. Make sure to align index marks on spark plug side.

2) Rotate crankshaft and intermediate shafts until index mark (punch mark) on intermediate shaft sprocket is positioned in "V" notch on crankshaft pulley.

NOTE – *Make sure sprockets are not moved after belt has been removed.*

3) Being careful not to move sprockets, fit belt from bottom first. Make sure there is no slack between sprockets. Tighten belt tensioner until belt can just be twisted 90°. Make twist half way between camshaft and intermediate sprockets. Tighten lock nut. Reverse removal procedure for remaining components.

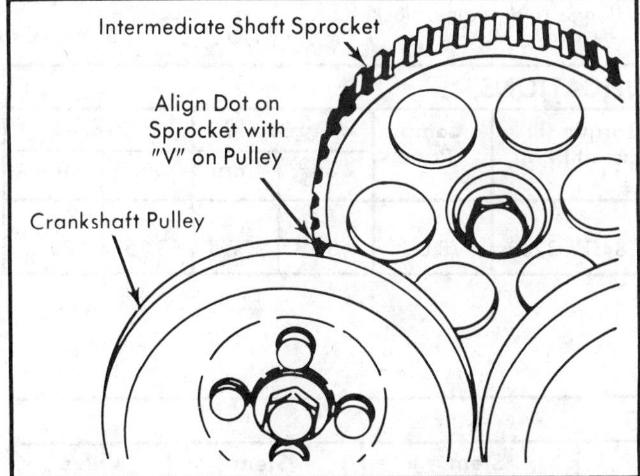

Fig. 7 Crankshaft and Intermediate Shaft Index Marks Aligned with Notch on Crankshaft Pulley

CAMSHAFT

Removal – 1) Remove camshaft cover. Loosen and remove bearing caps in following sequence: 5, 1, and 3, then loosen bearing caps 2 and 4 diagonally. Bearing caps are numbered front to rear.

2) Check camshaft end play. Remove camshaft and lift out cam followers. Install camshaft using only bearing caps 1 and 5. Fit dial indicator so tip of gauge touches front of camshaft. Pry camshaft back and forth. Reading should not exceed .006" (.15 mm). If end play is beyond limits, replace either camshaft or cylinder head.

3) Check camshaft runout. Fit dial indicator so gauge pin is against camshaft center journal. Turn camshaft and record runout range. Runout must not exceed .0004" (.01 mm). Replace camshaft as necessary.

4) Inspect camshaft lobes for wear. Worn lobes usually indicate lack of lubrication. Check engine oiling passages to make sure they are not restricted. Replace worn camshafts and worn discs.

5) Inspect cam followers for signs of seizure or lack of lubrication. If any aluminum particles from head are found on cam followers, replace followers. Cylinder head must be replaced if any follower bores are worn or excessively rough.

Installation – Lightly lube cam follower bores, then fit followers in their original bores. Install adjusting discs. Place camshaft on cylinder head. Loosely attach No. 2 and No. 4 bearing caps. Gradually tighten caps. Fit No. 5 and No. 3 bearing caps. Install new oil seal in front of camshaft. Install No. 1 bearing cap. Make sure all caps are torqued to proper specifications.

VALVE TIMING

With timing belt removed as previously described, rotate crankshaft and intermediate shaft until index mark (punch mark) on intermediate shaft is positioned in "V" notch on crankshaft pulley (*Fig. 7*). This is firing point of No. 1 cylinder. Next, turn camshaft until marking on rear of camshaft sprocket is in line with cylinder head cover (*Fig. 8*). Replace timing belt.

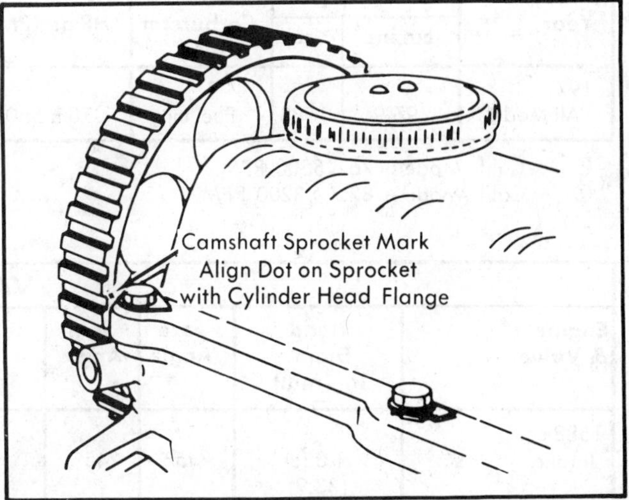

Fig. 8 Index Mark on Camshaft Sprocket Aligned with Cylinder Head Flange

RABBIT (GASOLINE), SCIROCCO & DASHER 4 CYLINDER (Cont.)

ENGINE OILING

Crankcase Capacity – On Rabbit and Scirocco models, 3.7 quarts with filter change. On Dasher models, 3.2 quarts with filter change.

Oil Filter – Replaceable spin-on type.

Normal Oil Pressure – 28 psi@2000 RPM (normal operating temperature).

ENGINE OILING SYSTEM

Oiling system is a pressure feed type. A gear oil pump lifts oil from pan and pressure feeds it to crankshaft journals, camshaft bearings, and intermediate shaft. Other parts of system receive oil mist or splash for lubrication.

OIL PUMP

Removal – **1**) Drain oil. Remove nuts mounting engine mounts on subframe. Remove four bolts holding subframe to body. Pull subframe downward to separate engine mounts and body. Remove pan. Remove pump mounting nuts and remove pump with pickup tube attached.

2) Separate pickup tube from pump. Check oil pump gear backlash. Clearance should be between .002-.008" (.05-.20 mm). If specification is exceeded, replace gears or pump.

3) Measure oil pump gear end play. If end play exceeds .006" (.15 mm), replace pump.

Installation – To install, reverse removal procedure. Make sure all mating surfaces are clean before installing gaskets. Oil pump drive shaft must align with distributor drive gear.

ENGINE COOLING

Cooling System Capacity

Application	Capacity
Rabbit/Scirocco	4.9 qts.
Dasher	
With Expansion Tank	6.9 qts.
Without Expansion Tank	6.4 qts.

Thermostat – Begins to open at 176° F (80° C) and is fully open at 200° F (94° C).

WATER PUMP

NOTE – *The front portion of water pump (shaft, seals, bearing, and housing) can be replaced separately. To do this camshaft drive belt and sprockets must be removed. To avoid removing drive belt, remove water pump as an assembly.*

Removal – Drain coolant. Remove alternator belt and alternator. On some Calif. models A.I.R. pump must be removed. Remove bolt holding camshaft belt cover to pump. Disconnect hoses from water pump. Remove water pump bolts.

Installation – To install, reverse removal procedure and make sure to use new "O" ring in recess in pump mounting flange.

NOTE – *Do not use sealer between water pump mounting flange and engine block.*

GENERAL SPECIFICATIONS

Year	Displ. cu. ins.	Displ. cc	Carburetor	HP at RPM	Torque (Ft. Lbs. at RPM)	Compr. Ratio	Bore in.	Bore mm	Stroke in.	Stroke mm
1977 All Models	96.9	1588	Fuel Inj.	①78 @ 5500	②84.1 @ 3200	8.0:1	3.13	79.5	3.15	80

① – Calif. Models: 76 @ 5500 RPM.
② – Calif. Models: 82.7 @ 3200 RPM.

VALVES

Engine & Valve	Head Diam. In. (mm)	Face Angle	Seat Angle	Seat Width In. (mm)	Stem Diameter In. (mm)	Stem Clearance In. (mm)	Valve Lift In. (mm)
1588 cc							
Intake	1.338 (33.9)	45°	45°	.079 (2.0)	.314 (7.98)	.001-.002 (.03-.05)	....
Exhaust	1.220 (31.0)	45°	45°	.095 (2.4)	.313 (7.95)	.002-.003 (.05-.07)	....

RABBIT (GASOLINE), SCIROCCO & DASHER 4 CYLINDER (Cont.)

VALVE SPRINGS

Engine	Free Length In. (mm)	PRESSURE Lbs. @ In. (kg @ mm) Valve Closed	Valve Open
1588 cc			
Inner	....	46-51@.719 (21-23@18.3)	....
Outer	....	96-106@.916 (43.5-48@22.3)	....

CAMSHAFT

Engine	Journal Diam. In. (mm)	Clearance In. (mm)①	Lobe Lift In. (mm)
1588 cc	.....	.0008-.002 (.02-.05)	.....

① — End play .006" (.15 mm)

PISTONS, PINS, RINGS

Engine	PISTONS Clearance In. (mm)	PINS Piston Fit In. (mm)	PINS Rod Fit In. (mm)	RINGS Rings	RINGS End Gap In. (mm)	RINGS Side Clearance In. (mm)
1588 cc	.0012 (.03)	Push Fit	.0004-.0008 (.01-.02)	Comp.	.012-.018 (.30-.45)	.0008-.002 (.02-.05)
				Oil	.010-.016 (.25-.40)	.0008-.002 (.02-.05)

CRANKSHAFT MAIN & CONNECTING ROD BEARINGS

Engine	MAIN BEARINGS Journal Diam. In. (mm)	Clearance In. (mm)	Thrust Bearing	Crankshaft End Play In. (mm)	CONNECTING ROD BEARINGS Journal Diam. In. (mm)	Clearance In. (mm)	Side Play In. (mm)
1588 cc	2.126 (54)	.0011-.0033 (.028-.088)	No. 3	.003-.007 (.07-.17)	1.81 (46)	.0011-.0033 (.028-.088)	①.015 (.37)

① — Wear Limit.

TIGHTENING SPECIFICATIONS

Application	Ft. Lbs. (mkg)
Timing Belt Tensioner Lock Nut	33 (4.5)
Intermediate Sprocket Bolt	58 (8.0)
Crankshaft Sprocket Bolt	58 (8.0)
Water Pump Pulley Bolts	14 (2.0)
Crankshaft Pulley Bolts	14 (2.0)
Main Bearing Cap Bolts	47 (6.5)
Flywheel-to-Crankshaft Bolts	54 (7.5)
Connecting Rod Cap Bolts	33 (4.5)
Camshaft Sprocket Bolt	58 (8.0)
Camshaft Bearing Cap Nuts	14 (2.0)
Cylinder Head Bolts	
Cold	54 (7.5)
Hot	61 (8.5)
Manifolds-to-Cylinder Head	18 (2.5)
Oil Pump Mounting Bolts	
Socket Head Bolt	14 (2.0)
Hex Head Bolt	7 (1.0)
Oil Pan Bolts	7 (1.0)

RABBIT (DIESEL) 4 CYLINDER

ENGINE CODING

ENGINE IDENTIFICATION

Engine coding for Volkswagen Diesel engines is CK. Engine identification is stamped on left side of block on machined pad near number three cylinder.

ENGINE, CYLINDER HEAD & MANIFOLDS

ENGINE

NOTE — *Manufacturer recommends removal of engine-transaxle as a unit.*

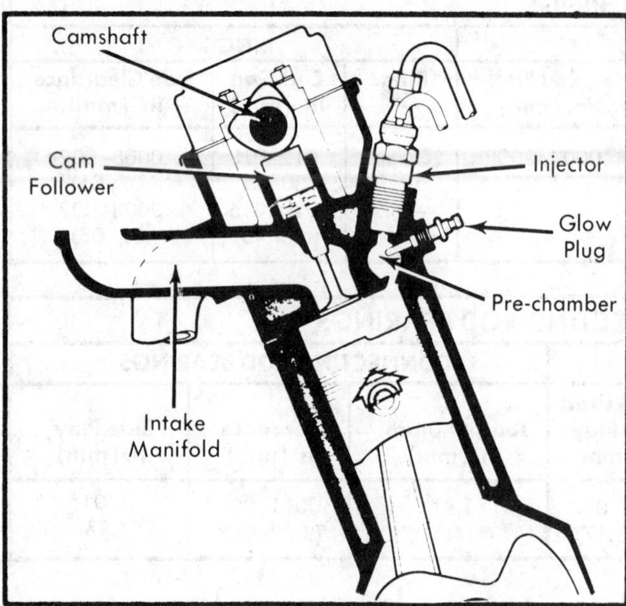

Fig. 1 End View of VW Diesel Engine

Removal — 1) Disconnect battery ground strap, open heater valve and drain all coolant. Remove radiator with fan, remove alternator and detach fuel filter from body.

2) Detach fuel supply and return lines from injection pump. Disconnect cold start cable, accelerator cable, and cable bracket from pump. Disconnect wires from oil pressure switch, temperature sensor, stop control, glow plugs, starter and back-up light switch.

3) Remove entire front transaxle mounting. Detach clutch cable and conduit from transaxle. Remove shift linkage relay shaft and detach from lever at rear. From underneath car, remove exhaust pipe supports, then remove nuts holding exhaust pipe to manifold. Remove rear transaxle mount.

4) Attach suitable sling to engine and lift slightly. Remove drive shafts at flanges from transaxle. Remove right engine mounting, then lift engine carefully to avoid damage to body, wires and cables.

5) Rotate crankshaft so that disassembly mark on flywheel is aligned with timing pointer. Remove cover plate over drive shaft flange. Remove engine/transmission mounting bolts and separate engine from transaxle.

NOTE — *Do not allow either engine or transaxle to be supported by transmission mainshaft. Damage could result to clutch, push rod or mainshaft if a strain is placed on them.*

Installation — To install, reverse removal procedures noting that recess in flywheel is level with clutch hub and drive shaft flange. Install left transaxle mounting loosely first, then complete alignment and assembly procedure.

CYLINDER HEAD & MANIFOLDS

NOTE — *Cylinder head may be removed and installed with engine in car.*

Removal — 1) Remove air cleaner and ducting, then drain cooling system. Remove camshaft drive belt. Unbolt thermostat housing from water pump. Disconnect battery ground strap.

2) Disconnect accelerator cable from injection pump. Detach fuel lines at injectors by unscrewing unions. Disconnect wire from glow plug bus, temperature sending wire and any other wires which could interfere with removal of cylinder head.

3) Remove nuts holding exhaust pipe to manifold and unbolt exhaust pipe support from engine/transaxle assembly. From underneath car, remove bolts and nuts holding exhaust manifold to cylinder head, then remove manifold from head. Disconnect coolant hoses from head and remove any other hoses which may interfere with head removal.

4) Remove cylinder head cover bolts and retaining plates. Carefully lift off cover and gasket. Loosen head bolts beginning at outer ends and work toward center. Lift off head and remove injectors and glow plugs to prevent damage while working on head.

5) Remove combustion chamber inserts by placing drift through injector hole and tapping out with hammer. Prior to installation, pre-chamber inserts must be reinstalled. When replacing injectors, new heat shields must be used between each injector and cylinder head. Remove old heat shield and place new shield in position with recess upward, towards injector. Tighten injector to 50 ft. lbs. (7.0 mkg).

Installation — 1) Clean gasket surface and ensure that cylinder head and block are not warped. Maximum distortion of .004" (.010 mm) is allowed. If installing on original piston and block assembly select a new head gasket that has the same marks as the original.

2) To determine proper gasket, measure projection of piston above block when at TDC. Select proper gasket from following table:

Available Cylinder Head Gaskets

Piston Projection in Inches (mm)	Gasket Thickness in Inches (mm)	Identification Notches
.017-.025 (.43-.63)	.051 (1.30)	2
.025-.032 (.63-.82)	.055 (1.40)	3
.032-.036 (.82-.92)	.059 (1.50)	4
.036-.040 (.92-1.02)	.063 (1.60)	5

Gasket must be installed with word "OBEN" facing up.

RABBIT (DIESEL) 4 CYLINDER (Cont.)

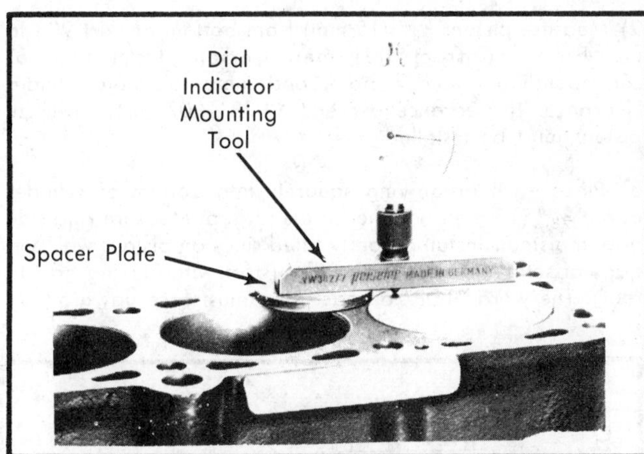

Fig. 2 Measuring Piston Projection

CAUTION — *Due to the aluminum construction of the head, do not use metal brushes or scrapers to clean gasket sealing surface or combustion chambers. Use solvent and wooden or plastic scrapers to remove foreign material. Do not mar piston tops when cleaning cylinder block. Ensure that all bolt holes and cylinder bores are absolutely free of debris prior to installing head or bolts.*

3) Lower head carefully onto gasket using two of the outermost bolts and washers to keep gasket and head aligned with block. Tighten head bolts in the sequence shown, first to 22 ft. lbs. (3.0 mkg), then to 43 ft. lbs. (6.0 mkg) and finally to 61 ft. lbs. (8.5 mkg). Complete installation in reverse order of removal.

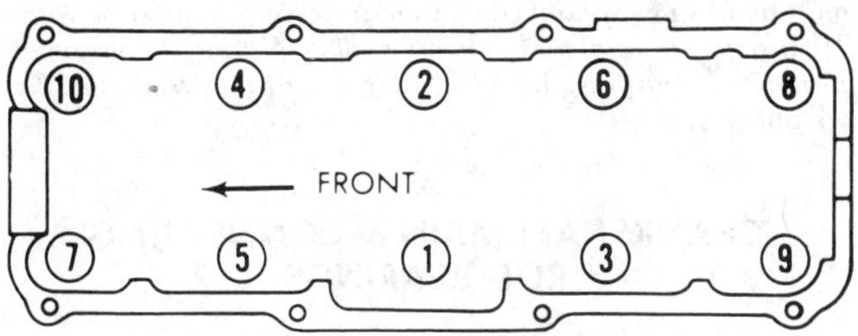

Fig. 3 Cylinder Head Tightening Sequence

VALVES

VALVE ARRANGEMENT

E-I-E-I-I-E-I-E (front to rear).

VALVE GUIDE SERVICING

1) To check for wear, insert NEW valve in clean valve guide until stem end is flush with spring end of guide. Use dial indicator to check that no more than .051" (1.3 mm) lateral (rocking) movement is indicated at valve head when moved back and forth against indicator.

2) Prior to replacing worn guides, check that head is not cracked and that valve seats can be refaced. Press out old guides and coat new guides with oil. Press new guides in up to shoulder but do not use more than one ton of pressure once shoulder is seated. Hand ream guides to proper uniform diameter of .315-.316" (8.013-8.035 mm).

VALVE STEM SEALS AND SPRINGS

NOTE — *It is possible to replace valve springs and seals with head installed provided camshaft and tappets are removed. Piston of cylinder concerned must be at top dead center position.*

Use suitable spring compressor to depress spring and retainer. Remove keepers, then remove retainer and springs. Remove stem seal. Use protective sleeve over valve stem and install new seal. Complete assembly in reverse order of disassembly.

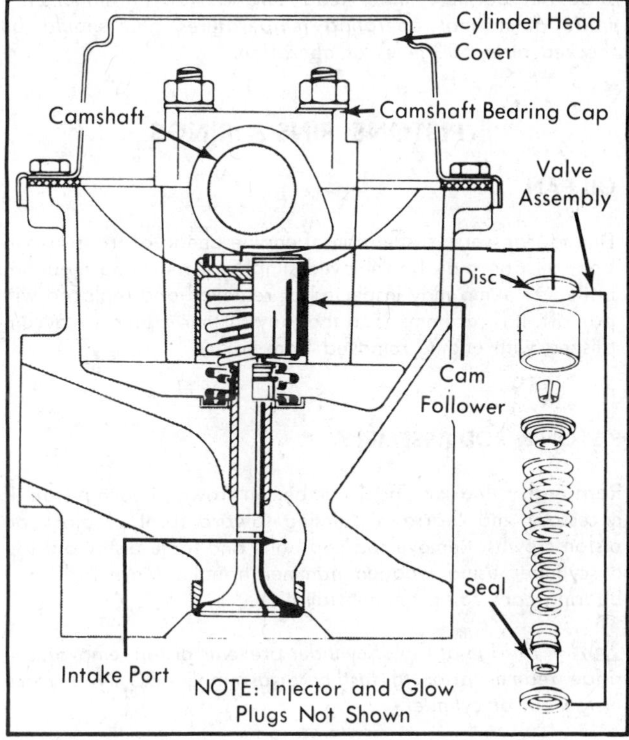

Fig. 4 View of Valve and Camshaft

VALVE CLEARANCE ADJUSTMENT

1) Engine should be near operating temperature (coolant at about 95°F (35°C). Rotate crankshaft so that cam lobes for No. 1 cylinder (curb side) point upward. Check intake and exhaust clearance between heel of cam lobe and follower.

2) Use crankshaft pulley to rotate crankshaft 180° at a time and check No. 3, No. 4, and No. 2 clearance. If clearances are not within specifications, use thinner or thicker adjusting discs to increase or decrease clearance.

NOTE — *Do not turn engine by camshaft pulley. Use crankshaft pulley with wrench or put vehicle in 4th gear and push to move crankshaft/valve train.*

3) Twenty-six different thicknesses of discs are available in increments of .0019" (.05 mm) from .1181" (3.0 mm) to .1673" (4.25 mm). To install, turn crankshaft about 1/4 turn past TDC and press cam follower down with suitable tool (VW 546). Remove old disc with special pliers (VW 10-208) and insert new disc with etched thickness marking toward cam follower.

RABBIT (DIESEL) 4 CYLINDER (Cont.)

Valve Clearance Specifications

Application	In. (mm)
Intake	
Hot	.008-.012 (.20-.30)
Cold	.006-.010 (.15-.25)
Exhaust	
Hot	.016-.020 (.40-.50)
Cold	.014-.018 (.35-.45)

NOTE – *Cold settings are given for reference as initial settings to be used during cylinder head rework. Final adjustments are made at normal operating temperatures and should be checked after 600 miles of operation.*

PISTONS, PINS & RINGS

OIL PAN

Due to transverse suspension of engine ahead of front suspension, oil pan may be removed simply by removing mounting bolts. Oil pump may inspected or removed and replaced with pan off. It is recommended that any further repairs be accomplished with engine removed from car.

PISTON & ROD ASSEMBLY

Removal – Mark cylinder number on crown of each piston. If necessary, mark arrows pointing toward front of block on piston crowns. Remove rod cap bolts and force piston out top of cylinder using wooden hammer handle. Mark rods and bearing caps for proper installation.

NOTE – *If ridge at top of cylinder prevents piston removal, use ridge reamer prior to further disassembly. DO NOT force piston out of cylinder.*

Installation – Turn crankshaft so No. 1 journal is at BDC. Install piston/rod assembly until ring compressor contacts block. Guide rod over journal and use wooden handle of hammer to push piston into cylinder. Repeat with No. 4 piston and rod assembly ensuring that tabs on bearing halves engage notches in respective rod and cap. Tighten caps on rods 1 and 4, then rotate crankshaft 180° and install No. 2 and No. 3 piston/rod assemblies.

PISTON PINS

Removal – Use needle-nose pliers to remove circlips. Press out pin and remove piston, noting direction piston is fitted to rod.

Installation – Check piston/pin fit for thumb push fit. Connecting rod/pin wear limit is .0015" (.04 mm). Connecting rod may be rebushed and honed to proper size if required. If pin is too loose in piston, replace both pin and piston.

FITTING PISTONS

1) Measure cylinder at three points: 3/8" (10 mm) from top and bottom, and at center of bore. Measure in line with and at 90° to thrust face. Cylinder wear limit is .0015" (.04 mm) beyond standard dimensions and/or out of round. If limits are exceeded, cylinders must be honed and new pistons fitted.

2) Measure pistons 5/8" (15 mm) from bottom of skirt 90° to pin bore. Subtract this measurement from that of corresponding cylinder bore and note piston-to-cylinder clearance. If clearance exceeds .0028" (.07 mm), oversize pistons must be installed.

3) Place each piston ring squarely into bottom of cylinder about 5/8" (15 mm) and measure end gap. Measure ring side gap in pistons. Install properly fitted rings on pistons with end gaps offset 120° from each other (start with oil ring gap to rear). The word "TOP" on each ring must face upward.

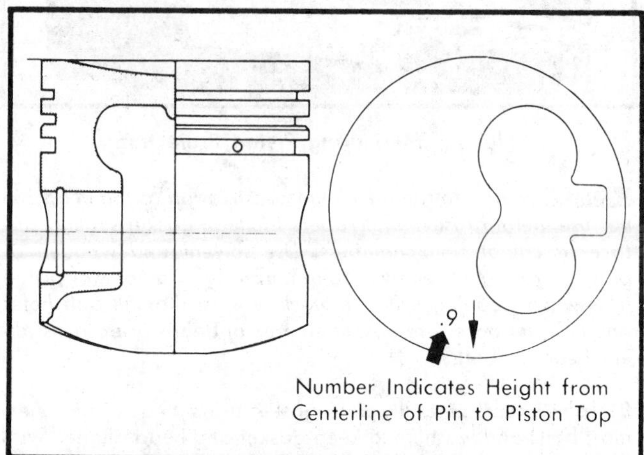

Fig. 5 Side and Top View of Diesel Piston

NOTE – *In case any pistons require replacement, new pistons must be of same weight class. Unmarked pistons must be within 10 grams of weight of other installed pistons. Replacement piston rods must also be installed in sets of four from the same weight group.*

CRANKSHAFT MAIN & CONNECTING ROD BEARINGS

MAIN & CONNECTING ROD BEARINGS

1) Push crankshaft toward one end and measure end play at No. 3 (thrust) bearing. Main bearing caps are numbered "1" to "5" with "1" at drive belt end and "5" at flywheel end. Measure connecting rod end play (side play). Check all bearing clearances by the Plastigage method.

2) Measure crankshaft journals to determine size and any out-of-round. Maximum allowable out of round is .0012" (.03 mm). Install main inserts with bearing half having oil groove into block. Lubricate bearings and install caps in original positions.

Crankshaft Journal Diameters

Size	Main Bearing In. (mm)	Con. Rod. Bearing In. (mm)
Standard	2.126 (54.00)	1.81 (46.00)
1st US	2.116 (53.75)	1.80 (45.75)
2nd US	2.106 (53.50)	1.79 (45.50)
3rd US	2.096 (53.25)	1.78 (45.25)

RABBIT (DIESEL) 4 CYLINDER (Cont.)

REAR MAIN BEARING OIL SEAL

NOTE — *Rear main bearing oil seal may be replaced with engine in vehicle. Transmission and flywheel must be removed.*

Insert screwdriver between crankshaft flywheel flange and inside lip of oil seal. Pry oil seal out. Install guide sleeve tool 2003/2A (or equivalent) over crankshaft flange. Start new oil seal into recess in carrier. Remove guide sleeve then fit drive plate 2003/1 (or equivalent) and seat seal by tightening flywheel bolts in plate.

FRONT MAIN BEARING OIL SEAL AND INTERMEDIATE SHAFT OIL SEAL

NOTE — *Diesel engine intermediate shaft rotates counterclockwise and utilizes a different seal than the gas engine. Arrow pointing counterclockwise on seal indicates correct application for Diesel model.*

Remove camshaft belt and crankshaft sprocket. Pry seal from carrier carefully to avoid damage to carrier. Use tool 10-219 or equivalent to remove seal. Use suitable installing tool (10-203 or equivalent) and press new seal into carrier until flush with front of carrier. Remove steel driving sleeve from carrier and use aluminum part of tool to drive seal further in until it is recessed .080" (2 mm) from front of seal carrier.

NOTE — *Same procedures are used for intermediate shaft seal except that intermediate shaft sprocket is removed. Seal is pressed in only until flush with carrier.*

CAMSHAFT

TIMING BELT

NOTE — *Sprockets do not have to be removed to replace drive belt.*

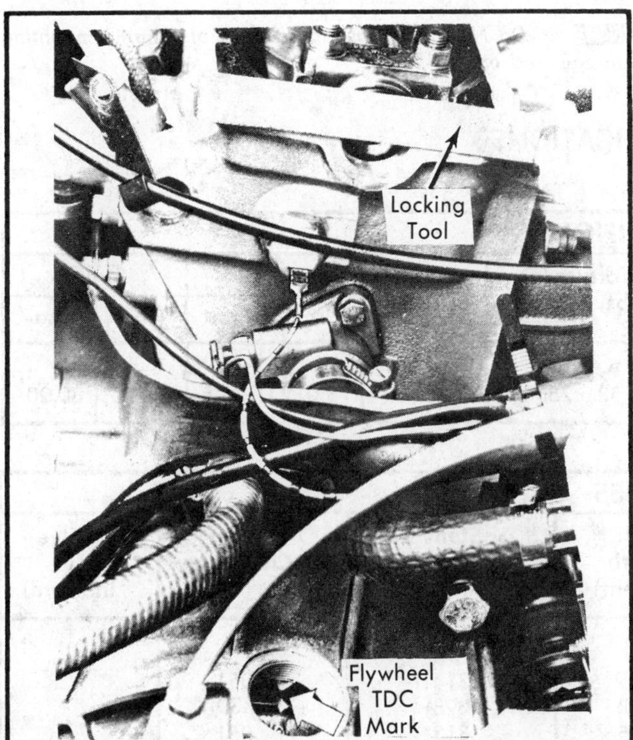

Fig. 6 Flywheel TDC Mark and Camshaft Locking Tool

Removal — Loosen alternator and remove V-belt, then remove crankshaft V-belt pulley. Remove air cleaner and ducting. Remove drive belt cover and cylinder head cover. Remove timing plug on top of bell housing and rotate crankshaft to No. 1 cylinder at TDC with both No. 1 cam lobes pointed upward. Using tool 2065 (or equivalent), lock camshaft in position. Lock injection pump in position with special pin (2064) and loosen tensioner. Remove drive belt toward right side of car.

Installation — Assure that flywheel is aligned with TDC mark. Loosen camshaft bolt ½ turn and tap camshaft gear loose from camshaft. Ensure that injection pump marks are aligned and install drive belt. Tension belt by turning tensioner to right until scale reads 12 to 13 on VW 210 tool. Tighten camshaft sprocket bolt to 32 ft. lbs. (4.5 mkg). Turn crankshaft two turns in direction of engine rotation, strike belt with rubber hammer between camshaft sprocket and injection pump sprocket. Recheck belt tension and replace remaining components.

CAMSHAFT

Removal — With camshaft drive sprocket and cylinder head cover removed, loosen bearing caps in following sequence: 5, 1, and 3, then loosen caps 2 and 4 diagonally. Bearing caps are numbered front (sprocket end) to rear (flywheel end).

Inspection — **1)** Number and remove cam followers, then reinstall camshaft using only end (1 and 5) bearing caps. Check axial play of camshaft with dial indicator. If play exceeds .006" (.15 mm), either head or camshaft is worn and must be replaced.

2) To measure camshaft bearing clearance, install caps one at a time and check with either a dial indicator or Plastigage. Check camshaft runout by installing shaft between centers and applying dial indicator at center bearing journal. Runout must not exceed .0004" (.01 mm) when camshaft is rotated.

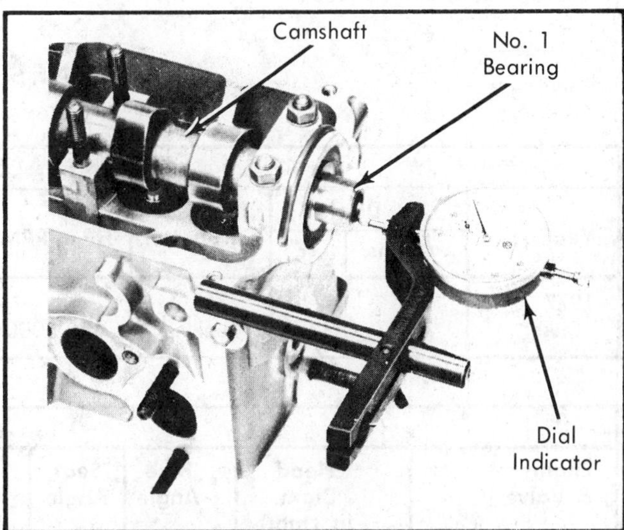

Fig. 7 Measuring Camshaft Endplay

3) Inspect cam lobes, followers, and all bearing surfaces. Ensure that all oil passages are clean. Replace any components showing signs of pitting, galling or signs of seizure.

RABBIT (DIESEL) 4 CYLINDER (Cont.)

Installation – Lightly lubricate all components for assembly. Install cam followers in original bores with matching adjusting discs. Place camshaft and number 2 and 4 bearing caps in position. Gradually tighten all four bearing cap nuts until camshaft is fully seated, then install caps 5, 3, and 1. Use tool 10-203 (or equivalent) to install front oil seal and complete installation in reverse order of removal.

VALVE TIMING

See TIMING BELT procedures in this article.

INJECTION PUMP TIMING

See ADJUSTING INJECTION PUMP TIMING in BOSCH DIESEL INJECTION section.

ENGINE OILING

Crankcase Capacity – 3.7 quarts with filter change; 3.2 quarts without filter change.

Oil Filter – Replaceable spin-on type.

Normal Oil Pressure – 28 psi @2000 RPM (normal operating temperature).

ENGINE OILING SYSTEM

Gear type oil pump provides oil for pressure feed to crankshaft journals, camshaft bearings, and intermediate shaft. A larger, heavy-duty oil filter and revised oil pump drive are used in the Diesel. Other lubrication characteristics are similar to the spark ignition engines.

OIL PUMP

Removal – Drain oil and remove oil pan. Remove pump mounting bolts and pump along with pick-up tube. Install in vise and remove pick-up tube.

Inspection – Check oil pump gear backlash with feeler gauge. Clearance should be between .002-.008" (.05-.20 mm). Measure pump gear end play using machinist's square and feeler gauge for .006" (.15 mm) clearance or less. If specifications are exceeded, replace gears or pump.

Installation – To install, assure that all mating surfaces are clean, install gaskets and reverse removal procedure.

ENGINE COOLING

Cooling System Capacity – 6.8 U.S. quarts.

Thermostat – Begins to open at 176°F (80°C) and is fully open at 200°F (94°C). Radiator fan thermo switch causes fan to operate above 194°-203°F (90°-95°C) and switch off at 185°-194°F (85°-90°C) and below. Radiator relief pressure should be 13-15 psi.

CAUTION – *Never drain the coolant while the engine is hot. Cylinder head or engine block could warp if not allowed to cool prior to draining.*

WATER PUMP

NOTE – *Front portion of water pump (shaft, seals, bearing, and housing) can be replaced separately. To do this, camshaft drive belt and sprockets must be removed. To avoid removing drive belt, remove water pump as an assembly.*

Removal – Drain cooling system. Disconnect battery ground strap and unplug alternator wires. Remove alternator. Disconnect thermostat housing and hoses from water pump. Remove bolts holding pump to engine block and remove pump.

Installation – To install, reverse removal procedure and use new "O" ring in recess in pump mounting flange.

NOTE – *Do NOT use sealer between water pump mounting flange and engine block.*

ENGINE SPECIFICATIONS

GENERAL SPECIFICATIONS

Year	Displ.		Carburetor	HP at RPM	Torque (Ft. Lbs. at RPM)	Compr. Ratio	Bore		Stroke	
	cu. ins.	cc					in.	mm	in.	mm
1977 Diesel	89.7	1471	Fuel Inj.	48@5000	58@2500	23.5:1	3.012	76.5	3.150	80.00

VALVES

Engine & Valve	Head Diam. In. (mm)	Face Angle	Seat Angle	Seat Width In. (mm)	Stem Diameter In. (mm)	Stem Clearance In. (mm)	Valve Lift In. (mm)
1977 Diesel							
Intake	1.338 (33.9)	45°	45°	.079 (2.0)	.314 (7.98)	.051 (1.30)	.....
Exhaust	1.220 (31.0)	45°	45°	.095 (2.4)	.313 (7.95)	.051 (1.30)	.....

RABBIT (DIESEL) 4 CYLINDER (Cont.)

ENGINE SPECIFICATIONS (Cont.)

PISTONS, PINS, RINGS						
	PISTONS	PINS		RINGS		
Engine	Clearance In. (mm)	Piston Fit In. (mm)	Rod Fit In. (mm)	Rings	End Gap In. (mm)	Side Clearance In. (mm)
Diesel	.001 (.03)	Push Fit	.0004-.0008 (.01-.02)	Comp. Oil	.012-.018 (.30-.45) .010-.016 (.25-.40)	.0008-.002 (.02-.05) .0008-.002 (.02-.05)

CRANKSHAFT MAIN & CONNECTING ROD BEARINGS							
	MAIN BEARINGS				CONNECTING ROD BEARINGS		
Engine	Journal Diam. In. (mm)	Clearance In. (mm)	Thrust Bearing	Crankshaft End Play In. (mm)	Journal Diam. In. (mm)	Clearance In. (mm)	Side Play In. (mm)
Diesel	2.126 (54)	.0011-.0033 (.02-.088)	No. 3	.014 .37	1.81 (46)	.0011-.0035 (.028-.088)	①.014 (.37)

① — Wear Limit

VALVE SPRINGS			
Engine	Free Length In. (mm)	PRESSURE Lbs. @ In. (kg @ mm) Valve Closed	Valve Open
Diesel Inner	.....	46-51@.719 (21-23@18.3)	....
Outer	.....	96-106.875 43.5-48@22.3	....

CAMSHAFT			
Engine	Journal Diam. In. (mm)	Clearance In. (mm)①	Lobe Lift In. (mm)
Diesel	.....	.0008-.002 (.02-.05)	....

① — End play .006" (.1 mm)

TIGHTENING SPECIFICATIONS	
Application	Ft. Lbs. (mkg)
Timing Belt Tensioner Lock Nut	32 (4.5)
Intermediate Sprocket Bolt	32 (4.5)
Crankshaft Sprocket Bolt	58 (8.0)
Water Pump Pulley Bolts	14 (2.0)
Crankshaft Pulley Bolts	14 (2.0)
Main Bearing Cap Bolts	47 (6.5)
Flywheel-to-Crankshaft Bolts	54 (7.5)
Connecting Rod Cap Bolts	32 (4.5)
Camshaft Sprocket Bolt	32 (4.5)
Camshaft Bearing Cap Nuts	14 (2.0)
Cylinder Head Bolts	
Cold	61 (8.5)
Hot	68 (9.5)
Manifolds-to-Cylinder Head	18 (2.5)
Oil Pump Mounting Bolts	14 (2.0)
Oil Pan Bolts	14 (2.0)
Fuel Injectors in Head	50 (7.0)
Fue Injector Line Unions	18 (2.5)
Fuel Injection Pump Mounting Bolts	18 (2.5)

240 SERIES 4 CYLINDER

ENGINE CODING

ENGINE IDENTIFICATION

Engine may be identified by Vehicle Identification Number located on metal tab fastened to left windshield pillar and visible from outside. The VIN number contains fifteen digits. Example: VC 24245 H 1 123456. Number is decoded as follows:

1st, 2nd Digit – Manufacturers Prefix
3rd, 4th and 5th Digit – Model
6th Digit – Engine Type (4 - B21)
7th Digit – Engine Version (5 - "F" Fuel Injection U.S.)
8th Digit – Model Year (H - 1977)
9th Digit – Assembly Plant
Last Six Digits – Serial Number.

ENGINE, CYLINDER HEAD & MANIFOLD

ENGINE

1) Disconnect rubber boot and lock ring at base of gearshift lever (manual transmission). Remove battery. Disconnect windshield washer hose and engine compartment lamp. Remove hood.

2) Remove cap from expansion tank. Open radiator drain cock and drain coolant. Disconnect lower radiator hose at radiator, crankcase ventilation hose at cylinder head, and upper radiator hose at engine. Detach expansion tank hoses from radiator. Disconnect oil cooler pipes for automatic transmission at radiator. Remove fan shroud screws, disconnect radiator, and lift radiator and fan shroud from car.

3) Remove air cleaner and hose assembly. Loosen tensioner nut and remove belt from air pump. Disconnect hoses at pump and remove pump and bracket assembly. Remove vacuum pump after disconnecting hoses, including hose to brake power cylinder. Remove tensioner bar bolts, drive belt and power steering pump.

4) If equipped with air conditioning, remove crankshaft pulley and A/C drive belt. Reinstall pulley loosely. Disconnect and remove compressor and bracket.

5) Mark and disconnect four vacuum hoses at engine and two carbon filter hoses. Remove wire or connector from distributor, high tension lead from coil, and starter motor cables and clutch cable clamp from starter.

6) Detach wiring harness from voltage regulator. Disconnect throttle cable at pulley and A/C wire at solenoid on intake manifold.

7) Remove fuel cap to relieve pressure, and remove fuel hoses from filter and return pipe. Remove guard plate for ballast resistor, and disconnect two wire connectors from intake manifold micro switch, four in wiring harness, and two at ballast resistor.

8) Disconnect heater hoses at firewall and drain oil from engine. Remove exhaust pipe flange nuts and gasket. Remove front engine mounting bolts and front exhaust pipe mounting bracket. Disconnect gearshift control rod (automatic transmission) or clutch cable (manual transmission).

9) Disconnect speedometer cable, propeller shaft U-joint, and gearshift selector from control rod. If manual transmission has overdrive, disconnect wire to gearshift selector. Using a wooden block, place jack under transmission. Remove transmission support member.

10) Attach lifting yoke assembly (5035) to three engine lifting eyes, and adjust lifting beam (2810) to its rearmost position. Hoist slightly to release front engine mount dowels. Check for wires or hoses, and disconnect as necessary. Adjust lifting beam to forward position and lift engine from car.

INTAKE & EXHAUST MANIFOLDS

Removal – **1)** Disconnect battery ground cable, then remove air bellows from CI unit to intake manifold. Disconnect PCV hoses at intake manifold and flame arrester. Disconnect vacuum pump hose at intake manifold. Disconnect diverter valve hoses. Disconnect air pump with tensioner and position to one side.

2) Disconnect the following fuel lines: control pressure regulator (one hose), cold start injector (one hose), distributor pipe to engine (two hoses) front fuel filter to engine (two hoses), and injector hoses (four hoses). Disconnect wiring at control pressure regulator, cold start injector, and auxiliary air valve.

3) Remove air injection pipe. Disconnect throttle cable from intake manifold. Disconnect charcoal canister hoses and EGR valve hose from intake manifold. Remove intake manifold brace, attaching nuts, and intake manifold. Disconnect transmission fill pipe from flywheel housing (automatic transmissions only). Remove attaching nuts and exhaust manifold.

Installation – To install, reverse removal procedure and use new manifold gaskets. Tighten nuts and bolts to specifications.

CYLINDER HEAD

Removal – **1)** Drain cooling system at radiator and cylinder block. Disconnect battery ground cable. Disconnect upper radiator hose at engine. Disconnect air bellows between CI unit and air cleaner. Remove PCV hoses from intake manifold and oil trap on block. Disconnect vacuum pump hose at intake manifold.

2) Disconnect diverter valve hoses. Remove air pump and bracket. Disconnect the following fuel lines: control pressure regulator (one hose), cold start injector (one hose), distributor pipe to engine (two hoses), front fuel filter to engine (two hoses), and injector hoses (four hoses).

240 SERIES 4 CYLINDER (Cont.)

3) Disconnect wires at following components: control pressure regulator, cold start injector, auxiliary air valve, and temperature sender. Disconnect throttle cable from intake manifold. Disconnect charcoal canister hoses and EGR valve hose from intake manifold. Disconnect transmission fill pipe from transmission housing (automatic transmissions only).

4) Remove water pipe rear clamp from manifold. Remove exhaust manifold to exhaust pipe attaching nuts. Remove intake manifold brace. Disconnect spark plug cables at plugs, then disconnect upper water hose at firewall. Remove valve cover and cylinder head bolts. Lift cylinder head from engine.

Installation – 1) Install new head gasket with "TOP" mark upward. Be sure all contact surfaces are clean. Position cylinder head over gasket.

2) Dip head bolts and washers in engine oil before installation. Install and torque, in two steps, to specifications shown in table, and according to sequence shown in *Fig. 1*.

3) Adjust valves to .014-.016" (.35-.40 mm) with engine cold. **NOTE** – *See Valve Clearance Adjustment for procedure.* Reverse remainder of removal procedure, and then make final valve adjustment after running engine for 10 minutes. Adjust to .016-.018" (.40-.45 mm). Retorque cylinder head bolts.

Cylinder Head Tightening Specifications

Sequence	Ft.Lbs (mkg)
Step One	44 (6.0)
Step Two	①76-83 C10.5-11.5)

① – Run engine for 10 minutes until hot, allow engine to cool 30 minutes, and retorque.

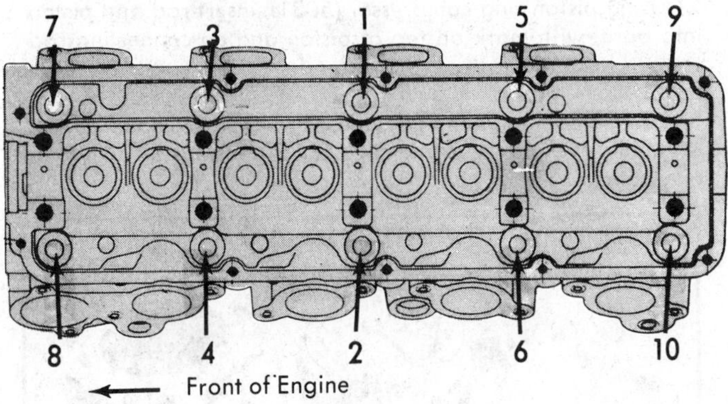

Fig. 1 Cylinder Head Tightening Sequence

VALVES

VALVE ARRANGEMENT

E-I-E-I-E-I-E-I – Front to Rear.

VALVE GUIDE SERVICING

Removal – Heat cylinder head to 212° ± 18°F (100° ± 10°C). Use drift 9992818-6 (or equivalent) to press out old guide. Make sure guide is not scored when being pressed out. If it is, the hole must be machined oversize.

Valve Guide Identification – New guides are grooved for identification. Guide must be same size as old guide. Guides are marked as follows:

No. of Grooves	Std.
1	Os 1
2	Os 2
3	Os 3

Installation – With cylinder head heated, use drift 9995027-1 or equivalent)) to press in intake valve guide. Use drift 9995028-9 for exhaust valve guide. Press guide down until drift touches cylinder head. This establishes correct location. Force required to press in guide should be at least 2023 lbs. If force used does not reach this figure, guide seat must be reamed to nearest oversize.

VALVE SPRINGS

Removal & Installation – With cylinder head removed, compress valve springs using suitable valve spring compression tool, and remove valve retainers. Disassemble valve spring components and place valves in order in suitable valve rack. To install, place valves in position, fit valve guide seal, valve spring, upper washer and retainer.

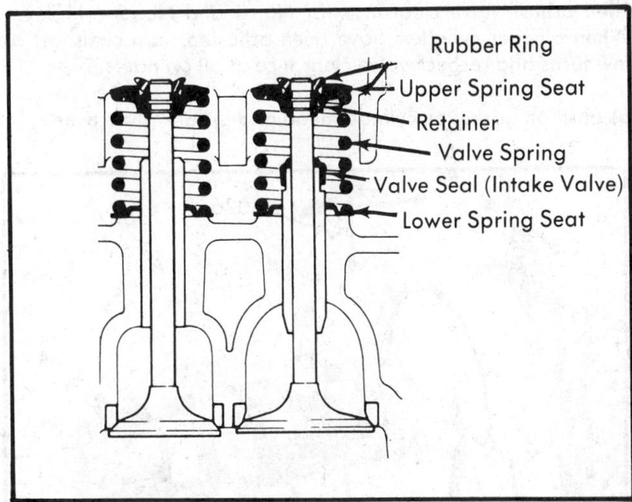

Fig. 2 Valve & Guide Assembly

VALVE SPRING INSTALLED HEIGHT

Valve spring ends must be square. Installed height of valve spring cannot exceed specifications. Measure spring height from base of spring pad on cylinder head to underside of spring retainer.

VALVE CLEARANCE ADJUSTMENT

1) Valve clearance is adjusted with engine off, and may be done either warm or cold. Remove valve cover. Turn crankshaft center bolt until camshaft is in position for firing No. 1 cylinder. Both cam lobes should point up at equally large angles. Pulley timing mark should be on 0°.

240 SERIES 4 CYLINDER (Cont.)

2) Using feeler gauge, check valve clearance of No. 1 cylinder, measuring between camshaft lobe and discs. Intake and exhaust valves should have same clearances:

Valve Clearances

When Checking	In. (mm)
Cold engine	.012-.018" (.30-.45 mm)

When Setting	In. (mm)
Cold engine	.014-.016" (.35-.40 mm)
Hot engine	.016-.018" (.40-.45 mm)

3) If clearance is incorrect, line up notches in valve depressors, so they are at right angles to engine center line. Install valve adjustment tool (5022) and turn handle downward until depressor groove is just above edge of cylinder head. Remove adjusting disc with special pliers (5026).

4) Using micrometer, measure thickness of disc. Then determine proper thickness required of new disc to bring clearance within specifications. For example: Measure existing clearance and subtract correct clearance. Difference should be added to thickness of old disc to determine thickness of new disc required. Discs are available in thicknesses ranging from 3.30 to 4.50 mm in increments of .05 mm.

5) Discs should be oiled and installed with marks down. Remove valve adjustment tool (5022), rotate crankshaft to correct firing position for No. 3 cylinder and repeat procedure. Then adjust valve clearance for No. 4 and No. 2 cylinders. When all four cylinders have been adjusted, turn camshaft a few turns and recheck valve clearance at all cylinders.

6) Position gasket on cylinder head and install valve cover.

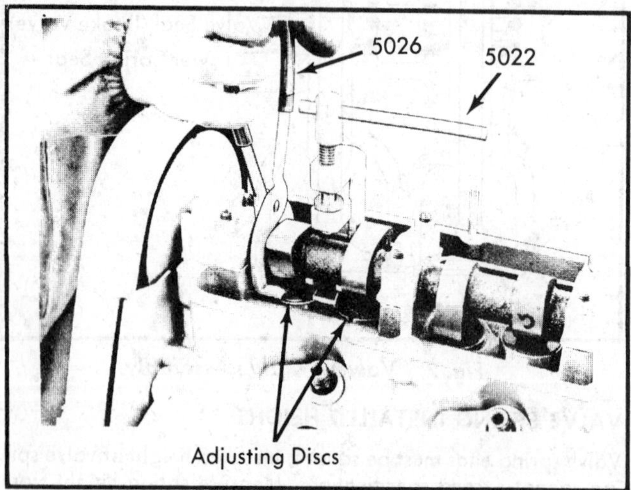

Fig. 3 Removing Valve Adjusting Discs

PISTONS, PINS & RINGS

OIL PAN

Removal – Position lifting tools (5006, 5033 & 5115) as shown in *Fig. 4*. Disconnect A/C compressor (if equipped). Remove bolts from left engine mount. Lift engine slightly and drain oil. Remove splash guard, left engine mount, and brace. Remove bolts from oil pan and tap to loosen.

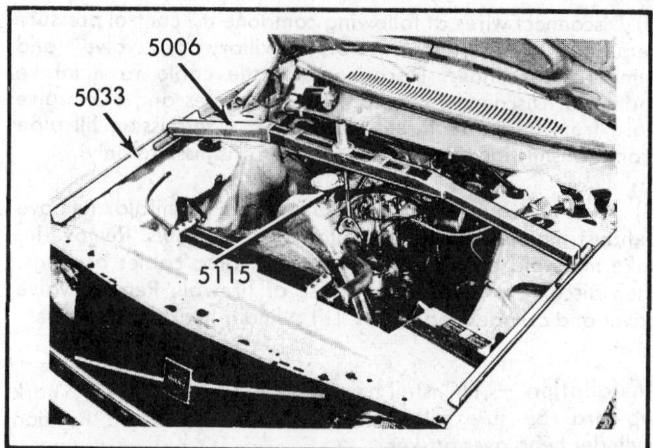

Fig. 4 Removing Oil Pan

Installation – Place new gasket on oil pan. Turn and lift into position. Install bolts, brace, left engine mount, and splash guard. Lower engine and install bolts in left engine mount. Remove tools and connect A/C compressor. Fill engine with oil.

PISTON & ROD ASSEMBLY

Removal – Remove cylinder head, oil pan and oil pump. Be sure connecting rods and caps are properly marked, so they may be reinstalled in original location. Remove carbon ridge from cylinder bores. Remove rod cap, and using wooden hammer handle, push piston out top of cylinder bore. Reinstall rod cap on piston and rod from which removed.

Installation – 1) Remove rod cap from connecting rod. Secure piston pin with retaining rings. Be sure "TOP" mark on rings is facing top of piston and end gaps are 120 degrees from each other and rings are properly installed. Install bearings in connecting rods and caps. Lubricate cylinder bores, pistons and bearings.

2) Using piston ring compressor (5031), insert rod and piston into bore, with mark on top of piston and on connecting rod toward front of engine.

3) Using wooden hammer handle, tap lightly on top of piston. Align marks and torque end caps to 43 ft. lbs. Install oil pump, oil pan and cylinder head.

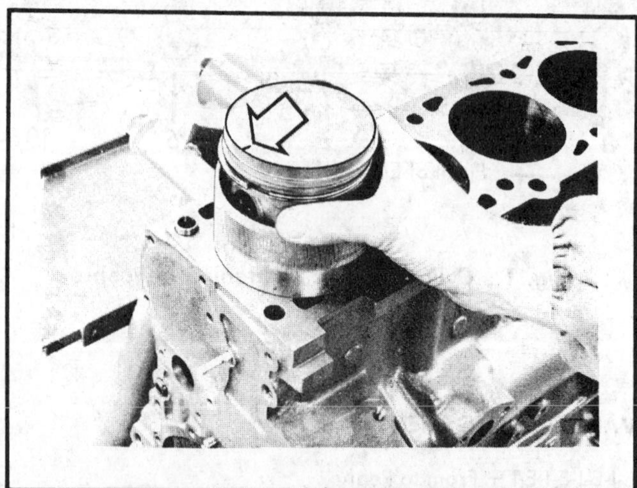

Fig. 5 Installation of Piston in Cylinder Block

240 SERIES 4 CYLINDER (Cont.)

FITTING PISTONS

Measure piston diameter at right angle to piston pin bore and .25" (7 mm) from lower edge. Measure cylinder bore at several positions. If difference exceeds clearance specifications, oversize pistons are available.

PISTON PINS

Piston pins are available in .002" (.05 mm) oversize from standard diameter. If replacement oversize pins are needed, piston pin hole should be reamed out to correct measurement using suitable reaming tool. Use reamer fitted with pilot guide, take only small cuts at a time. Pin fit is correct when pin can be pushed through connecting rod hole by hand, with only light resistance.

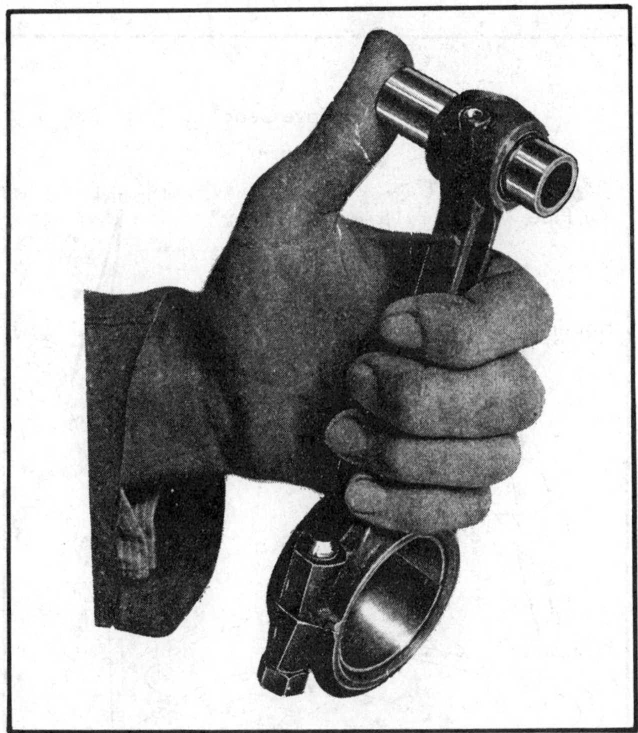

Fig. 6 Thumb Pressure Piston Pin Fit

CRANKSHAFT MAIN & CONNECTING ROD BEARINGS

MAIN & CONNECTING ROD BEARINGS

Removal & Installation — **1**) Remove oil pan and related parts. *See Oil Pan Removal.* Identify and mark connecting rod caps and main bearing caps to ensure correct replacement.

2) Remove connecting rod caps and push pistons towards top of cylinders. Remove main bearing caps (one at a time) and thoroughly clean all bearing surfaces.

3) Measure all journals, using a micrometer. Out-of-roundness on connecting rod bearings should not exceed .003" (.07 mm) and on main bearings, it should not exceed .002" (.05 mm). If values obtained are close to, or in excess of wear limits, crankshaft must be reground to next suitable undersize.

4) If all journals check out to standard size, refit with replacement bearings. Reinstall main bearing caps, refit connecting rods to crankshaft and tighten all nuts and bolts to specifications. Reassemble engine in reverse order of removal.

REAR MAIN BEARING OIL SEAL

Removal & Installation — **1**) Remove transmission, clutch, and flywheel from engine. Remove two bolts from oil pan (into rear flange). Slacken two bolts on each side of flange, and remove flange. Use a suitable drift (2817) to remove oil seal.

2) Clean flange area thoroughly and inspect seal mating surface of crankshaft. Install new seal to flange using drift (2817). **NOTE** — *If a new crankshaft has been installed, screw center bolt of tool in fully and install seal to its outer position in flange. If crankshaft has not been replaced, install seal with center bolt of tool screwed out a couple of turns.*

3) Oil new seal and install flange with new gasket to cylinder block. Install attaching bolts and tighten. Install oil pan attaching bolts and tighten. Install flywheel, clutch, and transmission.

CAMSHAFT

ENGINE FRONT COVER

Removal — **1**) Remove fan shroud, fan belt and fan pulley. Remove water pump pulley and camshaft drive belt cover. Remove crankshaft hub, sprocket and belt guide. Remove sprocket from intermediate shaft. Detach wiring harness across front of engine. Remove two oil pan bolts from base of front cover and loosen two on each side of them. Remove drive belt guard plate and front cover.

2) Using suitable tool (5025) press out intermediate shaft seal from front cover. Using similar tool (5024) press out crankshaft seal. Use same tools to install new seals.

Installation — **1**) Using new gasket, install front cover. Install oil pan, drive belt guard plate, and wiring harness.

2) Using tool (5024), install crankshaft seal. Using similar tool (5025), install intermediate shaft seal in front cover. **NOTE** — *Oil seals prior to installation.* Install inner belt guide on camshaft (collar facing away from belt). Install camshaft sprocket, aligning notch with dowel on camshaft. Install outer belt guide, washer and center bolt. Use suitable tool (5034) to hold sprocket and torque to 37 ft. lbs.

3) Install sprocket on intermediate shaft, aligning notch with dowel on shaft. Use tool (5034) to hold shaft while tightening center bolt to 37 ft. lbs.

4) Install belt guide and sprocket on crankshaft. Install front hub and torque center bolt to 122 ft. lbs. Install drive belt and complete installation of previously removed parts.

240 SERIES 4 CYLINDER (Cont.)

Fig. 7 Timing Marks for Crankshaft, Intermediate Shaft & Camshaft

INSTALLING DRIVE BELT

1) Install belt tensioner if previously removed. Align notch in crankshaft belt guide with timing mark on front cover. Rotate intermediate shaft so timing mark on sprocket aligns with mark on belt guard. Align marks on camshaft belt guide with timing mark on valve cover.

2) New drive belts have yellow markings. Two lines should fit toward crankshaft marks and next mark toward intermediate shaft mark. Place belt over crankshaft sprocket first, then intermediate shaft. Stretch belt on tension side and fit over camshaft sprocket. Slide back of belt inside tension roller.

3) Loosen nut on belt tensioner to permit spring tension to act against drive belt. Recheck timing marks for proper location and torque nut on tensioner to 37 ft. lbs. Attach pulley to front hub on crankshaft.

ENGINE OILING

Crankcase Capacity – 4 qts. including filter.
Oil Filter – Full-flow canister, disposable type.
Normal Oil Pressure – 35-85 psi @2000 RPM with engine hot.

ENGINE OILING SYSTEM

Engine utilizes a force-feed lubricating system. Oil circulates through oil pump to oil filter on outside of engine block assembly. From filter, oil is forced to drilled gallery in center of block, where it moves under pressure to main bearings. Main bearings are drilled to permit lubricant to pass on to connecting rod and camshaft bearings.

Oil from camshaft bearings is used to lubricate discs, valves, and cylinder head assembly. Cylinder walls and rings are lubricated by the splash from connecting rods. Excess oil from all areas returns to sump through drain holes in block assembly.

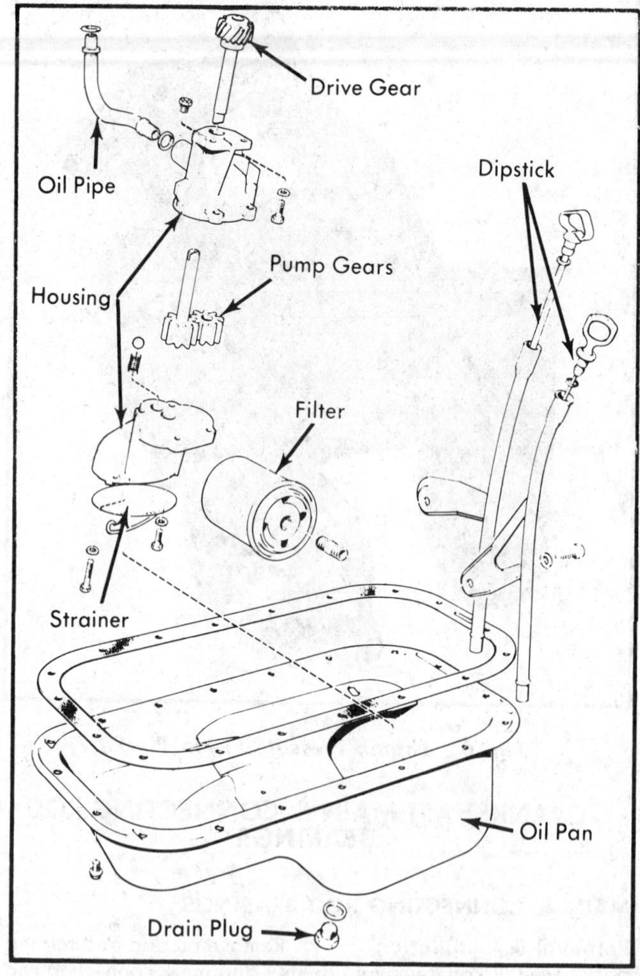

Fig. 8 Oiling System Components

OIL PUMP

1) Remove oil pan and related parts. *See Oil Pan Removal.* Pull oil pump out of engine, disassemble and clean all parts thoroughly. Check all parts for excessive wear or signs of fatigue.

240 SERIES 4 CYLINDER (Cont.)

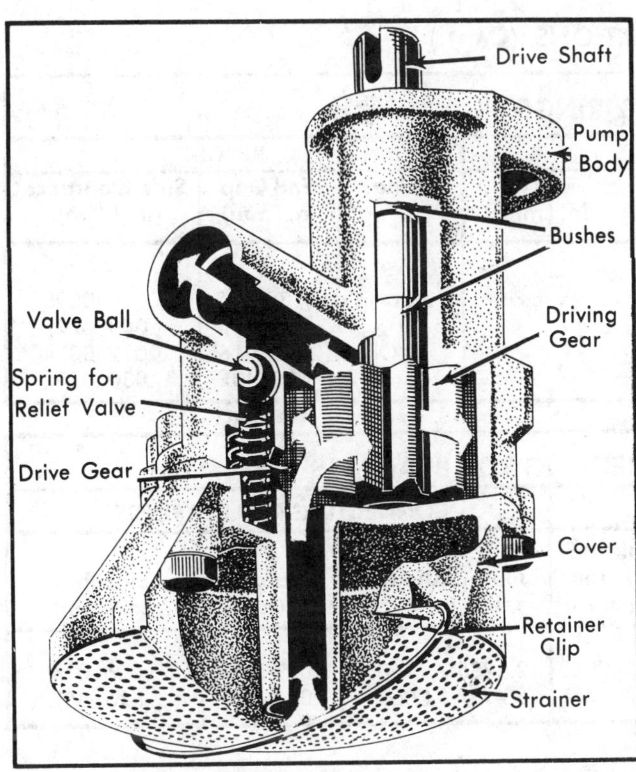

Fig. 9 Cutaway & Operational View of Oil Pump Assembly

2) Measure backlash (clearance) between pump gears. It should be .006-.014" (.15-.35 mm). Also measure end play of gears. Allowable end play is .0008-.0048" (.02-.12 mm). If any parts show excessive wear or play, replace necessary components. Drive shaft and gear are matched set and must be replaced as an assembly.

3) Reinstall oil pump, making sure that sealing rings on oil delivery pipe are securely in place. Be sure oil pump properly engages pump drive shaft. Replace oil pan and related components.

ENGINE COOLING

WATER PUMP

Removal & Installation – 1) Remove expansion tank cap, open engine block drain cock, and disconnect lower radiator hose at radiator. Remove fan shroud and fan. Loosen alternator and air pump and remove drive belts.

2) Remove water pump pulley, timing gear cover, and lower radiator hose. Remove retaining bolt and slide coolant pipe rearward. Remove pump.

3) Clean all surfaces. Place new sealing ring on coolant pipe. Install new gasket when mounting pump. Install other components previously removed. Fill with coolant.

Thermostat – Standard wax-type (marked 87°) opens at 189° F (87° C); fully open at 207° F (97° C).

ENGINE SPECIFICATIONS

GENERAL SPECIFICATIONS

Year	Displ.		Carburetor	HP at RPM	Torque (Ft. Lbs. at RPM)	Compr. Ratio	Bore		Stroke	
	cu. ins.	cc					in.	mm	in.	mm
1977										
B21F										
Federal	130.0	2130	F.I.	102@5200	114@2500	8.5-1	3.623	92	3.150	80
Calif.	130.0	2130	F.I.	99@5200	114@2500	8.5-1	3.623	92	3.150	80

VALVES

Engine & Valve	Head Diam. In. (mm)	Face Angle	Seat Angle	Seat Width In. (mm)	Stem Diameter In. (mm)	Stem Clearance In. (mm)	Valve Lift In. (mm)
B21F							
Intake	1.732 (44)	45.5°	44.75°	.068-.092 (1.7-2.3)	.3134-.3138 (7.96-7.97)	.0012-.0024 (.030-.060)	.44 (11.2)
Exhaust	1.278 (35)	45.5°	44.75°	.068-.092 (1.7-2.3)	.3122-.3126 (7.93-7.94)	.0024-.0035 (.060-.090)	.28 (11.2)

240 SERIES 4 CYLINDER (Cont.)

ENGINE SPECIFICATIONS (Cont.)

PISTONS, PINS, RINGS						
	PISTONS	PINS		RINGS		
Engine	Clearance In. (mm)	Piston Fit In. (mm)	Rod Fit In. (mm)	Rings	End Gap In. (mm)	Side Clearance In. (mm)
B21F	.0004-.0012 (.010-.030)	Push Fit	Push Fit	2 Comp. 1 Oil	.0138-.217 (.35-.55) .010-.016 (.25-.40)	.0016-.0028 (.040-.072) .0012-.0024 (.030-.062)

CRANKSHAFT MAIN & CONNECTING ROD BEARINGS							
	MAIN BEARINGS				CONNECTING ROD BEARINGS		
Engine	Journal Diam. In. (mm)	Clearance In. (mm)	Thrust Bearing	Crankshaft End Play In. (mm)	Journal Diam. In. (mm)	Clearance In. (mm)	Side Play In. (mm)
B21F	2.4981-2.4986 (63.451-63.464)	.0011-.0033 (.028-.083)	.....	.0015-.0058 (.037-.147)	2.1255-2.1260 (53.987-54.000)	.0009-.0028 (.024-.070)	.006-.014 (.15-.35)

VALVE SPRINGS			
Engine	Free Length In. (mm)	PRESSURE Lbs. @ In. (kg @ mm)	
		Valve Closed	Valve Open
B21F	1.77 (45)	63-72@1.50 (29-33@38)	160-178@1.06 (73-81@27)

CAMSHAFT			
Engine	Journal Diam. In. (mm)	Clearance In. (mm)	Lobe Lift In. (mm)
B21F	1.1437-1.1445 (29.050-29.070)	.0012-.0028 (.030-.071)	.....

TIGHTENING SPECIFICATIONS

Application	Ft. Lbs (mkg)
Cylinder Head Bolts	
Step One	44 (6.0)
Step Two	①76-83 (10.5-11.5)
Main Bearing Caps	85-91 (11.8-12.6)
Connecting Rod Caps	43-48 (6.0-6.6)
Camshaft Bearing Caps	13-16 (1.8-2.2)
Exhaust & Intake Manifold Bolts	15 (2.0)
Flywheel Bolts	47-54 (6.5-7.5)
Engine Mount Bolts	15 (2.0)
Spark Plugs	25-29 (3.5-4.0)
Sprockets	
Camshaft	37 (5.1)
Intermediate Shaft	37 (5.1)
Crankshaft	122 (16.9)
Fan Bolt	33 (4.6)
Drive Belt Tensioner Nut	37 (5.1)
Oil Pan Bolts	8 (1.1)

① Run engine for 10 minutes, until hot, allow engine to cool 30 minutes, and retorque.

260 SERIES V6

ENGINE CODING

ENGINE IDENTIFICATION

Engine may be identified by Vehicle Identification Number located on metal tab fastened to left windshield pillar visble from outside. The VIN number contains fifteen digits. Example: VC 24265 H 1123456. Number is decoded as follows:

1st, 2nd Digit – Manufacturers Prefix
3rd, 4th and 5th Digit – Model
6th Digit – Engine Type (6- B27)
7th Digit – Engine Version (5- "F" Fuel Injection U.S.)
8th Digit – Model Year (H-1977)
9th Digit – Assembly Plant
Last six digits – Serial number.

ENGINE, CYLINDER HEADS & MANIFOLDS

ENGINE

1) Remove gearshift lever (manual) or place lever in "Park" (automatic). Remove battery, hood, air cleaner and engine splash guard.

2) Drain cooling system (each side of block), and disconnect all coolant hoses. Disconnect automatic transmission oil cooler pipes at radiator. Remove radiator and fan shroud. Disconnect heater hose at intake pipe, power brake hose at intake manifold, and vacuum pump hose at pump. Remove vacuum pump.

3) Disconnect fuel hoses at filter and return pipe. Disconnect wiring harness and relay connectors. Remove high tension lead from distributor and heater hoses at fire wall. Disconnect carbon filter hose at filter, and hose from EGR valve. Remove connector at voltage regulator and wire clamp. Disconnect connector for distributor, throttle cable, vacuum amplifier hose at T-pipe, and wax thermostat hoses.

4) Remove hose from air pump to backfire valve and wires from solenoid valve and micro switch. Remove nuts from both exhaust manifold flanges. Remove A/C compressor and drive belt without disconnecting hoses. Drain engine oil. Remove power steering pump and belt.

5) Remove nuts from front engine mounts. Remove exhaust pipe clamps (front exhaust pipe with catalytic converter). Disconnect shift control lever at automatic transmission.

6) Disconnect slave cylinder from clutch (manual transmission) and detach speedometer cable. Disconnect propeller shaft. Put stands under front of car, and using wooden block, place jack under oil pan. Remove transmission attachment member.

7) Using safe hoisting equipment, lift engine from car.

NOTE – *When removing engine, check for hoses and wires not previously removed.*

CYLINDER HEAD (ENGINE IN VEHICLE)

Removal – 1) Disconnect battery ground cable. Remove air cleaner and disconnect throttle cable. Disconnect kick-down cable (automatic transmission) and remove pipe from EGR valve and intake manifold. Disconnect vacuum hose at EGR valve. Remove oil filler cap and stuff rag in filler hole. Disconnect crankcase ventilation pipe from intake manifold and remove intake manifold front, gaskets, and rubber rings.

2) Disconnect fuel line and connector from cold start injector. Disconnect vacuum hose, connector and two fuel lines from control pressure regulator. Disconnect hoses, pipes and electrical connectors, and remove auxiliary air valve. Remove connector at fuel distributor and wiring harness. Disconnect high tension leads from spark plugs and injectors from holders in both banks.

3) Disconnect vacuum hose at distributor, and remove vacuum, carbon filter, diverter valve, power brake, and heater hoses at intake manifold. Disconnect wires at throttle micro switch and solenoid valve, and fuel lines from filter and return pipe. Remove fuel distributor.

4) Disconnect EGR valve hose from throttle housing. Remove cold start injector and pipe. Remove intake manifold and rubber rings. Remove splash guard under engine and drain coolant from both sides of block. Remove air pump, vacuum pump and vacuum hoses at thermostat. Disconnect upper radiator hose and remove A/C compressor (do not remove hoses).

5) Remove distributor and EGR valve and bracket. Disconnect relay connectors and remove rear A/C bracket. Remove lower radiator hose at water pump and hoses from pump to cylinder heads. Disconnect supply hose from cylinder heads, and separate air manifold at rear of engine. Remove backfire valve and air hose. Remove valve covers.

6) On left side, remove four upper timing gear cover bolts and Allen head screw (not camshaft center bolt). On right side, remove four upper timing gear cover bolts and cover plate. Remove exhaust pipe clamps under vehicle and oil dipstick and pipe. Remove exhaust pipe flange and exhaust manifold. Remove cover plates at rear of cylinder heads.

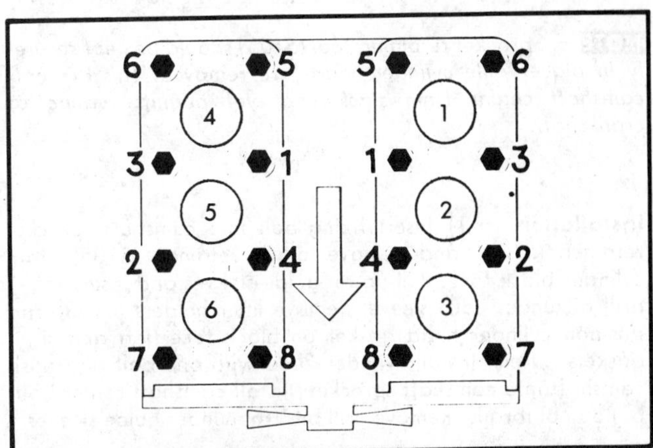

Fig. 1 Sequence for Removing and Installing Cylinder Head Bolts

260 SERIES V6 (Cont.)

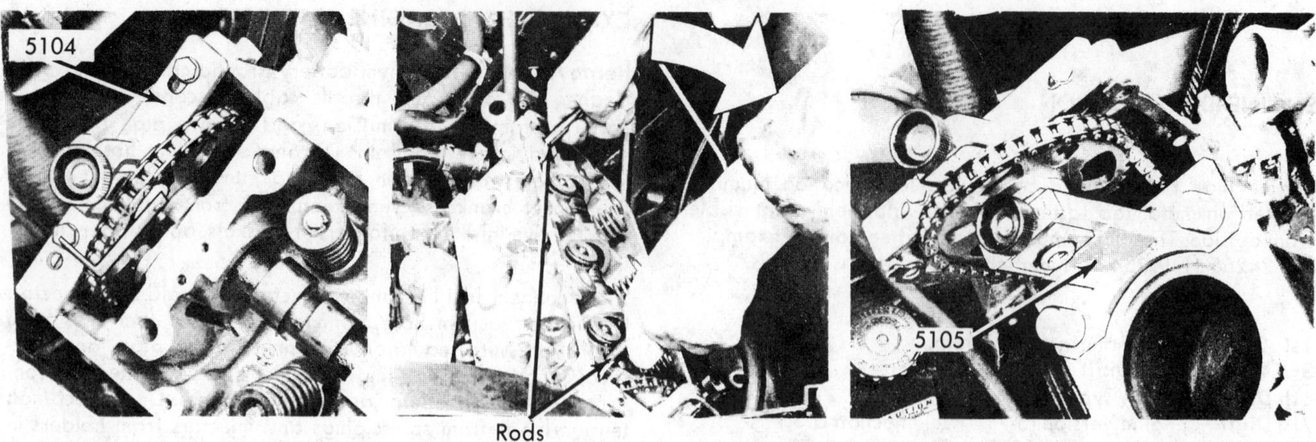

Fig. 2 Special Tools for Removing Cylinder Heads

7) Rotate each camshaft until large hole in sprocket aligns with rocker arm shaft. Remove rocker arm and shaft assembly by removing bolts in sequence shown in *Fig. 1.* Loosen bolt and push camshaft lock fork to one side.

8) Install tool to hold camshaft sprocket in place (5104). With tool installed, remove camshaft center bolt and slide camshaft to rear. Be sure camshaft stud is free from sprocket.

NOTE — *If tool is not used, camshaft chain will slacken and be held by chain tensioner. Sprocket then cannot be pulled upward when installing camshaft. If this should occur, timing gear cover must be removed for access to chain tensioner.*

9) Insert two 12" long rods into cylinder head bolt holes, *Fig. 2,* and push downward to loosen cylinder head from block. Do not attempt to remove cylinder head by lifting straight upward. If liners are not to be removed, be sure they do not separate from their seals in lower liner seat. If seals are damaged, coolant will enter crankcase. Lift out cylinder head carefully.

10) Tap guide sleeves flush with block face and remove gasket. Install liner holders (5093) to secure liners against seat seals. Clean gasket surfaces and install camshaft retaining tool (5105). After tool is securely in place, remove fixing bolt from previously installed tool (5I04). See *Fig. 2.*

NOTE — *Sprocket retaining tool (5105) should be kept securely in place while cylinder heads are removed. This prevents camshaft chains from slackening, yet permits turning of crankshaft.*

Installation — 1) Insert fixing bolt into camshaft sprocket retainer (5104) and remove other retainer (5105) from cylinder block face. Pull up on guide sleeves and insert a ⅛" drill bit under each sleeve. Remove liner holders (5093) and position cylinder head gasket on block face (left and right gaskets differ). Install cylinder head with one bolt and push camshaft into camshaft sprocket. Install camshaft center bolt, but do not torque. Remove drill bits from under guide sleeves

2) Position rocker arm and shaft assembly and install cylinder head bolts. Tighten all bolts in sequence shown in *Fig. 1* in three stages:

Cylinder Head Tightening Specifications

Sequence	Ft. Lbs. (mkg)
Step One	7 (1.0)
Step Two	22 (3.0)
Step Three	①44 (6.1)

① — After 10-15 minutes retorque with protractor (5098).

3) Torque camshaft center bolt and remove sprocket retainer (5104). Center lock fork over camshaft and tighten. Back off all cylinder head bolts in sequence, *Fig. 1*. Tighten to 11-14 ft. lbs. Using protractor (5098) on standard socket, torque head bolts as follows:

1. Use rocker arm and shaft as a guide line for protractor.
2. Fit socket over bolt 1 and take up slack of tool. Rotate protractor so that "0" mark aligns with rocker arm and shaft assembly.
3. Tighten bolt until protractor angle of 116-120° aligns with rocker arm guide line.
4. Repeat procedure in proper tightening sequence for other head bolts.
5. After engine is assembled, run at operating temperature for 15 minutes and cool for 30 minutes. Back off head bolts once more and torque to 11-14 ft. lbs. Then use protractor to torque bolts in sequence shown (*Fig. 3*) to 113-117°.

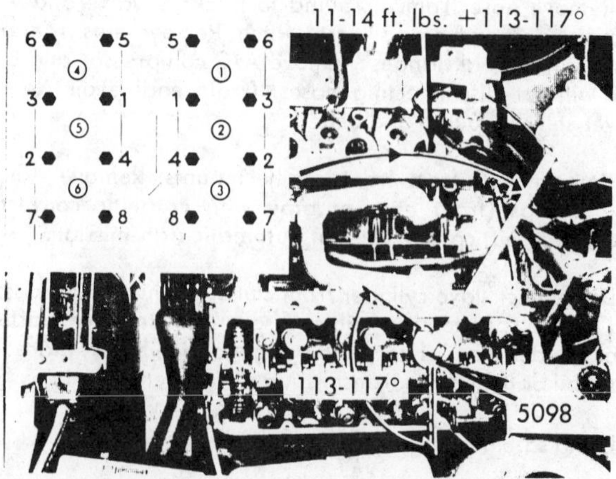

Fig. 3 Final Torquing of Cylinder Head Bolts After Running and Cooling Engine

260 SERIES V6 (Cont.)

4) Install remainder of components in reverse order of removal procedure, noting the following:

1. Before installing valve cover, adjust valves (cold setting).
2. When installing distributor, rotor should initially point to clamp clockwise from mark on distributor housing. Crankshaft should still be in position for firing No. 1 cylinder following valve adjustment. When distributor is pushed into place, rotor will point to mark on housing. *Fig. 4 and 5.*
3. Use new gaskets and rubber sealing rings.
4. When installing spark plug wires, firing order is 1-6-3-5-2-4.
5. Be sure to fill engine with oil and coolant. Retorque cylinder head bolts after assembly is completed.

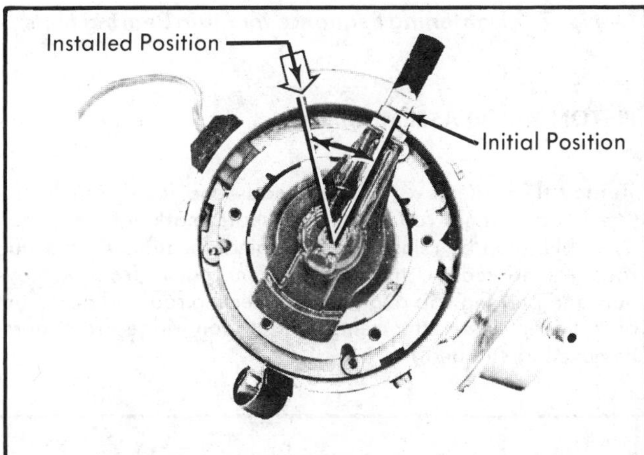

Fig. 4 Distributor Rotor Position Prior to Final Positioning

VALVES

VALVE ARRANGEMENT

Right Bank .... E-I-E-I-E-I (Front-to-Rear)
Left Bank .... I-E-I-E-I-E (Front-to-Rear)

ROCKER ARM ASSEMBLY

1) Mark rocker arm assemblies for right and left bank. Disassemble, keeping parts in same order as removed from shaft. Shaft-to-arm clearance should be .00047-.00213" (.012-.054 mm). Shaft diameter (new) is .7858-.7866" (19.96-19.98 mm). Replace parts as necessary.

2) Install rocker shaft support on shaft with lubricating holes downward and flat top surface of support pointing toward ring groove end of shaft. Tighten lock bolt. Install thick spacer, exhaust valve arm, thin spacer, intake valve arm, spring and rocker arm support in order. After installing three such sets, install lock ring in shaft groove.

VALVE STEM OIL SEALS AND VALVE SPRINGS

With cylinder head removed from engine, remove spark plugs, injectors, rear cover plate, lock fork and camshaft. Using valve spring compressor, remove valve collets, spring retainer, spring, lower spring seat and valve. Remove valve guide seal from guide. Place valves in order in suitable rack.

VALVE GUIDE SERVICING

1) Check valve guides for wear. If replacement is necessary, press out old guide using drift (2818). Ream hole in cylinder head to oversize class 1 or 2:

Valve Guide Specifications

Application	Diameter In. (mm)
Cylinder Head Hole, Class 1	.5193-.5209 (13.19-13.23)
Cylinder Head Hole, Class 2	.5311-.5327 (13.49-13.53)
Valve Guide, Class 1	①.5228-.5232 (13.28-13.29)
Valve Guide Class 2	①.5346-.5350 (13.58-13.59)

① — Oversize Valve Guides Shown

2) Using drifts (5108 for intake; 5109 for exhaust), press in new guides. Ream guides to .3150-.3158" (8.00-8.02 mm). Check for burrs and be sure valves move freely in guides.

RECONDITIONING VALVES

After inspection, grind valves, mill or grind valve seats, and lap valves with grinding paste, as necessary. Check valve springs for proper length and tension. Install seals, valves, spring seats, spring, and spring retainers. Compress spring and install collets. Remove tool, and reinstall all parts previously removed from cylinder head.

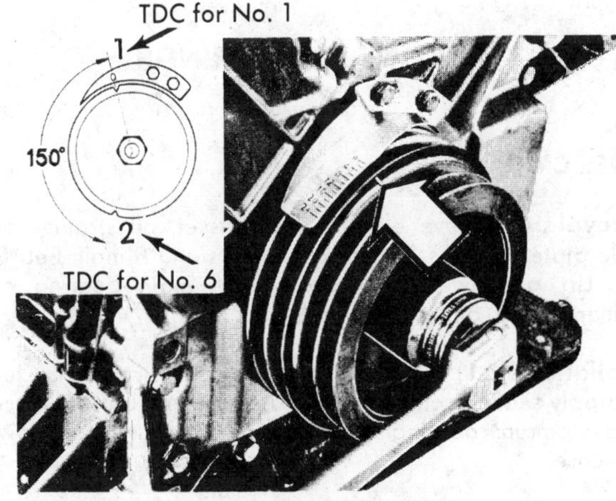

Fig. 5 Adjusting Crankshaft to Firing Position for No. 1 Cylinder

VALVE CLEARANCE ADJUSTMENT

1) Rotate crankshaft to firing position for No. 1 cylinder. See *Fig.5.* In this position, both rocker arms should have clearance. Check and adjust the following cylinders for clearance: Intake

260 SERIES V6 (Cont.)

valves on cylinders 1, 2, and 4; exhaust valves on cylinders 1, 3, and 6 (White valves in *Fig.* 6).

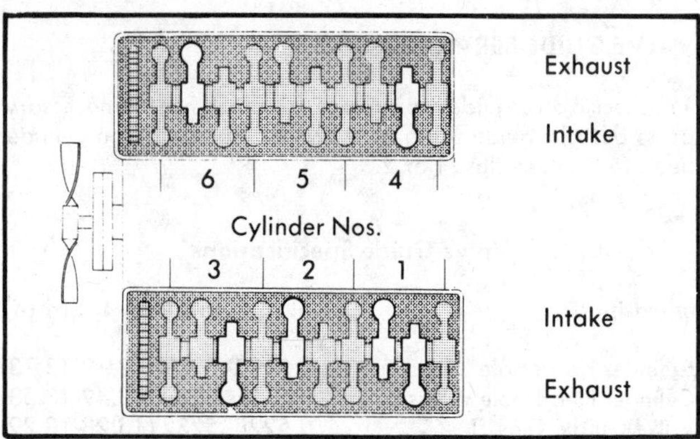

Fig. 6 Valve Clearance Adjustment Sequence

Valve Clearance Specifications①

Valve	In. (mm)
Intake	.004-.006 (.10-.15)
Exhaust	.010-.012 (.25-.30)

① – Specifications are for cold engine.

2) Rotate crankshaft one full turn so marking is again opposite 0° mark. Rocker arms for No. 1 cylinder will now rock. Check and adjust the following cylinders for clearance: Intake valves on cylinders 3, 5, and 6; exhaust valves on cylinders 2, 4, and 5 (Grey valves in *Fig.* 6).

PISTONS, PINS & RINGS

LOWER CRANKCASE

Removal – Remove oil pan and gasket, oil strainer and baffle plate. Remove 14 crankcase bolts and 8 main bearing nuts. Lift off lower crankcase. Install main bearing cap retainers (5096) on two outer bearings.

Installation – **1)** Install rubber ring for oil channel. Clean and apply sealing compound to crankcase and block surfaces. Remove main bearing cap retainers and install lower crankcase.

2) Be sure crankcase and block are flush at rear end, and tighten main bearing nuts to 22 ft. lbs. torque. Use sequence shown in *Fig.* 7. Then back off No. 1 nut and retorque to 22-25 ft. lbs. Using a protractor tool (5098), tighten nut an additional 73-77°. Continue in sequence retorquing one nut at a time.

3) Tighten 14 lower crankcase bolts to 11-15 ft. lbs. Install baffle plate, oil strainer, gasket and oil pan.

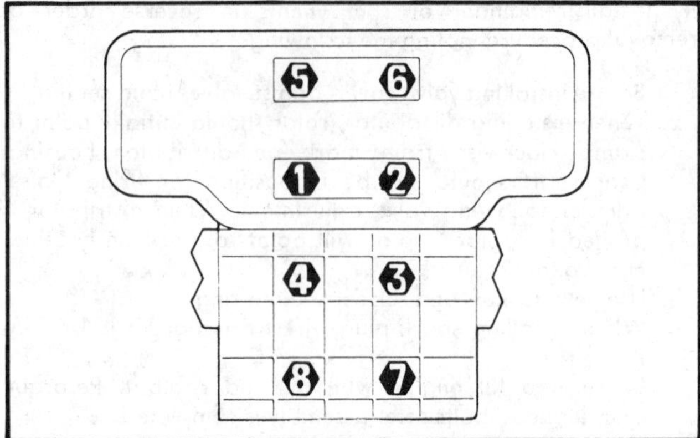

Fig. 7 Tightening Sequence for Main Bearing Nuts

PISTON & ROD ASSEMBLIES

Removal – Remove cylinder heads and lower crankcase. Check connecting rod and crankshaft markings so piston assemblies can be reinstalled in original location. Connecting rods are marked "A" through "F" from rear to front. Remove nuts and bearing cap and press connecting rod and piston out of cylinder liner after removing carbon ridge from bore. Remove big-end bearing.

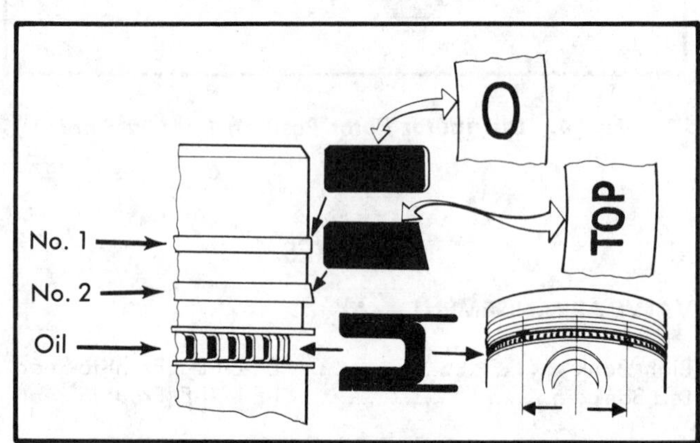

Fig. 8 Piston Ring Location & Markings

Installation – Install piston & rod assemblies one cylinder at a time. Connecting rods and caps are marked "A" through "F" from rear to front for cylinders 1-4-2-5-3-6. Adjust rings so end gaps are not aligned. Oil rings and install piston with arrow marking on top pointing toward front of engine. Using installation tool (5106) press piston into liner. Install connecting rod cap after oiling the bearing. Tighten cap to 33-37 ft. lbs.

PISTONS AND LINERS

1) Pistons and liners are matched. Pistons are marked "A", "B", or "C" according to diameter and correspond to liners "1", "2", or "3" (marked in recesses at top of liners). Pistons and piston pins are also marked blue, white or red for proper matching.

260 SERIES V6 (Cont.)

2) Two types of pistons are used, Demolin (overall height 2.695" or 68.45 mm) and Mahle (overall height of 2.474" or 62.85 mm). Measure piston diameter at right angles to pin bore. Measure Demolin pistons .433" (11 mm) above lower edge of piston; Mahle pistons .236" (6 mm) above lower edge.

Piston and Liner Diameters①

Piston	In. (mm)
Demolin A	3.4610-3.4614 (87.910-87.920)
Demolin B	3.4617-3.4618 (87.928-87.930)
Demolin C	3.4618-3.4622 (87.930-87.940)
Mahle A	3.4634-3.4638 (87.970-87.980)
Mahle B	3.4638-3.4642 (87.980-87.990)
Mahle C	3.4642-3.4646 (87.990-88.000)
Liner	**In. (mm)**
No. 1 for A Piston	3.4646-3.4650 (88.00-88.01)
No. 2 for B Piston	3.4650-3.4653 (88.01-88.02)
No. 3 for C Piston	3.4653-3.4657 (88.02-88.03)

① — Measurements for new parts.

3) To determine piston-to-cylinder clearance, subtract piston diameter from maximum and minimum bore diameters. Do not remove pistons from connecting rods, unless piston and liner replacement is necessary.

4) If liner is to be removed for cleaning or inspection, mark liner and block with colored pen. Do not damage gasket surface. Remove liner holders and pull up liners. When installing liners, be sure contact surfaces on block and liner are clean and without defect. Install No. 1 liner first (without shims) using previous pen markings for alignment. Tighten liner by hand, using two liner holders (5093). Using dial indicator, measure liner height above block at three points. Largest measurement should not exceed smallest measurement by more than .002" (.05 mm). Liner should be as close to .0091" (.23 mm) above block face as possible. Use correct shims to achieve dimension:

Liner Shim Thicknesses①

Color	Thickness - In. (mm)
Blue	.0028-.0041 (.070-.105)
White	.0033-.0047 (.085-.120)
Red	.0041-.0055 (.105-.140)
Yellow	.0051-.0065 (.130-.165)

① — Use same thickness shims for all liners.

5) Install shims with color marking up and positioned as shown in *Fig. 9*. Inner tabs on shims should be in liner groove.

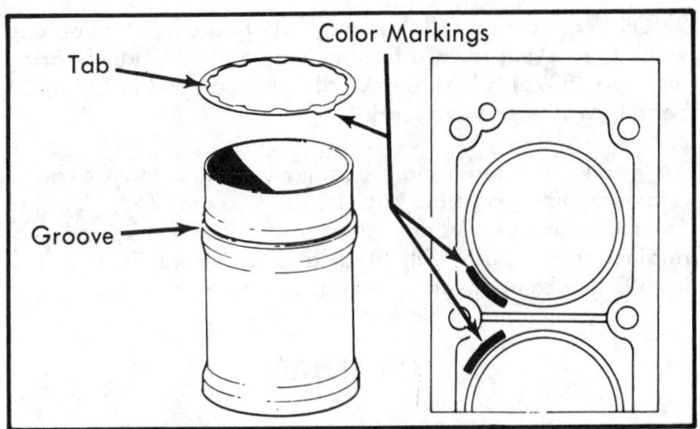

Fig. 9 Positioning Shims on Liners

6) After shimming, install four liner holders (5093) for each bank. Again measure each liner at three points. Largest and smallest dimensions should be within .002" (.05 mm). Measure three liners at points shown in *Fig. 10*. Difference in measurements between points "1" and "2" and between "3" and "4" should not exceed .0016" (.04 mm). If height difference is excessive, change shims.

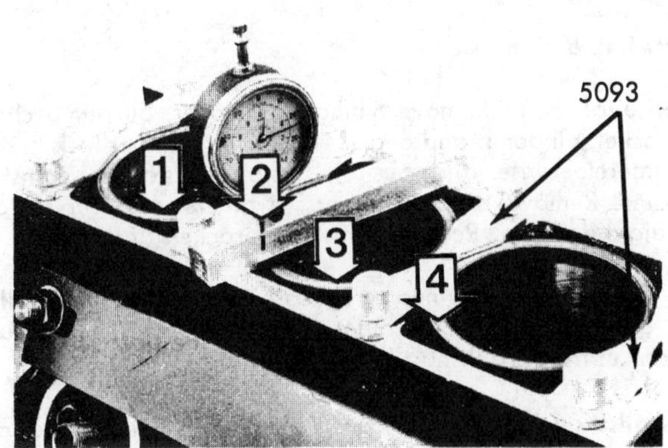

Fig. 10 Checking Liner Height Above Block Face

CRANKSHAFT MAIN & CONNECTING ROD BEARINGS

CRANKSHAFT

Removal — 1) Remove oil pan, lower crankcase, cylinder heads, clutch, drive plate or flywheel, spacer (automatic transmission) and input shaft pilot bearing (manual transmission). Remove seal holder and use drift (5107) to press out seal. Press new seal in flush with retainer.

2) Check main bearing cap markings (marked 1 through 4, from rear-to-front). Remove main bearing retainers and caps. Remove upper and lower thrust bearings and lift out crankshaft. Remove main bearings from block and caps.

Installation — 1) Oil and install main bearings (with lubricating holes) in block. Place crankshaft in block. Oil and install "hooked" thrust bearings in block groove. Oil and install "non-hooked" thrust bearings on crankshaft.

260 SERIES V6 (Cont.)

2) Oil bearing and install in main bearing cap. Position cap with "1" marking toward front of engine. Install main bearing retainers (5096). Check crankshaft end play and install thrust bearing washers as necessary.

3) Install other three main bearing caps and main bearing retainers (5096) on front cap. Install caps with "2", "3", and "4" marks toward front of engine. Position gasket on seal retainer, align flush with block and torque to 7-11 ft. lbs. Install other components previously removed.

CAMSHAFT

TIMING GEAR COVER

Removal – Remove both valve covers, lock flywheel (5112), and remove crankshaft nut. Remove pulley while key is on top of shaft (prevents dropping key in crankcase). Use puller (5069) to remove crankshaft seal. Remove timing gear cover.

Installation – Clean surfaces and place gaskets on block and timing gear cover. Install cover and tighten bolts to 7-11 ft. lbs. Install crankshaft seal (drift 5103). Block flywheel with locking tool (5112), install pulley and tighten crankshaft nut to 118-132 ft. lbs.

CHAINS & SPROCKETS

Removal – **1)** Remove timing gear cover, oil pump chain, sprocket, oil pump and gears. Turn each tensioner lock ¼ turn counterclockwise and push in piston to slacken camshaft chains. Remove both tensioners, strainers, and curved and straight dampers. Remove camshaft sprockets and chains.

2) Stuff rag in holes near crankcase to keep key from falling in crankcase. Remove outer sprocket and inner double sprocket from crankshaft (either by hand or with puller).

Installation – **1)** Place key in crankshaft. Oil sprocket and shaft. Install double sprocket (drift 4028) with mark outward. Install spacer ring and outer key. Install oil pump sprocket, strainers and chain tensioners, and curved and straight dampers.

2) Rotate crankshaft so key aligns with camshaft in left bank (No. 1 cylinder at TDC). Position camshaft so key points upward (rocker arms for No. 1 cylinder rock). Place chain on camshaft sprocket so that link between two white lines is centered over camshaft sprocket timing mark. Place chain on inner crankshaft sprocket so timing mark on sprocket is aligned with white mark on chain. Install left camshaft sprocket onto camshaft so that pin on sprocket slips into recess in camshaft. Chain should be stretched on tension side. Use screwdriver to hold sprocket and tighten center bolt to 51-59 ft. lbs.

3) Rotate crankshaft clockwise 150° so that key points straight downward. Set right camshaft so keyway is in position shown in *Fig. 11*. Place chain on sprocket so link between white lines on chain aligns with sprocket timing mark. Place chain on crankshaft center sprocket so that chain and sprocket timing marks align. Fit sprocket on camshaft with chain stretched on tension side. Pin on sprocket should slip into camshaft recess. Use screwdriver to hold sprocket and torque center bolt to 51-59 ft. lbs.

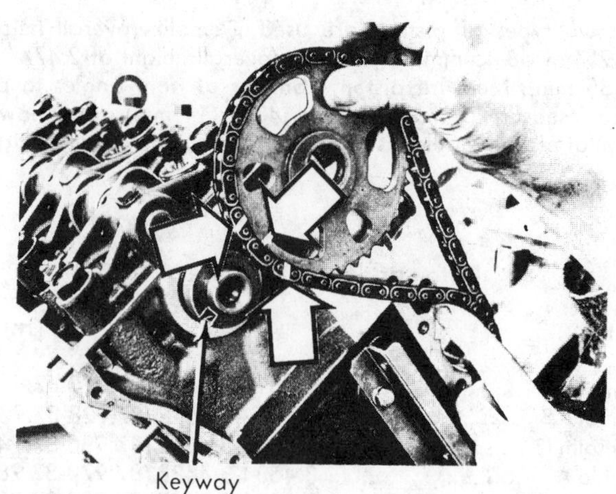

Fig. 11 Right Camshaft Keyway and Timing Marks

4) Turn lock on each chain tensioner ¼ turn clockwise. Tension chains by rotating crankshaft 2 full turns in direction of rotation (clockwise). Remove crankshaft nut. Markings on chains and sprockets will no longer align. Reassemble oil pump, install chain and chain sprocket. Install timing gear cover after removing rag from crankcase holes.

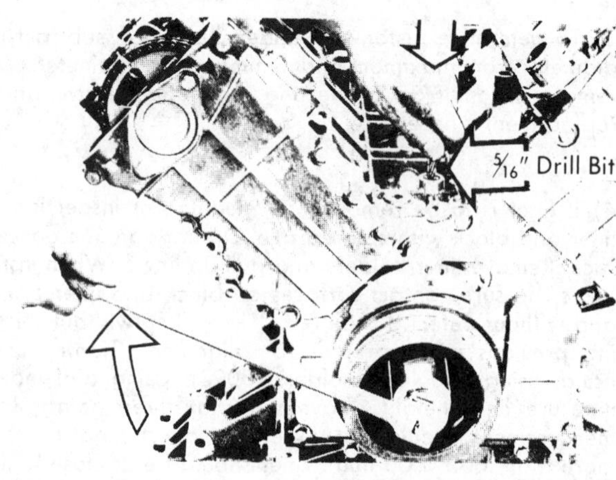

Fig. 12 Locating Top Dead Center for No. 1 Cylinder

IGNITION TIMING PLATE

1) Rotate crankshaft so that mark No. 1 (*See Fig. 5*) is at 20° mark on ignition timing plate. Remove plug and insert 5/16" drill bit or similar rod into hole and against crankshaft counterweight, *See Fig. 12.* Rotate crankshaft in direction of rotation until drill bit can be pressed into recess in counterweight (TDC for No. 1 cylinder).

NOTE – *Do not drop drill bit into engine. Use drill or pin up to 10" long.*

260 SERIES V6 (Cont.)

2) Loosen two bolts and adjust ignition timing plate so that "0" mark is aligned with pulley mark. Tighten two bolts, remove drill bit or rod and install plug. Check camshaft setting. Valve clearance should be .28" (.7 mm). Intake valve should open at:

Intake Valve Opening

Valve	Crankshaft Degrees
Left bank	9°±3°BTDC
Right bank	7°±3°BTDC

ENGINE OILING

Crankcase Capacity — 7.4 quarts including filter.

Oil Filter — Full-flow type, disposable spin-on element.

Oil Pressure — 26 psi @900 RPM; 58 psi @3000 RPM with engine warm and new filter.

ENGINE OILING SYSTEM

Engine utilizes a force-feed lubrication system. Oil moves from oil pan through strainer to oil pump and full-flow oil filter mounted outside of engine block assembly. Oil is pressure fed from filter to drilled galleries in block.

Lubricant moves under pressure to main bearings, which are drilled to pass oil on to connecting rod and camshaft bearings, upward in block to rocker arm shafts. Excess or rι off oil drains back down into oil pan through drain holes in cylinder head. Cylinder walls and piston rings are lubricated by splash from connecting rods.

OIL PUMP

Removal & Installation — **1)** See *Chains and Sprockets.* Inspect housing, cover and gears for damage or wear. Replace if necessary.

2) Oil pumps are serviced as complete units (pump cover with impeller and relief valve).

Oil Pump Specifications ①

Application	Dimension In. (mm)
Pump Gear Width, Class 1	1.2167-1.2175 (30.905-30.925)
Pump Gear Width, Class 11	1.2175-1.2183 (30.925-30.945)
Pump Housing Width, Class 1	1.2185-1.2195 (30.950-30.975)
Pump Housing Width, Class 11	1.2195-1.2209 (30.975-31.010)
End Play	.0010-.0033 (.025-.084)
Clearance (Tooth-to-Housing)	①.0043-.0073 (.11-.185)
Backlash	①.0067-.0106 (.17-.27)
Bearing Clearance, Driving Shaft	.0006-.0021 (.015-.053)
Bearing Clearance, Trailing Shaft	.0006-.0020 (.015-.051)
Relief Valve Spring Length, No Load	3.52 (89.5)
Relief Valve Spring Length, 19.8 lbs.	2.22-2.38 (56.5-60.5)

① — Excluding bearing clearance.

ENGINE COOLING

Thermostat — Wax-type. Begins to open at 176-181° F (80-83° C); fully open at 194-201° F (90-94° C). Marking, 180° F (82° C).

Cooling System Capacity — 12 quarts (10.0 liters).

Radiator Cap — 9-12 psi.

WATER PUMP

1) Drain coolant from both sides of block. Remove intake manifold, two expansion tank hoses from radiator, upper radiator hose and automatic transmission oil cooler pipes. Remove fan shroud, radiator and fan.

2) Remove hoses from pump to block. Remove fan belts, water pump pulley, and remaining hose clamps. Remove senders from water pump, and pump from block. Remove cover and thermostat and cover from body. Install in reverse order.

ENGINE SPECIFICATIONS

GENERAL SPECIFICATIONS

Year	Displ.		Carburetor	HP at RPM	Torque (Ft. Lbs. at RPM)	Compr. Ratio	Bore		Stroke	
	cu. ins.	cc					in.	mm	in.	mm
1977 B27F										
Federal	162.3	2660	F.I.	125@5500	150@2750	8.2-1	3.4646	88	2.8740	73
Calif.	162.3	2660	F.I.	121@5500	148@2750	8.2-1	3.4646	88	2.8740	73

260 SERIES V6 (Cont.)

ENGINE SPECIFICATIONS (Cont.)

VALVES							
Engine & Valve	Head Diam. In. (mm)	Face Angle	Seat Angle	Seat Width In. (mm)	① Stem Diameter In. (mm)	① Stem Clearance In. (mm)	② Valve Lift In. (mm)
B27F							
Intake	1.73 (44)	30°	30°	.067-.083 (1.7-2.1)	.3140-.3146 (7.97-7.99)	.0004-.0018 (.010-.046)	LB .327 (8.3)
Exhaust	1.46 (37)	30°	30°	.079-.094 (2.0-2.4)	.3136-.3142 (7.96-7.98)	.0008-.0022 (.020-.056)	RB .321 (8.1)

① — Stem diameter gets larger from disc toward collet end of valve, where measurement above is taken.

② — Exhaust and intake valves have same lift, but valves in right bank (RB) vary from those in left bank (LB).

PISTONS, PINS, RINGS						
	PISTONS	PINS		RINGS		
Engine	Clearance In. (mm)	Piston Fit In. (mm)	Rod Fit In. (mm)	Rings	End Gap In. (mm)	Side Clearance In. (mm)
B27F	Demolin .0035-.0043 (.090-.110)	Push Fit .0005-.0008 (.013-.020)	Press Fit .0008-.0016 (.020-.041)	Comp. 1	.016-.022 (.40-.55)	.0018-.0029 (.045-.074)
				Comp. 2	.016-.022 (.40-.55)	.0010-.0021 (.025-.054)
	Mahle .0008-.0016 (.020-.040)	Push Fit .0004-.0006 (.010-.015)	Press Fit .0008-.0016 (.020-.041)	Oil	.015-.055 (.38-1.4)	.0004.0092 (.009-.233)

CRANKSHAFT MAIN & CONNECTING ROD BEARINGS							
	MAIN BEARINGS				CONNECTING ROD BEARINGS		
Engine	Journal Diam. In. (mm)	Clearance In. (mm)	Thrust Bearing	Crankshaft End Play In. (mm)	Journal Diam. In. (mm)	Clearance In. (mm)	Side Play In. (mm)
B27F	2.7576-2.7583 (70.043-70.062)	.0015-.0035 (.038-.088)	.....	.0028-.0106 (.070-.270)	2.0578-2.0585 (52.267-52.286)	.0012-.0031 (.030-.080)	.008-.015 (.20-.38)

CAMSHAFT			
Engine	Journal Diam. In. (mm)	Clearance In. (mm)	Lobe Lift In. (mm)
B27F			
Front	1.5921-1.5931 (40.440-40.465)	①.0014-.0033 (.035-.085)	.....
2nd	1.6157-1.6173 (41.040-41.065)		
3rd	1.6394-1.6404 (41.640-41.665)		
4th	1.6630-1.6640 (42.240-42.265)		

① — End play should be .0028-.0057" (.070-.144 mm).

VALVE SPRINGS			
Engine	Free Length In. (mm)	PRESSURE Lbs. @ In. (kg @ mm)	
		Valve Closed	Valve Open
B27F	1.81 (47.2)	52-60@1.57 (24-27@40)	117-132@1.27 (53-60@32)

260 SERIES V6

ENGINE SPECIFICATIONS (Cont.)

TIGHTENING SPECIFICATIONS

Application	Ft. Lbs. (mkg)
Cylinder Head Bolts	
Step One	7 (1.0)
Step Two	22 (3.1)
Step Three	①44 (6.1)
Main Bearing Cap Nuts	②22-25 (3.1-3.5)
Connecting Rod Cap Nuts	33-37 (4.6-5.1)
Flywheel Bolts	33-37 (4.6-5.1)
Clutch-to-Flywheel Bolts	15-18 (2.1-2.5)
Camshaft Center Bolts	51-59 (7.1-8.2)
Crankshaft Pulley Nut	118-132 (16.3-18.3)
Alternator Attaching Bolts	29-37 (4.0-5.1)
Fan Hub	22-37 (3.1-5.1)
Spark Plugs	13-15 (1.8-2.1)
Oil Pressure Sensor	26-37 (3.6-5.1)
Temperature Sensor	18-22 (2.5-3.1)
Transmission-to-Engine	30-36 (4.2-5.0)
Front Engine Mounts	11-18 (1.5-2.5)
Oil Pan Plug	18-25 (2.5-3.5)
Exhaust & Intake Manifolds	7-11 (1.0-1.5)
Valve Covers	7-11 (1.0-1.5)
Water Pump-to-Block	11-15 (1.5-2.1)

① – After step 3, wait 10-15 minutes, slacken bolts and retorque to 11-14 ft. lbs. (1.5-1.9 mkg). Protractor torque to 116-120°. Run engine until hot and cool for 30 minutes. Slacken and retorque each individual bolt in stages again to 11-14 ft. lbs. (1.5-1.9 mkg) and protractor torque 113-117°.

② – Torque all nuts to 22 ft. lbs. (3.1 mkg). Slacken No. 1 nut, retorque to 22-25 ft. lbs. (3.1-3.5 mkg), and protractor torque 73-77°. Repeat procedure for other seven nuts in sequence.

Section 6

CLUTCHES

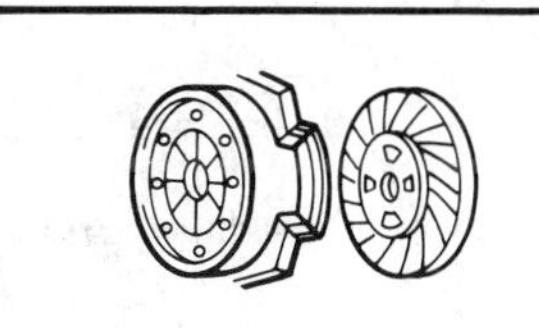

Contents

NOTE — ALSO SEE GENERAL INDEX

CLUTCH TROUBLE SHOOTING

CONDITION	POSSIBLE CAUSE	CORRECTION
▸ **Chattering or Grabbing**	1) Incorrect Lever Adjustment	1) Adjust Clutch
	2) Oil or Grease on Facings	2) Check for Oil Leaks
	3) Loose "U" Joint Flange	3) Check "U" Joint Flange and Tighten
	4) Worn Input Shaft Spline	4) Replace Shaft
	5) Binding Pressure Plate	5) Check for Binding, Replace as Necessary
	6) Binding Release Lever	6) Free Binding Levers or Replace
	7) Binding Disc Hub	7) Replace Disc and Adjust Clutch
	8) Glazed Facings	8) Replace Disc After Checking Pressure Plate and Flywheel for Scoring. Replace as Necessary
	9) Unequal Pressure Plate Contact	9) Check Release Lever Clearance, Disc Thickness, and Pressure Plate for Paralleism with Flywheel
	10) Bent Clutch Disc	10) Replace Clutch Disc
	11) Uneven Spring Pressure	11) Adjust Spring Tension
	12) Incorrect Transmission Alignment.	12) Check Clutch Housing Alignment
	13) Loose Facings	13) Replace Clutch Disc
	14) Scored Pressure Plate	14) Replace Pressure Plate if Warped More Than .015"
	15) Worn Pressure Plate, Disc or Flywheel	15) Replace When There are Signs of Excessive Wear, Heat Checking or Scoring
	16) Clutch Disc Hub Sticking on Shaft	16) Check Shaft for Excessive Wear or Burrs, Check Shaft for Distortion and Replace as Necessary
	17) Worn or Binding Release Levers	17) Replace Levers and Release Bearing
	18) Broken or Weak Pressure Springs	18) Replace Springs
	19) Sticking Clutch Pedal	19) Check for Worn or Misaligned Components
	20) Incorrect Disc Facing	20) Replace Clutch Disc
	21) Engine Loose in Chassis	21) Check Motor Mounts and Replace or Tighten
▸ **Spinning**	1) Dry or Worn Bushings	1) Replace Bushings
	2) Misaligned Clutch Housing	2) Check Clutch Housing Alignment
	3) Bent or Distorted Clutch Disc.	3) Replace Clutch Disc
	4) Warped Pressure Plate	4) Replace Pressure Plate
	5) Excessive Pedal Free Play	5) Readjust Pedal Free Play

CLUTCH TROUBLE SHOOTING

CONDITION	POSSIBLE CAUSE	CORRECTION
▸ Dragging	1) Oil or Grease on Facings	1) Free Release Levers
	2) Incorrect Lever Adjustment	2) Check for Damage and Readjust Lever
	3) Incorrect Pedal Adjustment	3) Adjust Pedal
	4) Dust or Dirt on Clutch	4) Disassemble Clutch and Clean Throughly
	5) Worn or Broken Facings	5) Replace Clutch Disc
	6) Bent Clutch Disc	6) Replace Clutch Disc, Check for Cause
	7) Clutch Disc Hub Binding on Shaft	7) Check Shaft for Burrs or Gummed Splines
	8) Binding Pilot Bushing	8) Replace Pilot Bushing
	9) Sticking Release Bearing Sleeve	9) Free Sleeve, Check for Scoring or Rough Spots
	10) Warped Pressure Plate	10) Replace Pressure Plate if Worn More Than .015″
▸ Rattling	1) Weak or Broken Release Lever Spring	1) Replace Spring
	2) Damaged Pressure Plate	2) Replace Pressure Plate and Adjust Clutch
	3) Broken Clutch Return Spring	3) Replace Return Spring
	4) Worn Splines in Clutch Disc Hub or Transmission Input Shaft	4) Replace Clutch Disc or Transmission Input Shaft
	5) Worn Clutch Release Bearings	5) Replace Release Bearing, Check Tips of Release Levers for Wear, Replace as Necessary
	6) Dry or Worn Pilot Bushing	6) Lubricate or Replace Pilot Bushing
	7) Unequal Release Lever Contact	7) Readjust Release Levers
	8) Incorrect Pedal Freeplay	8) Adjust Pedal Free Play
	9) Warped Clutch Disc	9) Replace Clutch Disc, Check Pressure Plate for Wear and Replace as Necessary
▸ Slipping	1) Pressure Springs Worn or Broken	1) Replace Springs
	2) Worn Facing	2) Replace Clutch Disc
	3) Incorrect Clutch Alignment	3) Adjust Clutch
	4) Oil or Grease on Facings	4) Replace Clutch Disc, Fix Oil Leaks
	5) Warped Clutch Disc	5) Replace Clutch Disc
	6) Warped or Scored Pressure Plate	6) Replace Pressure Plate if Scored, Heat Checked, or Warped More Than .015″, Test Spring Tension and Replace Clutch Disc
	7) Binding Release Levers	7) Free Release Lever
	8) Binding Clutch Pedal	8) Check for Worn or Misaligned Parts

CLUTCH TROUBLE SHOOTING

CONDITION	POSSIBLE CAUSE	CORRECTION
▸ **Squeaking**	1) No Lubrication in Release Bearing	1) Lubricate
	2) Worn Release Bearing	2) Replace Release Bearing
	3) Dry or Worn Pilot Bushing	3) Lubricate or Replace Pilot Bushing
	4) Pilot Bearing Turning in Crankshaft	4) Replace Pilot Bearing
	5) Worn Input Shaft Bearing	5) Replace Input Shaft Bearing
	6) Incorrect Transmission Alignment	6) Check Clutch Housing Alignment
	7) No Lubrication Between Clutch Fork and Pivot	7) Lubricate
	8) No Lubrication in Torque Shaft	8) Lubricate
▸ **Heavy, Stiff Pedal**	1) Dry or Binding Linkage Components	1) Lubricate Linkage Components
	2) Sticking Release Bearing Sleeve	2) Check Release Bearing Sleeve for Wear, Burrs or Roughness on Mating Surface
	3) Dry or Binding Pedal Hub	3) Replace Bushing or Bearings in Pedal Hub and Lubricate
	4) Pedal Interference With Floorboard or Mat	4) Check for Pedal Interference
	5) Rough, Dry or Binding Pivot Ball, or Fork Pivots	5) Lubricate All Moving Points
▸ **Grinding**	1) Dry Release Bearing	1) Replace Release Bearing
	2) Worn or Dry Pilot Bearing	2) Lubricate or Replace Release Bearing
	3) Worn Input Shaft Bearing	3) Replace Input Shaft Bearing
▸ **Whirring**	1) Incorrect Pedal Free Play	1) Adjust Pedal Free Play
	2) Incorrect Transmission Alignment	2) Check Clutch Housing Alignment

ARROW & COLT

Arrow
Colt

DESCRIPTION

Clutch is a diaphragm spring, single disc type. Operation is controlled mechanically by a cable. Clutch release bearing is sealed and permanently lubricated.

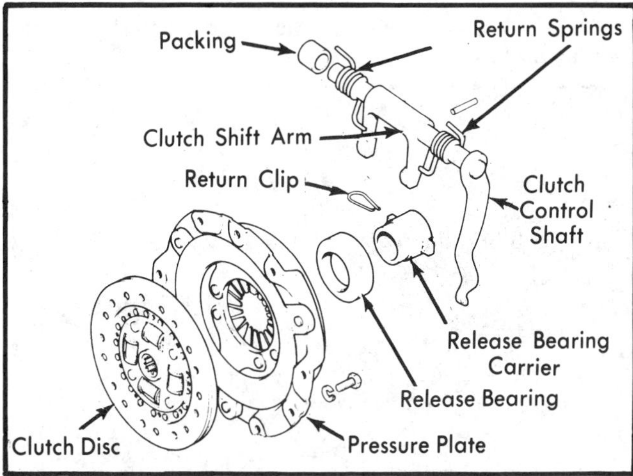

Fig. 1 Exploded View of Clutch Assembly

REMOVAL & INSTALLATION

CLUTCH ASSEMBLY

1) With battery disconnected, air cleaners removed and battery cables disconnected from starter, remove starter. Remove two bolts from top of transmission.

2) Inside vehicle, remove dust cover retaining plate and four bolts securing gearshift lever assembly to vehicle. **NOTE** — *Lever should be in 2nd gear on 4-speed transmission models and in 1st gear on 5-speed transmission models.*

3) With car raised and supported on jack stands, drain transmission fluid. Remove speedometer cable and electrical leads from transmission, then remove bolts from rear of propeller shaft and remove shaft from transmission.

4) Disconnect exhaust system from brackets, then disconnect clutch cables. With transmission supported by a jack, remove insulators from crossmembers by removing attaching bolts. **NOTE** — *Jack should be placed under transmission oil pan, making sure support area is as wide as possible.*

5) Remove each crossmember from frame by pulling off sideways. Remove clutch inspection cover, then remove remaining transmission to engine attaching bolts. Pull transmission to rear and remove from vehicle. **NOTE** — *Use care not to twist front end of main drive gear.*

6) Insert a suitable clutch centering tool (MD998017) into center of clutch to prevent clutch disc from falling. Loosen clutch attaching bolts alternately and evenly until pressure plate can be removed. Remove pressure plate and clutch disc.

7) To install, reverse removal procedure and note the following: Use a suitable clutch centering tool (MD998017) to center clutch disc on flywheel. Adjust clutch cable and clutch pedal.

CLUTCH CABLE

Removal — Loosen cable adjusting wheel inside engine compartment, then loosen clutch pedal lock nut. Remove clutch cable from pedal lever, then remove cable from clutch shift lever and remove.

Installation — To install clutch cable, reverse removal procedure and note the following: Apply engine oil as necessary to install cable. On 2000 cc models, install pads at battery cable area of starter and at rear of engine front insulator. On 1600 cc models, pads are installed at alternator side and at side of engine front support insulator.

CLUTCH RELEASE BEARING & SHIFT ARM

Removal — With transmission removed, remove return clip on transmission side, then slide off release bearing carrier and release bearing. Using a 3/16" punch, remove shift arm spring pin and control lever assembly, then remove the shift arm and return springs.

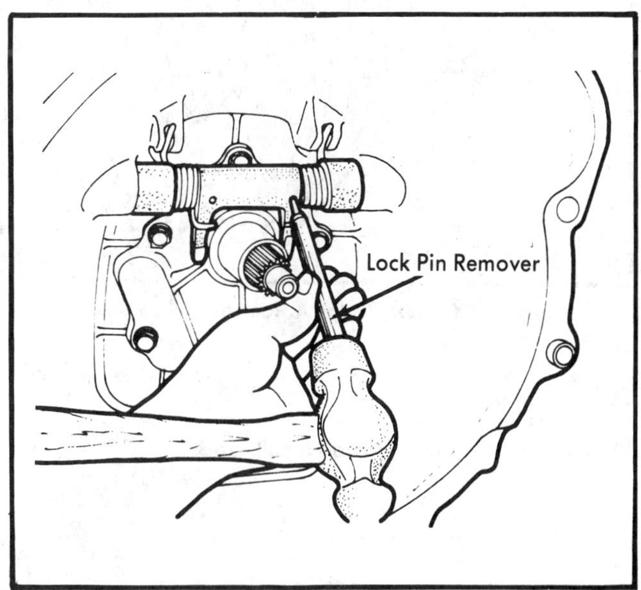

Fig. 2 Using a 3/16" Punch to Remove Shift Arm Spring Pin

Installation — 1) Insert lever and shaft into transmission case from left side.

2) Install onto shaft:
- Shift arm
- 2 felt packings
- Return springs

3) Apply grease to inside of bushing. Oil seal lips.

4) Oil felt packings.

5) Drive in 2 shift arm springs pins. Face spring pin slots UP. *See Fig. 2.*

ARROW & COLT (Cont.)

ADJUSTMENT

PEDAL ADJUSTMENT

1) Move pedal adjusting bolt *(See Fig. 3)* until distance between toe board and top face of clutch pedal is 6.5-6.7" (165-170 mm).

2) Make sure pedal stroke is at least:
- 5.9" (170 mm) Coupe, Hatchback, and Sedan
- 5.1" (130 mm) Hardtop and Station Wagon

NOTE – *Make sure height difference between clutch pedal and brake pedal is not more than .4" (10 mm).*

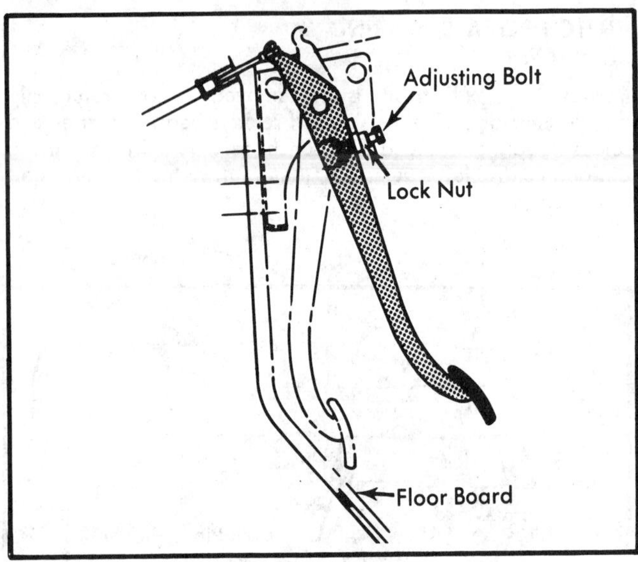

Fig. 3 Clutch Pedal Adjustment Procedure

CLUTCH CABLE

1) Pull outer cable from holder at bulkhead.

2) Set cable-to-adjuster wheel clearance to .20-.24" (5-6 mm). *See Fig. 4.*

NOTE – *One full turn of adjuster wheel will change clearance approximately .06" (1.5 mm).*

3) Check that pedal free play is 0.8-1.4" (20-35 mm).

4) Make sure distance between floor board and clutch pedal (in released position) is 1.4" (35 mm).

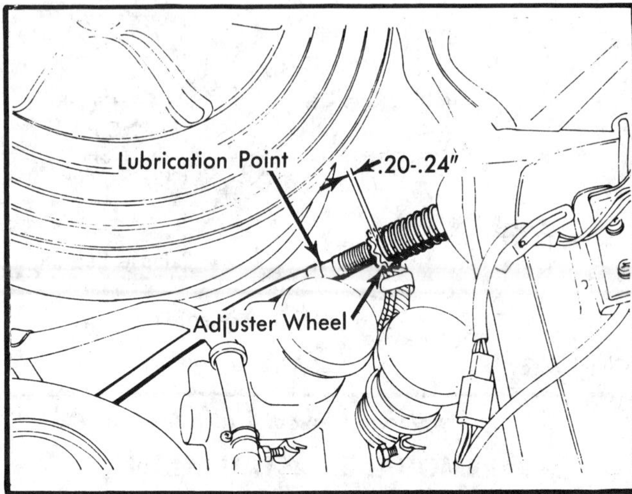

Fig. 4 Clutch Cable Adjustment Procedure and Lubricant Point

TIGHTENING SPECIFICATIONS

Application	Ft. Lbs. (mkg)
Transmission-to-Engine	22-30 (3.0-4.15)
Transmission-to-Engine Flange Bolts	32-39 (4.4-5.4)
Starter Bolts	16-23 (2.2-3.2)

AUDI 100LS

100LS

DESCRIPTION

Clutch is of the single plate dry disc type, using a diaphragm type pressure plate and a pre-lubricated clutch release bearing. Clutch is cable actuated.

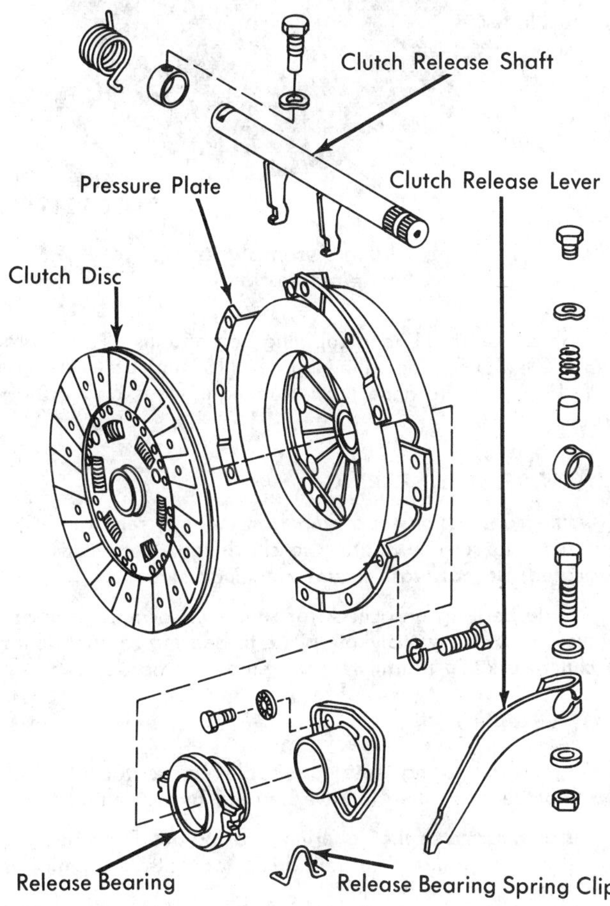

Fig. 1 Exploded View of Audi 100LS Clutch Assembly

REMOVAL & INSTALLATION

CLUTCH ASSEMBLY

1) Remove engine and transmission assembly from vehicle. *See Audi Engine Removal in ENGINE Section.* Separate transmission from engine.

2) Mark all parts for reassembly reference, then remove clutch attaching bolts and clutch assembly. To install, reverse removal procedure and note the following: Use a suitable centering tool (Ku-2) to center clutch disc when installing clutch assembly. Tighten all bolts evenly.

CLUTCH CABLE

1) Remove lower dash panel to gain access to clutch pedal assembly. In engine compartment, loosen adjusting nuts and lift cable out of mounting. Disconnect threaded eyelet from hook at clutch pedal, then remove eyelet and nut from pedal end of cable.

2) Remove cable from engine compartment side. To install, reverse removal procedure and note the following: Position clutch lever so that distance between edge of cable mount and hook portion of lever is 6.3". Adjust clutch pedal free play. See *Pedal Free Play*.

CLUTCH RELEASE BEARING

1) With transmission separated from engine, remove clips securing release bearing to clutch fork. Rotate bearing and check for roughness or noise. **NOTE** — *Bearing is pre-lubricated and should not be washed in any cleaning solution.*

2) To install, reverse removal procedure, making sure that clips engage cut-outs in back side of release shaft arms. Apply Molykote paste to bearing contact points on clutch fork.

PILOT BEARING

1) Bearing is needle roller type and is pressed into flywheel end of crankshaft. Rotate bearing and check for roughness or noise. If defective, remove using a suitable puller.

2) Lubricate new bearing when driving in. Drive bearing in so that flat side with lettering is facing out.

ADJUSTMENT

PEDAL FREE PLAY

With upper and lower adjusting nuts loose, tighten upper nut until clutch pedal free travel is .6-.8". Tighten lower adjusting nut to secure adjustment, then check operation of clutch assembly.

TIGHTENING SPECIFICATIONS

Application	Ft. Lbs. (mkg)
Clutch Assembly-to-Flywheel	25-28 (3.5-3.9)
Clutch Lever Pinch Bolt	10 (1.4)
Transmission-to-Engine	
12 mm Bolts	54 (7.5)
10 mm Bolts	33 (4.6)
8 mm Bolts	18 (2.5)

AUDI FOX

Fox

DESCRIPTION

Clutch is single plate dry disc type, using a diaphragm type pressure plate and a pre-lubricated clutch release bearing. Clutch is cable actuated.

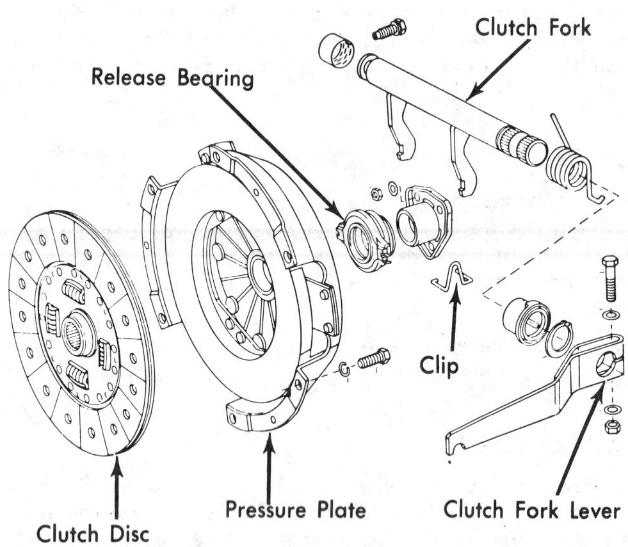

Fig. 1 Exploded View of Clutch Assembly

REMOVAL & INSTALLATION

CLUTCH ASSEMBLY

Removal – 1) Disconnect battery ground strap. Disconnect exhaust pipe from transaxle bracket and engine. Remove square bolt and push shifter assembly coupling from rear of transmission shifting shaft. Unhook clutch cable and disconnect speedometer cable.

2) Disconnect CV joints at inner drive flanges. Remove starter, front mounting plate, and transaxle mounting bolts. Disconnect back-up light wires. Support transaxle away from engine and lower out of vehicle.

Installation – 1) Place clutch disc on suitable aligning tool and insert tool into guide bearing in end of crankshaft. Bolt pressure plate to flywheel, making sure that three dowel pins in flywheel engage appropriate holes in pressure plate. Tighten mounting bolts in steps before final torque.

2) Install crossmember to transaxle. Raise transaxle and fit crossmember bolts (do not tighten). Slide transaxle up to engine and install mounting bolts. Install front mounting plate and starter. Install CV joint Allen screws and tighten. Now, tighten crossmember mounting bolts.

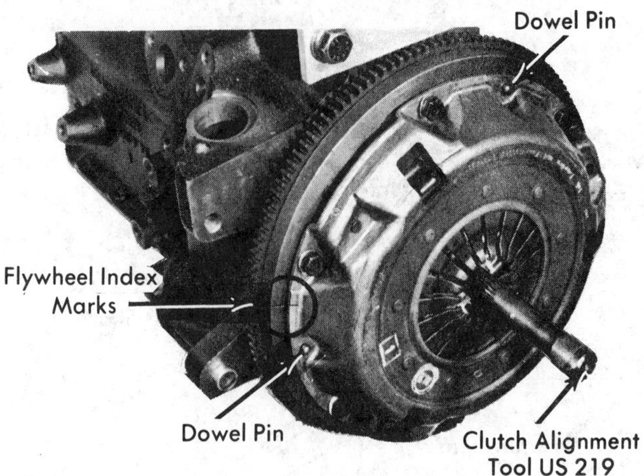

Fig. 2 Aligning Clutch Assembly Reference Marks for Reinstallation

3) Tighten square headed coupling bolt and install lock wire. Connect exhaust pipe, allowing 3/8' (10 mm) between pipe and floor pan. Reconnect back-up light wires and battery ground strap.

CLUTCH RELEASE BEARING

1) With transmission separated from engine, remove spring clips securing release bearing to clutch fork. Bearing is pre-lubricated; do not wash in any cleaning solution.

2) Rotate bearing and check for roughness or noise, replace as necessary. Apply Molykote paste to bearing contact points on clutch fork. To install, reverse removal procedure.

PILOT BEARING

1) To remove bearing, install a suitable remover tool (10-202) into pilot bearing, then remove bearing by tightening tool.

2) Install bearing so that lettering is facing out. Drive bearing into crankshaft using a suitable driver tool (US 219) until it is flush, then lubricate bearing.

ADJUSTMENT

CLUTCH PEDAL FREE PLAY

To obtain correct free play between clutch release bearing and clutch, clutch pedal free play must be correct. Free play can be adjusted by loosening and adjusting both counternuts at clutch cable to obtain .590" (15 mm) free play at pedal.

TIGHTENING SPECIFICATIONS

Application	Ft. Lbs. (mkg)
Clutch Assembly-to-Flywheel	18 (2.5)
Transmission-to-Engine	40 (5.5)
Clutch Lever-to-Transmission	12-18 (1.7-2.5)
Drive Shaft-to-Transmission	25.5 (3.5)

BMW

320i
530i
630CSi

DESCRIPTION

BMW clutch system consists of the following major components:

- Dry, single plate disc
- Diaphragm spring pressure plate
- Pre-lubricated clutch release bearing with release lever

Clutch is hydraulically operated. Clutch master cylinder is mounted to fire wall and provides hydraulic fluid to slave cylinder. Slave cylinder is mounted off the clutch housing. Release portion of system is self-adjusting. Pedal travel is the only adjustment that may have to be made.

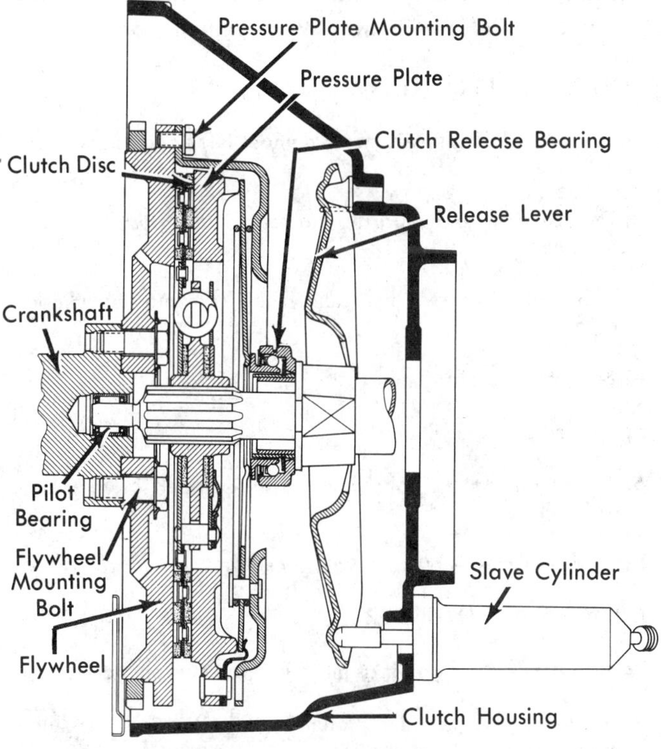

Fig. 1 Sectional View of Clutch Assembly for Part Identification and Component Relationship (630CSi Shown; 320i and 530i Similar)

REMOVAL & INSTALLATION

CLUTCH ASSEMBLY

Removal, 320i – 1) Remove console.

2) Disengage circlip, remove washer, and pull out gear shift selector rod. Gear shift lever will remain in vehicle.

3) Remove all upper clutch housing mounting bolts.

4) Remove exhaust pipe support bracket. Separate exhaust pipe at manifold.

5) Remove bolts mounting propeller shaft to transmission.

NOTE – *Coupling remains on propeller shaft.*

6) Remove heat shield. Separate center support bearing. Maneuver propeller shaft downward and pull it from center support journal. Place shaft out of way.

7) Disconnect speedometer cable.

8) Disconnect back-up light wires. Separate wiring harness from mounting clips.

9) Remove 2 clutch slave cylinder bolts and hydraulic line mounting bracket (located on clutch housing).

10) Remove flywheel inspection cover.

11) Place support under engine and an adjustable jack under transmission.

12) Unbolt remaining clutch housing bolts. Slide transmission rearward until free.

13) Retain flywheel. Loosen clutch assembly mounting bolts alternately and evenly. Remove clutch assembly.

Installation – Make the following notes during installation:

- Slide clutch disc into place. Fit pressure plate over flywheel dowels.
- Center clutch assembly with alignment tool 21 2 100 (or equivalent).
- Tighten mounting bolts evenly.
- Make sure exhaust pipe support bracket is loose when pipe-to-manifold nuts are tightened.
- Preload center bearing on propeller shaft by moving bracket .078" (2 mm) forward. Slots are provided for adjustment.
- Slave cylinder bleed screw must face down.

Removal, 530i & 630CSi – 1) From under vehicle, remove circlip and washer from selector rod. Disengage rod from control arm.

2) Remove any exhaust system parts that may interfere with transmission removal.

3) Separate propeller shaft from transmission.

NOTE – *Special propeller shaft coupler (Guido) stays on propeller shaft.*

4) Remove heat shield.

5) Remove center support bearing.

6) Maneuver propeller shaft out of center bearing housing and place out of way.

7) Support engine. Place an adjustable jack under transmission.

8) Disconnect speedometer from transmission.

9) Remove 2 crossmember-to-body nuts and bolts. Slightly lower transmission.

10) Separate clip on clutch housing. Clip is bolted to driver's side.

BMW (Cont.)

11) Remove slave cylinder. Hydraulic line does not have to be disconnected.

12) Disconnect brake back-up light wires.

13) Remove bolts holding transmission-to-engine. Slide transmission back until clear, then remove from vehicle.

14) Remove clutch housing mounting bolts. Take off flywheel inspection cover. Slide clutch housing off.

15) Retain flywheel from rotating. Loosen pressure plate mounting bolts alternately and evenly. Slide out clutch assembly.

Installation – Note the following when reinstalling transmission and clutch assembly:
- Place pressure plate over dowels. Center entire clutch assembly on flywheel using tool 21 2 100 (or equivalent).
- Temporarily fit slave cylinder. Face cylinder face down.
- Align release lever and slave cylinder.
- Fill lubricating groove in release bearing with Molykote BR 2-750 (or equivalent).
- Make sure transmission is in gear before inserting into clutch assembly.
- Carefully slide transmission guide sleeve into release bearing and clutch assembly.
- Rotate output flange until input shaft is fitted into clutch.
- Remove slave cylinder.
- Tighten transmission mounting bolts.

NOTE – *Remaining components are installed in reverse of removal procedure with following notes:*
- Tighten from nut side when installing propeller shaft.
- Preload center bearing by sliding bracket .078" (2 mm) forward. Adjustment slots are provided.

RELEASE BEARING & RELEASE BEARING LEVER

Removal – **1)** Remove transmission.

2) On 320i models, remove clutch housing.

3) Remove spring clip from mounting holes in clutch housing.

4) Slide off release lever and separate lever from bearing.

Inspection – Measure bearing at points "A" and "B". *See Fig. 2.* Refer to table for correct dimensions. If bearing is not within specifications it must be replaced.

Clutch Release Bearing Dimensions

Application	Spec. "A"	Spec. "B"
All Models①	2.067±.016" (52.5±.4 mm)	1.00±.010" (25.5±.25 mm)

① – Specification "B" does not apply to model 530i.

Installation – To install, reverse removal procedure.

Fig. 2 Release Bearing Measurement Locations

CLUTCH MASTER CYLINDER

Removal – **1)** Remove trim from under left side of instrument panel.

2) Remove bolt and separate master cylinder push rod from clutch pedal.

3) Siphon off most of hydraulic fluid from master cylinder reservoir.

4) Separate reservoir line.

5) Separate slave cylinder line.

6) Remove mounting bolts. Pull master cylinder forward and out of vehicle.

Installation – Reverse removal procedure.

CLUTCH SLAVE CYLINDER

Removal – **1)** Siphon off as much hydraulic as possible.

2) Remove slave cylinder mounting bolts located on clutch housing.

3) Once slave cylinder is pulled back, disconnect hydraulic line.

Installation – Reverse removal procedure and note:
- Bleed screw faces DOWN.
- Push rod must be coated with Molykote 2 (or equivalent).
- Bleed hydraulic system.

OVERHAUL

CLUTCH MASTER CYLINDER

Disassembly – **1)** Remove push rod, if necessary.

2) Side back dust boot.

3) Remove circlip.

4) Extract internal components.

BMW (Cont.)

Cleaning & Inspection – **1)** Clean all internal components with alcohol.

2) If master cylinder bore is badly scored or has excessive corrosion, replace cylinder.

Reassembly – **1)** Replace following parts with new ones provided in overhaul kit:
- Cap
- Circlip
- Seals
- Seal Plug
- Plain Washer
- Dust Boot

2) Insert master cylinder push rod and adjust length to approximately 5.5" (140 mm). *See Fig. 3.*

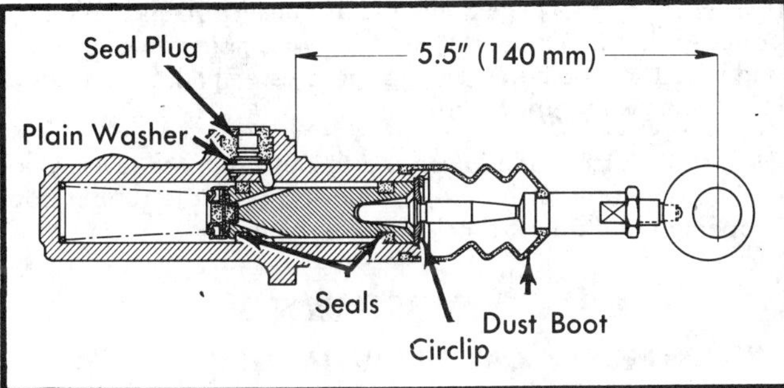

Fig. 3 Sectional View of Clutch Master Cylinder

CLUTCH SLAVE CYLINDER

Disassembly – **1)** Remove push rod.

2) Remove retainer ring.

3) Tip slave cylinder in a manner that will allow internal components to fall out.

Cleaning & Inspection – **1)** Clean all internal components with alcohol.

2) If slave cylinder bore is badly scored or has excessive corrosion, replace cylinder.

Reassembly – Replace following parts with new ones provided in overhaul kit:
- Retainer ring
- Dust Cap
- Sleeve

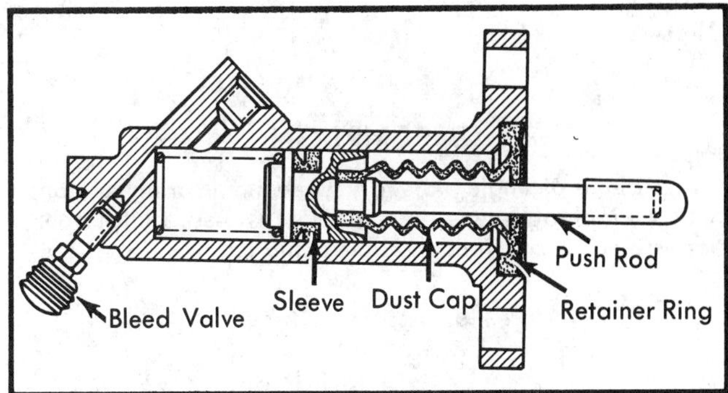

Fig. 4 Sectional View of Clutch Slave Cylinder

ADJUSTMENT

320i & 530i Only – Adjust pedal at master cylinder push rod. Vary rod length by loosening lock nut and turning rod in or out to obtain a total pedal travel of approximately 6.1" (155 mm).

HYDRAULIC BLEEDING

1) Fill fluid reservoir.

2) Attach bleeder hose to slave cylinder bleed screw. Submerge the free end of hose into a container part full with brake fluid.

3) Pump clutch pedal about 10 times. Hold pedal down on last pump stroke.

4) Loosen bleed screw and allow air to escape.

5) Close bleed screw.

6) Repeat steps **3-5** until all air is bled from clutch hydraulic system.

TIGHTENING SPECIFICATIONS

Application	Ft. Lbs. (mkg)
Clutch-to-Flywheel	16-17 (2.2-2.4)
Master Cylinder Mounting Bolts	16-17 (2.2-2.4)
Slave Cylinder Mounting Bolts	
Except 530i	18-20 (2.5-2.8)
Clutch Housing-to-Engine	
530i	
8 mm Bolts	16-17 (2.2-2.4)
10 mm Bolts	31-35 (4.3-4.8)
320i and 630CSi	
8 mm Bolts	18-19 (2.5-2.7)
10 mm Bolts	34-37 (4.7-5.1)
Transmission-to-Clutch Housing	
630CSi	52-57 (7.2-8.0)

CAPRI

2300 cc
2800 cc

DESCRIPTION

Clutch disc is of single plate, dry type with a spring cushioned hub. A diaphragm type pressure plate is used. Clutch operation is mechanical through cable actuation.

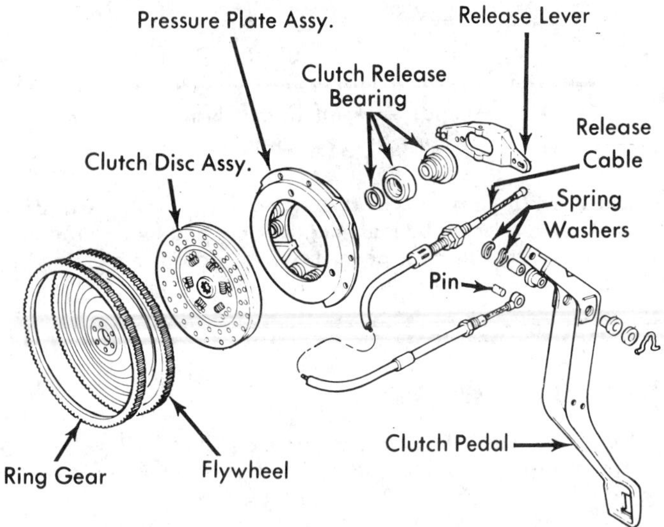

Fig. 1 Exploded View of Clutch Assembly & Linkage

REMOVAL & INSTALLATION

CLUTCH ASSEMBLY

Removal – **1**) With battery disconnected, raise vehicle on a hoist. Remove four bolts securing drive shaft to rear axle pinion flange. Remove two bolts securing center bearing carrier to bracket, then lower rear of shaft down and slide front yoke from transmission. Install a dummy yoke in transmission to prevent oil leakage.

2) Remove speedometer cable from extension housing, then disconnect exhaust pipe from transmission bracket and secure out of way. Lift up clutch release lever boot and disconnect clutch cable from lever. Unclip spring retainers and disconnect shift rods from transmission.

3) Remove starter attaching bolts, then place starter out of way. Remove clutch housing-to-engine attaching bolts and bolts securing engine rear plate to front lower part of flywheel housing.

4) Place a suitable transmission jack under transmission, remove four bolts securing crossmember to body, then slide transmission assembly rearward and detach from engine. Loosen clutch attaching bolts working diagonally across clutch, then remove clutch assembly.

Installation – To install, reverse removal procedure noting the following: Apply a light coat of molybdenum-based grease to clutch disc splines. Insure input shaft fully extends into crankshaft pilot bearing.

CLUTCH RELEASE BEARING

With transmission and clutch assembly removed, withdraw release lever and bearing assembly from clutch housing. Remove release lever from hub and bearing assembly. Before installing, apply molybdenum-based grease to hub and release lever. To install, reverse removal procedure.

PILOT BEARING

With transmission and clutch assembly removed, insert a suitable puller behind bearing, then screw puller attachment (T69L-1102-A) into puller. Tighten thrust nut on center shaft to remove bearing. Install bearing into end of crankshaft using a suitable driver, making sure that bearing is .156-.175" (3.96-4.44 mm) below crankshaft flange.

CLUTCH CABLE

Removal – Raise vehicle on a hoist. Loosen clutch cable at adjuster on clutch housing, then remove spring clip securing clutch cable to top of pedal. Remove pivot pin (*Fig. 1*) and pull top of cable into engine compartment. Move clutch release lever boot on clutch housing and free cable from lever, then remove cable from vehicle.

Installation – **1**) Pass top end of clutch cable through dash panel so that it is near clutch pedal. Assemble cable to pedal and install pivot pin (lubricate prior to assembly). Secure cable in position with spring clip.

2) Install clutch cable lower end to clutch release lever. Coat ball end of cable with ball joint lubricant. Locate rubber boot in opening and adjust clutch pedal free play.

ADJUSTMENT

CLUTCH PEDAL & CABLE ADJUSTMENT

2300 cc – **1**) Pull clutch pedal against back stop and retain with a wood block. Loosen adjustment lock nut. Pull cable forward taking up slack. Hold cable forward and turn adjusting nut until a clearance of .124-.144" (3.15-3.65 mm) is obtained between nut and clutch housing cable bushing. Tighten lock nut.

2) Before making further adjustments, depress clutch pedal to floor twice. With clutch pedal retained in position against back stop, measure distance "A" (*Fig. 2*). Depress clutch pedal fully and release easily; measure distance "B" (*Fig. 2*). Difference between measurements should be .866-1.02" (22-26 mm).

2800 cc – **1**) Pull clutch pedal against back stop and retain with a wood block. Pull cable forward until adjusting nut is accessible. Apply enough pressure to clutch cable to eliminate free play in release lever. Rotate adjusting nut until it just contacts recess. Release cable and allow adjusting nut to re-enter recess.

2) Before making further adjustments, depress clutch pedal to floor twice. With clutch pedal retained in position against back stop, measure distance "A" (*Fig. 2*). Depress clutch pedal fully and release easily; measure distance "B" (*Fig. 2*). Difference between measurements should be 1.06-1.22" (27-31 mm).

TIGHTENING SPECIFICATIONS

Application	Ft. Lbs. (mkg)
Pressure Plate-to-Flywheel	11-14 (1.5-1.9)
Clutch Housing-to-Transmission	40-47 (5.5-6.5)
Clutch Housing-to-Engine	22-27 (3.0-3.7)

CAPRI (Cont.)

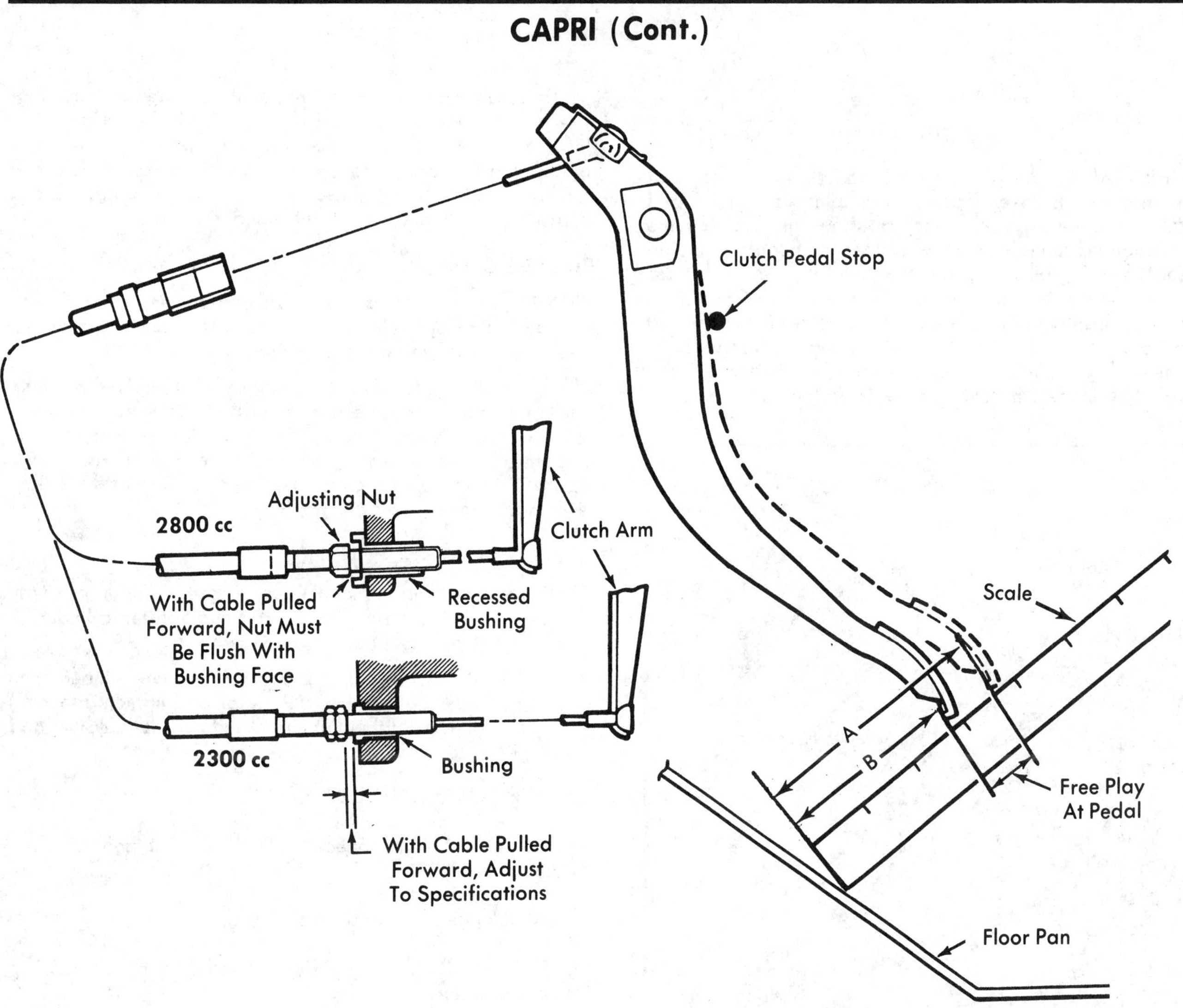

Fig. 2 Capri Clutch Cable Adjustment Procedures

COURIER

Courier

DESCRIPTION

Clutch is of single dry disc type. Clutch assembly consists of clutch disc, clutch cover and pressure plate assembly, and clutch release mechanism. Clutch housing also acts as the transmission input shaft bearing retainer, and contains the input shaft bearing oil seal and a selective fit thrust washer for controlling input shaft end play. Clutch release mechanism is hydraulic, consisting of a firewall mounted master cylinder and a slave cylinder mounted on flywheel housing. To control clutch engagement, a one-way valve mounted on master cylinder controls flow of return fluid when pressure on clutch pedal is released.

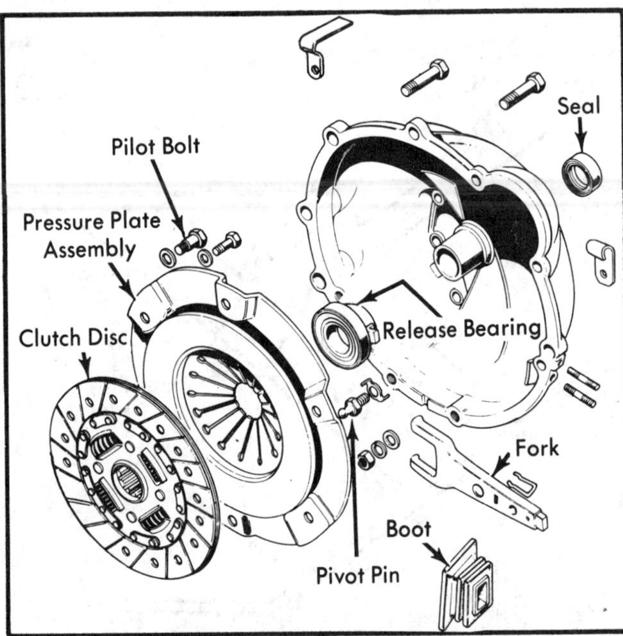

Fig. 1 Exploded View of Courier Clutch Assembly with Detail of Internal Components – Note That Fork Return Spring and Release Bearing Retainer Spring are No Longer Used

REMOVAL & INSTALLATION

CLUTCH ASSEMBLY

1) Place gear shift lever in neutral and remove shift lever, tower and boots as an assembly. Raise vehicle, disconnect drive shaft at rear axle and at center bearing support and remove from transmission.

2) Disconnect exhaust pipe brackets from transmission case and clutch housing. Remove exhaust pipe and resonator assembly. Disconnect clutch release lever return spring. Remove clutch slave cylinder and secure to one side.

3) Remove speedometer cable from extension housing and disconnect wiring from starter and transmission. Using a suitable jack, support engine and remove starter. Support transmission and remove transmission-to-engine rear plate attaching bolts.

4) Remove crossmember attaching bolts at transmission and frame side rails, and remove crossmember. Lower jack supporting engine and remove transmission by sliding rearward and downward. Mark location of two pilot bolt holes on flywheel and pressure plate and remove clutch attaching bolts and clutch assembly.

5) To install, reverse removal procedure noting the following: Use a suitable centering tool to align clutch disc to flywheel. Install pressure plate, four standard, and two pilot bolts finger tight. To avoid distorting pressure plate, tighten bolts a few turns at a time until tight, using a criss-cross pattern. Bleed hydraulic system and adjust clutch pedal free play.

RELEASE LEVER & BEARING

1) With transmission removed, disconnect release collar spring and slide out release lever, boot and release bearing. Inspect all parts for wear or damage.

2) To install, apply lubricant to input shaft bearing retainer portion of clutch housing and pivot bolt. Drive release lever onto pivot. Apply lubricant to bearing contact surface of lever and install release bearing and hook release collar spring. Apply lubricant to face of release bearing. Check to see that lever and bearing operate freely.

CLUTCH MASTER CYLINDER

1) Disconnect fluid outlet line at master cylinder one-way valve. Remove nuts and bolts attaching master cylinder to firewall and pull cylinder out and away.

2) To install, start pedal push rod into master cylinder, then position cylinder against firewall. Install and tighten attaching bolts and connect fluid outlet line. Bleed hydraulic system and check pedal free play.

CLUTCH SLAVE CYLINDER

Removal – 1) Disconnect brake fluid inlet hose at slave cylinder.

2) Unhook release lever from push rod.

3) Remove nuts attaching slave cylinder to clutch housing. Remove cylinder.

Installation – 1) Locate cylinder on studs in housing. Tighten nuts.

2) Connect fluid inlet hose.

3) Fill master cylinder. Bleed hydraulic system.

4) Hook clutch release lever into slave cylinder push rod.

OVERHAUL

CLUTCH MASTER CYLINDER

1) Clean outside of cylinder, drain fluid, and remove dust boot. Using a screwdriver, remove piston stop ring and washer. Remove piston, piston cup and return spring from cylinder, then carefully remove and disassemble one-way valve.

2) Wash all parts in clean alcohol or brake fluid. Check all rubber components and replace if damaged, worn, softened or swollen. Check cylinder bore for wear or damage, and check clearance between cylinder bore and piston. Replace cylinder or piston if clearance is more than .004" (.102 mm)

3) To assemble, dip all parts in clean brake fluid and reverse disassembly procedure. When assembled, fill reservoir with fluid and operate piston with a screwdriver until fluid is ejected at outlet fitting.

COURIER (Cont.)

CLUTCH MASTER CYLINDER

ONE-WAY VALVE

Disassembly – Remove cap from side of clutch master cylinder. *See Fig. 2.* Slide out washer, one-way valve and spring.

Reassembly – Position spring along with one-way valve into cylinder housing. Fit cap and washer.

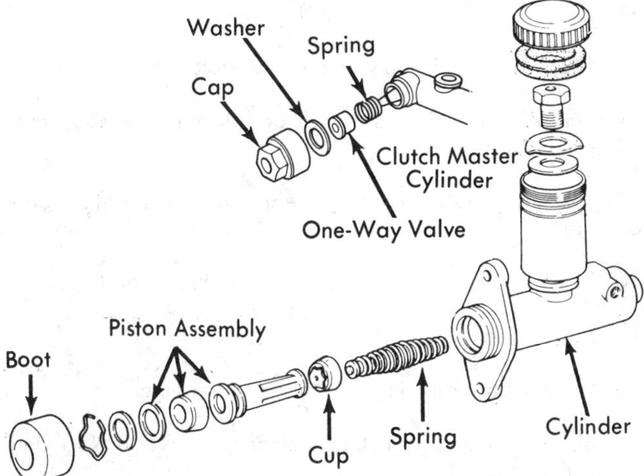

Fig. 2 Exploded View of Clutch Master Cylinder Assembly with Detail of One-Way Valve Used on Models Equipped with 2300 cc Engine

SLAVE CYLINDER

1) Clean outside of housing.

2) Remove dust boot and clutch release rod.

3) Remove piston assembly and return spring.

4) From slave cylinder, remove:
- Bleeder screw cap
- Bleeder screw
- Steel ball

Inspection – **1)** Check cylinder bore and piston for:
- Wear
- Roughness
- Scoring

2) Clearance between cylinder bore and piston should be .004" (.102 mm). Replace piston or cylinder if specification is exceeded.

Reassembly – **1)** Lightly coat piston and cups with brake fluid.

2) Fit cups to piston.

3) Install piston into cylinder.

4) Install release rod and boot.

5) Put steel ball into cylinder.

6) Screw in bleeder. Fit dust cap.

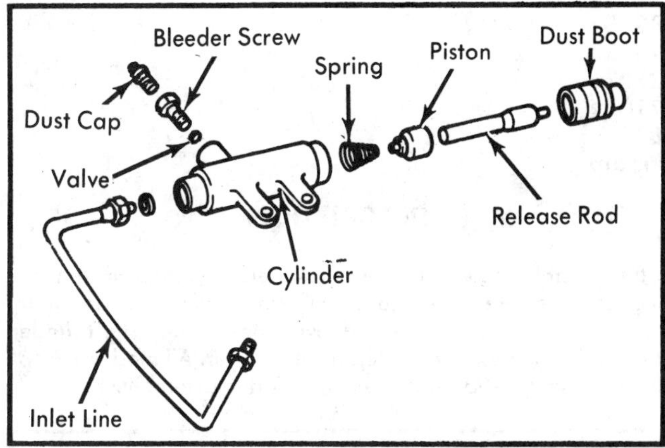

Fig. 3 Exploded View of Courier Slave Cylinder

ADJUSTMENT

CLUTCH PEDAL

Pedal free play is adjusted by loosening lock nut on push rod and rotating rod until .025-.121" (.64-3.07 mm) free travel is obtained at pedal pad. *See Fig. 4.* Tighten lock nut when adjustment is completed.

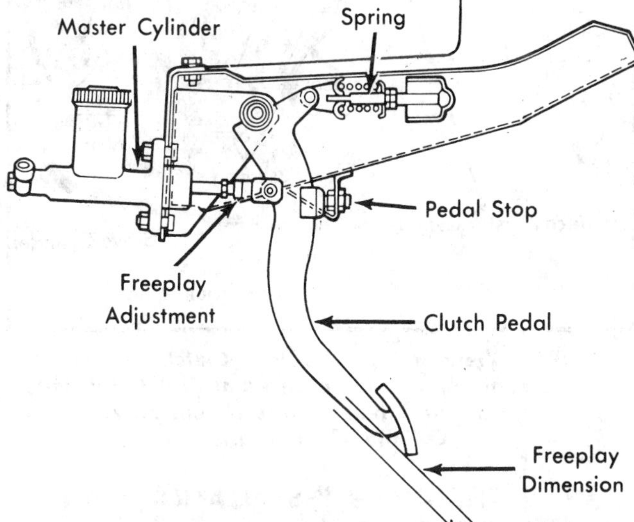

Fig. 4 Clutch Pedal Adjustment Procedure

HYDRAULIC SYSTEM BLEEDING

Remove rubber cap from bleeder valve and attach a bleeder tube and fixture to bleeder screw. Place other end of tube in a glass jar of brake fluid and open bleeder screw. Depress clutch pedal and allow to return slowly. Continue pumping action until air bubbles cease to appear in glass jar, then close bleeder screw. Install rubber cap on bleeder screw and fill master cylinder. **NOTE** – *During bleeding, master cylinder must be kept ¾ full of brake fluid.*

TIGHTENING SPECIFICATIONS

Application	Ft. Lbs. (mkg)
Clutch Housing-to-Engine	
1800 cc Engine	34-45 (4.7-6.2)
2300 cc Engine	28-40 (3.9-5.5)
Pressure Plate-to-Flywheel	13-20 (1.8-2.8)
Slave Cylinder-to-Clutch Housing	12-17 (1.7-2.4)
Pivot Pin	23-34 (3.2-4.7)

DATSUN EXCEPT F10

B210
200SX
280Z
710
810
Pickup

DESCRIPTION

Clutch is dry, single disc type. All models use a diaphragm spring type pressure plate and pre-lubricated clutch release bearing. Clutch is operated by a firewall mounted master cylinder and a clutch housing mounted slave cylinder. All models except B210 have non-adjustable slave cylinder assembly.

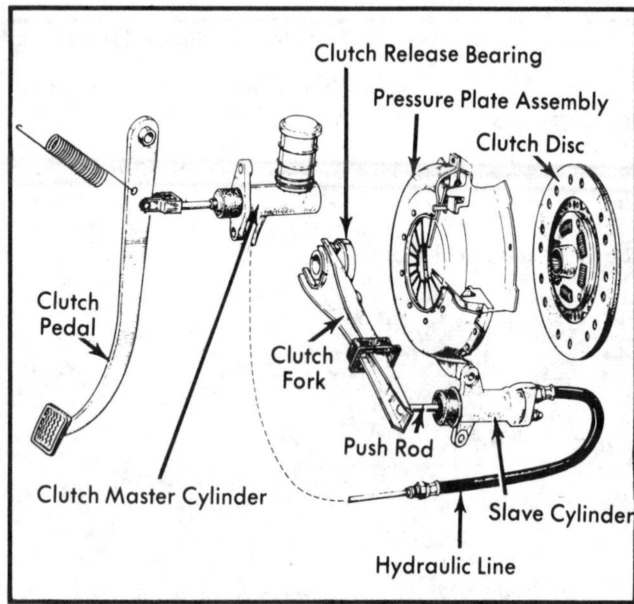

Fig. 1 View of Typical Datsun Clutch System — Note Some Models have Different Clutch Release Forks and Others Have Different Slave Cylinder Configurations

REMOVAL & INSTALLATION

CLUTCH ASSEMBLY

NOTE — *Removal procedure is general. Not all steps apply to each model.*

Removal — 1) Disconnect battery ground.

2) Remove console. Place gear shift lever in "N". Disconnect shift lever.

3) On 280Z models only, disconnect accelerator linkage.

4) Raise vehicle and place on safety stands.

5) Disconnect front exhaust pipe from exhaust manifold. It may be necessary to remove entire pipe on some models.

6) On 710, California models only, remove lower CAT shield before disconnecting front exhaust pipe.

7) Disconnect speedometer cable.

8) Disconnect electrical leads from transmission.

9) Remove slave cylinder from clutch housing.

10) On 280Z models only, remove insulator mounting bolts and place insulator on exhaust pipe.

11) Remove propeller shaft.

12) Support engine under oil pan with a jack and block of wood.

13) Support transmission with an adjustable jack.

14) On California, Pickup models only, separate exhaust pipe bracket from mounting.

15) Remove nut mounting rear crossmember-to-rubber bushing.

16) Remove bolts mounting rear crossmember-to-body.

17) Remove starter.

18) Remove bolts securing transmission-to-engine.

19) Slide transmission back until clear and lower on jack until it can be removed.

20) Loosen bolts attaching pressure plate to flywheel. Use a criss-cross loosening pattern.

Installation — To install, reverse removal procedure and note:
- Lubricate clutch disc splines with small amount of multipurpose grease.
- Slip clutch assembly over guide dowels.
- Use clutch aligning tool to center disc and pressure plate.
- Adjust linkage.
- Refill transmission, if necessary.
- Bleed clutch hydraulic system if it was opened.

CLUTCH MASTER CYLINDER

Removal & Installation — Disconnect master cylinder push rod at clevis. Disconnect hydraulic line to slave cylinder. Remove cylinder attaching bolts and remove cylinder from firewall. To install, reverse removal procedure, bleed hydraulic system and adjust clutch pedal height.

CLUTCH SLAVE CYLINDER

Removal & Installation — Remove clutch fork return spring (if equipped). Disconnect hydraulic line from cylinder, remove bolts attaching cylinder to clutch housing, and remove slave cylinder. To install, reverse removal procedure and bleed hydraulic system.

CLUTCH RELEASE BEARING & LEVER

Removal — With transmission removed from vehicle, remove dust boot from clutch housing. Disconnect release lever retaining spring or return spring, as required, and retaining clips holding release bearing to lever. Remove bearing and lever through front of clutch housing. Remove bearing from collar using a puller.

DATSUN EXCEPT F10 (Cont.)

Installation – To install, reverse removal procedure and note the following: Apply multi-purpose grease to inside surface of bearing collar, release bearing contact points, release bearing, ball pin in clutch housing, and ball contact points on release lever.

OVERHAUL

CLUTCH MASTER CYLINDER

1) With master cylinder removed, remove filler cap and drain brake fluid. Pull back dust boot and remove snap ring. Remove stopper, push rod and piston assembly. Remove spring seat from piston and take off piston cup. Thoroughly clean all components in brake fluid.

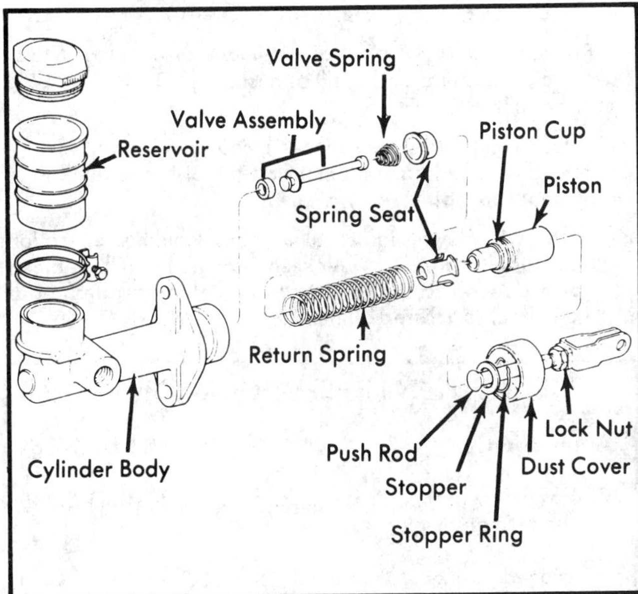

Fig. 2 Exploded View of Clutch Master Cylinder

2) Inspect all parts for wear or damage. If clearance between cylinder and piston exceeds .006", replace master cylinder. Replace piston cup any time master cylinder is disassembled.

3) Lubricate all parts with clean brake fluid before assembly. To assemble, reverse disassembly procedures.

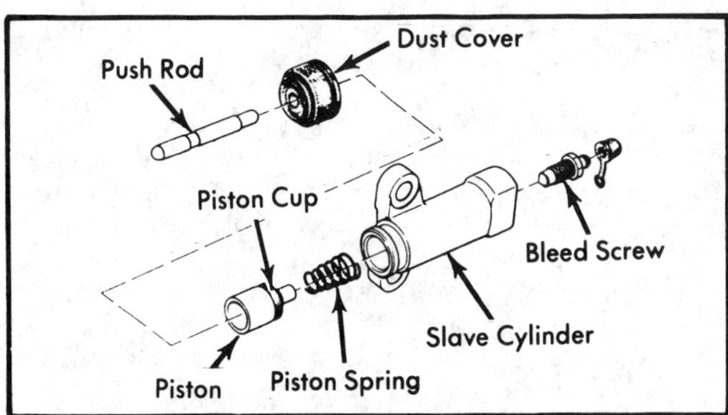

Fig. 3 Exploded View of of Clutch Slave Cylinder Assembly – (Except B210 Models)

CLUTCH SLAVE CYLINDER

1) With slave cylinder removed, take out push rod along with dust boot. Remove entire piston assembly and piston spring. Remove bleed screw.

2) Visually inspect all parts and replace those determined unuseable. To assemble, reverse disassembly procedure noting the following: Dip all components in clean brake fluid and ensure cup is installed in correct direction.

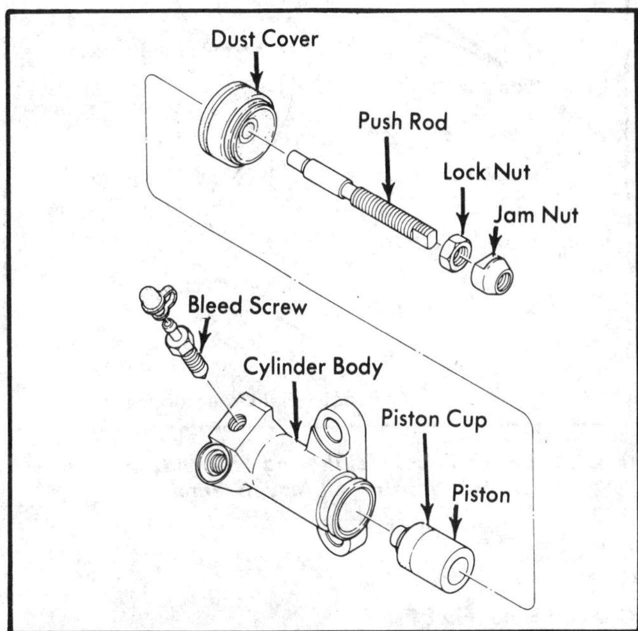

Fig. 4 Exploded View of Clutch Slave Cylinder (B210 Models Shown)

ADJUSTMENT

PEDAL HEIGHT & FREE PLAY

Adjust clutch pedal height to specification "A" by turning pedal stopper adjusting nut in or out. Tighten lock nut. Adjust pedal free play to specification "B" (clearance between clevis pin and clutch pedal) by turning clutch master cylinder rod in or out.

Pedal Height; Free Play Specifications

Application	"A" Height In. (mm)	"B" Free Play In. (mm)
B210	6.02-6.26 (153-159)	.039-.118 (1-3)
200SX	7.36-7.6 (187-193)	.039-.118 (1-3)
280Z	8.78 (223)	.039-.118 (1-3)
710	7.08 (180)	.039-.197 (1-5)
810	6.9 (175.5)	.039-.197 (1-5)
Pickup	6.02 (153)	.039-.118 (1-3)

DATSUN EXCEPT F10 (Cont.)

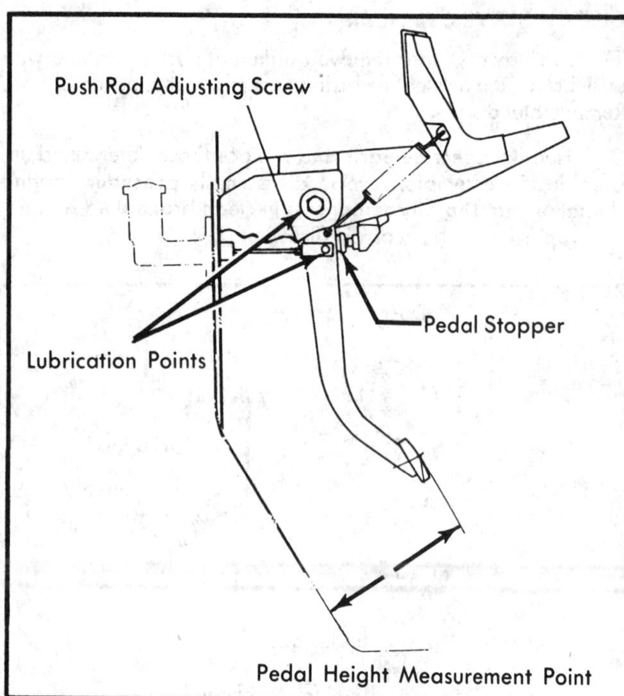

Fig. 5 Clutch Pedal Height and Free Play Adjustment Locations – All Models Similar

CLUTCH FORK FREE PLAY

1) Loosen lock nut and push nut. *See Fig. 6.*

2) Turn push rod until release bearing lightly touches clutch diaphragm spring.

3) Turn rod back (opposite direction) about 1¼ turns. This provides about .039-.079" (1-2 mm) clearance between push nut and lever.

4) Tighten lock nut.

5) Work clutch pedal several times. Recheck pedal free play.

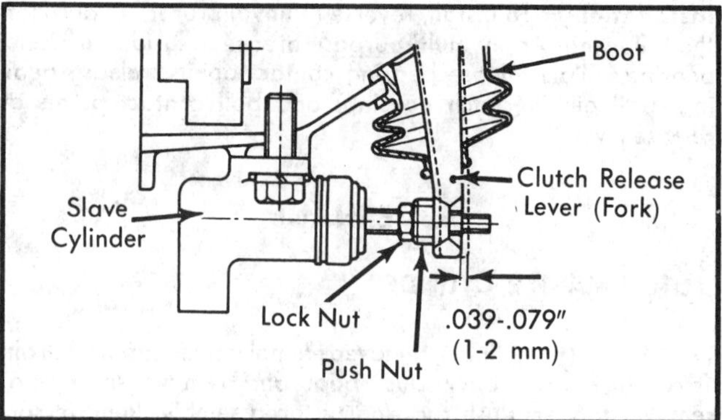

Fig. 6 Clutch Fork Free Play Adjustment Locations for Datsun B210

HYDRAULIC SYSTEM BLEEDING

1) Remove dust cap from slave cylinder bleed plug. Check fluid level in master cylinder, fill as necessary. Open bleed plug approximately ¾ turn.

2) Attach a tube to slave cylinder bleed plug, and place opposite end of tube in a container half-full of brake fluid. Push clutch pedal to bottom of travel.

3) With pedal down, tighten bleed plug. Continue operation until air bubbles are no longer seen in container. Close bleed plug on a downward stroke of pedal. Install dust cap and adjust fluid level in master cylinder.

TIGHTENING SPECIFICATIONS

Application	Ft. Lbs. (mkg)
Clutch-to-Flywheel	11-16 (1.5-2.2)
Engine-to-Transmission	
B210	
4-Speed	12-16 (1.6-2.2)
5-Speed & 200SX	27-36 (3.7-5.0)
280Z, 810, Pickup	32-43 (4.4-5.9)
710	29-36 (4.0-4.8)
Slave Cylinder-to-Clutch Housing	
280Z	18-25 (2.5-3.5)
Pickup	18-22 (2.5-3.0)
All Others	22-30 (3.1-4.1)

DATSUN F10

Datsun F10

DESCRIPTION

Clutch is a single, dry disc, diaphragm spring type. Main components consist of: clutch cover, pressure plate, and diaphragm spring. Clutch plates are riveted together. A release bearing and fork control clutch engagement and disengagement. Clutch is hydraulic type with a firewall mounted master cylinder and clutch housing mounted slave cylinder.

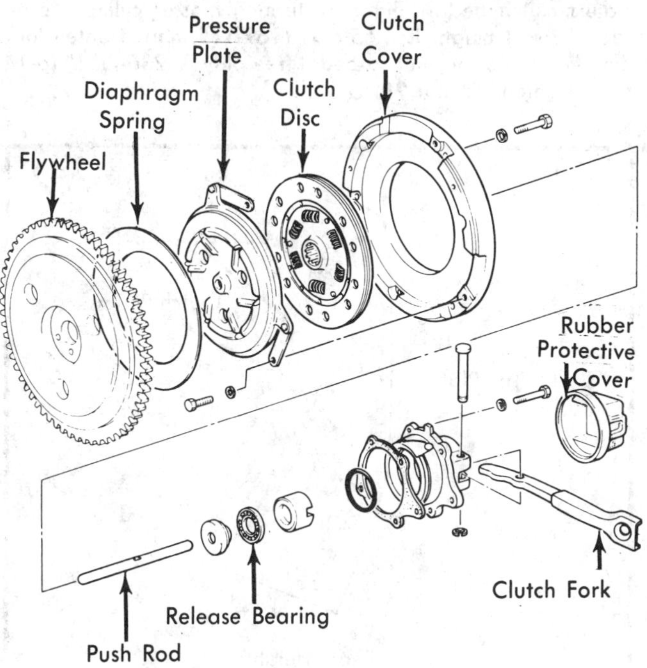

Fig. 1 Exploded View of Clutch Components

REMOVAL & INSTALLATION

CLUTCH ASSEMBLY

NOTE – *Clutch assembly can be serviced, removed, or overhauled while transmission and engine remain in vehicle. Also, transmission cannot be removed without removing engine.*

Removal – 1) Disconnect the following: Battery ground cable, fresh air duct, electrical connectors on clutch housing and carbon cannister hoses. Remove upper portion of clutch housing inspection cover, then take out six bolts mounting clutch cover.

NOTE – *To gain access to mounting bolts, raise right front wheel and rotate by hand until bolts are visible.*

2) Turn wheels to left stop, then remove right side inspection cover and disconnect clutch release fork. Remove six bolts on bearing housing. Pull out primary drive gear assembly. *(See Fig. 2).* Lift out clutch cover and disc through inspection opening. Remove strap securing pressure plate to clutch cover. Keep strap in relative position since it is part of dynamic balance.

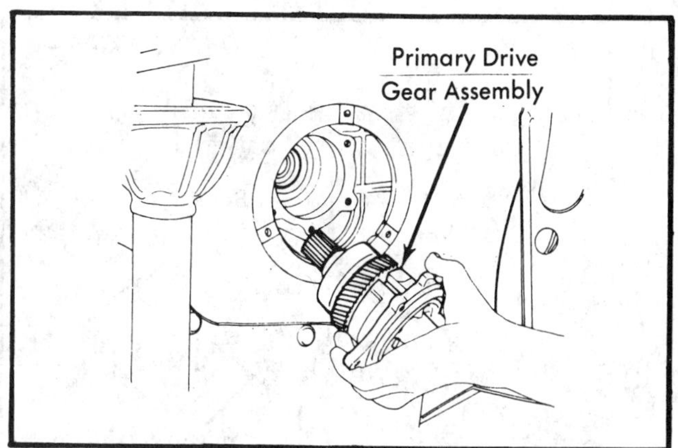

Fig. 2 Removing Primary Drive Gear Assembly

Installation – To install, reverse removal procedure and note the following: Make sure all alignment marks are positioned before tightening.

RELEASE BEARING

Removal – Separate release lever by removing pivot pin and removing bearing housing. Remove "O" ring and bearing. Hold bearing and rotate outer race, replace if operation is rough or noisy.

Installation – To install, reverse removal procedure and apply multi-purpose grease to sliding parts of release lever.

CLUTCH MASTER CYLINDER

Removal – Remove lock ring from clevis pin and pull out clevis pin. Disconnect and plug clutch line from master cylinder. Remove nuts mounting master cylinder to insturment panel.

Installation – To install, reverse removal procedure and note the following: Adjust pedal play and bleed air from hydraulic system.

SLAVE CYLINDER

Removal – Disconnect clutch hose from slave cylinder. Remove two bolts mounting slave cylinder to clutch housing.

Installation – To install, reverse removal procedure and note the following: Bleed air from hydraulic system.

OVERHAUL

MASTER CYLINDER

Disassembly – Remove dust cover and pull stopper ring from cylinder body. Remove push rod, then take out entire piston assembly.

Inspection – Wash all internal parts in clean brake fluid. Check cylinder bore and piston for burrs or score marks. Check bore for wear. If clearance between bore and piston is more than .006" (.15 mm), piston must be replaced. Check all passages to make sure they are clear.

DATSUN F10 (Cont.)

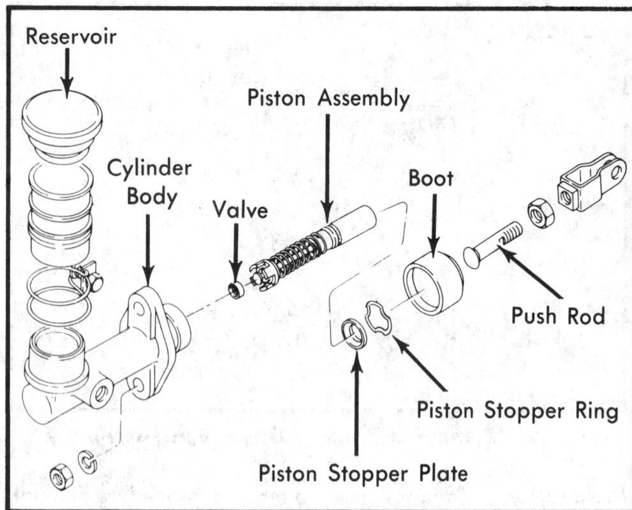

Fig. 3 Exploded View of Master Cylinder

Reassembly – To reassemble, reverse disassembly procedure and note the following: Make sure piston cup is correctly positioned. Apply a light coat of brake fluid to cylinder and piston.

SALVE CYLINDER

Disassembly – Remove dust boot. Separate remaining components as shown in *Fig. 4*.

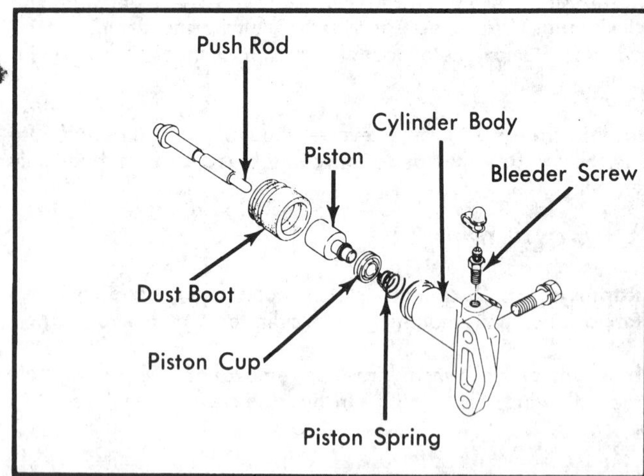

Fig. 4 Exploded View of Clutch Slave Cylinder

Inspection – Visually inspect all components and replace those which indicate signs of damage or wear. Clean all components in brake fluid. Check cylinder piston and bore for score marks and rust. Inspect cylinder bore and piston for wear. If clearance is more than .006" (.15 mm), replace piston. Make sure bleed hole is dirt free.

Reassembly – To reassemble, reverse disassembly procedure and note the following: Apply a light coat of brake fluid to cylinder and piston before reassembly.

NOTE – *When pressure plate and clutch disc are replaced, or if any components of release mechanism is replaced, a new push rod may have to be installed.*

ADJUSTMENTS

CLUTCH PEDAL HEIGHT & FREE PLAY

Adjust clutch pedal height by turning master cylinder push rod. Correct height is 6.65-6.9" (169-175 mm). Tighten lock nut. Adjust stopper nut so pedal free play is .236-.551" (6-14 mm). Tighten lock nut. *Fig. 5*.

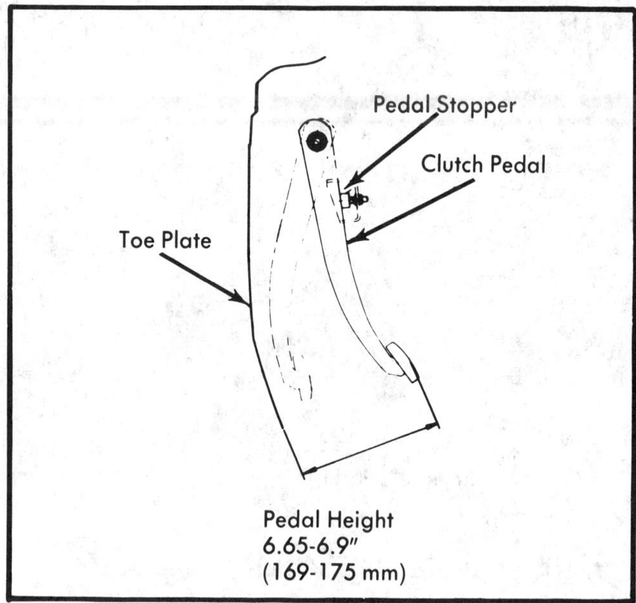

Fig. 5 Pedal Height and Free Play Adjustment

HYDRAULIC SYSTEM BLEEDING

Fit bleeder hose to bleeder valve. Place opposite end into a clear container partically filled with brake fluid. Pump clutch pedal two or three times and hold to floor. Break bleeder valve loose and allow air to vent. Close bleeder screw and allow pedal to return. Repeat procedure several times.

TIGHTENING SPECIFICATIONS

Application	Ft. Lbs. (mkg)
Clutch Cover Assembly	5.1-7.2 (.7-1.0)
Pressure Plate Strap	5.1-5.8 (.7-.8)
Bleeder Screw	5.1-6.5 (.7-.9)
Push Rod Lock Nut	5.8-8.0 (.8-1.1)
Master Cylinder-to-Instrument Panel	5.8-8.0 (.8-1.1)
Slave Cylinder Bolts	12-15 (1.6-2.1)

FIAT X1/9

X1/9

DESCRIPTION

Clutch is a dry, single plate, diaphragm spring type. Clutch actuation is hydraulic, using a firewall mounted master cylinder and a clutch housing mounted slave cylinder. A prelubricated clutch release bearing is also used.

REMOVAL & INSTALLATION

CLUTCH ASSEMBLY

Removal 1) – Disconnect positive battery cable. Remove air cleaner and carburetor duct cooling. From inside engine compartment, separate slave cylinder from transmission case. Install engine support. Remove upper transmission-to-crankcase mounting bolts.

2) – Working from under vehicle, disconnect and swing out-of-way shifting flexible link. Disconnect back-up lights and seat belt warning system wire. Remove starter. Disconnect and remove exhaust pipe.

3) – Remove nuts from hub end of half shaft. Remove attaching hardware mounting suspension control arm to supports. Free half shaft from hub end and fix other end to transmission to prevent premature disconnection.

4) – Remove the following: Flywheel cover, engine cross-member support, and lower engine-to-transmission bolts. Remove transmission/differential from below vehicle. Mark clutch position on flywheel and remove clutch.

Installation – To install, reverse removal procedure using suitable tool (A. 70210) to center clutch assembly.

CLUTCH MASTER CYLINDER

Removal – Steering column must be removed to gain access to clutch master cylinder. Disconnect and cap master cylinder hydraulic line. Remove two bolts attaching cylinder to support plate. Withdraw cylinder from actuating rod and remove from vehicle.

Installation – To install, reverse removal procedure and bleed hydraulic system.

CLUTCH SLAVE CYLINDER

Removal – Remove slave cylinder hydraulic hose and union. Disconnect cylinder push rod from clutch release bearing fork. Slightly compress return spring and remove two mounting bolts; slowly withdraw cylinder from support plate.

Installation – To install, reverse removal procedure ensuring slave cylinder snugly fits against support and that hydraulic system is bled.

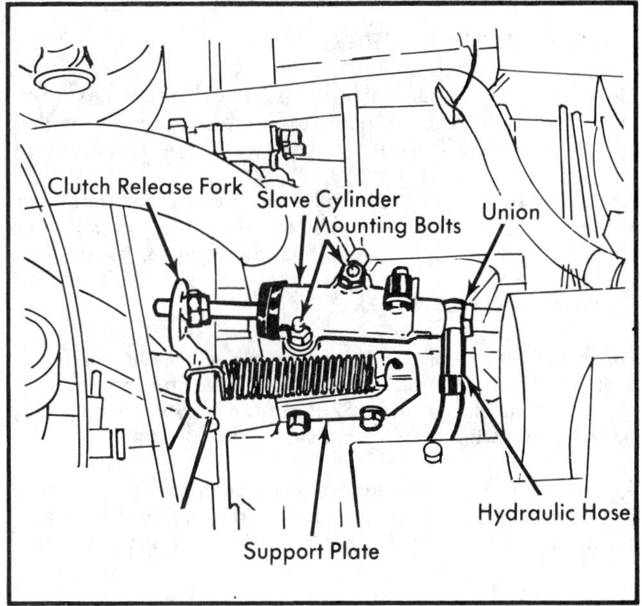

Fig. 1 Clutch Slave Cylinder Location

ADJUSTMENT

CLUTCH PEDAL HEIGHT & FREE PLAY ADJUSTMENT

1) Check clutch pedal travel, it should be approximately 6.7" (170 mm). If specification is not met, adjust screw on top of clutch pedal assembly until travel is correct. Turn screw out to reduce travel and in to increase it.

2) Check clutch pedal for approximately 1.25" (31.8 mm) free play. If specification is incorrect, adjust nut on slave cylinder until free play is to specification.

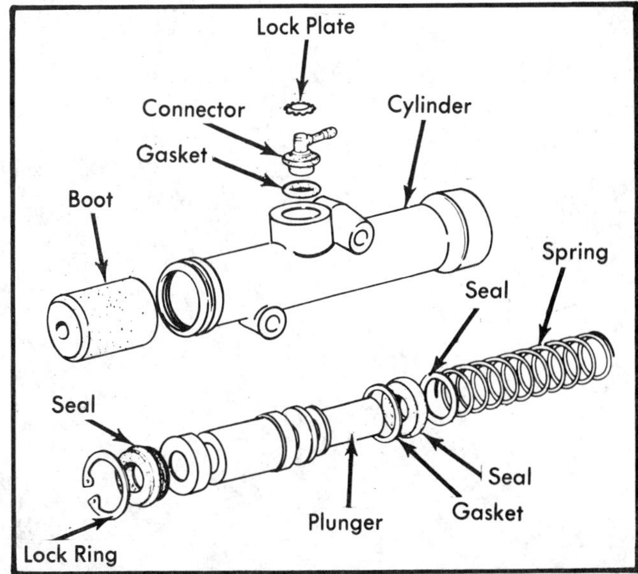

Fig. 2 Exploded View of Clutch Master Cylinder

FIAT X1/9 (Cont.)

OVERHAUL

CLUTCH MASTER CYLINDER

Disassembly – Ease rubber dust boot back and remove snap ring, using long nosed pliers. Remove seal and complete plunger assembly. Pull out remaining gasket, seal and spring.

Reassembly – Lightly coat all components with brake fluid. Insert spring and seal into position. Fit piston assembly and seal, then install snap ring. Slip boot over cylinder housing.

CLUTCH SLAVE CYLINDER

Disassembly – Pull push rod from slave cylinder. Slide dust boot off housing. Remove lock ring, washer, and spring, then shake out piston assembly. Seal at rear of cylinder bore may not come out with piston assembly.

Reassembly – Lightly coat all components with brake fluid before reassembly. Insert rear seal, and piston assembly. Refit spring, washer, and lock ring. Install dust boot and push rod.

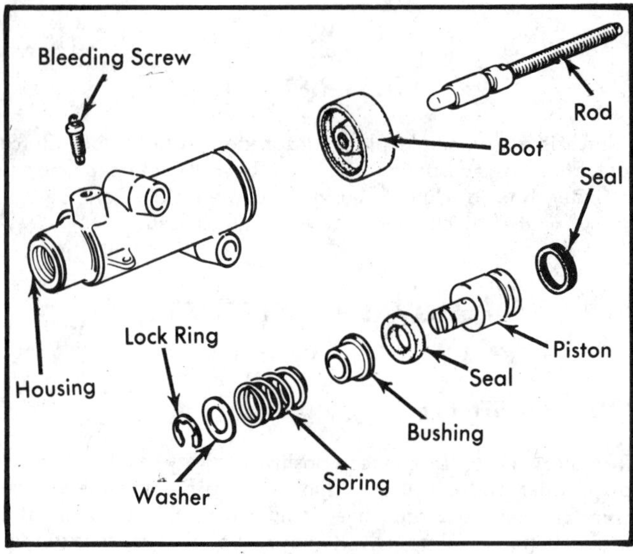

Fig. 3 Exploded View of Clutch Slave Cylinder

TIGHTENING SPECIFICATIONS

Application	Ft. Lbs. (mkg)
Clutch Flywheel Bolts	10.8 (1.5)
Clutch Release Fork Bolt	18 (2.5)
Slave Cylinder Piston Adjusting Nut	18 (2.5)
Slave Cylinder Support Plate-to-Transmission Case	18 (2.5)
Support Plate-to-Transmission Case Stud Nut	18 (2.5)

FIAT 124

124 Spider

DESCRIPTION

Clutch is a dry, single-disc, diaphragm spring type. Clutch is engaged or disengaged through a cable which is actuated by the clutch pedal.

REMOVAL & INSTALLATION

CLUTCH

1) Raise and suitably support vehicle. From inside drivers compartment, press down on gearshift lever and pry out retaining ring with screwdriver. Remove transmission cover.

2) From under vehicle, disconnect drive shaft from transmission and remove drive shaft safety cross strap. Remove drive shaft center pillow block. Disconnect speedometer drive from transmission. Disconnect back-up light switch (if equipped). Disconnect clutch fork return spring and remove adjusting rod.

3) Remove inspection cover from bottom of clutch housing. Disconnect exhaust pipe support bracket from rear of transmission and remove starter from clutch housing. Position a suitable transmission holding fixture (A. 70509) to a floor jack and position under transmission.

4) Remove bolts securing transmission to engine and remove rear crossmember. With transmission supported by jack, pull to rear until input shaft clears release bearing. Lower jack when transmission is clear and remove from under vehicle. Remove clutch assembly from flywheel after marking their relationship for reinstallation.

5) To install transmission and clutch assembly, reverse removal procedures noting the following: Lightly lubricate transmission input shaft splines. Ensure clutch and flywheel are properly aligned.

ADJUSTMENT

CLUTCH PEDAL

Clutch pedal should have approximately 1" (25 mm) free play. If specification is not met, loosen lock nut and rotate adjustment nut *(Fig. 1)* until clutch pedal free play is to specification. When free play is correctly adjusted maximum pedal travel (measured from first resistance) should be about 4.72" (120 mm).

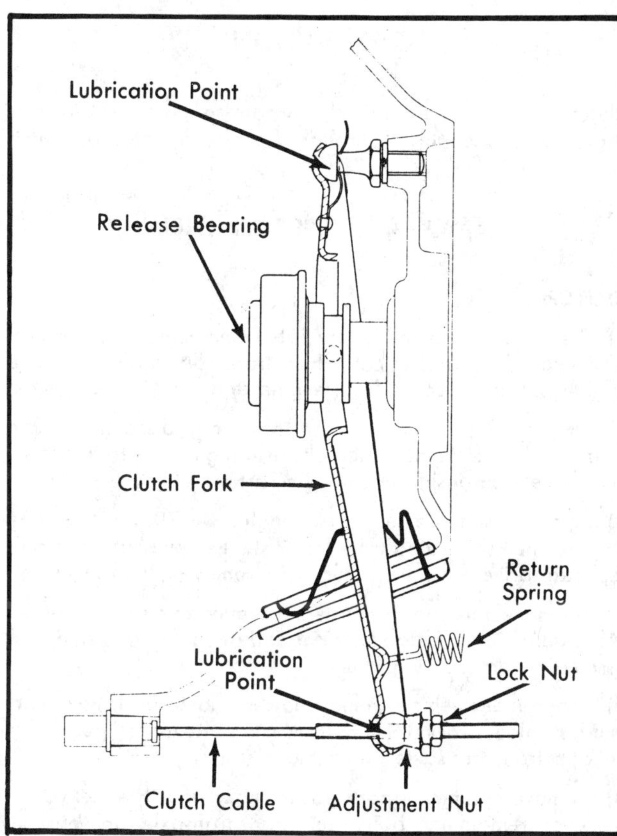

Fig. 1 ***Clutch Actuating Components Showing Cable Adjustment Point***

TIGHTENING SPECIFICATIONS

Application	Ft. Lbs. (mkg)
Clutch-to-Flywheel	22 (3.0)
Transmission Case-to-Bell Housing Bolts	36 (5.0)
Transmission Case-to-Bell Housing Nut	18 (2.5)
Bell Housing-to-Engine Mounts	61 (8.4)

FIAT 128

128
Sedan
Station Wagon
3P

DESCRIPTION

Clutch is a dry, single disc, diaphragm spring type. Clutch is engaged or disengaged through a cable, actuated by clutch pedal.

REMOVAL & INSTALLATION

CLUTCH

1) Disconnect positive battery cable and remove spare tire. Disconnect speedometer cable from transaxle housing. Remove engine protective cover from engine and front of body.

2) Disconnect clutch fork return spring and disconnect cable from clutch fork. Remove all bolts securing engine to transaxle accessible from inside engine compartment.

3) Attach a suitable support to engine (A. 70526) to secure engine when separated from transaxle. Remove hub caps and separate drive axles from hubs and remove left front wheel.

4) Disconnect tie rod from steering arm using a suitable puller (A. 47035). Remove stabilizer bar and disconnect left side strut assembly from steering knuckle.

5) From under vehicle, remove lower guards and disconnect exhaust pipe bracket from transaxle. Disconnect gear shift linkage from transaxle and remove starter.

6) Remove engine support crossmember and flywheel cover. Remove remaining bolts securing transaxle to engine. Disconnect ground cable from transaxle.

7) Secure drive axles to transaxle with wire to prevent axles from slipping out of transaxle during removal. Secure a suitable lifting fixture (A. 70547) to a floor jack.

8) Position floor jack and lifting fixture to transaxle and remove transaxle from vehicle. Mark position of clutch on flywheel and remove clutch assembly.

9) To install clutch assembly, reverse removal procedure. Align clutch and flywheel marks and tighten evenly on flywheel. Drive axle to hub nuts must be tightened to specification.

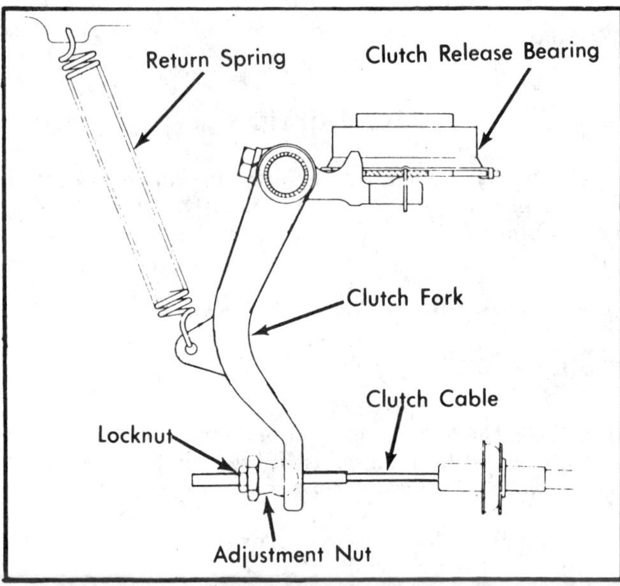

Fig. 1 Clutch Actuating Components Showing Cable Adjustment Point

ADJUSTMENT

CLUTCH PEDAL

1) Clutch pedal should have about 1" (25 mm) free play. If specification is not met, loosen adjustment lock nut and rotate adjusting nut until pedal free play is within specification.

2) When free play is correctly adjusted maximum pedal travel (measured from first resistance) should be about 4.72" (120 mm) for sedan and station wagon models or 4.02" (102 mm) for 3P models.

TIGHTENING SPECIFICATIONS

Application	Ft. Lbs. (mkg)
Clutch Assembly-to-Flywheel	11 (1.5)
Transmission-to-Clutch Housing	18 (2.5)
Clutch Housing-to-Engine	58 (8.0)

FIAT 131

DESCRIPTION

Clutch is a dry, single disc type using a diaphragm spring pressure plate. Clutch disc is a conventional friction lining kind. Clutch operation is accomplished by a control cable attached at upper end directly to clutch pedal and lower end to clutch release fork.

REMOVAL & INSTALLATION

CLUTCH ASSEMBLY

1) Disconnect battery ground cable. Remove exhaust pipe-to-manifold bracket. From inside vehicle, remove transmission cover, then pry snap ring from gear shift lever. Disconnect electrical lead on fast idle switch and pull wire through tunnel.

2) Disconnect drive shaft at flexible coupler. Remove protection shield and bracket (if necessary) and secure drive shaft out of way. Disconnect remaining electrical leads from transmission.

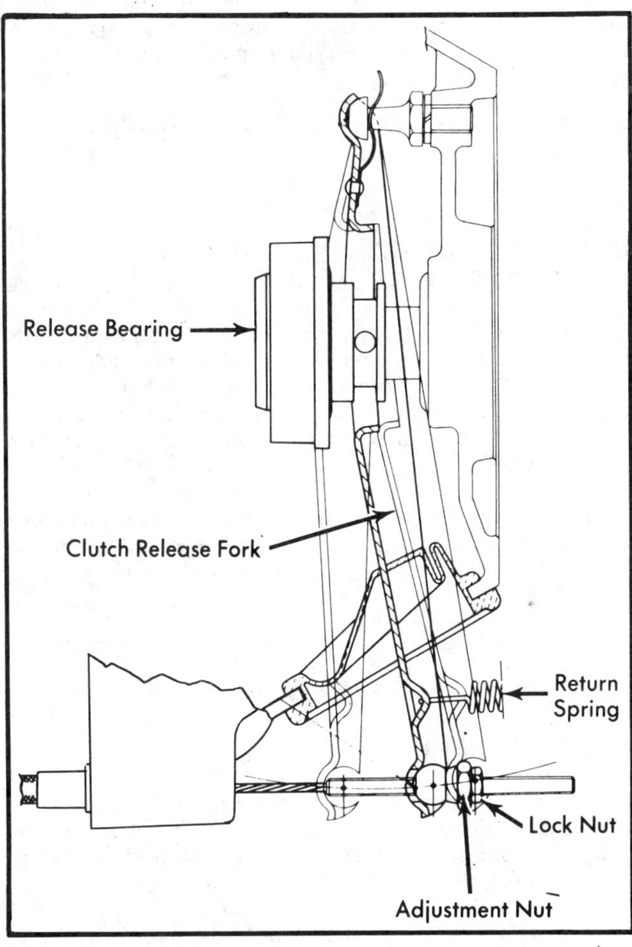

***Fig. 1** Clutch Actuating Components Showing Cable Adjustment Point*

3) Fit a hydraulic jack with necessary adaptors (if any) under transmission, then suitably support the engine. Take out starter bolts. Disconnect clutch linkage and speedometer cable.

4) Remove flywheel cover bolts, then remove exhaust pipe support and place out of way. Remove transmission support mount. Pull transmission rearward, tilting to slide input shaft out of clutch. Lower transmission to floor. Index mark clutch position on flywheel, then remove clutch.

5) To install clutch and transmission assembly, reverse removal procedure noting the following: Clutch disc must be installed with protrusion on hub facing transmission. Lightly coat input shaft splines with oil and use centering tool to align clutch disc.

ADJUSTMENT

CLUTCH PEDAL

Clutch pedal free play should be approximately 1" (25 mm). If pedal is out of adjustment, loosen lock nut (near firewall) and rotate adjustment nut until free play is to specification.

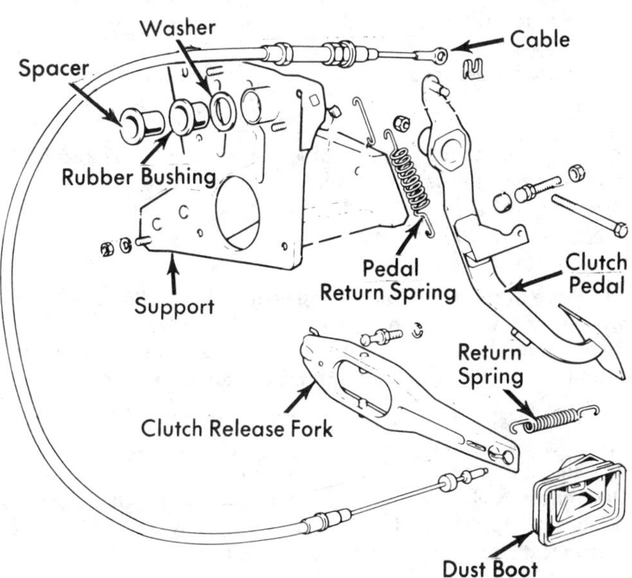

***Fig. 2** Exploded View of Clutch Cable & Pedal Components*

TIGHTENING SPECIFICATIONS

Application	Ft. Lbs. (mkg)
Clutch-to-Flywheel	22 (3.0)

HONDA ACCORD

Accord

DESCRIPTION

Clutch is a single plate, dry disc type. Clutch assembly consists of clutch disc, clutch cover and pressure plate assembly, and clutch release mechanism. Clutch release mechanism is hydraulic, consisting of a firewall mounted master cylinder and a slave cylinder mounted to clutch housing. Clutch release fork free play is adjustable.

REMOVAL & INSTALLATION

CLUTCH

Removal – 1) Disconnect battery ground at transmission. Put gear shift in Neutral. Disconnect following electrical wiring.

- Positive battery cable at starter.
- Black/White wire from starter solenoid.
- Yellow/Green wire from temperature sending unit.
- Black/Yellow and Yellow wires from temperature sensor A.
- Black/White and Red wires from temperature sensor B
- Black/Green and Yellow wires from back-up light switch.

2) Disconnect clutch control cable at firewall and release fork. Remove the right side starter bolt and two upper transmission mounting bolts.

3) Raise vehicle. Drain transmission fluid. Remove front wheels. Fit transmission jack squarely under transmission. Remove rightside inner fender panel. Remove speedometer from transmission. Take off sub-frame center support.

4) Remove stop bracket from front of clutch housing. Disconnect lower torque rod at transmission. Use suitable driver and force out shift linkage spring pin at transmission. Disconnect stabilizer bar from both radius rods.

5) Remove lower control arm bolt at rear of arm. Disconnect tie rods at steering knuckle. With steering knuckle at outer most position, pry constant velocity (CV) joint outward approximately ½". Pull stub axle from transmission housing. Remove clutch cover. Remove left starter bolt and starter.

6) Remove engine mounting bolts (3 rear) from transmission housing. Remove single front transmission mounting bolt. Remove transmission. Fit suitable flywheel holding device into flywheel. Remove eight (8) pressure plate mounting bolts. Separate pressure plate from diaphragm spring by removing retainers. Remove clutch disc. Remove six (6) flywheel mounting bolts and slide off flywheel.

Installation – To install reverse removal procedure and note: Make sure flywheel and pressure plate alignment marks are matched. **NOTE** – *New pressure plates are not indexed.* Use clutch disc alignment tool to ensure all components are properly set. Torque pressure plate bolts in criss-cross pattern. Refill transmission with SAE 10W-40 oil.

CLUTCH MASTER CYLINDER

Removal – Separate clutch pedal operating rod from master cylinder push rod by removing through pin at clevis. Disconnect and plug hydraulic lines. Remove nuts mounting master cylinder to firewall. Make sure brake fluid does not spill on painted surfaces.

Installation – To install master cylinder, reverse removal procedure and note: Bleed hydraulic system.

CLUTCH SLAVE CYLINDER

Removal – Disconnect hydraulic line from slave cylinder. Unhook return spring. Separate threaded rod from end of slave cylinder. Remove slave cylinder mounting bolts and take cylinder off clutch housing.

Installation – To install, reverse removal procedure and note: Bleed hydraulic system.

CLUTCH RELEASE FORK AND BEARING

Removal – With transmission removed, separate slave cylinder push rod from release fork. Slide release fork through slot in clutch housing (inward) and remove fork. Release fork bolt can now be removed, if necessary. Slide bearing out of release fork. Using a driver, release bearing can be separated from holder, if necessary.

Installation – To install, reverse removal procedure and lightly coat all moving parts and contact areas with grease.

OVERHAUL

MASTER CYLINDER

Disassembly – Remove boot and take off snap ring. Use compressed air and force piston assembly from master cylinder. Separate piston, cups, spring retainer, return spring and valve assembly.

Inspection – Check all components for damage or excessive wear. Check cylinder to piston for wear. Clearance should not exceed .006" (.15 mm). Make sure all rubber components are replaced.

Reassembly – To reassemble, reverse disassembly procedure.

HONDA ACCORD (Cont.)

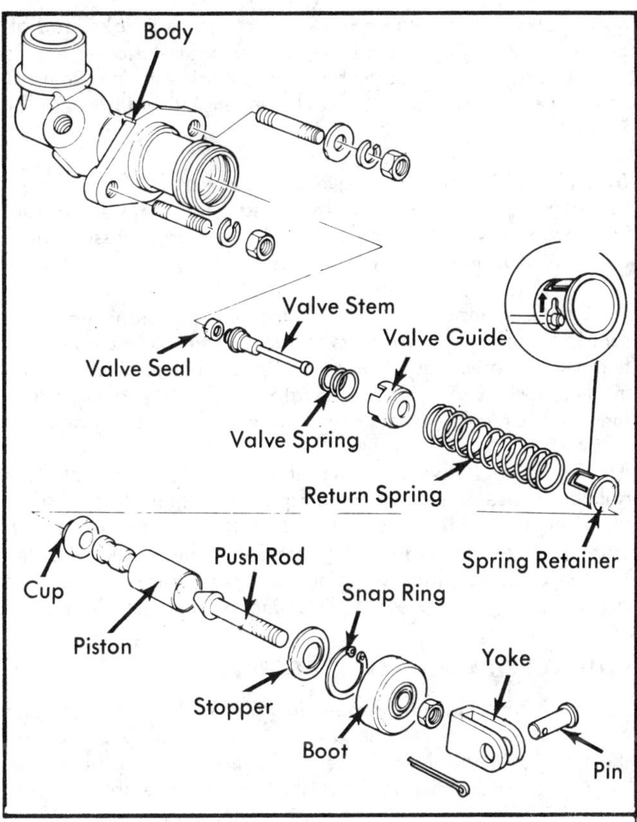

Fig. 1 Exploded View of Master Cylinder

CLUTCH SLAVE CYLINDER

Disassembly – Remove air bleed screw. Pull off dust boot. Force piston out of slave cylinder using compressed air. Take off piston rubber cup. Remove union plug with metal gasket. Carefully lift off valve plate. Remove spring.

Inspection – Check cylinder to piston wear. Clearance should not exceed .006" (.15 mm). Inspect all components for excessive wear or damage. Replace all rubber components with new parts.

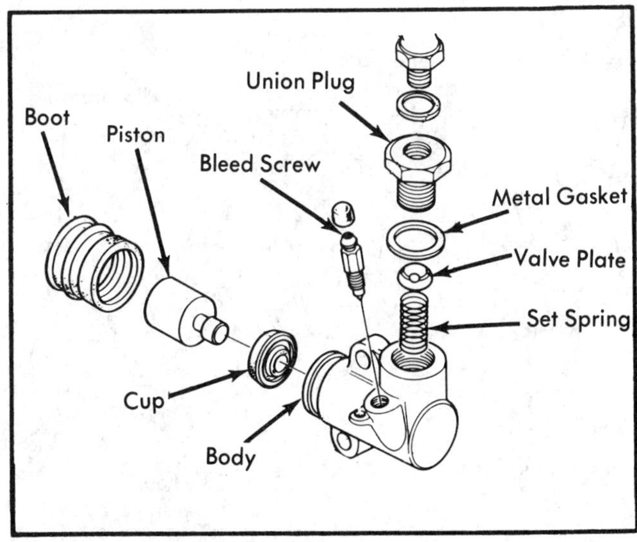

Fig. 2 Exploded View of Slave Cylinder

Reassembly – Reverse disassembly procedure. Lightly coat all components with brake fluid before reassembly.

ADJUSTMENT

CLUTCH PEDAL HEIGHT AND FREE PLAY

Adjust clutch pedal height to 7.24" (184 mm) using pedal stopper bolt. Rotate bolt in direction necessary to bring pedal height into specifications. Adjust pedal free play (clearance between clutch pedal push rod and master cylinder) using nut on master cylinder push rod. Pedal free play should be approximately .04-.12" (1-3 mm).

CLUTCH RELEASE FORK FREE PLAY

Loosen lock nut. Hold push rod end nut stationary and rotate Push rod with screw driver. Rotate counterclockwise to increase free play. After eliminating free play, back out rod 1¾ to 2 turns. Final free play should be .08-.1" (2.0-2.6 mm).

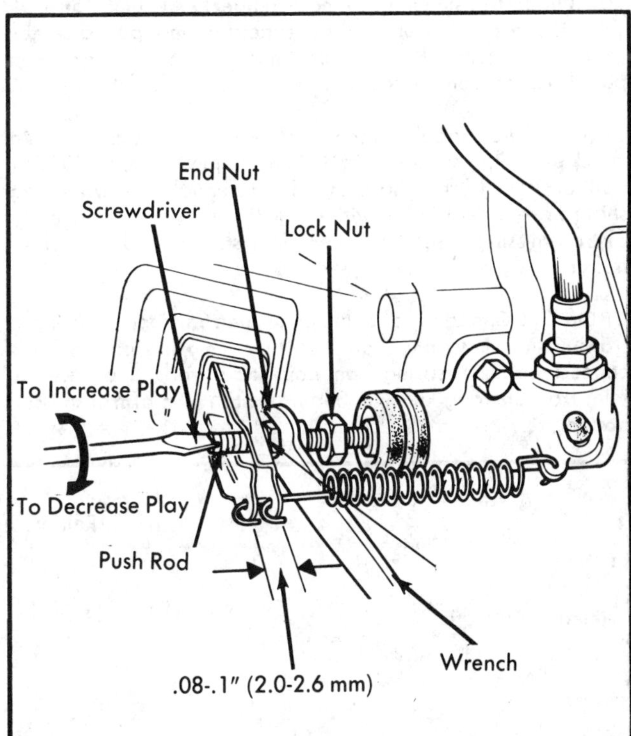

Fig. 3 Clutch Release Fork Adjustment Locations

TIGHTENING SPECIFICATIONS

Application	Ft. Lbs. (mkg)
Master Cylinder-to-Firewall	5-9 (.7-1.2)
Slave Cylinder-to-Clutch Housing	14-18 (1.9-2.5)
Slave Cylinder Hydraulic Line	11-18 (1.5-2.5)
Flywheel	34-38 (4.7-5.3)
Master Cylinder Push Rod Lock Nut	22-29 (3.0-4.0)

HONDA CIVIC & CIVIC CVCC

Civic
Civic CVCC

DESCRIPTION

Clutch is single plate dry disc type, using a diaphragm spring to engage pressure plate. Clutch has a mechanical release system consisting of clutch pedal, cable, clutch release lever, and release bearing.

REMOVAL & INSTALLATION

CLUTCH ASSEMBLY

1) Raise and support vehicle, then remove front wheels. Disconnect battery ground cable at battery and transmission case. Disconnect electrical leads from starter and separate connections for back-up lights. On CVCC models, disconnect leads to temperature sending units. Disconnect clutch cable and on Civic models, remove speedometer cable.

2) On CVCC models, remove right starter motor bolt and two upper transmission mounting bolts. Drain transmission. Place jack under transmission. Remove fender well shield on right side. Remove speedometer drive holder and pull assembly from transmission. Remove subframe crossmember and support bracket from clutch housing front.

3) On Civic models, disconnect lower arm ball joints at knuckles with suitable ball joint remover tool (07941-6340000). Pull drive shafts out of differential case. Drive gear shift rod retainer pin out with a pin driver, then disconnect rod at transmission case. Disconnect gear shift extension at clutch housing.

4) On CVCC models, disconnect torque rod from mounting at transmission. Disconnect gear shift by removing pin, then disconnect stabilizer spring from both radius rods. Separate ball joint from steering knuckle. Separate stub axle of transmission housing.

5) On Civic models, raise and support engine to take load off engine mounts. Remove the two center beam-to-lower engine mount nuts. Remove center beam and engine mount. Reinstall center beam (less mount) and lower engine until it rests on beam.

6) On CVCC models, remove clutch cover, left starter bolt, then remove starter. Remove three rear engine mounting bolts from transmission housing. Remove front transmission bolts and pull transmission rearward off dowels.

7) On Civic models, place a jack under transmission and remove four attaching bolts. Slide transmission away from engine and lower jack until transmission clears vehicle. On all models, loosen pressure plate retaining bolts two turns at a time in a circular pattern, and remove clutch assembly.

8) To install, reverse removal procedure and note the following: Use a suitable aligning pin to center clutch disc on flywheel. When installing pressure plate, align mark on outer edge of flywheel with alignment mark on pressure plate. Tighten pressure plate retaining bolts two turns at a time in a circular pattern to prevent distorting diaphragm spring.

CLUTCH RELEASE LEVER & BEARING

1) With transmission removed, unbend locking tab and remove the 8 mm release arm retaining bolt. Slide release shaft out of transmission case. Slide release arm and release bearing off transmission input shaft as an assembly.

2) Separate release bearing from arm taking care not to damage retaining clip. **NOTE** — *Attempting to remove or install release bearing with release arm in case will damage retaining clip.* Using a suitable bearing driver, separate release bearing from holder.

3) **NOTE** — *Bearing is filled with grease and should not be immersed in cleaning solvent.* To install, reverse removal procedure and note the following: Install release bearing with radiused (rounded) side opposite holder. When installing release shaft and arm, place a lock tab washer under retaining bolt.

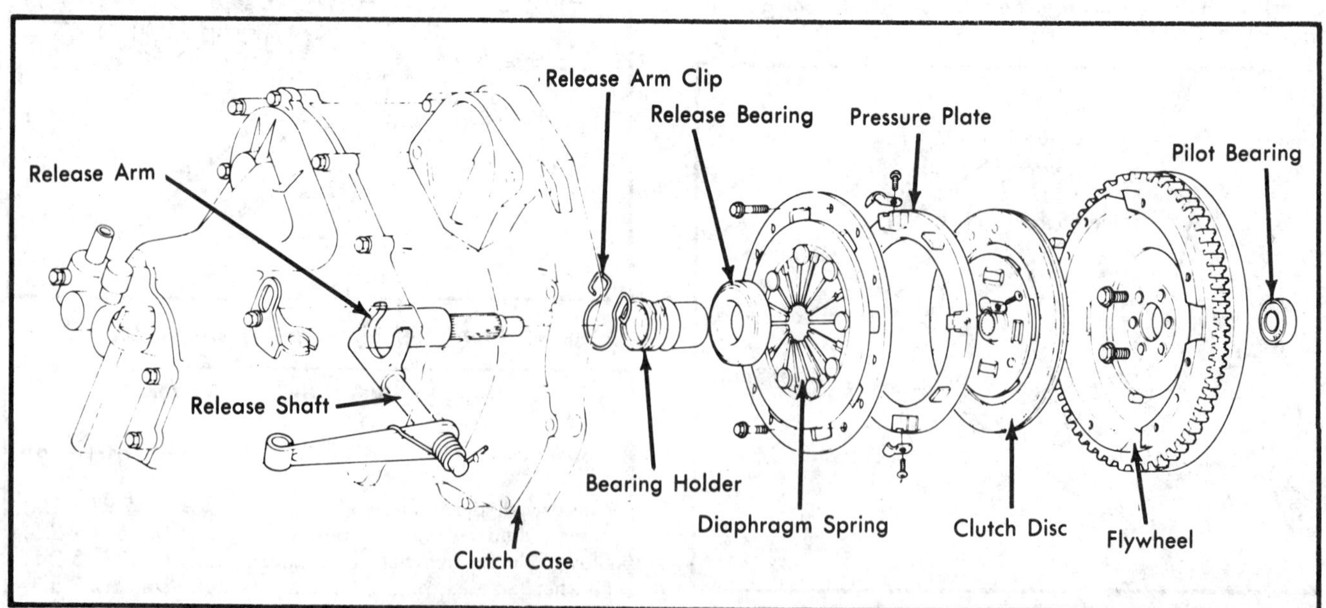

Fig. 1 Exploded View of Clutch Assembly with Bell Housing

HONDA CIVIC & CIVIC CVCC (Cont.)

ADJUSTMENT

CLUTCH PEDAL

1) Check clutch pedal height and if necessary, adjust upper stop so that clutch and brake pedals rest at approximately same height from floor. **NOTE** — *Before adjusting clutch pedal height, make sure brake pedal free play is properly adjusted.*

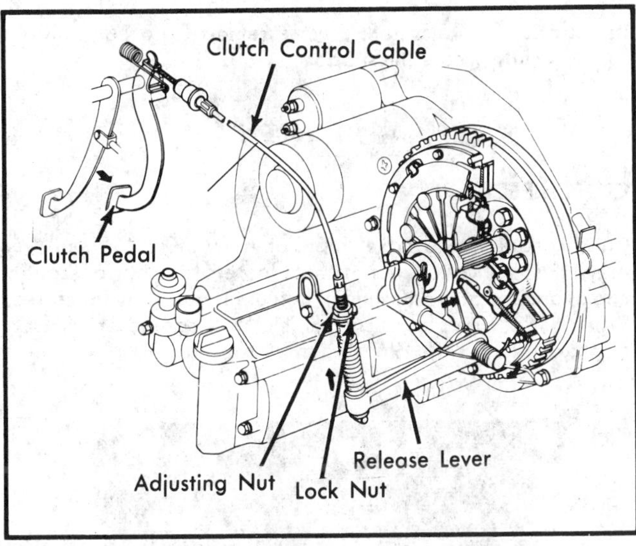

Fig. 2 Clutch Adjustment Point for Civic

2) On Civic models, adjust clutch release lever to .12-.16" (3-4 mm) free play, measured at release lever. Adjustment is made at outer cable housing adjuster near release lever. **NOTE** — *Insure upper and lower adjusting nuts are tightened after adjustment.*

3) On Civic CVCC models, adjust clutch cable clip (near firewall) until pedal free play is approximately .6-.8" (15-20 mm).

4) Check clutch pedal release height as follows: Raise front wheels off ground and place transmission in fourth gear. Depress clutch pedal and start engine. Release pedal until wheels start to turn, and measure pedal height at this point. Pedal release height should be greater than 1.18".

NOTE — *If release lever free play and pedal height are properly adjusted, but pedal release height is not within specifications, clutch components are damaged.*

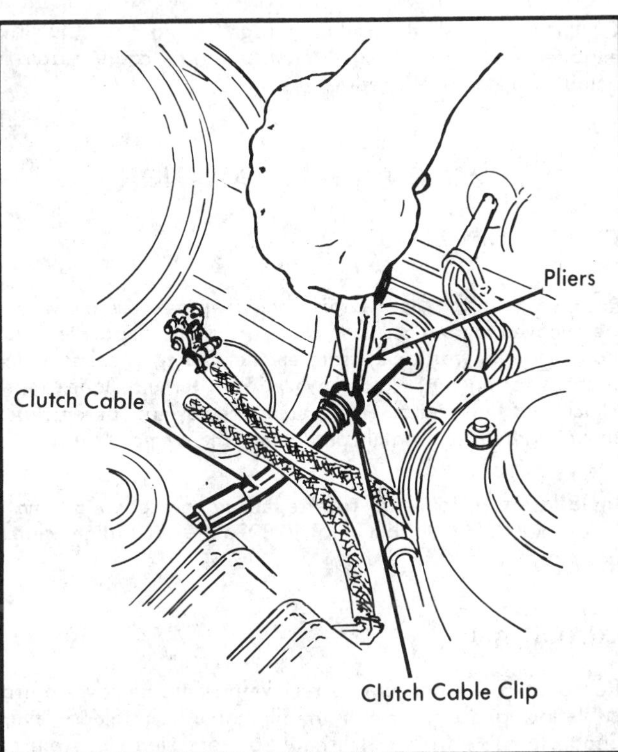

Fig. 3 Clutch Pedal Adjustment Point for CVCC

TIGHTENING SPECIFICATIONS

Application	Ft. Lbs (mkg)
Clutch-to-Flywheel	7-10 (.97-1.3)
Flywheel-to-Crankshaft	34-38 (4.7-5.2)
Release Arm Bracket Bolt	14-20 (1.9-2.7)
Clutch Case-to-Engine (Civic)	29-36 (4.0-4.9)

LANCIA

Lancia
(Except Scorpion)

DESCRIPTION

Clutch is a dry, single disc, diaphragm spring type. Clutch is engaged and disengaged through a control cable. Cable is actuated by the clutch pedal.

REMOVAL & INSTALLATION

CLUTCH ASSEMBLY

Removal – **NOTE** – *Engine and Transaxle assembly must be removed to gain access to clutch assembly.* Separate clutch housing (with transaxle) from engine. Set flywheel so index mark is facing top. Hold flywheel from turning. Index mark clutch and flywheel assembly before removing. Loosen clutch mounting bolts alternately and evenly, then remove clutch.

Installation – To install, reverse removal procedure and note following: Use suitable tool (88023030) to align clutch assembly.

CLUTCH CABLE

Removal – Disconnect and remove battery. Remove control cable lock and adjustment nut. Slip cable from release lever. Separate cable from clutch pedal by removing clevis pin on pedal arm. Remove cable out through engine compartment.

Installation – To install, reverse removal procedure. Make clutch pedal adjustment.

CLUTCH PEDAL

Removal – Loosen lock and adjustment nut on clutch cable. Unhook pedal spring from upper pin. Remove pedal mounting bolt. Pull clutch pedal downward, disconnect cable, remove hook and spring. Remove pedal.

Installation – To install pedal, reverse removal procedure and adjust pedal free play.

RELEASE BEARING

Removal – With transaxle removed or slid back, slide bearing off input shaft. Remove clutch operating lever and bushings. Inspect bushings and replace if excessively worn. Inspect bearing and replace if found worn or defective.

Installation – To install, reverse removal procedure. Make sure to lightly grease the support.

ADJUSTMENT

CLUTCH PEDAL

Clutch pedal should have approximately .590" (15 mm) free play. If specification is not met, loosen lock nut on control cable and rotate adjustment nut until free play is correct. When pedal free play is correct, clutch release lever will have approximately .118-.196" (3-5 mm) free play.

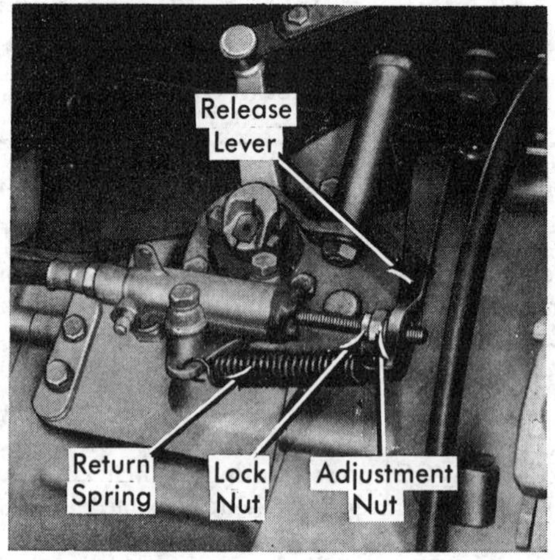

Fig. 1 Clutch Free Play Adjustment Location

LUV

LUV

DESCRIPTION

Clutch assembly is a single disc dry type using a diaphragm spring to disengage pressure plate. Clutch release system is hydraulic, using a firewall mounted master cylinder, a bell housing mounted slave cylinder, and a prelubricated clutch release bearing.

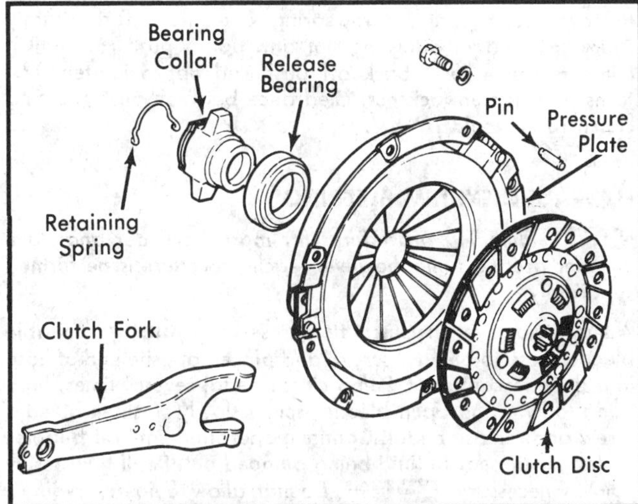

Fig. 1 Exploded View of LUV Clutch Assembly

REMOVAL & INSTALLATION

CLUTCH ASSEMBLY

1) Disconnect negative battery terminal and remove air cleaner assembly. Slide gearshift lever boot upwards on lever, remove gearshift lever attaching bolts, and remove lever assembly. Remove starter attaching bolts, and lay starter aside.

2) Raise vehicle on hoist and disconnect exhaust pipe hanger at transmission. Disconnect speedometer cable at transmission. Remove propeller shaft. **NOTE** — *Drain transmission oil or insert a plug into rear extension to prevent oil spillage.*

3) Disconnect clutch slave cylinder from transmission, and wire cylinder to frame. Remove flywheel inspection cover. Disconnect transmission from crossmember, raise transmission and engine assembly slightly, and remove crossmember. Lower engine and transmission assembly, and support rear of engine.

4) Disconnect electrical leads at transmission. Remove transmission to engine attaching bolts and remove transmission. **NOTE** — *When removing transmission, pull straight back until disengaged from clutch, then tip front of transmission downward to remove.*

5) Mark pressure plate and flywheel for reassembly reference. Loosen clutch to flywheel attaching bolts one turn at a time until spring pressure is released. Support clutch assembly with a suitable clutch aligning tool, remove bolts, and remove clutch.

6) To install, apply a thin coat of Lubriplate or equivalent to clutch disc splines. Install clutch assembly to flywheel, matching alignment marks made at disassembly. Use a suitable clutch alignment tool to center clutch assembly on flywheel, then install and tighten attaching bolts. To complete installation, reverse removal procedure.

CLUTCH MASTER CYLINDER

Disconnect clutch pedal arm from push rod, and disconnect hydraulic line from master cylinder. Remove nuts attaching master cylinder, and remove cylinder towards engine compartment. To install, reverse removal procedure, adjust pedal height, and bleed hydraulic system.

CLUTCH SLAVE CYLINDER

Remove slave cylinder mounting bolts and push rod from clutch fork. Disconnect hydraulic line from slave cylinder, and remove cylinder. To install, reverse removal procedure, adjust free play at clutch fork, and bleed hydraulic system.

CLUTCH RELEASE BEARING

1) Remove shift fork boot from transmission case. Disconnect shift fork spring clip from shift fork ball stud, and remove shift fork and release bearing. If necessary, remove shift fork ball stud from front cover.

2) Inspect all parts for wear, damage or distortion, replace as necessary. **CAUTION** — *Do not wash release bearing in any cleaning solution as bearing is permanently lubricated.* To install, lubricate all contact surfaces with graphite grease, and reverse removal procedure.

PILOT BEARING

Check pilot bearing for seizing, sticking, abnormal noise or wear. If replacement is required, use a suitable tool (J-23907) to remove bearing. **NOTE** — *Do not wash bearing in any cleaning solution as bearing is permanently lubricated.*

OVERHAUL

CLUTCH MASTER CYLINDER

1) Drain clutch fluid reservoir completely. Remove boot and retaining clip, and remove push rod. Remove stopper, piston, cup and return spring. Clean all parts in clean brake fluid.

2) Inspect all parts for wear or damage. Piston-to-bore clearance should be no more than .001-.004" (.025-.102 mm). **NOTE** — *Manufacturer recommends that cup seal be replaced any time master cylinder is disassembled.*

3) Lubricate all parts with clean brake fluid, then reassemble in reverse order of disassembly and note the following: Reinstall cup seal carefully to prevent scratching lipped portions.

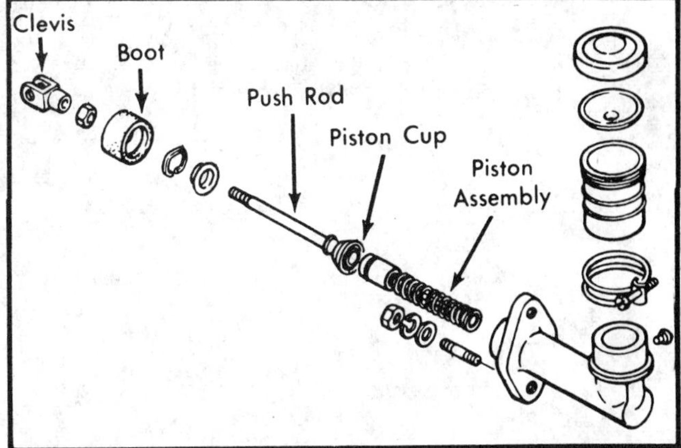

Fig. 2 Exploded View of Clutch Master Cylinder Showing Relationship of Internal Components

LUV (Cont.)

CLUTCH SLAVE CYLINDER

1) Remove push rod and boot, then force out piston by blowing compressed air into cylinder at hose connection. Clean all parts in clean brake fluid. Inspect all parts for wear or damage. Piston to bore clearance should be no more than .001-.004" (.025-.102 mm).

2) **NOTE** — *Manufacturer recommends that piston cup be replaced any time slave cylinder is disassembled.* Lubricate all parts with clean brake fluid, then reassemble in reverse order of disassembly and note the following: Reinstall cup seal carefully to prevent scratching lipped portions. Fill slave cylinder with brake fluid before bleeding.

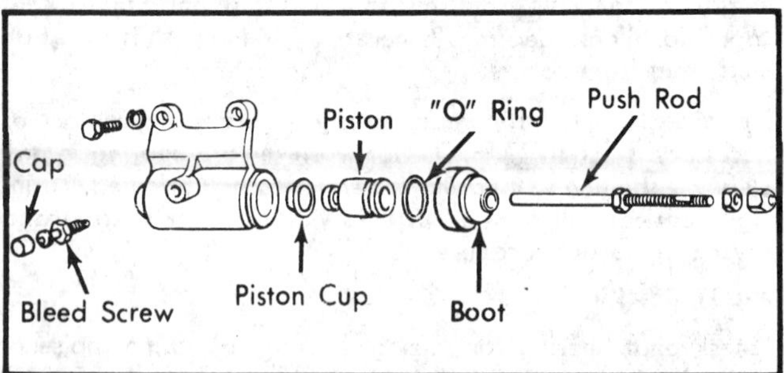

Fig. 3 Exploded View of Clutch Slave Cylinder

ADJUSTMENT

CLUTCH PEDAL HEIGHT

1) Disconnect battery ground cable. Measure clutch pedal height after making sure pedal is fully returned by pedal return spring. Correct pedal height is 5.9-6.3". If adjustment is required, disconnect clutch switch wiring, remove switch lock nut, and remove switch from bracket by rotating counterclockwise.

2) Loosen lock nut on pedal push rod, rotate push rod to obtain specified pedal height, and tighten lock nut. Install clutch switch. Adjust clearance between switch housing (not switch actuating pin) and clutch pedal tab to .02-.04", and tighten lock nut. Connect clutch switch wiring and battery cable. Insure clutch pedal has approximately 25/32" free travel.

CLUTCH FORK FREE PLAY

Remove clutch fork return spring and move fork slightly rearward. Loosen adjusting nut and adjust push rod until it contacts clutch fork. Back off push rod approximately 1¾ turns and tighten lock nut. Clearance between push rod and clutch fork should be 5/64".

HYDRAULIC SYSTEM BLEEDING

NOTE — *Bleeding procedures for master cylinder and slave cylinder are the same, however, each procedure is performed separately.*

Adjust fluid level in clutch fluid reservoir. Attach a suitable bleeder hose to bleeder screw, and place opposite end of hose into a clean container. Pump clutch pedal several times, hold pedal down, and open bleeder screw slowly. Tighten bleeder screw and release pedal. Continue operation until air bubbles no longer appear in fluid being pumped out. Refill fluid reservoir as necessary. **NOTE** — *Do not allow fluid reservoir to empty during bleeding operation.* Check operation of clutch assembly.

TIGHTENING SPECIFICATIONS

Application	Ft. Lbs. (mkg)
Clutch-to-Flywheel	13 (1.8)
Transmission-to-Engine	27 (3.7)
Shift Fork Ball Stud	30 (4.2)

MAZDA, EXCEPT GLC

808 (1300 cc) Mizer
808 (1600 cc)
RX-3SP
RX-4
Cosmo
Rotary Pickup

DESCRIPTION

Clutch is a dry, single disc, diaphragm spring type. Clutch actuation is hydraulic. A firewall mounted master cylinder inconjunction with a clutch housing mounted slave cylinder is used. System uses a prelubricated clutch release bearing. All clutch assemblies are similar but, some models (808) have different clutch fork configurations. Also, 808 (1300 cc) models have adjustable clutch fork free play.

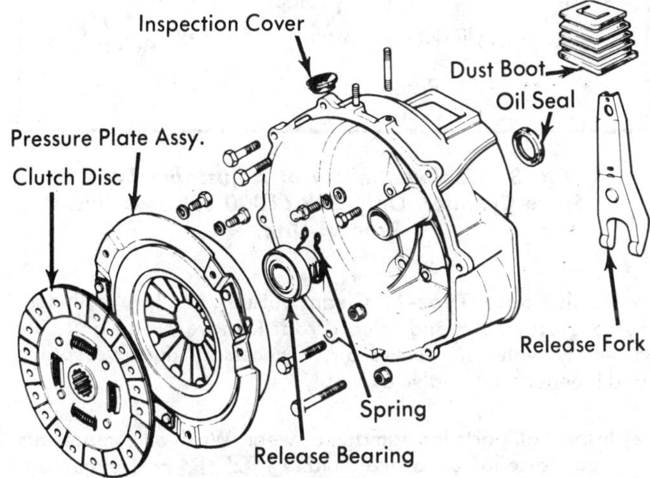

Fig. 1 Exploded View of Mazda Clutch Assembly. Illustration Shown is for Cosmo, RX-3SP, RX-4 and Rotary Pickup. 808 Models Have Clutch Release Fork Mounted Through Side of Clutch Housing.

REMOVAL & INSTALLATION

CLUTCH ASSEMBLY

NOTE — *Removal procedure outlined is designed for all models. Procedure is general. Some models may have slight individual differences.*

1) Disconnect battery ground cable. From inside driver's compartment, remove console (if equipped) and disassemble gearshift lever. Raise and suitably support engine and transmission.

2) Remove electrical leads from starter and transmission mounted switches. Disconnect power brake vacuum line from clutch housing (if equipped). Separate electrical wire harness from bracket located near starter housing. Disconnect exhaust pipe from manifold. It may be necessary to remove entire front portion of exhaust pipe on some models. Remove speedometer cable from extension housing.

3) Disconnect slave cylinder from transmission housing and remove starter. Disconnect propeller shaft at rear axle and slide shaft from transmission. Insert suitable plug (49 0259 440) into transmission to prevent fluid loss.

4) Support transmission with a jack, disconnect crossmember at transmission and side supports, and remove crossmember. Remove transmission attaching bolts, slide transmission rearward until input shaft clears clutch splines, and remove transmission.

5) Note flywheel and pressure plate index marks for reassembly reference. Install a suitable flywheel holding tool, and loosen clutch attaching bolts (noting where special bolts go) one turn at a time until spring pressure is released. Remove clutch assembly.

6) To install, reverse removal procedure and note the following:

- On piston engine models, lubricate pilot bearing in crankshaft with grease prior to installing clutch.
- Use clutch aligning tool to center disc and pressure plate on flywheel.
- Bleed hydraulic system.

CLUTCH MASTER CYLINDER

Removal & Installation — Disconnect hydraulic line from master cylinder. Remove nuts mounting cylinder to firewall. Unhook clutch pedal from cylinder push rod. Remove cylinder. To install, reverse removal procedure and bleed hydraulic system.

CLUTCH SLAVE CYLINDER

Disconnect hydraulic line from cylinder, disconnect return spring from clutch fork, remove cylinder attaching nuts and remove slave cylinder from clutch housing. To install, reverse removal procedure, adjust clutch fork free play (if applicable) and bleed hydraulic system.

CLUTCH RELEASE BEARING & FORK

With transmission removed, disconnect return spring for release bearing and slide bearing off transmission front cover. Pull release fork outward until spring clip releases from ball pivot, and remove fork from clutch housing. To install, apply a light coat of grease to all contact surfaces and reverse removal procedure. NOTE — *Bearing is prelubricated and should not be washed in any solevent or cleaning solution.*

PILOT BEARING

Rotary Engine Models — 1) Remove nut mounting flywheel to eccentric shaft. Free flywheel from shaft. It may be necessary to use puller to remove flywheel.

2) Use suitable puller (49 0823 070A) to remove pilot bearing and seals.

3) Use same tool mentioned in step **2)** or a driver to seat new bearing into shaft. Fit new seals.

Piston Engine Models — Pilot bearing is pressed into flywheel. If replacement is required, remove using a suitable puller. To install lubricate bearing with grease and install into flywheel using a driver.

MAZDA, EXCEPT GLC (Cont.)

OVERHAUL

CLUTCH MASTER CYLINDER

1) Clean outside of master cylinder thoroughly and drain brake fluid. Remove dust boot, retaining clip, and retaining washer. Remove piston assembly, primary cup and return spring from cylinder. Remove reservoir from cylinder.

2) Wash all parts in clean alcohol or brake fluid. **CAUTION** – *Do not use gasoline or kerosene.* Check all parts for wear or damage, replace as necessary. Check clearance between piston and cylinder bore. If clearance exceeds .006", replace piston or cylinder as necessary. Ensure that compensating port on cylinder is open.

3) To assemble, reverse disassembly procedure and note the following: Before assembly, dip piston and cups in clean brake fluid. Install primary cup so that flat side of cup is against piston. When assembled, fill reservoir with brake fluid and operate piston with a screwdriver until fluid is ejected at outlet port.

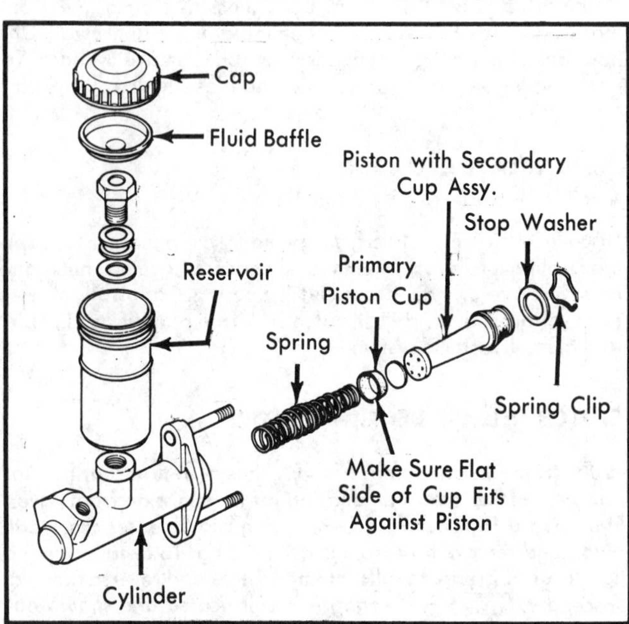

Fig. 2 Exploded View of Clutch Master Cylinder. All Models Use Same Basic Master Cylinder 808 Models Have Slightly Different Fluid Reservoir.

CLUTCH SLAVE CYLINDER

Adjustable Type-1) Clean outside of slave cylinder thoroughly, and remove dust boot, release rod, and spring assembly. Remove piston and cups from cylinder. **NOTE** – *If necessary, apply compressed air to fluid inlet passage to remove piston and cups.*

2) Inspect all parts for wear or damage. Wash all parts in clean alcohol or brake fluid. **CAUTION** – *Do not use gasoline or kerosene.*Check clearance between piston and cylinder bore. If clearance exceeds .006", replace cylinder or piston as necessary.

3) Coat all components with clean brake fluid. Fit cups to piston and install into cylinder. Install rubber dust boot and bleeder valve assembly. Install clutch release rod.

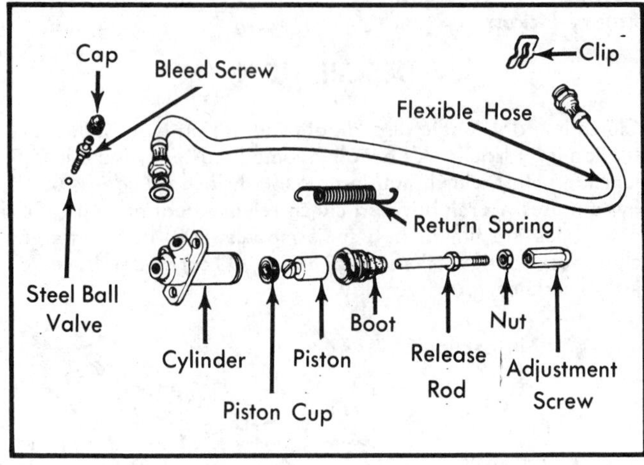

Fig. 3 Exploded View of Adjustable Type Slave Cylinder. Only 808 (1300 cc) Uses this Type of Unit.

Nonadjustable Type-1) Clean outside of slave cylinder. Remove dust boot and release rod. Remove piston and cup assembly with compressed air, if necessary. Remove spring and bleeder screw/valve assembly.

2) Inspect all parts for damage or wear. Wash all components in clean alcohol or brake fluid. **CAUTION** – *Do not use gasoline or kerosene.* Check clearance between piston and cylinder bore. If clearance exceeds .006" (.15 mm), replace cylinder or piston as necessary.

3) Install spring into cylinder. Fit piston cup to piston and slip them into cylinder. Install release rod into cylinder and fit dust boot. Install valve and bleeder screw.

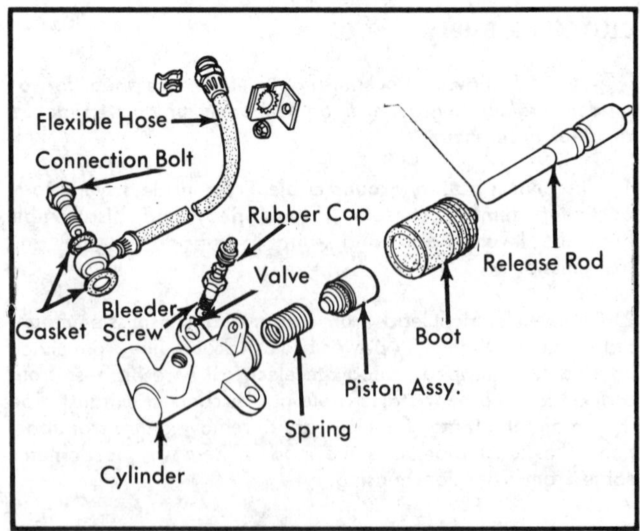

Fig. 4 Exploded View of Nonadjustable Slave Clyinder. Only 808 (1300 cc) DOES NOT Use This Type Unit.

MAZDA, EXCEPT GLC (Cont.)

ADJUSTMENT

CLUTCH PEDAL FREE PLAY

Loosen lock nut and turn push rod until clutch pedal free play is .02-.12" (.5-3.0 mm).

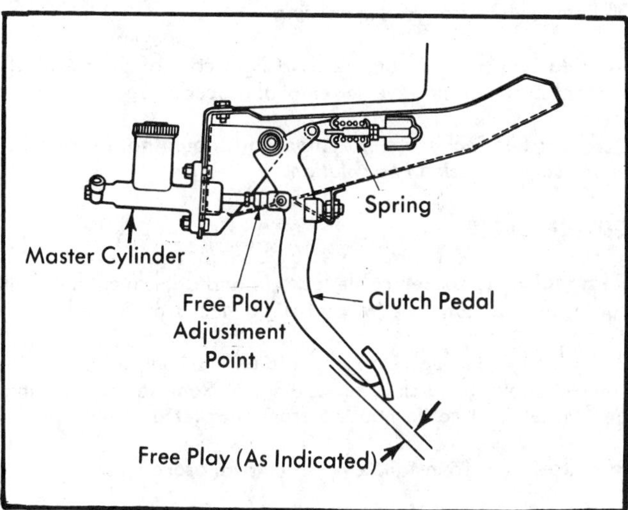

Fig. 5 Clutch Pedal Free Play Adjustment Location

CLUTCH FORK FREE PLAY

808 (1300 cc) Models – Remove clutch fork return spring. Loosen lock nut. Turn adjustment nut until free play is approximately .010-.140" (2.5-3.5 mm). Tighten lock nut. Reconnect return spring to clutch fork.

HYDRAULIC SYSTEM BLEEDING

1) Clutch hydraulic system must be bled whenever a fluid line has been disconnected or air has entered system. To bleed system, remove rubber cap on slave cylinder bleeder screw and attach a hose.

2) Place opposite end of hose into a jar partially filled with brake fluid. Open bleeder screw, depress clutch pedal, and allow pedal to return slowly. Continue operation until air bubbles cease to appear in discharged fluid, then close bleeder screw. **NOTE** – *During bleeding operation, master cylinder reservoir must be kept at least ¾ full of brake fluid.*

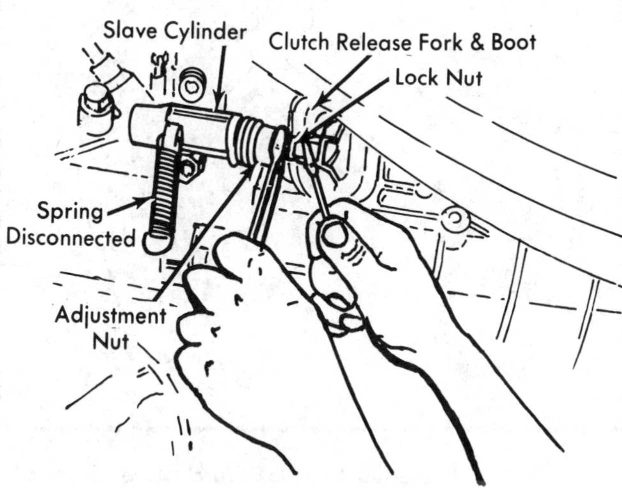

Fig. 6 Making Clutch Release Fork Free Play Adjustment on 808 (1300 cc) Models

TIGHTENING SPECIFICATIONS

Application	Ft. Lbs. (mkg)
Flywheel-to-Crankshaft (Piston Engines)	112-118 (15.5-16.3)
Flywheel-to-Eccentric Shaft (Rotary Engines)	289-362 (40-50)
Clutch-to-Flywheel	13-20 (1.8-2.7)

MAZDA GLC

DESCRIPTION

Clutch is a dry, single disc, diaphragm type, and cable actuated. A prelubricated clutch release bearing is used and is located in the transmission housing.

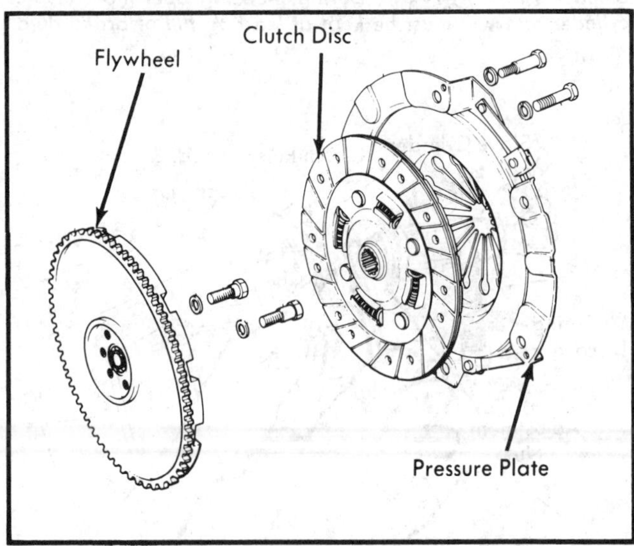

Fig. 1 Exploded View of Clutch Assembly

REMOVAL & INSTALLATION

CLUTCH ASSEMBLY

Removal – 1) Disconnect battery ground cable. Remove gear shift lever from inside of driver's compartment.

2) Raise vehicle and then support engine and transmission. Disconnect electrical wires from transmission. Remove electrical wires from starter then remove starter.

3) Disconnect exhaust pipe from exhaust manifold and speedometer cable from extension housing on transmission. Disconnect propeller shaft at rear axle and slide shaft from transmission.

NOTE – *Insert a suitable plug into transmission tail housing to prevent fluid leakage.*

4) Support transmission with a jack, disconnect crossmember at transmission and at side supports. Remove crossmember.

5) Remove transmission attaching bolts and slide transmission rearward until input shaft clears clutch splines. Remove transmission.

6) Note flywheel and pressure plate index mark for reassembly reference. Install a flywheel holding tool and loosen clutch attaching bolts one turn at a time until spring pressure is released. Remove clutch assembly.

Installation – To install, reverse removal procedure while noting the following:
Lubricate clutch pilot bearing in crankshaft with grease prior to installing clutch.
Use a clutch aligning tool to center disc on flywheel.
Adjust clutch pedal free play.

CLUTCH RELEASE BEARING & FORK

Removal – 1) With transmission removed, disconnect return spring for release bearing.

2) Slide bearing off transmission front cover. Pull release fork outward until spring clip releases from ball pivot.

3) Remove fork from clutch housing.

Installation – To install, apply a light coat of grease to all contact surfaces and reverse removal procedure.

NOTE – *Bearing is prelubricated and should not be washed in any solvent or cleaning solution.*

CLUTCH CABLE

Removal – 1) Loosen cable lock nut and adjustment nut. Pull cable toward clutch pedal and disconnect from pedal.

2) Push cable through stop ring into engine compartment. Disconnect cable at clutch lever. See *Fig. 2.* Remove retainer ring at bracket. Pull cable housing from bracket and remove.

Installation – To install, reverse removal procedure.

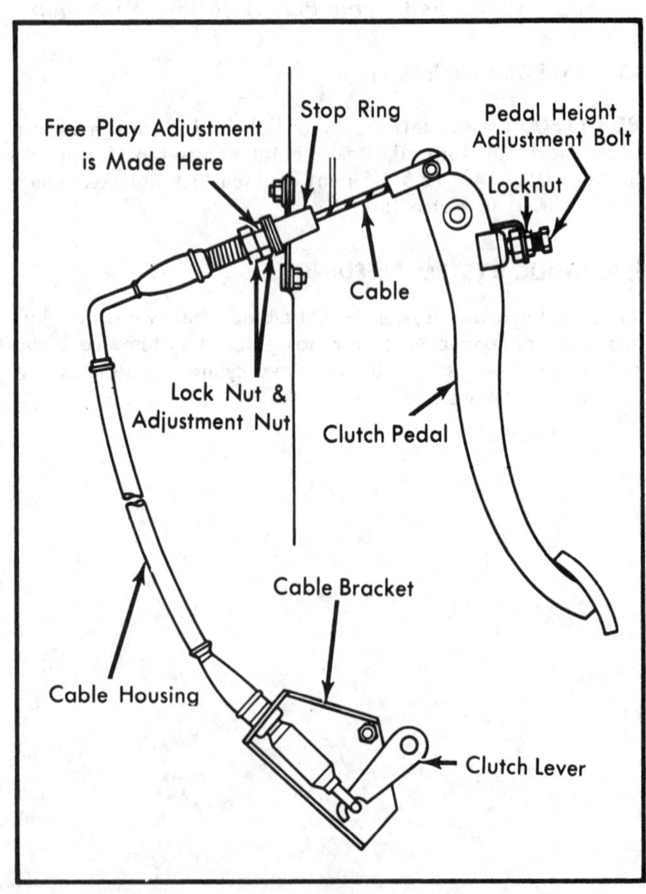

Fig. 2 Installed View of Clutch Cable with Detail of Items to Disconnect for Cable Removal. Illustration Also Shows Pedal Height Location.

MAZDA GLC (Cont.)

PILOT BEARING

Pilot bearing is pressed into flywheel. If replacement is required, remove using a puller. To install, lubricate bearing with grease and install into flywheel using a driver.

ADJUSTMENT

CLUTCH PEDAL HEIGHT

Loosen lock nut *(Fig. 2)* and turn adjusting bolt until pedal height is approximately 7.48" (190 mm). Tighten lock nut. Check clutch pedal free play.

CLUTCH PEDAL

Pedal Free Play – **1)** Loosen lock nut on clutch cable (engine compartment side of firewall).

2) Pull outer clutch cable (housing) away from firewall and measure distance from adjusting nut to cable housing protruding through firewall.

3) Measurement should be .06-.09" (1.5-2.25 mm). If not, turn adjusting nut until correct specification is obtained.

4) Tighten lock nut then check clutch pedal free play. Free play should now be .39-.59" (10-15 mm). If not, readjust clutch cable.

TIGHTENING SPECIFICATIONS

Application	Ft. Lbs. (mkg)
Flywheel-to-Engine	60-65 (8.0-9.0)
Pressure Plate Assembly-to-Flywheel	13-20 (1.8-2.7)

MERCEDES-BENZ

240D

DESCRIPTION

Dry single disc type clutch uses a diaphragm spring type pressure plate. Clutch actuation is hydraulic, using a clutch pedal mounted master cylinder and a clutch housing mounted slave cylinder. A pedal mounted over-center spring assists in clutch pedal actuation. A sealed prelubricated clutch release bearing is also used.

REMOVAL & INSTALLATION

Removal – 1) Disconnect battery ground cable. Remove rear crossmember, after supporting transmission on a suitable jack or stand. Remove exhaust pipe and supporting bracket. Loosen propeller shaft center bearing, remove propeller shaft-to-transmission bolts. Push propeller shaft towards the rear.

2) Remove tachometer drive from rear of transmission. Remove clutch slave cylinder and pull towards the rear with lines connected, until rod is released from clutch housing. Remove shift linkage from transmission shift levers. Remove starter.

3) Remove transmission-to-intermediate flange attaching bolts (removing two upper bolts last). Pull transmission out horizontally, until input shaft is clear of clutch. Then remove in a downward direction.

4) Loosen pressure plate attaching bolts 1 to 1½ turns at a time until tension is released, then remove all bolts, pressure plate and clutch disc.

Installation – 1) To install, center clutch disc on flywheel using an aligning tool and install pressure plate. Tighten bolts 1 to 1½ turns at a time until tight.

CAUTION – *During installation, make sure that clutch is fully pulled into recess in flywheel.*

2) To complete installation, reverse removal procedure. Bleed slave cylinder and check hydraulic fluid level. Check clutch adjustment and shift linkage adjustment.

RELEASE BEARING & LEVER

1) Remove release bearing from bearing tube on front transmission cover. Move release lever down and to the left, and pull from ball pin on clutch housing.

2) To install, apply a suitable lubricant to all bearing and lever contact surfaces, and reverse removal procedure.

CLUTCH MASTER CYLINDER

1) Remove floor mats and lining from driver compartment, and remove cover under instrument panel. Siphon sufficient fluid from fluid reservoir to bring level below minimum mark. Loosen input line by pulling elbow out of rubber clamping ring on master cylinder.

2) Disconnect pressure line from master cylinder and unscrew master cylinder from pedal assembly. Remove master cylinder with connecting hose. Push rod remains on clutch pedal.

3) To install, reverse removal procedure, adjust fluid level in fluid reservoir, adjust master cylinder push rod length, and bleed hydraulic system.

CLUTCH SLAVE CYLINDER

1) Disconnect hydraulic line from slave cylinder, then plug line with a rubber cap to prevent loss of fluid. Remove bolts attaching cylinder to clutch housing, and remove slave cylinder and push rod from housing as an assembly.

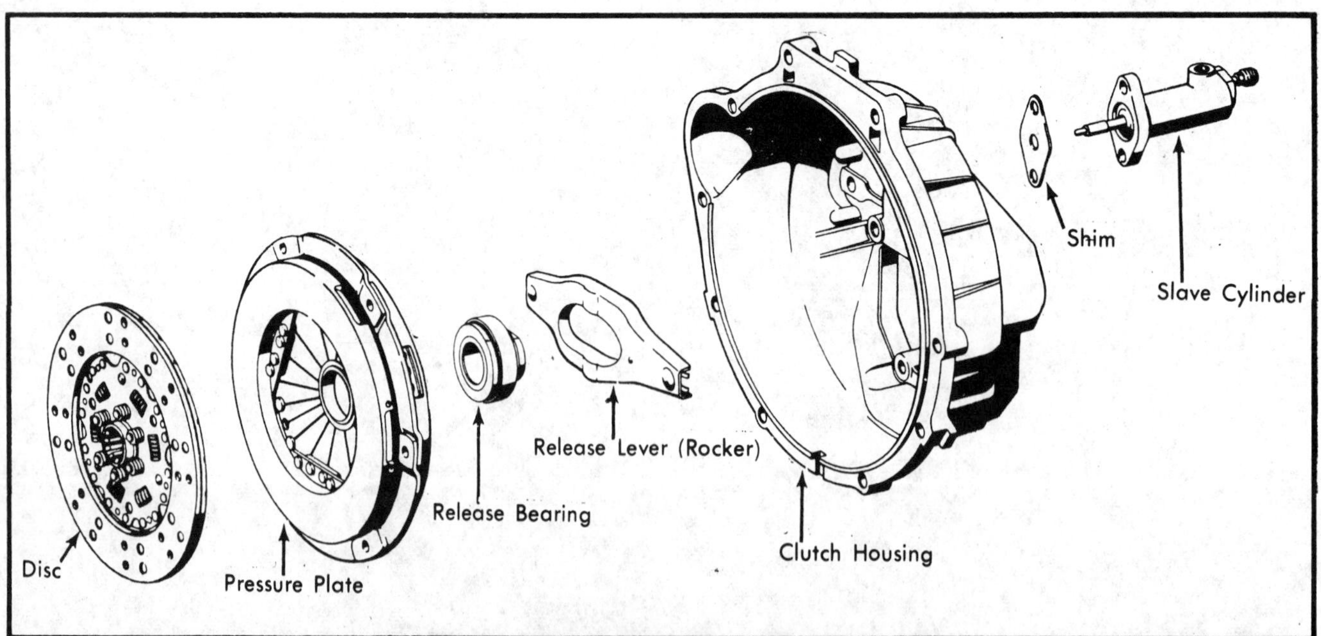

Fig. 1 Mercedes 240D Clutch Components

MERCEDES-BENZ (Cont.)

NOTE – *Take care not to lose plastic shim installed between cylinder and housing. Shim is recessed to accomodate inspection gauge.*

2) To install, place shim with grooved end against clutch housing and hold in position. Insert slave cylinder with push rod into clutch housing, and install and tighten mounting bolts. Connect hydraulic line to cylinder, and bleed hydraulic system.

NOTE – *Wear on clutch disc may only be checked using special inspection gauge inserted in groove of plastic shim. Disc is serviceable if notches on gauge disappear in flange. If notches remain visible, wear limit is exceeded and disc must be replaced. See illustration.*

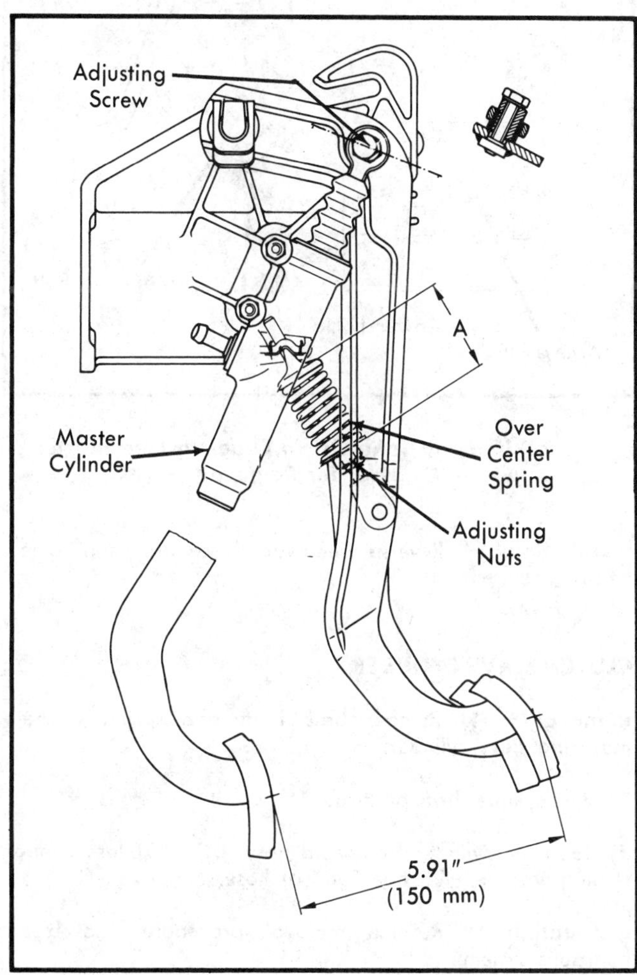

Fig. 2 Clutch Pedal Assembly with Master Cylinder and Over Center Spring

Clearance between master cylinder piston and push rod should be .008" (.2 mm). To adjust, loosen hex nut of eccentric adjusting screw and turn screw until proper clearance is obtained.

OVER CENTER SPRING

Adjust nuts at bottom of over center spring so that spring length measured across retainers is 2.05±.02" (52±.5 mm). Improper adjustment will result in failure of pedal to return when released or excess pressure required to depress pedal.

HYDRAULIC SYSTEM BLEEDING

With Pressure Bleeder – **1** Connect pressure line of bleeder to opened bleeder screw of slave cylinder. Fluid reservoir of vehicle should be almost empty so that brake fluid can flow from bottom upward through system, allowing air to escape in upward direction.

2) Make sure bleeder is set at lowest possible pressure, and watch reservoir to prevent overflow of fluid. When fluid approaches maximum level in reservoir, remove bleeder and close bleeder screw. Adjust fluid level in reservoir, if necessary, to maximum level in reservoir.

With Assistance of Brake System – **1**) Check fluid level in reservoir and make sure it is at maximum level. Place a hose on bleeder screw of right front brake caliper and open screw. Press down on brake pedal until hose is filled with brake fluid and no more air bubbles are showing.

2) Place opposite end of hose on clutch slave cylinder bleeder screw, and open screw. Keep pressure on brake pedal. Close bleeder screw on caliper and release brake pedal. Repeat operation until no more air bubbles appear at fluid reservoir.

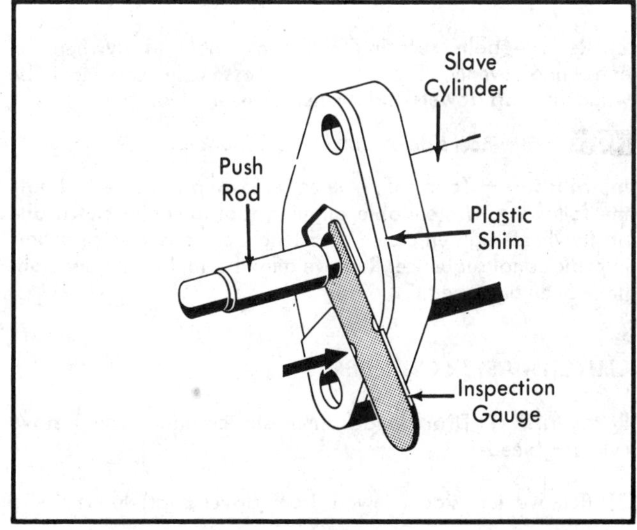

Fig. 3 Checking for Clutch Disc Wear

MGB

MGB

DESCRIPTION

Clutch is single dry disc type, using a diaphragm spring type pressure plate. Clutch actuation is hydraulic, using a firewall mounted master cylinder and a bell housing mounted slave cylinder. Release bearing is graphite type, and is mounted in a cup which fits into fork of clutch release lever.

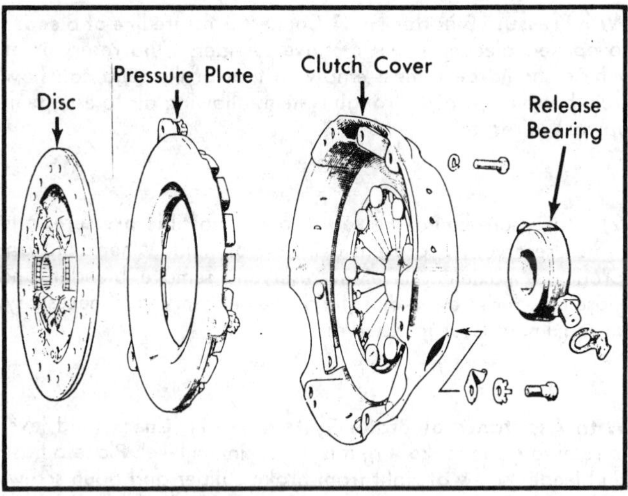

Fig. 1 Exploded View of Clutch Assembly

REMOVAL & INSTALLATION

CLUTCH ASSEMBLY

1) Remove engine. *See Engine Removal in ENGINE Section.*

2) Remove bolts securing clutch assembly to flywheel by extracting evenly. Pressure plate assembly can now be withdrawn off dowels and further disassembled.

NOTE – *Flywheel side of clutch disc is marked.*

Installation – To install, reverse removal procedure and note the following: Use suitable aligning tool to center clutch disc on flywheel. Tighten clutch attaching bolts one turn at a time in a diagonal sequence. Remove aligning tool only after bolts have been tightened.

CLUTCH MASTER CYLINDER

Removal – 1) Drain fluid from master cylinder through slave cylinder bleeder.

2) Remove left side (viewed from drives seat) lower facia panel.

3) Pull out rubber access plug in bulkhead. *See Fig. 2.*

4) Remove 8 screws holding cover plate and seal to pedal box.

5) Separate push rod from clutch pedal at clevis pin.

6) Disconnect hydraulic outlet line.

7) Remove mounting hardware holding master cylinder to pedal box.

NOTE – *Access to lower bolt is achieved inside car through hole in bulkhead.*

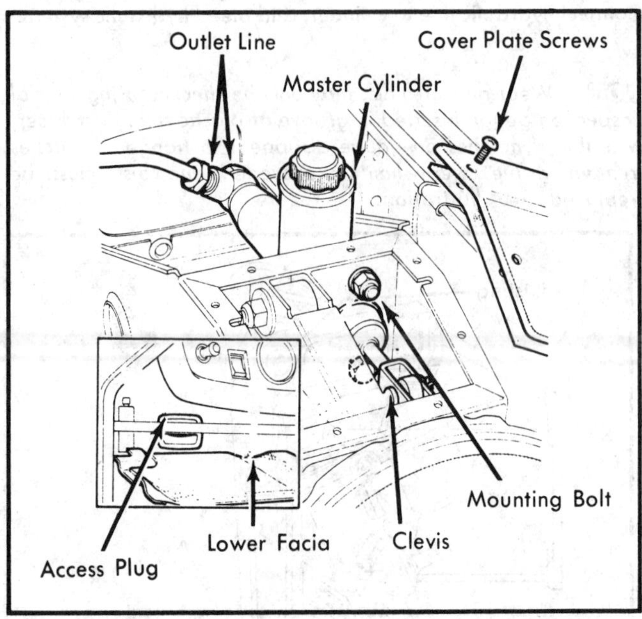

Fig. 2 Items to Take Off in Order to Free Master Cylinder for Removal

Installation – Reverse removal procedure and bleed hydraulic system.

CLUTCH SLAVE CYLINDER

Removal – 1) Remove both bolts and spring washers mounting slave cylinder.

2) Slide cylinder from push rod.

3) Separate cylinder from fluid hose. DO NOT lose copper sealing washer. Plug open end of hose.

Installation – Reverse removal procedure and bleed hydraulic system.

CLUTCH RELEASE BEARING

Removal – 1) Remove transmission.

2) Separate clutch assembly from transmission.

3) Release clips keeping release bearing to clutch fork by rotating clips forward.

4) Slide out release bearing and remove mounting clips.

MGB (Cont.)

Installation – Reverse removal procedure and note: Make sure clips are installed with spring arm of clip facing AWAY from release bearing.

OVERHAUL

CLUTCH MASTER CYLINDER

Disassembly – 1) Make sure all fluid is drained.

2) Separate dust boot from body by sliding along push rod.

3) Free circlip retaining push rod.

4) Withdraw push rod along with circlip, dished washer and rubber boot.

5) Remove piston with secondary seal cup.

6) Remove piston washer, main cup, seal spring retainer and spring.

7) Remove secondary cup seal from piston by stretching over end of piston.

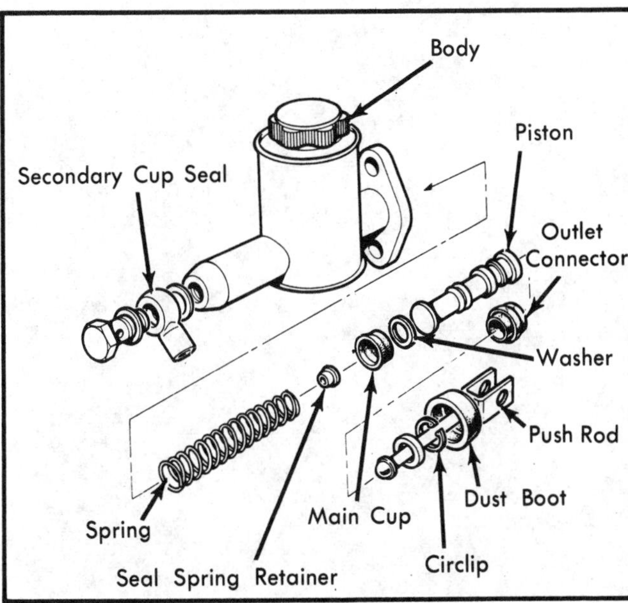

Fig. 3 Exploded View of MGB Clutch Master Cylinder Internal Components – Note That Seals are Normally Replaced During Each Overhaul

Inspection – 1) Wash master cylinder body in alcohol and dry.

2) Clean internal parts in brake fluid.

3) Check cylinder bore for score marks or deep ridges. New seal will hold if damage is slight.

Reassembly – 1) Lightly coat all internal components in brake fluid.

2) Slip new secondary cup seal over piston. Make sure seal lip faces toward rear of piston.

3) Fit spring retainer into small end of spring. Insert spring into body, large diameter first.

4) Install main cup seal, washer, piston, and push rod. Fit lip edge of cup seals first.

5) Put circlip on, then boot.

CLUTCH SLAVE CYLINDER

Disassembly – 1) Release retaining ring. Pull dust cover back.

2) Remove the small inside retaining ring from dust cover.

3) Force air pressure into fluid connector port. This will remove:

- Piston
- Cup
- Spring Retainer
- Spring

4) Remove bleeder screw.

Inspection – 1) Wash cylinder body in alcohol.

2) Clean internal parts with brake fluid.

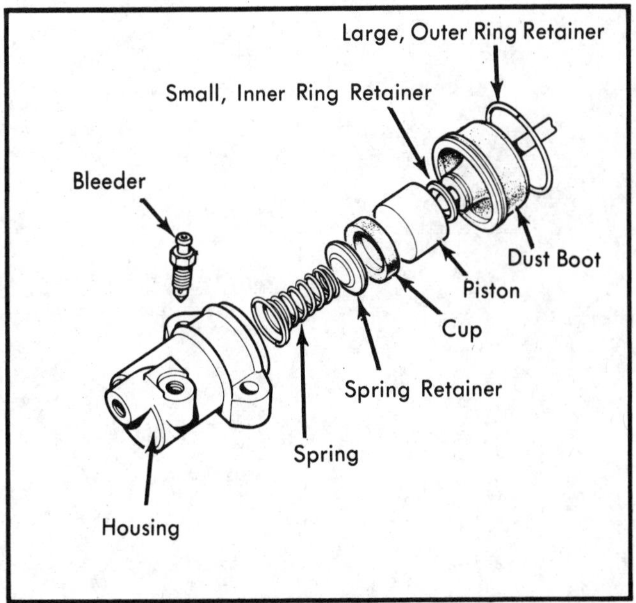

Fig. 4 Exploded View of MGB Clutch Slave Cylinder Showing Detail of Internal Components

MGB (Cont.)

3) Check bore for scoring or ridge marks, replace as necessary.

Reassembly – **1)** Lightly coat all internal components with brake fluid.

2) Insert return spring with small end fitted to spring retainer.

3) Fit NEW cup seal, lip toward spring retainer.

4) Fit flat surface of piston to seal.

5) Fit small inner retaining ring, dust boot and large outer ring retainer.

6) Install bleed screw after making sure there is no restriction in orifice.

ADJUSTMENT

HYDRAULIC BLEEDING

1) Fill master cylinder.

2) Attach bleed tube to bleed valve on slave cylinder. Submerge free end into container part full with brake fluid.

3) Open bleed valve ¾ turn.

4) Slowly depress clutch pedal to let air escape.

5) Close bleed valve.

6) Let pedal return unassisted.

7) Pause.

8) Repeat procedure never letting master cylinder run dry.

MG MIDGET

Midget

DESCRIPTION

The clutch is a single, dry-disc type, using a diaphragm spring type pressure plate. Clutch actuation is hydraulic. Hydraulic components are a firewall-mounted master cylinder and a clutch housing-mounted slave cylinder. The hydraulic design of the clutch control eliminates the necessity of pedal adjustment.

REMOVAL & INSTALLATION

CLUTCH ASSEMBLY

Remove engine. See *Engine Removal in ENGINE Section*. If engine and transmission are removed as an assembly, disconnect and remove transmission. Mark all parts for reassembly reference, then loosen clutch attaching bolts one turn at a time until pressure plate spring tension is released. Remove attaching bolts and clutch assembly. To install, use a suitable aligning tool to center disc on flywheel, and reverse removal procedure.

CLUTCH MASTER CYLINDER

Removal – Remove the high tension lead from ignition coil and white/blue lead from ballast resistor. Remove the four screws mounting cover plate and remove with ignition coil. Remove cotter pin and separate clevis pin. Disconnect and plug hydraulic line at master cylinder. Remove bolts mounting master cylinder and lift from pedal box.

Installation – To install master cylinder, reverse removal procedure and note the following: Bleed clutch hydraulic system.

CLUTCH SLAVE CYLINDER

Removal – Disconnect hydraulic line from slave cylinder and plug open line. Remove mounting hardware and withdraw slave cylinder from housing.

Installation – Center push rod in cylinder housing. Align groove in slave cylinder with bolt hole in housing. Attach mounting hardware, reconnect hydraulic line and bleed slave cylinder.

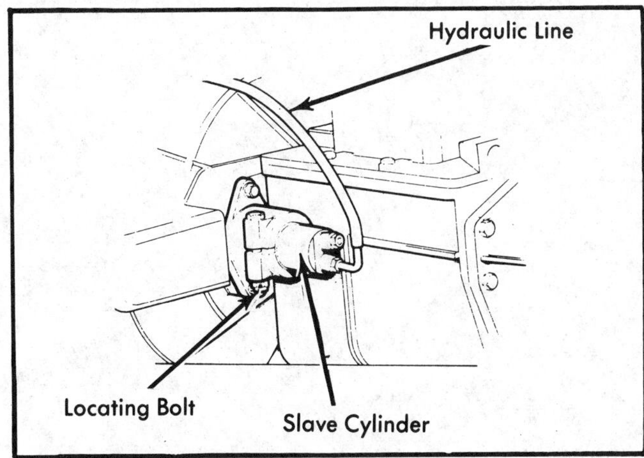

Fig. 1 Installed View of Clutch Slave Cylinder

CLUTCH RELEASE LEVER & RELEASE BEARING

Removal – With transmission and clutch housing removed, drive out pin retaining clutch release bearing lever in clutch housing. Press out pins from release lever. Remove both bearing sleeve plugs and separate bearing from release lever. Sleeve can now be pressed from bearing.

Installation – Grease sleeve and bearing, then press bearing onto sleeve. **NOTE** – *Do not apply pressure to outer race.* Fit bearing in release lever and insert sleeve locating plugs. Press in both pins to retain plugs. Reinstall release lever.

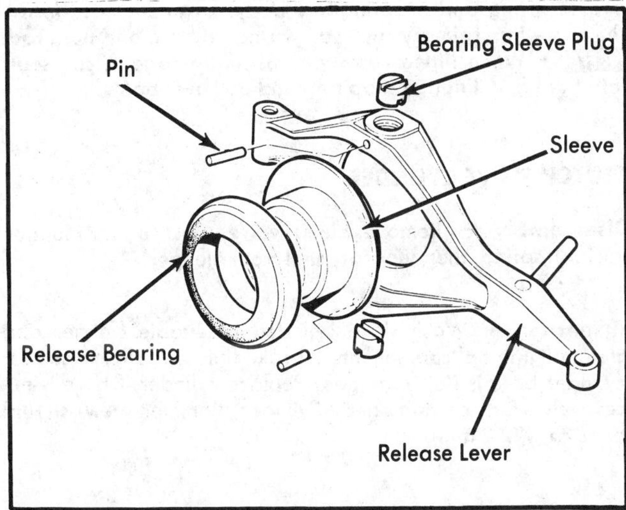

Fig. 2 Exploded View of Clutch Release Bearing & Lever

OVERHAUL

CLUTCH MASTER CYLINDER

Disassembly – Drain fluid from reservoir. Separate rubber boot from housing and slide off push rod. Disengage snap ring holding push rod, then pull out push rod with snap ring, dished washer, and rubber boot. Extract piston with secon-

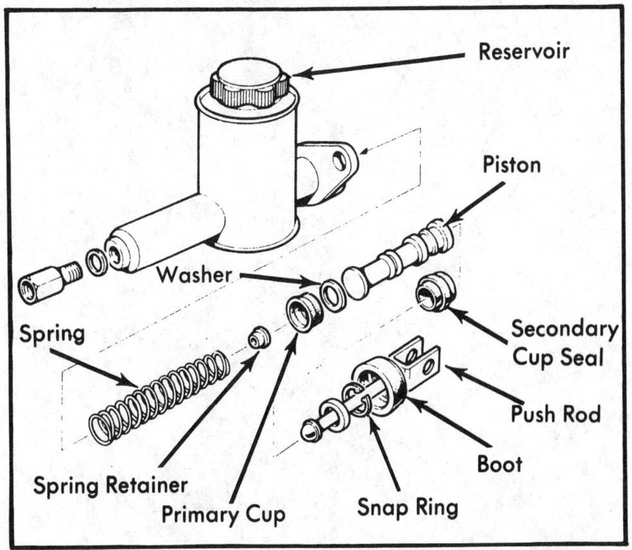

Fig. 3 Exploded View of Clutch Master Cylinder

MG MIDGET (Cont.)

dary cup seal. Remove piston washer, primary cup seal spring retainer, and spring. Separate secondary cup seal from piston; it must be stretched over end of piston.

Inspection – Wash master cylinder in suitable cleaner and clean internal components with brake fluid. Check cylinder for ridges or score marks. Cylinder bore diameter (new) should be approximately .704" (17.88 mm). New seals can be used if cylinder is not damaged.

Reassembly – Fit new secondary cup seal over piston with lip of seal facing piston head. Insert spring retainer into small end of spring and fit spring into body, large end first. Install the following: primary cup seal, washer, piston, and push rod. **NOTE** – *When fitting cup seals, install lip edge of cup seals into bore first.* Engage snap ring and pull over boot.

CLUTCH SLAVE CYLINDER

Disassembly – Remove bleed valve, dust boot, plunger (piston), spring, then separate seal from plunger.

Inspection – Wash slave cylinder in suitable cleaner and clean all internal components in brake fluid. Install new seals if cylinder bore is not damaged. Replace cylinder if bore is excessively worn or damaged. Cylinder diameter (new) should be .875" (22.2 mm).

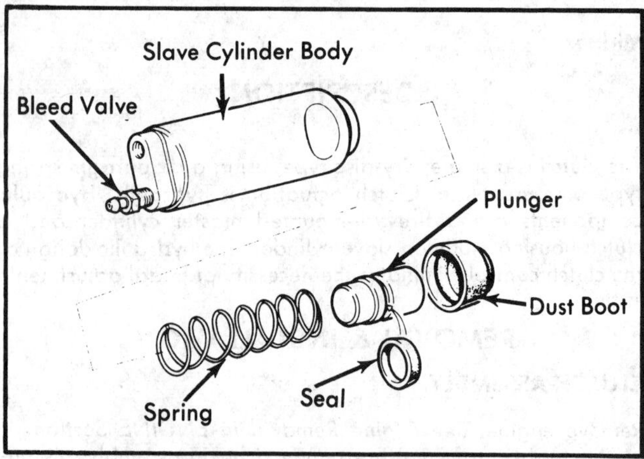

Fig. 4 Exploded View of Clutch Slave Cylinder

Reassembly – Fit seal to plunger. Refit spring and plunger into cylinder bore. Install bleed valve. Slip dust boot into position, install slave cylinder, and bleed hydraulic system.

ADJUSTMENT

HYDRAULIC SYSTEM BLEEDING

Fill master cylinder and attach a bleed hose to slave cylinder bleed valve; submerge free end of hose in a half-full container of brake fluid. Pump clutch pedal, open bleed valve approximately three-quarters turn; at end of down stroke close bleed valve. Continue procedure until air bubbles stop.

OPEL

All Models

DESCRIPTION

Clutch is a dry, single disc diaphragm spring type. Clutch operation is mechanical by cable. Release lever holds throwout bearing and support in place with spring clip.

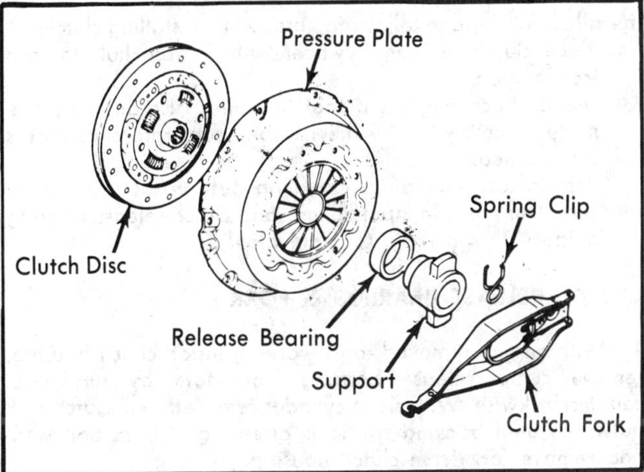

Fig. 1 Exploded View of Clutch Components

REMOVAL & INSTALLATION

CLUTCH ASSEMBLY

Removal – 1) Disconnect battery ground cable. Remove gearshift assembly. From left side of engine, loosen clutch cable adjusting nuts. Disconnect starter wiring and remove upper starter mounting bolt.

2) Raise and support vehicle at front and rear. Remove propeller shaft. Disconnect speedometer cable. Remove clutch heat shield and cable.

3) Remove lower starter bolt and take out starter. Disconnect exhaust pipe at manifold. Take off flywheel inspection cover.

4) Remove rear crossmember support bolt. With jack placed under transmission, remove crossmember from frame. Slightly lower transmission and disconnect back-up light and CRS switches. Remove transmission-to-engine mounting bolts and pull straight back.

5) Index mark clutch assembly. Insert clutch alignment tool, then remove six mounting bolts and pull out clutch assembly.

Installation – To install, reverse removal procedure noting the following: Use alignment tool to center clutch assembly while tightening mounting bolts. Lightly lubricate transmission input shaft before installing. Refill transmission with SAE 30 engine oil. Adjust clutch.

CLUTCH CABLE

Removal – Loosen clutch lock and adjusting nuts. Raise vehicle and support. Remove heat shield, then separate return spring from release fork. Remove clutch cable from release fork and slide cable through mounting bracket.

Installation – To install, reverse removal procedure and make sure cable is properly fitted to clutch pedal.

ADJUSTMENT

CLUTCH PEDAL HEIGHT

Adjust clutch pedal height, measured from floor, to 6.2" (153 mm) by rotating clutch switch located behind pedal. When correct height is reached, tighten lock nut. Check and adjust clutch pedal free play.

CLUTCH FREE PLAY

Loosen both locking nut and adjusting nut on clutch cable. See *Fig. 2*. Take up cable slack by pulling cable forward. Turn adjustment nut until pedal free play is about ⅝" (.625 mm). Tighten lock nut.

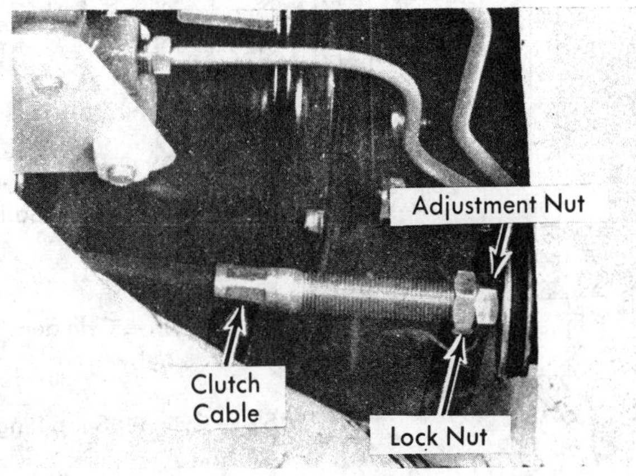

Fig. 2 Clutch Free Play Adjustment Location – Adjustment Nut Moves Along Threaded Rod

TIGHTENING SPECIFICATIONS

Application	Ft. Lbs. (mkg)
Clutch Assembly-to-Flywheel	13 (1.8)
Release Fork Ball Stud	30 (4.2)

PEUGEOT

504
604

DESCRIPTION

Clutch is a dry, single disc, diaphragm spring type. Clutch actuation is hydraulic, using a firewall mounted master cylinder and a bell housing mounted slave cylinder. A pre-lubricated clutch release bearing is also used. Due to hydraulic system design, no adjustments, with the exception of bleeding hydraulic system, is necessary.

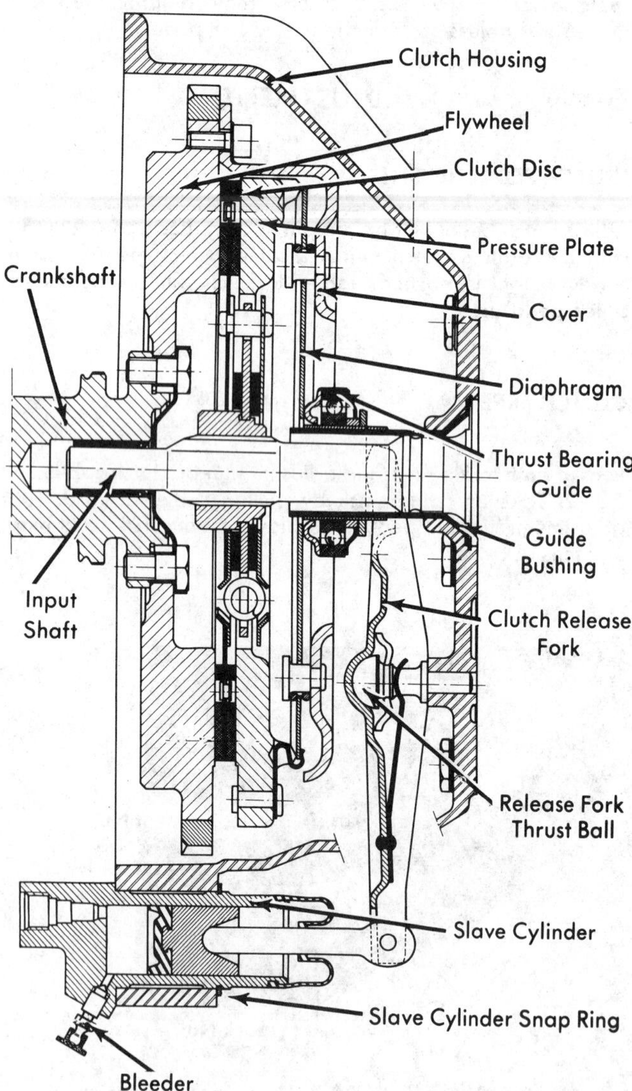

Fig. 1 Sectional View of Clutch Assembly

REMOVAL & INSTALLATION

CLUTCH ASSEMBLY

NOTE — *Engine and transmission must be removed as an assembly. See Peugeot article in ENGINE Section.*

Removal — 1) Remove engine and transmission assembly.

2) Lower engine and transmission assembly to floor or onto a support.

3) On 604 models, remove 2 bolts mounting starter casing.

4) Remove bolts mounting clutch housing to engine.

5) Mark pressure plate and flywheel for reassembly reference. Remove Allen head bolts and remove clutch assembly.

Installation — Make following notes when installing clutch:
- Place clutch disc on flywheel with flexible hub toward transmission.
- Use a clutch alignment tool to center disc and pressure plate assembly on flywheel. Make sure reference marks are aligned.
- Replace pressure plate mounting bolt washers.
- Lube transmission input splines and clutch release bearing guide with Molykote (or equivalent).

CLUTCH RELEASE BEARING & FORK

1) With engine removed, and working inside clutch housing, remove clutch release bearing from fork by turning it counterclockwise. With slave cylinder removed, pull clutch fork outwards until backing spring is disengaged from ball stud, and remove fork from clutch housing.

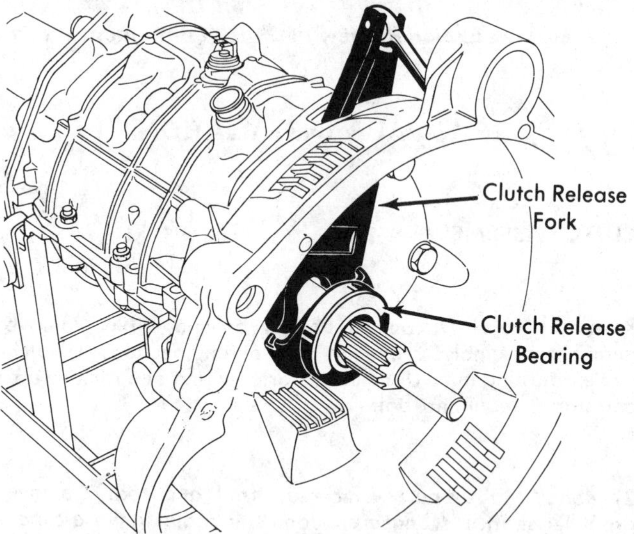

Fig. 2 Installed View of Clutch Release Bearing and Fork

2) Pack rubber cup on ball stud with grease, then slide release fork from inside toward outside of clutch housing. Using a screwdriver, lift fork backing spring, engage fork on ball stud with spring being backed against rubber cup. Install release bearing by engaging onto fork and turning clockwise.

PILOT BUSHING

Bushing is press fit in rear of crankshaft. Bushing must be replaced if excessive clearance with transmission input shaft is evident. Remove and install bushing using suitable pullers and drivers. **NOTE** — *Bushing is self-lubricated. Do not wash in any cleaning solution. Lubricate with motor oil when installing.*

PEUGEOT (Cont.)

CLUTCH MASTER CYLINDER

Disconnect and plug master cylinder hydraulic lines from fluid reservoir and to slave cylinder. Remove bolts securing master cylinder to pedal assembly and remove master cylinder. To install, reverse removal procedure and bleed hydraulic system.

CLUTCH SLAVE CYLINDER

Disconnect hydraulic line at slave cylinder. Remove snap ring securing cylinder in bell housing, then slide slave cylinder from bell housing mounting. To install, reverse removal procedure and bleed hydraulic system.

ADJUSTMENT

HYDRAULIC SYSTEM BLEEDING

1) Attach a suitable adapter (0.0204) to bleeder plug on slave cylinder. Attach a suitable pressure bleeder (ARC 50) to adapter.

2) Adjust pressure of bleeder to approximately 25.6 psi. Open bleeder screw on slave cylinder and check fluid level in master cylinder. Close bleeder screw when fluid reaches specified level.

PORSCHE

911S
924
930 Turbo Carrera

DESCRIPTION

All models use a dry, single disc, diaphragm spring type of clutch system. Clutch operation is mechanical. Pedal is connected to release lever by cables. All models have similar clutch disc designs: 930 models have thicker clutch lining, stronger springs, and larger diameter hubs. 930 models also have release lever mounted so a shorter, thicker cable can be used.

REMOVAL & INSTALLATION

CLUTCH ASSEMBLY

1) On 911 S and Turbo Carrera, remove engine and transaxle from vehicle. On 924, follow removal procedures except that it is only necessary to move central tube with transmission back far enough to remove clutch disc and pressure plate. See *Engine Removal in ENGINE Section.*

2) Index mark pressure plate and flywheel for reassembly. Insert clutch alignment tool. Loosen clutch mouting bolts alternately and evenly until spring pressure is released. Slip clutch assembly from vehicle.

Inspection – **1)** Check pressure plate and disc for wear, cracks, burning or loose rivets. Replace any part found defective. Check ends of diaphragm spring for wear marks from release bearing.

2) Lay a straightedge across pressure plate face and check for distortion; up to .011" (.3 mm) is permissible. Place clutch disc on input shaft and see that it moves freely on splines. Check disc for maximum allowable runout of .24" (.6 mm).

3) Check clutch release bearing for noise or rough operation. Do not wash bearing in any cleaning solution; clean with a lint free cloth only. Replace bearing if contaminated or loud. Check pilot bearing in crankshaft for rough operation, replace as necessary.

Installation – **1)** Place graphite grease or molybdenum disulphide grease in crankshaft pilot bearing, and moisten felt seal with engine oil. Install clutch disc on flywheel using a suitable aligning tool to center disc. Coat diaphragm spring of pressure plate with a thin coat of molybdenum disulphide grease see *Fig. 2.*

2) Install pressure plate to flywheel, aligning marks made at disassembly. **NOTE** – *If a new clutch is installed, balancing marks on clutch and flywheel should be offset 180°.* Install and tighten clutch attaching bolts one turn at a time in a diagonal sequence to prevent distorting pressure plate.

3) On 911 models, when transmission is installed on engine, pull release lever in a direction opposite engine. There must be a distance of at least .787" between release lever and transmission housing.

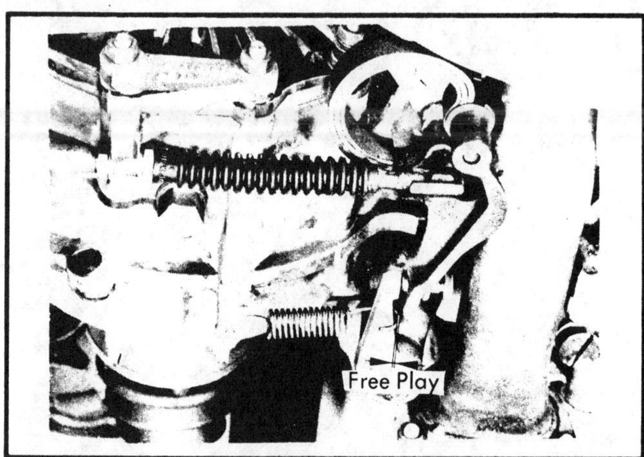

Fig. 2 View of Clutch Adjusting Mechanism (911S & 930)

CLUTCH RELEASE BEARING

Removal (911S & 930) – Bearing is removed with pressure plate and must be removed by laying pressure plate on bearing. Remove snap ring and take out bearing together with washers.

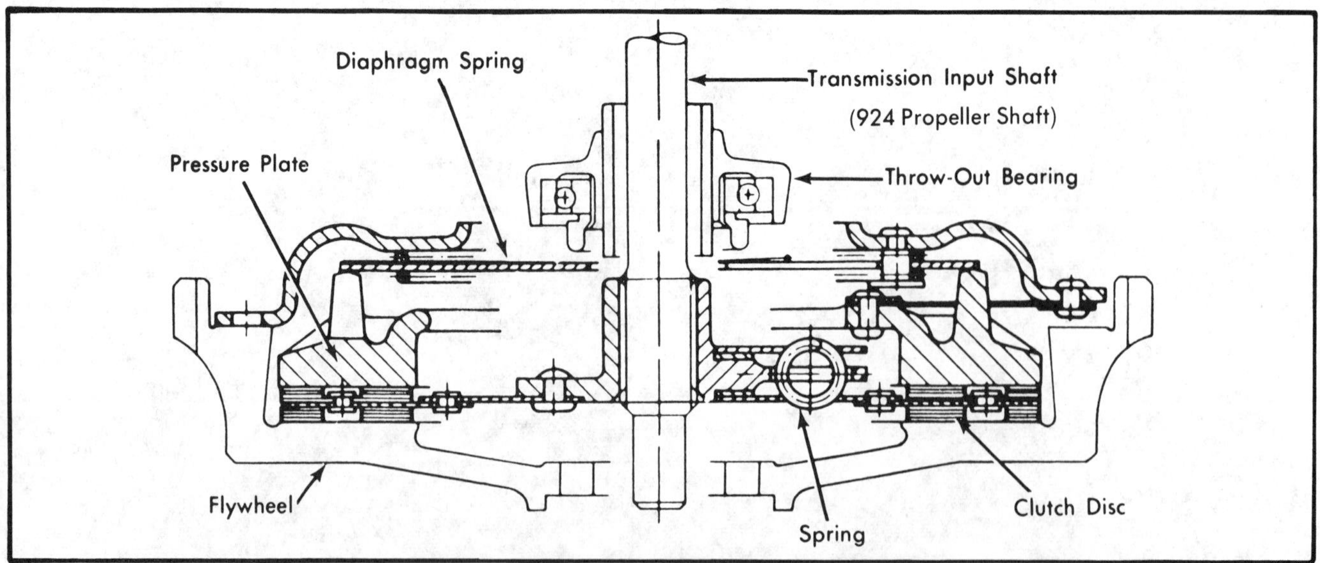

Fig. 1 Sectional View of Clutch Assembly

PORSCHE (Cont.)

Removal (924) – With clutch removed, detach bearing spring clips from release lever. Move lever forward and take release bearing off of guide tube.

Installation – Apply thin coat of suitable lubricant to guide tube and reverse removal procedures.

NOTE – *Do not wash clutch release bearing in cleaning solvent. Bearing is pre-packed and requires no lubrication.*

ADJUSTMENT

CLUTCH ADJUSTMENT

911S & 930 – Clutch free play must be checked at transmission adjusting lever due to auxiliary clutch spring. With cable snug, adjust play to .004" (1.0 mm). See *illustration*. Clutch pedal travel may be adjusted at stop on floor plate, if required. Release travel distance for 91 should be .984±.002" (25±.5 mm) and for 930 should be 1.063±.002" (27±.5 mm) when measured at cable end.

924 – Lower end of clutch cable should measure 5.438±.078" (138±2 mm) when measured from lower edge of cable holder to pin at release lever with release bearing against diaphragm spring. To adjust, turn outboard release lever on shaft and tighten in position. Adjust cable with counternuts on holder to give .8-1" (20-25 mm) free play at clutch pedal.

Clutch Pedal Free Play

Application	Free Play
911S & 924	.8-1.0" (20-25 mm)
930	.9" (23 mm)

PEDAL ADJUSTMENT

All Models – 1) With engine and transmission warm, depress clutch pedal to stop. In this position reverse gear must just be able to be engaged silently.

2) When clutch pedal is fully depressed, clutch release lever should move .6" (15mm) to completely disengage clutch. If cable housing rests on bottom of guide clamp when pedal is fully depressed, inner cable must be adjusted at yoke end.

3) Measure from threaded cable end of yoke to outer edge of lock nut. Measurement should be .7-.9" (17-22mm), adjust if necessary. If cable housing rests on bottom of guide clamp when clutch pedal is fully depressed, inner cable must be lengthened at yoke end.

4) If arc of cable is too large, allowing cable to come out of guide clamp when pedal is released, inner cable must be shortened at yoke end.

TIGHTENING SPECIFICATIONS

Application	Ft. Lbs. (mkg)
Flywheel (All Models)	108 (15)
Clutch	
911S	25 (3.5)
924	23 (3.2)
930	14-18 (2.0-2.5)

RENAULT

R-5
R-12
R-17

DESCRIPTION

Clutch system is single disc dry plate type. Main components are: Disc, diaphragm spring operated pressure plate, ball bearing type clutch release bearing, release fork, and pilot bearing. Clutch operation is mechanical through cable actuation.

REMOVAL & INSTALLATION

CLUTCH ASSEMBLY

Removal, Exc. R-5 – 1) Disconnect and remove battery with bracket. Remove air filter and starter. Disconnect clutch cable and remove bracket. Remove camshaft and water pump pulley. Slide alternator inward as far as possible.

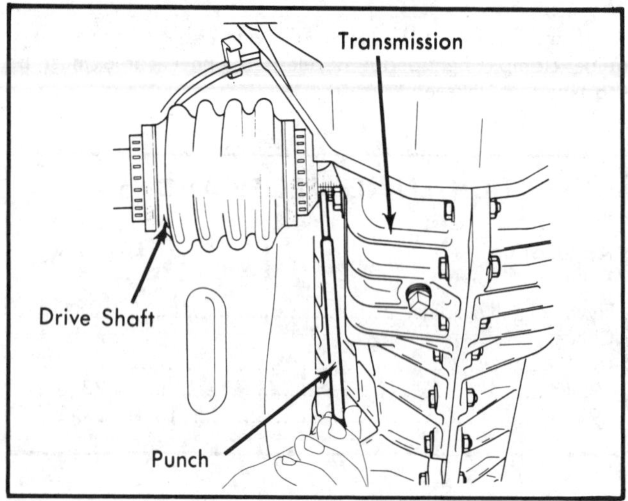

Fig. 1 View Showing Removal of Drive Shaft Roll Pin

2) Install retaining tool (T. Av. 509) between shock absorber lower mounting and lower suspension arm hinge pins. Suitably support front of vehicle. Drain transmission fluid.

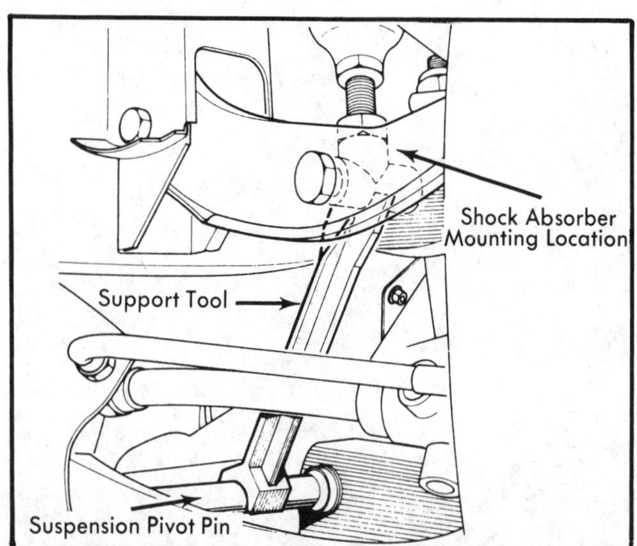

Fig. 2 Installed Position of Support Tool Av. 509

3) Using a suitable drift (B. Vi. 31 B), punch out drive shaft roll pins and disengage from transmission drive flanges. Using a suitable extractor (T. Av. 476) detach upper ball joint and steering arm ball joint from each front wheel.

4) Disconnect speedometer cable, gear shift lever, and back-up light switch. Remove tubular crossmember, exhaust pipe (if necessary), and transmission crossmember. Using a suitable jack, support rear of transmission. **NOTE** – *It may be necessary to raise rear of transmission to remove crossmember.*

5) Tilt engine and transmission assembly. Remove clutch shield and bolts securing transmission to engine, and remove transmission. Mark pressure plate and flywheel for reassembly reference, and remove clutch assembly.

Installation – 1) To install, reverse removal procedure and note the following: Lightly lubricate clutch disc splines with Molykote BR 2 grease. When installing drive shafts, lightly lubricate drive shaft splines and drive flange splines with Molykote BR 2 lubricant, align splines and slide together. Use a suitable elbow drift (B. Vi. 31B) to align roll pin holes. Make sure new roll pins are used.

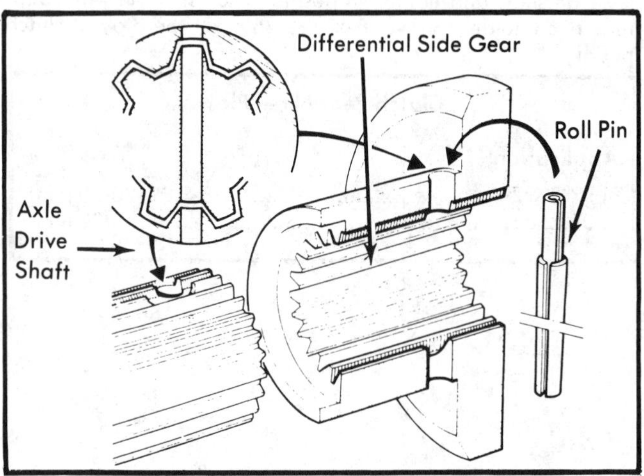

Fig. 3 Axle Drive Shaft Alignment Using New Roll Pin Assembly

2) To adjust transmission gearshift lever, place transmission and shift lever in fourth gear and, without holding lever, tighten gearshift control lever link bolt. Adjust clutch free play, and refill transmission with EP 80 grade oil.

Removal, R-5 – 1) Disconnect battery. Separate speedometer. Remove water pump belt, camshaft belt, and A.I.R. components. Remove both upper starter bolts (it may be necessary to use special wrench ele 565).

2) Remove clutch housing mounting bolts. Take off calipers and support out of way. Disconnect tie rods at steering rack end. Disconnect upper ball joints. Separate axle drive shafts by pulling stub axle out and down. **NOTE** – *Be careful not to damage oil seal lips on differential adjusting ring nuts.*

RENAULT (Cont.)

3) Remove bolts from support tab on underside of transaxle. Disconnect and free clutch cable lever. Remove tubular crossmember bolts and slide crossmember out rearward. Use a jack and support front of transaxle. Remove front mount. Remove lower starter bolt. Remove clutch cover and any side reinforcement bolts. Remove transaxle from vehicle. Mark pressure plate assembly for installation reference and remove entire clutch assembly.

Installation – To install, reverse removal procedure and note following: Larger end of clutch disc hub should face engine. Use centering tool to align pressure plate and disc. Lightly grease input shaft and axle drive shaft splines. Make sure axle drive shafts fully seat into side gears.

CLUTCH CABLE

Removal – 1) Disconnect cable from lever on transmission. Remove the bolt securing mounting pad (if equipped). From inside vehicle, remove pedal shaft retaining clip, push shaft to the right, and disconnect clutch pedal.

2) Disconnect clutch pedal return spring from pin retaining cable end-to-pedal, remove pin, and disconnect cable end from pedal. Free cable from sleeve stop on pedal assembly bracket, and remove cable.

Installation – To install, reverse removal procedure and note the following: Lubricate pedal bores and retaining pins with Molykote BR 2 lubricant. Adjust clutch free play.

CLUTCH RELEASE BEARING & FORK

Removal – With transmission removed, disconnect return spring from release bearing and fork, and slide bearing off transmission input shaft. Using a suitable tool (Emb. 384), extract fork retaining roll pins. Remove fork shaft, fork, and return spring.

Installation – 1) Lubricate fork shaft with Molykote BR 2 grease, and slide shaft into transmission housing (fitted with rubber seal), and through release fork and return spring.

2) Align holes in shaft with those in fork and install roll pins, making sure that pins protrude 1/32" on forward side of fork. Lubricate bearing sleeve and fork fingers with Molykote BR 2 grease, and slide bearing onto transmission input shaft.

3) Install return spring, placing ends in holes of release bearing support and in fork. Lubricate bearing face and portion of clutch diaphragm spring which bearing contacts with Molykote BR 2 grease. Install transmission and adjust clutch free play.

PILOT BEARING

Removal – Remove transmission, clutch assembly, and flywheel. Using a suitable tool (Mot. 11), extract bearing from crankshaft.

Installation – Using a suitable driver, install pilot bearing into crankshaft. **NOTE** – *Bearing is pre-greased, do not clean.* Install flywheel, clutch assembly, and transmission. Adjust clutch free play.

OIL SEAL

Removal – Remove transmission from vehicle. Remove clutch housing attaching bolts and separate clutch housing from transmission. Using a suitable tool, remove oil seal from clutch housing.

Installation – Fit oil seal into place over special tool B. Vi. 526 or 488. Coat paper gasket with sealer. Place tool inside clutch release bearing guide to spread seal lip. Refit clutch housing on transaxle and slide tool along clutch shaft, then remove tool. Tighten clutch housing nuts.

ADJUSTMENT

CLUTCH FREE PLAY

Loosen lock nut. Turn adjusting nut to obtain free travel at end of release lever.

Clutch Free Play Adjustment

Application	Measurement
R-5	1/8-5/32"
R-12	7/64-9/64"
R-17	5/64-1/8"

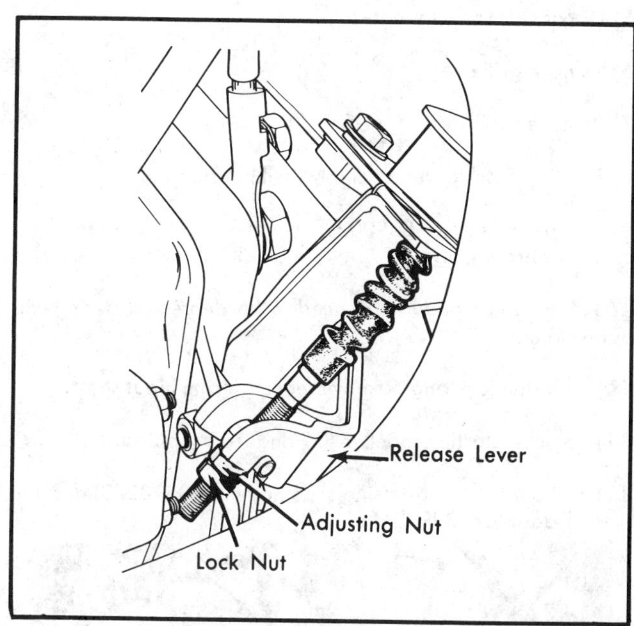

Fig. 4 Adjustment Point for Clutch Cable (R-17 Shown)

TIGHTENING SPECIFICATIONS

Application	Ft. Lbs. (mkg)
Flywheel-to-Crankshaft	35 (4.8)
Clutch Housing-to-Transmission	
8 mm Bolts	15 (2.0)
10 mm Bolts	30 (4.1)

SAAB

99

DESCRIPTION

Clutch is dry, single plate, diaphragm spring type. Primary components are: Disc, pressure plate assembly, and release bearing. Release bearing is a special design ball bearing with elongated outer ring which presses directly against diaphragm when clutch pedal is let out. Clutch operation is hydraulic. Clutch pedal operates on a master cylinder which is connected to slave cylinder. Slave cylinder is located inside clutch cover around input shaft. Slave cylinder acts directly on release bearing. Clutch adjustment is automatic.

REMOVAL & INSTALLATION

CLUTCH ASSEMBLY

Removal – 1) Drain coolant.

2) Remove hood.

3) Disconnect battery ground cable.

4) Disconnect wiring harness from fan housing and disconnect following electrical leads:
- Ignition coil.
- Oil pressure switch.
- Temperature switch.
- Headlight wiper motor.
- Thermal fan switch (located on radiator).

5) Disconnect radiator hoses.

6) Remove grille.

7) Remove radiator.

8) Remove clutch cover assembly (bell housing).

9) Fit special spacer 8390023 (or equivalent) between cover and diaphragm spring.

NOTE – *Clutch pedal may need to be depressed during this operation.*

10) Dislodge lock ring. Remove seal cap from input shaft.

11) Remove plastic propeller "O" ring from input shaft.

12) Pull out input shaft using slide hammer (8390270) and universal adaptor (8390015).

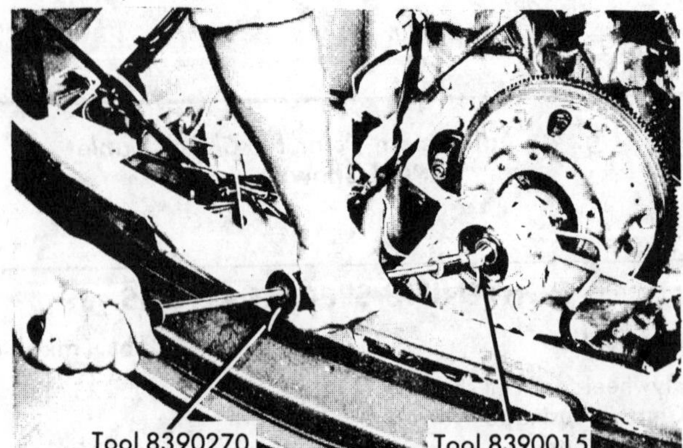

Fig. 1 Pulling Input Shaft Using Special Tools

13) Remove 3 bolts securing slave cylinder guide sleeve to primary gear case.

14) Remove bolts mounting clutch pressure plate and remove together:
- Pressure plate.
- Disc.
- Slave cylinder (guide sleeve).
- Release bearing.

NOTE – *Slave cylinder does not need to be disconnected.*

Fig. 2 Lifting Out Clutch Assembly – Illustration Shows Relationship of Clutch Assembly to Surrounding Engine Components

NOTE – *Before beginning clutch installation, make sure input shaft seal located in seal retainer inside slave cylinder is in good condition.*

Installation – 1) Install collective clutch parts and loosely install two clutch pressure plate bolts.

NOTE – *Make sure:*
- Diaphragm spring does not damage slave cylinder sleeve because piston may sieze.
- Hardened side of release bearing faces diaphragm spring.

2) Bolt slave cylinder to primary gear casing.

3) Install input shaft.

4) Fit plastic propeller and "O" ring to input shaft.

5) Fit sealing cap and "O" ring at input shaft.

6) Tighten clutch assembly (pressure plate) to flywheel.

7) Depress clutch pedal and remove spacer.

NOTE – *DO NOT depress clutch pedal any further than necessary. Seal lip may be pressed to far resulting in a hydraulic leak.*

8) Install remaining components in reverse of removal procedure.

CLUTCH MASTER CYLINDER

Removal – 1) Separate cylinder hydraulic line.

SAAB (Cont.)

2) On left side, remove screen under instrument panel. This provides access to master cylinder push rod and mounting nuts.

3) Remove clevis pin holding push rod to clutch pedal.

4) Remove mounting nuts under instrument panel. These nuts hold master cylinder to bulkhead.

5) Pull off master cylinder inlet hose (from reservoir) and position so fluid does not leak.

Installation – Reverse removal procedure and bleed hydraulic system.

CLUTCH SLAVE CYLINDER

NOTE – *Slave cylinder removal is accomplished during clutch assembly removal. See Clutch Assembly Removal in this article.*

OVERHAUL

CLUTCH MASTER CYLINDER

Disassembly – Pull back sealing bellows and remove retaining ring. Remove push rod and washer. Remove piston, convex washer, piston seal, and spring. Inspect cylinder bore for wear or damage. Replace complete assembly if cylinder is worn or damaged. Replace seal if worn or swollen.

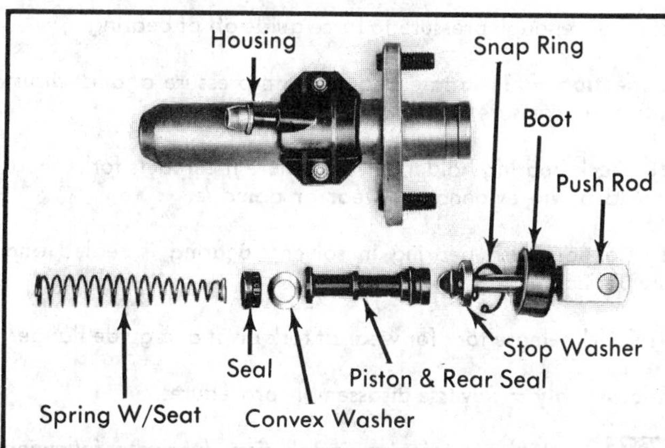

Fig. 3 Exploded View of Clutch Master Cylinder This is Same Cylinder That Has Been Used in Earlier Years

Reassembly – Install return spring and spring retainer. Lubricate piston and seals with Girling Rubber Grease No. 3. Install seals, convex washer and piston. Install push rod followed by washer and retaining ring. Install sealing bellows.

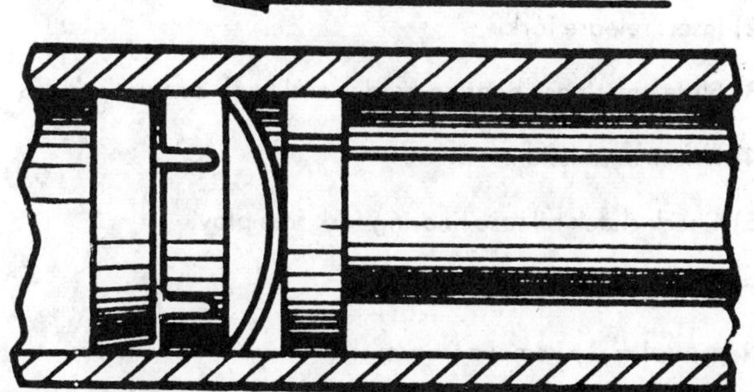

Fig. 4 Cut-Away View of Clutch Master Cylinder Bore Showing Convex Washer Correctly Installed. Convex Side MUST Face Master Cylinder Piston

CLUTCH SLAVE CYLINDER

Disassembly – 1) Remove clutch release bearing from slave cylinder.

2) Set slave cylinder with release bearing end facing up. Press cylinder sleeve out.

3) Remove "O" ring from sleeve.

4) Remove piston and lip seal.

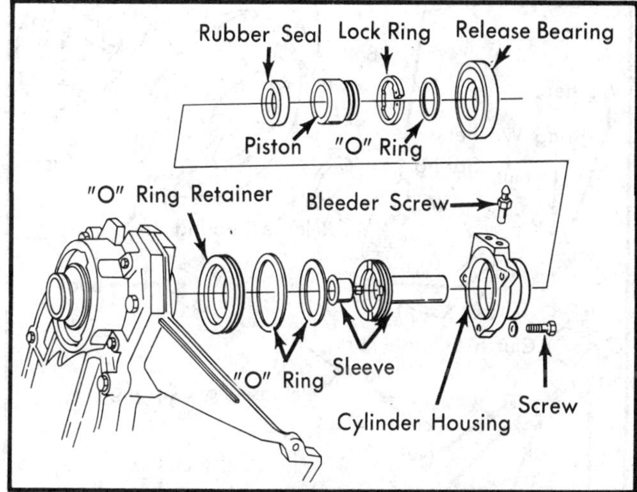

Fig. 5 Exploded View of Clutch Slave Cylinder New Design Slave Cylinder was Introduced in Early 1976 Models

NOTE – *Before beginning reassembly, lightly coat lip seal and piston (not "O" ring) with Caster Rubber Grease (or equivalent).*

Reassembly – 1) Fit "O" ring to sleeve flange.

2) Slide seal lip on sleeve.

3) Coat sleeve flange with brake fluid. Insert sleeve into cylinder. Push seal lip part way into cylinder.

4) Guide sleeve and cylinder together by pushing on piston until lock rings and "O" ring are fitted.

5) Place slave cylinder on support and seat sleeve into cylinder.

6) Fit release bearing to piston.

ADJUSTMENT

HYDRAULIC SYSTEM BLEEDING

1) Connect a ¼" hose to slave cylinder bleeder screw, and place opposite end in a container partially filled with hydraulic fluid. Fill master cylinder reservoir with hydraulic fluid. Open bleeder screw on slave cylinder ½ turn.

2) Place a coolant system tester over filler opening of master cylinder. Pump tester until all air has been removed from system. Close slave cylinder bleeder screw and check to see that all air has been expelled by depressing clutch pedal.

SUBARU

Subaru

DESCRIPTION

Clutch is a diaphragm spring, single dry disc type, with mechanical actuation through a clutch cable. Release bearing is a sealed unit and requires no lubrication.

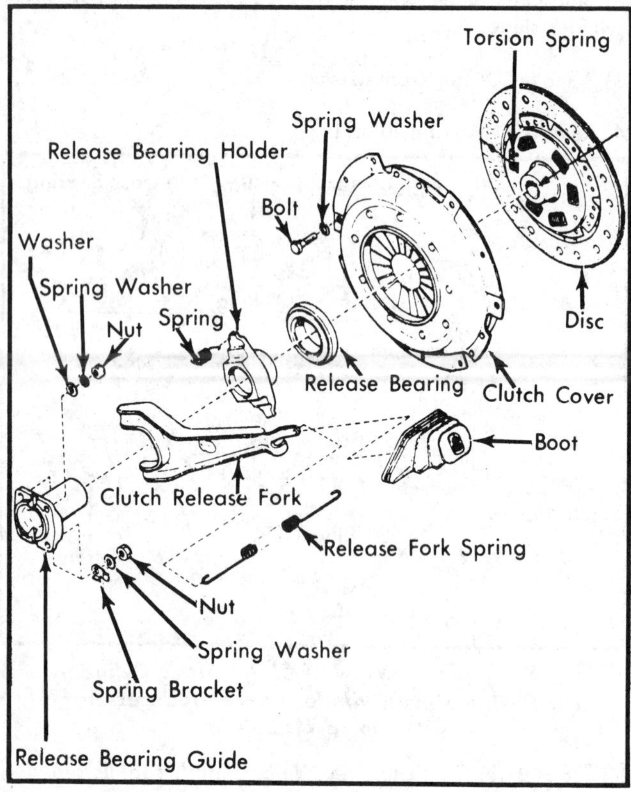

Fig. 1 Exploded View of Clutch Assembly

REMOVAL & INSTALLATION

CLUTCH ASSEMBLY

Removal – 1) Disconnect battery and remove spare tire and air cleaner. Remove transmission stabilizer bar and disconnect wiring from starter and back-up light switch. Remove starter. Remove clutch return spring and loosen clutch release fork. Loosen adjusting nut and remove cable from lever.

2) Disconnect speedometer cable from transmission. Remove shift lever knob and console. Remove shift lever boot, loosen rod clamping nut and remove lever from rod. Raise and support front of vehicle. Disconnect exhaust pipe from manifold (sedan), or disconnect exhaust manifold from engine (coupe).

3) Remove nuts and bolts attaching transmission to engine. Loosen clamps and brace on gear shift rod, pull assembly rearward, and drive spring pin from hole. Disconnect gear shift from transmission and leave it attached to body. Remove axle shaft spring pin using a hammer and pin remover.

4) Remove nut, washer and bushing connecting stabilizer to transverse link. Place a jack under transmission and loosen bolts of hand brake cable mounting bracket. Remove bracket from crossmember. Loosen stabilizer bracket-to-rear crossmember bolts and pull stabilizer out of transverse link.

5) Loosen lock nut holding transverse link to crossmember and pull link to rear, out of crossmember. A lever may be used to ease removal. Pull axle shafts from transmission by pushing struts outward. Pull transmission out to rear.

6) **NOTE** – *Engine is tilted forward when transmission is removed. To aid in removal, a stop may be provided at front of engine.* Remove bolts attaching clutch assembly to flywheel and remove clutch pressure plate and disc.

Installation – To install, reverse removal procedure and note the following: Use a suitable aligning tool (399740100) to center clutch disc on flywheel. When installing pressure plate, make sure residual balance marks are placed at least 120° from each other. After installing transmission, adjust clutch cable.

CLUTCH RELEASE BEARING & HOLDER

Removal – 1) Remove transmission from engine.

2) Disconnect return springs from release bearing holder.

3) Remove release bearing and holder from bearing guide.

4) Remove clutch release fork and fork seal.

Disassembly, Release Bearing – 1) Fit bearing to suitable press (899754112).

2) Apply enough pressure to force guide off of bearing.

Inspection – 1) Rotate bearing with pressure against thrust side to make sure of smooth operation.

2) Check bearing holder surface where it contacts fork. There should be no evidence of wear or damage.

3) Do not wash bearing in solvent. Bearing is sealed and prelubricated.

4) Check release fork for wear at fork pivot and guide flange.

Reassembly – Reverse disassembly procedure.

NOTE – *Before beginning installation, lubricate following locations with multipurpose grease:*
- Inner release bearing sleeve groove.
- Fork, fork ball pin, and guide contact surfaces.
- Transmission input shaft.

Installation – 1) Fit release fork seal.

2) Insert release fork.

3) Slide on release bearing holder and hook 2 return springs.

4) Refit transmission.

5) Check clutch release bearing fork free play.

PILOT BEARING

Removal – 1) Remove transmission.

2) Remove pressure plate and clutch disc.

3) Remove oil seal and pilot bearing seated in crankshaft.

SUBARU (Cont.)

Inspection – 1) Check bearing fit in crankshaft.

2) Check inner surface of pilot bearing for wear. Replace bearing if excessively worn.

3) If pilot bushing is worn, also check transmission input shaft for wear.

Installation – 1) Thoroughly clean bearing location in crankshaft.

2) Use an aluminum rod and plastic mallet to seat bearing in crankshaft.

3) Insert oil seal in crankshaft.

4) Install clutch and pressure plate.

5) Install transmission.

ADJUSTMENT

CLUTCH FREE PLAY

1) Remove release fork spring.

2) Loosen lock nut.

3) Rotate adjustment nut to obtain .14-.18" (3.6-4.6 mm) play measured at fork end (center of adjustment nut).

NOTE – When adjustment is correct pedal free play will be approximately .94-1.18" (24-30 mm).

4) Tighten lock nut.

Clutch Adjustment Specifications

Application	Specifications
Clutch Pedal Stroke	5.04-5.43" (128-138 mm)
Release Fork Stroke	.67-.71" (17-18 mm)
Clutch Release Fork Free Play	.14-.18" (3.6-4.6 mm)
Pedal Free Play	.94-1.18" (24-30 mm)

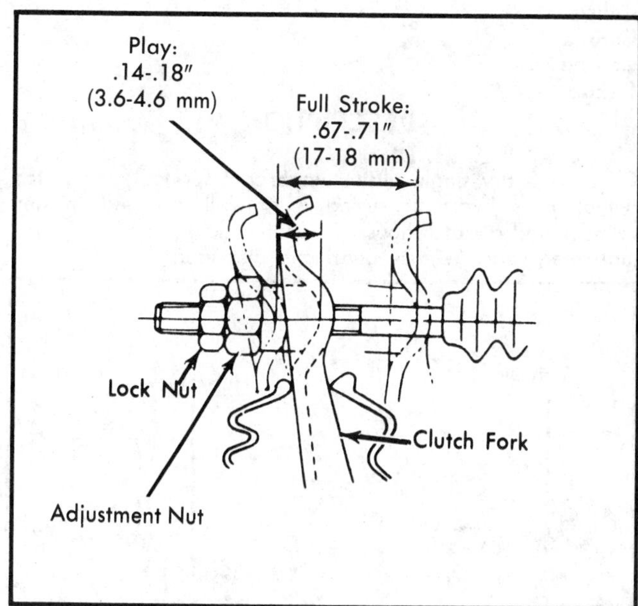

Fig. 2 Clutch Cable Adjustment Locations and Specifications

TIGHTENING SPECIFICATIONS

Application	Ft. Lbs. (mkg)
Clutch Cover-to-Flywheel Bolts	
Four Wheel Drive Models	11.6 (1.6)
All Others	7-9 (.97-1.2)
Transverse Link-to-Front Crossmember	72-87 (9.9-12.0)
Stabilizer-to-Transverse Link	72-87 (9.9-12.0)
Stabilizer Bracket-to-Rear Crossmember	22-33 (3.0-4.7)
Engine Mounts	15-22 (2.0-3.0)
Transmission Stabilizer Bar	5-9 (.69-1.2)

TOYOTA EXCEPT LAND CRUISER

Celica
Corolla
Corona
Pickup

DESCRIPTION

Clutch is a dry, single plate, diaphragm spring type. Clutch actuation is hydraulic, using a firewall mounted master cylinder and a clutch housing mounted slave cylinder. A pre-lubricated clutch release bearing is also used.

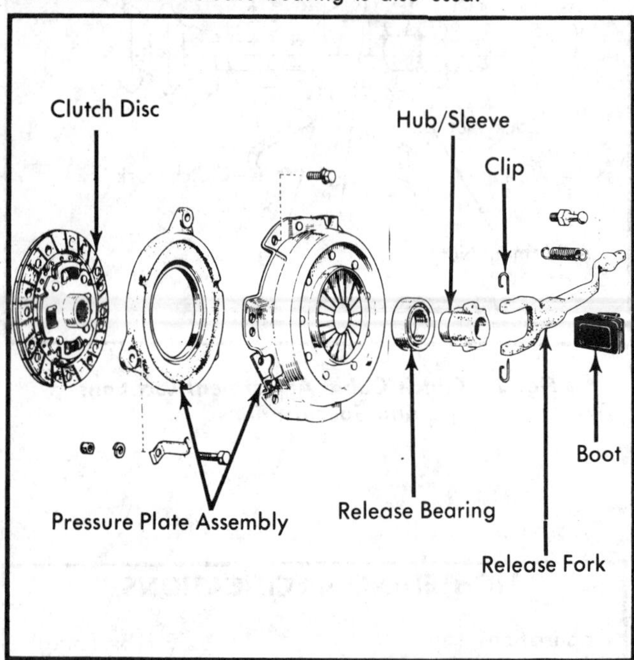

Fig. 1 Exploded View of Typical Clutch Arrangement

REMOVAL & INSTALLATION

CLUTCH ASSEMBLY

NOTE – *Engine removal procedures are of a general nature written to cover all Toyota models.*

Removal – **1**) Disconnect battery cable. Remove air cleaner and drain cooling system, then disconnect top radiator hose. Disconnect accelerator control rod linkage. Remove shift lever boot and shifter assembly. Remove starter.

2) Raise vehicle and support at front and rear with jack stands. If equipped, remove protective cover from under engine.

3) Remove clutch slave cylinder, but only disconnect hydraulic line if necessary. Disconnect exhaust pipe support bracket from mounting and separate exhaust pipe from manifold. Disconnect speedometer cable and electrical leads from transmission.

4) Scribe index marks on drive shaft and coupling for reinstallation reference, then remove drive shaft. Insert suitable plug into extension housing to prevent oil spillage.

5) Support transmission using a floor jack and remove rear support crossmember. Lower jack and remove bolts mounting transmission to engine. Index mark clutch assembly and flywheel for reassembly. Loosen bolts securing clutch assembly alternately and evenly until pressure is released from clutch. Lift out clutch assembly.

Installation – To install, reverse removal procedure and note the following: Use a suitable aligning tool to center clutch disc on flywheel. Tighten clutch pressure plate attaching bolts alternately and evenly in a diagonal progression. With transmission installed, adjust clutch.

CLUTCH MASTER CYLINDER

Removal – Remove cotter pin and clevis pin connecting master cylinder push rod to clutch pedal, then disconnect push rod. Disconnect hydraulic line from cylinder, remove cylinder attaching nuts at firewall, and remove cylinder from vehicle.

Installation – To install, reverse removal procedure and note the following: When installing master cylinder, make sure rubber boot hole faces downward. Adjust pedal height and free play, and bleed hydraulic system.

CLUTCH SLAVE CYLINDER

Removal – Raise front of vehicle and support with safety stands. If equipped, remove protective cover under engine. Remove return spring and disconnect hydraulic line. Back off push rod and remove slave cylinder attaching nuts and slave cylinder.

Installation – To install, reverse removal procedure and note the following: After installing slave cylinder, adjust free play at release lever and bleed hydraulic system.

CLUTCH RELEASE BEARING

Removal – With transmission removed, check release bearing for freedom of rotation with bearing still installed on hub. To remove, disconnect spring clips from bearing collar and slide bearing off transmission input shaft. Use a press to remove and install bearing on collar.

Installation – Slide bearing and collar over transmission input shaft and secure to release lever with new retaining clips. Apply grease to diaphragm spring contact points before installing transmission.

PILOT BEARING

Removal – With transmission and clutch assembly removed, check pilot bearing in crankshaft for roughness or noise. If required, remove bearing using a suitable puller (09303-35010).

Installation – Apply grease to new bearing and install into crankshaft using a suitable driver (09304-30012 for Corona and Hi-Lux models, or 09304-12011 for all other models).

OVERHAUL

CLUTCH MASTER CYLINDER

Disassembly – **1**) With cylinder removed from vehicle, clamp it into a soft jawed vise. Remove reservoir, snap ring, and push rod. Pull out piston, cup, and remaining internal components. Further disassemble piston by prying up spring retainer and separating retainer from piston.

TOYOTA EXCEPT LAND CRUISER (Cont.)

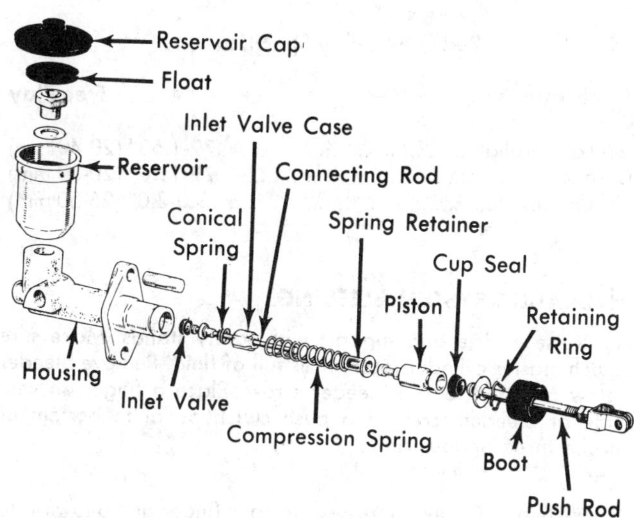

Fig. 2 Exploded View of Clutch Master Cylinder Celica, Corona, Corolla Shown

Inspection – Wash all parts in clean brake fluid. Check master cylinder piston to bore for a clearance of .006" (.15 mm); replace components as necessary. Check compression spring for distortion or weakening and reservoir for damage. Make sure vent hole in reservoir is open.

Reassembly – Dip cylinder cups into clean brake fluid or coat with rubber grease before assembly. Assemble piston components in reverse order of disassembly. Install piston assembly, push rod, and reservoir into master cylinder.

CLUTCH SLAVE CYLINDER

Disassembly – With slave cylinder removed from vehicle, remove rubber boot and push rod. Remove piston and cups, then remove bleeder screw.

Inspection – Thoroughly clean all parts with clean brake fluid and inspect for wear or damage. **NOTE** – *Manufacturer recommends replacing seals each time slave cylinder is disassembled.*

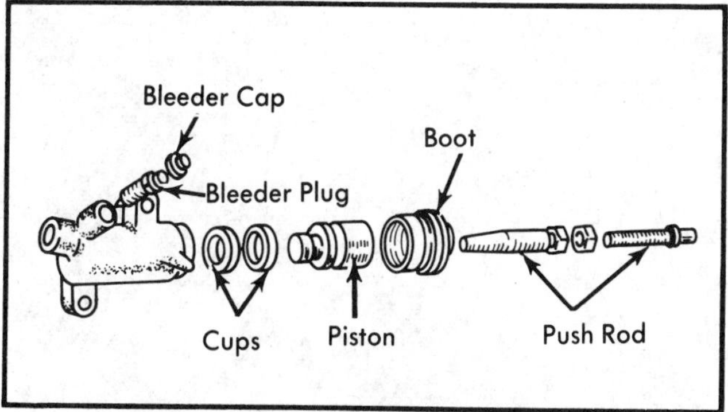

Fig. 3 Exploded View of Slave Cylinder Pickup Cylinder Shown – Other Similar

Reassembly – Soak all parts in clean brake fluid before assembly. Install seals on piston, then install piston into cylinder. Install rubber boot and push rod. Install bleeder screw and cap.

ADJUSTMENT

PEDAL HEIGHT

Adjust pedal stop bolt at top of pedal assembly until specified pedal height is obtained. Height is measured from floor mat to top of pedal pad.

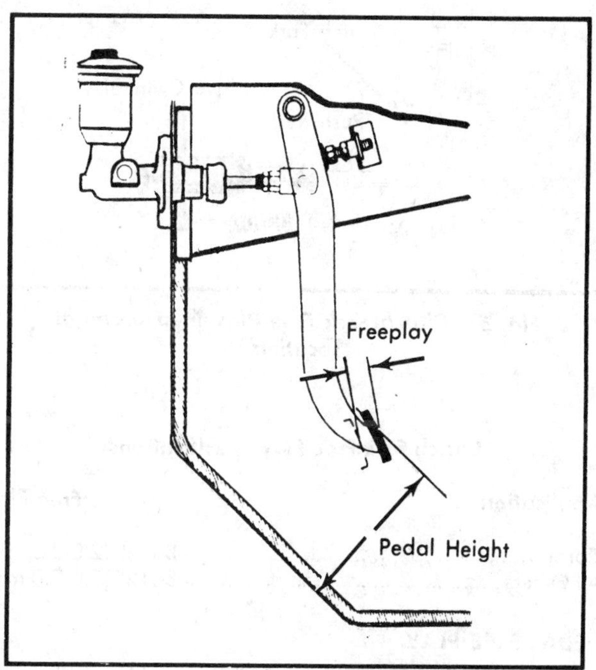

Fig. 4 Pedal Height and Free Play Measuring Points

Pedal Height Specifications

Application	Height
Celica	6.59" (167 mm)
Corolla	6.65" (169 mm)
Corona	6.3-6.8" (160-170 mm)
Pickup	6.3" (160 mm)

MASTER CYLINDER PUSH ROD FREE PLAY

To obtain specified free play between pedal push rod and master cylinder piston, loosen lock nut on push rod and adjust rod until specified free play is obtained.

Master Cylinder Push Rod Free Play Specifications

Application	Free Play
Celica	.04-.12" (1.0-3.0 mm)
Corona	.04-.28" (1.0-7.0 mm)
Hi-Lux Pickup	.02-.12" (.5-3.0 mm)

TOYOTA EXCEPT LAND CRUISER (Cont.)

CLUTCH FORK FREE PLAY

Clutch fork free play determines amount of clearance between clutch release bearing and clutch. To obtain specified free play, loosen lock nut on slave cylinder push rod and screw push rod in or out until specified free play is obtained.

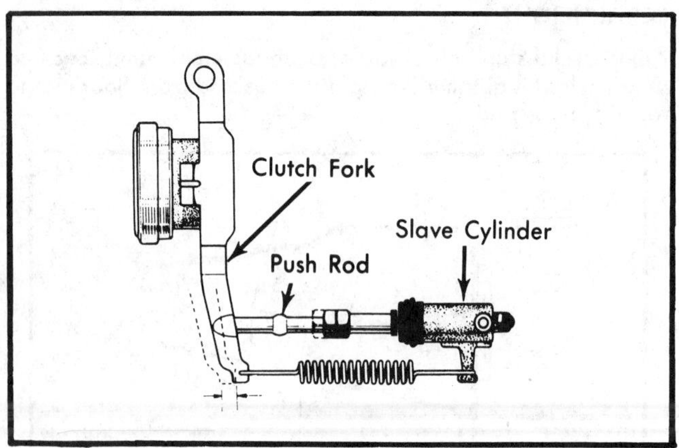

Fig. 5 Clutch Fork Free Play Measurement Location

Clutch Fork Free Play Specifications

Application	Free Play
Corolla	.08-.14" (2.0-3.5 mm)
All Others	.08-.12" (2.0-3.0 mm)

PEDAL FREE PLAY

Pedal free play is total of clutch fork free play and master cylinder push rod free play, and is measured at pedal pad. If other measurements are to specification, pedal free play should be as specified in table.

Pedal Free Play Specifications

Application	Free Play
Celica, Corolla	.79-1.58" (20-40 mm)
Corona	.79-1.18" (20-30 mm)
Pickup	1.0-2.0" (25-50 mm)

HYDRAULIC SYSTEM BLEEDING

1) Raise vehicle and support with safety stands. Make sure clutch master cylinder reservoir is full of fluid. Remove bleeder screw cap and loosen bleeder screw. Place a finger on vent hole of bleeder screw and push clutch pedal to bottom of stroke three or four times.

2) With pedal fully depressed, remove finger and allow air to vent out. Repeat procedure three or four times or until pressure is felt. Install a flexible hose on bleeder screw and insert free end into a container partially full of brake fluid.

3) Push pedal to bottom of stroke, loosen bleeder screw, and allow fluid to bleed into container. Tighten bleeder screw and release clutch pedal. Repeat procedure until air bubbles are no longer seen in container, then close screw on a down stroke of pedal. Check system for leaks and fill master cylinder.

TORQUE SPECIFICATIONS

Application	Ft. Lbs. (mkg)
Clutch Housing-to-Engine	
Corolla, Pickup	36-50 (5.0-7.0)
Corona, Celica	36-58 (5.0-8.0)
Master Cylinder Set Screw	14-22 (2.0-3.0)
Pressure Plate-to-Flywheel	11-16 (1.5-2.2)

TOYOTA LAND CRUISER

FJ40 Series
FJ55 Series

DESCRIPTION

Clutch is dry, single plate, coil spring type. Clutch actuation is hydraulic, using a master cylinder mounted at pedal bracket on firewall and a slave cylinder attached to the engine mounting rear bracket. A prelubricated clutch release bearing is also used.

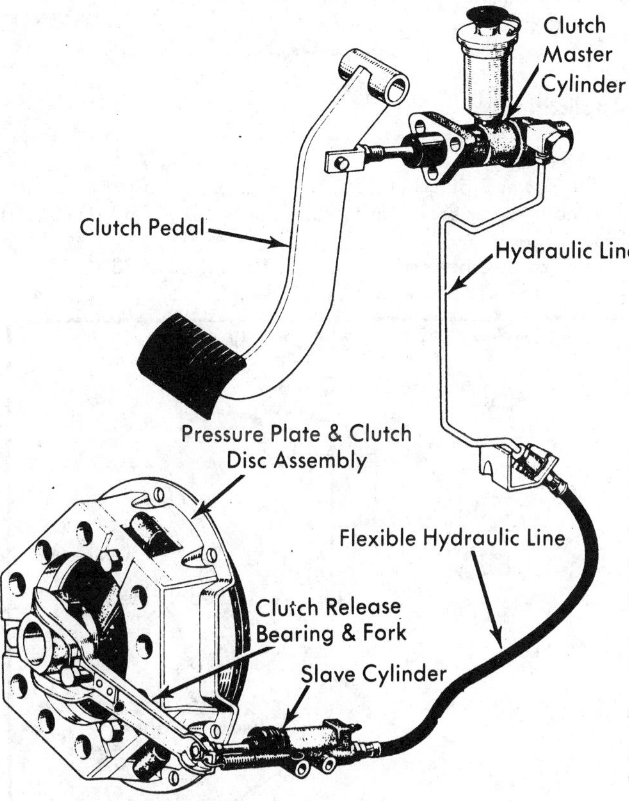

Fig. 1 Toyota Land Cruiser Clutch System

REMOVAL & INSTALLATION

CLUTCH ASSEMBLY

Removal – 1) Remove protective cover under transmission, and disconnect front and rear drive shafts from transfer case. Drain lubricant from transmission and transfer case. Disconnect parking brake cable from link lever. On FJ40 Series, drain fuel tank.

2) On FJ40 Series only, remove front seats, seat frames and console. Separate rear heater line clamp from tunnel. Remove fuel tank cover and fuel tank. On all series, remove shift lever boot and shift lever. Remove transmission cover.

3) Disconnect all electrical wires and vacuum lines from transfer case and transmission. Support transmission/transfer case assembly and remove mounting bolts.

4) Disconnect clutch fork return spring and remove slave cylinder, but do not disconnect hydraulic line unless necessary. Remove release bearing retaining clips, and release bearing with collar. Remove clutch lever assembly.

5) Mark pressure plate and flywheel for reassembly reference. Loosen clutch attaching bolts one turn at a time until spring pressure is released, then remove bolts and clutch assembly

Installation – To install, reverse removal procedure and note the following: Use suitable aligning tool to center disc on flywheel. Tighten clutch attaching bolts alternately and evenly. After reinstallation, adjust clutch fork free play and bleed hydraulic system if necessary.

CLUTCH MASTER CYLINDER

Removal – Remove clevis pin connecting master cylinder push rod to clutch pedal. Disconnect hydraulic line from cylinder body and plug opening. Remove cylinder attaching bolts at firewall and remove master cylinder. **CAUTION** – *Do not allow fluid to spill on painted surfaces.*

Installation – To install, reverse removal procedure, adjust pedal height and clutch pedal free play, and bleed hydraulic system. Check hydraulic system for leaks.

CLUTCH SLAVE CYLINDER

Removal – Plug master cylinder reservoir cap. Disconnect clutch return spring from hanger. Disconnect flexible hose from metal line and remove clip. Remove slave cylinder retaining bolts and remove slave cylinder.

Installation – To install, reverse removal procedure, adjust clutch fork free play and bleed hydraulic system.

CLUTCH RELEASE BEARING

NOTE – *Procedure for removal and installation of clutch release bearing is identical to that of clutch assembly. See Clutch Assembly Removal & Installation.*

PILOT BEARING

Removal & Installation – With clutch assembly removed, check pilot bearing in end of crankshaft for roughness or noise during rotation. If defective, remove using a suitable puller (09303550011). To install, lubricate bearing with multi-purpose grease and insert into crankshaft using suitable driver (0930447010).

OVERHAUL

CLUTCH MASTER CYLINDER

Disassembly – Remove reservoir cap, drain fluid, and remove float. Remove reservoir and rubber boot from cylinder body. Remove snap ring, push rod, piston stop plate and boot. Remove piston and return spring from cylinder, then remove cylinder cup from piston. Clamp cylinder cap in a vise and, using a pipe wrench on cylinder body, remove body from cap. Remove cylinder cup spacer from cylinder.

Inspection – Clean all parts in clean brake fluid or alcohol and inspect for wear or damage. Check clearance between

TOYOTA LAND CRUISER (Cont.)

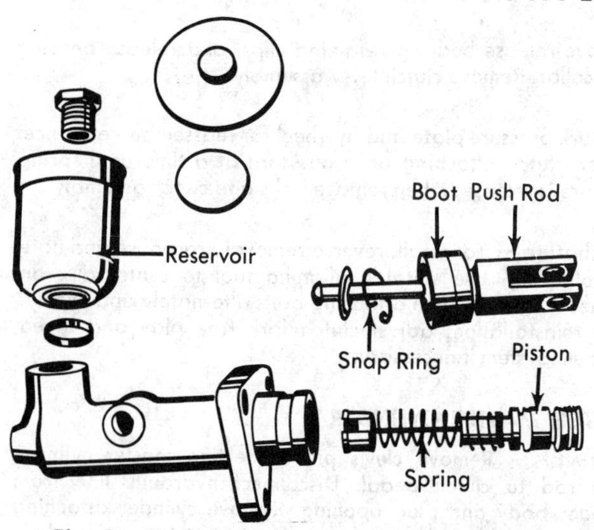

Fig. 2 Exploded View of Clutch Master Cylinder

master cylinder bore and piston; if clearance exceeds .006", replace parts as necessary. Check return spring for wear or distortion. Replace spring if length is less than 3.31" with 4.5 lbs. load applied.

Reassembly – 1) **NOTE** – *Manufacturer recommends replacing cylinder cups each time cylinder is disassembled.* Soak all parts in clean brake fluid before assembly. Install piston stop plate, push rod, boot and snap ring into cylinder body.

2) Install a new cylinder cup onto piston, and insert piston into cylinder through front of bore. Install cup spacer and cylinder cup into cylinder bore. Install return spring with spring seat into cylinder and onto piston, then install cylinder cap with a new gasket.

3) Install reservoir onto master cylinder, install bolt and washer and tighten securely. Install float into fluid reservoir, and install reservoir cap.

CLUTCH SLAVE CYLINDER

Disassembly – Remove push rod assembly and rubber boot from cylinder body. Withdraw cylinder piston and cup seal. Loosen and remove bleeder screw.

Inspection – Clean all parts thoroughly and inspect for wear or damage. Check clearance between slave cylinder bore and piston; if clearance exceeds .006", replace parts as necessary. Inspect spring for wear or distortion, and check bleeder screw and its seat in cylinder body for damage or distortion.

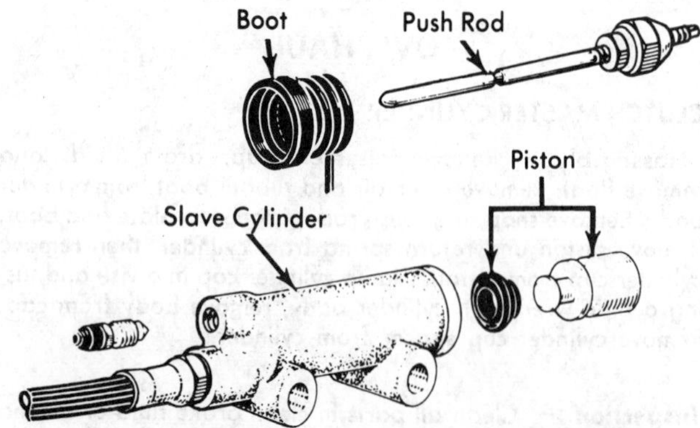

Fig. 3 Exploded View of Clutch Slave Cylinder

Reassembly – Soak all parts in clean brake fluid and reverse disassembly procedures. **NOTE** – *Manufacturer recommends that cylinder cups be replaced whenever cylinder has been disassembled.*

ADJUSTMENT

PEDAL HEIGHT

Pedal height is measured from floor mat to top of pedal pad as shown in *Fig. 4*. Loosen lock nut and push rod. Adjust stop bolt until specified pedal height is obtained.

Pedal Height

Application	Height
FJ40 Series	
With Power Brake Unit	8.47" (215 mm)
Without Power Brake Unit	7.80" (198 mm)
FJ55 Series	
With Power Brake Unit	7.28" (185 mm)
Without Power Brake Unit	6.77" (172 mm)

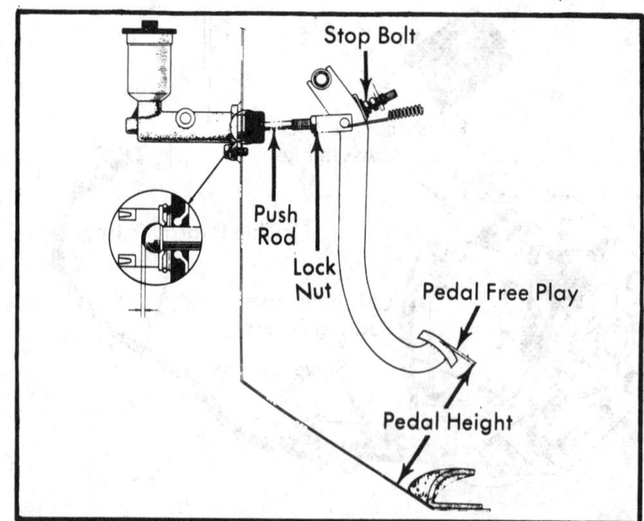

Fig. 4 Pedal Height Measuring and Adjustment Points

PEDAL FREE PLAY

Clutch pedal free play is measured from a point where pedal is in fully up position to a point where master cylinder push rod just contacts piston. Adjust free play by loosening lock nut and turning push rod to obtain specified pedal free play.

Pedal Free Play

Application	Free Play
All Models	.02-.12" (.5-3.0 mm)

CLUTCH FORK FREE PLAY

To obtain correct amount of clearance between release bearing and pressure plate, adjust push rod tip to specifications.

Clutch Fork Free Play

Application	Free Play
All Models	.12-.16 (3-4 mm)

TOYOTA LAND CRUISER (Cont.)

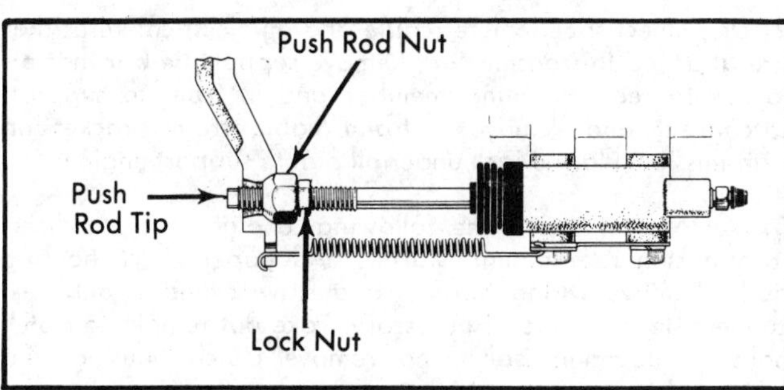

Fig. 5 Clutch Fork Adjustment Location

HYDRAULIC SYSTEM BLEEDING

1) Connect a flexible tube to slave cylinder bleeder screw, and place opposite end in a container partially filled with brake fluid.

2) Pump clutch pedal several times. With pedal depressed, loosen bleeder screw one-third to one-half turn and allow air to bleed out. Tighten bleeder screw.

3) Continue operation until air bubbles are no longer seen in fluid being discharged into container. Tighten bleeder screw securely and install cap. Check fluid level in master cylinder reservoir, and check system for leaks.

TIGHTENING SPECIFICATIONS

Application	Ft. Lbs. (mkg)
Engine-to-Clutch Housing	36-58 (5.0-8.0)
Pressure Plate-to-Flywheel	11-16 (1.5-2.2)
Reservoir	15-22 (2.0-3.0)

TRIUMPH

Spitfire
TR7

DESCRIPTION

Clutch is dry, single plate, diaphragm spring type. Clutch actuation is hydraulic, using a firewall mounted master cylinder and a clutch housing-mounted slave cylinder. Due to self-adjusting feature of clutch assembly, no adjustment, with the exception of bleeding hydraulic system, is necessary.

REMOVAL & INSTALLATION

CLUTCH ASSEMBLY

Removal – 1) Disconnect battery.

2) Remove gear shift lever. On models equipped with overdrive, pry off gear shift knob cap. Disconnect electrical wires. Loosen lock nut, unscrew retaining ring and remove shift knob.

3) Remove transmission tunnel cover.

4) Remove propeller shaft cover. Disconnect propeller shaft from transmission.

5) Disconnect speedometer.

6) Remove clutch slave cylinder.

7) Raise vehicle. Drain transmission.

8) Position an adjustable jack and wood block under oil pan.

9) Disconnect exhaust pipe bracket from transmission.

10) Remove rear transmission mounting nuts.

11) Remove restraint cable from clutch housing.

12) Remove lower clutch housing bolts.

13) Lower vehicle.

14) Remove starter bolts.

15) Disconnect electrical leads from transmission.

16) Remove upper clutch housing bolts. Slide transmission from vehicle.

17) Remove 6 Allen bolts mounting clutch assembly to flywheel.

Installation – Reverse removal procedure and note:

- Use clutch alignment tool to center clutch assembly.
- Tighten clutch assembly bolts evenly.

Removal, TR7 – 1) Raise and support vehicle, then disconnect battery. Remove gear shift lever assembly. Remove transmission tunnel cover, if equipped. Index mark and separate drive shaft from transmission. Disconnect entire exhaust system and remove those brackets that may interfer with removal process.

2) Disconnect speedometer cable and all electrical wires that are attached to transmission. Remove support tie-bar that attaches to rear mounting member and in front to support. Disconnect and remove restraint cable from bracket on transmission. Place a jack under oil pan to support engine.

3) Remove, in order, the following: engine rear stabilizer, transmission rear mount, starter, and upper clutch housing bolts. Remove wiring harness and slave cylinder, only disconnect slave cylinder if necessary. Take out remaining clutch housing mounting bolts and remove clutch housing and transmission as an assembly.

4) Separate clutch housing and index mark pressure plate and flywheel. Remove pressure plate bolts evenly and alternately until all pressure is off clutch disc.

Installation – To install, reverse removal procedure and note the following: Ensure index marks on clutch assembly match with those on flywheel. Make sure engine rear stabilizer is properly adjusted. Adjust restraint cable as follows: Loosen front nut at rear of cable, then tighten rear nut to 5-8 ft. lbs. (.69-1.1 mkg) to settle cable into position. Loosen rear nut and holding cable with fingers, position rear nut so a clearance of .031-.063" (.79-1.6 mm) clearance exists between cable and bracket, tighten front nut.

CLUTCH MASTER CYLINDER

Removal – 1) Disconnect hydraulic line and drain fluid. Plug open port and line.

2) Disconnect clevis mounting push rod to clutch pedal.

3) Remove 2 bolts (Spitfire) or 2 nuts (TR7) mounting master cylinder to bracket (Spitfire) or bulkhead (TR7).

Installation – Reverse removal procedure and bleed hydraulic system.

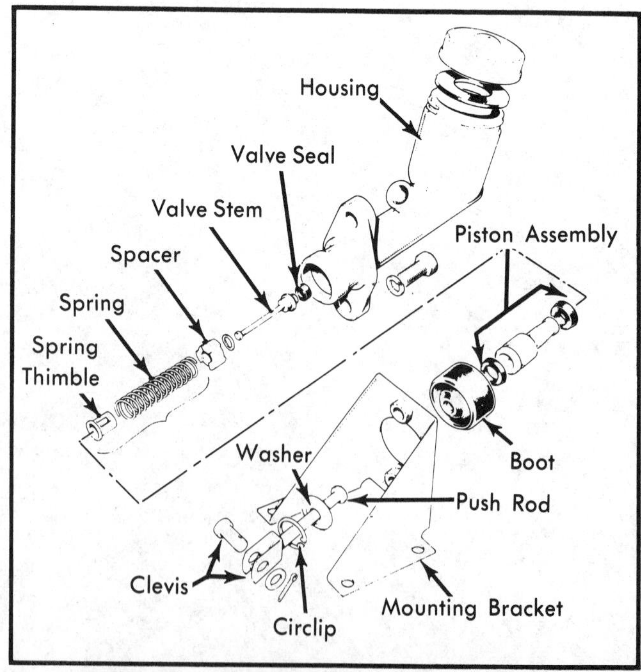

Fig. 1 Exploded View of Spitfire Clutch Master Cylinder – Note How Master Cylinder is Mounted

TRIUMPH (Cont.)

CLUTCH SLAVE CYLINDER

Removal – 1) Raise vehicle and place on safety stands.

2) Disconnect hydraulic line. Plug openings.

3) Remove bolts and nuts mounting slave cylinder.

4) Pull out slave cylinder.

NOTE – *On TR7 models, do not move operating rod in a forward direction. Forward movement may cause release lever to dislodge. Transmission removal would then become necessary for installation of release lever.*

Installation – Reverse removal procedure and note:

- On Spitfire models, centralize push rod in housing before sliding slave cylinder in position.
- On TR7 models, slave cylinder must be mounted with bleed screw ABOVE fluid pipe.
- Bleed hydraulic line.

CLUTCH RELEASE BEARING

Spitfire – With transmission assembly removed, remove clutch fork pivot pin and remove fork and bearing assembly. Drive pins from fork and remove bearing and sleeve. Using a suitable press, remove bearing from sleeve. To install, reverse removal procedure. Lubricate all bearing contact points with multi-purpose grease.

TR7 – With transmission removed, use suitable tool (ST 1136) and unscrew clutch release lever pivot bolt from clutch housing. Pull release lever, complete with pivot bolt and release bearing. To install, reverse removal procedure making sure fork and collar engage evenly.

OVERHAUL

CLUTCH MASTER CYLINDER

Disassembly; Spitfire – 1) Drain fluid reservoir.

2) Remove master cylinder.

3) Pull rubber boot back along push rod.

4) Disengage circlip from push rod end of master cylinder. Remove push rod and washer.

5) Force air pressure through fluid outlet union to remove piston, spring and seal assembly.

6) Straighten edge of prong on spring thimble. Separate thimble and spring from piston.

7) Dislodge valve stem from key hole slot in thimble.

8) Slide seal spacer off valve stem.

9) Remove seal from piston.

Reassembly – 1) Fit new valve seal.

2) Refit components to valve.

3) Fit new seal, lip first, toward spring.

4) Engage spring thimble on piston and carefully depress thimble prong.

5) Lubricate master cylinder bore. Insert seal assembly, spring, and piston.

6) Refit push rod boot.

7) Fit push rod and washer; secure with circlip. Slide boot into place.

Disassembly, TR7 – Slide dust boot free of mounting flange and with push rod exposed, disengage snap ring. Remove boot and push rod. Withdraw piston and rear cup seal, front cup, seal and washer, spring and spring retainer.

Inspection – Discard dust boot, front and rear cups, then clean remaining components in clean beake fluid. Inspect cylinder bore and piston for scoring or damage, replace components as necessary.

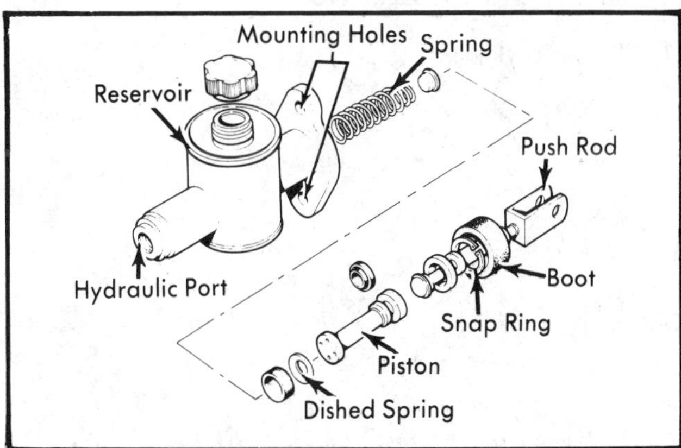

Fig. 2 Exploded View of TR7 Master Cylinder

Reassembly – Fit a new rear cup to piston. Lubricate cylinder bore with clean brake fluid. Insert large end of spring, with spring retainer, into cylinder bore. Fit dished spring and piston, complete with rear cup, into bore. Install new dust boot and push rod, then fit snap ring.

CLUTCH SLAVE CYLINDER

Disassembly – 1) Remove slave cylinder.

2) Remove dust cover.

3) On Spitfire models, remove circlip.

4) Remove piston, seal, and spring.

Inspection – Look at cylinder bore and piston for signs of damage. Replace either or both parts if wear is excessive.

Reassembly – 1) Fit new seal to piston.

2) Lube cylinder bore with brake fluid.

3) Fit small end of spring to piston.

4) Fit spring, piston, and seal into cylinder.

TRIUMPH (Cont.)

5) On Spitfire models, install circlip.

6) Install dust cover.

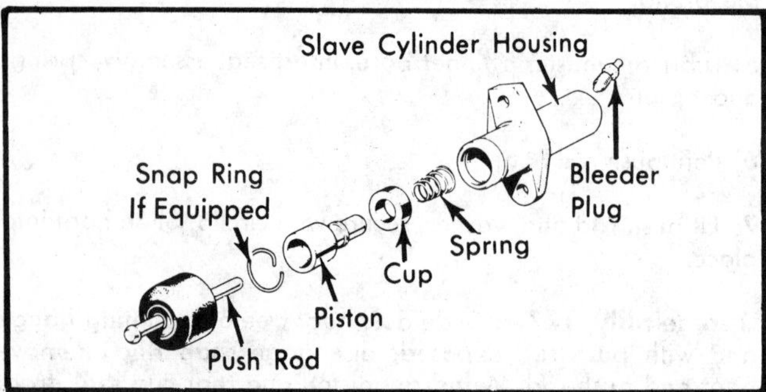

Fig. 3 Exploded View of Clutch Slave Cylinder (TR7 Shown, Spitfire Similar)

ADJUSTMENT

HYDRAULIC SYSTEM BLEEDING

1) Fill master cylinder.

2) Attach a bleeder hose to slave cylinder bleed screw. Insert free end of hose into a container part full with brake fluid.

3) Loosen bleed screw about 1 turn.

4) Push clutch pedal down 1 full stroke.

5) Allow pedal to return unassisted.

6) Pause.

7) Repeat procedure until all air is bled from system.

8) Hold pedal down on last stroke and tighten bleed screw.

TIGHTENING SPECIFICATIONS

Application	Ft. Lbs. (mkg)
Clutch Assembly-to-Flywheel	22 (3.0)
Clutch Housing-to-Transmission	32 (4.4)
Slave Cylinder-to-Clutch Housing	21 (2.9)

VOLKSWAGEN TYPE 1 & 2

Type 1
Type 2

DESCRIPTION

Clutch is dry, single disc, diaphragm spring type. Clutch operation is mechanical through cable actuation. A prelubricated clutch release bearing is also used.

REMOVAL & INSTALLATION

CLUTCH ASSEMBLY

Removal – With engine removed, install a suitable holding tool to prevent flywheel from turning. Mark position of clutch assembly on flywheel for reassembly reference. Loosen clutch mounting bolts alternately and evenly, then remove clutch.

Installation – Apply multi-purpose grease to pilot bearing and light oil to felt ring. Lubricate transmission input shaft with molybdenum disulphide powder. Position clutch disc against flywheel and align using a suitable centering tool. Install pressure plate and mounting bolts, tightening alternately and evenly.

CLUTCH CABLE

Removal (Type 1) – Disconnect clutch cable from clutch operating lever, then withdraw rubber sleeve from guide tube and cable. Remove accelerator pedal and disconnect accelerator cable. Remove push rod lock plate and disconnect brake pedal return spring at push rod pin. Remove pedal cluster mounting bolts, pull back pedal cluster and remove clutch cable by pulling toward front of vehicle.

Installation – Lubricate cable with multi-purpose grease. Insert threaded end of cable in guide tube and push completely through. Install pedal assembly with cable connected. Ensure rubber boot is seated correctly on rear of guide tube, connect clutch cable lever, then lubricate and install wing nut. Adjust free play.

Removal (Type 2) – Disconnect cable from clutch operating lever on transmission. Pull rubber boot from guide tube and rear of cable. Pull guide tube and cable out of bracket on transmission. From under vehicle, remove pedal cover plate. Unbolt clutch pedal and remove pedal lever assembly from frame. Disconnect cable, bend up lock plate and pull out cable toward front of vehicle.

Installation – Lubricate cable with multi-purpose grease and install into guide tube. Connect cable to pedal, push cable through boot, and install boot onto cable guide. Lubricate and install wing nut. Adjust clutch free play.

CLUTCH RELEASE BEARING

Removal – With engine removed, pry clutch release bearing retaining clips from bearing and clutch arm. **NOTE** – *Do not wash bearing in solvent or any cleaning solution; use a clean cloth to clean bearing.*

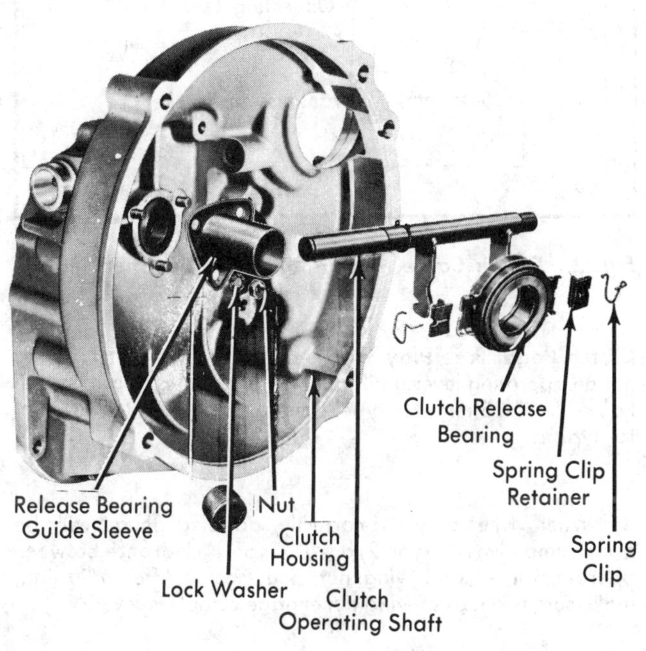

Fig. 1 Clutch Release Bearing Assembly

Installation – Roughen plastic ring with coarse emery paper and apply a light coating of molybdenum disulphide paste. Coat pivoting points between bearing and operating shaft with multi-purpose grease. Position bearing to shaft and install retaining clips, making sure they are correctly positioned. With engine installed, check and adjust clutch free play.

CLUTCH PILOT BEARING

Clutch pilot bearing is integral with flywheel gland nut. If bearing is defective, flywheel nut must be replaced. See *Volkswagen Engines in ENGINE Section for removal and installation procedures.*

ADJUSTMENT

CLUTCH ADJUSTMENT

Guide Tube – Clutch cable guide tube should sag approximately 1-1¾" (25-45 mm). See *Fig. 2.* This preload is obtained by inserting or removing washers between bracket on transmission and end piece of guide tube. **NOTE** – *If sag is greater than 1 ¾", stiff operation and/or damage may result.*

VOLKSWAGEN TYPE 1 & 2 (Cont.)

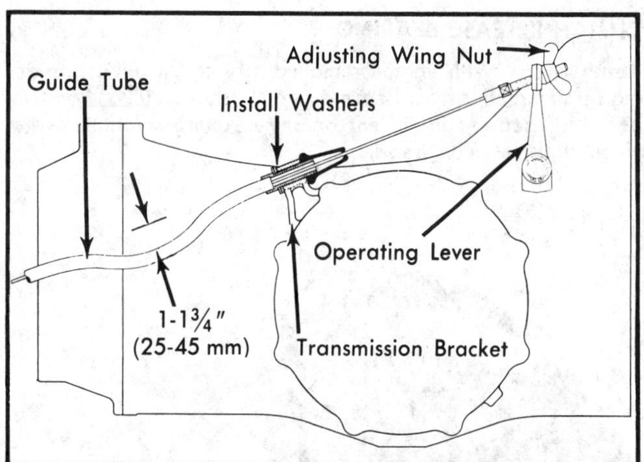

Fig. 2 Clutch Cable Measuring and Adjustment Points

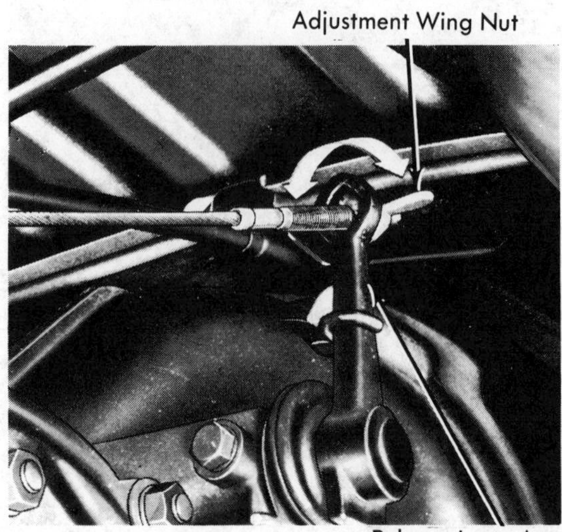

Fig. 3 Clutch Free Play Adjustment Point

Clutch Pedal Free Play — 1) Adjust clutch by turning wing nut on operating lever until free play at pedal is approximately ⅝-1" (15-25 mm) for type 2 models or ⅜-¾" (10-20 mm) for type 1.

2) When free play is correctly adjusted there will be approximately 3/32" (Type 2) or 1/16" (Type 1) clearance between operating lever and wing nut. *See Fig. 3.* After adjusting, make sure two lugs of wing nut engage cutouts in lever.

TIGHTENING SPECIFICATIONS

Application	Ft. Lbs. (mkg)
Engine-to-Transmission Nuts	22 (3.0)
Flywheel-to-Crankshaft Bolt	80 (11.0)
Clutch-to-Flywheel Bolts	18 (2.5)

VOLKSWAGEN DASHER

Dasher

DESCRIPTION

Clutch is single plate dry disc type, using a diaphragm type pressure plate and a pre-lubricated clutch release bearing. Clutch is cable actuated.

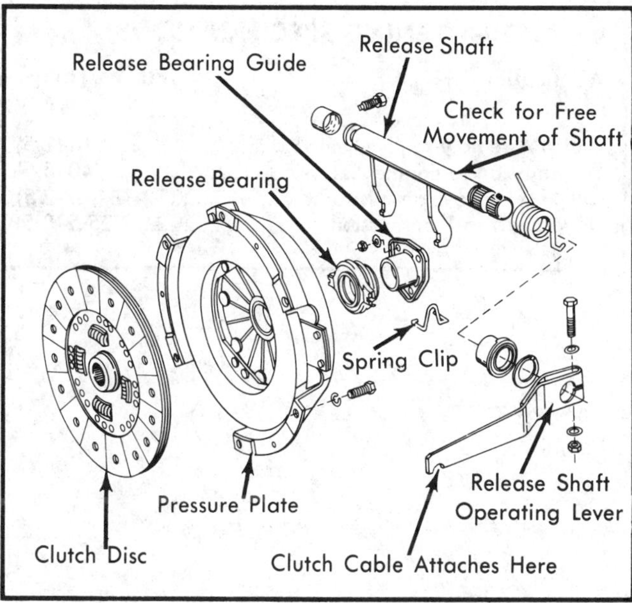

Fig. 1 Exploded View of Clutch Assembly

REMOVAL & INSTALLATION

CLUTCH ASSEMBLY

Removal – 1) Disconnect battery ground strap. Disconnect exhaust pipe from transaxle bracket and engine. Remove square bolt and push shifter assembly coupling from rear of transmission shifting shaft. Unhook clutch cable and disconnect speedometer cable.

2) Disconnect CV joints at inner drive flanges. Remove starter, front mounting plate, and transaxle mounting bolts. Disconnect back-up light wires. Support transaxle away from engine and lower out of vehicle.

Installation – 1) Place clutch disc on suitable aligning tool and insert tool into guide bearing in end of crankshaft. Bolt pressure plate to flywheel, making sure that three dowel pins in flywheel engage appropriate holes in pressure plate. Tighten mounting bolts in steps before final torque.

2) Install crossmember to transaxle. Raise transaxle and fit crossmember bolts (do not tighten). Slide transaxle up to engine and install mounting bolts. Install front mounting plate and starter. Install CV joint Allen screws and tighten. Now, tighten crossmember mounting bolts.

3) Tighten square headed coupling bolt and install lock wire. Connect exhaust pipe, allowing 3/8' (10 mm) between pipe and floor pan. Reconnect back-up light wires and battery ground strap.

Fig. 2 View Showing Clutch Assembly Alignment on Flywheel

CLUTCH RELEASE BEARING

Removal – 1) Remove transmission.

2) Remove spring clips keeping release bearing to release bearing shaft.

3) Slide release bearing off release bearing guide sleeve.

Inspection – 1) Rotate bearing and check for roughness or noise.

2) Bearing is pre-lubricated, DO NOT wash in solvent.

3) Apply Molykote paste to bearing contact points on clutch release shaft.

Installation – 1) Slide release bearing into bearing guide sleeve.

2) Fit spring clips keeping release bearing in position on shaft.

3) Check fit closely.

4) Install transmission.

CLUTCH CABLE

Removal – 1) Loosen clutch cable adjusting nuts.

2) Free clutch cable housing from support bracket.

3) Separate end of cable from clutch operating lever. Operating lever is mounted to side of clutch housing.

4) Disconnect clutch cable from clutch pedal.

5) Force cable and housing through bulkhead into passenger compartment.

Installation – Refit new cable in reverse of removal procedure. Readjust clutch pedal free play.

NOTE – If new clutch cable has been installed, make sure to recheck clutch pedal free play after 300 miles.

VOLKSWAGEN DASHER (Cont.)

PILOT BEARING

1) To remove bearing, install a suitable remover tool (10-202) into pilot bearing, then remove bearing by tightening tool.

2) Install bearing so that lettering is facing out. Drive bearing into crankshaft using a suitable driver tool (US 219) until it is flush, then lubricate bearing.

ADJUSTMENT

CLUTCH PEDAL FREE PLAY

1) Raise hood and find adjusting nuts located just ahead of oil filter.

- **To Increase Free Play** – Loosen top adjusting nut 2 or 3 turns. Tighten bottom nut until locked against bracket. Pedal free play should be ⅝" (15.87 mm).
- **To Decrease Free Play** – Loosen nut under bracket 2 or 3 turns. Tighten top nut until locked against bracket. Pedal free play should be ⅝" (15.87 mm).

2) Check clutch pedal operation. Repeat adjustment procedure until clutch pedal free play is within specifications.

TIGHTENING SPECIFICATIONS

Application	Ft. Lbs. (mkg)
Clutch Assembly-to-Flywheel	18 (2.5)
Transmission-to-Engine	40 (5.5)
Clutch Lever-to-Transmission	12-18 (1.7-2.5)
Drive Shaft-to-Transmission	25.5 (3.5)

VOLKSWAGEN RABBIT/SCIROCCO

Rabbit
Scirocco

DESCRIPTION

Clutch is a single plate dry disc type, using a diaphragm type pressure plate and a transmission mounted clutch release bearing. Clutch is cable operated.

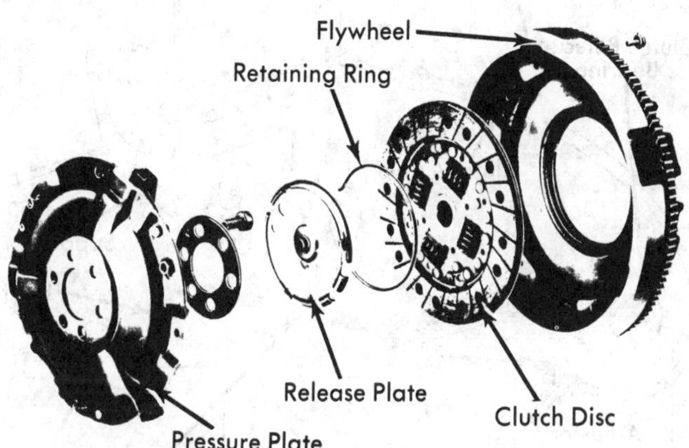

Fig. 1 Exploded View of Clutch and Flywheel Assembly

REMOVAL & INSTALLATION

TRANSMISSION

1) Disconnect battery ground strap and attach an engine support assembly. Remove four attaching bolts and left transmission mount. Remove TDC sender unit and rotate flywheel until flywheel lug appears in sender unit hole. **NOTE** — *Engine and transmission can be separated only when flywheel is in this position.*

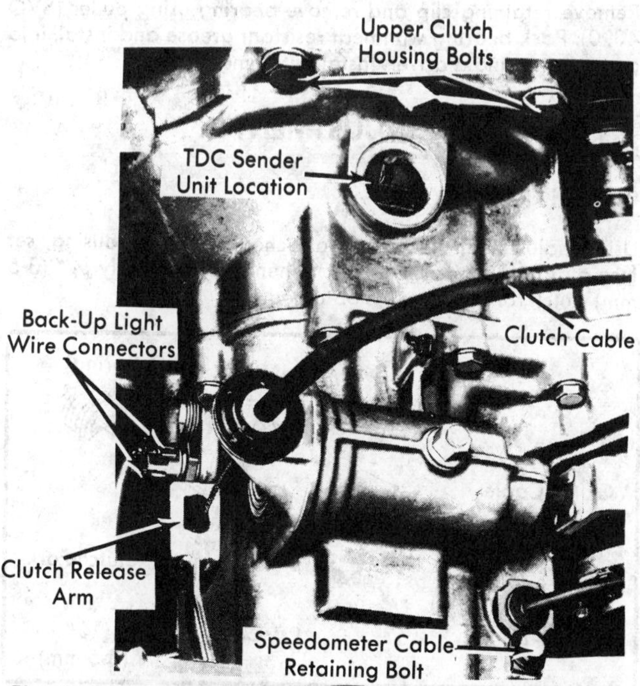

Fig. 2 Top View of Transmission and Clutch Housing Note Where Clutch Cable Mounts on Transmission Case

2) Disconnect speedometer drive cable and plug hole in transmission with a rubber cap. Disconnect back-up light wires and clutch cable. Remove two upper clutch housing-to-engine bolts. Disconnect shift linkage from rod lever and relay lever.

3) Disconnect ground strap from transmission. Remove starter and engine mount next to starter. Remove lower transmission mount. Disconnect left and right drive shafts and hang aside with wire. While supporting transmission, remove bolts from large housing plate and small housing plate (large housing plate remains on engine). Slide transmission from locating dowels and lower out bottom of vehicle. To install, reverse removal procdure making sure recess in flywheel is level with drive shaft flange. Adjust clutch cable so that clutch pedal has ⅝" (15.87mm) of free play.

CLUTCH ASSEMBLY

1) Using a diagonal loosening pattern, gradually loosen and remove flywheel bolts and flywheel. Pry retaining ring from release plate and lift release plate from pressure plate.

NOTE — *A special dual purpose holding tool (VW558) may be used to lock either flywheel or pressure plate for removal purposes.*

2) Remove bolts attaching pressure plate to engine. Use Loctite 270 or 271 when installing pressure plate bolts. If a new flywheel is to be installed a new timing mark must be cut into flywheel ¼" (6 mm) to right of TDC mark. Install clutch assembly in reverse of disassembly with ends of retaining ring between two slots in release plate. Use a centering disc (VW 547) to center clutch disc in flywheel.

CLUTCH RELEASE BEARING

NOTE — *It is not necessary to remove transmission from engine to replace clutch release bearing as bearing is located on opposite end of transmission from clutch assembly.*

Remove cover plate from transmission. Disconnect clutch cable and rotate clutch arm until clutch lever is clear of release bearing. Lift out release bearing. Inspect clutch push rod for signs of wear or burning. To install, reverse removal procedure.

ADJUSTMENT

CLUTCH PEDAL FREE PLAY

Adjust cable housing at transmission until there is ⅝" (15.87 mm) of free play at clutch pedal.

TIGHTENING SPECIFICATIONS

Application	Ft. Lbs. (mkg)
Transmission-to-Engine	47 (5.5)
Drive Shaft-to-Transmission	32 (4.5)
Pressure Plate Bolts	54 (7.5)
Flywheel Bolts	14 (2.0)
Cover Plate	11 (1.5)

VOLVO

240
260

DESCRIPTION

Clutch is diaphragm spring type. Clutch assembly consists of the following components:

- Pressure plate
- Diaphragm spring
- Sheet metal clutch housing
- Clutch disc
- Clutch release bearing

Clutch actuation is mechanical. Cable is connected between clutch pedal and release fork.

REMOVAL & INSTALLATION

CLUTCH ASSEMBLY

Removal, M45 & M46 Transmission – 1) Disconnect battery ground cable. Pull back-up light wiring harness connector. Working from under vehicle, disconnect gear shift lever from gear shift rod.

2) Separate gear shift boot from carpet. Using a 4 mm Allen wrench, remove reverse gear detent fork. With snap ring pliers, remove lock ring and pull up lever. Unhook clutch fork return spring and separate cable from housing.

3) Remove bolts at clutch housing and nut at exhaust pipe, then remove front exhaust pipe bracket. Position a support under engine. Remove transmission crossmember. Index mark and disconnect drive shaft. Separate speedometer cable from transmission.

4) Slightly lower rear of engine and take out all clutch housing bolts except top right. Fit jack to transmission for support and remove last clutch housing bolt. Pull transmission from vehicle. Remove upper starter mounting bolt. Remove bolts mounting clutch assembly, loosening in a criss-cross pattern. Make sure bolts are loosened evenly.

Installation – To install transmission and clutch assembly, reverse removal procedure and note the following: Insert clutch plate with long side of hub facing backward. Use aligning tool (2484 or equivalent) to center clutch assembly. Tighten clutch mounting bolts in a criss-cross pattern. Adjust clutch pedal free play.

CLUTCH CABLE

Removal – Remove return spring and disconnect clutch cable at clutch fork; extract cable. Remove cover panel under instrument cluster. Remove clevis pin at upper end of cable. Separate clutch fork adjustment mechanism from clutch housing, if necessary. Force cable out of rubber grommet located in firewall.

Installation – Insert new cable into rubber grommet, feed it through cable guide and attach at upper end with clevis pin. Position adjustment mechanism into clutch housing. Attach cable to clutch fork, then refit return spring.

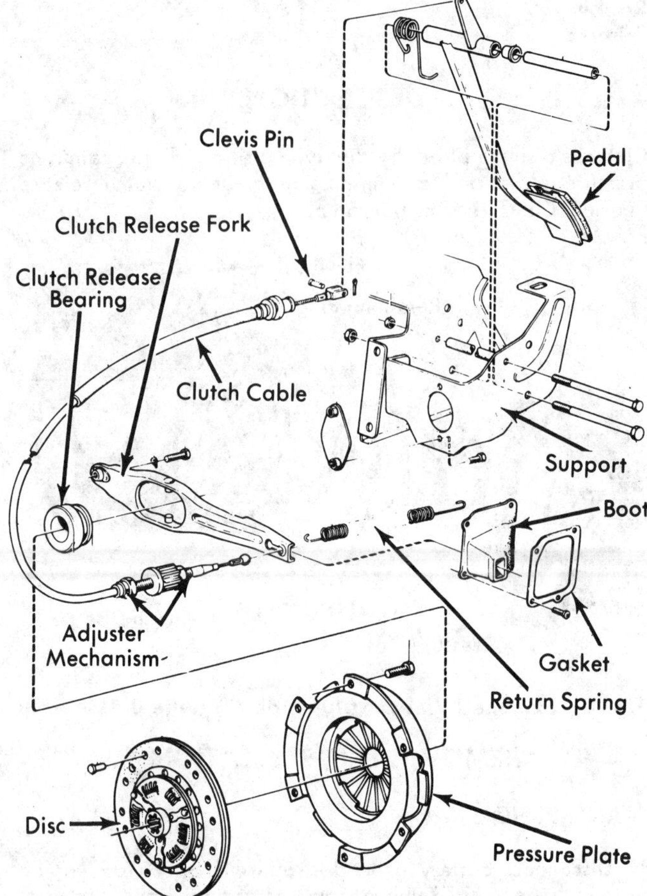

Fig. 1 Exploded View of Clutch System

PILOT BEARING

Remove retaining clip and remove bearing using puller (SVO 4090). Pack bearing with heat resistant grease and install into crankshaft using a driver. Install retaining clip.

ADJUSTMENT

CLUTCH FREE PLAY

Using adjustment mechanism attached to clutch housing, set free play. Adjustment is correct when approximately ⅛" (3-5 mm) clutch fork free play is obtained.

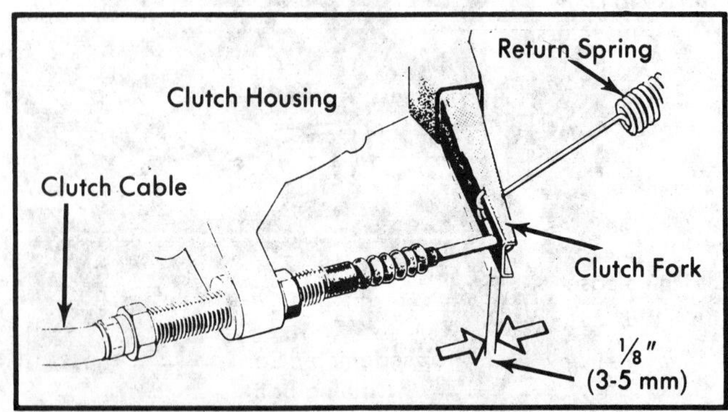

Fig. 2 Clutch Fork Free Play Measuring Point

Section 7

BRAKES

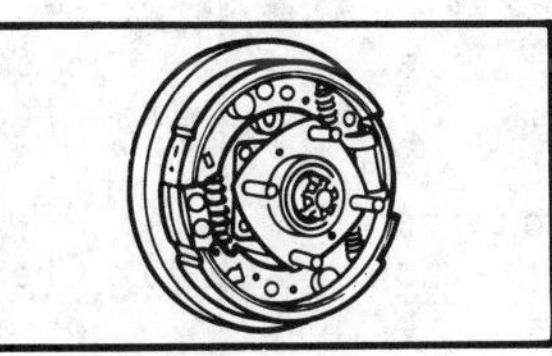

Contents

NOTE — ALSO SEE GENERAL INDEX.

BRAKE SYSTEM TROUBLE SHOOTING

NOTE — *This is a general trouble shooting guide. Not all steps will apply to all brake systems. When using this guide, locate the condition in column one that corresponds to your problem and determine the possible causes in column two. Match the number of the possible causes with the same number in column three.*

CONDITION	POSSIBLE CAUSE	CORRECTION
▸ Brake chatter, squeal, squeak	1) Dust on drums/rotors, oil stained linings 2) Weak shoe return spring 3) Drum out of round 4) Excessively worn pads or shoes 5) Uneven rotor surface 6) Excessive lateral rotor runout 7) Excessive wheel bearing play	1) Remove drum/rotor, clean 2) Check, replace springs 3) Turn drum on lathe 4) Replace pads or shoes 5) Check rotor surface in various locations with micrometer 6) Check runout with dial indicator, resurface or replace rotor 7) Readjust or replace bearings
▸ Excessive pedal travel	1) Excessive rotor runout 2) Brake fluid boil 3) Warped or excessively worn pads or shoes 4) Rear brakes out of adjustment 5) Power brake unit malfunction	1) Check rotor with dial gauge, resurface or replace 2) Drain system, refill with fluid of correct specification 3) Check and replace pads or shoes 4) Adjust shoe to drum clearance 5) Check and either overhaul or replace unit
▸ Poor brake operation	1) Too long brake lever stroke 2) Brake cable sticking 3) Excessive shoe to drum clearance	1) Readjust brake pedal lever 2) Check brake cable routing and lubricate 3) Check self-adjuster machanism; readjust or replace components
▸ Shock when pedal applied	1) Brake durm cracked or distorted 2) Uneven brake drum wear 3) Broken return spring	1) Replace drum 2) Resurface drum or replace 3) Replace springs
▸ Leaks in caliper piston cylinder	1) Damaged or excessively worn caliper piston seal 2) Deep scores or corrosion on surface of cylinder bore	1) Overhaul caliper and install new seals 2) Overhaul caliper and hone (unless not recommended by manufacturer); install new seals
▸ Rattling in front brakes	1) Pad anti-rattle spring clip broken or missing 2) Excessive clearance between pads and caliper	1) Install new part or reposition existing one 2) Fit caliper with new pads
▸ Pull when brake applied	1) Incorrect tire pressure 2) Front end out of alignment 3) Unmatched tires 4) Restricted brake lines or hoses	1) Inflate tires evenly as indicated in owners manual 2) Check and align front end 3) Make sure all tires have approximately equal amounts of tred and pressure 4) Inspect for soft hoses or damaged lines. Replace with new hoses or brake tubing

BRAKE SYSTEM TROUBLE SHOOTING (Cont.)

CONDITION	POSSIBLE CAUSE	CORRECTION
▶ Excessive pedal pressure required	1) Linings coated with brake fluid, oil or grease 2) Entire pad not contacting rotor 3) Scored brake rotors 4) Incorrect pads 5) Seized piston 6) Power brake failing	1) Fit new pads or shoes 2) Replace pads 3) Resurface rotor according to specs. 4) Check pads 5) Overhaul caliper, check piston 6) Check power unit and replace
▶ Low pedal effect	1) Air in hydraulic system, brakes not properly bled 2) Hydraulic fluid leaking past primary cup in master cylinder 3) Bleeder screw not tight	1) Check for air leaks and bleed hydraulic system 2) Overhaul master cylinder making sure to replace cups 3) Tighten bleeder screw
▶ Uneven braking	1) Linings contaminated 2) Unmatched disc pads 3) One or more seized pistons 4) Incorrect tire pressure 5) Front wheel out of alignment 6) Brake hose or line clogged 7) Caliper alignment improper	1) Clean or refit with new pads/shoes 2) Ensure all pads on any axle are same quality 3) Overhaul caliper to free piston 4) Inflate tires according to manufacturers recommendations 5) Align front wheels 6) Free restriction 7) Remove and realign caliper
▶ Brake pedal pulsation	1) Excessive rotor lateral runout 2) Rotor not parallel 3) Wheel bearings out of adjustment 4) Rear drums out of round	1) Check rotor runout with dial gauge 2) Check rotor and replace 3) Adjust 4) Check drums and turn or replace
▶ Spongy pedal	1) Air in brake system 2) Swollen brake hose(s) 3) Brake fluid boiling point too low 4) Filler cap vent hole plugged	1) Bleed system 2) Replace hose and bleed system 3) Drain, flush and refill with fluid of proper specifications 4) Clean, then bleed system
▶ Pedal yield under slight pressure	1) Deteriorated check valve 2) External brake fluid leaks 3) Internal leak in master cylinder	1) Replace valve, bleed system 2) Check master cylinder, lines, and wheel cylinders; replace 3) Overhaul master cylinder
▶ Brake failure or heavy pedal	1) Power unit diaphragm damaged 2) Check valve malfunctioning 3) Defective vacuum hose 4) Twisted air valve and valve rod plunger	1) Check and/or replace diaphragm 2) Replace valve 3) Replace hose 4) Disassemble and repair
▶ Brakes react slowly	1) Check valve malfunction 2) Vacuum hose blocked or broke 3) Air cleaner clogged or restricted	1) Clean or replace check valve 2) Replace hose 3) Clean or replace air cleaner
▶ Brake drag or slow return	1) Push rod out of alignment 2) Operating rod out of adjustment 3) Air valve and push rod plunger twisted	1) Disassemble and repair 2) Adjust 3) Adjust

ARROW & COLT

Arrow
Colt

DESCRIPTION

Brake system is hydraulically actuated, using a tandem master cylinder and a power brake unit. All models are equipped with disc brakes on front wheels and drum brakes on the rear wheels. Front disc brakes consist of a rotor and a single piston floating caliper assembly. Rear brakes are self-adjusting, leading-trailing shoe/drum type. Rear brakes are actuated by a dual piston wheel cylinder. Parking brake is cable actuated, operating on the rear wheel brake assemblies. All models use a combination valve to control pressure to rear wheels.

ADJUSTMENT

FRONT DISC BRAKE PADS

Front brakes are self-adjusting.

REAR BRAKE SHOES

Rear brakes are self-adjusting.

PEDAL HEIGHT & FREE PLAY

Adjust pedal height (distance from top of brake pedal to toe board) to specifications by adjusting master cylinder push rod. Set clearance between end of stop light switch and stop to .020-.040" (.51-1.0 mm). After making these two adjustments correct free play should be obtained.

Pedal Height & Free Play Adjustment

Application	Pedal Height In. (mm)	Free Play In. (mm)
All Models	6.5-6.7	.4-.6
	(160-165)	(10-15)

PARKING BRAKE

Coupe, Sedan, Hatchback – Fully release parking brake. Remove parking lever cover to gain access to adjustment nut. Adjust nut until clearance between lever and stop is about .008-.08" (.2-2 mm).

Hardtop, Station Wagon – **1**) Release parking brake lever. Loosen cable attaching bolt and adjusting nut. Move cable lever to right. Adjust clearance of left side to .04" (1.0 mm). Tighten attaching bolt. Clearance is measured between extension lever and stopper.

2) With left cable adjusted, turn adjusting nut until same clearance is obtained on right extension lever. With parking brake properly adjusted, lever stroke should be 4-6 notches (8-12 clicks).

COMBINATION VALVE

NOTE – *Valve accomplishes three functions: Pressure control of rear service brakes; trouble warning; deactivating rear brake pressure control when front service brakes fail.*

Pressure Test – Use two pressure gauges that will measure at least 1,500 psi. Hook one gauge to master cylinder rear side and one to rear wheel cylinder. Pressure reading should be as shown in chart. Replace defective as required.

Brake Hydraulic Pressure Chart

Application	Pressure
Wheel Cylinder	460±28.4 psi
Master Cylinder	640 psi

Warning Light Test – Slightly loosen bleeder screw of one wheel cylinder and depress brake pedal. At this time warning light should come on. If light doesn't work, check switch and wire connector.

Combination Valve Reset – Tighten whichever bleeder screw has been opened (ie: drum wheel cylinder), then loosen the opposite system bleeder screw (ie: caliper wheel cylinder). Press brake pedal down until light goes out, close bleeder.

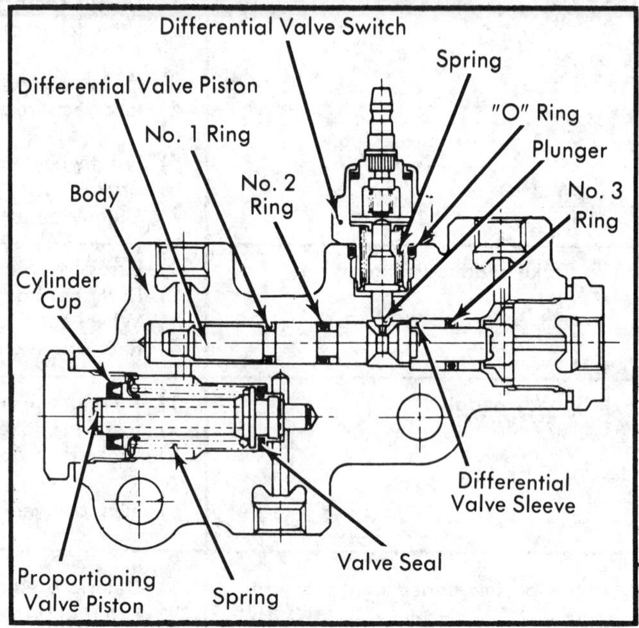

Fig. 1 Section View of Combination Valve Showing Detail of Internal Components

HYDRAULIC SYSTEM BLEEDING

Attach a bleed tube to wheel cylinder bleeder screw and immerse opposite end of tube in a container partially filled with brake fluid. Depress and release pedal several times, hold in applied position, loosen bleeder screw, allow air to escape, and tighten bleeder screw. Continue operation until air bubbles are no longer seen in discharged fluid. Repeat procedure at remaining brake lines until all air is bled from system. Bleeding sequence is right-rear, left-rear, left-front, and right-front.

REMOVAL & INSTALLATION

FRONT DISC BRAKE PADS

Removal – Raise and support vehicle and remove front wheel. Remove pad protector by prying up edge of clip at center of protector. Hold center of "M" clip, detach "M" clip

ARROW & COLT (Cont.)

from pad and its ends from retaining pins, remove clip. Remove retaining pins from caliper and remove "K" spring. Remove pads from caliper by grasping backing plate area of pads with pliers.

NOTE – *Replace all pads (left and right side) at same time.*

Installation – Press piston to bottom of bore using a suitable tool, install disc pads and retaining pins. Install "K" spring and "M" clip, making sure positions are not reversed. *See Fig. 2.* Install pad protector, making sure clips face outward.

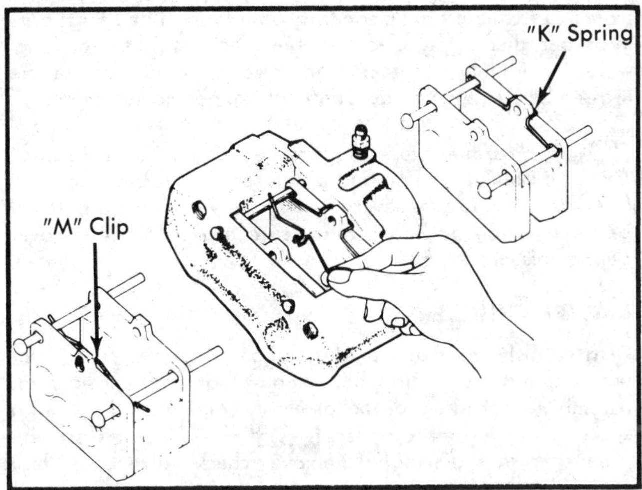

Fig. 2 Installing Spring and Clip on Brake Pads and Retaining Pins

FRONT DISC BRAKE CALIPER

Removal – With disc pads removed, disconnect hydraulic line and remove bolts attaching caliper assembly to steering knuckle, and remove caliper assembly.

Installation – Reverse removal procedure, tighten caliper mounting bolts evenly, and bleed hydraulic system.

FRONT DISC BRAKE ROTOR

Removal – With caliper assembly removed, remove hub dust cap, cotter pin, lock nut, and adjustment nut. Pull hub and rotor assembly from spindle, taking care not to drop outer wheel bearing. Remove bolts attaching rotor to hub, then separate.

Installation – Reverse removal procedure, tighten rotor-to-hub bolts evenly, and adjust wheel bearings. *See Wheel Bearing Adjustment in WHEEL ALIGNMENT Section.*

REAR BRAKE SHOES

Removal – Raise and support vehicle and remove brake drum. Remove shoe hold-down springs. Disconnect strut-to-shoe spring and upper shoe return spring end from trailing shoe. Remove trailing shoe and lower return spring. Hold adjusting latch downward, pull adjusting lever toward center of brake, and remove leading shoe assembly. Remove upper shoe return spring and strut-to-shoe spring.

Installation – Reverse removal procedure and note the following: Apply brake grease to all shoe contact points of backing plate, adjuster assembly, and wheel cylinder. Adjust amount of engagement of adjusting lever with strut only after pulling lever fully toward center of brake. Note that adjusting lever and latch spring differ between right and left sides.

REAR WHEEL CYLINDER

Removal – With rear drum and brake shoes removed, disconnect hydraulic line from wheel cylinder at rear of backing plate, remove bolts attaching cylinder, and remove wheel cylinder.

Installation – Reverse removal procedure, tighten mounting bolts evenly, and bleed hydraulic system.

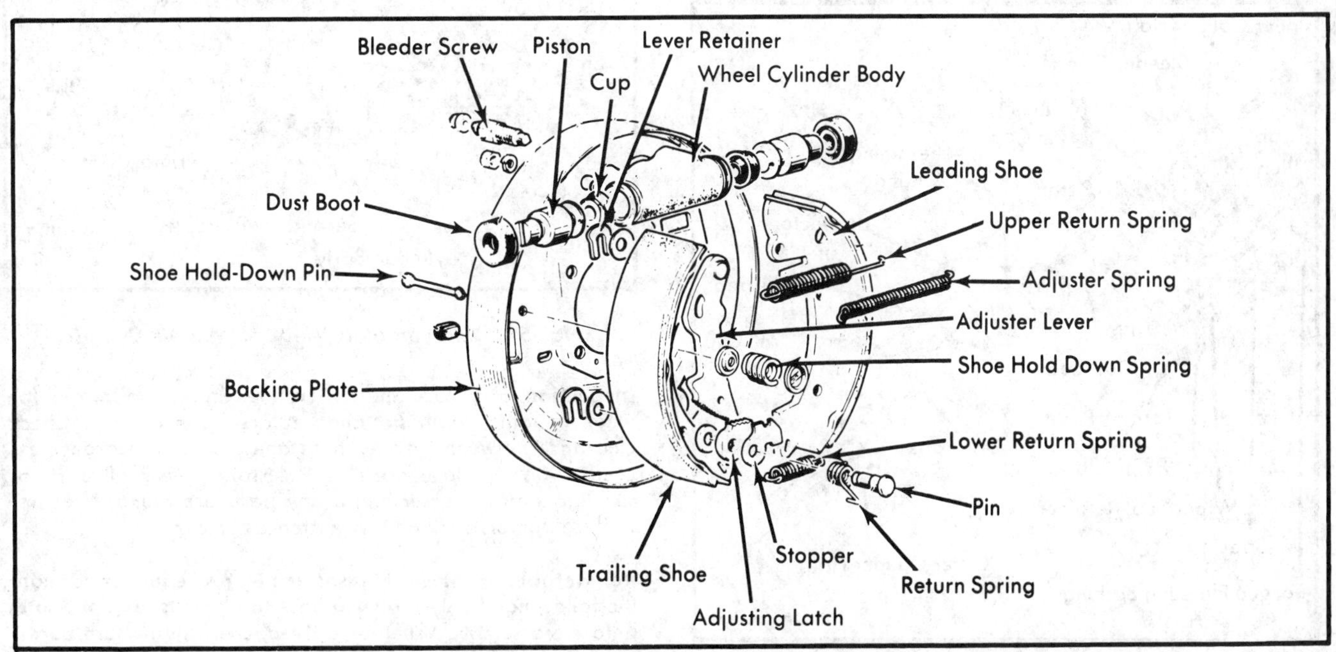

Fig. 3 Exploded View of Rear Brake Assembly for Component Identification

ARROW & COLT (Cont.)

MASTER CYLINDER

Removal – Disconnect hydraulic lines from master cylinder, then depress brake pedal slowly several times to discharge brake fluid. On models with power brakes, remove clevis bolt retaining master cylinder push rod to brake pedal, then on all models, remove cylinder attaching bolts and lift off master cylinder.

Installation – Reverse removal procedure, check and adjust pedal height, and bleed hydraulic system.

POWER BRAKE UNIT

NOTE – *Before removal or overhaul test check valve. Pull off vacuum hose, place finger over check valve and crank engine; vacuum should be created.*

Removal – With master cylinder removed, disconnect vacuum hose from power brake unit. Remove pin connecting power unit operating rod to brake pedal, then loosen attaching nuts and remove power unit.

Installation – Reverse removal procedure and note the following: Apply a suitable sealer to power unit mounting surface and vacuum line connections. Adjust pedal height and bleed hydraulic system.

OVERHAUL

FRONT DISC BRAKE CALIPER

Disassembly – Remove caliper attaching bridge bolts and separate outer and inner halves. Remove retaining ring and dust seal, apply compressed air to fluid inlet, and remove piston. Remove piston seal taking care not to damage caliper bore or seal groove.

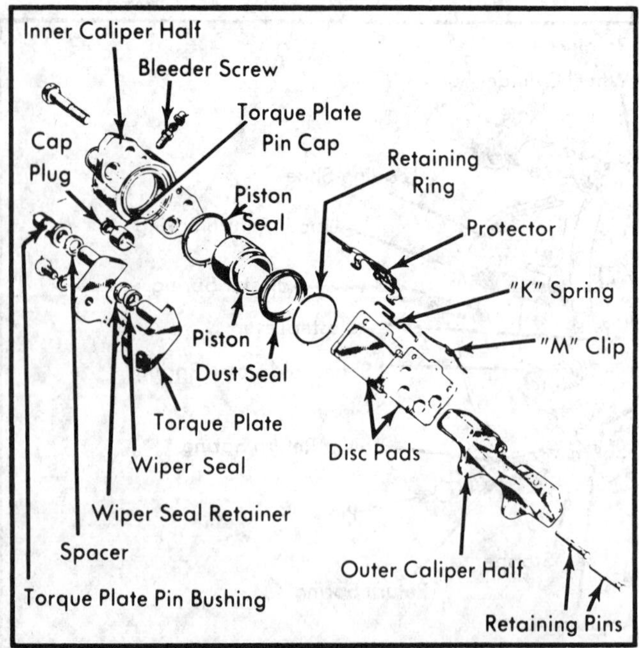

Fig. 4 Disassembled View of Disc Brake Caliper

Cleaning & Inspection – Clean all metal parts in trichloroethylene, alcohol, or brake fluid; clean piston seal in brake fluid or alcohol; clean dust seal and other rubber parts in alcohol only. Inspect caliper bore and piston for wear, damage or rust; replace parts as necessary.

NOTE – *Manufacturer recommends replacing piston seal and dust seal whenever piston has been removed.*

Reassembly – Reverse disassembly procedure and note the following: Apply rubber grease to piston seal and brake fluid to piston when reassembling. If torque plate was removed from inner caliper half, clean torque plate shaft and shaft bore in caliper, then apply special rubber grease to rubber bushing, wiper seal inner surface, and torque plate shaft before reassembly. Tighten bridge bolts of caliper halves evenly.

NOTE – *Possible cause of increased pedal stroke is: Insufficient fit between piston and piston seal. Correct by manually levering piston to seat several times. This will create a better fit between piston and seal. Make sure brake pad is removed during this procedure.*

MASTER CYLINDER

Disassembly – Remove dust boot, retaining ring, stop washer, and piston stop bolt, and withdraw primary piston assembly, secondary piston assembly, and secondary return spring from master cylinder. NOTE – *Do not disassemble primary piston assembly.* Remove check valve caps, tube seats, check valves, and check valve springs.

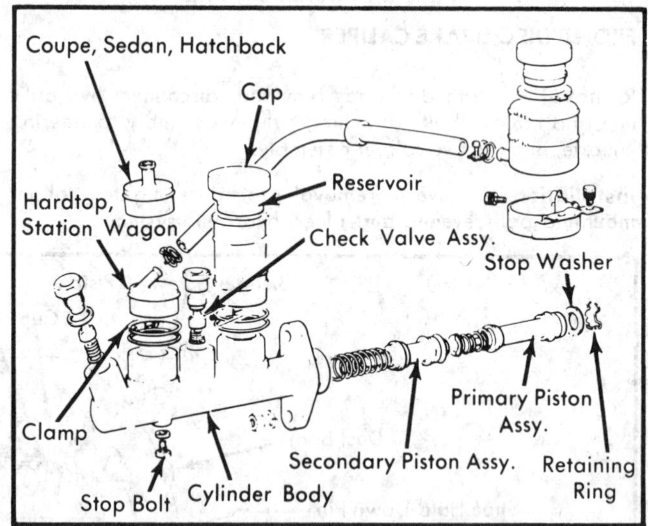

Fig. 5 Disassembled View of Master Cylinder

Inspection – Check master cylinder bore and piston for wear or other damage and replace as necessary. Check clearance between cylinder bore and piston; if clearance exceeds .006", replace parts as necessary. Check all parts of secondary piston assembly; if any parts are found defective, replace complete secondary piston assembly.

Reassembly – Reverse disassembly procedure and note the following: Apply rubber grease to all parts (except boots) before reassembly. When assembled, check that return port is not blocked by piston cup when piston is located at return position.

ARROW & COLT (Cont.)

POWER BRAKE UNIT

Disassembly – **1**) Hold front shell flange (master cylinder end of power unit) in a vice and remove clevis and lock nut. Scribe alignment mark on front and rear shells for reassembly reference. Holding neck of rear shell on both sides with pipes, remove rear shell by turning it counterclockwise. **NOTE** – *The diaphragm spring can be removed at the same time.* Remove diaphragm plate assembly from rear shell.

2) Using suitable driver, remove rear shell retainer and lift out bearing and valve body seal. Pull diaphragm from diaphragm plate assembly, then using a screwdriver, remove silencer retainer and lift out silencer and filter. Hold valve plunger, with key hole facing down and remove stop key by lightly pushing valve rod while shaking unit, then remove valve rod and plunger assembly. Remove reaction disc. **NOTE** – *Valve rod plunger assembly can not be disassembled.* Remove flange from front shell, then pull off plate and seal assembly.

Cleaning & Inspection – Thoroughly clean and dry each part. **NOTE** – *Cups and plastic parts must be wiped off only.* Inspect diaphragm plate for damage and cracks. **NOTE** – *Diaphragm plate is made of plastic and should be handled carefully at all times.* Check push rod for damage and straightness. Check front and rear shells for cracks, damage and deformation. Repair or replace any defective part.

Reassembly – **1**) Apply a sufficient amount of silicone grease to the following parts (see illustration): Front shell seal and push rod sliding surfaces (A); push rod and seal contact surfaces (B); diaphragm lug-to-rear shell contacting surface (C); outside surface of reaction disc (D); reaction disc inserting part of diaphragm plate (E); rear shell seal and diaphragm plate sliding surfaces (F); interior of piston plate into which plunger assembly is inserted and seal sliding surfaces (G).

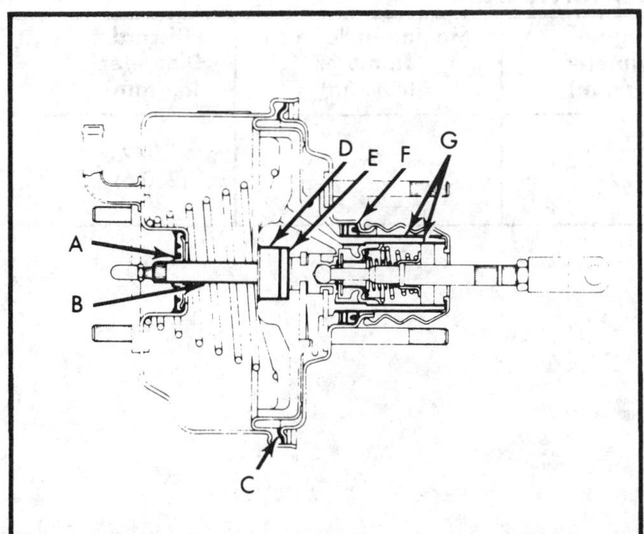

Fig. 6 Lubricate at Points Indicated in Illustration

2) Install seal and bearing into rear shell, then press in retainer. Gently install valve rod and plunger, then install stop key with chamfered end toward piston side. **NOTE** – *After installing stop key, pull plunger assembly to ensure plunger is securely locked by stop key.* Install reaction disc and diaphragm in diaphragm plate assembly, then install silencer filter and silencer into rear of diaphragm plate and press in retainer.

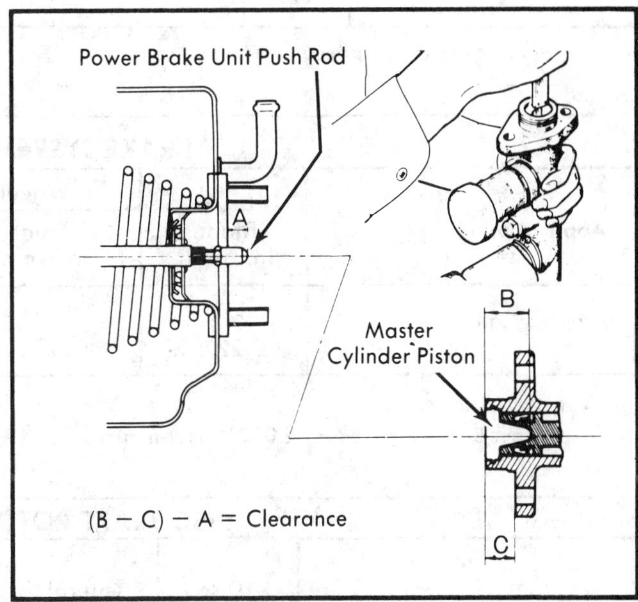

Fig. 7 Locations for Measuring Master Cylinder Push Rod-to-Piston Clearance

3) Install diaphragm plate assembly into rear shell, then install valve body guard (rear end first) into end of seal retainer. Install rear shell into front shell, then install push rod and front shell flange. Align marks made at disassembly, then turn rear shell until its notch touches stopper fully. Check clearance between power unit push rod and master cylinder piston (see illustration); clearance should be .30" (7.6 mm) or less. If clearance is not to specifications, correct by adjusting push rod length. Install yoke onto threaded end of power unit operating rod.

TIGHTENING SPECIFICATIONS

Application	Ft. Lbs (mkg)
Master Cylinder	
Check Valve Caps	18-25 (2.5-3.5)
Piston Stop Bolt	1-2 (.14-.28)
Retaining Nuts	6-9 (.83-1.2)
Hydraulic Lines	9-12 (1.2-1.7)
Caliper Mounting Bolts	58-72 (8.0-10.0)
Caliper Bridge Bolts	58-69 (8.0-9.5)
Rotor-to-Hub Bolts	25-29 (3.5-4.0)
Hydraulic Line-to-Caliper	9-12 (1.2-1.7)
Wheel Cylinder Bolts	4-7 (.55-.97)
Bleeder Screw	4-7 (.55-.97)

ARROW & COLT (Cont.)

BRAKE LINING SPECIFICATIONS							
Application	Drum Dia.	Width		Length		Thickness	
		Front	Rear	Primary	Secondary	Primary	Secondary
	In. (mm)	In. (mm)	In. (mm)	In. (mm)	In. (mm)	In. (mm)	In. (mm)
Arrow & Colt	9 (229)	①	1.57 (39.8)	9.57 (243)	9.57 (243)	.169 (4.29)	.169 (4.29)

① — Front disc brake equipped.

BRAKE SYSTEM SPECIFICATIONS				
Application	Drum Diam. In. (mm)	Wheel Cylinder Diameter		Master Cylinder
		Front In. (mm)	Rear In. (mm)	Diameter In. (mm)
Arrow & Colt	9 ① (229)	②	.750 (19.1)	.815 (20.69)

① — Rear Drum.
② — Caliper Bore Diameter — 2.012" (51.1 mm).

DISC BRAKE ROTOR SPECIFICATIONS						
Application	Disc Diameter In. (mm)	Lateral Runout In. (mm)	Parallelism In. (mm)	Original Thickness In. (mm)	Minimum Refinish Thickness In. (mm)	Discard Thickness In. (mm)
Arrow & Colt	....	.006 (.152)	....	.51 (12.9)	.....	.45 (11.4)

BRAKE DRUM SPECIFICATIONS				
Application	Drum Diameter In. (mm)	Original Diameter In. (mm)	Maximum Refinish Diameter In. (mm)	Discard Diameter In. (mm)
Arrow & Colt	9 (229)	9.000 (229)	.....	9.079 (230.6)

AUDI 100LS

100LS

DESCRIPTION

Brake system is hydraulically operated, utilizing a tandem master cylinder and power brake unit. Front disc brakes consist of rotors attached to wheel hub and drive shaft and two-piston calipers attached to strut assembly. Disc pads are equipped with a ceramic transmitter-type wear sensor. Transmitter is mounted on cross spring and will break when contact is made with pad plates, interrupting control circuit and causing indicator light on instrument panel to be activated. All models are equipped with pressure regulator that is mounted to body and operated by a spring connected to rear axle. Rear brakes are leading-trailing shoe/drum type, using a dual piston wheel cylinder. Parking brake is cable actuated, operating secondary shoes of rear brake assemblies.

ADJUSTMENT

NOTE — *Adjustments or readjustments should be carried out on cold brakes. However, brakes must be warm when testing. Instrument panel trim must be removed to adjust master cylinder push rod free play.*

MASTER CYLINDER PUSH ROD FREE PLAY

Adjustment of piston rod play at master cylinder is made by loosening lock nut and turning piston rod until correct free play, measured at brake pedal, is obtained. When correct free play of .039" is obtained between push rod and piston, free play measured at brake pedal will be approximately .2".

FRONT DISC BRAKES

Front disc brakes are self-adjusting, therefore, no adjustment in service is required.

REAR DRUM BRAKES

Raise and support rear of vehicle and release parking brake. Using a 17 mm wrench, tighten eccentric adjusters until wheels can no longer be turned by hand. Loosen eccentric adjusters until wheels are just free to turn.

PARKING BRAKE

NOTE — *Because of the residual pressure in brake regulator, the right rear brake shoes might not fully release from drum. Before adjustment, move lever on pressure regulator rearward.*

Raise and support rear of vehicle and adjust rear brakes. Lift parking brake lever until it engages third ratchet stop. Adjust nut at equalizer until rear wheels are just free to turn. When parking brake lever is pulled up one additional notch (to fourth ratchet stop), rear wheels should be locked.

BRAKE PRESSURE REGULATOR

Checking & Adjusting — **1)** Rock vehicle back and forth several times, then measure distance from top of rim to bottom of fender lip. Measurement must be made with trunk empty, gas tank full, and driver in vehicle.

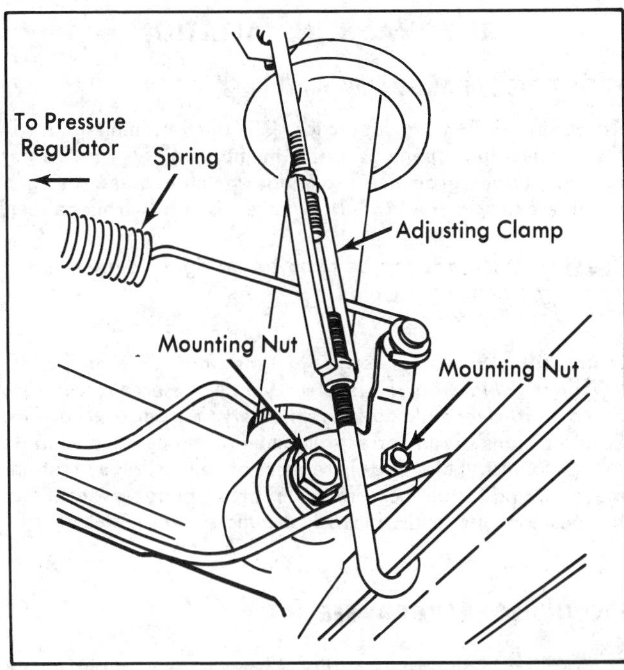

Fig. 1 Brake Pressure Regulator Adjustment Points

2) Raise vehicle on a hoist and make measurement again. If there is a difference in measurements, adjust by turning clamps. *See Fig. 1.*

3) Connect pressure gauges to left front and right rear wheels. Bleed pressure gauges. Apply pressure to foot pedal and note reading at gauge. Repeat procedure on right and left rear wheels.

Brake Pressure Values

Application	Pressure (psi)
Left Front	700
Right Rear	475-625
Right Front	1400
Left Rear	765-945

NOTE — *DO NOT adjust brake pressure regulator when pressure is applied to brake pedal.*

4) If pressure at rear wheels is too high, release spring and move spring support arm forward. If pressure at rear wheels is too low, move support arm rearward.

HYDRAULIC SYSTEM BLEEDING

Fill master cylinder reservoir with brake fluid and maintain level throughout bleeding operation. Attach a hose to bleeder screw, and immerse opposite end in a container partially full of brake fluid. Open bleeder screw approximately one-half turn, depress brake pedal, close bleeder screw, and slowly return pedal. Continue operation until air bubbles are no longer seen in discharged fluid. Bleeding sequence is left-rear, right-rear, right-front, left-front.

AUDI 100LS (Cont.)

REMOVAL & INSTALLATION

FRONT DISC BRAKE PADS

Removal – Remove lock clips. Pull out retaining pins so they project into openings in side members. **NOTE** – *Do not remove rubber grommets from side member holes.* Using a suitable extractor tool (SB-3), remove disc pads from caliper.

NOTE – *Disc pads can be removed on right side only after removing front exhaust pipe.*

Installation – Press both pistons into caliper bores. **NOTE** – *Fluid level in master cylinder reservoir will rise. Siphon sufficient fluid to prevent reservoir from overflowing.* Ensure pistons are in correct alignment in bores using suitable tool (B-5). Install disc pads in recesses of caliper, slide in retaining pins, and install lock clip. Pump brake pedal several times to position disc pads. Bleed hydraulic system if necessary.

FRONT DISC BRAKE CALIPER

Removal – With wheel and tire removed, take out disc brake pads. Disconnect hydraulic line from caliper. Remove bolts securing caliper and take off caliper.

Installation – To install brake caliper, reverse removal procedure and bleed hydraulic system.

FRONT DISC BRAKE ROTOR

Removal – With wheel and tire assembly removed, take off caliper. Do not disconnect hydraulic line unless necessary. Remove screw retaining rotor to wheel hub (if equipped) and withdraw rotor.

Installation – To install rotor assembly, reverse removal procedure and bleed hydraulic system.

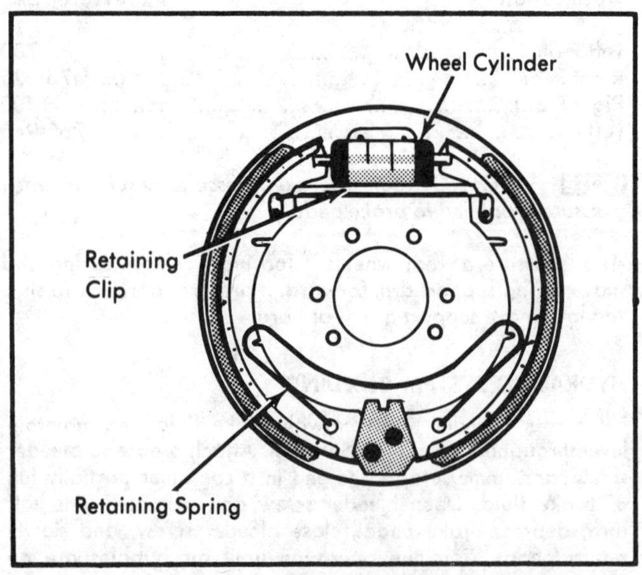

Fig. 2 Audi 100LS Rear Brake Assembly

REAR BRAKE DRUM

Removal – Raise and support vehicle, remove wheel and tire assembly. Pry off dust cap, remove cotter pin from hex nut, and remove nut. Remove brake drum making sure that retaining washer and wheel bearing do not fall out.

Installation – To install, reverse removal procedure, adjust brakes, and adjust wheel bearings. *See Wheel Bearing Adjustment in WHEEL ALIGNMENT Section.*

REAR BRAKE SHOES

Removal – With brake drum removed, remove retaining spring for brake shoes. Remove shoes as an assembly by disconnecting spring at bottom, pulling shoes back from wheel cylinder, and disconnecting parking brake cable.

Installation – To install, reverse removal procedure and note the following: Make sure long ends of retaining clip and spring are installed on secondary shoe and parking brake lever. Ensure brake shoes are correctly positioned on wheel cylinder pistons.

REAR BRAKE WHEEL CYLINDER

Removal – With drum and shoes removed, depress pedal approximately 1.2" and hold in position using a suitable pedal support. Disconnect hydraulic line from rear of backing plate and plug line to prevent loss of fluid. Remove retaining screws and wheel cylinder.

Installation – To install, reverse removal procedure, adjust brakes and bleed hydraulic system.

MASTER CYLINDER

Removal – Disconnect hydraulic line at rear of master cylinder. Depress brake pedal 1.2-1.6" and hold in position using a suitable pedal support. Disconnect remaining hydraulic line and cylinder mounting nuts. Separate master cylinder from power unit taking care not to lose"O" ring installed between them.

Installation – To install, reverse removal procedure and bleed hydraulic system.

POWER BRAKE UNIT

Removal – Siphon brake fluid from master cylinder reservoir and disconnect hydraulic lines. Loosen hose clamp and disconnect vacuum hose from power unit. From inside vehicle, remove trim below instrument panel as necessary. Disconnect push rod from brake pedal, remove power unit adapter attaching nuts, and remove power unit and master cylinder from engine compartment as an assembly. Separate master cylinder and adaptor from power unit.

Installation – To install, reverse removal procedure and note the following: Be sure to install "O" ring between master cylinder and power unit. Install adaptor to power unit so that center punch mark on adaptor is located on lower right hand side facing engine. To complete installation, adjust pedal push rod free play and bleed hydraulic system.

AUDI 100LS (Cont.)

Check Valve Replacement – A vacuum check valve is located in vacuum line between intake manifold and power unit. To remove, loosen hose clamps, separate vacuum hoses from check valve, and remove check valve. To install, reverse removal procedure and note the following: Check valve is stamped with the word "MOTOR" and an arrow. End of valve in which arrow points must be connected to shorter hose from intake manifold.

OVERHAUL

FRONT DISC BRAKE CALIPER

Disassembly – Remove disc pads. Pry out retaining ring and remove dust seal by hand. Place a small block of wood in caliper cavity, and remove piston by applying compressed air to fluid inlet. Remove remaining piston in same manner. Remove seal from caliper bore using a piece of wood or plastic. **NOTE** – *Do not use hard or sharp tools for this purpose. Do not separate caliper halves.*

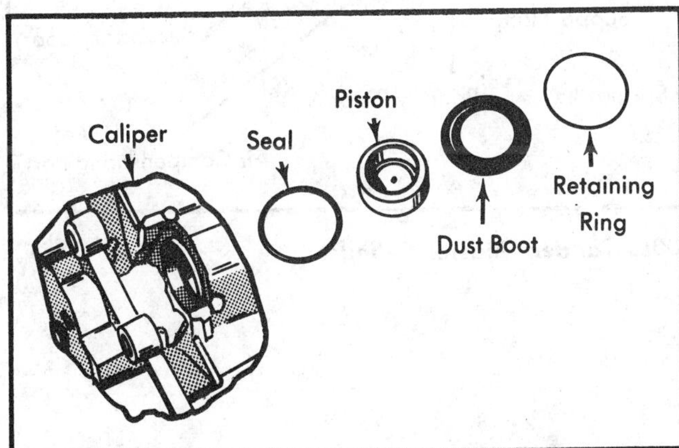

Fig. 3 Front Disc Brake Caliper Assembly

Cleaning & Inspection – Clean all parts in alcohol only. Check cylinder bore and piston for damage. **NOTE** – *Do not machine caliper bore or piston. Parts are serviced by replacement only.*

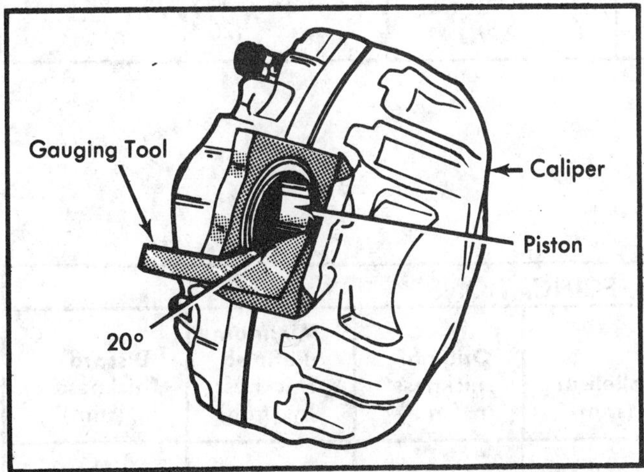

Fig. 4 Using a 20°Gauge to Position Caliper Piston

Reassembly – Coat all parts with ATE brake cylinder paste (or equivalent), reverse disassembly procedure, and note the following: Use new seals, dust boots, and retaining rings when reassembling. When installing piston, make sure machined surface of piston face makes a 20° angle to wall of caliper bore (see illustration). Install disc pads after caliper has been installed on vehicle.

REAR WHEEL CYLINDER

Disassembly – Thoroughly clean outside of cylinder. Remove end caps, piston and seal assemblies, and spring. Remove dust cap and bleeder screw.

Cleaning & Inspection – Clean all parts in alcohol only. Check all parts for rust, corrosion, or other damage. Check cylinder bore and piston for wear. Maximum allowable cylinder diameter is .6287"; minimum allowable piston diameter is .6197". Manufacturer recommends replacing rubber components each time cylinder is disassembled.

Reassembly – Reverse disassembly procedure and note the following: Apply a thin coat of ATE brake cylinder paste (or equivalent) to all parts during assembly.

MASTER CYLINDER

Disassembly – Thoroughly clean outside of master cylinder. Remove hydraulic fluid reservoir, remove retaining ring, and remove primary piston assembly. Loosen or remove (if necessary) piston stop screw and remove secondary piston assembly. Disassemble primary and secondary piston assemblies.

Cleaning & Inspection – Clean all parts in alcohol only. Dry all parts with compressed air and check that compensating ports of cylinder are free of obstructions. Check cylinder bore and pistons for rust, corrosion or other damage. Inspect cylinder bore and piston for wear. Maximum allowable cylinder diameter is .817"; minimum allowable piston diameter is .807". Manufacturer recommends replacing all rubber parts whenever cylinder has been disassembled.

Reassembly – Reverse disassembly procedures and note the following: Do not apply grease to push rod as damage may result to rubber components.

POWER BRAKE UNIT

NOTE – *Manufacturer does not recommend overhaul of power brake unit.*

TIGHTENING SPECIFICATIONS

Application	Ft. Lbs. (mkg)
Caliper-to-Transmission	68-75 (9.5-10.5)
Brake Line Nuts	7-10 (1.0-1.2)
Drive Shaft-to-Transmission	70-78 (9.7-10.7)

AUDI 100LS (Cont.)

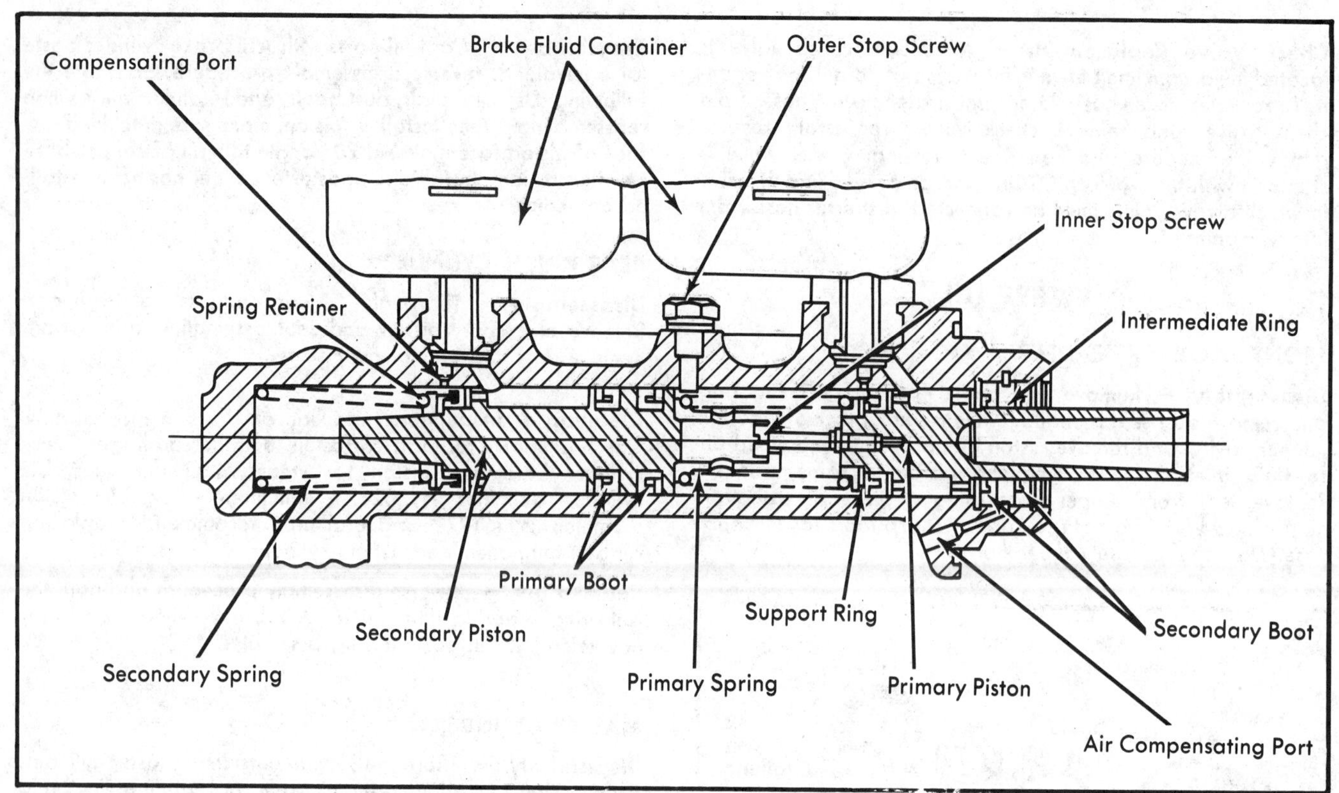

Fig. 5 Sectional View of Audi 100LS Tandem Master Cylinder

BRAKE SYSTEM SPECIFICATIONS				
Application	Drum Diam. In. (mm)	Wheel Cylinder Diameter		Master Cylinder
		Front In. (mm)	Rear In. (mm)	Diameter In. (mm)
100LS	7.87 (200)	①	.625 (15.8)	.813 (20.6)

① — Front disc equipped.

DISC BRAKE ROTOR SPECIFICATIONS						
Application	Disc Diameter In. (mm)	Lateral Runout In. (mm)	Parallelism In. (mm)	Original Thickness In. (mm)	Minimum Refinish Thickness In. (mm)	Discard Thickness In. (mm)
100LS	11.45 (291)	.004 (.1)	.0008 (.02)	.413 (10.5)	.....	.354 (9.0)

AUDI FOX

Fox

DESCRIPTION

Brake system is hydraulically operated, utilizing a tandem master cylinder and a Teves power brake unit. Front disc brakes consist of rotors attached to wheel hubs, and single piston floating caliper assemblies attached to steering knuckles. The disc brake pads are equipped with wear indicators that create a pulsation in the brake pedal when the pads are worn. Rear brakes are leading-trailing shoe/drum type, using a dual piston wheel cylinder. Parking brake is cable actuated, operating secondary shoes of rear brake assemblies. Pressure regulator valves for rear wheels mount to power brake unit.

ADJUSTMENT

FRONT DISC BRAKE PADS

Front disc brakes are self-adjusting, therefore, no adjustment in service is required.

REAR DRUM BRAKE SHOES

Raise and support rear of vehicle, release parking brake. Use a brake spoon, tighten rear star adjuster until wheel can no longer be turned by hand. Loosen star until wheels are just free to turn.

PARKING BRAKE

With rear brake shoes properly adjusted, pull parking brake handle to second notch. Tighten parking brake adjusting nut until rear wheels can just be turned by hand, then tighten lock nut. Release handle and ensure both rear wheels rotate freely.

PRESSURE REGULATOR VALVE

Operation Test – Place hand around pressure regulator. Depress brake pedal relatively hard. Release pedal; listen and feel for a slight "knock" in each regulator. This is the piston returning in regulator.

Pressure Test – **1**) Use two pressure gauges that will record at least 1400 psi. Hook one gauge to left rear wheel cylinder. Attach other gauge to right front caliper cylinder. Bleed both hoses through bleeder in gauges. Operate pedal vigorously several times.

2) Depress brake pedal until gauge on right front caliper reads 497 psi at the same time the gauge hooked to left rear wheel cylinder should read 384 psi.

3) Continue depressing pedal and hold it in position when right front gauge reads 1400 psi, left rear wheel cylinder gauge should read between 768-862 psi. Repeat procedure to check other side. Replace any regulator that does not meet specifications outlined here.

HYDRAULIC SYSTEM BLEEDING

Fill master cylinder reservoir with brake fluid and maintain level throughout bleeding operation. Attach a hose to bleeder screw, and immerse opposite end in a container partially full of brake fluid. Open bleeder screw approximately one-half turn, depress brake pedal, close bleeder screw, and slowly return pedal. Continue operation until air bubbles are no longer seen in discharged fluid. Bleeding sequence is right-rear, left-rear, right-front, left-front.

REMOVAL & INSTALLATION

FRONT DISC BRAKE PADS

Removal – Raise and support front of vehicle and remove wheel and tire assembly. Pull spring locks out of retaining pins, drive retaining pins out toward outside of vehicle, and remove cross spring. Using a suitable tool (P 86), remove inboard brake pad. Pull mounting frame and brake cylinder outwards until outboard pad can be removed.

Installation – Press piston to bottom of travel in cylinder and floating frame. **NOTE** – *Level in master cylinder reservoir will rise. Siphon off sufficient fluid to prevent overflowing.* Ensure machined portion of piston face makes a 20° angle to lower caliper wall. Install disc pads by reversing removal procedure.

FRONT DISC BRAKE CALIPER

Removal – With wheel and tire assembly and disc brake pads removed, disconnect hydraulic line from caliper. Remove bolts securing caliper to steering knuckle and remove caliper.

Installation – Reverse removal procedure and bleed hydraulic system.

FRONT DISC BRAKE ROTOR

Removal – With wheel and tire assembly removed, remove caliper. **NOTE** – *Do not disconnect hydraulic line unless necessary.* Remove screw securing rotor to wheel hub and withdraw rotor.

Installation – Reverse removal procedure and bleed hydraulic system if necessary.

REAR BRAKE DRUM

Removal – Pry off grease cap. Remove cotter pin, castle nut, hex nut, and washer. Pull off brake drum making sure that inner race of outer bearing is not lost.

Installation – Reverse removal procedure, adjust brake shoes, and adjust wheel bearings. *See Wheel Bearing Adjustment in WHEEL ALIGNMENT Section.*

REAR BRAKE SHOES

Removal – With brake drum removed, disconnect lower spring by removing from primary shoe. Remove shoe vibration cups, springs, and pins. Remove primary shoe from backing plate, disconnect parking brake cable from lever, and remove secondary shoe and parking brake lever assembly.

Installation – Reverse removal procedure and note the following: Before installing secondary brake shoe, make sure that rear wheel cylinder piston is positioned so that web faces outward and opening inward. Adjust brakes and bleed hydraulic system if necessary.

AUDI FOX (Cont.)

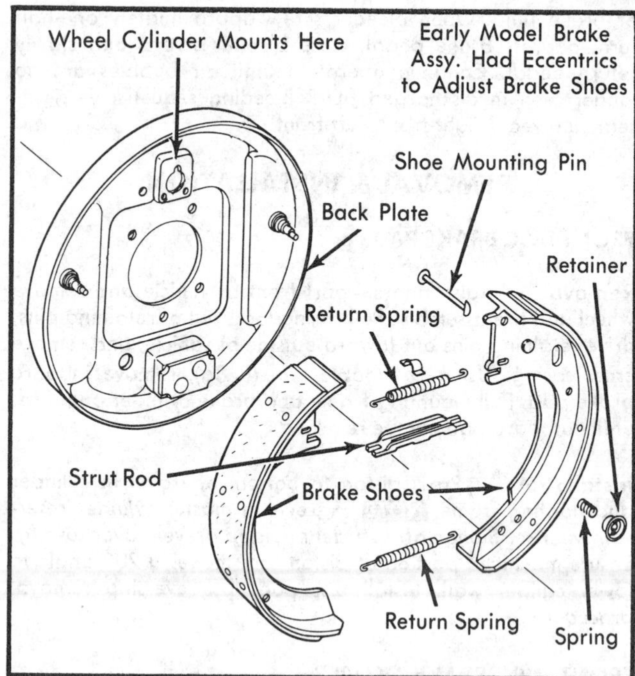

Fig. 1 Exploded View of Rear Brake Assy.

REAR BRAKE WHEEL CYLINDER

Removal – Depress brake pedal approximately 1.2" to close compensator bore in master cylinder, and hold in position using a suitable pedal support. Disconnect hydraulic line from cylinder and plug with rubber cap from bleeder screw. Remove bolts attaching wheel cylinder to backing plate. Remove cylinder by maneuvering out of backing plate.

Installation – Reverse removal procedure and note the following: Make sure that rear piston is installed in wheel cylinder so that web faces outward and opening inward. Bleed hydraulic system.

MASTER CYLINDER

Removal – Siphon brake fluid from master cylinder reservoir. Disconnect hydraulic lines at cylinder, remove nuts attaching master cylinder to power unit, and remove master cylinder.

Installation – Reverse removal procedure and note the following: Make sure "O" ring is installed between master cylinder and power unit. After installing master cylinder, bleed hydraulic system.

OVERHAUL

FRONT DISC BRAKE CALIPER

Disassembly – Remove disc pads and pry mounting frame and piston assembly off floating frame. Remove brake cylinder and guide spring from floating frame. Remove clamp and dust cap from brake cylinder, then withdraw piston. **NOTE** – *If necessary, apply compressed air to fluid inlet.* Remove seal from cylinder.

Cleaning & Inspection – Thoroughly clean all parts in alcohol. Check all parts for rust, corrosion, or other damage; replace parts as necessary. **NOTE** – *Manufacturer recommends replacing rubber parts whenever caliper has been disassembled.*

Reassembly – Apply a thin coat of ATE brake cylinder paste (or equivalent) to cylinder, piston and seal, and reassemble. Place guide spring in groove of brake cylinder, then drive cylinder on floating frame with a brass mandrel. Place mounting frame in guide spring, then slide it on floating frame.

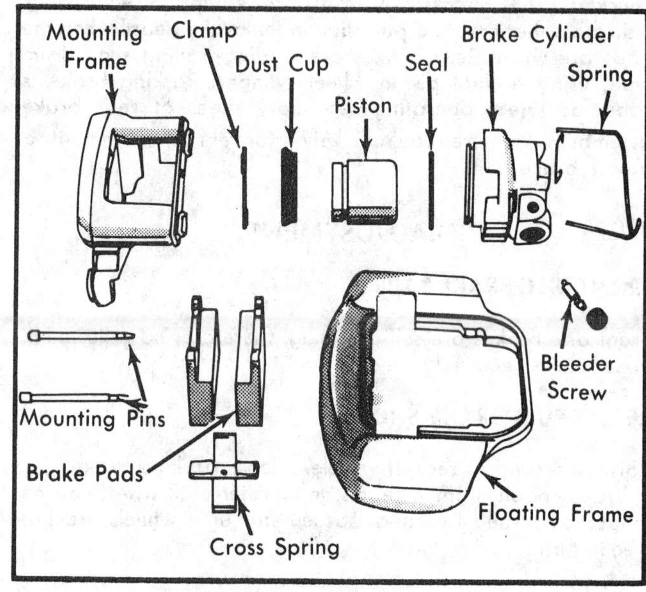

Fig. 2 Audi Fox Disc Brake Caliper Assy.

REAR BRAKE WHEEL CYLINDER

Disassembly – Remove rubber dust caps, then withdraw front and rear piston and seal assemblies. Remove seals from pistons. Remove bleeder screw and dust cap.

Cleaning & Inspection – Thoroughly clean all components in alcohol. Inspect cylinder and pistons for rust, corrosion, or scoring; replace parts as necessary. **NOTE** – *Manufacturer recommends replacing all rubber parts whenever cylinder has been disassembled.*

Reassembly – Reverse disassembly procedure and note the following: Pistons are not interchangeable. Install notched piston in front of cylinder so that it will engage primary shoe when installed on backing plate.

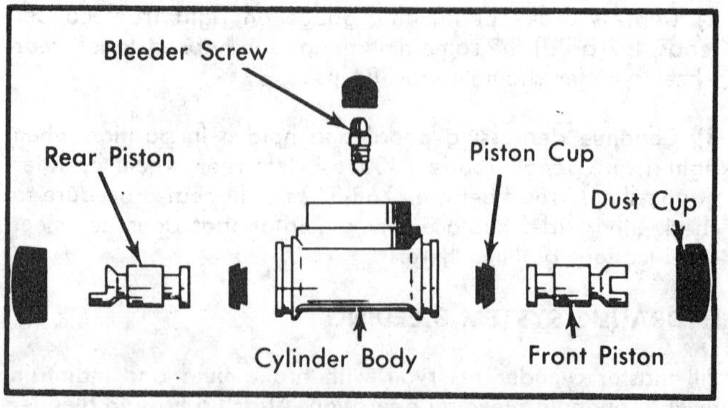

Fig. 3 Exploded View of Rear Wheel Cylinder

AUDI FOX (Cont.)

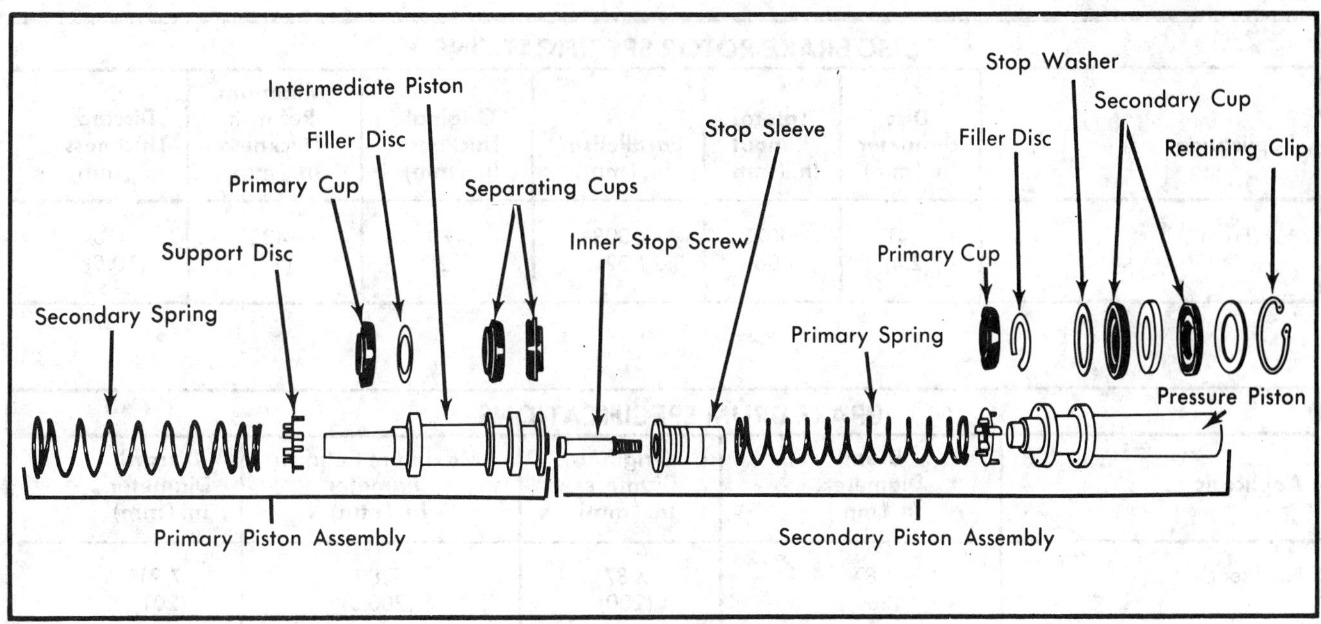

Fig. 4 Master Cylinder Piston Assembly

MASTER CYLINDER

Disassembly – Remove "O" ring from master cylinder housing. Remove retaining ring and loosen piston stop screw, then remove both pistons from housing. Remove pressure valves and reservoir from master cylinder housing. Disassemble piston assemblies as necessary.

Cleaning & Inspection – Clean all parts in alcohol and check for rust, corrosion, or other damage; replace parts as necessary. Make sure compensating and filler holes are not plugged.

Reassembly – Reverse disassembly procedure and note the following: Make sure pressure and intermediate piston cups are installed correctly. *See Fig. 4*. Use new "O" ring on master cylinder between cylinder and power unit.

POWER BRAKE UNIT

NOTE – *No information available for Overhaul of power brake unit.*

TIGHTENING SPECIFICATIONS	
Application	**Ft. Lbs. (mkg)**
Power Unit-to-Adapter	14 (2)
Adapter-to-Firewall	14 (2)
Caliper-to-Steering Knuckle	43 (6)
Splash Guard-to-Steering Knuckle	7 (1)
Rotor-to-Hub Screw	5 (.7)
Hydraulic Line-to-Master Cylinder	7 (1)
Hydraulic Line-to-Caliper	9 (1.2)
Hydraulic Line-to-Wheel Cylinder	9 (1.2)

BRAKE SYSTEM SPECIFICATIONS

Application	Drum Diam. In. (mm)	Wheel Cylinder Diameter Front In. (mm)	Wheel Cylinder Diameter Rear In. (mm)	Master Cylinder Diameter In. (mm)
Fox	7.87 (200)	1.73① (44)	.....	.813 (20.6)

① – Front disc brake cylinder.

AUDI FOX (Cont.)

DISC BRAKE ROTOR SPECIFICATIONS						
Application	Disc Diameter In. (mm)	Lateral Runout In. (mm)	Parallelism In. (mm)	Original Thickness In. (mm)	Minimum Refinish Thickness In. (mm)	Discard Thickness In. (mm)
Fox (Front)	9.41 (2.4)	.0023 (.06)	.0008 (.02)	.470 (12)	.430 (11)	.410 (10.5)

BRAKE DRUM SPECIFICATIONS				
Application	Drum Diameter In. (mm)	Original Diameter In. (mm)	Maximum Refinish Diameter In. (mm)	Discard Diameter In. (mm)
Fox (Rear)	7.87 (200)	7.87 (200)	7.89 (200.5)	7.91 (201)

BMW

320i
530i
630CSi

DESCRIPTION

Brake system is hydraulically operated. System uses both a tandem master cylinder and power brake unit. 530i and 630CSi models have 4 piston ATE front disc brakes and 2 piston ATE rear brakes. 320i models are equipped with 2 piston ATE front disc brakes and drum rear brakes. Parking brake is lever actuated and cable operated. On 530i and 630CSi models, brake shoes work against a drum machined in rear disc brake rotor/hub. On 320i models, shoes lock against rear brake drum. All models are equipped with a brake pressure regulator to reduce line pressure to rear brakes.

ADJUSTMENT

DISC PADS

Front and rear disc brake assemblies are self-adjusting, therefore, no adjustment in service is required.

REAR DRUM BRAKES

320i – Raise vehicle. Release parking brake. Using special tool 34 2 000 (or equivalent wrench), tighten brake shoes by turning left cam counterclockwise and right cam clockwise. Loosen cam ⅛ turn or until wheel is just free to turn.

PARKING BRAKE

530i & 630CSi – **1)** Release parking brake lever, raise and support vehicle, and remove rear wheels. Insert a brake adjusting tool through .6" hole in rotor, turn adjuster until rotor can no longer be rotated, then back off adjuster 2 or 3 teeth.

2) Work inside driver compartment, tighten adjustment nuts on lever until parking brake holds vehicle securely before fifth ratchet stop is reached.

320i – **1)** Raise and support rear of vehicle. Fully release parking brake. Tighten brake shoes until wheel is locked. Back off adjusters about ⅛ turn or until wheel can just barely turn.

2) Work inside drivers compartment and tighten nuts on lever until parking brake holds vehicle securely before fifth ratchet stop is reached.

HYDRAULIC SYSTEM BLEEDING

NOTE – *Manufacturer recommends replacing brake fluid in entire system once a year to avoid moisture build-up.* Attach a pressure bleeder to master cylinder reservoir.

CAUTION – *Do not exceed 29 psi.* Raise and support vehicle and remove wheels. Attach a bleeder hose to bleeder screw, and immerse opposite end of hose into a container partially filled with brake fluid. Open bleeder screw, allow all air to escape, then close bleeder screw. Continue operation until all air has been expelled from system. **NOTE** – *On front wheel four piston calipers, bleed lower inboard screw before bleeding lower outboard screw.*

REMOVAL & INSTALLATION

DISC PADS

Removal – Raise and support vehicle and remove wheels. Drive out retaining pins toward inside of vehicle and remove cross spring. Using an extractor tool, remove disc pads from caliper assembly. If disc pad thickness (including backing) has been worn to .080" (.02 mm), replace pads. Only replace pads in sets.

Installation – **1)** Using a cylinder brush, clean guide surface and support surface in caliper. Siphon sufficient fluid from master cylinder reservoir to prevent overflowing, then press pistons to bottom of bores.

2) On rear two piston calipers, ensure machined postion of piston face makes a 20° angle to lower caliper wall. Install disc pads, cross spring, and retaining pins. After installation, depress brake pedal several times to position pads against rotor.

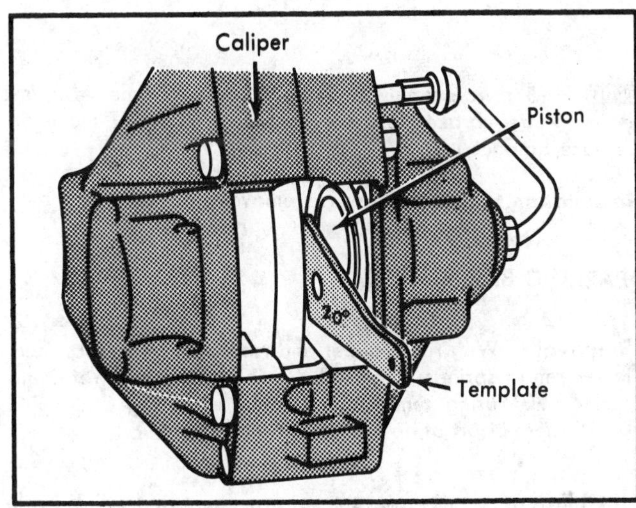

Fig. 1 Piston Alignment for Dual Piston Calipers

CALIPER ASSEMBLY

Removal – Drain brake fluid from master cylinder reservoir. Remove caliper mounting bolts. Disconnect disc pad wear indicator electrical lead. Disconnect brake fluid inlet lines. Lift caliper off rotor.

Installation – Reverse removal procedure and bleed hydraulic system.

ROTOR

Removal: 530i; Front – With caliper assembly removed, remove hub grease cap, cotter pin, and nut. Remove hub and rotor assembly. Remove Allen head bolts retaining rotor to hub and remove rotor.

NOTE – *Both brake rotors must be replaced at same time.*

BMW (Cont.)

Installation – To install, reverse removal procedure. Tighten all bolts and fittings evenly. Bleed hydraulic system if necessary. Adjust front wheel bearings. *See Wheel Bearing Adjustment in WHEEL ALIGNMENT Section.*

Removal: 320i & 630CSi; Front – Raise and support front of vehicle. Separate bracket from strut. Remove caliper and tie out of way with brake line still connected. Remove mounting bolt from hub and take off rotor.

NOTE – *Inboard vented brake discs are balanced, DO NOT move or replace balance clips.*

Installation – To install, reverse removal procedure.

Removal: 530i & 630CSi; Rear – Raise vehicle and support on safety stands. Remove tire and wheel. Remove caliper and support out of way leaving brake line connected. Slip brake line out of clamp. Take out mounting bolt and remove brake rotor.

NOTE – *Both rotors must be replaced at same time. Also, inboard vented brake discs are balanced, DO NOT move or replace balance clips.*

Installation – To install, reverse removal procedure.

PARKING BRAKE SHOES

Removal – With rear caliper and rotor removed, disconnect lower return spring using brake spring pliers. Turn retaining springs 90° using removal tool, then set spring aside. Pull brake shoes apart at bottom and lift upward.

Installation – Reverse removal procedure and adjust parking brake shoes and cables.

BRAKE DRUM

Removal & Installation: 320i; Rear – Loosen brake adjuster cams. Remove countersunk Allen bolt and slide off brake drum. To install, reverse removal procedure and note: If one brake drum is reground, drum on other side must also be machined.

BRAKE SHOES

Removal: 320i; Rear – Remove brake drum. Disengage mounting spring, retainer, and pin from each shoe. Disconnect bottom return spring. Pull shoes apart and out of wheel cylinder. Disconnect parking brake cable and remove brake shoes. If brake shoe lining has worn to .118" (3.0 mm) or less, replace brake shoes.

Installation – Reverse removal procedure and note: Connect long end of spring between parking brake lever and brake shoe.

WHEEL CYLINDER

Removal: 320i; Rear – Remove brake drum. Disconnect brake fluid inlet line. Remove wheel cylinder bleeder valve. Remove cylinder mounting bolts and take off cylinder being careful not to drop brake fluid on brake shoes.

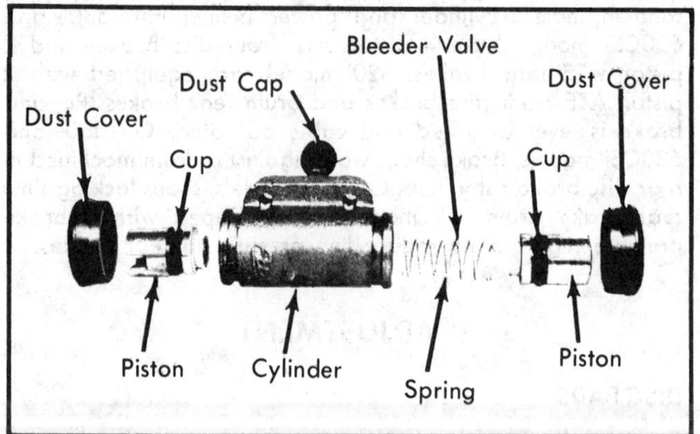

Fig. 2 Exploded View of 320i Rear Wheel Cylinder

Installation – To install, reverse removal procedure and make sure to bleed brake system.

MASTER CYLINDER

Removal – Siphon off brake fluid from reservoir. On 320i models, disconnect clutch hose connection. On 630CSi models, remove air cleaner. Disconnect all hydraulic lines from master cylinder. Remove nuts mounting master cylinder to power booster. On 320i models, remove nuts mounting master cylinder support to inner fender panel. Remove support and master cylinder.

Installation – To install, reverse removal procedure and note: Make sure "O" ring on master cylinder is not damaged. An imperfect fit will not allow correct vacuum build-up.

POWER BRAKE UNIT

NOTE – *Mixture control unit must be removed to take off power brake unit (with master cylinder).*

Removal: 320i – **1)** Remove air intake ducting. Remove 3 screws located in top of control unit. Spread open cable clips. Remove wire holder. Lift up mixture control unit and retain piston with fingers until it can be tapped into place. Disconnect remaining vacuum lines. Remove unit mounting nuts and lift off unit.

2) Siphon out brake fluid from reservoir. Disconnect push rod from brake pedal. Separate hydraulic lines from master cylinder. Also, disconnect clutch hose.

3) Disconnect vacuum hose from brake unit. Remove brake unit mounting nuts and bolts. Separate master cylinder support

BMW (Cont.)

from inner fender panel. Slide master cylinder and power brake assembly from vehicle.

Installation – To install master cylinder and power brake assembly as a unit, reverse removal procedure.

Removal: 530i & 630CSi – Disconnect power brake push rod from brake pedal at clevis pin. Disconnect vacuum hose at power brake unit. Disconnect and plug brake lines at master cylinder. Remove brake unit at mounting bracket and slide entire unit out of vehicle.

Installation – To install brake unit with master cylinder connected, reverse removal procedure. Bleed brake system after assembly is installed.

Check Valve Replacement – Check valve is located in power unit vacuum line at intake manifold. To remove, loosen hose clamps, remove vacuum hoses, and remove valve. To install, reverse removal procedure, making sure arrow or black portion of valve faces intake manifold.

Filter Replacement – With power brake unit removed from vehicle, pull back rubber dust boot and remove retaining ring. Remove silencer and filter. To install, reverse removal procedure.

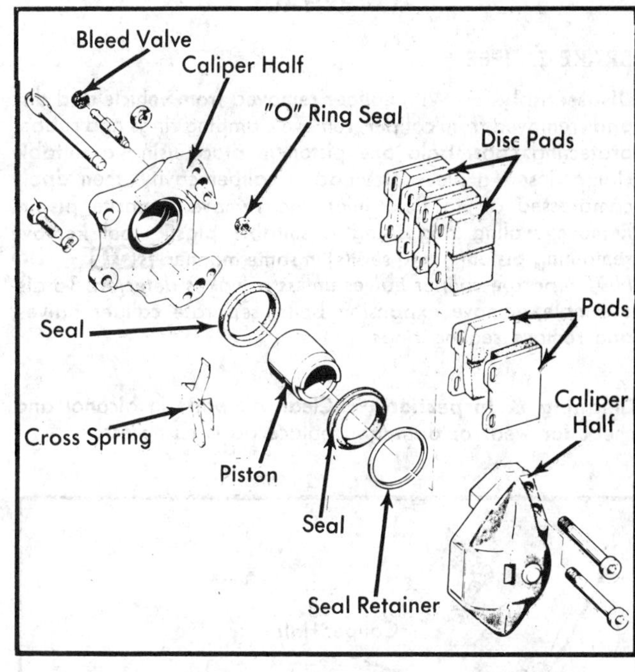

Fig. 3 Disassembled View of Dual Piston Rear Disc Brake for 530i & 630CSi. Front Caliper for 320i is Similar

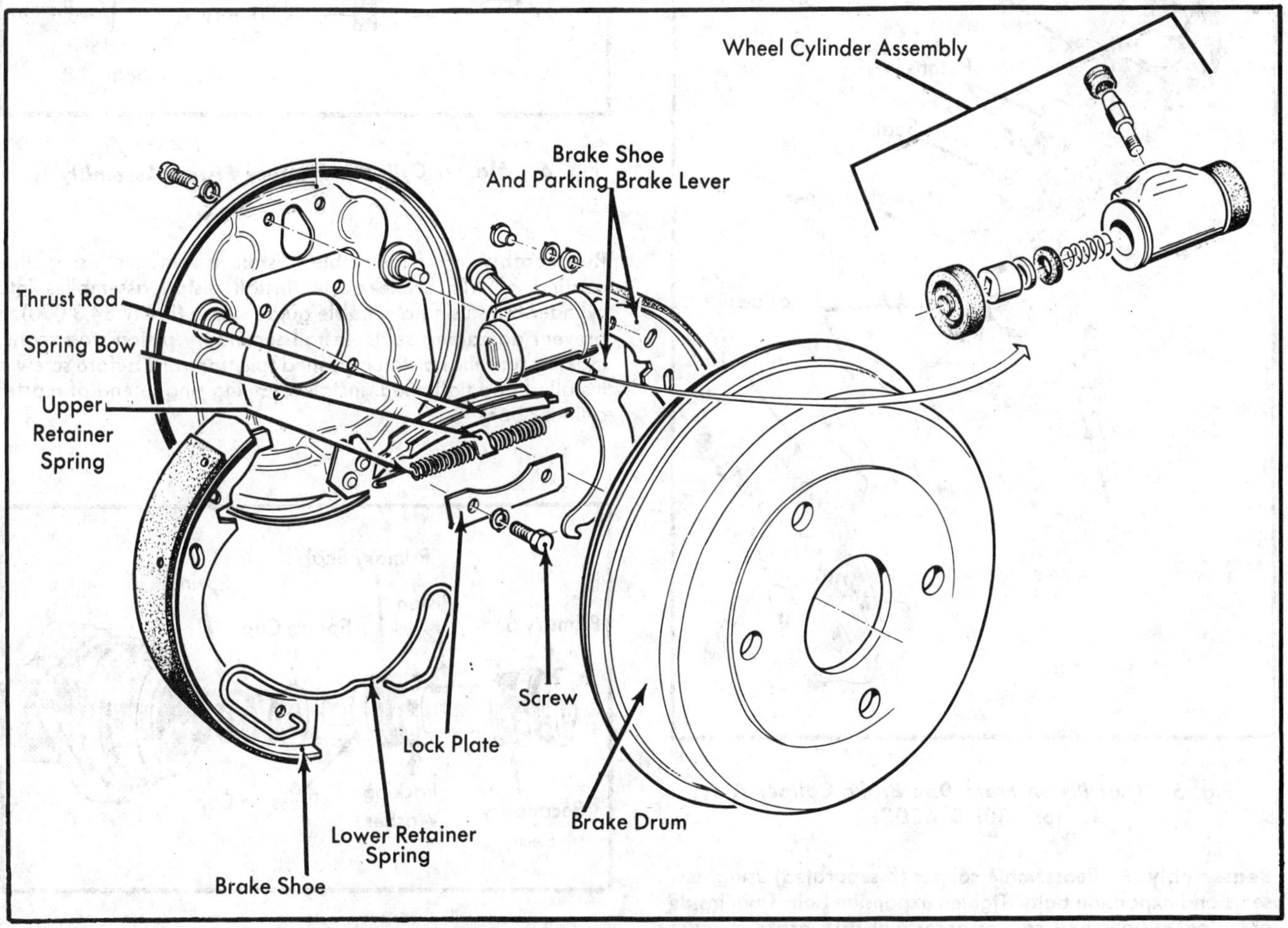

Fig. 4 Exploded View of 320 Rear Drum Brake Assy.

BMW (Cont.)

OVERHAUL

BRAKE CALIPER

Disassembly – With caliper removed from vehicle and disc pads removed from caliper, remove clamping rings and rubber protecting caps. Hold one piston in place using a suitable clamp, insert a piece of wood in caliper cavity, then apply compressed air to fluid inlet and remove opposite piston. Remove sealing ring using a suitable plastic tool. Remove remaining piston(s) and seal(s) in same manner. **NOTE** – *DO NOT separate caliper halves unless a leak is detected.* To disassemble, remove expansion bolts, separate caliper halves, and remove sealing rings.

Cleaning & Inspection – Clean all parts in alcohol and check for wear or damage; replace parts as necessary.

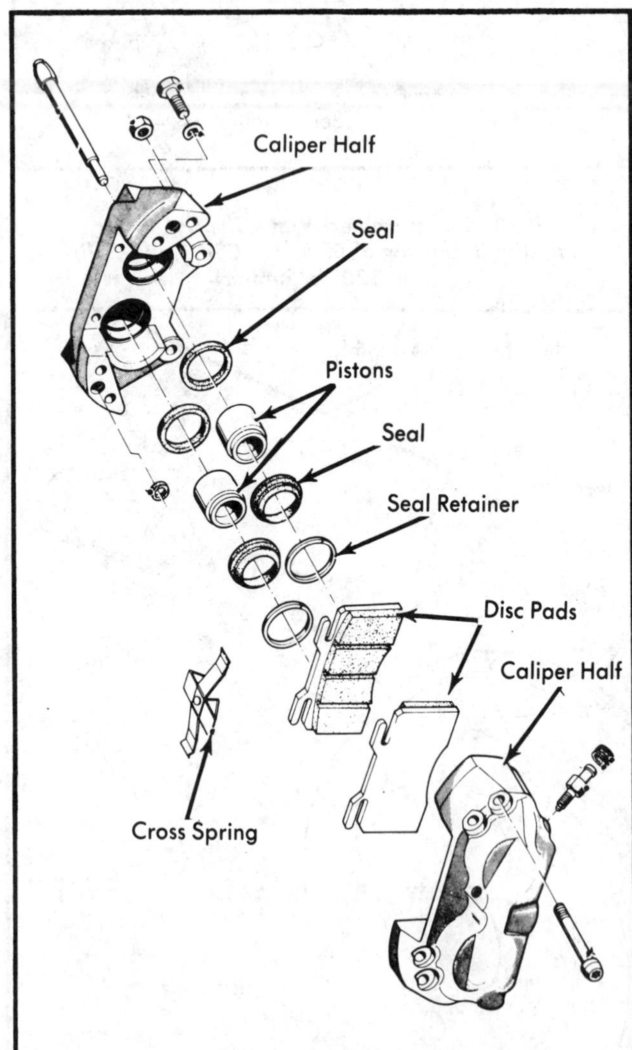

Fig. 5 Four Piston Front Disc Brake Caliper Assy. for 530i & 630CSi

Reassembly – Reassemble caliper (if separated) using new seals and expansion bolts. Tighten expansion bolts from inside out. Coat pistons and caliper bores with ATE brake cylinder paste (or equivalent), install sealing rings, then install pistons into bores. Make sure pistons are not tilted when inserting. On two piston calipers, make sure machined surface of piston face makes a 20° angle to lower caliper wall. Install rubber protecting caps and clamp rings.

MASTER CYLINDER

Disassembly – Push in on primary piston and remove secondary piston stop screw. Remove snap ring from end of cylinder and remove primary and secondary piston assemblies and return spring. Dissassemble piston assemblies noting number and position of parts used.

Cleaning & Inspection – Clean all parts in alcohol and inspect for wear or damage. **NOTE** – *Cylinders with surface defects in bores must be replaced; do not overhaul.*

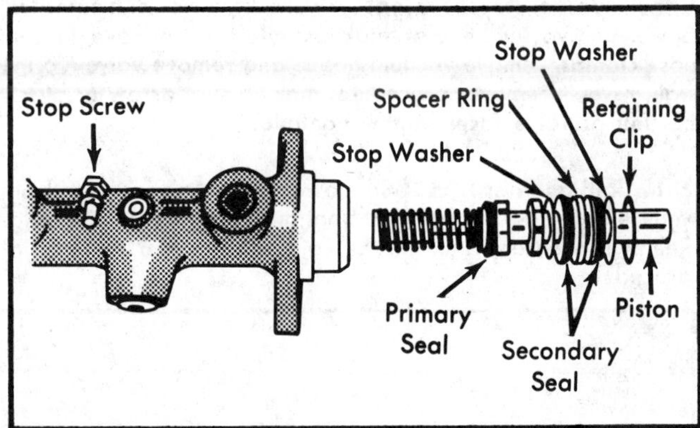

Fig. 6 Master Cylinder Primary Piston Assembly

Reassembly – Reassemble piston assemblies using thin coating of ATE brake paste. Install piston assemblies into cylinder bore using a suitable guide sleeve (BMW 34 3 000) to prevent damaging seals. Install secondary piston stop screw, making sure that piston is pushed fully forward before screw is installed and tightened. Install retaining ring in end of master cylinder bore.

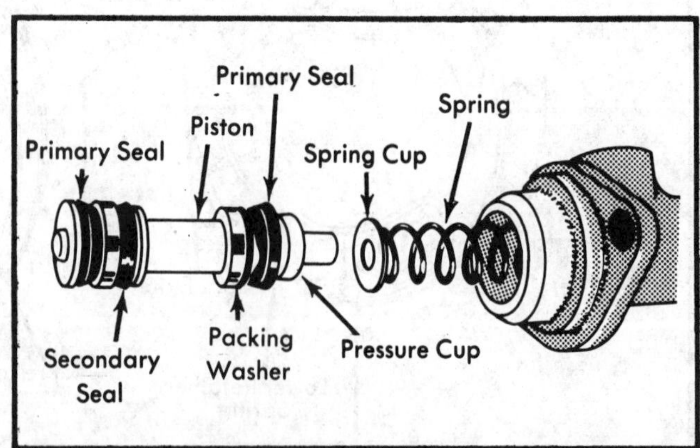

Fig. 7 Master Cylinder Secondary (Front) Piston Assy.

BMW (Cont.)

TIGHTENING SPECIFICATIONS

Application	Ft. Lbs. (mkg)
Caliper Mounting Bolts	
Front	58-69 (8.0-9.5)
Rear	43-48 (6.0-6.7)
Rotor-to-Wheel Hub	
320i & 630CSi	3.0-3.5 (.4-.5)
530i	43-48 (6.0-6.7)
Brake Line-to-Caliper	9-12 (1.3-1.6)
Caliper Expansion Bolts	
530i, Front	33-41 (4.6-5.7)
530i, Rear	16 (2.2)
Master Cylinder-to-Power Unit	
320i	12-14 (1.6-2.0)
630SCi	16-21 (2.1-2.9)
Power Brake Unit-to-Holder	
320i & 630CSi	16-17 (2.2-2.4)

DISC BRAKE ROTOR SPECIFICATIONS

Application	Disc Diameter In. (mm)	Lateral Runout In. (mm)	Parallelism In. (mm)	Original Thickness In. (mm)	Minimum Refinish Thickness In. (mm)	Discard Thickness In. (mm)
320i						
Front	10.040① (255)	.008② (.2)	.0008 (.02)	.866 (22)	.....	.827 (21)
530i						
Front	10.708① (272)	.008② (.2)	.0008 (.02)	.499 (12.7)	.....	.460 (11.7)
Rear	10.708① (272)	.008② (.2)	.0008 (.02)	.374 (9.5)	.....	.334 (8.5)
630CSi						
Front	11.024① (280)	.008② (.2)	.....	.866 (22)	.....	.827 (21)
Rear	10.708① (272)	.008② (.2)	.....	.748 (19)	.....	.709 (18)

① — ±.008" (.2 mm).
② — Installed on vehicle.

BRAKE SYSTEM SPECIFICATIONS

Application	Drum Diam. In. (mm)	Wheel Cylinder Diameter Front In. (mm)	Wheel Cylinder Diameter Rear In. (mm)	Master Cylinder Diameter In. (mm)
320i	9.842① (250)	1.890② (48)	.750 (19.05)	.....
530i & 630CSi	6.300③ (160)	1.575② (40)	1.652② (42)	.....

① — Rear
② — Piston Diameter
③ — Parking brake inside diameter.

CAPRI

Capri

DESCRIPTION

The brake system is hydraulically operated, utilizing a tandem master cylinder and a power brake unit. Front disc brakes consist of rotors attached to wheel hubs, and dual piston floating caliper assemblies. Rear brakes are leading-trailing shoe/drum type, using dual piston wheel cylinders. A combination valve is used to distribute correct pressure to each rear brake wheel cylinder. Parking brake system is cable and rod operated, acting on rear brake assemblies.

ADJUSTMENT

FRONT DISC BRAKE PADS

Front disc brakes are self-adjusting; therefore, no adjustment in service is required.

REAR BRAKE SHOES

Rear drum brakes are self-adjusting (actuated by parking brake linkage); therefore, no adjustment in service is required.

PARKING BRAKE LINKAGE

NOTE – *It should only be necessary to adjust parking brake system in the event of wear on linkage components or replacement of parts. DO NOT adjust for rear brake wear.*

Ensure parking brake is fully released, then raise and support vehicle. To adjust primary cable, engage keyed sleeve (A) into abutment slot (B), then turn adjuster nut (C) until all slack is removed from cable. Parking brake is properly adjusted when clearance between parking brake lever stop and brake backing plate is .039-.059" (1.0-1.5 mm).

COMBINATION VALVE

Warning Light Test – **1**) Turn ignition switch to on position and set parking brake, warning light should be on. If there is no light, electrical problem is indicated.

2) Release parking brake and operate pedal a few times; light should not work. If light comes on, hydraulic problem is indicated.

NOTE – *Piston in combination valve is self-centering.*

BLEEDING HYDRAULIC SYSTEM

1) Fill master cylinder reservoir with brake fluid and maintain level throughout bleeding operation. **NOTE** – *Piston in combination valve is self-centering and does not need to be held in central position while brakes are being bled.* Attach a hose to right front brake bleeder screw and immerse opposite end in a container partially full of brake fluid.

2) Open bleeder screw approximately one-half turn, depress brake pedal fully, then allow it to return to its off position. Continue depressing brake pedal, pausing after each return stroke to allow full recuperation of master cylinder, until fluid entering container is clean and free from air bubbles. Press brake pedal to the floor and hold it there while bleeder screw is tightened. Repeat operation on remaining brakes in the following sequence: left front, left rear and right rear.

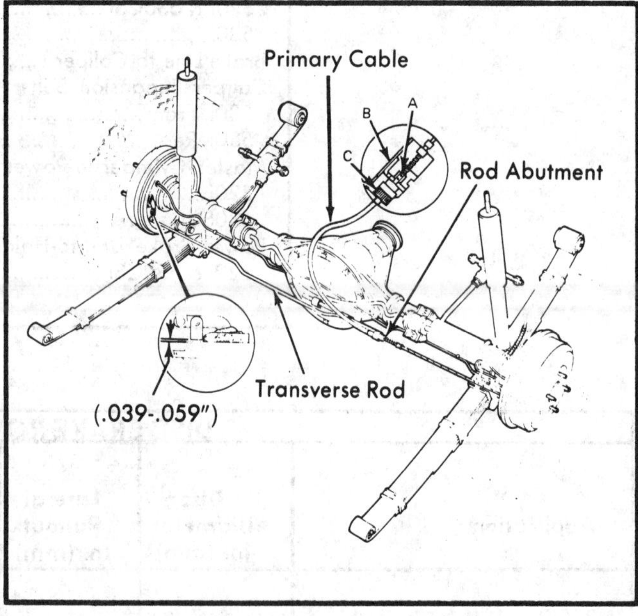

Fig. 1 Parking Brake Adjustment Points

REMOVAL & INSTALLATION

FRONT DISC BRAKE PADS

Removal – Remove retaining pin clips and pins. Lift-out brake pads, tension springs and shim, (if equipped). **NOTE** – *Clean any foreign matter from rotor. Ensure new pads are correct.*

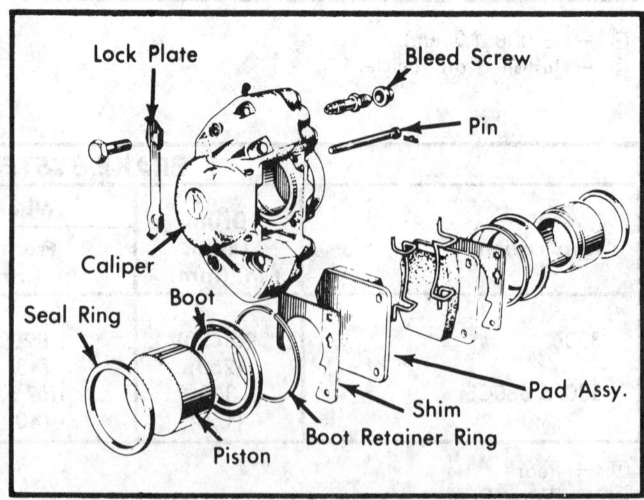

Fig. 2 Exploded View of Front Disc Brake Assy.

CAPRI (Cont.)

Installation – Press pistons to bottom of caliper bores. **NOTE** – *Siphon sufficient fluid from master cylinder to prevent overflowing when pistons are pressed back into bores.* Place tension springs on brake pads and shims, then install pads and shims into caliper assembly with arrow on shims pointing up. Install retaining pins and secure with pin clips. Pump brake pedal several times to position pads against rotor.

FRONT DISC BRAKE CALIPER

Removal – With disc pads removed from caliper, disconnect hydraulic line from caliper and plug openings. Bend up lock tabs, remove caliper retaining bolts, and detach caliper assembly.

Installation – Position caliper on steering knuckle, install new lock tabs, then install and tighten retaining bolts. Install disc pads and bleed hydraulic system.

FRONT DISC BRAKE ROTOR

Removal – With caliper assembly removed, remove dust cap, cotter pin, adjusting nut, thrust washer, and outer bearing. Remove hub and rotor assembly, bend back lock tabs, remove attaching bolts, and separate rotor from hub. Discard lock tabs and bolts.

Installation – Thoroughly clean mating surfaces of hub and rotor, position rotor on hub aligning mating marks, and install and tighten lock tabs and retaining bolts. To complete installation, reverse removal procedure, tighten all bolts evenly and adjust wheel bearings. *See Wheel Bearing Adjustment in WHEEL ALIGNMENT Section.*

REAR BRAKE SHOES

Removal – Raise and support vehicle and remove rear wheels. Ensure parking brake is fully released, then remove brake drum. Remove brake shoe hold down springs and pins, then pull shoes from bottom guides and remove lower spring. Pull primary shoe from wheel cylinder slot and self-adjuster arm, then undo spring and remove shoe. Unhook secondary shoe from parking brake lever, disconnect spring and remove shoe.

Installation – Hook spring and parking brake lever to secondary shoe. Connect upper spring to both shoes and position primary shoe over self-adjuster arm. Connect lower spring to shoes, then install lower end of shoes into guides. Install hold down springs and pins. Ensure brakes are centered and install brake drum.

REAR BRAKE WHEEL CYLINDER

Removal – Remove wheel, drum and brake shoe assemblies. Ensure there is no vacuum in booster system, then disconnect brake line from wheel cylinder. Remove wheel cylinder attaching bolts and lock washers and remove cylinder.

Installation – Place wheel cylinder into position, then connect brake line to cylinder and tighten fitting finger tight. Install and tighten cylinder attaching bolts with lock washers, then tighten brake line fitting. Install links in ends of cylinder, then install shoe and adjuster assemblies. Install brake drum and bleed hydraulic system.

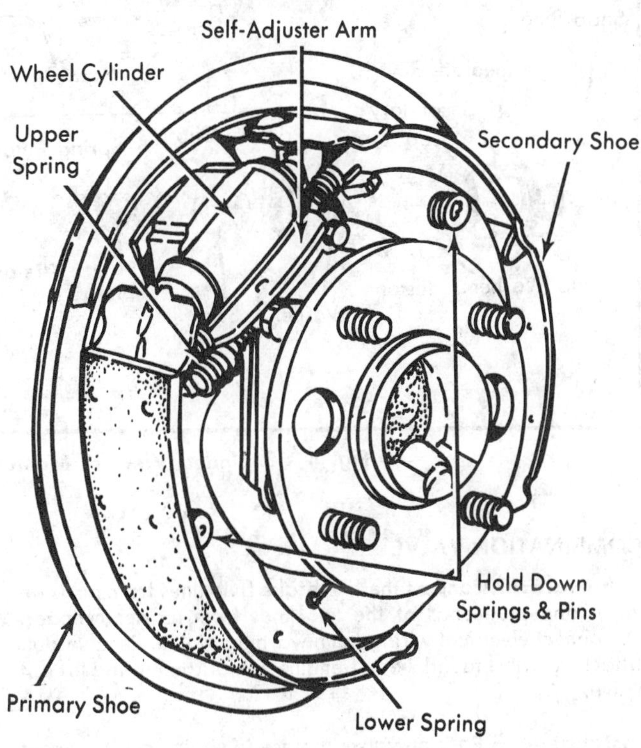

Fig. 3 Assembled View of Rear Drum Brake Components

MASTER CYLINDER

Removal – Siphon fluid from reservoir, then disconnect hydraulic lines from master cylinder. Remove master cylinder-to-booster attachings nuts, then lift master cylinder from booster using care not to damage vacuum seal.

Installation – Position master cylinder and fluid seal onto push rod and start all brake line union nuts. Connect master cylinder to booster and tighten attaching nuts. Tighten brake line union nuts and fill master cylinder with brake fluid. Bleed hydraulic system and check operation of brakes.

POWER BRAKE UNIT

Removal – Disconnect power unit push rod from brake pedal. Remove nuts retaining master cylinder to power unit and position master cylinder out of way. Remove vacuum hose from power unit, power unit-to-firewall retaining screws, and remove power unit from vehicle. Remove retaining bracket and gasket from power unit.

Installation – Reverse removal procedure and note the following: Assemble retaining bracket to power unit using a new gasket. Make sure seal ring is installed on master cylinder between cylinder and power unit.

CAPRI (Cont.)

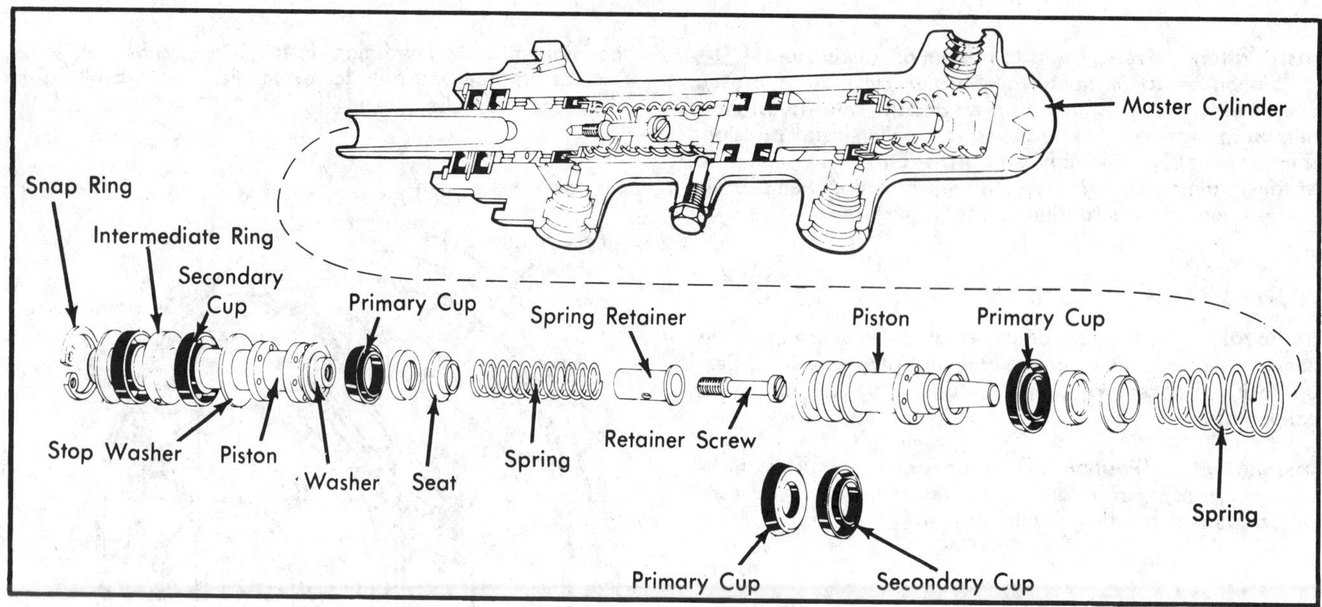

Fig. 4 Exploded View of Master Cylinder and Related Components

COMBINATION VALVE

Removal – Disconnect the five brake fluid lines from ports on valve and plug ends of the two lines from master cylinder. Disconnect electrical wiring from warning switch. Remove bolt attaching valve to left side of engine compartment and lift out valve.

Installation – Position valve in place in engine compartment and loosely install attaching bolt. Reconnect brake lines, then tighten attaching bolt. Fill master cylinder reservoir with brake fluid and bleed hydraulic system.

OVERHAUL

FRONT DISC BRAKE CALIPER

Disassembly – Partially remove one piston from cylinder bore, remove snap ring, and remove sealing bellows from piston skirt. Remove piston by appling air pressure or hydraulic pressure to fluid inlet in caliper. Remove sealing bellows from annular ring in cylinder bore, and remove piston sealing ring. Repeat operation for remaining piston. **NOTE** – *DO NOT separate caliper halves.*

Cleaning & Inspection – Clean pistons and cylinder bores in alcohol or brake fluid. **CAUTION** – *DO NOT use mineral based solvents.* Check all parts for wear, scoring, or other damage; replace parts as necessary.

Reassembly – Install piston seal and sealing bellows into caliper bore. Lubricate piston with brake fluid and install through sealing bellows (crown first). Install inner edge of bellows in piston skirt, push piston to bottom of cylinder, and install snap ring. Repeat operation for remaining piston.

REAR WHEEL CYLINDER

Disassembly – Remove dust boots and slide out piston assemblies. Remove seal from piston and spring from cylinder bore. Remove bleeder screw.

Cleaning & Inspection – Ensure pistons and cylinder are free of dirt, burrs and scratches. Thoroughly clean and dry all parts with a lint free cloth. Replace parts as necessary.

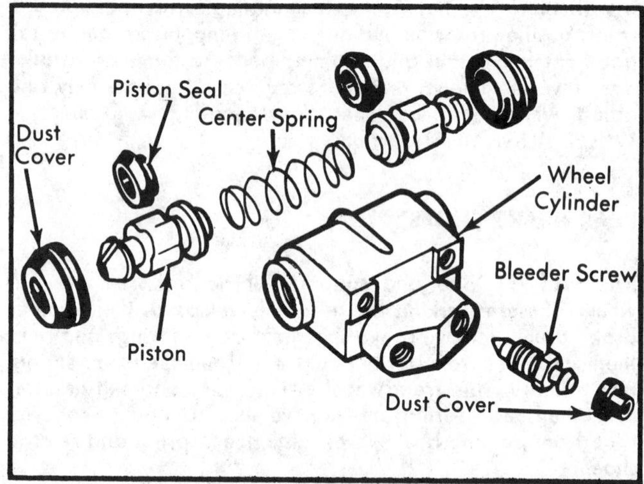

Fig. 5 Expanded View of Rear Wheel Cylinder Assy.

Reassembly – Install bleeder screw and tighten to specifications. Install new seals on pistons. Slide one piston into cylinder bore, then insert spring and remaining piston from opposite end and install dust boots.

MASTER CYLINDER

Disassembly – Remove reservoir from body. Loosen stop screw and push piston inward; remove snap ring. From primary chamber remove stop washer and primary piston assembly. With compressed air, force secondary piston assembly from its chamber.

Cleaning & Inspecting – While apart clean master cylinder and inner components with alcohol. Thoroughly dry all parts before reassembly.

CAPRI (Cont.)

Reassembly – Install secondary piston and replacement parts together in secondary chamber. Press piston inward and install stop screw. Release piston and let it contact stop screw. **NOTE** – *Length of stop screw must not change with new seal.* Reassemble primary piston and insert it into chamber. Position stop screw. **NOTE** – *Prevent burrs on secondary piston face by filling chambers with fluid before moving piston.* Install reservoir.

COMBINATION VALVE

Disassembly – Unscrew and remove warning switch. Remove retaining bolt, then using a small screwdriver, gently push piston assembly out of valve bore. Remove two rubber seals from piston and slide off sleeves.

Cleaning & Inspection – Thoroughly clean all parts and dry with a lint free cloth. Inspect all parts for wear or damage and replace as necessary. Inspect retaining clips on piston for wear and tightness and replace if necessary.

Reassembly – Slide sleeves on piston and install new rubber seals. Slide piston assembly into cylinder, then install retaining bolt. Install warning switch.

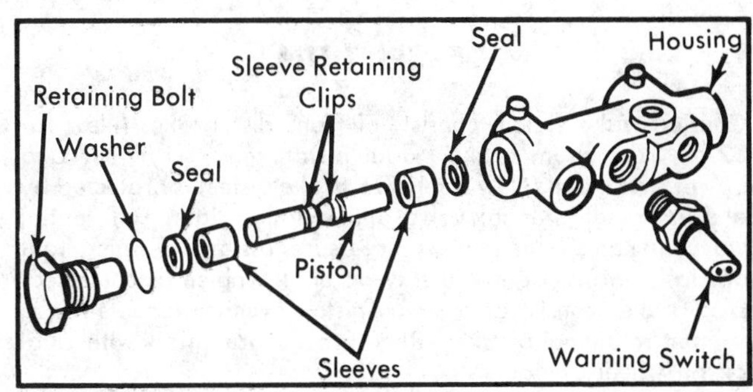

Fig. 6 Exploded View of Combination Valve Parts

TIGHTENING SPECIFICATIONS

Application	Ft. Lbs. (mkg)
Caliper Mounting Bolts	45-50 (6.2-6.9)
Rotor-to-Hub Bolts	30-34 (4.2-4.7)
Rear Backing Plate Bolts	15-18 (2.1-2.5)
Hydraulic Line Union Nuts	5-7 (.7-1.0)
Bleeder Screws	5-7 (.7-1.0)

BRAKE SYSTEM SPECIFICATIONS

Application	Drum Diam. In. (mm)	Wheel Cylinder Diameter		Master Cylinder
		Front In. (mm)	Rear In. (mm)	Diameter In. (mm)
Capri II	9 (229)	2.125 ① (53.9)	.700 (17.8)	....

① – Caliper bore diameter.

DISC BRAKE ROTOR SPECIFICATIONS

Application	Disc Diameter In. (mm)	Lateral Runout In. (mm)	Parallelism In. (mm)	Original Thickness In. (mm)	Minimum Refinish Thickness In. (mm)	Discard Thickness In. (mm)
Capri II	9.625 (244.4)	.0035 (.089)	.0004 (.010)	.500 (12.7)	.460 (11.6)	.450 (11.3)

COURIER

Courier

DESCRIPTION

Courier brake system consists of front disc brakes (New for 1977), rear drum brakes, dual piston master cylinder and power brake unit (New for 1977). Brake system is protected by a pressure differential valve and warning light. Differential valve indicates when there is a pressure loss by a warning light on dash board. Light will stay on until problem is corrected. Disc brakes consist of a single piston cylinder mounted in a caliper retaining bracket. Rear brakes are fitted with dual piston wheel cylinders.

ADJUSTMENT

PEDAL FREE PLAY

Loosen lock nut on master cylinder push rod at clevis. Turn push rod in or out to obtain .33-.39" (8.5-10.0 mm) free play, measured at pedal pad. When clearance is correct, tighten lock nut.

FRONT DISC BRAKES

No adjustment is necessary.

REAR DRUM BRAKES

All shoe to drum adjustments must be made with brake shoes at normal room temperature. Turn lower wheel cylinder rachet to expand brake shoe locking it against drum. Back-off rachet 5 notches or until drum rotates freely. Repeat procedure for upper wheel cylinder.

PARKING BRAKE CABLE

NOTE — *Service brakes must be properly adjusted before adjusting parking brake.* Adjust length of cable at equalizer so that rear brakes are locked when parking brake lever is pulled out five to ten ratchet clicks (1 ⅝-3 ⅛"). After adjustment, apply and release parking brake several times, and make sure wheels rotate freely when parking brake is released.

COMBINATION VALVE

Combination Valve Reset — Place ignition switch in the on position. Depress brake pedal and piston will center itself. This will cause brake warning light to go out.

HYDRAULIC SYSTEM BLEEDING

NOTE — *Front and rear hydraulic systems are individual systems and are bled separately. Bleed longest line first on individual system being serviced.*

CAUTION — Do not bleed hydraulic system through master cylinder stop screw.

Manual Bleeding-1) Attach a bleeder tube to right rear lower brake cylinder, and immerse opposite end of tube in a container partially filled with brake fluid. Open bleeder screw ¾ turn, push brake pedal through full travel, close bleeder screw, and return pedal. Continue operation until air bubbles are no longer seen in discharged fluid.

2) Repeat procedure at upper right rear wheel cylinder, and at wheel cylinders on left rear brake. If primary system is to be bled, repeat procedure at each right front wheel cylinder and each left front wheel cylinder. When bleeding operation is completed, fill master cylinder reservoirs to within ¼" of top of reservoirs. Centralize pressure differential valve.

REMOVAL & INSTALLATION

DISC BRAKE PADS

Removal — 1) Raise vehicle and place on safety stands. Remove front wheel. Remove 4 locking spring clips. Drift out both stopper plates.

2) Remove caliper piston and anti-rattle spring from pad bracket. Support caliper piston out of way. Pull out disc pads and shims (if any). Note position of shims.

NOTE — *All pads must be replaced at one time.*

Installation — 1) Pull bleeder cap off caliper and attach a tube over bleed screw. Open bleed screw and seat piston in cylinder with "C" clamp. Tighten bleed screw and remove "C" clamp.

2) Install new pads and shims if thickness of pads (including shoe) has worn to .315" (8 mm). Fit anti-rattle spring and caliper piston. Apply a light coat of grease to stopper plates. Install plates and spring clips.

FRONT DISC BRAKE CALIPER

Removal — Raise vehicle and support with safety stands. Remove front wheel. Disconnect hydraulic line at flexible hose. Remove "U" clip to free hose. Take out 2 mounting bolts holding caliper bracket, then remove entire assembly.

Installation — To install, reverse removal procedure and note: Bleed brake system.

BRAKE ROTOR

Removal — Remove caliper. Remove dust cap, cotter pin, adjustment nut, thrust washer and outer bearing. Slide out hub and rotor assembly. Index mark and separate hub from rotor.

Installation — Thoroughly clean mating surface of hub and rotor. Position rotor on hub aligning index marks. Tighten mounting bolts. To complete installation, reverse removal procedure. *See Wheel Bearing Adjustment in WHEEL ALIGNMENT Section.*

BRAKE DRUM

Removal — Remove tire and wheel. Remove brake drum attaching screws and install them in tapered holes in brake drum. Turn screws in evenly to force drum away from wheel hub. Lift off drum.

Installation — Align attaching screw holes with ones in wheel hub. Transfer screws to retaining position and tighten evenly. Install tire and wheel.

COURIER (Cont.)

BRAKE SHOES

Removal – Remove tire, wheel and brake drum. Remove brake shoe return springs, withdraw shoe retaining pin and spring. Disconnect handbrake link and cable from lever. Lift out brake shoes.

Installation – Reassemble handbrake. Position new brake shoes to backing plate with slots toward wheel cylinders. Install retaining springs and clips. Replace brake drum and adjust brakes.

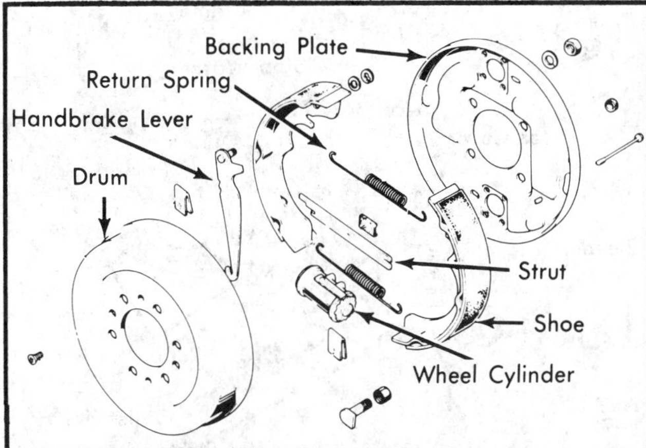

Fig. 1 Rear Brake Assembly Showing Relationship of Internal Components

WHEEL CYLINDER

Removal – With brake drum and shoes removed, disconnect hydraulic line from cylinder. Remove stud nuts and bolt which retain cylinder to backing plate and remove cylinder.

Installation – Reverse removal procedure, adjust brake shoes and bleed hydraulic system.

MASTER CYLINDER

Removal & Installation – Disconnect brake hydraulic lines at master cylinder outlets and inlet ports from cylinder reservoir. Remove 2 nuts mounting master cylinder to power brake booster. Lift assembly outward and upward away from booster push rod. To install reverse removal procedure and make sure to guide power brake booster push rod into master cylinder piston.

COMBINATION VALVE

Removal – Disconnect warning light wire. Disconnect hydraulic lines from combination valve. Remove bolt mounting valve assembly and take off combination valve.

Installation – To install combination valve, reverse removal procedure and note the following: Bleed hydraulic system and reset piston in valve.

POWER BRAKE BOOSTER

Removal – Remove master cylinder as previously outlined. Disconnect vacuum hose for power booster. Disconnect push rod from brake pedal. Work under instrument panel and remove 4 nuts mounting power brake booster.

Installation – Slide booster into position. Fit 4 mounting nuts. Install push rod to brake pedal. Connect vacuum line from intake manifold. Refit master cylinder to booster. Bleed brake system.

OVERHAUL

FRONT DISC BRAKE CALIPER

Disassembly – Clean outside of caliper. Separate cylinder from bracket. Remove boot retainer and slide off dust boot. Force compressed air into brake line hole to remove piston from caliper.

2) It may be necessary to tap outside of piston housing with plastic hammer while applying air pressure to unseat piston. Dig out piston seal from inside caliper bore.

Cleaning and Inspection – Wash all disassembled parts in clean brake fluid and completely dry with compressed air. Inspect caliper bore and piston for scratches, grooves or rust. Minor imprefections can be eliminated with crocus cloth. Piston seal and dust boot must be replaced during each overhaul.

Reassembly – Lightly coat piston seal with brake fluid and insert into groove in caliper bore. Make sure seal is not twisted in groove. Lubricate piston and bore with brake fluid, then slide piston into place. Fit dust boot with flange seated in inner groove of caliper. Fit dust boot retainer.

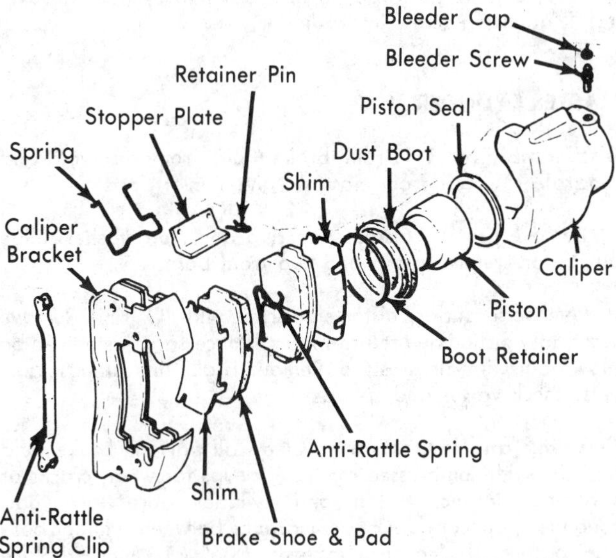

Fig. 2 Exploded View of Front Disc Brake

REAR WHEEL CYLINDER

Disassembly – Remove piston, adjusting screw, and boot assemblies from each end of cylinder and separate parts. Press in on either piston cup and force out piston cups, expanders, and return spring.

Cleaning & Inspection – Wash all parts in isopropyl alcohol. Examine cylinder bore, pistons, and adjuster for wear or damage. Check clearance between cylinder bore and pistons; if greater than .006" (.15 mm), replace parts as necessary.

COURIER (Cont.)

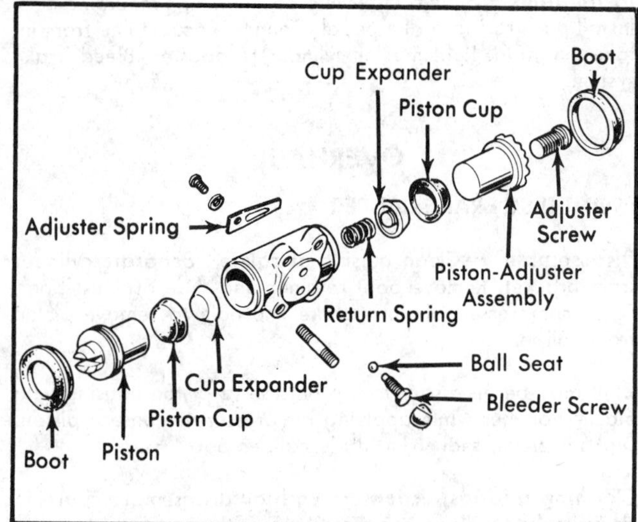

Fig. 3 Disassembled View of Courier Rear Wheel Cylinder

Reassembly – Apply brake fluid to cylinder bore, adjuster, and cylinder cups. Position return spring in cup expanders, place cups against expanders, and install into cylinder bore with flat side of cups facing outward. Install boot to piston with smaller lip of boot in groove of piston, install piston into cylinder, and install larger lip of boot into cylinder groove. Install adjusting screw into adjuster.

MASTER CYLINDER

Disassembly – 1) Drain brake fluid from reservoir and separate reservoir from master clyinder inlet ports.

2) Remove primary piston snap ring and stop washer. Slide out piston, return spring and cup from bore.

3) Remove secondary piston stop screw with "O" ring. Remove secondary pistion and return spring. If necessary, piston can be blown out with air pressure. Remove brake line fittings, gaskets, check valves and springs.

Cleaning and Inspection – Clean all parts in brake fluid and dry with compressed air. Check cups for wear, cracks or softening. Inspect piston and cylinder bore for wear, roughness, or scoring. Check clearance between cylinder bore and pistons. If clearance exceeds .006" (.15 mm), replace piston.

Reassembly – 1) Lightly coat all components with brake fluid. Install check valve springs and valves into outlet ports. Install gasket and brake line fittings.

NOTE – *Make sure check valve with hole is installed in hole on side of master cylinder.*

2) Insert secondary and primary cup onto secondary piston. Fit piston assembly and spring into cylinder. Seat piston with a screwdriver and install stop screw with washer.

3) Fit cup to primary piston. Insert primary piston assembly with return spring into cylinder. Install washer and snap ring.

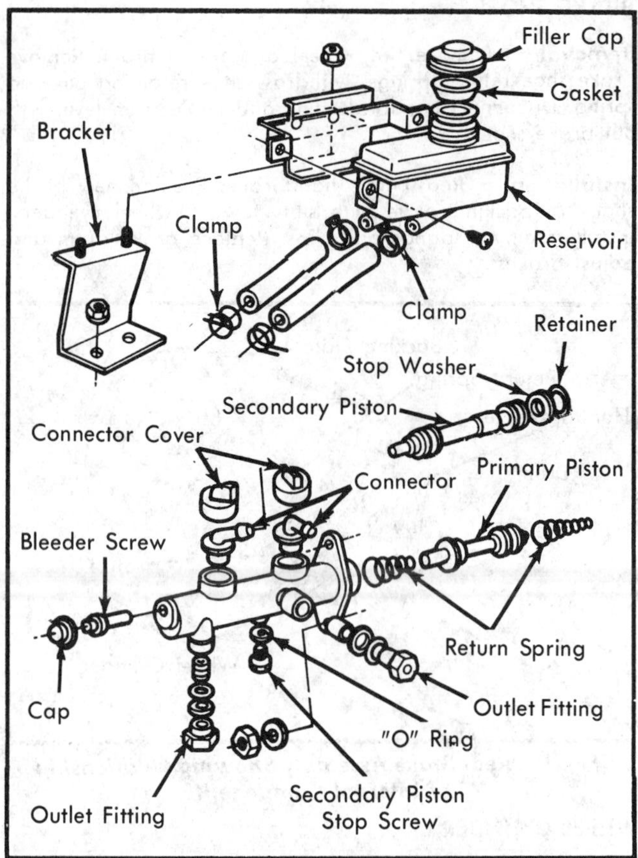

Fig 4 Exploded View of Master Cylinder and Related Components

POWER BRAKE BOOSTER

Disassembly – 1) Fit booster in vise with rod facing up. Index mark shell sides with a scribe. Remove lock nut and boot. Rotate rear shell clockwise to unlocked position and lift off shell complete with:

- Diaphragm
- Power Piston Assembly
- Valve Rod
- Plunger Assembly

2) Remove spring from front shell. From inside rear shell remove:

- Diaphragm
- Power Piston Assembly
- Valve Rod
- Plunger Assembly

3) Remove rear seal, with punch, from rear shell only if seal needs replacing. Take out air silencer retainer and air filter from power piston. DO NOT damage piston.

4) Press in valve rod and remove retainer key. Take valverod and plunger assembly off power piston. Press out reaction disc. Slide push rod out of front shell.

Cleaning – 1) Wipe down all components. Carefully inspect all components for damage. Especially look at rubber parts for cuts, nicks or deformation.

COURIER (Cont.)

2) Check power piston for cracks, distortion, chipping or damage.

3) Inspect reaction disc, valve rod and plunger. Replace components as necessary.

Reassembly – 1) Apply brake fluid to inside of power piston bore and to surface of valve rod plunger assembly. Insert valve rod and plunger assembly into power piston. Press in valve rod and align plunger groove with slot in power piston. Insert key.

2) Install diaphragm on power piston. Be sure diaphragm is squarely seated on piston groove. Fit air silencer retainer and filter and fit over rod, then place in power piston. Coat surface of reaction disc with brake fluid and install in power piston.

3) Lightly coat outer edge of diaphragm and rear shell seal with brake fluid. Carefully guide tube end of power piston through seal in real shell. Fit push rod to front of power piston.

4) Put return spring in front shell. Position complete rear shell assembly over front half, press down and rotate counterclockwise until scribe marks align. Install dust boot, fork end and lock nut.

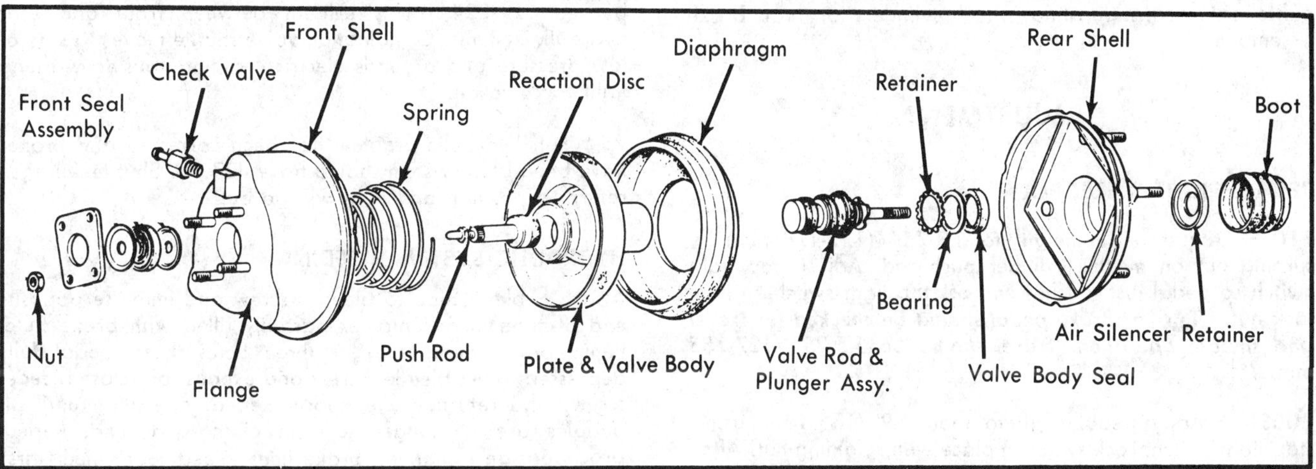

Fig. 5 Exploded View of Power Brake Booster

BRAKE DRUM SPECIFICATIONS

Application	Drum Diameter In. (mm)	Original Diameter In. (mm)	Maximum Refinish Diameter In. (mm)	Discard Diameter In. (mm)
Courier	10.236 (260)	10.236 (260)	10.2756 (261)	

DISC BRAKE ROTOR SPECIFICATIONS

Application	Disc Diameter In. (mm)	Lateral Runout In. (mm)	Parallelism In. (mm)	Original Thickness In. (mm)	Minimum Refinish Thickness In. (mm)	Discard Thickness In. (mm)
Courier	10.079 (256)	.004 (.10)	.....	.472 (12)	.433 (11)	.....

BRAKE SYSTEM SPECIFICATIONS

Application	Drum Diam. In. (mm)	Wheel Cylinder Diameter Front In. (mm)	Wheel Cylinder Diameter Rear In. (mm)	Master Cylinder Diameter In. (mm)
Courier	10.236 (260)	①	.750 (19)	.875 (22.2)

① – Front disc brake cylinder bore 2.12" (53.8 mm).

DATSUN F10, 200SX, B210

F10
200SX
B210

DESCRIPTION

Brake system is hydraulically operated, utilizing a tandem master cylinder and a Master-Vac power brake unit. Front disc brakes consist of rotors attached to wheel hubs, and single cylinder, dual-piston, floating-calipers attached to steering knuckles. Rear brakes are leading-trailing shoe/drum type, using a single piston sliding wheel cylinder. Parking brake is cable actuated, operating wheel cylinders of rear brake assemblies.

ADJUSTMENT

PEDAL HEIGHT & FREE PLAY

F10 – Adjust pedal height to 6.8-7.0" (172-178 mm) by turning nut on master cylinder push rod. Adjust stop light switch so pedal just touches end of stop light switch; tighten lock nut. **NOTE** – *Brake pedal should be checked for travel and smooth operation. Travel should be 5-5.25" (127-133 mm).*

200SX – Adjust pedal height to about 6.9" (175.5 mm) using stop light switch. Lock switch in place with retaining nut. After pedal height is adjusted, loosen push rod lock nut and adjust pedal free play to .039-.118" (1-3 mm).

B210 – Adjust pedal height to specifications by moving stop lamp switch. Pedal height should be 6.14" (156 mm) on vehicles equipped with manual transmission and 6.22" (158 mm) on vehicles with automatic transmission. After pedal height is adjusted, loosen push rod lock nut and adjust pedal free play to .039-.197" (1-5 mm).

FRONT DISC BRAKE PADS

Front disc brakes are self-adjusting, therefore, no adjustment in service is required.

REAR BRAKE SHOES

F10 – Raise and support vehicle. Pump brake pedal several times to center brake shoes. Using a screwdriver, turn adjuster star until considerable drag is evident. Back off adjuster five or six notches and make sure drum rotates freely.

200SX – No adjustment required.

B210 – Raise and support vehicle. Using a suitable brake adjusting tool, tighten adjuster eccentric clockwise until brake shoe contacts drum. Return adjuster eccentric until shoe is slightly separated from drum. Check operation by turning drum and applying brakes; if shoe interferes with drum rotation, readjust.

PARKING BRAKE

With rear brakes properly adjusted, adjust parking brake cable turnbuckle until rear brakes are locked when parking brake lever is pulled to sixth or seventh ratchet stop. Release parking brake lever and ensure rear wheels turn freely and that all parts are returned to their original position.

COMBINATION VALVE

Function Test, All Models – Accelerate engine to 30 mph and rapidly apply brakes. If rear wheels lock before front wheels, malfunction of combination valve assembly (200SX & B210), or of separate proportioning valve (F10) is indicated.

Warning Light Operation & Reset, Except 200SX – 1) Instrument panel light will come on when a pressure difference of between 71-224 psi is evident between front and rear hydraulic systems. Combination valve shuttle moves to side of low pressure and grounds electrical circuit, causing warning light to come on.

2) When hydraulic problem has been corrected and brakes have been bled, system should have 427 psi. Shuttle will then return to position and light will go out.

HYDRAULIC SYSTEM BLEEDING

Attach a bleed tube to bleeder screw and immerse opposite end of tube in a container partially filled with brake fluid. Pump brake pedal two or three times, keep pedal fully depressed, open bleeder screw and exhaust air, close bleeder screw, and return brake pedal. Repeat operation until air bubbles are no longer seen in discharged fluid. Repeat procedure on remaining brake lines. Bleed rear wheels first, then front wheels.

REMOVAL & INSTALLATION

FRONT DISC BRAKE PADS

Removal – Raise front of vehicle and support in place, then remove front wheels. Remove clips from retaining pins and pull out pins, coil springs and pad springs. Remove pads from caliper assembly using a suitable pair of pliers.

Inspection – With friction pads removed, measure their thickness. Replace any pad that is worn to less than .063" (1.6 mm) in thickness (not including metal backing plate). It is recommended that friction pads be replaced as a set to prevent any possibility of uneven braking.

NOTE – *Replace all pads at same time.*

Installation – Clean and apply P.B.C. grease (or equivalent) on yoke guide groove of cylinder body, sliding contact portions of yoke and end surface of piston. Loosen bleeder screw and push outer piston in cylinder until end surface of piston coinsides with end surface of retaining ring on boot. Install inner brake pad. Push inner piston in cylinder by pulling on yoke, then install outer brake pad. After installing pads, depress brake pedal several times to seat pads.

FRONT DISC BRAKE CALIPER

Removal – Raise vehicle and suitably support on safety stands; remove tire and wheel. Remove brake friction pads as previously described. Disconnect brake line from wheel cylinder. To ease removal of caliper, remove strut assembly and knuckle arm mounting bolt. Withdraw caliper mounting bolt and separate it from strut assembly.

DATSUN F10, 200SX, B210 (Cont.)

Installation – To install brake caliper assembly, reverse removal procedures, noting the following: Bleed hydraulic system.

FRONT DISC BRAKE ROTOR

Removal – With caliper removed, remove hub dust cap, cotter pin and nut. Remove hub and rotor assembly with wheel bearing and washer in place. Remove bolts attaching rotor to wheel hub, and separate rotor from hub.

Installation – Reverse removal procedure, tighten rotor-to-hub bolts securly, and adjust wheel bearings. *See Wheel Bearing Adjustment in WHEEL ALIGNMENT Section.* Use a dial indicator to measure rotor runout. Resurface rotor if runout exceeds .0047" (.12 mm) for 200SX & B210 or .006" (.15 mm) for F10.

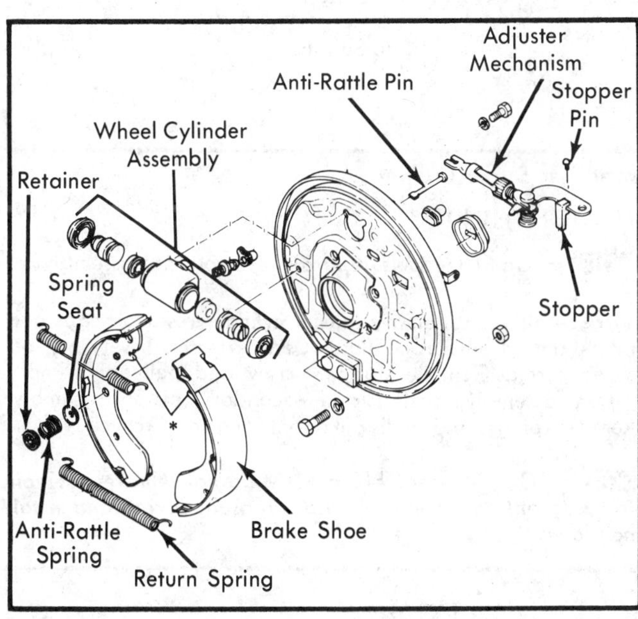

Fig. 1 Exploded View of Datsun 200SX Rear Brake Assembly

REAR BRAKE ASSEMBLY

Removal (Rear) – Raise vehicle and suitably support on safety stands; remove tire and wheel. Loosen parking brake linkage at clevis pin and place out of way. Remove brake drum. Remove shoe retainer and return spring, then lift off shoe assembly. Disconnect brake line from wheel cylinder. If necessary, wheel cylinder can now be removed by taking out mounting bolt.

Inspecting – Inspect all brake components for damage or excessive wear and replace those found defective. Replace brake lining if it is oil soaked or lining is less than .059" (1.5 mm) thick.

Installation – To install rear brake lining, reverse removal procedures, noting the following: Readjust shoe-to-drum clearance and, if necessary, bleed hydraulic system.

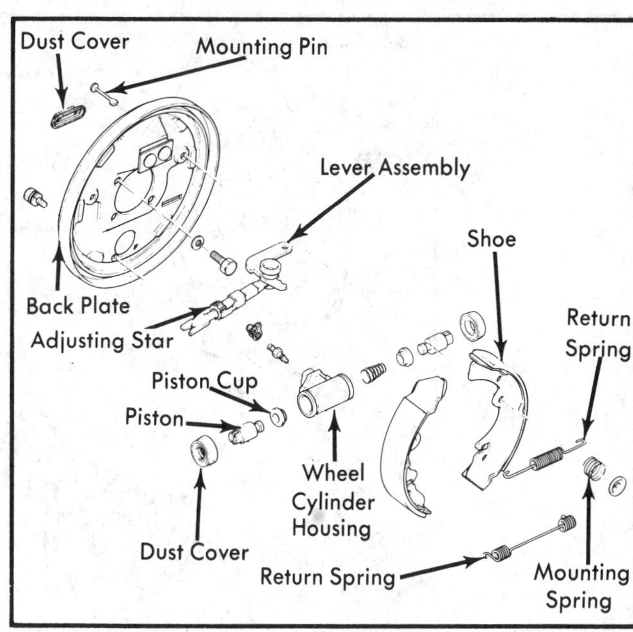

Fig. 2 Exploded View of F10 and B210 Rear Brake Assembly – 200SX Similar

MASTER CYLINDER

Removal – Disconnect any electrical leads attached to cylinder reservoir. Disconnect front and rear brake lines from master cylinder outlet ports. On models equipped without power brakes, separate master cylinder push rod from pedal. Remove cylinder mounting nuts and slide unit off studs. Make sure brake fluid does not drop on paint.

NOTE – *On F10 models, fluid reservoir can be removed attached to cylinder.*

Installation – To install master cylinder, reverse removal procedures, noting the following: Bleed hydraulic system and check pedal height.

POWER BRAKE UNIT

Removal – Disconnect power unit push rod from brake pedal by removing clevis pin. Disconnect hydraulic lines from master cylinder and vacuum line from power unit, remove master cylinder attaching nuts, and remove master cylinder. Remove nuts attaching power unit to firewall, and remove power unit from engine compartment.

Installation – Reverse removal procedure, adjust brake pedal height, and bleed hydraulic system.

Check Valve Removal – Check valve is located in vacuum line between intake manifold and power unit on firewall. To remove, disconnect retaining clip from firewall, remove hose clamps, separate hoses from valve, and remove check valve. To install, reverse removal procedure.

OVERHAUL

FRONT DISC BRAKE CALIPER

Disassembly – With caliper removed, drain brake fluid and remove bleeder screw. Push both pistons into cylinder bore, then place yoke in a vise and tap the top of yoke lightly with a

DATSUN F10, 200SX, B210 (Cont.)

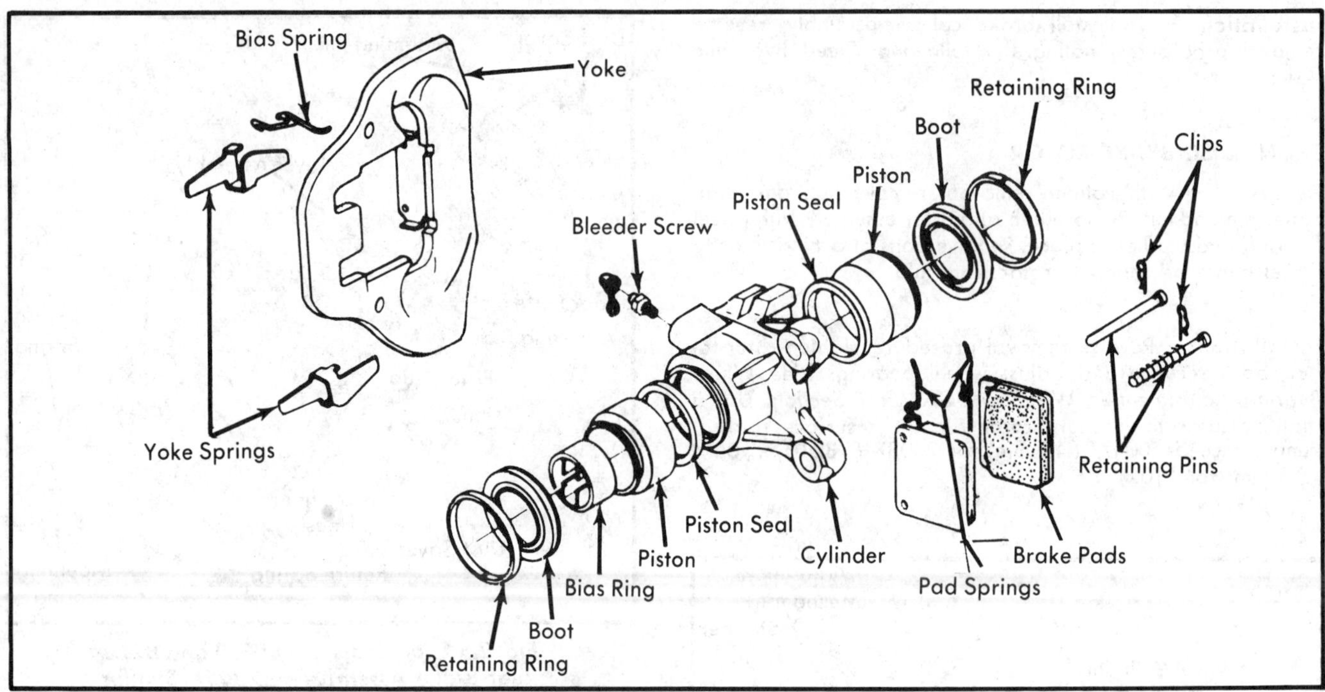

Fig. 3 Exploded View of Front Disc Brake Caliper

hammer to separate cylinder from yoke. Remove bias ring from outer piston, then remove retaining rings and boots. Push both pistons out in one direction. Remove piston seals from cylinder and yoke spring from yoke.

Inspecting – Thoroughly clean all internal parts and check each component for excessive wear or damage. If caliper bore is damaged or excessively rusted, it must be replaced. If, however, slight imperfections are evident, honing will eliminate them. It is recommended to replace all seals when overhauling.

Reassembly – Before assembling components, lightly coat with suitable brake grease. Insert bias ring into piston so round portion of ring fits to bottom of piston. Insert piston into cylinder. Do not fully seat piston. Install dust boot and retaining ring. Install yoke bias ring so it coincides with yoke groove of cylinder. Fit bias spring to yoke so bias spring faces bleeder side of cylinder. With yoke spring inserted in cylinder groove, properly align position of bias spring so groove of spring aligns with yoke. Assemble body-to-yoke, tapping lightly if necessary.

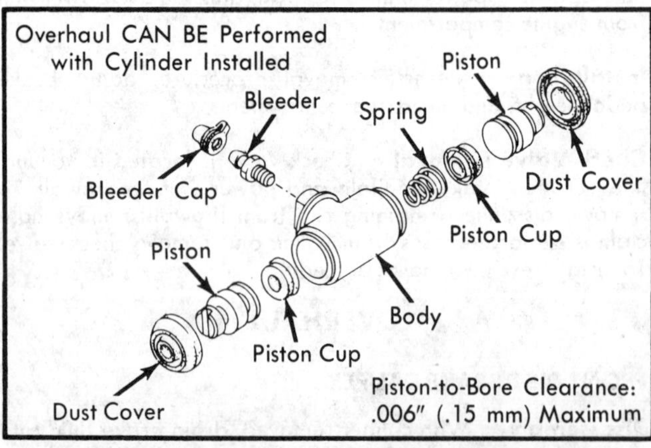

Fig. 4 Exploded View of Datsun Wheel Cylinder Used on F10, 200SX and B210 Models

MASTER CYLINDER

NOTE – *On F10 models, separate reservoir tank assembly.*

Disassembly – Remove master cylinder reservoir caps and filters and drain brake fluid. Using a screwdriver, pry off stopper ring. Remove stopper screw and pull out primary piston assembly, spring and secondary piston assembly. Remove plugs and pull out front and rear check valves.

NOTE – *On all except F10 models, do not remove reservoir tanks. If tanks are removed for any reason, discard and install new ones.*

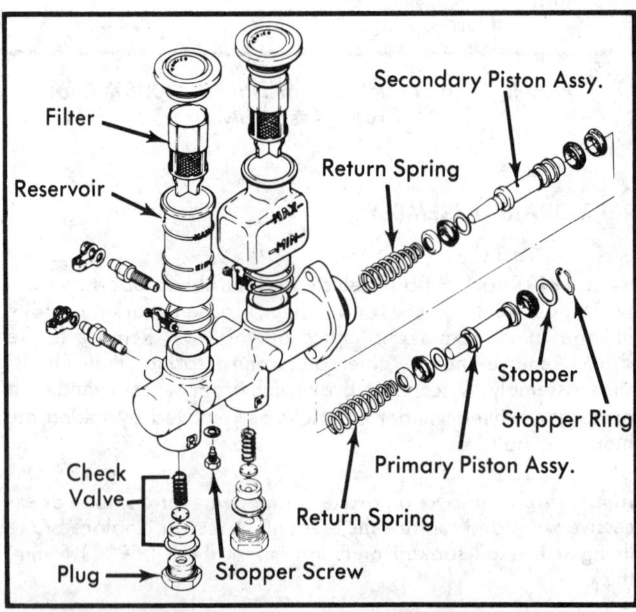

Fig. 5 Exploded View of Datsun 200SX and B210 Master Cylinder – F10 Models Have Different Reservoir Arrangement

BRAKES

DATSUN F10, 200SX, B210 (Cont.)

Inspecting – Thoroughly clean all components in approved grade brake fluid. Inspect all components for excessive wear or damage and replace parts as necessary.

Reassembly – Reverse disassembly procedure and note the following: Coat all parts with brake fluid (rubber parts with brake grease) when assembling.

POWER BRAKE UNIT

Disassembly – **1**) Place power unit in a soft jaw vise with operating rod pointing up. Scribe an alignment mark on front and rear shell to assure reassembly in original position, then remove lock nut, clevis and dust boot from rear shell.

2) Place suitable wrench (ST08080000) over rear shell mounting studs. Press down on wrench while rotating counterclockwise and remove rear shell, then lift out diaphragm plate assembly, diaphragm spring and push rod assembly. Pry off retainer and remove bearing and valve body seal assembly.

3) Remove diaphragm from diaphragm plate assembly, then pry off air silencer retainer and remove silencer and filter. Rotate diaphragm plate assembly until valve plunger key slot is down, then press in on plunger and shake out stop key. Remove reaction disc from plate assembly. Detach flange from front shell and remove front seal assembly.

Cleaning & Inspection – Clean all parts in denatured alcohol and blow dry with compressed air. Inspect front and rear shells for wear or damage. If slight rust is found on inside surface of shells, polish clean with fine emery cloth. Inspect all parts for cracks, nicks, distortion or other damage and replace as necessary.

Reassembly – Reverse disassembly procedure and note the following: Apply a thin coat of silicone grease to parts before installation. When assembling front shell to rear shell ensure marks made during disassembly are aligned. After reassembly, measure distance from master cylinder mounting surface of power unit to end of power unit push rod; distance should be .38-.39" (9.8-10.0 mm). If distance is not to specifications, correct by adjusting end of push rod.

TIGHTENING SPECIFICATIONS

Application	Ft. Lbs. (mkg)
Master Cylinder Attaching Nuts	6-9 (.8-1.2)
Hydraulic Lines	11-13 (1.5-1.8)
Rotor-to-Hub	
200SX & B210	28-38 (3.9-5.3)
F10	18-25 (2.5-3.4)
Caliper Mounting Bolts	
200SX & B210	53-72 (7.3-9.9)
F10	40-47 (5.5-6.5)

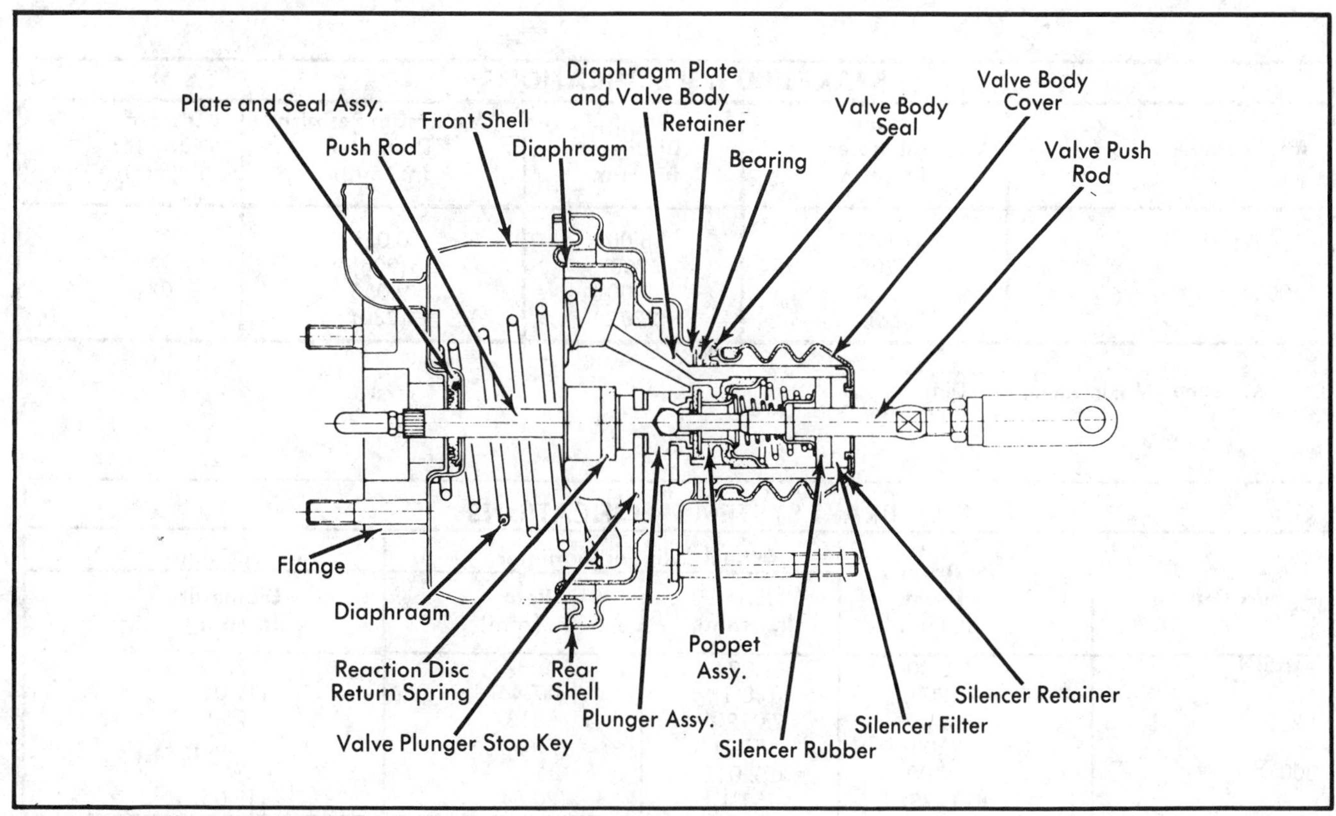

Fig. 6 Sectional View of Datsun Master Vac

DATSUN F10, 200SX, B210 (Cont.)

DISC BRAKE ROTOR SPECIFICATIONS						
Application	Disc Diameter In. (mm)	Lateral Runout In. (mm)	Parallelism In. (mm)	Original Thickness In. (mm)	Minimum Refinish Thickness In. (mm)	Discard Thickness In. (mm)
F10	9.45 (240)	.005① (.13)	.....	.....	.339 (8.6)	②
B210	9.65 (245)	.0047① (.12)	.....	.374 (9.5)	.331 (8.4)	②
200SX	9.65 (245)	.0047① (.12)	.....	.394 (10.0)	.331 (8.4)	②

① — Maximum.
② — Less than minimum refinish thickness.

BRAKE LINING SPECIFICATION							
Application	Drum Dia.	Width		Length		Thickness	
		Front	Rear	Primary	Secondary	Primary	Seondary
	In. (mm)	In. (mm)	In. (mm)	In. (mm)	In. (mm)	In. (mm)	In. (mm)
F10 & B210	8.00 (203)	①	1.378 (35)	7.68 (195)	7.68 (195)	.189 (4.8)	.189 (4.8)
200SX	9.00 (228.6)	①	1.575 (40)	8.64 (219.5)	8.64 (219.5)	.177 (4.5)	.177 (4.5)

① — Front disc equipped.

BRAKE DRUM SPECIFICATIONS				
Application	Drum Diameter In. (mm)	Original Diameter In. (mm)	Maximum Refinish Diameter In. (mm)	Discard Diameter In. (mm)
F10 & B210	8.00 (203)	8.00 (203)	8.051 (204)	①
200SX	9.00 (228.6)	9.00 (228.6)	9.055 (230)	①

① — More than Maximum Refinish Diameter.

BRAKE SYSTEM SPECIFICATIONS				
Application	Drum Diam. In. (mm)	Wheel Cylinder Diameter		Master Cylinder
		Front In. (mm)	Rear In. (mm)	Diameter In. (mm)
F10	8.00 (203)	1.894 (48.1)	.687 (17.46)	.750 (19.05)
B210	8.00 (203)	2.012① (51.1)	.813 (20.64)	.750 (19.05)
200SX	9.00 (228)	①2.012 (51.1)	.813 (20.64)	.750 (19.05)

① — Caliper cylinder diameter.

DATSUN 280Z

280Z

DESCRIPTION

Brake system is hydraulically operated, using a tandem master cylinder and a Master-Vac power brake unit. Front brakes are Girling-Sumitomo dual piston fixed caliper type. Rear brakes are leading-trailing, shoe/drum type. Brake system is equipped with a combination valve to prevent premature locking of rear wheels. A brake warning light works off the combination valve and indicates when a pressure drop occurs in either front or rear circuit. Parking brake is mechanically actuated through cables and levers. Parking brake locks rear drums.

ADJUSTMENT

BRAKE PEDAL

Loosen lock nut, turn push rod clevis, and adjust push rod length so that height of pedal, measured from pedal pad to floor, is 8.11" (206 mm). **NOTE** – *Make sure pedal stopper (stop light switch) does not contact pedal arm at this time.* With push rod adjusted, adjust stop light switch until pedal height is reduced to 7.99" (203 mm).

FRONT DISC BRAKE PADS

Front disc brakes are self-adjusting, therefore, no adjustment in service is required.

REAR DRUM BRAKE SHOES

Rear drum brakes are self-adjusting (actuated by parking brake), therefore, no adjustment in service is required.

PARKING BRAKE

Adjust shoe-to-drum clearance on rear brakes. Loosen adjusting rod lock nut and rotate adjuster nut to reduce linkage play. Actuate parking brake lever several times to stabilize cable. Make sure cables are free to operate.

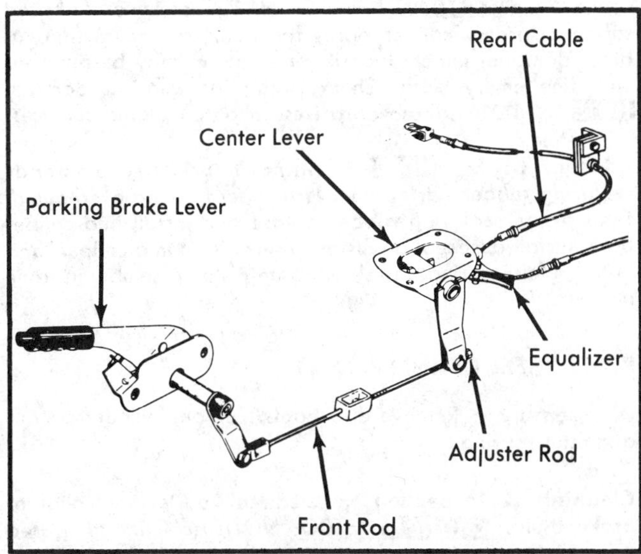

Fig. 1 280Z Parking Brake Adjustment Point Adjuster Rod

COMBINATION VALVE

Function Test – Accelerate engine to 30 mph and quickly apply brakes. If rear wheels lock before front wheels, malfunction of combination valve is indicated.

Warning Light Operation and Reset – Instrument panel light will come on when a pressure difference of between 71-244 psi is evident between front and rear hydraulic systems. Combination valve shuttle moves to side of low pressure and grounds electrical circuit, causing waring light to come on. When hydraulic problem has been corrected and brakes have been bled, system should have normal psi. Shuttle will then return to position and light will go out.

REMOVAL & INSTALLATION

FRONT DISC BRAKE PADS

Removal – Remove tire and wheel. Remove clip, retaining pin, damper spring and remove pad with shim.

Installation – Depress piston into cylinder so new pad may be inserted. Install pad, shim, damper spring and retaining pin securing with clip. Depress pedal several times to position new pads.

FRONT DISC BRAKE CALIPER

Removal - With disc pads removed, disconnect hydraulic line from caliper and plug openings. Remove caliper mounting bolts and separate caliper from steering knuckle and rotor.

Installation – Reverse removal procedure, tighten caliper mounting bolts securely, and bleed hydraulic system.

FRONT DISC BRAKE ROTOR

Removal – With caliper assembly removed, remove wheel hub dust cap, cotter pin, and adjusting nut. Remove wheel hub and rotor assembly, wheel bearing, and washer from spindle as an assembly. Remove bolts attaching rotor to wheel hub, and detach rotor.

Installation – Reverse removal procedure and adjust front wheel bearings. *See Wheel Bearing Adjustment in WHEEL ALIGNMENT Section.*

REAR BRAKE SHOES

Removal – Remove tire. Pull off brake drum. If drum is hard to remove, apply parking brake and drive out clevis pin. Release brake and pull on drum. Once drum is removed, disconnect all springs, clips and release brake shoes. Wheel cylinders are now accessible.

Installation – Apply brake grease to adjuster and all pivot points on backing plate. Refit brake shoes, springs, and clips. Refit drum. Connect parking brake and continually apply until click sound from adjuster is gone.

DATSUN 280Z (Cont.)

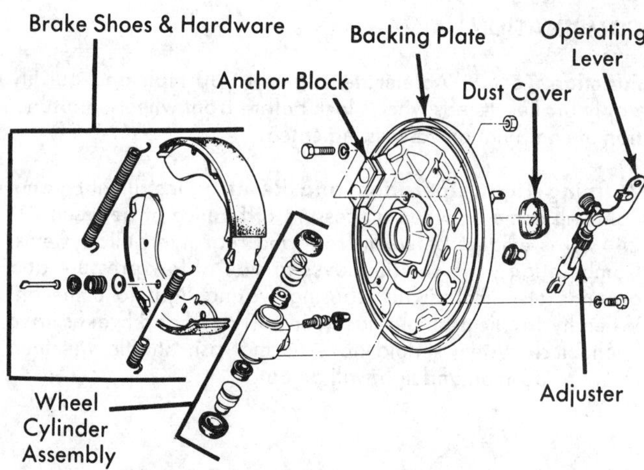

Fig. 2 Exploded View of Rear Brake Assembly

REAR WHEEL CYLINDER

Removal – Remove rear brake shoes. Disconnect and plug hydraulic line. Separate parking brake linkage. Remove mounting bolt and slide off cylinder.

Installation – Reverse removal procedure and note the following: Apply brake grease (or equivalent) to wheel cylinder, backing plate, and adjusting plate sliding surfaces; also lubricate wheel cylinder lever fulcrum and ensure wheel cylinder assembly operates freely.

MASTER CYLINDER

Removal – Disconnect hydraulic lines from master cylinder, remove nuts attaching cylinder to power unit, and separate master cylinder from power brake unit.

Installation – Reverse removal procedure, adjust brake pedal height, and bleed hydraulic system.

POWER BRAKE UNIT

Removal – Disconnect power unit push rod from brake pedal by removing clevis pin. Disconnect hydraulic lines from master cylinder, vacuum line from power unit, remove master cylinder mounting nuts, and remove master cylinder. Remove nuts attaching power unit to firewall, and remove power unit from engine compartment.

Installation – Reverse removal procedure, adjust brake pedal height, and bleed hydraulic system.

Check Valve Replacement – Check valve is located in vacuum line between intake manifold and power unit on firewall. To remove, disconnect retaining clip from firewall, remove hose clamps, separate hoses from valve, and remove check valve. To install, reverse removal procedure.

COMBINATION VALVE

Removal – Disconnect all hydraulic lines from combination valve. Plug openings. Remove mounting bolts and take off valve.

NOTE – *280Z combination valve looks similar to some used on other models. DO NOT mix-up or interchange valves.*

Installation – To install, reverse removal procedure and note: "F" mark indicates where front brake circuit is attached. Arrows indicate where to attach rear brake circuit. Note that there are arrows to show where inlet and outlet lines attach.

OVERHAUL

FRONT DISC BRAKE CALIPER

Disassembly – Clean exterior of brake caliper. Remove retaining ring and dust seal. Using a small block of wood, (or equivalent), hold one piston and blow air into brake line inlet to force piston from bore. Remove piston seal from cylinder bore. Remove other piston in similar manner.

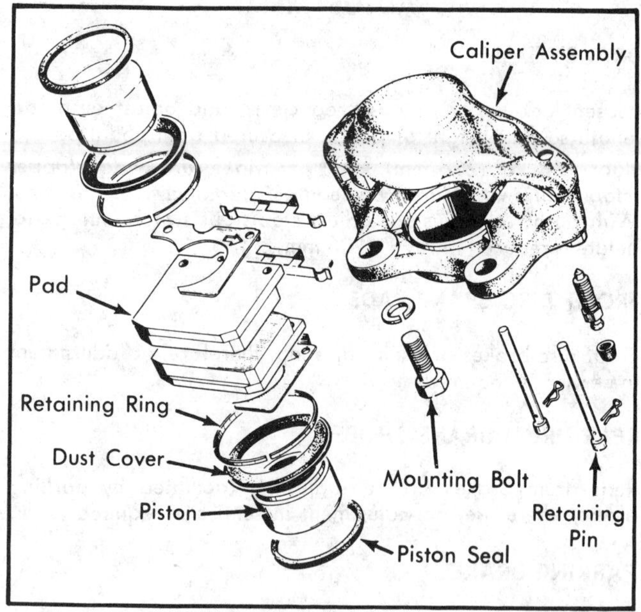

Fig. 3 Exploded View of Front Disc Brake Caliper

Cleaning & Inspection – Clean all parts in alcohol or brake fluid. **CAUTION** – *DO NOT use mineral based solvents.* Inspect caliper bores for wear, rust, corrosion, or other damage; minor deposits or scratches may be removed with fine emery cloth. Check piston for wear or damage **NOTE** – *DO NOT use abrasives on piston plated surfaces.*

Reassembly – **NOTE** – *Manufacturer recommends replacing rubber parts whenever caliper is being overhauled.* Coat piston seal with rubber grease and install into caliper bore. Install dust seal on piston, insert piston into caliper, and install retaining ring. Install opposite piston assembly in same manner.

REAR WHEEL CYLINDER

Disassembly – Remove dust boots. Pull out cylinder pistons and return spring.

Cleaning & Inspection – Clean all parts in alcohol or brake fluid. **CAUTION** – *DO NOT use mineral based solvents.* Check all parts for wear or damage; replace parts as necessary. Check clearance between cylinder bore and piston; if clearance exceeds .006", replace cylinder or piston as

DATSUN 280Z (Cont.)

necessary. Check spring for damage or distortion. NOTE — *Manufacturer recommends replacing seal whenever wheel cylinder has been disassembled.*

Reassembly — Reverse disassembly procedure and note the following: Apply rubber grease to all parts when reassembling to prevent damage.

MASTER CYLINDER

Disassembly — Remove reservoir filler caps, drain brake fluid, and remove secondary piston stop bolt. Remove snap ring and withdraw primary piston, secondary piston and return springs. Remove valve caps and withdraw check valve assemblies. NOTE — *Do not remove reservoirs unless necessary.*

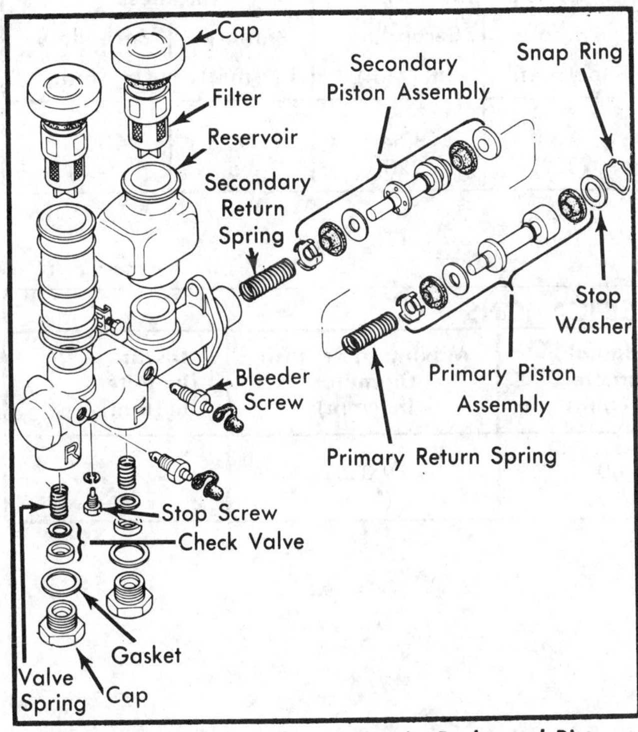

Fig. 4 Master Cylinder Reservoir, Body and Piston Assembly

Cleaning & Inspection — Clean all parts in alcohol or brake fluid and inspect for wear or damage. Check clearance between cylinder bore and pistons; if clearance exceeds .006", replace cylinder or pistons as necessary. NOTE — *Manufacturer recommends replacing piston cups, gaskets, and valves whenever master cylinder has been disassembled.*

Reassembly — Reverse disassembly procedure and note the following: Apply rubber grease to all rubber parts and brake fluid to remaining parts when assembling to prevent damage.

POWER BRAKE UNIT

Disassembly — 1) Place power unit in a soft jawed vise with operating rod pointing up. Scribe alignment marks on front and rear shells to assure reassembly in original position. Remove operating rod lock nut and clevis, then remove dust boot from rear shell.

2) Place a suitable wrench (ST08080000) over rear shell mounting studs. Press down on wrench while rotating counterclockwise and remove rear shell, then remove diaphragm plate assembly, diaphragm spring and push rod assembly. Pry off retainer and remove bearing and valve body seal from rear shell.

3) Remove diaphragm from diaphragm plate assembly, then pry off air silencer retainer and remove silencer and filter. Rotate diaphragm plate assembly until valve plunger key slot is down, then press in on plunger and shake out stop key. Remove reaction disc from plate assembly. Detach flange from front shell and remove plate and seal assembly.

Cleaning & Inspection — Clean all parts in denatured alcohol and blow dry with compressed air. Inspect inside of front and rear shells for wear or damage and replace as necessary. If slight rust is found on inside surface of shells, polish clean with fine emery cloth. Inspect all parts for cracks, nicks, distortion or other damage and replace as necessary.

Reassembly — Reverse disassembly procedure and note the following: Apply a thin coat of silicone grease to parts before installation. When assembling front shell to rear shell ensure marks made at disassembly are aligned. After reassembly, measure distance from master cylinder mounting surface to end of power unit push rod; distance should be .38-.39" (9.8-10.0 mm). If distance is not to specifications, correct by adjusting end of push rod.

TIGHTENING SPECIFICATIONS

Application	Ft. Lbs. (mkg)
Caliper-to-Knuckle Flange	53-72 (7.3-9.9)
Rotor-to-Hub	28-38 (3.9-5.3)
Hydraulic Lines	11-13 (1.5-1.8)
Master Cylinder	
Piston Stop Screw	3-4 (.4-.5)
Check Valve Caps	58-65 (8-9)
Anchor Block-to-Backing Plate	10-13 (1.4-1.8)

BRAKE SYSTEM SPECIFICATIONS

Application	Drum Diam. In. (mm)	Wheel Cylinder Diameter Front In. (mm)	Wheel Cylinder Diameter Rear In. (mm)	Master Cylinder Diameter In. (mm)
280Z	9.0① (229)	2.125② (53.9)	.875 (22.2)	.875 (22.2)

① — Rear drum.
② — Caliper bore diameter.

DATSUN 280Z (Cont.)

DISC BRAKE ROTOR SPECIFICATIONS

Application	Disc Diameter In. (mm)	Lateral Runout In. (mm)	Parallelism In. (mm)	Original Thickness In. (mm)	Minimum Refinish Thickness In. (mm)	Discard Thickness In. (mm)
280Z	10.67 (271)	.0059 (.15)	.0028① (.07)	.492 (12.5)	.413 (10.5)	②

① — Maximum allowable.
② — Less than Minimum Refinish Thickness.

BRAKE LINING SPECIFICATION

Application	Drum Dia.	Width		Length		Thickness	
		Front	Rear	Primary	Secondary	Primary	Secondary
	In. (mm)	In. (mm)	In. (mm)	In. (mm)	In. (mm)	In. (mm)	In. (mm)
280Z (Rear)	9.0 (229)	①	1.575 (40)	8.64 (220)	8.64 (220)	.177 (4.5)	.177 (4.5)

① — Front disc brake equipped.

BRAKE DRUM SPECIFICATIONS

Application	Drum Diameter In. (mm)	Original Diameter In. (mm)	Maximum Refinish Diameter In. (mm)	Discard Diameter In. (mm)
280Z (Rear)	9.0 (229)	9.0 (229)	9.055 (230)	①

① — More than Maximum Refinish Diameter.

DATSUN 710 & 810

710
810

DESCRIPTION

Brake system is hydraulically operated, using a tandem master cylinder and a Master-Vac power brake unit. Front brakes are single cylinder, dual piston type. Rear brakes are leading-trailing drum type. A combination valve is used in brake system to prevent premature locking of rear brakes. Parking brake is cable operated by an actuating lever. Parking brake works on rear wheels only.

ADJUSTMENT

BRAKE PEDAL HEIGHT & FREE PLAY ADJUSTMENT

Adjust brake light switch bolt until end face is flush with front face of bracket, then tighten lock nut. Adjust pedal stopper until pedal height, measured from pedal pad to floor, is 7.28" (185 mm) for 710 models or 7.09" (180 mm) for 810 models. Adjust master cylinder push rod length until free play, measured at pedal, is .039-.197" (1-5 mm).

FRONT DISC BRAKE PADS

Front disc brakes are self-adjusting; therefore, no adjustment in service is required.

REAR BRAKE SHOES

710 – With parking brake fully released, depress brake pedal several times so that shoes are settled to normal positions. Turn adjusting cam on backing plate until shoes lock against drum. Loosen adjusting cam until drum is just free to rotate.

810 – No adjustment is required. Brakes are adjusted when parking brake is applied.

PARKING BRAKE

Station Wagon – Make sure rear brakes are correctly adjusted. Adjust front cable adjusting nut so that when parking brake lever is pulled with specified force (see specifications), the lever stroke or the number of notches is as specified (see specifications). With parking brake off, make sure cables are slack and the rear levers are in their original positions.

Sedan – Make sure rear brakes are correctly adjusted. Adjust front cable adjusting nut so that when parking brake is off, dimension "A" (*see Fig. 1*) is .28" (7 mm). Tighten lock nut. Now adjust rear cable adjuster so that when parking brake lever is pulled with specified force (see specifications) the lever stroke or the number of notches is as specified (see specifications). With parking brake off, make sure cables are slack and the rear levers are in their original positions.

Parking Brake Adjustment Specifications

Adjustment	Station Wagon	Sedan
Pulling Force①	53 lbs. (24 kg)	44 lbs. (20 kg)
Lever Stroke	4.49" (114 mm)	4.02-4.49" (102-114 mm)
No. of Notches	6	5-6

① – Measured 1.97" (50 mm) from the end of the parking brake lever (less release button).

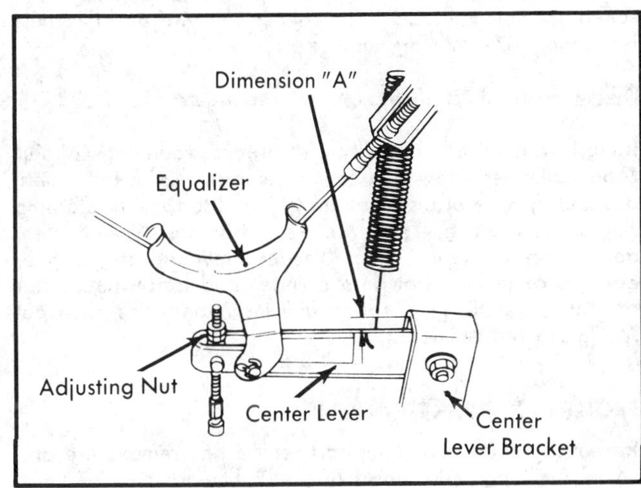

Fig. 1 Adjusting Center Lever (Sedan Models)

BRAKE WARNING LIGHT

Brake Warning Light – Light indicates parking brake is engaged. To adjust warning light, bend switch plate down until light operates when ratchet handle is pulled up one notch and so light goes out when handle is returned to normal position.

COMBINATION VALVE

Function Test – Accelerate to about 30 mph on a dry concrete surface and harshly apply brakes. If rear wheels lock at same time as fronts do, or if front wheels lock before rears, combination valve is operating properly. If rear wheels lock first, combination valve is malfunctioning; replace valve.

Warning Light Operation & Reset – Instrument panel light will come on when a pressure difference of between 71-224 psi is evident between front and rear hydraulic systems. Combination valve shuttle moves to side of low pressure and grounds electrical circuit causing warning light to come on. When hydraulic problem has been corrected and brakes have been bled, system should have 427 psi. Shuttle will then return to centered position and light will go out.

HYDRAULIC SYSTEM BLEEDING

Attach a bleed tube to bleeder screw and immerse opposite end of tube in container partially filled with brake fluid. Depress pedal, open bleeder allowing air to escape, close bleeder screw, and allow pedal to return slowly. Continue

DATSUN 710 & 810 (Cont.)

operation until air bubbles are no longer seen in discharged fluid. Repeat procedure on remaining brake lines until all air is bled from system. Bleeding sequence is: Master cylinder first, rear brakes, and front brakes.

REMOVAL & INSTALLATION

FRONT DISC BRAKE PADS

Removal – Raise and support front of vehicle. Remove retaining spring clip. Remove disc pad pins retaining anti-squeal springs. Pull pads from caliper cavity. If pad thickness is less than .079" (2 mm), replace pads.

NOTE – *Pads must always be replaced in sets.*

Installation – Clean cavity and area surrounding caliper. Loosen bleeder screw and seat outer piston in cylinder until dust seal groove of piston aligns with end surface of retaining ring on dust seal. **NOTE** – *Make sure piston groove does not go inside piston seal.* Tighten bleeder screw and fit new inner pad. Force inner piston into cylinder and install new outer pad. Install anti-squeal spring and insert pad pins, then put spring clip into position.

FRONT DISC BRAKE CALIPER

Removal – Raise and support vehicle and remove tire and wheel assembly. Disconnect hydraulic line from caliper and plug openings. Remove bolts securing caliper to steering knuckle and remove caliper.

Installation – Reverse removal procedure, tighten mounting bolts securely, and bleed hydraulic system.

FRONT DISC BRAKE ROTOR

Removal – With caliper assembly removed, remove hub dust cap, adjusting cap, adjustment nut and washer. Slide hub and rotor assembly from spindle taking care not to lose outer wheel bearing. Remove bolts attaching rotor to hub, then separate.

Installation – Reverse removal procedure, tighten rotor mounting bolts securly, and adjust wheel bearings. *See Wheel Bearing Adjustment in WHEEL ALIGNMENT Section.* Using a dial indicator, measure rotor runout. If runout exceeds .005" (.12 mm), resurface or replace rotor.

REAR BRAKE SHOES

Removal, 710 – Raise and support vehicle, remove tire and wheel. Remove brake drum. Disconnect anti-rattle springs and shoe return springs. Take shoes off bracking plate. If necessary, remove bolts securing adjuster to backing plate and remove adjuster mechanism. *See Fig. 2.*

Installation – Reverse removal procedure and note the following: Apply grease to sliding areas of backing plate and adjuster, taking care not to contaminate linings. When installed, adjust brake shoes, parking brake, and bleed hydraulic system.

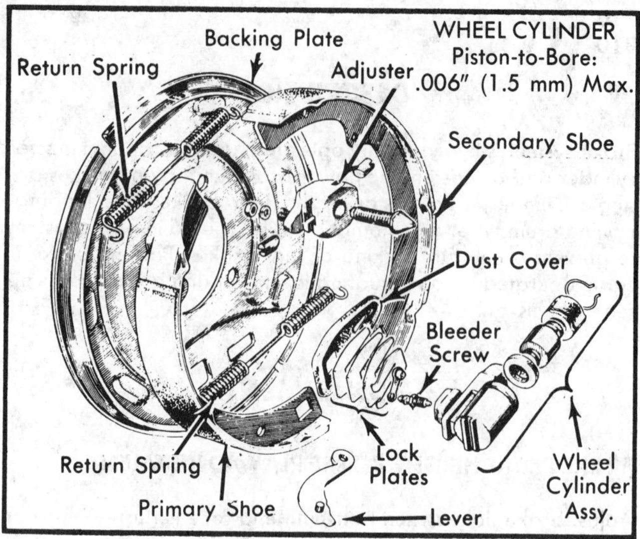

Fig. 2 Rear Brake Assembly for Datsun 710. Also Note Detail of Sliding Wheel Cylinder for Disassembly Purposes

Removal, 810 Sedan – 1) Raise rear of vehicle, remove tire and brake drum. Apply parking brake. Lightly tap stopper head. Remove stopper and fastner as an assembly. Release parking brake.

2) If necessary, remove rear axle to gain access to rear brake components. Remove anti-rattle spring and pin. Remove return springs and brake shoes. Remove parking brake cable from lever. Pry off snap ring and remove lever from brake shoe.

Installation – To install, reverse removal procedure. Apply grease to adjuster nut and threads on rod. Also, apply grease to mating surfaces between adjuster and back plate.

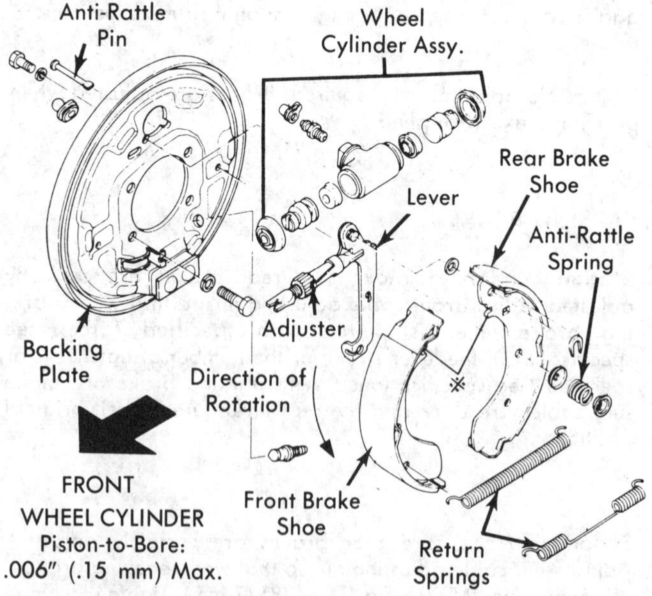

Fig. 3 Exploded View of Rear Brake Assembly for Datsun 810 Sedan Models. 810 Station Wagon Models Are Similar But Have Different Brake Adjuster Mechanism Configuration

DATSUN 710 & 810 (Cont.)

Removal, 810 Station Wagon – 1) Raise rear of vehicle, remove tire and brake drum. Apply parking brake. Pull out pin and remove stopper from toggle lever. Release parking brake.

2) If necessary, remove rear axle shaft to gain access to brake components. Remove anti-rattle spring and pin. Remove return springs and brake shoes. Remove parking brake return spring, then remove cross-rod cotter pin. Remove dust cover and toggle lever with adjuster assembly.

Installation – To install, reverse removal procedure. Apply grease to adjuster nut and rod threads. Also apply grease to mating surface between adjuster and toggle lever.

Removal, 710 – With rear drum and brake shoes removed, disconnect and plug hydraulic line at wheel cylinder. Pull out clevis pin and separate rod from cylinder operating lever. Remove dust cover, adjusting shims and lock plates, then remove wheel cylinder.

Installation – Reverse removal procedure and note the following: After wheel cylinder is installed, measure wheel cylinder sliding resistance using a spring pull gauge; resistance should be 4.4-15.4 lbs. (2.0-7.0 kg.). Install brake shoe assemblies and bleed hydraulic system.

Removal, 810 – With brake drum and shoes removed, disconnect hydraulic line at rear of wheel cylinder. Remove bolt securing wheel cylinder to backing plate and remove cylinder.

Installation – To install, reverse removal procedure. Bleed hydraulic system after installation.

MASTER CYLINDER

Removal – Disonnect and plug front and rear hydraulic lines from master cylinder and drain brake fluid from cylinder. Remove master cylinder attaching nuts and lift off master cylinder.

Installation – Reverse removal procedure and bleed hydraulic system.

POWER BRAKE UNIT

Removal – With master cylinder removed, disconnect vacuum line from power unit. From inside vehicle, disconnect pedal return spring, push rod from brake pedal, and power unit mounting nuts. Remove power unit from engine compartment.

Installation – Reverse removal procedure, adjust pedal height and free play, and bleed hydraulic system.

Check Valve Replacement – Check valve is located near identification plate on firewall. To remove, disconnect clip, remove hose clamps, separate hoses from valve, and remove valve. To install, reverse removal procedure.

OVERHAUL

FRONT DISC BRAKE CALIPER

Disassembly – Drain any remaining fluid from cylinder. Remove holding mounting nut, See *Fig. 4*. Separate yoke and cylinder body. Remove yoke holder from piston. Take off retaining ring and dust seals from both inner and outer pistons. Force pistons from cylinder using compressed air. Carefully pry out piston seals.

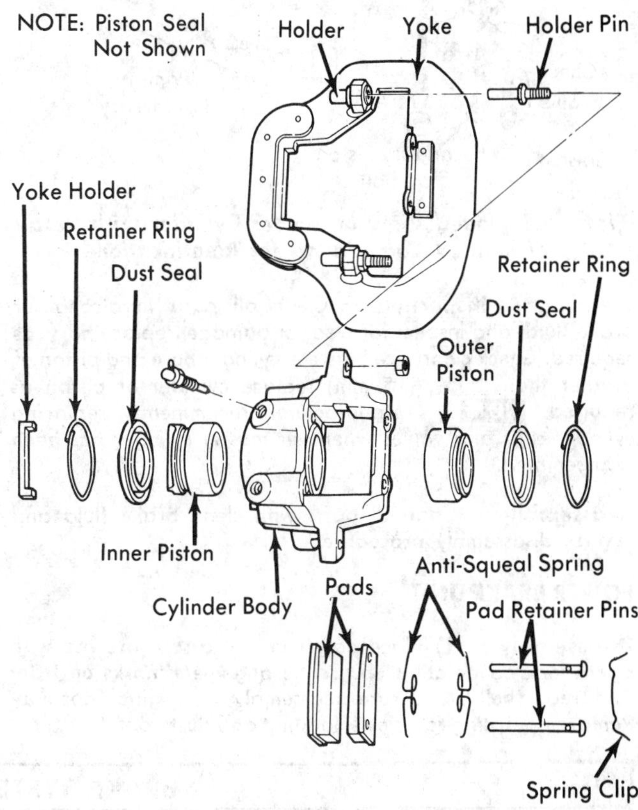

Fig. 4 Exploded View of Front Disc Brake Caliper 710 Caliper is Shown – 810 Models Have Slightly Different Holder Pins and Anti-Rattle Springs

Inspection – Clean all components in brake fluid. Inspect for rust, score marks, damage, or wear. Minor damage can be polished out with a fine emery cloth, except on piston head.

Reassembly – Carefully refit piston seals. Apply a light coat of brake fluid to sliding surfaces. Insert inner piston so yoke groove aligns with groove in cylinder. Fit dust seal and insert retainer ring. Fit yoke holder to inner piston. Drive in holding pin. Support end of piston, then press yoke into holder.

MASTER CYLINDER

Disassembly – Remove reservoir cap and drain fluid. Remove dust cover, retaining ring and piston stop screw. Remove washer, primary piston assembly, secondary piston assembly and return spring. Remove valve plugs and remove check valves. **NOTE** – *Do not remove master cylinder reservoir tanks; if removed new tanks must be reinstalled.*

DATSUN 710 & 810 (Cont.)

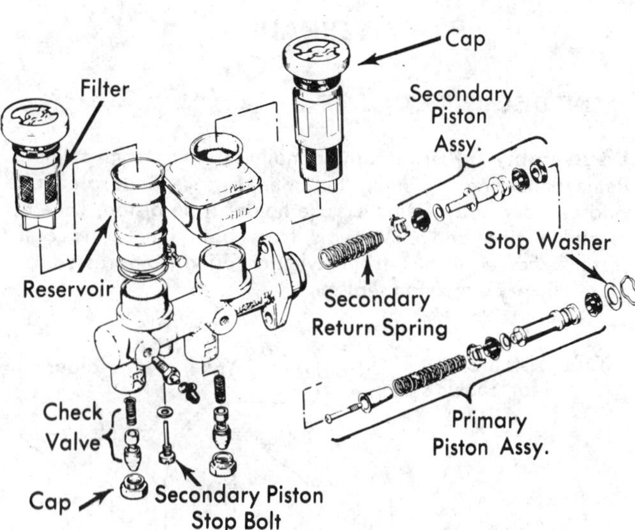

Fig. 5 Exploded View of Master Cylinder with Detail of Related Components for Identification

Cleaning & Inspection – Clean all parts in alcohol or brake fluid, and inspect for wear or damage; replace parts as required. Check clearance between cylinder bore and piston; if greater than .006" (.15 mm) replace cylinder or piston as required. **NOTE** – *Manufacturer recommends replacing cylinder cups and valves whenever master cylinder has been disassembled.*

Reassembly – Coat all parts with clean brake fluid and reverse disassembly procedure.

POWER BRAKE UNIT

Disassembly – **1)** Place power unit in a soft jaw vise with operating rod pointing up. Scribe alignment marks on front and rear shells to assure reassembly in original position. Remove operating rod clevis, lock nut and dust boot.

2) Place Master-Vac wrench (ST08080000) over rear shell mounting studs. Press down on wrench while rotating counterclockwise and separate rear shell from front shell, then remove diaphragm plate assembly, diaphragm spring and push rod assembly. Pry off retainer and remove bearing and valve body seal from rear shell.

3) Remove rubber diaphragm from diaphragm plate assembly, then pry off air silencer retainer and remove silencer and filter. Rotate plate assembly until valve plunger key slot is down, then press in on plunger and shake out stop key. Remove reaction disc from plate assembly. Detach flange from front shell and remove plate and seal assembly.

Cleaning & Inspection – Clean all parts in denatured alcohol and blow dry with compressed air. Inspect front and rear shells for wear or damage. If slight rust is found on inside surface of shell, polish clean with fine emery cloth. Inspect all parts for cracks, nicks, distortion or other damage and replace as necessary.

Reassembly – Reverse disassembly procedure and note the following: Apply a thin coat of silicone grease to parts before reassembly. When assembling front shell to rear shell, ensure marks made during disassembly are aligned. After reassembly, measure distance from master cylinder mounting surface of power unit to end of power unit push rod; distance should be .38-.39" (9.8-10.0 mm). If distance is not to specifications, correct by adjusting tip of push rod.

TIGHTENING SPECIFICATIONS

Application	Ft. Lbs. (mkg)
Hydraulic Lines	11-13 (1.5-1.8)
Rotor-to-Hub	28-38 (3.9-5.3)
Caliper-to-Steering Knuckle	53-72 (7.3-9.9)

BRAKE SYSTEM SPECIFICATIONS

Application	Drum Diam. In. (mm)	Wheel Cylinder Diameter Front In. (mm)	Wheel Cylinder Diameter Rear In. (mm)	Master Cylinder Diameter In. (mm)
710	9 (229)	2.012① (51.1)	.813 (20.6)	.750 (19.0)
810	9 (229)	2.125① (53.98①)	.813 (20.6)	.813 (20.6)

① – Caliper cylinder diameter.

DISC BRAKE ROTOR SPECIFICATIONS

Application	Disc Diameter In. (mm)	Lateral Runout In. (mm)	Parallelism In. (mm)	Original Thickness In. (mm)	Minimum Refinish Thickness In. (mm)	Discard Thickness In. (mm)
710	9.65 (245)	.0024 (.06)	.0028① (.07)	.394 (10.0)	.331 (8.4)	②
810	10.67 (271)	.0059 (.15)	.0028① (.07)	.492 (10.67)	.413 (10.5)	②

DATSUN 710 & 810 (Cont.)

BRAKE LINING SPECIFICATION							
Application	Drum Dia. In. (mm)	Width		Length		Thickness	
		Front In. (mm)	Rear In. (mm)	Primary In. (mm)	Secondary In. (mm)	Primary In. (mm)	Secondary In. (mm)
710 & 810	9.0 (229)	①	1.575 (40)	8.642 (219.5)	8.642 (219.5)	.177 (4.5)	.177 (4.5)

① — Front disc brake equipped.

BRAKE DRUM SPECIFICATIONS				
Application	Drum Diameter In. (mm)	Original Diameter In. (mm)	Maximum Refinish Diameter In. (mm)	Discard Diameter In. (mm)
710 & 810	9 (229)	9.000 (229)	9.055 (230)	①

① — More than maximum refinish diameter.

DATSUN PICKUP

Pickup

DESCRIPTION

Brake system is hydraulically operated, using a tandem master cylinder and a Master-Vac power brake unit. Leading-trailing shoe/drum brakes are used on all four wheels, with front brakes actuated by a uni-servo wheel cylinder, and rear brakes actuated by a duo-servo wheel cylinder. Parking brake is cable actuated, operating secondary shoes of rear brake assemblies.

ADJUSTMENT

BRAKE PEDAL

Loosen stop light switch adjusting nuts and rotate switch until pedal height, measured from pedal pad to floor, is approximately 5.5". With pedal height adjusted, adjust brake pedal push rod adjusting nut so that .039-.118" free play is obtained when depressing pedal. With pedal assembly properly adjusted, total pedal travel should be 4.96-5.20" with no interference.

BRAKE SHOES

Remove rubber boot from hole in front backing plate and lightly tap adjuster housing to move it forward. Using a suitable brake adjusting tool, turn adjuster downward until drum locks, then back off adjuster 12 ratchet stops and ensure brake drum rotates freely without dragging. Adjustment procedure for rear brake shoes is the same, with parking brake fully released.

PARKING BRAKE

With parking brake lever applied 3.15-3.94", adjust equalizer link with adjusting nut until rear wheels are locked. Release parking brake and insure rear wheels turn freely.

BRAKE WARNING LIGHT

Brake Warning Light – Light indicates parking brake is engaged. To adjust warning light, bend switch plate down until light operates when ratchet handle is pulled up one notch and so light goes out when handle is returned to normal position.

COMBINATION VALVE

Function Test – Accelerate vehicle to 30 mph and sharply apply brakes. If rear wheels lock ahead of fronts, or if stopping distance is greater than 43 feet (rear wheels locked), valve must be replaced.

NOTE – *Stopping distance is same whether loaded or not. Lighter pedal pressure is required to lock rear wheels of unloaded vehicles.*

MASTER VAC

Vacuum Test – **1)** Insert vacuum gauge in line between check valve and master vac.

2) Start engine and raise RPM until vacuum gauge reads 19.69 in. Hg (500 mm Hg). Stop engine.

3) After 15 minutes lapse time, check pressure drop indicated by gauge. A drop of more than .98 in. Hg (25 mm Hg) indicates master vac is loosing pressure too quickly. Several problems are indicated:

- Check valve air leak
- Push rod seal air leak
- Air leak; valve body and seal
- Damaged hydraulic lines

4) Repeat step **2)** Fully apply brake pedal and read vacuum gauge after 15 minutes. Note if pressure drop has exceeded .98 in. Hg (25 mm Hg). Several problems are indicated if pressure drop is excessive:

- Check valve air leak
- Damaged diaphragm
- Disengaged reaction rod
- Air leak at poppet seat and valve body

Check Valve Test – **1)** Using suitable master vac tester gauge set or equivalent, apply 7.87 in Hg (200 mm Hg) to master vac side of check valve. If pressure drops more than .39 in. Hg (10 mm Hg) in 15 seconds, replace valve.

2) When pressure is applied to master vac side of check valve and valve fails to open, replace check valve.

HYDRAULIC SYSTEM BLEEDING

Attach a bleed tube to wheel cylinder bleeder screw, and immerse opposite end into a container partially filled with brake fluid. Pump brake pedal two or three times, open bleeder screw to allow air to escape, then close bleeder screw. Continue operation until air is no longer seen in discharged fluid. Repeat procedure on remaining brake lines. Bleed rear wheels first, front wheels last.

REMOVAL & INSTALLATION

BRAKE SHOES

Removal (Front) – Remove tire, wheel and brake drum. Disconnect all mounting and return springs. Remove brake shoes. Remove backing plate plug, spring plate, lock plate, shim and adjuster assembly.

Installation – Reverse removal procedure. **NOTE** – *Apply a thin coat of suitable brake grease to pivot points on backing plate, adjuster and spring sliding surfaces.*

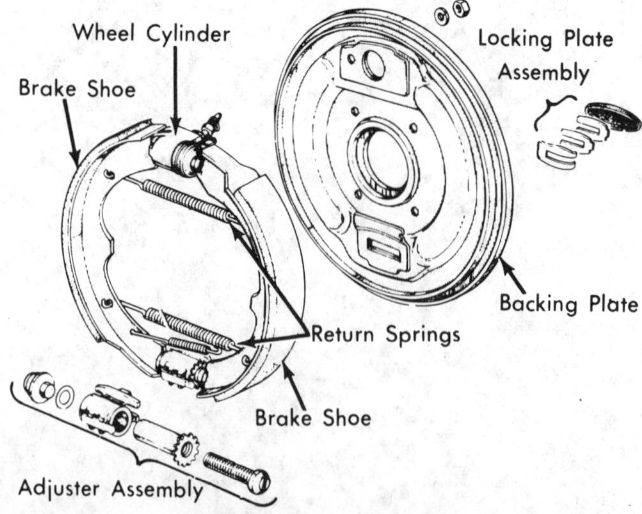

Fig. 1 Exploded View of Front Brake Assy.

DATSUN PICKUP (Cont.)

Removal (Rear) – Remove rear wheel and brake drum. Remove mounting springs, clips and pins. Spread shoe assembly and remove parking brake strut. Disconnect return springs and parking brake cable, then lift off brake shoes. Remove adjuster assembly from backing plate.

Installation – Reverse removal procedure. *See* **NOTE** *in preceding installation procedure.*

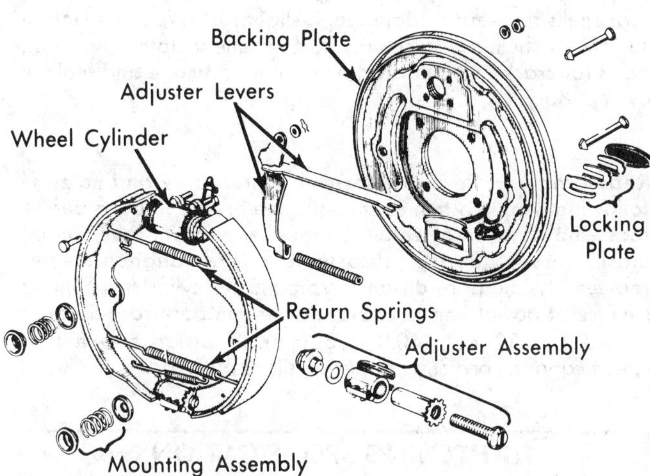

Fig. 2 Exploded View of Rear Brake Assy.

WHEEL CYLINDER

Removal (All) – With brake shoes removed, disconnect hydraulic line from cylinder and nuts attaching cylinder to backing plate. Remove wheel cylinder.

Installation – Reverse removal procedure, adjust brake shoes, and bleed hydraulic system.

MASTER CYLINDER

Removal – Disconnect hydraulic lines from master cylinder, taking care not to spill brake fluid on paint. Remove nuts attaching master cylinder to power unit and remove cylinder.

Installation – Reverse removal procedure and bleed hydraulic system.

POWER BRAKE UNIT

Removal – With master cylinder removed, disconnect vacuum line from power unit. From inside vehicle, disconnect brake pedal return spring, power unit push rod clevis from brake pedal, and remove nuts attaching power unit to firewall. Remove power unit from engine compartment.

Installation – Reverse removal procedure, adjust brake pedal assembly, and bleed hydraulic system.

Check Valve Replacement – Vacuum check valve is located in vacuum line between intake manifold and power unit. To remove, loosen hose clamps, separate hoses from valve, and remove check valve. To install, reverse removal procedure.

OVERHAUL

WHEEL CYLINDER

Disassembly (All) – Remove snap ring and rubber dust boots. Remove piston and seal assemblies, then remove seals from pistons.

Cleaning & Inspection – Clean all parts in clean alcohol or brake fluid. **NOTE** – *DO NOT use mineral based solvents.* Inspect all parts for wear or damage; replace parts as necessary. Check clearance between piston and cylinder bore; if clearance exceeds .006" (.15 mm), replace cylinder or piston as necessary.

Reassembly – Reverse disassembly procedure and note the following: Coat all parts with clean brake fluid when reassembling. When securing connector bolt, insert location tip to hole of wheel cylinder firmly and tighten securely.

MASTER CYLINDER

Disassembly – Remove reservoir caps and drain fluid. Remove retaining ring and secondary piston stop bolt, then withdraw stop washer, primary piston assembly, secondary piston assembly, and return springs. Remove valve caps and check valve assemblies. **NOTE** – *DO NOT remove reservoir. If removed, a new replacement reservoir must be installed.*

Cleaning & Inspection – Clean all parts in alcohol or brake fluid. Inspect all parts for wear, deformation, or other damage; replace parts as necessary. Check clearance between pistons and cylinder bore; if greater than .006" (.15 mm), replace parts as necessary. **NOTE** – *Manufacturer recommends replacing cups and valves whenever master cylinder has been disassembled.*

Reassembly – Reverse disassembly procedure and note the following: Coat all parts with brake fluid or rubber grease when reassembling to prevent damage. Replace all gaskets and packings with new parts.

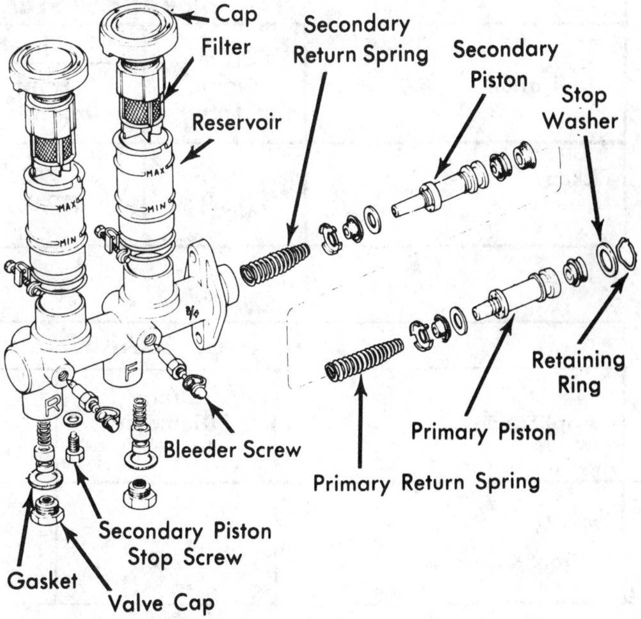

Fig. 3 Exploded View of Datsun Pickup Master Cylinder

DATSUN PICKUP (Cont.)

POWER BRAKE UNIT

Disassembly — **1)** Place power unit in a soft jaw vise with operating rod pointing up. Scribe alignment marks on front and rear shells to assure reassembly in original position. Remove operating rod clevis, lock nut and dust boot.

2) Place Master-Vac wrench (ST08080000) over rear shell mounting studs. Press down on wrench while rotating counterclockwise and separate rear shell from front shell, then remove diaphragm plate assembly, diaphragm spring and push rod assembly. Pry off retainer and remove bearing and valve body seal from rear shell.

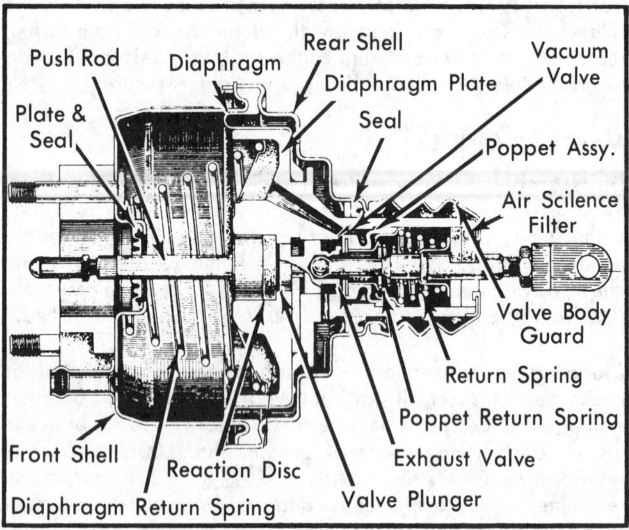

Fig. 4 Sectional View of Master Vac Power Brake Unit

3) Remove rubber diaphragm from diaphragm plate assembly, then pry off air silencer retainer and remove silencer and filter. Rotate plate assembly until stop key slot is down, then press in on plunger and shake out stop key. Remove reaction disc from plate assembly. Detach flange from front shell and remove plate and seal assembly.

Cleaning & Inspection — Clean all parts in denatured alcohol and blow dry with compressed air. Inspect front and rear shells for wear or damage. If slight rust is found on inside surface of shell, polish clean with fine emery cloth. Inspect all parts for cracks, nicks, distortion or other damage and replace as necessary.

Reassembly — Reverse disassembly procedure and note the following: Apply a thin coat of silicone grease to parts before reassembly. When assembling rear shell to front shell, ensure marks made during disassembly are aligned. After reassembly, measure distance from master cylinder mounting surface of power unit to end of power unit push rod; distance should be .39-.41" (10.0-10.5 mm). If distance is not to specifications, correct by adjusting tip of push rod.

TIGHTENING SPECIFICATIONS

Application	Ft. Lbs. (mkg)
Master Cylinder-to-Master Vac	5.8-8.0 (.8-1.1)
Combination Valve-to-Body	5.8-8.0 (.8-1.1)
Brake Back Plate	
Front	30-36 (4.2-5.0)
Rear	39-46 (5.4-6.4)
Master Vac-to-Body	5.8-8.0 (.8-1.1)

BRAKE SYSTEM SPECIFICATIONS

Application	Drum Diam. In. (mm)	Wheel Cylinder Diameter Front In. (mm)	Wheel Cylinder Diameter Rear In. (mm)	Master Cylinder Diameter In. (mm)
Pickup	10.0 (254)	.750 (19.05)	.750 (19.05)	.750 (19.05)

BRAKE DRUM SPECIFICATIONS

Application	Drum Diameter In. (mm)	Original Diameter In. (mm)	Maximum Refinish Diameter In. (mm)	Discard Diameter In. (mm)
Pickup Front & Rear	10.00 (254)	10.00 (254)	10.059 (255.5)	①

① — More than Maximum Refinish Diameter.

FIAT

124 Spider
128
131
X1/9

DESCRIPTION

Brake system is hydraulically actuated, using a tandem master cylinder and a Master Vac power brake unit. All front brakes are single piston, sliding caliper type. 128 and 131 models use leading-trailing rear drum brakes, while 124 and X1/9 models use single piston rear disc brakes. All models except X1/9 use pressure differential valves. Parking brakes are cable operated and work either on rear drums or rear brake calipers.

ADJUSTMENT

DISC BRAKE PADS

Front disc brakes are self-adjusting, no in-service adjustment is required.

REAR BRAKE SHOES

Rear drum brakes are self-adjusting, no in-service adjustment is required.

PARKING BRAKE

Fully release parking brake lever, then pull up approximately two notches. On 124 and X1/9 models, tighten nut on equalizer until cable is tight. X1/9 models have an opening provided in floor pan under body for access to equalizer. On 128 models, loosen lock nut on tensioner located along under body and tighten adjuster nut until rear wheels are locked. On 131 models, loosen lock nut located near parking brake handle and tighten until rear wheels lock.

BRAKE PRESSURE REGULATOR

124 Spider – 1) Bring end of torsion bar (E) to distance (X) from rubber buffer resting surface.

2) Lift dust boot (C) and check contact of regulator piston (D) with torsion bar end (E).

3) Pivot regulator body on screw (A) until piston (D) is just touching torsion bar end (E).

4) First, tighten screw (B) and then screw (A) in all the way. Connect link (G) to torsion bar eye end (E) with screw and nut while inserting rubber bushings and spacer.

NOTE – *Fluid inlet from master cylinder must be connected to lower union (R) and fluid line to rear brakes must be connected to upper union (S).*

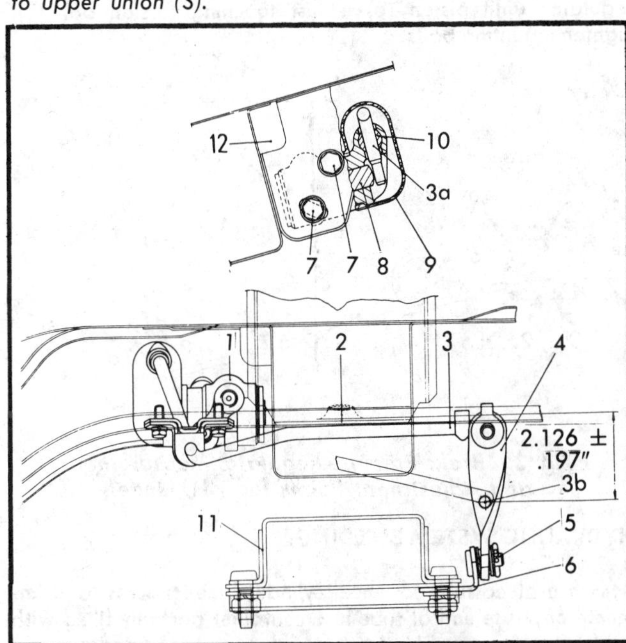

Fig. 1 Brake Pressure Regulator Measurement and Adjustment Points for 128

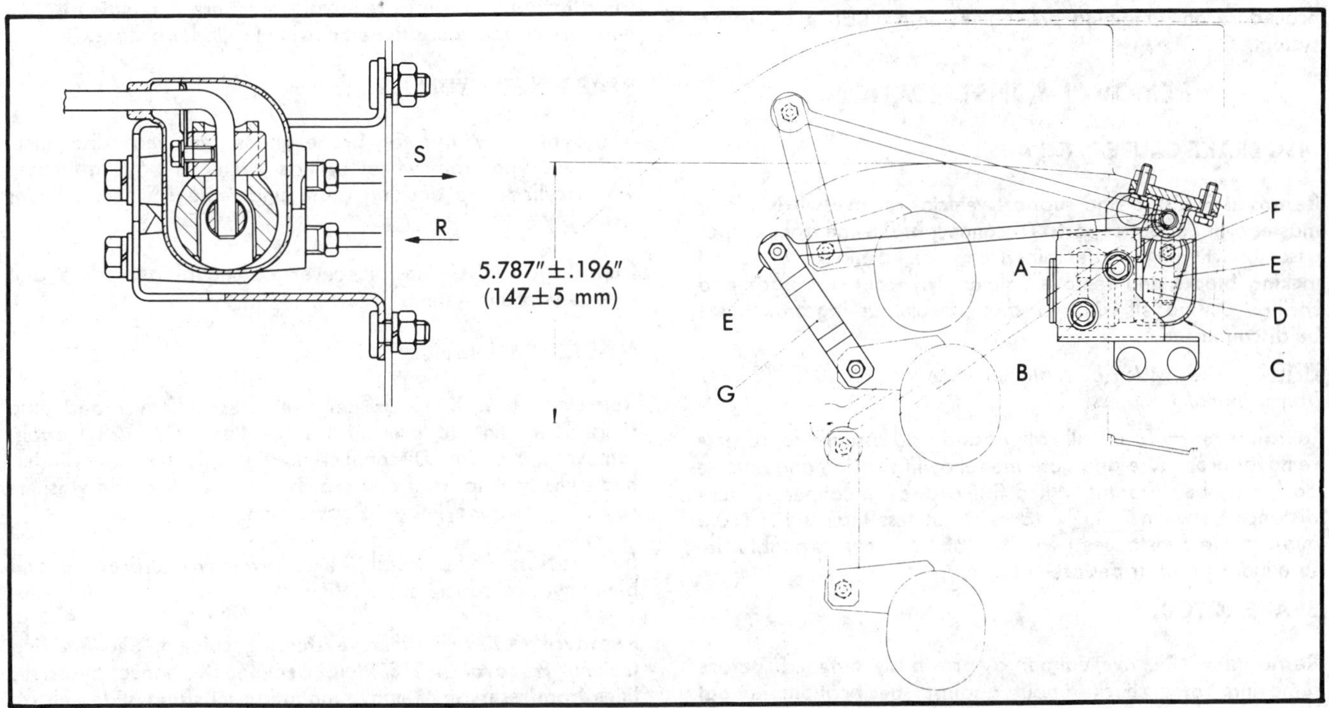

Fig. 2 Brake Pressure Regulator Measurement and Adjustment Points for 124

FIAT (Cont.)

128 – With pressure regulator mounting bolts loosened and link (4) disconnected from control arm anchor pin (5), check that the axis of torsion bar end (3b) is 2.126"±.197" from center of rubber buffer seat (2). Once obtained, position pressure regulator with piston (8) just touching torsion bar end (3a). Tighten regulator mounting bolts (7) on bracket (12), then connect link (4) to control arm anchor pin (5).

131 – Install regulator and leave mounting bolts loose. Bring torsion bar (7) to dimension (X) from the base of buffer end (11). Remove rubber boot (3) from regulator, then rotate regulator until piston (6) is just touching torsion bar (1). Tighten mounting bolts.

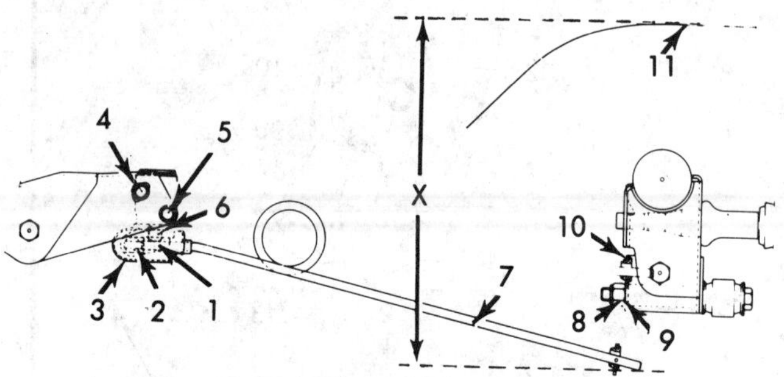

Fig. 3 Brake Pressure Regulator Measurement and Adjustment Points for 131 Models

HYDRAULIC SYSTEM BLEEDING

Attach a bleed tube to wheel cylinder bleeder screw and immerse opposite end of tube in a container partially filled with brake fluid. Loosen bleeder screw, depress brake pedal quickly and allow to return slowly. Continue operation until air bubbles are no longer seen in discharge fluid. Tighten bleeder screw on a down stroke of pedal application. Repeat procedure on remaining brake lines until all air is bled from system.

REMOVAL & INSTALLATION

DISC BRAKE CALIPERS & PADS

Removal – Raise and support vehicle; remove wheels. Plug master cylinder outlet ports. Disconnect brake line from caliper assembly. Remove cotter pins from locking blocks, drive out locking blocks and remove caliper. Take out disc pads and springs. On models with rear disc brakes, parking brake must be disconnected.

NOTE – *Pads MUST be replaced when worn to .079" (2 mm) from original thickness.*

Installation – To install caliper and pad assemblies, reverse removal procedure and note the following: Inside and outside pads may be different. When fitting pads to calipers, ensure distance between inner surfaces is not less than .413" (10.5 mm). In most instances two kinds of pads are available, be sure index paint stripes are not mixed.

BRAKE ROTOR

Removal – Remove caliper as previously outlined. Before removing rotor check runout against specification. Runout should not exceed .006" (.15 mm). Remove caliper support bracket from support plate (front) or from axle housing (rear). Remove bolts mounting rotor to wheel hub, remove hub plate, then remove rotor using a suitable drift or puller.

Installation – Fit rotor onto wheel hub, install attaching bolts and tighten evenly.

REAR BRAKE SHOES

Removal – Raise and support rear of vehicle and remove wheels. Remove bolts attaching drum. Install a suitable tool to retain wheel cylinder pistons, remove upper and lower shoe return springs, shoe guide pins, springs, and cups, then remove brake shoes.

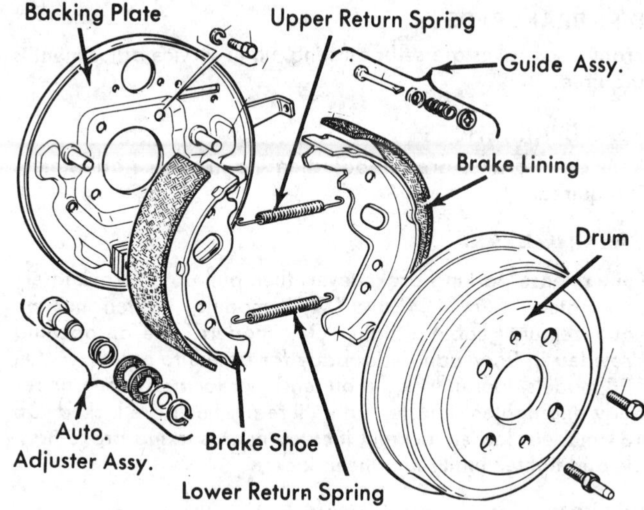

Fig. 4 Typical Rear Drum Brake Assembly for 128 Models

Installation – Reverse removal procedure making sure shoe ends are correctly positioned in wheel cylinder pistons.

REAR WHEEL CYLINDER

Removal – With rear brake shoes removed, disconnect hydraulic line from wheel cylinder, remove bolts attaching wheel cylinder to backing plate and remove wheel cylinder assembly.

Installation – To install, reverse removal procedure and bleed hydraulic system.

MASTER CYLINDER

Removal, Exc. X1/9 – Remove reservoir cover and plug fluid outlet line to prevent loss of fluid. On 128 models, remove spare tire. Disconnect fluid supply line at cylinder, hydraulic lines to front and rear brakes and nuts and washers retaining master cylinder to power unit.

Installation – To install, reverse removal procedure and bleed hydraulic system.

Removal, X1/9 – Remove steering column. *See Steering Column Removal in STEERING Section.* Disconnect hydraulic lines from reservoir. Remove mounting nuts and slide unit off supports. Disconnect outlet lines from master cylinder.

FIAT (Cont.)

Installation – To install, reverse removal procedure and bleed hydraulic system.

OVERHAUL

Disassembly, Front – With caliper assembly on bench, remove dust boot. Apply light air pressure to brake fluid inlet union and gently force piston from caliper. Remove piston seal from groove in piston cylinder bore. **NOTE** – *Be sure bore is not scratched during removal process.*

Inspection – Clean all components in suitable solvent (Fiat LDC). Inspect each part for damage or excessive wear. Replace all piston seals and dust boots.

Reassembly – Fit piston seal in caliper. Insert piston to bottom end of cylinder bore. Position dust boot on caliper body. Fit caliper body into caliper bracket and reinstall on vehicle.

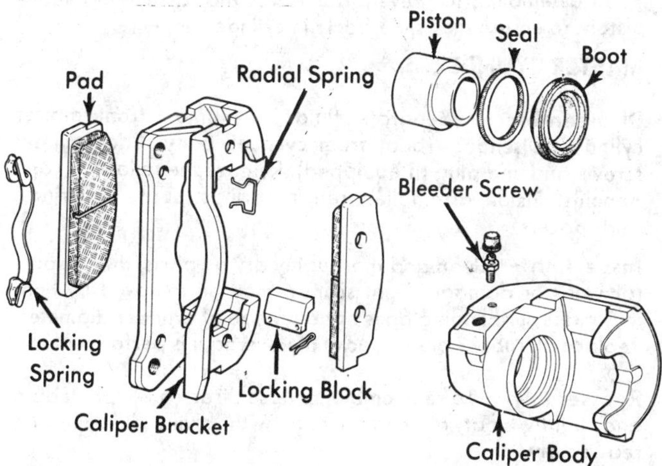

Fig. 5 Front Brake Caliper Assembly for 124 and 131 Models

Disassembly, Rear – With caliper assembly on bench, remove dust boot. With a screwdriver, separate piston from plunger. Remove piston seal from groove in piston cylinder bore. Remove cam lever, pivot pin, and lever. Lift out self-adjusting plunger, plunger seal, disc spring, and spring thrust washer.

Inspection – Clean all components in suitable solvent (Fiat LDC). Inspect each part for damage or excessive wear. Replace all piston seals and dust boots.

Reassembly – Fit self-adjusting plunger complete with seal, disc springs, and thrust washer. Fit parking brake cam lever complete with pivot pin. Fit pivot pin bushing and snap ring. Fit piston sealing ring into caliper cylinder. Screw piston into cylinder until fully seated. Align piston slot so it is opposite bleed connection. Refit dust boot.

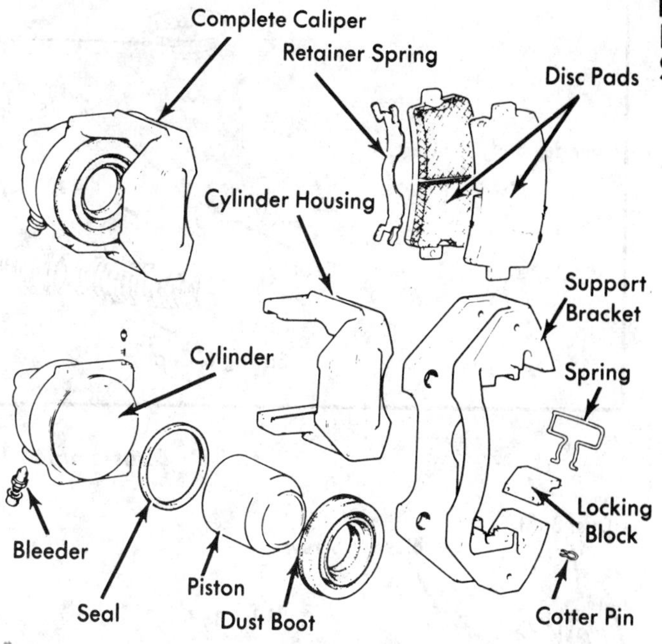

Fig. 6 Front Brake Caliper Assembly for 124 Models

REAR WHEEL CYLINDER

Disassembly – Remove boots, then remove pistons, seal rings, backing washers and reaction spring. Take out bleeder valve.

Inspection – Clean and dry all parts and inspect for excessive wear or damage. Light damage may be removed by honing; make sure bore size is not altered. Replace all rubber components at each overhaul.

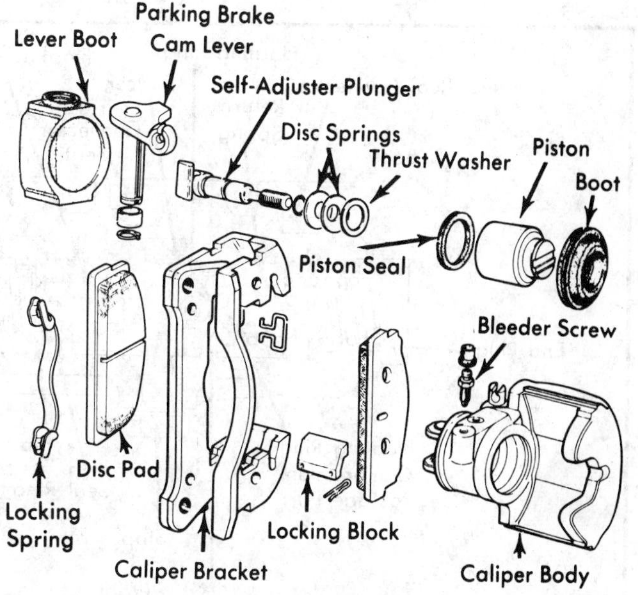

Fig. 7 Exploded View of Rear Brake Caliper for 124 Models

FIAT (Cont.)

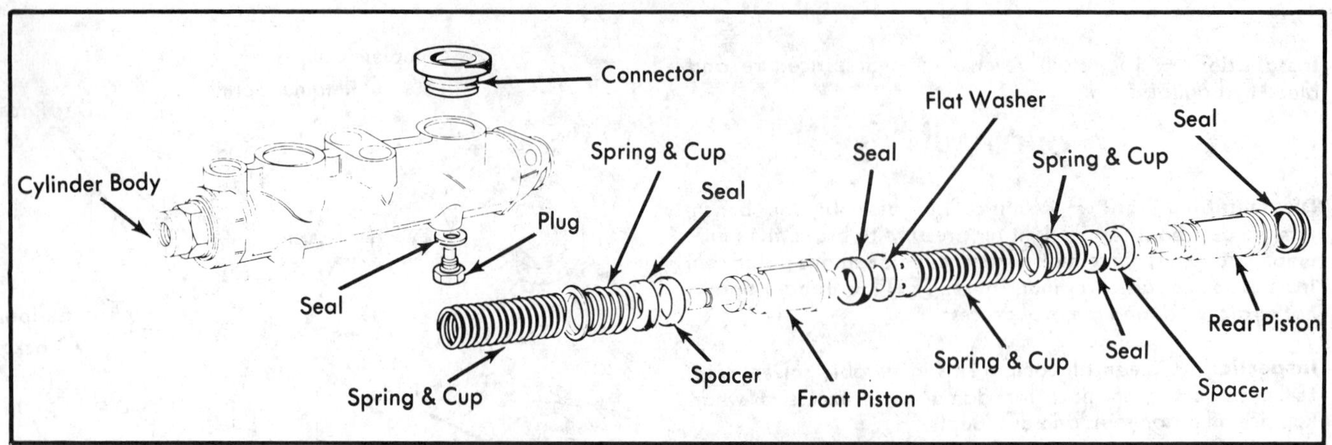

Fig. 8 Disassembled View of X1/9 Master Cylinder

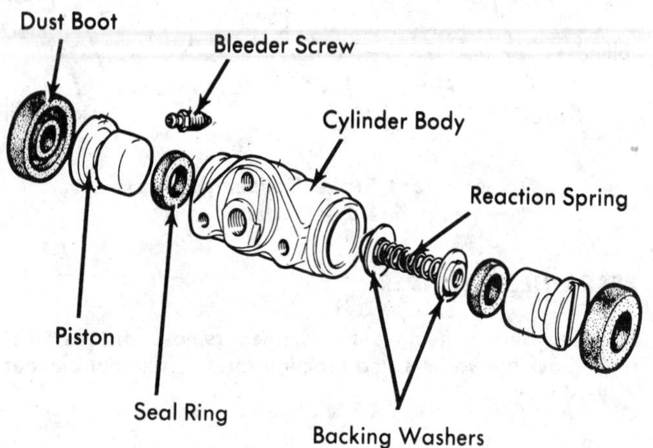

Fig. 9 Fiat Rear Wheel Cylinder Assembly

Reassembly – To reassemble, reverse disassembly procedure and note the following: Lightly coat all parts with brake fluid when assembling to prevent damage. Once assembled, move pistons to ensure they slide freely in cylinder bore.

MASTER CYLINDER

Disassembly – Separate fluid inlet union from master cylinder. Disengage boot from cylinder body. Back out set screws and end plug (if equipped). Remove the following components: Piston assemblies, return springs, cups, seal rings, and spacers.

Inspection – Clean and thoroughly dry all parts, then inspect for wear or damage. Light scoring may be removed by honing, make sure honing does not alter size of cylinder diameter. Replace all rubber pieces each time overhaul is performed.

Reassembly – To reassemble, reverse disassembly procedure and lightly coat all components with brake fluid before reassembly.

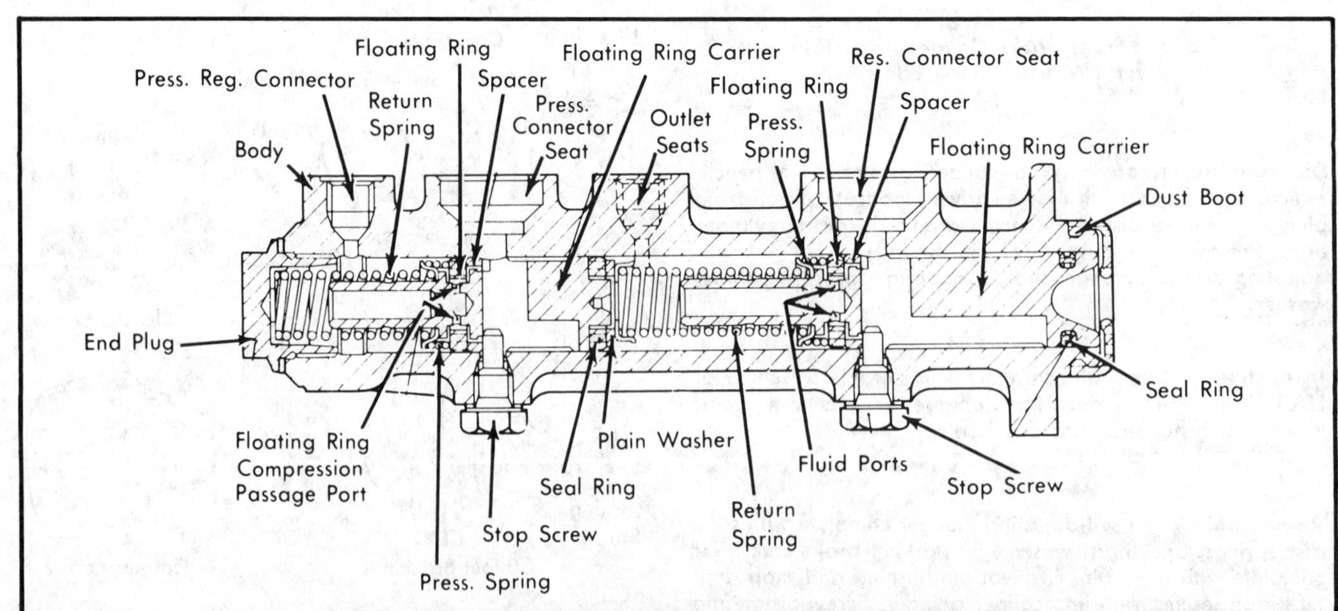

Fig. 10 Sectional View of Master Cylinder Assembly for 128 models

FIAT (Cont.)

BRAKE DRUM SPECIFICATIONS				
Application	Drum Diameter	Original Diameter	Maximum Refinish Diameter	Discard Diameter
128 Rear (Exc. X1/9)	7.3 (185)	7.293-7.304 (185.2-185.5)	7.325 (186)	7.355 (186.6)
131 Rear	9.0 (228.6)	8.988-9.000 (228.3-228.6)	9.03 (229.4)	9.055 (230)

BRAKE SYSTEM SPECIFICATIONS				
Application	Drum Diam. In. (mm)	Wheel Cylinder Diameter Front In. (mm)	Wheel Cylinder Diameter Rear In. (mm)	Master Cylinder Diameter In. (mm)
128 (Exc. X1/9	7.30① (185)	1.89② (48)	.750 (19.05)	.750 (19.05)
124 & X1/9	.....	1.89② (48)	1.34③ (34)	.750 (19.05)
131	9.00① (228.6)	1.89② (48)	.874 (22.2)	.750 (19.05)

① — Rear.
② — Caliper Bore Diameter.
③ — Rear Caliper Bore Diameter.

DISC BRAKE ROTOR SPECIFICATIONS						
Application	Disc Diameter In. (mm)	Lateral Runout In. (mm)	Parallelism In. (mm)	Original Thickness In. (mm)	Minimum Refinish Thickness In. (mm)	Discard Thickness In. (mm)
All Models	8.937 (227)	.0059 (.15)	.0019① (.05)	.392-.400 (9.95-10.2)	.368② (9.35)	.354 (9.0)

① — 128 3P Only.
② — 124 Rear is .372" (9.45 mm).

HONDA

Civic
Civic CVCC
Accord

DESCRIPTION

Brake system is hydraulically actuated, using a tandem master cylinder and a power brake booster unit. On Civic models and Civic CVCC sedan models, front brakes are dual piston floating caliper type. CVCC station wagon models and Accord models utilize single piston front disc brakes. All models use leading-trailing shoe/drum type rear brakes actuated by a dual piston wheel cylinder. Parking brake is cable and lever operated, actuating shoes of rear brake assemblies. All models use proportioning valve arrangements to differentiate pressure to rear wheels. All vehicles are equipped with a brake warning light that indicates hydraulic pressure loss and when parking brake is engaged.

ADJUSTMENT

PEDAL FREE PLAY

Brake pedal free play is distance pedal travels from pedal stop (brake light switch) before push rod contacts vacuum booster. Adjust pedal free play to .039-.196" (1-5 mm), measured at pedal pad, by adjusting brake light switch.

FRONT DISC BRAKE PADS

Front disc brakes are self-adjusting, therefore, no adjustment in service is required.

REAR BRAKE SHOES

With parking brake released, depress brake pedal two or three times and release. Turn adjuster on backing plate clockwise until wheel no longer turns. Back off adjuster two clicks and ensure wheel rotates freely. If brakes are dragging, back off one additional click.

PARKING BRAKE

With rear brakes adjusted, pull parking brake lever to check operation. Rear wheels should be locked when lever is pulled one to five notches on ratchet. Adjustment is made at equalizer located between rear lower control arms.

HYDRAULIC SYSTEM BLEEDING

1) Attach a bleed tube to cylinder bleed screw and immerse opposite end of tube in a container partially filled with brake fluid.

2) Pump pedal several times. Hold steady pressure on pedal. Open bleed screw. Allow air to escape into container. Close bleed screw with pedal still depressed. Let pedal return unassisted.

3) Repeat procedure on remaining brake cylinders until all air is bled from system. Bleeding sequence is left front, right rear, right front, right rear.

REMOVAL & INSTALLATION

FRONT DISC BRAKE PADS

Removal; Civic & CVCC Sedan – Raise and support front of vehicle; remove front wheels. Remove pin retaining clip, retaining pins and springs. Note that springs are not interchangeable, reference mark for reassembly. Remove disc pads and shims from one side. DO NOT remove pads from both sides at one time.

Installation – Clean exposed portions of caliper pistons and cavity. Manually seat caliper pistons into cylinders. Check disc pad thickness, if less than .060" (1.5 mm), replace with new lining. Install pads, shims (index arrow facing up), pad springs, and retaining pins. Secure retaining pin with clips.

Removal; CVCC Station Wagon – Raise and support front of vehicle; remove front wheels. Remove pad shield. Take off pad retainer clips. Drive out retaining pins and pull pads from caliper housing.

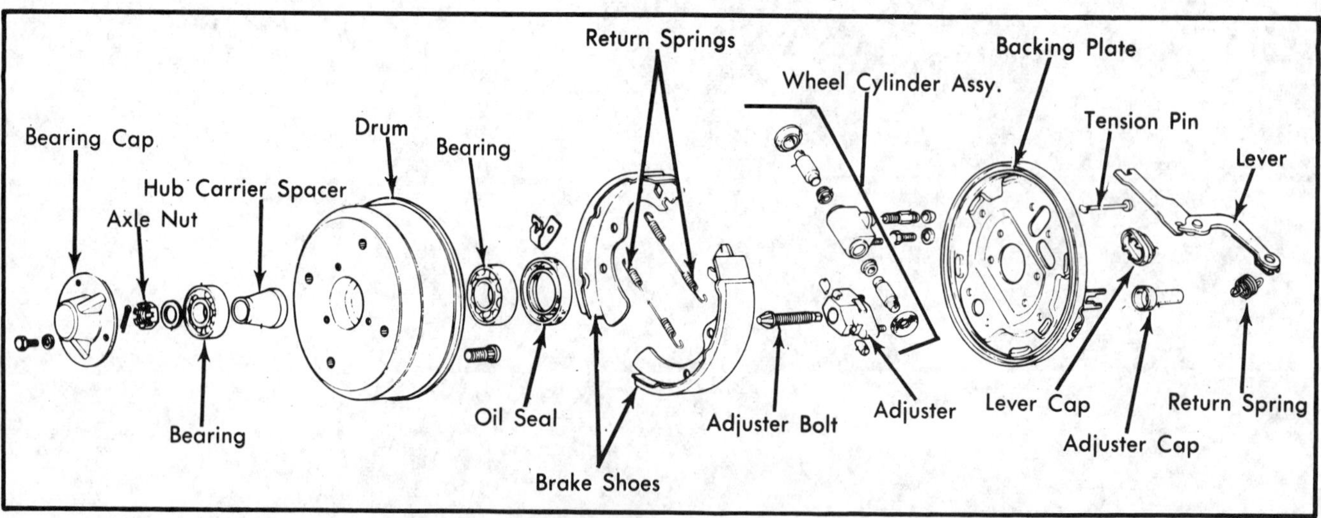

Fig. 1 Honda Rear Drum Brake Assembly – Civic Shown – Others Similar

HONDA (Cont.)

Installation – To install, reverse removal procedure and note: Make sure all rust has been removed from brake pad retaining pins. Inspect brake pad thickness. If pads are worn more than .060" (1.5 mm), replace.

Removal; Accord – Raise and support front of vehicle. Remove wheel. Using a pair of pliers, remove spring clips. Pull off top and bottom side plates. Lift off caliper and suspend out of way. Remove disc pad anti-rattle clip and slide off pads.

Installation – To install, reverse removal procedure and note: Clean exposed areas of caliper. Check disc pad thickness, if less than .060" (1.5 mm), replace with new lining.

FRONT DISC BRAKE CALIPER

Removal; Civic & CVCC Sedan – Raise and support front of vehicle. Remove front wheels. Disconnect hydraulic line at caliper, remove bolts retaining caliper to steering knuckle. Lift off caliper assembly.

Installation – Reverse removal procedure and bleed hydraulic system.

Removal; CVCC Station Wagon – Raise vehicle and remove disc pads as previously outlined. Disconnect and plug brake fluid line. Remove caliper mounting bolt and lift off vehicle.

Installation – To install, reverse removal procedure and bleed brake system.

Removal; Accord – Raise and suitably support front of vehicle. Remove wheel. Disconnect and plug brake lines. Remove spring pins and caliper side plate covers. Pull off caliper cylinder. Mounting bracket can now be removed if necessary.

Installation – To install, reverse removal procedure and bleed brake system.

DISC BRAKE ROTOR

Removal – 1) Raise and support front of vehicle; remove front wheel. Before continuing removal procedure, check rotor runout and compare to specifications. Remove spindle nut and caliper assembly.

NOTE – *Do not allow caliper to hang by brake line.*

2) Using a slide hammer with hub puller attachment, remove hub and rotor assembly. Index mark hub and rotor, then remove bolts and separate.

NOTE – *Since removing hub and rotor assembly involves use of a slide hammer and subjects wheel bearings to severe loads, it is suggested that both inner and outer wheel bearings be replaced each time hub and rotor assembly is removed.*

Installation – Reverse removal procedure, tighten rotor-to-hub bolts evenly, and bleed hydraulic system if necessary.

REAR BRAKE DRUM

Removal – Raise and support rear of vehicle and remove rear wheels. Remove bearing retaining cap and rear axle nut, then remove brake drum. **NOTE** – *If drum is difficult to remove, use a slide hammer with a hub puller attachment.*

Installation – Reverse removal procedure and tighten axle nut.

REAR BRAKE SHOES

NOTE – *All models have same basic brake system design; however, there may be some minor differences.*

Removal – With rear brake drum removed, remove tension pin clips and brake shoe return springs, and remove brake shoes.

Installation – 1) Reverse removal procedure and note the following: Upper and lower return springs are not interchangeable.

2) On Civic models, upper spring is identified by tight bends on each end and is designed so spring coils are located on outside of shoes when installed. Lower springs are designed so spring coils ride inside of shoes.

3) On all other models, 2 upper return springs are used to support shoes.

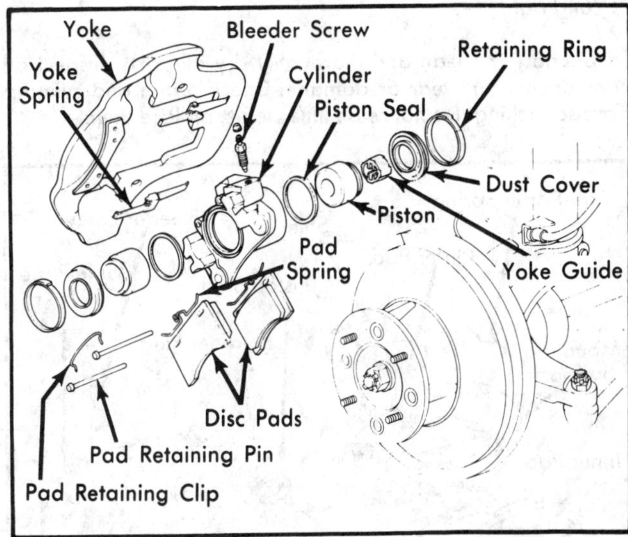

Fig. 2 Disc Brake Assembly for Civic and CVCC Sedan

REAR BRAKE WHEEL CYLINDER

Removal – With rear brake drum and brake shoes removed, disconnect hydraulic line from wheel cylinder at rear of backing plate. Remove retaining nuts and wheel cylinder assembly.

Installation – Reverse removal procedure, tighten retaining nuts, and bleed hydraulic system.

HONDA (Cont.)

MASTER CYLINDER

Removal – Disconnect hydraulic lines at master cylinder, remove retaining nuts, and remove master cylinder from power brake unit.

Installation – Reverse removal procedure and bleed hydraulic system.

POWER BRAKE UNIT

Removal – Disconnect vacuum hose at power brake unit, and hydraulic lines at master cylinder. Remove clevis pin retaining power brake unit push rod to brake pedal, and bolts attaching power unit to firewall, then remove power brake unit and master cylinder as an assembly.

Installation – Reverse removal procedure, tighten all nuts and bolts, and bleed hydraulic system.

OVERHAUL

DISC BRAKE CALIPER

Disassembly; Civic & CVCC Sedan – Holding caliper assembly in hands, press caliper down to compress piston. Keep pistons compressed and lift up on caliper removing yoke. Remove yoke return springs. Using light air pressure, force out pistons. Remove seals from cylinder bore grooves being careful not to scratch bore. **NOTE** – *Calipers are marked left "L" and right "R".*

Inspection – Clean and thoroughly dry all parts. Inspect all components for wear or damage. Check piston and cylinder bore scratching. Do not reuse inner seals, replace them.

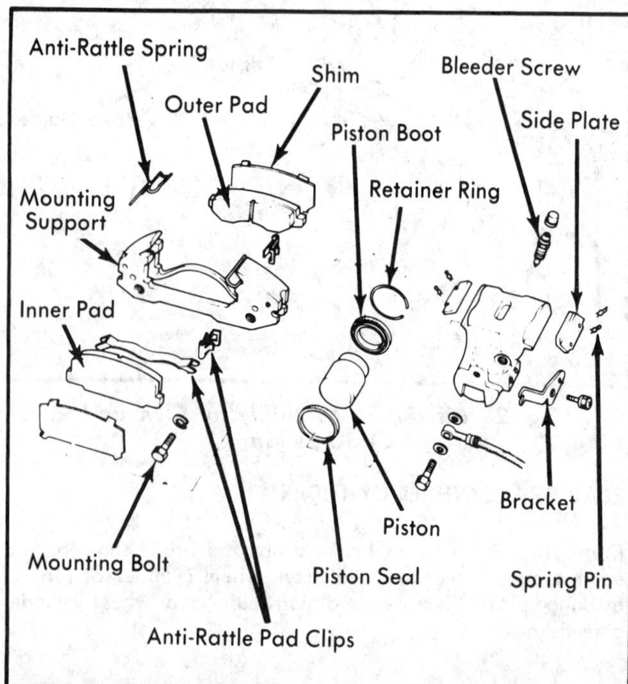

Fig. 3 Exploded View of Accord Disc Brake Assembly

Reassembly – 1) Install piston seals into grooves in cylinder. Lubricate pistons with brake fluid and install into cylinder. Install yoke guide into inboard piston. Hold yoke with retaining pin bracket facing up, and install yoke springs so long thin portion of spring is on upper side.

2) Hold yoke with retaining pin bracket facing up and to left. Place cylinder so that inlet port is facing up and to right. Slide yoke over cylinder. When yoke springs contact cylinder sliding surface, push down firmly and slide yoke to left until securely engaged with cylinder. Install disc pads, springs, pins and retainer.

Disassembly; CVCC Station Wagon – Remove caliper bridge bolt and carefully separate inner caliper with piston from torque plate and outer caliper. Remove rubber bushing insert from inner caliper housing. Take out retainer ring and wiper seal. Remove snap ring and dust seal, then force from cylinder. Using a pointed, but not sharp tool, remove "O" ring seal.

Inspection – Clean all components in brake fluid and inspect for excessive damage or wear. Replace all rubber parts. Look inside cylinder bore for signs of scoring or rough surfaces. Check outer caliper for cracks or metal fatigue.

Reassembly – Reverse disassembly procedure and note: Lightly grease shafts of torque plate. Lightly lubricate all internal components with brake fluid before reassembly. Make sure "O" ring seal is not twisted in cylinder groove.

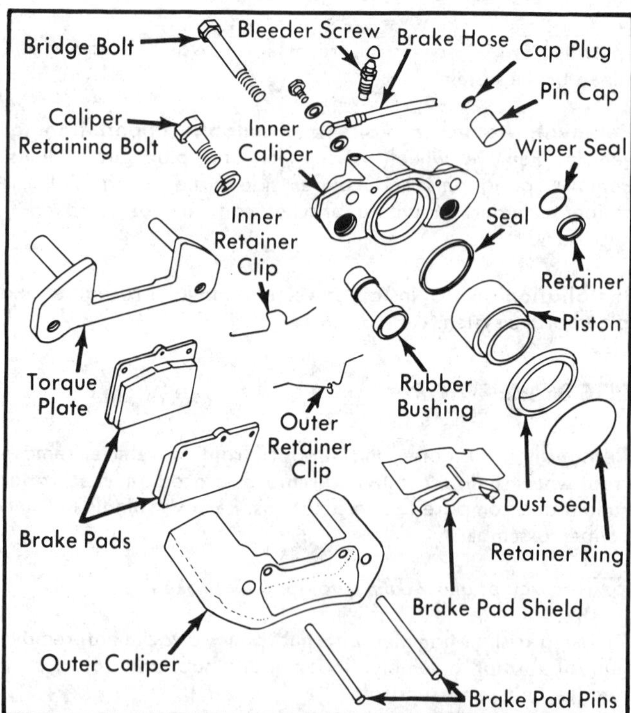

Fig. 4 Exploded View of CVCC Station Wagon Disc Brakes

Disassembly; Accord – Remove snap ring retainer and piston boot. Apply light air pressure to caliper through brake fluid inlet port. Using a pointed tool, remove piston seal.

Inspection – Examine cylinder piston and bore for scoring, rough spots or excessive wear. Replace all rubber components.

HONDA (Cont.)

Reassembly – Reverse disassembly procedure and note: Make sure seal is properly fitted to cylinder groove.

REAR WHEEL CYLINDER

Disassembly – Remove dust seals and pistons. Remove cylinder cups from pistons. If necessary, remove bleeder screw.

Cleaning & Inspection – Clean and dry all parts and inspect for wear or damage; replace parts as necessary. Check cylinder bore-to-piston clearance; if clearance exceeds .005", replace piston or cylinder as necessary.

Reassembly – Coat cylinder walls, pistons, and cups with brake fluid and install into cylinder bore. **NOTE** – *Install cups on pistons so that lips of cups face center of cylinder.* Install dust covers making sure lips engage grooves on cylinder body.

MASTER CYLINDER

NOTE – *Accord and Civic models have some minor external modifications that make physical appearance different. Overhaul Procedures are same as for earlier models.*

Disassembly – Remove reservoir caps and floats and drain brake fluid. Loosen retaining clamps and remove reservoirs. Remove primary piston stop bolt, retaining clip, and washer, then remove primary piston. Hold a finger over stop bolt hole, apply compressed air to secondary outlet, and remove secondary piston. Remove two union caps, washers, check valves, and springs.

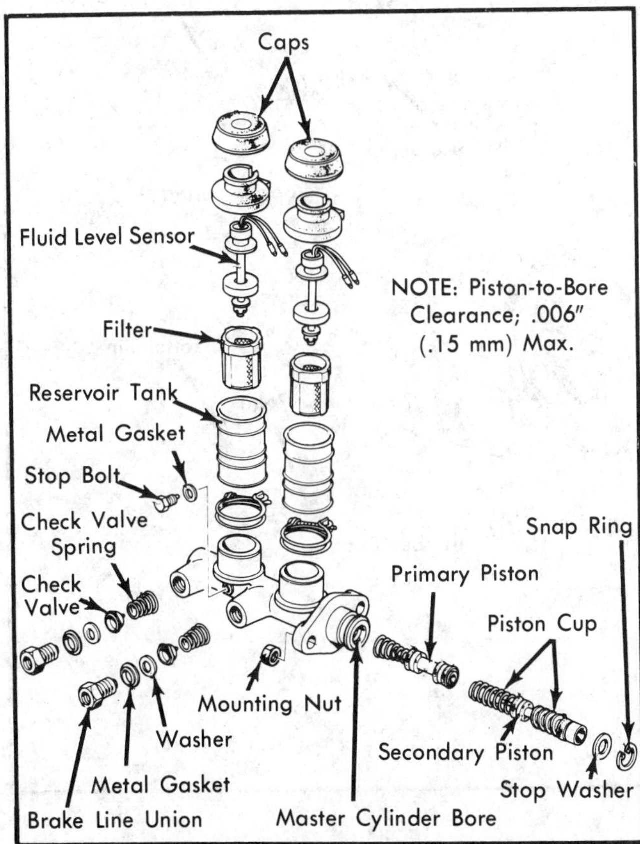

Fig. 5 Exploded View of Honda Accord Master Cylinder Assembly – Others Similar

Cleaning & Inspection – Clean and dry all parts and inspect for wear or damage. Check clearance between master cylinder bore and pistons; if greater than .005", replace pistons or cylinder assembly as required. Check for clogged orifices in pistons and cylinder. **NOTE** – *Manufacturer recommends replacing piston cups and check valves whenever cylinder has been disassembled.*

Reassembly – Reverse disassembly procedure and note the following: Coat all parts with brake fluid when assembling. When installing pistons, push in while rotating to prevent damaging cups.

POWER BOOSTER UNIT

Disassembly – 1) Separate master cylinder from booster assembly, but leave retaining plate attached to booster shell. Remove spring clip and booster shell retaining tab, then separate push rod from master cylinder.

2) Place booster assembly in vise. Index-mark shell halves and separate halves with suitable tool. Turn tool clockwise, noting that shell is spring-loaded. Take booster from vise and remove master retaining plate, check valve, seal retainer and seal.

3) Remove booster push rod and boot. Separate housing from diaphragm and piston. Take off seal retainer, seal (note position), and bushing. Disengage snap ring, spring, and seat, then pull out diaphragm.

4) Remove retaining cover, push rod actuator, retaining plate, center seat, and spring washer (note position). Push piston from diaphragm plate. Extract "O" ring from inside piston. Remove filter retaining clip, then take off filter, push plate, spring, and poppet valve.

Inspection – Thoroughly wash all components in alcohol and blow dry with compressed air. Check all parts for wear and carefully look at booster plate and piston for scratches.

Reassembly – Reverse disassembly and note the following: Coat lip of seal with silicon before installing into booster housing. Be sure bushing fully seats into position. Make sure piston "O" ring has a perfect fit. Install reaction plates with curved side facing up. Lightly coat piston with silicon before installing in booster housing. After fitting master cylinder push rod, measure distance between booster shell and end of push rod. Clearance should be .024" (.6 mm).

PROPORTIONING VALVES

NOTE – *Some models use two proportioning valves. Proportioning valves are NOT to be overhauled; if determined defective, replace.*

TIGHTENING SPECIFICATIONS

Application	Ft. Lbs. (mkg)
Caliper Mounting Bolts	
Civic & CVCC Sedan	29 (4.0)
CVCC Wagon	63 (8.5)
Accord	58-66 (8.0-9.0)
Rear Axle Nut	
Except Accord	83 (11.5)
Master Cylinder Nuts	9 (1.2)

HONDA (Cont.)

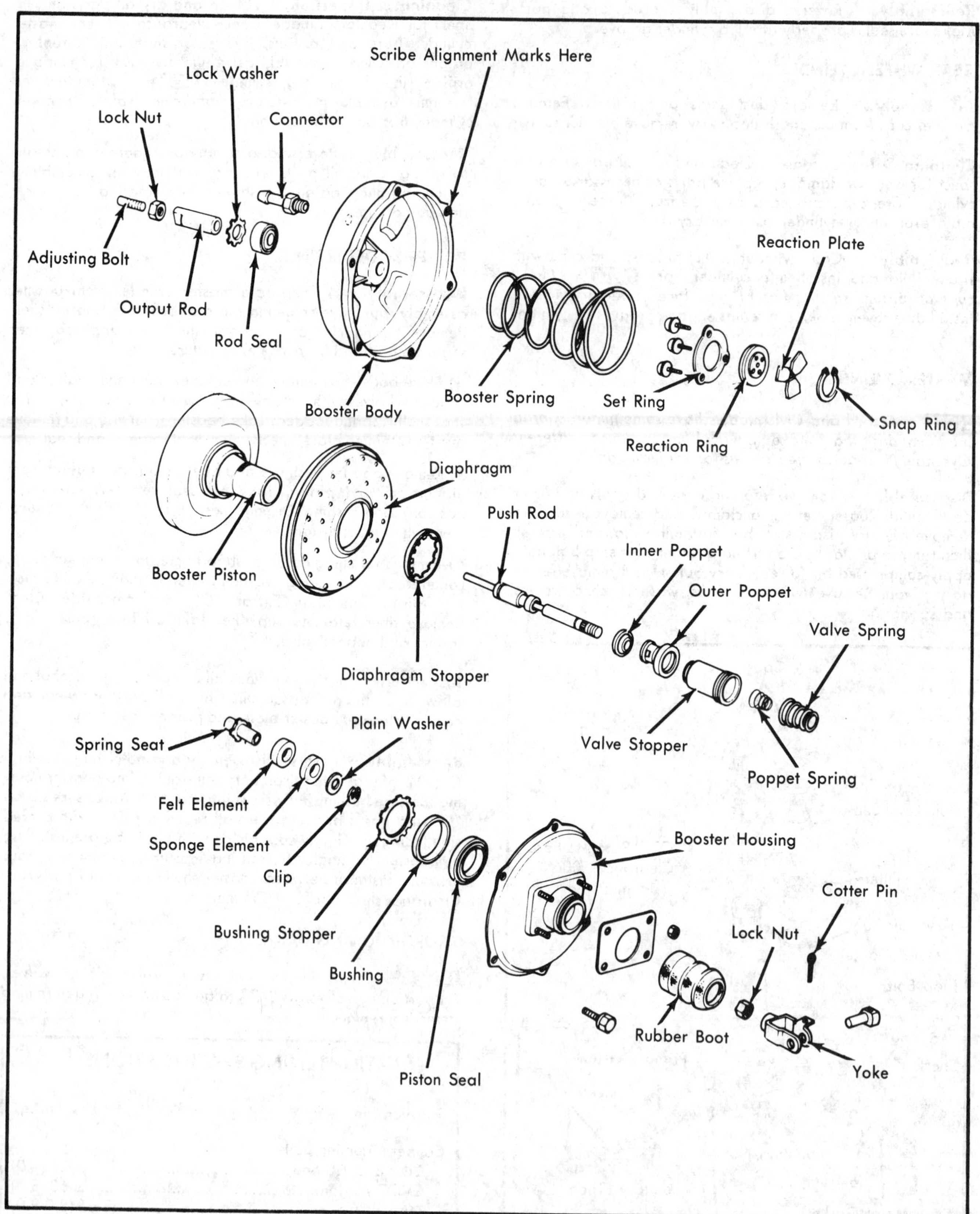

Fig. 6 Exploded View of Honda Accord Power Booster Assembly — Other Models Similar

HONDA (Cont.)

DISC BRAKE ROTOR SPECIFICATIONS

Application	Disc Diameter In. (mm)	Lateral Runout In. (mm)	Parallelism In. (mm)	Original Thickness In. (mm)	Minimum Refinish Thickness In. (mm)	Discard Thickness In. (mm)
Civic	.....	.006 (1.5)	.003 (.07)	.378 (9.6)	.354 (9.0)	.343 (8.7)
CVCC						
Sedan	.....	.006 (.15)	.003 (.07)	.378 (9.6)	.354 (9.0)	.343 (8.7)
Sta. Wgn.	.....	.006 (.15)	.003 (.07)	.473 (12.0)	.449 (11.4)	.437 (11.1)
Accord	.....	.006 (.15)	①	.473 (12.0)	.449 (11.4)	.437 (11.1)

① — Max. difference between measurements .006" (.15 mm).

BRAKE DRUM SPECIFICATIONS

Application	Drum Diameter In. (mm)	Original Diameter In. (mm)	Maximum Refinish Diameter In. (mm)	Discard Diameter In. (mm)
Civic	7.08 (180)	7.08 (180)	7.13 (181)	7.15 (181.5)
CVCC Sedan	7.08 (180)	7.08 (180)	7.13 (181)	7.15 (181.5)
CVCC St.Wgn	7.87 (200)	7.87 (200)	7.91 (201)	7.93 (201.5)
Accord	7.08 (180)	7.01 (180)	7.13 (181)	7.15 (181.5)

JAGUAR

XJ6
XJ12
XJS

DESCRIPTION

Brake system utilizes four wheel disc brakes and a tandem master cylinder connected to a power unit (servo). Front calipers are four piston type. Master cylinder supplies hydraulic pressure to two individual brake circuits (front and rear). A combination valve is used to indicate a pressure difference between brake circuits. Front calipers are mounted on stub axle carriers and rear calipers are mounted inboard on differential housing. Rear rotors are connected to differential drive shaft flanges. Each front caliper consists of four pistons (two inboard and two outboard) and each rear caliper has two opposing pistons. Parking brake consists of independent, lever operated, disc pads mounted on rear calipers. Parking brake pads operate on rear brake rotor.

ADJUSTMENT

DISC BRAKE PADS

Due to self-adjusting feature of calipers, no adjustment in service is required.

PARKING BRAKE

Parking Brake Caliper – Caliper is self-adjusting to compensate for pad wear, therefore, no adjustment is required.

Parking Brake Cable – On XJS models only, pull back carpet near rear of drivers seat for access. Put caliper levers in fully released position. Loosen lock nut and turn adjusting nut until there is a slight amount of slack in cable. Operate brake several times to ensure proper braking has been achieved.

HYDRAULIC SYSTEM BLEEDING

1) Keep hydraulic fluid reservoirs filled with clean brake fluid during bleeding operation. Attach a bleed tube to bleeder screw on left-rear brake caliper, and immerse opposite end of tube in a container partially filled with brake fluid.

2) Run engine at idle speed. Loosen bleeder screw, operate pedal through full stroke until discharged fluid is free of air bubbles, close bleeder screw. Repeat procedure on right-rear caliper and front calipers.

COMBINATION VALVE

Operation Testing – 1) Put gear selector lever in Park. When ignition switch is on and parking brake is applied, brake warning light should be on. Run engine at idle. Release parking brake. Apply pedal hard.

2) Open any bleeder screw. Brake warning light should light. Close bleeder, then release and reapply brake pedal. Brake warning light should go out. Carefully repeat procedure if warning light will not go on. Replace component as necessary.

REMOVAL & INSTALLATION

DISC PADS (SERVICE BRAKES)

Removal – Raise vehicle and remove wheels. Remove pin clips, pad retaining pins, anti-chatter springs (if equipped) and lining pads.

Installation – Draw out about half the brake fluid from reservoir(s). This will enable caliper pistons to be pushed back into cylinders without overflowing fluid. Lever pistons back, insert new pads, springs and replace retaining pins and clips. Check pads for freedom of movement within caliper. Check reservoirs for correct fluid level.

DISC PADS (PARKING BRAKE)

Removal & Installation – Parking brake calipers must be removed to replace disc pads. *See Parking Brake Caliper Removal & Installation.*

PARKING BRAKE CALIPER

Removal – 1) Raise and support vehicle. On XJS models only, adjust some slack into parking brake cable. Remove nuts and bolts attaching rear suspension mounting plate to rear suspension unit and remove plate from vehicle. Disconnect parking brake cable and return spring from caliper.

2) Remove caliper mounting bolts and release lever, then slide caliper around rotor and remove through hole left by suspension plate. To remove disc pads, remove nut and spring washer securing pads to pad carriers.

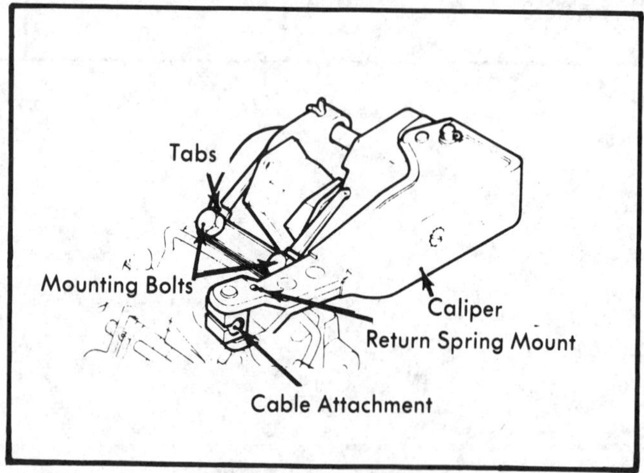

Fig. 1 Detail of Parking Brake Caliper

Installation – 1) To install, reverse removal procedure and note the following: On XJ6 and XJ12 models only, adjust caliper if new pads have been installed or if caliper has been overhauled. Adjust by holding one pad carrier stationary and turning remaining carrier until there is a clearance of .75" (19.0 mm) between disc pad surfaces.

2) On all models, operate caliper actuating lever until adjuster ratchet ceases to click. Install remaining components and check operation of brakes.

JAGUAR (Cont.)

SERVICE BRAKE CALIPER

NOTE — *Do not separate caliper halves for repair. If a leak exists between halves, replace caliper.*

Removal (Front) — Raise vehicle and remove wheels. Disconnect caliper fluid line and plug. Discard locking wire from mounting bolts. Remove caliper.

NOTE — *Check position and number of shims between steering arm and caliper; replace shims in order.*

Installation — **1)** Place caliper in position. If original caliper is being reinstalled, refit shims. Install mounting bolts and safety wire. Bleed brakes.

2) If new caliper is being used, check gap between caliper abutment and rotor face. Gap should be no more than .010" (.25 mm). Gap on upper and lower abutment on SAME SIDE must be equal. If rotor is not centered, remove one caliper mounting bolt and add or subtract shims as necessary. Repeat procedure on other bolt.

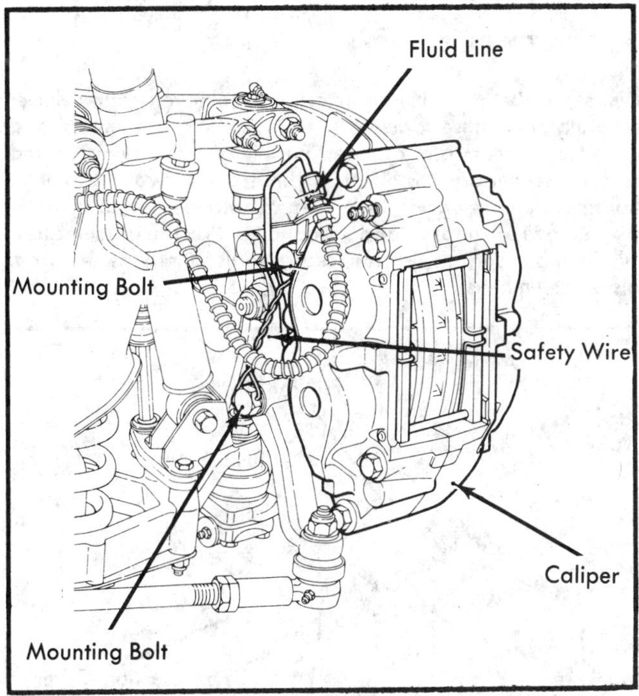

Fig. 2 Components to Remove to Take Off Caliper

Removal (Rear) — Remove parking brake caliper as previously outlined. Disconnect and plug hydraulic line from caliper mounting bolts and lock wire. Slide caliper around brake rotor and out hole left by suspension plate.

Installation — Place caliper in position, install shims if equipped, and secure bolts. Torque bolts to 49-55 ft. lbs. Check rotor for center between caliper. If necessary, adjust shims between drive flange and rotor. If shim adjustment is performed, rear wheel camber must be checked. See *Jaguar Rear Wheel Camber Adjustment in WHEEL ALIGNMENT Section*. Complete installation by reversing removal procedures.

BRAKE ROTOR

Removal (Front) — Remove brake caliper disc pads as previously outlined. Remove hub-to-rotor attaching bolts and washers. Remove hub dust cap, then remove cotter pin, axle nut and washer from axle stub and remove hub. Insert a punch through access hole in splash shield and lightly tap on it to free water deflector. Remove rotor assembly by sliding it from caliper jaws and over axle stub.

Installation (Front) — To install, reverse removal procedure and note the following: Pack hub and wheel bearings with suitable grease and adjust wheel bearing end play. *See Wheel Bearing Adjustment in WHEEL ALIGNMENT Section.*

Removal (Rear) — Remove brake caliper as previously outlined. Disconnect shock absorber from lower mount and remove radius arm locking bolt and lower control arm outer grease fitting. Place stands under hub assembly and slide radius arm from anchor point. Loosen clamp and slide boot away from inner universal joint, then remove universal joint-to-rotor attaching bolts and separate universal joint from rotor.

NOTE — *DO NOT move shims mounted between drive axle flange and brake rotor.*

Installation — To install, reverse removal procedure and note the following: Ensure caliper is centered on rotor; adjust by adding or removing shims between rotor and drive axle flange. Caliper is centered when gap is not more than .010" (.25 mm). Check rear wheel camber and adjust if necessary. *See Camber Adjustment in WHEEL ALIGNMENT Section.*

MASTER CYLINDER

Removal & Installation — Disconnect electrical wires from master cylinder reservoir. Remove filter. Disconnect clips mounted to cylinder. Separate all hydraulic lines and plug openings. Remove nuts mounting cylinder to power unit studs. To install, reverse removal procedure.

POWER BRAKE UNIT (SERVO)

Removal — **1)** On XJ6 and XJ12, disconnect battery and remove air cleaner. On all models, disconnect and plug master cylinder lines. Pry vacuum hose from power unit. Remove fluid reservoir.

2) On XJS models, swing pedal box bracket into vertical position. Remove 4 pedal box mounting nuts. Slide off master cylinder. Lift off pedal box and power unit, then separate.

3) On XJ6 and XJ12 models, disconnect choke cable clips. Remove bolt securing upper pedal box. Remove reservoir mounting bracket. Remove stop light switch. Remove 6 bolts

JAGUAR (Cont.)

attaching pedal box. Remove brake pedal pad. Withdraw pedal box, master cylinder, and power brake unit as an assembly, then separate.

Installation – To install, reverse removal procedure and bleed hydraulic system.

COMBINATION VALVE

Removal & Installation – Disconnect battery. Remove air cleaner. Disconnect electrical lead. Separate fluid lines and plug openings. Remove mounting nut and bolt. To install, reverse removal procedure and bleed brakes.

OVERHAUL

BRAKE CALIPER

NOTE – *DO NOT separate caliper halves for service; pistons and seals may be changed without splitting caliper. If a leak is detected between caliper halves, replace caliper as a unit.*

Disassembly – With disc pads removed, install a suitable piston clamp to retain outboard piston(s), then apply compressed air to fluid inlet port and remove inboard piston(s). Pull dust seal from piston(s) and caliper grooves. Carefully remove piston seal from cylinder. **NOTE** – *Inboard piston(s) must be installed before outboard piston(s) can be removed.*

Cleaning & Inspection – Clean all parts in alcohol and inspect for wear or damage. Check cylinder bore and pistons for scratches, rust or corrosion; replace all damaged parts.

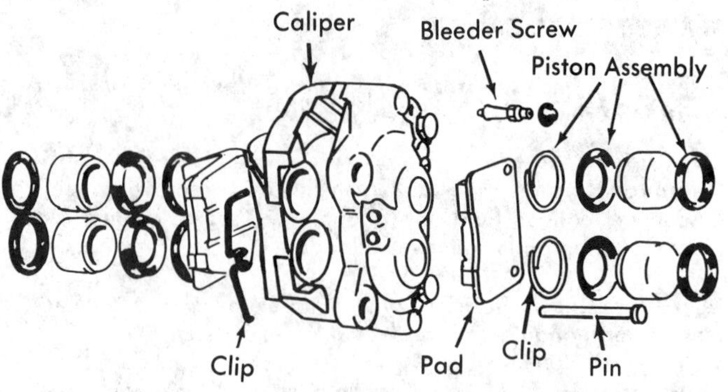

Fig. 3 Exploded View of Front Four Piston Caliper Assembly

Reassembly – Coat cylinder, piston and seal with brake fluid before installing. Place piston seal in bore. Install dust seal over cylinder groove and carefully insert piston through dust seal. Pull dust seal into groove in piston. Use piston clamp to press piston completely into cylinder. Repeat procedure for outer piston seal replacement. Install caliper as previously outlined.

MASTER CYLINDER

Disassembly – With master cylinder removed from vehicle, carefully pry hose adaptors from sealing grommets and grommets from master cylinder. Push in on primary piston and remove secondary piston stop pin from forward grommet housing. Remove spring lock, then tap flange end of cylinder to remove primary and secondary piston assemblies. Disassemble springs, spring seats, seals and washers from piston assemblies.

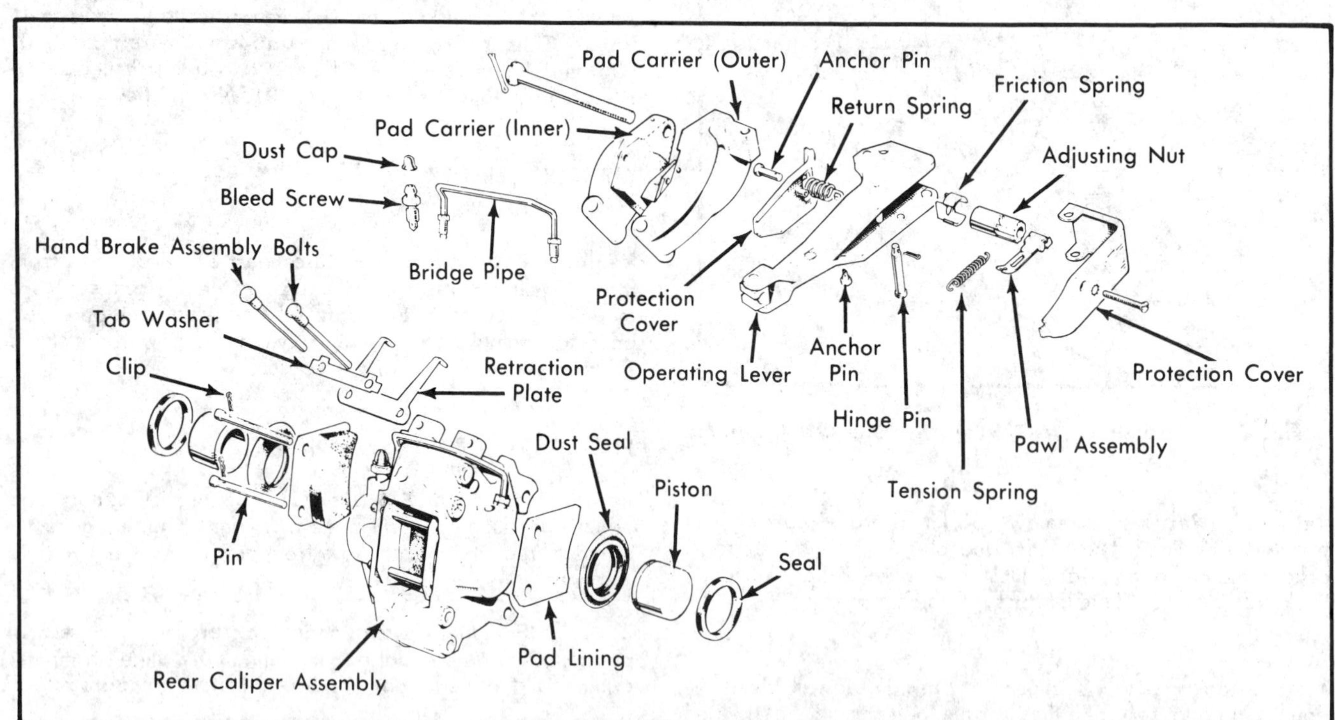

Fig. 4 Exploded View of Rear Brake Caliper with Detail of Parking Brake Assembly

JAGUAR (Cont.)

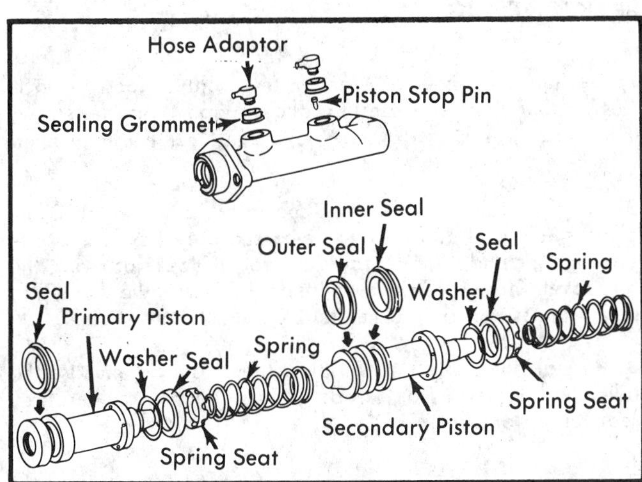

Fig. 5 Exploded View of Dual Piston Master Cylinder

Cleaning & Inspection – Clean all parts in alcohol and dry with a lint-free cloth. Inspect pistons and bore for wear, scores, or corrosion; replace damaged parts as necessary.

Reassembly – To reassemble, reverse disassembly procedure and note the following: Lubricate all parts with clean brake fluid. Install secondary piston inner seal with lip facing away from primary piston and install outer seal with lip facing primary piston. Install primary piston seal with lip facing away from spring lock. Install master cylinder and bleed brake system.

COMBINATION VALVE

NOTE – *Combination valve CANNOT be overhauled.*

POWER BRAKE UNIT (SERVO)

NOTE – *Power brake unit CANNOT be overhauled; if determined defective, replace entire unit.*

TIGHTENING SPECIFICATIONS

Application	Ft. Lbs. (mkg)
Pedal Box-to-Body	11-13 (1.5-1.8)
Caliper Mounting Bolts	
Front	50-60 (7.0-8.3)
Rear	49-55 (6.7-7.6)
Wheel Lug Nuts	40-60 (5.5-8.3)

DISC BRAKE ROTOR SPECIFICATIONS

Application	Disc Diameter In. (mm)	Lateral Runout In. (mm)	Parallelism In. (mm)	Original Thickness In. (mm)	Minimum Refinish Thickness In. (mm)	Discard Thickness In. (mm)
All Models						
Front	11.18 (284)	.004 (.1)	....	.950 (24.1)	....	....
Rear	10.38 (263.5)	.004 (.1)	....	.500 (12.7)	....	....

LANCIA

Lancia
Except Scorpion

DESCRIPTION

Brake system is hydraulically operated. System utilizes a tandem (dual piston) master cylinder and on some models, a power brake assist unit. Front and rear brakes are disc type. The brake system is fitted with an adjustable brake pressure limiter valve which regulates brake operating pressure on rear wheels. Parking brake is lever operated with cables acting on rear calipers. All models are equipped with brake wear limit indicator on front wheels. When brake lining reaches wear limit a warning light on instrument panel comes on.

ADJUSTMENT

PARKING BRAKE

Raise and support vehicle. Make sure brake system has no air trapped in lines. Apply parking brake three notches up from full released position. Loosen lock nut, turn adjuster rod until control cable is stretched and wheels are locked. Tighten lock nut. Check operation.

PRESSURE LIMITER

1) Raise and support vehicle. Leave vehicle in unloaded state (fuel tank empty, spare tire and jack assembly removed, no driver). Remove limiter dust cover. Loosen limiter mounting bolts. Twist limiter housing counterclockwise until there is .001" (.03 mm) clearance between control rod and limiter plunger.

2) Rotate limiter housing clockwise until feeler gauge contact is broken. Do not load control rod. Tighten mounting bolts and recheck clearance. Refit dust cover.

BRAKE BLEEDING

1) Begin work on either one of the front calipers. Attach bleeder tube to inner (closest to caliper support) bleeder screw. Immerse opposite end of tube in a container partially filled with brake fluid.

2) Pump pedal several times. Keep pressure on pedal. Open bleed screw and allow air to be forced out of system. Make sure that as pedal moves toward floor, it does not swing the full travel. Close bleed screw with pedal down. Allow pedal to return unassisted before next stroke.

3) Repeat procedure until all air is bled from system. Use the following sequence for bleeding: Front; either caliper first, rear; either one first.

REMOVAL & INSTALLATION

FRONT & REAR DISC BRAKE PADS

Removal – **1)** Remove wheels. Remove spring clips. Drive out component keeping pad carrier to caliper. Remove pad carrier then slip out disc pads. Do not lose mounting springs.

2) Check disc pads for wear. Replace pads if they have less than .039" (1 mm) of lining left. Always replace pads in sets.

NOTE – *Front caliper assemblies are fitted with pad wear warning devices. Unit must be replaced when pads are renewed.*

Installation – Thoroughly clean brake rotor. Completely seat pistons in cylinders. On rear calipers, pistons must be turned clockwise in cylinder while pushing to fully seated position. Fit new pads and spring clips. If old pads are being reinstalled, make sure they are put back in original position. Reverse removal procedure for remaining components.

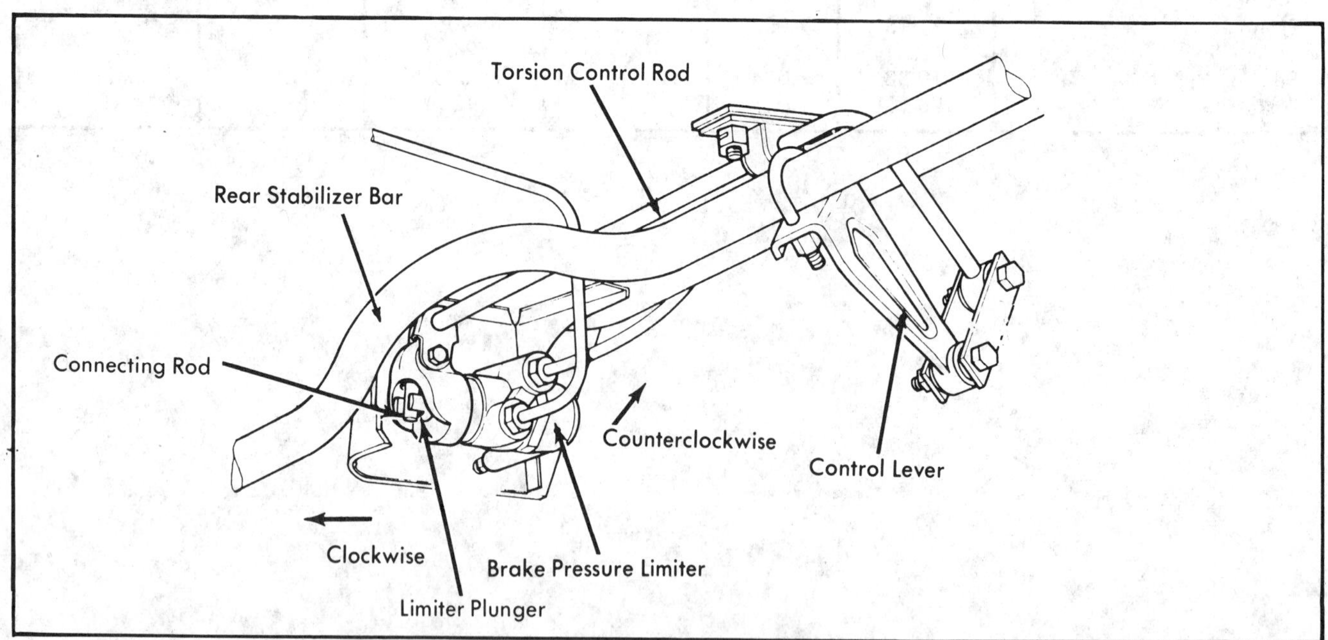

Fig. 1 Installed View from Under Vehicle Showing Adjustment Direction of Rear Brake Pressure Limiter

LANCIA (Cont.)

FRONT & REAR BRAKE CALIPER

Removal – Raise and support vehicle. Remove wheel. Disconnect hydraulic inlet lines at caliper cylinder. On rear calipers, disconnect parking brake from control lever. Pull out spring clips. Drive off retaining component and remove pad carrier. Disconnect electrical lead on front caliper. Remove caliper mounting bolts and slide assembly from mounting.

Installation – To install caliper assembly, reverse removal procedure and note: Bleed hydraulic system. Check parking brake operation.

FRONT & REAR ROTOR

Removal – Raise and support vehicle. Remove wheel. Remove caliper assembly, but do not disconnect hydraulic line; lay caliper out of way. Remove rotor mounting bolts and pull rotor off. It may be necessary to use a puller to free rotor before sliding it off vehicle.

Installation – To install rotor, reverse removal procedure and check runout. On front wheels, attach dial gauge to front strut. On rear wheels, attach dial gauge to support tool 88095768 (or equivalent). Clean rotor surface and set gauge .08" (2 mm) from outer diameter. Slowly turn rotor and record reading. Runout must not exceed .002" (.05 mm).

MASTER CYLINDER & POWER ASSIST UNIT (SERVO)

Removal – Disconnect battery. Disconnect electrical leads from master cylinder. Separate hydraulic lines and remove master cylinder from servo. Disconnect vacuum hose from power assist unit. Work under instrument panel and unhook brake pedal return spring. Remove operating rod from brake pedal. Remove servo from support by extracting mounting nuts and sliding servo off.

Installation – To install, reverse removal procedure and note: Adjust control rod length. Bleed hydraulic system.

PRESSURE LIMITER

Removal – Raise vehicle and place on safety stands. Remove top bolt connecting control rod to mounting (shackle support), then loosen bottom bolt. Remove torsion control rod clamp from underbody. Loosen hydraulic fittings. Separate pressure limiter and take off with control rod. Remove rubber cover from pressure limiter, take out bolt mounting plate to limiter and separate control rod from plate.

Installation – To install, reverse removal procedure and note: Adjust pressure limiter. Bleed hydraulic system.

PRESSURE LIMITER TORSION CONTROL ROD

Removal – Remove top bolt connecting control rod to shackle support. Remove torsion control rod clamp from underbody. Remove rubber cover from pressure limiter. Remove bolts keeping pressure limiter to bracket. Leave hydraulic lines connected. Lower control rod limiter, remove control rod and bracket from underbody.

Installation – To install, reverse removal procedure and adjust brake limiter.

OVERHAUL

FRONT DISC BRAKE CALIPER

Disassembly – 1) Completely clean outside of caliper. Fit caliper in vice. Remove pad carrier. Take off both bleeder screws. Slide off dust guard. Force compressed air into inner inlet port to remove piston from cylinder.

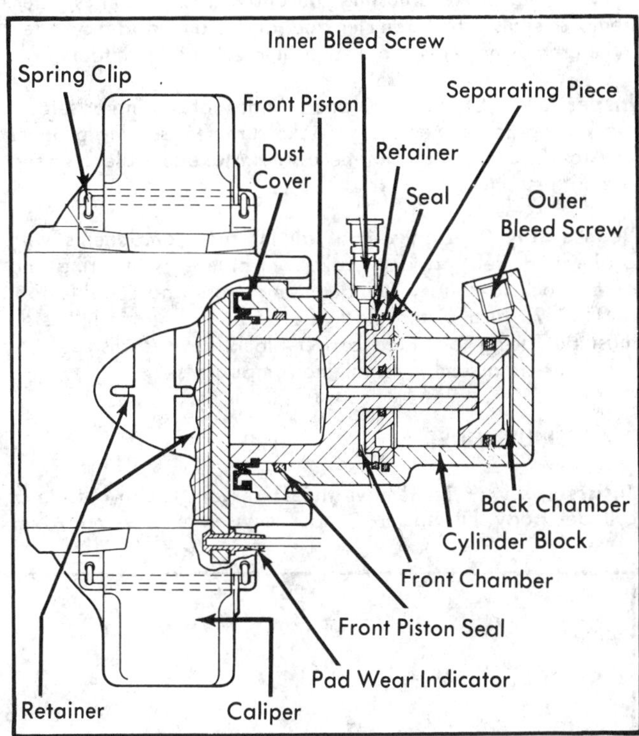

Fig. 2 Sectional View of Lancia Front Disc Brake Assembly

2) Take out front piston seal. Use a small diameter tool to lift edges and remove retainer. Access to retainer is gained through bleeder screw hole.

3) Refit piston to caliper. Again apply compressed air to inner inlet port this time removing front piston and separating piece. Force air pressure into outer bleeder screw and remove back piston. Remove seals from cylinder.

Inspection – Look at both pistons and replace if severely scored or pitted. Examine cylinder for signs of scoring, if excessively damaged, replace cylinder. Free any restriction in bleed screws.

Reassembly – Insert back piston and separating piece in cylinder. Fit retainer. Make sure retainer gap aligns with bleed hole. Refit cylinder to carrier. Reverse disassembly procedures for remaining components.

LANCIA (Cont.)

REAR DISC BRAKE CALIPER

Disassembly – 1) Thoroughly clean outer cylinder housing of grease before beginning disassembly. Fit caliper in vise. Remove pad carrier and retaining spring. Turn piston counterclockwise and separate dust shield. Apply air pressure to brake fluid inlet port and remove piston.

2) Remove snap ring from inside piston, then remove washer, bearing, self-adjuster and piston return spring. Take out parking brake snap ring and remove control lever, return spring, and drive block.

3) Take out brake adjusting rod and washers from cylinder. Remove seals from adjuster rod and from inside cylinder. When removing seals avoid scratching cylinder with tool.

Inspection – Check piston and cylinder for scoring or seizure marks, replace as necessary. Make sure seal seating grooves are not distorted, replace if necessary. Make sure bleed screws are not restricted.

Reassembly – Lightly coat all internal components with brake fluid. Refit parking brake control lever with spring and drive block to caliper cylinder using press and suitable tool 88053067. Turn piston clockwise and seat. Notch in piston must be facing top. Refit carrier block. Reverse disassembly procedure to assemble remaining components.

MASTER CYLINDER

Disassembly – 1) Remove fluid reservoir. Clean outside of cylinder body. Fit master cylinder to vise. Remove snap ring. Remove back piston assembly. Separate following components from piston:

- Washers
- Seals
- Guide bushing seal
- Piston guide bushing
- Floating spacer and piston seal
- Seal spring
- Spring caps and return spring

2) Back out piston stop screw. Remove front piston in assembled state. Separate following components from piston: *(Also, refer to Fig. 3)*

- Spring thrust washer
- Piston seals
- Seal spring
- Spring caps
- Piston return spring

Inspection – Check that all components slide freely in cylinder. Make sure both pistons and cylinders are free of score marks. Replace components if scoring is evident.

Reassembly – 1) Before reassembling pistons, lightly coat components with Castrol B.N.G. grease (or equivalent). Reassemble pistons in reverse of disassembly procedure. Make sure to replace all seals with new parts.

2) Fit front piston in master cylinder with groove aligning with threaded bore. Install stop screw and tighten. Check piston for free movement. Slide back piston into bore and fit snap ring. Fit grommets and install fluid reservoir.

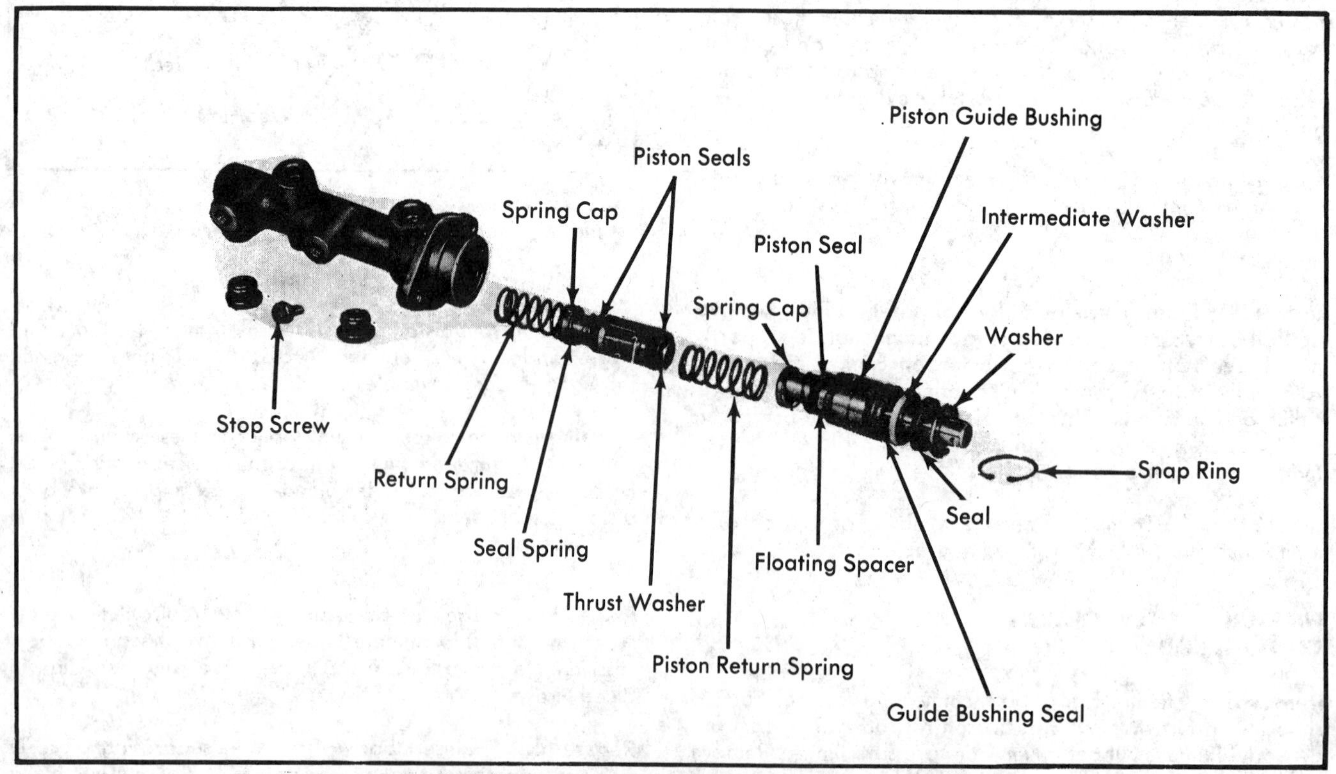

Fig. 3 Exploded View of Master Cylinder Internal Components. Primary and Secondary Pistons are Shown Removed, but Assembled

LUV

LUV

DESCRIPTION

Brake system is hydraulically actuated using a tandem master cylinder and a Master Vac power brake unit. Front brakes are single piston, floating disc type. Rear brakes are leading-trailing, shoe/drum type. Drum brakes are actuated by dual piston wheel cylinder. Parking brake is cable and lever operated, actuating shoes of rear drum.

ADJUSTMENT

PEDAL HEIGHT

Pedal height, measured from top of pedal pad to floor, should be 5.9-6.3". If adjustment is required, disconnect battery ground cable and stop lamp switch wiring harness. Remove stop lamp switch from bracket, then rotate master cylinder push rod until proper pedal height is obtained. Install stop lamp switch, then adjust clearance between switch housing (not actuating pin) and brake pedal tab to .02-.04". Tighten lock nuts and connect stop lamp switch wiring harness.

FRONT DISC BRAKE PADS

Disc brakes are self-adjusting

REAR BRAKE SHOES

Rear brakes have a self-adjusting mechanism. No in-service adjustment is required. Initial adjustment may be necessary after changing brake lining. Pull adjuster mechanism out of star. Rotate star until shoes just contact drum. Final adjustment will be accomplished with self-adjuster mechanism.

PARKING BRAKE

Apply parking brake two notches from fully released position. Loosen equalizer check nut and adjust front jam nut until a light to moderate drag is felt when rear wheels are rotated forward. Tighten nuts securely, release parking brake lever, and ensure no drag is present.

HYDRAULIC SYSTEM BLEEDING

NOTE — *Make sure engine is running while bleeding brakes. This will prevent damage to push rod.*

Attach a bleed tube to wheel cylinder bleeder screw and immerse opposite end of tube in a container partially filled with brake fluid. Open bleeder screw ¾ turn, depress pedal, close bleeder screw before bottom of pedal stroke, and allow pedal to return slowly. Continue operation until no air bubbles are seen in discharged fluid. Bleed wheel cylinder closest to master cylinder first, then repeat procedure at remaining cylinders, ending with cylinder furthest from master cylinder.

REMOVAL & INSTALLATION

FRONT DISC BRAKE PADS & BRAKE CALIPER ASSEMBLY

Removal — Raise and support vehicle. Remove tire and wheel. Take out caliper pin stops and remove stops. Remove caliper off support, take out stop plates, then suspend caliper from frame with wire. Remove pads and shims. Mark pad location for reassembly, if necessary. Separate anti-rattle springs from support.

Inspection — Replace disc pads when thickness is reduced to .039" (1 mm). Always replace pads in axle sets. Check caliper, supports and adaptors for distortion or cracking. Inspect inside caliper cavity for leaks. Replace any parts found defective.

Installation — To install, reverse removal procedure and note the following: Original pads must be installed according to in-

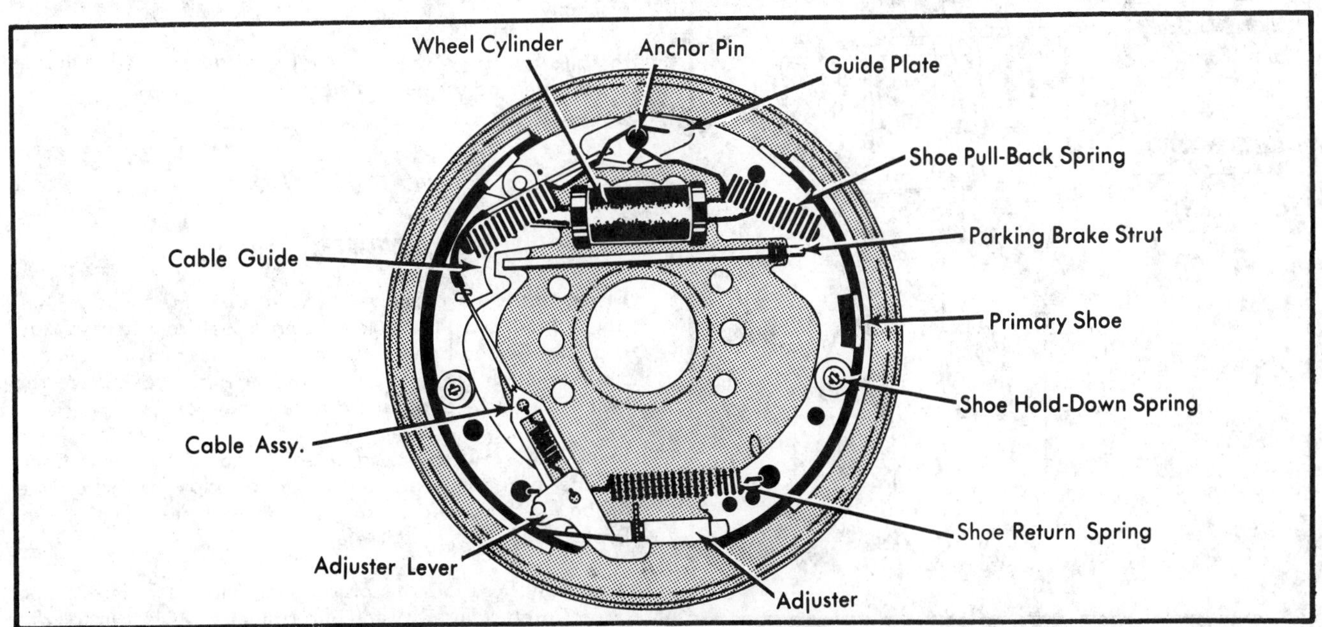

Fig. 1 Assembled View of Rear Drum Brake Assembly

LUV (Cont.)

dex marks. Install pads to supports with wear indicators facing LOWER SIDE. Make sure brake lubricant is applied to sliding portion of caliper.

FRONT DISC BRAKE ROTOR

Removal – Raise and support vehicle. Remove tire and wheel. Remove caliper assembly. Remove grease cap, nut, and outer bearing. Pull hub and rotor assembly from vehicle. It is not necessary to separate hub and rotor, except to replace either component.

Inspection – Adjust all play out of wheel bearings and inspect rotor runout using a dial gauge. If runout exceeds .005" (.13 mm), replace or resurface. Check parallelism at four or more points. Value obtained must not exceed .0005" (.001 mm) in 360°. Make all measurements at same distance from edge of rotor.

Installation – To install, reverse removal procedure and note the following: Adjust wheel bearings. *See Wheel Bearing Adjustment in WHEEL ALIGNMENT Section.*

REAR BRAKE SHOES

Removal – Remove tire and wheel. Remove tension from parking brake cable, remove retaining screws and remove brake drum. **NOTE** – *Mark drum for reassembly reference.* Remove return springs, hold-down springs, and self-adjuster assembly. Separate primary and secondary brake shoes, adjuster mechanism, return spring, and parking brake strut.

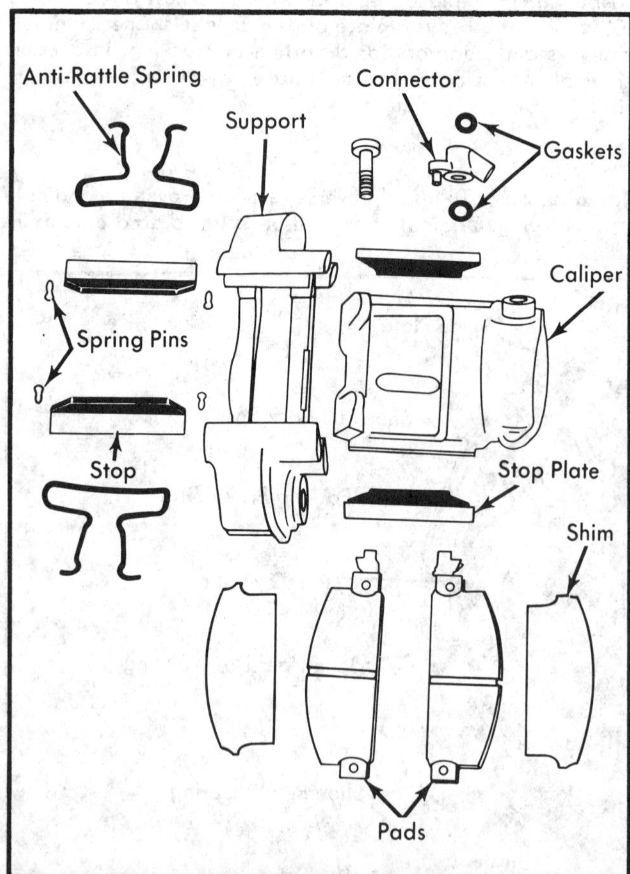

Fig. 2 Exploded View of Front Disc Brake Assy.

Separate parking brake lever and rear cable, and remove lever from secondary shoe.

Installation – Install parking brake lever to secondary shoe and rear cable to lever. Connect brake shoes together with return spring, and place adjuster screw into position, making sure star wheel is nearest secondary shoe. Install parking brake strut with spring on primary shoe end, then fit shoes to wheel cylinder push rods. Install hold-down springs, self-adjuster assembly, and return springs.

WHEEL CYLINDER

Removal – With brake drum removed, disconnect brake shoe return springs. Disconnect hydraulic line and bolts retaining cylinder to backing plate. Disengage cylinder push rod(s) from brake shoe(s) and remove cylinder.

Installation – Reverse removal procedure and bleed hydraulic system.

MASTER CYLINDER

Removal – Disconnect battery ground cable. Disconnect hydraulic lines at master cylinder and cover ends to prevent entry of dirt. Remove bracket bolt at front end of cylinder, and nuts retaining cylinder to power unit, then remove master cylinder and gasket from power unit.

Installation – Reverse removal procedure, bleed hydraulic system and adjust pedal height if necessary.

POWER BRAKE UNIT

Removal – Disconnect battery ground cable. Disconnect hydraulic lines at master cylinder and cover ends to prevent entry of dirt. Remove bolts attaching bracket to master cylinder and fender and remove bracket. Disconnect vacuum line at power unit and place out of way. Disconnect brake pedal return spring and push rod. Remove nuts attaching power unit to firewall, and remove power unit and master cylinder as an assembly.

Installation – Reverse removal procedure, bleed hydraulic system, and adjust pedal height if necessary.

OVERHAUL

FRONT DISC BRAKE CALIPER

Disassembly – Remove flex hose from caliper. Using pointed, but blunt instrument, remove seal from caliper. Place a block of wood between piston and caliper cavity wall, then apply enough compressed air pressure to force piston from cylinder. Remove and discard piston ring seal.

Inspection – Replace dust seal and piston seal. Check cylinder bore for wear, scuffing or corrosion. Inspect cylinder piston for damage or wear. Never attempt to refinish piston. Replace any parts found defective.

Assembly – Lubricate piston seal and insert into caliper bore. Carefully insert piston into caliper assembly. Install dust seal to piston and caliper. Fit seal ring into dust seal.

LUV (Cont.)

WHEEL CYLINDER

Disassembly — Remove boots from cylinder ends. Remove pistons and cups. Remove expander springs, if equipped.

NOTE — *Front wheel cylinder pistons and cups are serviced as an assembly.*

Cleaning & Inspection — Clean all parts in clean brake fluid. **NOTE** — *Do not use mineral based solvents.* Inspect cylinder bore and pistons for rust, corrosion, or other damage; replace parts or cylinder as necessary. Measure clearance between piston and cylinder bore; if clearance exceeds .006", replace wheel cylinder assembly.

Reassembly — Lubricate cylinder bore with clean brake fluid. Install spring expander into bore, then install new cups with flat surfaces toward outside. Install new pistons into cylinder with flat surfaces toward inside. **NOTE** — *Do not lubricate pistons or cups before installation.* Press new boots onto cylinder.

MASTER CYLINDER

Disassembly — Remove reservoir caps, plates and strainers and drain brake fluid. Place cylinder in a vise and remove reservoirs. Remove connector bolt, connector and gaskets from rear outlet, then withdraw end plug, gasket, check valve, return spring and spring seat. Remove check valve assembly from front outlet. Push in on primary piston, remove stop bolt and snap ring, and remove primary and secondary piston assemblies.

Cleaning & Inspection — Wash all parts in clean brake fluid and dry using compressed air. Blow out all passages, orifices and valve holes. If slight rust is found, polish clean with crocus cloth or emery paper. Inspect cylinder bore for scoring, pitting, or other damage. Check clearance between pistons and cylinder bore; if greater than .006", replace cylinder. **NOTE** — *Manufacturer recommends replacing rubber parts whenever master cylinder has been disassembled.*

Reassembly — Lubricate cylinder bore and all parts with clean brake fluid, reverse disassembly procedure, and note the following: Use all new gaskets and seals when reassembling. When reassembly is complete, bench bleed master cylinder as follows: Install plugs in all outlet ports of cylinder, fill reservoirs with clean brake fluid, and press in and out on primary piston until air bubbles are no longer seen in fluid.

POWER BRAKE UNIT

Disassembly — 1) Remove master cylinder reservoir and drain remaining brake fluid from cylinder. Scribe alignment marks on front and rear shells to assure reassembly in original position. Clamp flange of master cylinder in a vise with power unit up. Loosen push rod clevis lock nut and remove clevis and lock nut, then remove push rod boot.

2) Place suitable wrench (J-9504) over rear shell mounting studs. Press down on wrench while rotating counterclockwise and remove rear shell, piston rod, power piston, return spring and spring retainer. Remove nuts and lock washers and separate master cylinder and power unit front shell, then remove and discard gasket.

3) Pry retainer off power piston and remove air silencer and filter, then remove rubber diaphragm from piston. Rotate power piston until push rod retainer slot is down, then press in on rod, allowing retainer to fall out of power piston. Remove push rod assembly and reaction disc. **NOTE** — *Do not disassemble push rod assembly; if defective, replace complete assembly.*

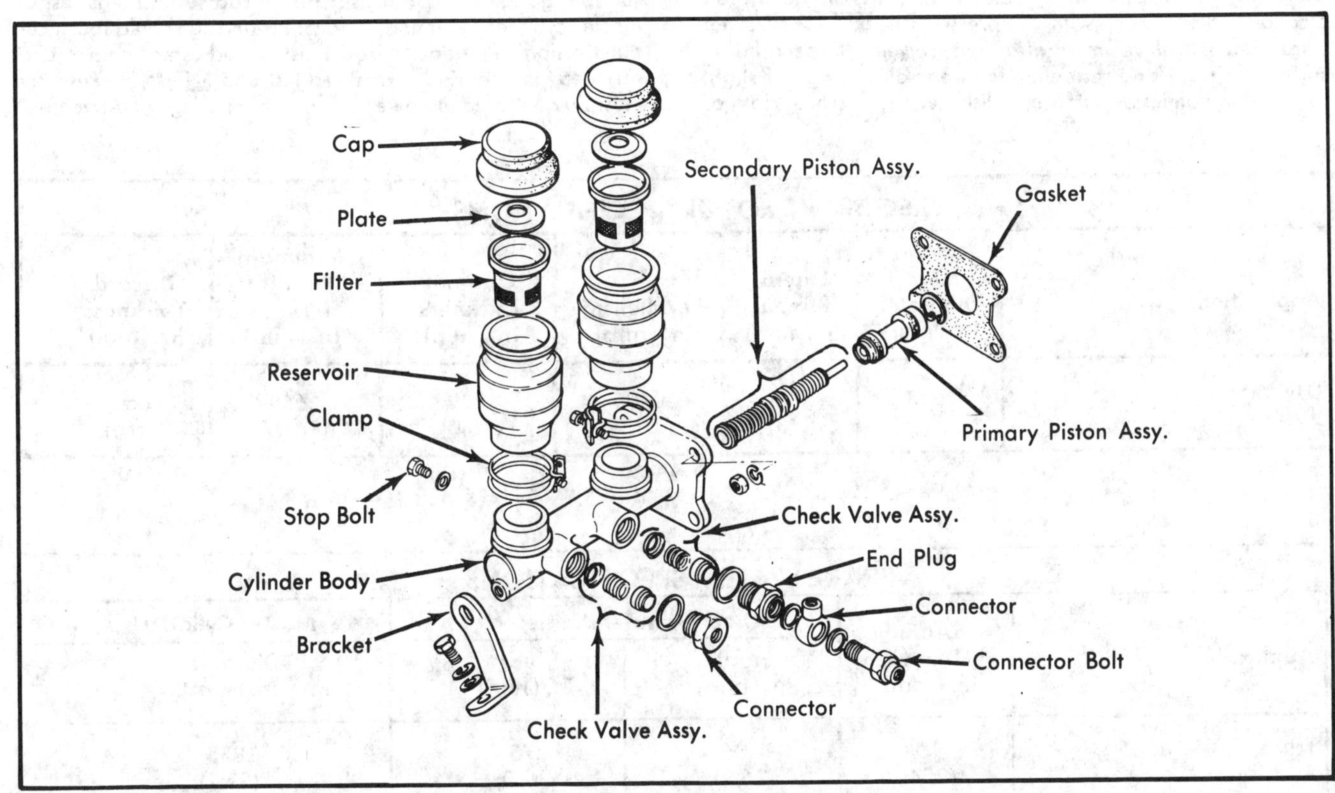

Fig. 3 Master Cylinder Reservoir, Body and Piston Assembly

LUV (Cont.)

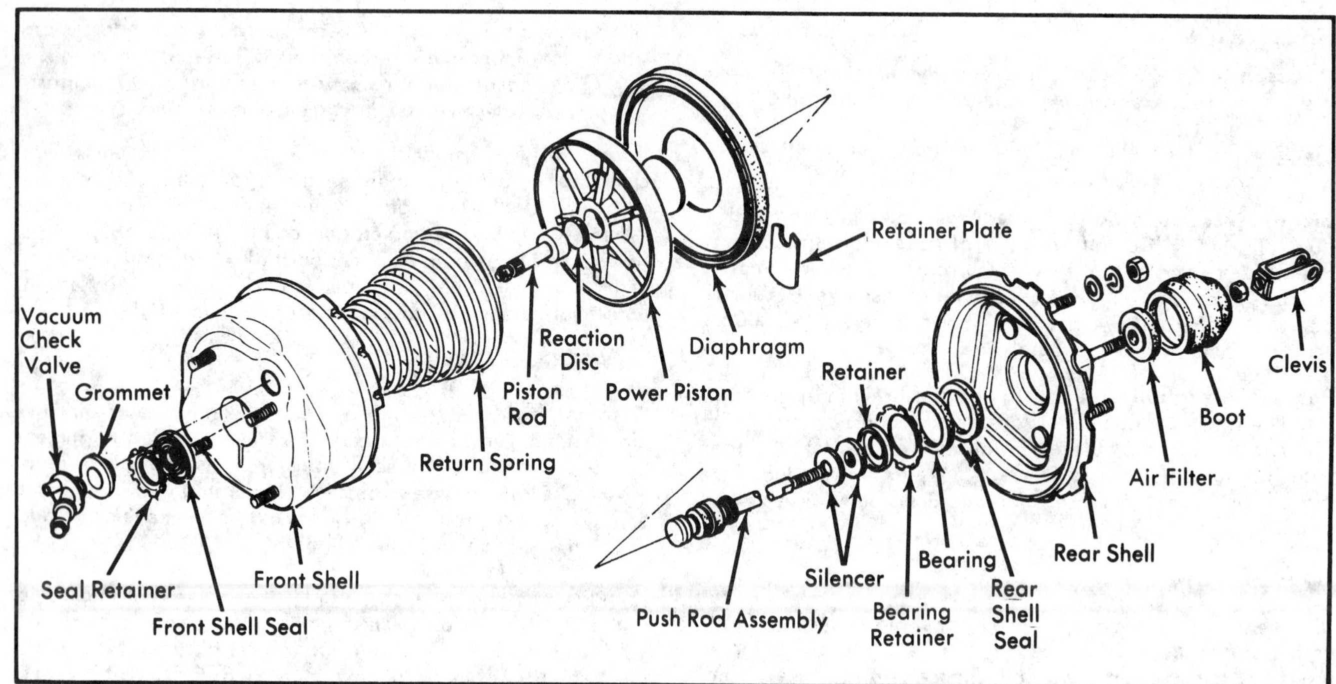

Fig. 4 Exploded View of Power Brake Assembly

4) If rear shell is defective, pry out seal retainer and remove spacer and seal assembly. If front seal is defective, pry out retainer and remove seal. If vacuum check valve is defective, remove using a twisting motion, then remove grommet.

Cleaning & Inspection – Clean all parts in denatured alcohol and blow dry with compressed air. **NOTE** – *Do not clean parts with a mineral based solvent.* Inspect inside surface of front and rear shell for wear or damage. If slight rust is found on inside surface, polish clean with crocus cloth or fine emery cloth. Inspect all parts for cracks, nicks, distortion or other damge and replace as necessary.

Reassembly – Reverse disassembly procedure and note the following: Apply a coat of silicone grease to parts before installation. When assembling front shell to rear shell, ensure marks made at disassembly are aligned. When reassembly is completed, remove master cylinder from power unit. Place suitable gauge (J-24568) over piston rod so that legs rest on master cylinder mounting surface. Piston rod should touch cut-out portion of gauge. If rod must be adjusted, hold rod at serrated portion and turn threaded end. **NOTE** – *Push rod must be bottomed in power unit before making adjustment.*

DISC BRAKE ROTOR SPECIFICATIONS

Application	Disc Diameter In. (mm)	Lateral Runout In. (mm)	Parallelism In. (mm)	Original Thickness In. (mm)	Minimum Refinish Thickness In. (mm)	Discard Thickness In. (mm)
LUV	.....	.005 (.13)	.0005 (.013)	.709 (18.0)	.668 (16.97)	.653 (16.6)

BRAKE SYSTEM SPECIFICATIONS

Application	Drum Diam. In. (mm)	Wheel Cylinder Diameter Front In. (mm)	Wheel Cylinder Diameter Rear In. (mm)	Master Cylinder Diameter In. (mm)
LUV	10 (254)	1.06 (26.9)	.75 (19.0)	.875 (22.2)

LUV (Cont.)

BRAKE DRUM SPECIFICATIONS				
Application	**Drum Diameter In. (mm)**	**Original Diameter In. (mm)**	**Maximum Refinish Diameter In. (mm)**	**Discard Diameter In. (mm)**
LUV	10 (254)	10.000 (254)	10.059 (255)	10.079 (256)

TIGHTENING SPECIFICATIONS

Application	Ft. Lbs. (mkg)
Backing Plate-to-Axle Housing	55 (7.7)
Wheel Cylinder	10 (1.4)
Master Cylinder	
End Plug	90 (12.4)
Connector Bolt	35 (4.8)
Stopper Bolt	14 (1.9)
Mounting Nuts	10 (1.4)
Power Brake Unit Mounting Nuts	10 (1.4)
Rotor-to-Hub	36 (5.0)
Caliper Connector	22 (3.0)
Support-to-Adaptor	64 (9.0)
Caliper Assembly-to-Knuckle	
Large Bolt	55 (7.6)
Small Bolt	35 (4.8)

MAZDA

808 1300 cc (Mizer)
808 1600 cc
GLC 1300 cc
RX-3SP
RX-4
Cosmo
Rotary Pickup

DESCRIPTION

Brake system is hydraulically actuated using a dual piston master cylinder and power brake unit. All models use single piston front disc brakes. Cosmo models have single piston rear disc brakes with integral parking brake shoes covered by hub/rotor assembly. All other models are equipped with leading-trailing drum brakes. All models use lever and cable operated parking brake actuating shoes of rear brake assemblies or, on Cosmo models, operating the separate parking brake shoes. All models are equipped with a proportioning valve to regulate brake pressure to rear wheels and prevent rear wheel lockup.

ADJUSTMENT

BRAKE PEDAL FREE PLAY

Brake pedal free play must be set to specifications (see table) to ensure compensating port is not covered by master cylinder piston. To adjust free play, loosen lock nut, adjust brake pedal push rod until proper free play is obtained, and tighten lock nut.

Brake Pedal Free Play Adjustment

Application	Inches (mm)
Rotary Pickup	.33-.39 (7-9)
All Others	.28-.35 (8.5-10)

FRONT DISC BRAKE PADS

Front disc brakes are self-adjusting; therefore, no adjustment in service is required.

REAR DISC BRAKE PADS

No adjustment is required.

NOTE – *On self-adjusting brakes, perform adjustment procedures only after overhaul or when servicing other components affects brake adjustment.*

REAR DRUM BRAKES

1) Raise and support rear of vehicle. Release parking brake. Remove adjusting hole plugs from back plate. Use suitable tool and expand one shoe at a time by rotating star adjuster until wheel locks.

NOTE – *Direction for star rotation may be marked on back plate.*

2) Back off adjuster about 4-6 notches or until wheel rotates freely without drag. Repeat procedure on each adjuster mechanism.

PARKING BRAKE

RX-3SP, RX-4, 808, GLC – With rear brakes properly adjusted, raise parking brake lever boot inside vehicle and turn lever adjusting screw so parking brake begins to apply when pulling lever 3 to 7 notches.

Cosmo – **1)** Raise rear of vehicle and place on safety stands. Release parking brake. Remove dust plug and rotate star wheel in direction printed on backing plate. When drum locks, back off 7 to 9 notches. Clearance between shoe and drum should be .006-.008" (.15-.20 mm).

2) Work inside vehicle and free shift lever boot. Adjust brake lever screw so rear wheels will lock when lever is pulled 5 to 7 notches with normal application force.

Rotary Pickup – With rear brakes properly tightened, adjust length of front cable with adjusting nut (located under vehicle where cable guide attaches to threaded shaft) so rear wheels lock when parking brake is pulled 5-10 notches. Apply parking brake several times, release, and check that rear wheels rotate freely.

BRAKE FAILURE SWITCH RESET

All Models – Turn ignition switch "On". Depress brake pedal and piston will center itself and light will go out. Turn ignition switch to "Off".

HYDRAULIC SYSTEM BLEEDING

NOTE – *DO NOT use secondary stop bolt to bleed hydraulic system.*

Bleed hydraulic system in sequence starting with line furthest from master cylinder, and ending with line closest to master cylinder. Attach a bleed tube to wheel cylinder or caliper bleeder screw, and immerse opposite end of tube in a container partially filled with brake fluid. Pump brake pedal several times, and with pedal depressed, open bleeder screw ¾ turn allowing air to escape, tighten bleeder screw, and release brake pedal. Continue operation until air bubbles are no longer seen in discharged fluid. Repeat procedure at remaining brake lines until all air is bled from system.

REMOVAL & INSTALLATION

FRONT DISC BRAKE PADS

Removal, Cosmo, RX-4, GLC, Pickup – Raise and support front of vehicle. Remove retainers and take out stopper plate. Take off caliper and anti-rattle spring. DO NOT allow caliper to hang by brake hose. Pull out disc pads and shims. If pad lining has worn to less than .276" (7 mm), replace disc pads. Make sure to always replace pads in sets of same make.

Installation – To install, reverse removal procedure and note: It may be necessary to open bleed valve and seat piston into caliper bore so disc pads can be inserted.

Removal, RX-3SP, 808 – Raise and support front of vehicle. Remove retainers and pull out locating pins. Remove pad return spring and remove disc pads. If pad lining has worn to less than .256" (6.5 mm), replace. Always replace all disc pads at same time and DO NOT mix pad types.

Installation – To install, reverse removal procedure.

MAZDA (Cont.)

FRONT DISC BRAKE CALIPER

Removal, Cosmo, RX-4, GLC, Pickup – **1)** Raise and support vehicle. Remove front wheel(s). Disconnect brake hose from caliper and plug openings to prevent entry of dirt and loss of fluid.

2) Remove fastening clips and stopper plates, then remove caliper and anti-rattle spring. Remove disc pads. If necessary, lift off disc pad (caliper) bracket.

Installation – If removed, reinstall caliper bracket. Attach a bleed tube to caliper bleeder screw, open bleeder screw, press caliper piston to bottom of bore, and tighten bleeder screw. Install disc pads and replace anti-rattle spring, caliper, stopper plates, and fastening clips. Install hydraulic line and bleed hydraulic system.

Removal, RX-3SP, 808 – With disc pads removed, disconnect hydraulic line from caliper and plug openings to prevent entry of dirt and loss of fluid. Remove bolts attaching caliper to front suspension and remove caliper.

Installation – Reverse removal procedure, tighten caliper mounting bolts evenly, and bleed hydraulic system.

FRONT DISC BRAKE ROTOR

Removal – With caliper assembly removed, remove wheel hub grease cap, cotter pin, nut lock, and bearing adjusting nut. Remove thrust washer and outer bearing from hub, then slide hub and rotor assembly from spindle. Remove bolts attaching rotor to hub, and separate.

Installation – Reverse removal procedure, tighten rotor-to-hub bolts evenly, and adjust wheel bearings. *See Wheel Bearing Adjustment in WHEEL ALIGNMENT Section.*

REAR DISC BRAKE PADS

Removal, Cosmo – Raise vehicle and place on safety stands. Remove wheel. Remove lock pins, then take out stopper plates. Slide off caliper and anti-rattle springs. DO NOT hang caliper from chassis by rubber brake hose. Pull out disc pads and shims. If pads have worn to .276" (7 mm) or less, disc pads must be replaced. Always replace all pads at one time and do not mix lining types.

Installation – To install, reverse removal procedure.

REAR DISC BRAKE CALIPER

Removal, Cosmo – Raise rear of vehicle and place on safety stands. Disconnect brake line from caliper and plug openings. Remove lock pins, then take out stopper plates. Slide off caliper and anti-rattle spring.

Installation – To install, reverse removal procedure and bleed brakes.

REAR DISC BRAKE ROTOR

Removal, Cosmo – Raise and support rear of vehicle. Remove caliper mounting bolts and remove caliper and mounting bracket assembly. Suspend caliper out of way with a wire hanger. Fully release parking brake. Unscrew hub/rotor mounting screws. Insert screws into tappered holes and tighten evenly until hub/rotor is free. Before removal of hub/rotor index mark axle shaft flange and hub/rotor assembly.

Installation – To install, reverse removal procedure and note following: Make sure index marks on axle shaft flange and hub/rotor assembly are aligned.

BRAKE DRUM

Removal – Raise and support vehicle and remove wheels to be serviced. Remove set screws securing drum to wheel hub or axle flange, fit screws into tapped holes in drum, and tighten evenly to force drum from hub or flange.

Installation – Mount brake drum to hub or axle flange, install and tighten set screws, and adjust brake shoes.

REAR BRAKE SHOES

Removal – With brake drum removed, remove brake shoe return springs. Remove brake shoe retaining springs and guide pins by compressing retaining spring and turning guide pin 90°. Remove brake shoes. Remove parking brake strut and disengage parking brake cable from operating lever of secondary shoe.

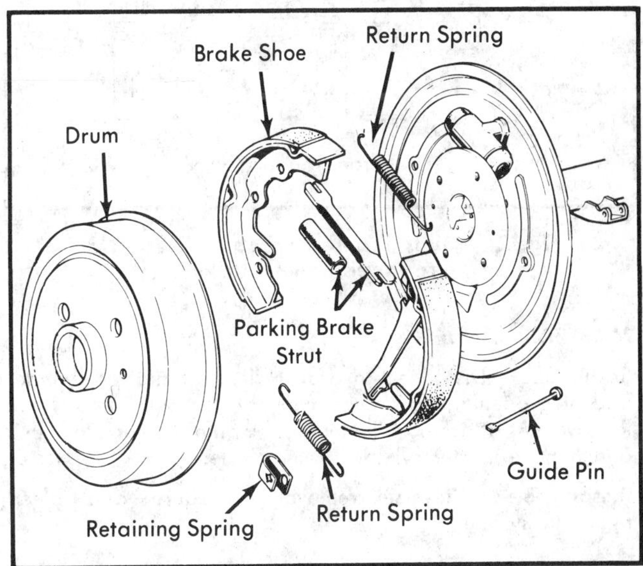

Fig. 1 Disassembled View of GLC Rear Brakes Other Models Similar

Installation – **1)** Lubricate adjusting screw threads and contact surfaces of shoes and backing plate with brake grease. Install parking brake operating lever to secondary shoe and secure with clip. Engage lever in parking brake cable.

2) Position operating strut between slots of shoes. Mount assembly to backing plate so slots in shoes are toward adjusting screws. Install return springs and retainer springs.

WHEEL CYLINDERS

Removal – With brake drum and shoes removed, remove hydraulic lines from cylinders at rear of backing plate and cover openings to prevent entry of dirt and loss of fluid. Remove nuts and/or bolts securing wheel cylinder to backing plate, and remove cylinders.

Installation – Reverse removal procedure. With brake shoes and drum installed, bleed hydraulic system.

MAZDA (Cont.)

PARKING BRAKE SHOES

Removal, Cosmo – Remove rear hub/rotor assembly as previously outlined. Disengage parking brake shoe return springs. Take off secondary brake shoe mounting spring, pin, and retainer. Pull out brake shoe. Repeat procedure on primary shoe.

Installation – To install, reverse removal procedure.

PROPORTIONING VALVE

Removal & Installation – Disconnect and plug all hydraulic lines. Remove mounting bolts and lift off valve. When installing valve make sure lines are connected as shown in *Fig. 2*.

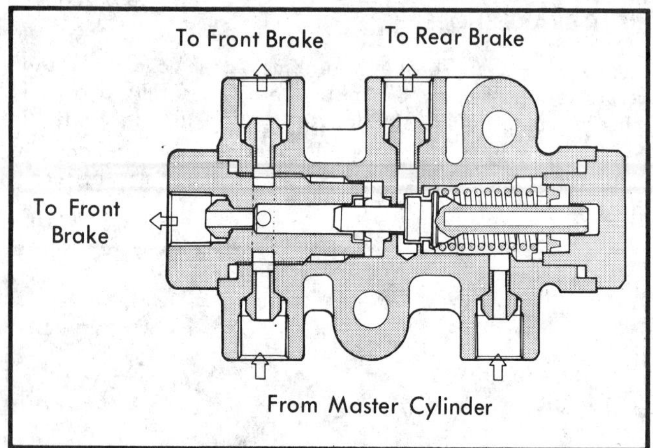

Fig. 2 Points Where Hydraulic Lines Attach to Proportioning Valve

MASTER CYLINDER

Removal – Disconnect hydraulic lines at master cylinder and plug openings to prevent entry of dirt and loss of fluid. Remove nuts attaching cylinder to firewall or power brake unit and remove master cylinder from vehicle.

Installation – Reverse removal procedure and bleed hydraulic system.

POWER BRAKE UNIT

Removal - Disconnect hydraulic lines at master cylinder, and vacuum line at power brake unit. From inside vehicle, remove cotter pin and clevis pin retaining push rod to brake pedal, and separate. Remove nuts retaining power unit to firewall, and remove power brake unit and master cylinder as an assembly from engine compartment.

Installation – Reverse removal procedure and bleed hydraulic system.

OVERHAUL

DISC BRAKE CALIPER

Disassembly – Thoroughly clean exterior of caliper and remove retainer and dust boot. On 808 and RX-3SP models, remove bolts which attach caliper bracket to caliper. On all models, place a piece of wood in front of piston, apply compressed air to fluid inlet and remove piston. Remove piston seal from caliper bore. Take out bleed screw if necessary.

NOTE – *If piston is stuck, tap lightly with hammer while forcing compressed air into caliper.*

Cleaning & Inspection – Wash all parts in clean alcohol or brake fluid and air dry. Inspect cylinder bore and piston for scoring, scratches or rust; replace piston or caliper as necessary. Minor damage may be removed using crocus cloth.
NOTE – *Manufacturer recommends replacing piston seal and dust boot whenever caliper has been disassembled.*

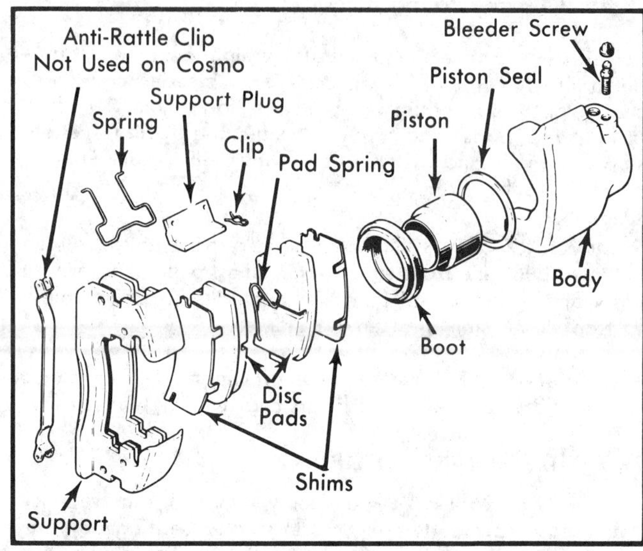

Fig. 3 Exploded View of Front Disc Brake Caliper Cosmo, RX-4, GLC and Rotary Pickup Shown

Reassembly – 1) Apply clean brake fluid to cylinder bore, piston and piston seal, then seat piston seal in caliper bore. On Cosmo, RX-4, GLC and Pickup models, install piston carefully into cylinder bore and install dust boot and retainer.

2) On RX-3SP and 808 models, spread dust boot over piston and seat in piston groove. Insert piston and boot carefully into cylinder bore. Position dust boot by setting flange squarely into outer groove in cylinder bore. Install retainer. Install bracket to caliper.

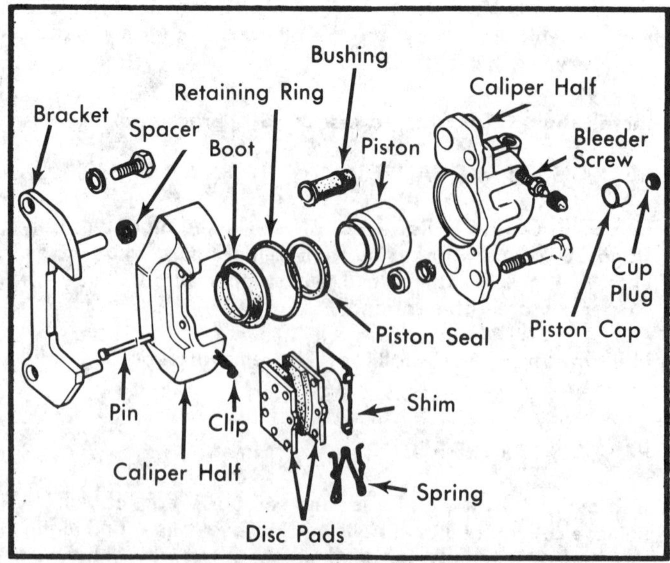

Fig. 4 Front Disc Brake Assembly for RX-3SP and 808 Models

MAZDA (Cont.)

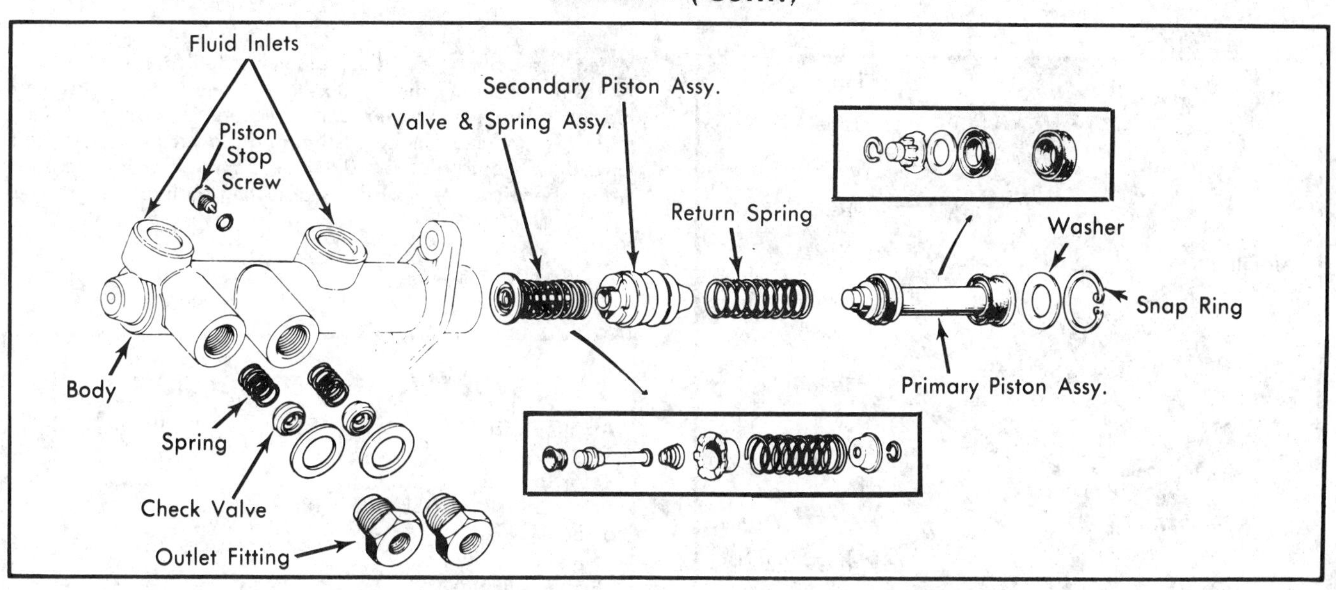

Fig. 5 Exploded View of Master Cylinder Assembly. All Models are Similar. Major Difference Occurs in Area of Piston Shape and Reservoir Attachment.

WHEEL CYLINDERS

Disassembly – Remove rubber dust boots and withdraw pistons with adjuster assemblies. Press in on piston cup allowing cups, filling blocks and return spring to be removed.

Cleaning & Inspection – Clean all parts in alcohol or brake fluid. **CAUTION** – *DO NOT use gasoline or kerosene.* Check cylinder bore, pistons and/or adjusters for scores, roughness, or wear. Check clearance between cylinder bore and pistons; replace if clearance exceeds .006". Check cups for softening, swelling, wear, or other damage; replace as necessary.

Reassembly – Reverse disassembly procedure and note the following: Coat all parts with clean brake fluid before reassembly. When installing cylinder cups, make sure flat side of cup faces outward. On models so equipped, coat threads of adjuster with brake grease and install into piston.

MASTER CYLINDER

Disassembly – Thoroughly clean exterior of cylinder and pour out any remaining brake fluid. If equipped, remove reservoir and dust boot. Depress primary piston assembly, remove retaining ring from rear of cylinder bore, and remove washer, primary piston assembly, and return spring. Depress secondary piston, remove secondary piston stop bolt, and withdraw secondary piston assembly and return spring. Remove joint bolts from outlets, and withdraw check valves and return springs.

Cleaning & Inspection – Clean all parts in alcohol or brake fluid. **CAUTION** – *DO NOT use gasoline or kerosene.* Check all parts for scoring, roughness or wear. Check clearance between cylinder bore and piston; if clearance exceeds .006", replace parts as required. Check all recesses, openings and internal passages for foreign matter; remove with compressed air. Check cylinder cups for softening, swelling, or wear; replace as necessary.

Reassembly – Reverse disassembly procedure and note the following: Coat all parts with clean brake fluid before reassembly. Use new gaskets at all hydraulic unions. When assembled, make sure piston cups do not cover compensating ports. Make sure valve with hole in center faces front side outlet hole.

POWER BRAKE UNIT

Disassembly – 1) Remove master cylinder and check valve from power unit, then place power unit in a vise with push rod up. Scribe alignment marks on front and rear shells to assure reassembly in original position. Remove clevis, lock nut and dust boot from rear shell.

2) Attach suitable removal tool to rear shell mounting studs, then press down on tool while rotating clockwise to unlock rear shell. **NOTE** – *Loosen shell carefully because it is under spring tension.* Lift rear shell assembly from power unit, then separate diaphragm and power piston assembly, valve rod and plunger assembly from rear shell. Remove return spring from power unit.

3) Remove diaphragm from power piston, then lift air silencer and filter from piston. Press in on valve rod and remove retainer key, then remove valve rod and plunger assembly. Press reaction disc from power piston. Remove push rod from front shell and if necessary, remove front seal.

Cleaning & Inspection – Clean all parts and blow dry with compressed air. Inspect all rubber parts for cuts, nicks, deterioration or other damage. Check power piston for cracks, distortion, chipping and damaged seats. Inspect front and rear shells for scratches, scores, pits, dents or other damage. Replace any defective parts.

Reassembly – Reverse disassembly procedure and note the following: Apply clean brake fluid to parts before reassembly.

MAZDA (Cont.)

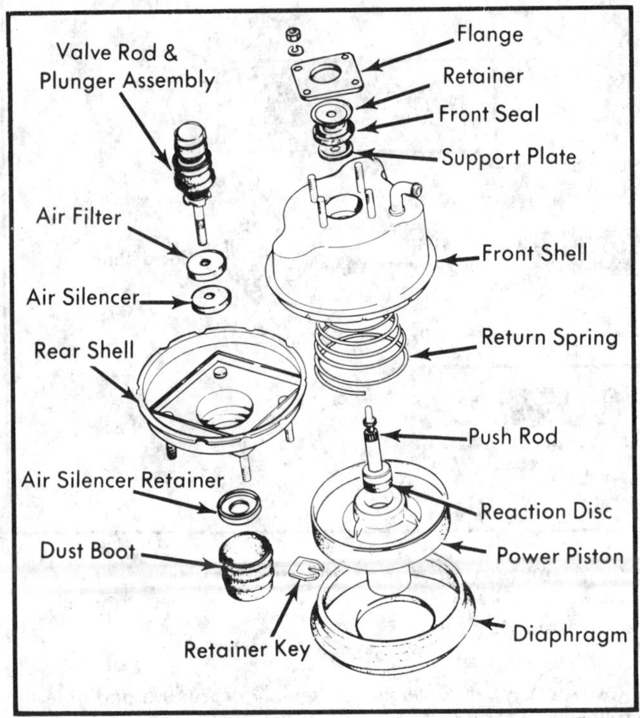

Fig. 6 Exploded View of Power Brake Unit. All Models are Similar. Some Models May Have Slightly Different Internal Design.

When assembling rear shell assembly to front shell, ensure marks made during disassembly are aligned. Before installing master cylinder to power unit, measure clearance between master cylinder primary piston and power unit push rod. Clearance should be .004-.020" (.1-.5 mm). If clearance is not within specifications, correct by adjusting push rod length.

TIGHTENING SPECIFICATIONS

Application	Ft. Lbs. (mkg)
Rotor-to-Hub	36 (5)
UNLESS OTHERWISE SPECIFIED:	
6T Bolts/Nuts	
6 mm Bolt/Nut	5-7 (.7-1)
8 mm Bolt/Nut	12-17 (1.6-2.3)
10 mm Bolt/Nut	23-34 (3.2-4.7)
12 mm Bolt/Nut	41-59 (5.6-8.2)
14 mm Bolt/Nut	56-76 (7.7-10.5)
8T Bolts/Nuts	
6 mm Bolt/Nut	6-9 (.8-1.2)
8 mm Bolt/Nut	13-20 (1.8-2.7)
10 mm Bolt/Nut	27-40 (3.7-5.5)
12 mm Bolt/Nut	46-69 (6.4-9.5)
14 mm Bolt/Nut	75-101 (10.4-14)

DISC BRAKE ROTOR SPECIFICATIONS

Application	Disc Diameter In. (mm)	Lateral Runout In. (mm)	Parallelism In. (mm)	Original Thickness In. (mm)	Minimum Refinish Thickness In. (mm)	Discard Thickness In. (mm)
RX-3 & 808	9.055 (230)		.....	.433 (11)	.394 (10)	②
RX-4	9.055 (230)	.004① (.10)	.....	.472 (12)	.433 (11)	②
Cosmo Front	9.843 (250)	.002① (.06)	.....	.709 (18)	.669 (17)	②
Rear	11.024 (280)	.004① (.10)	.....	.394 (10)	.354 (9)	②
Pickup	10.079 (256)	.004① (.10)	.....	.472 (12)	.433 (11)	②
GLC	8.150 (207)	.02① (.06)	.....	.512 (13)	.472 (12)	②

① — Maximum allowable.
② — Less than Minimum Refinish Thickness.

MAZDA (Cont.)

BRAKE DRUM SPECIFICATIONS				
Application	**Drum Diameter In. (mm)**	**Original Diameter In. (mm)**	**Maximum Refinish Diameter In. (mm)**	**Discard Diameter In. (mm)**
RX-3SP, 808, GLC	7.874 (200)	7.874 (200)	7.914 (201)	①
RX-4	9.000 (228.6)	9.000 (228.6)	9.040 (229.6)	①
Rotary Pickup	10.236 (260)	10.236 (260)	10.276 (261)	①
Cosmo	.....	.....	.....	②

① — More than Maximum Refinish Diameter.
② — Max refinish diameter for PARKING BRAKE drum 6.535" (166 mm).

BRAKE SYSTEM SPECIFICATIONS				
Application	**Drum Diam. In. (mm)**	**Wheel Cylinder Diameter**		**Master Cylinder**
		Front In. (mm)	**Rear In. (mm)**	**Diameter In. (mm)**
RX-3 & 808	7.874① (200)	2.012 ② (51.1)	.750 (19.05)	.813 (20.6)
RX-4	9.00① (228.6)	2.125② (54)	.687 (17.5)	.875 (22.2)
Cosmo	.....	2.0② (50.8)	1.375② (34.9)	.875 (22.2)
Pickup	10.236 (260)	2.125② (54)	.750 (19.05)	.875 (22.2)
GLC	7.874 (207)	2.0② (50.8)	.750 (19.05)	.813 (20.6)

① — Rear.
② — Caliper bore diameter.

MERCEDES-BENZ

230
240D
280 Series
300D
450 Series
6.9

DESCRIPTION

All models incorporate four wheel disc brake systems. Brakes are manufactured by either Bendix or Teves. Disc brake calipers are actuated by a power assisted, dual piston master cylinder. Parking brakes are cable actuated, internal expanding shoe type. Rear brake rotors house parking brake shoes.

ADJUSTMENT

DISC BRAKES

Disc brakes are self-adjusting, therefore no adjustment in service is required.

PARKING BRAKE

Remove one wheel lug bolt at each rear wheel. Raise and support vehicle, and rotate wheels until lug bolt hole is positioned over parking brake adjuster (approximately 45° in upward and forward direction from wheel center). Using a screwdriver inserted through lug bolt hole, turn adjuster until wheel cannot be turned by hand. Back off adjuster until wheel can be turned by hand without restriction.

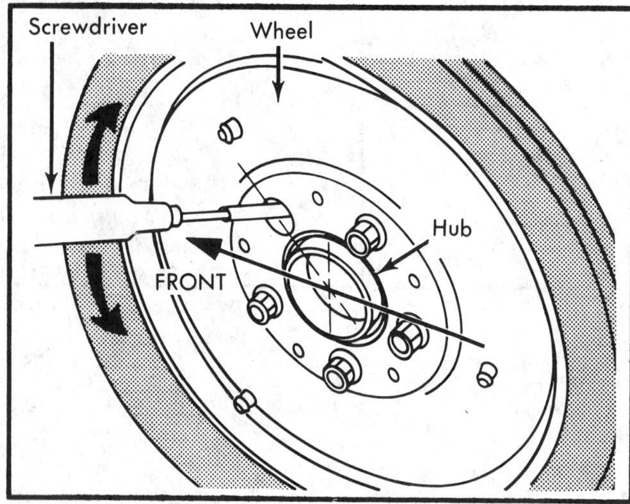

Fig. 1 Fitting Parking Brake Adjuster Tool Into Adjusting Mechanism

HYDRAULIC SYSTEM BLEEDING

Beginning with cylinder farthest from master cylinder, attach one end of bleeder tube to bleeder screw, and submerge opposite end in a jar half full of clean brake fluid. Pump brake pedal several times, and with pedal at bottom of stroke, open bleeder screw. Close bleeder screw when fluid stops flowing from tube, then release pressure on brake pedal. Repeat procedure until fluid flowing from tube shows no sign of air.

REMOVAL & INSTALLATION

DISC PADS

Removal — Raise and support vehicle with safety stands, remove wheels. If equipped, remove shaft cover plate from caliper. Drive out retaining pins toward inside of vehicle and remove cross spring. Using a suitable extractor tool, remove disc pads from caliper assembly.

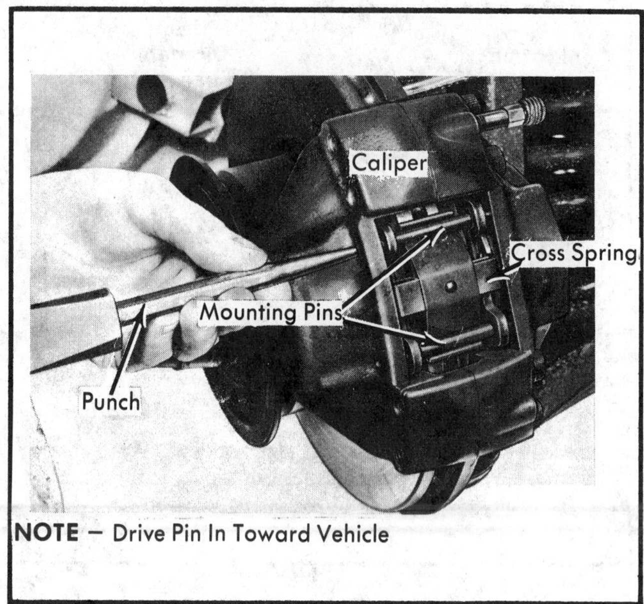

NOTE — Drive Pin In Toward Vehicle

Fig. 2 Knocking Out Disc Pad Mounting Pins On Teves Model Brakes

Installation — Using a cylinder brush, clean disc pad guide surface in caliper. Siphon sufficient fluid from master cylinder reservoir to prevent overflowing, then press pistons to bottom of bores. Install disc pads, cross spring, retaining pins and cover plate (if equipped). After installation, depress brake pedal several times to position pads against rotor.

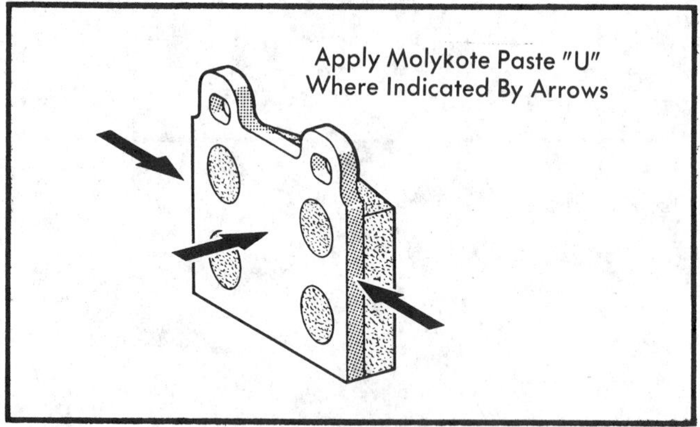

Fig. 3 Typical Mercedes-Benz Disc Brake Pad Illustration Shows Molykote Application Points

BRAKE CALIPER

Removal — Raise and support vehicle, and remove wheel. Disconnect brake lines at caliper assembly, and plug lines to prevent entry of foreign matter. Remove caliper attaching bolts, and remove caliper assembly from vehicle.

Installation — To install caliper assembly, reverse removal procedure. Tighten all nuts and bolts, and bleed hydraulic system.

BRAKE ROTOR

Removal & Installation (Front) — With caliper assembly removed, remove hub grease cap. Remove contact spring for radio shielding, loosen socket screw on clamping nut on wheel

MERCEDES-BENZ (Cont.)

spindle, remove clamping nut and washer, then remove wheel hub and rotor assembly. Remove Allen head bolts securing rotor to hub and remove rotor. To install, reverse removal procedure, tighten all bolts and fittings evenly, and bleed hydraulic system if necessary. Adjust front wheel bearing. *See Wheel Bearing Adjustment in WHEEL ALIGNMENT Section.*

Removal & Installation (Rear) – Remove rear wheel and caliper assembly, then pull rotor out from axle shaft flange. To install, reverse removal procedure, tighten all bolts and fittings evenly, and bleed hydraulic system if necessary.

Fig. 4 Assembled View of Rear Hub and Caliper

MASTER CYLINDER

Removal – Drain master cylinder of brake fluid. Disconnect and plug brake lines, disconnect electrical wires. Remove bolts securing master cylinder to power booster and remove master cylinder.

Installation – Reverse removal procedure and note the following: Always replace rubber "O" ring seal between master cylinder and power unit. Bleed hydraulic system and check complete system for fluid leaks.

POWER BRAKE UNIT

Removal – Drain master cylinder brake fluid, and remove master cylinder from vehicle. Disconnect vacuum line at power booster, and disconnect push rod at brake pedal. Remove power brake unit attaching hardware, and remove assembly from vehicle.

Installation – To install, reverse removal procedure, tighten all nuts and bolts, and bleed hydraulic system.

OVERHAUL

BRAKE CALIPER

Disassembly – With caliper removed from vehicle and disc pads removed from caliper, remove dust cap from piston housing. Hold one piston in place using a suitable clamp, then apply compressed air to fluid inlet and remove opposite piston. Remove piston seal from groove of cylinder bore. Remove remaining piston and seal in same manner. **CAUTION** – *Do not separate caliper halves.*

Cleaning & Inspection – Remove deposits on piston with a soft brass wire brush. **NOTE** – *Do not use polishing or emery cloth on pistons, as they could damage chrome plated surface.* Check cylinder bore of caliper for wear or damage. Small rust spots in bore can be removed with polishing cloth and heavier rust spots in front of piston seal groove with fine emery paper.

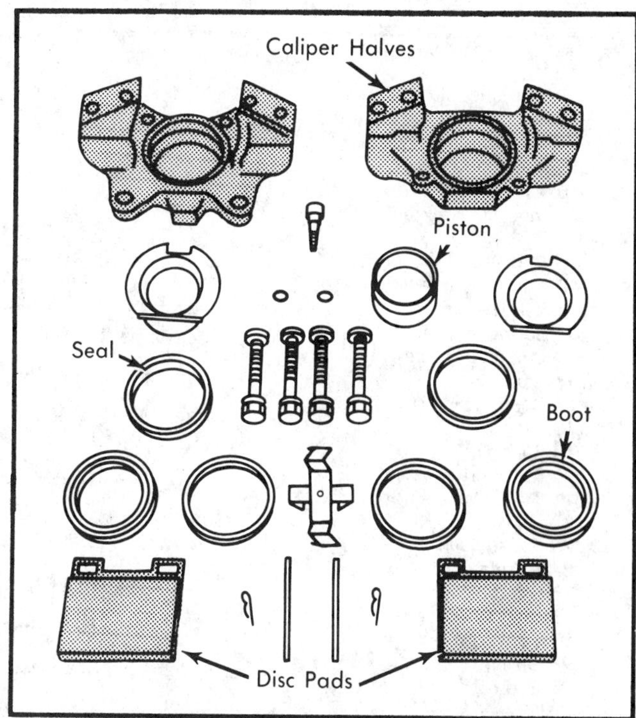

Fig. 5 Disassembled View of Typical Mercedes-Benz Brake Caliper

Reassembly – Coat piston and caliper bore with ATE brake cylinder paste (or equivalent), install piston seal into groove of bore, then install piston. **NOTE** – *Install piston so that elevation on piston is facing downward.* Install dust cap. Install heat shield into piston with recess in shield fitting into elevation of piston. **NOTE** – *Elevation should project at least .004" (.1 mm) above shield.*

MASTER CYLINDER

Disassembly – Remove fluid reservoir from master cylinder. Remove check valves from cylinder housing. Push piston into cylinder bore slightly, and remove forward piston stop screw. Remove lock ring from open end of cylinder bore. Remove rear piston, washer, seals, and rings from cylinder. Remove front piston and spring from cylinder. Disassemble front piston by removing connecting screw.

Inspection – Clean all parts with alcohol or brake fluid. Check bore in housing and piston for scoring and rust. Small rust spots in housing may be removed with polishing cloth. Scored or badly rusted parts cannot be repaired, replace complete master cylinder.

Reassembly – Reverse disassembly procedure and bleed hydraulic system.

TIGHTENING SPECIFICATIONS

Application	Ft. Lbs. (mkg)
Front Caliper Mounting Bolts	83 (11.5)
Rear Caliper Mounting Bolts	65 (9)
Master Cylinder Attaching Bolts	9-10 (1.2-1.4)
Rotor-to-Wheel Hub Bolts	83 (11.5)
Hydraulic Line Fittings	11 (1.5)

MERCEDES-BENZ (Cont.)

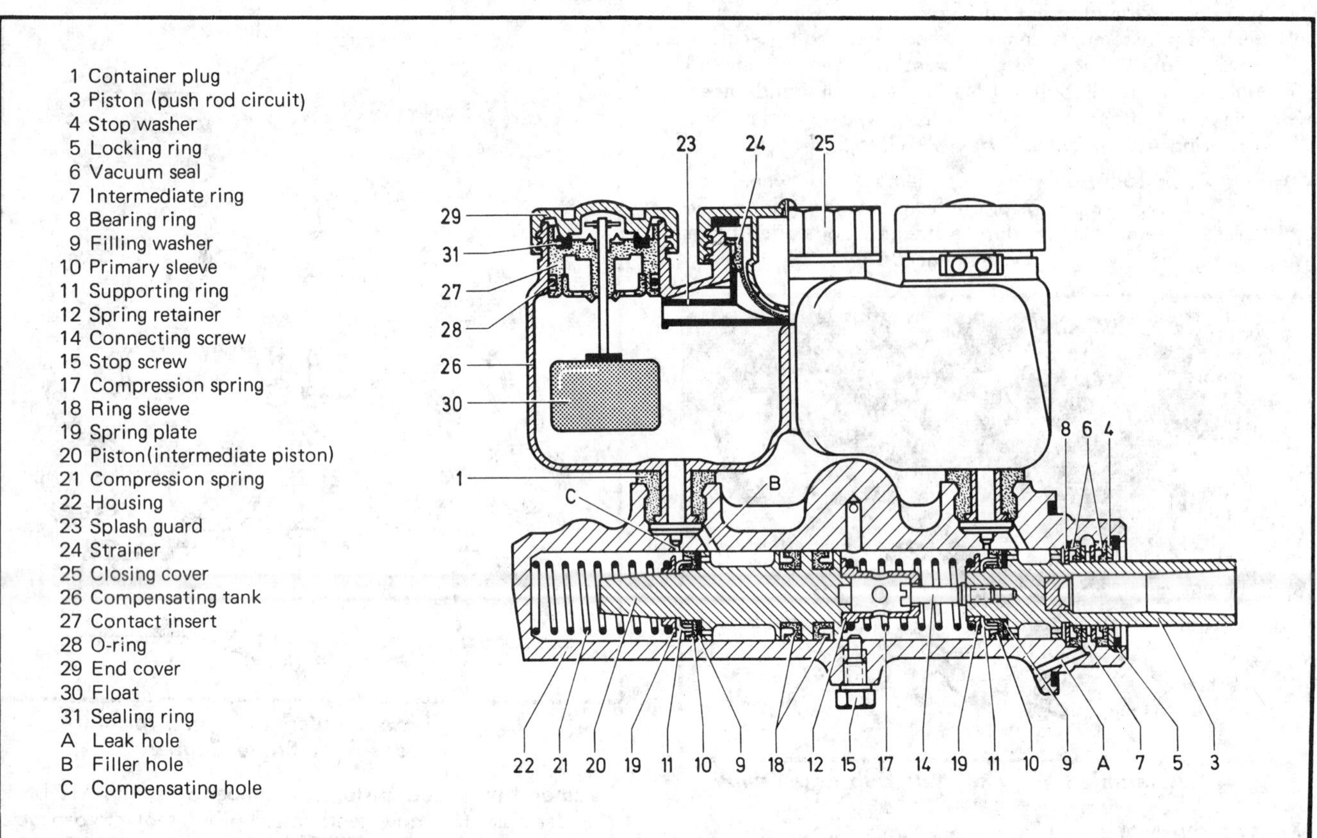

Fig. 6 Sectional View of Late Model Mercedes-Benz Tandem Master Cylinder

DISC BRAKE ROTOR SPECIFICATIONS

Application	Disc Diameter In. (mm)	Lateral Runout In. (mm)	Parallelism In. (mm)	Original Thickness In. (mm)	Minimum Refinish Thickness In. (mm)	Discard Thickness In. (mm)
240D & 300D						
Front	10.75 (273)	.0047 (.12)	.0008 (.02)	.496 (12.6)	.457 (11.6)	.435 (11.05)
Rear	10.98 (279)	.0059 (.15)	.0008 (.02)	.394 (10)	.370 (9.4)	.355 (9.02)
280 Models						
Front	10.94 (278)	.0047 (.12)	.0008 (.02)	.496 (12.6)	.457 (11.6)	.435 (11.05)
Rear	10.98 (279)	.0059 (.15)	.0008 (.02)	.394 (10)	.370 (9.4)	.355 (9.02)
450 & 6.9 Models						
Front	10.94 (278)	.0047 (.12)	.0004 (.01)	.866 (22)	.827 (21)	.815 (20.7)
Rear	10.98 (279)	.0059 (.15)	.0004 (.01)	.394 (10)	.370 (9.4)	.355 (9.02)

MGB

MGB

DESCRIPTION

Lockheed type brake system consists of a tandem type master cylinder, self-adjusting disc brakes, manually adjusted leading-trailing type drum rear brakes, and a lever operated parking brake. Front brakes are of rotating disc and rigid mounted caliper type. Each caliper carries two disc pad assemblies, one on each side of the rotating disc. Rear brakes are internal expanding, shoe and drum type. Rear brakes are operated by a single wheel cylinder which is hydraulically actuated by a foot pedal. A brake pressure warning switch is mounted to master cylinder and connected to a warning light on instrument panel.

ADJUSTMENT

DISC BRAKES

Disc brakes are self-adjusting, therefore no adjustment in service is required.

DRUM BRAKES

Raise and support rear of vehicle and fully release parking brake. Turn shoe adjuster clockwise until wheel is locked. Back off adjuster until wheel is free to rotate without binding.

NOTE — *Adjustment on drum brakes also tightens up parking brake.*

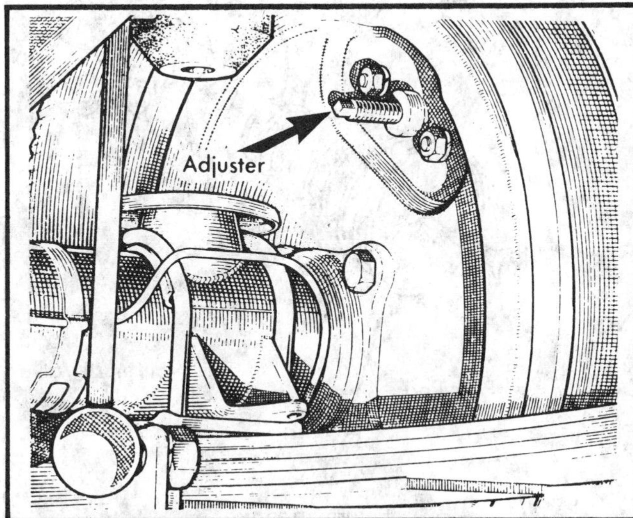

Fig. 1 Rear Drum Brake Shoe Adjuster Location

PARKING BRAKE

With service brakes properly adjusted, check for excessive parking brake cable stretch. Turn brass cable adjuster nut until total parking brake lever travel required to fully set parking brake is three to four serrations.

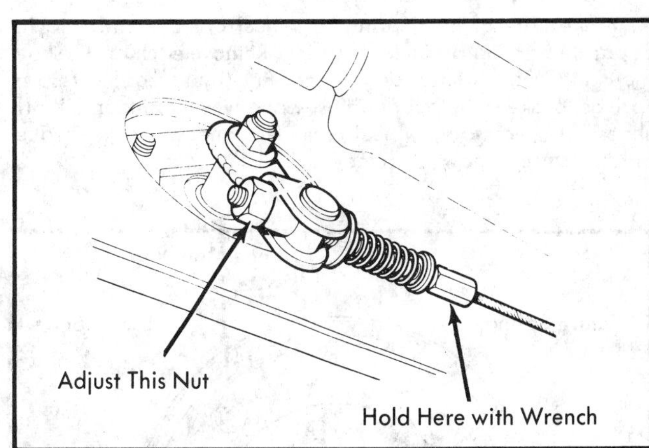

Fig. 2 Parking Brake Cable Adjustment Location

BRAKE SYSTEM BLEEDING

1) Release parking brake. Disconnect electrical wiring from brake failure switch. Unscrew switch about 3 ½ turns to ensure switch plunger is clear.

2) Fit bleed tube to caliper nearest master clyinder. Submerge opposite end of tube into a container partially filled with brake fluid. Open bleed screw about ½ turn.

3) Depress pedal rapidly through several full strokes allowing pedal to return unassisted. Repeat procedure (pedal pumping) with short pauses between each full stroke. Continue until all air bubbles stop. Tighten bleed screw with pedal on down stroke.

4) Repeat above procedure on other front caliper and each rear wheel cylinder. Tighten brake failure switch and connect wiring. If warning light remains on with parking brake released and pedal applied, repeat bleeding procedure.

REMOVAL & INSTALLATION

FRONT DISC BRAKE PADS

Removal — Raise vehicle and remove tire and wheel. Depress pad retaining springs and remove cotter pins with retaining springs. Carefully lift out pads from caliper. Measure pad lining and replace if lining is worn to .063" (1.59 mm).

Installation — Before inserting disc pads, clean any foreign material from piston head and caliper cavity. Using suitable clamp, seat piston in cylinder bore. **NOTE** — *During this operation fluid level will rise.* Ensure machined portion of piston face is correctly positioned at inner end of caliper. Insert friction pads, reposition retaining springs and fit cotter pins. Check that pads have some degree of movement in caliper. It is acceptable to file high spots from friction pads if necessary. Pump brake pedal several times to readjust pistons.

REAR BRAKE SHOES

Removal — **1)** Raise and support rear of vehicle. Remove wheel. Release parking brake. Loosen brake shoe adjuster. Remove screws and pull off brake drum.

MGB (Cont.)

2) Make note of how springs at wheel cylinder end attach. Separate parking brake lever spring. Remove each brake shoe mounting pin, retainer, and spring. Pry (by spreading return springs) brake shoes out of adjuster and wheel cylinder. Lift off shoes. If necessary, wheel cylinder and parking brake mechanism can now be removed.

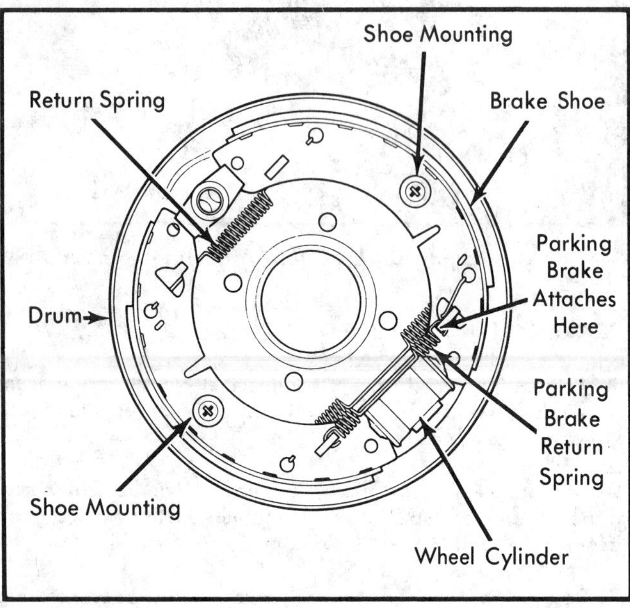

Fig. 3 Installed View of Rear Brake Drum Assembly

Installation – To install, reverse removal procedure and note: Apply suitable brake grease to shoe contact points. Adjust brake shoes.

BRAKE CALIPER

Removal – Raise vehicle and remove tire, wheel, and friction pads. Drain fluid through bleed screw. Disconnect fluid hoses on mounting half of caliper and plug end of hose. Bend locking ears and withdraw mounting bolts. Lift off caliper.

Installation – To install, reverse removal procedure noting the following: Torque mounting bolts to 43 ft. lbs. (6.0 mkg).

MASTER CYLINDER

Removal – After removing pedal box cover drain fluid from master cylinder reservoir. Disconnect hydraulic lines from master cylinder and separate electrical connections from warning switch. move two nuts mounting master cylinder to power brake unit, then remove cylinder.

Installation – To install, reverse removal procedure. Start hydraulic lines before tightening master cylinder. Bleed hydraulic system and adjust brakes, if necessary.

WHEEL CYLINDER

Removal – Remove rear brake shoes as previously outlined. Disconnect wheel cylinder fluid line. Pull line clear of cylinder and plug opening. Remove bleed screw. Pry out spring clip holding wheel clyinder to back plate. Slide out wheel cylinder.

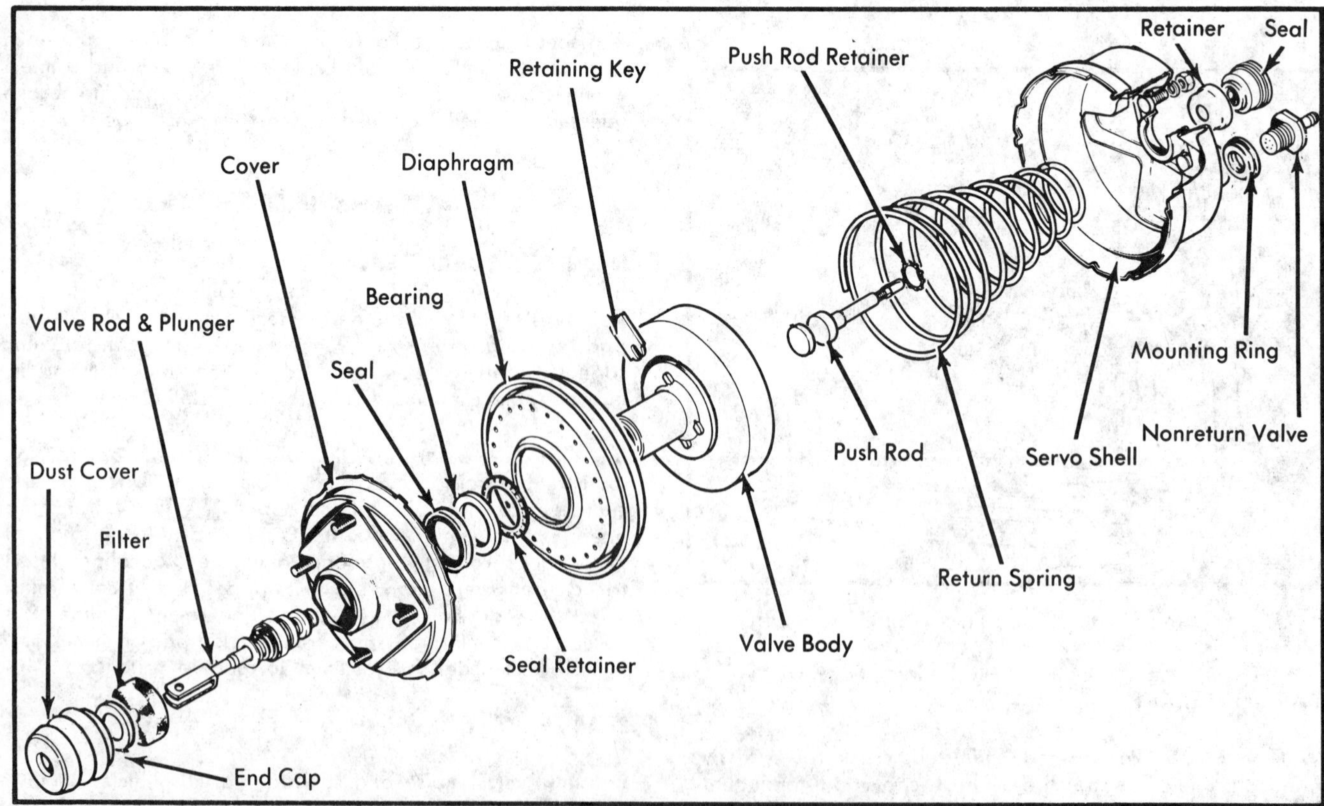

Fig. 4 Power Brake Unit Components

MGB (Cont.)

Installation – Coat face of wheel cylinder with heat resistant grease. Slide wheel cylinder through back plate and install new spring clip. Insert bleed screw. Reconnect brake line. To install remaining components, reverse removal procedure.

POWER BRAKE UNIT

Removal – Disconnect throttle return spring from air cleaner, then remove air cleaner from vehicle. Remove pedal box cover. Disconnect hydraulic lines from mounting clips. Separate master cylinder from power brake unit and support cylinder out of way. Disconnect vacuum source and pedal return spring, then remove pin securing pedal to push rod. Remove nuts and spring washers mounting power brake unit to pedal box and lift out unit.

Installation – To install, reverse removal procedure and bleed hydraulic system.

OVERHAUL

BRAKE CALIPER

Disassembly – 1) Remove brake caliper, leaving inlet hose connected. Clamp piston in mounting half of caliper and gently apply service brakes. This procedure will force rim half piston out enough to be removed by hand.

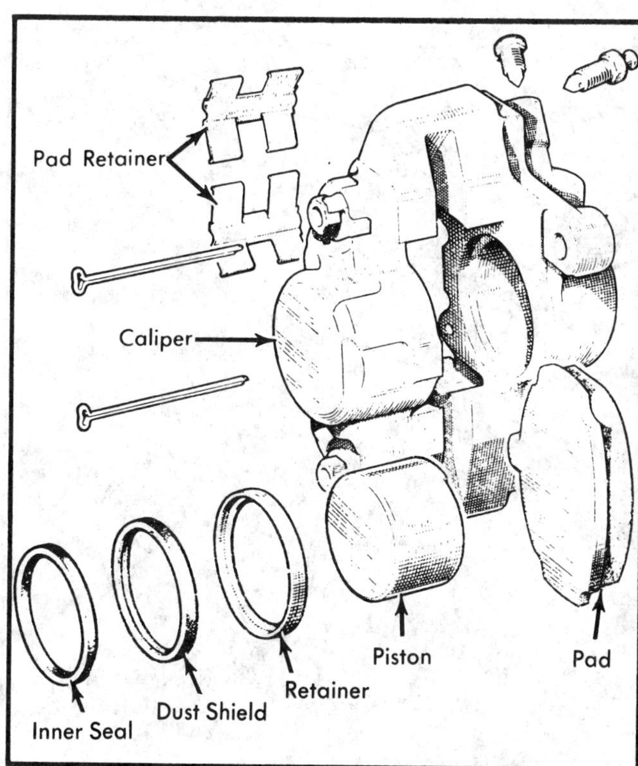

Fig. 5 Exploded View of Brake Caliper

2) Using a blunt instrument, remove fluid seal, taking care not to damage bore or retaining groove. To remove dust seal, insert a screwdriver between retainer and seal, and gently pry retainer from mouth of caliper bore. Disassembly procedure is same for mounting half. **NOTE** – *Caliper rim half must be reassembled before disassembling mounting half.*

Reassembly – 1) Coat new seal with brake fluid and ease seal into groove. Loosen bleed screw in rim half one turn. Coat piston with brake fluid and locate piston squarely in cylinder bore with cut-away portion facing inner edge of caliper.

2) Press piston down until 5/16" protrudes from bore. Fit dust seal into retainer. Position seal assembly on extended portion of piston with seal innermost. Seat piston and seal assembly with clamp and retighten bleed screw. Rim half of caliper is reassembled in same manner.

POWER BRAKE UNIT

Disassembly – Remove seal and retainer from servo (power brake unit). Fix servo into a vice and mark both cover and shell. Remove dust cover and pull out filter. Remove end cover by pressing down and turning counterclockwise. **NOTE** – *Cover is under spring tension.* Remove seal retainer, bearing, and seal from cover. Remove diaphragm from valve body. Push in on valve rod and plunger to release retaining key. Remove remaining components.

Inspection – Clean all components in brake fluid. Examine components for damage and wear. Replace all retainers and rubber parts. Valve rod and plunger must be replaced as an assembly.

Reassembly – To reassemble, reverse disassembly procedure and note the following: Coat all rubber components with brake fluid. Ensure push rod protrusion from servo is .400" (10.16 mm). One turn on adjuster alters rod length .035" (.088 mm)

WHEEL CYLINDER

Disassembly – Pry off dust seals from each end of wheel cylinder. Slide pistons out. Remove seals taking care not to damage the seal groove.

Inspection – Clean all components in alcohol and allow to dry. If cylinder bore shows any signs of scoring or roughness, replace wheel cylinder.

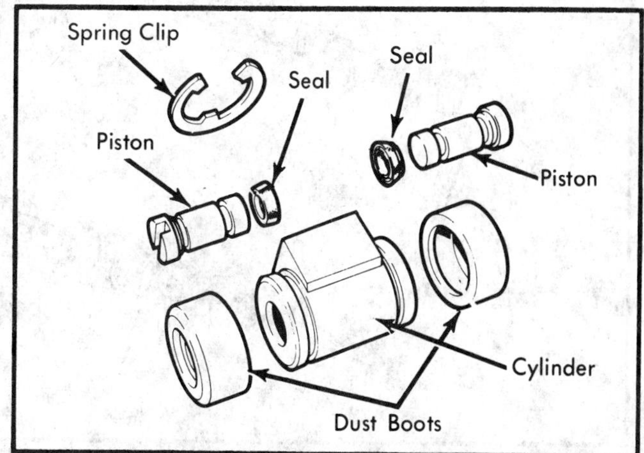

Fig. 6 Exploded View of Rear Wheel Cylinder

MGB (Cont.)

Reassembly – Lightly coat all internal components with brake fluid. Slide in each seal with flat surface toward slotted end of piston. Push piston into bore. Pull seal over end of assembly.

MASTER CYLINDER

Disassembly – 1) Remove brake pressure failure switch. Place cylinder in vice and remove reservoir. Take out seal and adaptor assembly from primary feed port, then remove secondary port seal. Extract spring clip from cylinder bore and take out primary piston, return spring, and cup.

2) Insert a rod into bore and depress secondary piston, take out stop plug from secondary feed port and withdraw secondary piston assembly. Remove pressure differential piston assembly. Pull rubber seals from pistons.

Inspection – Clean all components in brake fluid. Examine cylinder bore for scoring or ridges, replace components as necessary.

Reassembly – 1) Lubricate all components with brake fluid. Fit "O" ring seals to pressure warning piston. Place a shim on primary and secondary pistons. Install seal to both pistons, lip facing away from shim. Fit the thinner of remaining seals to secondary piston with lips toward primary seat. Fit the secondary seal to primary piston with lip toward first seal. Fit return spring and cup to secondary piston and insert assembly.

2) Depress secondary piston and insert stop plug when piston head has passed feed port. Fit return spring and cup to primary piston and insert assembly. Refit spring clip.

3) Reinstall pressure differential valve into its bore and fit end plug. Fit "O" ring and seal to primary feed port adaptor and install into port recess. Install secondary feed port seal, round edge first. Reposition reservoir and brake pressure switch.

TIGHTENING SPECIFICATIONS

Application	Ft. Lbs. (mkg)
Caliper Mounting Bolts	43 (6.0)
Master Cylinder End Plug	33 (4.5)
Master Cylinder Reservoir Screws	5 (.70)
Brake Hub-to-Rotor	43 (6.0)

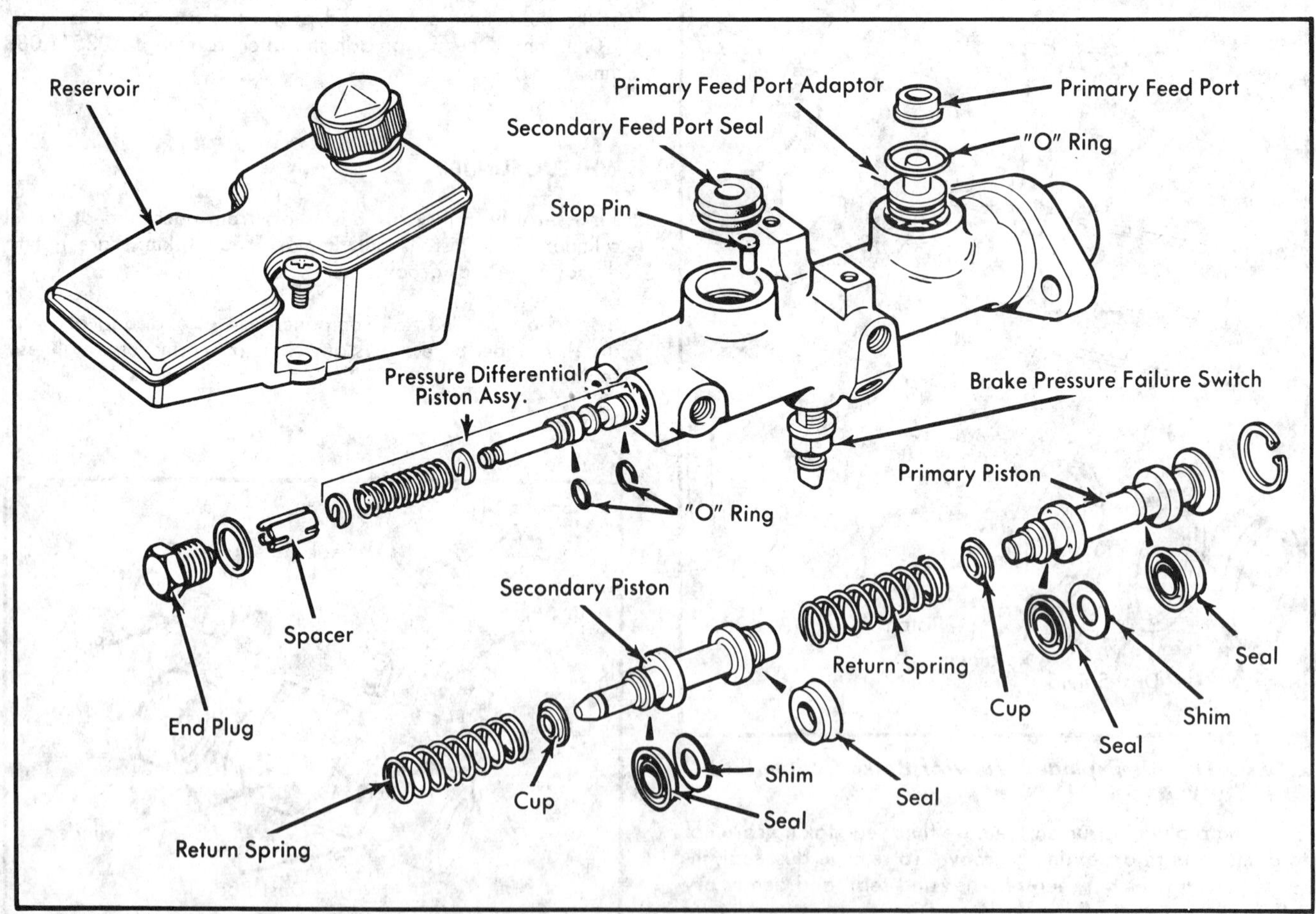

Fig. 7 Master Cylinder Reservoir, Body and Piston Assemblies

MG MIDGET

Midget

DESCRIPTION

Midget brake system is made up of two independent curcuits: a hydraulic foot brake and a mechanical hand brake. Hand brake is lever operated and, when set, locks rear wheels. Foot brakes are either leading-trailing drum type or dual piston caliper disc type. Rear brakes in all instances are leading-trailing drum type with manual adjusters. Master cylinder is tandem type with each of its halves feeding a separate circuit. There is a brake warning light located on instrument panel to indicate fluid loss in either side of master cylinder.

ADJUSTMENT

DISC BRAKES

Disc brakes are self-adjusting, therefore no adjustment in service is required.

DRUM BRAKES

Raise and support vehicle, and remove wheel to be serviced. Rotate drum until front hole and adjuster mechanism are aligned. Using a screwdriver, turn adjuster clockwise until brake shoe contacts drum. Back off adjuster until drum is just free to turn. Repeat adjustment on rear shoe adjuster.

PARKING BRAKE

With service brakes correctly adjusted, apply parking brake three ratchet notches. Adjust sleeve nut on parking brake cable until drum can just be rotated.

BLEEDING HYDRAULIC SYSTEM

Fit a bleeder tube to both right front and right rear wheel cylinders, then submerge free ends into a partially filled container of brake fluid. Pump brake pedal, but do not go entire pedal stroke. Repeat bleeding process until all air is expelled from system. With pedal down, and on next to last stroke, close bleeder screws. Perform same procedure on left front and left rear wheels.

COMBINATION VALVE

Reset – Make sure brake fluid reservoir is full. Correct any hydraulic leaks. Bleed brakes to make sure all air is out of system. Bleed brakes of one wheel of system that was not at fault. Slowly depress pedal, as soon as light goes out, release pedal and close bleeder screw. **NOTE** – *If pedal isn't released immediately, piston will move too far and procedure will have to be repeated.*

FRONT DISC BRAKE PADS

Removal – Remove tire and wheel. Depress friction pad retaining spring and remove cotter pins. Remove retaining springs. Carefully twist friction pads and remove damper shims. Lift out friction pads. Using a clean rag, wipe any foreign material from piston head and cylinder cavity.

Installation – Using suitable clamp, fully seat piston in cylinder bore. **NOTE** – *Fluid level will rise during this procedure.* Insert friction pads into caliper and ensure they have free movement. Install damper shims between pistons and friction pads. Fit pad retaining springs, press down spring and insert cotter pins. Install tire.

BRAKE SHOES

Removal – Remove tire. Loosen brake shoes at adjuster and remove drum. Disconnect brake mounting springs. Pull trailing shoe against tension of return springs and away from its abutment at either end. With return spring tension released, detach mounting springs and remove both shoes. Remove brake adjuster.

Installation – To install, reverse removal procedure and ensure adjuster is in slot in shoe.

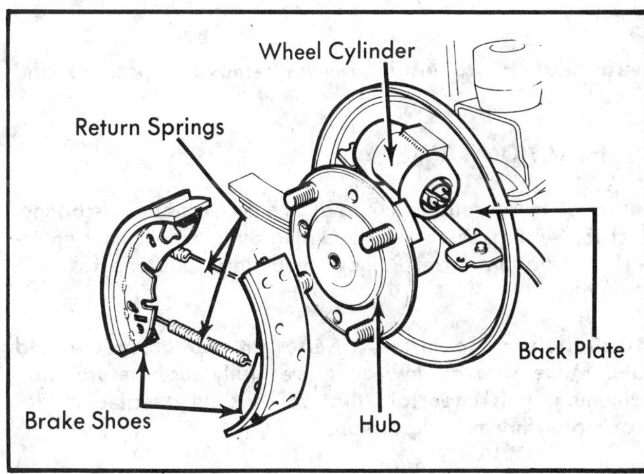

Fig. 1 MG Midget Rear Drum Brake Assembly

REMOVAL & INSTALLATION

BRAKE CALIPER

Removal – Remove tire and wheel. Remove friction pads. Disconnect brake caliper line. Remove nuts securing caliper hose mounting plate to caliper. Remove studs securing caliper to axle stud and lift off caliper.

Installation – To install, reverse removal procedure, tighten all nuts and bolts, and bleed hydraulic system.

FRONT DISC BRAKE ROTOR

Removal – Remove tire and wheel. Extract friction pads and brake caliper. Remove dust cover cap, cotter pin, locking nut and washer. Withdraw hub assembly from axle, using suitable puller (18G-304 with adaptors 18G-304-F for standard wheels, or 18G-363 for wire wheels, early models, or 18G-1032 for wire wheels, late models). Remove bolts securing brake rotor to hub and remove rotor.

Installation – To install, reverse removal procedure.

MG MIDGET (Cont.)

MASTER CYLINDER

Removal – Disconnect high tension lead from ignition coil and blue-white lead from resistor. Remove four screws and pull cover plate with ignition coil from vehicle. Remove cotter pin and clevis from push rod. Disconnect and separate hydraulic lines from master cylinder, then plug open lines. **NOTE** – *Keep brake fluid off paint.* Remove bolts securing master cylinder pedal box and pull out cylinder.

Installation – To install master cylinder, reverse removal procedure and bleed brake system.

REAR WHEEL CYLINDER

Removal – Remove rear wheel and brake drum. Disconnect the brake line at wheel cylinder and plug line opening. Remove cylinder bleed screw. Take out spring clip and washer retaining wheel cylinder to back plate and withdraw cylinder assembly.

Installation – To install, reverse removal procedure and bleed brakes.

COMBINATION VALVE

Removal – Thoroughly clean all line connections. Disconnect electrical wiring. Disconnect and plug all hydraulic lines entering combination valve. Remove mounting bolts and take off assembly.

Installation – To install, reverse removal procedure and note: Make sure all hydraulic lines fully seat before final tightening. It is important that valve is fully seated in approximately horizontal position.

OVERHAUL

BRAKE CALIPER

Disassembly – 1) Remove brake caliper as previously described. Clean outside of caliper and note position of relieved portion of piston face. Using suitable clamp, retain piston in mounting half of caliper.

2) Holding caliper on bench, apply compressed air to hydraulic inlet port until dust seal retainer and seal can be removed. Remove fluid seal from groove in caliper bore. **NOTE** – *Exercise care not to score caliper bore.* Refit piston into caliper bore and install suitable clamp.

3) Remove mounting half dust seal, piston, and fluid seal. Remove clamp and piston. **NOTE** – *Do not separate caliper halves.*

Inspection – Clean all components with brake fluid. Check pistons and cylinder bores for wear or damage, replace parts as necessary.

Reassembly – Lubricate pistons and all new seals in brake fluid. Insert fluid seals into grooves fit pistons in bore with relieved portion toward bleed screw. Install dust seal and retainer.

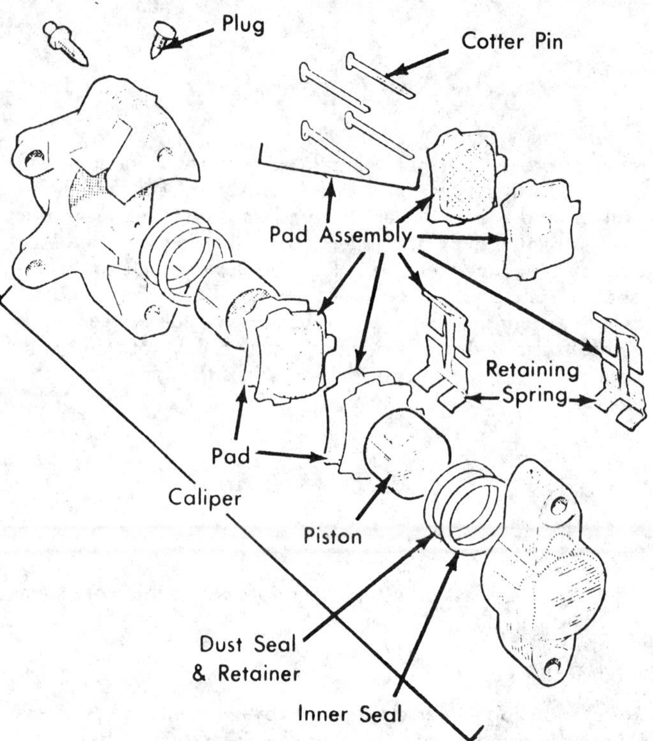

Fig. 2 Exploded View of Front Disc Brake Caliper Assembly

REAR WHEEL CYLINDER

Disassembly – Separate dust cover boot from both ends of wheel cylinder. Pull out both pistons with seals and inspect pistons for excessive wear or damage. Separate seals from pistons and replace seals.

Reassembly – After cleaning cylinder bore and related components in brake fluid, check wheel cylinder bore for scoring or pitting. While components are still damp, fit new seals to pistons with flat surfaces of seals facing slotted end of piston. Insert new pistons into wheel cylinder bore, plain end first. Install new dust cover boots.

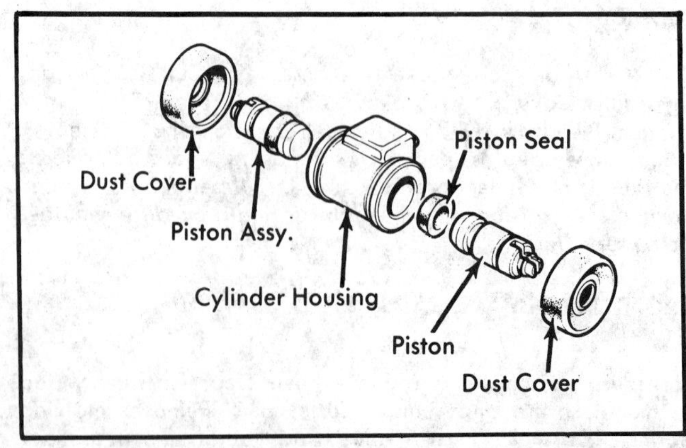

Fig. 3 Disassembled View of Rear Wheel Cylinder

MG MIDGET (Cont.)

COMBINATION VALVE

Disassembly – Remove the end plug and discard copper washer. Unscrew nylon switch. Remove shuttle valve piston from assembly bore. Use air pressure to force out piston. Remove two piston seals and discard.

Inspection – Thoroughly clean all components in clean brake fluid. Check bore of assembly for scoring or ridges. New seals can be used if bore isn't damaged.

Reassembly – Lightly coat all components in brake fluid. Install both new seals with lips facing outward from piston center. Fit piston into bore, taking care that lead seal is not cocked. Fit new copper seal and tighten end plug to 200 INCH lbs. (230 cmkg). Refit nylon switch and torque to 15 INCH lbs. (17.25 cmkg).

MASTER CYLINDER

Disassembly – Thoroughly clean dirt from outside of cylinder. Detach rubber boot and remove snap ring. Compress return spring and remove circlip. Move piston around in bore to free nylon guide bearing and cap seal. Remove bearing seal and plain washer. Remove inner circlip. Withdraw primary and secondary piston assemblies complete with stop washers. When component parts have been removed, they can be further disassembled.

Cleaning & Inspecting – Clean all parts in approved grade brake fluid. Examine all components for signs of rust, grooves or distortion. Replace any parts found out of tolerance.

Reassembly – To reassemble, reverse disassembly procedure.

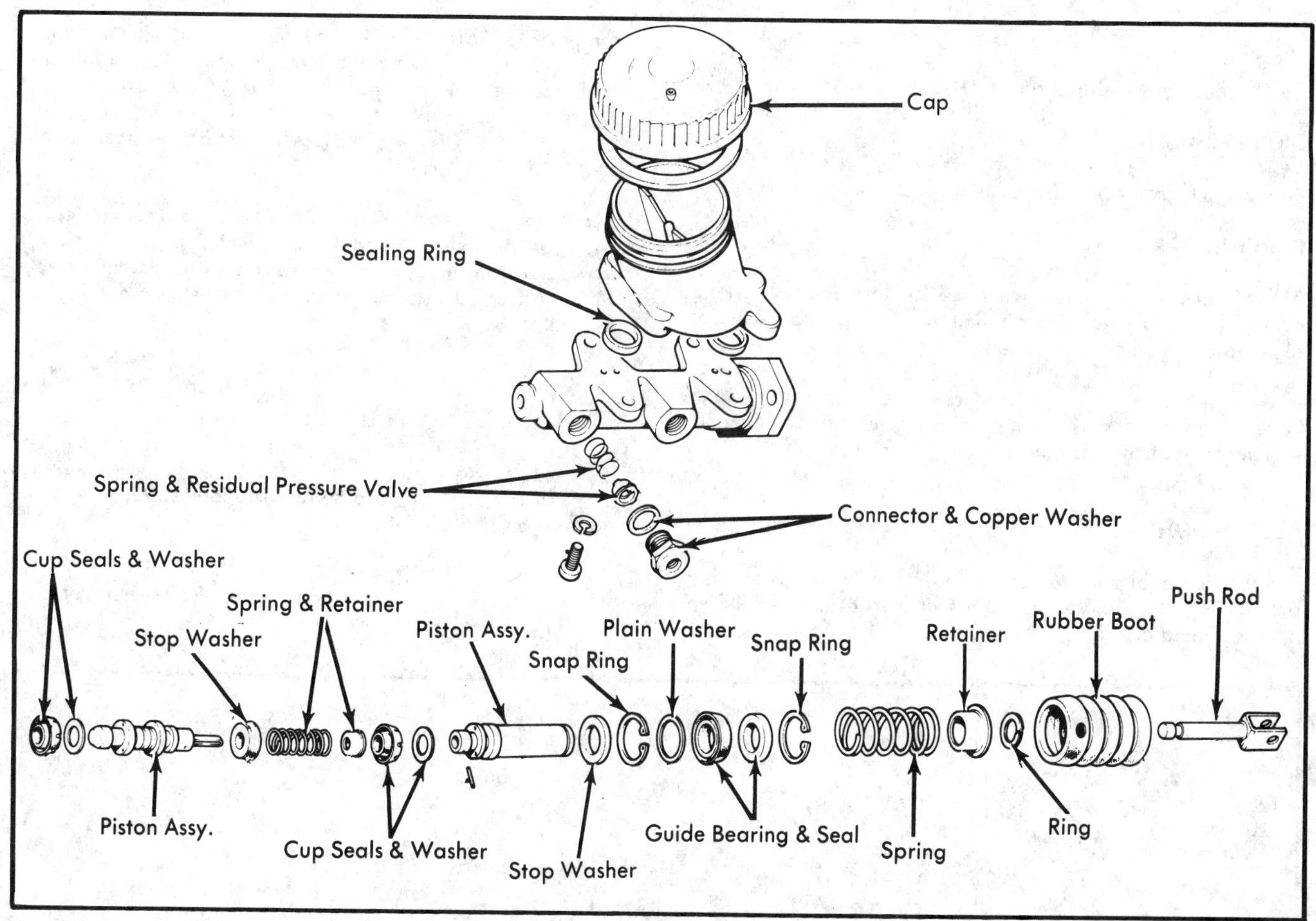

Fig. 4 Exploded View of Master Cylinder Reservoir, Body and Piston Assemblies

BRAKE SYSTEM SPECIFICATIONS				
Application	Drum Diam. In. (mm)	Wheel Cylinder Diameter		Master Cylinder
		Front In. (mm)	Rear In. (mm)	Diameter In. (mm)
Midget	7 (177.8)	①	.687 (17.46)	.750 (19.05)

① – Front wheel disc brakes

OPEL

All Models

DESCRIPTION

Brake system has a two-part circuit. Front brakes are one circuit, consisting of a dual piston caliper and a rotor. Leading-trailing, rear drum brakes make up other circuit. Drum brakes are self-adjusting. A dual piston master cylinder supplies the hydraulic pressure for brake system. Some models may be equipped with a Master-Vac power brake unit. All models are fitted with a mechanical parking brake. Control handle for parking brake is mounted between front seats and, when actuated, locks rear wheels.

ADJUSTMENT

DISC BRAKES

Disc brakes are self-adjusting.

DRUM BRAKES

Rear drum brakes are self-adjusting.

PARKING BRAKE

1) Adjustment is required when service brakes are working properly but parking brake handle must be pulled excess of eight notches to lock rear wheels.

2) Release parking brake and check cable for free movement. Take up cable slack by turning adjusting nut at yoke connection until lever travel is from five to eight notches.

PEDAL HEIGHT

Turn brake pedal push rod until pedal height is approximately 6¾" (171 mm). Adjust stop light switch so brake pedal free play is eliminated. Tighten lock nuts.

HYDRAULIC SYSTEM BLEEDING

NOTE — *To avoid damage to push rod seal, engine must be running during bleeding operation.*

Attach a bleeder tube to bleeder screw and immerse opposite end of tube in a container partially filled with brake fluid. Open bleeder screw and allow pedal to be pushed through its full travel. Close bleeder screw and let pedal return to normal height. Continue procedure until all air is expelled from cylinder. Repeat bleeding procedure at remaining wheels.

REMOVAL & INSTALLATION

FRONT DISC BRAKE PADS

Removal — Raise vehicle and support on safety stands. Remove spring clips, mounting pins, damper ("M") spring, pad shims, and disc pads. Inspect pads for wear or damage and replace pads if worn beyond .067" (1.70 mm). Inspect caliper cavity for leaks. **NOTE** — *All pads must be replaced at one time.*

Installation — Seat piston into caliper bore using tool J-22430 (or equivalent). Fit anti-squeal shims to disc pads with arrow facing in direction of normal disc rotation. Fit damper ("M") spring and insert mounting pins. Install mounting pin spring clips.

FRONT DISC BRAKE CALIPER

Removal — Raise and suitably support vehicle. Remove wheel. Disconnect and plug caliper brake line. Remove mounting bolts and lift off caliper.

Installation — To install caliper assembly, reverse removal procedure. Bleed hydraulic system.

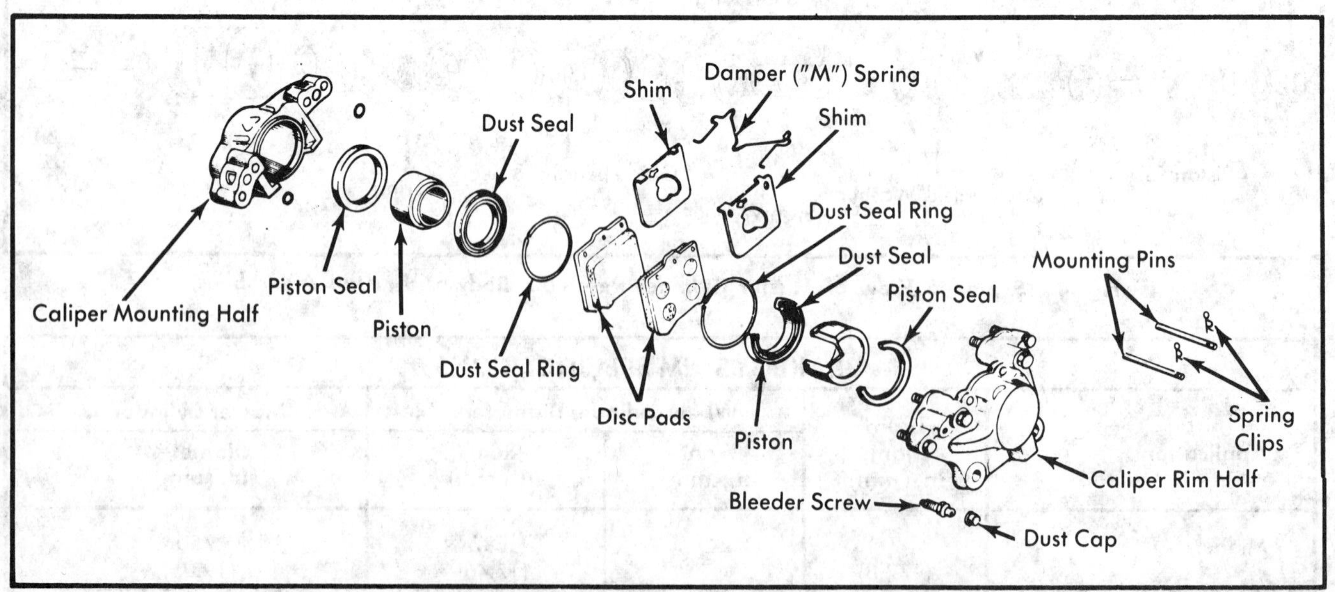

Fig. 1 Exploded View of Opel Front Disc Brake Assembly

OPEL (Cont.)

FRONT DISC BRAKE ROTOR

Removal – Raise and suitably support vehicle. Remove wheel. Remove caliper without disconnecting brake fluid line. Suspend caliper from upper control arm using a wire hanger. Remove grease cap and take out the outer wheel bearing assembly. Pull hub and rotor assembly from spindle. Remove bolts mounting rotor to hub and index mark before separating.

Installation – To install, reverse removal procedure and note the following. Make sure wheel bearings are properly tightened. *See Wheel Bearing Adjustment in WHEEL ALIGNMENT Section.* Measure brake rotor runout. If runout exceeds .006" (.15 mm), resurface or replace rotor.

REAR BRAKE SHOES

Removal – Raise and suitably support vehicle on safety stands. Remove wheel and drum. Remove return springs, shoe hold down pins, retainers and springs. Fully expand adjuster mechanism and disconnect strut. Remove primary shoe. Disconnect parking brake lever from cable; then remove secondary shoe. If necessary, wheel cylinder can now be removed.

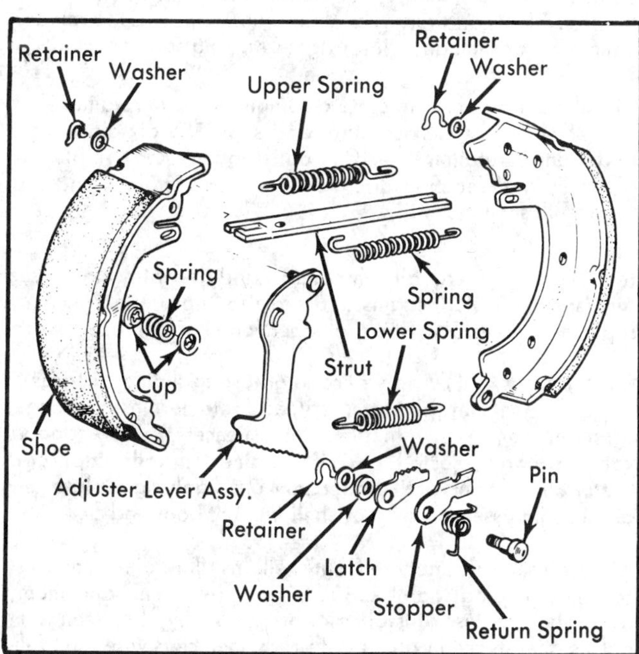

Fig. 2 Exploded View of Rear Brake Assembly

Installation – To install brake shoes, reverse removal procedure and note the following: Make sure brake shoes do not scratch wheel cylinder boots during installation. Halves of adjuster mechanism are not reversible. Right and left side self-adjuster components are not interchangeable.

MASTER CYLINDER

Removal – Disconnect front and rear brake lines from master cylinder. Take off nuts mounting cylinder to power brake unit support bracket. Separate brake fluid reservoir bracket and lift off master cylinder assembly complete with fluid reservoir and hoses.

Installation – To install master cylinder, reverse removal procedure.

POWER BRAKE UNIT

Removal – Remove master cylinder as previously outlined. Disconnect vacuum hose from check valve. Remove clevis pin and brake pedal arm. Remove nuts mounting power brake unit to fire wall spacer and lift unit from vehicle.

Installation – To install, reverse removal procedure and note the following: Adjust push rod length to .733" (18.6 mm). Adjust brake pedal height as previously outlined.

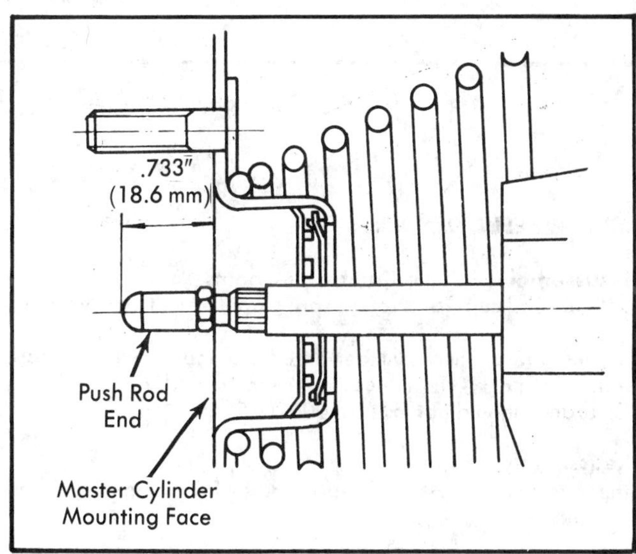

Fig. 3 Power Brake Unit Push Rod Measurement Points for Adjustment

OVERHAUL

FRONT DISC BRAKE CALIPER

Disassembly – Remove each piston dust seal ring, then take out dust seal. Fit clamp J-2242 (or equivalent) to caliper mounting half piston, then force air pressure into fluid inlet to push rim half piston from caliper bore. Repeat procedure on opposite side to remove other piston. Remove seals from grooves in piston bores. **NOTE** – *Use a pointed, but not sharp instrument to dig out seal.*

Inspection – Inspect cylinder bores for signs of wear or scoring. Check calipers and adaptor plates for distortion, replace as necessary.

Installation – Lightly coat seals and cylinder bore walls with suitable grease. Fit new seals to grooves in caliper bore. Insert one piston and push to bottom of caliper bore. Install dust seal and seal ring. Repeat procedures on opposite side piston.

OPEL (Cont.)

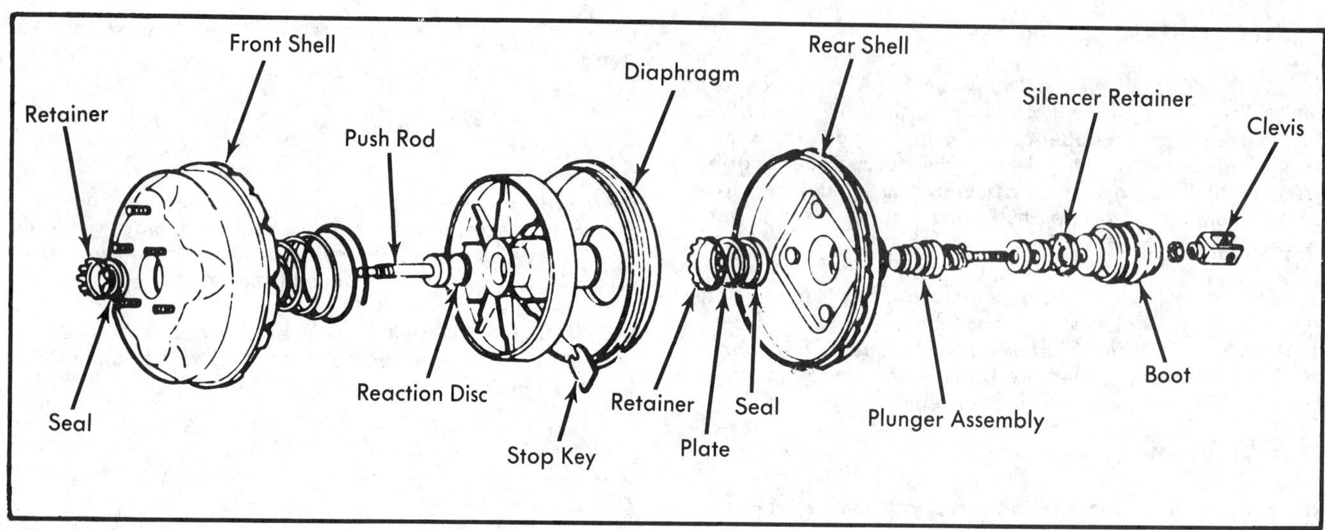

Fig. 4 Exploded View of Opel Master-Vac Power Brake Assembly

REAR WHEEL CYLINDER

Disassembly – Pull off rubber dust boots. Push from one side until pistons, cups, and return spring are forced from cylinder.

Inspection – Check cylinder bore for damage, wear or score marks. Check clearance between cylinder and bore. Clearance should not exceed .006" (.15 mm).

Reassembly – Lightly coat pistons, cups, and return spring, then reverse disassembly procedure for remaining components.

MASTER CYLINDER

Disassembly – Empty excess brake fluid from master cylinder reservoir. Separate reservoir from cylinder body. Remove brake line connectors and take out check valves, springs and retainers. Insert screwdriver and push in primary piston enough to remove secondary stop bolt and snap ring. Withdraw both piston assemblies and separate remaining components.

Inspection – Clean all parts in brake fluid and dry with compressed air. Inspect master cylinder bore for damage or wear. Measure bore diameter, value should be .875" (22.2 mm). If pistons are found defective or damaged, replace entire piston assembly. Always replace piston cup during overhaul. Master cylinder to piston clearance should be no more than .006" (.15 mm).

Reassembly – To reassemble, reverse disassembly procedure and not the following: Lightly coat all components with brake fluid before reassembling. Make sure check valve with hole is installed on front side. Insert primary piston and fit snap ring, then push in with screwdriver and install stop bolt.

POWER BRAKE UNIT

Disassembly – 1) Index mark shell halves. Remove nuts and spacer from rear shell. Remove clevis. Use tool J-22805-01 (or equivalent) and clamp front shell in vise. Use tool J-9504-01 (or equivalent) and turn rear shell counterclockwise to remove. Take off rear shell and diaphragm retaining spring.

2) Take out diaphragm plate assembly. Remove retainer from rear shell, then take out plate and seal. Slip off diaphragm and silencer retainer, then pull out stop key. Remove plunger assembly and reaction disc. Pull push rod, retainer and seal from front shell assembly.

Inspection – Clean all components and dry with compressed air. Check all diaphragms and seals for signs of weakening; replace as necessary. Check plunger for wear; replace if worn.

Reassembly – 1) Apply silicone grease to sliding surfaces of all components. Install plate, seal, and retainer. Install plunger assembly complete with filter and silencer. Be sure poppet valve is not projected beyond retainer. Install diaphragm plate. Fit retainer and diaphragm on diaphragm plate. Put diaphragm assembly on rear shell, then fit boot and clevis.

2) Install seal assembly to front shell. Install retainer and push rod. Use holding tool J-22805-01 (or equivalent) and mount front shell in vise. Install diaphragm spring between shell halves, then force in and rotate rear shell clockwise until fully seated and aligned with index marks.

TIGHTENING SPECIFICATIONS

Application	Ft. Lbs. (mkg)
Caliper Mounting Bolts	36 (4.9)
Caliper Brake Line	11 (1.5)
Master Cylinder-to-Power Brake Unit	10 (1.4)
Master Cylinder Brake Line	12 (1.6)
Master Cylinder Brake Line Connector	87 (12.0)
Master Cylinder Stop Bolt	14 (1.9)
Wheel Cylinder Mounting Bolt	7 (.97)

OPEL (Cont.)

BRAKE SYSTEM SPECIFICATIONS

Application	Drum Diam. In. (mm)	Wheel Cylinder Diameter		Master Cylinder
		Front In. (mm)	Rear In. (mm)	Diameter In. (mm)
All Models	8.980 (228.1)	①	.812 (20.6)	.875 (22.2)

① — Front disc brakes.

BRAKE DRUM SPECIFICATIONS

Application	Drum Diameter In. (mm)	Original Diameter In. (mm)	Maximum Refinish Diameter In. (mm)	Discard Diameter In. (mm)
All Models	8.980 (228.1)	8.980 (228.1)	9.040 (229.6)	9.060 (230.1)

PEUGEOT

504
604

NOTE — *604 coverage in this article is limited to disc pad removal and installation.*

DESCRIPTION

Brake system is hydraulically operated, using a tandem master cylinder and a Bendix Mastervac power brake unit. Sedan models are equipped with Girling disc brakes, consisting of a brake rotor and dual piston floating caliper, on all four wheels. Station Wagons use Girling disc brakes on the front wheels and leading-trailing shoe/drum type brakes on the rear wheels. A load actuated compensator is used on all models to provide equal pressure distribution at front and rear brakes. Parking brake lever actuates rear wheel brakes through two cables.

ADJUSTMENT

DISC PADS

Disc brakes are self-adjusting, therefore no adjustment in service is required.

REAR BRAKE SHOES (STATION WAGON)

Raise and support rear of vehicle. To adjust, rotate front adjustment eccentric clockwise until wheel locks, then back off until wheel just turns freely. Repeat procedure for rear adjustment eccentric, but rotate the eccentric counterclockwise. **NOTE** — *Do not alter the adjustment of brake pedal.*

PARKING BRAKE

Sedan (Dashboard Mounted Handbrake) — With parking brake lever fully released, and rear control lever against nylon spacers, tighten adjusting nut until cup washer deflection is .04-.06" (1-1.5 mm). Tighten adjusting lock nut.

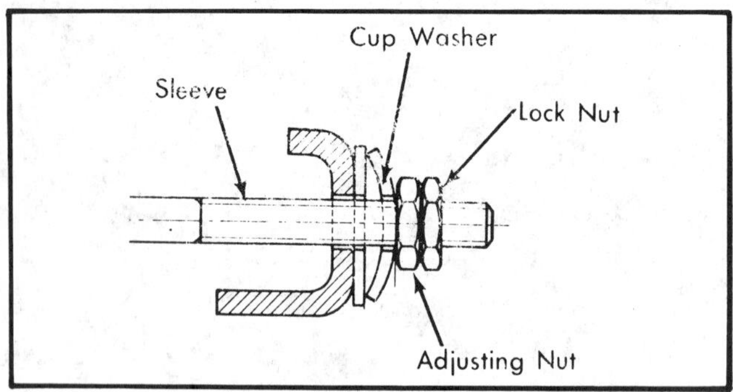

Fig. 1 Sectional View of Parking Brake Adjusting Nut and Cup Washer

Sedan (Handbrake Mounted Between Front Seats) — With parking brake lever fully released, loosen lock nuts on parking brake cables. Loosen adjusting nuts simultaneously until control lever almost touches nylon spacer, then tighten adjusting nuts ½ turn. Tighten lock nut and ensure rear wheels rotate freely with parking brake released.

Station Wagon — With parking brake lever fully released, loosen lock nut on parking brake cable. Tighten adjusting nut until parking brake is operational when lever is pulled 4 to 7 notches. Tighten lock nut and ensure rear wheels rotate freely with parking brake released.

BRAKE COMPENSATOR

NOTE — *During compensator adjustment, spare tire should be in place, and fuel tank should be full.*

Raise and support vehicle under frame. Place an 11 lb. (5 kg) weight on upper rear of compensator lever, and place a .05" (1.4 mm) feeler gauge between adjuster screw and compensator piston. **NOTE** — *If reservoir is empty, use a .06" (1.6 mm) feeler gauge.* Adjust screw to obtain a tight sliding fit with feeler gauge. Tighten lock nut, and remove weight.

HYDRAULIC SYSTEM BLEEDING

Attach a bleed tube to bleeder screw and immerse opposite end of tube in a container partially filled with brake fluid. Pump brake pedal two or three times, keep pedal fully depressed, open bleeder screw and exhaust air, close bleeder screw, and return brake pedal. Repeat operation until air bubbles are no longer seen in discharged fluid. Repeat procedure on remaining brake lines until air is bled from complete hydraulic system.

REMOVAL & INSTALLATION

DISC PADS

Removal, Except 604 Front — Raise and support vehicle under frame. Remove wheel for brake caliper to be serviced. Disconnect disc pad wear indicator electrical lead. Remove disc pad thrust spring, retaining fork mounting bolt and retaining fork. Remove pad assembly from caliper.

Installation — To install, reverse removal procedure and note the following: Using a suitable tool press pistons to bottom of caliper bore before installing pads. Replace retaining fork and springs when fitting new pads.

Removal, 604 Front — Raise and support front of vehicle. Remove tire and wheel. Disconnect disc pad wear indicator wire. Use a small diameter drift and remove disc pad retaining pins. Pry out spreader spring. Force piston into caliper bore and pull out inner pad. Pull caliper back so retaining boss on outer pad is uncovered. Remove outer pad.

Installation — To install, reverse removal procedure and note: Make sure retaining boss of outer pad is securly seated.

REAR BRAKE SHOES

Raise and support rear of vehicle, remove wheel and brake drum. Disengage return springs and mounting assemblies. Separate parking braking linkage from shoe. Pull brake shoes from wheel cylinder and lift from backing plate. To install reverse removal procedure and adjust brakes.

PEUGEOT (Cont.)

BRAKE CALIPER

Removal – Raise and support vehicle under frame. Mark wheel and hub for reassembly reference, then remove wheel. Disconnect brake pad wear indicator lead, and remove hydraulic hose from caliper housing. Disconnect parking brake cable and housing on rear calipers. Remove caliper mounting bolts, and remove caliper assembly from vehicle.

Installation – To install, reverse removal procedure, making sure hub and wheel reference marks are aligned. Bleed hydraulic system.

BRAKE ROTOR

Inspection – Mount a dial indicator to wheel hub carrier such that indicator contact tip is .984" from outer edge of rotor. Rotate disc through at least one complete revolution, and note indicator reading. Maximum allowable deflection is .003".

Removal (Front) – Remove caliper mounting bolts, and support caliper out of way to prevent damage to brake hose. Remove wheel bearing adjusting nut and outer wheel bearing. Remove rotor assembly from vehicle. Hub and disc may now be separated by removing disc attaching bolts from rear of hub.

Removal (Rear – Exterior Mounted Rotor) – Remove flexible brake hose from bracket on rear control arm. Remove brake line from clamp on rear arm. Remove disc pads, then remove caliper assembly and support it out of the way. Remove rotor attaching nut, and remove rotor assembly from vehicle.

Removal (Rear – Interior Mounted Rotor) – Remove flexible brake hose from bracket on rear control arm. Remove brake line from clamp on rear arm. Remove disc pads, then remove caliper assembly and support it out of the way. Remove drive shaft. Disconnect control arm and support it out of the way. Remove hub carrier attaching nut and remove rotor assembly from vehicle. Hub and disc may now be separated.

Installation (All Models) – To install, reassemble hub and disc (if disassembled), and reverse removal procedure.

MASTER CYLINDER

Removal & Installation – Using a siphon, drain brake fluid from master cylinder. Disconnect all hydraulic lines from master cylinder. Remove master cylinder-to-power brake unit attaching nuts and lift off master cylinder. To install, reverse removal procedure, fill master cylinder with new brake fluid and bleed hydraulic system.

OVERHAUL

FRONT DISC BRAKE CALIPER

Disassembly – Clamp caliper assembly in a soft-jawed vise. Remove thrust spring, retaining fork bolt, retaining fork, and disc pads. Using suitable tool (8.0803 E), bottom piston in caliper bore. Remove caliper armature, and disengage armature from grooves in caliper housing. Remove spring clips securing piston protectors, and remove protectors. Force both pistons out of caliper bore. Remove nylon spacer from piston on armature side. Remove sealing rings from caliper bore. Clean pistons and caliper with denatured alcohol.

Reassembly – Lubricate new rubber parts with suitable lubricant prior to reassembly. Install sealing rings in caliper bore. Fit pistons in caliper bores, with piston groove inclined ⅛ turn from vertical. Install protectors with thin spring clip on rotor side. Position nylon spacer in piston, and install thrust plate. Install caliper armature, retaining fork, retaining fork bolt, and disc pads.

REAR DISC BRAKE CALIPER

Disassembly – Clamp caliper assembly in a soft-jawed vise. Remove thrust spring, retaining fork, and disc pads. Turn piston so that groove in piston is ⅛ turn from vertical toward disc pad guide. Remove thrust spring from armature, and remove armature from caliper housing. Remove parking brake return spring, then remove parking brake lever. Remove nylon spacer from piston, and remove piston protectors. Remove both pistons by pushing against grooved piston. Remove sealing rings from caliper bore, and clean pistons and caliper with denatured alcohol.

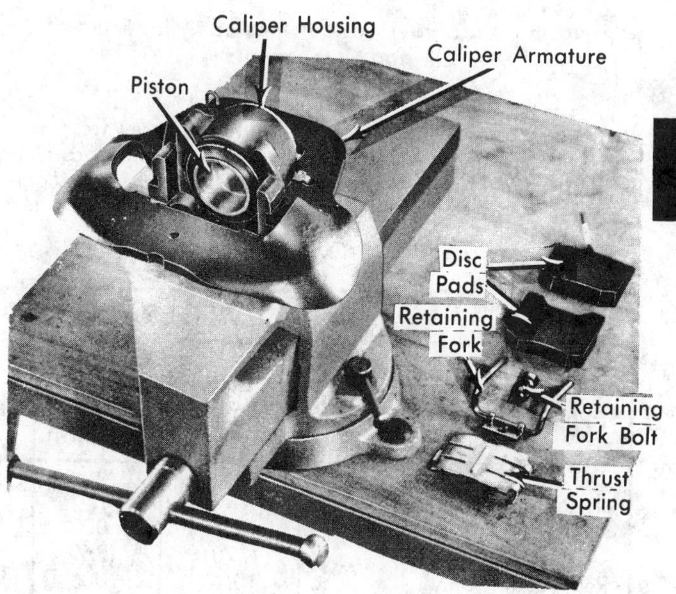

Fig. 2 Disassembling Disc Brake Caliper

Reassembly – Lubricate new rubber parts with suitable lubricant prior to reassembly. Install sealing rings in caliper bores. Fit pistons into caliper bores, with piston groove inclined ⅛ turn from vertical. Install parking brake lever. Install protectors, with thin spring clip on rotor side. Raise parking brake lever, and install nylon spacer on piston. Install thrust plate, and install parking brake return spring. Install caliper armature, retaining fork, retaining fork bolt, and disc pads.

PEUGEOT (Cont.)

MASTER CYLINDER

Disassembly – 1) Mount master cylinder in a soft jaw vise. On Lockheed master cylinders, remove reservoir attaching screw from inside each reservoir and separate each reservoir from master cylinder. On Teves master cylinders, separate reservoir from master cylinder by pulling it from sealing grommets, then remove grommets.

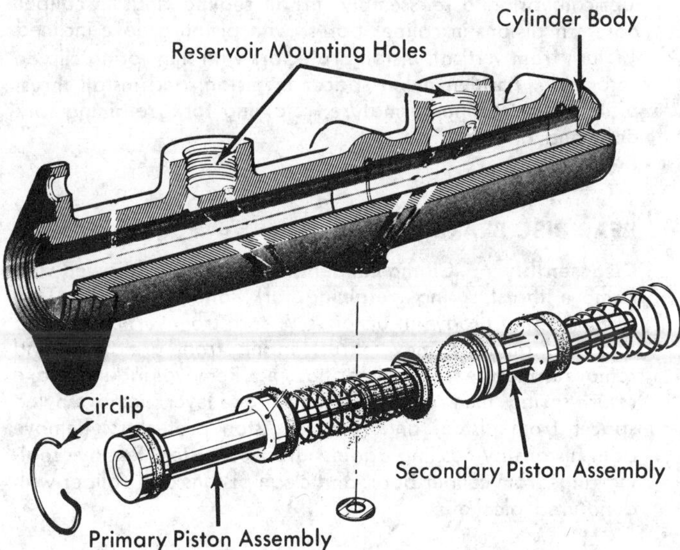

Fig. 3 Cutaway View of Master Cylinder Body and Components

2) On all master cylinders, remove piston stop screw from rear reservoir mounting hole. Remove piston circlip and stop washer, then lift out primary piston assembly. Using compressed air, remove secondary piston assembly. NOTE – *Do not disassemble piston assemblies, if either assembly is damaged or worn, replace both piston assemblies.*

Inspection – Wash all parts in denatured alcohol and blow dry with compressed air. Inspect all parts for scoring, burrs, corrosion, wear or distortion and replace as necessary. NOTE – *Do not polish cylinder bore with emery cloth.*

Reassembly – Reverse disassembly procedure and note the following: Coat all parts with clean brake fluid prior to reassembly. After reassembly is completed, push in primary piston several times and ensure it returns fully and smoothly to its stop each time.

POWER BRAKE UNIT

NOTE – *Power brake unit is serviced as an assembly only. Do not attempt to overhaul.*

TIGHTENING SPECIFICATIONS

Application	Ft. Lbs. (mkg)
Caliper Mounting Bolts	
Front	51 (7)
Rear	31 (4.3)
Retaining Fork Bolt	13 (1.8)
Rotor-to-Hub Bolts	34 (4.7)
Hub Carrier Nut	181(25)
Wheel Stud Nut	43 (6)
Parking Brake Cable Bracket Bolt	7 (1)

DISC BRAKE ROTOR SPECIFICATIONS

Application	Disc Diameter In. (mm)	Lateral Runout In. (mm)	Parallelism In. (mm)	Original Thickness In. (mm)	Minimum Refinish Thickness In. (mm)	Discard Thickness In. (mm)
All Models						
Front	10.75 (273)	.003 (.07)	.0008 (.02)	.502 (12.75)	.443 (11.25)	.423 (10.75)
Rear (Sedan Only)	10.75 (273)	.003 (.07)	.0008 (.02)	.394 (10)	.354 (9)	.335 (8.5)

BRAKE DRUM SPECIFICATIONS

Application	Drum Diameter In. (mm)	Original Diameter In. (mm)	Maximum Refinish Diameter In. (mm)	Discard Diameter In. (mm)
Station Wagon (Rear)	11.024 (280)	11.024 (280)	11.063 (281)	11.083 (281.5)

PORSCHE

911 & Turbo Carrera
924

DESCRIPTION

Brake systems are hydraulically operated, utilizing a tandem master cylinder and a power brake unit. 911 models are equipped with front and rear disc brakes. 924 models are equipped with front disc brakes and rear shoe brakes. All models utilize mechanical parking brakes that operate off of the rear brakes. All models have a brake warning light that is activated when there is a pressure drop in hydraulic system. Warning light on instrument panel comes on and will not go out until problem is corrected.

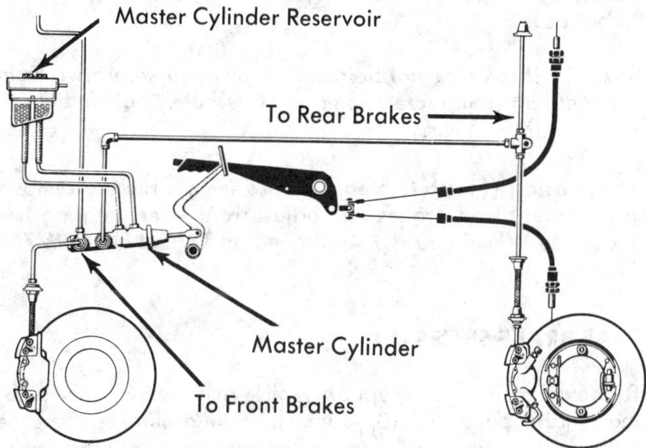

Fig. 1 Hydraulic Fluid Distribution for Dual Circuit Brake System

ADJUSTMENT

DISC BRAKES

Disc brakes are self adjusting, therefore no adjustment in service is required.

REAR BRAKE SHOES

924 (Rear Brakes) – Turn adjuster until a slight drag is felt when rotating brake drum. Back off adjuster until drum is just free to rotate.

PARKING BRAKE

911 Models – Raise and support vehicle, and remove rear wheels. Release parking brake lever and push pistons and pads into caliper to allow rotor to turn freely. Loosen parking brake cable lock nuts until cable is slack. Working through access hole in parking brake drum, turn star wheel adjuster until rotor can no longer be turned by hand. Adjust parking brake cable at rear cable end until it just begins to pull and tighten lock nuts. Back off on star wheel adjuster until rotor turns freely without drag. Repeat procedure on opposite wheel and check parking brake operation.

924 Models – Raise and support vehicle and ensure rear brakes are properly adjusted. From inside of vehicle, pull parking lever up by two notches. At base of lever adjust nut until both wheels can just be turned by hand.

BLEEDING SYSTEM

Bleeding Sequence – If equipped with outer and inner caliper half bleed screws, always bleed outer caliper half fist and inner half second. Bleed brakes as follows: Left rear first, right rear second, right front third, and left front last.

CAUTION – *When any fluid fitting is disconnected, fluid will drain from reservoir through master cylinder and out open fitting. To avoid this, depress brake pedal far enough so piston cup will pass the compensating (resupply) port.*

Pressure Bleeding – Fill pressure bleeder with brake fluid and pressurize tank to 32.3 psi (2.2 atm). Connect bleeder to reservoir and connect a small bleed hose to first bleed screw. See *Bleeding Sequence*. Place other end in container partially filled with brake fluid. Open bleed screw 1/2 – 3/4 turn and allow fluid to drain until no air bubbles are apparent in fluid. Close bleed screw and repeat operation for each bleed screw in turn.

NOTE – *If brake system was completely drained, it may be necessary to perform bleeding, in sequence, more than once.*

Manual Bleeding – Fill reservoir with brake fluid and connect a small hose to first bleed screw. See *Bleeding Sequence*. Place other end in container partially filled with brake fluid. Have an assistant rapidly pump brake pedal until slight pressure is felt, then hold pedal depressed. Open bleed screw and allow fluid to drain. Close bleed screw before slowly releasing pedal. Repeat pedal action until fluid flows into container with no bubbles. Repeat at each bleed screw in turn.

REMOVAL & INSTALLATION

NOTE – *On 911 models, in late 1975 a new "Type A" caliper was introduced to replace both previously used "Type M&S" calipers. All calipers are similar. The main differance is the disc pads. Because of clearance problems, redesignated pads are used.*

DISC PADS

NOTE – *Mark pads and calipers before removal. If pads are to be reused, they must be installed in original location. If only one pad on front or rear needs replacing, all four pads must be replaced.*

Removal – Raise and support vehicle and remove wheels. Remove retaining pin clips and using a punch, drive retaining pins out of caliper (toward center of vehicle). On 924 models remove inside brake pad first, outside brake pad is guided by a tab on caliper frame, press out this frame to pull out brake pad.

NOTE – *Depress spreader spring if required. Using a suitable extractor (P86) pull pads from caliper.*

CAUTION – *If fluid level is too high in reservoir, overflow will result when pistons (during installation) are pushed back into calipers.*

Installation – Push piston back into caliper using suitable tool (P83), or wooden block. Remove anti-rotation locks (if equipped) and clean all parts with alcohol. Inspect all parts for damage or wear. Ensure piston 20° position is correct using suitable gauge (P84). Install remaining parts in reverse order of removal, replace parts as necessary.

PORSCHE (Cont.)

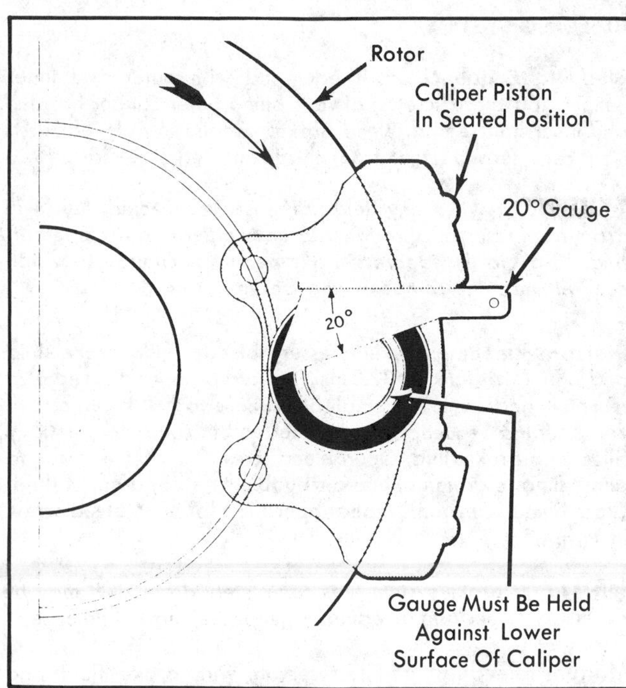

Fig. 2 Using a 20° Gauge to Properly Position Caliper Piston

BRAKE CALIPER

CAUTION – *When any fluid fitting is disconnected, fluid will drain from reservoir through master cylinder and out open fitting. To avoid this, depress brake pedal far enough so piston cup will pass the compensating (resupply) port.*

Removal (Front & Rear) – Raise and support vehicle, and remove wheels. Remove brake pads as previously outlined. Remove splash shield (if necessary), disconnect hydraulic line. Remove mounting bolts and remove caliper assembly.

Installation (Front & Rear) – To install, reverse removal procedure and note the following: Clean and inspect all parts for wear or damage and replace as necessary. Tighten all bolts and fittings to specifications and bleed complete brake system.

BRAKE ROTOR

Removal (Front) – Remove caliper assembly as previously outlined. Remove dust cap from wheel hub, loosen clamp lock screw, then remove clamp nut and thrust washer. Remove rotor and wheel bearings as a unit. On 911 models, mark rotor and hub for reassembly reference, remove attaching bolts and separate rotor from hub.

Removal (Rear) – Remove caliper assembly as previously outlined. Remove the two rotor attaching bolts and pull rotor from hub.

NOTE – *If rotor cannot be removed by hand, insert two 8mm bolts into attaching screw holes and alternately tighten bolts to press rotor from hub.*

Installation (Front & Rear) – To install, reverse removal procedure, bleed brakes and adjust front wheel bearing free play. *See Wheel Bearing Adjustment in WHEEL ALIGNMENT Section.*

REAR BRAKE SHOES

Removal – Raise and support vehicle and remove wheels. Using suitable puller (40-107) remove brake drum. Remove shoe hold down springs. Remove upper and lower return springs and pressure rod. Remove emergency brake rod from brake shoe.

Installation – Reverse removal procedures and note the following: Lubricate adjusting screws and sliding surfaces of brake shoes slightly. Use new bearing pin and clip when installing emergency brake rod.

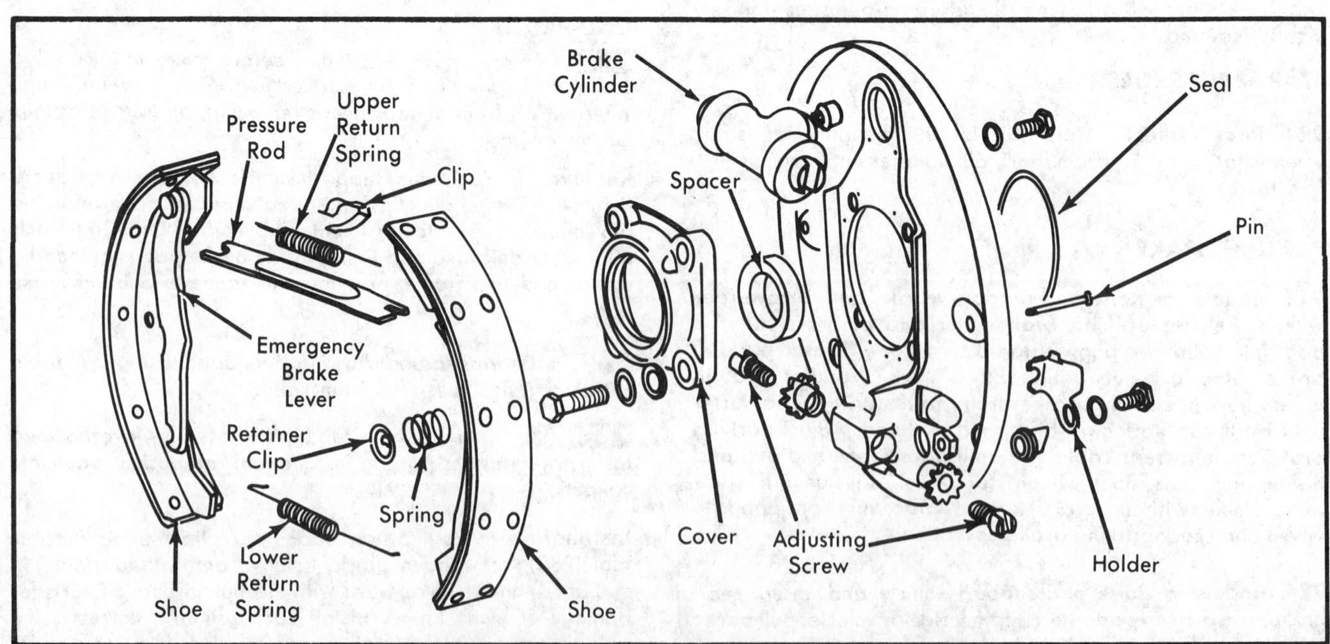

Fig. 3 Exploded View of 924 Rear Wheel Brakes

PORSCHE (Cont.)

REAR WHEEL CYLINDER

Removal – With rear drum and brake shoes removed, disconnect brake line from wheel cylinder at rear of backing plate, remove bolts attaching cylinder and remove cylinder.

Installation – Reverse removal procedure, tighten mounting bolts and bleed hydraulic system.

PARKING BRAKE ASSEMBLY

Removal & Installation – On 911 models, remove cotter pin, castle nut and washer from cable, then remove cable from brake assembly. Remove expander and springs and shoe retaining pins, then springs from upper shoes. Raise upper shoe, withdraw adjuster and spring. Remove shoe retainer from lower shoe and remove both shoes from vehicle. On 924 models, loosen mounting screws and remove entire parking brake lever. It may be necessary to remove tension spring and adjusting rod to remove assembly. To install, reverse removal procedures.

BRAKE PRESSURE REGULATOR

Removal – Disconnect brake lines at pressure regulator. Remove bolts from regulator flange and take out unit.

Checking – Step down hard on the brake pedal while feeling theregulator body; note if piston in regulator is moving. When the brake pedal is released, a slight "knock" should be felt on regulator body.

Installation – To install, reverse removal procedure and bleed brake system.

NOTE – *Brake pressure units can not be overhauled.*

MASTER CYLINDER

Removal – On 911 models, raise and support vehicle and drain fluid from reservoir. Pull back on accelerator pedal to detach pedal from rod. Remove floor mat and floor board and withdraw boot from master cylinder. Remove underpanel covering front axle, remove brake lines, electrical leads and reservoir tubes from cylinder and remove master cylinder from vehicle. On 924 models, remove hydraulic lines from master cylinder and remove electrical connections. Remove mounting nuts and remove master cylinder.

Installation – Reverse removal procedures and note the following: On 911 models, be sure push rod is correctly installed and that clearance between push rod and piston is about .04" (1mm). Use a sealing material on cylinder flange to prevent water leakage into drivers compartment. Bleed both systems as previously outlined.

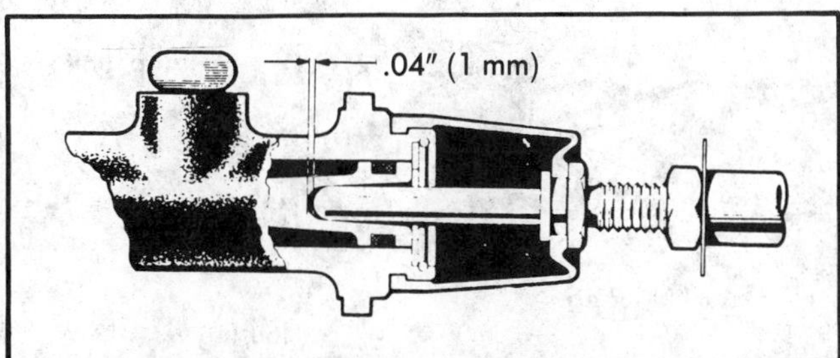

Fig. 4 Illustrating Push Rod-to-Master Cylinder Piston Clearance on 911 Models

POWER BRAKE UNIT

NOTE – *Before removal or overhaul test check valve and power brake unit for operation. To check valve, pull off vacuum hose, place finger over check valve and crank engine, vacuum should be created. To check power brake unit, push on brake pedal several times with engine stopped, hold pedal down and start engine. If power brake unit is operating properly brake pedal will drop slightly.*

Removal – With master cylinder removed, disconnect vacuum hose from power brake unit. Remove pin connecting power brake unit operating rod to brake pedal assembly, remove nuts and remove power brake unit from vehicle.

Installation – Reverse removal procedures and note the following: Apply a suitable sealer to power brake unit mounting surface and vacuum line connections. Adjust pedal height and bleed hydraulic system.

OVERHAUL

BRAKE CALIPER

NOTE – *Cylinders can only be overhauled one at a time, because with one piston removed air pressure is unattainable in second cylinder.*

Disassembly – With pads and piston retaining plates removed, clamp caliper (by mounting flange) in vise. Remove dust cover retaining ring and dust cover. Install suitable piston

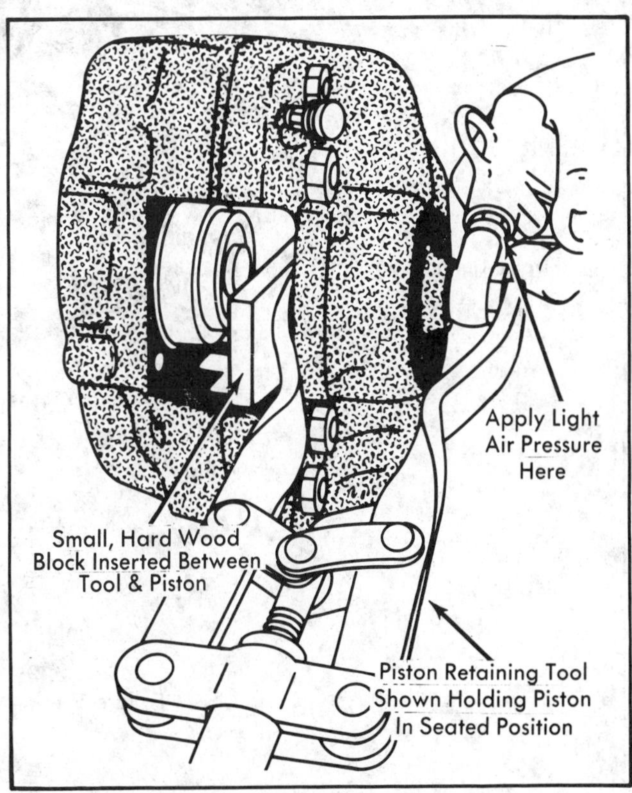

Fig. 5 Using Air Pressure to Remove Piston from Caliper Assembly

PORSCHE (Cont.)

retaining tool (P83) to one piston and place a thin wood block between tool and piston to be removed. Apply air pressure to fluid inlet hole to remove piston. Remove cylinder to piston seal using a plastic or hard rubber tool.

Cleaning & Inspection – Clean all parts in alcohol or clean brake fluid. Check all parts for wear or damage and replace as necessary. If caliper piston or bore show any signs of wear or damage, complete caliper assembly must be replaced.

Separating Caliper Halves – Caliper halves should only be separated if "O" ring seals between caliper halves show signs of leaking. To separate, remove bolts attaching caliper halves, separate caliper and discard "O" ring seals. To reassemble, install new "O" ring seals and reassemble caliper using new bolts, spring washers and nuts.

NOTE – *Install shorter bolts in outside holes. Tighten two inside bolts first and then tighten outside bolts. Bolts must be tightened in two stages; first to 50% of torque value, then to 100% of torque value.*

Reassembly – Reverse disassembly procedure and note the following: Use new rubber components, dust cover retaining ring and pad retaining plates. Apply brake cylinder paste to piston, and cylinder seal. Assure piston is straight with cylinder by using a suitable piston installing clamp. Check 20° position of piston with suitable gauge and correct using piston rotating pliers (if required).

MASTER CYLINDER

Disassembly – Push in on primary piston to remove lock ring, then remove stop plate and primary piston assembly. Remove piston stop screw, and using compressed air, remove secondary piston. Remove secondary piston support washer, spring seat and return spring. To remove hydraulic warning system assembly, remove sending unit and retaining bolt from master cylinder, and using compressed air, remove pistons and springs.

Cleaning & Inspection – Clean all parts with alcohol. Check all pistons and cylinders for out-of-round, corrosion or damage. Inspect all other parts for scoring, excessive wear, corrosion or other damage.

Reassembly – To install reverse disassembly procedure using illustration as a reference and note the following: Lightly coat all parts with a suitable brake cylinder paste before installation. Use new "O" ring seals on warning system sending unit and retaining bolt. Tighten all brake lines and fittings and bleed complete brake system.

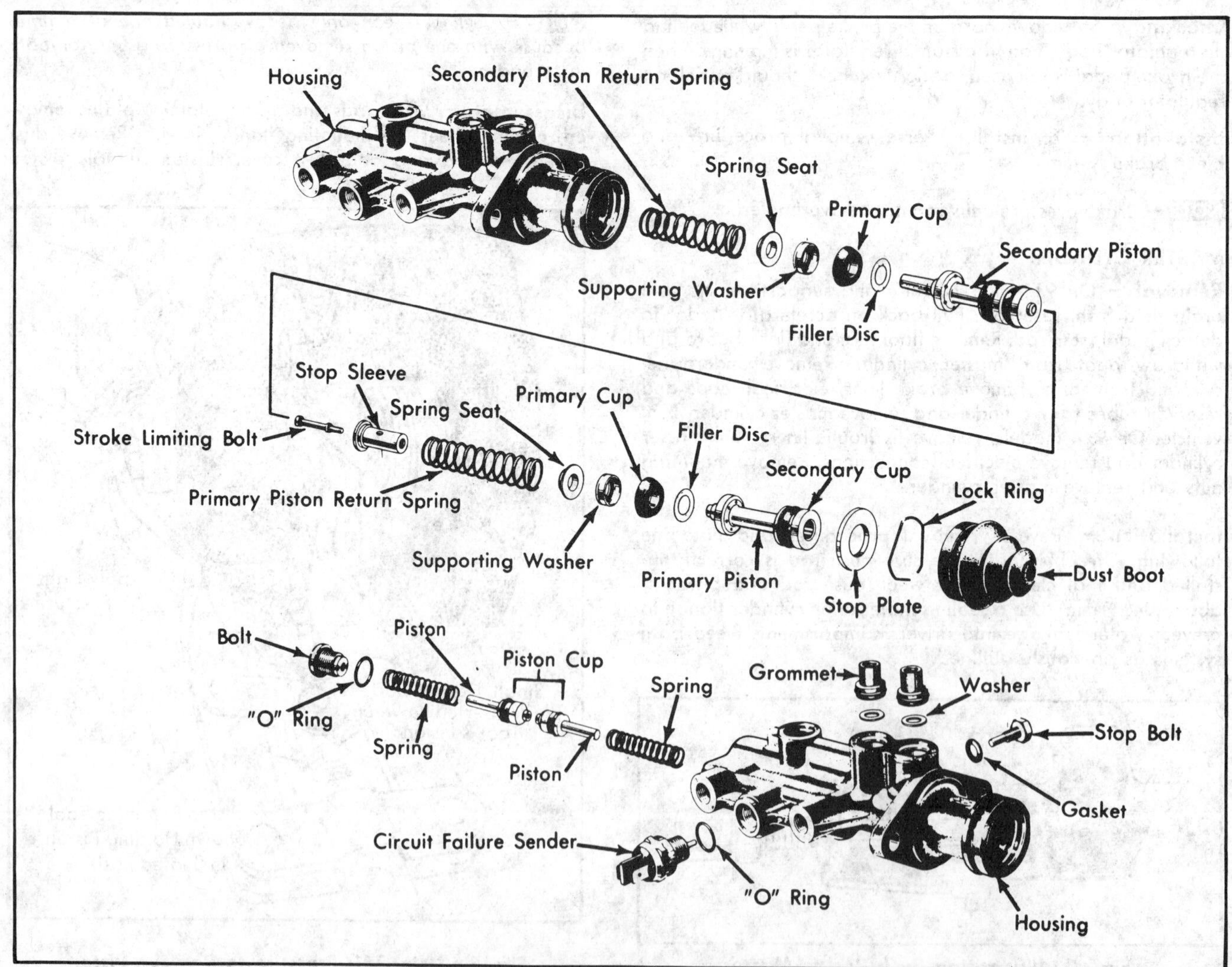

Fig. 6 Master Cylinder Housing, Pistons and Internal Components on 911 Models

PORSCHE (Cont.)

DISC BRAKE ROTOR SPECIFICATIONS

Application	Disc Diameter In. (mm)	Lateral Runout In. (mm)	Parallelism In. (mm)	Original Thickness In. (mm)	Minimum Refinish Thickness In. (mm)	Discard Thickness In. (mm)
911 Models						
Front	11.122 (282.5)	.008 (.2)	.0012 (.03)	.787 (20)	.732 (18.6)	.709 (18)
Rear	11.417 (290)	.008 (.2)	.0012 (.03)	.787 (20)	.732 (18.6)	.709 (18)
924 Models						
Front	10.1 (257)	.....	.....	.5 (13)	.47 (12)	.45 (11.5)

BRAKE SYSTEM SPECIFICATIONS

Application	Drum Diam. In. (mm)	Wheel Cylinder Diameter		Master Cylinder Diameter In. (mm)
		Front In. (mm)	Rear In. (mm)	
924 Models	9.05 (230)	.....	.75 (19.05	.81 (20.64)

TIGHTENING SPECIFICATIONS

Application	Ft. Lbs. (Mkg)
911 Models	
Master Cylinder Mounting Bolts	18 (2.5)
Brake Line Connections	11 (1.5)
Caliper Mounting Bolts (Front & Rear)	50 (7.0)
Caliper Housing Bolts	
Front	25 (3.4)
Rear	16 (2.2)
Rotor-to-Hub	17 (2.3)
Brake Carrier Bolts	34 (4.7)
Splash Shield Bolts	18 (2.5)
924 Models	
Master Cylinder Mounting Bolts	9 (1.3)
Brake Line Connections	9 (1.2)
Caliper Mounting Bolts	60 (8.5)
Rear Brake Cylinder-to-Backing Plate Bolts	15 (2.1)
Splash Shield Bolts	7 (1.0)
Power Brake Unit Mounting Bolts	15 (2.1)
Axle Holding Nut Allen Bolt	11 (1.6)
Rear Wheel Brake Drum Shaft Nut	7 (1.0)

RENAULT

R-5
R-12
R-17

DESCRIPTION

Brake system is hydraulically operated by a tandem master cylinder. Some vehicles may be equipped with a power brake unit. All models are fitted with front disc brakes and rear drum brakes. A pressure limiter valve is used to regulate pressure to rear wheels and prevent rear wheel lock-up. Parking brake cable is lever operated from between the front seats.

ADJUSTMENT

DISC BRAKES

Disc brakes are self adjusting; therefore, no adjustment in service is required.

DRUM BRAKES

NOTE — *R-17 Gordini models have self-adjusting rear drum brakes.*

Remove plastic dust plug and insert screwdriver into opening. Turn star wheel until linings just contact drum. Back off adjuster until wheels rotate freely.

PARKING BRAKE

Manual Adjuster Type — Adjust drum brake shoe clearance. Bleed disc brakes. Fully release parking brake lever. Back off lock nut on parking brake rod. Adjust other nut forward until linings just touch drum. Check that parking brake lever travel is approximately six notches, then tighten lock nut.

Self-Adjuster Type — Place vehicle on hydraulic hoist or leave all wheels on ground. Put parking brake lever in fully released position. Tighten adjustment nut until secondary cable is 25/32" (20 mm) from floor section. NOTE — *If proper adjustment is not maintained at all times, lever will become detached and wear take-up will be out of adjustment.* Normal lever travel is 12-13 notches.

REAR BRAKE PRESSURE LIMITER

NOTE — *Limiter must always be checked and adjusted with vehicle on level ground, trunk empty and driver in driver's seat.*

1) To check limiter, remove one rear wheel cylinder bleeder screw and connect a pressure gauge to wheel cylinder. Bleed hydraulic system. Depress brake pedal and check pressure obtained at rear wheel cylinder. Pressure should be as shown in table.

2) On all models except R-5, rotate one of the nuts on adjustment rod *(See Fig. 1)*. Rotating top nut upward will reduce pressure, while rotating the lower nut upward will increase pressure.

3) To adjust limiter on R-5, release lock nut and tighten adjustment nut to increase pressure or loosen it to reduce pressure.

4) On all models, apply brake pedal several times and recheck adjustment. Remove pressure gauge and bleed hydraulic system.

Pressure Limiter Adjustment

Application	①Psi
R-12	
Sedan	610-655
Station Wagon	500-585
R-17TL	
Coupe	770-810
Convertible	825-870
R-17 Gordini	
Coupe	700-740
Convertible	725-770
R-5	433-437

① — With fuel tank full.

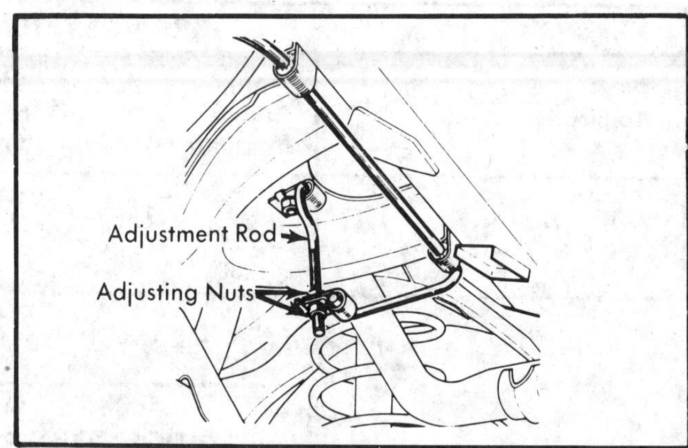

Fig. 1 Pressure Limiter Adjustment Points

HYDRAULIC SYSTEM BLEEDING

NOTE — *On vehicles equipped with power assisted brakes, release vacuum from servo unit prior to bleeding brakes.*

Fill brake reservoir, and connect pressure bleeder. NOTE — *Do not exceed 30 psi with pressure bleeder.* Check each bleeder screw for fluid flow. Close bleeder screw when fluid flowing from screw is free of air. Remove pressure bleeder, and check fluid level in reservoir.

REMOVAL & INSTALLATION

DISC BRAKE PADS

Removal & Installation — Caliper must be removed to replace disc pads. See *Disc Brake Caliper Removal & Installation*.

DISC BRAKE CALIPER

Removal — Raise and support vehicle and remove front wheels. Remove spring clips and slide keys out of caliper and mounting bracket. Disconnect brake line fitting from flexible hose and remove hose retaining clip from body. NOTE — *Brake lines and hoses should not be disconnected for removal of brake pads.* Remove caliper from mounting bracket and disconnect flexible hose from caliper. Remove brake pads and pad spring from caliper.

Installation — To install, reverse removal procedure and note the following: Install longest pad spring on outside of caliper. Tighten all fittings and bleed hydraulic system.

RENAULT (Cont.)

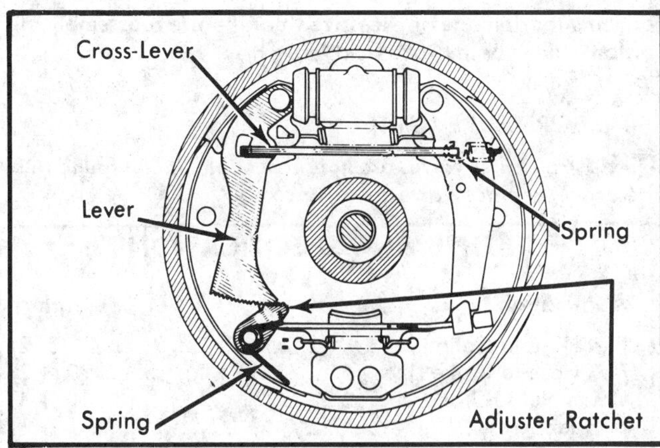

Fig. 2 Assembled View of Early Type Self-Adjusting Drum Brakes

DISC BRAKE ROTOR

Removal & Installation – Remove caliper assembly and pad mounting bracket from vehicle. Take out the three screws securing brake disc. Remove stub axle nut. Fit slide hammer and remove disc/hub assembly. To install, reverse removal procedure.

BRAKE DRUM

Removal – Remove plug in backing plate and insert a screwdriver through hole. Push parking brake operating lever in until peg on lever is clear of brake shoe, then push lever to rear to back off brake shoes. Remove hub grease cap and attaching hardware. Remove drum assembly using a suitable puller.

Installation – To install reverse removal procedure and note the following: Apply a suitable grease to wheel bearings. After installing drum assembly, adjust wheel bearings. See *Wheel Bearing Adjustment in WHEEL ALIGNMENT Section.* Apply brake pedal several times to adjust brake shoes.

DRUM BRAKE SHOES

Removal & Installation – Remove wheel and brake drum from vehicle. Install wheel cylinder clamp, then remove upper brake shoe return spring. On rear brake assembly, disconnect parking brake cable. Unhook shoe hold down springs, and tilt long self-adjuster lever inward. Ease leading shoe away from backing plate, and pull cross lever from shoe. Turn leading shoe at right angle to backing plate and remove lower return spring. Remove both brake shoes. To install, reverse removal procedure.

WHEEL CYLINDER

Removal & Installation – Remove brake drum and brake shoes from vehicle. Disconnect brake line from wheel cylinder, and remove cylinder attaching bolts. Remove cylinder from vehicle. To install, reverse removal procedure and bleed hydraulic system.

MASTER CYLINDER

Removal & Installation – Siphon fluid from master cylinder, and disconnect hydraulic lines at master cylinder. Remove pressure loss indicator bolt (if equipped). Remove cylinder mounting bolts, and remove cylinder from vehicle. To install, reverse removal procedure, and adjust push rod clearance.

POWER BRAKE UNIT

NOTE – *Power brake unit is not serviceable, only the air filter and check valve can be serviced.*

Removal – Disconnect battery, and remove fluid from master cylinder. Remove engine air filter (if necessary). Disconnect hydraulic lines at master cylinder, and remove pressure loss indicator valve bolt (if equipped). Disconnect vacuum hose, and remove clevis from brake pedal. Remove power brake unit attaching nuts from pedal side of firewall, and remove master cylinder and power brake unit as an assembly. Separate master cylinder from power brake unit.

Installation – Measure push rod-to-master cylinder clearance at master cylinder mounting flange, and adjust by turning push rod nut. To install power brake unit, reverse removal procedure, and bleed hydraulic system.

OVERHAUL

DISC BRAKE CALIPER

Disassembly – Remove caliper assembly from vehicle, and remove piston dust cover. Using compressed air, introduced at caliper fluid port, carefully remove piston from caliper assembly. Remove piston seal from cylinder. Using a wedge, spread legs of caliper piston bracket a small amount. Remove caliper stop peg from piston bracket. Slide cylinder assembly from bracket.

Inspection – Clean all parts in denatured alcohol, and inspect for piston and cylinder wear. Replace worn parts as necessary. Replace all rubber seals.

Reassembly – Lubricate cylinder bore, piston, and seals with brake fluid prior to reassembly. To reassemble, reverse disassembly procedure.

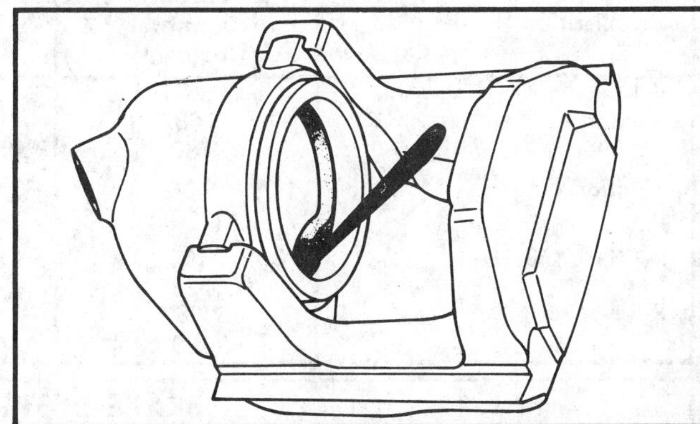

Fig. 3 Prying Seal Out of Caliper Cylinder Bore

MASTER CYLINDER

Disassembly – Clamp master cylinder in a soft-jawed vise. Remove reservoirs, and rubber reservoir sleeves. Using a wooden dowel, push piston into cylinder bore, and remove piston stop screw. Remove snap ring and stop washer from end of cylinder bore, and remove piston assemblies.

Inspection – Clean all parts in denatured alcohol, and check pistons and cylinder bore for wear. If either are worn, replace cylinder as an assembly. Replace all rubber seals.

Reassembly – Lubricate all parts with brake fluid prior to reassembly. To reassemble master cylinder, reverse disassembly procedure.

RENAULT (Cont.)

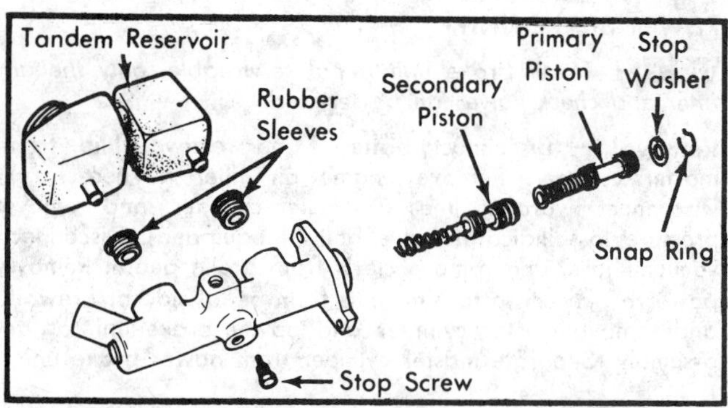

Fig. 4 Master Cylinder and Internal Components

WHEEL CYLINDER

Disassembly & Reassembly – Using the following illustration, disassemble wheel cylinder and examine components for damage or excessive wear. Before reassembly, dip pistons and cups in brake fluid.

BRAKE PRESSURE LIMITER

NOTE – *Limiter valves are not serviceable. If unit found to be defective, replace valve as an assembly.*

TIGHTENING SPECIFICATIONS

Application	Ft. Lbs. (mkg)
Flex Hose-to-Caliper	15 (2)
Flex Hose-to-Brake Line	9 (1.2)
Union Nut-to-Brake Line	10 (1.4)
Bleeder Screw	7 (1)
Caliper Mounting Bracket	50 (7)
Rotor-to-Hub	20 (2.8)
Wheel Stud Nuts	50 (7)

DISC BRAKE ROTOR SPECIFICATIONS

Application	Disc Diameter In. (mm)	Lateral Runout In. (mm)	Parallelism In. (mm)	Original Thickness In. (mm)	Minimum Refinish Thickness In. (mm)	Discard Thickness In. (mm)
R-12 & R-17GTL	9.00 (228)	.004 (.1)	.....	.395 (10)	.355 (9)	.....
R-17 Gordini	9.00 (228)	.004 (.1)	.....	.788 (20)	.433 (11)	.....
R-5	9.00 (228)	.004 (.1)	.....	.395 (10)	.355 (9)	.....

BRAKE DRUM SPECIFICATIONS

Application	Drum Diameter In. (mm)	Original Diameter In. (mm)	Maximum Refinish Diameter In. (mm)	Discard Diameter In. (mm)
R-12				
Sedan	7.087 (180)	7.087 (180)	7.136 (181)	.....
Station Wagon	9.00 (228)	9.00 (228)	9.040 (229)	.....
R-17GTL & Gordini	9.00 (228)	9.00 (228)	9.040 (229)	.....
R-5	7.087 (180)	7.087 (180)	7.136 (181)	.....

BRAKE SYSTEM SPECIFICATIONS

Application	Drum Diam. In. (mm)	Wheel Cylinder Diameter Front In. (mm)	Wheel Cylinder Diameter Rear In. (mm)	Master Cylinder Diameter In. (mm)
R-5	7.087 (180)	1.772① (45)	.866 (22)	.812 (20.6)
R-12				
Sedan	7.87 (180)	1.890① (48)	.866 (22)	.748 (19)
St. Wgn.	9.00 (228.5)	1.890① (48)	.866 (22)	.748 (19)
R-17GTL & Gordini	9.00 (228.5)	2.126① (54)	.866 (22)	.812 (20.6)

① – Caliper cylinder.

SAAB

99

DESCRIPTION

Brake system is hydraulically operated by a tandem master cylinder and power brake unit. Front disc brakes are Girling type consisting of a brake rotor and dual piston, fixed caliper (sliding yoke). Rear brakes are either Girling type with sliding yoke or ATE dual piston type. Parking brake is mechanically actuated and works on FRONT brake assemblies.

ADJUSTMENT

DISC BRAKES

Disc brakes are self adjusting; therefore, no adjustment in service is required.

PARKING BRAKE CABLE

Before adjusting cable, apply brake lever several times to stretch cables. Rotate cable adjusting nuts located at rear of parking brake lever under plastic cover until distance between lever on front caliper and yoke is .016-.022" (.41-.56 mm). Check distance with parking brake fully released.

NOTE – *Parking brake cables are crossed, so to adjust left parking brake mechanism (cable), right adjusting nut must be rotated and vice versa.*

HYDRAULIC SYSTEM BLEEDING

Connect bleeder tube to bleeder screw, and submerge open end of tube in a jar half full of clean brake fluid. Open bleeder screw, and push brake pedal down quickly, allowing it to return slowly. Repeat procedure until fluid flows from bleeder tube with no sign of air. On last downward stroke, close bleeder screw. Bleeding sequence is left-rear, right-front, right-rear, left-front.

REMOVAL & INSTALLATION

DISC BRAKE PADS

Removal, Girling Type – Rotate brake rotor until one of the recesses in edge of rotor is aligned with brake pads. Remove damper spring, pin retaining clips and retaining pins, then lift out brake pads.

Installation – Open bleeder screw and press pistons back into caliper bore, then close bleeder screw. **NOTE** – *On the front brakes, it will be necessary to rotate direct piston while pressing it into caliper bore.* Insert brake pads into caliper, then install retaining pins, clips and damper spring. After installation, apply brake pedal several times to position pads against rotor.

Removal, ATE Type – Clean outside of caliper housing. Turn rotor until recess in edge of rotor is inline with pad. Remove cover plate, mounting pins and spring that retains brake pads. Pull pads out of caliper.

NOTE – *If pads are siezed, use suitable extractor tool (8995771) to remove pads.*

Installation – Seat pistons in bores. Insert new pads. Install spring, lock pins, and cover plate. Pump pedal several times to ensure proper brake operation is taking place.

DISC BRAKE CALIPER

Removal – Raise and support vehicle and remove wheels. On front wheel calipers, disconnect parking brake cable from lever on caliper. On all wheels, disconnect hydraulic line from hose, then plug lines to prevent entry of dirt and loss of fluid. Remove caliper attaching bolts and lift off caliper.

Installation – To install, reverse removal procedure and note the following: Tighten all attaching bolts, bleed hydraulic system and adjust parking brake cables.

DISC BRAKE ROTOR

Removal (Front) – Apply parking brake and remove rotor and hub attaching nut from spindle, then release parking brake. Remove caliper assembly (without disconnecting hydraulic line) and support out of way. Using a puller, remove rotor and hub assembly from spindle. Remove the four attaching bolts and separate rotor from hub.

Removal (Rear) – Remove caliper assembly (without disconnecting hydraulic line) and support out of way. Remove the two rotor attaching bolts and lift off rotor.

Installation (Front & Rear) – To install, reverse removal procedure and note the following: Tighten all nuts and bolts and adjust parking brake if necessary.

MASTER CYLINDER

Removal – Disconnect electrical lead to warning switch on master cylinder. Disconnect clutch master cylinder hose from fluid reservoir, then plug reservoir nipple to prevent loss of fluid. Disconnect hydraulic lines from master cylinder. Remove master cylinder-to-power brake unit attaching nuts and lift off master cylinder.

Installation – To install, reverse removal procedure and bleed hydraulic system.

POWER BRAKE BOOSTER

Removal – From inside engine compartment, remove upper circlip from brake pedal push rod. Disconnect all electrical leads, hydraulic lines and vacuum lines from master cylinder and power brake unit. Remove the four attaching nuts and lift off master cylinder and power unit as an assembly. **NOTE** – *Three attaching nuts are removed from inside vehicle while the fourth nut is removed from engine compartment.* Separate master cylinder from power unit.

Installation – To install, reverse removal procedure and bleed hydraulic system.

OVERHAUL

FRONT CALIPER ASSEMBLY

Disassembly, Girling Type – **1)** With caliper removed from vehicle, mount assembly in a soft jawed vise. Remove parking brake return spring. Then remove yoke from caliper assembly and spring and parking brake lever from yoke.

SAAB (Cont.)

2) Remove retaining ring and dust boot, then using compressed air, force out indirect piston assembly from caliper. Press direct piston push rod and remove piston from caliper. Remove "O" rings and seal rings from caliper bore and pistons.

Cleaning & Inspection – Clean all parts, except indirect piston assembly, in clean brake fluid and dry with a clean, lint-free cloth. **NOTE** – *Indirect piston assembly should only be wiped clean to prevent washing off parking brake mechanism lubricant.* Inspect all parts for wear, damage or corrosion and replace as necessary. **NOTE** – *Manufacturer recommends replacing all rubber parts whenever caliper assembly has been disassembled.*

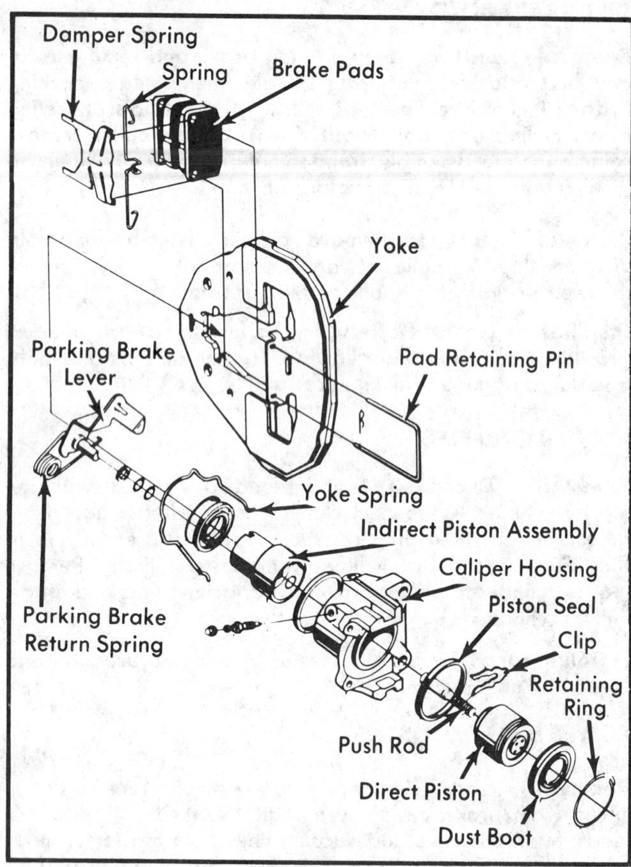

Fig. 1 Exploded View of Girling Front Brake Caliper

Reassembly – 1) Lubricate pistons and caliper bore with clean brake fluid, then install new "O" rings and seal rings to pistons and caliper bore. Install indirect piston into caliper with recess for yoke aligned with groove in caliper housing, then install direct piston in the same manner. Press in indirect piston and screw in direct piston until edges of dust boot grooves are flush with caliper housing.

2) Install dust boots and retaining rings. Fit yoke spring and parking brake lever to yoke, then align yoke guide edges with groove on caliper housing and install yoke. Lift parking brake lever and install axle pin into hole in indirect piston. **NOTE** – *Ensure yoke fits into recess of indirect piston.* Install parking brake return spring. Check clearance between sliding surfaces of yoke and caliper housing; clearance on one side should be .006-.012" (.15-.30 mm), while there should be no clearance on the other side (see illustration).

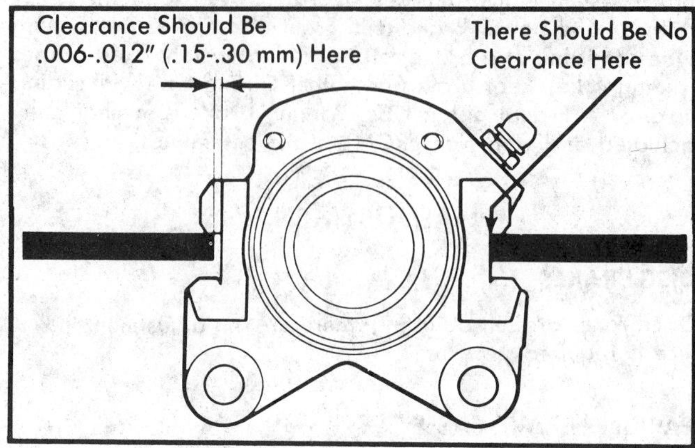

Fig. 2 Girling Front Brake Caliper Clearance Measuring Points

REAR CALIPER ASSEMBLY

Disassembly, Girling Type – 1) With caliper assembly removed from vehicle, mount assembly in soft jawed vise. Remove yoke from caliper assembly by lifting it toward bleeder screw. Then remove yoke spring.

2) Remove retaining ring and dust boot. Using compressed air, force indirect piston from caliper assembly. Push direct piston from caliper assembly. Remove piston seals from caliper bore.

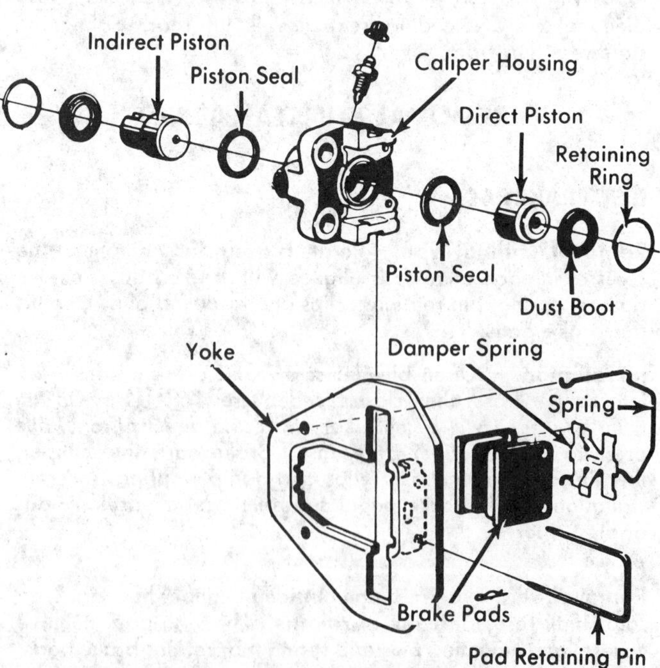

Fig. 3 Disassembled Girling Rear Brake Caliper Showing Internal Component Relationships

SAAB (Cont.)

Cleaning & Inspection – Clean all parts in clean brake fluid and dry with a clean, lint-free cloth. Inspect all parts for wear, damage or corrosion and replace as necessary.

Reassembly – Lubricate caliper bore with clean brake fluid and install new piston seals. Press pistons into caliper bore, then rotate indirect piston until recess for yoke is aligned with groove in caliper housing. Install new dust boot and retaining ring. Install yoke spring on yoke, then install yoke into groove of caliper housing and indirect piston. Check clearance between sliding surfaces of yoke and caliper housing; clearance should be .006-.012" (.15-.30 mm) on bleeder screw side of caliper housing (see illustration).

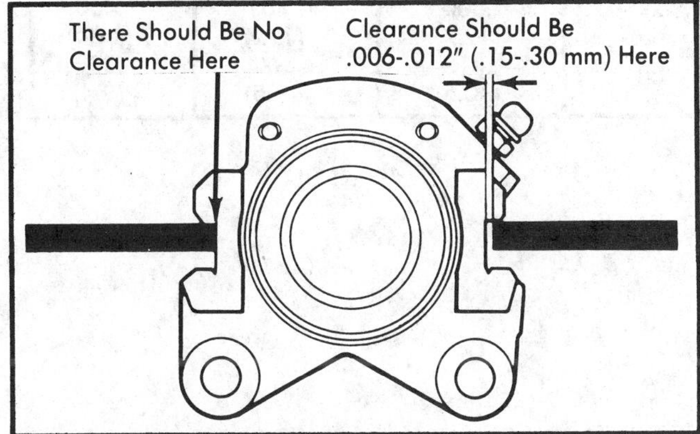

Fig. 4 Girling Rear Brake Caliper Clearance Measuring Points

Disassembly, ATE Type – 1) Clean outside of caliper assembly. Remove pads and caliper as previously outlined. Using suitable clamp (7841323), secure one piston in bore. Apply air pressure to fluid inlet port and force out piston.

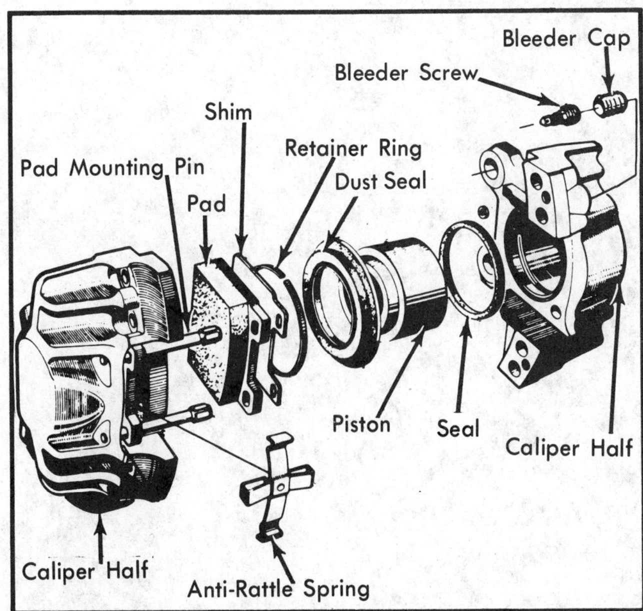

Fig. 5 Exploded View of ATE Type Rear Caliper

2) Carefully remove seals from cylinder bore using a pointed but not sharp instrument. Make sure seal groove is not damaged when removing seal.

NOTE – *Before second piston can be removed and seal replaced, reassembly operation must be completed on first piston.*

Reassembly – Lubricate caliper bore with clean brake fluid and slide new seal into machined groove. Lubricate piston with brake fluid and fit it into cylinder. Install new dust seal and retainer ring. Seat piston into bore and begin disassembly of other piston.

MASTER CYLINDER

Disassembly – 1) With master cylinder removed from vehicle, drain brake fluid from reservoir and mount cylinder in a soft jaw vise. Remove retaining pins and separate reservoir from master cylinder, then remove rubber seals from reservoir mounting holes in cylinder.

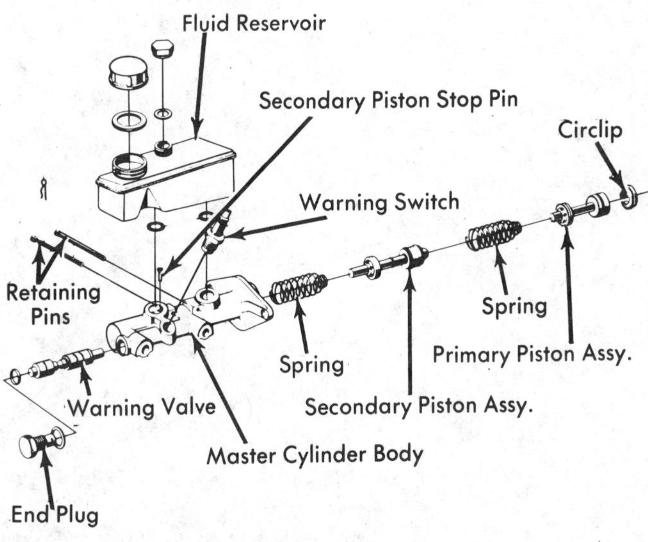

Fig. 6 Master Cylinder Reservoir, Housing and Pistons

2) Push in on primary piston and pull secondary piston stop pin from forward reservoir mounting hole. Remove circlip and take out primary piston assembly and spring. Remove cylinder from vise and carefully knock it against a block of wood to remove secondary piston assembly and spring. Remove brake warning switch from master cylinder, then remove end plug and lift out warning valve assembly.

Cleaning & Inspection – Wash all parts in clean brake fluid and dry with a clean, lint-free cloth. Inspect all parts for wear, damage or corrosion and replace as necessary. **NOTE** – *Manufacturer recommends replacing all rubber parts whenever master cylinder is disassembled.*

SAAB (Cont.)

Reassembly – Reverse disassembly procedure and note the following: Coat all parts with clean brake fluid prior to reassembly. Use care when installing piston assemblies to prevent damage to seals.

POWER BRAKE UNIT

NOTE – *Power brake unit is serviced as a complete assembly only. Do not attempt to overhaul.*

DISC BRAKE ROTOR SPECIFICATIONS						
Application	Disc Diameter In. (mm)	Lateral Runout In. (mm)	Parallelism In. (mm)	Original Thickness In. (mm)	Minimum Refinish Thickness In. (mm)	Discard Thickness In. (mm)
Model 99						
Front	11.024 (280)	.004 (.10)	.....	.500 (12.7)	.461 (11.7)	.460 (11.6)
Rear	10.614 (269.5)	.004 (.10)	.....	.413 (10.5)	.374 (9.5)	.373 (9.4)

SUBARU

1600

DESCRIPTION

Subaru brake system utilizes hydraulically operated service brakes. All models except Coupe use a duo-servo, single anchor front brake with self-adjuster mechanisms. Coupe models use front, single cylinder disc brakes with self-adjuster components. Rear brakes on all models are drum type with leading-trailing shoes. Parking brake operates on front brakes and is mechanically actuated. A tandem master cylinder is located under the hood and supplies hydraulic pressure. Some models use a power brake cylinder to improve the effectiveness of the brake system.

NOTE – *Because of the front wheel drive construction, brakes are mounted inboard to drive axle and are connected directly to differential carrier.*

ADJUSTMENT

PEDAL FREE PLAY

Adjust brake pedal free play to .24-.55" (4-14 mm) by disconnecting wiring from stop light switch and turning switch.

FRONT BRAKES

Self-adjusting, no adjustment required.

REAR BRAKES

Raise vehicle and loosen lock nut. Turn adjusting wedge until wheel locks, then back-off adjuster until wheel is just free to rotate. Tighten lock nut.

PARKING BRAKE

Engage parking brake lever a few serrations. Loosen cable lock nut and adjust turnbuckle for necessary length. Parking brake is correctly adjusted when ratchet travel is between 6-10 notches.

HYDRAULIC SYSTEM BLEEDING

Begin bleeding with wheel furthest from master cylinder and end with wheel nearest master cylinder. With pressure on pedal, open bleed fitting and push pedal its full travel. When pedal is fully depressed, close fitting and let pedal return to fully released position. Repeat procedure until all air is bled from system.

REMOVAL & INSTALLATION

FRONT DISC BRAKE PADS

Removal – Disconnect handbrake cable. Remove pin and stop plug. Force caliper body from brake pad and lift-off pad.

NOTE – *It is not necessary to disconnect brake line to change pads.*

Installation – Return piston to bottom of caliper bore by turning it clockwise with a screwdriver. Place new lining in position. Re-install stop plug and pin and connect handbrake cable.

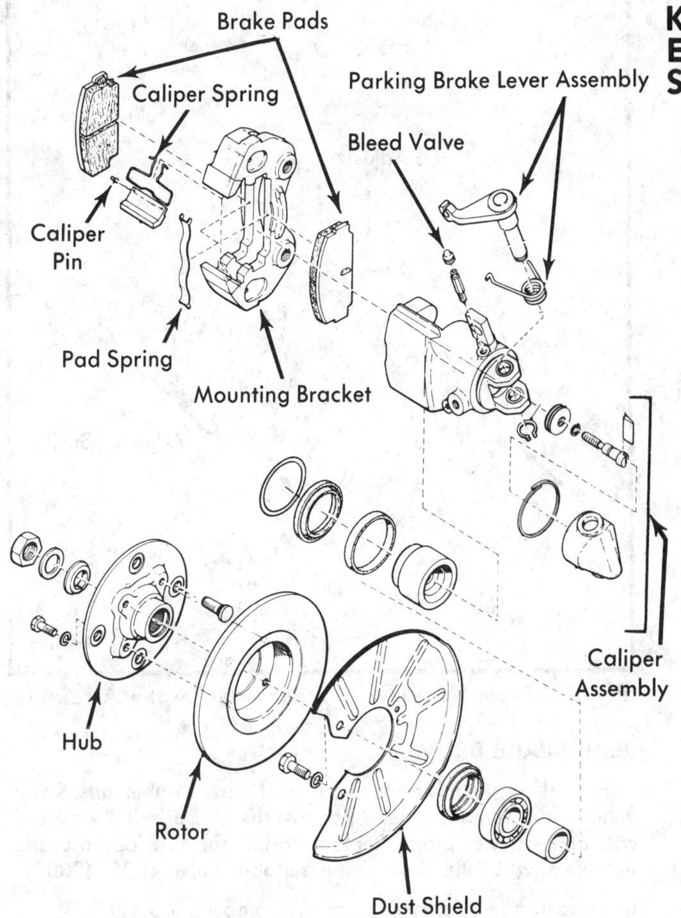

Fig. 1 Exploded View of Front Disc Brake Assembly

FRONT DISC BRAKE ROTOR

Removal – Remove wheel, handbrake cable, stoppers and calipers. Remove two bolts and lift off caliper bracket. Pull rotor from axle using suitable tool (925200000). Remove four bolts to separate rotor from hub.

Installation – To install, reverse removal procedure.

FRONT BRAKE DRUM

Removal – Remove wheel cap and loosen axle nut. Raise vehicle and remove wheel. Remove axle nut and pull off drum using suitable tool (925200000).

Installation – To install, reverse removal procedure.

FRONT BRAKE SHOES

Removal – Remove brake drum. Remove automatic adjuster spring and lever. Remove handbrake cable. Remove shoe return springs using suitable tool (925110000), then remove adjuster cable. Remove shoe set springs using suitable tool (925110000) and remove brake shoes.

Installation – To install, reverse removal procedure.

SUBARU (Cont.)

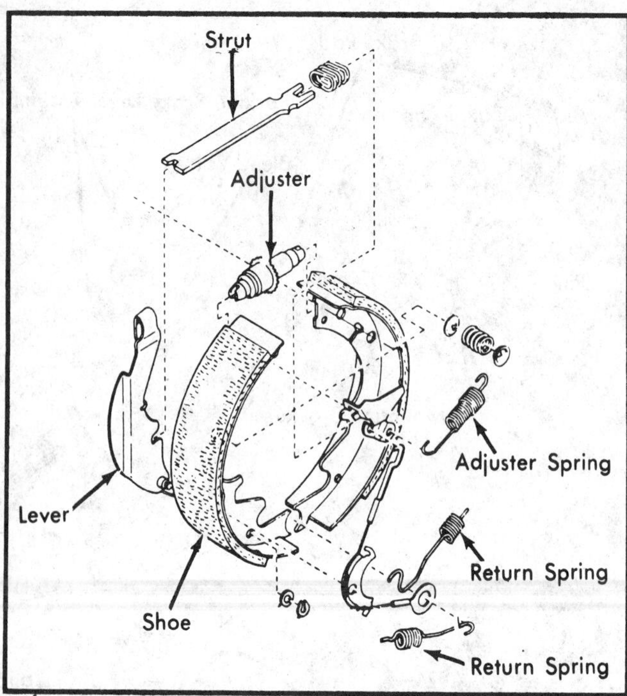

Fig. 2 Exploded View of Front Drum Brake Assembly

REAR BRAKE DRUM

Removal – Remove wheel cap and loosen wheel nuts. Raise vehicle and remove wheel. Remove three cap bolts, washers, cap and stopper plate. Remove cotter pin and loosen castle nut. Remove brake drum using suitable puller (925240000).

Installation – To install, reverse removal procedure.

REAR BRAKE SHOES

Removal – Remove brake drum. Remove three bolts securing back plate and remove brake assembly. Remove shoe setting spring and remove anchor side of shoe first.

Installation – To install, reverse removal procedure.

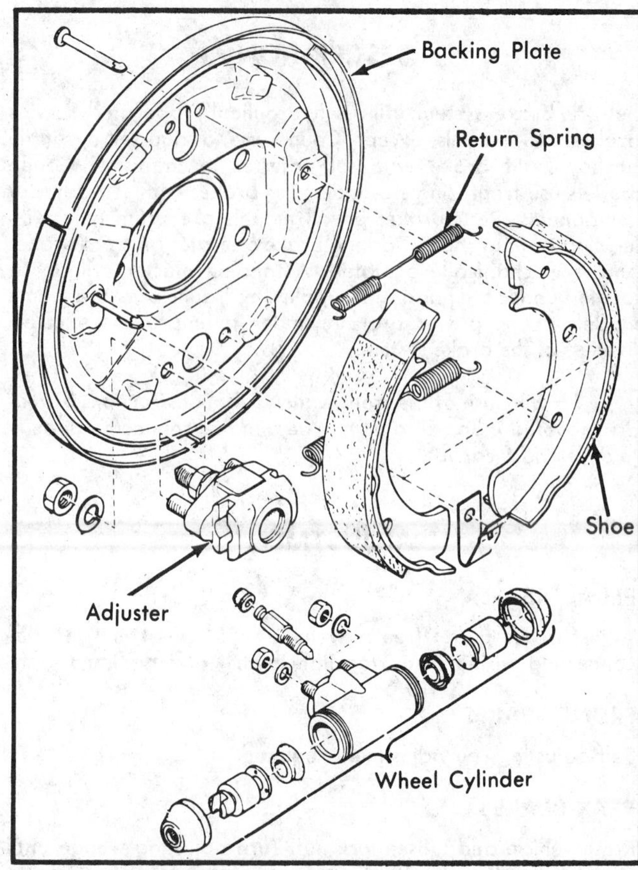

Fig. 3 Exploded View of Rear Drum Brake Assembly

MASTER CYLINDER

Removal – Remove nuts securing brake lines to cylinder. Remove nuts securing cylinder to firewall and remove master cylinder.

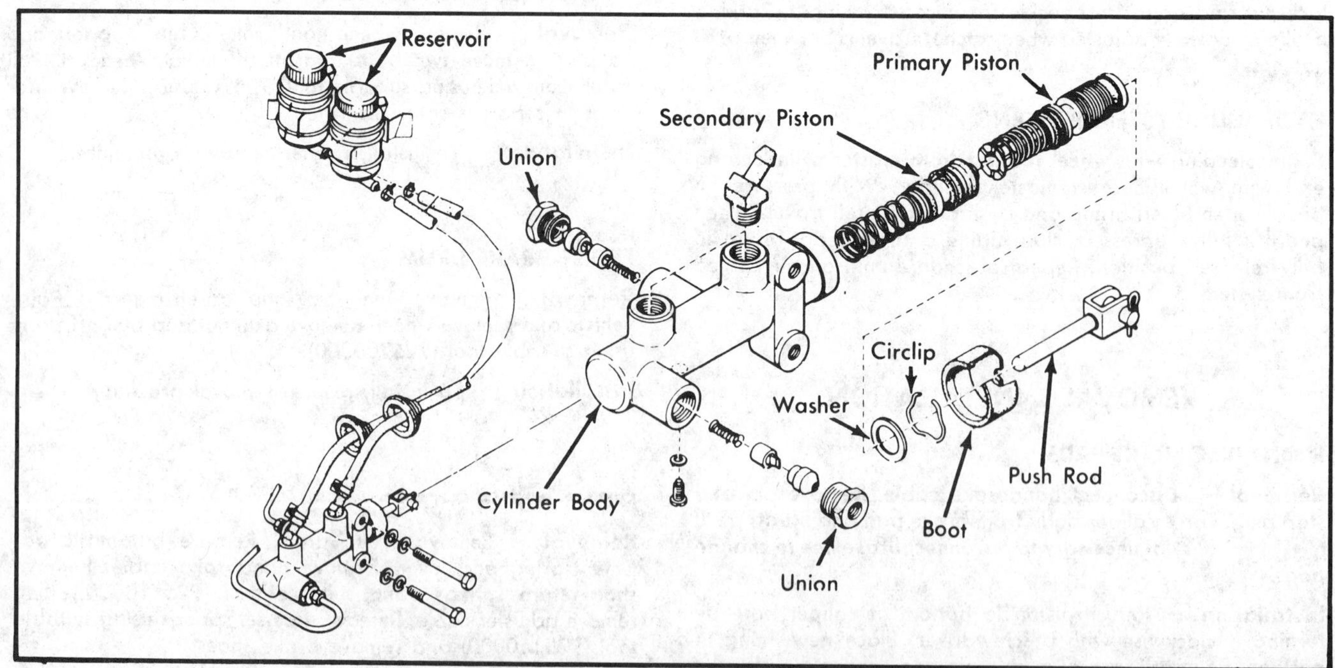

Fig. 4 Exploded View of Components in Tandem Master Cylinder

SUBARU (Cont.)

Installation – To install, reverse removal procedure.

POWER BRAKE CYLINDER

Removal – Extract cotter key, pull out lock pin and separate brake pedal from push rod. Disconnect power brake unit vacuum hose and remove master cylinder mounting nuts. Remove power brake unit attaching hardware and lift unit from engine compartment. Support master cylinder and leave it in vehicle.

Installation – To install, reverse removal procedure noting the following: Arrow on power brake unit should face toward engine.

OVERHAUL

WHEEL CYLINDER

Disassembly – Remove boot and take out wheel cylinder, taking care not to scratch cylinder bore. Also remove spring located in center of rear wheel cylinder.

Cleaning & Inspection – Clean all components in brake fluid. Inspect piston-to-cylinder bore for .001-.004" (.025-.105 mm) clearance. Check cylinder bore for out of round and burrs. If cylinder bore is damaged, it cannot be honed; it must be replaced.

Reassembly – To reassemble, reverse disassembly procedure.

MASTER CYLINDER

Disassembly – Remove boot from cylinder, then remove stop ring and plate. Remove stopper pin and gasket, pull out primary and secondary piston assembly. Remove return spring, screw, retainer and secondary cup.

Cleaning & Inspection – Clean all parts in clean brake fluid. Inspect cylinder bore for smoothness and roundness. Replace cylinder if scored or out of round. Do not hone cylinder. Inspect piston-to-cylinder clearance and replace if worn.

Reassembly – To reassemble, reverse disassembly procedure.

TIGHTENING SPECIFICATIONS

Application	Ft. Lbs. (mkg)
Front Brake Mounting Bolt	30 (4.2)
Backing Plate Mounting Bolts	24 (3.3)
Drum-to-Double Offset Joint	54 (7.5)
Brake Lines	14 (1.9)
Wheel Bearing Nut	115-133 (15.9-18.4)
Power Cylinder-to-Firewall	5.0-9.0 (.69-1.20)
Master Cylinder-to-Power Cylinder	5.0-9.0 (.69-1.2)

DISC BRAKE ROTOR SPECIFICATIONS

Application	Disc Diameter In. (mm)	Lateral Runout In. (mm)	Parallelism In. (mm)	Original Thickness In. (mm)	Minimum Refinish Thickness In. (mm)	Discard Thickness In. (mm)
Coupe	7.2 (184)	.....	.....	.39 (10)	.33 (8.5)	.....

BRAKE DRUM SPECIFICATIONS

Application	Drum Diameter In. (mm)	Original Diameter In. (mm)	Maximum Refinish Diameter In. (mm)	Discard Diameter In. (mm)
All Models				
Front	9.00① (229)	9.00 (229)	.....	9.08 (230)
Rear	7.09 (180)	7.09 (180)	.....	7.17 (182)

① – Coupe models use front disc brakes.

BRAKE SYSTEM SPECIFICATIONS

Application	Drum Diam. In. (mm)	Wheel Cylinder Diameter		Master Cylinder
		Front In. (mm)	Rear In. (mm)	Diameter In. (mm)
All Models	9.00① (229)	.938② (23.8)	.625③ (15.9)	.750 (19.0)

① – Front drum. Rear drum is 7.09" (180 mm).
② – Coupe models use front disc brakes. Caliper bore diameter is 2.125" (53.9 mm).
③ – Station Wagon and Four Wheel Drive .687" (17.46 mm).

TOYOTA

Celica
Corolla
Corona
Pickup
Land Cruiser

DESCRIPTION

All models use front disc brakes and drum rear brakes. Dual piston master cylinders are used on all models. All vehicles are equipped with some kind of pressure differential valve (combination valve). Any model can be fitted with a power assist unit. Not all power units are the same. All parking brakes are cable actuated, internal expanding shoe type. Land Cruiser parking brake is mounted on rear of transfer case, all other models use a parking brake incorporated in rear wheel brakes. Land Cruiser models use a separate vacuum pump to supply vacuum to power assist unit.

BRAKE PEDAL HEIGHT

All Models (Exc. Land Cruiser) – Loosen stop light switch lock nut and turn switch to obtain correct brake pedal height. If correct height cannot be obtained by adjusting switch, loosen push rod lock nut and lengthen or shorten push rod as necessary to obtain correct height.

Brake Pedal Height

Application	Height In. (mm)
Celica	6.60 (167.6)
Corolla	6.65 (169)
Pickup	
Man. Trans.	6.3 (160)
Auto. Trans.	6.5 (166)
Corona	6.2-6.6 (161-168)

Land Cruiser – On models with power brake unit, loosen stop light switch and adjust pedal height with push rod. Readjust stop light switch to make proper contact. On models without power brake unit, loosen push rod and adjust pedal height by turning stop light switch.

Brake Pedal Height

Application	Height In. (mm)
FJ40 Series	8.46 (215)
FJ55 Series	7.28 (185)

DISC BRAKES

Disc brakes are self-adjusting; therefore, no adjustment in service is required.

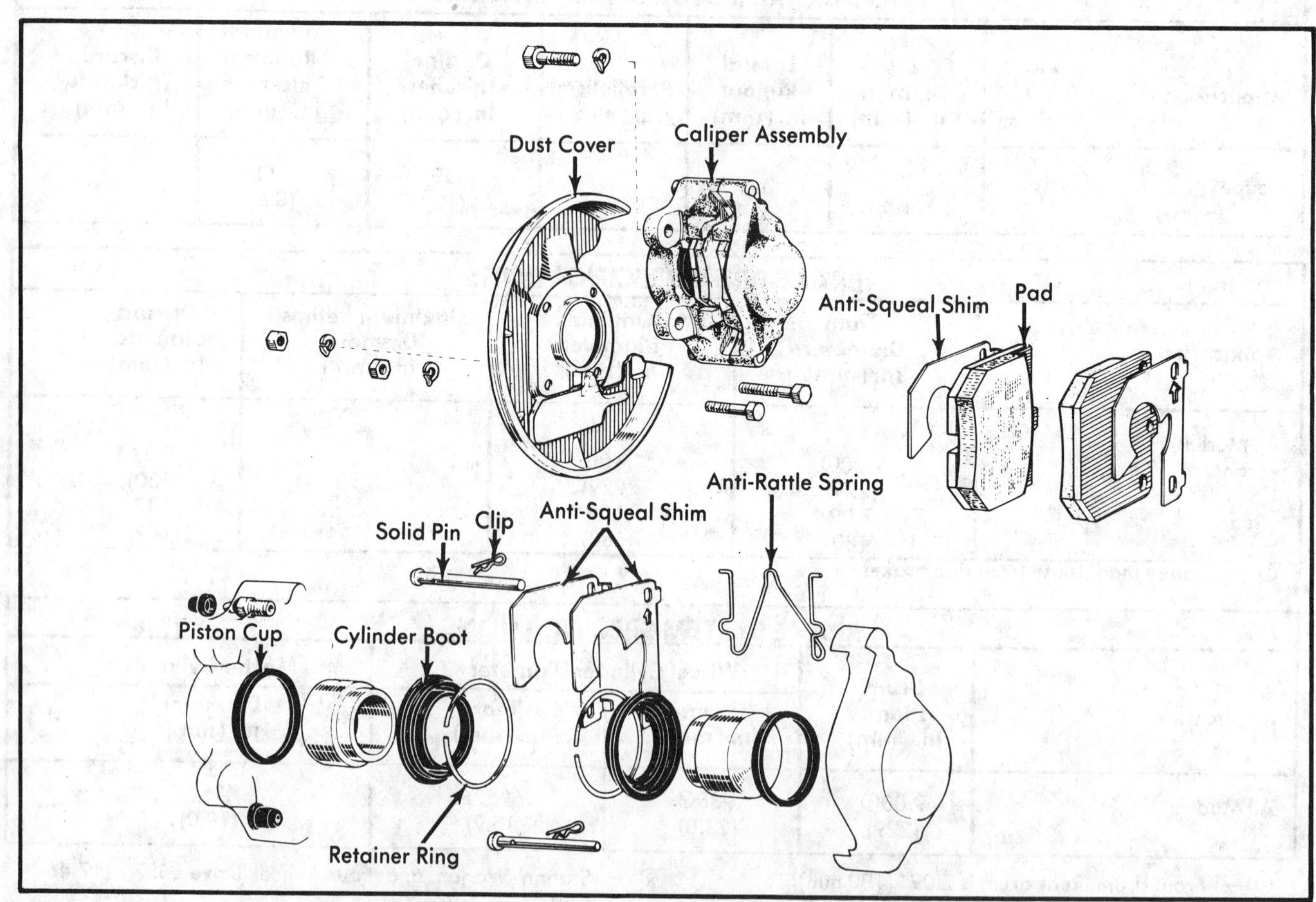

Fig. 1 Exploded View of Girling Type Disc Brake Components

TOYOTA (Cont.)

DRUM BRAKES

Manual Adjusting – One or two adjusting screws may be used on some vehicles. **CAUTION** – *On double adjusting screw type, do not adjust both screws at the same time.* Pump brake pedal several times, and ensure brake cylinder reservoir is full. Raise vehicle and remove adjusting hole plug from backing plate. Using a suitable adjusting tool, turn adjusting screw until shoes make full contact with brake drum, and wheel will not turn. Pump brake pedal, then turn adjuster back until wheel turns with light shoe drag.

Self-Adjusting – Adjustment, except at time of overhaul, should not be required. If self-adjusters are not functioning properly, hold self-adjuster screw and perform procedure described under manual adjusting.

PARKING BRAKE

Land Cruiser – With brake handle fully released, turn shaft of adjusting cam (on brake backing plate) counterclockwise until shoe seats against drum. Back off adjuster one notch at a time until drum locks when foot brake is applied, and spins freely when released. After adjusting shoes, adjust brake handle for travel of 6-9 notches from released to applied position. Adjust by turning cable adjusting nut or turnbuckle.

All Others (Instrument Panel Mounted) – With brake handle fully released, turn cable adjusting nut at equalizer on frame until cables to rear wheels are slightly slack, and there is no drag on rear wheels. After adjustment, brake handle travel should be about eight notches, and brake warning light should be off. If light remains on, adjust switch position so light is on when brake is applied, and off when handle is released.

All Others (Floor Mounted) – Correct adjustment is obtained when rear wheels are locked, and brake lever travel is 5-8 notches. To adjust, remove cable adjusting cap at rear of lever, and turn cable adjusting nut until correct lever travel is obtained. Replace and lightly tighten adjusting cap. Check and adjust brake warning light switch so that light is off when brake lever is released.

HYDRAULIC BRAKE BLEEDING

NOTE – *Master cylinder reservoir(s) must be kept full at all times during bleeding.* Starting at wheel cylinder farthest from master cylinder, connect a tube to bleeder screw and put other end of tube in a glass container half full of clean brake fluid. Slowly pump brake pedal several times, then hold pedal in depressed position. Open bleeder screw slightly, and close screw when fluid stops flowing from tube. Repeat procedure until fluid coming from tube shows no sign of air.

REMOVAL & INSTALLATION

DISC BRAKE PADS

Removal, F Type – Raise and support front of vehicle; remove wheel. Pull four spring clips out and remove cylinder guides. Hang disc cylinder assembly out of way. Remove disc pads and inspect for wear.

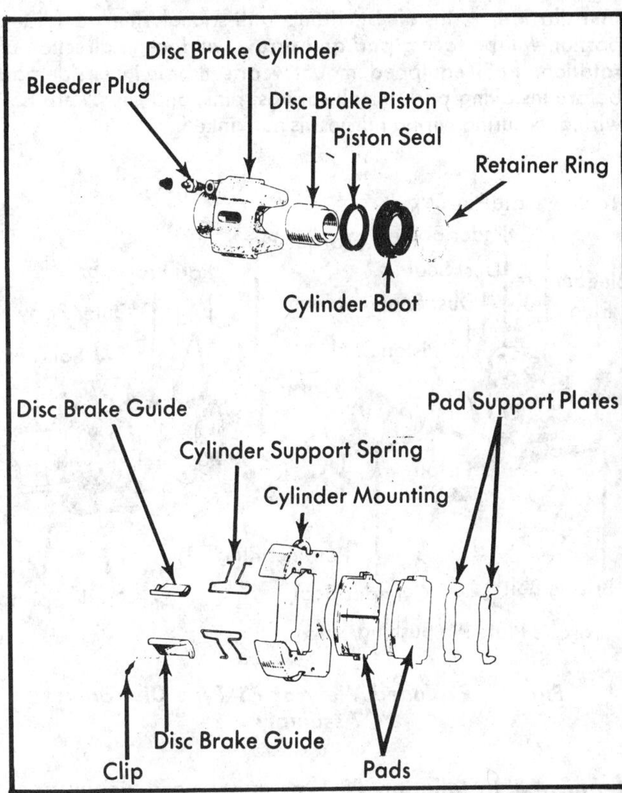

Fig. 3 Expanded View of F Type Disc Brake Components

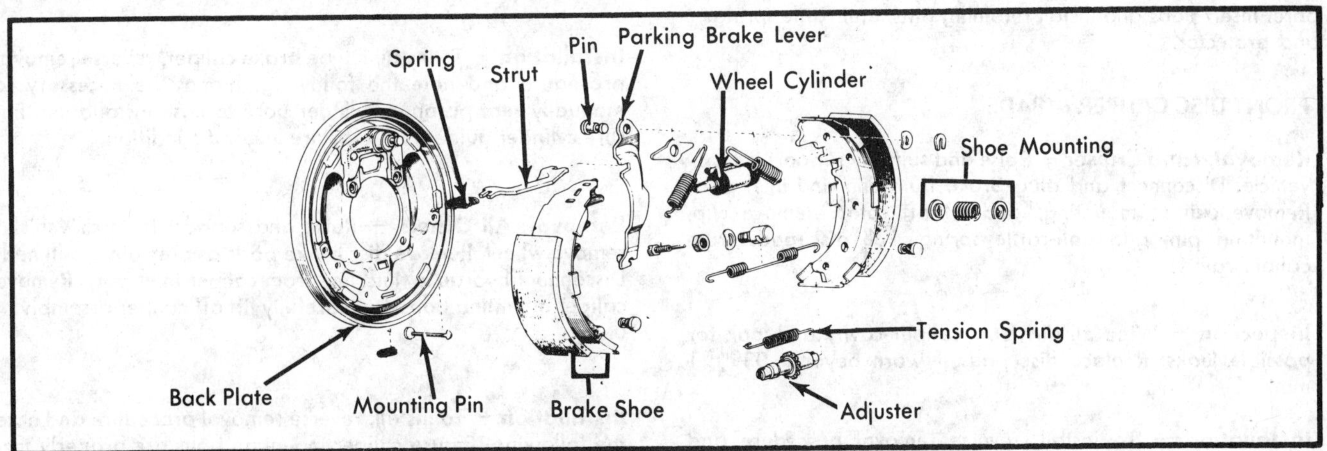

Fig. 2 Exploded View of Typical Toyota Self-Adjusting Rear Brake Assembly – Pickup Shown

TOYOTA (Cont.)

Installation – Clean piston and cylinder assembly, then seat piston into cylinder bore. If piston won't easily reseed into cylinder bore, crack bleed valve to relieve pressure. Insert cylinder assembly into position. Refit new disc pads, cylinder guides, and spring clips. If hydraulic line has been disconnected, bleed brake system.

Removal, Girling Type – Raise and support front of vehicle; remove wheel. Remove clips, pins, and springs; then take out pads and anti-squeal shims. If vehicle is equipped with Electrical Sensor Panel, separate wire harness from steering knuckle wire harness clamp. Pull out pads and separate connection between pad and wear sensor.

Installation – Install by fitting anti-squeal shim so folded portion will be facing pad and arrow will face in direction of rotation. If ESP equipped, mount wear sensor in inner side pad before installing pad. Install springs, pins, and clips. Refit ESP wiring, ensuring wiring harness is not kinked.

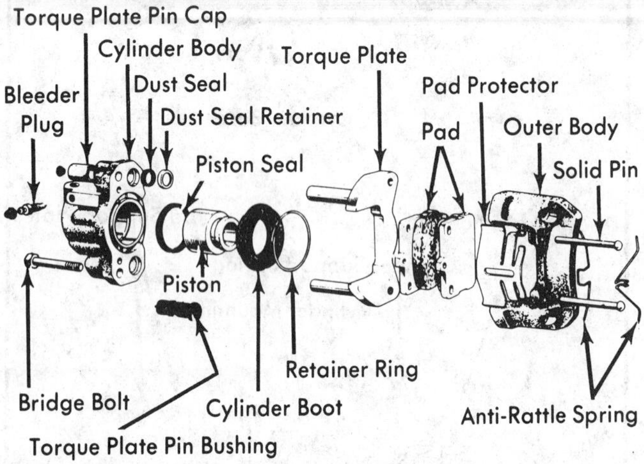

Fig. 4 Exploded View of PS Type Disc Brake Assembly

Removal & Installation, PS Type – Raise and support front of vehicle; remove wheel. Take out pad protector, anti-rattle springs, spring pins, and pads. Clean dirt from pin portion of torque plate. After cleaning piston assembly, seat into cylinder bore. Insert pads and install retaining pins, anti-rattle springs, and protector.

FRONT DISC CALIPER & PADS

Removal, Land Cruiser – Raise and suitably support front of vehicle. Disconnect and plug brake fluid line and inlet port. Remove caliper mountings and lift off rotor. Remove clip, mounting pin, and anti-rattle spring. Pull disc pads from caliper cavity.

Inspection – Wipe all dirt from caliper cavity and look for possible leaks. Replace disc pads if worn beyond .039" (1 mm).

Installation – To install, reverse removal procedure and note: Tighten mounting bolts. Make sure brake tube is properly seated and that anti-rattle spring is tight.

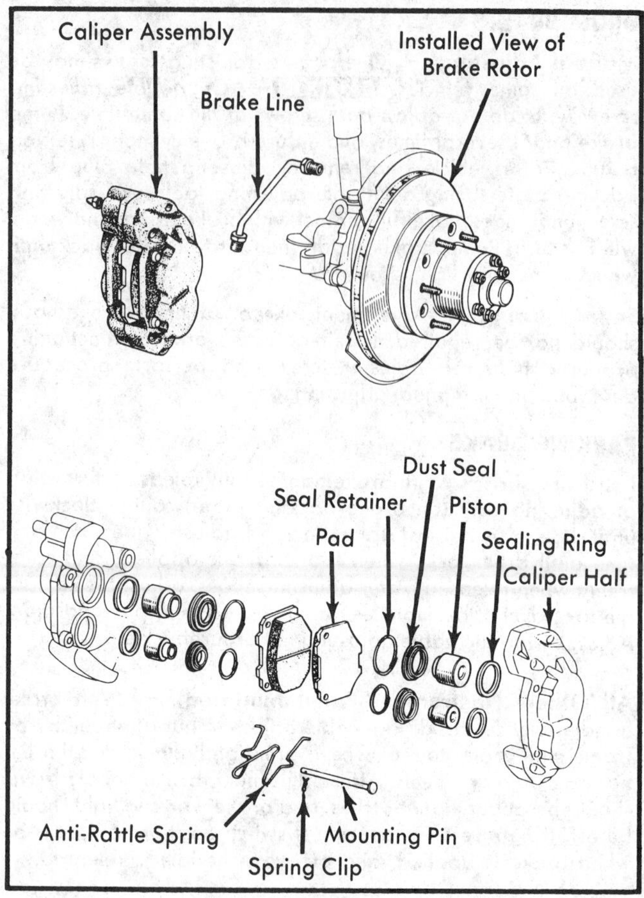

Fig. 5 Exploded View of Land Cruiser Front Disc Brakes

DISC BRAKE CALIPER

Removal, F Type – Raise and support front of vehicle; remove wheel. Pull four clips out and remove cylinder guides. Hang disc cylinder assembly out of way. Remove disc pads. Remove two bolts from rear of disc brake cylinder mounting and remove mounting along with cylinder support springs and pad support plates.

Installation – To install F type brake caliper, reverse removal procedure and note the following: It may be necessary to manually seat piston in cylinder bore to ease installation. Ensure cylinder guides and clips are in good condition.

Removal, All Others – Raise and support front of vehicle; remove wheel. Remove disc brake pads as previously outlined. Disconnect hydraulic fluid line from caliper inlet port. Remove caliper mounting bolts and carefully lift off caliper assembly.

Installation – To install, reverse removal procedure and note the following: Ensure caliper mounting bolts are properly torqued. Make sure disc pads are installed according to prevoiusly outlined procedure.

TOYOTA (Cont.)

DISC BRAKE ROTOR

Removal, Except Land Cruiser – Raise and support vehicle; remove tire. Before removing rotor, measure runout and check against specifications. Proceed by removing hub grease cap, cotter pin, washer, and castle nut; carefully ease outer wheel bearing from hub. Remove caliper assembly as previously outlined. Pull hub and rotor from vehicle as an assembly. If necessary, hub and rotor can be further disassembled after index marking relationship.

Installation – To install hub and rotor assembly, reverse removal procedure and note the following: Ensure wheel bearings are packed with grease and that wheel bearing grease seal is satisfactory. Make sure wheel bearings are properly adjusted. *See Wheel Bearing Adjustment in WHEEL ALIGNMENT Section.*

Removal, Land Cruiser – Remove caliper assembly as previously outlined. Remove hub grease cap and take off snap ring. Remove cover nuts, washers and cone washers. Using suitable socket or wrench SST 09607-60020, remove lock nut, lock washer and wheel bearing adjusting nut. Slide off rotor and hub assembly. If necessary, index mark rotor and hub, then separate.

Inspection – Before rotor removal check runout. Set up dial indicator, remove play from wheel bearings, and take measurement. Runout must not exceed .005" (.13 mm). With rotor removed, measure thickness. Rotor thickness must not be less than .790" (20 mm).

Installation – To install, reverse removal procedure and note: Adjust wheel bearings. *See Wheel Bearing Adjustment in WHEEL ALIGNMENT Section.*

BRAKE DRUM

Removal, All Models Rear – Raise and support rear of vehicle; remove wheel. Remove set screws from brake drum, if equipped. Using hands only, pull drum from vehicle. It may be necessary to first loosen brake shoes if an adjustment hole is provided.

Installation – To install, reverse removal procedure and readjust brake shoes, if necessary.

BRAKE SHOES

Removal, All Models Rear – Raise and support vehicle. Remove wheel and brake brum. Remove parking brake cable from lever, and remove tension springs from shoes. Remove self-adjuster mechanism (if equipped). Remove shoe guide plate, shoe hold down pins and springs. Take out parking brake strut. Remove brake shoes from backing plate. Remove parking brake actuating lever, self-adjusting lever, and latch from brake shoe.

Installation – To install, reverse removal procedure and bleed hydraulic system.

PARKING BRAKE

Removal, Land Cruiser – Drain oil from transfer case. Disconnect front of drive shaft and wire out-of-way. Remove drum mounting nut and slide drum off splines. Remove return springs and tension springs, then take off hold down springs and pins. Disconnect parking brake cable from shoes.

Inspection – Inspect shoes for excessive damage or wear. Replace shoes when lining thickness is less than .06" (1.5 mm).

Installation – To install, reverse removal procedure and note: Make sure lower tension spring is installed so it lies between back plate and shoes. Refill transfer case with 1.8 quarts of SAE 90. Tighten drum mounting nut.

VACUUM PUMP

Removal, Land Cruiser – Disconnect vacuum line from pump assembly. Disconnect and plug oil lines. Remove mounting nuts and gently pry pump off studs.

Installation – To install, reverse removal procedure and note: Run engine at idle speed. Loosen screw at vacuum pump outlet and check that oil is circulating.

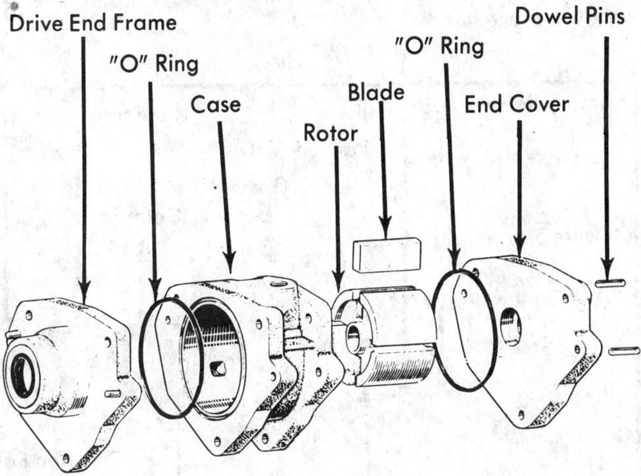

Fig. 6 Exploded View of Vacuum Pump for Land Cruiser

MASTER CYLINDER

Removal, All Models – Disconnect any electrical lead from master cylinder switches. Separate hydraulic outlet lines and plug open ends of line. Remove nuts mounting master cylinder to power unit, if equipped. If vehicle is not power brake equipped, disconnect master cylinder push rod and lift from vehicle.

Installation – To install, reverse removal procedure and bleed hydraulic system.

TOYOTA (Cont.)

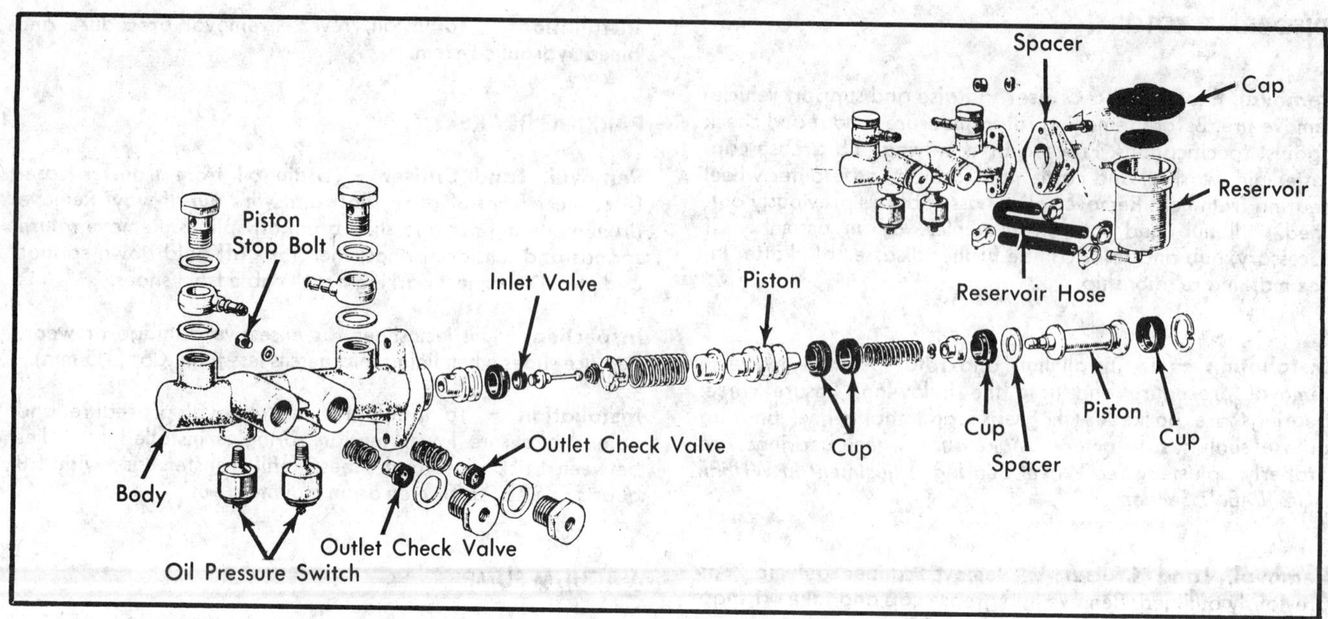

Fig. 7 Exploded View of a Typical Master Cylinder with Detail of Each Component

POWER BRAKE UNIT

Removal & Installation – Remove master cylinder assembly from vehicle. Disconnect push rod clevis at brake pedal. Remove power booster attaching hardware, and remove booster assembly from vehicle. To install, reverse removal procedure.

OVERHAUL

NOTE – *When overhauling caliper, wheel cylinder, or master cylinder assemblies, all rubber components should be replaced. If cylinder bores in any part are pitted, or scored more than light honing will repair, entire assembly should be replaced.*

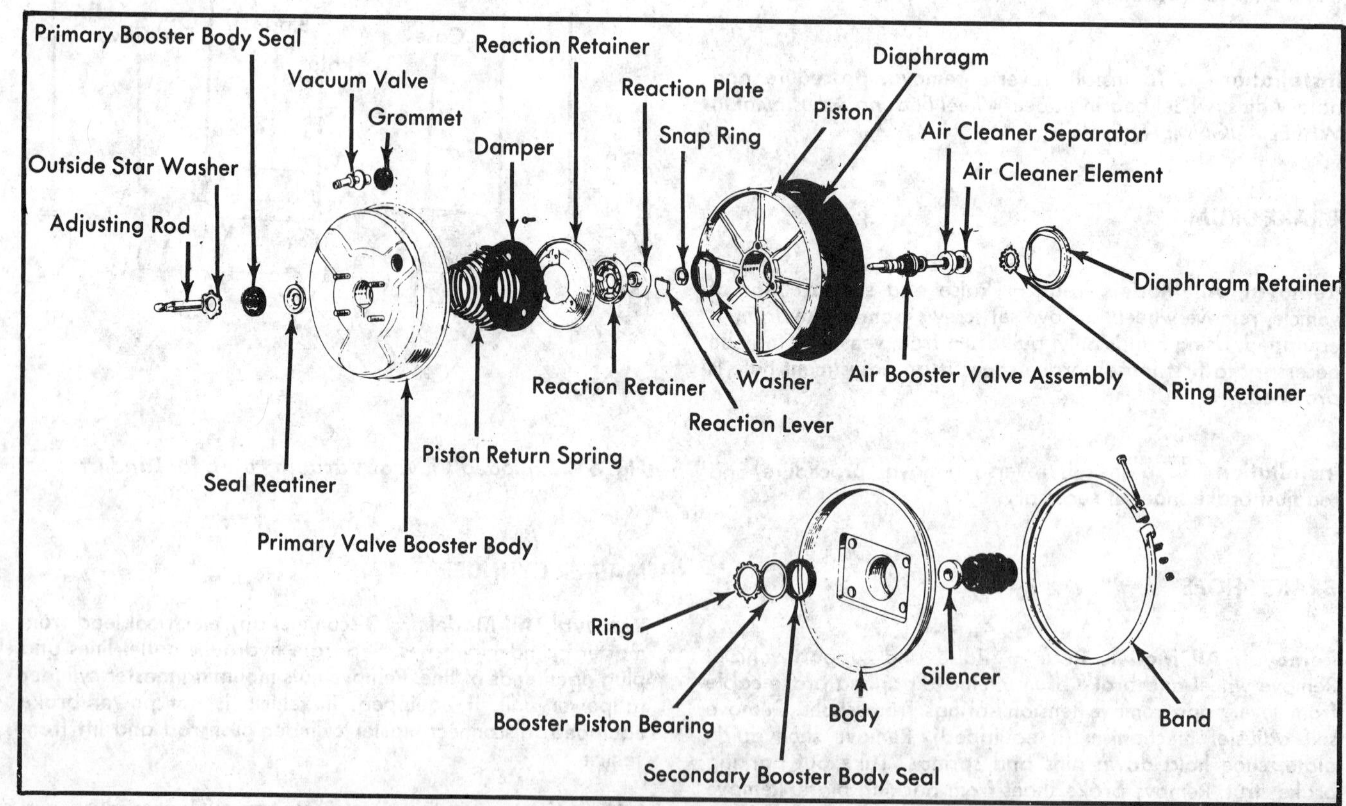

Fig. 8 Exploded View of ASC Type Brake Booster Unit

TOYOTA (Cont.)

DISC BRAKE CALIPER

Disassembly, F Type – Remove retainer ring and take off cylinder boot. Apply light air pressure to fluid inlet port and force piston from cylinder. Remove seal from cylinder, being careful not to damage cylinder bore.

Inspection – Clean and inspect all components. Replace any parts found defective.

Reassembly – To reassemble, reverse disassembly procedure and note the following: Apply light coat of suitable grease/brake fluid to all components before reassembly. Bleed hydraulic system after installation.

Disassembly, Girling Type – Remove retainer ring from dust boot and pull off dust boot. Insert a small block of wood between pistons and apply light air pressure to inlet port to force pistons from cylinder bores. Remove seals from grooves in cylinder bores. **NOTE** – *Do not separate caliper halves.*

Inspection – Clean and inspect all components. Replace any parts found defective.

Reassembly – Lightly coat all components with brake fluid, then insert seal into cylinder bore groove. Carefully push pistons into cylinder, install rubber dust boots and retainer rings.

Disassembly, PS Type – Loosen both bridge bolts (caliper half mounting bolts) and separate cylinder casting from outer body. Pull out torque plate. Remove retainer ring and dust boot. Force light air pressure through fluid inlet port and expel piston. From caliper, remove following: Piston seal, bushings, hole plug, retainers and dust seals.

Inspection – Inspect all parts for wear or damage and replace as necessary. If torque plate pins are excessively worn or if pin weld parts are abnormally corroded, caliper must be replaced.

Reassembly – **1)** Lightly coat all parts prior to reassembly with clean brake fluid. Fit dust seal, retainers, and bushings to cylinder. Ensure pin sliding surfaces and bushing bores are clean and smear with suitable grease from repair kit.

2) Fit piston seal on cylinder and push piston in by hand. Install dust boot and ring. Reassemble torque plate pins in cylinder body. Make sure torque plate is free to slide smoothly. Install bridge bolts and torque.

Disassembly, Land Cruiser – Remove caliper assembly and take out disc pads. Remove dust seal retainer ring and dust seal. Place a small block of wood into caliper cavity. Blow compressed air into brake fluid inlet port until piston is forced out; repeat procedure on opposite side. Using a pointed, but blunt tool, dig piston seal from caliper groove. **NOTE** – *Do not separate caliper halves.*

Inspection – Check cylinder bore and piston for excessive wear, damage or corrosion; replace parts as necessary. Inspect pad thickness, pad must not be worn beyond .039" (1 mm).

Reassembly – Lightly coat all components with brake fluid. Insert new piston seal, being careful that seals properly enter grooves. Fit piston and slide dust seal into position. With dust seal seated, fit retainer ring.

MASTER CYLINDER

Disassembly, All Models – Remove pressure switches and clamp cylinder flange in a soft jawed vise. Remove unions and bolts, outlet plugs, valves, and springs. Remove push rod boot. Take off snap ring, then remove push rod and rear piston assembly. Remove stop bolt from side of cylinder and remove front piston. Remove inlet valve seat and inlet valve. Disassemble pistons by removing springs, retainers, and cups.

Reassembly – To reassemble, reverse disassembly procedure using all new rubber parts and lubricating all components with clean brake fluid.

WHEEL CYLINDER

NOTE – *Removal of wheel cylinder from backing plate is not necessary, except when replacement of cylinder assembly is required.*

Disassembly – Remove adjuster lock spring and adjuster (if equipped). Remove bleeder screw. Remove cylinder boot(s), piston(s), cup(s), spring seat (if equipped), and spring.

Inspection – Clean all parts with solvent, and blow dry with compressed air. Check cylinder bore for out-of-round, corrosion, or scoring.

Reassembly – To reassemble, reverse disassembly procedure, using new rubber parts.

VACUUM PUMP

Disassembly, Land Cruiser – Drive dowel pins from end cover toward case. Separate end cover. Continue to drive dowels through case and stop with them flush with end frame. Remove end frame with pins still fitted. Remove both "O" rings and discard. Slide rotor and blades from case.

Inspection – Inspect end cover and casing for damage or wear. Casing bore must not be worn beyond 2.29" (5.82 mm). Check rotor-to-alternator shaft spline play. Rotor wear must not exceed .095" (2.4 mm). Inspect rotor blades for following wear limits: Height .47" (12 mm); length 1.377" (34.98 mm); width .036" (.92 mm). Check end frame bushing and oil seal. Bushing bore must not exceed .635" (16.14 mm). Replace oil seal by prying out and pressing in new one.

Reassembly – Lightly coat new "O" rings and insert into grooves. Refit rotor and blades. Drive in dowel pins.

POWER BRAKE UNIT

Disassembly, ASCO Type – Remove booster push rod. Remove clamping band and separate primary and secondary booster body halves. Remove boot and booster piston assembly from secondary body half. Remove outside star washer from secondary body and remove bearing and body seal. From primary body, remove seal and retainer. Disassemble booster piston by removing reaction retainers, lever, air valve, air cleaner element and separator. Using suitable remove tool (SST 09736-30020), take out diaphragm rotating it 45°, then remove diaphragm from piston. Remove vacuum check valve and grommet from booster body.

TOYOTA (Cont.)

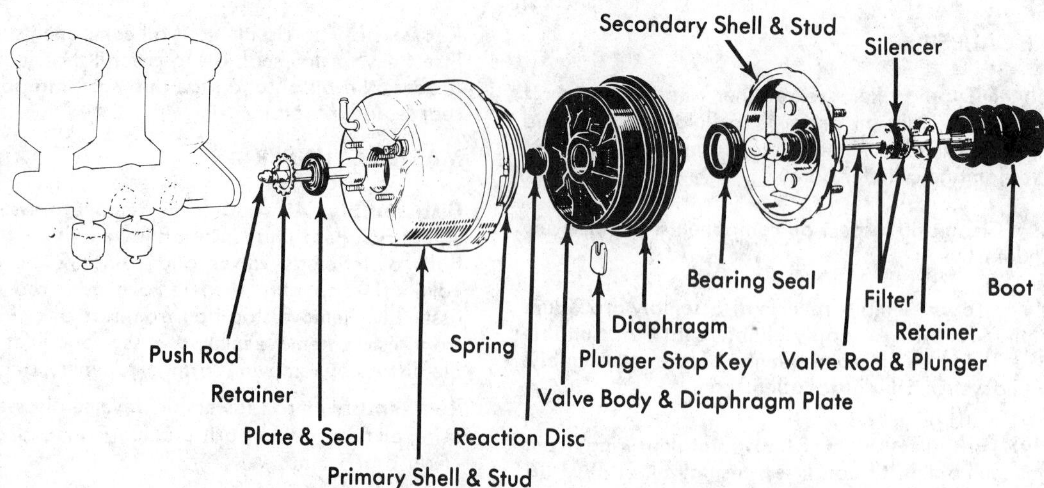

Fig. 9 Exploded View of JKK Type Brake Booster Unit

Inspection – Wash all parts in suitable cleaner. Inspect all components for excessive wear or damage and replace those that are found damaged.

Reassembly – To reassemble, reverse disassembly procedure and note the following: When assembling booster body seal to seal retainer, ensure seal retainer side is in the body inner side. When assembling body halves, align index marks.

Disassembly, JKK Type – Remove push rod clevis, nut, and boot. Index mark primary and secondary shell halves. Separate halves using suitable tool (SST 09738-22012). Remove diaphragm spring and push rod. Take out diaphragm plate and diaphragm spring from secondary shell half. Disengage the diaphragm from plate, then remove silencer. Remove plunger stop key by lining up valve rod and plunger toward key hole with pieces facing downward; then remove valve and plunger rod from diaphragm plate. **NOTE** – *Valve rod and plunger assembly can not be further disassembled.* Remove reaction disc from diaphragm plate. If necessary, remove retainer and seal from primary shell. With a press, force bearing seal from secondary shell.

Inspection – Wash all parts in suitable cleaner. Inspect all components for any damage and replace those found defective. Ensure all rubber pieces are replaced during each overhaul.

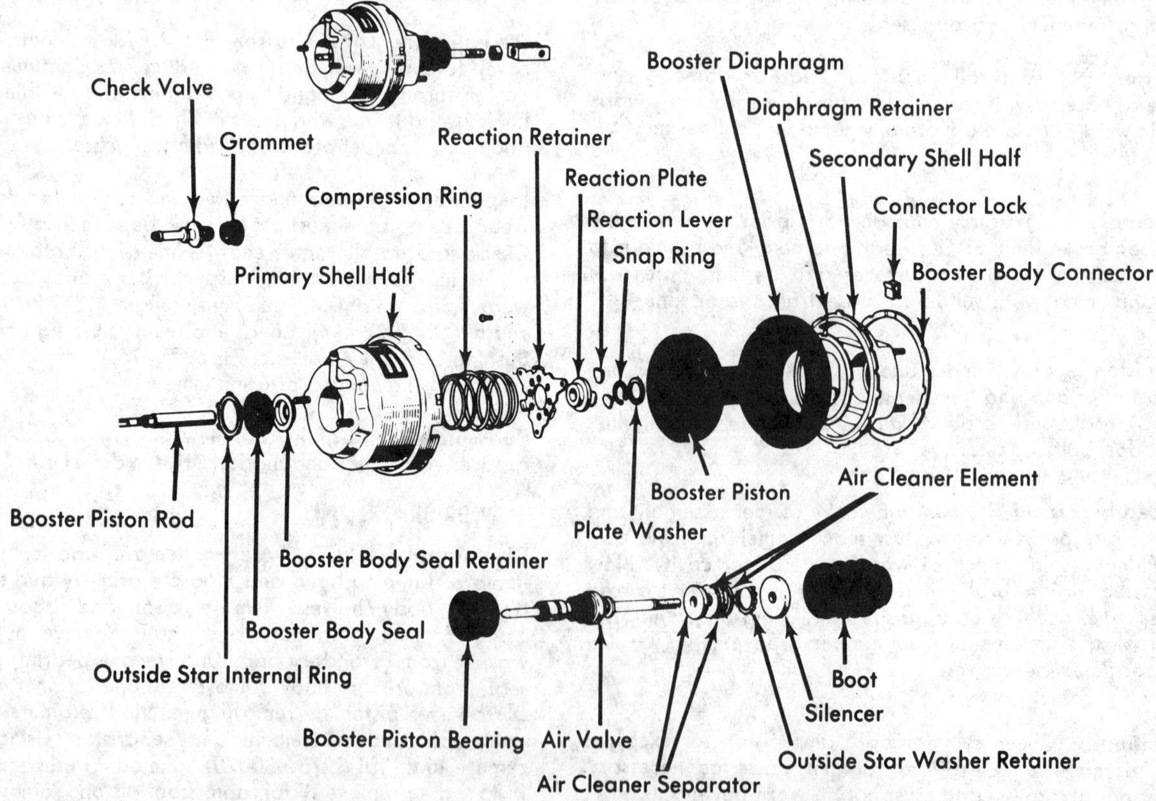

Fig. 10 Exploded View of Aisan Type Brake Booster Assembly

TOYOTA (Cont.)

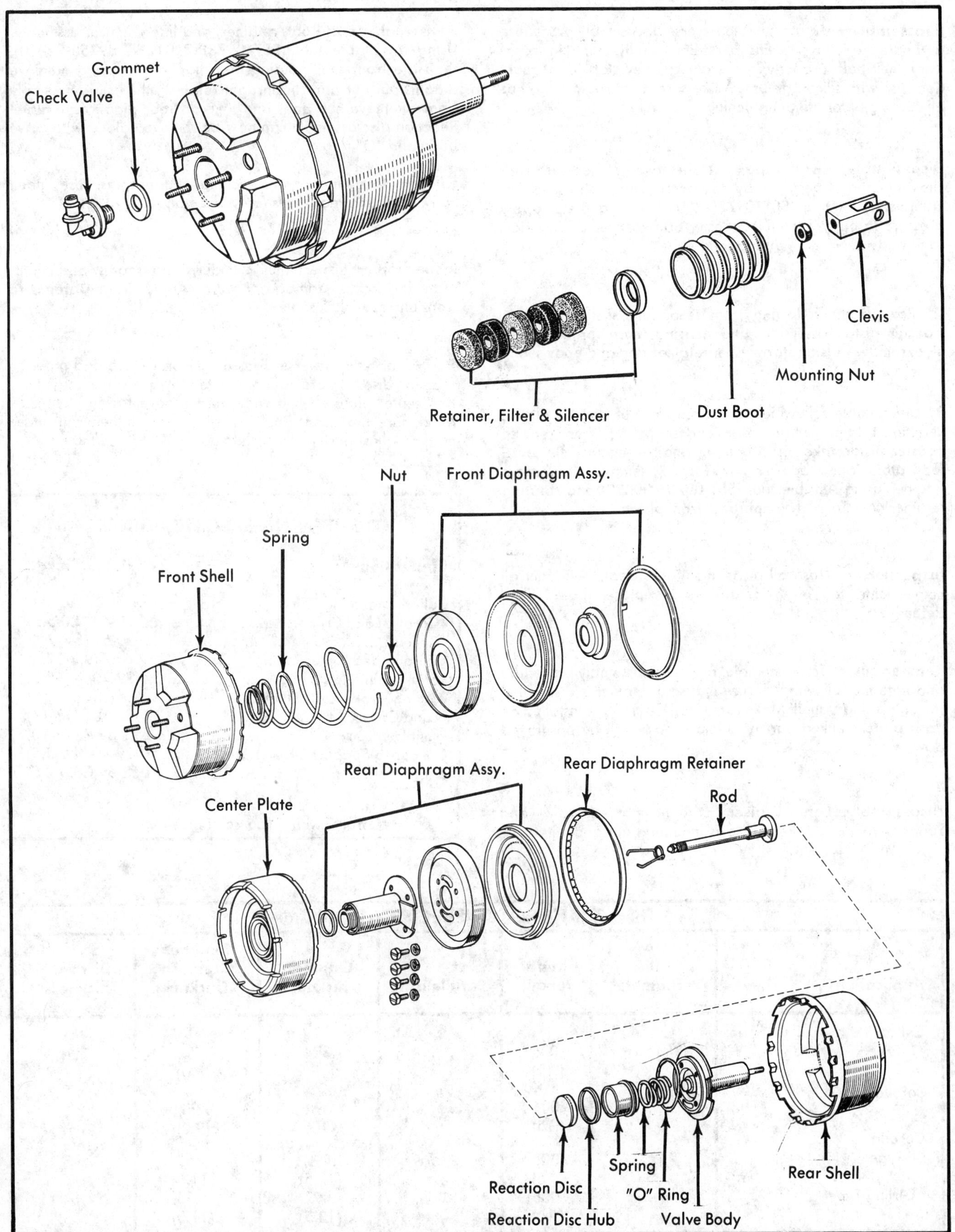

Fig. 11 Exploded View of Land Cruiser Power Brake Booster Assembly

TOYOTA (Cont.)

Reassembly – To reassemble, reverse disassembly procedure and note the following: Ensure retainer is fully seated in secondary shell half. Properly locate plunger key stop. Coat reaction disc with silicon grease. Make sure diaphragm edge has oil coating before final tightening.

Disassembly, Aisan Type – 1) Remove booster push rod, clips mounting booster body connector, and push rod clevis. Using suitable tool (SST 09738-20010) and a press, apply pressure to body; then turn booster body connector until slots (and body halves) are disengaged.

2) Remove the following from secondary shell half: Boot, booster piston assembly, and bearing. From primary shell side, remove outside star washer retainer ring and body seal.

3) Disassemble following parts from front of booster piston: Reaction retainer, plate, lever, and snap ring. From rear of booster piston take off: Mounting ring, air cleaner elements, separators and booster air valves. Remove diaphragm retainer using suitable tool (SST 09736-30020) and rotating retainer 45°. Take off diaphragm from piston.

Inspection – Wash all parts in suitable cleaner. Inspect all components for any damage and replace those found defective.

Reassembly – To reassemble, reverse disassembly procedure and note the following: Ensure that seal retainer is assembled to inner primary shell. Make sure when assembly is installed on dash panel, sunken part of primary body will be positioned downward.

Disassembly, Land Cruiser – Remove check valve and rubber grommet. Take off clevis mounting nut and withdraw clevis, rubber dust boot, retainer, and filter/silencer assembly. Using a suitable tool (SST 09738-22012 & 09753-22010), separate front shell housing and diaphragm spring. Remove diaphragm nut and diaphragm retainer, then slide assembly apart. Remove hub bolts and take off rear diaphragm plate. Reaction disc assembly can now be removed along with valve body and "O" ring.

NOTE – *Index mark front and rear diaphragms. Also, index mark front and rear shells for reassembly.*

Inspection – Inspect shell cylinder, diaphragms, and center plate for cracks, damage or wear. Apply silicone grease to front and rear shell seals.

Reassembly – Reverse disassembly procedure and note: Fit reaction disc with protrusion directed toward valve body. Position center plate on hub with large groove facing front side. Make sure that front and rear shells are aligned with index marks. Adjust push rod length to .004-.020" (.1-.5 mm)

TIGHTENING SPECIFICATIONS

Application	Ft. Lbs. (mkg)
Caliper Mounting Bolts	
Corolla Land Cruiser	29-40 (4.0-5.5)
Celica	39-54 (5.4-7.5)
Corona and Pickup	67-87 (9.3-12.0)
Rotor-to-Hub	29-40 (4.0-5.5)
Parking Brake Drum Nut	
Land Cruiser	80-101 (11-14)
Front Hub Lock Nut	58-72 (8-10)
Caliper-to-Support Bracket	①29-40 (4.0-5.5)
Bridge Bolt	①58-69 C8.0-9.5)

① – Corolla with 1166 cc engine.

DISC BRAKE ROTOR SPECIFICATIONS ①

Application	Disc Diameter	Lateral Runout	Parallelism	Original Thickness	Minimum Refinish Thickness	Discard Thickness
Celica F Type	.....	.006 (.15)	.....	.394 (10)	.354 (9.0)	.....
Corolla F Type & PS Type	.....	.006 (.15)	.....	.394 (10)	.354 (9.0)	.....
Corona F Type	.....	.006 (.15)	.....	.492 (12.5)	.453 (11.5)	.....
Girling Type	.....	.006 (.15)	.....	.492 (12.5)	.453 (11.5)	.....

① – All measurements given in Inches with millimeters in parens.

TOYOTA (Cont.)

DISC BRAKE ROTOR SPECIFICATIONS

Application	Disc Diameter In. (mm)	Lateral Runout In. (mm)	Parallelism In. (mm)	Original Thickness In. (mm)	Minimum Refinish Thickness In. (mm)	Discard Thickness In. (mm)
Pickup Girling	.....	.006 (.15)	.....	.492 (12.5)	.453 (11.5)	.....
Land Cruiser	.....	.0047 (.12)	.....	.790 (20.1)	.740 (19)	.....

BRAKE DRUM SPECIFICATIONS

Application	Drum Diameter In. (mm)	Original Diameter In. (mm)	Maximum Refinish Diameter In. (mm)	Discard Diameter In. (mm)
Corolla (3K-C)	7.87 (200)	7.87 (200)	.....	7.953 (202)
Corolla (2T-C), Celica Corona	9.0 (228.6)	9.0 (228.6)	.....	9.079 (230.6)
Pickup	10.0 (254)	10.0 (254)	.....	10.078 (256)
Land Cruiser	.....	.....	.....	11.50 (292)

BRAKE SYSTEM SPECIFICATIONS

Application	Drum Diam. In. (mm)	Wheel Cylinder Diameter		Master Cylinder
		Front In. (mm)	Rear In. (mm)	Diameter In. (mm)
Corolla (3K-C)	7.87 (200)	1.89 (48.1)	.811 (20.6)	.....
Corolla (2T-C)	9.0 (228.6)	2.00 (50.8)	.811 (20.6)	.....
Celica	9.0 (228.6)	1.87 (47.5)	.748 (19)	.811 (20.6)
Pickup	10.0 (254)	.....	.875 (22.2)	1.0 (25.4)

① — Information not available for Corona and Land Cruiser.

TRIUMPH

Spitfire
TR7

DESCRIPTION

All models use front disc and rear drum brakes. A tandem piston master cylinder which consists of two independent and complete hydraulic circuits is used. A pressure differential valve is used on all models to detect low pressure in either front or rear brake systems. When a pressure differential exists between the two circuits, indicating a failure, the pressure differential valve completes the circuit to the brake failure warning light on the instrument panel. A vacuum servo unit for power braking is also used on some models.

ADJUSTMENT

DISC BRAKES

No adjustment required.

DRUM BRAKES

Spitfire – Release parking brake and raise rear wheels off ground. Rotate rear wheel clockwise while tightening adjuster. After wheel locks back off adjuster until wheel is just free to turn.

PARKING BRAKE

NOTE – *Adjustment of rear brakes will normally provide satisfactory parking brake adjustment. If cables are stretched, further adjustment is performed as follows:*

1) Hoist vehicle in rear, release parking brake and lock both rear brake drums with adjusters. Remove clevis pins from levers on brake back plates.

2) Adjust each clevis equal amounts until clevis pin can be easily inserted to relay levers. Secure clevis pins and check operation. **NOTE** – *If system is equipped with return spring, adjust bracket to provide proper tension.*

HYDRAULIC SYSTEM BLEEDING

NOTE – *TR7 system incorporates a self-centering Pressure Differential Shuttle. On all others, hard pedal application will cause shuttle to go over-center and warning light be activated.*

1) Attach a bleed tube to wheel cylinder farthest from master cylinder and submerge free end into a half full container of brake fluid.

2) On TR7 models, remove pressure differential switch. Open bleed valve and FULLY depress brake pedal, then follow with three rapid, successive strokes.

3) On Spitfire models, open bleed valve and lightly depress brake pedal, but DO NOT allow pedal to make complete stroke.

4) Continue either steps 2) or 3) until all air is bled from brake system.

Bleeding Sequence

Application	Sequence
Spitfire	RR,LR,RF,LF
TR7	RF,LF,RR,LR

REMOVAL & INSTALLATION

DISC BRAKE PADS

Removal – Raise vehicle and remove front wheels. Withdraw the two retaining pins and springs. Lift out brake pads complete with damper shims.

Installation – Clean surfaces of pistons and caliper cavity. Ease caliper pistons into bores to provide clearance. **NOTE** – *Brake fluid will raise during this operation.* Insert new pads and shims. On TR7 models only, larger cut outs face upper most in cylinder recess. On Spitfire models only, arrow on disc pad faces UP. Insert retaining pins and secure in place.

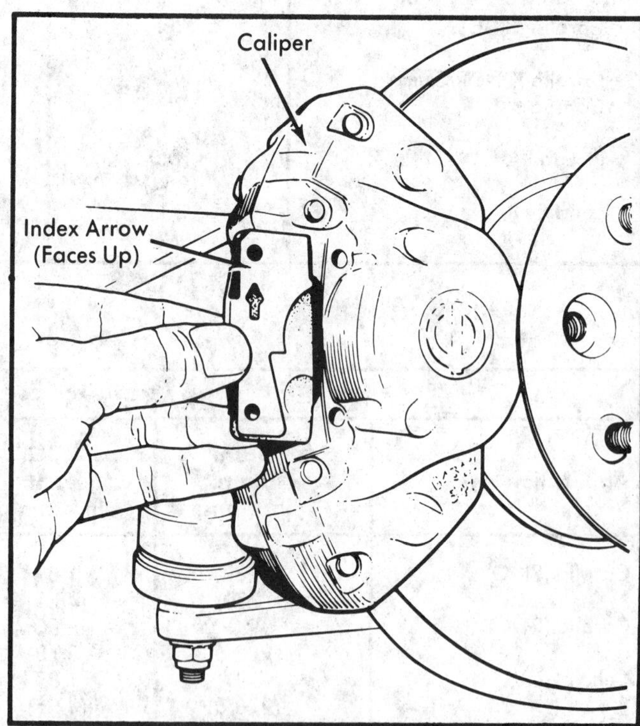

Fig. 1 Installing Disc Brake Pad on Spitfire Models

MASTER CYLINDER

Removal – Disconnect all hydraulic lines from master cylinder. On models equipped with power brake unit, remove mounting nuts and spring washers, then pull cylinder off studs. On models without power unit, disconnect master cylinder push rod from brake pedal. Remove four mounting bolts securing cylinder to mounting bracket. Take off bolt mounting master cylinder flange to bracket and withdraw entire assembly.

Installation – To install master cylinder assemblies, reverse removal procedure and bleed brake system.

TRIUMPH (Cont.)

VACUUM SERVO UNIT

Removal & Installation – Remove master cylinder as previously outlined. Disconnect vacuum hose from check valve. Remove clevis pin from servo operating rod and brake pedal lever. Remove servo with spacer. To install, reverse removal procedure.

DISC BRAKE CALIPER

Removal – Disconnect brake union at caliper and plug opening in line. On Spitfire models, remove two bolts mounting caliper assembly to stub axle. On TR7 models, remove two bolts mounting steering arm and caliper lower mounting to stub axle assembly. Push steering clear, then remove upper mounting.

Installation – To install caliper assembly, reverse removal procedure and torque mounting bolts. Bleed hydraulic system.

BRAKE DISC (ROTOR)

Removal – Raise front of vehicle and place on safety stands; remove tire. Disconnect and remove brake caliper; hang out of way. Remove grease cap and cotter pin. Take off mounting nut and washer. Withdraw complete disc assembly, then remove the four bolts and spring washers securing disc to hub.

Installation – To install, reverse removal procedure and torque all nuts and bolts. Install wheel bearing seal as required. Hub end play on Spitfire models must be approximately .002-.005" (.051-.127 mm). On TR7 models, eliminate end play as required, but DO NOT tighten hub nut more than 5 ft. lbs. (.69 mkg).

REAR BRAKE DRUM

Removal & Installation – Hoist vehicle and remove rear wheel. Remove two countersunk screws securing brake drum to hub. Release parking brake and remove brake drum. To install, reverse removal procedure.

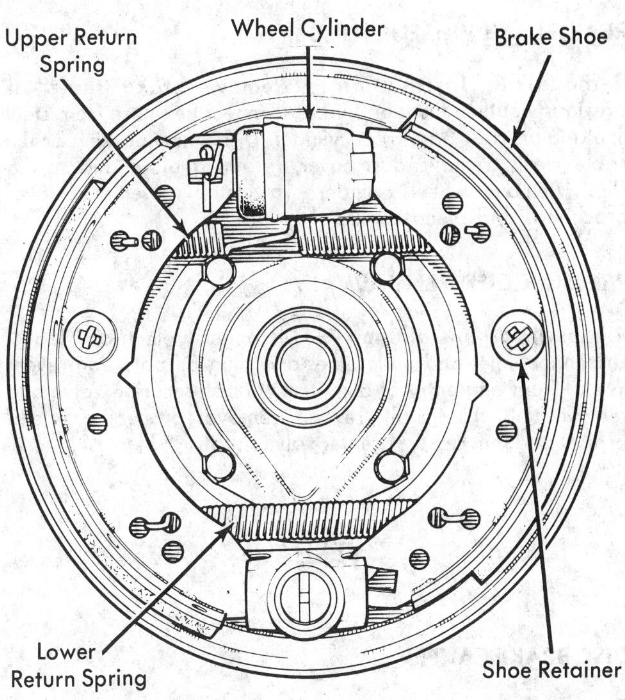

Fig. 2 Assembled View of Triumph Spitfire Rear Drum Brake Unit

REAR BRAKE SHOES

Removal – Remove brake drum as previously outlined. Remove parking brake cotter pin, shoe anchor pins, cups and springs. Disconnect return springs and lift shoes from abutments. Disconnect front shoe from parking brake lever and remove shoes.

Installation – Reverse removal procedure and lightly apply white grease (zinc base) to ends of shoes and cam faces. **CAUTION** – *Do not allow grease to contact lining material.* Readjust brakes when lining replacement is complete.

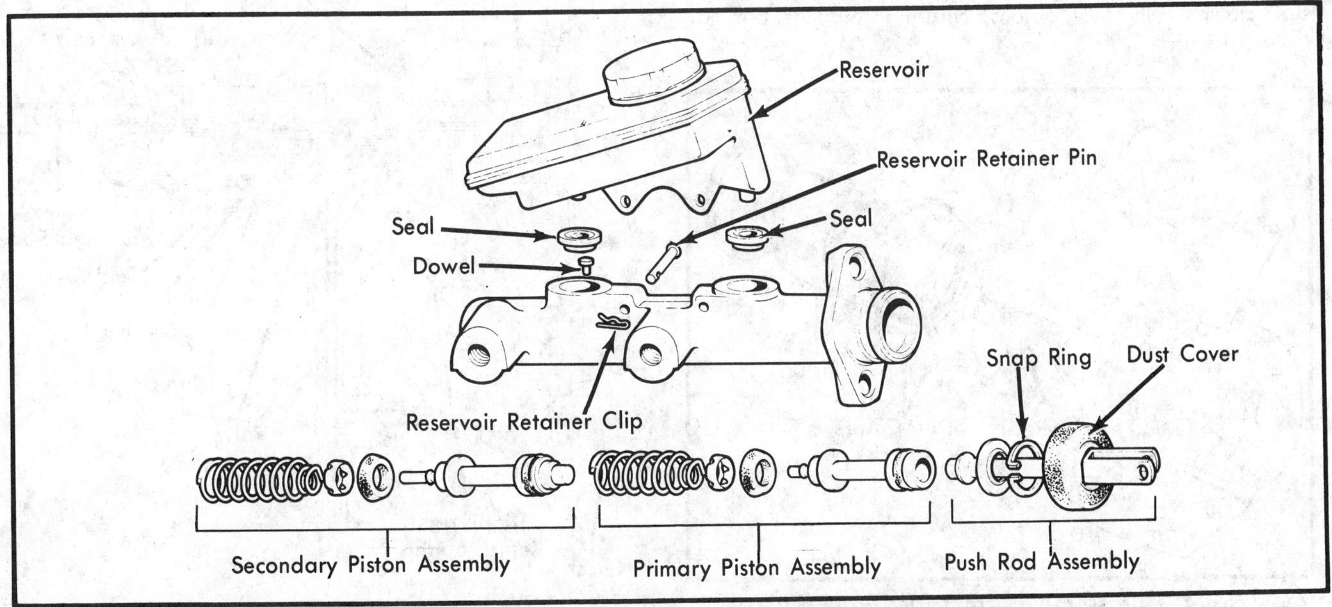

Fig. 3 Exploded View of Master Cylinder – Spitfire Shown

TRIUMPH (Cont.)

REAR BRAKE WHEEL CYLINDER

Removal & Installation – Remove brake shoes as previously outlined. Drain fluid, disconnect flex hose from steel line and unscrew hose from cylinder. Disconnect parking brake cable clevis, remove dust cover, retaining plate and spring clips. Remove wheel cylinder. To install, reverse removal procedure and bleed brakes.

PRESSURE DIFFERENTIAL VALVE

Removal & Installation – Disconnect electrical leads. Disconnect inlet and outlet lines and plug all ports to prevent loss of fluid and entry of dirt. Remove bolt securing valve and remove unit. To install, reverse removal procedure, bleed brakes and if necessary, center valve shuttle.

OVERHAUL

DISC BRAKE CALIPER

Disassembly – Using low air pressure, force pistons from caliper bores. If pistons are seized, the whole caliper assembly must be renewed. Carefully pry wiper seal retainer from groove, using a blunt instrument. **NOTE** – *Spitfire uses circlips for retainers.* Take out wiper seal and then fluid seal.

Inspection – Clean caliper bores and inspect for deep scratches or pitting. Look at pistons and ensure they are not corroded or damaged. Replace components as necessary.

Reassembly – Fit new fluid seals into caliper bores, making sure they are properly located. Lightly coat bores with clean brake fluid. Insert pistons into calipers, with approximately 5/16" (7.94 mm) of each piston protruding from mouth of each bore. Fit new wiper seal into each retainer, then slide assembly, seal first, into mouth of bore. **NOTE** – *Use piston as a guide for seal.* On Spitfire models, insert dust seals and install circlip. Fully seat pistons, ensuring retainers are not distorted.

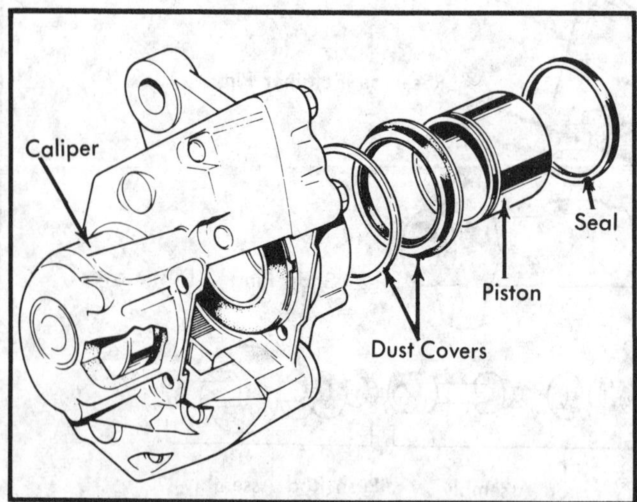

Fig. 4 Disassembled Front Disc Brake Caliper Spitfire Shown

REAR WHEEL CYLINDER

Disassembly – Remove wheel cylinder as previously outlined. Remove dust cover and withdraw piston. Remove seal from piston using fingers only.

Cleaning & Inspection – Clean all parts in alcohol or brake fluid and examine cylinder bore and piston for score marks, ridges or corrosion. If either bore or piston is damaged, replace entire cylinder assembly.

Reassembly – Install new seal with lip towards bottom of cylinder. Lubricate seal with clean brake fluid, insert piston into cylinder and install dust cover. Reinstall cylinder and bleed brakes.

VACUUM SERVO UNIT

NOTE – *Overhauling unit consists of changing check valve, filter, dust cover, seal and plate assembly. Any other component failure requires complete unit replacement. Replacing filter is the only normal service required. A service repair kit is available for limited service.*

Disassembly – 1) Remove servo unit as previously outlined. To remove check valve, note angle of valve in relation to servo housing. Use a suitable wrench to press down on valve and rotate counterclockwise 1/3 turn.

2) Remove filter by pulling back dust cover and pulling out filter. For ease of filter installation, cut new filter diagonally.

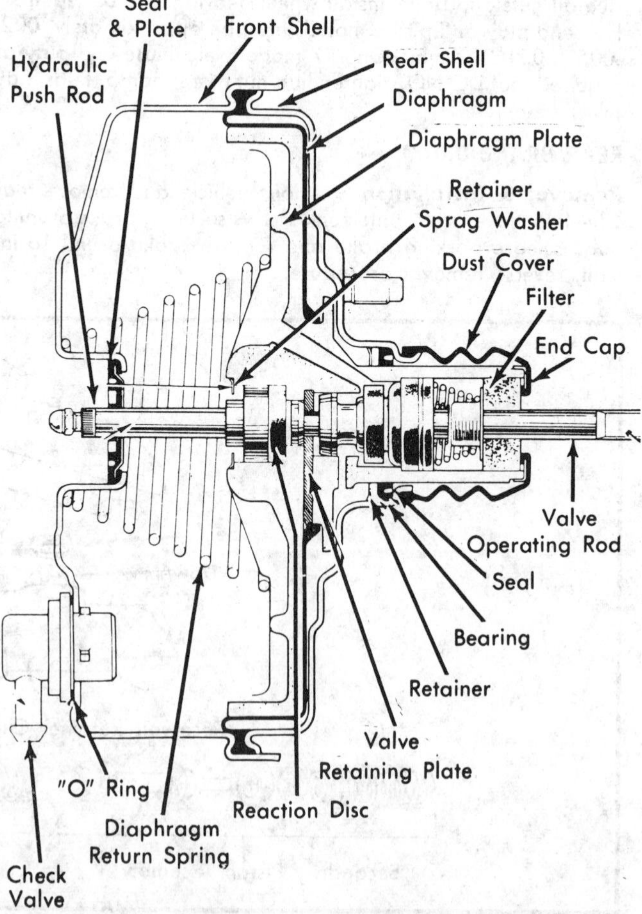

Fig. 5 Sectional View of Vacuum Servo Unit

TRIUMPH (Cont.)

3) Remove seal and plate assembly from front shell recess by gripping center rib with needle nose pliers. Use grease supplied in service kit to lubricate new seal and plate assembly when installing.

4) To check push rod for wear, place a straight edge across front shell recess. Measure clearance between end of push rod and straight edge. Clearance should be .011-.016" (.28-.41mm). Replace servo unit if clearance is incorrect.

NOTE – *Servo push rod to master cylinder clearance is set by factory and secured with Locktite. No attempt should be made to alter setting.*

Reassembly – To reassemble components to servo unit, reverse disassembly procedures.

MASTER CYLINDER

Disassembly, Spitfire – 1) Remove master cylinder as previously outlined. Drain and discard fluid. Remove screws securing reservoir to cylinder. Depress push rod, remove snap ring and withdraw push rod with abutment plate. Use an Allen wrench to unscrew tipping valve securing nut and remove seal. Depress primary plunger and remove tipping valve.

2) Remove internal parts either with compressed air at inlet or by shaking cylinder body. Separate plunger and intermediate spring. Lift leaf of spring retainer, remove spring and center valve sub-assembly from secondary plunger. From valve stem, remove spring, valve spacer, spring washer and valve seal. Remove seals from primary and secondary plungers.

Cleaning & Inspection – Clean all serviceable parts in brake fluid or alcohol. Examine cylinder bore for score marks, ridges or corrosion. Discard cylinder body even if only slight imperfections are found.

NOTE – *Replace all seals with those contained in service repair kit. Prior to assembly, lubricate all parts in clean brake fluid.*

Reassembly – 1) Install seal on primary and secondary plungers. Install seal, smaller diameter leading, to valve head. Place spring washer on valve stem ensuring that convex side of washer is to valve. Place spring retainer to valve stem with keyhole leading. Slide secondary spring over spring retainer and up to secondary plunger.

2) Place secondary plunger and valve assembly between protected jaws of a vise and compress spring. Use a small screwdriver to press leaf spring retainer against secondary plunger and then compress leaf spring retainer with needle nose pliers against plunger. Remove plunger and valve assembly from vise and check retainer spring.

3) Install intermediate spring between primary and secondary plungers and insert into cylinder. Replace push rod, snap

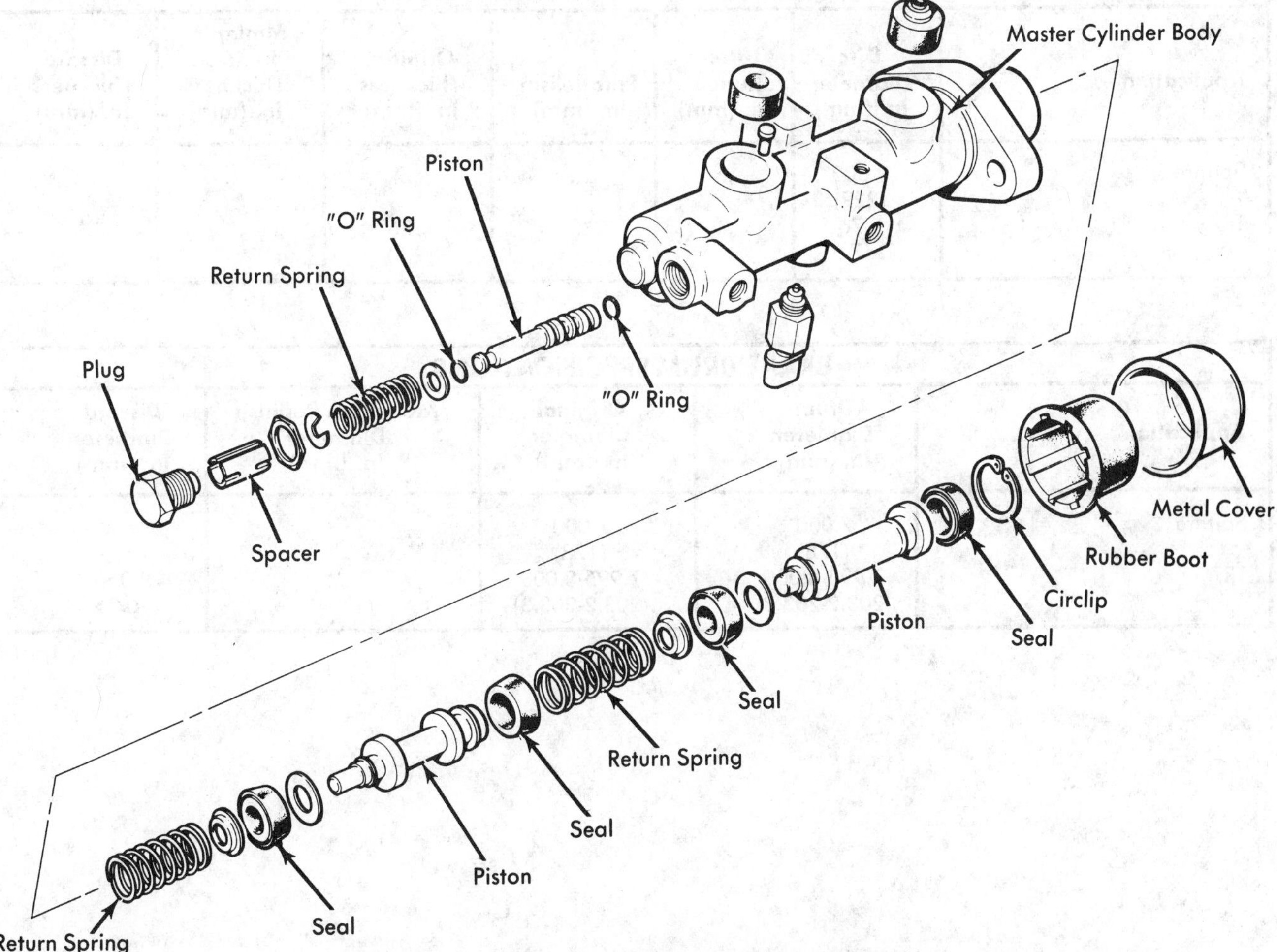

Fig. 6 Exploded View of Master Cylinder Assembly

TRIUMPH (Cont.)

ring and rubber boot. Depress push rod and insert tipping valve. Install seal, secure nut and torque to specifications. Install reservoir and seal. Install master cylinder and bleed brakes.

Disassembly, TR7 – 1) Separate fluid reservoir from master cylinder. Pull out rubber seals from cylinder body. Take off metal cap and rubber boot, then disengage circlip and pull out primary piston assembly.

2) Insert a rod into bore and depress secondary piston. This releases stop pin for removal. Withdraw secondary piston, spring retainer and return spring.

3) Unscrew failure switch from cylinder body. Remove end plug and extract washer, spacer and piston with spring. Carefully separate rubber seals.

Inspection – Clean all components in brake fluid, then thoroughly dry. Carefully inspect all components for wear. If cylinder bore is even slightly corroded, cylinder must be replaced. Ensure all fluid passages are unobstructed.

Reassembly – 1) Fit new seals and washers to primary and secondary pistons. Insert secondary return spring, spring retainer, and piston into cylinder bore.

2) Using a rod, depress secondary piston until head of piston passes secondary fluid port, then fit stop bolt. Fit primary return spring, spring retainer and piston into bore. Be sure lip of seal is not bent back.

3) Fit circlip at mouth of cylinder and check for correct seating in groove. Reinstall both rubber seals into cylinder body recesses. Ensure reservoir is clean and fit to master cylinder.

4) Fit new "O" rings into grooves on pressure warning switch piston and spring assembly. Insert assembly into bore and take care not to damage "O" rings. Install spacer, fuel line, copper washer, and end plug.

TIGHTENING SPECIFICATIONS

Application	Ft. Lbs. (mkg)
Disc Brake Rotor-to-Hub	
Spitfire	26-34 (3.6-4.7)
Disc Brake Caliper-to-Mount Plate	
Spitfire	50-65 (7.0-9.0)
Master Cylinder Tipping Valve Nut	35-40 (4.8-5.5)

DISC BRAKE ROTOR SPECIFICATIONS

Application	Disc Diameter In. (mm)	Lateral Runout In. (mm)	Parallelism In. (mm)	Original Thickness In. (mm)	Minimum Refinish Thickness In. (mm)	Discard Thickness In. (mm)
Spitfire	9.000 (229)	...	...	...	...	...
TR7	9.76 (247.6)	...	...	.375 (9.5)	...	...

BRAKE DRUM SPECIFICATIONS

Application	Drum Diameter In. (mm)	Original Diameter In. (mm)	Maximum Refinish Diameter In. (mm)	Discard Diameter In. (mm)
Spitfire	7.000 (178)	7.000 (178)	...	...
TR7	7.995-8.000 (203.2-203.3)	7.995-8.000 (203.2-203.3)	...	8.050 (204.5)

VOLKSWAGEN

Type 1
Type 2
Dasher
Rabbit
Scirocco

DESCRIPTION

Brake system is hydraulically actuated, using a tandem master cylinder and on some models, a power brake unit. Type 1 models are equipped with drum brakes on all four wheels. All other models are equipped with disc brakes on the front wheels and drum brakes on the rear wheels. All models with disc brakes are equipped with a pressure regulator in the rear brake circuit. The pressure regulator limits pressure to the rear brakes when foot brake is applied, preventing rear wheel lock-up. All models are equipped with a mechanical parking brake, operating on the rear brakes.

ADJUSTMENT

DISC BRAKES

Disc brakes are self-adjusting; therefore, no adjustment in service is required.

DRUM BRAKES

Type 2 (Rear Brakes) – Turn adjusting nut for both shoes three notches at a time, alternating from one nut to the other, until both shoes are rubbing on brake drum. Turn both nuts back alternately, until brake drum just rotates freely.

All Others – Turn adjuster until a slight drag is felt when rotating brake drum. Back off adjuster 3-4 notches, or until drum is just free to rotate.

PARKING BRAKE

Type 2 & Dasher – Raise and support vehicle and ensure rear brakes are properly adjusted. From under vehicle, loosen parking brake cable lock nut(s). Pull parking brake handle up six notches (Type 2), or two notches (Dasher) and tighten cable adjusting nut(s) until rear wheels can just be turned by hand. Tighten lock nut(s) and ensure rear wheels rotate freely with parking brake fully released.

All Others – Raise and support vehicle and ensure rear brakes are properly adjusted. Pull back rubber (plastic) boot at base of parking brake handle and loosen parking brake cable lock nuts. Pull handle up three notches and tighten each adjusting nut until rear wheels just lock. Tighten lock nuts and refit rubber (plastic) boot. Ensure rear wheels rotate freely with parking brake fully released.

HYDRAULIC SYSTEM BLEEDING

Pressure Bleeding – Attach bleeder connector cap to cylinder reservoir, and pressurize system to 43 psi. Attach one end of bleeder tube to cylinder bleeder screw, and submerge opposite end of tube in a jar half full of clean brake fluid. Open each bleeder screw in turn, and allow fluid to flow into container until fluid flows with no sign of air in fluid.

Manual Bleeding – Attach one end of bleeder tube to bleeder screw, and submerge opposite end in a jar half full of clean brake fluid. Pump brake pedal several times, and with pedal at bottom of stroke, open bleeder screw. Close bleeder screw, then release pressure on brake pedal. Repeat procedure until fluid flows from bleeder tube with no sign of air in fluid.

BRAKE PRESSURE REGULATOR

NOTE – *Scirocco models do not use pressure regulator.*

Type 2 – **1)** Install a hydraulic pressure gauge that will record 0-2300 psi in front and rear circuit. Bleed both hoses through gauge bleeder valves.

2) Pump pedal several times. Depress pedal until there is 1420 psi in each circuit. Release pedal. Loosen pressure regulator mounting bolts.

3) Apply pressure to pedal until both gauges read 710 psi. Tilt front of pressure regulator about 30° down from installed position. Leave regulator on angle and depress pedal until front brake circuit pressure reaches 1420 psi. Rear circuit MUST have 786-929 psi. If correct pressure is not obtained in rear circuit, replace regulator.

Dasher & Rabbit – **1)** Remove everything from luggage compartment. Fill fuel tank. Load drivers seat with about 165 lbs. Bounce vehicle several times and allow to settle normally.

2) Install spring tensioners under shock absorbers and attach at top to frame. See *Fig. 1*.

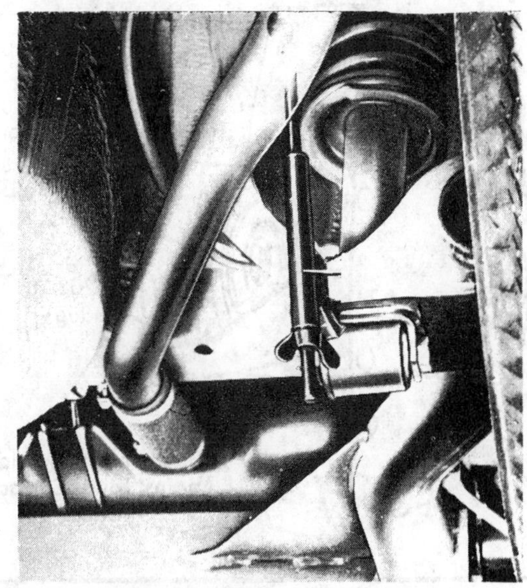

NOTE: Tensioners will keep vehicle in a settled position.

Fig. 1 Tensioner with Wing Nut Fitted on Left Side Shock Absorber of Rabbit

3) Connect 1 1500 psi minimum pressure gauge to right rear wheel cylinder and connect another to left front brake caliper. Bleed gauges.

VOLKSWAGEN (Cont.)

4) Pump pedal several times. Depress pedal until front wheel gauge reads 710 psi. Check rear wheel gauge for pressure of 440-497 psi.

5) Continue to depress pedal until front gauge reads 1400 psi. Rear gauge must read 753-810 psi.

NOTE – *Do NOT adjust spring tension with brake pedal depressed.*

6) If both pressures in test were too high on rear wheel, loosen regulator clamp bolt and REDUCE spring tension. If both pressures were consistently low, INCREASE spring tension. If correct specifications cannot be obtained by adjusting spring tension, replace pressure regulator.

REMOVAL & INSTALLATION

FRONT DISC BRAKE PADS

Removal: Girling, All Models – Raise and support vehicle. Remove wheel. Pry off spreader spring. On Rabbit and Scirocco models, remove spring retainer bolt. Using a pair of pliers, pull out pad retainer pins. NOTE – *Some models have "U" shaped retainer.* With a disc pad extractor tool, pull out pads. Inspect pads for wear or damage. Replace pads if lining thickness is less than .080" (2.0 mm).

Installation – To install Girling disc brake pads, reverse removal procedure and note: Tighten spring retainer bolt. Make sure spreader spring arrow faces upward.

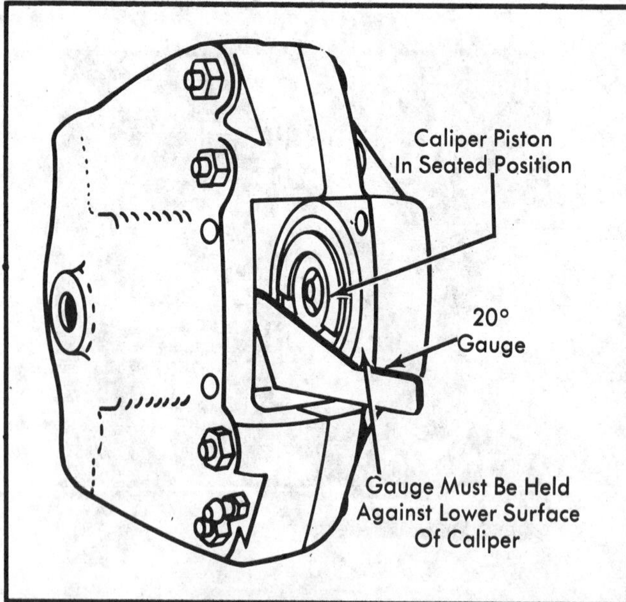

Fig. 2 Using a 20° Gauge to Properly Position Piston in Caliper Bore

Removal: ATE; Dasher, Rabbit and Scirocco – 1) Raise and support vehicle. Remove wheel. Remove spring clips from retaining pins. Using a punch, drive out retaining pins. Remove damper spring. With a disc pad extractor tool, remove inner pad. Outer pad is positioned in a notch and must be moved out of notch before removal.

2) Inspect disc pads for wear or damage. Replace pads if lining thickness is less than .008" (2.0 mm). Remove piston retaining plate and clean in denatured alcohol. Inspect plate for damage and replace as necessary.

Installation – **Using a suitable piston retaining device, push piston to bottom of cylinder bore. Check position of piston using a 20° gauge. Install piston retaining plate, insert disc pads and a NEW damper spring. Using a hammer, install retaining pins into caliper. Depress brake pedal several times to seat pistons and disc pads.**

Removal: ATE; Type 2 – Raise and support vehicle. Remove wheel. Pry off spreader spring. Using a pair of pliers, pull out pad retainer pins. Using a disc pad extractor tool, pull out pads. Inspect pads for wear or damage. Replace pads if lining thickness is less than .080" (2.0 mm).

Installation – To install disc pads, reverse removal procedure and note: Make sure spreader spring faces up.

DISC BRAKE CALIPER

Removal – Raise and support vehicle and remove wheel. Disconnect brake line from caliper and plug opening to prevent entry of dirt and foreign matter. Bend back locking tabs on mounting bolts at steering knuckle. Remove caliper mounting bolts and remove caliper assembly from vehicle.

Installation – To install, reverse removal procedure, using new lock plates and mounting bolts.

DISC BRAKE ROTOR

Removal – **Raise and support vehicle, remove wheel. Remove caliper mounting bolts and hang caliper from tie rod with wire. Remove wheel bearing mounting hardware and carefully pull hub and rotor assembly (with outer bearing) from spindle.** NOTE – ***On Type 2 models, if hub is stuck, DO NOT pound with hammer, screw bolts into three holes provided until assembly breaks loose.*** **Rotor can be separated from hub by removing the Allen head bolts.**

Installation – **To install hub and rotor assembly, reverse removal procedure and adjust wheel bearings.** ***See Wheel Bearing Adjustment in WHEEL ALIGNMENT Section.***

FRONT BRAKE DRUM

Removal – Raise and support vehicle, and remove wheel. Remove retainer from speedometer cable. Remove dust cap from hub, then remove wheel bearing adjusting nut, and outer wheel bearing. Back off brake shoe adjusters, and remove hub and drum assembly from vehicle.

Installation – To install, reverse removal procedure. Adjust and lubricate wheel bearings, and adjust brake shoes.

REAR BRAKE DRUM

Removal (Type 1) – **Remove cotter pin and castellated nut. Loosen castellated nut while vehicle is on ground. Raise and**

VOLKSWAGEN (Cont.)

support vehicle, then take off wheel. Release parking brake and back off adjusters. Fit puller to drum and take off drum.

Installation – To install, reverse removal procedure and note: Make sure castellated nut is tightened with vehicle on floor.

Removal (Type 2) – Raise and support vehicle, remove wheel. With parking brake released, back off on brake shoe adjuster. Remove two Allen head screws and pull brake drum from wheel hub.

Installation – To install, reverse removal procedure and make sure Allen head screws are tight.

Removal (Rabbit, Scirocco, Dasher) – Raise and support vehicle. Back off brake shoe adjusters. Remove grease cap and cotter pin. Loosen, then remove adjustment nut and washer. Slide drum off spindle being careful not to drop outer bearing.

Installation – To install, reverse removal procedure and note: Clean spindle and threads. Make sure wheel bearing is lubricated. Adjust wheel bearings. *See Wheel Bearing Adjustment in WHEEL ALIGNMENT Section.* Adjust brake shoes.

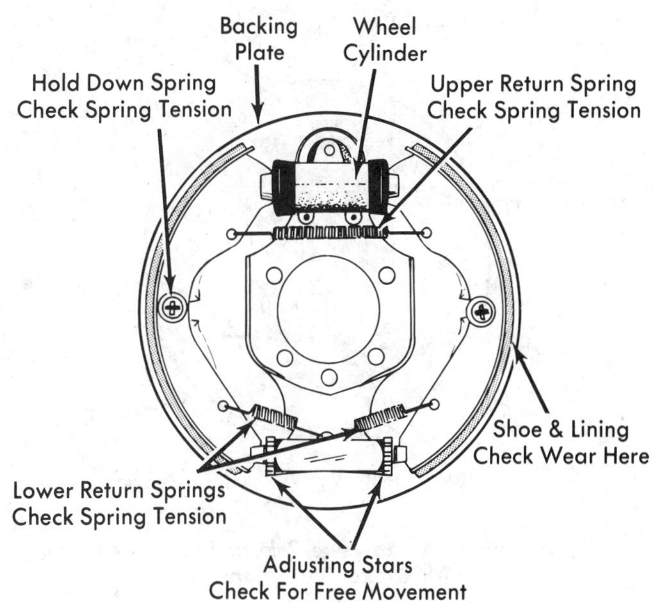

Fig. 4 Type 1 Front Brake Assembly with Brake Drum Removed

BRAKE SHOES

Removal (Front) – Raise and support vehicle. Remove wheel, and brake drum. Remove brake shoe hold down pins and springs. Remove brake shoe return springs, and pry shoes from adjusting screws. Remove brake shoes from vehicle.

Removal (Rear) – Raise and support vehicle. Remove wheel, and brake drum. Remove brake shoe hold down pins and springs. Remove lower shoe return spring, and disconnect parking brake cable from lever. Remove brake shoes, connecting link, upper return spring, and clip from vehicle as an assembly. Separate shoes from attaching hardware.

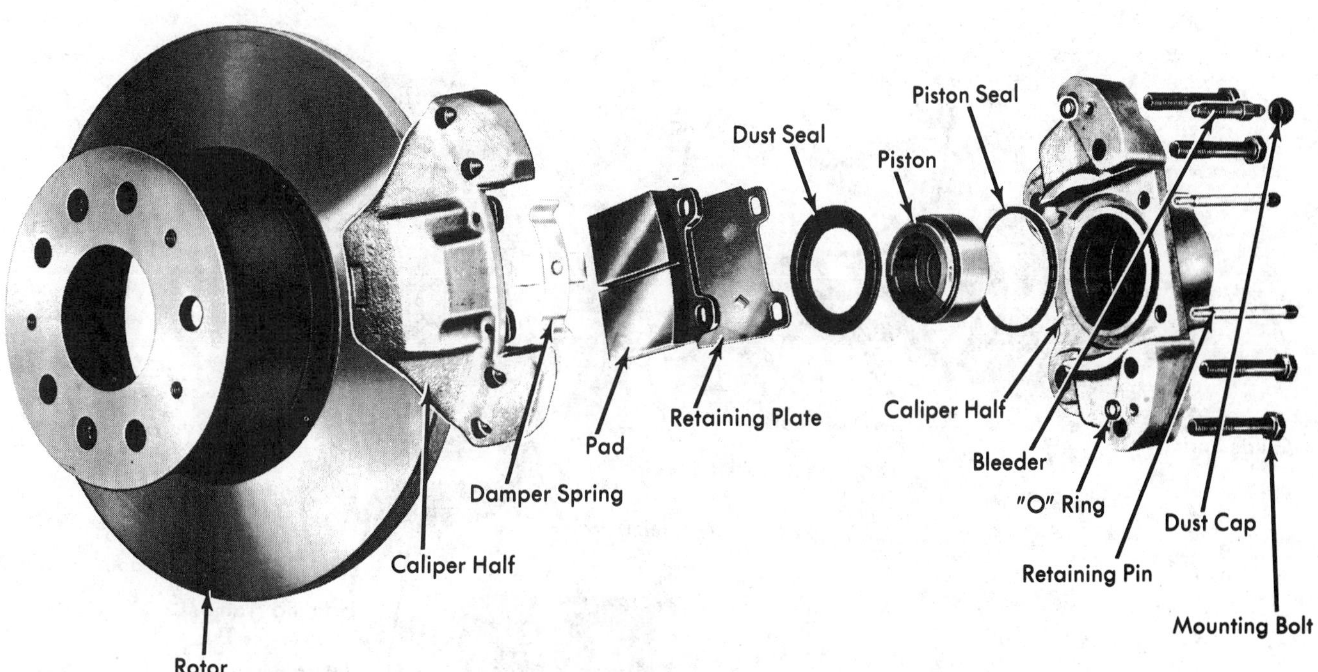

Fig. 3 Volkswagen Type 2 ATE Front Disc Brake Assembly. Girling Caliper Internal Design is Only Slightly Different. Girling Has a Retainer Ring for Dust Seal that is not Integral with Seal.

VOLKSWAGEN (Cont.)

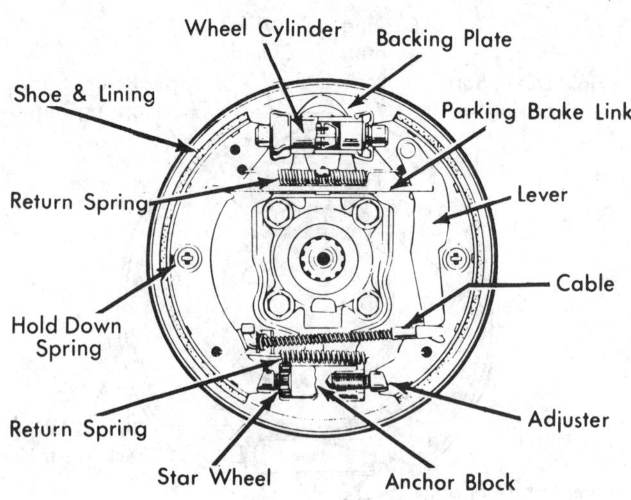

Fig. 5 Volkswagen Type 2 Rear Brake Assembly with Brake Drum Removed

Installation (All Models) – To install reverse removal procedure. Adjust brakes and bleed hydraulic system if necessary.

MASTER CYLINDER

NOTE – *Removal and installation of all master cylinders is basically the same. The following variations may apply: Location of cylinder, removal of wheel for accessibility, number of fluid connections, and number of electrical connections.*

Removal – Drain or siphon fluid from reservoir(s). Raise and support vehicle, and remove cover plate (if equipped). Disconnect fluid lines at master cylinder. Disconnect electrical connections at cylinder, and remove push rod at brake pedal connection. Remove master cylinder attaching bolts, and remove master cylinder from vehicle. **NOTE** – *If spacers are used on attaching bolts, do not allow spacers to drop into pedal assembly recess.*

Installation – To install, reverse removal procedure and note the following: On vehicles equipped with a power brake unit, install a new "O" ring seal between master cylinder and power unit. After installation, bleed hydraulic system.

POWER BRAKE BOOSTER

Removal & Installation – Remove master cylinder from power brake unit. Remove vacuum hoses and cover plate, then back off push rod lock nut at power booster end. Disconnect push rod at brake pedal, pull rod to one side, and unscrew push rod from booster. Remove booster attaching hardware, and pull booster out and back. To install booster, reverse removal procedure.

OVERHAUL

DISC BRAKE CALIPER

Disassembly: ATE & Girling; Type 2 – 1) Remove disc pads and retaining plates from caliper assembly. Clamp mounting flange in a vise. Remove retainer and dust seal from caliper assembly.

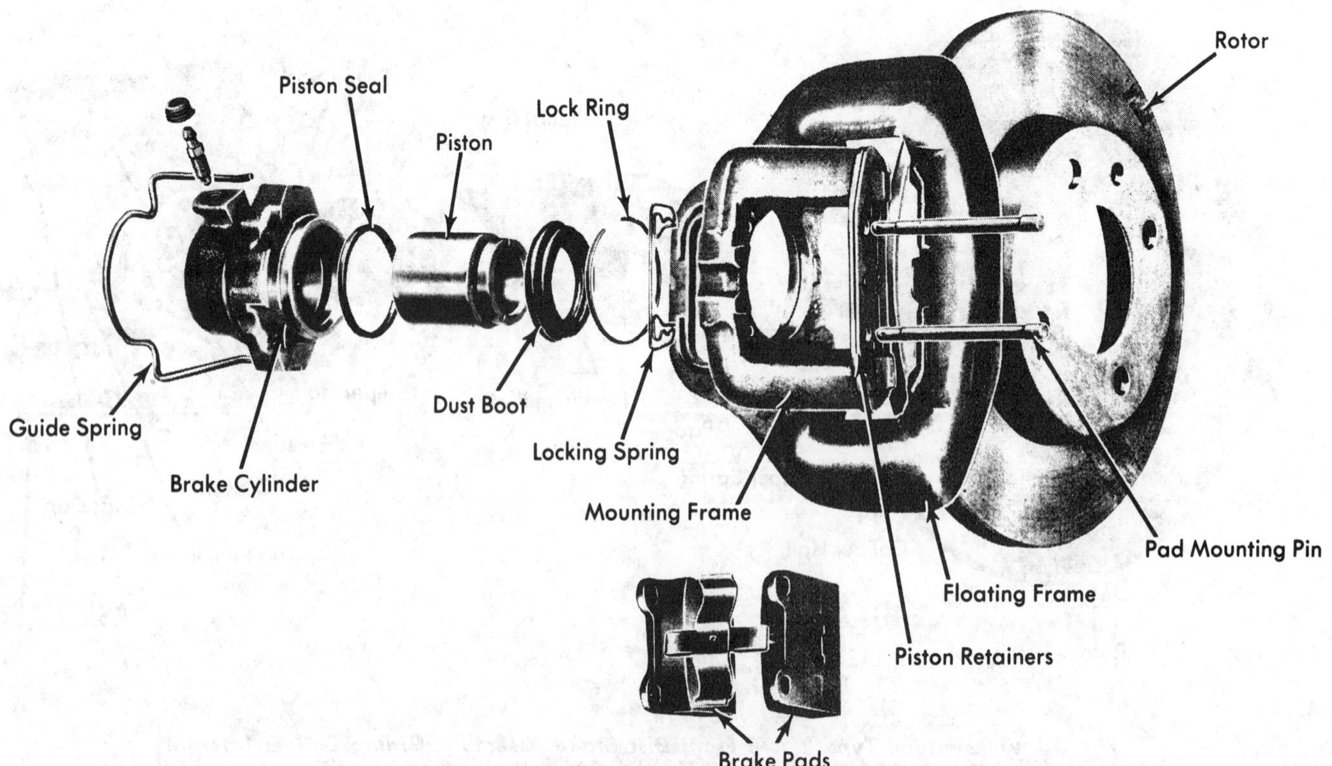

Fig. 6 Exploded View of ATE Disc Brake Assembly Used on Dasher, Rabbit and Scirocco

VOLKSWAGEN (Cont.)

2) Install a piston retaining tool on one piston and fit a thin block of wood between tool and piston to be removed. Carefully apply air pressure to fluid inlet port and remove piston. Remove piston seal from groove with a pointed tool.

Inspection – Clean all parts in brake fluid. Check piston and caliper bore for wear or damage; replace as necessary. **NOTE** – *Manufacturer recommends replacing rubber parts during caliper overhaul.*

Reassembly – Apply light coat of brake paste to piston and seal. Fit seal in groove. Install piston and clamp at bottom of bore. Lightly coat inside of dust seal with paste and fit to piston. Using suitable tool (VW 442), press seal and piston into caliper. Fit retaining plate and position piston in bore. Repeat procedure on other half of caliper.

Disassembly: ATE; Dasher, Rabbit, Scirocco – Remove disc pads. Pry mounting frame and piston assembly off floating frame. Separate guide spring and brake cylinder. Remove clamp and dust cap from brake cylinder, then withdraw piston. Compressed air may be used to force out piston.

Inspection – Clean all parts in brake fluid. Check piston and caliper bore for damage or wear; replace as necessary. **NOTE** – *Manufacturer recommends replacing all rubber parts during overhaul.*

Reassembly – To reassemble, reverse disassembly procedure and note following: Coat piston with brake paste. Use a vise to seat piston. Use a brass drift to fit brake cylinder to floating frame. Make sure two grooves in mounting frame are pushed over ribs on floating frame. Ensure piston is in proper position.

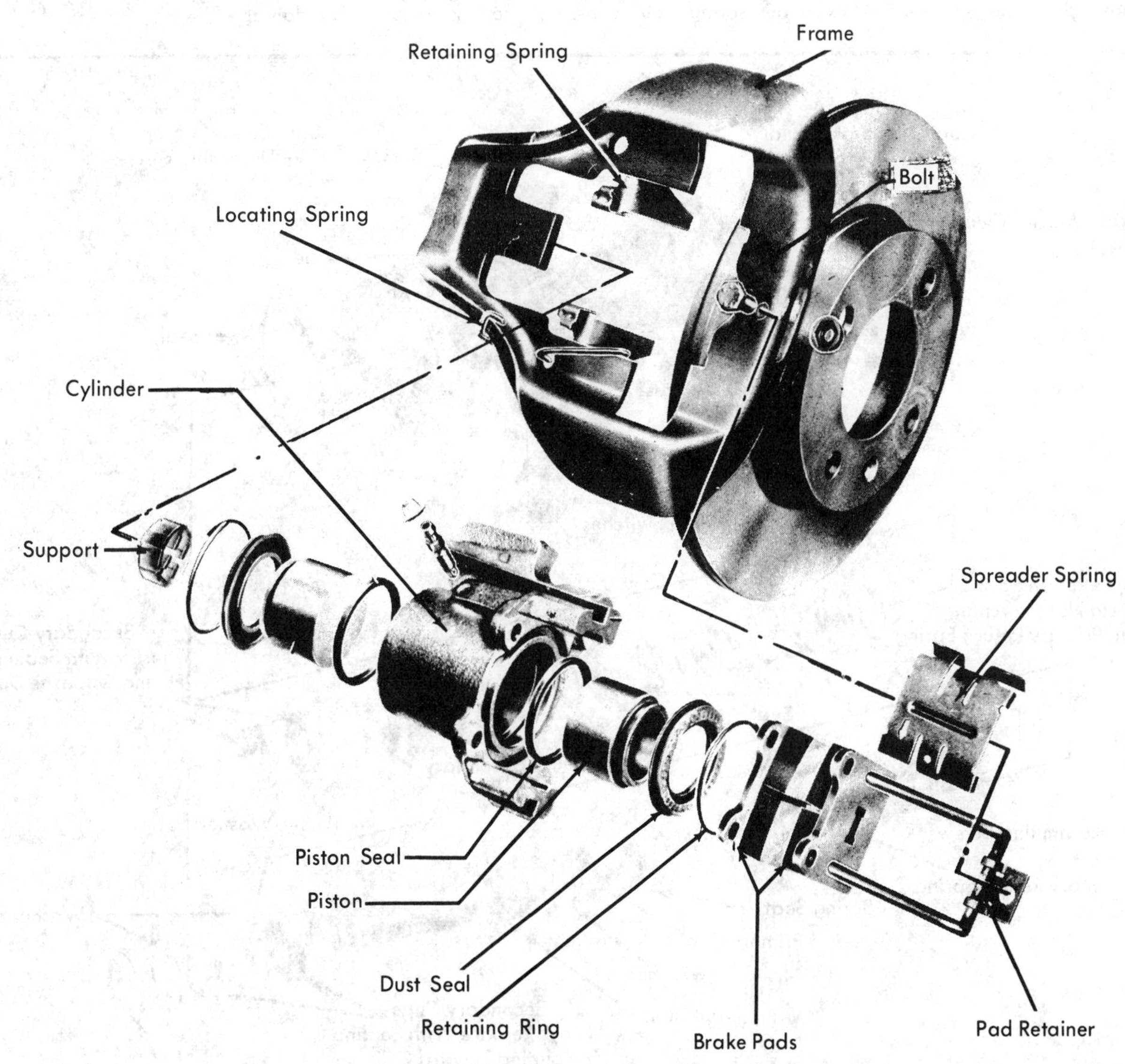

Fig. 7 Exploded View of Girling Disc Brake Assy. Use on Dasher, Rabbit and Scirocco

VOLKSWAGEN (Cont.)

Disassembly: Girling; Dasher, Rabbit, Scirocco – Press brake cylinder out of yoke. Hold brake cylinder between two jaws of a vise with a slight gap. This will prevent piston from flying out of cylinder when compressed air is introduced into fluid port to remove pistons. With a pointed tool, remove sealing rings.

Inspection – Clean all parts in brake fluid. Check piston and caliper bore for damage or wear; replace as necessary. **NOTE** – *Manufacturer recommends replacing all rubber parts at time of overhaul.*

Reassembly – To reassemble, reverse disassembly procedure and note: Coat pistons and seals with brake paste before refitting.

WHEEL CYLINDER

Disassembly – With wheel cylinder removed from vehicle, remove dust boot(s), piston(s), expander spring, and cups.

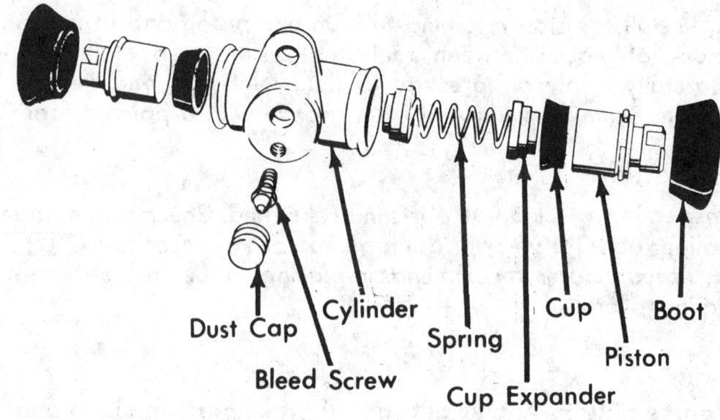

Fig. 8 Volkswagen Type 1 Wheel Cylinder Assembly

Inspection – Clean all parts with clean brake fluid or denatured alcohol. Check piston and cylinder bore for out-of-round, corrosion, or damage.

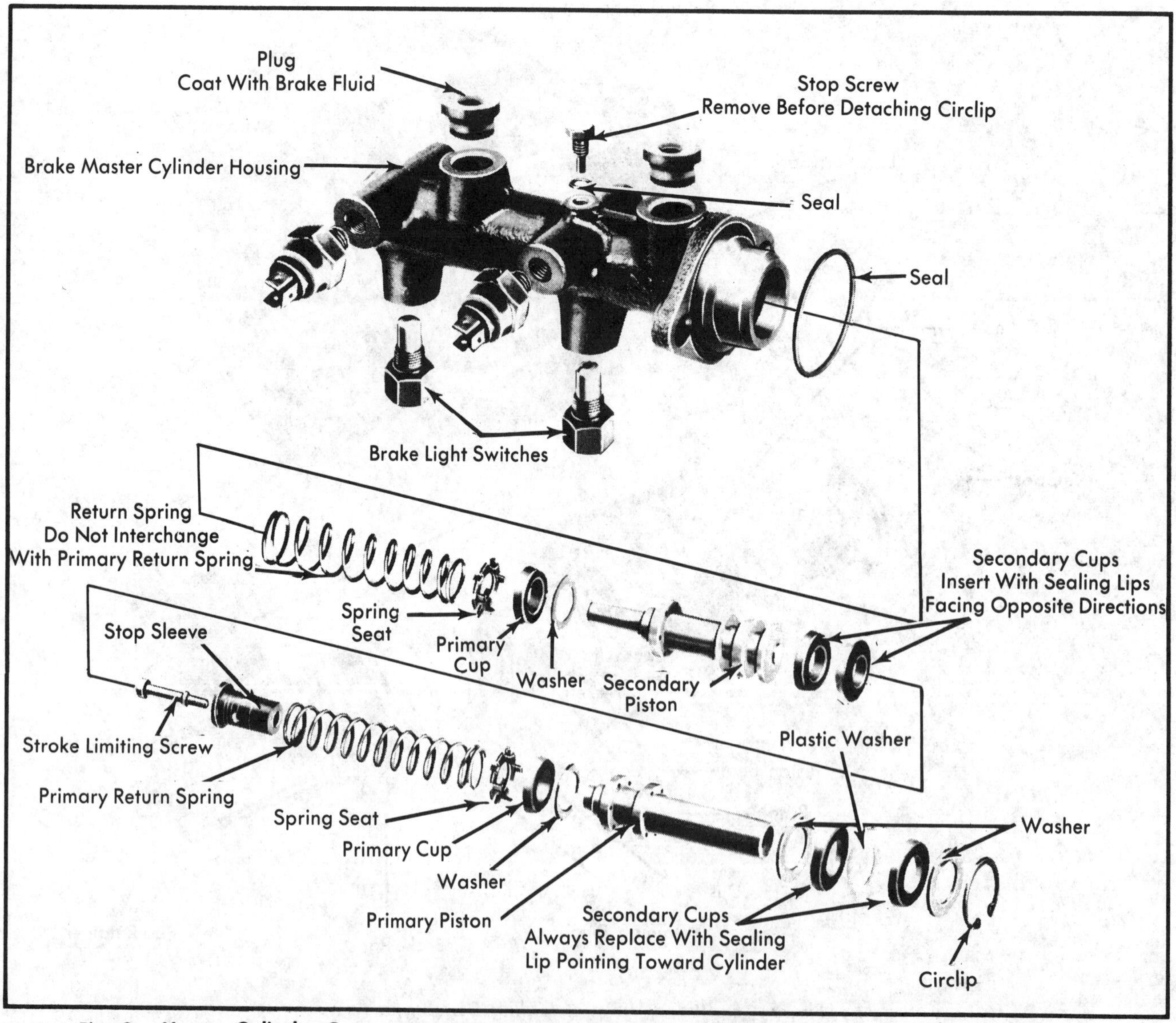

Fig. 9 Master Cylinder Component Relationship – Rabbit, Scirocco, Dasher Shown – Others Similar

VOLKSWAGEN (Cont.)

Reassembly – To reassemble, reverse disassembly procedure, using new rubber components. Replace piston(s) and spring as necessary. Use brake cylinder paste on pistons and cups.

MASTER CYLINDER

Disassembly – Remove front brake circuit piston stop screw. On Type 2 vehicles with power booster, remove snap ring and stop washer. On all other models, remove dust boot, stop ring, and stop washer. Remove both pistons and springs from cylinder by tapping open end of cylinder on a wood surface, or by carefully applying air pressure to front brake circuit fluid port will all other openings plugged. Remove all externally mounted fittings and switches from cylinder housing.

Inspection – Clean all parts with clean brake fluid or denatured alcohol. Check all pistons and cylinder for out-of-round, corrosion, or damage. If light honing will not remove blemishes from cylinder, replace cylinder. Inspect all other parts for scoring, wear, corrosion, or other damage.

Reassembly – **1)** Install cups on pistons. Place cup washer, primary cup, support washer, spring retainer, and spring onto front piston, and insert piston assembly into cylinder bore. Assemble cup washer, primary cup, support washer, spring retainer, spring, and stop sleeve onto rear piston. Secure assembly with stroke limiting screw.

2) Except on Type 2 vehicles with power booster, install rear piston assembly into cylinder. Install stop washer, and lock ring. On Type 2 vehicles with power booster, install rear piston with washer, cup, plastic washer, second cup, and second washer into cylinder, followed by snap ring.

3) Install piston stop screw, pushing front piston assembly forward as required to clear stop screw hole. Install all externally mounted switches and fittings. Tighten all nuts and bolts.

POWER BRAKE UNIT & PRESSURE REGULATING VALVE

Replace these units as an assembly, do not try to overhaul units. When installing booster, use new boot, filter, damping washer, and sealing ring.

TIGHTENING SPECIFICATIONS

Application	Ft. Lbs. (mkg)
Master Cylinder-to-Booster	9 (1.3)
Master Cylinder-to-Frame	
Type 1 & 2	18 (2.5)
Master Cylinder Piston Stop Screw	
Type 1 & 2	3.5-7.0 (.5-1.0)
Dasher, Rabbit, Scirocco	11-14 (1.5-2.0)
Caliper Mounting	
Type 2	116 (16.0)
Dasher, Rabbit, Scirocco	43 (6.0)
Slotted Axle Shaft Nut (Type 2)	253 (35.0)

BRAKE SYSTEM SPECIFICATIONS

Application	Drum Diam. In. (mm)	Wheel Cylinder Diameter Front In. (mm)	Wheel Cylinder Diameter Rear In. (mm)	Master Cylinder Diameter In. (mm)
Type 1	② 9.055 (230)	.874 (22.2)	.678 (17.5)	.750 (19.05)
Type 2	9.921 (252)	2.126① (54)	.937 (23.8)	.874 (22.2)
Dasher	7.87 (200)	①	.....	.813 (20.6)
Rabbit & Scirocco	7.1 (180)	①	.....	.....

① – Front disc brakes. ② – Front and rear.

DISC BRAKE ROTOR SPECIFICATIONS ①

Application	Disc Diameter	Lateral Runout	Parallelism	Original Thickness	Minimum Refinish Thickness	Discard Thickness
Type 2	10.95 (278)	.004 (.10)	.0008 (.02)	.512 (13)	.472 (12)	.452 (11.5)
Dasher	9.41 (239)	.004 (.10)	.0008 (.02)	.472 (12)	.433 (11)	.410 (10.5)
Rabbit & Scirocco	...	...	...	.472 (12)	.433 (11)	.410 (10.5)

① – In. (mm)

VOLKSWAGEN (Cont.)

BRAKE DRUM SPECIFICATIONS				
Application	Drum Diameter In. (mm)	Original Diameter In. (mm)	Maximum Refinish Diameter In. (mm)	Discard Diameter In. (mm)
Front				
Type 1	9.055 (230)	9.055 (230)	9.114 (231.5)	.....
Rear				
Type 1	9.055 (230)	9.055 (230)	9.114 (231.5)	.....
Type 2	9.921 (252)	9.921 (252)	9.980 (253)	.....
Dasher	7.87 (200)	7.87 (200)	7.89 (200.5)	7.91 (201)
Rabbit & Scirocco	7.08 (180)	7.08 (180)	7.10 (180.5)	7.125 (181)

VOLVO

240 Series
260 Series

DESCRIPTION

Volvo models may be equipped with either Girling or ATE four wheel disc brake systems. Also, it is possible that a vehicle may have a combination of Girling and ATE brakes. Brake system incorporates two separate circuits: hydraulic disc brake and mechanical parking brake. Service brakes are operated by a tandem master cylinder attached to a vacuum operated power assist unit. Master cylinder feeds hydraulic pressure to each circuit. One circuit feeds lower front caliper pistons and right rear caliper. Other circuit feeds upper front caliper pistons and left rear caliper. Additionally, valves are installed in both circuits to equally distribute braking power. A warning light, mounted on instrument panel, indicates pressure differences between circuits as they may occur.

ADJUSTMENT

DISC BRAKES

Disc brakes are self-adjusting; therefore, no adjustment in service is required.

PARKING BRAKE

1) Remove center console rear ash tray, then working through ash tray hole, loosen parking brake cables adjusting screw until cables are slack. Raise and support rear of vehicle, then remove wheels. Align hole in parking brake drum with starwheel adjuster.

2) Tighten starwheel until drum can just be rotated by hand, then back off adjuster until drum just rotates freely. Install rear wheels. Tighten parking brake cable adjusting screw until parking brake is fully applied when lever is pulled three or four notches. Install ash tray and lower vehicle.

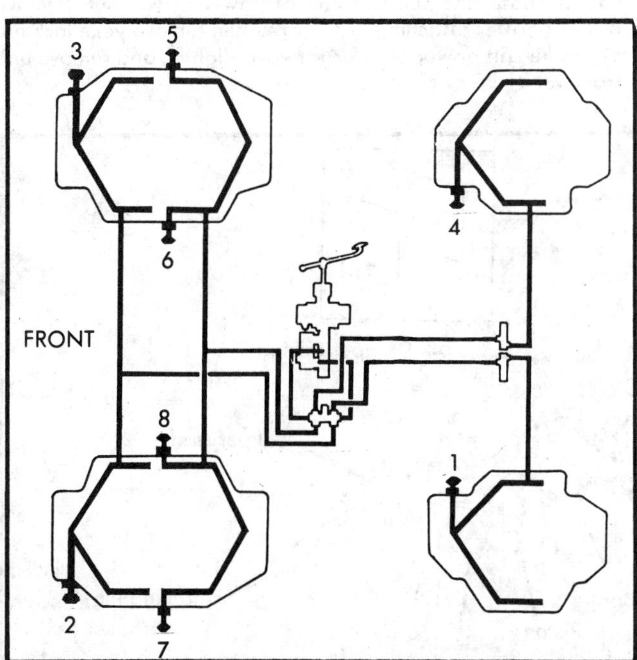

Fig. 1 Schematic of Bleeding Sequence

HYDRAULIC SYSTEM BLEEDING

NOTE — *To ensure the best possible results, bleed brakes in proper sequence.*

1) Start at left front brake. Connect bleed tubes to all three bleeder screws and immerse opposite end of tubes in a container partially filled with brake fluid. Pump brake pedal ten times, then keep pedal depressed and using assistants, open all three bleeder screws simultaneously. When pedal reaches end of travel, close all bleeder screws. Continue operation until all air is bled from caliper assembly. Repeat procedure on right front brake.

2) Depress brake pedal several times to level out master cylinder. Connect a bleed tube to right rear brake bleeder screw and immerse opposite end of tube in a container partially filled with brake fluid. Open bleeder screw and gravity bleed (no pumping of pedal) caliper assembly. Close bleeder screw when brake fluid is free of air bubbles. Repeat procedure on left rear brake.

REMOVAL & INSTALLATION

DISC PADS

Removal, All Types — Raise and support vehicle. Remove wheel. On Girling brakes, remove spring locks. Pull out one lock pin and hold damper springs in place. Remove springs and other lock pin. On ATE brakes, drive out upper guide pin, remove tension spring, then tap out lower guide pin. On all brakes, use tool 2917 (or equivalent) and pull disc pads from caliper. If pads are to be reinstalled, index mark.

Installation, All; Front — Using tool 280 (or equivalent), seat pistons in caliper bore. **NOTE** — *Use of screwdriver is discouraged because pads, seals or piston can be easily damaged.* Insert pads and fit guide or lock pins, spring locks and tension springs.

Installation, Rear; ATE — Press pistons into caliper until bottomed in bore. Before installing disc pads, ensure pistons are in proper position to prevent brake squeal; piston recess should incline 20° in relation to lower guide area on caliper *(See Fig. 2)*. Check piston angle using template SVO 2919 (or equivalent) and correct if necessary. Install disc pads and one guide pin. Install damper spring and remaining guide pin and secure with locking clips. After installation, depress brake pedal several times to position pads against rotor.

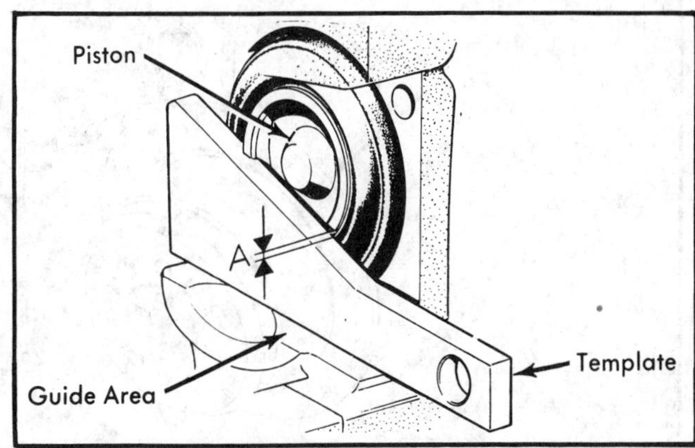

Fig. 2 Checking Piston Angle on Rear Brakes

VOLVO (Cont.)

Installation, Rear; Girling, – Select new disc pads and fit to caliper. If caliper is equipped with intermediate plates between pad and caliper, reinstall plates. If round damper washers are used, reinstall with smaller contact face toward pad. **NOTE** – *DO NOT install intermediate plates in caliper with round damper washers.* Fit one lock pin and install damper spring, then insert last lock pin. Check free movement of pads.

CALIPER ASSEMBLY

Removal – Raise and support vehicle, and remove wheel. Disconnect brake line connections at caliper, and cap lines to prevent entry of foreign matter. Remove caliper mounting bolts and lift caliper from vehicle.

Installation – Position caliper assembly on mounting bracket, and install attaching bolts. After installing bolts, check clearance between disc pads and rotor on both sides of rotor; maximum deviation between sides should not exceed .022" (.01 mm). If clearance is not within specifications, correct by adding shims to caliper. Connect hydraulic lines to caliper and bleed brakes.

DISC BRAKE ROTOR

Removal – Raise and support vehicle, remove wheel. Remove caliper assembly as previously outlined. Unscrew rotor lock bolts. Pull rotor from wheel hub.

Inspection – Before removing rotor, mount a dial indicator and check rotor runout. Runout must not exceed .004" (.1 mm). Measure rotor thickness through one revolution, thickness must not vary more than .001" (.03 mm).

Installation – To install, reverse removal procedure.

PARKING BRAKE SHOES

Removal – Remove center console rear ash tray and loosen parking brake cable adjusting nut until cables are slack. Raise and support rear of vehicle and remove wheels. Remove caliper (without disconnecting hydraulic line) and support out of way, then remove rotor. Remove brake shoe return springs and lift off shoes and adjuster.

Installation – Reverse removal procedure and note the following: Replace brake drum (rotor) if out-of-round more than .008" (.2 mm). Apply a thin coat of heat resistant graphite grease to brake shoe sliding surfaces and to adjusting starwheel. After installation, adjust parking brake. See *Parking Brake*.

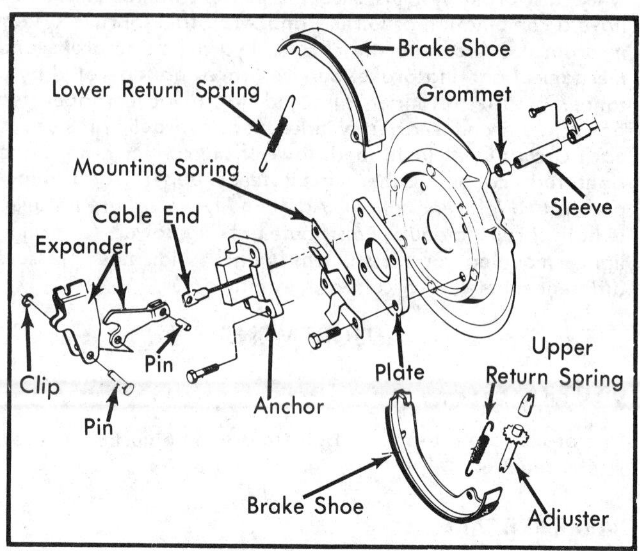

Fig. 3 Exploded View of Parking Brake Assembly

MASTER CYLINDER

Removal & Installation – Disconnect hydraulic lines at master cylinder and cap openings to prevent entry of foreign matter. Remove cylinder attaching hardware, and remove cylinder assembly from vehicle. To install, reverse removal procedure, and bleed hydraulic system.

POWER BRAKE UNIT

Removal – Remove master cylinder from vehicle. Disconnect vacuum hose and support unit at power brake unit. Remove power booster attaching hardware, then remove yoke lock nut and yoke. Tilt power booster forward slightly, and remove unit from vehicle.

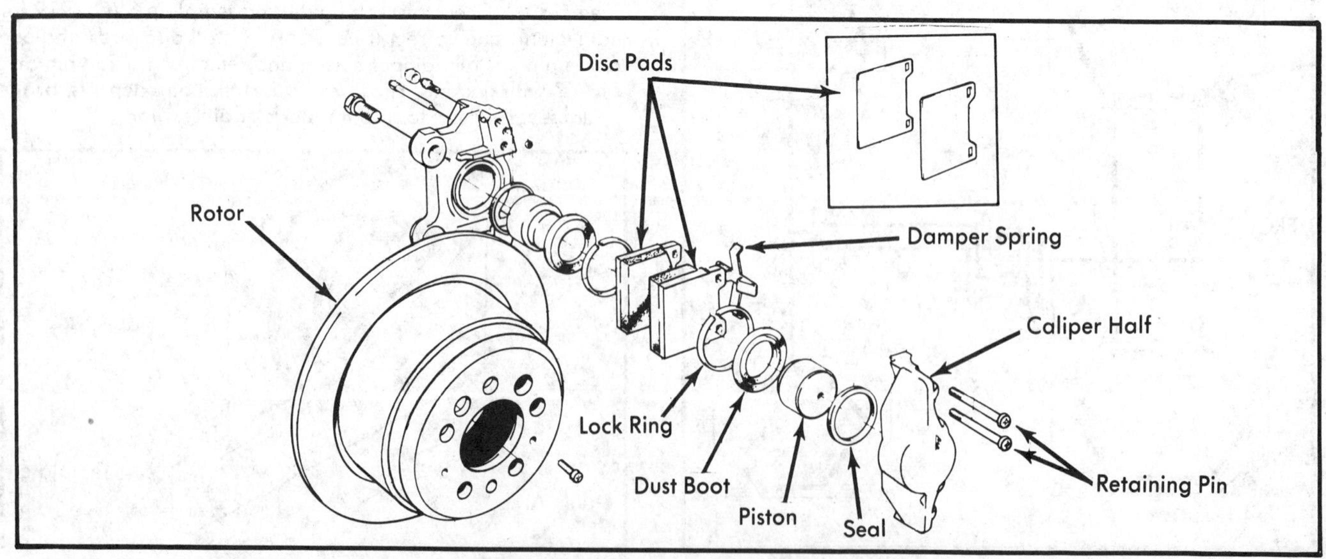

Fig. 4 ATE Rear Caliper Assembly Components

VOLVO (Cont.)

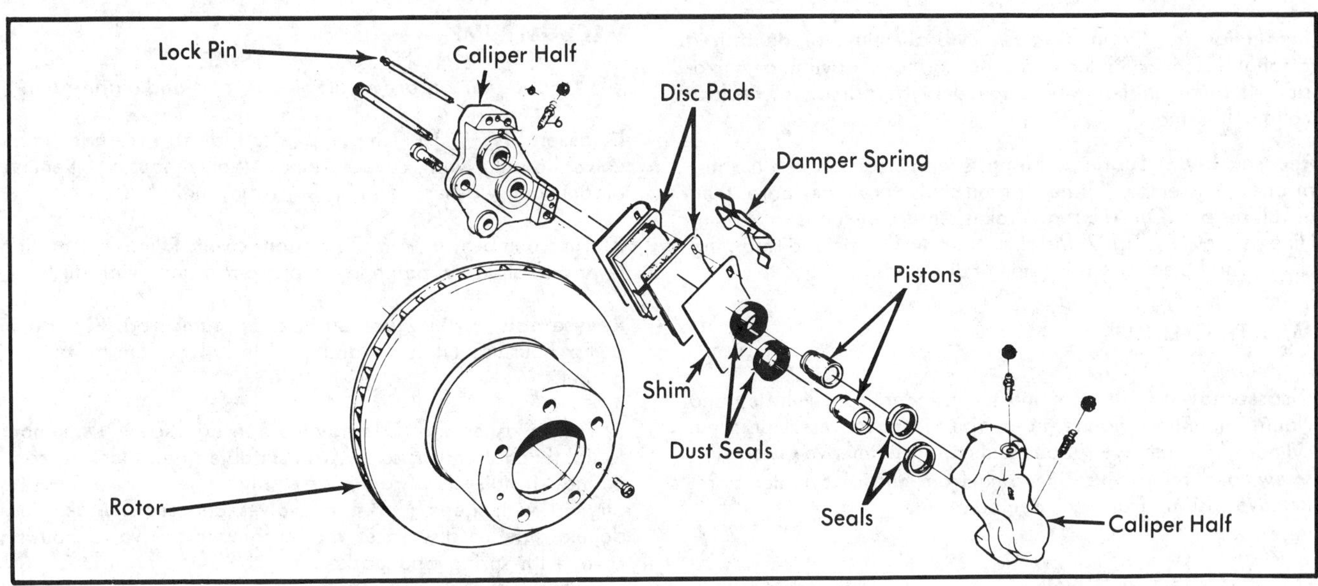

Fig. 5 ATE Front Caliper Assembly Components

Installation – Position power brake unit on vehicle, and attach yoke to push rod. Install and tighten push rod lock nut.

Install and tighten power booster mounting hardware, and install master cylinder to booster. Install vacuum hose, and bleed hydraulic system.

Check Valve Replacement – Remove vacuum hose clamps at check valve, and remove check valve from vehicle. When installing check valve into vacuum hose, install valve with arrow on valve housing pointing toward intake manifold.

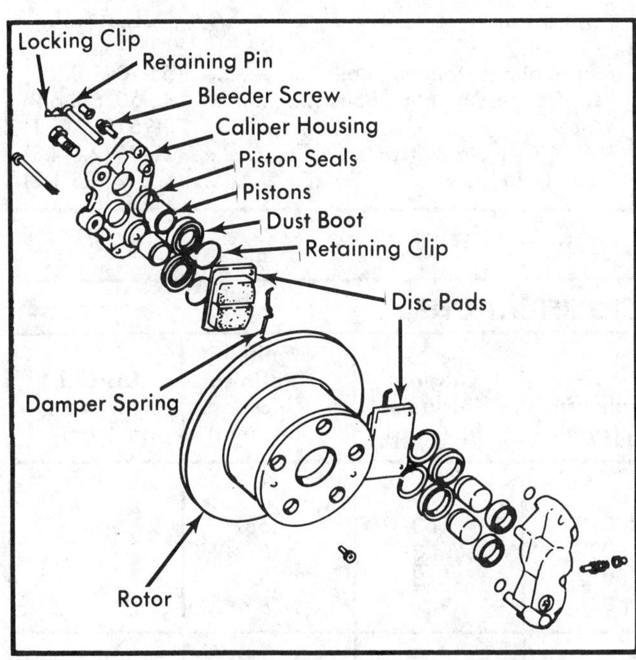

Fig. 6 Girling Front Caliper Assembly

Filter Replacement – Remove power brake unit from vehicle. Remove rubber dust boot, and filter retainer washer. Withdraw silencer and filter from end of booster. To install, reverse removal procedure, making sure slots in filter and silencer are 180° apart.

OVERHAUL

BRAKE CALIPER

Disassembly – Remove caliper from vehicle. Remove disc pads from caliper. Remove piston dust covers and retaining clips. Position a piece of wood between pistons, and carefully apply compressed air at fluid inlet port to force pistons out of cylinder bores. Remove piston seal from cylinder bore, then remove bleeder screw. **NOTE** – *DO NOT separate caliper halves.*

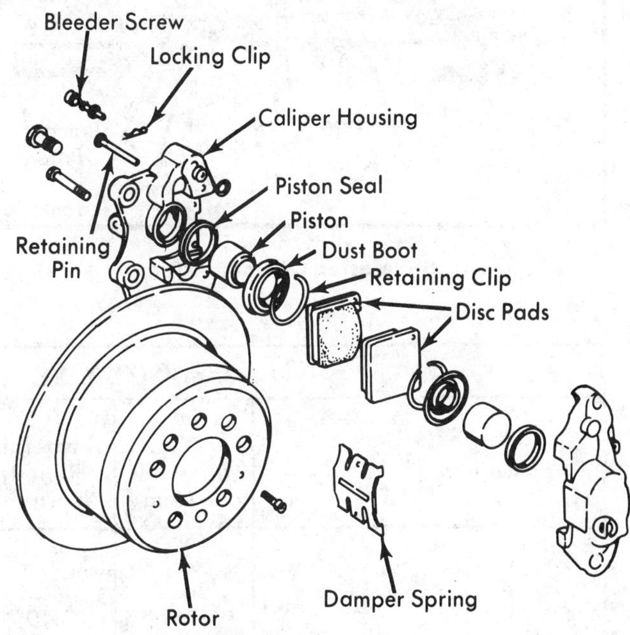

Fig. 7 Girling Rear Caliper Assembly

VOLVO (Cont.)

Inspection – Clean all parts in brake fluid or denatured alcohol. Inspect cylinder bores for scoring, grooving, or corrosion. If any cylinder bore is found to be damaged, replace caliper housing.

Reassembly – Lubricate all parts with clean brake fluid just prior to reassembly. Fit new piston seals in cylinder bore, then install pistons. On ATE rear brakes, ensure piston is at 20° incline as shown in *Fig. 2*. Install rubber dust boots and retaining clips. Install bleeder screw, then fit disc pads.

MASTER CYLINDER

Disassembly – Remove master cylinder from vehicle, and clamp mounting flange in a vise. Remove reservoir from cylinder, and remove rubber sealing rings. Remove piston stop screw, and remove retainer ring from end of cylinder bore. Remove pistons from cylinder bore.

Inspection – Clean all parts in clean brake fluid or denatured alcohol and blow dry with compressed air. Inspect cylinder bore for scratches, scoring or corrosion. If cylinder is scored or scratched, it should be replaced.

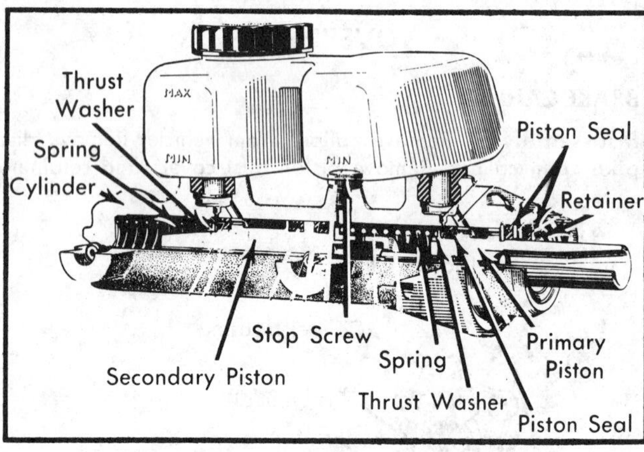

Fig. 8 Master Cylinder Assembly

VACUUM PUMP

NOTE – *Repair kits are available for valve and diaphragm.*

Disassembly – 1) Place pump in soft jawed vise. Index mark valve housing with cover. Remove valve housing. Remove diaphragm, washers, and spring from pump.

2) Turn pump over. Remove bottom cover. Remove actuating lever pin. Slide out pump lever, pump rod and nylon bushing.

Reassembly – 1) Place bushing on pump rod. Put rod in pump housing. Fit lever and pin. Install bottom cover and gasket.

2) Place washer and "O" ring on diaphragm screw. Remember to lightly coat end of screw with suitable thread locking compound. Install diaphragm assembly. Insert valve housing aligned with index marks. Fit valves and seals. Make sure domed side of disc faces diaphragm. Install valve housing cover with spring and gasket.

Reassembly – Lubricate all parts with clean brake fluid prior to reassembly. Position washer, seal, and back-up ring on secondary piston. Install spring thrust washer on piston, and install piston assembly into cylinder bore. Install washer, seal, and back-up ring on primary piston. Install spring, with plate and sleeve on piston, then install piston assembly into cylinder bore. Push piston into cylinder bore, and install piston stop screw. Install reservoir sealing rings, and install reservoir.

TIGHTENING SPECIFICATIONS

Application	Ft. Lbs. (mkg)
Front Caliper Mounting Bolts	65-70 (9.0-9.7)
Rear Caliper Mounting Bolts	45-50 (6.2-6.9)
Wheel Nuts	70-95 (9.7-13.1)
Master Cylinder Bolts	20-35 (2.8-4.8)
Brake Fluid Lines	6-9 (.83-1.2)

DISC BRAKE ROTOR SPECIFICATIONS

Application	Disc Diameter In. (mm)	Lateral Runout In. (mm)	Parallelism In. (mm)	Original Thickness In. (mm)	Minimum Refinish Thickness In. (mm)	Discard Thickness In. (mm)
240						
Front	10.35 (263)	.004 (.10)	.0012 (.03)	.563 (14.3)	.557 (13.14)	...
Rear	11.06 (281)	.004 (.10)	.0012 (.03)	.378 (9.6)	.331 (8.4)	...
260						
Front	10.35 (263)	.004 (.10)	.0012 (.03)	.95 (24)	.90 (22.8)	...
Rear	11.06 (281)	.004 (.10)	.0012 (.03)	.378 (9.6)	.331 (8.4)	...

Section 8
WHEEL ALIGNMENT

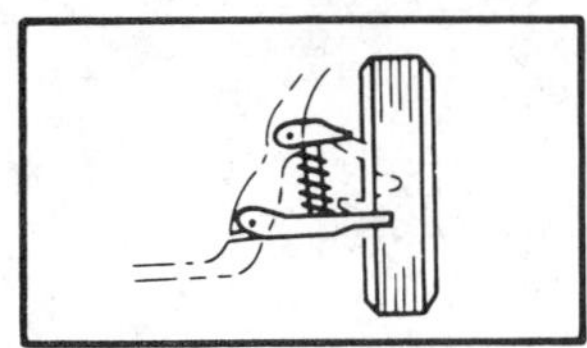

Contents

NOTE — ALSO SEE GENERAL INDEX.

WHEEL ALIGNMENT TROUBLE SHOOTING

NOTE – *This is a general trouble shooting guide. When using this guide, locate the condition in column one that corresponds to your problem and determine the possible causes in column two. Match the number of the possible cause with the same number in column three, and you will have the suggested correction.*

CONDITION	POSSIBLE CAUSE	CORRECTION
► Tire wear	1) Tire pressure too low 2) Wheel alignment out of tolerance 3) Excessively worn wheel bearings 4) Improper or no tire rotation	1) Check manufacturer's recommended pressure and set to specifications. 2) Check alignment and set to specs or replace components 3) Check, adjust or replace bearings 4) Follow manufacturer's recommended procedures. Perform a 4 or 5-tire rotation
► Grating tire noise	1) Improper tire pressure 2) Wheel alignment out of tolerance 3) Damaged or defective spindle or suspension components	1) Check manufacturer's recommended pressure and set to specifications 2) Reset alignment or replace necessary suspension components 3) Inspect and replace components
► Uneven tire wear	1) Uneven tire pressure 2) Tire pressure too low (shoulders on tire worn) 3) Tire pressure too high (center of tred worn) 4) Bent rotor or wheel 5) One side of front tred worn 6) Inside of tred worn 7) Outside of tred worn 8) Excessive wheel bearing play 9) Brake operation on only one side	1) Check manufacturer's recommended pressure and set to specifications 2) See correction 1 3) See correction 1 4) Check and replace part 5) Inadequate camber 6) Inadequate toe-in 7) Excessive toe-in 8) Inspect and adjust bearings 9) Check and adjust brakes
► Road noise	1) Abnormal tire wear 2) Tire out of balance 3) Tire pressure too low	1) Replace tire 2) Rebalance tire 3) Check manufacturer's recommended pressure and set to specifications

WHEEL ALIGNMENT SPECIFICATIONS

Application	Caster (Degrees)	Camber (Degrees)	Toe-In (Inches)	Remarks
ARROW				
All Models	2 1/12 ± 1/2	1 ± 1/2	5/64 to 15/64	
AUDI				
Fox				
Front	1/2 ± 1/2	1/2 ± 1/2	−1/32 to 7/32	
Rear	.....	1/2 ± 1/2	−13/32 to 13/32	
100LS	0 ± 1/4	0 ± 1/2	3/32 to 11/32	
BMW				
320i				
Front	8 1/3 ± 1/2	0 ± 1/2	3/64 to 3/32	
Rear	.....	−2 ± 1/2	0 to 5/64	
530i				
Front	7 2/3 ± 1/2	1/2 ± 1/2	3/64 to 3/32	
Rear	.....	−2 ± 1/2	0 to 1/12	
630CSi				
Front	7 2/3 ± 1/2	1/2 ± 1/2	1/32 to 3/32	
Rear	.....	−2	0 to 1/16	
CAPRI				
All Models	1 5/8 ± 5/8	1 1/2 ± 3/4	1/4 to 3/8	
COLT				
All Models	2 1/12 ± 1/2	1 ± 1/2	5/64 to 15/64	
COURIER				
All Models	1 ± 1/4	7/8 ± 3/8	0 to 1/4	
DATSUN				
200SX	1 5/16 ± 3/4	1 ± 5/6	5/16 to 5/32	① – Radial tires; 1/4 ± 1/32 for bias tires.
F10	1 1/8 ± 3/4	1 5/8 ± 3/4	0 to 13/16①	
B210	1 3/4 ± 3/4	1 1/8 ± 3/4	3/32 to 5/32	
710	1 5/6 ± 3/4	2 ± 3/4	5/32 to 1/4②	② – Radial tires; 15/64 to 5/16 for bias tires.
810	1 1/2 ± 3/4	3/4 ± 3/4	0 to 5/64	
280Z				
Front	2 3/4 ± 3/4	1 ± 3/4	0 to 1/8	
Rear	.....	3/4 ± 3/4	−13/64 to 13/64	
280Z 2+2				
Front	2 3/4 ± 3/4	1 1/16 ± 3/4	0 to 1/8	
Rear	.....	−3/4 ± 7/12	−13/64 to 13/64	
Pickup	1 5/6 ± 2/3	1 1/4 ± 1	5/64 to 1/8	
FIAT				
124 Spider	3 1/6 ± 1/2	1/2 ± 1/6	1/32 to 7/32	
128				
Front	2 1/4 ± 1/2	1 1/2 ± 1/2	1/4 to 15/32	
Rear	.....	−3 1/4 ± 1/2	5/64 to 15/64	
X1/9				
Front	7 ± 1/2	1/2 ± 1/2	5/64 to 15/64	
Rear	.....	−1 2/3 ± 1/2	5/32 to 15/64	
131	3 3/4 ± 1/2	3/4 ± 1/4	15/64 to 25/64	
HONDA				
Civic				
Front	1 3/4	1/2	3/64①	① – All Honda "Toe" measurements are "Toe-out".
Rear	.....	1/2	0	
CVCC Sedan				
Front	2 ± 1/2	1/2 ± 1/2	0 to 3/32	
Rear	.....	1/2 ± 1/2	0 to 5/64	

Wheel Alignment

WHEEL ALIGNMENT SPECIFICATIONS				
Application	**Caster (Degrees)**	**Camber (Degrees)**	**Toe-In (Inches)**	**Remarks**
HONDA (Cont.)				
CVCC ST. Wagon	1 ± 1/2	1/2 ± 1/2	0 to 1/16	
Accord				
Front	2 ± 1	1/2 ± 1	−3/32 to 5/32	
Rear	.....	3/8 ± 1/2	1/16 to 1/8	
JAGUAR				
XJ6				
Front	2 1/4 ± 1/4	1/2 ± 1/4	1/16 to 1/8	
Rear	.....	−3/4 ± 1/4	−1/32 to 1/32	
XJ12				
Front	2 1/4 ± 1/4	1/2 ± 1/4	1/16 to 1/8	
Rear	.....	−3/4 ± 1/4	−1/32 to 1/32	
XJS				
Front	3 1/2 ± 1/4	1/2 ± 1/4	1/16 to 1/8	
Rear	.....	−3/4 ± 1/4	−1/32 to 1/32	
LANCIA				
All Models				
Front	1 1/2 ± 3/8	1/2 ± 3/8	1/16 to 1/8	
Rear	.....	−1 ± 3/8	−1/32 to 1/32	
LUV				
All Models	−1/6 ± 1/2	1/2 ± 1/2	0 to 1/8	
MAZDA				
808 (1300)				① – With power steering, 2 1/4 ± 3/4.
Sedan & Wagon	1 5/12 ± 3/4	5/6 ± 1	0 to 1/4	
Coupe	1 3/4 ± 3/4	11/12 ± 1	0 to 1/4	
808 (1600)				
Sedan	1 5/6 ± 3/4	1 1/2 ± 1	0 to 1/4	
Coupe	2 1/12 ± 3/4	1 1/2 ± 1	0 to 1/4	
Wagon	1 5/6 ± 3/4	1 1/8 ± 1	0 to 1/4	
RX3	2 1/8 ± 3/4	1 1/8 ± 1	0 to 1/4	
RX4				
Sedan & Coupe	1 5/6 ± 3/4	1 ± 1	0 to 1/4	
Wagon	1 5/6 ± 3/4	1 1/4 ± 1	0 to 1/4	
Cosmo	1 5/6 ± 3/4 ①	1 ± 1	0 to 1/4	
GLC	1 5/8 ± 3/4	5/8 ± 1	0 to 1/4	
Pickup	1 ± 1/3	1 1/3 ± 1	0 to 1/4	
MERCEDES-BENZ				
230,240D				
280,300D	8 1/4 ± 1/2	0 ± 1/4	3/32 to 5/32	
280SE,450SE/SEL	10 ± 1/2	−1/8 ± 1/8	3/32 to 5/32	
450 SL/SLC	3 2/3 ± 1/3	−1/12 ± 1/4	3/64 to 7/64	
6.9 Sedan	9 3/4 ± 1/2	3/8 ± 1/8	3/32 to 5/32	
MG				
Midget	3	3/4	0 to 1/8	
MGB	6 1/8 ± 1 1/4	1/2 ± 3/4	1/16 to 1/8	
OPEL				
All Models	5 ± 1	0 ± 1/2	5/64 to 11/64	
PEUGEOT				
All Models	2 2/3 ± 1/2	2/3 ± 1/2	3/32 to 5/32	

WHEEL ALIGNMENT SPECIFICATIONS

Application	Caster (Degrees)	Camber (Degrees)	Toe-In (Inches)	Remarks
PORSCHE				
911S				
Front	$6\frac{1}{8} \pm \frac{1}{4}$	$\frac{1}{2} \pm \frac{1}{8}$	0	
Rear	.....	$0 \pm \frac{1}{8}$	0 to $\frac{5}{32}$	
924				
Front	$2\frac{3}{4} \pm \frac{1}{2}$	$-\frac{3}{8} \pm \frac{1}{8}$	$-\frac{1}{32}$ to $\frac{1}{32}$	
Rear	.....	$-1 \pm \frac{1}{2}$	$-\frac{5}{32}$ to $\frac{5}{32}$	
930				
Front	$5\frac{1}{2} \pm \frac{1}{2}$	$\frac{1}{2} \pm \frac{1}{8}$	0	
Rear	.....	$0 \pm \frac{1}{8}$	0 to $\frac{5}{16}$	
RENAULT ①				① — All Renault "Toe" measurements are "Toe-out".
R-5				
Front	10 ± 1	$1\frac{1}{2}$	$-\frac{3}{16}$ to $\frac{1}{16}$	
Rear	.....	$\frac{3}{4} \pm \frac{3}{4}$	0 to $\frac{5}{32}$	
R-12,R-17				
Front	2 ± 2	$1\frac{1}{2}$	$-\frac{1}{8}$ to 0	
Rear	.....	$0 \pm \frac{1}{2}$	0 to $\frac{1}{16}$	
SAAB				
All Models	$1 \pm \frac{1}{2}$	$1 \pm \frac{1}{2}$	0 to $\frac{1}{16}$①	① — With power steering, $-\frac{1}{32}$ to $\frac{1}{32}$.
SUBARU				
4WD				
Front	$\frac{3}{4} \pm \frac{3}{4}$	$2\frac{1}{2} \pm \frac{1}{2}$	$\frac{7}{32}$ to $\frac{15}{32}$	① — Station Wagon is $1\frac{1}{2} \pm \frac{1}{2}$.
Rear	.....	$1 \pm \frac{1}{2}$	$\frac{5}{64}$ to $\frac{15}{64}$	② — Station Wagon is $\frac{5}{64}$ to $\frac{15}{64}$.
1600				
Front	$\frac{3}{4} \pm \frac{3}{4}$	$1\frac{3}{4} \pm \frac{1}{2}$	$\frac{1}{16}$ to $\frac{5}{16}$	
Rear	.....	$\frac{3}{4} \pm \frac{1}{2}$①	$\frac{3}{4}$ to $\frac{13}{64}$②	
TOYOTA				
Corolla	$1\frac{5}{6} \pm \frac{1}{2}$	$1 \pm \frac{1}{2}$	$\frac{3}{32}$ to $\frac{5}{32}$①	① — Radial tires; 0 to $\frac{1}{16}$ for bias tires.
Corona	$1\frac{3}{4} \pm \frac{1}{2}$	$1 \pm \frac{1}{2}$	0 to $\frac{1}{16}$	
Celica	$1\frac{3}{4} \pm \frac{1}{2}$	$1 \pm \frac{1}{2}$	$\frac{3}{64}$ to $\frac{1}{8}$②	
Pickup	$\frac{1}{2} \pm \frac{1}{2}$	$1 \pm \frac{1}{2}$	$\frac{13}{64}$ to $\frac{17}{64}$	② — Radial tires.
Land Cruiser	1	1	$\frac{1}{8}$ to $\frac{13}{64}$	
TRIUMPH				
Spitfire				① — All Triumph "Toe" measurements are "Toe-out".
Front	4 ± 1	3 ± 1	$\frac{1}{16}$ to $\frac{1}{8}$①	
Rear	.....	-1 ± 1	$\frac{1}{32}$ to $\frac{3}{32}$	
TR7	$3\frac{1}{2} \pm 1$	$-\frac{1}{4} \pm 1$	0 to $\frac{1}{16}$	
VOLKSWAGEN				
Type 1				
Front	$3\frac{3}{8} \pm 1$	$\frac{5}{8} \pm \frac{1}{2}$	$-\frac{1}{16}$ to $\frac{1}{8}$	
Rear	.....	$\frac{1}{4} \pm 1$	$-\frac{3}{32}$ to $\frac{1}{32}$	
Type 2				
Front	$3 \pm \frac{5}{8}$	$\frac{5}{8} \pm \frac{3}{8}$	$-\frac{1}{16}$ to $\frac{1}{8}$	
Rear	.....	$3\frac{1}{2} \pm \frac{1}{2}$	$-\frac{1}{4}$ to 0	
Dasher				
Front	$\frac{1}{2} \pm \frac{1}{2}$	$\frac{1}{2} \pm \frac{1}{2}$	$\frac{1}{32}$ to $-\frac{7}{32}$	
Rear	.....	$-\frac{1}{2} \pm \frac{1}{2}$	0 to $\frac{13}{32}$	
Rabbit/Scirocco				
Front	$1\frac{7}{8} \pm \frac{1}{2}$	$\frac{3}{8} \pm \frac{1}{2}$	$-\frac{1}{4}$ to $-\frac{1}{16}$	
Rear	.....	$-1\frac{1}{4} \pm \frac{5}{8}$	$\frac{1}{32}$ to $\frac{9}{32}$	
VOLVO				
All Models	$2\frac{1}{2} \pm \frac{1}{2}$	$1\frac{1}{4} \pm \frac{1}{4}$	$\frac{1}{8}$①	① — 240 series and 260 series with power steering is $\frac{1}{16}$.

ARROW & COLT

ADJUSTMENT

TIRE INFLATION (COLD)

Before attempting to check or adjust wheel alignment, ensure that tires are properly inflated. Refer to specifications in owners handbook for proper inflation procedures.

CASTER

Generally caster is stated as nonadjustable, and that if not within specifications parts are to be replaced. However, in some instances when slight adjustment will alleviate the problem, adjustment of strut bar nut is permitted.

CAMBER

Camber is nonadjustable. If not within specifications, check front suspension for damage. Repair or replace parts as necessary.

TOE-IN

Position wheels in straight-ahead position. If toe-in is not within specifications, loosen locking nuts on tie rod turn buckles. Rotate buckles until toe-in is within specifications. Tighten lock nuts. **NOTE** — *Adjustment must be made equally to both sides of vehicle to maintain correct wheel lock angles; difference of tie rod length when adjusted should not exceed .20" (5.1 mm).*

AUDI

ADJUSTMENT

TIRE INFLATION (COLD)

Before attempting to check and adjust wheel alignment, ensure tires are properly inflated. Model 100LS requires 26 psi in front and 28 psi in rear. Fox requires 27 psi in front and rear, (31 psi in rear with maximum load).

CASTER

Fox — Caster angle is not adjustable. However, if not to specifications, check suspension for wear or damage and repair or replace necessary components.

Model 100LS — Caster and camber adjustment must be made at the same time. See *Camber Adjustment Procedure.*

CAMBER

Fox — With vehicle loaded down or placed on blocks, measure camber angle. If not to specifications, loosen ball joint nuts and attach tool US 4471 (or equivalent). Tighten tool nut to break loose joint from control arm. **NOTE** — *When tool nut is loosened weight of vehicle will move wheel to negative camber.* After adjustment retorque ball joint nuts to 47 ft. lbs. (6.5 mkg).

Model 100LS — 1) With vehicle equipped with spare tire and full fuel tank, measure caster and camber angle. If not to specifications, remove inner ball joint-to-lower control arm mounting bolt and install camber adjusting tool (US 9020) as shown in *Fig. 1*. Install and slightly tighten an 8 mm bolt and washer in threaded hole between inner and outer ball joint mounting bolts on lower control arm, then loosen outer mounting bolt. Tighten tensioner bolt on adjusting tool to break loose ball joint, then tighten or loosen tensioner bolt until camber angle is set to specifications.

2) To adjust caster angle, leave camber adjusting tool installed to maintain adjusted camber angle, then install caster adjusting tool as shown in *Fig. 1*. Adjust caster angle to specifications by moving ball joint forward or backward by means of adjusting tool. Hold adjusting tool stationary and tighten outer ball joint mounting bolt to 80 ft. lbs. (11 mkg). Remove caster and camber adjusting tools and tighten inner bolt to 47 ft. lbs. (6.5 mkg), then remove 8 mm bolt and washer.

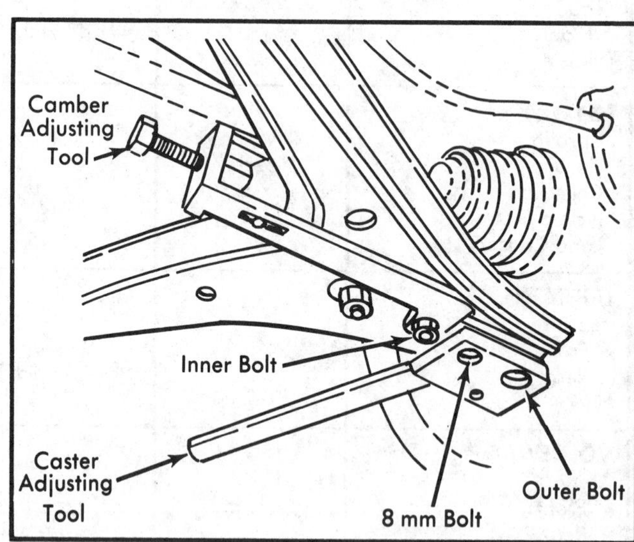

Fig. 1 Adjusting Caster and Camber on Audi 100LS with Special Tool. Fox Camber Adjusting Tool is Similar

TOE-IN

All Models — Before checking toe-in, check wheel rim run-out and replace rim if necessary. If toe-in is not to specifications, adjust by loosening tie rod outer locking nut and clamp and turning tie rods until correct toe-in is obtained. Tighten lock nut and clamp and recheck toe-in.

BMW

ADJUSTMENT

TIRE INFLATION (COLD)

Before attempting to check or adjust wheel alignment, ensure tires are properly inflated. The 320i series requires 27 psi front and rear. The 530i series requires 28 psi front and 26 psi rear. The 630CSi series requires 33 psi front and 31 psi rear.

CASTER & CAMBER

All Models – Before checking caster and camber, vehicle must be in loaded condition. Loaded condition consists of two 143 lbs. weights on front seat, one 143 lbs. weight on rear seat, gas tank full and 66 lbs. on left side of luggage compartment. If caster and camber are not within specifications check suspension for damage. Repair or replace parts as necessary.

TOE-IN

All Models – Before checking toe-in, vehicle must be in loaded condition (see Caster & Camber). Check toe-in with front wheels in straight ahead position. If not within specifications, loosen tie rod clamping bolts. Rotate both tie rod tubes until toe-in is within specifications. Tighten clamping bolts.

CAPRI

ADJUSTMENT

TIRE INFLATION (COLD)

Before attempting to check or adjust wheel alignment, make sure that tires are properly inflated. Refer to manufacturers specifications, located inside glove box door.

CASTER

All Models – Caster is nonadjustable. If not within specifications, check front suspension for damage. Repair or replace parts as necessary.

CAMBER

All Models – Camber is nonadjustable. If not within specifications, check front suspension for damage. Repair or replace parts as necessary.

TOE-IN

All Models – Position wheels in straight-ahead position and loosen tie rod end lock nut and clips securing bellows. To adjust toe-in, rotate tie rods until specifications are within limits. Tighten lock nuts and secure clips. Tie rods lengths should be equal within 1/4".

COURIER

ADJUSTMENT

TIRE INFLATION

Before attempting caster or camber adjustments, ensure tires are correctly inflated. Specifications are located on glove box door; especially consider radial tires, they require a different pressure than conventional tires.

NOTE – *Vehicle must be unloaded, except fuel, water, and oil should be at their proper levels.*

CASTER

To correct caster, adjust shims between upper control arm and frame or turn control arm shaft until correct angle is obtained (see specifications).

CAMBER

The camber is adjusted by adding or subtracting shims between the upper control arm and frame. Shims are available in the following sizes: .039", .063", .079", and .126". Set camber to specifications as shown in chart.

TOE-IN

1) Raise vehicle until front wheels clear ground. Turn wheel by hand and scribe a line in center of each tire tread. Measure distance between marked lines in front of front wheel and at rear of front wheel. Both measurements must be taken at equal distances from ground.

2) If distance between wheels at rear is greater than that at front, but within specifications, adjustment is correct. If adjustment is wrong, loosen clamp bolts and adjust tie rod to specifications.

NOTE – *Tighten clamping bolts with bolts horizontal and below steering link to prevent interference with center steering link.*

DATSUN

ADJUSTMENT

TIRE INFLATION (COLD)

Before attempting to check or adjust wheel alignment, make sure that tires are properly inflated. Refer to manufacturer's specifications given in owner's manual.

Pickup Only – Make measurement with vehicle empty: Fuel tank full, radiator filled, oil levels up to marks, spare tire and hardware in position. Measure distance from center of lower control arm bushing (where it contacts to body) and lower steering knuckle bushing *(See "H" In Fig. 1)*. To adjust, raise vehicle to release tension on anchor bolt adjusting nut and turn anchor bolt to adjust to specified height.

DATSUN (Cont.)

Riding Height Specifications

Application	Height In. (mm)
620 Pickup (All Models)	3.1-3.3 (79-84)

CASTER

All Models Exc. Pickup – Preset at factory and cannot be adjusted. If not to specifications, check suspension for wear or damage and repair or replace components as necessary.

Pickup – Caster is adjusted by increasing or decreasing thickness of shims inserted between upper link spindle and upper link mounting bracket. When front shim thickness increases, caster decreases. **NOTE** – *Do not adjust caster with difference between front and rear shim thickness beyond .079" (2 mm).*

CAMBER

All Models (Exc. Pickup) – Preset at factory and cannot be adjusted. If not to specifications, check suspension for wear or damage and repair or replace components as necessary.

Pickup – Camber is adjusted by increasing or decreasing the thickness of shims inserted between upper link spindle and upper link mounting bracket. When thickness of shims increase, camber decreases.

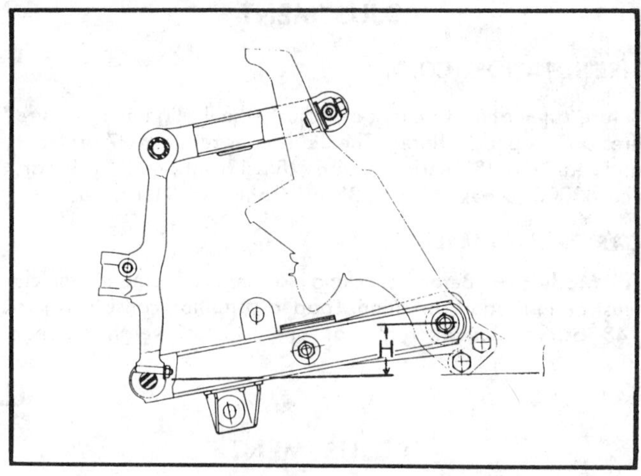

Fig. 1 Pickup Front Suspension Riding Height Measurement Point

TOE-IN

All Models Except Pickup – Adjust by loosening each side steering link lock nut and adjusting steering link to change toe-in. **NOTE** – *Left and right side steering links should be adjusted equally.* Tighten lock nuts.

Pickup – Adjust by loosening steering cross link lock nuts, and adjusting steering cross link to change toe-in. Tighten lock nuts.

FIAT

ADJUSTMENT

TIRE INFLATION (COLD)

Before attempting to check or adjust wheel alignment, make sure tires are properly inflated. Refer to manufacturers specifications given in owner's manual.

CASTER

Model 128 & 131 (Except 128 3P) – If caster is not to specifications, raise front of vehicle. Remove stabilizer bar-to-control arm nut and disconnect control arm from body. Remove end of stabilizer bar from control arm. To adjust caster, addition of shims between end of stabilizer bar and rubber pad of control arm will decrease caster angle and removal of shims will increase caster angle. Reverse removal procedure and recheck caster.

Model 124 – If caster is not within specifications, raise front of vehicle and remove wheel and shock absorber. Using suitable tool (A.74174), compress spring to relieve lower control arm and loosen nuts holding control arm pivot bar to crossmember. To adjust caster, remove shims from front stud and move to rear stud to increase caster. To decrease caster, remove shims from rear stud and move shims to front stud. Reverse removal procedure and check caster.

Model X1/9 – If caster is not to specifications, adjust by adding or removing shims located between stabilizer bar and stabilizer bar support.

CAMBER

Model 124 – If camber is not within specifications, adjust by changing shims. Raise front of vehicle, remove wheel and shock absorber. Using suitable tool (A.74174), compress spring to relieve lower control arm and loosen nuts holding control arm pivot bar to crossmember. To increase camber, remove equal amount of shims from both studs and add equal amount of shims to decrease camber. **NOTE** – *Adding or removing equal amounts of shims will not affect caster.* Reverse removal procedure and check camber.

Model 128 & 131 Front – Camber is nonadjustable. If not within specifications, inspect suspension for damage and repair or replace parts as necessary.

Model 128 Rear – If rear camber is not within specifications raise rear of vehicle and compress one end of leaf spring, shifting it from flexible guide anchoring spring to control arm. Remove guide and slowly release spring. Remove nuts attaching pivot to body and loosen screw to free adjustment shims. To increase camber, add an equal number of shims on both screws attaching control arm to body. To decrease, remove equal number of shims from both screws. Reverse removal procedure and check camber.

FIAT (Cont.)

Model X1/9 Front & Rear – Camber is nonadjustable. If not within specifications, inspect suspension for damage and repair or replace parts as necessary.

TOE-IN

Model 124 Front – Place front wheels in straight-ahead position. If toe-in is not within specifications, loosen four clamps securing sleeves on tie rods. Rotate tie rods in opposite direction (by equal amounts) to set toe-in to specifications. Tighten clamp nuts. **NOTE** – *Expansion slot in sleeve must coincide with clamp joint when clamp is fully tightened.*

Model 128, 131 & X1/9 Front – Place front wheels in straight-ahead position. If toe-in is not within specifications, loosen sleeve locking nut on tie rods. To adjust, rotate hexagon on ball pin to set toe-in to specifications. Hold hexagon in position and lock nut against tie rod sleeve.

Model 128 Rear – If rear toe-in is not within specifications raise rear of vehicle and compress one end of leaf spring, shifting it from flexible guide anchoring spring to control arm. Remove guide and slowly release spring. Remove nuts attaching pivot to body and loosen screws to free adjustment shims. To increase toe-in, add shims to rear screw or remove shims from front screw. To decrease, add shims to front screw or remove shims from rear screw.

Model X1/9 Rear – If rear wheel toe-in is not within specifications, loosen clamps securing sleeves to reaction rods. Adjust toe-in by lengthening or shortening reaction rods. Tighten clamps and recheck toe-in.

HONDA

ADJUSTMENT

TIRE INFLATION (COLD)

Before checking or adjusting wheel alignment, make sure tires are correctly inflated. Refer to manufacturers specifications located in glove box.

RIDING HEIGHT

Make sure tires are properly inflated.Measure from bottom of side marker lamps to ground. If height measurement is not within specifications, check rear height before attempting to repair front suspension.

Riding Height Specifications

Application	Front	Rear
Civic	25.78" (655 mm)	24.01" (610 mm)
CVCC		
Sedan	24.2" (615 mm)	20.7" (525 mm)
Station Wgn.	24.2" (615 mm)	23.5" (598 mm)
Accord	24.0" (610 mm)	25.4" (645 mm)

CASTER

Caster is nonadjustable. If alignment is not within specifications, inspect for damaged parts and replace as necessary.

CAMBER

Camber is nonadjustable. If alignment is not within specifications, inspect for damaged parts and replace as necessary.

TOE-OUT

Front, CVCC and Accord – Loosen lock nuts at each end of tie rods. Turn tie rod until toe-out is within specifications. Use same procedure for both sides. To center steering wheel after toe has been adjusted, turn both tie rods in same direction until steering wheel (spokes) are centered. Tighten lock nuts.

TOE-IN

Rear, CVCC and Accord – To adjust toe-in, loosen nuts on radius rods. Rotate radius rods until toe-in is within specifications, then tighten lock nuts. **NOTE** – *Each notch on cam plate is equal to 5/64" movement.*

JAGUAR

ADJUSTMENT

TIRE INFLATION (COLD)

Before attempting to check or adjust wheel alignment, make sure tires are properly inflated. Refer to owner's manual for manufacturer's specifications.

RIDING HEIGHT

All Models (Front) – 1) Check that vehicle is full of fuel, oil, and water, and that tires are properly inflated. Press down on front bumper and slowly release, then lift up on bumper and slowly release, this will settle front suspension.

JAGUAR (Cont.)

2) On XJ6 and XJ12 models, measure distance between center of outer headlight and ground on both sides of vehicle. Height should be 24.6" (611 mm) minimum.

3) On XJS models, measure distance between lower face of crossmember and ground on both sides. Height should be 6.0" (152 mm) minimum, plus thickness of slip plates.

4) On all models, adjust by installing or removing spring spacers from front coil springs. **NOTE** — *Spring spacers are 1/8" (3.2 mm) thick and will change riding height approximately 5/16" (7.9 mm).*

All Models (Rear) — Check that vehicle is full of gasoline, water and oil, and that tires are properly inflated. Roll vehicle forward three car lenghts to settle suspension system. Measure distance between lower surface of rear crossmember and ground on both sides of vehicle. Correct height should be 7.45±.25 (189±6 mm). If height is correct, it will be unnecessary to proceed further, however if height is incorrect, all four rear springs will need to be replaced.

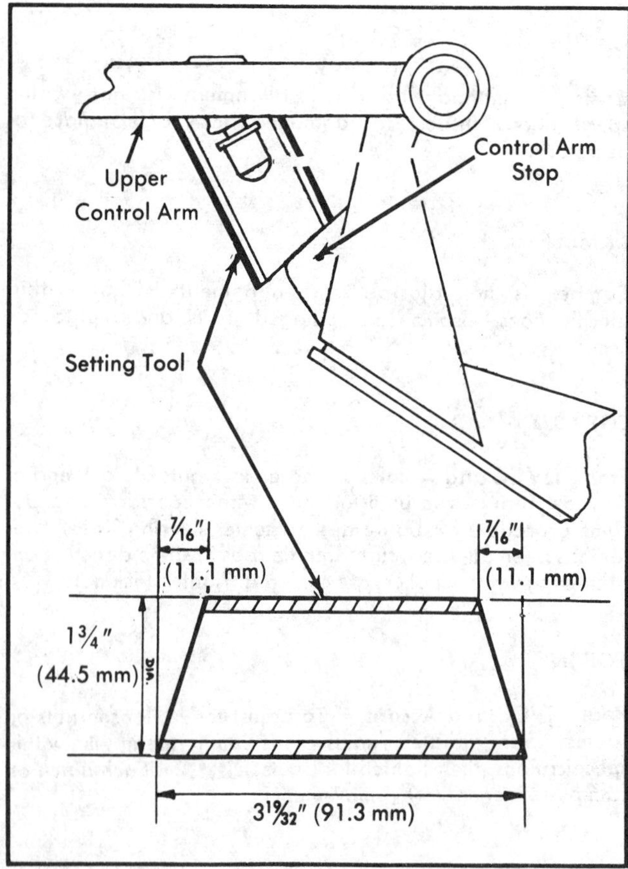

Fig. 1 Dimensions for Fabricating the Two Necessary Setting Tools

PREPARATION FOR CASTER & CAMBER ADJUSTMENT

1) Ensure vehicle is on level ground and that tires are properly inflated. Before checking or adjusting caster or camber it will be necessary to fabricate two setting tools *(See Fig. 1)*.

2) Compress front suspension and insert tools under upper control arms, adjacent to control arm rubber stops and over brackets welded to bottom of control arms.

3) Compress rear suspension and install suitable suspension setting links (J. 25), to lock rear suspension in place *(See Fig. 2)*. Vehicle is now locked in half-loaded condition and caster and camber can be checked and adjusted.

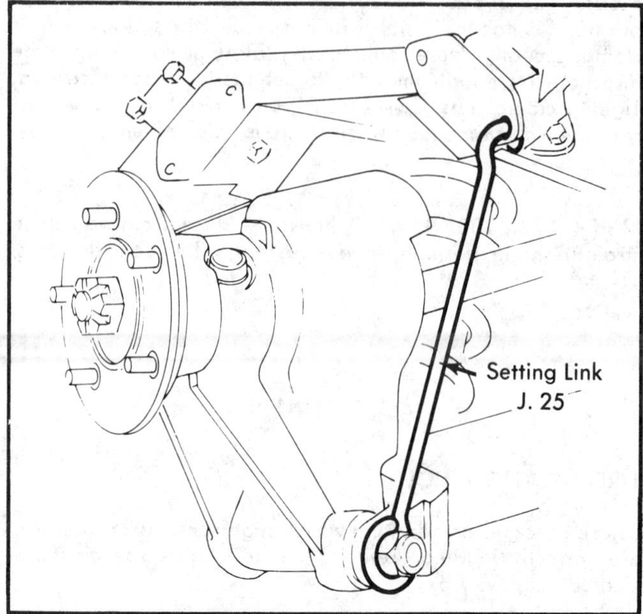

Fig. 2 Rear Suspension in Locked Position with Special Tool

CASTER

NOTE — *Before adjusting caster angle, make sure car is standing at normal riding height.*

All Models — If caster angle is not within specifications, adjust by moving shims on front and rear of upper control arm ball joint. To increase caster, loosen bolts securing upper ball joint and move shims from rear of ball joint to front of ball joint. To decrease caster, reverse procedure. Tighten ball joint attaching bolts and recheck caster angle.

CAMBER

NOTE — *Before attempting to check or adjust camber angle it will be necessary to make sure that vehicle is in half-loaded condition.*

All Models (Front) — With wheels in straight-ahead position, measure camber angle. **NOTE** — *Two front wheels must be within 1/4° of each other.* Adjustment is accomplished by means of shims placed between control arm mounting bracket and the frame. Adding shims increases camber angle. **NOTE** — *Be sure to use the same number of shims on each bolt, otherwise caster angle will be affected.*

All Models (Rear) — Before checking rear wheel camber, rear suspension must be in the half-loaded position. See *Preparation for Caster & Camber Adjustment.* To adjust, remove suspension setting links (JD.25), raise and support rear of vehicle and remove wheels. Loosen nuts securing half-shaft to brake disc, then add or remove shims as reqired to bring camber angle within specifications. **NOTE** — *Addition of one*

JAGUAR (Cont.)

.020" (.5 mm) shim will alter camber ¼°. Retighen nuts and bolts and check camber angle.

TOE-IN

All Models – Place vehicle in straight-ahead position. Remove grease nipple from rack adjuster nut. Put centralizing tool 12279 (or equivalent) into locating hole. Push tool on to back of rack bar. Slowly turn steering wheel until tool drops into back of rack bar. Measure toe-in. If toe-in is not within specifications, adjust by loosening steering link lock nuts and rotating adjuster sleeves equal amounts, as necessary. Tighten lock nuts and recheck toe-in.

LUV

ADJUSTMENT

TIRE INFLATION

Before checking or adjusting wheel alignment, ensure tires are correctly inflated. Refer to manufacturers specifications located in glove box or on right hand door jam.

RIDING HEIGHT

1) Place vehicle on smooth level surface. Bounce vehicle several times. Raise vehicle and allow to settle at normal height. Measure distance as shown in *Fig. 1 and 2.*

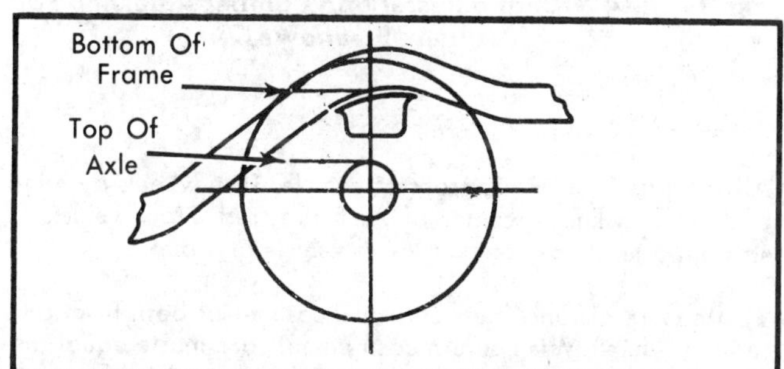

Fig. 1 Rear Suspension Riding Height Measuring Point

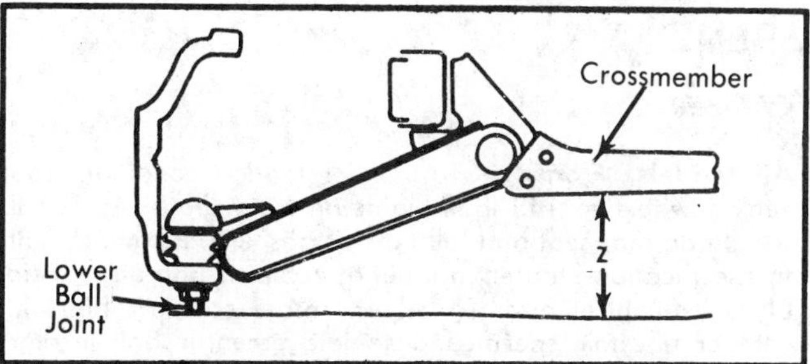

Fig. 2 Front Suspension Riding Height Measuring Point

NOTE – *Height check should be made with a full tank of gas, spare tire installed, and jack included. No passengers should be in vehicle.*

2) Difference between measurements of each side must not be more than 1/2". If an adjustment is necessary, it can be made at bolt on height control arm.

Riding Height Specifications

Application	Front	Rear
LUV	4.6"	6.0"

CASTER

Adjustment is made with shims inserted between upper control arm pivot shaft and frame. Adding or subtracting shims from either front or rear bolts will effect a change in caster. Shims may be transfered from front to rear or from rear to front.Transfer of one shim from front bolt to rear bolt will decrease positive caster. For correct specifications, refer to table.

CAMBER

Camber is adjusted by adding or subtracting shims. Adding an equal number of shims at both front and rear of pivot shaft will decrease positive camber. For correct specifications, refer to table.

TOE-IN

NOTE – *Toe-in must be adjusted after caster and camber adjustment.*

Toe-in can be adjusted by rotating the intermediate rod after loosening lock nuts. Rotating intermediate rod towards front of vehicle reduces toe-in and towards rear of vehicle increases toe-in. For correct specifications, refer to specifications table.

MAZDA

ADJUSTMENT

TIRE INFLATION (COLD)

Before attempting to check or adjust wheel alignment, make sure tires are properly inflated. Refer to manufacturer's specifications given in owner's manual.

CASTER

808, RX3SP & GLC – Caster is not adjustable. If caster is not to specifications, inspect suspension for wear or damage and repair or replace components as necessary.

RX4 and Cosmo – Caster and camber angles are adjusted by changing position of shock absorber support. To adjust,

MAZDA (Cont.)

remove four nuts attaching shock absorber support to fender apron. Raise front of vehicle and support with jack stands, then remove wheel on side to be adjusted.

2) Press shock absorber downward and change position of support according to table and *Fig. 1*. Tighten shock absorber support mounting nuts. Install wheel, lower vehicle and recheck caster and camber.

Caster and Camber Adjustment			
Adjustment		Variation	
	Shock Absorber Support	Caster	Camber
A	0	0	0
B	90°	½ °	0
C	180°	½ °	½ °
D	-90°	0	½ °

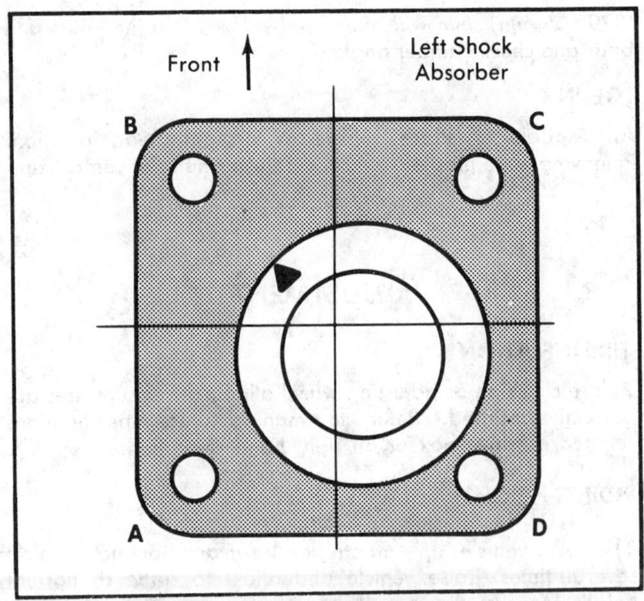

Fig. 1 RX4 & Cosmo Caster and Camber Adjusting Pad (Position "B" Shown)

Pickup – To adjust, change shims between upper arm shaft and support bracket or turn upper arm shaft until specifications are obtained.

CAMBER

808, RX3SP & GLC – Camber is not adjustable. If camber is not to specifications, inspect suspension for wear or damage and repair or replace components as necessary.

RX4 and Cosmo – *See procedure given under Caster adjustment.*

Pickup – To adjust, change shims between upper arm shaft and support bracket until specifications for camber are within limits.

TOE-IN

All Models – **1)** Raise front of vehicle. Turn wheels by hand and mark a line in center of each tire tred. Place vehicle in straight-ahead position and lower vehicle to ground.

2) Measure distance between marked lines at both front and rear of wheel. Make sure measurements are made equal distances from ground. Distance at rear of wheel should be .24" (6 mm) more than that at front wheels. Loosen lock nuts and turn tie rods until adjustment is correct.

MERCEDES-BENZ

ADJUSTMENT

TIRE INFLATION (COLD)

Before attempting to check or adjust wheel alignment, make sure tires are properly inflated. Refer to manufacturers specifications given in owner's manual.

CASTER

All Models (Front) – Test under loaded condition. Load vehicle with two 143 lb. weights on rear seat and full tank of gasoline. If caster is not to specifications, loosen lock nut on eccentric bolt on front side of lower control arm. To adjust, rotate eccentric bolt until caster angle is to specifications. Hold eccentric bolt in place and tighten lock nut.

CAMBER

All Models (Front) – Test under loaded condition. Load vehicle with two 143 lb. weights on front seat, one 143 lb. weight on rear seat and full tank of gasoline. If camber is not to specifications, loosen lock nut of eccentric bolt on rear side of lower control arm. To adjust, rotate eccentric bolt until camber is within specifications. Hold eccentric bolt in place and tighten lock nut.

TOE-IN

All Models (Front) – Place wheels in straight-ahead position. If toe-in is not within specifications, adjust by loosening lock nuts on outer steering links and rotating links to obtain specified toe-in. Make sure steering links are adjusted equally.

MG

ADJUSTMENT

TIRE INFLATION (COLD)

Before attempting to check or adjust wheel alignment, make sure tires are properly inflated. Refer to manufacturers specifications given in owner's manual.

NOTE – *All checks must be made with vehicle unloaded, tires properly inflated and steering wheel in straight-ahead position. Before making checks, ensure suspension components are in good condition. If necessary, repair damaged components before making wheel alignment checks.*

MG (Cont.)

CASTER

All Models – Caster is nonadjustable. If alignment not within specifications, inspect for damaged suspension parts and repair or replace as necessary.

CAMBER

All Models – Camber is not adjustable. If alignment is not within specifications, inspect suspension parts for wear or damage and repair or replace components as necessary.

TOE-IN

All Models – Turn front wheels to straight-ahead position and check toe-in measurement. Move vehicle ahead so front wheels rotate 180° and take second reading. Take average of two readings to check toe-in. If not within specifications, loosen lock nut for each tie rod and loosen clips securing rubber gaiters to tie rods. To adjust, rotate both tie rods equally to set toe-in to specifications. **NOTE** – *Tie rods must be equal lengths.* Tighten lock nuts and clips on tie rods.

OPEL

ADJUSTMENT

TIRE INFLATION (COLD)

Before attempting to check or adjust wheel alignment, make sure tires are properly inflated. Refer to manufacturer's specifications given in owner's manual.

CASTER

1) If caster is not within specifications, adjust by changing washers on upper control arm shaft. Raise vehicle and place jack stands under lower control arms. Remove wheel on side which requires caster adjustment.

NOTE – *The replacement of washers requires the same diameter as those being changed and a combination such that the total thickness of front and rear equals 12 mm. If specifications are not achieved, frame alignment is required.*

2) Loosen hex. nut from upper control arm shaft and remove shaft. Adjust caster by replacing washers on control arm shaft. Put smaller washer on leg nearest front of vehicle.

CAMBER

Raise front of vehicle and place jack stands below lower control arms. Remove wheel on side to be adjusted. Remove ball joint from upper control arm and front steering knuckle. To adjust camber, lift upper control arm and rotate ball joint flange 180°. **NOTE** – *Only two adjustments are possible.* Rotating ball joint flange will make camber more negative.

TOE-IN

1) Position front wheel in straight-ahead position. Remove clamp on tie rod bellows and push bellows back. Loosen tie rod clamping bolts. To adjust, rotate tie rod sleeves equally to obtain specified toe-in. **NOTE** – *Never grip tie rod on inner ball joint stud.*

2) Pull bellows over tie rods and secure wire clamps. Bellows must not be twisted and wire ends showing towards steering gear adjusting screw opening. Tighten clamp bolts. Rotate wheel back and forth several times to check bellows for correct attachment to tie rods.

PEUGEOT

ADJUSTMENT

TIRE INFLATION (COLD)

Before attempting to check or adjust wheel alignment, make sure tires are properly inflated. Refer to manufacturers specifications given in owner's manual.

CASTER

Caster angle is not adjustable. If not to specifications, check suspension system for wear or damage and repair or replace components as necessary.

CAMBER

Camber angle is not adjustable. If not to specifications, check suspension system for wear or damage and repair or replace components as necessary.

TOE-IN

Position wheels in straight-ahead position. If toe-in is not to specifications, loosen clamping bolts on the two steering links. To adjust, rotate two steering links simultaneously in either direction necessary to obtain specified toe-in. Tighten clamping bolt and recheck toe-in.

PORSCHE

ADJUSTMENT

TIRE INFLATION (COLD)

Before attempting to check or adjust wheel alignment, make sure tires are properly inflated. Refer to manufacturer's specifications given in owner's manual.

RIDING HEIGHT

NOTE – *Riding height should be set with full tank of gasoline and spare tire included.*

All Models (Front) – Checking or adjusting riding height can only be performed with vehicle on level surface. Mark center of front wheel hub cap (grease retainer cup). Bounce vehicle several times to settle suspension. Measure distance "a" as shown in illustration, then measure distance "b". Difference

PORSCHE (Cont.)

between "a" and "b" should be to specifications. If necessary to adjust, loosen or tighten torsion bar adjusting bolt until correct height is obtained. Bounce vehicle several times and recheck height. **NOTE** — *Difference between right and left measurement must not exceed .20".*

Riding Height Specifications①

Application	Front	Rear
911/S	4.25±.20" (108±5 mm)	.468±.20" (12±5 mm)
Turbo Carrera	3.3±.20" (84.5±5 mm)	1.5±.20" (37±5 mm)
924	②	②

① — Measurement is expressed as difference between "a" and "b".

② — No specifications are available for Model 924.

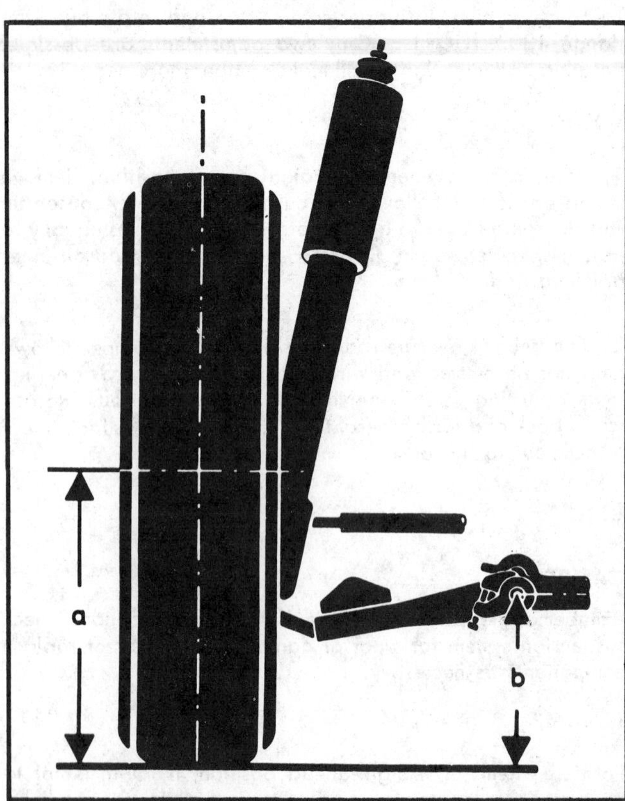

Fig. 1 Front Suspension Riding Height Measuring Points

911 Series (Rear) — Checking or adjusting riding height can only be performed with vehicle on level surface. Mark center of rear wheel. Bounce vehicle several times to settle suspension. Measure distance "a" as shown in illustration. Distance "a" plus .468" (12 mm) equals "b"; however, distance "b" is difficult to measure because the torsion bar is mounted off center in its rubber bushing. Therefore it is necessary to measure distance "b1" and add .585" (14.8 mm), radius of bushing. This total should be equal to "b". After calculating "b", difference between "a" and "b" should be .468"±.20" (12±5mm). Difference in height from left to right should not exceed .197" (8 mm). If values are not within specifications, check front eight and rear torsion bar adjustment. Correct as required.

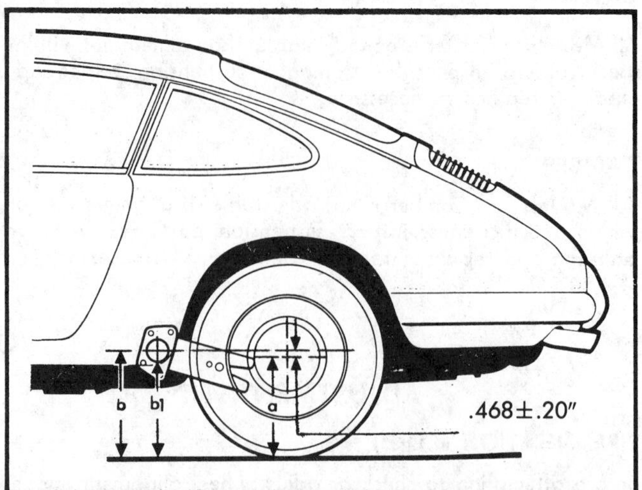

Fig. 2 Porsche 911/S Rear Suspension Riding Height Measuring Points and Dimensions

NOTE — *Caster and Camber cannot be adjusted on vehicles up to chassis serial number 302.694, also on chassis number 302.736 and 302.805. If velicles are not within specifications, check for damage or worn suspension parts.*

CASTER

911 Series & Turbo Carrera — If caster angle is not to specifications, it will be necessary to remove adjuster plate which attaches to front shock absorber. Remove enough front compartment carpet to allow access to top of each shock absorber. Mark position of each movable plate, located below each Allen screw. Loosen each screw and upper shock absorber nut. Move assembly lengthwise to obtain correct caster angle. Tighten all three screws and shock absorber nut.

NOTE — *Movement of adjuster plate from side to side will affect camber angle.*

924 — Adjust caster by moving the rear of suspension control arm from side-to-side. See *Fig. 3*.

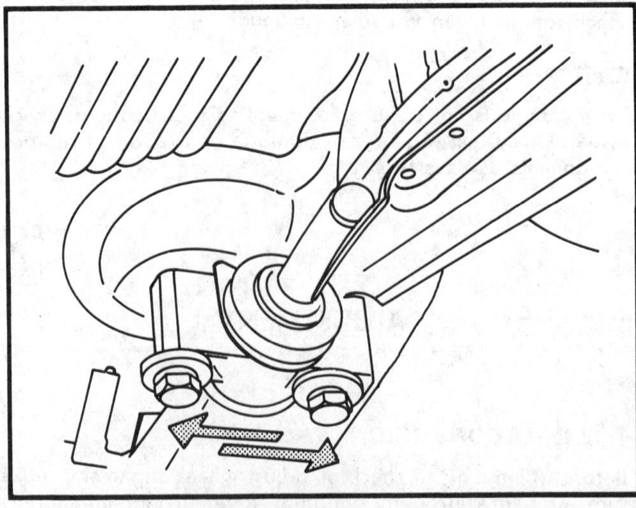

Fig. 3 View Showing 924 Caster Adjustment

PORSCHE (Cont.)

CAMBER

911 Series & Turbo Carrera (Front) – If camber angle is not to specifications, it will be necessary to move adjuster plate which attaches to front shock absorber. Remove enough carpet to allow access to top of each shock absorber. Mark position of each movable plate located below each Allen screw. Loosen each screw and upper shock absorber nut. Move assembly from side to side-to-obtain correct camber angle. Tighten all three screws and shock absorber nut.

924 – Adjust camber by turning eccentric bolt. *See Fig. 4.*

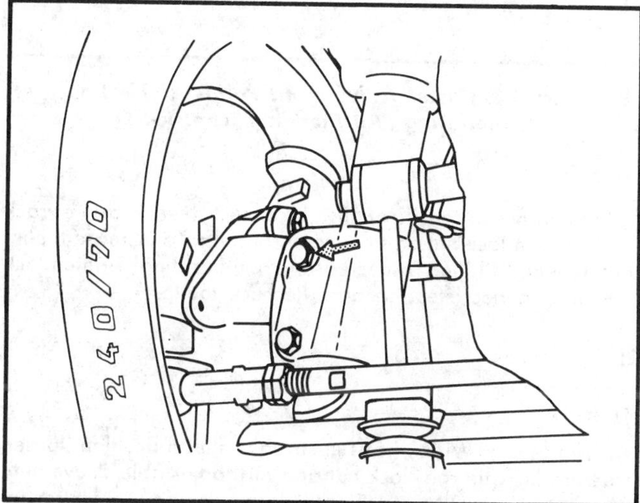

Fig. 4 Eccentric Bolt for Camber Adjustment on 924 Models

NOTE – *Rear wheel camber is not adjustable on 924 models.*

911 Series (Rear) – In order to obtain correct camber value at rear wheels, it is necessary that rear torsion bars be adjusted first. *See Torsion Bar Adjustment.* Now, loosen nuts on retaining bolts and on eccentric bolt at rear axle flange. Turn camber eccentric until camber angle is within specifications. Tighten retaining nuts and eccentric bolt nuts.

TOE-IN

NOTE – *All toe-in specifications are given in inches.*

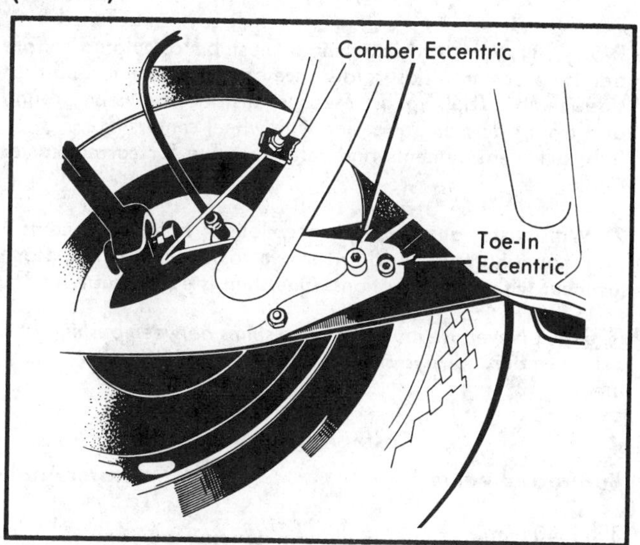

Fig. 5 911 Rear Wheel Adjustment Points

All Models (Front) – Place front wheels in straight-ahead position. Adjust left and right steering links (tie rods) equally to obtain specified setting. Coat each steering link with anti-corrosive compound after adjustment.

911 Series (Rear) – To adjust rear wheel toe-in, loosen nuts on retaining bolts and adjusting eccentrics at rear axle flange. Turn toe-in eccentric until toe-in is set to specifications. Hold eccentric stationary and tighten all lock nuts.

TORSION BAR ADJUSTMENT

911 Series (Rear) – Place torsion bar into transverse tube with inner end splines first. Slip radius arm onto outer end splines of torsion bar. Place suitable leveling tool (VW 261) on lower edge of door opening and adjust level so bubble is in center of glass. Check adjustment (degrees) of free hanging radius arm with same leveling tool. If not to specifications, adjust by turning torsion bar and radius arm in opposite directions. Adjustment of both radius arms must each equal 36°45′±15′.

RENAULT

ADJUSTMENT

TIRE INFLATION (COLD)

Before attempting to check or adjust wheel alignment, make sure tires are properly inflated. Refer to manufacturers specifications given in owner's manual.

CASTER

R-12 & R-17 – If caster angle is not within specifications, loosen lock nuts "C" and "D" on strut rod. *See Fig. 2.* To reduce caster angle, unscrew nut "B" and tighten nut "A". To increase caster angle, unscrew nut "A" and tighten nut "B". When caster angle is within specifications, tighten all nuts.

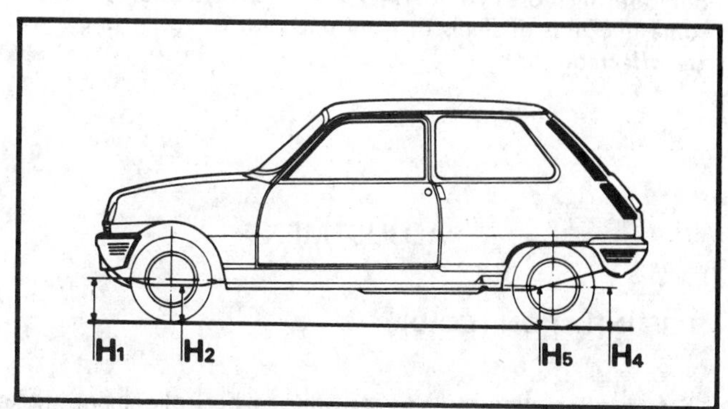

Fig. 1 Riding Height Measurement Points

RENAULT (Cont.)

R-5 – 1) Vehicle riding height must be calculated before adjusting caster. Measure distance between ground and rear side member (H5, *Fig. 1*). Measure distance between ground and front side member in line with wheel centers (H2, *Fig. 1*). Subtract measurements and refer to table for correct caster angle.

2) With caster angle determined, loosen both lower control arm mounting bolts. Add or remove caster shims to bring adjustment within specifications. One shim is equal to about 1°.

NOTE – *Never use more than two shims between bushing and side member. Always check steering box height after adjustment.*

Caster Angle Table

Subtracted Value	Caster Angle
1⁹⁄₁₆" (40 mm)	12½°
2⅜" (60 mm)	12°
3⅛" (80 mm)	11½°
3¹⁵⁄₁₆" (100 mm)	11°
4¾" (120 mm)	10½°
5½" (140 mm)	10°

CAMBER

Camber angle is not adjustable. If not within specifications, inspect front suspension for wear or damage and repair or replace components as necessary.

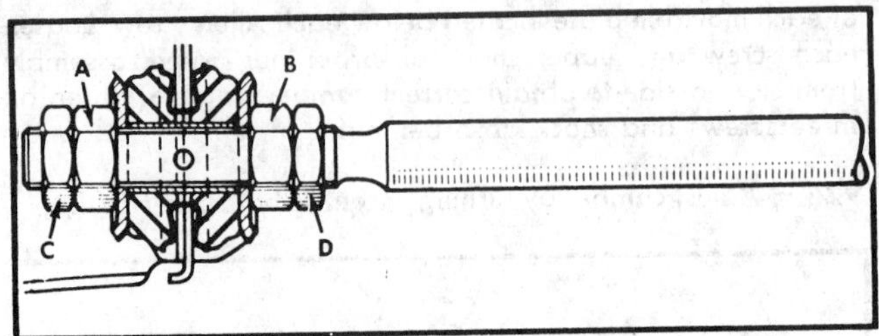

Fig. 2 Caster Adjustment Points at Tie Rod Mounting (All Models Except R-5)

TOE-IN

If toe-in is not to specifications, disconnect steering arm at rack end. Loosen lock nut on steering end fitting. To increase toe-in, unscrew end fitting. To decrease, screw in fitting. Tighten lock nut and connect steering arm. Recheck toe-in.

SAAB

ADJUSTMENT

TIRE INFLATION (COLD)

Before attempting to check or adjust wheel alignment, make sure tires are properly inflated. Refer to manufacturers specifications given in owner's manual.

CASTER

All Models – To adjust caster, add or remove shims under upper control arm bushing brackets. Changing shims from front to rear bracket increases caster angle. Moving shims from rear to front decreases caster angle. **NOTE** – *Same thickness of shims removed from front must be placed under rear and vice versa. Change in caster also effects camber.*

CAMBER

All Models – To adjust camber, add or remove shims under upper control arm bushing brackets. Increasing shims under both brackets reduces camber angle and removing shims under both increases camber. **NOTE** – *Always add or remove same thickness of shims at front and rear or caster angle will be affected.*

TOE-IN

All Models – With wheels in straight-ahead position, loosen steering link (tie rod) lock nut and turn adjustable sleeve until correct toe-in is obtained. Tighten lock nuts and recheck toe-in.

NOTE – *After adjustment of toe-in, measurement "A" (Fig. 1) of tie rod must not exceed 1.0" (25 mm). For tie rods opposite to each other, the difference between measurement "A" must not exceed .08" (2 mm).*

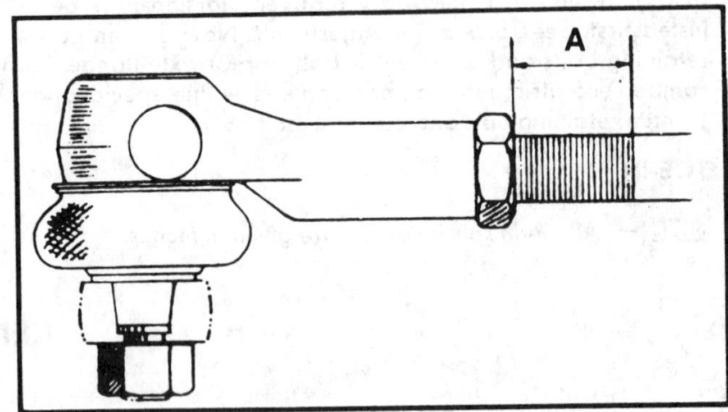

Fig. 1 View Showing Tie Rod Length Measurement

SUBARU

ADJUSTMENT

TIRE INFLATION (COLD)

Before attempting to check or adjust wheel alignment, make sure tires are properly inflated. Refer to manufacturers specifiations given in owner's manual.

RIDING HEIGHT (REAR)

Riding height is adjusted by changing the size of the angle between trailing arm center line and the markings on outer bracket. See *Fig. 1*. The trailing arm and outer bracket have full serrations around the torsion bar mounting hole, while torsion bar has one missing serration, thus allowing torsion bar to be inserted at any angle.

SUBARU (Cont.)

Raising vehicle height is accomplished by turning outer end and inner end of torsion bar in direction opposite to cast-in arrow on outer end of bar. Height changes .20" (5mm) per each serration shifted.

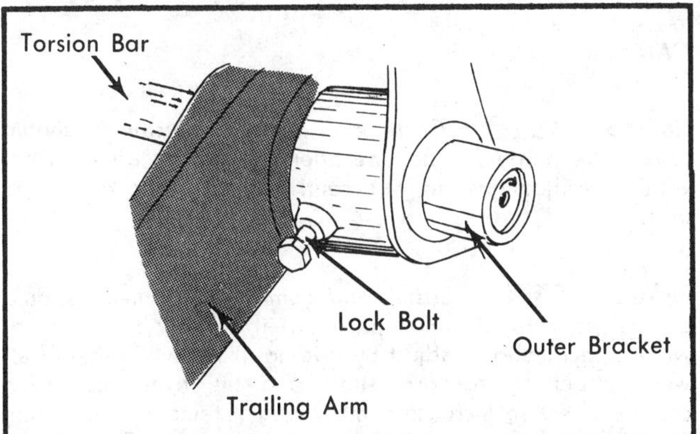

Fig. 1 Installed View of Torsion Bar Outer End Attachment

1) Initially set vehicle rear riding height by inserting torsion bar with its missing serration aligned with markings on outer bracket surface and trailing arm inner surface. This will give approximately the specified riding height as indicated in table.

2) Measure road clearance from center of trailing arm bushing to ground. **NOTE** – *Vehicle must be in unloaded condition.* Raise rear of vehicle and remove rear wheel.

3) Unscrew shock absorber lower mounting nut and remove it from trailing arm. Unscrew lock bolt on outer bushing.

4) Scribe mark position of torsion bar by making a mark on upper half of inner end surface and lower half of outer end surface. Outer end surface mark should be continued onto trailing arm shaft and outer bracket boss.

5) Holding trailing arm so torsion bar does not twist, disengage serrations by tapping inner end surface of torsion bar See *Fig. 2.*

6) Pull torsion bar out of trailing arm. Determine amount of turn necessary to make proper height adjustment and turn inner end of torsion bar to this value. Then, insert outer end of torsion bar to its proper adjusted position.

7) Install rear wheel and lower vehicle. Reattach lower end of shock absorber. Recheck vehicle rear ground clearance as originally measured. If correct, tighten lock bolt on outer trailing arm bushing. If incorrect, repeat adjustment.

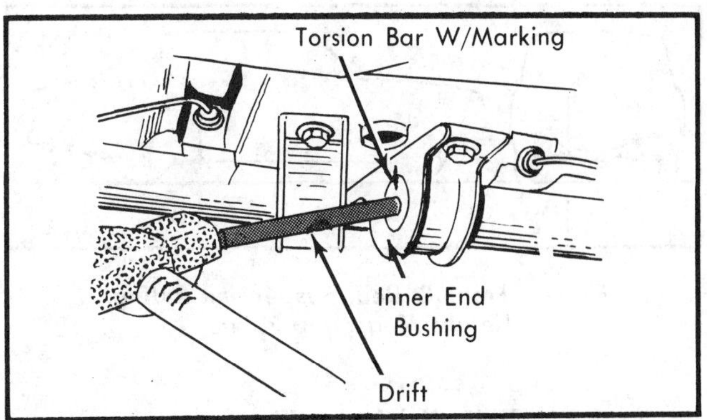

Fig. 2 View Showing Removal Procedure for Torsion Bar

Rear Riding Height Specifications

Application	Height
1600	
Sedan	11.34-11.89" (288-302 mm)
Station Wagon	12.21-12.76" (310-324 mm)
4WD Station Wagon	14.17-14.76" (360-375 mm)

CASTER

Caster angle is not adjustable. If angle is not to specifications, inspect suspension for wear or damage and repair or replace components as necessary.

CAMBER

All Models (Front) – Camber angle is not adjustable. If angle is not to specifications, inspect suspension for wear or damage. Repair or replace components as necessary.

All Models (Rear) – Camber angle is adjusted by altering number of shims inserted between torsion bar bracket and chassis mounting. Fitting shims changes camber to negative and removing shims changes camber to positive. One shim corresponds to ¼° adjustment.

TOE-IN

All Models (Front) – If toe-in is not within specifications, loosen steering link (tie rod) lock nut and turn sleeve until correct toe-in is obtained.

All Models (Rear) – If toe-in is not within specifications, loosen bolts holding torsion bar bushing to body. Bushing is fixed to body at elongated holes. Moving bushing forward decreases toe-in and moving it rearward increases toe-in. Tighten bolts and recheck toe-in.

TOYOTA

ADJUSTMENT

TIRE INFLATION (COLD)

Before attempting to check or adjust wheel alignment, make sure tires are properly inflated. Refer to manufacturers specifications given in owner's manual.

RIDING HEIGHT

Corona – Place vehicle on level surface. Bounce several times and allow suspension to settle. Check riding height dimensions *(See Fig. 1)* and if not within specifications, inspect suspension components. Replace or repair parts as required.

TOYOTA (Cont.)

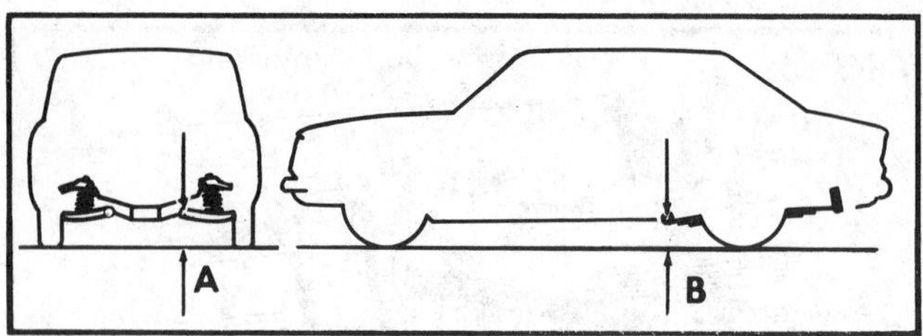

Fig. 1 Front & Rear Suspension Riding Height Measuring Points

Riding Height Specifications

Application	A In. (mm)	B In. (mm)
Corona		
Sedan & Hdtop	9.92 (252)	9.01 (229)
Wagon	9.92 (252)	10.0 (254)

CASTER

Corona – **NOTE** – *Camber and caster adjustments should always be made in one operation.* If caster angle is not within specifications, adjust eccentric on front of lower control arm.

Pickup – **NOTE** – *Camber and caster adjustments should always be made in one operation.* If caster angle is not within specifications, adjust by adding or removing shims between the upper control arm shaft and the front suspension crossmember. To increase caster, add shims to rear side of the upper control arm shaft mounting bolt or remove shims from the front side. To decrease caster, reverse procedure.

All Other Models – Caster angle is not adjustable. If caster angle is not within specifications, inspect front suspension for wear or damage and repair or replace components as necessary.

CAMBER

Corona – **NOTE** – *Caster and camber adjustments should always be made in one operation.* If camber angle is not within specifications, adjust eccentric on rear of lower control arm.

Pickup – **NOTE** – *Caster and camber adjustments should always be made in one operation.* If camber angle is not within specifications, adjust by adding or removing shims between upper control arm shaft and the front suspension crossmember. To increase camber angle, remove shims from, upper control arm shaft bolts in equal amounts. To decrease camber, reverse procedure.

All Other Models – Camber angle is not adjustable. If camber angle is not with specifications, inspect front suspension for wear or damage and repair or replace components as necessary.

TOE-IN

All Models – If toe-in is not within specifications, loosen steering link (tie-rod) clamping bolts and rotate adjusting sleeves an equal amount until correct toe-in is obtained. Position clamp bolts at right angles to slot in tie rod and tighten bolts.

TRIUMPH

ADJUSTMENT

TIRE INFLATION (COLD)

Before attempting to check or adjust wheel alignment, make sure tires are properly inflated. Refer to manufacturers specifications given in owner's manual.

CASTER

All Models – Caster angle is not adjustable. If caster angle is not to specifications, inspect suspension system for wear or damage and repair or replace components as necessary.

CAMBER

All Models (Exc. TR7) – Before adjusting camber angle, inspect suspension for wear or damage and repair or replace components as necessary. To adjust, raise vehicle and support chassis on jack stands. Loosen nuts securing lower control arm bracket to chassis. Add shims equally to front and rear of bracket to decrease camber, or remove shims equally to increase camber angle. After each adjustment is made, tighten bracket-to-chassis bolts, remove jack stands and measure camber angle.

TR7 – Camber angle is not adjustable. If camber angle is not within specifications, inspect suspension system for wear or damage and repair or replace components as necessary.

TOE-IN

All Models (Front) – Set front wheels in straight ahead position. If adjustment is necessary, loosen steering link (tie rod) lock nuts and gaiter clips. Rotate adjusting sleeves equal amounts until correct toe-in is obtained. Tighten lock nuts and recheck toe-in.

Spitfire (Rear) – If toe-in is not to specifications, loosen bolts holdings strut front support. Adjust as necessary by adding to or removing from the shims fitted between support and body. Tighten bolts and recheck toe-in.

VOLKSWAGEN

ADJUSTMENT

TIRE INFLATION (COLD)

Before attempting to check or adjust wheel alignment, make sure tires are properly inflated. Refer to manufacturers specifications given in owner's manual.

CASTER

Caster angle is part of front axle design and is not adjustable. If not within specifications, inspect front suspension for wear or damage and repair or replace components as necessary.

CAMBER

Type 1 & 2 (Front) – Camber is adjusted by an eccentric bushing. Loosen nut on upper torsion arm, then rotate eccentric bushing until specified camber angle is obtained. **NOTE** – *Basic setting is with eccentric notch facing in forward position. Adjustment must be made within 90° either direction.*

Dasher (Front) – If adjustment is necessary, loosen nuts attaching ball joint to track control arm. To adjust, insert suitable adjusting tool (40-200) in adjusting holes in control arm and pry ball joint sideways until camber is set to specifications. **NOTE** – *Difference in camber between* wheels should not vary more than 1°. Tighten attaching nuts and recheck camber.

NOTE – *On Dasher models, insert tool from front on right side and from rear on left side.*

Rabbit & Scirocco (Front) – If adjustment is necessary, loosen nuts of suspension strut-to-wheel bearing housing mounting bolts. Turn eccentric bolt (upper mounting bolt) until specified camber angle is obtained. Tighten mounting bolt nuts and recheck camber angle.

Type 1 (Rear) – Camber angle is dependent on torsion bar adjustment. If camber angle is not within specifications, see *Torsion Bar Adjustment.*

Type 2 (Rear) – If minor adjustment is necessary, loosen bolts attaching bearing housing to spring plate and diagonal arm. Adjust by changing position of bearing housing in elongated holes in spring plate. Tighten bolts and recheck camber. **NOTE** – *Range that this procedure will cover is very small.*

Dasher, Rabbit & Scirocco (Rear) – Rear camber is not adjustable. If camber angle is not to specifications, inspect rear suspension for wear or damage and repair or replace components as necessary.

TOE-IN

Type 1 (Front) – Working on inner end of right tie rod, bend up lockplate. Loosen lock nut and clamp bolts from tie rods. Tap tapered rings from inner end of right side tie rod. Rotate tops of tie rods. Forward rotation increases toe-in; rearward rotation decreases toe-in. When specified toe is achieved, place tie rods so ball joints are not angled. Tighten clamp bolts and lock nuts. If steering wheel is not centered after making adjustment, use *Fig. 1* to recenter steering wheel. **NOTE** – *Centering steering wheel will not alter toe-in.*

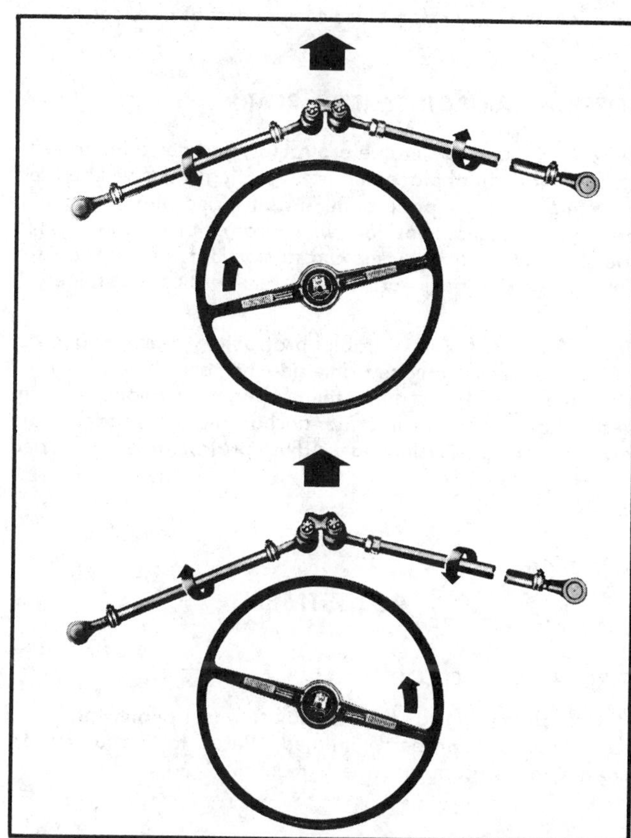

Fig. 1 Direction of Tie Rod Rotation to Align Steering Wheel (Type 1 Only)

Type 2 (Front) – 1) Right side tie rod adjusts front wheel toe. Press drag link off steering drop arm. Place left side wheel in straight-ahead position. Adjust right side tie rod until specified toe is obtained.

2) Place steering gear so protrusion on dust cap is properly aligned. Attach drag link to drop arm. Drag link must enter mounting with no tension against it. Readjust drag link if necessary.

Dasher, Rabbit, Scirocco (Front) – Place front wheels in straight-ahead position. Loosen lock nut on adjustable tie rod end (left side, Dasher; right side, Rabbit and Scirocco). Hold axle boot to avoid twisting. Adjust right side tie rod until specified toe-in is obtained. Tighten lock nut and recheck toe-in.

Type I (Rear) – If adjustment is necessary, remove nuts securing spring plate but do not remove bolts. To adjust, move diagonal arm forward or backward in slotted spring plate mounting holes until toe-in is set to specifications. Install spring plate attaching nuts and recheck toe-in.

Type 2 (Rear) – If adjustment is necessary, loosen bolts attaching bearing housing to spring plate and diagonal arm. Change position of bearing housing in elongated holes on spring plate. Tighten bolts and recheck toe-in.

VOLKSWAGEN (Cont.)

All Other Models (Rear) — Toe-in is not adjustable. If toe-in is not within specifications, inspect rear suspension for wear or damage and repair or replace components as necessary.

TORSION BAR ADJUSTMENT (REAR)

Type I — Using a suitable protractor, find deviation of vehicle from horizontal plane and note reading which will be used in setting angle of spring plate. Install spring plate on torsion bar and measure position with protractor. If not within specifications, adjust by moving torsion bar, one spline at a time, forward or backward until correct position is obtained.

Type 2 — Using a suitable protractor, check horizontal position of vehicle on one frame side member. Reading should be noted; it will be used in setting spring plate angle. Insert inner end of torsion bar in center anchor and press spring plate on outer end of torsion bar. Adjust protractor on unloaded spring plate until bubble is in center position. Adjust torsion bar one spline forward or rearward until correct specifications are obtained.

Torsion Bar Specifications

Application	Setting (Degrees)
Type 1	$21\frac{1}{3} \pm \frac{5}{6}$
Type 2	
Kombi & Campmobile	
From Chassis 218 000 002	① $21 \pm \frac{5}{6}$
From Chassis 212 2000 001	② $23 \pm \frac{5}{6}$
Station Wagon	
From Chassis 218 000 002	① $20 \pm \frac{5}{6}$
From Chassis 212 2000 001	② $23 \pm \frac{5}{6}$

① — Man. Trans.
② — Man. Trans. and Auto. Trans.

VOLVO

ADJUSTMENT

TIRE INFLATION (COLD)

Before attempting to check or adjust wheel alignment, make sure tires are properly inflated. Refer to manufacturers specifications given in owner's manual.

CASTER

Caster cannot be adjusted. If not within specifications, check front end components for damage.

CAMBER

If camber is not within specifications, loosen nuts at strut assembly upper attachment. Use special tool 5038 (or equivalent) at strut upper attachment to adjust camber. Tighten lock nuts. Recheck camber.

TOE-IN

Place wheels in straight-ahead position and loosen lock nut and rubber dust boot outer clamp. Turn tie rods until toe is within specifications. Make sure length of tie rods does not differ more than .08" (2 mm). Measure difference between groove in tie rod and lock nut.

ARROW & COLT

All Models – Tighten adjusting nut to 14.5 ft. lbs. After seating bearing components, loosen nut to 0 ft. lbs. Now make final adjustment to 3.6 ft. lbs. After installing lock cap, insert cotter pin. **NOTE** – *Do not loosen adjusting nut more than 15 degrees to align spindle holes.*

AUDI

NOTE – *The folllowing procedure can only be performed using special tools indicated.*

Model 100 (Front) – **1)** Raise and support front of vehicle. Remove lower wheel bolt and replace with special wheel bolt adapter (V-104) and special dial indicator (G-43). By means of retaining screw on special tool (V-104), adjust dial indicator to pretensioned position of 1 millimeter.

2) Grasp wheel at front and rear. First push inward on front while pulling outward on rear, record dial indicator reading. Reverse this procedure and record dial indicator reading. Difference between these two readings is wheel bearing play. If play exceeds .04-.07 mm, adjustment will be necessary.

3) Remove cotter pin and castle nut. If there was too much play, tighten spindle nut until play is within specifications. If there was insufficient play, remove wheel, spindle nut and its shim. Replace and tighten spindle nut. Using 1 millimeter feeler gauge, loosen spindle nut until it is possible to insert feeler gauge between spindle nut and wheel hub. Attach special hub puller (V-26) and withdraw hub until it is firmly in contact with spindle nut. Remove puller and retighten spindle nut until it is within specifications.

Model 100 (Rear) – Raise and support rear of vehicle. Remove grease cup and one wheel bolt. Attach special dial indicator (30-43), using wheel bolt adapter (40-104) and attachment (10-22). Dial indicator actuator foot should be pretensioned to 1 millimeter against the stub axle. Grasp wheel at front and rear. Move wheel on horizontal axis. If reading on dial indicator is not .02-.04 mm, adjustment will be necessary. Adjust by loosening or tightening spindle nut.

NOTE – *Fox front wheel bearing is not adjustable. Torque stub axle nut to 13 ft. lbs.*

Fox (Rear) – Remove grease cup, cotter pin and castle nut. Tighten spindle nut and loosen for adjustment. Adjust by lightly tightening spindle nut until plain washer (beneath spindle nut) can just be moved from side to side, using screwdriver. This adjustment will correspond to .0012-.0027" (.03-.06 mm) wheel bearing play.

BMW

320i & 630CSi – While rotating wheel hub, tighten castle nut to 22-24 ft. lbs., then rotate hub at least two more times. Loosen castle nut until bearing end play is noticed. Tighten castle nut to a maximum of 2.2 ft. lbs., then loosen nut to nearest hole and install cotter key.

NOTE – *After adjustment, slotted washer should move easily, without noticeable resistance.*

530i Models – While rotating wheel hub, tighten castle nut to 7 ft. lbs. Loosen castle nut approximately ¼ turn. Insert screwdriver in recess of bearing retainer washer and ensure washer can be rotated easily. Install suitable gauge holder (BMW 00 2 500) on wheel hub and install dial indicator with tip touching front axle stub. Move wheel hub back and forth several times and check bearing end play. Adjust castle nut until bearing end play is .0008-.0024".

NOTE – *Set bearing end play as close to lowest limit as possible.*

Install cotter key.

CAPRI

All Models – Rotate wheel, hub and drum assembly while turning adjusting nut to 17-25 ft. lbs. Back adjusting nut off 120°. Install cotter pin and check front wheel rotation.

COURIER

All Models – While rotating wheel, hub and drum assembly, tighten adjusting nut to 17-25 ft. lbs. Back adjusting nut off ¼ turn and retighten nut where castellations on the lock nut are aligned with cotter pin hole in spindle. Install new cotter pin and check wheel rotation.

DATSUN

All, Except F10 – Tighten spindle nut to torque specifications in table. Spin wheel and retorque spindle nut. Loosen nut according to specifications in table and then tighten to align cotter key hole. Insert cotter key.

Wheel Bearing Adjustment

Application	Torque (Ft. Lbs.)	Loosen
B210	18-22	90°
Pickup	22-25	40-70°
200SX,710,810,280Z	18-22	60°

F10 – Raise vehicle and place on safety stands. Remove tire and wheel. Make sure mounting nut is torqued to 87-145 ft. lbs. (12-20 mkg). Spin wheel hub several times in both directions to ensure free rotation. Measure bearing preload by attaching a spring pull scale to lug stud and turning hub. It should take about 3-11 lb. (1.4-4.9 kg) to turn hub.

FIAT

Model 124 & 131 – While rotating hub, torque spindle nut to 14.5 ft. lbs. Completely loosen nut and retighten to 5 ft. lbs. Loosen nut 30° and stake collar of spindle nut into machined slot on spindle. Attach dial indicator with magnetic base on brake drum and actuating foot on spindle. Hub end play should not exceed .004". **NOTE** – *When ever spindle nut has been removed it must be replaced with a new nut.*

Models 128 & X1/9 – Tighten front and rear spindle nuts to 112 ft. lbs. When spindle nuts are properly tightened, stake collar of spindle nut into machined slot on spindle.

Wheel Bearing Adjustment

HONDA

All Models (Front) – Front wheel bearings are not adjustable. Torque front spindle nut to 87-130 ft. lbs. (Civic and Accord) or 109 ft. lbs. (Civic CVCC).

All, Except Accord (Rear) – Rear wheel bearings are not adjustable. Torque rear spindle nut to 72-94 ft. lbs. (Civic) or 83 ft. lbs. (Civic CVCC).

Accord (Rear) – Tighten spindle nut to 18 ft. lbs. (2.5 mkg) and rotate drum several times. Loosen lock nut. Tighten spindle nut to 1.1-3.6 ft. lbs. (.15-.5 mkg). Insert cotter pin.

JAGUAR

All Models – While rotating hub, tighten nut until no end play is evident. Loosen nut 1 or 2 flats to line up cotter key and install cotter key. End play should be measured with a dial indicator and should be .002-.006". If not within specifications, adjust axle nut to correct end play.

LANCIA

All Models – Front wheel bearing and rear wheel bearings are pressed into stub axle housings. Stub axle must be removed to replace bearings. Spindle nut torque not available.

LUV

All Models – While rotating wheel, tighten spindle nut to 22 ft. lbs. Turn hub through two or three turns and loosen nut until just finger tight. Check free play. Using a pull scale attached to wheel stud, measure turning torque; adjust nut until pull recorded on scale is 1.1-2.6 lbs. when wheel begins to rotate.

MAZDA

All Models – With vehicle raised and supported under lower control arms, measure amount of bearing preload using a pull scale hooked on hub bolt. Preload should be 1.3-2.4 lbs. (Pickup) or .88-2.0 lbs. (all other models). If not to specifications, adjust by tightening spindle nut until correct bearing preload is obtained. Align slot of spindle nut with hole in spindle and install new cotter key.

MERCEDES-BENZ

All Models – While rotating hub, tighten clamping nut until hub can just be turned. Loosen clamping nut and release bearing tension by striking steering knuckle spindle with plastic hammer. Using a suitable dial indicator, check wheel bearing end play. End play should be .0004-.0008". Adjust clamping nut until end play is within limits. Tighten socket bolt of clamping nut. Washer between outer bearing and clamping nut should rotate with light pressure applied to it.

MG

Midget – Raise front of vehicle and remove each wheel. Remove caliper assembly, but do not disconnect hydraulic brake hose. Support caliper to prevent damage to hose. Attach suitable dial indicator and measure runout of hub at outer edge of brake rotor. If runout exceeds .006" remove rotor and reposition on hub. Torque spindle nut to 46 ft. lbs. and recheck runout.

MG (cont.)

MGB – Raise front of vehicle and remove front wheels. Using suitable dial indicator, measure hub end play. Correct end play is .002-.004" (.05-.10 mm). If not within specifications, remove spindle nut, washer, and outer bearing. Add or remove shims behind outer bearing until correct end play is obtained with spindle nut torqued to 40-70 ft. lbs. (5.5-9.7 mkg).

OPEL

All Models – Raise and support front of vehicle. While rotating wheel, torque spindle nut to 21 ft. lbs. Back off spindle nut completely. Now turn the nut all the way in using fingers only. If slot and hole are not aligned, tighten enough to align and install cotter key.

PEUGEOT

All Models – While turning wheel, tighten spindle nut to 22 ft. lbs. Loosen and retorque nut to 7 ft. lbs. Lock nut in this position, by staking nut collar into slot of spindle.

PORSCHE

All Models (Front) – Turn wheel and tighten clamping nut just enough to seat roller bearings. Loosen nut until tab washer can be easily moved laterally with a screwdriver. There should be no bearing play felt when hub is moved axially. Tighten screw on clamping nut and recheck adjustment.

930 (Rear) – Torque axle nut to 217 ft. lbs. (30 mkg) and check axial play. Adjust axle nut in small steps until axial play is about .001" (.04 mm) (torque may be increased to 325 ft. lbs.; 45 mkg, during this procedure). Loosen axle nut. Retorque nut to 217 ft. lbs. (30 mkg) and insert cotter pin.

RENAULT

R5 (Front) – Nonadjustable. Torque stub axle nut to 90 ft. lbs. (12.4 mkg).

R5 (Rear) – Tighten stub axle nut to 25 ft. lbs. (3.5 mkg). Loosen nut about 1/4 turn. Check bearing end play, it should be between .0004-.002" (.01-.05 mm). Adjust stub axle as necessary. Fit lock plate and cotter pin. Refill hub dust cover cap with 1/3 oz. of grease.

R-12 & R-17 (Front) – Front wheel bearings are not adjustable. Torque spindle nut to 115 ft. lbs. (14.5 mkg), while holding hub-disc assembly.

R-12 & R-17 (Rear) – Tighten rear spindle nut to 25 ft. lbs. (3.5 mkg) while rotating drum. Loosen nut 1/4 turn and check end play using a dial indicator. End play should be .001-.002" (.025-.051 mm). Adjust spindle nut until end play is set to specifications, then install a new cotter key.

SAAB

All Models (Front) – Front wheel bearings are not adjustable. Torque front spindle nut to 145 ft. lbs.

All Models (Rear) – Install washer and lock nut. Tighten lock nut to 36 ft. lbs. (5 mkg) to seat bearings. Loosen lock nut completely, then tighten nut to 1.4-2.9 ft. lbs. (.2-.4 mkg) and lock nut in place by bending flange into slot of lock nut.

SUBARU

All Models (Front) – Front wheel bearing is not adjustable. Tighten spindle nut to 174 ft. lbs.

4WD Station Wagon (Rear) – Rear wheel bearings are not adjustable. Tighten spindle lock nut to 145-181 ft. lbs.

All Other Models (Rear) – While rotating brake drum, snug down spindle nut to seat bearings. Back spindle nut off 1/8 turn and bend down tab of locking washer to secure spindle nut. If adjustment is correct, a force of 6.1-8.7 INCH lbs. will be required to rotate wheel.

TOYOTA

Land Cruiser – Install claw washer and tighten front wheel adjusting nut with suitable tool (09607-60010). Rotate drum to seat bearings. Loosen nut 1/8-1/6 turn. If brake drum rotates properly, install lock washer and tighten lock nut with suitable tool (09607-60010).

Pickup – Tighten front axle castle nut to 36 ft. lbs. to seat bearings, then back off until nut is finger tight. Retighten nut to 36 ft. lbs. and back off 1/6-1/3 turn and install cotter key. When properly adjusted, bearing preload should be as shown in table, when checked with pull scale attached to hub bolt.

All Other Models – Tighten castle nut bearing retainer nut 18.8-23.2 ft. lbs. and turn brake drum back and forth to seat bearing. Loosen nut until can be turned with fingers. Tighten nut to finger tight using a socket without the handle. If not aligned for cotter key installation, tighten until installation possible. Preload at hub (hub rotating) should be within specifications.

Bearing Preload Specifications

Application	Preload (Oz)
Corona	12.3-30.6
Pickup	18.6-61.8
All Others	10.6-24.7

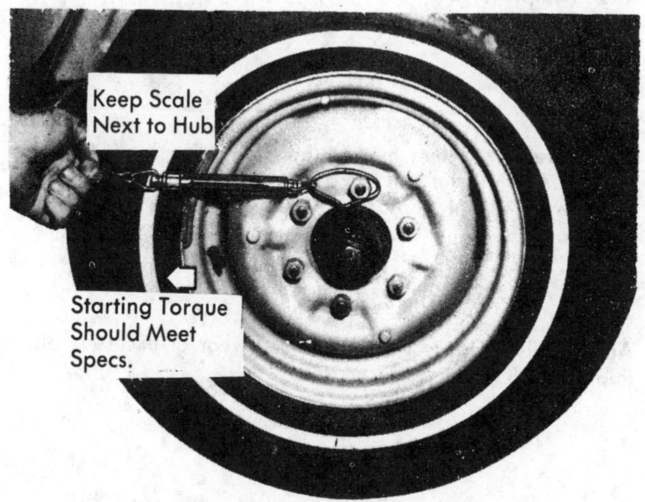

Fig. 1 Using a Pull Scale to Measure Wheel Bearing Starting Torque

TRIUMPH

TR7 – Raise and support front of vehicle, then remove wheel and tire. Check hub for excessive end play. If adjustment is necessary, remove grease cap and cotter key. Tighten spindle nut to 5 ft. lbs. (.7 mkg), then back nut off one flat and install cotter key.

All Others – Raise and support front of vehicle, then remove wheel and brake caliper. Attach a dial indicator and measure wheel bearing end play. If end play exceeds .003-.005" (.08-.13 mm), remove cotter key and loosen or tighten spindle nut until end play is within specifications. Install new cotter key.

VOLKSWAGEN

Type 1 (Front) – Raise and support front of vehicle. While rotating wheel, tighten spindle clamp nut to seat bearings. Loosen clamp nut until axial play is .001-.005" (.025-.027 mm). Tighten clamp nut.

Type 2 (Front) – Adjust clamp nut while rotating wheel. Adjustment is completed when thrust washer can be moved with a screwdriver and finger pressure.

All Other Models (Front) – Front wheel bearings are pressed into bearing housing and no adjustment is necessary. Tighten front axle nut to 167 ft. lbs. (23 mkg) on Dasher models or 175 ft. lbs. (24.2 mkg) on Rabbit and Scirocco models.

Dasher, Rabbit & Scirocco (Rear) – Wheel bearings are correctly adjusted if thrust washer can be moved slightly with a screwdriver. **NOTE** – *This will provide axial play of approximately .001-.003".*

VOLVO

All Models – While rotating hub, torque nut to 50 ft. lbs. Loosen nut 1/3 turn and check for hub rotating freely with no end play. If necessary to align cotter key holes loosen nut and install cotter key.

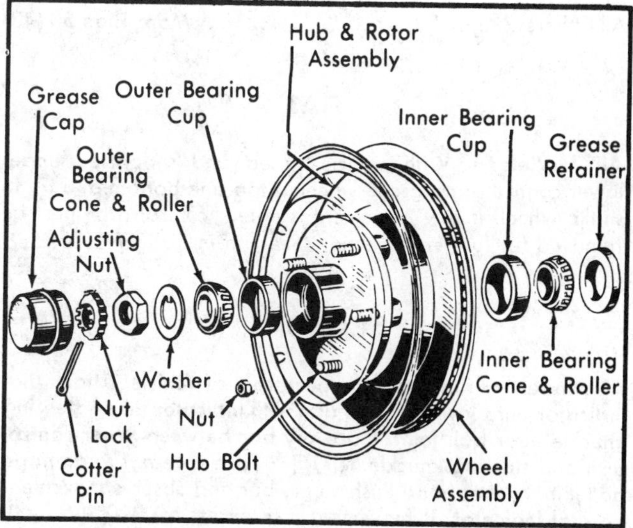

Fig. 2 Exploded View of Wheel Bearing Components with Disc Brakes

Ball Joint Checking

ARROW/COLT

All Models – With components removed from control arm and ball joint still installed, check following: Horizontal and vertical free play (0"), and ball joint rotation starting torque 4-6 ft. lbs. (6-8Nm). Replace ball joints if correct specifications are not obtained.

AUDI

Fox – Clearance of ball joint with pressure applied by leverage should be .04-.10" (1.0-2.5 mm). If not replace ball joints.

BMW

All Models – With lower control arm removed, measure axial (up and down) movement of ball joint stud. If movement exceeds .0945", replace ball joint. *See BMW in SUSPENSION Section.*

COURIER

All Models – Check working surfaces of ball joints and studs for wear or damage. End play should not exceed .031" (.8 mm). If end play is excessive, replace ball joint. *See Courier in SUSPENSION Section.*

DATSUN

All Models (Exc. 620 Pickup) – Remove lower control arm. *See Datsun in SUSPENSION Section.* Use appropriate spring tension gauge and attach it to top of ball joint stud nut. Measure force (INCH Lbs.) required to move ball joint stud laterally. If measurement is not within specifications, replace ball joint.

Ball Joint Specifications

Application	Lateral Movement INCH Lbs. (cmkg)
F10	30 (35)
All Others	More Than 50 (43)

FIAT

All Models – With vehicle raised and supported under lower control arms, grasp wheel at top and bottom and try to shake wheel. If any movement is noted, control arm must be removed for further inspection. *See Fiat in SUSPENSION Section.*

HONDA

All Models – Raise and support front of vehicle. Attach dial indicator onto lower control arm with indicator tip on steering knuckle near ball joint. Place pry bar between lower control arm and steering knuckle. **NOTE** – *Take care not to damage ball joint rubber boot.* Push on pry bar and observe movement on dial indicator. If movement is in excess of .020" (.5 mm), ball joint must be replaced. *See Honda in SUSPENSION Section.*

JAGUAR

All Models – Upper ball joint must be replaced if signs of wear or play are evident. The lower ball joint is adjustable with shims if axial play exceeds .004-.006" (.10-.15 mm). Shims must not be removed to take up excessive wear in ball pin and socket. If parts are excessively worn, replacement is required.

LANCIA

All Models – If ball joint shows excessive amounts of wear (play), replace ball joints. *See Lancia in SUSPENSION Section.*

LUV

With vehicle raised and supported under lower control arms, grasp wheel at top and bottom. Try to move wheel and replace ball joint if movement exceeds .06" (1.52 mm).

MAZDA

All Models – Check ball joint dust seal for wear or damage and, if necessary, replace seal. Ball joint end play must not exceed .039" (1 mm). If end play exceeds specifications, replace ball joint. *See Mazda in SUSPENSION Section.*

MERCEDES-BENZ

There should be no lateral movement of ball joint. Vertical movement is adjusted by adding or removing washers.

OPEL

All Models – Raise and support front of vehicle. Inspect ball joint rubber boots for damage and replace as necessary. If lower ball joint axial play exceeds .008" (2 mm), ball joint must be replaced. *See Opel in SUSPENSION Section.*

PEUGEOT

All Models – Inspect ball joints for roughness or excessive wear. Replace ball joints as necessary. *See Peugeot in SUSPENSION Section.*

PORSCHE

All Models – When moving ball pin some friction torque should be felt. If ball pin can be moved without resistance and end play is shown, replace ball joint.

RENAULT

All Models – Inspect ball joints for wear or excessive play. Replace ball joints as necessary.

SAAB

All Models – If ball joint exhibits excessive play, it must be replaced as a complete unit. *See Saab in SUSPENSION Section.*

SUBARU

All Models – Check ball joint for excessive play by pushing and pulling on ball joint stud. Allowable looseness is less than .012". If play exceeds this specification, ball joint must be replaced. *See Subaru in SUSPENSION Section.*

TOYOTA

Corona & Pickup – To check lower ball joint, jack up lower suspension arm and check for ball joint looseness by moving wheel vertically and horizontally. Movement limit in vertical direction should be less than .04" (1 mm) Corona and .20" (5.0 mm) Pickup. Movement limit in horizontal direction should be less than .08" (2 mm) Corona and .09" (2.3 mm) Pickup.

NOTE – *Ensure other suspension parts are tight before checking ball joints. To check upper ball joints, disconnect upper suspension arm from steering knuckle. Turn ball stud and check for excessive looseness or tightness. Replace ball joint if it is excessively loose or tight.*

All Other Models – Check for excessive looseness, proper operation and damaged ball stud. Replace as necessary.

TRIUMPH

All Models – Inspect ball joints for excessive wear or play. Replace ball joint as necessary. *See Triumph in SUSPENSION Section.*

VOLKSWAGEN

Type 1 – Raise front of vehicle and turn steering to one side. Place pry bar tool over nut or bolt head mounting steering knuckle to strut. Compress ball joint spring and place vernier caliper over top of ball joint and over bottom stud. Note caliper reading, then release lever and record caliper travel. Increased reading is ball joint play. Replace ball joints as necessary.

Type 2 – Raise front of vehicle and turn steering to one side. Insert pry bar tool VW 281a (or equivalent) under lower control arm and over top of strut mounting. Fit a vernier caliper on lower or upper torsion arm and steering knuckle. Record measurement. Press down with lever and measure travel of vernier caliper. If travel exceeds specifications, replace ball joint.

All Other Models – Raise and support, then turn steering to one side. Install suitable levering tool so that ball joint spring may be compressed. With spring compressed, postion a vernier caliper with lower jaw on ball joint stud and upper jaw on top of clamping bolt for ball joint stud. Note reading. Slowly release tension from spring and note travel of caliper. This reading indicates ball joint play. If specified play is exceeded, replace ball joint. *See Volkswagen in SUSPENSION Section.*

Ball Joint Specifications

Application	Travel In.(mm)
Type 2	.08 (2)
All Others	.10 (2.5)

VOLVO

All Models – Maximum permitted axial play for lower ball joint is .12" (3 mm). Check ball joint by prying back and forth with a bar. If specifications are exceeded, replace ball joints. *See Volvo in SUSPENSION Section.*

ALL MANUFACTURERS

NOTE – *Information not available for Lancia models.*

NOTE – *These illustrations are not intended to represent exact structure of the manufacturer's frame, underbody, or body outline. These are presented only to give the mechanic some point of reference.*

FRAME & UNDERBODY

The following illustrations indicate areas (parts) of the underbody and frame which may be used to raise and support the vehicle, using either floor jack or hoist. These points are indicated by shaded areas on the frame (see sample illustration).

OUTERBODY

Those points designated on the outline of the body were specifically designed to facilitate the use of the vehicle's own jack, but may also be used to raise and support the vehicle by means of a floor jack or hoist. These jacking points are indicated by circular dots on the outline of the body (see sample illustration). If floor jack or hoist is employed, extreme care should be exercised to prevent damaging the outer body shell.

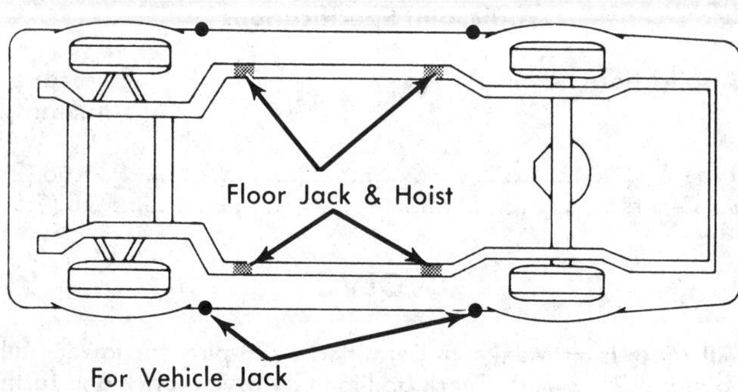

Fig. 1 Sample Jacking & Hoisting Points (Typical Illustration)

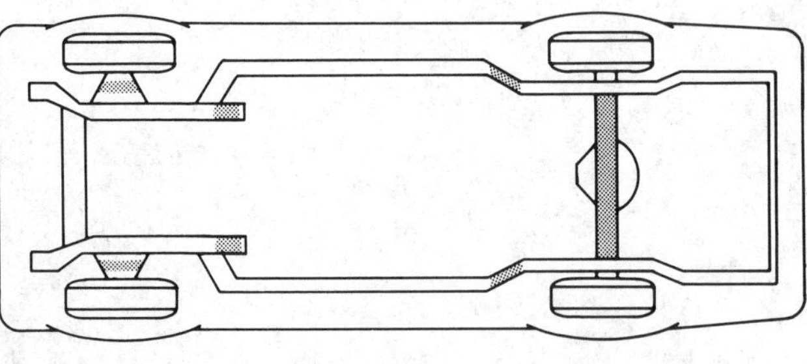

Arrow/Colt

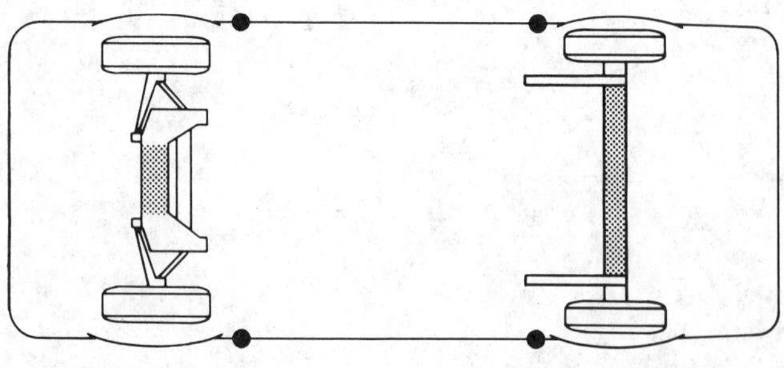

Audi

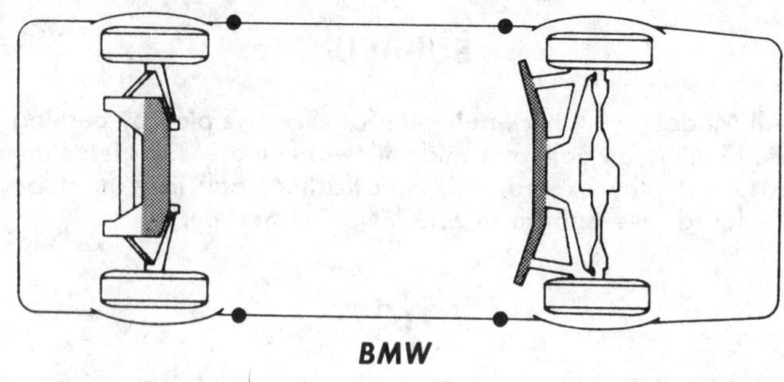

BMW

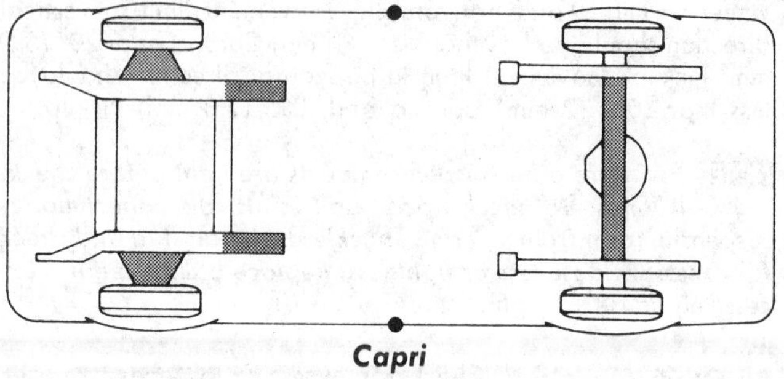

Capri

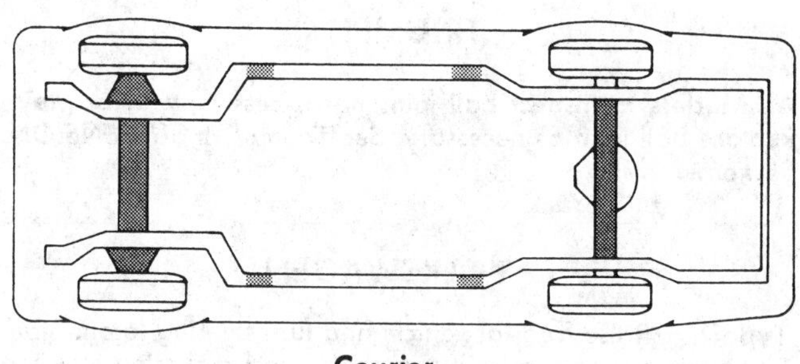

Courier

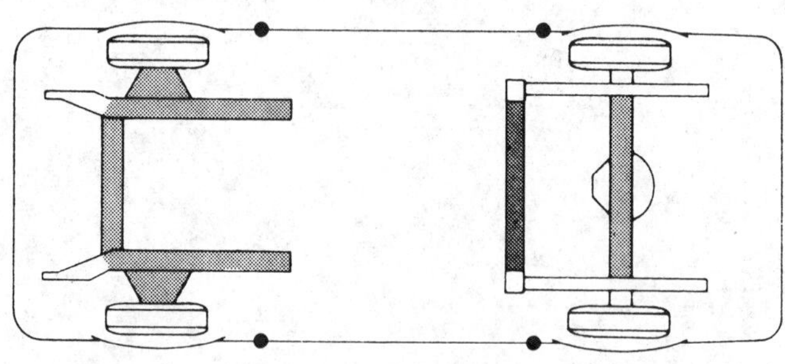

Datsun (Except Pickup)

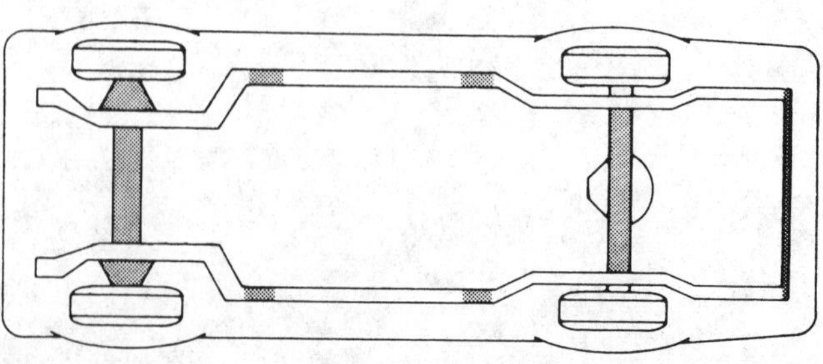

Datsun Pickup

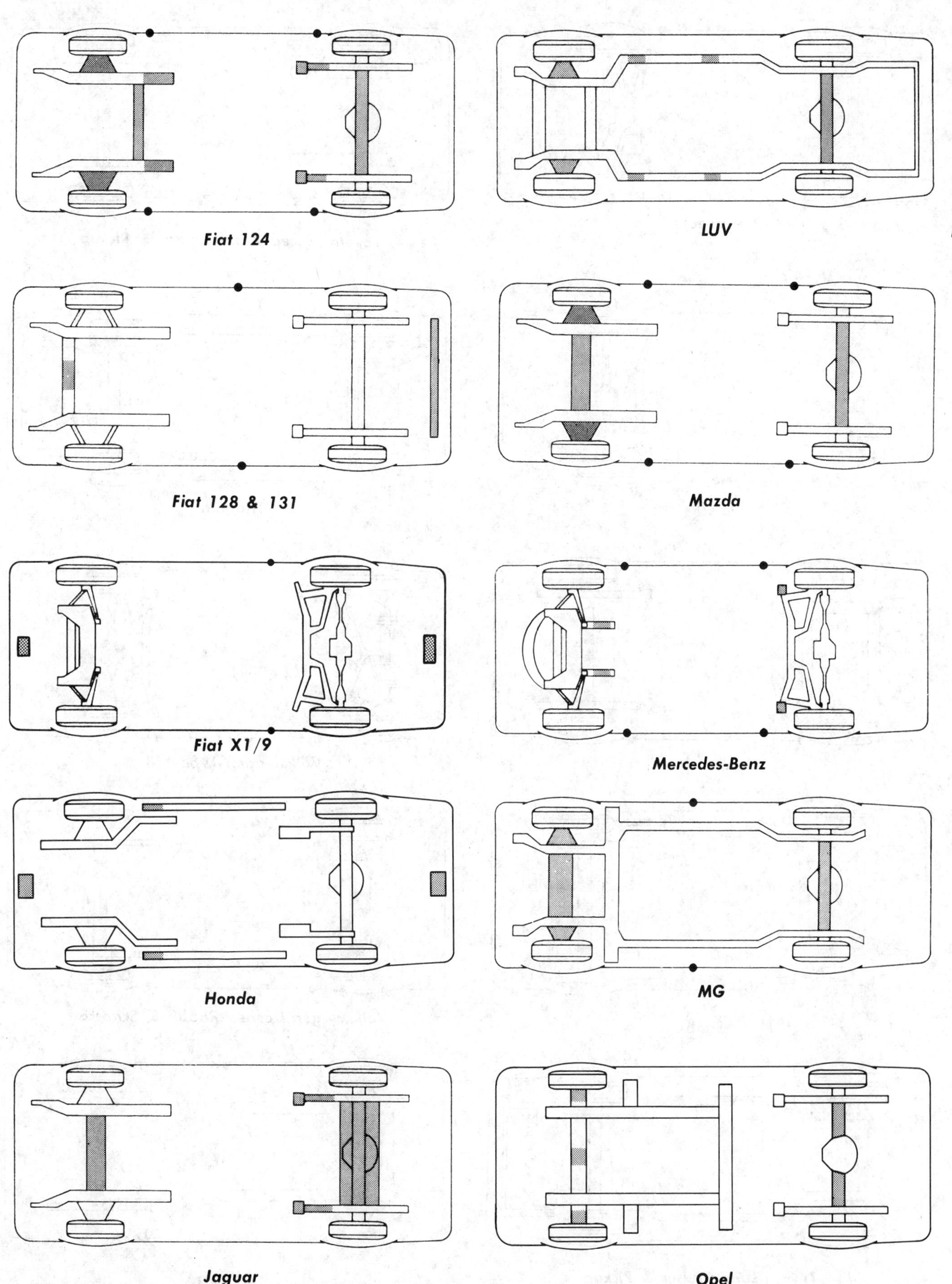
Fiat 124
LUV
Fiat 128 & 131
Mazda
Fiat X1/9
Mercedes-Benz
Honda
MG
Jaguar
Opel

Jacking & Hoisting

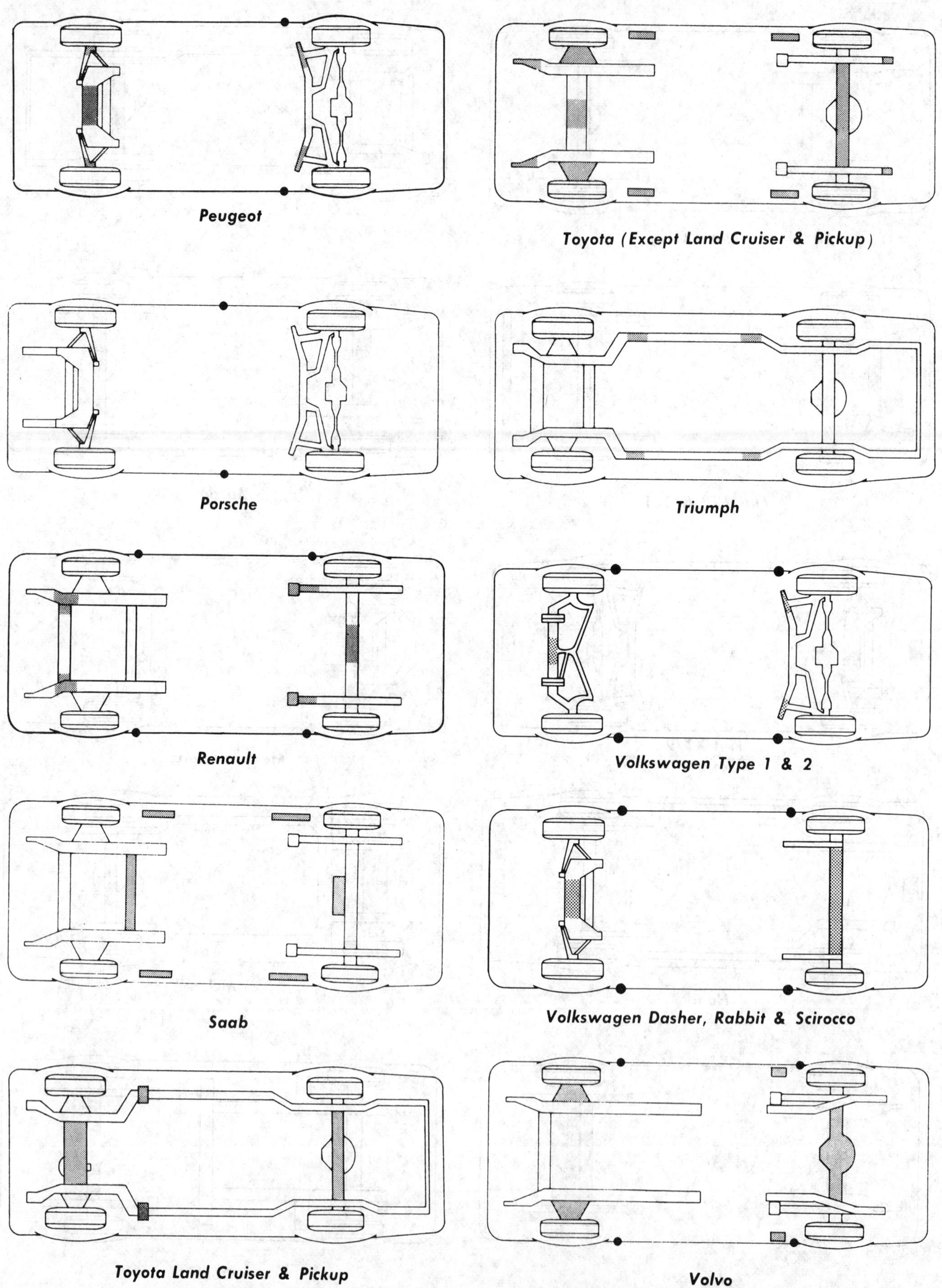
Peugeot
Toyota (Except Land Cruiser & Pickup)
Porsche
Triumph
Renault
Volkswagen Type 1 & 2
Saab
Volkswagen Dasher, Rabbit & Scirocco
Toyota Land Cruiser & Pickup
Volvo

Section 9

SUSPENSION

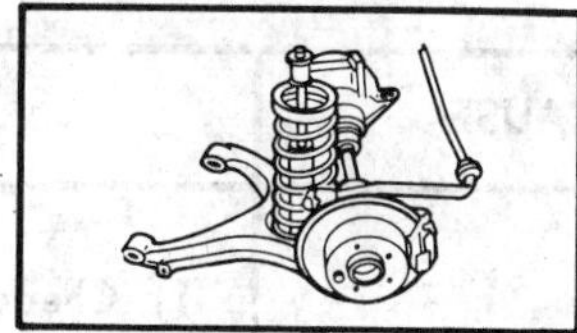

Contents

NOTE — ALSO SEE GENERAL INDEX.

SUSPENSION TROUBLE SHOOTING

NOTE— *This is a general trouble shooting guide. When using this guide, locate the condition in column one that corresponds to your problem and determine the possible causes in column two. Match the number of possible cause with the same number in column three, and you will have the suggested correction.*

CONDITION	POSSIBLE CAUSE	CORRECTION
▶ Hard Steering	1) Tire pressure too low 2) Front wheels out of alignment 3) Lower control arm ball joint siezed	1) Check manufacturers recommended pressure and set to specifications 2) Check alignment and set to specifications or replace parts 3) Check specifications set or replace parts
▶ Pulls to one side	1) Crossmember broken, cracked or loose 2) Left and right side wheel base uneven 3) Loose or excessively worn wheel bearings 4) Loose wheel lug nuts	1) Replace crossmember 2) Check frame and repair 3) Adjust wheel bearings or replace 4) Tighten lug nuts
▶ Steering wheel wander	1) Excessive ball joint wear 2) Lower control arm and strut 3) Lower control arm pivot bolt (shaft) loose or sloppy 4) Lower control arm and strut damaged or worn	1) Replace ball joint or adjust if possible 2) Replace defective component bar(s) damaged 3) Tighten or replace parts 4) Inspect bushings and replace as required
▶ Body roll	1) Stabilizer broken or damaged 2) Shock absorbers worn out	1) Replace parts 2) Check and replace
▶ Noise	1) Coil spring broken 2) Bad shock absorber 3) Insufficient lubrication 4) Components loose or excessively worn 5) Damaged wheel bearing 6) Improper tire pressure	1) Replace, may be matched set 2) Check operation and replace 3) Grease fittings 4) Tighten or replace 5) Adjust or replace wheel bearings 6) Check inflation
▶ Steering hard to control	1) Broken front coil spring 2) Defective shock absorber 3) Loose control arm bushings 4) Strut assembly loose 5) Tire pressure 6) Wheel alignment out of tolerance 7) Damaged suspension links	1) Replace coil spring 2) Replace shock absorber 3) Replace bushings 4) Tighten or replace assembly 5) Check and set to specifications 6) Check and adjust or replace components 7) Replace parts

ARROW & COLT

Arrow
Colt

DESCRIPTION

Strut type suspension consists of a vertically mounted strut assembly, lower control arm, and stabilizer bar. Strut assembly is mounted to top of fender panel by a thrust bearing. Strut assembly mounts at bottom to steering arm and pivots in ball joint. Strut components are: shock absorber built into strut outer tube, coil spring around outside of strut tube, and wheel spindle integral with bottom of strut tube. A stabilizer bar is attached to front chassis members and at ends to lower control arms. Some models are also equipped with strut bars.

ADJUSTMENT

WHEEL ALIGNMENT SPECIFICATIONS & PROCEDURES

See Wheel Alignment Specifications & Procedures in WHEEL ALIGNMENT Section.

WHEEL BEARING ADJUSTMENT

See Wheel Bearing Adjustment in WHEEL ALIGNMENT Section.

BALL JOINT CHECKING

See Ball Joint Checking in WHEEL ALIGNMENT Section.

REMOVAL & INSTALLATION

STABILIZER & STRUT BAR

Removal – Raise vehicle and support on safety stands. Disconnect stabilizer and strut bars from mountings on lower control arm. Remove strut bracket from body mounting position. Remove stabilizer bracket on each side and take off stabilizer. Next, lift off strut bar after noting position of all washers and bushings.

Installation – To install, reverse removal procedure and note the following: Make sure distance between strut bar end and lock nut is 3.1" (78.7 mm). Install strut bar bushing with convex surface to front side.

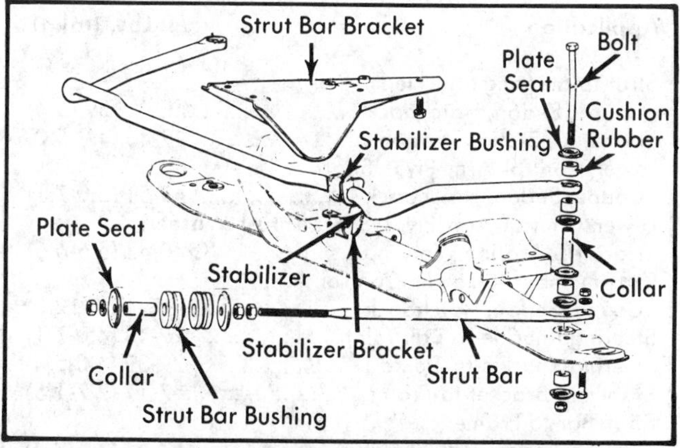

Fig. 1 Exploded View of Coupe, Sedan and Hatchback Strut/Stabilizer Bar Assembly

LOWER CONTROL ARM

Removal – 1) Raise vehicle and place on safety stands. Remove tire and wheel.

2) Disconnect stabilizer bar from lower control arm.

3) On Coupe, Sedan and Hatchback models, take out strut rod.

4) Remove 3 bolts mounting strut assembly to steering arm. Remove nut from ball joint stud and pull steering arm from ball joint.

5) On Coupe, Sedan and Hatchback models, remove control arm pivot shaft bolt.

6) On Hardtop and Station Wagon models, remove bolts mounting control arm to crossmember.

7) Remove control arm from vehicle.

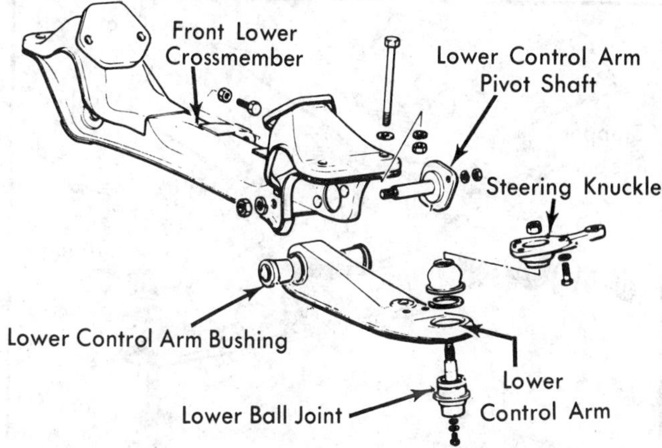

Fig. 2 Exploded View of Colt and Arrow Front Suspension. Coupe, Sedan and Hatchback Use Suspension Shown

Ball Joint Replacement – 1) Pry out ball joint dust seal.

2) Remove snap ring from groove in ball joint seat.

3) Press ball joint from control arm.

4) Select new ball joint. Position ball joint in control arm. Seat ball joint into position so ball joint and lower control arm reference marks are aligned.

NOTE – *It should take approximately 11,000 lbs. (5000 kg) to fully seat ball joint.*

5) Fit new snap ring into ball joint groove. It may be necessary to tap snap ring into place.

NOTE – *Make sure not to open snap ring wider than necessary.*

6) Apply packing sealer inside of dust cover metal ring. Seat metal ring into snap ring surface by tapping with hammer.

Bushing Replacement – Hardtop, Station Wagon – 1) Remove bolts and washers from both ends of pivot shaft.

2) Press pivot shaft with rear bushing out of control arm. Remove rubber stopper *(Fig. 3)* and press out front bushing.

3) Select new pivot shaft bushings and washers. Press front bushing with pivot shaft into control arm. Place a holder between rear branches of control arm. Press in rear bushing.

ARROW & COLT (Cont.)

4) Install pivot shaft bolts and new washers. Do not tighten pivot bolts until weight of vehicle is on ground.

Installation – To install lower control arm, reverse removal procedure and note following:

- On Hardtop and Station Wagon models, make sure mounting nut on crossmember has chamfered edges facing rounded corners of bracket.
- Smear grease on strut mounting surface before fitting to steering knuckle.

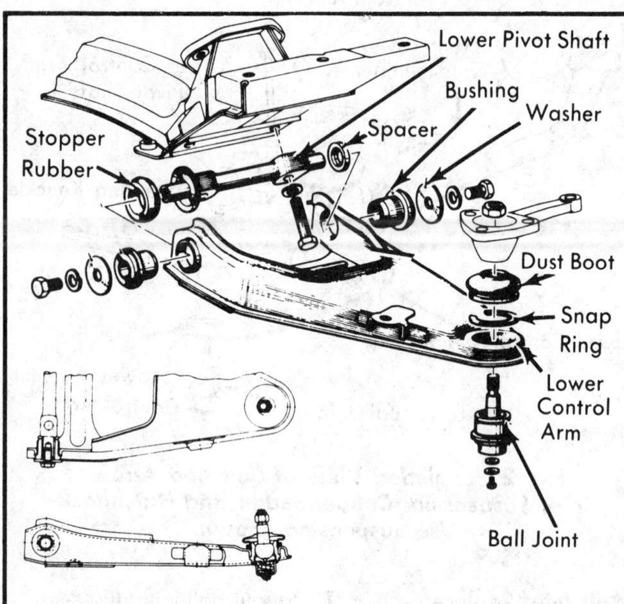

Fig. 3 Exploded View of Lower Control Arm Assembly. Only Hardtop and Station Wagon Models Use Suspension Shown

STRUT ASSEMBLY

Removal – Raise vehicle and place safety stands under chassis members. Disconnect strut assembly from lower control arm as previously outlined. Remove brake caliper and hub. Remove dust cover and disc brake adapter. Remove three bolts retaining strut assembly to fender panel and remove strut assembly from vehicle.

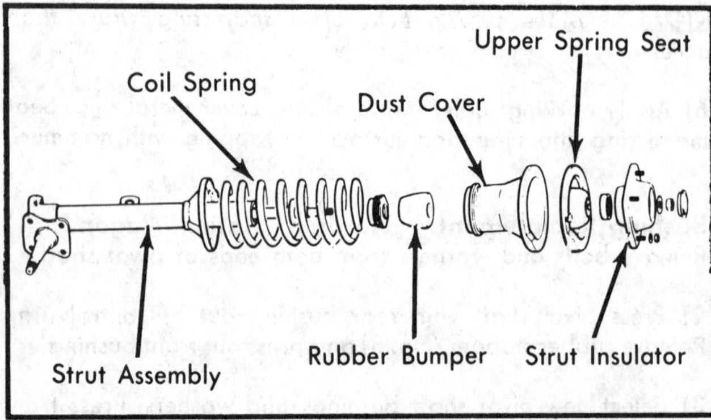

Fig. 4 Internal Strut Assembly Components

Disassembly – **1)** Secure strut assembly in vise and remove small dust cover in middle of thrust bearing assembly. Compress spring using tool CT-1105 (or equivalent) and remove nut retaining thrust bearing. Remove thrust bearing, coil spring, upper spring seat, and rubber bumper.

2) Hold strut assembly vertical in vise and use wrench CT01112 (or equivalent) to remove shock absorber seal. Push piston rod to lowest position and drain oil. Remove "O" ring from top of strut tube and drain piston rod assembly and guide up and out of tube. Remove guide from piston rod and rod from cylinder.

Reassembly – **1)** Thoroughly clean all components and check for wear or distortion. Coat piston rod with shock absorber oil and install in cylinder. Insert cylinder and piston rod in strut tub. Push piston rod to bottom of stroke and fill cylinder with 10 ounces of shock absorber oil. Slowly move piston rod up and down until air is removed from cylinder.

2) Install guide over cylinder and push down until it contacts upper edge of cylinder. Install "O" ring between guide and strut tube. **NOTE** – *Always use new "O" ring when removed.* Using seal guide CT-1111B (or equivalent), slide shock absorber seal over piston rod and tighten until edge of seal nut touches strut tube. **NOTE** – *Always use new seal when removed.*

3) Compress spring and install over strut tube. Pull piston rod to end of travel and slide on rubber bumper. Install upper spring seat, thrust bearing and nut, and tighten temporarily. Make sure spring is seated and release tool. Using holding tool CT-1112 (or equivalent), hold upper spring seat and tighten piston rod nut.

Installation – To install, reverse removal procedure and tighten all nuts and bolts.

TIGHTENING SPECIFICATIONS

Application	Ft. Lbs. (mkg)
Strut-to-Steering Knuckle	
Coupe, Sedan, Hatchback	39 (5.4)
Hardtop, Station Wagon	29-36 (4.0-5.0)
Lower Control Arm Pivot Shaft	
Coupe, Sedan, Hatchback	43-51 (6.0-7.1)
Lower Control Arm Pivot Shaft Thrust Washers	
Hardtop, Station Wagon	①40-47 (5.5-6.5)
Crossmember-to-Lower Control Arm	
Coupe, Sedan, Hatchback	72-87 (10.0-12.0)
Steering Knuckle-to-Ball Joint	29-43 (4.0-7.1)
Steering Knuckle-to-Tie Rod	29-39 (4.0-5.4)
Stabilizer Bracket-to-Frame	7-11 (.97-1.5)
Strut Bar-to-Frame	
Coupe, Sedan, Hatchback	54-61 (7.5-8.4)
Strut Bar-to-Lower Control Arm	
Coupe, Sedan, Hatchback	36-43 (4.0-7.1)
Strut Bar Bracket	
Coupe, Sedan, Hatchback	29-33 (4.0-4.6)
Stabilizer Bar-to-Lower Control Arm	22-25 (3.0-3.5)

① – With wheel on ground.

AUDI 100LS

100LS

DESCRIPTION

Audi is front wheel drive with independent type front suspension utilizing upper and lower control arms and coil spring/shock absorber assemblies. Upper and lower control arms pivot in mounts connected to chassis. Steering knuckles are mounted between upper and lower control arms by means of ball joints. Steering knuckles support drive axle bearing carriers. A stabilizer bar is mounted to chassis and connected at ends to lower control arms.

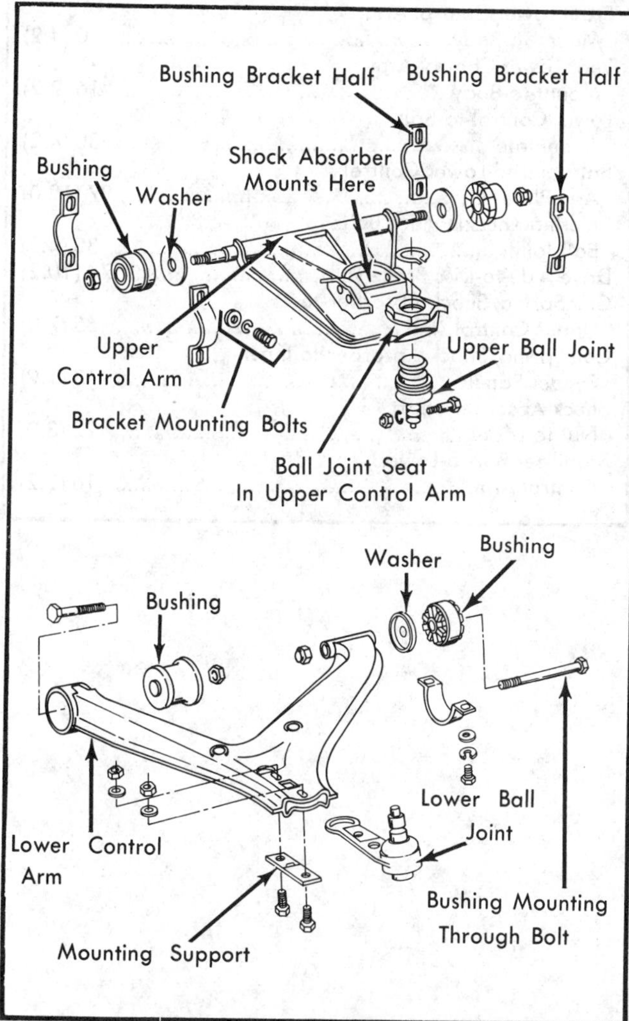

Fig. 1 Exploded View of Audi 100LS Front Suspension Assembly

ADJUSTMENT

WHEEL ALIGNMENT SPECIFICATIONS & PROCEDURES

See *Wheel Alignment Specifications & Procedures* in *WHEEL ALIGNMENT* Section.

WHEEL BEARING ADJUSTMENT

See *Wheel Bearing Adjustment* in *WHEEL ALIGNMENT* Section.

BALL JOINT CHECKING

See *Ball Joint Checking* in *WHEEL ALIGNMENT* Section.

REMOVAL & INSTALLATION

COIL SPRING/SHOCK ABSORBER ASSEMBLY

Removal – Raise vehicle, position safety stands under chassis and remove wheel and tire. Disconnect shock absorber lower mount from upper control arm. Remove nuts securing shock absorber upper mount from fender well. Pull shock absorber down and pivot to outside. Turn shock absorber and spring assembly 90° and remove from lower control arm.

Disassembly – Mount coil spring/shock absorber assembly in a suitable spring compressor. Compress spring until lock nut and nut can be removed from shock absorber shaft. With nuts removed, withdraw shock absorber from spring compressor. Release spring compressor and remove coil spring and mounting components.

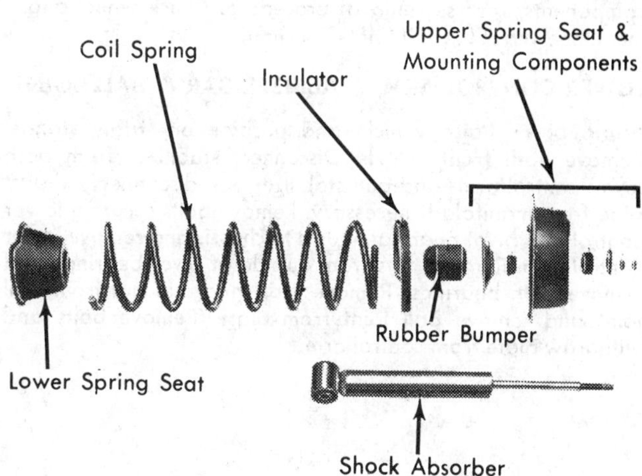

Fig. 2 Exploded View of Coil Spring and Shock Absorber Assembly

Reassembly – 1) Coil springs are identified as to length by colored lines on spring. If spring is marked with one line, a thick insulator ring in upper spring seat must be installed. If spring is marked with two lines, a medium thickness ring must be installed and if coil spring has three colored lines, a thin ring must be installed. When installing ring, make sure lug on ring fits into notch in upper spring retainer.

2) Position spring in upper retainer, making sure that end of spring coil fits into notch in insulator. Install rubber stop on shock absorber shaft. Install coil spring and upper and lower spring seats in a suitable spring compressor. Compress spring, making sure that there is at least .080" of clearance between inside of spring and lower spring seat. A noise will occur if spring touches spring seat on inside. Insert shock absorber and position so that centerline of lower mount eye on shock is parallel with straight edge on upper spring seat. Tighten shock absorber shaft nut and lock nut.

Installation – To install coil spring/shock absorber assembly, reverse removal procedure. Make sure that straight edge of upper spring seat is facing center of vehicle.

AUDI 100LS (Cont.)

UPPER CONTROL ARM & BALL JOINT

Removal – Raise vehicle, position safety stands under chassis and remove wheel and tire. Separate upper ball joint stud from steering knuckle, as previously outlined. Remove pivot bearing mounts from chassis and remove upper control arm. Remove nuts at outside of pivot bearings and remove bearing. Remove snap ring retaining ball joint in control arm and press ball joint from control arm.

Installation – 1) Lower control arm must be removed to install upper control arm. *See Lower Control Arm, Stabilizer Bar and Ball Joint in this section.* With lower control arm installed, fit tool 3007 (or equivalent). Tool mounts between inside nuts of lower control arm halves with threaded bore facing rearward.

2) Turn arms of tool up and position upper control arm on tool arms (loosen bushing retainers, if necessary) and tighten upper control arm pivot bearing mounts. To install remaining components, reverse removal procedure. Check wheel alignment. See *WHEEL ALIGNMENT Section.*

LOWER CONTROL ARM, STABILIZER BAR & BALL JOINT

Removal – Raise vehicle and position on safety stands. Remove both front wheels. Disconnect stabilizer from both lower control arms and pull stabilizer out, disconnect exhaust pipe from manifold if necessary. Remove bolts securing lower control arm pivot bearing mounts to chassis and remove lower control arm. Remove nuts from outside of pivot bearings and remove both bearings. Remove snap ring and nut from ball joint and remove ball joint from plate. Remove bolts and withdraw plate from control arm.

Installation – To assemble and install lower control arm, reverse removal procedure. When installing stabilizer bar, position rubber bushings at correct distances on stabilizer bar (see illustration). Check front wheel alignment. See *WHEEL ALIGNMENT Section.*

TIGHTENING SPECIFICATIONS

Application	Ft. Lbs. (mkg)
Upper Control Arm-to-Body	16 (2.2)
Pivot Bearing End Nuts	36 (5.0)
Front Lower Control Arm Mount-to-Body	30 (4.2)
Rear Lower Control Arm Mount-to-Body	16 (2.2)
Lower Control-to-Ball Joint Plate	30 (4.2)
Ball Joint-to-Lower Control Arm Plate	87 (12.0)
Steering Knuckle Pinch Bolts-to-Ball Joints	30 (4.2)
Drive Axle-to-Disc Brake Hub	74 (10.2)
Coil Spring/Shock Absorber-to-Upper Control Arm	65 (7.0)
Coil Spring/Shock Absorber-to-Inner Fender Panel	13 (1.9)
Shock Absorber Shaft Nut-to-Lock Nut	22 (3.0)
Stabilizer Bar-to-Lower Control Arm	16 (2.2)

AUDI FOX

Fox

DESCRIPTION

Audi Fox is front wheel drive with independent strut type front suspension. Axles are supported by lower control arms, vertically mounted strut assemblies, and a stabilizer bar. Strut assemblies consist of double action shock absorbers with coil springs mounted over the outside. The top part of strut is attached to the inner fender panel and the lower portion is attached directly to steering knuckle. Tie rods are connected to supports under coil springs. Stabilizer bar is connected to lower control arms at each end and to crossmember below engine.

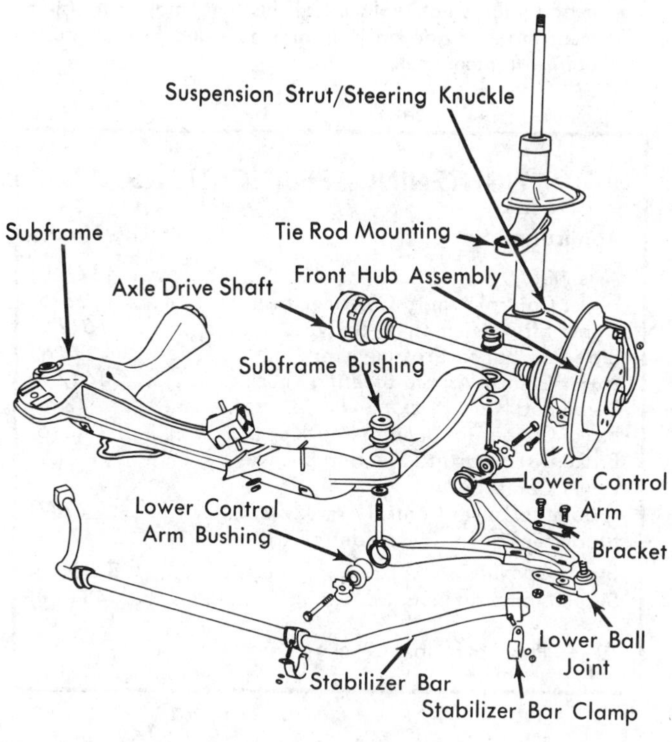

Fig. 1 Exploded View of Audi Fox Front Suspension Components

ADJUSTMENT

WHEEL ALIGNMENT SPECIFICATIONS & PROCEDURES

See Wheel Alignment Specifications & Procedures in WHEEL ALIGNMENT Section.

WHEEL BEARING ADJUSTMENT

See Wheel Bearing Adjustment in WHEEL ALIGNMENT Section.

BALL JOINT CHECKING

See Ball Joint Checking in WHEEL ALIGNMENT Section.

REMOVAL & INSTALLATION

STRUT ASSEMBLY

Removal – **1)** Remove brake caliper mounting bolts. Remove bolt mounting steering knuckle to ball joint.

2) Remove cotter pin and nut mounting tie rod end to suspension strut. Press out ball joint.

3) Loosen brake fluid line clamp. Swing caliper over to control arm and support there.

4) Scribe alignment marks on ball joint mount bracket near nuts. Remove nuts.

5) Remove 2 upper mounting nuts inside engine compartment. Pull coil spring downward.

6) Separate axle drive shaft from steering knuckle/suspension strut:

a. Remove axle shaft nut.

b. Remove socket head bolts at transaxle.

NOTE – *If work is being done on right side, exhaust pipe must be separated from manifold and bracket on transmission.*

c. Pry axle drive shaft out of transaxle and place on transaxle case.

d. Put steering in locked position. Pull drive shaft out of steering knuckle.

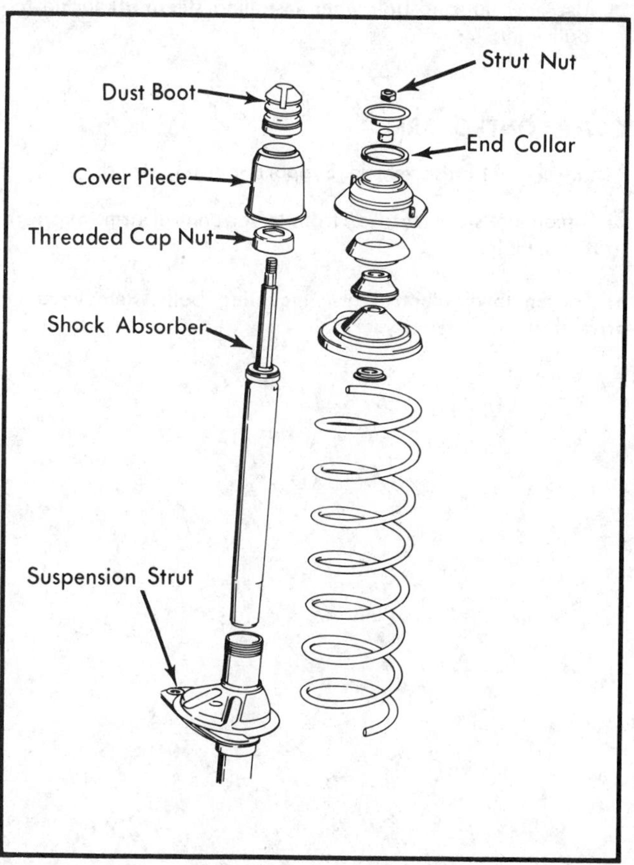

Fig. 2 Exploded View of Front Suspension Strut Assembly

AUDI FOX (Cont.)

Shock Absorber Replacement – 1) Slightly collapse and secure coil spring. Remove strut end nut (piston rod). Slowly release spring pressure. Remove coil spring assembly.

2) Clamp steering knuckle end of strut in a vise. Remove boot and cover piece. Remove threaded cap nut (turn counter-clockwise) from strut tube.

3) Refit strut nut. Place open end wrench under strut nut on shock absorber and tap on wrench to pull shock absorber out of strut tube.

4) Select new shock absorber. Guide shock absorber into strut tube. Fully seat shock absorber but do not force into place with a hammer. Tighten mounting (cap) nut.

5) Fit cover piece and dust boot. Refit coil spring assembly. With shock absorber piston rod pulled out as far as necessary and held with pliers, tighten strut nut.

NOTE – *If coil spring is replaced both sides do not have to be changed at same time.*

NOTE – *Entire subframe assembly can be removed as long as engine/transaxle assembly is suitably supported in vehicle. Audi reccommends use of tool 10-222 to retain components that remain in vehicle. Tool mounts on each inner fender panel and attaches at a point to engine.*

Installation – To install, reverse removal procedure and note:
- Use new nut and bolt when installing steering knuckle to ball joint.

LOWER CONTROL ARM

Removal – 1) Raise vehicle. Support on safety stands.

2) Disconnect stabilizer bar from lower control arm. Support strut assembly.

3) Loosen lower control arm mounting bolts. Remove axle drive shaft, if necessary.

4) Index mark ball joint-nuts and bracket. Remove ball joint mounting nuts, bolts and bracket. Separate ball joint from strut.

5) Remove mounting bolts at crossmember.

Bushing Replacement – 1) Check control arm bushings. If bushings are worn they must be replaced.

2) Fit control arm to press and force bushing out.

3) Select new bushing. Coat outer surface of bushing with brake paste. Support control arm. Force new bushing into control arm with press.

Installation – To install lower control arm, reverse removal procedure and note:
- If ball joint is not replaced at this time, make sure alignment marks made on ball joint nuts and bracket match before tightening nuts.

TIGHTENING SPECIFICATIONS

Application	Ft. Lbs. (mkg)
Axle Nut	137 (19)
Lower Control Arm-to-Crossmember	33 (5)
Upper Strut Assembly-to-Body	16 (2.2)
Stabilizer Bar-to-Crossmember	7 (.9)
Lower Control Arm-to-Steering Knuckle	16 (2.2)
Piston Rod Nut	43 (6)
Brake Caliper-to-Steering Knuckle	43 (6)
Brake Disc Guard-to-Steering Knuckle	7 (.9)
Lower Control Arm Joint-to-Lower Control Arm	47 (7)
Stabilizer Bar-to-Lower Control Arm	7 (.9)
Strut Cap Nut	①87 (12.0)
Suspension Strut Nut	43 (6.0)

① – Plus 36 ft. lbs. (5 mkg).

BMW

320i
530i
630CSi

DESCRIPTION

Strut type suspension consisting of a vertically mounted strut assembly. Strut assembly is mounted to chassis frame at top by means of thrust bearing. Lower end of strut assembly is mounted to ball joint which is bolted to lower control arm. Strut assembly connects to ball joint by means of a steering knuckle which is bolted to strut assembly and ball joint. Strut assembly consists of a shock absorber built into strut tube. A coil spring is mounted on outside of strut assembly. A stabilizer bar is mounted to front of crossmember and is connected at ends to lower control arms. A strut rod connects lower control arm to crossmember.

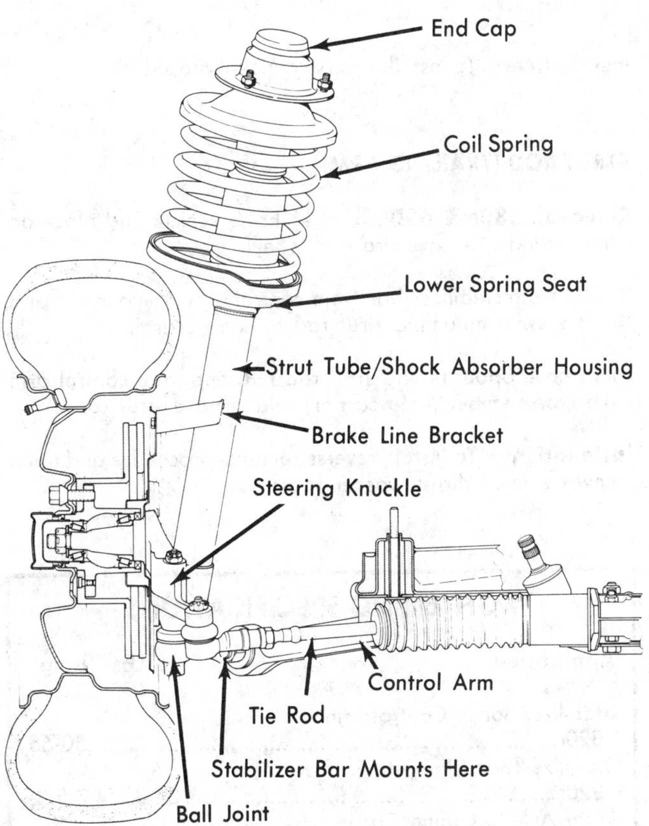

Fig. 1 BMW 320i Front Suspension Assembly

ADJUSTMENT

WHEEL ALIGNMENT SPECIFICATIONS & PROCEDURES

See Wheel Alignment Specifications and Procedures in WHEEL ALIGNMENT Section.

WHEEL BEARINGS

See Wheel Bearings in WHEEL ALIGNMENT Section.

BALL JOINT CHECKING

See Ball Joint Checking in WHEEL ALIGNMENT Section.

REMOVAL & INSTALLATION

FRONT SUSPENSION ASSEMBLY

Removal – 1) Raise and suitably support vehicle. Remove bracket mounting brake lines on strut tube. Disconnect disc brake caliper and hang out of way. On 320i models, disconnect stabilizer bar at frame.

2) Disconnect steering shaft at pinch bolt and index mark shaft. Disconnect power steering hoses, if equipped, then plug openings. Remove nuts securing left and right engine mounts. Remove clamps mounting automatic transmission cooling lines, if equipped.

3) Disconnect strut assembly at top inside fender panel. Loosen heat shield and remove, if equipped. Support engine with an overhead hoist and place a jack under suspension. Disconnect crossmember from chassis, lower and remove complete suspension assembly.

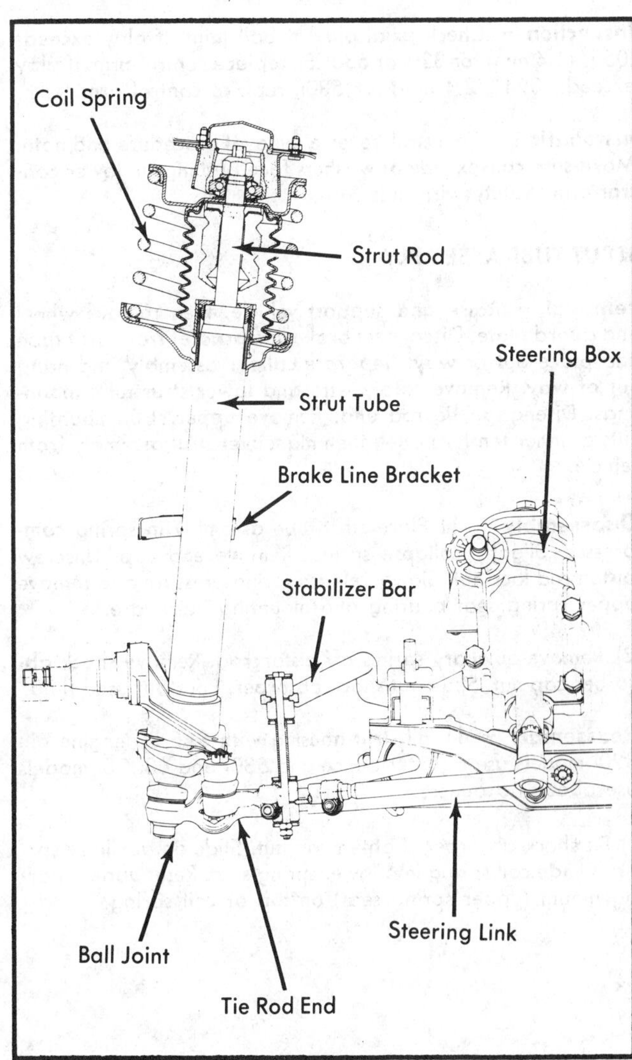

Fig. 2 BMW 530i and 630CSi Front Suspension Assembly

Installation – To install reverse removal procedure and note the following: Make sure shoulder of engine mount engages

BMW (Cont.)

properly in opening. Reconnect steering shaft while front wheels are pointing straight ahead. Ensure steering shaft index marks are aligned and that mounting screw engages safety groove. Check wheel alignment and bleed power steering unit, if equipped.

LOWER CONTROL ARM AND STEERING KNUCKLE

Removal – 1) Raise and support vehicle with safety stands. Remove tire and wheel. Disconnect stabilizer bar from lower control arm. On 530i and 630CSi models, disconnect strut rod from its mounting through the control arm.

2) On 320i models, remove castle nut mounting control arm to steering knuckle. Press off control arm.

3) On 530i and 630CSi models, take off safety wire. Remove nuts and separate control arm from shock absorber assembly. Remove cotter pin and castle nut, then press off tie rod. Remove control arm.

Inspection – Check axial play of ball joint. If play exceeds .055" (1.4 mm) for 320i or 630CSi, replace control arm. If play exceeds .094" (2.4 mm) for 530i, replace control arm.

Installation – To install, reverse removal procedure and note: Make sure convex side of washers face bushings in lower control arm. Safety wire nuts.

STRUT TUBE ASSEMBLY

Removal – Raise and support vehicle, then remove wheel and guard plate. Disconnect brake line bracket from strut tube and place out of way. Separate caliper assembly and hang out of way. Remove safety wire and lower strut tube mountings. Disengage tie rod end. Remove upper strut mounting nuts at inner fender panel, then maneuver strut assembly from vehicle.

Disassembly – 1) Place strut tube assembly in spring compressor. Slightly collapse spring. Remove end cap. Unscrew piston rod lock nut. Slowly release spring pressure and remove upper spring seat bearing and mounting hardware.

2) Remove auxiliary spring off piston rod. Remove shock absorber cap nut. Slide out shock absorber. Pour out used fluid.

Reassembly – 1) Fill strut housing with SAE 30 engine oil. 320i models use about 1 ounce and 530i and 630CSi models use about 1.5 ounces.

2) Fit shock absorber. Tighten cap nut. Slide on auxiliary spring. Guide coil spring into lower spring seat. Reset upper bearing mount (upper spring seat) on top of coil spring.

piston rod through opening. Extend piston rod as far as possible. Collapse coil spring enough to install upper mounting nut.

Installation – To install, reverse removal procedure and tighten all nuts and bolts.

STABILIZER BAR

Removal, 320i – Raise and support vehicle. Remove tire and wheel for easier access. Remove nuts mounting stabilizer bar through control arms. Disengage bushing clamps that mount stabilizer to frame near front of vehicle. Pull stabilizer bar toward front of vehicle and remove downward.

NOTE – *Before installation, inspect bushings for excessive wear and replace as necessary.*

Installation – To install, reverse removal procedure.

STRUT ROD (TRAILING ARM)

Removal, 530i & 630CSi – 1) Raise vehicle and place on safety stands. Remove tire and wheel.

2) Separate stabilizer bar from control arm. Remove nut and thrust washer mounting strut rod to control arm.

3) Remove opposite end strut rod nut. Separate control arm from crossmember (axle carrier) and remove strut rod.

Installation – To install, reverse removal procedure and note: Convex side of thrust washer faces nut.

TIGHTENING SPECIFICATIONS

Application	Ft. Lbs. (mkg)
Stabilizer Bar-to-Control Arm	
320i	50-65
Stabilizer Bar Clamp-to-Frame	
320i	34-37 (4.7-5.2)
Front Axle-to-Engine Carrier	
320i	31-35 (4.3-4.8)
530i & 630CSi	58-65 (8.1-9.0)
Shock Absorber Cap Nut	87-101 (12.0-14.0)
Tie Rod Castle Nut	25-29 (3.5-4.0)
Caliper-to-Steering Knuckle	
530i & 630CSi	58-69 (8.0-9.5)

CAPRI

Capri

DESCRIPTION

Strut type suspension with strut assemblies mounted vertically between lower control arms and upper body members. Strut assemblies are mounted to lower control arms by means of ball joints. Strut assembly consists of a coil spring mounted over strut tube with a hydraulic shock absorber built into strut tube. A wheel spindle is integral with bottom of strut tube. A stabilizer bar is mounted to front chassis members and at ends to lower control arms.

ADJUSTMENT

WHEEL ALIGNMENT SPECIFICATIONS & PROCEDURES

See *Wheel Alignment Specifications & Procedures in WHEEL ALIGNMENT* Section.

WHEEL BEARING ADJUSTMENT

See *Wheel Bearing Adjustment in WHEEL ALIGNMENT Section.*

BALL JOINT CHECKING

See *Ball Joint Checking in WHEEL ALIGNMENT Section.*

REMOVAL & INSTALLATION

STABILIZER BAR

Removal — Raise vehicle and place safety stands under chassis members. Disconnect clamps holding stabilizer bar to chassis and remove cotter pins and nuts retaining stabilizer bar to control arms. Slide stabilizer bar forward and remove from vehicle.

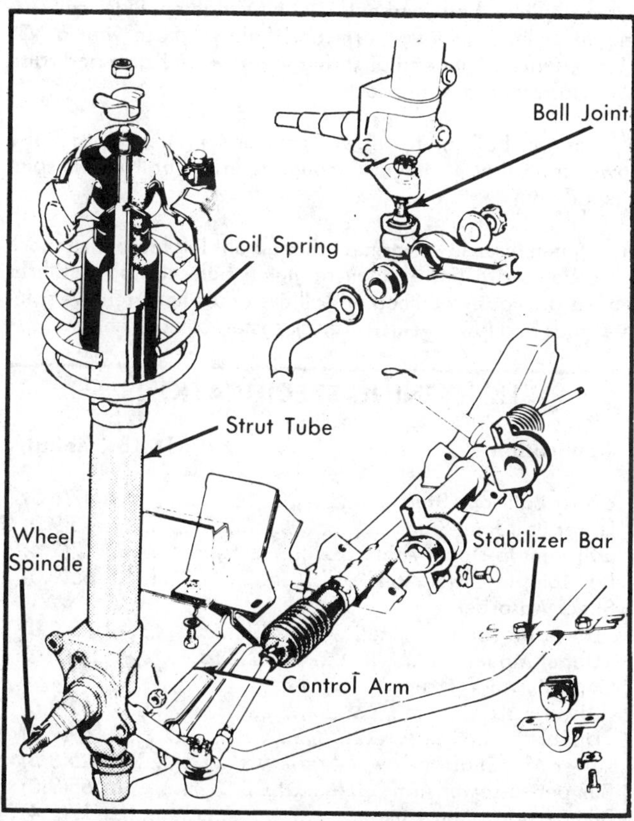

Fig. 1 Front Suspension Assembly with Detail of Lower Ball Joint

Installation — To install, reverse removal procedure noting the following: Tighten all nuts and bolts when vehicle weight is on ground.

LOWER CONTROL ARM

Removal — Raise vehicle and place safety stands under chassis members. Disconnect stabilizer bar from control arm as previously outlined. Remove self-locking nut and flat washer and slide out control arm pivot bolt. Remove cotter pin and nut from ball joint stud and separate ball joint from steering knuckle. Remove control arm from vehicle.

Installation — To install, reverse removal procedure noting the following: Tighten all nuts and bolts. Bleed brakes when all operations are completed.

STRUT ASSEMBLY

Removal — Raise vehicle and place safety stands under chassis members. Remove tire and wheel. Disconnect brake flex line from bracket on strut tube. Place a jack under control arm and raise enough to release connecting rod from steering arm when cotter pin and nut are removed. Lower jack and remove. Remove cotter pin and nut from ball joint stud and separate ball joint from strut assembly. Remove three bolts securing strut assembly top mount to fender panel and remove strut assembly from vehicle.

Disassembly — Using a suitable spring compressor (T70P-5045), compress spring enough to remove piston rod nut. **NOTE** — *Force nut collar out of keyway by using a small punch*. Remove cranked retainer. Remove top mount, then lift off spring upper seat, suspension spring, and rubber bumper. Use a suitable wrench to remove the shock cartridge.

Reassembly — Install shock cartridge into top of outer casing, then tighten to specifications using a suitable wrench. Install coil spring, rubber bumper, plug, and spring upper seat. Assemble top mount and cranked retainer, then install collared piston rod nut. Tighten nut to 5-10 ft. lbs. (.7-1.4 mkg) but do not bend collar. Remove coil spring retainers from front spring.

Installation — Reverse removal procedure for installation while noting the following: Tighten piston rod nut when unit is installed in vehicle and weight of vehicle is on front wheels, then force collar into keyway with a small punch. Bleed brakes when all operations are completed.

TIGHTENING SPECIFICATIONS

Application	Ft. Lbs. (mkg)
Piston Rod Nut	①28-32 (3.9-4.4)
Strut Assembly Upper Mount	15-18 (2.1-2.5)
Ball Joint Stud Nut	30-35 (4.2-4.9)
Connecting Rod-to-Steering Arm	18-22 (2.5-3.0)
Lower Control Arm Pivot Bolt	22-27 (3.0-3.7)
Stabilizer Bar Clamps	15-18 (2.1-2.5)
Stabilizer Bar-to-Control Arm Nut	①15-45 (2.1-6.2)
Brake Caliper Bolts	45-50 (6.2-6.9)

① — Tighten with front wheels straight ahead.

COURIER

Courier

DESCRIPTION

Independent type suspension, consisting of upper and lower control arms and wheel spindle mounted between upper and lower arms by means of ball joints. Upper control arm pivots on a shaft attached to frame, lower control arm pivots on a shaft mounted to crossmember. A coil spring is mounted between lower control arm and frame. Shock absorber is hydraulic double action type, mounted between lower control arm and frame inside coil spring.

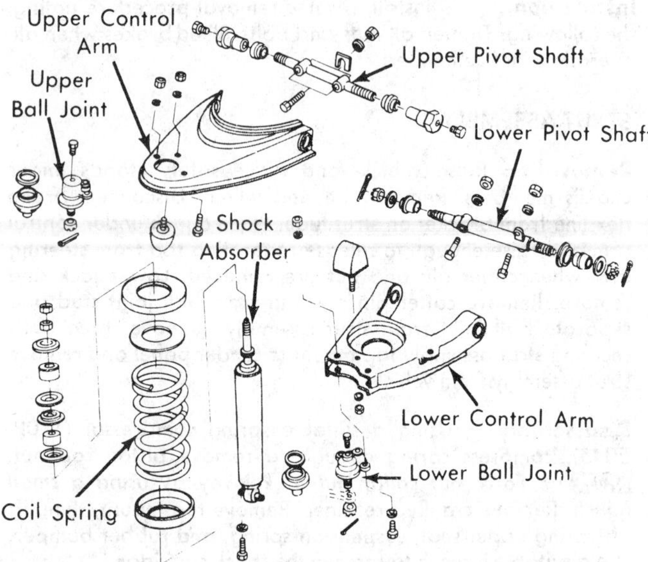

Fig. 1 Exploded View of Front Suspension Assembly

ADJUSTMENT

WHEEL ALIGNMENT SPECIFICATIONS & PROCEDURES

See Wheel Alignment Specifications & Procedures in WHEEL ALIGNMENT Section.

WHEEL BEARING ADJUSTMENT

See Wheel Bearing Adjustment in WHEEL ALIGNMENT Section.

BALL JOINT CHECKING

See Ball Joint Checking in WHEEL ALIGNMENT Section.

REMOVAL & INSTALLATION

SHOCK ABSORBERS

Removal – Remove nut, rubber bushing and washer attaching upper end of shock absorber to crossmember. Remove lower retaining bolts holding shock absorber to lower control arm, and remove shock absorber from vehicle.

Installation – Reverse removal procedure and tighten mounting bolts to specifications.

UPPER BALL JOINT & CONTROL ARM

Removal – 1) Raise and suitably support vehicle under lower control arm. Lower vehicle until arm is off rubber bumper stop. Remove tire and wheel. Remove cotter pin and nut attaching upper ball joint to spindle.

2) Strike tapered fit with a hammer to break loose and separate ball joint from spindle. Remove three retaining nuts and bolts and remove ball joint from control arm. To remove, open hood and remove two upper arm retaining bolts, then remove control arm from vehicle.

Installation – Position ball joint in upper arm and tighten bolts to specifications. Install control arm in vehicle and tighten bolts to specifications. Install spindle on ball joint, tighten nut to specification and install cotter pin. Install tire and wheel, remove safety stands and lower vehicle. Check caster, camber and toe-in.

LOWER CONTROL ARM, BALL JOINT & COIL SPRING

Removal – 1) Raise vehicle and place safety stands under frame behind both lower control arms. Remove wheel and tire. Remove lower shock absorber bolts and collapse shock absorber up into spring. Remove retaining bolt attaching stabilizer bar to lower control arm.

2) Install a floor jack under spring area of lower arm and raise arm to relieve spring pressure. Remove cotter pin and nut attaching lower control arm to spindle, strike tapered fit with hammer and separate ball joint from spindle.

3) Remove three bolts and nuts retaining ball joint to lower control arm and remove ball joint. Release jack and lower arm enough to remove coil spring. Remove three bolts and nuts retaining lower control arm to crossmember and remove arm from vehicle.

Installation – 1) Place lower control arm in position, install three retaining bolts and nuts, DO NOT tighten. Place coil spring in position in lower arm and hold in place with a "C" clamp. Place upper end of spring in pocket in frame and raise lower control arm with a jack.

2) Position ball joint in lower arm and tighten bolts. Raise lower control arm with jack enough to install ball joint in spindle, refit nut.

3) Tighten three lower arm retaining bolts left loose. Pull shock absorber down and tighten retaining bolts. Install stabilizer bar as previously outlined. Install tire and wheel, remove safety stands and lower vehicle. Check caster, camber and toe-in.

TIGHTENING SPECIFICATIONS

Application	Ft. Lbs. (mkg)
Upper Ball Joint Stud	47(6.5)
Lower Ball Joint Stud	65(9.0)
Ball Joint-to-Upper Arm	17(2.4)
Ball Joint-to-Lower Arm	65(9.0)
Shock Absorber	
Lower Mount	14.5(2.0)
Upper Mount	①
Control Arm-to-Frame	
Lower	62(8.6)
Upper	69(9.5)
Lower Arm Shaft-to-Lower Arm	61.5(8.5)
Bumper-to-Lower Arm	65(9.0)
Bumper-to-Upper Arm	17(2.4)

① – Distance from top of lock nut to top of shock absorber stud should be .256" (6.5 mm).

DATSUN F10

F10

DESCRIPTION

All models use a strut type front suspension system. Shock absorbers are built into each strut. Upper end of strut is mounted to inner fender panel. Lower end is connected by a ball joint to lower control arm. Control arm mounts at two points on subframe. Steering knuckle is removable from strut. Knuckle bolts to strut with four bolts and has a hole for axle drive shafts to pass through.

ADJUSTMENTS

WHEEL ALIGNMENT SPECIFICATIONS & PROCEDURES

See Wheel Alignment Specifications and Procedures in WHEEL ALIGNMENT Section.

WHEEL BEARING ADJUSTMENT

See Wheel Bearing Adjustment in WHEEL ALIGNMENT Section.

BALL JOINT CHECKING

See Ball Joint Checking in WHEEL ALIGNMENT Section.

REMOVAL & INSTALLATION

CONTROL ARM

Removal – Raise and support vehicle with safety stands. Remove tire and wheel. Remove bolts securing lower control arm to ball joint. Take off nut mounting stabilizer bar to control arm. Disconnect control arm from subframe by removing two mounting bolts.

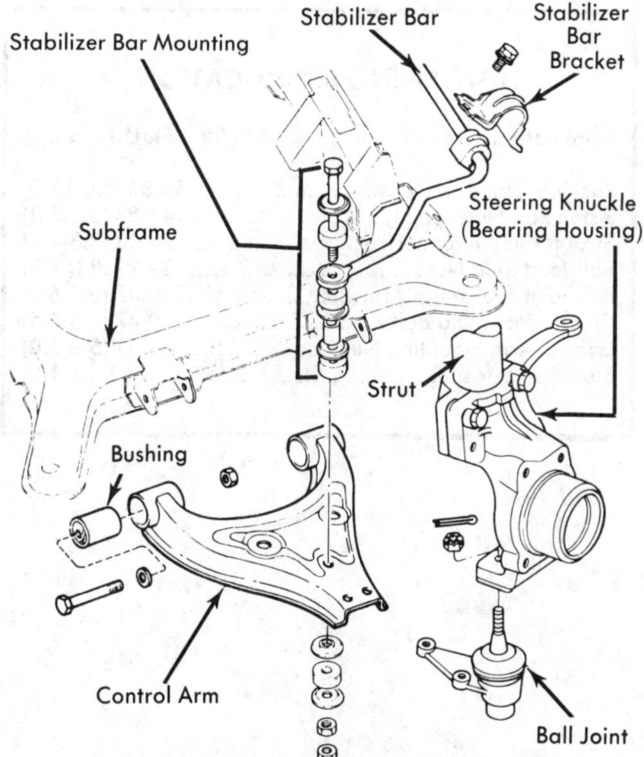

Fig. 1 Exploded View of Control Arm and Stabilizer Bar

Inspection – Inspect arm for distortion. Replace control arm bushings using a press. Make sure new bushings extend evenly on both sides of hole.

Installation – To install, reverse removal procedure and note: Control arm bolts must be tightened with weight of vehicle on ground.

STEERING KNUCKLE (INNER BEARING HOUSING)

Removal – Raise vehicle and place on safety stands. Remove tire and wheel. Remove caliper and suspend out of way. Remove stub axle. Remove rotor. Disconnect ball joint and support control arm. Remove four bolts securing steering knuckle (inner bearing housing) to strut.

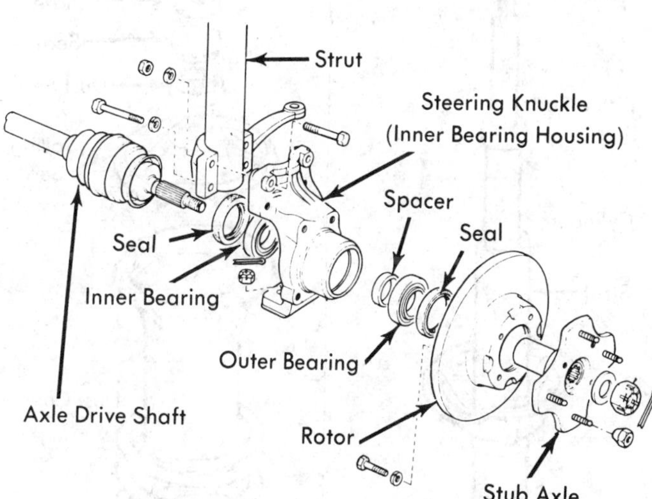

Fig. 2 Exploded View of Steering Knuckle and Strut

Installation – To install, reverse removal procedure an note: Adjust wheel bearings.

BALL JOINT

Removal – Raise vehicle and support on safety stands. Remove tire and wheel. Remove ball joint stud nut. Use ball joint driver and hammer to remove ball joint. **NOTE** – *Avoid damage to ball joint dust cover. Remove bolts securing ball joint to lower control arm.*

Installation – To install ball joint, reverse removal procedure and make sure new cotter pin is installed. Replace ball joint dust cover if cracked.

STABILIZER BAR

Removal – Raise and support vehicle with safety stands. Remove nuts mounting stabilizer bar to control arm. Disconnect and remove brackets mounting stabilizer bar to subframe.

Installation – To install, reverse removal procedure and replace any bushing that is worn or cracked.

DATSUN F10 (Cont.)

STRUT ASSEMBLY

Removal – 1) Raise vehicle and suitably support with safety stands. Remove tire and wheel. Working from inside engine compartment, remove cap. Partially loosen lock nut mounting piston rod. Disconnect brake line and plug opening. Detach tie rod from steering knuckle.

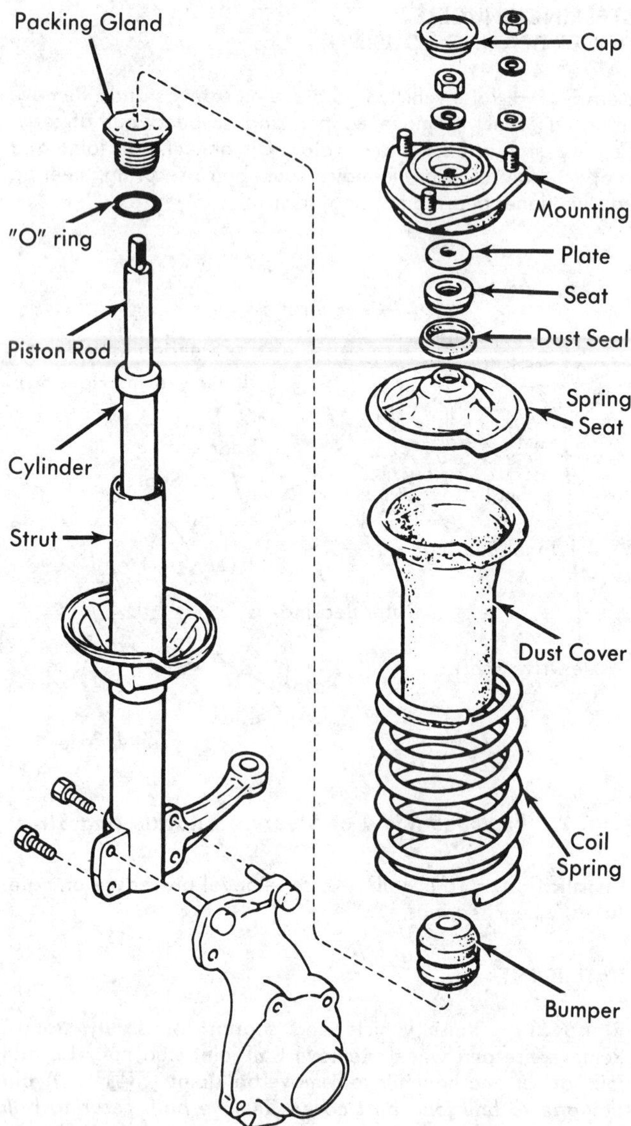

Fig. 3 ***Exploded View of F10 Strut Assembly***

2) Place safety stand under control arm for support. Remove four bolts mounting strut to steering knuckle. Remove three nuts keeping upper portion of strut to inner fender panel. Maneuver strut and coil spring assembly from vehicle.

Disassembly – 1) Place strut in a vise and slightly compress coil spring. Remove piston rod nut and take off all upper mounting hardware. See *Fig. 2*.

2) Remove packing gland. Remove "O" ring, then remove piston rod assembly and guide bushing. Drain oil from inner shock absorber cylinder, then pull out cylinder.

Inspection – Inspect all components for damage or excessive wear. Always replace packing gland and "O" ring.

Reassembly – Install cylinder and piston rod in strut. Add 7 ounces (210 cc) of shock absorber oil for AMPCO struts or 7 1/3 ounces (220 cc) of oil for K.Y.B. struts. Fit guide bushing in cylinder. Slide "O" ring over guide bushing. Install new packing gland. **NOTE** – *Lubricate sealing lip with multi-purpose grease.* Torque packing gland. Pump piston rod several times and bleed air from cylinder. Refit coil spring. **NOTE** – *Only torque piston rod nut after strut has been reinstalled.*

Installation – To install strut assembly, reverse removal procedure and note following: Make sure all contact surfaces are clean and dirt free.

TIGHTENING SPECIFICATIONS

Application	Ft. Lbs. (mkg)
Packing Gland	58-80 (8.0-11.0)
Piston Rod Nut	46-53 (6.3-7.3)
Strut-to-Steering Knuckle	24-33 (3.3-4.5)
Ball Joint Stud Nut	22-29 (3.0-4.0)
Ball Joint-to-Control Arm	40-47 (5.5-6.5)
Caliper Mounting Bolt	40-47 (5.5-6.5)
Control Arm Mounting Nut	42-51 (5.8-7.0)
Stabilizer Bar	6-9 (.8-1.2)

DATSUN B210, 200SX & 810

B210
200SX
810

DESCRIPTION

Strut type suspension consisting of a vertically mounted strut assembly, lower control arm, stabilizer bar and compression rod. Strut assembly is mounted at top to chassis frame by a thrust bearing and at bottom to lower control arm by a ball joint. Strut assembly consists of a shock absorber built into outer strut tube, a coil spring mounted on outside of strut tube, and a wheel spindle integral with bottom of strut tube. Compression rod is mounted between lower control arm and chassis. Stabilizer bar is mounted to front chassis member and is connected at end of lower control arm.

ADJUSTMENT

WHEEL ALIGNMENT SPECIFICATIONS & PROCEDURES

See Wheel Alignment Specifications & Procedures in WHEEL ALIGNMENT Section.

WHEEL BEARING ADJUSTMENT

See Wheel Bearing Adjustment in WHEEL ALIGNMENT Section.

BALL JOINT CHECKING

See Ball Joint Checking in WHEEL ALIGNMENT Section.

REMOVAL & INSTALLATION

STRUT ASSEMBLY

NOTE – *On 810 models, strut rod mounts on underside of lower control arm.*

Removal – Raise vehicle and support with safety stands; remove tire and wheel. Disconnect brake line flare nut and plug openings. Remove caliper mounting bolts and lift complete assembly from vehicle. Remove bolts connecting strut to steering knuckle arm. Using suitable pry bar, force steering knuckle arm from strut. Place a jack under strut. Working from under hood, remove nuts holding top portion of strut to body. While guiding strut assembly with hand, slowly lower jack and remove entire strut assembly from vehicle.

Disassembly – Using suitable holding tool (ST27700002) mount strut assembly in vise. Compress coil spring, using suitable tool, enough to turn mounting insulator by hand. Remove self-locking nut. Remove insulator, strut bearing, oil seal, upper spring seat, dust cover, and rubber bumper. With coil spring still compressed, remove from strut tube. Depress piston rod to bottom of stroke and remove packing gland using suitable wrench (ST35500001). Remove "O" ring from top of piston rod guide. Pull piston rod and cylinder assembly upward to remove from strut tube. **NOTE** – *Do not remove piston rod and guide from cylinder assembly, it is an assembly and must be serviced as a unit.* Drain oil from cylinder and from strut tube.

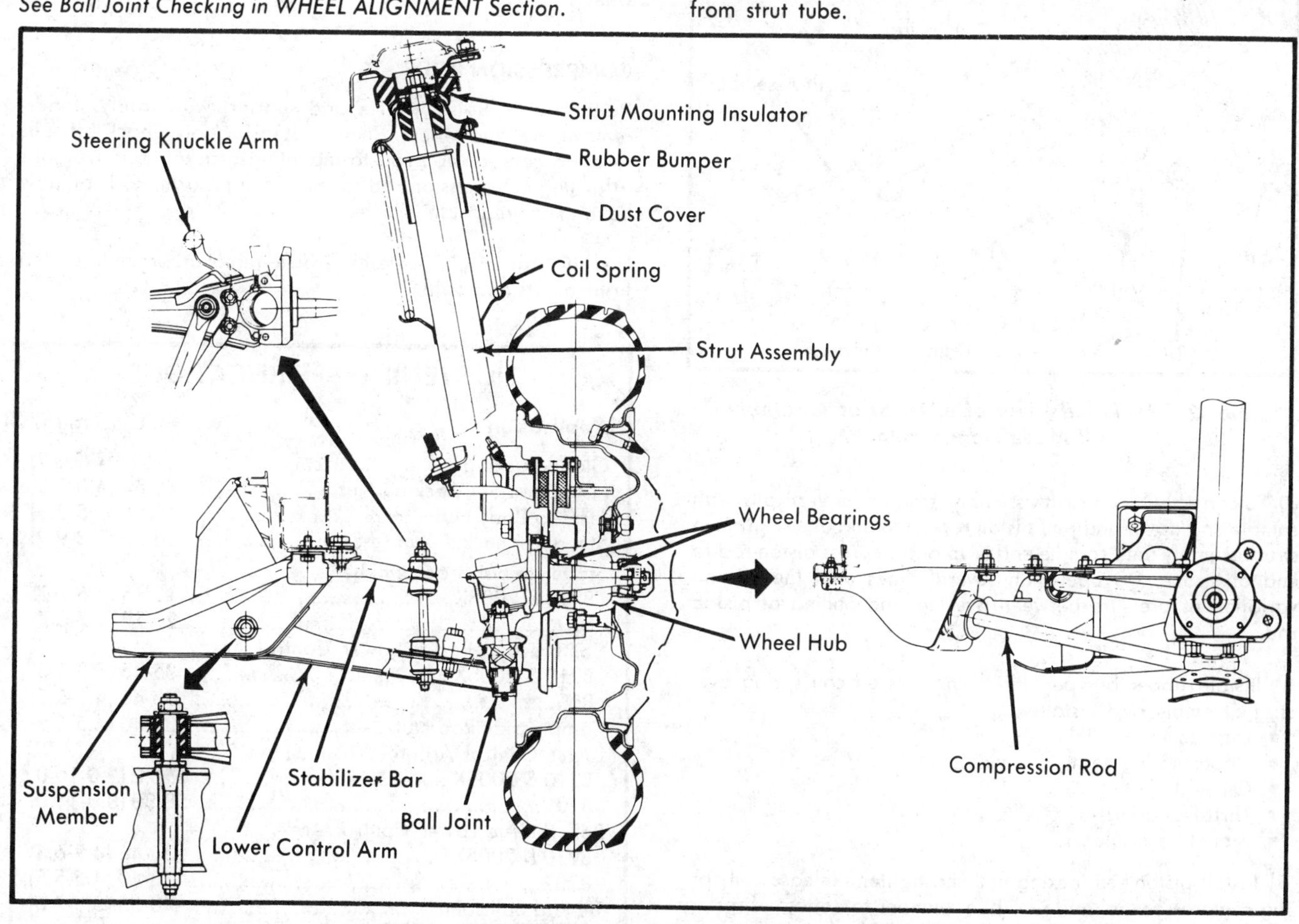

Fig. 1 Assembled View of B210 Front Suspension. Note That Some Items are Shown in Detail. 200SX and 810 Models are Similar

DATSUN B210, 200SX & 810 (Cont.)

Reassembly – 1) Inspect all components for wear or damage. Clean all parts thoroughly before reassembly. Mount strut tube in vise using suitable holding tool. Install piston rod and cylinder into place in outer casing. Pour correct amount of suitable shock absorber oil (Nissan Genuine Strut Oil) into outer casing.

Shock Absorber Oil Specifications

Application	Amount of Oil In Ounces
B210	11
200SX	
Ampco Type	10.4
Tokico Type	10.8
810	10.4

2) Install "O" ring on top of piston guide. Using suitable guide (ST35530000) install packing gland over piston rod. Tighten packing gland.

NOTE – *When tightening packing gland nut it is important that piston rod be extended approximately 4.72" (120 mm) from end of outer casing.*

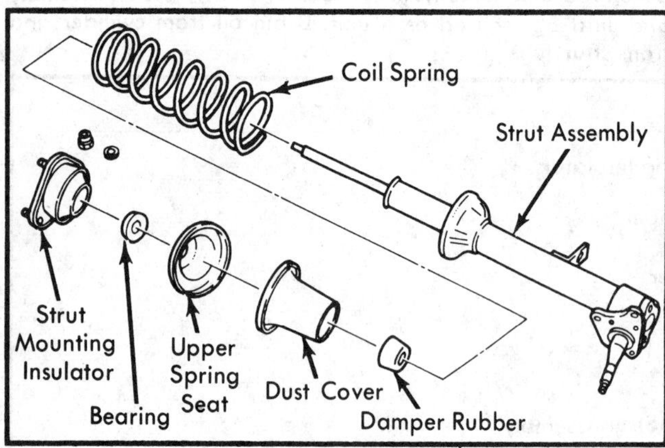

Fig. 2 Exploded View of B210 Strut Assembly All Models are Similar

3) To correctly bleed strut assembly, stand strut vertically with spindle end down and pull piston rod up to end of stroke. Turn strut assembly until spindle end is up and depress piston rod to end of stroke. Do operation several times until there is no variation of pressure between pushing and pulling of piston rod.

4) Install rubber bumper. Place compressed coil spring over strut assembly and install:

- Dust cover.
- Upper spring seat.
- Oil seal.
- Thrust bearing
- Mounting insulator.

5) Install piston self-locking nut and tighten. Release coil spring compressor tool and fit rubber bumper to bottom of spring seat.

Installation – To install, reverse removal procedure and tighten all nuts and bolts.

LOWER CONTROL ARM & BALL JOINT

Removal – Raise vehicle and support with safety stands; remove tire and wheel. Disconnect tie rod at ball socket. Remove steering knuckle arm bolts and separate arm from bottom of strut. Separate compression rod and stabilizer bar from lower control arm. Remove bolt connecting lower control arm complete with ball joint and knuckle arm. After placing lower control arm in vise loosen control arm ball joint bolts and remove ball joint. Place steering knuckle arm in vise and remove cotter pin and nut; remove knuckle from control arm. Using suitable tool (ST36720000) extract bushings from lower control arm.

NOTE – *On 810 models, steering gear arm must be separated from sector shaft and steering linkage lowered to remove lower control arm from driver's side. On passenger side, idler arm assembly must be separated from frame and linkage lowered.*

Installation – Using suitable bushing replacement tool set (ST36700000) press bushing into control arm. To install lower control arm, reverse removal procedure. Do not tighten nuts and bolts to final torque until weight of vehicle is on front wheels.

COMPRESSION RODS

Removal – Raise vehicle and support with safety stands; remove tire and wheel. Remove splash board, back off nuts securing compression rod to mounting bracket. Remove bolts attaching compression rod to lower control arm. Rod can now be maneuvered from vehicle.

Installation – To install, reverse removal procedure and tighten nuts and bolts.

TIGHTENING SPECIFICATIONS

Application	Ft. Lbs. (mkg)
Gland Packing	51-94 (7-13)
Piston Rod Self Locking Nut	43-54 (6.0-7.5)
Strut-to-Body Nuts	18-25 (2.5-3.5)
Steering Knuckle Arm-to-Strut	53-72 (7.3-9.9)
Stabilizer Bar Bracket Bolts	
B210 & 200SX	12-15 (1.6-2.1)
810	20-27 (2.7-3.7)
Compression Rod-to-Lower Control Arm	
B210 & 200SX	35-46 (4.9-6.3)
810	33-40 (4.5-5.5)
Compression Rod Nut	33-40 (4.5-5.5)
Lower Control Arm-to-Crossmember	
B210 & 200SX	65-72 (9.0-10.0)
810	58-80 (8.0-11.0)
Ball Joint-to-Lower Control Arm	
B210 & 200SX	35-46 (4.9-6.3)
810	33-40 (4.5-5.5)
Tie Rod Ball Joint	40-55 (5.5-7.6)

DATSUN 280Z

280Z

DESCRIPTION

Strut type suspension consisting of a vertically mounted strut assembly. Strut assembly is mounted to chassis frame at top by means of a thrust bearing. Lower end of strut assembly is mounted to a ball joint which is bolted to lower control arm. Strut assembly connects to ball joint by means of a steering knuckle which is bolted to strut assembly and ball joint. Strut assembly consists of a shock absorber built into strut outer tube; a coil spring is mounted on outside of strut assembly; a spindle is integral with bottom of strut. A compression rod is mounted between lower control arm and chassis. A stabilizer bar is mounted to front chassis member and is connected at ends to lower control arm.

ADJUSTMENT

WHEEL ALIGNMENT SPECIFICATIONS & PROCEDURES

See Wheel Alignment Specifications & Procedures in WHEEL ALIGNMENT Section.

WHEEL BEARING ADJUSTMENT

See Wheel Bearing Adjustment in WHEEL ALIGNMENT Section.

BALL JOINT CHECKING

See Ball Joint Checking in WHEEL ALIGNMENT Section.

REMOVAL & INSTALLATION

STRUT ASSEMBLY

Removal – Raise vehicle and support with safety stands, then remove wheel and tire. Loosen brake hose, remove spring and plate, then remove hose from strut assembly bracket. Remove caliper mounting bolts and lift complete assembly from vehicle. Remove strut-to-steering knuckle arm bolts, then force arm from strut and support strut with a jack. Working from under hood, remove nuts holding top portion of strut to body. While guiding strut assembly with hand, slowly lower jack and remove entire strut assembly from vehicle.

Disassembly – Mount strut assembly in vise using a holding tool. Remove snap ring from dust cover. Using spring compressor, compress coil spring enough to turn mounting insulator by hand. Remove self-locking nut, then remove insulator, strut bearing, oil seal, upper spring seat, and rubber bumper. Remove coil spring and compressing tool from strut

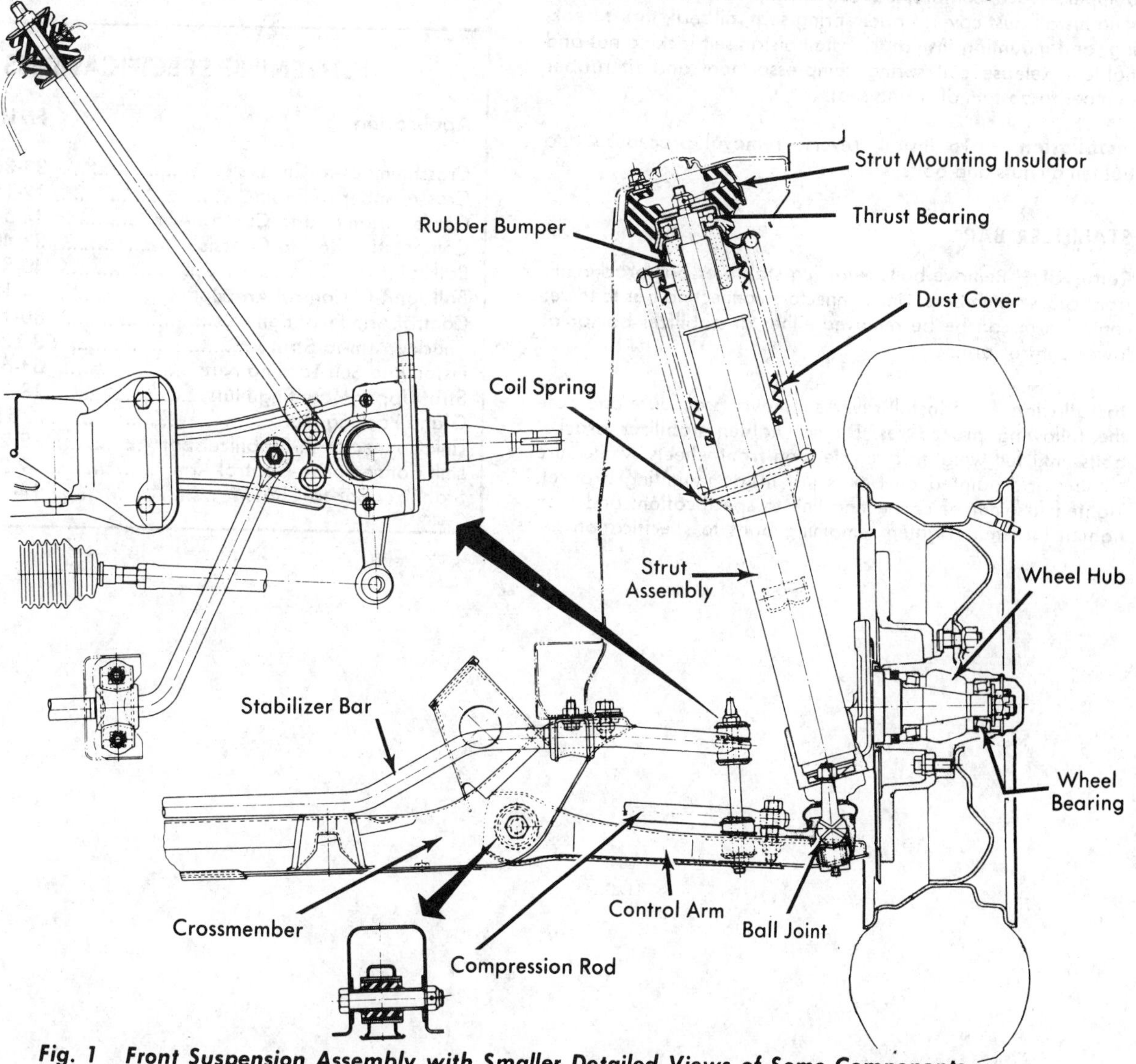

Fig. 1 Front Suspension Assembly with Smaller Detailed Views of Some Components

DATSUN 280Z (Cont.)

tube. Depress piston rod to bottom of stroke and remove packing gland using a suitable wrench (KV40100800). Remove "O" ring from top of piston rod guide. Pull piston rod and cylinder assembly upward to remove from strut tube. **NOTE** — *Do not remove piston rod and guide from cylinder assembly as they must be serviced as an assembly.* Drain oil from cylinder and from strut tube.

Reassembly — Inspect all components for wear or damage. Clean all parts thoroughly before reassembly. Mount strut tube in vise using a holding tool. Install piston rod and cylinder into place in outer casing. Fill strut assembly with 11.5 ounces of shock absorber oil (Nissan Genuine Strut Oil or equivalent). Install "O" ring on top of piston rod guide. Use a guide (ST35530000) to install packing gland over piston rod. Tighten packing gland to specification. **NOTE** — *When tightening packing gland nut it is important that piston rod be extended approximately 4.72" (120 mm) from end of outer casing to aid in bleeding assembly.* To correctly bleed strut assembly, stand strut vertical with spindle end down and pull piston rod up to end of stroke. Turn strut assembly so spindle end is up and depress piston rod to end of stroke. Repeat operation several times until there is no variation of pressure between pulling or depressing of piston rod. Install rubber bumper. Place compressed coil spring over strut assembly, then install dust cover, upper spring seat, oil seal, thrust bearing, and mounting insulator. Install piston self-locking nut and tighten. Release coil spring compressor tool and fit rubber bumper to bottom of spring seat.

Installation — To install, reverse removal procedure and tighten all nuts and bolts.

STABILIZER BAR

Removal — Remove bolts retaining stabilizer bar brackets to front chassis members. Link connectors connecting bar to lower control arm can be be removed either at stabilizer bar or at lower control arm.

Installation — To install reverse removal procedure and note the following procedures. Do not tighten stabilizer bracket bolts until full weight of vehicle is on front wheels. Make sure white stripe painted on bar is just inside mounting bracket. Tighten first nut of connecting link to specification, and then tighten lock nut. Tighten remaining bolts to specifications.

COMPRESSION ROD

Removal — Remove bolts retaining compression rod to lower control arm. Remove nut retaining compression rod to chassis member.

Installation — To install reverse removal procedure. Tighten all bolts and nuts to specification.

LOWER CONTROL ARM & BALL JOINT

Removal — Raise vehicle and remove tire and wheel. Remove stabilizer bar and compression rod as previously outlined. Remove two bolts retaining steering knuckle to strut assembly. Remove lower control arm pivot bolt and remove control arm from vehicle. Remove cotter pin from ball joint stud, remove nut and seperate steering knuckle from ball joint. Remove ball joint retaining bolts and remove ball joint from control arm. If control arm bushing is being replaced, press out using a suitable tool (ST36710000).

Installation — Inspect all components for wear or damage. Using a suitable tool (ST36710000), press a new bushing in control arm. Install ball joint in control arm and tighten bolts to specification. Reverse removal procedure for installing control arm in vehicle. Tighten all bolts and nuts to specifications.

TIGHTENING SPECIFICATIONS

Application	Ft. Lbs.(mkg)
Crossmember-to-Chassis	33-36(4.5-5.0)
Crossmember-to-Engine	12-15(1.6-2.1)
Compression Rod-to-Control Arm	44-51(6.1-7.1)
Compression Rod-to-Chassis	33-40(4.5-5.5)
Ball Joint Nut	40-54(5.5-7.5)
Ball Joint-to-Control Arm Bolts	14-18(1.9-2.5)
Control Arm Pivot Bolt	80-101(11-14)
Knuckle Arm-to-Strut	53-72(7.3-10.0)
Piston Rod Self-Locking Nut	54-69(7.5-9.5)
Strut Upper Mounting Nuts	18-25(2.5-3.5)
Gland Packing Nut	51-94(7-13)
Link Connector-to-Stabilizer Bar	9-20(1.2-2.7)
Link Connector-to-Control Arm	9-20(1.2-2.7)
Stabilizer Bar-to-Chassis	14-18(1.9-2.5)

DATSUN 710

710

DESCRIPTION

Strut type suspension consisting of a vertically mounted strut assembly. Strut assembly is mounted to chassis frame at top by means of a thrust bearing. Lower end of strut assembly is mounted to a ball joint. Strut assembly consists of a shock absorber built into strut outer tube and a coil spring mounted to outside upper portion of strut tube. The spindle is integral with bottom of strut. A stabilizer bar is mounted to front of crossmember and is connected at ends to lower control arms.

ADJUSTMENT

WHEEL ALIGNMENT SPECIFICATIONS & PROCEDURES

See Wheel Alignment Specifications & Procedures in WHEEL ALIGNMENT Section.

WHEEL BEARING ADJUSTMENT

See Wheel Bearing Adjustment in WHEEL ALIGNMENT Section.

BALL JOINT CHECKING

See Ball Joint Checking in WHEEL ALIGNMENT Section.

REMOVAL & INSTALLATION

STRUT ASSEMBLY

Removal – Raise vehicle and support with safety stands, then remove wheel and tire. Loosen flare nut attaching brake hose-to-tube on frame, then remove locking spring and plate. Separate brake hose from tube and remove hanger spring. Disconnect brake hose from brake cylinder and plug openings. Remove caliper mounting bolts and lift complete assembly from vehicle. Remove bolts connecting strut to steering knuckle arm. Using suitable pry bar, force steering knuckle arm from strut. Position a jack under strut. Working from under hood, remove nuts holding top portion of strut to body. While guiding strut assembly with hand, slowly lower jack and remove entire strut assembly from vehicle.

Disassembly – Using suitable holding tool (ST27700002) mount strut assembly in vise. Remove snap ring from dust cover. Compress coil spring, using suitable tool, enough to turn mounting insulator by hand. Remove self-locking nut. Remove insulator, strut bearing, oil seal, upper spring seat, and rubber bumper. With coil spring still compressed, remove from strut tube. Depress piston rod to bottom of stroke and remove packing gland using suitable wrench (ST35500001). Remove "O" ring from top of piston rod guide. Pull piston rod and cylinder assembly upward to remove from strut tube. **NOTE** – *Do not remove piston rod and guide from cylinder assembly, it is an assembly and must be serviced as an assembly.* Drain oil from cylinder and from strut tube.

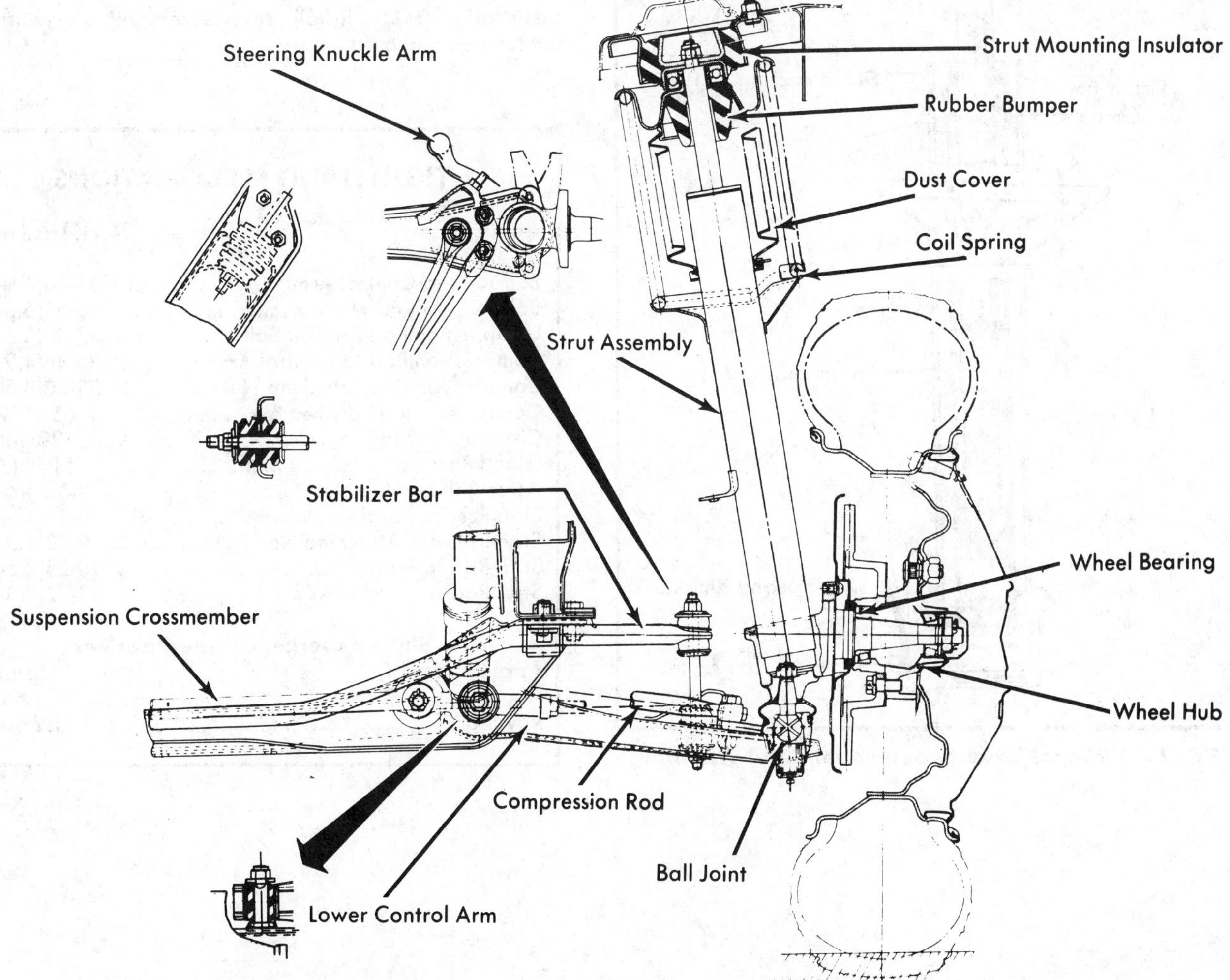

Fig. 1 Front Suspension Assembly Including Small Detailed Views

DATSUN 710 (Cont.)

Reassembly – Inspect all components for wear or damage. Clean all parts thoroughly before reassembly. Mount strut tube in vise using a suitable holding tool. Install piston rod and cylinder into place in outer casing. Fill strut assembly with specified amount of shock absorber oil (see specifications). Install "O" ring on top of piston rod guide. Using suitable guide (ST35530000) install packing gland over piston rod. Tighten packing gland to specification. **NOTE** – *When tightening packing gland nut it is important that piston rod be extended approximately 4.72" (120 mm) from end of outer casing.* To correctly bleed strut assembly, stand strut vertically with spindle end down and pull piston rod up to end of stroke. Turn strut assembly until spindle end is up and depress piston rod to end of stroke. Do this operation several times until there is no variation of pressure between pulling or depressing of piston rod. Install rubber bumper. Place the compressed coil spring over strut assembly and install dust cover, upper spring seat, oil seal, thrust bearing and mounting insulator. Install piston self-locking nut and tighten. Release coil spring compressor tool.

Installation – To install, reverse removal procedure and tighten all nuts and bolts.

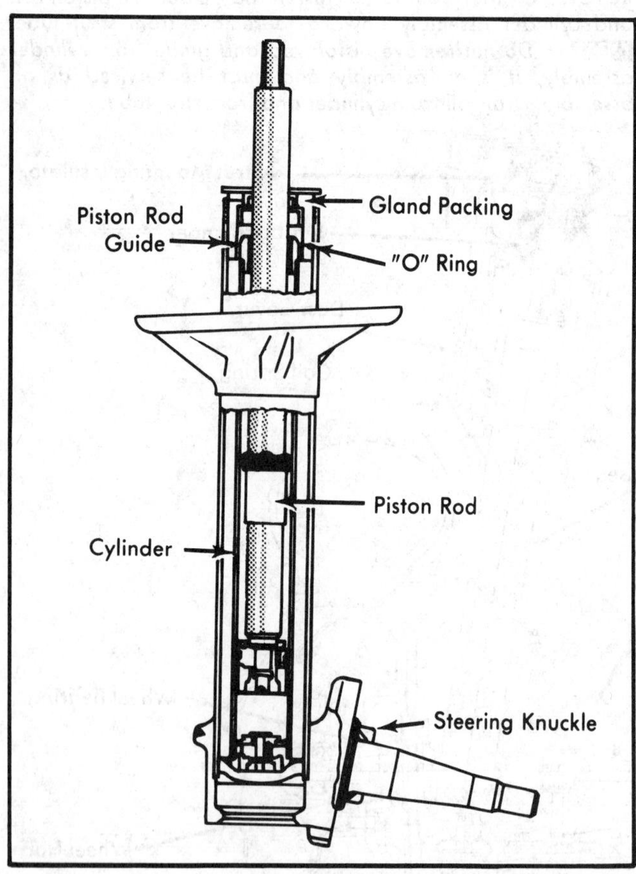

Fig. 2 Sectional View of Suspension Strut Assembly

LOWER CONTROL ARM & BALL JOINT

Removal – Raise vehicle and support with safety stands, then remove tire and wheel. Remove splash board. Disconnect tie rod at ball socket. Remove steering knuckle arm bolts and separate arm from bottom of strut. Separate compression rod and stabilizer bar from lower control arm. Remove bolt connecting lower control arm complete with ball joint and knuckle arm. After placing lower control arm in vise loosen control arm ball joint bolts and remove ball joint. Place steering knuckle arm in vise and remove cotter pin and nut; remove knuckle from control arm. Using suitable tool (ST36700000) extract bushings from lower control arm.

Installation – Using suitable bushing replacement tool set (ST36700000) press bushing into control arm. To install lower control arm, reverse removal procedure. Do not tighten nuts and bolts to final torque until weight of vehicle is on front wheels.

COMPRESSION RODS

Removal – Raise vehicle and support with safety stands, then remove tire and wheel. Remove splash board, back off nuts securing compression rod to mounting bracket. Remove bolts attaching compression rod to lower control arm. Rod can now be maneuvered from vehicle.

Installation – To install, reverse removal procedure and tighten nuts and bolts.

TIGHTENING SPECIFICATIONS

Application	Ft. Lbs.(mkg)
Ball Joint-to-Control Arm	14-18(1.9-2.5)
Ball Joint-to-Knuckle Arm	40-55(5.5-7.6)
Compression Rod Bracket Bolt	37-50(5.1-6.9)
Compression Rod-to-Control Arm	35-46(4.9-6.3)
Compression Rod Attaching Nut	33-40(4.5-5.5)
Control Arm-to-Crossmember	65-72(9-10)
Crossmember-to-Frame	29-36(4-5)
Gland Packing	51-95(7-13)
Piston Self Locking Nut	43-54(6-7.5)
Stabilizer Bar Bracket Bolt	10-13(1.4-1.8)
Stabilizer Bar Attaching Nut	9-12(1.3-1.7)
Strut Rod-to-Body	18-25(2.5-3.5)
Strut Rod-to-Knuckle Arm	53-72(7.3-9.9)

Shock Absorber Oil Specifications

Application	Quantity
Atsugi	11 ounces
Kayaba	11.2 ounces

DATSUN PICKUP

Pickup

DESCRIPTION

Independent type suspension with torsion bars. Upper and lower control arms pivot on brackets which are integral with chassis. A steering knuckle spindle support is mounted between upper and lower control arms. Wheel spindle pivots on steering knuckle spindle support. A strut bar is mounted between lower control arm and chassis. A torsion bar is mounted outboard to lower control arm by means of a torque arm and mounted inboard to chassis by means of an adjustable spring anchor. A hydraulic shock absorber is mounted between lower control arm and upper control arm mounting bracket. A stabilizer bar is optional and may be installed on some vehicles; it is mounted to front chassis members and connected at ends to lower control arms.

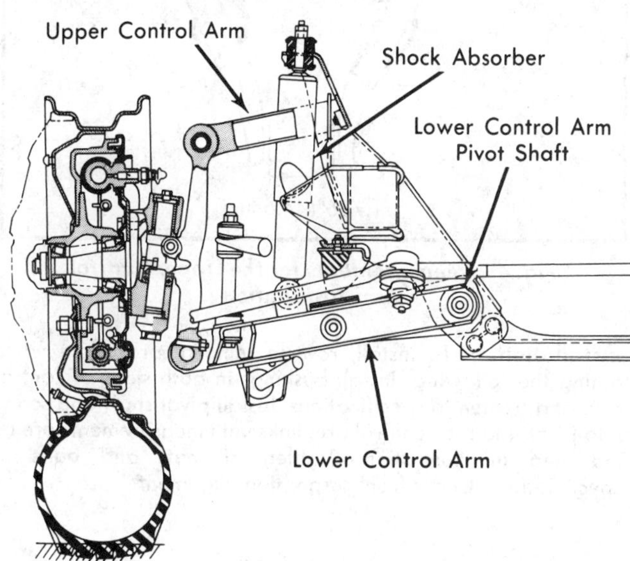

Fig. 1 Sectional View of Front Suspension Assembly

ADJUSTMENT

WHEEL ALIGNMENT SPECIFICATIONS & PROCEDURES

See Wheel Alignment Specifications & Procedures in WHEEL ALIGNMENT Section.

WHEEL BEARING ADJUSTMENT

See Wheel Bearing Adjustment in WHEEL ALIGNMENT Section.

BALL JOINT CHECKING

See Ball Joint Checking in WHEEL ALIGNMENT Section.

REMOVAL & INSTALLATION

SHOCK ABSORBER

Removal – Remove nut and slide out bolt retaining shock absorber to lower control arm. Remove upper shock absorber retaining nut and remove shock absorber from vehicle.

Installation – To install, reverse removal procedure and tighten all nuts and bolts.

STABILIZER BAR

Removal – Raise and support vehicle, then remove wheel and tire. Loosen nut at lower link side of stabilizer bar. Remove stabilizer bracket-to-frame bolt, then remove stabilizer from link bolt and remove from vehicle.

Installation – To install, reverse removal procedure and note the following: Tighten nut on link bolt enough to create a distance of 3.84" (97.6 mm) between top of lower control arm and center of stabilizer bar.

TORSION BAR

Removal – Raise and support vehicle and remove wheel and tire. Loosen nut securing spring anchor bolt. Remove dust cover at rear of torsion bar spring and remove snap ring. Remove anchor arm by pulling out rearward, then remove torsion bar.

Installation – To install, reverse removal procedure and note the following:

1) Coat serrated end of torsion bar with suitable grease and install it in torque arm. **NOTE** – *Torsion bars are marked left and right on ends of bars. If both bars are removed at one time, make sure they are installed on their correct sides.*

2) Install anchor arm and adjust to obtain dimension "A" as shown. After installing snap ring and dust cover, tighten adjusting nut until dimension "B" is obtained.

Application	Dimension "A"	Dimension "B"
7 Ft. Bed	.591-.984"	2.362-2.756"
	(15-25 mm)	(60-70 mm)

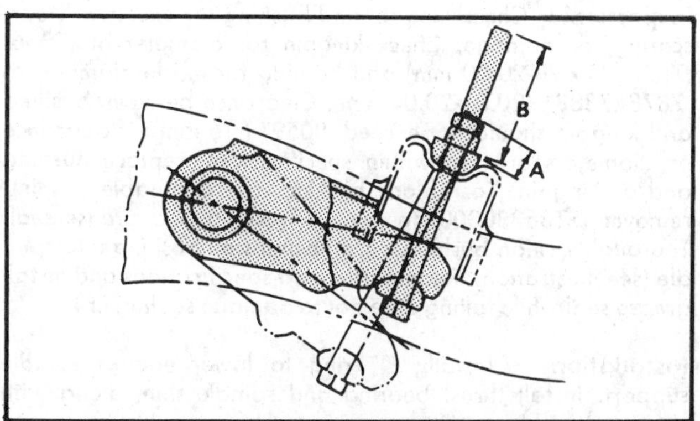

Fig. 2 View Showing Measuring Points for Installation of Anchor Pin

STRUT BAR

Removal – Raise and suuport vehicle, then remove wheel and tire. Remove retaining nuts, washers, and rubber grommets from both front and rear of strut bar. Remove mounting bracket bolts and remove strut bar from vehicle.

Installation – To install, reverse removal procedure while noting the following: Tighten nut so rubber bushings are each approximately .433" (11 mm) in width when compressed, then tighten lock nut to specifications.

DATSUN PICKUP (Cont.)

STEERING KNUCKLE SPINDLE

Removal – Raise and support vehicle, then remove wheel and tire. Disconnect brake hose from wheel cylinder and install a plug to line to prevent dirt from entering system. Remove brake drum. Remove dust cover, cotter pin, spindle nut, then remove brake hub with bearings and grease seal as an assembly. Remove backing plate and brake assembly from steering knuckle. Disconnect steering arm from spindle. Remove kingpin lock bolt. Drill a .413" (10.5 mm) diameter hole in plug at top of kingpin, thread the hole with a tap, then screw a bolt into hole and pull out plug. Drive out kingpin with a drift punch. Tap spindle using a soft faced hammer, and separate from spindle support while taking care not to drop thrust bearing.

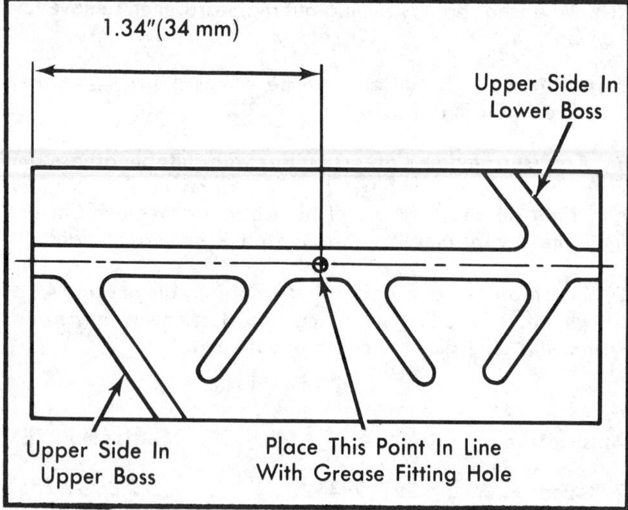

Fig. 3 View Showing Details of King Pin Bushing Installation

Inspection – Check kingpin and bushing for excessive wear, scoring, or damage. Check kingpin for diameter of .7866-.7874" (19.98-20.00 mm) and bushing for inside diameter of .7878-.7888" (20.01-20.04 mm). Clearance between bushing and kingpin should not exceed .0059" (.15 mm). If clearance or diameters are not within specifications, replace bushing and/or kingpin. To replace bushing, use a suitable bushing remover (ST35380000) to remove bushing and grease seal. Thoroughly clean bushing bore, then install bushing into spindle (see illustration). Ream bushing to specifications and install grease seal while taking care not to damage sealing lip.

Installation – Install "O" ring to lower end of spindle support. Install thrust bearing and spindle shim along with steering knuckle spindle to support. Clearance between spindle and spindle support should be .004" (.1 mm) or less, change shims as required to achieve this clearance. Thrust bearing must be installed with covered side upward. Install kingpin and lock bolt, making sure spindle moves smoothly. Install remaining components in reverse order of removal, then tighten all nuts and bolts.

UPPER CONTROL ARM & BUSHINGS

Removal – Raise and support vehicle, then remove wheel, tire, and brake drum. Disconnect brake hose from wheel cylinder and install a plug in line to prevent dirt from entering system. Remove dust cover, cotter pin, spindle nut, then remove brake hub with bearings and grease seal as an assembly. Remove steering arm from spindle, torsion bar, stabilizer bar, shock absorber, and strut bar from vehicle. Remove upper control arm-to-spindle support bolt and separate arm from support. Remove control arm spindle-to-frame attaching bolts, then remove upper control arm taking care not to lose camber adjusting shims.

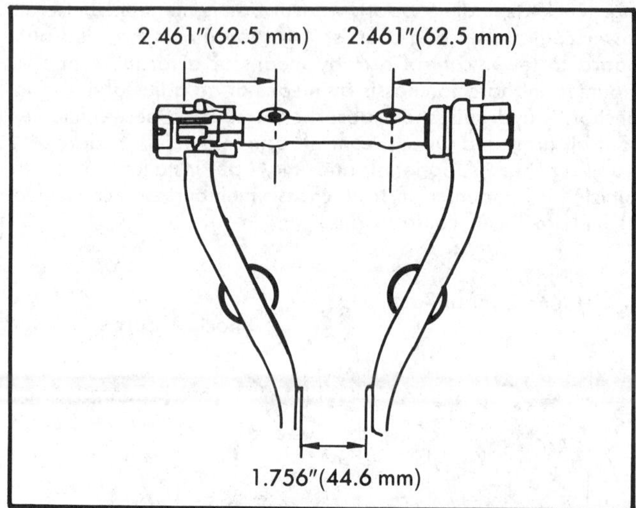

Fig. 4 Measurements for the Upper Control Arm Installation

Installation – To install, reverse removal procedure while noting the following: Install bushings in both sides of control arm and tighten to specifications. Install pivot shaft and screw into front and rear control arm links until measurements are as indicated in illustration. Tighten all nuts and bolts to specifications. Check front suspension alignment.

LOWER CONTROL ARM & BUSHINGS

Removal – 1) Raise and support vehicle, then remove wheel, tire, and brake drum. Disconnect brake hose from wheel cylinder and install a plug in line to prevent dirt from entering system.

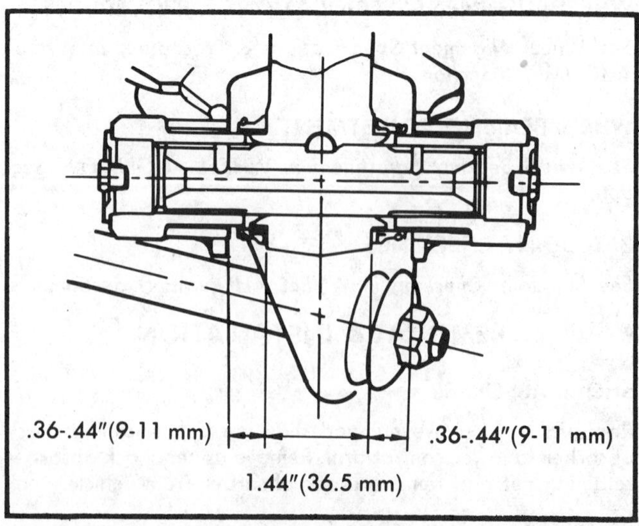

Fig. 5 Measurements for Lower Control Arm Installation

DATSUN PICKUP (Cont.)

2) Remove dust cover, cotter pin, spindle nut, then remove brake hub with bearings and grease seal as an assembly. Remove steering arm from spindle, torsion bar, stabilizer bar, shock absorber, and strut from vehicle.

3) Remove lower control arm bushings, then remove nut attaching cotter pin to spindle support. Remove cotter pin, then use a suitable drift to tap out lower control arm fulcrum pin and separate control arm from spindle support. Remove lower control arm-to-frame attaching bolt and nut, then remove control arm from vehicle.

Installation — To install, reverse removal procedure while noting the following: Install fulcrum pin while lining up notch of pin with spindle support to allow inserting of cotter pin. Install cotter pin and tighten lock nut. Coat bushing insides with grease and tighten bushings by hand temporarily. With dimensions as shown in illustration, tighten screw bushings to specifications. Tighten all nuts and bolts to specifications. Check front suspension alignment.

TIGHTENING SPECIFICATIONS

Application	Ft. Lbs. (mkg)
Anchor Bolt Lock Nut	22-30(3.1-4.1)
Backing Plate-to-Spindle	30-36(4.2-5.0)
Brake Hose Connecting Nut	14-18(1.9-2.5)
Cotter Pin Lock Nut	5.8-8.0(.8-1.1)
Kingpin Lock Bolt	15-18(2.1-2.5)
Upper Control Arm Bushing	174-253(24-35)
Lower Control Arm Pivot	54-58(7.4-8.0)
Rubber Bumper Bolt	5.8-8.0(.8-1.1)
Shock Absorber Lower Bolt	23-30(3.1-4.1)
Shock Absorber Upper Nut	12-16(1.6-2.2)
Stabilizer Bar Bracket Bolts	12-16(1.6-2.2)
Steering Arm-to-Spindle	75-88(10.3-12.1)
Steering Knuckle Upper Pivot	28-38(3.9-5.3)
Strut Rod Bracket Bolts	12-16(1.6-2.2)
Strut Rod Lock Nut	12-16(1.6-2.2)
Torque Arm (Arm End)	20-27(2.7-3.7)
Torque Arm (Serration Boss)	13-19(1.8-2.6)
Lower Control Arm Bushing	181-231(25-32)
Upper Control Arm Pivot Bolt	51-65(7-9)

FIAT X1/9

X1/9

DESCRIPTION

Independent type front suspension consisting of lower control arms and hydraulic shock absorbers, surrounded by coil springs. Steering knuckle is attached to lower control arm at sealed ball joint. Shock absorber is attached to steering knuckle at bottom and to fender panel at top. Lower control arm pivots in rubber bushings attached to crossmember. Stabilizer bar is mounted to lower control arm and at front, to frame.

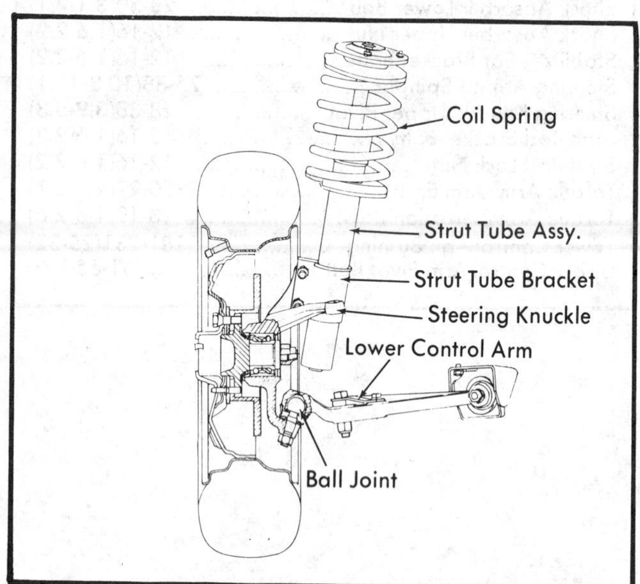

Fig. 1 Sectional View of Front Suspension Assembly

ADJUSTMENT

WHEEL ALIGNMENT SPECIFICATIONS & PROCEDURES

See Wheel Alignment Specifications and Procedures in WHEEL ALIGNMENT Section.

WHEEL BEARING ADJUSTMENT

See Wheel Bearing Adjustment in WHEEL ALIGNMENT Section.

BALL JOINT CHECKING

See Ball Joint Checking in WHEEL ALIGNMENT Section.

REMOVAL & INSTALLATION

FRONT SUSPENSION ASSEMBLY

Removal – Raise and support vehicle; remove tire and wheel. Remove front disc brake caliper assembly. **NOTE** – *See appropriate article in BRAKE Section.* Remove bolts and plate holding shock absorber tube to steering knuckle. Separate shock absorber at top by removing upper mounting nuts. Disconnect lower control arm from stabilizer bar bracket and ball joint. Remove tie rod nut and force tie rod from steering knuckle. Maneuver assembly from vehicle.

Inspection – Check rubber bushings in control arm and replace any that appear worn. Inspect ball joints for excessive play or damage; replace as necessary.

Installation – To install suspension assembly, reverse removal procedure ensuring all nuts and bolts are properly torqued.

STRUT ASSEMBLY

Removal – Raise and support vehicle under chassis. Disconnect upper strut assembly mount from inner fender panel. Remove bolts securing strut assembly to steering knuckle and carefully maneuver strut from vehicle.

Disassembly – **1)** Install strut assembly in suitable spring compressor and collapse coil. Remove nut from center of upper mount. Release spring compressor and remove upper mount and coil spring.

2) Inspect springs for cracks or distortion. Springs are manufactured in two classes and identified by paint markings. Class A springs are marked with a yellow stripe on outside of center coils and class B springs are marked with a green stripe. If springs are replaced for any reason, use a spring of same class.

Reassembly – Using same spring compressor as previously outlined, reverse disassembly procedure to assemble strut assembly.

Installation – To install strut assembly, reverse removal procedure. Do not tighten strut assembly lower mount until weight of vehicle is on ground.

CONTROL ARM, BUSHINGS & BALL JOINTS

Removal – Remove complete front suspension assembly as previously outlined. Remove ball joint stud nut and separate ball joint from steering knuckle with a suitable puller.

Disassembly – Inspect ball joint for wear or distortion. If ball joint is defective, complete control arm must be replaced. Inspect bearings for wear or damage. If defective, drill out metal sleeve from inside rubber bushing and extract bushing.

Reassembly – Position outer washer, bushing and sleeve on centering pin of a suitable bushing installation tool. Place control arm over bushing and washer for opposite side. Place control arm, components and tool into a press. Position remaining tool components in sleeve and press into position with a pressure of approximately 2200-2645 pounds.

Installation – To install control arm, attach to steering knuckle, tighten ball joint stud nut and install suspension assembly as previously outlined.

FIAT X1/9 (Cont.)

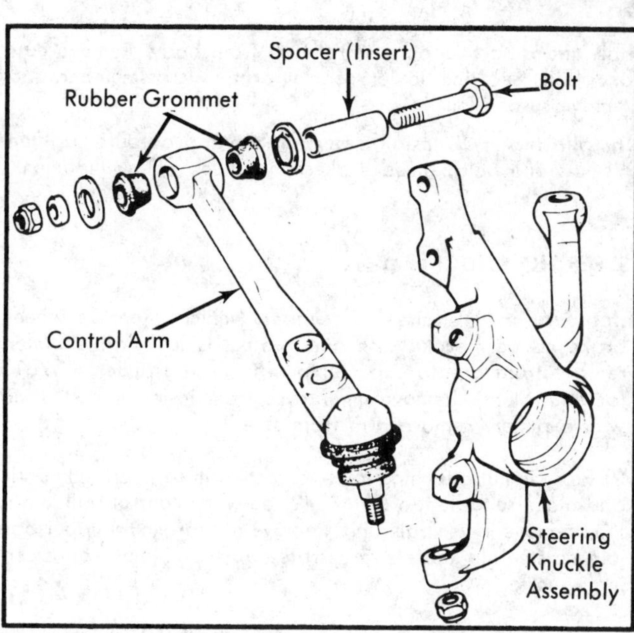

Fig. 2 Exploded View of Lower Control Arm Assembly

STABILIZER BAR

Removal – Raise and support vehicle. Disconnect stabilizer mounting bolt from lower control arm. Remove stabilizer attaching hardware from front end of stabilizer and carefully maneuver bar from vehicle.

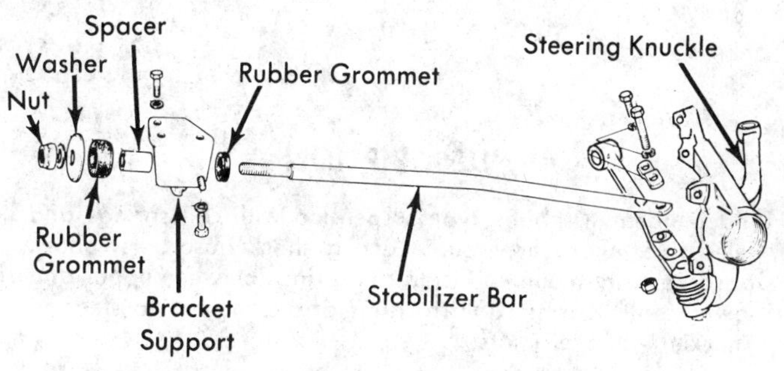

Fig. 3 Exploded View of Stabilizer Bar Assembly

Installation – To install stabilizer bar, reverse removal procedure noting the following: Replace any rubber grommet that appears distorted or severely worn.

TIGHTENING SPECIFICATIONS

Application	Ft. Lbs. (mkg)
Tie Rod Nut	58 (8.0)
Stabilizer Bar-to-Lower Control Arm	51 (7.0)
Lower Control Arm-to-Crossmember	29 (4.0)

FIAT 124

124 Spider

DESCRIPTION

Independent wishbone type suspension with coil springs and telescopic, hydraulic, double acting shock absorbers. Shock absorbers are mounted inside coil springs between upper and lower control arms. Control arms are connected to steering knuckle with ball joints.

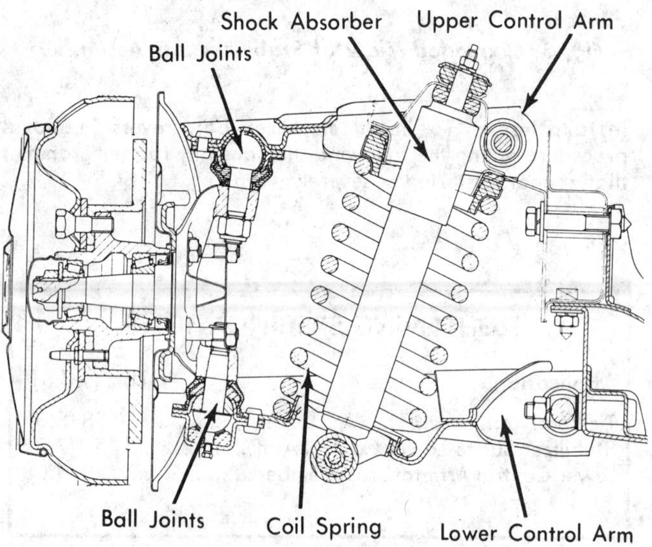

Fig. 1 Sectional View of Front Suspension Assembly

ADJUSTMENT

WHEEL ALIGNMENT SPECIFICATIONS & PROCEDURES

See Wheel Alignment Specifications and Procedures in WHEEL ALIGNMENT Section.

WHEEL BEARING ADJUSTMENT

See Wheel Bearing Adjustment in WHEEL ALIGNMENT Section.

BALL JOINT CHECKING

See Ball Joint Checking in WHEEL ALIGNMENT Section.

REMOVAL & INSTALLATION

FRONT SUSPENSION ASSEMBLY

Removal – Raise and support vehicle. Place cross-support over engine compartment and attach to engine. Remove wheels and shock absorbers. Using suitable tool (A. 74174) compress spring to relieve lower control arm. Disconnect stabilizer bar from lower control arm. Block brake lines and disconnect from brake cylinder. Disconnect tie rod from steering knuckle arm using suitable puller (A. 47044). Remove pivot bolt and detach upper control arm from body. Remove nuts and bolts securing lower control arm to crossmember and remove suspension.

Installation – To install, reverse removal procedure. Tighten all nuts and bolts, bleed brakes and check wheel alignment.

STEERING KNUCKLE

Removal – **1)** Raise and support vehicle. Remove wheel, brake caliper, brake disc and plate. Using suitable puller, remove front grease cap. Remove hub using puller A.47015 (or equivalent). Remove inner race from inside hub bearing with a puller. Remove arm from steering knuckle.

2) Remove nut attaching lower control arm to steering knuckle and place suitable tool (A.47042) between control ball joints, then remove lower ball joint. Remove nut attaching upper ball joint to steering knuckle. Separate upper ball joint from steering knuckle.

Installation – Inspect all parts for signs of wear or damage. To install, reverse removal procedure and tighten all nuts and bolts.

COIL SPRINGS

Removal – Raise and support vehicle so that suspension hangs freely. Remove wheels and shock absorbers. Disconnect stabilizer bar from lower control arm. Support lower control arm with a jack and disconnect lower ball joint stud from steering knuckle. Install suitable spring compressor tool and rotate lower control arm down carefully. Coil spring may now be removed.

Installation – To install reverse removal procedure.

STABILIZER BAR

Removal – Remove front stabilizer bar by removing nuts and bolts securing bar to crossmember. Remove nuts and bolts attaching ends of stabilizer bar to lower control arms and remove stabilizer bar.

Installation – To install, reverse removal procedure.

TIGHTENING SPECIFICATIONS

Application	Ft. Lbs. (mkg)
Lower Control Arm Pin-to-Crossmember	43 (6.0)
Lower Control Arm-to-Crossmember	72 (10.0)
Upper Control Arm	65 (9.0)
Lower Shock Absorber	43 (6.0)
Steering Arm-to-Steering Knuckle	43 (6.0)
Brake Caliper	36 (5.0)
Crossmember-to-Side Member	69 (10.0)

FIAT 128

128
Sedan
Station Wagon
3P

DESCRIPTION

Fiat 128 is front wheel drive utilizing independent, strut type front suspension. Strut assemblies consist of double action hydraulic shock absorbers with coil springs mounted over outside. Strut assemblies are mounted to inner fender panel at top and to steering knuckle at bottom. Steering knuckles are also bearing carriers for drive axles. Steering knuckles are supported by control arms connected to steering knuckle at outside and to chassis at inside. A stabilizer bar is mounted to chassis and connected at ends to lower control arms.

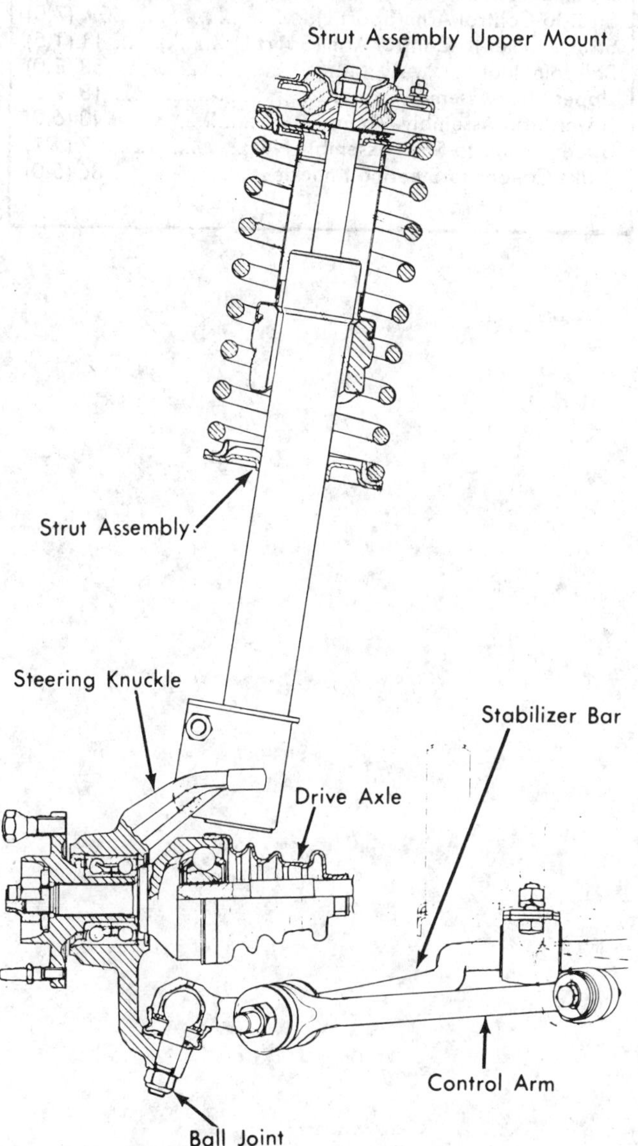

Fig. 1 Sectional View of Front Suspension Assembly

ADJUSTMENTS

WHEEL ALIGNMENT SPECIFICATIONS & PROCEDURES

See Wheel Alignment Specifications and Procedures in WHEEL ALIGNMENT Section.

WHEEL BEARING ADJUSTMENT

See Wheel Bearing Adjustment in WHEEL ALIGNMENT Section.

BALL JOINT CHECKING

See Ball Joint Checking in WHEEL ALIGNMENT Section.

REMOVAL & INSTALLATION

COMPLETE SUSPENSION ASSEMBLY

NOTE — *This procedure is for complete suspension assembly for one side.*

Removal — 1) Raise front of vehicle, position on safety stands and remove front wheels. Remove disc brake caliper from mount without disconnecting brake line and secure to body to prevent damaging brake line. Remove nut from tie rod end stud and separate tie rod end from steering arm with a suitable puller (A. 47035). Remove nut from stabilizer bar end at control arm. **NOTE** — *When removing nut from stabilizer bar end, note number of shims between end of bar and control arm for reassembly.*

2) Remove control arm pivot bolt from chassis mount. Remove nuts securing strut assembly upper mount to inner fender panel. Remove axle nut from hub. Pull out on suspension assembly, separating axle from hub and remove suspension assembly. Secure axle to prevent pulling out of differential.

Installation — To install suspension assembly, reverse removal procedure. Make sure axle nut is tightened to specification before lowering vehicle. Tighten all remaining bolts to specifications with weight of vehicle on all four tires. Make sure correct amount of shims are installed on stabilizer to control arm mount.

STRUT ASSEMBLY

Removal — Raise vehicle, position safety stands under chassis and remove wheel. Disconnect upper strut assembly mount from inner fender panel. Remove bolts securing strut assembly to steering knuckle, pull down on steering knuckle and remove strut assembly.

Disassembly — 1) Install strut assembly in a suitable spring compressor (A. 74241) and compress coil spring. With spring compressed, remove nut from center of upper mount. Release spring compressor and remove upper mount and coil spring.

2) Inspect springs for cracks or distortion. Springs are manufactured in two classes of strengths. Springs are identified as to class by a paint mark on spring. Class A springs are marked with a yellow stripe on outside of center coils and class B springs are marked with a green stripe. If springs are replaced for any reason, replace with a spring of same class.

Reassembly — Using same spring compressor as previously outlined, reverse disassembly procedure to assemble strut assembly.

Installation — To install strut assembly, reverse removal procedure. Do not tighten strut assembly lower mount to specification until weight of vehicle is on front wheels.

CONTROL ARM, BUSHINGS & BALL JOINTS

Removal — Remove complete front suspension assembly as previously outlined. Remove ball joint stud nut and separate ball joint from steering knuckle with a suitable puller (A. 47038).

FIAT 128 (Cont.)

Disassembly – Inspect ball joint for wear or excessive play. If ball joint is defective, complete control arm must be replaced. Inspect bushings for wear or damage. If defective, drill out metal sleeve from inside rubber bushings and remove bushings.

Reassembly – Position outer washer, bushing and sleeve on centering pin of a suitable bushing installation tool (A. 74221). Place control arm over bushing and install bushing and washer for opposite side. Place control arm, components and tool in a press. Position remaining tool components in sleeve and press mandrel of tool into sleeve with a pressure of at least 2200 to 2645 pounds. Sleeve will bellow out over washers, securing rubber bushings in control arm.

Installation – To install control arm, attach to steering knuckle, tighten ball joint stud nut and install suspension assembly as previously outlined.

TIGHTENING SPECIFICATIONS

Application	Ft. Lbs. (mkg)
Front Axle-to-Hub Nut	
Sedan	101 (14.0)
Sport L	112 (16.0)
Control Arm-to-Pivot Bolt	
Sedan	18 (2.5)
Sport L	32.5 (4.5)
Stabilizer Bar-to-Control Arm (Sedan)	43 (6.0)
Stabilizer Bar-to-Chassis (Sedan)	22 (3.0)
Strut-to-Control Arm (Sport L)	50.6 (7.0)
Strut Bracket-to-Control Arm (Sport L)	11 (1.5)
Ball Joint Nut	58 (8.0)
Upper Strut Assembly Mount	18 (2.5)
Lower Strut Assembly Mount	43 (6.0)
Upper Mount-to-Strut Assembly Nut	7 (.97)
Brake Caliper-to-Steering Knuckle	36 (5.0)

FIAT 131

131

DESCRIPTION

Strut type front suspension consisting of a vertically mounted strut assembly. Strut assembly is mounted to body at the top by means of a thrust bearing and lower end of strut is connected to steering knuckle. Strut assembly consists of hydraulic shock absorber with a coil spring mounted over outside. Lower control arm is connected to steering knuckle through ball joint and to front crossmember. A stabilizer bar is mounted to lower control arm and to frame.

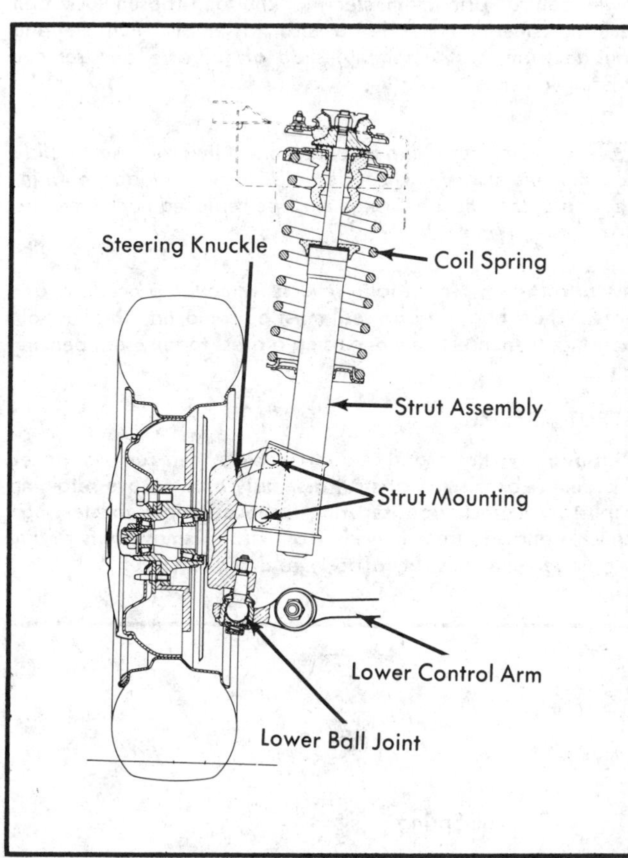

Fig. 1 Fiat 131 Front Suspension Assembly

ADJUSTMENTS

WHEEL ALIGNMENT SPECIFICATIONS & PROCEDURES

See Wheel Alignment Specifications and Procedures in WHEEL ALIGNMENT Section.

WHEEL BEARING ADJUSTMENT

See Wheel Bearing Adjustment in WHEEL ALIGNMENT Section.

BALL JOINT CHECKING

See Ball Joint Checking in WHEEL ALIGNMENT Section.

REMOVAL & INSTALLATION

FRONT SUSPENSION ASSEMBLY

Removal – Raise vehicle, support with safety stands, and remove wheel and tire. Disconnect brake hose from tube at clip mounted in fender well. Disconnect tie rod from steering knuckle. Disconnect stabilizer bar from lower control arm. Remove control arm-to-crossmember attaching bolt and separate control arm from crossmember. Position a jack under suspension assembly, then remove nuts and washers attaching top of strut assembly to body. Carefully lower suspension assembly from vehicle. Individual components may be removed from suspension assembly as follows: Disconnect control arm by removing ball joint stud nut and separating ball joint and lower control arm from steering knuckle. Remove shock absorber assembly by removing nuts and bolts attaching assembly to steering knuckle. Remove coil spring by using a coil spring compressor to compress the spring and removing spring retainer attaching nut.

Installation – Install suspension assembly in vehicle and secure strut assembly to body. Install control arm to stabilizer bar, and then to crossmember. Install attaching nuts and bolts loosely. Install tie rod to steering knuckle, and connect brake hose to tube. Install wheel and tire. Lower vehicle and tighten nuts and bolts to specifications with weight of vehicle on ground. Check wheel alignment.

CROSSMEMBER

Removal – Remove (4) bolts mounting steering box to crossmember. Remove engine mount bolts and suitably support engine. Disconnect lower control arms from crossmember. Remove (4) crossmember to frame bolts and remove crossmember.

Installation – To install, reverse removal procedure.

STRUT ASSEMBLY

Removal – 1) Remove (3) nuts mounting strut assembly to inner fender panel. Raise vehicle and place on safety stands. Remove wheel. Remove nuts and bolts mounting strut to steering knuckle. Remove strut complete with coil spring.

2) To remove coil spring from strut, proceed as follows: Use a spring compressor (A74277) and collapse coil until tension is relieved. Remove retainer mounting nut from top end of strut. Release spring compressor and remove coil.

Installation – To install, reverse removal procedure.

TIGHTENING SPECIFICATIONS

Application	Ft. Lbs.(mkg)
Ball Joint-to-Steering Knuckle	58(8)
Control Arm-to-Crossmember	65(9)
Strut Assembly-to-Knuckle	36(5)
Strut Assembly-to-Upper Mount	43(6)
Strut Upper Mount-to-Body	18(2.5)
Stabilizer Bar-to-Crossmember	65(9)
Stabilizer Bar-to-Control Arm	43(6)

HONDA

Civic
Civic CVCC
Accord

DESCRIPTION

Strut type front suspension consisting of a vertically mounted strut assembly. Strut assembly is mounted to body at the top by means of a thrust bearing. Lower end of strut is connected to steering knuckle which is mounted to lower control arm by means of a ball joint. Strut assembly consists of a shock absorber built into strut outer tube and a coil spring mounted to outside upper portion of strut tube. A two-piece stabilizer bar (with spring coil) is attached to crossmember and connected at ends to lower control arms. Control Spring mounts with brackets to stabilizer bars and crossmenber.

ADJUSTMENT

WHEEL ALIGNMENT SPECIFICATIONS & PROCEDURES

See Wheel Alignment Specifications & Procedures in WHEEL ALIGNMENT Section.

WHEEL BEARING ADJUSTMENT

See Wheel Bearing Adjustment in WHEEL ALIGNMENT Section.

BALL JOINT CHECKING

See Ball Joint Checking in WHEEL ALIGNMENT Section.

REMOVAL & INSTALLATION

STEERING KNUCKLE

Removal – 1) Raise and support vehicle and remove wheel. Remove spindle nut and brake caliper. Install hub puller with slide hammer and remove hub with brake disc attached, from steering knuckle.

2) Disconnect tie rod from steering knuckle using ball joint remover tool. **CAUTION** – *Care should be taken not to damage ball joint seals.* Use ball joint remover tool to detach lower control arm from steering knuckle. Loosen lock bolt securing steering knuckle to strut assembly. Pull steering knuckle from strut assembly, slide off of axle and remove steering knuckle.

NOTE – *Since removing hub assembly involves use of slide hammer and subjects wheel bearings to severe loads, both inner and outer wheel bearings must be replaced each time hub assembly is removed.*

Installation – To install, reverse removal procedure and note. Wheel bearing and seal must be replaced. Press out old bearing, then insert new one using a press to fully seat bearing and seal.

STRUT ASSEMBLY

Removal – Raise and support vehicle then remove wheel. Disconnect brake line at strut assembly and remove retaining clip. Loosen lock bolt securing strut assembly to steering knuckle and separate knuckle from strut. Remove nuts retaining upper end of strut to body and remove strut.

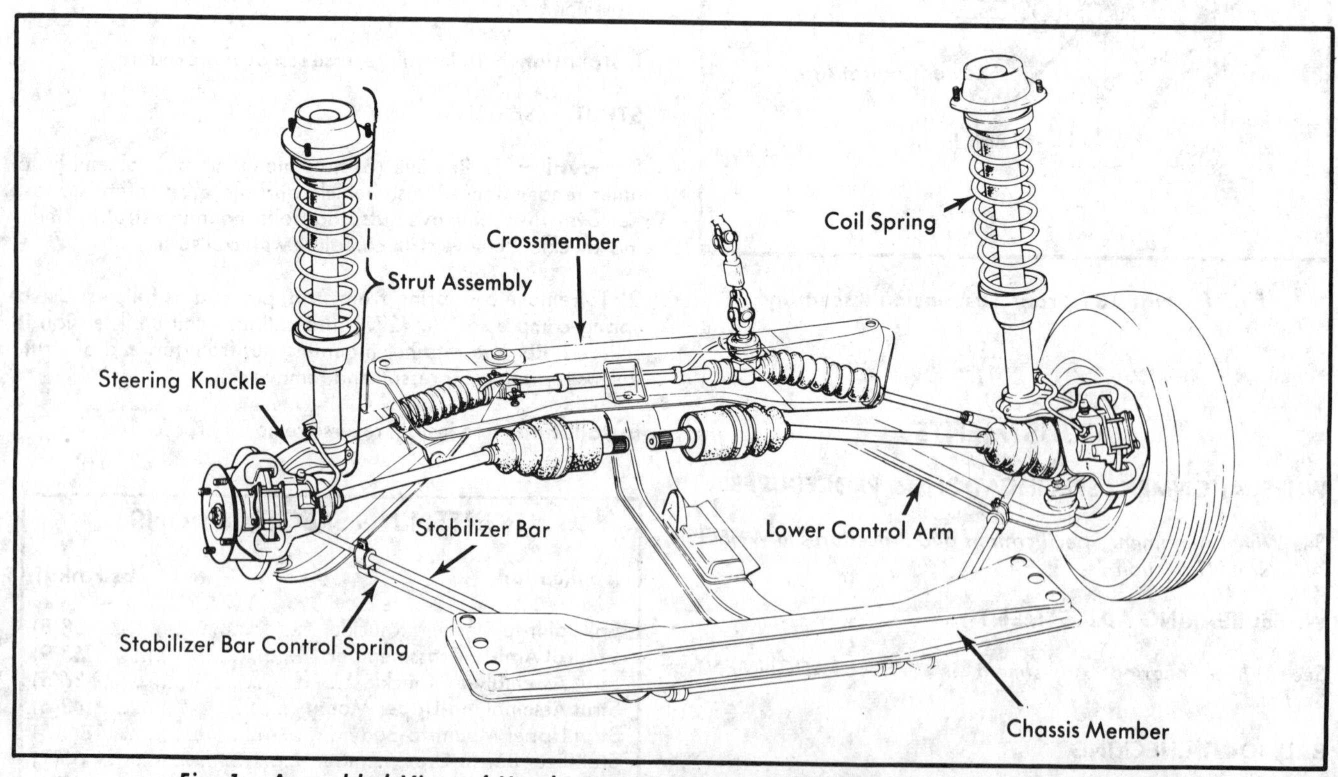

Fig. 1 Assembled View of Honda Front Suspension Showing Component Relationships Honda Civic Shown

HONDA (Cont.)

Disassembly – Assemble strut assembly to special spring compressor tool, and compress shock absorber approximately 2" (51 mm). Remove rubber cover and loosen self-locking nut on end of piston rod. Remove tool and upper mount, thrust bearing assembly and coil spring.

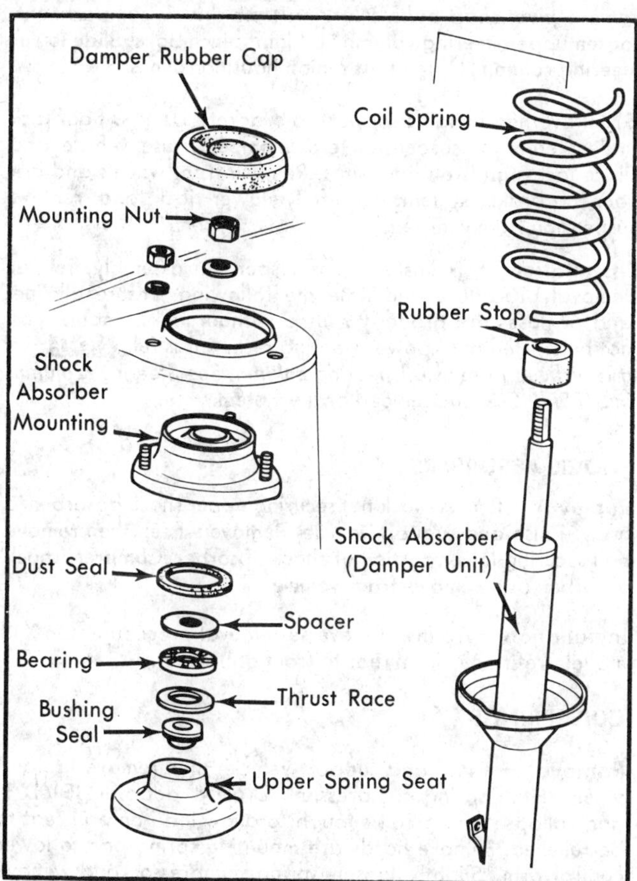

Fig. 2 Exploded View of Accord Strut Assembly. All Struts are Similar. Major Difference in Struts is Hardware Between Upper & Lower Spring Seats.

Reassembly – Reverse disassembly procedure using *Fig. 2* as a guide. Also, make sure shock absorber components do not show any signs of leaking.

Installation – Reverse removal procedure and note: Make sure slot in steering knuckle is engaged in tab on shock (strut) housing before seating it into steering knuckle.

LOWER CONTROL ARM

Removal – Raise and support vehicle. Remove wheel. Disconnect lower ball joint from steering knuckle using ball joint remover tool. Disconnect stabilizer retaining brackets and remove stabilizer bar. Remove lower control arm pivot bolt and disconnect radius rod (if equipped). Remove control arm.

Installation – To install, reverse removal procedure and note: On Accord models only, make sure bolt mounting lower control arm to crossmember is tightened with weight of vehicle on jack. This simulates normal riding height.

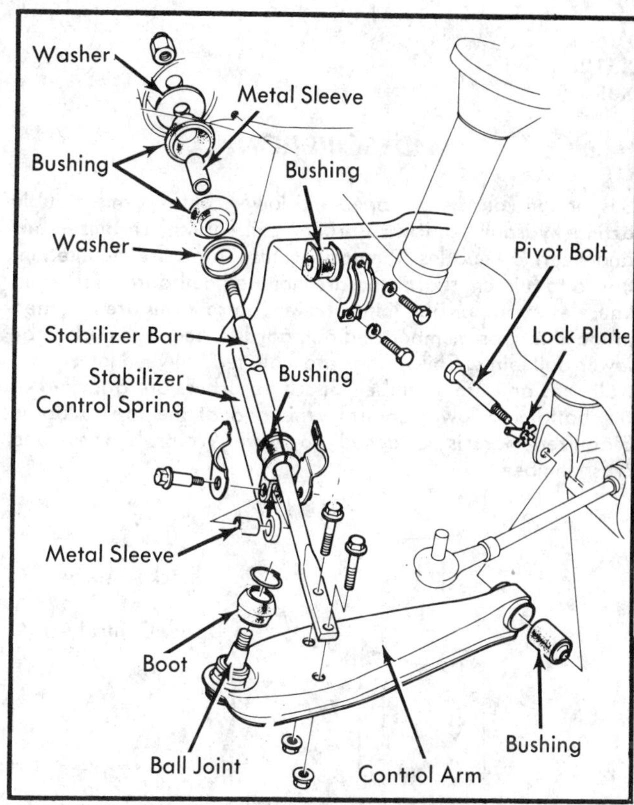

Fig. 3 Exploded View Showing Stabilizer Bar and Control Spring (Sway Bar). Note Mounting Locations. Accord Model Shown

STABILIZER BAR & CONTROL SPRING

Removal – Disconnect stabilizer bar mounting at lower control arm on both sides. Separate bracket and bushing mounting stabilizer bar control spring to stabilizer bar. Remove bracket securing control spring to crossmember. Loosen and remove stabilizer bar mounting at crossmember and slide both pieces from vehicle.

Inspection – Inspect all rubber bushings and metal sleeves for excessive wear or damage.

Installation – To install stabilizer and control spring, reverse removal procedure.

TIGHTENING SPECIFICATIONS

Application	Ft. Lbs. (mkg)
Spindle Nut	
Civic & Accord	87-130 (12-18)
CVCC	109 (15)
Ball Joint	
Civic	22-29 (3-4)
CVCC	25 (3.5)
Accord	29-36 (4-5)
Strut-to-Knuckle	
Civic	36-43 (5-6)
CVCC	40 (5.5)
Accord	43-51 (6-7)

JAGUAR

XJ6
XJ12
XJS

DESCRIPTION

Suspension consists of upper and lower control arms, double acting hydraulic shock absorbers, coil springs, stabilizer bar and steering knuckles. The upper control arms are mounted inboard to fulcrum shafts and are mounted outboard to steering knuckles by upper ball joints. Lower control arms are mounted inboard to crossmember and outboard to steering knuckles by lower ball joints. Coil springs are mounted between lower control arms and crossmember. Shock absorbers are attached at the bottom to lower control arms and at the top to body. Stabilizer bar is attached to lower control arms and crossmember.

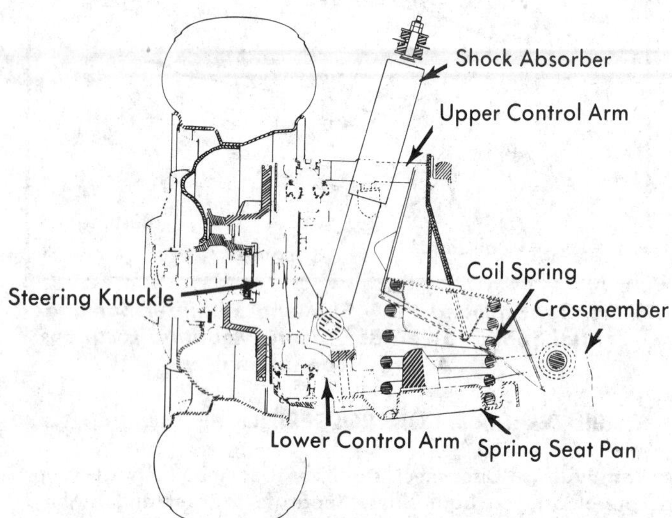

Fig. 1 Sectional View of Front Suspension Assembly

ADJUSTMENT

WHEEL ALIGNMENT SPECIFICATIONS & PROCEDURES

See Wheel Alignment Specifications and Procedures in WHEEL ALIGNMENT Section.

WHEEL BEARING ADJUSTMENT

See Wheel Bearing Adjustment in WHEEL ALIGNMENT Section.

BALL JOINT CHECKING

See Ball Joint Checking in WHEEL ALIGNMENT Section.

FRONT SUSPENSION ASSEMBLY

Removal – 1) Disconnect battery and remove air cleaners. Disconnect the upper end of shock absorber. Drain and discard power steering fluid. Disconnect and plug power steering inlet and outlet hoses.

2) Remove nuts securing engine mounts to brackets on frame crossmember. Disconnect rear crossmember mountings, then separate stabilizer bar from link. Turn steering until lower steering column pinch bolt is accessible, and remove bolt.

3) Return steering to straight ahead position, then disconnect horn wiring harness. Separate lower end of battery ground, then release wiring harness from clips.

4) Remove nuts from pivot bolts. **NOTE** – *Do not attempt to remove pivot shaft bolts.* Working from drivers compartment, loosen upper steering column "U" joint pinch bolts. Slide lower steering column "U" joint off pinion housing splines.

5) Fit overhead engine support to brackets. Using a floor jack under center of suspension crossmember, raise vehicle and place jack stands on lift points. Remove front wheels and disconnect brake system. Carefully lower jack and remove suspension from vehicle.

Installation – To install front suspension assembly, reverse removal procedure and note the following: Ensure all lines and/or hoses are properly routed without kinks. Engine must not be started until power steering reservoir is full. **NOTE** – *If it is difficult to reinstall steering column, See Steering Columns in STEERING Section.* Bleed brake system.

SHOCK ABSORBERS

Removal – Remove lock nut securing upper shock absorber to body. Raise and support vehicle. Remove wheel, then remove bolt securing lower portion of shock absorber. Compress shock absorber and remove from vehicle.

Installation – To install, reverse removal procedure. On XJS models, refit bolts from rear to front of bracket.

COIL SPRINGS

Removal – Raise and support vehicle, then remove tire and wheel. Fit a spring compressor (JD-6D & adaptor JD-6D-1) and collapse spring coil enough to allow load on pan seat to be relieved. Remove hardware mounting spring pan to lower control arm. Slightly loosen spring compressor and remove assembly complete. **NOTE** – *Keep track of number and placement of packing shims.*

Installation – To install coil spring, reverse removal procedure noting the following: Floor jack can be placed under lower ball joint to aid in aligning spring pan bolt. A maximum of three packers may be placed in spring pan and no more than two can be fitted on crossmember.

LOWER CONTROL ARM

Removal – Raise and support vehicle. Remove complete front suspension assembly as previously outlined. With assembly removed, disconnect tie rod ball joints from steering knuckle. Remove steering rack from crossmember and remove coil spring. Disconnect upper and lower ball joints from respective control arms. Remove stabilizer bar and using a suitable drift, remove pivot shaft from lower control arm.

Installation – To install, reverse removal procedure. **NOTE** – *Before tightening nuts on ends of pivot shaft, lower vehicle until full weight is on ground.*

UPPER CONTROL ARM

Removal – Raise and support vehicle, then remove wheel. Disconnect upper ball joint from control arm. Note number

JAGUAR (Cont.)

and position of caster adjusting shims for reinstallation. Wire steering knuckle to coil spring and remove bolts securing upper control arm pivot shaft to crossmember. Upper control arm can now be maneuvered from vehicle.

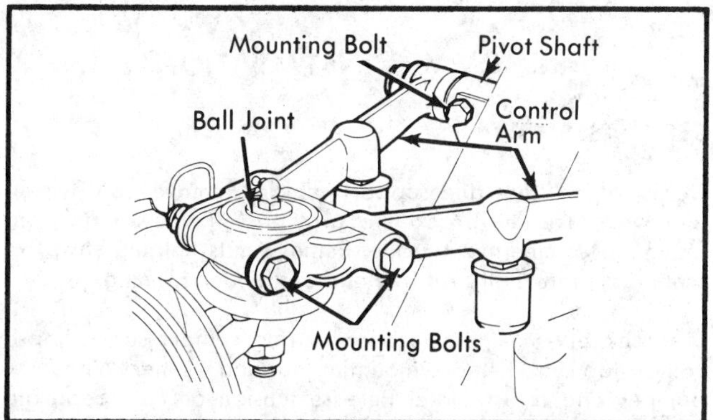

Fig. 2 Detail of Upper Control Arm Mounting Points

Installation – To install upper control arm, reverse removal procedure and tighten all nuts and bolts. Recheck wheel alignment.

STABILIZER BAR

Removal – Raise vehicle and place on safety stands, then remove both front wheels. Disconnect both ends of stabilizer bar from mounting links. Remove both mounting brackets from frame and separate stabilizer bar from all mounting bushings. Disconnect one tie rod end from steering knuckle and maneuver stabilizer bar from vehicle.

Installation – To install stabilizer bar, reverse removal procedure noting the following: Lightly coat rubber bushings with suitable liquid. Tighten all nuts, bolts, and fasteners when vehicle weight is on ground.

LOWER BALL JOINT

Removal – 1) Raise front of vehicle and place on safety stands. Remove wheel. Disconnect brake line from caliper and plug openings. Disconnect tie rod from steering arm. Twist stub axle carrier to gain access to bolts securing upper ball joint to control arm, then remove bolts. Note position and number of shims.

2) Remove nut mounting lower ball joint to control arm. Use tool JD 24 (or equivalent) to separate ball joint from control arm, then maneuver assembly from vehicle.

Disassembly & Reassembly – 1) Pry back tab washers and remove four screws keeping ball pin cap. Lift out ball pin. Release clip and remove upper socket from stub axle.

2) Clean all components and inspect for excessive wear or damage.

3) Install new upper socket to stub axle. Fit lip of boot clip in recess in socket. Lip MUST be near lower face of clip. Install new boot to clip and attach with plastic retaining ring. Grease new ball pin and put into position.

4) Put ball pin cap into vise and cut out lower socket. Clean shavings and fit new socket. Refit shims and replace ball cap. Fit four setscrews with lock tabs and tighten, continually checking ball joint movement.

5) If ball pin is loose in socket, remove shims. If pin is excessively tight, add shims until movement is correct. Movement should be slightly stiff.

Installation – Insert ball joint in lower control arm and tighten lock nut. Align stub axle with upper control arm and insert bolts (bolt heads MUST face front). Make sure packing pieces and shims are properly installed. Reconnect tie rod. Attach brake lines and bleed brakes. Check camber and caster angles.

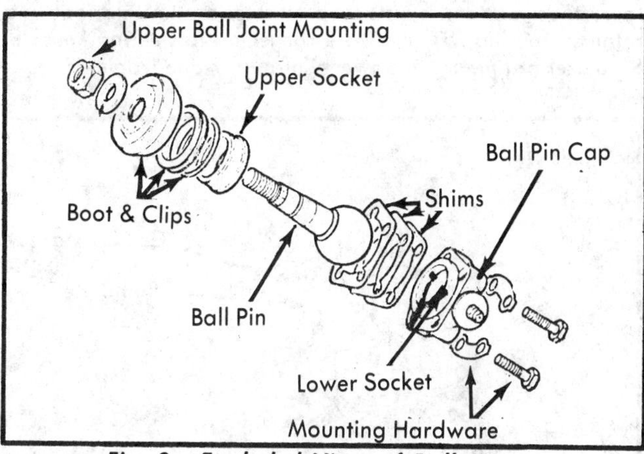

Fig. 3 Exploded View of Ball Joint

UPPER BALL JOINT

NOTE – *Upper control arm ball joint cannot be overhauled. If ball joint is excessively worn, assembly must be replaced.*

Removal – 1) Raise vehicle and place on safety stands. Remove wheel. Twist steering to full lock position. Wire stub axle to crossmember to prevent tension on brake hose when ball joint is separated.

2) Remove bolt mounting upper ball joint to control arm. Note number of shims and position of packing pieces. Remove ball joint lock nut and separate ball joint from control arm. Maneuver assembly from vehicle. Withdraw ball joint from stub axle.

Installation – Apply grease to replacement ball joint and place in position in stub axle. Hold ball joint against taper fit washer and tighten retaining nut. Refit upper control arm mounting bolts (bolt heads must face forward) and caster shims. Check camber and caster angles.

TIGHTENING SPECIFICATIONS

Application	Ft. Lbs. (mkg)
Upper Pivot Shaft-to-Crossmember	49-55 (6.8-7.6)
Upper Ball Joint-to-Control Arm	26-32 (3.6-4.4)
Pivot Shaft-to-Upper Control Arm	45-55 (6.3-7.6)
Pivot Shaft-to-Lower Control Arm	32-50 (4.4-6.9)
Upper Shock Absorber	27-32 (3.8-4.4)
Lower Shock Absorber	32-36 (4.4-5.0)
Spring Pan	27-32 (3.8-4.4)
Link-to-Lower Control Arm	14-18 (2.0-2.5)

LANCIA

Lancia
Except Scorpion

DESCRIPTION

Vehicles are equipped with front wheel drive and independent hydraulic strut type shock absorbers. Axles are supported by lower control arms and vertically mounted strut assemblies. Strut assemblies have shock absorbers with coil springs mounted over outside. Top of strut is attached at fender with four studs. Bottom is attached to steering knuckle (bearing retainer housing). Tie rods are connected to steering knuckle. Stabilizer bar mounts at lower control arm and frame.

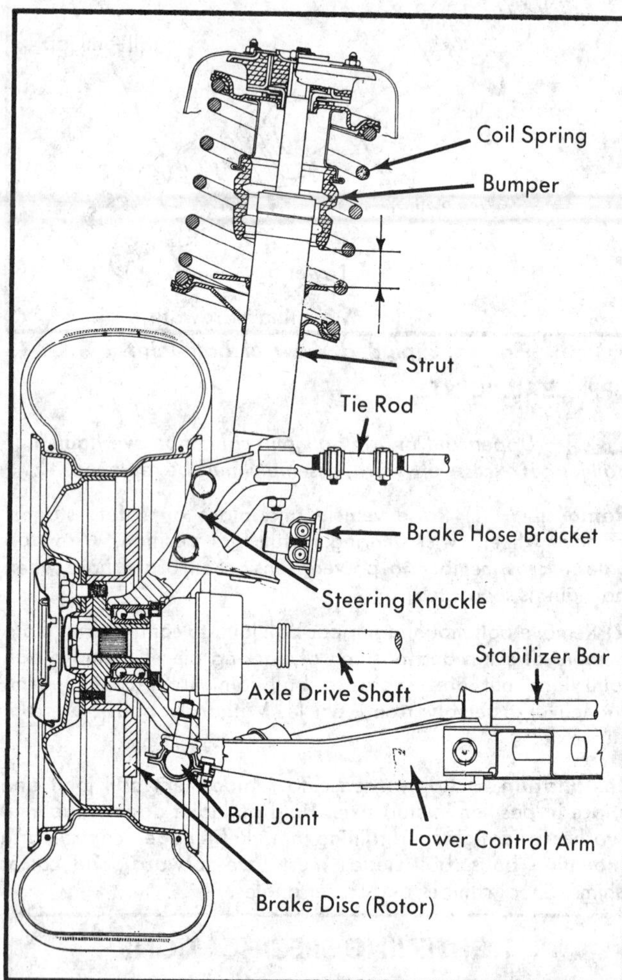

Fig. 1 Sectional View of Lancia Front Suspension Showing Component Relationship

ADJUSTMENT

WHEEL ALIGNMENT SPECIFICATIONS & PROCEDURES

See Wheel Alignment Specifications and Procedures in WHEEL ALIGNMENT Section.

WHEEL BEARING ADJUSTMENT

See Wheel Bearing Adjustment in WHEEL ALIGNMENT Section.

BALL JOINT CHECKING

See Ball Joint Checking in WHEEL ALIGNMENT Section.

REMOVAL & INSTALLATION

STRUT ASSEMBLY

Removal – Raise and support vehicle. Remove front wheel. Remove brake line bracket to strut base. Remove strut from mounting at steering knuckle. Remove nuts holding strut top mounting plate. Pull strut free and out fender opening.

Disassembly – 1) Using a coil spring compressor, collapse coil off top seat. Remove mounting nut and washer. Withdraw bumper and thrust plate. Release tension on coil. Separate base from strut and remove. Slide off coil spring, gasket, upper seat, and bumper.

2) Grip base of strut in vice. Remove retaining ring nut. Extract seals, cap and hose. Drain fluid from strut. Pull shaft assembly from strut tube. Remove buffer valve.

Reassembly – Reassembly buffer valve. *See Fig. 2.* Refill strut tube with fluid (10 ozs. for Cupe and 7 ozs. for others). Slowly insert strut assembly into tube exhausting air. Fit top cap assembly over strut shaft. This will seal tube. Make sure seals and hose fit properly. Tighten lock ring nut and stake in three places.

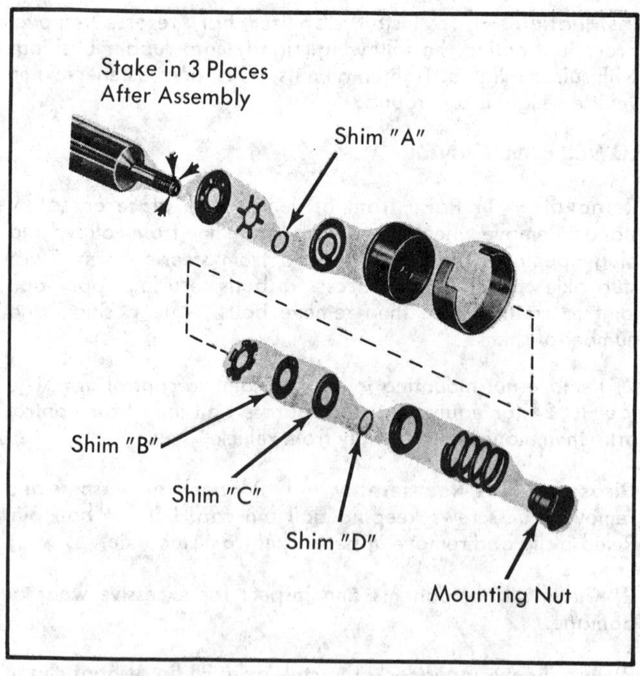

Fig. 2 Reassembly Sequence for Buffer Valve. Assemble Components Over Strut Shaft Stem. Refer to Table for Correct Shim Thickness.

Installation – To install strut assembly, reverse removal procedure and tighten all nuts and bolts.

LANCIA (Cont.)

Buffer Valve Shim Table

Application	Thickness In. (mm)
Early Coupe Models	
Shim A,C,D	.008 (.20)
Shim B	.006 (.15)
Late Coupe Models	
Shim A,D	.008 (.20)
Shim B	.004 (.10)
Shim C	.006 (.15)
Saloon	
Shim A	.020 (.50)
Shim B	.004 (.10)
Shim C,D	.008 (.20)

LOWER CONTROL ARM

Removal – Raise and support vehicle. Remove wheel. Disconnect axle drive shaft. Separate stabilizer bar from control arm. Disconnect headlight aiming link from left side control arm (if equipped). Using remover tool 88042104 (or equivalent), drive ball joint from steering knuckle. Remove bolts mounting control arm to subframe and pull control arm from vehicle.

Installation – To install, reverse removal procedure.

STABILIZER BAR

Removal – Raise and support vehicle. Remove front wheels. Remove clamps mounting stabilizer bar to lower control arms and subframe.

Installation – To install, reverse removal procedure.

TIGHTENING SPECIFICATIONS

Application	Ft. Lbs. (mkg)
Lower Control Arm Bolts	44 (6.0)
Ball Joint Mount Nuts	18 (2.5)
Ball Joint Nut	76 (10.5)
Buffer Nut	13 (1.8)
Strut-to-Steering Knuckle	31 (4.3)
Stabilizer Bar Bolts	17 (2.3)

LUV

LUV

DESCRIPTION

Independent type suspension, using torsion bars. Upper control arms are mounted to bracket which is part of shock tower. Lower control arm is mounted to crossmember. Ball joints attach both upper and lower control arms to steering knuckles, which are part of the front wheel spindle. Torsion bars are connected in front to lower control arm and at rear to frame crossmember. Back and forth movement of front suspension is regulated by a strut bar connecting lower control arm to frame, by means of a rubber bumper at frame end of strut.

ADJUSTMENT

WHEEL ALIGNMENT SPECIFICATIONS & PROCEDURES

See Wheel Alignment Specifications & Procedures in WHEEL ALIGNMENT Section.

WHEEL BEARING ADJUSTMENT

See Wheel Bearing Adjustment in WHEEL ALIGNMENT Section.

BALL JOINT CHECKING

See Ball Joint Checking in WHEEL ALIGNMENT Section.

REMOVAL & INSTALLATION

UPPER CONTROL ARM & BALL JOINT

Removal – Raise vehicle and place safety stands under lower control arm. Remove tire and wheel. Remove upper ball joint cotter pin and nut. Disconnect spindle from upper control arm.

CAUTION – *Do not let spindle and brake assembly hang from brake flex line, wire assembly to frame.* Remove two bolts holding upper control arm to bracket. Remove control arm from vehicle. Note the position and number of shims to keep correct caster and camber when installing control arm. If pivot shafts or bushings are to be removed, alternately loosen bushing nuts from pivot shaft and remove shaft from control arm. Check control arm and pivot shaft for cracks or distortion. Replace both pivot shaft and bushings if either are found defective. Replace rubber boots if necessary. Ball joint and control arm are a complete assembly. If ball joint needs replacing, entire control arm must be replaced.

Installation – Install boots on upper control arm pivot shaft. Pack inside of bushings with molybdenum disulfide grease and alternately screw right and left bushings into pivot shaft. Use a suitable tool to space pivot shaft when tightening bushings. Avoid getting grease on outer bushing face. Tighten bushings to specifications. Install grease fittings and grease all parts thru fittings. Place ball joint stud thru spindle. Install castillated nut and tighten to specifications. Install new cotter pin, if it does not align, tighten nut just enough for cotter pin to slide in. **NOTE** – *Do not loosen nut to allow cotter pin to be installed.* Install upper control arm to chassis frame, making sure shims equal in thickness to those that were removed, are installed. Tighten bolts to specifications. **NOTE** – *For better pivot shaft to frame retention, tighten thinner shim packs first.* Install dust cover, tire and wheel and lower vehicle.

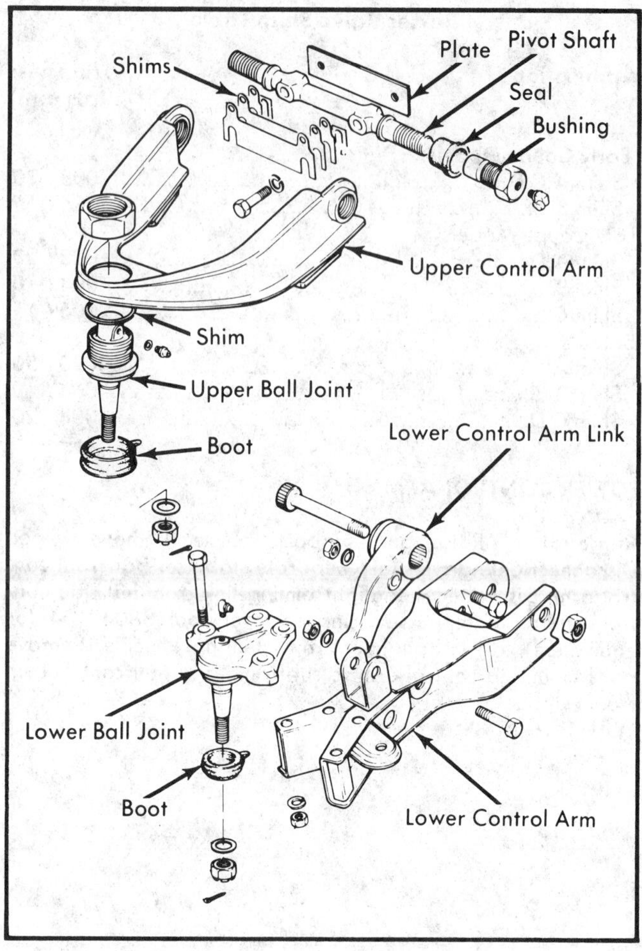

Fig. 1 Exploded View of LUV Front Suspension

LOWER CONTROL ARM & BALL JOINT

Removal – Raise vehicle and place safety stand under frame. Remove tire and wheel. Remove strut bar, torsion bar and disconnect stabilizer bar as previously outlined. Disconnect lower end of shock absorber. Remove cotter pin and nut retaining lower ball joint to spindle. Remove lower control arm retaining nuts and remove control arm. Ball joint can be removed with control arm either installed or out of vehicle, by removing two bolts retaining ball joint to control arm.

Installation – Check all parts for distortion, cracking or excessive wear. If ball joint was removed, install ball joint in lower control arm and tighten bolts to specification. Bolt lower control arm to chassis and tighten to specification. Place ball joint stud in spindle, tighten nut to specification, and install new cotter pin. **NOTE** – *Do not loosen nut to allow cotter pin to be installed.* Install torsion bar, strut bar and stabilizer bar as previously outlined. Install tire and wheel and lower vehicle.

SHOCK ABSORBER

Removal – Raise vehicle. Hold shock absorber upper stem with a wrench and remove retaining nut, retainer and rubber grommet. Remove lower shock absorber pivot bolt from lower control arm and remove shock absorber.

LUV (Cont.)

Installation — Check shock absorber and replace if necessary. Fully extend shock absorber, place lower retainer and grommet on stem and slide shock absorber into position. Install upper grommet and retainer on stem and tighten nut to specification. Slide bolt thru lower shock absorber mount and shock absorber. Tighten bolt to specification and lower vehicle.

STABILIZER BAR

Removal — Raise vehicle and disconnect stabilizer bar from lower control arm. Remove brackets holding bar to frame and remove bar. Remove link bolt, spacers and rubber grommets from lower control arm or stabilizer bar. Inspect all parts for wear or damage and replace if necessary.

Installation — Bolt brackets to frame over rubber bushings installed over stabilizer bar but do not tighten. Connect link bolts to lower control arm, making sure washers are installed in correct position. Connect link bolts to stabilizer, and tighten to specifications. Tighten bracket bolts to specifications.

TORSION BAR

Removal — Raise vehicle and place safety stands under front of vehicle. Mark position of height control arm adjusting bolt, then remove bolt. Remove height control arm from torsion bar and crossmember. Mark position, then remove torsion bar from lower control arm.

Installation — Thoroughly grease serrated portions at both ends of torsion bar. Raise lower control arm with a jack to position rubber bumpers in contact with lower control arm. Install front end of torsion bar into control arm. Install height control arm into position so its end is reaching the adjusting bolt. **NOTE** — *Grease portion of height control arm which fits into frame.* Turn height control adjusting bolt to position marked upon disassembly. Check riding height. *See Wheel Alignment Specifications and Procedures in WHEEL ALIGNMENT Section.*

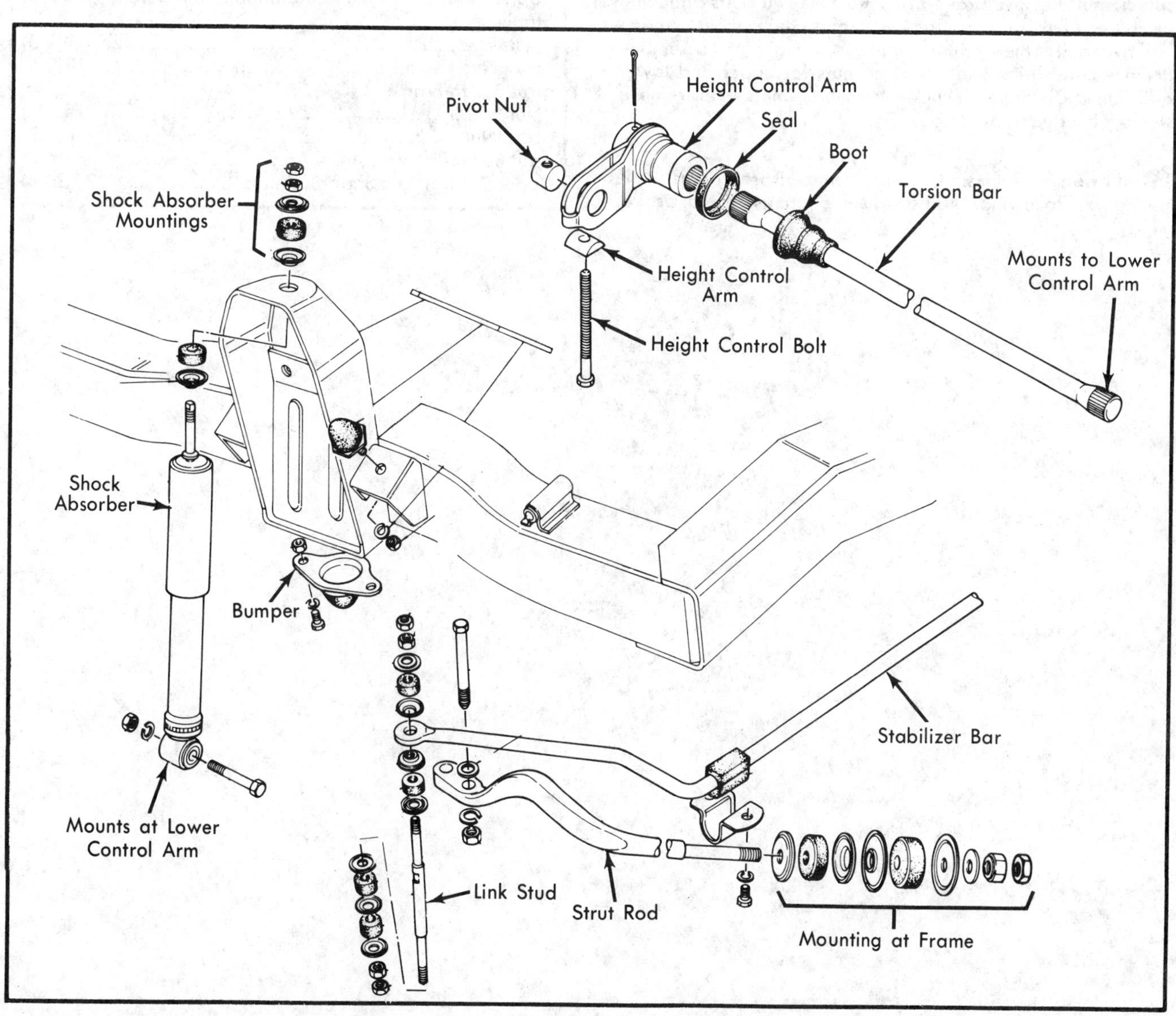

Fig. 2 Exploded View of Torsion Bar, Stabilizer Bar, Strut Bar and Shock Absorber Illustration Shows Component Relationships and Part Identification

LUV (Cont.)

LOWER CONTROL ARM STRUT BAR

Removal – Raise vehicle and remove double nuts, washers and rubber bushings from front side of strut bar. Remove two bolts holding strut bar to lower control arm and remove strut bar.

Installation – Place washer and bushing on strut bar and slide rod through frame bracket. Place second set of washers and bushings on end through bracket, then start on washer and one nut, but do not tighten. Bolt other end of strut to lower control arm and tighten to specifications. Lower vehicle and tighten bracket nut, install second nut and tighten to specifications.

STEERING KNUCKLE

Removal – Raise vehicle and place safety stands under front of vehicle. Remove tire and wheel. Disconnect brake hose from wheel cylinder. Remove dust cap, cotter pin, nut retainer, and spindle nut. Remove brake drum. Remove two bolts attaching tie rod end link, and position link to one side. Remove remaining two bolts, then remove brake backing plate assembly. Remove cotter pins and attaching nuts for upper and lower ball joints. Disconnect knuckle from ball joints, then remove steering knuckle from vehicle.

Installation – To install, reverse removal procedures while noting the following: Adjust wheel bearings. Bleed brakes after connecting brake hose to wheel cylinder. Tighten all bolts to specifications.

TIGHTENING SPECIFICATIONS

Application	Ft. Lbs. (mkg)
Backing Plate-to-Knuckle	
Small Bolts	35(4.8)
Large Bolts	50(6.9)
Ball Joint-to-Lower Control Arm	45(6.2)
Ball Joint Stud Nut	75(10.4)
Control Arm Pivot-to-Frame	
Lower	130(18.0)
Upper	50(6.9)
Lower Control Arm-to-Crossmember	130(18.0)
Shock Absorber	
Lower End	45(6.2)
Upper End	18(2.5)
Stabilizer Bar	
Nuts	7(1.0)
Lock Nuts	18(2.5)
Strut Bar-to-Frame	
Nut	15(2.1)
Lock Nut	50(6.9)
Strut Bar-to-Lower Control Arm	45(6.2)
Upper Control Arm Shaft Bushings	220(30.4)

MAZDA RX-3SP, RX-4, 808, COSMO & GLC

RX-3SP
RX-4
808
Cosmo
GLC

DESCRIPTION

Independent hydraulic strut type suspension with coil springs. Strut assemblies mount between lower control arms and upper fender panels. Strut assemblies consist of: hydraulic shock absorbers (built into strut tube), coil springs around outside of strut tube housing, and a steering knuckle that is connected to both lower control arm and strut. Lower control arms pivot at crossmember and are connected by ball joints to steering knuckle. A stabilizer bar is attached to chassis and at each end to lower control arm.

ADJUSTMENT

WHEEL ALIGNMENT SPECIFICATIONS & PROCEDURES

See Wheel Alignment Specifications & Procedures in WHEEL ALIGNMENT Section.

WHEEL BEARING ADJUSTMENT

See Wheel Bearing Adjustment in WHEEL ALIGNMENT Section.

BALL JOINT CHECKING

See Ball Joint Checking in WHEEL ALIGNMENT Section.

REMOVAL & INSTALLATION

LOWER CONTROL ARM

NOTE – *Check visual differences between models by comparing Figures 1, 2, and 3.*

Removal – **1)** Raise vehicle. Support weight with safety stands. Remove tire and wheel.

2) Remove cotter pin from tie rod nut. Remove nut. Separate tie rod ball joint using a puller.

3) Remove bolts mounting steering knuckle to strut tube. Remove nut from front of stabilizer bar. Begin to separate stabilizer bar from control arm.

4) Remove lower control arm pivot bolt mounting arm to crossmember. Pull strut outward and force control arm out of vehicle.

Ball Joint Replacement – **1)** Remove cotter pin and nut from ball joint stud. Separate ball joint from steering arm using a puller.

2) Remove retainer ring and dust seal from ball joint. Press joint from control arm.

3) Select new ball joint. Clean mounting bore in control arm. Press new ball joint into control arm. Position steering knuckle on ball joint and tighten nut.

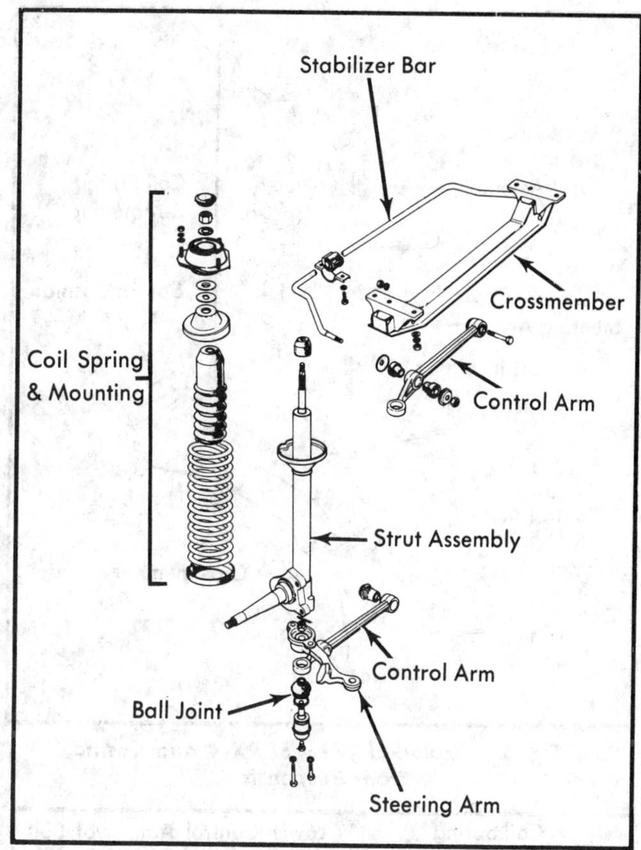

Fig. 1 Exploded View of 808 and RX-3SP Front Suspension

Installation – To install, reverse removal procedure and tighten all nuts and bolts. Do not use more than two adjusting plates at one side when installing coil spring.

STRUT ASSEMBLY

NOTE – *Check visual differences between models. See Figures 1, 2, and 3.*

Removal – **1)** Raise and suitably support vehicle. Remove tire and wheel.

2) Remove nuts (3 or 4) retaining strut to upper fender panel. Nuts are accessible from inside engine compartment.

3) Remove clip mounting brake hydraulic line to strut housing (if equipped). Remove bolts attaching caliper (bracket) and pull caliper assembly off disc. Hang caliper out of way using a short wire.

4) Remove hub grease cap, cotter pin, nut lock and bearing adjustment nut from spindle. Remove thrust washer and outer bearing. Pull off hub and brake assembly. Remove any remaining brake system components from steering knuckle.

5) Remove bolts mounting strut to steering knuckle. Drop lower control arm down. Slide strut assembly with coil spring out of vehicle.

MAZDA RX-3SP, RX-4, 808, COSMO & GLC (Cont.)

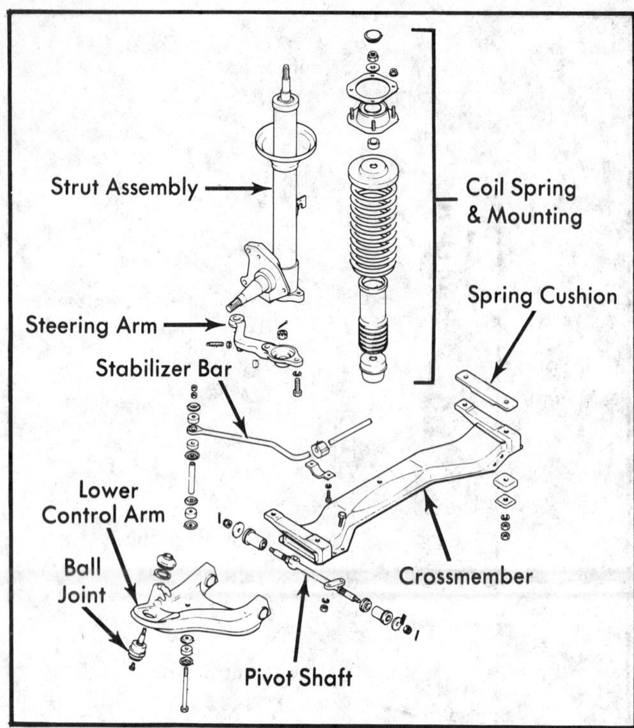

Fig. 2 Exploded View of RX-4 and Cosmo Front Suspension

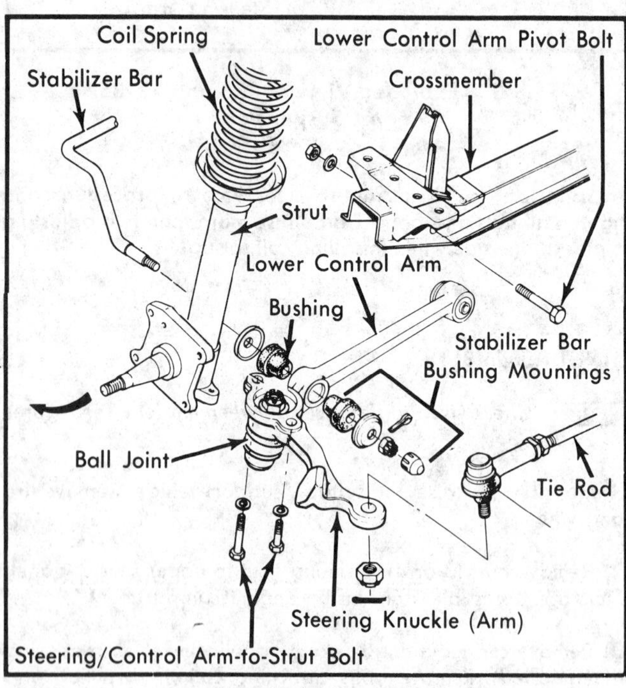

Fig. 3 Partical Exploded View of GLC Front Suspension

OVERHAUL

STRUT ASSEMBLY

NOTE – *All struts are not exactly the same. Check Figures 1, 2, and 3.*

Disassembly – **1**) Clamp strut in vise. Use spring compressor and collapse coil. Remove lock nut and washer from top of piston rod.

2) Remove shock absorber support, spring seat, coil spring, dust boot and damper stopper.

NOTE – *Check hydraulic strut (shock absorber) by forcing piston rod in and out several times. If resistance is weak or there is a free travel spot somewhere in the stroke, strut must be replaced or repaired.*

3) Place strut in a soft jawed vise. Remove cap nut and seal. Pry "O" ring from guide rod. Pull piston rod and pressure tube assembly out of strut (reservoir tube).

4) Remove piston rod, guide, base valve and pressure tube assembly from reservoir tube. Take strut from vise and drain hydraulic fluid.

NOTE – *Piston rod, guide, and base valve are serviced ONLY as an assembly. DO NOT remove items listed in step four from pressure tube. See Fig. 4.*

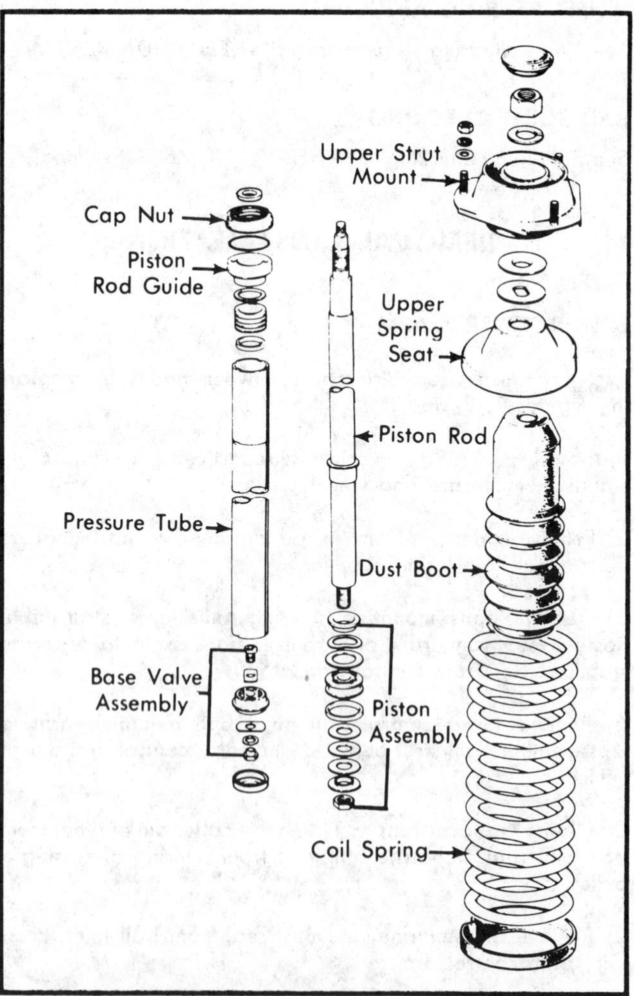

Fig. 4 Exploded View of Strut Assembly 808 Models Shown, Others Similar

MAZDA RX-3SP, RX-4, 808, COSMO & GLC (Cont.)

Inspection – 1) Check reservoir tube for cracks or damage. Replace tube if necessary.

2) Check mounting rubbers, replace if deteriorated.

3) Inspect coil spring for signs of fatigue, cracks or damage.

Reassembly – 1) Hold reservoir tube (strut) in a vise. Insert pressure tube, piston rod, and base valve assembly into tube as a set. Pour hydraulic fluid into reservoir.

Hydraulic Fluid Specifications

Application	Amount of Fluid In Ounces
Cosmo	11
All Others	9

2) Install piston rod guide into pressure tube. Fit new "O" ring between rod guide and reservoir tube.

3) Fit a pilot (49 0370 590) over threads of piston rod. Apply grease to lip of oil seal, insert cap nut through pilot onto piston rod.

4) Tighten cap nut and pull out piston rod. Seat piston and torque cap nut. Install coil spring and remaining components in reverse of removal procedure.

TIGHTENING SPECIFICATIONS

Application	Ft. Lbs. (mkg)
Control Arm Pivot Bolt	
Cosmo, RX-4	54-69 (7.5-9.5)
All Others	29-40 (4.0-5.5)
Steering Knuckle-to-Strut	
Cosmo, RX-4	75-101 (10.4-14.0)
All Others	46-69 (6.4-9.5)
Ball Joint-to-Steering Knuckle	
RX-4	25-36 (3.5-5.0)
RX-3SP, GLC, Cosmo	43-58 (6.0-9.0)
808 Models	43-51 (6.0-7.0)
Strut Cap Nut	
Cosmo	72-94 (10.0-13.0)
All Others	36-43 (5.0-6.9)
Piston Rod Nut	10-12 (1.35-1.65)

MAZDA ROTARY PICKUP

Rotary Pickup

DESCRIPTION

Independent type suspension, consisting of upper and lower control arms and wheel spindle mounted between upper and lower arms by means of ball joints. Upper control arm pivots on a shaft attached to frame, lower control arm pivots on a shaft mounted to crossmember. A coil spring is mounted between lower control arm and frame. Shock absorber is hydraulic double action type, mounted between lower control arm and frame inside coil spring.

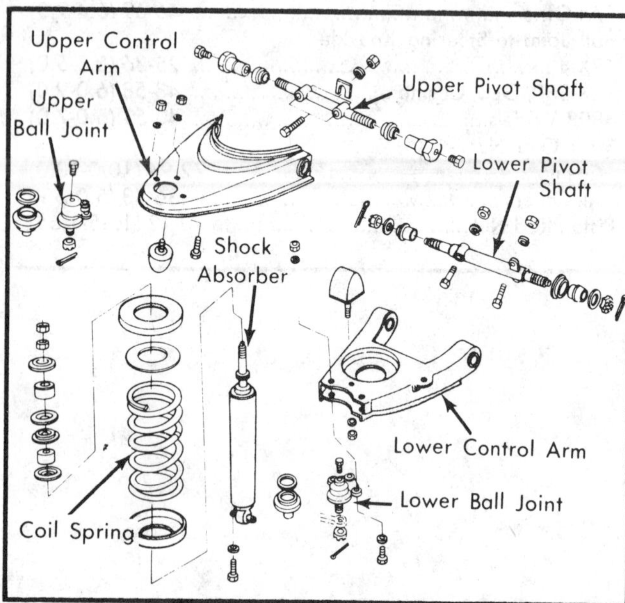

Fig. 1 Exploded View of Front Suspension Assembly for Component Identification

ADJUSTMENT

WHEEL ALIGNMENT SPECIFICATIONS & PROCEDURES

See Wheel Alignment Specifications & Procedures in WHEEL ALIGNMENT Section.

WHEEL BEARING ADJUSTMENT

See Wheel Bearing Adjustment in WHEEL ALIGNMENT Section.

BALL JOINT CHECKING

See Ball Joint Checking in WHEEL ALIGNMENT Section.

REMOVAL & INSTALLATION

SHOCK ABSORBERS

Removal — Remove nut, rubber bushing and washer attaching upper end of shock absorber to crossmember. Remove lower retaining bolts holding shock absorber to lower control arm, and remove shock absorber from vehicle.

Installation — Reverse removal procedure and tighten mounting bolts.

UPPER CONTROL ARM & BALL JOINT

Removal — 1) Raise vehicle and suitably support with safety stands located under lower control arm. Remove tire and wheel. Take off brake caliper assembly and suspend out of way. Disconnect and remove front shock absorber as previously outlined.

2) Remove cotter pin and nut mounting upper ball joint to steering knuckle. Use a suitable puller and disengage ball joint from knuckle. Note position and number of wheel alignment shims.

3) Remove 3 retaining nuts and bolts then remove ball joint from control arm. To remove control arm, open hood and remove 2 upper arm retaining bolts and pull control arm from vehicle.

Installation — Position ball joint in upper control arm and tighten bolts. Install control arm in vehicle and tighten. Install steering knuckle on ball joint, tighten nut, and remove safety stands; lower vehicle. Check wheel alignment.

LOWER CONTROL ARM, BALL JOINT & COIL SPRING

Removal — 1) Raise vehicle and place safety stands under frame behind both lower control arms. Remove tire and wheel. Take off brake caliper and suspend out of way. Disconnect stabilizer bar from lower control arm. Fit suitable spring compressor to coil and collapse spring.

2) Remove lower ball joint nut and disconnect stud from steering knuckle using a puller. Remove bolts attaching lower arm to crossmember and slide arm with coil spring from vehicle.

Installation — To install, reverse removal procedure noting the following: Ensure ball joint is greased. Install stabilizer bar with white stripe aligned with outside of support bracket.

TIGHTENING SPECIFICATIONS

Application	Ft. Lbs. (mkg)
Ball Joint-to-Steering Knuckle	58 (8.0)
Pivot Shaft-to-Frame	
Upper	69 (9.5)
Lower	62 (8.6)
Lower Control Arm-to-Pivot Shaft	62 (8.6)
Ball Joint-to-Control Arm	65(9.0)
Shock Absorber	
Upper Mount	①
Lower Mount	15(2.1)

① — Distance from top of lock nut to top of shock absorber stud should be .14" (3.5 mm)

MERCEDES BENZ EXCEPT 280SE, 450SEL & 6.9

230
240D
300D
280E
450SL and SLC

DESCRIPTION

Front suspension system is a coil spring type. Major components are upper and lower control arms, stabilizer bar, and shock absorbers. Stabilizer bar is attached to lower control arms and crossmember. Entire front suspension system can be removed as a assembly, if necessary.

WHEEL ALIGNMENT SPECIFICATIONS & ADJUSTMENTS

See Wheel Alignment Specifications and Adjustment in WHEEL ALIGNMENT Section.

WHEEL BEARING ADJUSTMENT

See Wheel Bearing Adjustment in WHEEL ALIGNMENT Section.

BALL JOINT CHECKING

See Ball Joint Checking in WHEEL ALIGNMENT Section.

REMOVAL & INSTALLATION

SHOCK ABSORBER

Removal — Raise and support vehicle, making sure stands are placed under lower control arms. Remove wheels. Disconnect upper and lower shock absorber mounting, then remove shock absorber from vehicle.

NOTE — *On some models, it may be necessary to unscrew water cooling compensating tank before removing right side of shock absorber.*

Installation — To install shock absorber, reverse removal procedure and tighten all nuts evenly.

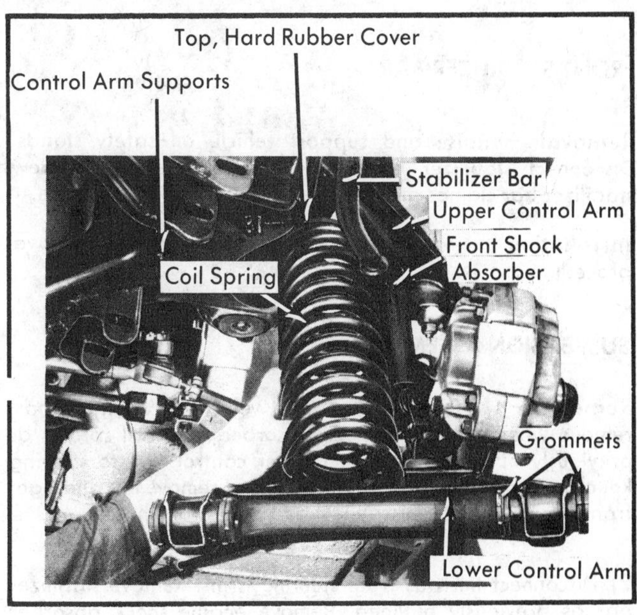

Fig. 1 Lowering Down Control Arm and Removing Coil

COIL SPRING

Removal — Raise and support vehicle on safety stands, remove wheel. Remove shock absorber as previously outlined. Disconnect stabilizer bar linkage. Support lower control arm inner side with a jack. Mark control arm cam bolts for correct installation. Remove control arm cam bolts (do not reverse front with rear), lower jack and remove coil spring with rubber ring.

Installation — To install coil spring, reverse removal procedure and note the following: Cam bolts affect caster/camber and should be installed in original position.

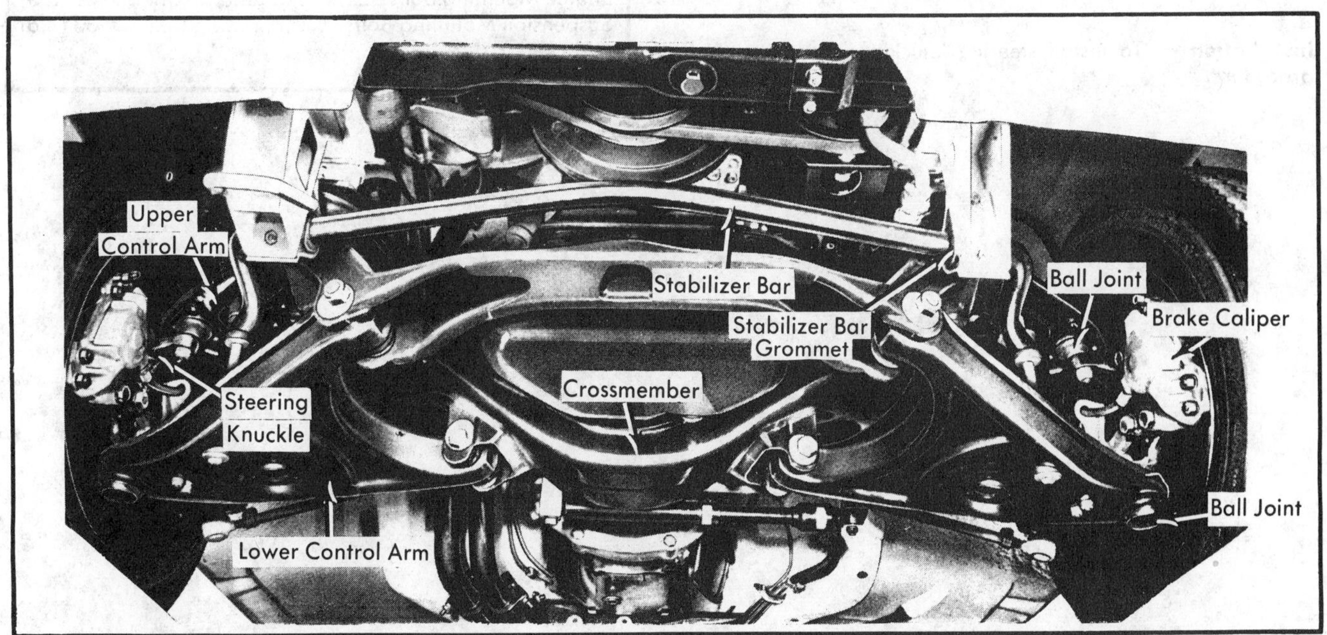

Fig. 2 Head on View of Mercedes-Benz 280 Front Suspension

MERCEDES BENZ EXCEPT 280SE, 450SEL & 6.9 (Cont.)

FRONT STABILIZER BAR

Removal – Raise and support vehicle on safety stands. Disconnect stabilizer bar linkage on both sides. Unscrew stabilizer bar clamps and remove stabilizer bar from vehicle.

Installation – To install stabilizer bar, reverse removal procedure.

SUSPENSION ASSEMBLY

Removal – **1**) Raise and support vehicle on safety stands, remove wheels. Remove shock absorbers and coil springs as previously outlined. Reconnect lower control arm to steering knuckle. Support engine. Disconnect and remove left and right front engine mounts. Disconnect and plug brake hoses.

2) Disconnect tie rods from steering arms. Remove stabilizer bar as previously outlined. Remove engine shock absorber from crossmember. Support crossmember on a jack, remove bolts from crossmember mounts and remove suspension assembly.

Installation – To install suspension assembly, reverse removal procedure.

STEERING KNUCKLE

Removal – Raise and support vehicle on safety stands, remove wheels. Place stands under front lower control arms. Disconnect steering arm from steering knuckle. Disconnect and plug brake hoses, remove caliper. Remove upper and lower ball joint nuts, remove steering knuckle.

Installation – To install steering knuckle, reverse removal procedurer

UPPER CONTROL ARM

Removal – Raise and support vehicle on safety stands, remove wheel. Remove steering arm from steering knuckle. Remove steering knuckle as previously outlined. Remove cam bolts on upper control arm, and remove control arm.

Installation – To install upper control arm, reverse removal procedure and note the following: Install front control arm cam bolts from rear in a forward direction, and rear cam bolts from the front in a rearward direction.

LOWER CONTROL ARM

Removal – Remove lower shock absorber mount. Raise and support vehicle on safety stands, remove wheel. Disconnect and plug brake hose. Remove coil spring as previously outlined. Remove nut on upper ball joint. Disconnect lower ball joint from steering knuckle and remove control arm.

Installation – To install lower control arm, reverse removal procedure and note the following: Use new lock nuts on upper and lower ball joints.

TIGHTENING SPECIFICATIONS

Application	Ft. Lbs. (mkg)
Lower Shock Absorber Mount	18 (2.5)
Stabilizer Bar Bolts	18 (2.5)
Steering Linkage Bolts	25 (3.5)
Steering Knuckle Arm Bolts	58 (8.0)
Upper Control Arm Cam Bolts	43 (6.0)
Lower Control Arm Cam Bolts	87 (12.0)
Upper Ball Joint	43 (6.0)
Lower Ball Joint	58 (8.0)
Engine Mounting Bolts	25 (3.5)
Suspension Mounting Bolts	33 (4.6)

MERCEDES BENZ 280SE, 450SEL & 6.9

280SE
450SEL
6.9

DESCRIPTION

Suspension is composed of a lower wishbone type control arm connected to steering knuckle by a ball joint. Upper end of steering knuckle attaches by a ball joint to control arm link. Shock absorber mounts off lower control arm and to upper control arm link. Stabilizer bar mounts at steering knuckle and upper control link junction. Lower control arm is attached to frame crossmember in front and to cross yoke at rear.

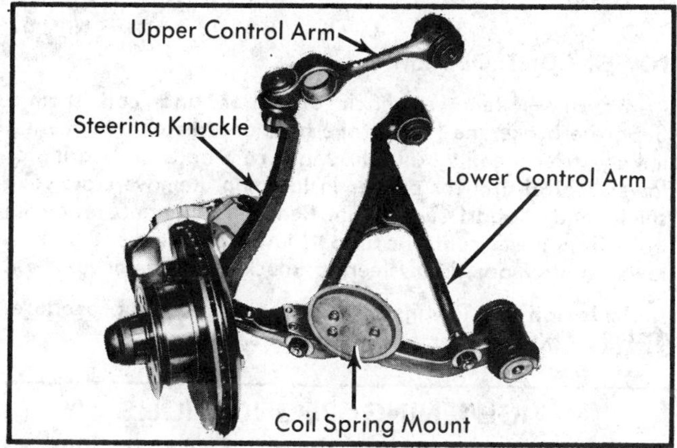

Fig. 1 Top View of Mercedes Benz Front Suspension

ADJUSTMENT

WHEEL ALIGNMENT SPECIFICATIONS & ADJUSTMENTS

See Wheel Alignment Specifications and Adjustments in WHEEL ALIGNMENT Section.

WHEEL BEARING ADJUSTMENT

See Wheel Bearing Adjustment in WHEEL ALIGNMENT Section.

BALL JOINT CHECKING

See Ball Joint Checking in WHEEL ALIGNMENT Section.

REMOVAL & INSTALLATION

SHOCK ABSORBER

Removal – Raise and support vehicle, place safety stands under lower control arm. Remove wheels. Disconnect upper and lower shock attaching bolts and nuts. Remove shock absorber.

Installation – To install shock absorber, reverse removal procedure and tighten nuts and bolts.

CAUTION – *On Bilstein shocks, do not reverse upper and lower shock absorber plates as lower plate may slide over locking ring while driving.*

COIL SPRING

Removal – Raise and support vehicle on safety stands, remove wheel. Loosen upper shock mount, it is not necessary to remove shock absorber. Install suitable spring compresser (116 589 01 31 00) through spring dome on engine side of fender panel. Remove spring together with rubber mount.

Installation – To install coil springs, reverse removal procedure and tighten upper shock abosrber attaching nut.

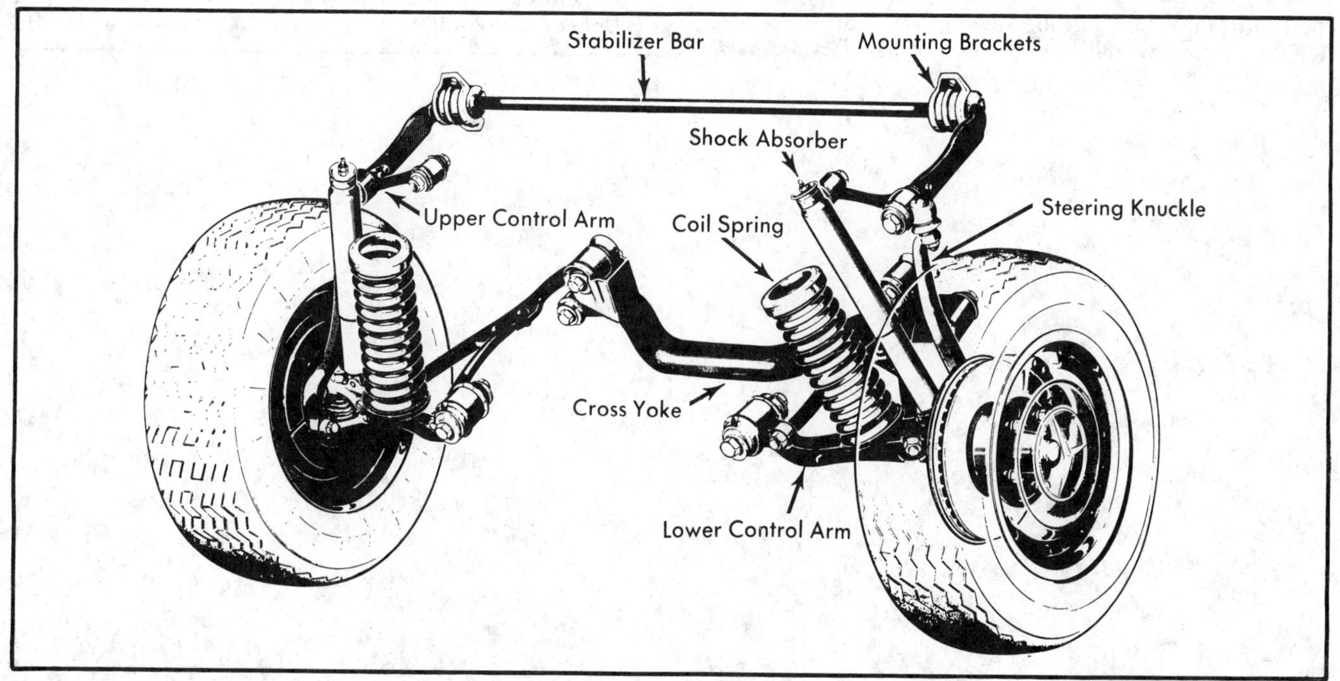

Fig. 2 Assembled View of Front Suspension Assembly

MERCEDES BENZ 280SE, 450SEL & 6.9 (Cont.)

FRONT STABILIZER BAR

Removal — Raise and support vehicle on safety stands located at outer ends of lower control arms, remove wheels. Remove bolts attaching stabilizer bar to upper control arm. Remove master cylinder, power brake booster, air cleaner, water hoses, regulating linkage and disconnect electrical wires to injection valves. Mark position of stabilizer bar mounting brackets, then remove mounting brackets, cover plates and stabilizer bar.

NOTE — *Make sure mounting brackets are installed in same spot as removed to prevent any changes of castor adjustments.*

Installation — To install stabilizer bar, reverse removal procedure. Tighten nuts and bolts.

CROSS YOKE

Removal — Mark position of rear cam bolts on lower control arms. Remove shields from cross yoke. Remove bolts attaching cross yoke to lower control arm and frame. Remove cross yoke.

Installation — To install, reverse removal procedure and make sure cam bolts are aligned with scribe marks.

STEERING KNUCKLE

Removal — Raise and support vehicle on safety stands at outer end of lower control arms. Remove wheel. Remove steering arm from steering knuckle. Remove and support brake caliper away from steering knuckle, then remove wheel hub. Remove brake hose clamp from brake cover plate then separate upper control arm ball joint from steering knuckle. Separate lower control arm ball joint from steering knuckle and remove steering knuckle.

NOTE — *Keep taper of ball joints free from grease.*

Installation — To install, reverse removal procedure. **NOTE** — *Use new self locking nuts and new lock washers.*

UPPER CONTROL ARM

Removal — Raise and uspport vehicle on safety stands at outer end of lower control arms, remove wheel. Separate upper control arm from steering knuckle. Support steering knuckle. Disconnect stabilizer bar from upper control arm and remove bolt attaching upper control arm to body from engine compartment side. Remove upper control arm.

Installation — Attach upper control arm to body and connect ball joint to steering knuckle.

NOTE — *Use new locking nut and keep taper of ball joint free of grease. Attach stabilizer bar to upper control arm.*

LOWER CONTROL ARM

Removal — Remove shock absorber and coil spring. Separate brake line from brake hose and disconnect steering linkage from steering knuckle. Mark cam bolts on bearing of lower control arm for proper installation. Remove cross yoke shield and support suspension. Remove front and rear cam bolts from lower control arm and lower cross yoke. Separate lower control arm from steering knuckle and remove.

Installation — To install reverse removal procedure. **NOTE** — *Keep taper of ball joint free of grease.*

TIGHTENING SPECIFICATIONS

Application	Ft. Lbs. (mkg)
Upper Control Arm Ball Joint Nut	29 (4)
Lower Control Arm Ball Joint Nut	29 (4)
Steering Linkage Ball Joint Nut	14 (2)
Cross Yoke-to-Frame	101 (14)
Lower Control Arm	130 (18)
Shock Absorber Lower Mount	14 (2)
Steering Arm-to-Steering Knuckle	57 (8)
Upper Control Arm Clamping Bolt	21 (3)
Upper Control Arm-to-Body	60 (8)

MGB

MGB

DESCRIPTION

Suspension is control arm coil spring type. Shock absorbers are lever arm type and act as the upper control arm. Shock absorber is attached to kingpin and bolted to crossmember. Lower control arm is attached to kingpin and crossmember with fulcrum shafts. Coil spring is mounted between lower control arm and crossmember. Front suspension can be removed as an assembly.

ADJUSTMENT

WHEEL ALIGNMENT SPECIFICATIONS & PROCEDURES

See Wheel Alignment Specifications and Procedures in WHEEL ALIGNMENT Section.

WHEEL BEARING ADJUSTMENT

See Wheel Bearing Adjustment in WHEEL ALIGNMENT Section.

REMOVAL & INSTALLATION

COIL SPRING

Removal – Raise and support vehicle on safety stands, remove wheels. Remove stabilizer bar link from spring pans. Using suitable spring compressor (18G 693), compress spring and remove spring pan bolts from lower control arm. Release spring compressor, remove spring pan and spring.

Inspection – Before reinstalling coil spring make sure free length of coil spring is 10.6" (269 mm). Also, check that under a load of approximately 1010-1050 lbs. (581-599 kg) spring height is 7.4" (190 mm).

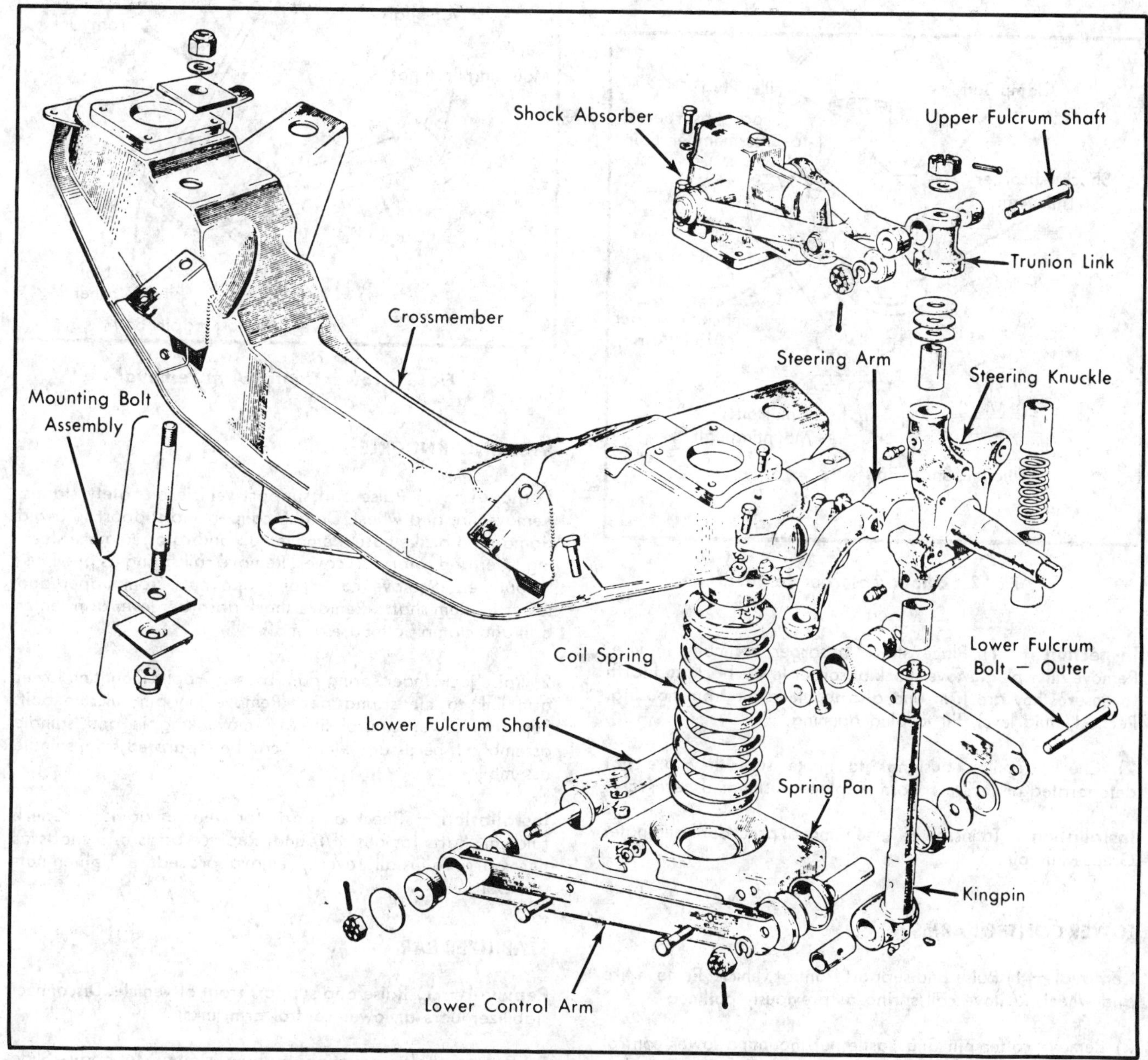

Fig. 1 Exploded View of Front Suspension Components for Part Identification

MGB (Cont.)

Installation – To install, reverse removal procedure and note: Shortest spring pan screw must be fitted to rear hole closest to wheel.

SHOCK ABSORBERS

Removal – **1)** Raise front of vehicle and place on safety stands. Use a floor jack placed under spring pan and raise spring until shock absorber is clear of rebound bumper.

2) Remove cotter pin and remove castle nut from fulcrum bolt. Loosen clamp bolt and center bolt on shock absorber arm.

3) Drive out fulcrum pin. Pry shock absorber halves apart and swing trunnion out of way. Wire steering knuckle to crossmember in an upright position. Remove 4 bolts mounting shock absorber to crossmember and slide out shock.

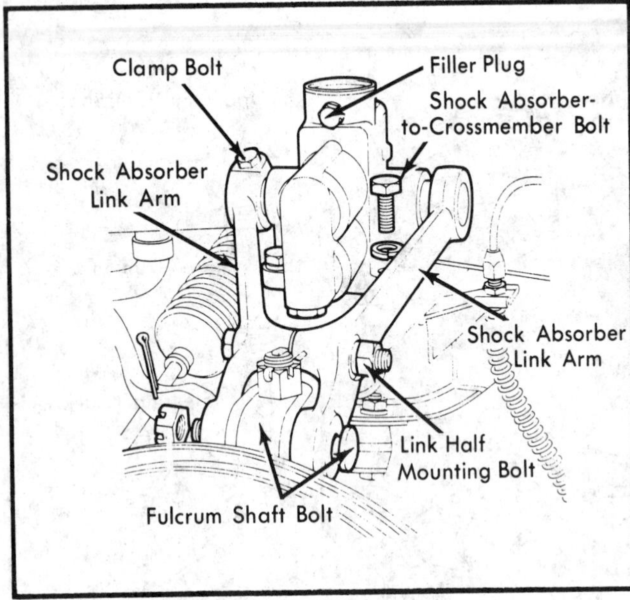

Fig. 2 Shock Absorber Removal

Inspection – **1)** Place shock absorber vertically in vise. Remove filler plug. Move shock absorber levers back and forth to ensure they are firm and also to bleed air from housing. Recheck fluid level, fill to plug opening.

2) Check trunnion bushings to make sure they are not deteriorated or severely worn. Replace bushings if necessary.

Installation – To install, reverse removal procedure and note: Grease kingpin.

LOWER CONTROL ARMS

Removal – **1)** Raise and support front of vehicle. Remove tire and wheel. Remove coil spring as previously outlined.

2) Remove cotter pin and castle nut mounting lower control arm link at kingpin. Remove cotter pin and castle nut mounting control arm link to pivot shaft.

3) Support hub assembly. Pull off front control arm link. Pull out control arm link mounting bolt at kingpin and force off back control arm link.

Inspection – Replace any bushings that show signs of excessive wear.

Installation – To install, reverse removal procedure and note: Make sure thrust washers face bushing correctly. Tighten castle nuts with vehicle weight on ground. If cotter pin cannot be fitted, tighten nut to next opening. Grease kingpin.

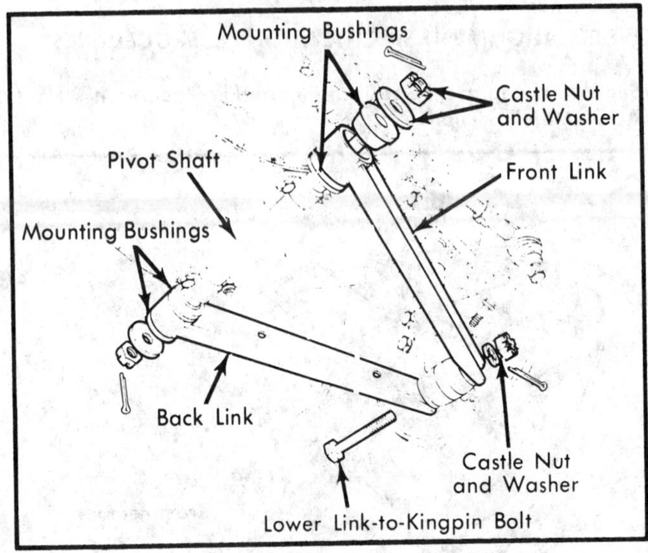

Fig. 3 Lower Control Arm Removal

STEERING KNUCKLE

Removal – **1)** Raise and support vehicle on safety stands. Remove tire and wheel. Detach caliper and support to avoid damage to brake hose. Remove hub and rotor. Remove steering lever and rotor dust cover. Remove coil spring as previously outlined. Remove cotter pins and nuts from upper and lower fulcrum shafts. Remove shock absorber lever arm center bolt and clamp bolt. Ease arm off.

2) Raise jack under spring pan. Loosen 2 bolts mounting lower arm link to the spring pan. Remove kingpin fulcrum bolt. Separate lower control links. Remove kingpin and spindle assembly. If necessary, kingpin can be separated from spindle assembly.

Installation – Check all parts for wear or damage. Check fulcrum shafts for out of round. Replace parts and shafts as necessary. To install, reverse removal procedure. Tighten nuts and bolts.

STABILIZER BAR

Removal – **1)** Raise and support front of vehicle. Disconnect stabilizer bars at lower control arm links.

2) Remove bolts mounting bushing clamps to body. Slide stabilizer bar from vehicle.

MGB (Cont.)

3) Pry mounting clamps away from bushings and slide bushings off stabilizer bar. Force link mounting bushings from each end of stabilizer bar. If bushings show signs of wear or severe deterioration, replace with new parts.

Installation – To install stabilizer bar, reverse removal procedure and note: If stabilizer bar is replaced put old locaters 9$^{5}/_{16}$" from center of new stabilizer bar.

FRONT SUSPENSION ASSEMBLY

Removal – **1)** Raise and support vehicle. Remove tire and wheel. Disconnect tie rods from steering knuckle. Disconnect stabilizer bar at lower control arm connecting links.

2) Remove 4 bolts mounting steering rack to crossmember. Tie rack to stabilizer bar.

3) Disconnect brake hose at bracket. Plug openings. Place floor jack under crossmember.

4) Put rods through holes in crossmember to retain body to crossmember studs. Loosen both REAR stud lock nuts keeping crossmember to body.

5) Work inside of engine compartment and remove lock nuts and washers from both FRONT mounting studs. Remove mounting pad from each rear stud. Lower suspension from vehicle.

Installation – To install suspension assembly, reverse removal procedure and note: Make sure all mounting pads are aligned. Make sure that REAR stud clamp plates have depressions facing toward mounting pad. Bleed brake system.

TIGHTENING SPECIFICATIONS

Application	Ft. Lbs. (mkg)
Shock Absorber Bolts	44 (6.1)
Brake Caliper Mounting Bolts	43 (6.0)
Crossmember-to-Body	55 (7.6)
Shock Absorber Pinch Bolt	28 (3.9)
Lower Control Arm Nuts	28 (3.9)
Stabilizer Bar Link Nut	60 (8.3)
Kingpin Nut	68 (8.3)

MG MIDGET

Midget

DESCRIPTION

Suspension is a control arm coil spring type. Shock absorber is a lever arm type and acts as upper control arm. Shock absorber is bolted to crossmember and attached to steering knuckle. Lower control arm is attached to frame and steering knuckle with fulcurm shafts. A coil spring is mounted between lower control arm and crossmember.

ADJUSTMENT

WHEEL ALIGNMENT SPECIFICATIONS & PROCEDURES

See Wheel Alignment Specifications & Procedures in WHEEL ALIGNMENT Section.

WHEEL BEARING ADJUSTMENT

See Wheel Bearing Adjustment in WHEEL ALIGNMENT Section.

REMOVAL & INSTALLATION

COIL SPRINGS

Removal – **1)** Place a wood block under shock absorber lever arm rubber stop. Raise and support vehicle on jack stands. Remove wheels.

2) Using a suitable spring compressor (18G 153) collapse spring. Remove nuts and bolts securing spring seat to lower control arm. Release spring pressure and remove spring.

Inspection – Before reinstalling coil spring make sure free length of coil spring is 9.85" (250 mm). Also, check that under a load of approximately 735-765 lbs. (331-343 kg) spring height is 7.08" (180 mm).

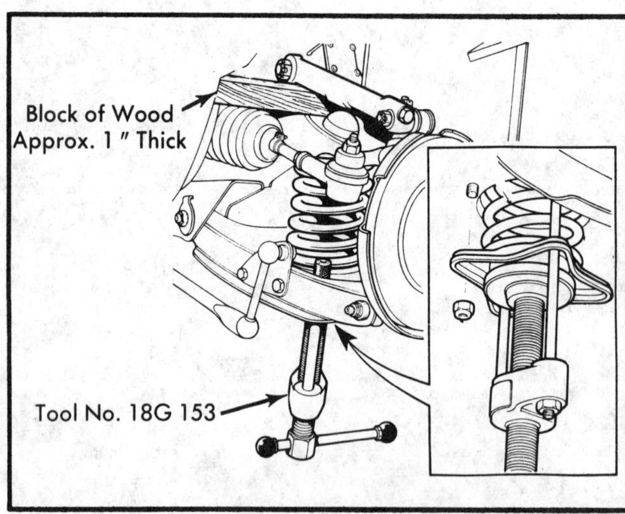

Fig. 1 Where to Place Tool When Compressing Front Spring for Removal

Installation – To install, reverse removal procedure. Remember to remove wood block.

STABILIZER BAR

Removal – Raise front of vehicle and place jack stands under front suspension. Remove screws and nuts to release end stops from stabilizer bar. Remove bolts mounting stabilizer bar rubber bushing bracket. Remove nuts mounting stabilizer bar links and remove from vehicle.

Installation – To install, reverse removal procedure and tighten all mounting hardware.

STUB AXLE ASSEMBLY

Removal – **1)** Remove front spring as previously outlined. Separate tie rod ball joint. Remove brake assembly. See *Midget in BRAKE Section.*

2) Remove dust shield. Separate stabilizer bar from lower arm. Remove clamp bolt at shock absorber. Remove trunnion link bolt. Remove bushings from trunnion link.

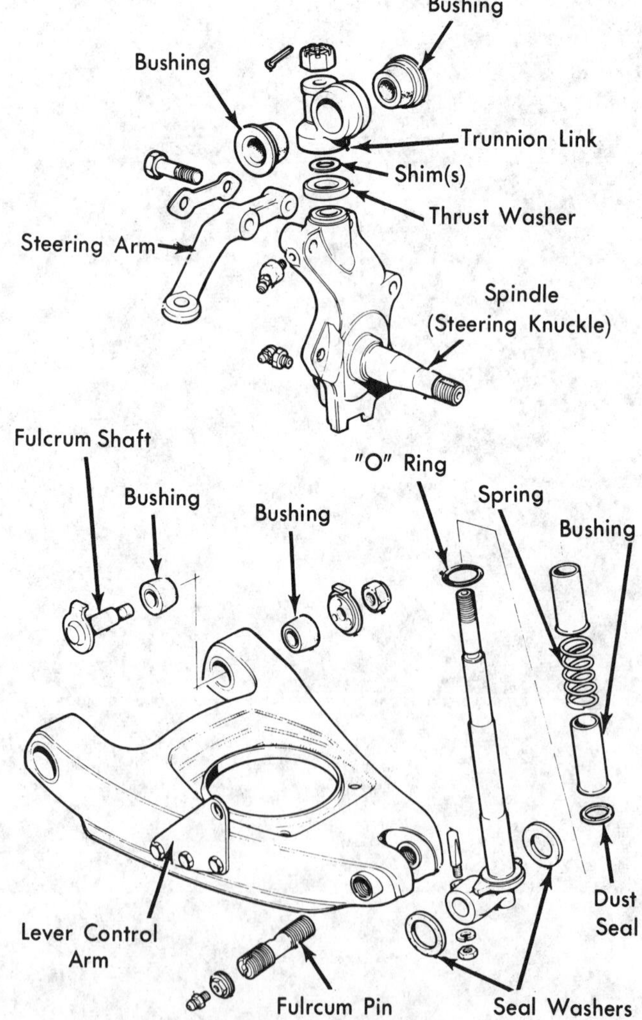

Fig. 2 Exploded View of Front Suspension Components

MG MIDGET (Cont.)

3) Remove nuts, washers, and fulcrum shaft from inside end of lower control arm. Force lower control arm down and remove from vehicle. Remove lower control arm bushings.

4) Remove upper kingpin mounting nut. Remove trunnion link with thrust washers and shims. Pivot out kingpin and separate spindle from kingpin.

5) Remove nut and take out fulcrum shaft. Tap out kingpin. Separate dust seal. Remove "O" ring. Take out steering arm mounting bolts and separate steering arm from spindle (steering knuckle).

Installation – **1)** Install new bushings with lubricating hole in bushing aligned with hole in kingpin. One end of bushing will easily enter housing. Bottom bushing must be flush with recess in housing. Ream bushings as necessary.

2) Fit dust seal. Install steering arm. Assemble kingpin to lower link arm by screwing fulcrum shaft into lower link. Use new dust seals. Install cotter pin.

3) Coat new "O" ring with oil and fit in bottom of kingpin. Fit thrust washers over kingpin. Refit shims.

4) Install trunnion with bore toward kingpin. Fit mounting nut. Check movement of kingpin from stop to stop, slight resistance should be felt. Make sure there is no vertical movement. Add or subtract shims to increase or decrease resistance.

5) To install the remaining components, reverse removal procedure.

SHOCK ABSORBERS

Removal & Installation – Raise and support vehicle on jack stands, remove wheels. Place jack under outer end of control arm and raise until shock lever arm is off its rubber stop. Remove nut and bolt from fulcrum shaft and remove shaft. Remove bolts securing shock absorber to frame. Remove shock absorber. Jack must remain under lower control arm while shock absorber is removed from vehicle. To install, reverse removal procedure; tighten bolts securing shock absorber-to-frame to 25-30 ft. lbs. (3.5-4.2 mkg).

OPEL

All Models

DESCRIPTION

Independent type suspension consisting of upper and lower control arms. Upper control arm pivots on a shaft bolt attached to crossmember and is connected to steering knuckle by a ball joint. Lower control arms are connected in same manor. A coil spring is mounted between lower control arm and crossmenber. Shock absorbers mount between top of upper control arm and inner fender panel. All vehicles are equipped with stabilizer bars.

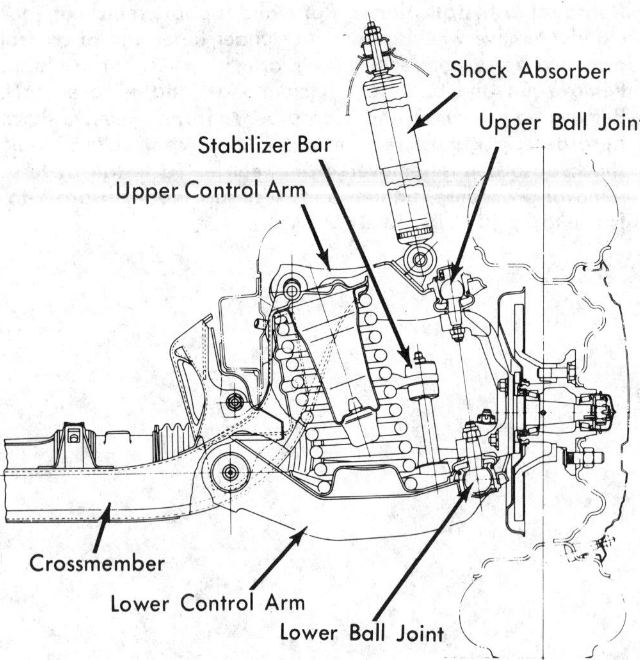

Fig. 1 Front View of Suspension Components Showing Relationship of Parts

ADJUSTMENTS

WHEEL ALIGNMENT SPECIFICATIONS & PROCEDURES

See Wheel Alignment Specifications and Procedures in WHEEL ALIGNMENT Section.

WHEEL BEARING ADJUSTMENT

See Wheel Bearing Adjustment in WHEEL ALIGNMENT Section.

BALL JOINT CHECKING

See Ball Joint Checking in WHEEL ALIGNMENT Section.

REMOVAL & INSTALLATION

SHOCK ABSORBER

Removal – Raise vehicle and suitably support with safety stands. Remove tire and wheel. Disconnect shock absorber from upper control arm. Working from inside engine compartment, remove shock absorber mounting nuts. Maneuver shock absorber from vehicle.

Installation – To install shock absorber, reverse removal procedure.

STABILIZER BAR

Removal – Raise vehicle and suitably support with safety stands. Remove protective under cover. Remove stabilizer bar mounting on lower control arm. Disconnect and remove clamps securing stabilizer bar to body.

Installation – Install new bushing on stabilizer bar. Install stabilizer bar and hold in place with mounting clamps. Fit stabilizer bar to lower control arms and tighten nut to end of bolt threads.

UPPER CONTROL ARM & BALL JOINT

Removal – 1) Raise vehicle and suitably support on safety stands. Remove tire and wheel. Remove upper brake caliper bolt and move hose clip back about 1/2". Disconnect lower end of shock absorber and compress upward. Using a jack, raise lower control arm until level, then support with jack stand.

2) Loosen upper ball joint and disconnect from steering knuckle using tool J-26407-1 (or equivalent). If only ball joint is being removed, take off two bolts connecting ball joint and control arm. If entire control arm is being taken off, remove pivot shaft bolt. Maneuver control arm from vehicle.

Installation – To install upper control arm and ball joint, reverse removal procedure and note the following. Fit ball joint so straight cut edge is outward.

LOWER CONTROL ARM, BALL JOINT AND COIL SPRING

Removal – Raise vehicle and suitably support with jack stands. Remove tire and wheel. Disconnect tie rod from steering knuckle. Disconnect and remove stabilizer bar from lower control arm. Remove upper caliper mounting bolt and slide hose clip back about 1/2".

2) Disconnect shock absorber lower mount and compress shock upward. Place a jack at outer edge of control arm and disconnect ball joint from steering knuckle. Suspend steering and hub assembly out of way.

3) With coil spring compressed until spring clears seat, lower jack under control arm. Using tools J-9519 and J-9519-14 (or equivalent) ball joint can be removed from control arm. If control arm is being removed, remove bolts connecting lower control arm to crossmember and body. Coil spring can now be removed.

Installation – To install, reverse removal procedure and note: Use installer J-9519 and receiver J-9519-4 (or equivalent) to install ball joint. **NOTE** – *DO NOT hammer on ball joint bottom.*

OPEL (Cont.)

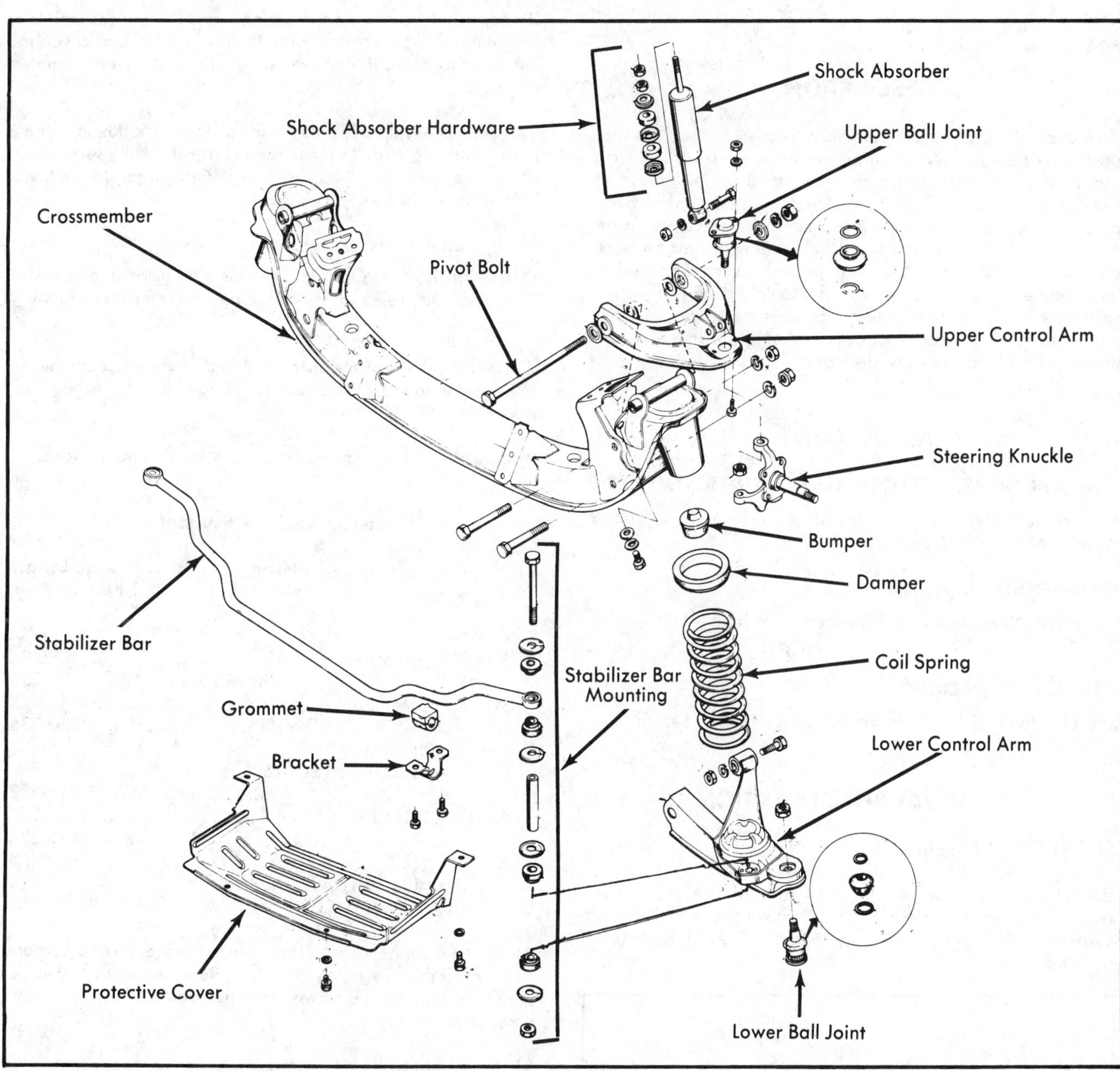

Fig. 2 Exploded View of Opel Front Suspension Components

STEERING KNUCKLE

Removal – 1) Raise vehicle and support on safery stands. Disconnect and compress shock absorber upward. Disconnect and remove caliper assembly, then hang with wire out of way. Disconnect tie rod from steering knuckle. Remove hub and rotor assembly from steering knuckle.

2) Raise lower control arm until level, then support at outside edge. Disconnect upper and lower ball joints from steering knuckle. Removal backing plate.

Installation – To install, reverse removal procedure and adjust wheel bearings.

TIGHTENING SPECIFICATIONS

Application	Ft. Lbs. (mkg)
Lower Control Arm Ball Joint-to-Steering Knuckle	58 (8.0)
Lower Control Arm-to-Crossmember	47 (6.5)
Lower Control Arm-to-Body	47 (6.5)
Upper Control Arm Ball Joint-to-Steering Knuckle	40 (5.5)
Upper Control Arm Ball Joint-to-Upper Control Arm	29 (4.0)
Shock Absorber-to-Upper Control Arm	29 (4.0)
Brake Caliper-to-Steering Knuckle	36 (5.0)

PEUGEOT

504
604

DESCRIPTION

An independent, strut front suspension is used. Wheels are supported by steering knuckles that are attached to vertical strut assemblies. Lower control arms are attached to bottom of steering knuckles by ball joints. Inner ends of control arms pivot on front crossmember. Attached to lower control arms are strut rods that run rearward to mounting points on back crossmember. Top of vertical strut assemblies are attached to inner fender panels. Coil springs fit into spring seats attached to strut assemblies. Hydraulic shock absorbers are built into strut assemblies. A stabilizer bar is mounted to frame and connected at ends to lower control arm.

ADJUSTMENT

WHEEL ALIGNMENT SPECIFICATIONS & ADJUSTMENTS

See Wheel Alignment Specifications and Adjustments in WHEEL ALIGNMENT Section.

FRONT WHEEL BEARINGS

See Front Wheel Bearing Adjustment in WHEEL ALIGNMENT Section.

BALL JOINT CHECKING

See Ball Joint Checking in WHEEL ALIGNMENT Section.

REMOVAL & INSTALLATION

FRONT STRUT ASSEMBLY

Removal – 1) Raise vehicle and place safety stands under front crossmember. Remove wheel. Remove brake caliper and suspend with a wire from underbody. DO NOT disconnect hydraulic line.

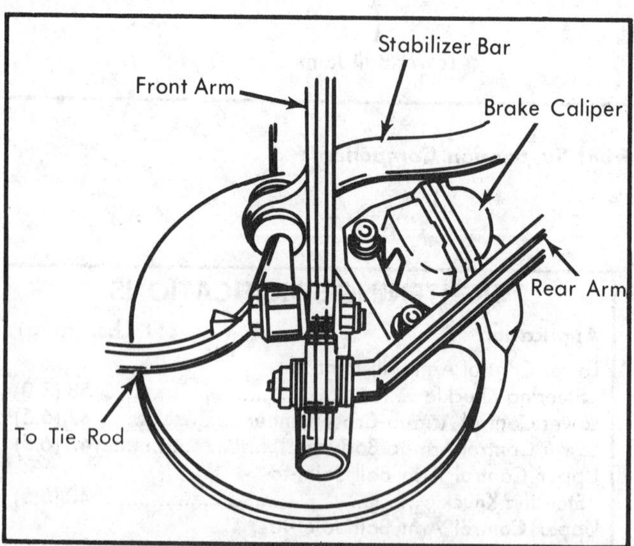

Fig. 1 Components That Must be Disconnected to Remove Strut Assembly

2) Separate tie rod from steering arm. Disconnect stabilizer bar at mounting on control arm. Remove control arm pivot bolt nut and tap bolt out. Remove nut mounting strut rod to control arm.

3) Take up weight of vehicle with a floor jack. Remove the 3 bolts mounting strut to inner fender panel. Make sure to disconnect ground wire. Support suspension and slowly lower jack with components to floor.

Disassembly, 504 Only – 1) Place strut horizontally in vise. Fit spring compressor over coil spring and compress enough to unseat spring.

2) Hold shock absorber piston rod and remove top nut. Slowly release tension on coil spring. Remove upper spring seat assembly and coil spring.

3) Measure coil spring free length and length under a load:

Coil Spring Specifications

Application	Free Length In. (mm)	Load Length 701 lbs. (318 kg)
Saloon①		
1 Red, 1 Green Stripe	19.7 (500)	8.86-9.1 225-230)
1 White, 1 Green Stripe	19.7 (500)	8.86-9.25 (230-235)
Coupes & Convertibles		
1 Red, 1 Yellow Stripe	16.8 (426.5)	8.42-8.66 (214-220)
1 Green, 1 Blue Stripe	16.8 (426.5)	8.66-8.82 (220-224)

① – From 504 A01, A02, A03.
② – From 504 B02, C02.

4) Remove rubber boot from shock absorber rod. Suspend strut assembly vertically in vise. Remove shock absorber mounting nut. Pull up slowly on piston rod and remove entire assembly.

5) Disassemble following components from piston rod:
- Support cup with rod seal.
- Thrust washer and upper spring.
- Bushing "O" ring.

6) Pry bumper and lower spring seat off strut housing. Take strut housing from vise and drain hydraulic fluid. Unscrew strut housing and remove compensator valve.

Inspection – Clean all components. Make sure that all components shown in *Fig. 2* are replaced during each overhaul.

Reassembly – 1) Place strut vertically in vise. Install recoil bumper with lower spring seat.

2) Install compensator valve to shock absorber tube by lightly tapping into position. Blow off valve and shock absorber tube with compressed air.

PEUGEOT (Cont.)

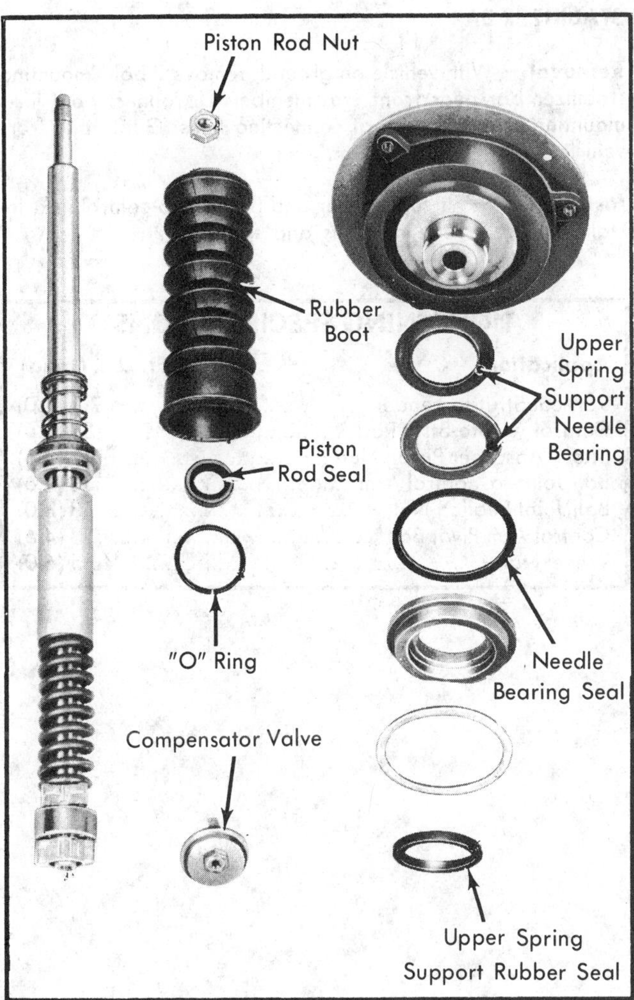

Fig. 2 Components That Must be Replaced

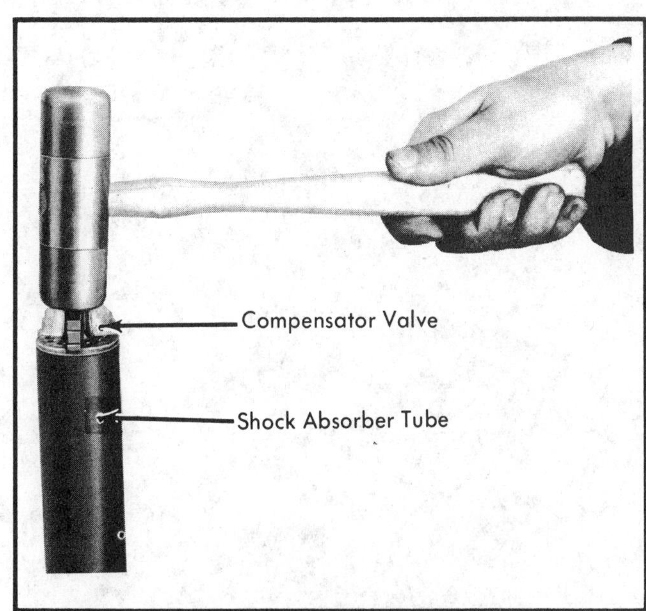

Fig. 3 How to Fit Compensating Valve to Shock Absorber Tube

3) Fit shock absorber tube to strut housing. Fill shock absorber with 10 ozs. (300 cc) of ESSO Olefluid 40X. Slide piston rod assembly into shock absorber tube. Make sure upper bushing has .12" (3 mm) clearance with upper shock absorber housing.

4) Next, insert components shown in *Fig. 4*.

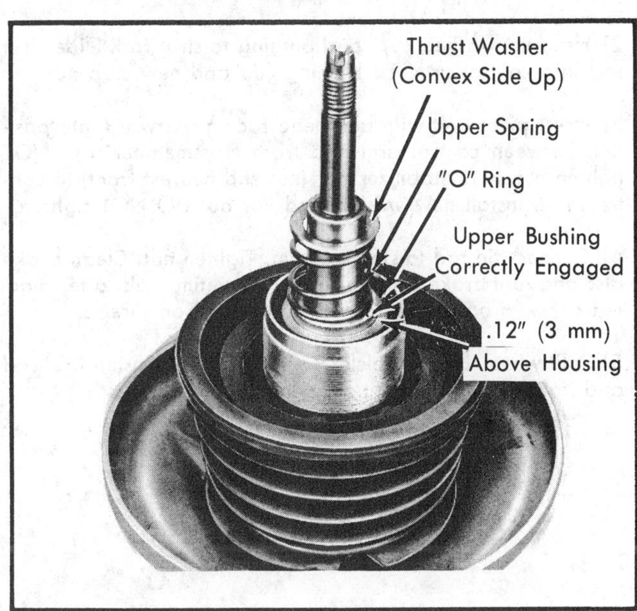

Fig. 4 Components That Mount on Top of Shock Absorber Piston Rod

5) Fit piston rod seal to cup. Place cup and seal over rod. Force assembly down until thrust washer engages spring. Tighten cap nut. Install rubber dust boot.

6) Fully extend piston rod and place holding clamp between bottom of dust boot and shock absorber cap nut. Place strut housing horizontally in vise.

7) Fit new seal to rebound buffer thrust ring. Reassemble upper spring seat components as shown in *Fig. 5*.

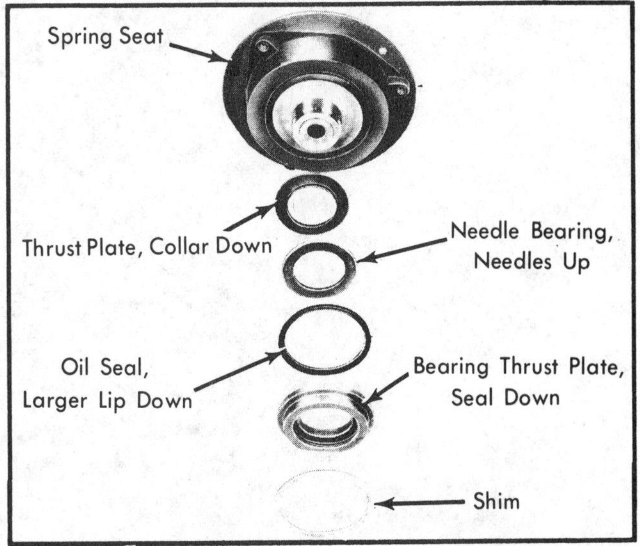

Fig. 5 Assembly Order for Upper Spring Seat Components

PEUGEOT (Cont.)

8) Fit coil spring and upper spring seat. Tighten spring compressor enough to fit locking nut.

Installation – **1)** Place assembled suspension on floor jack and guide upper mountings into position. Hook up ground wire. Install 3 upper mounting nuts.

2) Fit thrust washer, cup, and bushing to strut rod. Slide strut rod into control arm. Fit bushing cup and new stop nut.

3) Insert pivot bolt with bolt head facing rearward into position between control arm and front crossmember. DO NOT tighten nut. Refit stabilizer bar (nut end nearest front) to control arm. Install new washer and nut but DO NOT tighten.

4) Connect tie rod-to-steering arm. Tighten nut. Clean brake disc and refit brake caliper. Tighten mounting bolts after placing a few drops of Loctite (or equivalent) on threads.

5) Refit wheel. Lower vehicle. Push in front suspension strut rod and tighten all nuts to final torque.

STABILIZER BAR

Removal – With vehicle on ground, remove 2 bolts mounting stabilizer bar near front crossmember. Disconnect both links mounting stabilizer bar at connecting links. Guide bar from vehicle.

Installation – Fit cup, spacer and bushing to control link. Install stabilizer mounting bolts and spacers.

TIGHTENING SPECIFICATIONS

Application	Ft. Lbs. (mkg)
Vertical Strut-to-Fender	7.2 (1.0)
Control Arm-to-Strut Rod	33 (4.6)
Shock Absorber Piston Nut	33 (4.6)
Ball Joint-to-Control Arm	33 (4.6)
Ball Joint Sealing Nut	58 (8.0)
Control Arm Pivot Bolt	33 (4.6)
Wheel Nuts	43.5 (6.0)

PORSCHE 911S & TURBO CARRERA

911S & Turbo Carrera

DESCRIPTION

Independent strut type suspension with torsion bars. Strut assemblies are mounted to inner fender panels at top by thrust bearings. Bottom of strut assemblies are mounted to control arms by ball joints. Steering knuckle and shock absorbers are integral with individual strut assembly. Control arms pivot in mounts connected to body at front and in mounts integral with suspension crossmember at rear. Torsion bars anchor to control arm at front and to suspension crossmember at rear. Suspension crossmember also serves as mount for steering gear and is removable.

ADJUSTMENT

WHEEL ALIGNMENT SPECIFICATIONS & PROCEDURES

See Wheel Alignment Specifications & Procedures in WHEEL ALIGNMENT Section.

WHEEL BEARING ADJUSTMENT

See Wheel Alignment Specifications & Procedures in WHEEL ALIGNMENT Section.

BALL JOINT CHECKING

See Ball Joint Checking in WHEEL ALIGNMENT Section.

REMOVAL & INSTALLATION

STRUT ASSEMBLY AND THRUST BEARING

Removal – 1) Raise vehicle and place on safety stands under body. Remove wheel and tire. Remove brake rotor and brake caliper. **NOTE** – *See appropriate article in BRAKE SYSTEMS Section.*

2) Remove tie rod end strut nut and separate tie rod end from steering arm. Unscrew adjusting screw from torsion bar adjusting lever and remove lever. Remove ball joint retaining bolt at bottom of strut assembly and push control arm down to separate strut assembly from ball joint.

3) Remove center nut from upper strut assembly mount from inside luggage compartment. Remove lock washer, tab washer and strut assembly. Mark position of pressure plates on fender panel and remove Allen head bolts and pressure plates. Remove thrust , bearing and support.

NOTE – *Thrust bearing can be removed without completely removing strut assembly by disconnecting upper mount and pulling down on control arm to separate from thrust bearing.*

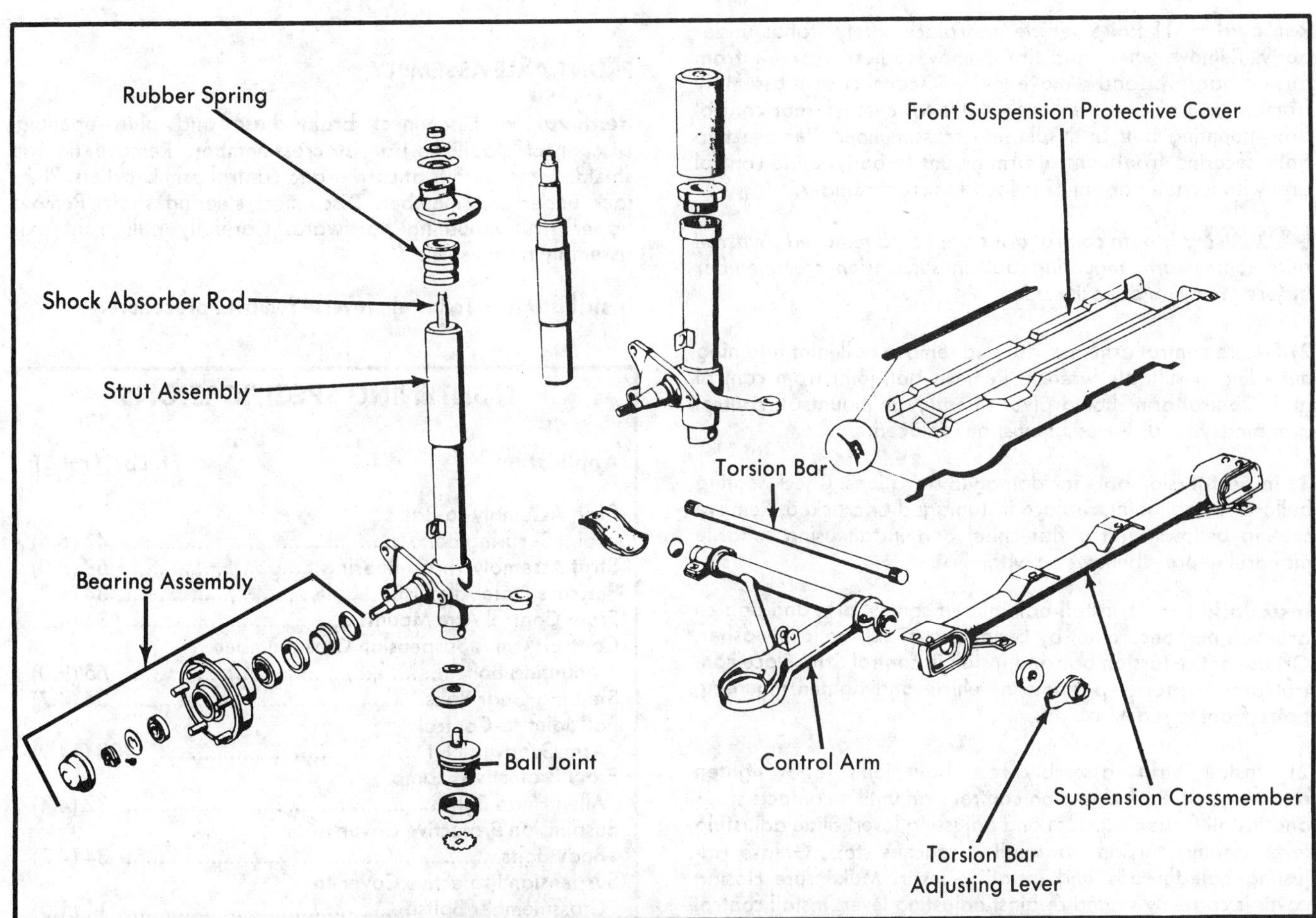

Fig. 1 Exploded View of Front Suspension Assembly

PORSCHE 911S & TURBO CARRERA (Cont.)

Installation – 1) Install thrust bearing and support. Place pressure plates in proper position and tighten Allen head bolts. Inspect strut assembly for leaks, if leak is discovered, strut assembly must be replaced.

2) Push rod to bottom of stroke, if flange does not bottom out against strut tube, replace strut assembly. There should be no variation of pressure when pushing in or pulling out on rod.

3) Install strut assembly in proper position in vehicle. Install hollow rubber spring, new lock washer, and tighten nut. Fit strut assembly to ball joint and tighten nut.

NOTE – *Make sure steel washer is between ball joint and stud.*

4) Push control arm lever down to stop and install adjusting lever on torsion bar. Grease threads of adjusting screw with suitable grease and install screw. Make sure closing cover is correctly seated against adjusting lever.

5) Install tie rod and retighten nut. Install remaining components. *See appropriate article in BRAKE SYSTEM Section.* Tighten all nuts and bolts, bleed brake system, check wheel alignment and riding height.

CONTROL ARM & BALL JOINT

Removal – 1) Raise vehicle and place safety stands under body. Remove wheel and tire. Remove adjusting screw from torsion bar lever and remove lever. Disconnect strut assembly from control arm as previously outlined. Remove rear control arm mounting bolt at suspension crossmember. Remove two bolts securing front control arm mount to body. Slide control arm with torsion bar out of suspension crossmember.

CAUTION – *If both control arms are being removed, reinstall rear control arm mounting bolt in suspension crossmember before removing opposite side.*

2) Secure control arm in a vise and remove ball joint retaining nut using a suitable wrench. Remove ball joint from control arm. Control arm should pivot smoothly in mounts. If control arm binds or is distorted, it must be replaced.

3) Inspect torsion bars for damaged serrations. Check sealing bellows on ball joint, replace if damaged or cracked. Remove sealing bellows with a flat chisel and install using suitable mandrel to press bellows on with.

Installation – 1) Install ball joint in control arm and tighten grooved nut. Secure nut by bending over tab on lock washer. Grease entire torsion bar and install in control arm. Place control arm in proper position in vehicle and tighten mounting bolts (front to rear).

2) Install strut assembly on ball joint and tighten retainingbolt. Push down on control arm until it contacts stops and install torsion bar seal and adjusting lever. Slide adjusting lever against torsion bar until it reaches stop. Grease adjusting bolt threads and install in lever. Make sure closing cover is correctly seated against adjusting lever. Install control arm protective cover. Install wheel and tire, lower vehicle and check riding height and wheel alignment.

SUSPENSION CROSSMEMBER

Removal – Raise vehicle and place safety stands under vehicle. Remove front axle protective cover. Remove steering gear bolts from crossmember. Remove rear control arm mounting bolts as previously outlined and remove suspension crossmember. Place crossmember on level surface and check for distortion. Inspect for cracks or damage.

Installation – Place crossmember in proper position in vehicle and install control arm mounting bolts as previously outlined. Install steering gear bolts and tighten. Install front suspension protective cover. Lower vehicle and check riding height and wheel alignment.

FRONT AXLE STABILIZER

Removal – Remove stabilizer shackles. Unbolt stabilizer lever retaining nuts and extract lever. Remove stabilizer mounting cover hardware and gently pry cover from vehicle.

Installation – Check all rubber grommets for signs of wear and replace components as necessary. Coat rubber parts with suitable lubricant. Reinstall stabilizer mounting cover, center stabilizer, then tighten attaching bolts. Seat stabilizer lever in position so stabilizer protrudes approximately .118" (3 mm) beyond lever. Tighten retaining nuts and install shackles.

FRONT AXLE ASSEMBLY

Removal – Disconnect brake hose and plug opening. Disconnect stabilizer bar at crossmember. Remove tie rod shield. Remove bolts at carrier and control arm brackets. Place jack under crossmember. Disconnect steering shaft. Remove upper strut mounting hardware. Carefully pull front axle assembly from vehicle.

Installation – To install, reverse removal procedure.

TIGHTENING SPECIFICATIONS

Application	Ft. Lbs. (mkg)
Strut Assembly-to-Ball Joint Securing Bolt	47 (6.5)
Strut Assembly Thrust Bearing	58 (8.0)
Pressure Plate Allen Head Bolts	34 (4.7)
Front Control Arm Mount	34 (4.7)
Control Arm & Suspension Crossmember Mounting Bolt	65 (9.0)
Steering Gear Bolts	34 (4.7)
Ball Joint-to-Control Arm Grooved Nut	108 (14.9)
Front Protective Clamp Allen Head Bolt	32 (4.4)
Suspension Protective Cover-to-Body Bolts	34 (4.7)
Suspension Protective Cover-to-Crossmember Bolts	11 (1.5)
Tie Rod End Strut Nut	32 (4.4)

PORSCHE 924

924

DESCRIPTION

Vehicle uses independent strut type front suspension. Lower control arms mount with a ball joint to steering knuckle. Back branch of control arm mounts to frame with "U" clamp around control arm pivot shaft. Front branch attaches to frame with bushings and pivot bolt. Strut assembly mounts at top to body with 3 nuts and at bottom to steering knuckle with 2 bolts. Tie rod mounts to steering knuckle with ball joint.

ADJUSTMENTS

WHEEL ALIGNMENT SPECIFICATIONS & PROCEDURES

See Wheel Alignment Specifications and Procedures in WHEEL ALIGNMENT Section.

WHEEL BEARING ADJUSTMENT

See Wheel Bearing Adjustment in WHEEL ALIGNMENT Section.

BALL JOINT CHECKING

See Ball Joint Checking in WHEEL ALIGNMENT Section.

REMOVAL & INSTALLATION

STRUT ASSEMBLY

Removal – 1) Raise vehicle so front suspension and front wheels are not supported.

2) Remove bolts mounting suspension strut to steering knuckle. Note that top bolt is one used to adjust front wheel camber.

3) Remove brake caliper assembly and suspend out of way. Pry or force suspension strut out of steering knuckle.

4) Support front suspension by hand. Also, support lower control arm and related components. Work inside engine compartment and remove upper strut mounting nuts. Guide out assembly.

Disassembly – 1) Fit strut to spring compressor. Slightly collapse coil spring. Remove shock absorber piston rod nut. Take off the following:

- Stop
- Seal
- Bearing flange
- Bearing
- Spring seat

2) Slowly release spring pressure, remove coil spring. Lift off rubber buffer and protective sleeve. Hold shock absorber upright and work piston rod through entire stroke several different times. Equal pressure must be felt in both directions. Remove cap nut and take out shock absorber.

Reassembly – 1) Place shock absorber in strut tube and fit cap nut. Slide on protective sleeve and buffer. Engage coil spring into lower seat.

NOTE – *If new coil is being installed, make sure it is same class of one on opposite side. Springs are available in 3 classes and each class is identified by RED paint stripe(s).*

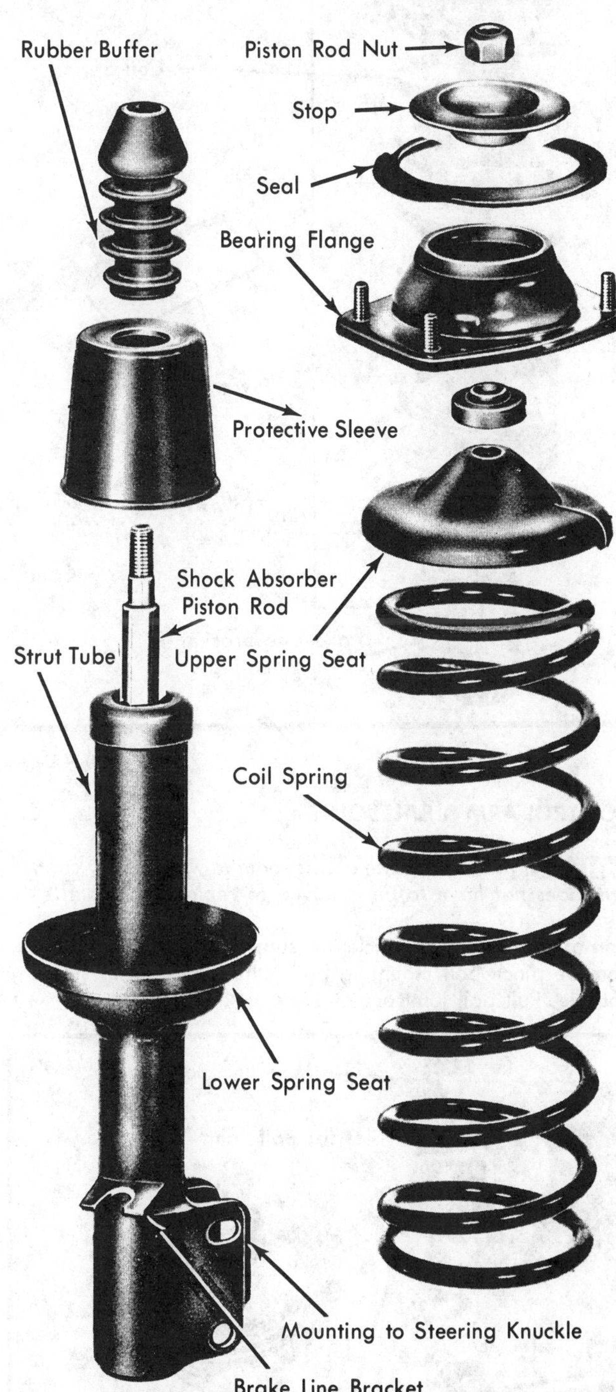

Fig. 1 Exploded View of Strut Assembly

2) Fit coil spring to compressor and collapse coil enough to allow piston rod threads to be exposed after upper mounting hardware is fitted. Tighten piston rod lock nut. Release spring pressure.

Installation – To install, reverse removal procedure and check front wheel alignment.

PORSCHE 924 (Cont.)

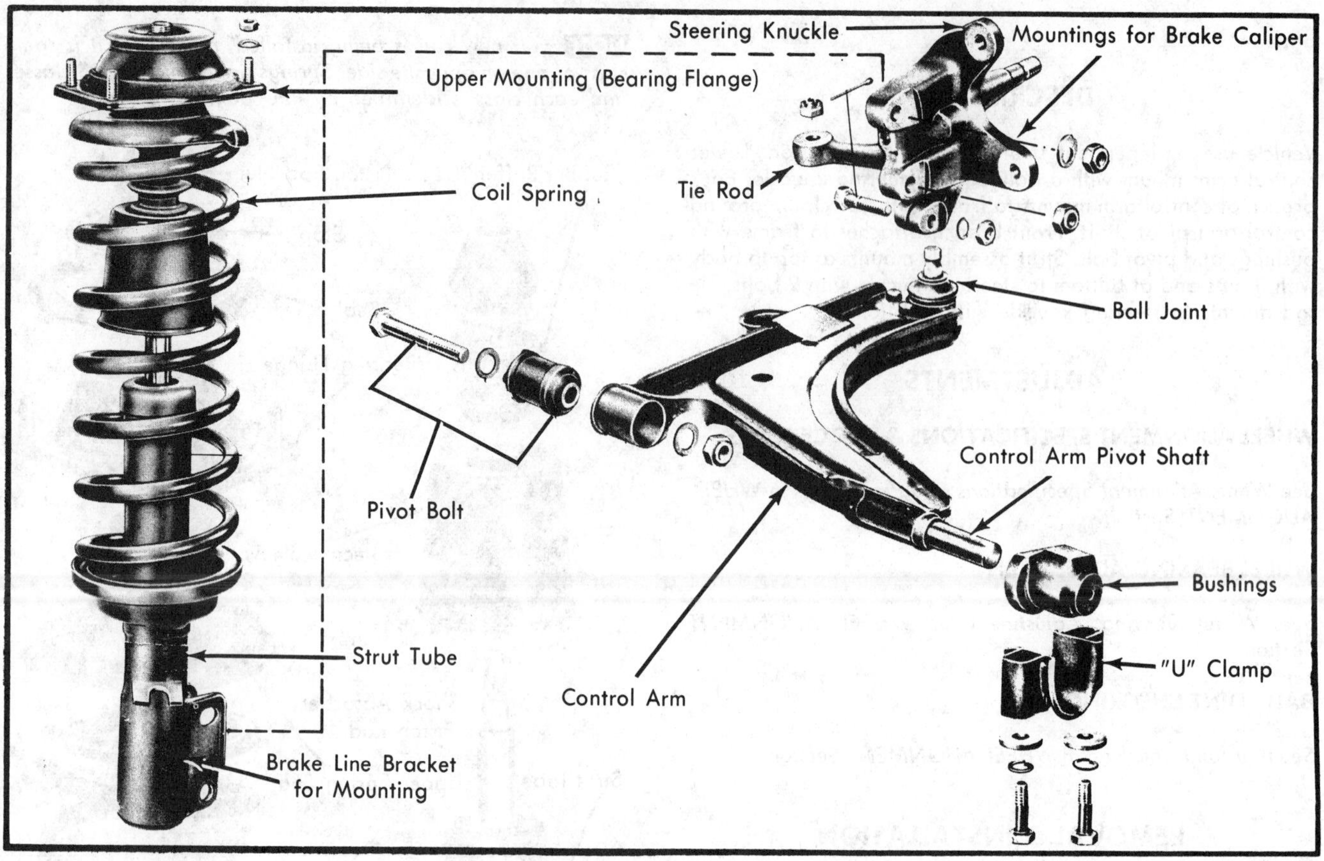

Exploded View of Front Suspension

CONTROL ARM & BALL JOINT

NOTE – *If there is enough access room to work, lower control arm does not have to be removed to replace ball joint.*

Removal – **1)** Raise vehicle and support so suspension is free. Remove pinch bolt mounting ball joint in bottom of steering knuckle. Pull ball joint out of steering knuckle.

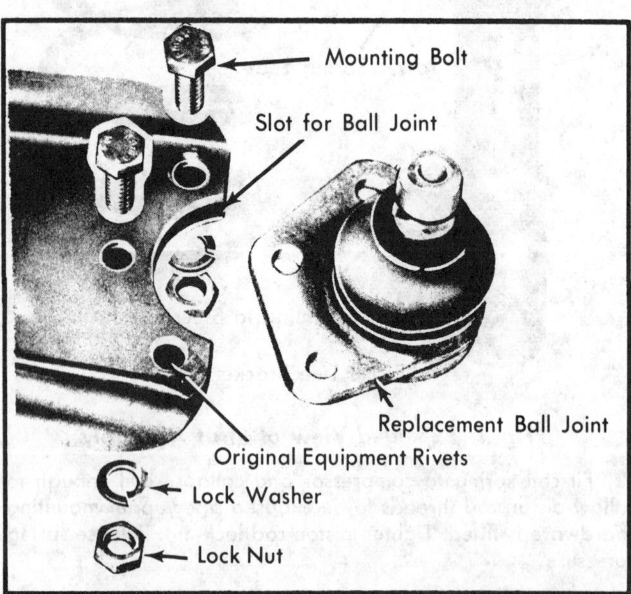

Fig. 3 Ball Joint Location in Control Arm.

2) If control arm is not being removed, drill through ball joint rivets with about 15/64" (6 mm) bit. Chisel off rivet heads. Fit new ball joint into slot on control arm and install bolts so heads are on top.

3) If control arm is being removed, take out mounting pivot bolt and "U" clamp housing inner pivot pin. Slide out control arm. For ball joint replacement, refer to step **2)**.

Inspection – Check control arm bushings. If bushings are bad they can be replaced. Press out worn bushings. Select new bushing and press into position. Make sure new bushings do not twist when seating into position.

Installation – To install, reverse removal procedure.

TIGHTENING SPECIFICATIONS

Application	Ft. Lbs. (mkg)
Control Arm-to-Crossmember	40-54 (5.5-7.5)
"U" Clamp Bolts	30 (4.2)
Toe Rod Castle Nut	21 (2.9)
Piston Rod Nut	56-58 (7.7-8.8)
Strut-to-Steering Knuckle	51-72 (7.0-10.0)
Upper Strut Mount	15-21 (2.1-2.9)
Ball Joint-to-Control Arm (Replacement)	18 (2.5)
Ball Joint Pinch Bolt	36-43 (5.0-6.0)

RENAULT R-5

R-5

DESCRIPTION

Independent type suspension, consisting of upper and lower control arms with stub axles mounted between upper and lower control arms by ball joints. Upper control arm pivots on shaft attached to frame. Lower arm pivots on shaft secured to crossmember. Shock absorbers mount off body brackets at top and off purchases built into control arm on bottom.

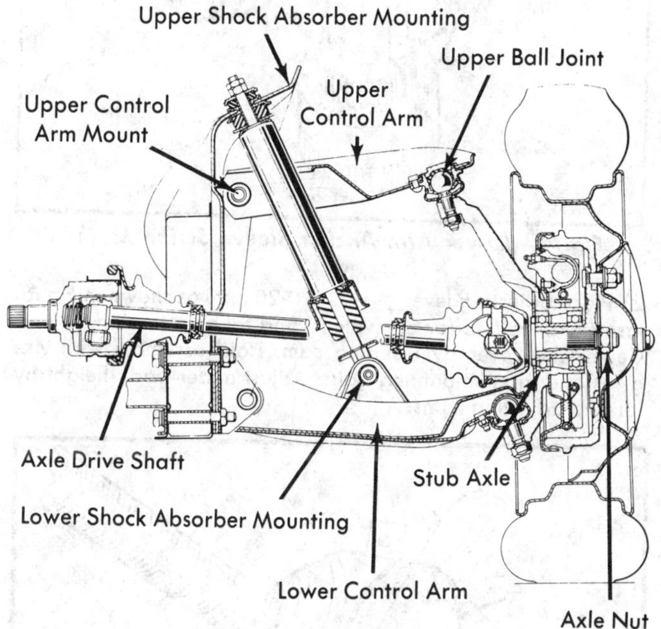

Fig. 1 Cut-Away View of Renault R-5 Front Suspension

ADJUSTMENT

WHEEL ALIGNMENT SPECIFICATIONS & PROCEDURES

See Wheel Alignment Specifications & Procedures in WHEEL ALIGNMENT Section.

WHEEL BEARING ADJUSTMENT

See Wheel Bearing Adjustment in WHEEL ALIGNMENT Section.

BALL JOINT CHECKING

See Ball Joint Checking in WHEEL ALIGNMENT Section.

RIDING HEIGHT ADJUSTMENT

See Riding Height Adjustment in WHEEL ALIGNMENT Section.

REMOVAL & INSTALLATION

SHOCK ABSORBERS

Removal – Raise vehicle and suitably support vehicle with safety stands. Remove lock nut, mounting nut, and bushing attaching shock absorber to upper bracket. Remove lower retaining bolt holding shock absorber to lower control arm. Maneuver shock absorber from vehicle.

Installation – To install, reverse removal procedure.

UPPER CONTROL ARM & BALL JOINT

Removal – Take out overflow tank and remove ignition coil. Using tool T. Av. 476 (or equivalent) disconnect upper ball joint. Remove nut from inboard edge of pivot shaft. Place a lock nut on outer end of pivot shaft and turn mounting nut to remove shaft. Pivot shaft will clear brake lines. Maneuver control arm from vehicle.

Inspection & Replacement – Inspect rubber bushings for cracks or distortion. Use a press and mandrel to remove and replace worn bushings. To replace ball joint, place control arm in a vise and drill out rivet heads. Fit new ball joint with shim placed on top of control arm. Tighten nuts and bolts (those that replaced rivets). Make sure bolt head is installed on dust cover side of joint.

Installation – To install, reverse removal procedure and note following: Apply a light coat of grease to pivot shaft before inserting in control arm. If ball joint has been replaced, check wheel alignment and steering box height.

LOWER CONTROL ARM & BALL JOINT

Removal – 1) Raise front of vehicle and place on safety stands. Remove stub axle nut. Disconnect and remove torsion bars. Disconnect sway bar from brackets and mounting on control arm. Separate bottom of shock absorber from mounting.

2) Remove lower control arm from crossmember. Put tool T. Av. 235 (or equivalent) in brake drum or hub. With a spacer located between thrust screw and axle drive shaft, force shaft inward and free ball joint from stub axle carrier. **NOTE** – *Make sure axle drive shaft is not removed.*

Inspection and Replacement – 1) Inspect rubber bushings and sleeve inserts for cracks, excessive damage or wear. Use a mandrel and press out worn bushings and press in new ones. Make sure each bushing is centered and has adequate protrusion out each side of control arm.

2) Place control arm in suitable holding fixture (vise). Chisel or drill out rivet heads. Remove nuts, if necessary. Separate joint from control arm. Fit new ball joint into control arm. Make sure bolt heads face dust cover side.

Installation – To install, reverse removal procedure and note following: Make sure castor adjusting shims are under bushing. Check wheel alignment after reinstallation.

STUB AXLE

Removal – Raise vehicle and place on safety stands. Remove hub and disc assembly. Using tool T. Av. 476 (or equivalent) disconnect upper and lower ball joints, then separate steering arm ball joint. Use a slide hammer and withdraw drum/hub assembly. Make sure axle drive shaft does not drop.

Installation – Install stub axle into position while guiding ball joints into position. Pull drive shaft into carrier housing. Refit brake components. Tighten stub axle nut.

RENAULT R-5 (Cont.)

TORSION BAR

Removal – 1) Slide seat forward and tilt seat. Loosen lock nut and turn cam screw counterclockwise to zero. Raise vehicle and place on safety stands. Remove dust cover from adjusting lever. Fit special tool 545 (or equivalent) in adjusting lever. From inside vehicle, remove lever housing attachment bolts. Remove housing cover cam assembly from adjusting lever, then slowly release pressure on wrench.

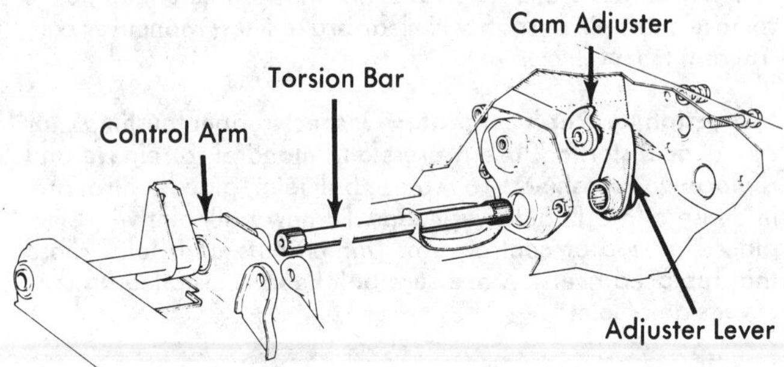

Fig. 2 Exploded View of Torsion Bar Assembly

2) Index mark position of adjusting lever with floor crossmember. Mark position of torsion bar on lower arm anchor sleeve. Disconnect stabilizer bar brackets. Remove bar from arm and check that mark made on lower arm anchor sleeve is aligned with punch mark on torsion bar. If punch marks do not align, count number of revolutions and spines displaced to align marks.

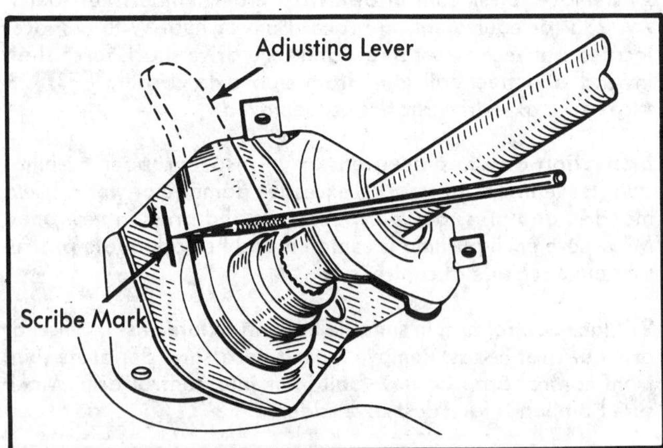

Fig. 3 Scribe Marks on Floor Crossmember

Installation – 1) Lightly grease torsion bar ends with grease. Reassemble cover seal, cam housing, and adjusting lever over torsion bar. Insert bar into lower control arm, aligning index mark made during installation. Fit adjusting lever on splines, aligning with mark on floor crossmember.

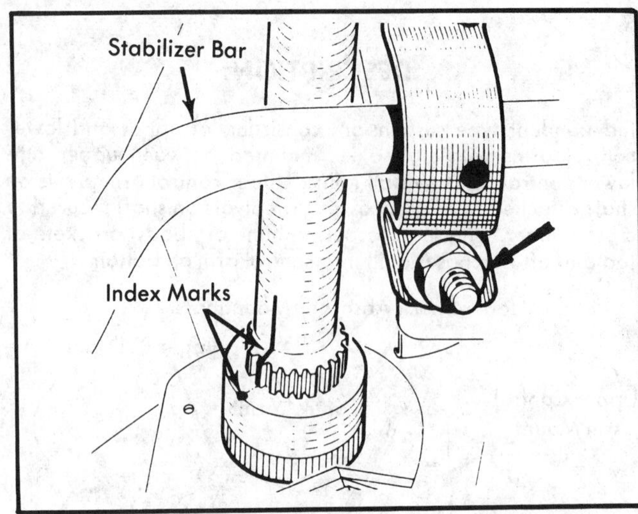

Fig. 4 Lower Arm Anchor Sleeve Scribe Mark

2) Place adjusting lever 3/8-3/4" (10-20 mm) as shown in *Fig. 5*. Insert wrench 545 (or equivalent) and take up tension on bar. Center the cover by resetting cam. Hold assembly with vise grips and insert mounting bolts. Adjust under body height by turning adjusting cams.

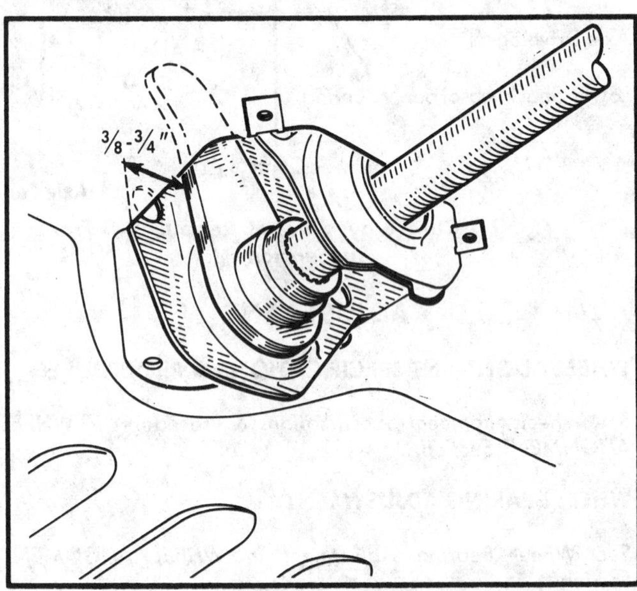

Fig. 5 Position of Adjusting Lever

TIGHTENING SPECIFICATIONS

Application	Ft. Lbs. (mkg)
Lower Shock Absorber Bolt	30 (4.2)
Lower Ball Joint	40 (5.5)
Upper Ball Joint	25 (3.5)
Lower Control Arm Nuts	75 (10.4)
Axle Nut	90 (12.4)

RENAULT R-12 & R-17

R-12
R-17

DESCRIPTION

Independent type front suspension with coil springs. Wheel is supported by steering knuckle mounted between upper and lower control arms by means of ball joints. Hydraulic double acting shock absorbers are mounted between upper control arm and chassis with coil spring mounted to upper portion of shock absorber. A strut rod is connected to chassis and upper control arm. A stabilizer bar is bolted to chassis and to ball joint of upper control arm link.

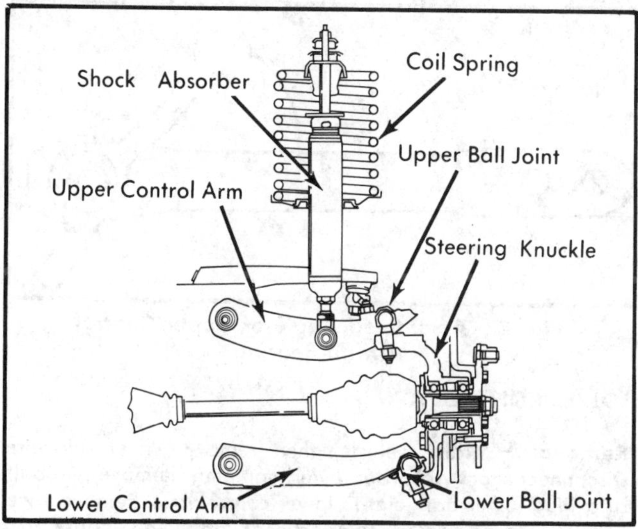

Fig. 1 Sectional View of Front Suspension Assembly

ADJUSTMENT

WHEEL ALIGNMENT SPECIFICATIONS & PROCEDURES

See Wheel Alignment Specifications and Adjustments in WHEEL ALIGNMENT Section.

WHEEL BEARINGS

See Wheel Bearing Adjustment in WHEEL ALIGNMENT Section.

BALL JOINT CHECKING

See Ball Joint Checking in WHEEL ALIGNMENT Section.

REMOVAL & INSTALLATION

FRONT SUSPENSION ASSEMBLY

Removal - Raise and support vehicle. Remove wheel and disconnect steering arm at rack end. Install spring compressor then disconnect top of shock absorber. Loosen lock nut at bottom of shock absorber and unscrew shock absorber until it can be removed with coil spring attached. Disconnect strut rod and stabilizer bar from upper control arm. Remove nuts and bolts secruing upper control arm. Remove nuts and bolts securing lower control arm. Remove hub and brake assembly without disconnecting brake hose. Slowly pull suspension assembly from vehicle separating steering knuckle from axle. **NOTE** – *Do not pull from gear box.*

Installation – Coat axle splines with Molykote and reverse removal procedure. Tighten all nuts and bolts.

UPPER CONTROL ARM & BALL JOINTS

Removal – Raise and support vehicle. Remove wheel and disconnect strut rod and stabilizer bar from upper control arm. Using suitable tool (T.Av 476), remove steering arm ball joint and steering knuckle ball joint. Remove nut secruing upper control arm pivot shaft and remove pivot shaft. Disconnect shock absorber from upper control arm and remove control arm.

Installation – To install, reverse removal procedure. Coat control arm pivot shaft with suitable grease and tighten all nuts and bolts.

LOWER CONTROL ARM & BALL JOINT

Removal – Raise and support vehicle and remove wheel. Using a suitable tool (T.Av 476), disconnect lower control arm ball joint. Disconnect and remove lower control arm pivot shaft and remove lower control arm.

Installation – To install, reverse removal proceedure. Coat control arm pivot shaft with suitable grease and tighten all nuts and bolts.

UPPER & LOWER BALL JOINTS

Removal – Using a suitable tool (T.Av 476) disconnect ball joint, then drill out rivets secruing ball jont and remove ball joint.

Installation – To install, reverse removal procedure, replacing rivets with nuts and bolts. **NOTE** – *Place bolt head on same side as dust cover.*

STEERING KNUCKLE

Removal – Raise and support vehicle, then remove wheel. Place spacer between lower schock absorber mount and lower control arm pivot shaft. Remove hub and brake assembly without disconnecting brake hose. Separate three ball joints using suitable tool (T.Av 476). After disconnecting ball joints, remove steering knuckle. NOTE – ***Do not pull axle from transaxle assembly.***

Installation – Coat axle splines with Molykote and reverse removal procedure. Tighten all nuts and bolts.

TIGHTENING SPECIFICATIONS

Application	Ft. Lbs. (mkg)
Upper Control Arm-to-Chassis	75 (10.4)
Lower Control Arm-to-Chassis	80 (11.1)
Steering Arm Ball Joint	25 (3.4)
Lower Ball Joint	35 (4.8)
Upper Ball Joint	35 (4.8)
Shock Absorber Lower Lock Nut	45 (6.2)

SAAB

99

DESCRIPTION

Independent front suspension with coil springs. Wheel is supported by steering knuckle mounted between upper and lower control arms by means of ball joints. Both upper and lower control arms pivot on shafts connected to body. Coil springs fit in pockets built into body at top and in supports attached to upper control arms at bottom. Hydraulic shock absorbers mount between lower control arm and body. If stabilizer bar is used, it is attached to frame and connected at ends to lower control arms.

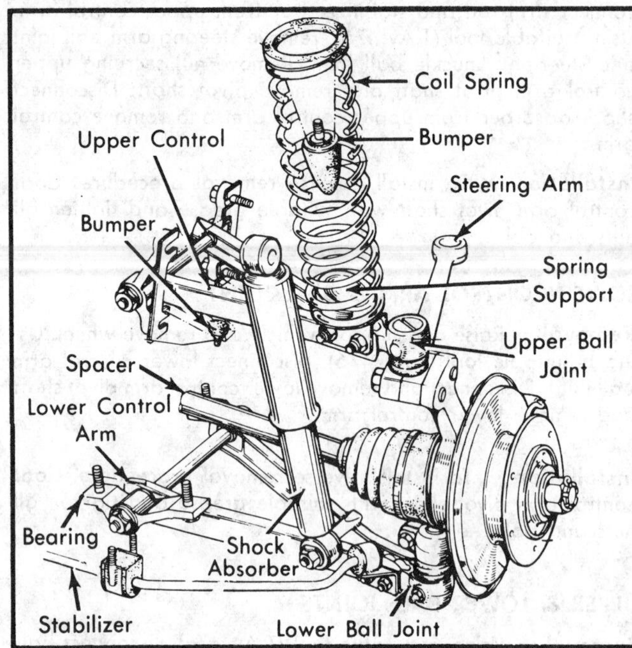

Fig. 1 Saab Front Suspension Assembly with Relationship of Components

ADJUSTMENT

WHEEL ALIGNMENT SPECIFICATIONS & PROCEDURES

See Wheel Alignment Specifications and Procedures in WHEEL ALIGNMENT Section.

WHEEL BEARING ADJUSTMENT

See Wheel Bearing Adjustment in WHEEL ALIGNMENT Section.

BALL JOINT CHECKING

See Ball Joint Checking in WHEEL ALIGNMENT Section.

REMOVAL & INSTALLATION

SHOCK ABSORBERS

Removal – Raise vehicle and place safety stands under frame. Remove wheel and tire. Remove nuts securing shock absorber and remove shock.

Installation – To install, reverse removal procedure.

UPPER CONTROL ARM

Removal – Raise and support front of vehicle. Remove tire and wheel. Remove shock absorber. Compress coil spring using a suitable compressor (8995839). Remove two bolts attaching upper ball joint to upper control arm. Remove bolts attaching upper control arm bearing brackets, remove compressed coil spring, upper control arm and bearings. **NOTE** – *Save spacers under bearings, and note number of spacers under each reassembly reference.*

Installation – Replace worn or damaged components. If bearings have been removed from control arm, position onto control arm so when both nuts are tightened and locked, angle between arm and bearing will be 52°±2°. Install upper control arm but do not install bearing locating bolts. Make sure spacer and support ring of upper spring seat are in position, then locate compressed coil spring with rubber buffer, and mount ball joint and lower spring seat onto control arm. Install bearing attaching bolts while ensuring that spacers are in position. Slowly release compressor tool to release coil spring. Install shock absorber, wheel and tire. Recheck wheel alignment.

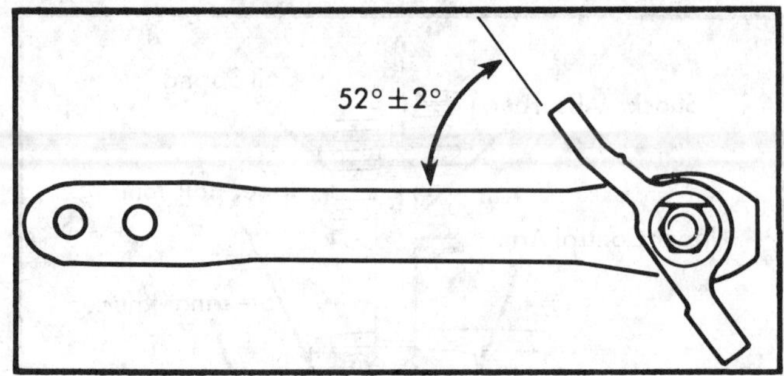

Fig. 2 Assembled Angle of Upper Control Arm-to-Bearing

LOWER CONTROL ARM

Removal – Raise vehicle, then remove wheel and tire. Disconnect shock absorber lower mounting. Remove two bolts attaching lower ball joint to lower control arm. Remove lower control arm-to-engine compartment attaching bolts, then remove lower control arm and brackets.

Installation – Replace worn or damaged components. if bearings have been removed from control arm, position onto control arm so when both nuts are tightened and locked, angle between arm and bearing will be 18°±2°. Install control arm and brackets, attach ball joint to control arm and tighten all attaching bolts. Install wheel and tire. Recheck wheel alignment.

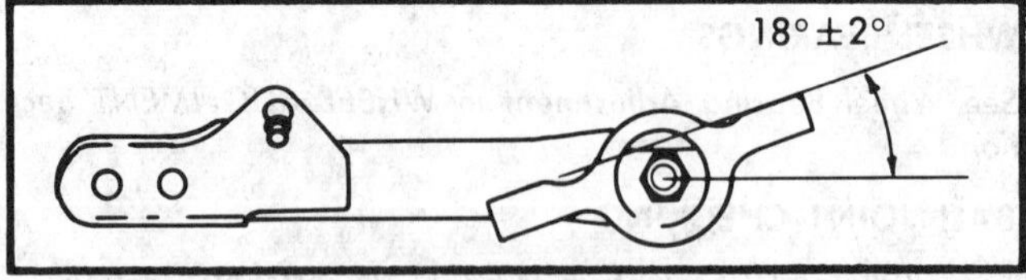

Fig. 3 Lower Control Arm-to-Bearing Angle

BALL JOINTS

Removal – Raise vehicle. Remove tire and wheel. Remove caliper and hang out of way. Remove ball joint nut. Using suitable tool (8995409) separate ball joint from steering knuckle.

Installation – Fit new ball joint to steering knuckle. Tighten nut. Insert ball joint mounting bock into control arm and tighten using new lock nuts. Reinstall brake caliper.

SUBARU

1600

DESCRIPTION

Suspension is strut type, utilizing a hydraulic shock absorber/coil spring assembly forming a strut. Strut is secured at top to body and at bottom to steering knuckle. Steering knuckle pivots on ball joint attached to lower control arm. Lower control arms are attached to front crossmember. Radius rods are welded to lower control arms and attached to rear crossmember with rubber bushings, washers, and nuts. A stabilizer bar is also used and attached to rear crossmember and to radius rods with clamps and rubber bushings.

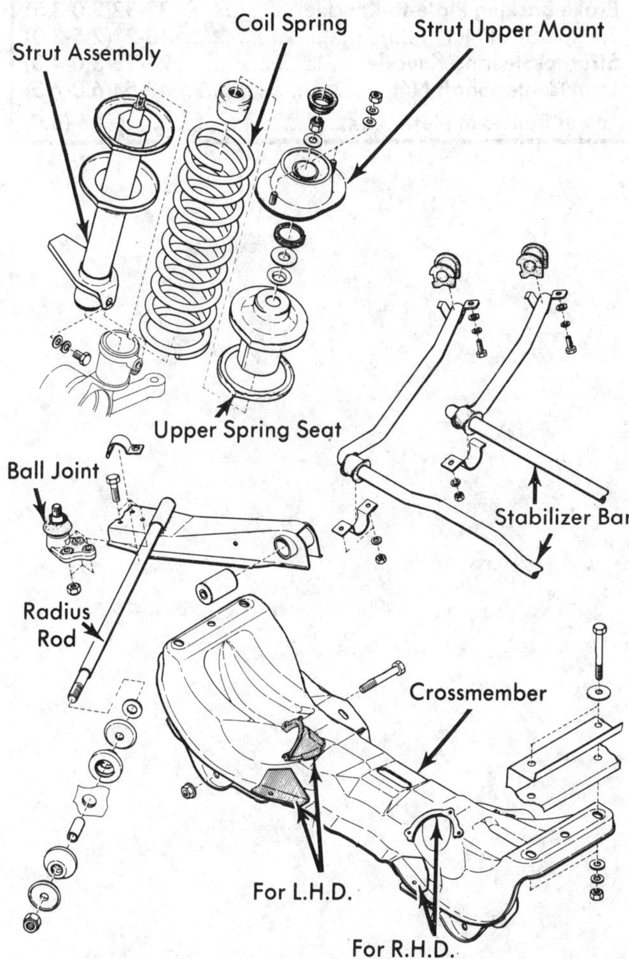

Fig. 1 Exploded View of Front Suspension

ADJUSTMENT

WHEEL ALIGNMENT SPECIFICATIONS & PROCEDURES

See Wheel Alignment Specifications and Procedures in WHEEL ALIGNMENT Section.

WHEEL BEARING ADJUSTMENT

See Wheel Bearing Adjustment in WHEEL ALIGNMENT Section.

BALL JOINT CHECKING

See Ball Joint Checking in WHEEL ALIGNMENT Section.

REMOVAL & INSTALLATION

FRONT SUSPENSION

Removal – 1) Disconnect battery ground cable. Disconnect parking brake cable bracket on control arm. Remove axle nut and pull brake drum off using a suitable puller (925200000). Disconnect flex brake lines from steel brake lines. Separate backing plate assembly from steering knuckle. On vehicles equipped with disc brakes, disconnect parking brake cable from caliper. Remove outer cable clip and remove cable bracket from housing mount.

2) Drive pins out of "U" joints at transaxle. Remove control arm pivot bolt. Disconnect stabilizer bar-to-radius rod clamps, then remove radius rod-to-rear crossmember attaching nut, washer, and rubber bushing. Remove tie rod stud nut and separate tie rod from steering knuckle using a puller. Remove strut assembly upper mounting nuts, pull "U" joint from transaxle and remove complete suspension assembly. Follow same procedure for removal of opposite side suspension assembly.

Installation – To install suspension assembly, reverse removal procedure. Tighten control arm-to-crossmember attaching bolt with weight off of front wheels. Replace all self-locking nuts with new ones during installation. Check wheel alignment. Bleed brake system.

STRUT ASSEMBLY

Removal – Raise and support front of vehicle on safety stands. Remove wheels. Remove bolt securing strut assembly to steering knuckle. Disconnect tie-rod from steering knuckle. Pull down on control arm, separating strut assembly from steering knuckle. Remove upper strut assembly mounting nuts and remove strut assembly.

Disassembly – 1) Install strut assembly in a holding fixture and spring compressor. Collapse coil spring until upper spring seat is clear of spring. Hold upper mount by attaching holding tool 925170000 (or equivalent) to bolts and remove nut from center shaft.

2) Pull strut mount from rod, remove thrust washer with oil seal and thrust bearing. Pull off upper spring retainer. Loosen spring compressor and remove spring when completely released.

Inspection – Push and pull center shaft in and out of strut assembly. Pressure should be equal during both strokes. Replace strut assembly if defective. Check outer layer of thrust washer for cracks or wear. Check sliding surface of thrust bearing for wear or cracking. Inspect sealing lip of oil seal for damage.

Reassembly – To assemble strut, reverse disassembly procedure. Apply grease to sealing lip of seal. Position thrust washer so that machined surface is facing coil spring. Tighten upper strut mount.

Installation – To install strut assembly, reverse removal procedure. Tighten all bolts and nuts, then check wheel alignment.

SUBARU (Cont.)

STABILIZER BAR

Removal – Raise front of vehicle, and support with safety stands. Remove clamps securing stabilizer bar to radius rod. Remove clamps attaching stabilizer bar to rear crossmember.

Installation – Check all bushings for wear or damage and replace as necessary. Check stabilizer bar for possible cracking. To install, reverse removal procedure.

LOWER CONTROL ARM

Removal – Raise front of vehicle, support with safety stands, and remove wheel and tire. Disconnect brake cable bracket from control arm. Disconnect stabilizer bar from radius rod. Disconnect radius rod from rear crossmember. Remove control arm-to-front crossmember attaching bolt. Remove ball joint-to-steering knuckle attaching nut and separate from knuckle. Remove control arm from vehicle.

Installation – Check ball joint for wear or damage. Check pivot bushing for wear or damage. To install lower control arm, reverse removal procedure and note: Torque ball joint castle nut, insert cotter pin, and tighten nut an additional turn.

TIGHTENING SPECIFICATIONS

Application	Ft. Lbs.(mkg)
Brake Backing Plate-to-Knuckle	21-32(3.0-3.5)
Tie Rod Strut Nut	18-21(2.5-3.0)
Strut-to-Steering Knuckle	21-28(3.0-4.0)
Strut Center Shaft Nut	43-54(6.0-7.5)
Lower Ball Joint Nut	36 (5.0)

TOYOTA CELICA & COROLLA

Celica
Corolla

DESCRIPTION

Independent strut type suspension consisting of vertically mounted strut assemblies, lower control arms, strut rods and a stabilizer bar. Individual strut assembly is mounted at top to inner fender by a thrust bearing and at bottom to lower control arm by means of a ball joint. Strut assembly consists of a shock absorber built into strut outer tube, a coil spring mounted on outside of strut tube and a steering knuckle integral with bottom of strut tube. A strut rod is mounted between lower control arm and frame. A stabilizer bar is mounted to front frame members and connected at ends to lower control arms. The suspension crossmember that serves as support for all suspension components is removable.

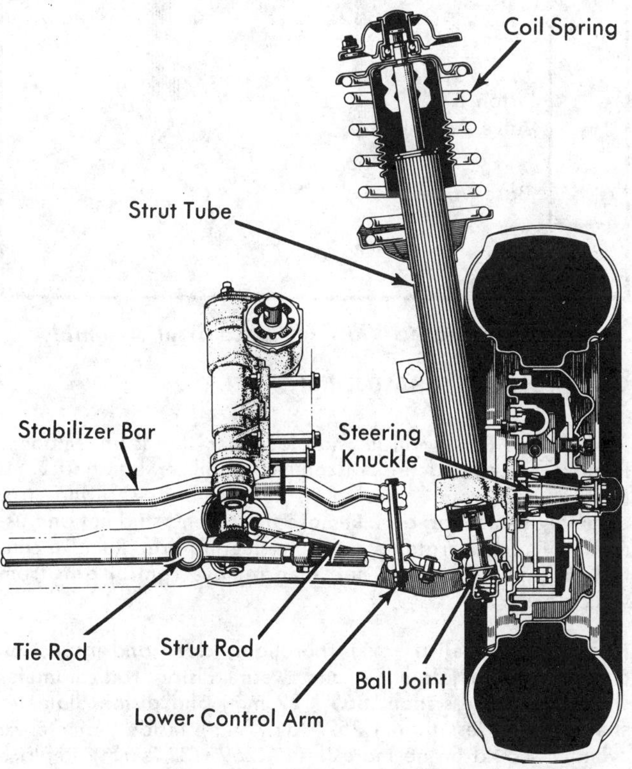

Fig. 1 Typical Front Suspension Assembly for Celica and Corolla

ADJUSTMENT

WHEEL ALIGNMENT SPECIFICATIONS & PROCEDURES

See Wheel Alignment Specifications & Procedures in WHEEL ALIGNMENT Section.

WHEEL BEARING ADJUSTMENT

See Wheel Bearing Adjustment in WHEEL ALIGNMENT Section.

BALL JOINT CHECKING

See Ball Joint Checking in WHEEL ALIGNMENT Section.

REMOVAL & INSTALLATION

STRUT ASSEMBLY

Removal – Raise vehicle and place jack stands under body. Remove wheel and tire. Disconnect brake flex line from bracket on strut tube by removing retaining clip. Remove three upper mounting nuts from strut assembly, accessible from inside engine compartment. Remove bolts securing steering arm to strut lower mount. Pull down on control arm and remove strut assembly complete with brake system components.

Disassembly, Corolla, Celica – 1) Bolt a holding fixture to bottom of strut tube and clamp assembly into vise. Compress coil spring. Remove dust cover from center of bearing support and remove nut from center of support. Remove support, upper spring seat, rubber bumper and coil spring.

2) Remove brake disc and backing plate from steering knuckle. *See appropriate article in BRAKE SYSTEMS Section.* Remove cap from upper portion of strut tube and straighten crimped edges of strut tube with a punch.

3) Remove ring nut from inside strut tube. Remove gasket and pull out piston rod and guide. Take out cylinder and drain fluid. Using a punch, drive base valve from bottom of cylinder. Pry base from case. Secure upper portion of piston rod in a vise and remove nut from bottom end. Remove valve assembly.

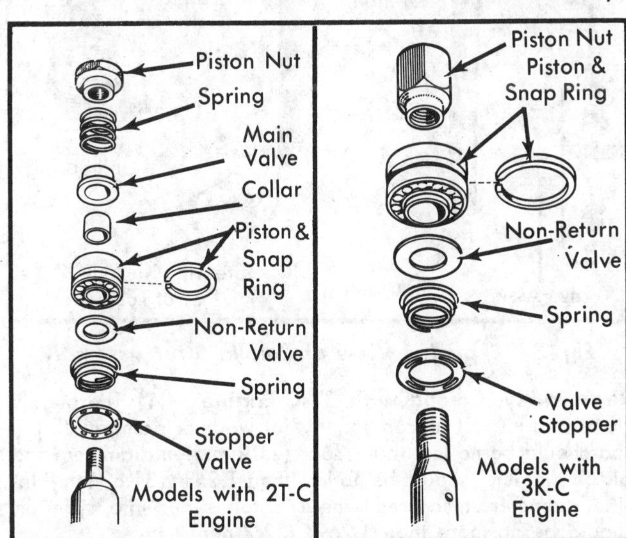

Fig. 2 Piston Valve Assemblies for Corolla Models

Reassembly, Corolla with 3K-C Engine – 1) Thoroughly clean and inspect all components for wear or damage. Piston rod should be no less than .783" (19.9 mm) in diameter and piston diameter should be no less than 1.183" (29.9 mm). Inside diameter of cylinder should be no more than 1.193" (30.2 mm).

2) Mount upper portion of piston rod in vise. Insert following parts from bottom end of piston rod:

- Stopper valve
- Spring
- Non-return valve
- Piston
- Piston ring
- Piston nut

3) Tighten piston nut.

4) Use a punch and stake piston nut against piston rod in two places. Avoid any damage to piston rod end.

TOYOTA CELICA & COROLLA (Cont.)

5) Use wrench SST 09720-12012 or equivalent to gradually screw piston valve into piston. When wrench becomes hard to turn, back out piston valve exactly 1½ turns. This sets damping force. Stake piston nut against piston valve in two places.

6) Press base valve into case, then force assembly into cylinder using a plastic hammer. Insert piston rod into cylinder, then fit cylinder into shell.

7) Fill shock absorber with 9.5 ozs. of fluid. Install rod guide into shell. Put new gasket on rod guide. Install ring nut. Pull piston rod out about 3-3½" before torquing nut.

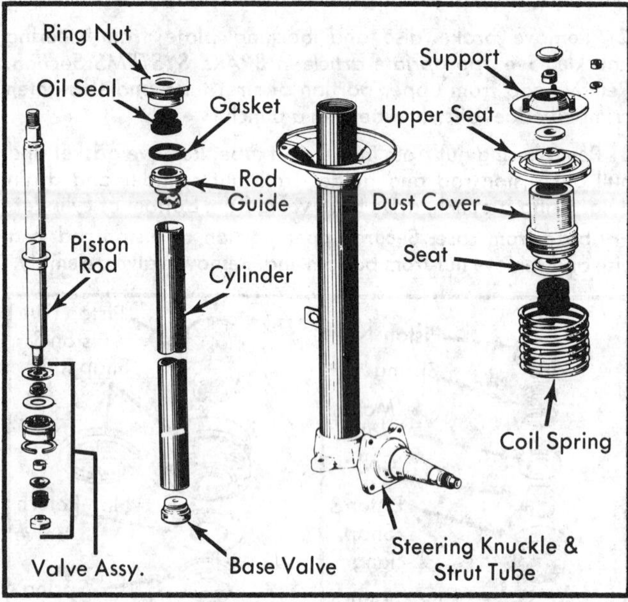

Fig. 3 Exploded View of Corolla Strut Assembly

Reassembly, Corolla with 2T-C Engine – **1)** Thoroughly clean and inspect all components for wear or damage. Piston rod should be no less than .865" (21.9 mm) in diameter, and piston diameter should be no less than 1.251" (31.80 mm). Inside diameter, measured where piston slides into cylinder, should be no more than 1.269" (32.2 mm).

2) Mount upper portion of piston in vise. Insert following into place:

- Stopper Valve
- Non-return valve
- Piston
- Piston
- Piston ring
- Collar
- Main Valve
- Compression Spring
- Piston nut

3) Tighten piston nut. Make sure non-return valve is squarely positioned into center of valve stopper before piston nut is tightened. Stake nut in four places.

4) Press base valve into case, then force assembly into caliper using a plastic hammer. Insert piston rod into cylinder, then fit cylinder into shell.

5) Fill shock absorber shell with 10.6 ozs. of fluid. Install rod guide into shell. Put new gasket on rod guide. Install ring nut. Pull piston rod out about 3-3½" before torquing nut.

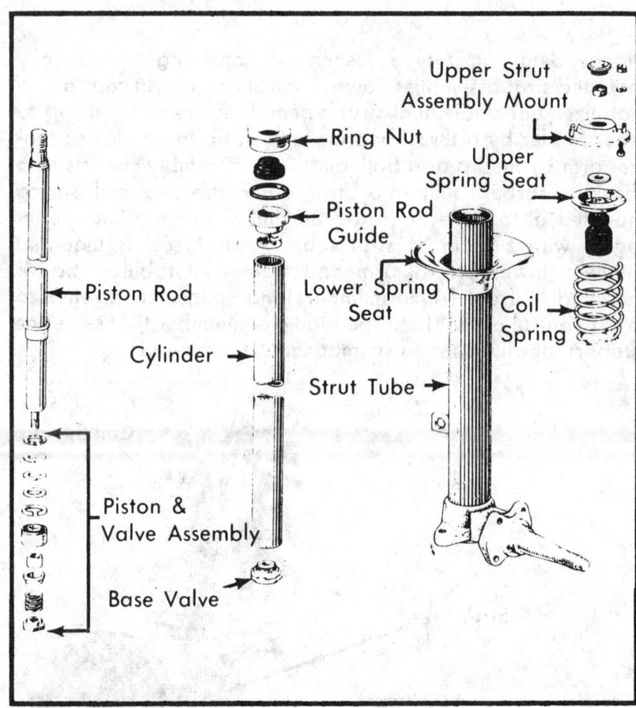

Fig. 4 Exploded View of Celica Strut Assembly

CONTROL ARM & BALL JOINT

Removal – Raise vehicle and place jack stands under body. Remove wheel and tire. Disconnect stabilizer bar and compression rod from control arm. Remove bolts securing strut assembly to steering arm. Remove tie rod end stud nut and using a puller, separate tie rod from steering arm. Remove control arm pivot bolt and nut, then remove control arm from vehicle.

Reassembly, Celica – **1)** Thoroughly clean and inspect all components for damage and wear. Piston rod diameter should be no less than .865" (22 mm) and piston diameter should be no less than 1.252" (31.7 mm). Inside diameter of cylinder should be no more than 1.269" (32.2 mm). Replace seal in ring nut by prying out with a screwdriver and pressing in with an available mandrel.

2) Place upper portion of piston rod in a vise and install internal components in reverse order of removal procedure. Tighten new nut. Stake center of piston nut and install ring on piston. Press valve into case and drive into base of cylinder. Install piston rod into cylinder and insert cylinder into strut tube.

3) Fill strut tube with approximately 10.7 ozs. of shock absorber fluid. Install piston rod guide and gasket into strut tube. Coat ring nut seal with grease and install into strut tube. Tighten ring nut. **NOTE** – *Raise piston rod 3-3½" from edge of strut tube before tightening fully.* Install coil spring and components in reverse order of removal.

Installation – To install, reverse removal procedure. Tighten all nuts and bolts and bleed brake system.

TOYOTA CELICA & COROLLA (Cont.)

SUSPENSION CROSSMEMBER

Disassembly – Remove nut from ball joint stud and using a puller, separate steering arm from ball joint. Ball joint is not removable from control arm, if either are defective, both must be replaced. Dust cover on ball joint is replaceable. Using a mandrel, press bushing out of control arm in a forward direction.

Reassembly – Using same mandrel used for disassembly, press new bushing into control arm in a forward direction. Install new dust cap on ball joint. Remove plug from bottom of ball joint and install grease fitting. Fill ball joint with grease. Install steering arm on ball joint and tighten nut. Install new cotter pin.

Installation – To install control arm, reverse removal procedure and tighten bolts and nuts, except control arm pivot bolt. Tighten control arm pivot bolt when weight of vehicle is on front wheels.

STABILIZER BAR

Removal – Disconnect stabilizer bar from both control arms. Remove engine protective cover, if equipped. Remove bolts securing mounting brackets to chassis and remove stabilizer bar.

Installation – To install, reverse removal procedure. Make sure components connecting stabilizer bar to control arms are installed properly.

STRUT ROD

Removal – Raise vehicle and place safety stands under vehicle. Remove nut from front of strut rod and remove washer, retainer, and rubber grommet. Remove bolts connecting strut rod to control arm and remove rod from vehicle.

Installation – Install first nut on rod so leading edge is 3.43"(87.2 mm) for Corolla or 3.22" (82 mm) for Celica from edge of threaded portion. Place in vehicle and tighten hardware.

Removal – Disconnect control arms as previously outlined. Place a jack under engine for support and remove nuts securing motor mounts to crossmember. Remove protective cover from under engine. Remove bolts securing crossmember to body and remove crossmember.

Installation – To install, reverse removal procedure. Make sure components connecting stabilizer bar to control arms are installed in correct order.

TIGHTENING SPECIFICATIONS

Application	Ft. Lbs. (mkg)
Ball Joint Stud Nut	
Upper	35 (4.8)
Lower	58 (8.0)
Control Arm Bushings	87 (12.0)
Control Arm Pivot Shaft-to-Crossmember	38 (5.3)
Lower Arm Ball Joint	
Large Nut	71 (9.8)
Small Nuts	14 (.19)

TOYOTA CORONA

Corona

DESCRIPTION

Independent front suspension with coil springs. Wheel is supported by steering knuckle mounted between upper and lower control arms by means of ball joints. Upper control arm pivots on shaft bolted to suspension crossmember. Lower control arm pivots on shaft bolted to suspension crossmember. Coil springs fit in pockets built into suspension crossmember at top and in pockets built into lower control arms at bottom. Hydraulic shock absorbers mount between lower control arms at bottom and suspension crossmember at top and are inside coil springs. A stabilizer bar is mounted to chassis members and connected at ends to lower control arms.

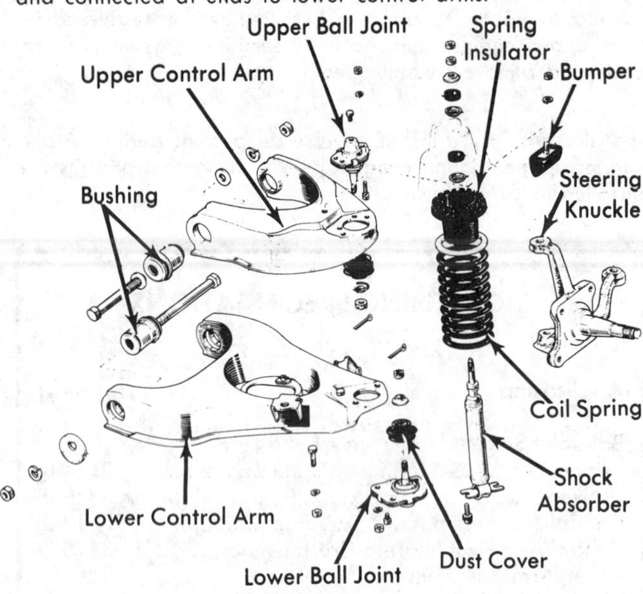

Fig. 1 Exploded View of Front Suspension Assy.

ADJUSTMENT

WHEEL ALIGNMENT SPECIFICATIONS & PROCEDURES

See *Wheel Alignment Specifications & Procedures* in *WHEEL ALIGNMENT Section.*

WHEEL BEARING ADJUSTMENT

See *Wheel Bearing Adjustment in WHEEL ALIGNMENT Section.*

BALL JOINT CHECKING

See *Ball Joint Checking in WHEEL ALIGNMENT Section.*

REMOVAL & INSTALLATION

STEERING KNUCKLE

Removal – 1) Raise vehicle by jacking up under lower control steering knuckle. **NOTE** – *See appropriate information in BRAKE SYSTEMS Section for removal.*

2) Detach tie rod end from steering knuckle using puller. Remove nuts from upper and lower ball joint studs and using puller, separate steering knuckle from ball joints. Remove steering knuckle from vehicle.

Installation – To install, reverse removal procedure and tighten all nuts and bolts.

LOWER CONTROL ARM, COIL SPRING & BALL JOINT

Removal – 1) Raise vehicle and place safety stands under body. Remove tire and wheel. Disconnect stabilizer bar from lower control arm. Remove shock absorber. Using a spring compressor, collapse coil spring until there is no pressure on lower control arm. On models with ESP, disconnect wiring harness for brakes and separate clamp from arm.

2) Remove nut securing ball joint stud to steering knuckle. Using a puller, separate ball joint from steering knuckle. Push down on control arm, release spring pressure, and remove coil spring. Remove bolts securing control arm pivot shaft to suspension crossmember and remove control arm from vehicle.

3) **NOTE** – *Ball joint can be removed from vehicle without removing control arm.* Remove bolts securing ball joint to control arm and separate ball joint from control arm. Unscrew bushings from control arm and remove pivot shaft.

Installation – 1) Install new bushings and pivot shaft into control arm. Tighten bushings securely. **NOTE** – *Make sure bushings are screwed in equal amounts on both sides.* Bolt pivot shaft to crossmember. Install coil spring and collapse using spring compressor. Place ball joint in control arm and tighten bolts.

2) **NOTE** – *Ball joint can be installed in control arm before control arm is fitted to vehicle.* Place ball joint stud in steering knuckle and tighten nut. Connect stabilizer bar to control arm. Remove spring compressor and install shock absorber. Install wheel and tire and lower vehicle. Check front wheel alignment. Thoroughly grease suspension components.

UPPER CONTROL ARM & BALL JOINT

Removal – 1) Raise vehicle and place jack stands under body, leave jack under control arm. Remove tire and wheel. On models equipped with ESP, disconnect wire harness clamp from upper arm. **NOTE** – *Ball joint can be removed with control arm in or out of vehicle.* Remove nut from upper ball joint stud.

2) Using puller separate ball joint from steering knuckle. Note number and thickness of shims between pivot shaft and mount. Remove bolts securing control arm pivot shaft to crossmember. Remove control arm from vehicle. Remove screw in bushings and pivot shaft from control arm. Remove ball joint from control arm.

Installation – 1) Install ball joint in control arm and tighten. Install bushings and pivot shaft in control arm. Tighten bushings, ensuring they are screwed in equal amounts on both sides. Install dust cover on ball joint.

2) Install control arm in vehicle with shims correctly positioned; tighten pivot shaft bolts. Install ball joint in steering knuckle and tighten nut. Install wheel and tire and lower vehicle. Thoroughly grease front suspension components and check front wheel alignment.

TIGHTENING SPECIFICATIONS

Application	Ft. Lbs. (mkg)
Lower Control Arm-to-Crossmember	
Celica	58-89 (8.0-12.3)
Corolla	51-65 C7.1-9.0)
Lower Ball Joint-to-Steering Knuckle	51-65 (8.0-12.3)
Strut Bar-to-Strut Bar Bracket	54-80 (7.5-11.1)
Crossmember-to-Frame	
Celica	29-36 (4.0-5.0)
Corolla	22-32 (3.0-4.4)
Strut-to-Steering Arm	
Celica	58-87 (8.0-12.0)
Corolla	51-65 C7.1-9.0)
Ring Nut	72-108 (9.9-14.9)

TOYOTA PICKUP

Pickup

DESCRIPTION

Independent front suspension with coil springs. Wheel is supported by steering knuckle mounted between upper and lower control arms by ball joints. Upper control arms pivot on shafts connected to frame. Lower control arms pivot on shafts connected to crossmember. Coil springs fit in pockets built into frame at top and in pockets built into lower control arms at bottom. Hydraulic shock absorbers mount between lower control arm and frame and are inside coil spring. A stabilizer bar is mounted to frame and connected at ends to lower control arms.

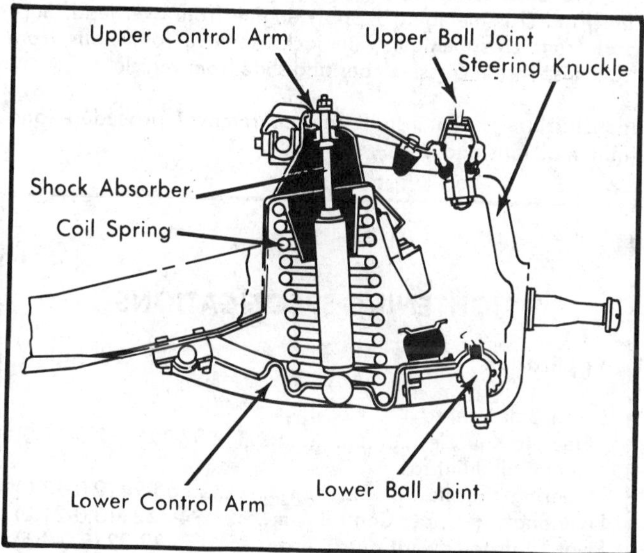

Fig. 1 Sectional View of Front Suspension Assembly

ADJUSTMENT

WHEEL ALIGNMENT SPECIFICATIONS & PROCEDURES

See Wheel Alignment Specifications & Procedures in WHEEL ALIGNMENT Section.

WHEEL BEARING ADJUSTMENT

See Wheel Bearing Adjustment in WHEEL ALIGNMENT Section.

BALL JOINT CHECKING

See Ball Joint Checking in WHEEL ALIGNMENT Section.

REMOVAL & INSTALLATION

SHOCK ABSORBERS

Removal – Raise vehicle and place on jack stands under frame. Remove wheel and tire. Remove nuts from upper shock absorber stem. Remove bolts securing shock absorber lower mount to lower control arm.

Installation – To install, reverse removal procedure. Tighten all nuts and bolts.

UPPER CONTROL ARM & BALL JOINT

Removal – Raise vehicle by placing jack under lower control arm. Place safety stands under frame and leave jack in place. Remove wheel and tire. Remove cotter pin and nut from upper ball joint stud. Using a suitable puller (09628-62010) separate ball joint from steering knuckle. Remove bolts securing upper control arm mount, noting size and number of shims between pivot shaft and mount. Remove control arm from vehicle. Remove bolts securing ball joint to control arm, and remove ball joint. Unscrew pivot shaft bushings and remove bushings and shaft.

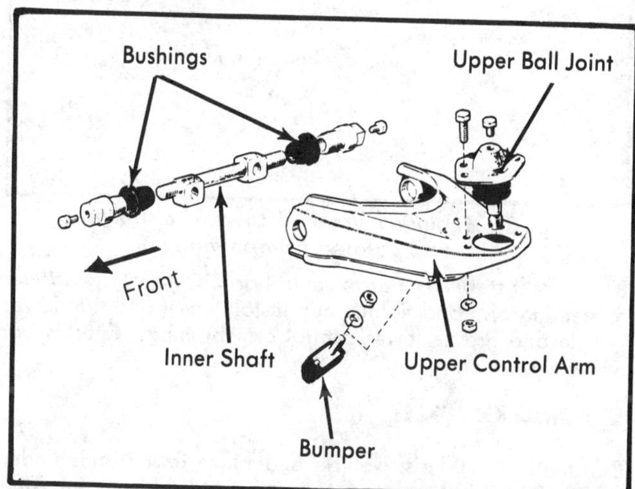

Fig. 2 Exploded View of Upper Control Arm Assembly

Installation – Inspect all components for wear or distortion. Install pivot shaft with offset mounting hole to front. Reverse removal procedure for installation making sure wheel alignment shims are installed in correct position. Tighten all bolts and nuts to specifications. Check wheel alignment.

LOWER CONTROL ARM, COIL SPRING & BALL JOINT

Removal – 1) Raise vehicle by jacking up under lower control arm. Place jack stands under frame and leave jack in place. Remove wheel and tire. Disconnect stabilizer bar from control arm. Remove cotter pin and nut from tie rod end stud and using a puller separate tie rod from steering arm. Remove shock absorber as previously outlined.

2) Remove cotter pin and nut from lower ball joint stud and using a puller, separate ball joint from steering knuckle. Lower jack slowly and remove coil spring and insulator. Remove bolts securing control arm to crossmember and remove control arm from vehicle. Secure control arm in a vise and remove ball joint from control arm. Remove bushings from both ends of pivot shaft and remove shaft.

Installation – 1) Install pivot shaft in control arm. Install bushings and tighten alternately and evenly. Install ball joint in control arm. Install control arm and tighten pivot shaft bolts. Install coil spring insulator in pocket.

2) Install a coil spring compressor on coil. Collapse coil spring until control arm can be connected to steering knuckle with coil spring in vehicle. With ball joint stud installed in steering knuckle, tighten nut.

TOYOTA PICKUP (Cont.)

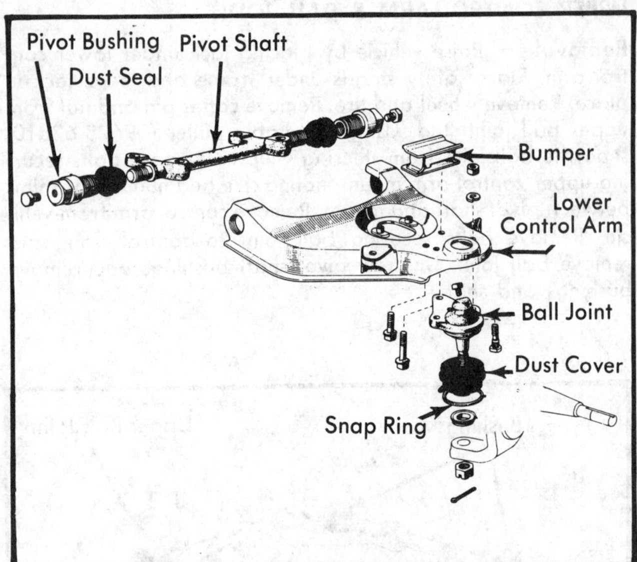

Fig. 3 Exploded View of Lower Control Arm and Related Components

3) Connect stabilizer bar to control arm. Connect tie rod end to steering arm and tighten nut. Install wheel and tire, lower vehicle and grease lower control arm bushings. Check front wheel alignment.

STEERING KNUCKLE

Removal — 1) Raise vehicle and place jack stands under frame. Remove wheel and tire. Remove brake system components from steering knuckle. **NOTE** — *See appropriate information in BRAKE SYSTEMS Section for removal.* Jack up under control arm to release spring tension from lower arm.

2) Remove cotter pin and nut from lower ball joint stud and using a suitable puller separate ball joint from steering knuckle. Separate upper ball joint from steering knuckle in same manner. Lower jack and remove steering knuckle.

Installation — To install, reverse removal procedure. Check wheel alignment.

FRONT SUSPENSION CROSSMEMBER

Removal — 1) Raise front of vehicle and support with jack stands. Remove front wheels. Disconnect tie rod ends from both steering knuckles. Disconnect each end of stabilizer bar from suspension lower arms. Remove engine compartment hood.

2) Disconnect brake system components from steering knuckle. **NOTE** — *See BRAKE SYSTEMS Section for removal procedure.* Remove bolts retaining front engine mounts. Separate brake line from crossmember. Support engine from overhead. Support front crossmember with jack. Remove four bolts from front suspension crossmember and slide from vehicle.

Installation — To install, reverse removal procedure and tighten all nuts and bolts.

TIGHTENING SPECIFICATIONS

Application	Ft. Lbs. (mkg)
Lower Ball Joint-to Steering Knuckle	87-123 (12.0-17.0)
Upper Ball Joint-to Steering Knuckle	65-94 (9.0-13.0)
Pivot Shaft-to-Upper Control Arm	94-152 (13.0-21.0)
Pivot Shaft-to-Lower Control Arm	22-32 (3.0-4.5)
Ball Joint-to-Upper Control Arm	14-22 (1.9-4.5)

TRIUMPH TR7

TR7

DESCRIPTION

Suspension is strut type with a coil spring around strut tube. Strut is secured at top to inner fender and at bottom to control arm link. A stabilizer bar is connected to chassis and lower control link. Control arm links are mounted by a ball joint at stub axles and through bolts at chassis.

ADJUSTMENT

WHEEL ALIGNMENT SPECIFICATIONS & PROCEDURES

See *Wheel Alignment Specifications and Procedures* in *WHEEL ALIGNMENT* Section.

WHEEL BEARING ADJUSTMENT

See *Wheel Bearing Adjustment* in *WHEEL ALIGNMENT* Section.

BALL JOINT CHECKING

See *Ball Joint Checking* in *WHEEL ALIGNMENT* Section.

REMOVAL & INSTALLATION

LOWER CONTROL LINK

Removal – 1) Raise and support vehicle with safety stands. Remove tire and wheel. Remove mounting hardware from end of stabilizer bar. Remove bolts holding steering arm to stub axle and move out of way. Remove nut and separate ball joint. Remove bolt and nut securing lower control link to chassis, then take out link.

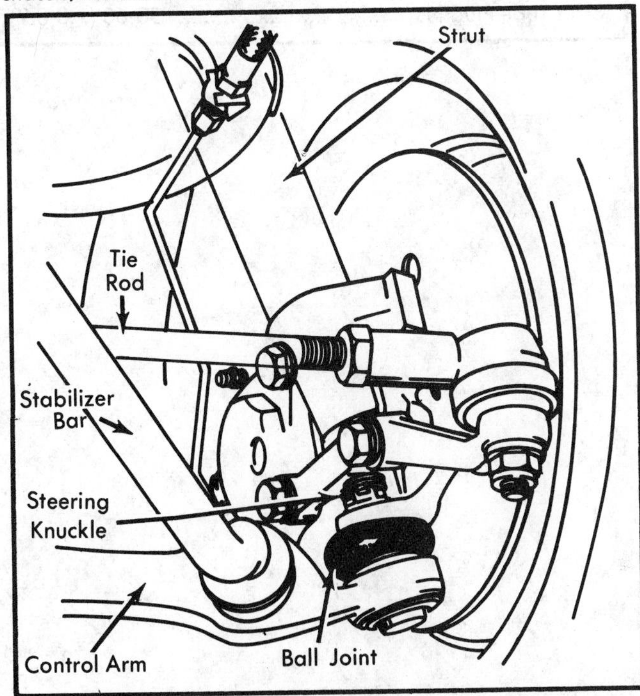

Fig. 1 Detail of Components to Remove in Order to Take Off Lower Control Link and Strut Assembly

2) Remove plastic and rubber ring from ball joint. Remove snap ring retaining ball joint housing to bottom link. Press or drive out ball joint and housing. Install new ball joint, fit snap ring, plastic, and rubber ring.

Installation – To install reverse removal procedure and tighten lower control link when vehicle weight is on ground.

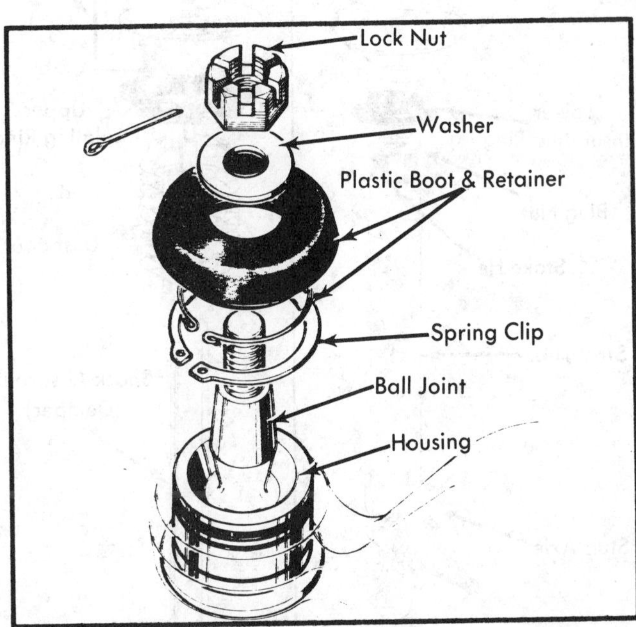

Fig. 2 Exploded View of Ball Joint Assembly

STRUT ASSEMBLY

Removal – 1) Raise vehicle and support with jack stands. Remove tire and wheel. Separate steering arm from stub axle assembly by removing two bolts. Disconnect brake hose from bracket on strut tube. Disconnect brake caliper and hang out of way.

2) Remove ball joint nut and separate from stub axle. Remove three nuts mounting strut assembly to inner fender panel. Pull strut downward and maneuver from vehicle.

3) Using a spring compressor, collapse coil and remove slotted nut from top of strut assembly. Take out spring pan complete with top mounting and swivel assembly. Remove spring from strut.

Disassembly – Remove retainer securing strut tube to plug nut using a 1/8" diameter drill. Using a suitable tool, remove plug nut. Slide shock absorber (damper) from strut tube.

Reassembly – Drill 1/4" diameter hole 1/16" deep at a 90° angle to the existing recess in plug nut. Fit shock absorber (damper) assembly to strut tube, then fit plug nut and tighten. Using center punch, stake strut tube into recess in plug nut.

TRIUMPH TR7 (Cont.)

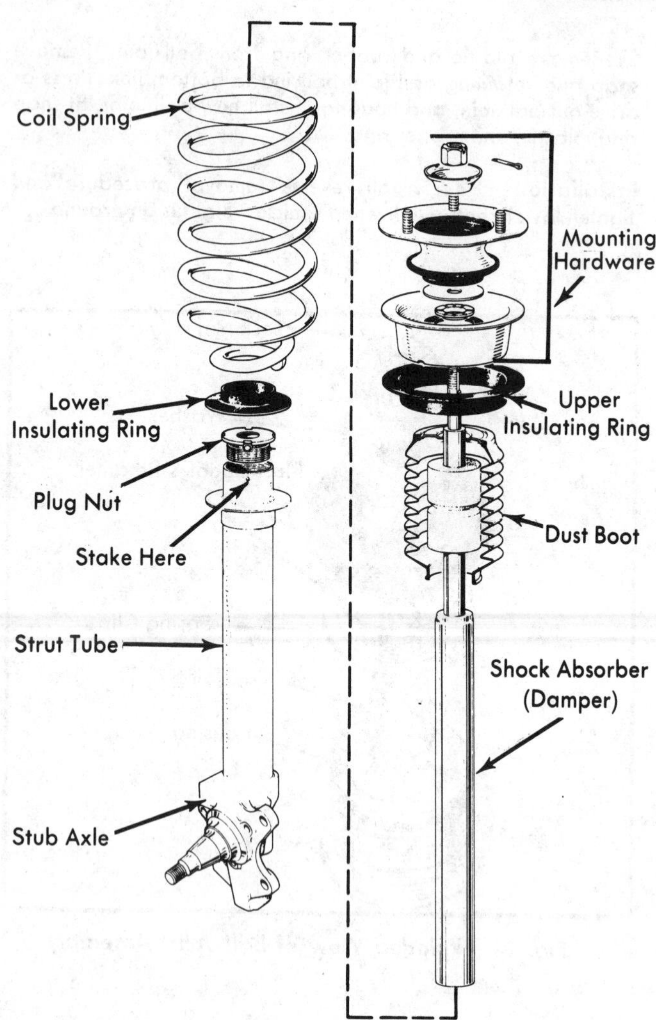

Fig. 3 Disassembled View of Strut

Installation – 1) Compress coil spring and ensure bumper stop is correctly positioned. Fully extend strut rod and fit the following: lower insulating ring, rubber seal, spring, upper insulating ring, and spring pan. Fit seal to thrust collar and place on upper spring pan.

2) Install plain washer, ground surface facing spring pan. Insert rubber mounting to strut and secure with dished washer and slotted nut. To complete installation, reverse removal procedure. Bleed brake system.

STABILIZER BAR

Removal – Raise vehicle and place on safety stands. Remove bolts and brackets mounting stabilizer bar to chassis. Remove mounting nut and rubber bushing securing stabilizer bar to lower control link. Pull out stabilizer, adjusting vehicle height as necessary. If necessary, inner bushing and mounting bushings can now be removed and replaced.

Installation – Refit inner dished washer with dish facing bushing, then install inner bushing on each end of stabilizer bar. Insert stabilizer bar and fit outer rubber bushings with dished washers. Reinstall mounting brackets and tighten all nuts and bolts.

TIGHTENING SPECIFICATIONS

Application	Ft. Lbs. (mkg)
Stabilizer Bar-to-Chassis	30-37 (4.2-5.1)
Stabilizer Bar-to-Lower Control Link	48-59 (6.7-8.1)
Strut Mounting-to-Body	16-21 (2.3-2.9)
Strut-to-Mounting	30-44 (4.2-6.0)
Tie Rod-to-Stub Axle	59-74 (8.2-10.2)
Strut Tube Plug Nut	50-60 (7.0-8.2)

TRIUMPH SPITFIRE

Spitfire

DESCRIPTION

Independent type front suspension consisting of upper and lower control arms, coil spring and shock assemblies and steering knuckles. Control arms pivot in mounts connected to chassis. Coil spring and shock assemblies are mounted between lower control arms and mounts integral with chassis. Steering knuckles are connected to upper control arms by means of ball joints and to lower control arms by means of trunion joints. Later models are equipped with a stabilizer bar.

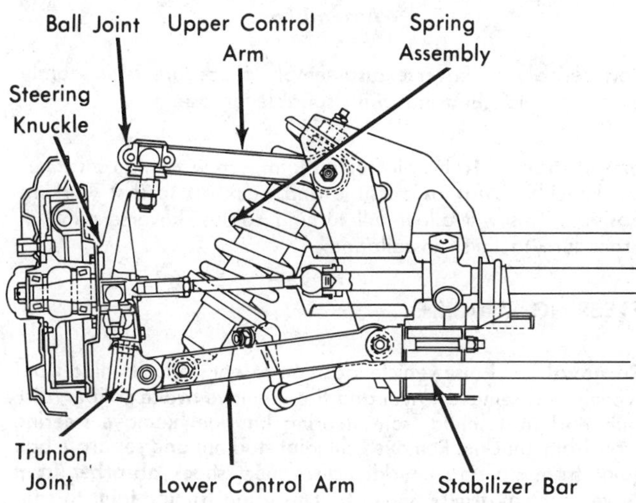

Fig. 1 Assembled View of Spitfire Front Suspension

ADJUSTMENT

WHEEL ALIGNMENT SPECIFICATIONS & PROCEDURES

See Wheel Alignment Specifications & Procedures in WHEEL ALIGNMENT Section.

WHEEL BEARING ADJUSTMENT

See Wheel Bearing Adjustment in WHEEL ALIGNMENT Section.

BALL JOINT CHECKING

See Ball Joint Checking in WHEEL ALIGNMENT Section.

REMOVAL & INSTALLATION

COIL SPRING & SHOCK ABSORBER

Removal – Raise and support vehicle. Place safety stands behind front wheels and remove wheel and tire. Loosen bolts securing lower control arm to trunion joints. Remove bolts securing bottom spring assembly mount to control arm. Remove three nuts securing upper spring assembly mount to chassis and remove spring and shock absorber as an assembly.

Disassembly – Using a suitable spring compressor, compress coil spring until spring is not contacting upper spring seat. Remove nut securing shaft from shock absorber to mount and remove rubber mounts, mount seats and mounting flange. Release spring compressor and remove coil spring.

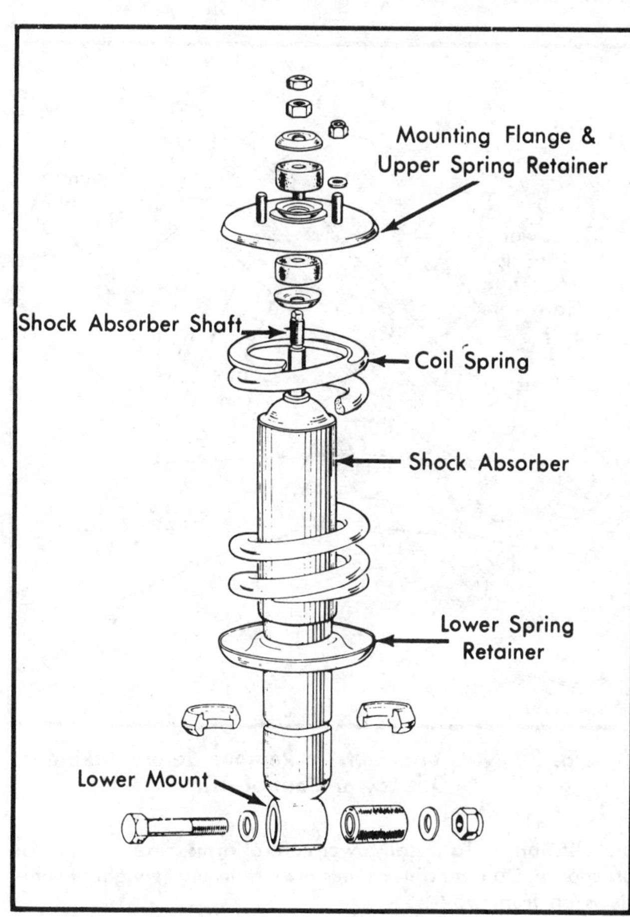

Fig. 2 Coil Spring and Shock Absorber Assembly

Assembly – Push shock absorber shaft in and out a few times, pressure should be constant and equal on either stroke. If little or no resistance is felt, or if shaft cannot be moved, replace shock absorber. To assemble coil spring and shock assembly, reverse disassembly procedure.

Installation – To install coil spring and shock absorber assembly, reverse removal procedure.

UPPER CONTROL ARMS

Removal – Raise vehicle, position safety stands behind front wheels and remove wheel and tire. Remove coil spring and shock assembly as previously outlined. Remove bolts securing upper control arms to ball joint. Remove both upper control arm pivot bolts and separate control arms from pivot mounts and ball joint.

Installation – To install upper control arms, reverse disassembly procedure. Do not tighten pivot bolts until weight of vehicle is on front wheels.

TRIUMPH SPITFIRE (Cont.)

LOWER CONTROL ARMS

Removal – Raise vehicle, position safety stands behind front wheels and remove wheel and tire. Disconnect stabilizer bar link from lower control arm. Disconnect bottom spring assembly mount from control arm. Remove bolt securing control arms to trunion joint. Remove inner pivot bolts and remove control arms.

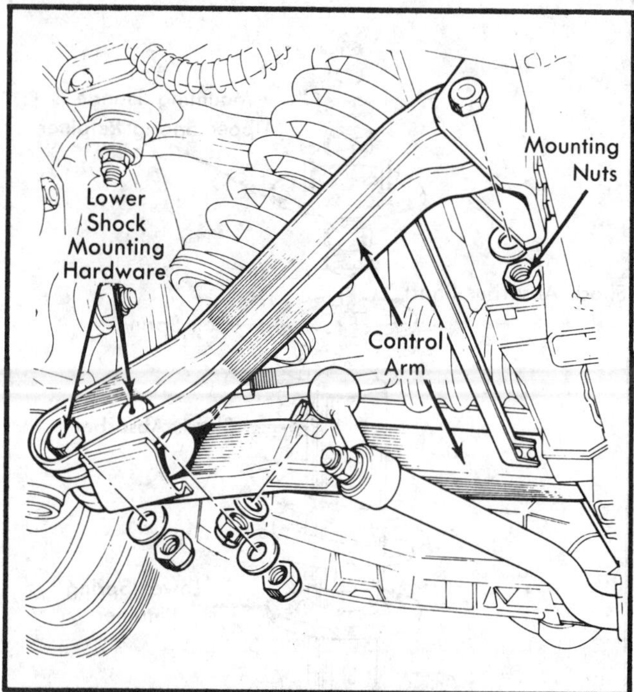

Fig. 3 Nuts and Bolts to Remove Before Taking Out Lower Control Arm

Installation – To install lower control arms, reverse removal procedure. Do not tighten inner pivot bolts until weight of vehicle is on front wheels.

UPPER BALL JOINT

Removal – Raise vehicle and place on safety stands; remove tire and wheel. Remove ball joint stud nut and separate ball joint from steeing knuckle. Remove bolts securing ball joint to control arm and remove ball joint.

Installation – To install ball joint, reverse removal procedure.

LOWER TRUNION JOINT

Removal – Raise vehicle, position safety stands behind front wheels and remove wheel and tire. Remove wheel hub and dust shield. Remove bolt securing trunion joint to lower control arm. Disconnect shock absorber mount from lower control arm. Pull trunion and steering knuckle from lower control arm and unscrew trunion from steering knuckle.

Disassembly – Pry loose 2 end washers. Slide out both dust seals. Lightly press out single spacer piece. Force out each of the nylon bearings and remove inner washers. Check all pieces for excessive wear and replace as necessary.

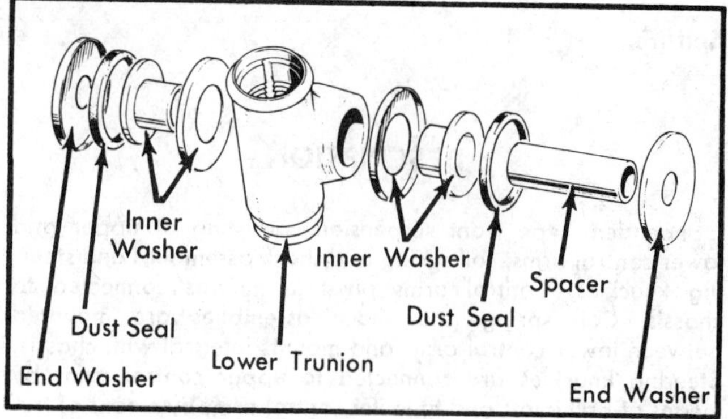

Fig. 4 Exploded View of Lower Trunion Assembly

Reassembly – Reverse disassembly procedure after lightly greasing nylon bearings with suitable grease.

Installation – To install trunion joint, screw trunion on steering knuckle as far as possible and back off to first working position. This will allow full turning radius. Reverse removal procedure to finish installation.

STEERING KNUCKLE

Removal – Raise vehicle, position safety stands behind front wheels and remove wheel and tire. Remove brake caliper, disc hub and dust shield from steering knuckle. Remove steering arm from knuckle. Remove ball joint stud nut and separate ball joint from steering knuckle. Disconnect shock absorber from lower control arm. Remove bolt securing trunion joint to control arm and remove steering knuckle. Remove trunion from steering knuckle. If necessary, remove nut securing spindle to steering knuckle and press spindle from knuckle.

Installation – To install steering knuckle, reverse removal procedure.

STABILIZER BAR

Removal – Remove nuts securing stabilizer bar to lower control arm. Remove nuts and plain washers holding bushing brackets to chassis. Remove bushing and withdraw stabilizer bar from vehicle.

Installation – To install stabilizer bar, reverse removal procedure.

TIGHTENING SPECIFICATIONS

Application	Ft. Lbs. (mkg)
Stabilizer Bar Stud	14 (1.9)
Ball Joint-to-Upper Control Arm	20 (2.8)
Ball Joint Stud Nut	38 (5.2)
Tie Rod End Ball Joint	32 (4.4)
Trunnion-to-Lower Control Arm	45 (6.2)
Lower Control Arm-to-Frame	25 (3.5)

VOLKSWAGEN TYPE 1

Type 1

DESCRIPTION

Independent strut type suspension consisting of vertically mounted strut assemblies, lower control arms and a stabilizer bar is used on Type 1 vehicles. Struts mount at top to fender panel and at bottom to side of steering knuckle. Steering knuckle mounts to a ball joint that is pressed into lower control arm. Control arm pivots in bushing mounted at chassis tube. Strut assembly consists of a shock absorber inside strut housing, coil spring mounted over strut housing, and a thrust bearing mounted on top attaching assembly. A stabilizer bar mounts to chassis and through lower control arms.

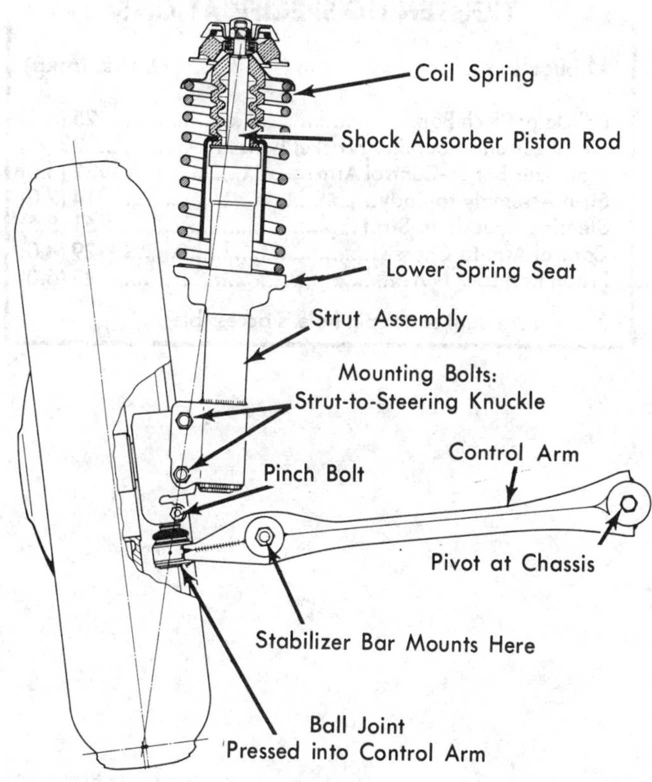

Fig. 1 Sectional View of Front Suspension

ADJUSTMENT

WHEEL ALIGNMENT SPECIFICATIONS & PROCEDURES

See Wheel Alignment Specifications & Procedures in WHEEL ALIGNMENT Section.

BALL JOINT CHECKING

See Ball Joint Checking in WHEEL ALIGNMENT Section.

WHEEL BEARING ADJUSTMENT

See Wheel Bearing Adjustment in WHEEL ALIGNMENT Section.

REMOVAL & INSTALLATION

STRUT ASSEMBLY

Removal – Raise vehicle and place safety stands under body. Remove wheel and tire. If left side strut assembly is to be removed pull speedometer cable out of steering knuckle. Pry loose brake hose retaining clip from strut. Remove two nuts and bolts that mount steering knuckle to strut and separate knuckle from strut. From inside luggage compartment, remove nuts securing assembly to fender panel and guide strut assembly from vehicle.

Disassembly – 1) Fit strut to suitable spring compressor. Pry off thrust bearing dust cap. Slightly compress coil.

2) Remove piston rod lock nut. Relieve spring pressure. Remove thrust bearing assembly. Separate coil spring from strut. Remove thrust bearing assembly. Take out rubber bumper and protective sleeve.

Inspection – 1) Hold shock absorber in assembled position. Work shock absorber back and forth; resistance must be uniform. Replace as necessary.

2) If new coil spring must be used make sure that both springs have the same identification markings.

Coil Spring Chart

Application	Spring Pressure Lbs. (kg)
1 Red Mark	500-514 (227-233)
2 Red Marks	516-529 (234-240)
3 Red Marks	531-545 (241-247)

Reassembly – Fit buffer and protective sleeve. Fit shock absorber and coil spring to compressor. Tighten compressor until piston rod threads project about $^5/_{16}$-$^3/_8$ (8-10 mm) over spring seat. Install thrust bearing assembly. Fit new piston rod lock nut.

Installation – Reverse removal procedure to refit strut assembly to vehicle.

CONTROL ARM

NOTE – *It is not necessary to remove suspension strut assembly or stabilizer bar when replacing control arm.*

Removal – 1) Loosen ball joint pinch bolt. Pull control arm down and free from steering knuckle. Remove cotter pin and castle nut from stabilizer bar. Remove nut from control arm pivot bolt.

2) Force stabilizer bar off mounting at control arm. Tap out control arm pivot bolt. Remove control arm from vehicle.

Installation – Check control arm for obvious cracks or distortion. Inspect rubber bushings and replace as necessary using suitable press. To install, reverse removal procedure and tighten all nuts and bolts. Check wheel alignment.

VOLKSWAGEN TYPE 1 (Cont.)

STEERING KNUCKLE

Removal – 1) Raise and support vehicle. Remove wheel and tire. Remove speedometer through back of steering knuckle.

2) Remove wheel bearing pinch bolt nut. Remove brake caliper and hang with wire hook out of way. Remove hub and rotor assembly. *See Volkswagen in BRAKE Section.*

3) Remove tie rod nut from end stud. Press tie rod out of steering arm.

4) Loosen pinch bolt on suspension ball joint stud. Pull lower control arm complete with ball joint down from steering knuckle.

5) Take out both bolts securing steering knuckle to strut assembly. Remove knuckle from vehicle.

Installation – Reverse removal procedure and note: Adjust wheel bearings and check front wheel alignment.

BALL JOINT

Removal – Raise vehicle and place safety stands under body. Remove control arm as previously described. Using a suitable press type tool, press ball joint downward and free from control arm.

Installation – Select new ball joint and press into control arm from deep side of arm. Reverse removal procedure for remaining components.

STABILIZER BAR

Removal – Remove cotter pin and nut from stabilizer bar end at control arm. Remove bolts from brackets securing stabilizer bar to chassis member. Pull stabilizer bar out of control arm and remove from vehicle.

Installation – Inspect rubber mounting components for wear or cracking. Reverse removal procedure for installation. Tighten all bolts and nuts to specifications.

TIGHTENING SPECIFICATIONS

Application	Ft. Lbs. (mkg)
Ball Joint Pinch Bolt	25 (3.5)
Stabilizer Bar Mounting Bracket Bolts	29 (4.)
Stabilizer Bar-to-Control Arm	①22 (3.0)
Strut Assembly-to-Body	14 (2.0)
Steering Knuckle-to-Strut	61 (8.5)
Control Arm-to-Chassis	29 (4.0)
Piston Rod Lock Nut	43 (6.0)

① – Turn until cotter pin hole is accessible.

VOLKSWAGEN TYPE 2

Type 2

DESCRIPTION

Independent ball joint type suspension with torsion bars. Front axle beam consists of two horizontal tubes held together at ends by endplates welded to tubes. Torsion bars are mounted inside tubes and anchor in center. Torsion arms are connected to end of torsion bars and mount to steering knuckles by means of ball joints. Hydraulic shock absorbers are mounted between lower torsion arms at bottom and to axle beam endplates at top. A stabilizer bar is mounted to lower torsion arms. Complete front axle assembly is removable.

ADJUSTMENT

WHEEL ALIGNMENT SPECIFICATIONS & PROCEDURES

See Wheel Alignment Specifications & Procedures in WHEEL ALIGNMENT Section.

WHEEL BEARING ADJUSTMENT

See Wheel Bearing Adjustment in WHEEL ALIGNMENT Section.

BALL JOINT CHECKING

See Ball Joint Checking in WHEEL ALIGNMENT Section.

REMOVAL & INSTALLATION

FRONT SUSPENSION ASSEMBLY

NOTE – *Most front suspension repairs can be accomplished without removing entire suspension.*

Removal – **1)** Raise vehicle and place safety stands under body. Remove tires and wheels. Disconnect brake fluid flex lines at brackets. Plug openings. On vehicles equipped with brake servo, remove push rod and take out servo.

2) Disconnect speedometer at left steering knuckle. Remove cover plate under pedal assembly. Engage 1st or 3rd gear. Remove gearshift rod lever at coupling.

3) On manual transmission models, remove gearshift lever and front rod. On automatic transmission models, remove gearshift rod from lower selector lever. Disconnect clutch cable pedal. Separate parking brake cables at parking brake lever.

4) Separate drag link from pitman arm. Remove steering damper from axle tube bracket and swing damper out of way.

5) Place floor jack (and adaptor VW 610) under axle. Raise jack until contact is made. Remove 4 axle beam mounting bolts. Lower jack and guide assembly from vehicle.

Installation – Reverse removal procedure. Tighten nuts and bolts. Bleed brake system. Check front wheel alignment.

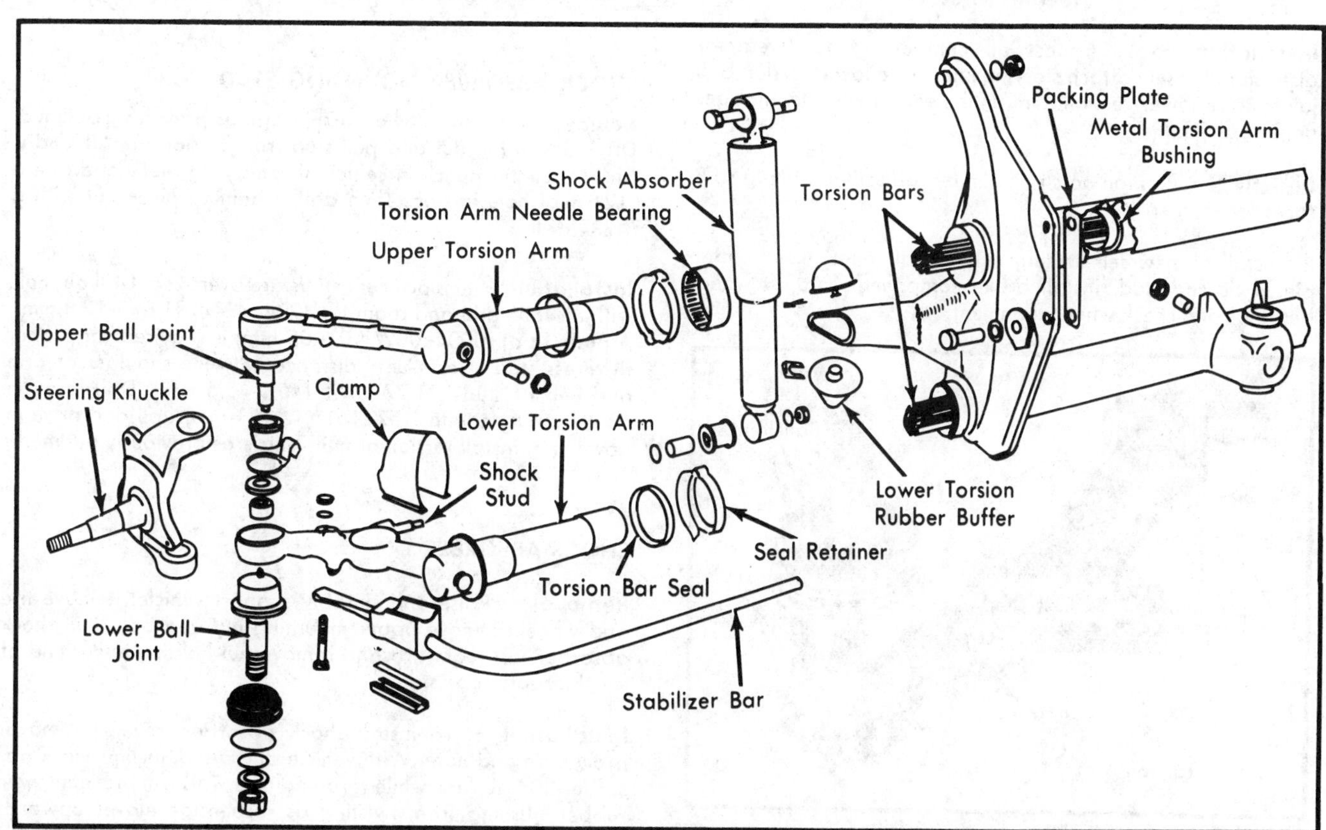

Fig. 1 Exploded View of Front Suspension Assembly

VOLKSWAGEN TYPE 2 (Cont.)

STEERING KNUCKLE

Removal – 1) Raise vehicle and place safety stands under body. Remove wheel and tire. If left side knuckle is being removed, pull out speedometer cable. Disconnect brake caliper and support out of way. Remove cotter pin and castellated nut from tie rod end. Use a press type tool and separate tie rod from steering knuckle.

2) Remove splash shield from steering knuckle. Take off lower ball joint nut and press joint from knuckle. Remove upper ball joint nut, then with suitable wrench, turn camber eccentric adjusting bushing until joint is free from knuckle.See Fig 2.

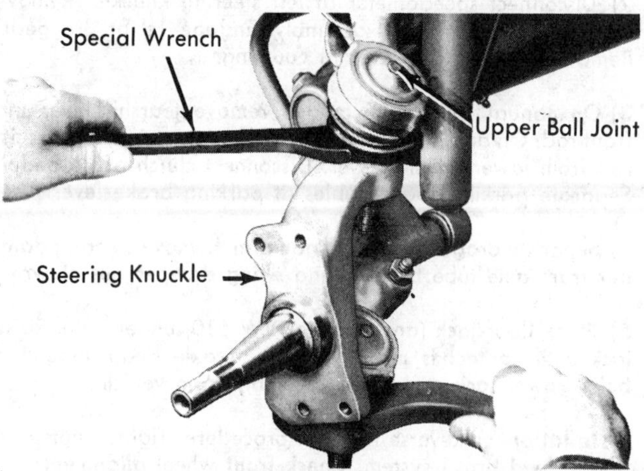

Fig. 2 Removing Upper Ball Joint from Steering Knuckle

Installation – 1) Inspect all components for wear or distortion. Loosely attach steering knuckle to lower torsion ball joint. Raise lower torsion arm until steering knuckle engages upper ball joint.

CAUTION – *Position notch on camber adjusting bushing so it faces forward.*

2) Install all new self locking nuts to ball joints. Insert cotter pin in tie rod stud. Install brake components. Adjust wheel bearings and check wheel alignment.

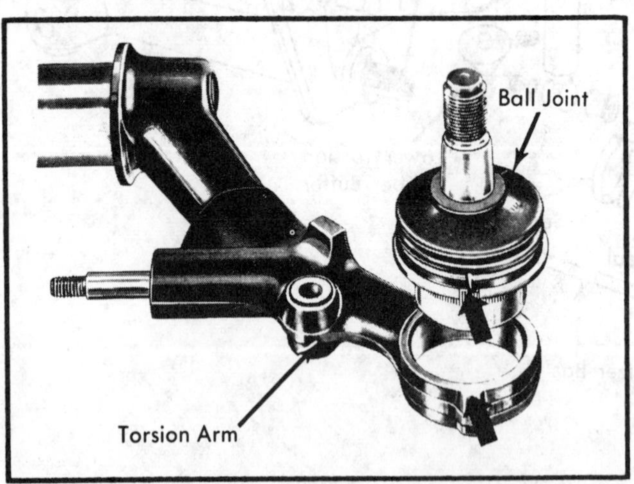

Fig. 3 Align Notch in Ball Joint with Boss on Torsion Arm

STABILIZER BAR

Removal – Knock retaining clip from clamp. Bend up clamp and remove plates. Remove nut from retaining bolt and remove bolt. Remove stabilizer bar from vehicle.

Installation – Inspect rubber components for wear or cracking. Inspect stabilizer bar for wear or distortion. Install stabilizer bar and retaining bolt and tighten nut to specification. Install clamp with cutout facing wheel. Press edges of clamp together with a pair of pliers and install clip. Made sure tongue edge of clip is facing axle beam. Lock clip by bending over tongue.

TORSION ARMS & BALL JOINTS

Removal – Raise vehicle and place safety stands under body. Remove wheel and tire. Remove steering knuckle and stabilizer bar as previously outlined. Back lock nuts from set screws and remove set screws. Pull torsion arms out of axle tubes. Press ball joints out of torsion arms.

Installation – Press ball joints into torsion arms. When pressing ball joints into control arms make sure that notches in shoulder of ball joint align with forged projections on torsion arm. Install a suitable peening tool (VW471) on press and peen ball joint 3 times with a pressure of 6 tons to insure ball joint is properly seated in torsion arm. Thoroughly grease pivot portion of torsion arm and install in axle tube. Reverse removal procedure for installation of remaining components. Tighten all bolts and nuts to specifications. Bleed brake system and check wheel alignment.

SHOCK ABSORBER MOUNTING STUD

Removal – Remove lower torsion arm as previously outlined. Drive dowel pin out and pull stud from torsion arm. If stud is broken, center punch in center of remaining piece and drill a .12" pilot hole in stud. Then drill remaining piece out with a .423" drill.

Installation – Replacement studs are oversized. Drill out hole with a .483" drill and ream to .4904-.4914" (12.45-12.8 mm). A press fit of .0004-.002" (.01-.05 mm) is required for proper fit. Press stud in arm until distance between shoulder of arm and end of stud is 1.77-1.79" (45.0-45.5 mm). Drill through dowel pin hole with .157-.161"(4.0-4.1 mm) drill and drive in dowel pin. Install torsion arm in vehicle as previously outlined.

SHOCK ABSORBER

Removal – Raise and suitably support vehicle. Remove tire and wheel. Remove upper mounting nut and bolt. Pull shock absorber top rearward and remove nut holding lower end of shock absorber on stud.

Installation – To install shock absorber, reverse removal procedure and note: With vehicle still raised, incline shock absorber 30° to rear while torquing nuts. This will prevent lower rubber bushing from twisting as suspension moves upward. **CAUTION** – *DO NOT incline shock absorber if vehicle weight is on ground.*

VOLKSWAGEN TYPE 2 (Cont.)

TORSION BARS, AXLE BUSHINGS & BEARINGS

Removal – 1) Raise vehicle and place on safety stands. Remove both tires and wheels. Remove steering knuckle from both sides. Remove torsion arm from one end of torsion bars. If lower bar is being removed, remove shock absorber. If upper bar is being removed, remove gearshift rod at coupling and set to one side.

2) Loosen lock nut and remove screw from center of axle tube. Pull out torsion bar. Remove torsion arm from bar.

Bearing Assembly Replacement – 1) Use a slide hammer and remove bearing. Measure metal bushing. If diameter of bushing exceeds 1.71" (43.4 mm), use slide hammer with fingers or washer inserted behind bushing and pull out bushing.

CAUTION – *DO NOT damage or pull out plastic sleeve in axle tube. Replacement sleeves are not available, axle tube must be replaced.*

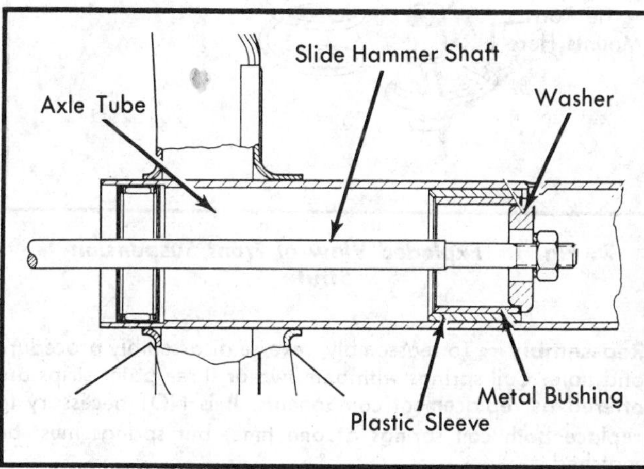

Fig. 4 Section View Showing Front Axle Tube

2) Clean off needle bearing seat. Measure inside diameter of bearing seat. If measurement is between 2.243-2.244" (56.97-56.99 mm), use standard bearings. If measurement is between 2.251-2.252" (57.17-57.19 mm), install oversize bearings. Oversize bearings are stamped with letter "U". Axle tubes that will not accept oversize bearing must be replaced.

3) Clean bearing and bushing seats. Insert bearing with hardened surface facing out. Drive bearing in using special drift VW 772 (or equivalent) until drift shoulder just meets outside edge of axle tube.

4) Use bearing as drift pilot and drive metal bushing into place. Fit new seal retainer to axle tube with lug in vertical position. Oversize seal retainers are available and can be identified by notch in lip. Fit new seals.

Installation – Reverse removal procedure and note: White stripe paint mark on end of torsion bar identifies left side bar.

TIGHTENING SPECIFICATIONS

Application	Ft. Lbs. (mkg)
Ball Joint Stud Nuts	72 (10.0)
Torsion Arm Set Screw	29 (4.0)
Torsion Arm Set Screw Lock Nut	29 (4.0)
Stabilizer Bar Retaining Nut	31 (4.3)
Shock Absorber	
Lower Mount Nut	18-25 (2.5-3.5)
Upper Mount Nut	36 (5.0)
Torsion Bar Set Screw	29 (4.0)
Torsion Bar Set Screw Lock Nut	29 (4.0)
Axle Assembly-to-Body	65-90 (9.0-12.5)
Tie Rod End Stud Nut	22 (3.0)

VOLKSWAGEN DASHER

Dasher

DESCRIPTION

Volkswagen Dasher is front wheel drive with independent strut type front suspension. Axles are supported by lower control arms, vertically mounted strut assemblies, and a stabilizer bar. Strut assemblies consist of double action shock absorbers with coil springs mounted over the outside. The top part of strut is attached to the inner fender panel and the lower portion is attached directly to steering knuckle. Tie rods are connected to supports under coil springs. Stabilizer bar is connected to lower control arms at each end and to crossmember below engine.

ADJUSTMENT

WHEEL ALIGNMENT SPECIFICATIONS & PROCEDURES

See Wheel Alignment Specifications & Procedures in WHEEL ALIGNMENT Section.

WHEEL BEARING ADJUSTMENT

See Wheel Bearing Adjustment in WHEEL ALIGNMENT Section.

BALL JOINT CHECKING

See Ball Joint Checking in WHEEL ALIGNMENT Section.

REMOVAL & INSTALLATION

STRUT & COIL SPRING ASSEMBLY

Removal – 1) Loosen axle nut and wheel lugs. Raise and support vehicle; remove wheel and tire. Remove brake hose clips, disconnect brake caliper and move out of way.

2) Loosen bolt holding suspension ball joint stud in bottom of strut assembly. Using suitable tool, remove tie rod end from mounting under coil spring seat. Disconnect stabilizer bar from lower control arm.

3) Force lower control arm down until ball joint stud is removed from suspension strut. Remove axle nut. Support axle drive shaft so it won't fall. Pull strut outward until off axle drive shaft. Remove both upper mounting nuts. Guide strut from vehicle.

Disassembly – 1) Place strut in a vise and install coil spring compressor. Tighten compressor until pressure is taken off upper retainer. Remove upper collar mounting nut. Take off upper mounting hardware. Release spring compressor and remove coil spring.

2) Hold shock absorber cartridge center shaft with suitable tool. Loosen and remove threaded cap nut. If shock absorber cartridge will not easily pull front strut tube, thread a nut on center shaft and tap until corrosion breaks free.

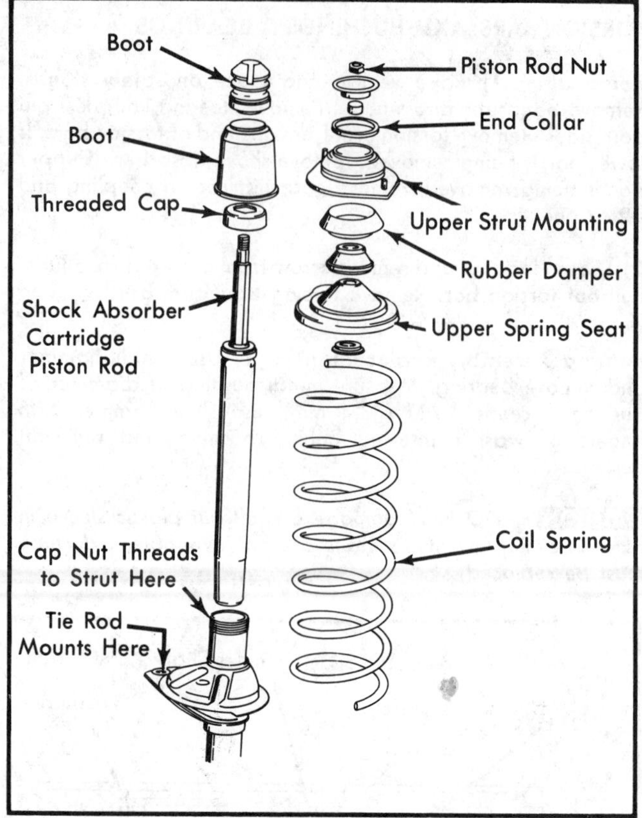

Fig. 1 Exploded View of Front Suspension Strut

Reassembly – To reassembly, reverse disassembly procedure and note: Coil springs with one, two or three paint strips are offered as replacement components. It is NOT necessary to replace both coil springs at one time, but springs must be matched.

Installation – To install, reverse removal procedure and note the following. When assembling ball joint to lower control arm always use a new bolt and nut. Face bolt head toward front of vehicle.

LOWER CONTROL ARM

Removal – Raise vehicle so that front wheel and suspension are not supported.

2) Disconnect stabilizer bar at control arm and subframe. Slide stabilizer bar out of vehicle.

3) Loosen ball joint clamp bolt. Force lower control arm down until ball joint stud is removed from suspension strut. Remove bolt mounting control arm to subframe. Guide arm from vehicle.

Bushing Replacement – 1) Check bushing in control arm for signs of excessive wear or damage. If bushings are bad they can be replaced.

2) Support wide points on control arm. Press bushings from each side of control arm.

VOLKSWAGEN DASHER (Cont.)

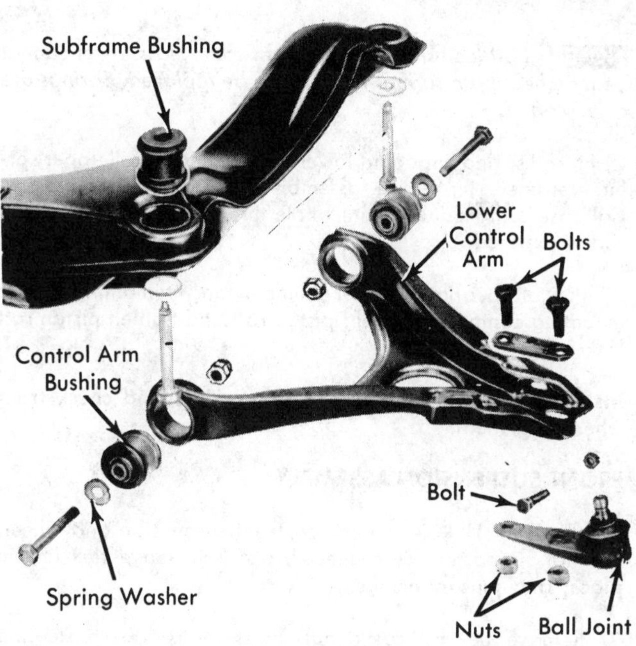

Fig. 2 Exploded View of Lower Control Arm Assembly

3) Select new bushings. Lightly coat each bushing with brake paste. Press bushing into position in control arm. Make sure bushing does not twist when pressing into place. Use bushing guide if necessary.

Installation – Reverse removal procedure and note: Use water pump pliers to compress clamps around bushing when trying to start bolts. Check front wheel alignment.

STABILIZER BAR

Removal – **1)** Raise vehicle and suitably support with safety stands. Remove brackets mounting stabilizer bar to lower control arm .

2) Loosen and remove "U" brackets mounting stabilizer bar to subframe. Guide stabilizer bar from vehicle. Inspect rubber bushings for damage or excessive wear and replace as necessay.

Installation – To install, reverse removal procedure.

TIGHTENING SPECIFICATIONS

Application	Ft. Lbs. (mkg)
Axle Nut	
18 mm Nut	145 (20.0)
20 mm Nut	175 (24)
Lower Control Arm-to-Subframe	50 (7.0)
Upper Strut Assembly-to-Body	18 (2.5)
Stabilizer Bar-to-Subframe	7 (.9)
Piston Rod Nut	43 (6)
Shock Absorber Cap Nut	108 (15.0)
Stabilizer Bar-to-Lower Control Arm	7 (.9)
Ball Joint-to-Suspension Strut	25 (3.5)
Tie Rod Castle Nut	29 (4.0)
Ball Joint-to-Lower Control Arm	47 (6.5)

VOLKSWAGEN RABBIT & SCIROCCO

Rabbit
Scirocco

DESCRIPTION

Vehicles are equipped with front wheel drive and independent strut type front suspension. Axles are supported by lower control arms, and vertically mounted strut assemblies. Strut assemblies consist of double action shock absorbers with coil springs mounted over the outside. The top portion of strut is attached to inner fender panel and lower portion is attached directly to steering knuckle. Tie rods are connected to steering knuckle.

ADJUSTMENT

WHEEL ALIGNMENT SPECIFICATIONS & PROCEDURES

See Wheel Alignment Specifications & Procedures in WHEEL ALIGNMENT Section.

WHEEL BEARING ADJUSTMENT

See Wheel Bearing Adjustment in WHEEL ALIGNMENT Section.

BALL JOINT CHECKING

See Ball Joint Checking in WHEEL ALIGNMENT Section.

REMOVAL & INSTALLATION

STRUT ASSEMBLY

NOTE – *Suspension strut does not need to be removed to replace end collar. Only requirement is to leave vehicle on ground.*

Removal – **1)** Raise vehicle so front suspension and front wheels are not supported.

2) Remove bolts mounting suspension strut to steering knuckle. Note that top bolt is one used to adjust front wheel camber.

3) Remove brake caliper assembly and suspend out of way. Pry or force suspension strut out of steering knuckle.

4) Support front suspension by hand. Also, support lower control arm and related components. Work inside engine compartment and remove upper strut mounting nuts. Guide out assembly.

Disassembly – **1)** Fit strut to spring compressor. Slightly collapse coil spring. Remove shock absorber piston rod nut. Slowly release spring pressure. Take off upper mounting hardware and coil spring.

2) Hold shock absorber cartridge center shaft with suitable tool. Loosen and remove threaded cap nut. If shock absorber cartridge will not easily pull from strut housing, thread a piston rod nut onto shaft and tap until corrosion breaks free.

Reassembly – **1)** Fit protective sleeve and buffer over piston rod. Insert shock absorber cartridge to strut housing and tighten cap nut.

NOTE – *Both coil springs must be of same class. If set cannot be matched, both springs will have to be replaced. Springs are color coded.*

2) Fit coil spring engaging lower spring seat. Install upper spring retainer. Fit entire assembly into spring compressor. Collapse coil gradually until whole threaded portion of piston rod is exposed.

3) Put on bearing, rubber bumper and remaining upper mounting components. Hold piston rod and tighten piston rod lock nut.

Installation – Reverse removal procedure and check front wheel alignment.

FRONT SUSPENSION ASSEMBLY

Removal – **1)** Raise vehicle so front suspension and wheels are not supported. Disconnect brake line, leave flex line in place, and plug openings.

2) Remove tie rod castle nut. Press tie rod from steering knuckle. Remove bolts mounting inner portion of constant velocity joint to transaxle drive flange.

3) Remove lower control arm front pivot bolt. Remove 2 bolts mounting "U" shaped bracket holding control arm rear pivot.

NOTE – *On vehicles equipped with automatic transmissions, engine may have to be slightly raised to gain access to pivot bolts.*

4) Support suspension assembly. Remove upper strut mounting nuts located in engine compartment. Guide assembly from vehicle.

Installation – Reverse removal procedure and note: Make sure convex side of thrust washer faces pivot bolt head.

LOWER CONTROL ARM & BALL JOINT

NOTE – *Ball Joint can be replaced while control arm is in vehicle.*

Removal – **1)** Raise vehicle and suitably support with front suspension free. Remove nut and clamp bolt mounting ball joint in bottom of steering knuckle. Force ball joint out of steering knuckle. Leave control arm hanging in mounts at subframe.

2) If control arm is not being removed, drill out 3 ball joint rivets with a $^9/_{32}$" (7 mm) drill. After drilling it still may be necessary to chisel off rivet heads. Remove ball joint.

3) If control arm is being removed, take out pivot bolt and "U" bracket housing inner pivot pin. Slide out control arm.

NOTE – *On vehicles equipped with automatic transmissions, engine may have to be slightly raised to gain access to pivot bolts.*

Inspection – Check lower control arm bushings. If bushings are bad they can be replaced. Press out worn bushing. Select new bushing and press into position. Make sure bushing does not twist when seating into place.

VOLKSWAGEN RABBIT & SCIROCCO (Cont.)

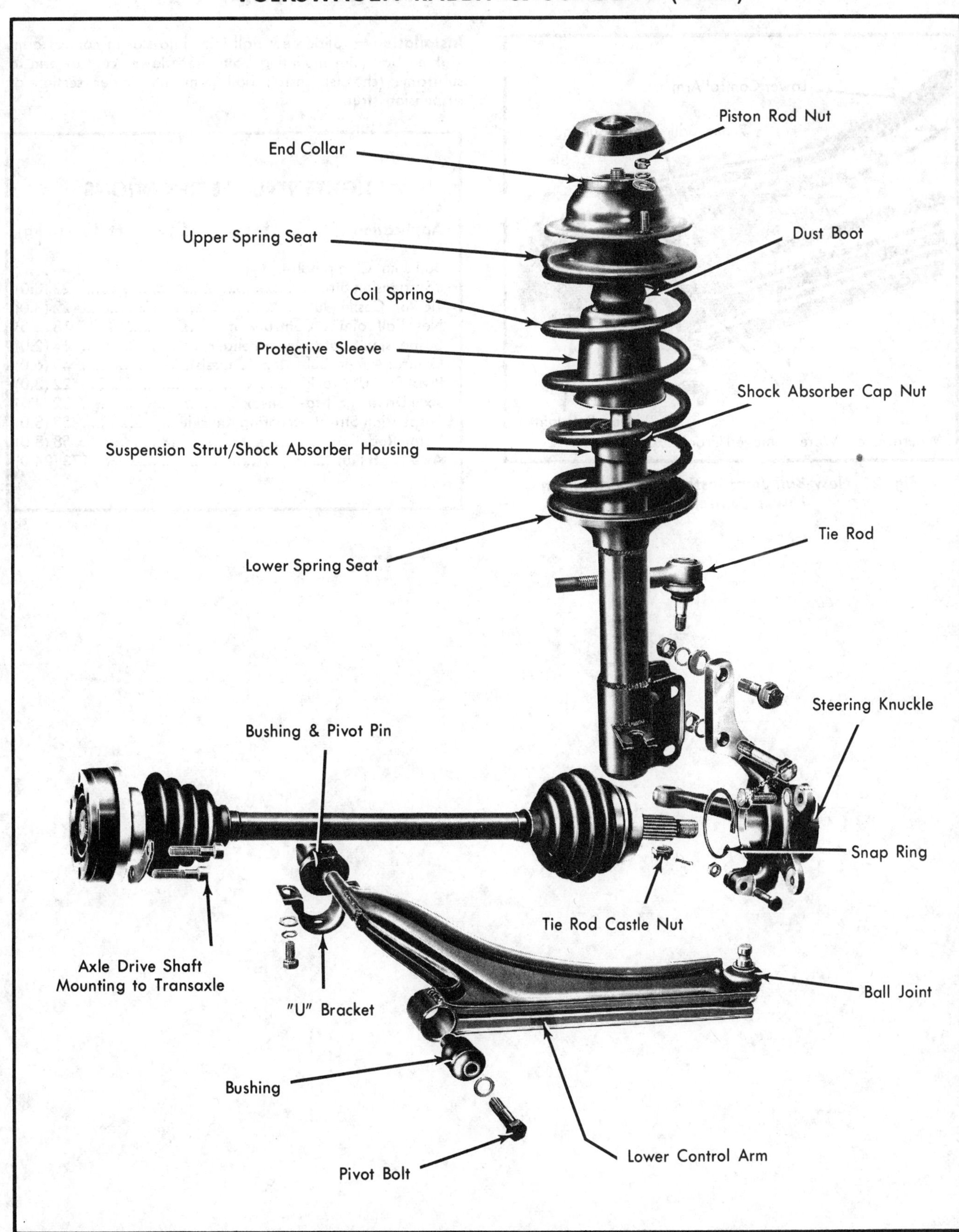

Fig. 1 Exploded View of Rabbit/Scricco Front Suspension

VOLKSWAGEN RABBIT & SCIROCCO (Cont.)

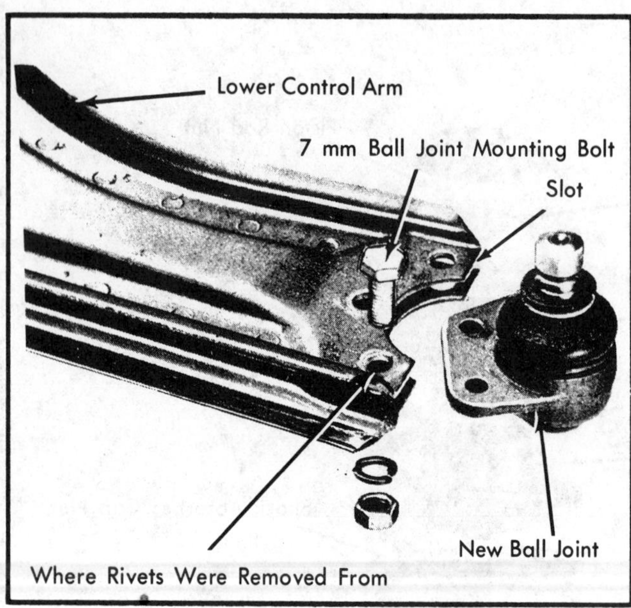

Fig. 2 New Ball Joint Installation Location in Lower Control Arm

Installation – Slide new ball joint into slot in control arm. Tighten ball joint mounting bolts. Refit lower control arm to subframe (chassis). Install ball joint into lower section of suspension strut.

TIGHTENING SPECIFICATIONS

Application	Ft. Lbs. (mkg)
Ball Joint Clamp Bolt-to Suspension Strut	22 (3.0)
Tie Rod Castle Nut	22 (3.0)
New Ball Joint-to-Control Arm	18 (2.5)
Suspension Strut-to-Inner Fender	14 (2.0)
Control Arm-to-Subframe (Chassis)	43 (6.0)
Pivot Pin "U" Bracket	22 (3.0)
Axle Drive Shaft-to-Transaxle	32 (4.5)
Suspension Strut-to-Steering Knuckle	58 (8.0)
Piston Rod Nut	58 (8.0)
Axle Shaft Nut	173 (24.0)

VOLVO

240 Series
260 Series

DESCRIPTION

Strut type suspension consisting of a vertically mounted strut assembly. Strut assembly is mounted to chassis frame at top by means of a thrust bearing. Lower end of strut assembly is mounted to a ball joint which is bolted to lower control arm. Steering knuckle is an integral part of strut assembly. Strut assembly consists of a shock absorber built into strut outer tube; a coil spring mounted on outside of strut assembly; and a spindle integral with bottom of strut. A stabilizer bar connects the control arms through rubber mounted links.

ADJUSTMENT

WHEEL ALIGNMENT SPECIFICATIONS & PROCEDURES

See Wheel Alignment Specifications & Procedures in WHEEL ALIGNMENT Section.

WHEEL BEARING ADJUSTMENT

See Wheel Bearing Adjustment in WHEEL ALIGNMENT Section.

BALL JOINT CHECKING

See Ball Joint Checking in WHEEL ALIGNMENT Section.

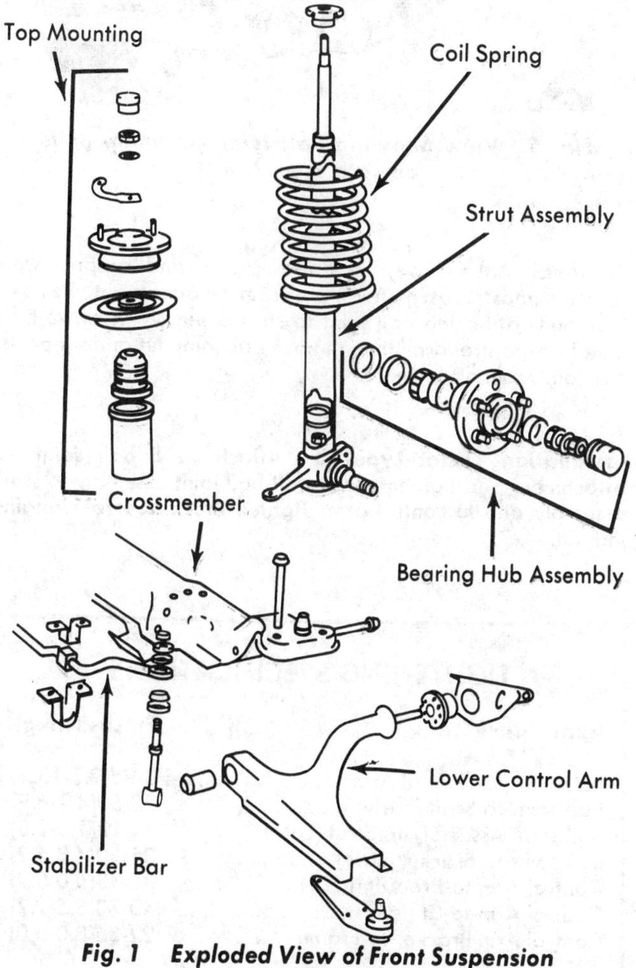

Fig. 1 Exploded View of Front Suspension Assembly

REMOVAL & INSTALLATION

CONTROL ARM

Removal – Raise vehicle and support on safety stands, then remove wheel and tire. Disconnect stabilizer bar-to-link assembly. Disconnect ball joint from control arm at three attaching bolts. Remove front attaching bolt for control arm. Remove bracket attaching rear of control arm to chassis, then remove control arm from vehicle. If control arm bushing is being replaced, press out using proper adapter (9995085) and driver (9995091).

Installation – Inspect all components for wear or damage. Use proper adapter (9995085) and driver (5555084) to install new bushings if necessary. If bushing in bracket is replaced, ensure that small slots on new bushing will point in a horizontal position when bracket is installed on vehicle. Install bracket, with control arm, to chassis but do not tighten bolts. Install front attaching bolt for control arm but do not tighten. Install ball joint to control arm and tighten bolts. Position a jack under control arm and raise so coil spring is compressed. Connect stabilizer bar to link. Tighten control arm attaching nuts and bolts. Install wheel and tire.

SHOCK ABSORBER

Removal – 1) Raise vehicle and support on safety stands, then remove wheel and tire. Position jack under control arm and raise slightly to provide support. Using a spring compressor, compress coil spring being sure to engage five coils with tool. Disconnect steering rod from steering arm and stabilizer bar from link at control arm. Remove bolt attaching brake line bracket. Remove cover on upper end of strut and spring assembly. Remove center nut using tool as indicated in *Fig. 2*.

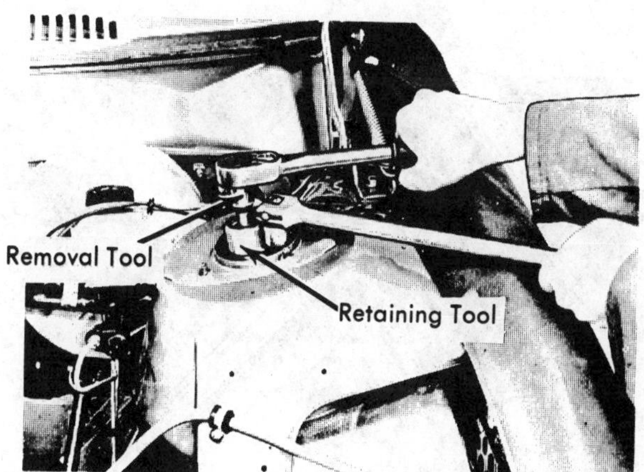

Fig. 2 View Showing Removal of Strut Assembly Center Nut

2) Lower jack supporting control arm while supporting strut assembly so brake lines and hoses are not damaged. Hook special tool (9995045) to strut assembly and stabilizer to support unit during remaining removal procedures. Remove the spring seat and rubber bumper. Remove coil spring with compressor tool attached. Remove shock absorber retaining nut while holding strut outer casing at the weld. Pull shock absorber from casing.

VOLVO (Cont.)

Installation – **1)** Install new shock absorber and retaining nut while holding strut outer casing at the weld. Pull shock absorber spindle to fully extended position. Install coil spring onto strut assembly making sure spring end is properly aligned on strut bracket. Install rubber bumper and install spring seat on coil spring. Guide strut assembly into upper mount and shock absorber spindle through upper mount. Connect stabilizer bar to stabilizer link.

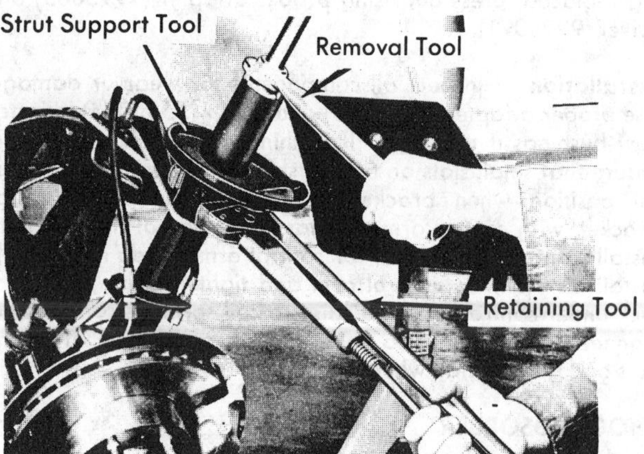

Fig. 3 View Showing Removal of Shock Absorber Nut

2) Position jack under control arm and raise slightly. Install and tighten washer and nut to shock absorber spindle while using proper retaining tool. Install cover, then connect brake line bracket to chassis. Connect steering arm to steering rod and remove coil spring compressor tool slowly. Install wheel and tire.

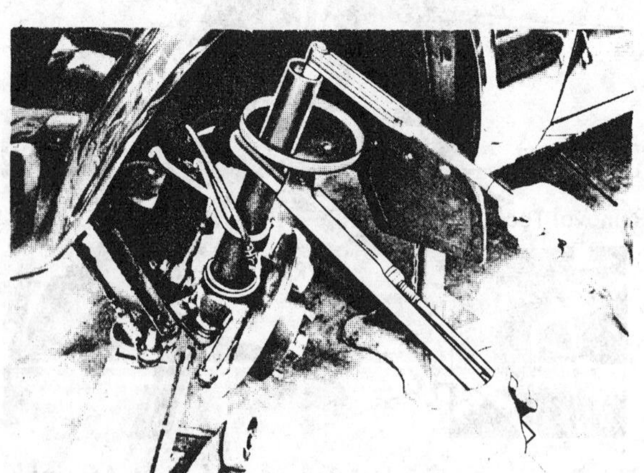

Fig. 4 View Showing Removal of Ball Joint Retaining Nut on Early Type Unit

BALL JOINTS

NOTE – *Early type ball joints have seat directly in the strut housing making removal of shock absorber necessary before access to ball joint mounting nut can be achieved. On late type ball joints, seat is bolted to shock absorber lower attachment.*

Removal (Early Type) – Remove shock absorber as previously described. Loosen ball joint retaining nut using ¾" (19 mm) socket with an extension while holding strut outer casing at the weld. Use a drift and hammer to break ball joint loose from strut assembly. Remove ball joint retaining nut, then secure strut assembly to frame with wire and disconnect ball joint from strut assembly. Disconnect ball joint from control arm and remove.

Installation (Early Type) – Install new ball joint to control arm and tighten bolts. Lift strut assembly into position, then install and tighten ball joint retaining nut while holding strut casing at the weld. Install shock absorber and remaining components.

Fig. 5 View Showing Ball Joint Retaining Bolts on Late Type Unit

Removal (Late Type) – Raise vehicle and support with safety stands. Loosen shock absorber retaining nut. Remove four bolts attaching ball joint to strut assembly. Remove ball joint from control arm, then remove ball joint nut and separate ball joint from attachment.

Installation (Late Type) – Attach new ball joint to attachment and tighten nut. Install ball joint assembly to strut assembly and to control arm. Tighten shock absorber retaining nut.

TIGHTENING SPECIFICATIONS

Application	Ft. Lbs.(mkg)
Ball Joint-to-Control Arm	70-95(9.7-13.1)
Ball Joint-to-Strut (Early)	30-50(4.1-6.9)
Ball Joint Assembly-to-Strut (Late)	11-18(1.5-2.5)
Ball Joint-to-Bracket (Late)	35-50(4.8-6.9)
Control Arm-to-Bracket (Rear)	36-43(5.0-5.9)
Control Arm-to-Chassis	40-70(5.5-9.7)
Control Arm Bracket-to-Frame	22-36(3.0-5.0)

AUDI 100LS

100LS

DESCRIPTION

Suspension is a torsion bar type utilizing a solid axle. Torsion bars are mounted inside a tube connected to chassis. Torsion bars are mounted solid inside tube and are connected at outside to spring plates. Spring plates are connected at rear to solid axle. A stabilizer bar is also employed.

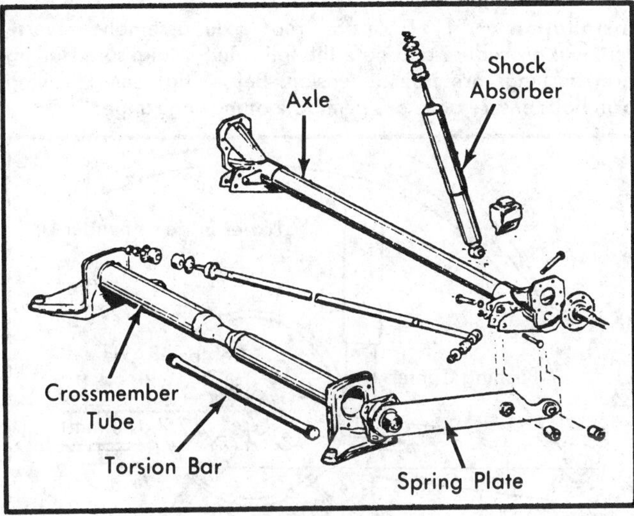

Fig. 1 Exploded View of Rear Suspension Assembly

ADJUSTMENT

WHEEL BEARING ADJUSTMENT

See Wheel Bearing Adjustment in WHEEL ALIGNMENT Section.

REMOVAL & INSTALLATION

REAR SUSPENSION ASSEMBLY

NOTE – *Complete rear suspension assembly, including solid axle can be removed as a unit.*

Removal – **1)** Push brake pedal down and secure at a position approximately 3" (76 mm) from full up position. This closes compensating port in brake master cylinder. Raise vehicle and position safety stands under chassis. Remove rear wheels. Disconnect both shock absorbers from rear axle.

2) Loosen nut at parking brake cable adjustment point until cable can be slid from bracket. Pull back plastic sleeve at cable mount on chassis and push back rubber boot. Pull cable to rear and slide through slot in holding bracket. This procedure applies to cable brackets on both sides.

3) Disconnect brake line from flex line. Plug both lines on both sides. Position a jack under suspension crossmember tube and remove bolts securing tube to chassis. Lower jack and remove complete rear suspension assembly.

NOTE – *When installing rear suspension assembly, a suitable centering tool (Centering Tool Gauge No. H-100) is required.*

Installation – **1)** Position suspension assembly in vehicle in approximate position and install front bolts and washers securing crossmember tube to chassis but do not tighten. Install centering tool on crossmember tube. Insert centering bolt in hole in crossmember tube.

2) **CAUTION** – *Bolt should not be inserted with force, move tool until bolt can be inserted easily.* With tool firmly attached to tube, move tube laterally until measuring bolts can be inserted easily into tool body. Install and tighten remaining crossmember tube bolts and remove centering gauge. Reverse removal procedure to complete installation.

CROSSMEMBER TUBE & TORSION BARS

Removal – **1)** Push brake pedal down and secure at a position approximately 3" (76 mm) from full up position. This closes compensating port in brake master cylinder. Raise vehicle and position safety stands under chassis. Remove both rear wheels.

2) Disconnect brake line at flex line and plug both openings. Remove stabilizer bar from crossmember tube and from axle. Remove bolts securing torsion bar spring plates to rear axle mounts. Remove bolts, bend open retaining clamps and remove parking brake cable from spring plates. Remove crossmember tube mounting bolts and remove crossmember tube assembly.

Disassembly – Position crossmember tube assembly on a work bench or stand and using a suitable puller, pull torsion bar spring plate from torsion bar. With spring plate removed, withdraw torsion bar from tube. If rubber mounts in spring plate are damaged, drive from spring plate with a suitable driver (H 103).

Assembly – Apply soapy water to bushing before driving into spring plate. Torsion bars are marked left and right and must be installed accordingly. Install spring plates and tighten bolts when distance "A" *(Fig. 2)* is 8.46" (215 mm). Install torsion bars, rotating bar a little at a time until bar slides in smoothly.

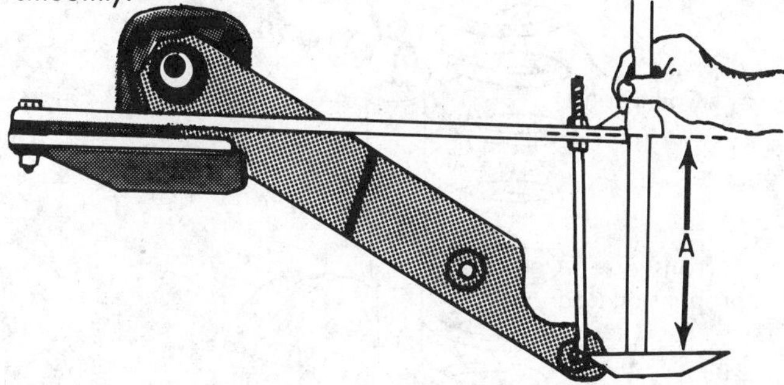

Fig. 2 Measurement Point for Spring Plate Installation

Installation – To install crossmember tube and torsion bars, reverse removal procedure.

TIGHTENING SPECIFICATIONS

Application	Ft. Lbs. (mkg)
Upper Shock Absorber Mount	22 (3.0)
Lower Shock Absorber Mount	50 (6.9)
Spring Plate-to-Rear Axle	30 (4.1)
Spring Plate-to-Crossmember Tube	16 (2.2)
Crossmember Tube-to-Body	30 (4.2)
Stabilizer Bar-to-Rear Axle	47 (6.5)
Stabilizer Bar-to-Crossmember Tube	29 (4.0)

AUDI FOX

Fox

DESCRIPTION

Rear suspension is coil spring type utilizing a transverse mounted suspension rod and a trailing arm. Suspension rod is used to improve stability. Shock absorbers mount off bracket on axle beam and to upper body. Coil spring rides in spring seat welded to axle beam and wedges against damper ring at chassis/body.

ADJUSTMENTS

WHEEL ALIGNMENT SPECIFICATIONS & PROCEDURES

See *Wheel Alignment Specifications and Procedures* in *WHEEL ALIGNMENT* Section.

WHEEL BEARING ADJUSTMENT

See *Wheel Bearing Adjustment* in *WHEEL ALIGNMENT Section*

REMOVAL & INSTALLATION

REAR AXLE BEAM ASSEMBLY

Removal – 1) Raise vehicle and place safety stands under body. Take nuts off parking brake linkage equalizer bar. Force parking brake plastic cable guide bushing from clip holder. Pry down and unhook muffler from front bracket. Separate all brake cables from body mountings.

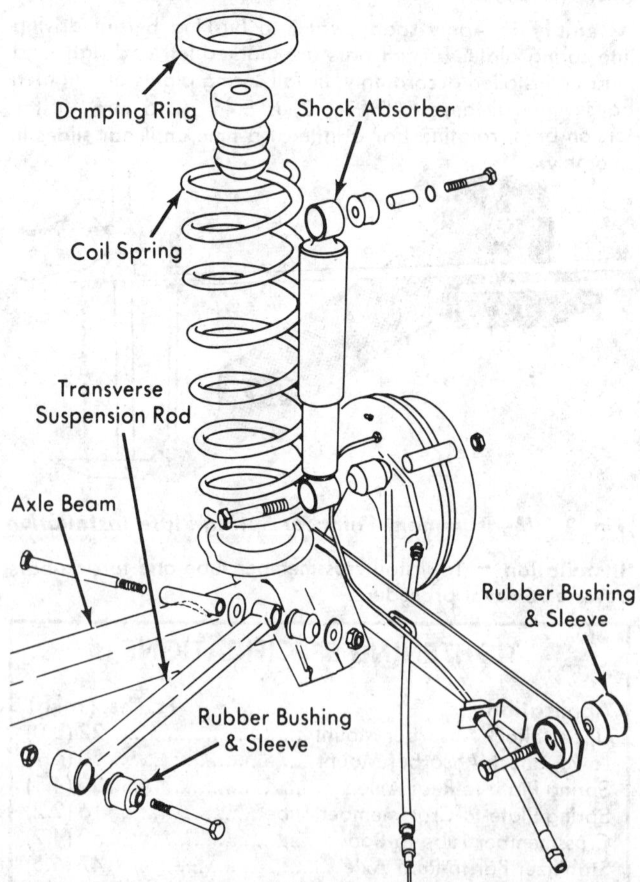

Fig. 1 Exploded View of Fox Rear Suspension

2) Disconnect brake lines and plug open ends. Using a jack, raise axle slightly. Unhook muffler at rear. Disconnect suspension rod from mounting on axle. Disconnect and wire lower end of shock absorber out of way. Guide rear axle assembly from mounting position.

Disassembly – Place trailing arm in press and force bushing from arm. Repeat process to install new bushing. **NOTE** – *Early model bushings are not interchangeable with late model bushings.* Make sure when new bushings are installed slots in bushings are aligned horizontally in trailing arm.

Installation – 1) To install rear axle assembly, reverse removal procedure and note the following: Make sure trailing arm bushings are free of tension. Before tightening trailing arm bolts ensure arms are in middle of moving range.

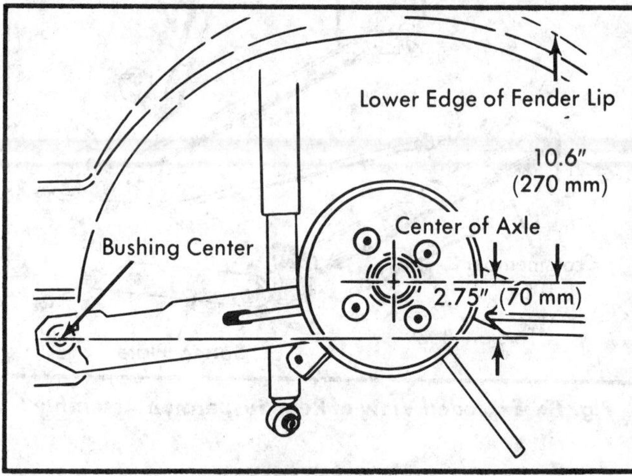

Fig. 2 Measurement Points for Installing Rear Axle Beam

2) Lift axle beam until center of axle *(See Fig. 2)* is 2.75" (70 mm) higher than center of bushing in trailing arm. Check distance between axle center to lower edge of fender lip. Distance should be 10.6" (270 mm). Tighten bolts. **NOTE** – *ONLY tighten bolts with axle located in this position.*

TRANSVERSE SUSPENSION ROD

Removal & Installation – Raise vehicle and place on safety stands. Remove suspension rod mounting bolts and tap bolts free from mounting bushings. Inspect mounting bushings and sleeves for excessive wear or damage; replace as necessary. To install, reverse removal procedure.

SHOCK ABSORBER

Removal & Installation – Raise vehicle and place on safety stands. Remove shock absorber lower mounting bolt. Remove upper mount bolt and slide shock absorber from vehicle. **NOTE** – *Lower mounting bolt must be removed first. Upper mounting bolt must be installed first.*

TIGHTENING SPECIFICATIONS

Application	Ft. Lbs. (mkg)
Shock Absorber Mounting Bolts	43 (6.0)
Suspension Rod Mounting Bolts	50 (7.0)
Trailing Arm Bolt	43 (6.0)

BMW

320i
530i
630CSi

DESCRIPTION

Independent type rear suspension with rear struts. Semi-trailing control arms pivot on crossmember and are integral with axle shaft bearing housing. Shock absorber (strut assembly) mounts to purchase on top of control arm and to body. A stabilizer bar is attached to each trailing arm and at two points on crossmember.

ADJUSTMENTS

WHEEL ALIGNMENT SPECIFICATIONS & PROCEDURES

See Wheel Alignment Specifications and Procedures in WHEEL ALIGNMENT Section.

REMOVAL & INSTALLATION

STRUT ASSEMBLIES (SHOCK ABSORBERS)

Removal – Raise vehicle and support with safety stands. Remove tire. Place a jack under control arm. Disconnect shock absorber at lower mount on control arm. From top end of shock absorber, remove centering shell and mounting nuts. Remove shock absorber complete with spring assembly.

Disassembly & Reassembly – Using a spring compressor, collapse spring and remove centering shell. Remove coil spring and boot. Pull retainer and auxiliary spring off shock absorber. Inspect spring and boot for wear and replace any parts found defective. To reassemble, reverse disassembly procedure and ensure coil spring is properly aligned before releasing spring compressor. Vent opening on auxiliary spring faces inside retainer.

Installation – To install shock absorber, reverse removal procedure and tighten all nuts and bolts.

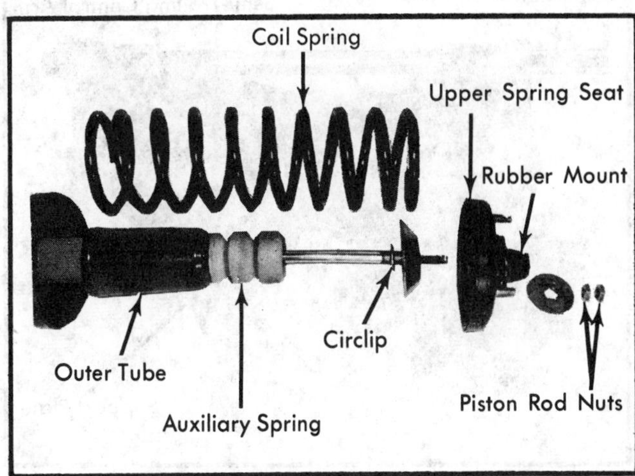

Fig. 2 Exploded View of BMW Rear Suspension Strut Assembly – 320i Shown

SEMI-TRAILING CONTROL ARM

Removal – **1)** Raise vehicle and place on safety stands. Remove tire and wheel. Remove parking brake lever. Disconnect and plug brake fluid line at union bracket; plug openings. Disconnect brake pad wear sensor from right trailing arm, if equipped.

2) Remove stabilizer bar from control arm. Remove strut assembly (shock absorber) from vehicle. Disconnect axle drive shaft from bearing carrier. Place jack under control arm. Remove trailing arm pivot bolts at crossmember and lower arm to ground.

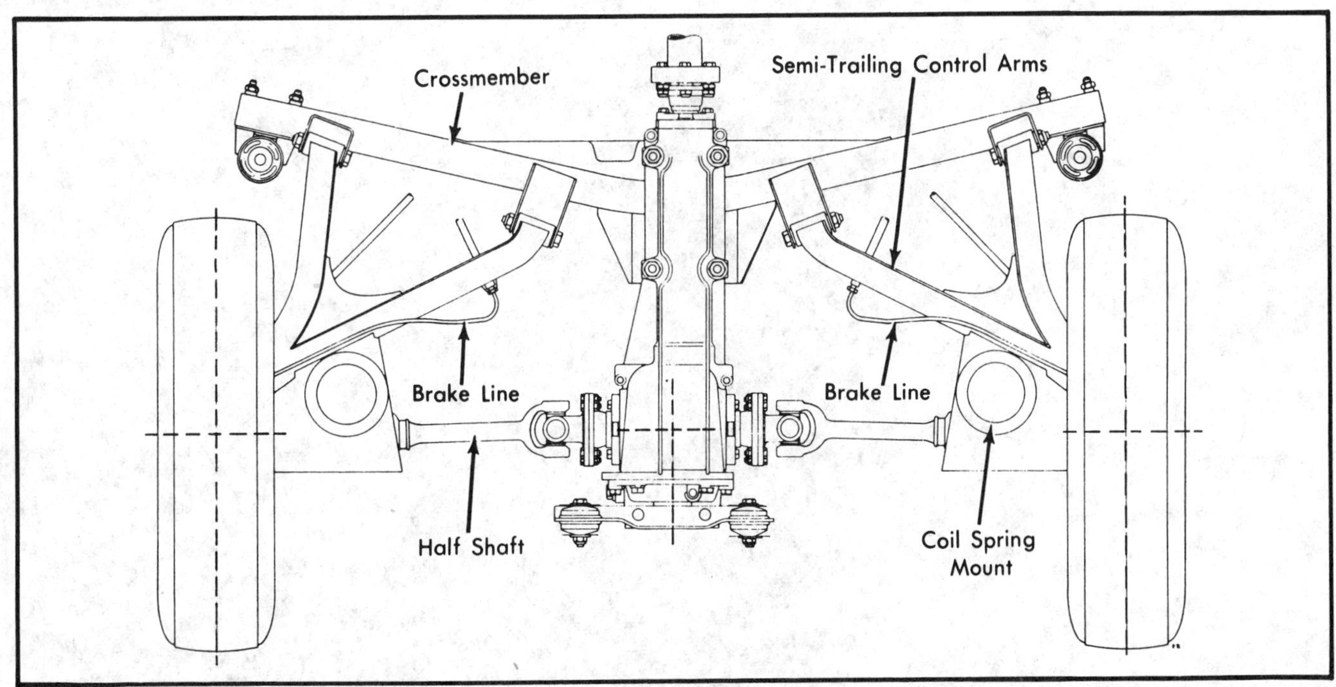

Fig. 1 Overhead View of BMW Rear Suspension

BMW (Cont.)

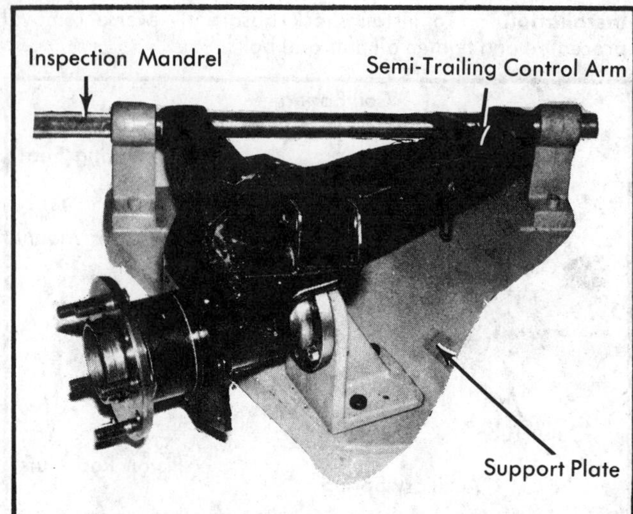

Fig. 3 Trailing Arm Fitted to Support Plate to Check Alignment

Inspection – **1**) Visually inspect bushing and replace those that have deteriorated. Before pressing out worn bushings, cut off collar. When pressing in new bushings lubricate them with oil. Note that collared edge faces out.

2) Check trailing arm alignment. Place arm in support plate. See *Fig. 3.* Slide inspection mandrel through control arm to crossmember mounting bushings bores (bushings removed). If control arm is out of alignment it can be straightened if there is no other damage to arm.

Installation – To install, reverse removal procedure and tighten all nuts and bolt. Bleed and adjust brakes.

TIGHTENING SPECIFICATIONS

Application	Ft. Lbs. (mkg)
Bottom Strut Mounting	
320i	36-39 (4.9-5.4)
530i and 630CSi	87-94 (12-13)
Upper Strut-to-Body	18-20 (2.5-2.8)
Trailing Arm-to-Crossmember	
320i	58-65 (8.1-9.0)
530i and 630CSi	49-54 (6.7-7.5)

DATSUN 280Z

280Z

DESCRIPTION

Rear suspension is a strut type independent suspension. Rear wheels are supported with strut and transverse link. The gear carrier is aligned independently and separately from the suspension, and gear carrier is mounted directly to body with rubber insulators. Rear axle housing is welded on lower end of strut which contains a shock absorber, and its lower side is connected to the transverse link through rubber bushings. At strut midpoint, the body is suspended with coil springs. The transverse link is attached to the body with rubber cushions.

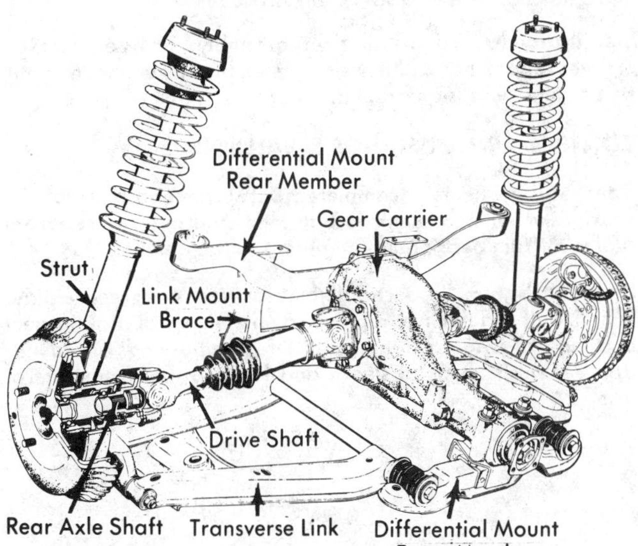

Fig. 1 Datsun 280Z Rear Suspension Assembly

REMOVAL & INSTALLATION

STRUT & COIL SPRING

Removal – 1) Block front wheels, raise rear end of vehicle, and support at body with stands. Remove rear wheels. Disconnect brake line coupler (body side) and parking brake linkage. Disconnect stabilizer bar from transverse link.

2) Remove transverse link outer self-locking nuts and bolt from lower end of bearing housing. Withdraw spindle and separate transverse link from strut assembly.

3) Disconnect drive half-shaft at wheel side. Remove strut mounting nuts from passenger side and remove strut assembly downward. **NOTE** – *When removing strut assembly, apply a jack to lower end of strut and remove it gradually.*

4) For removal of coil spring, clamp strut assembly in vise with suitable strut attachment (ST35650000). Compress coil spring until strut mounting insulator can be turned by hand, then remove self-locking nut. Remove strut insulator, mounting bearing, and upper spring seat. Remove coil spring with tool still attached to spring.

Installation – To install, reverse removal procedure, noting the following: Tighten transverse link outer self-locking nut after rear wheels are installed and vehicle is lowered to ground.

TRANSVERSE LINK

Removal – 1) Block front wheels, raise rear end of vehicle, and remove rear wheels. Remove stabilizer bar from transverse link. Separate transverse link from strut assembly. *Refer to Strut & Coil Spring above.* Support gear carrier with a jack.

2) Loosen transverse link inner bolts for both front and rear. Remove differential mount front insulator installation nut. Remove mount front member installation nuts, and remove differential mount front member.

3) Remove link mount rear bracket and withdraw the transverse link. Detach inner bushing and outer bushing from link.

Installation – To install, reverse removal procedure, noting the following: Tighten transverse link inner bolts and outer self-locking nut only after rear wheels are replaced and vehicle is under standard load (on the ground).

REAR SUSPENSION ASSEMBLY

Removal – 1) Remove strut assemblies from both sides as previously outlined. Detach main muffler. Disconnect stabilizer bar from body. Separate propeller shaft from final drive. Loosen transverse link inner bolts for front and rear. Support gear carrier with jack.

2) Remove differential mount front member installation bolts. Unscrew link brace mounting bolt and differential mount rear insulator attaching bolt (for both sides). Lower jack slowly and remove rear suspension assembly.

Disassembly – 1) Remove link mount rear bracket and remove transverse link (for both sides). Unscrew drive shaft installation bolt (in gear carrier side), and separate drive shaft from gear carrier (both sides).

2) Extract inner and outer bushings from transverse link. Remove differential mount rear member and differential mount front insulator from gear carrier. Drift out differential mount rear insulator from rear member.

Reassembly & Installation – Assemble and install rear suspension assembly in reverse of disassembly and removal procedures, while noting the following: When replacing transverse link inner bushing, position bushing to link shaft and align projection on bushing horizontally. Align center of bushing to center of bracket and temporarily tighten transverse link inner bolts. Do not fully tighten inner bolts until installation is complete and vehicle has been lowered to ground. When differential carrier front insulator is installed, ensure arrow points toward front.

TIGHTENING SPECIFICATIONS

Application	Ft. Lbs.(mkg)
Transverse Link Outer Self-Locking Nut	54-68(7.5-9.4)
Transverse Link Inner Bolt	101-106(14-16)
Strut Upper Mounting Nuts	18-25(2.5-3.5)
Strut Rod Self-Locking Nut	54-69(7.5-9.5)
Gland Packing	51-94(7-13)
Drive Shaft Installation Bolts	36-43(5-6)

FIAT X1/9

X1/9

DESCRIPTION

Fiat X1/9 is a rear engine mounted and rear wheel driven vehicle utilizing independent rear suspension. All rear suspensions consists of the following: Lower control arms, bearing housings, and hydraulic, strut type, shock absorbers. Control arms are attached to chassis in rubber bushings and to bearing housing with a ball joint. Hydraulic strut assembly attaches to bearing housing just above axle shaft and mounts at top to inside of engine compartment. A reaction rod is also attached to bearing housing and is used to adjust rear wheel alignment.

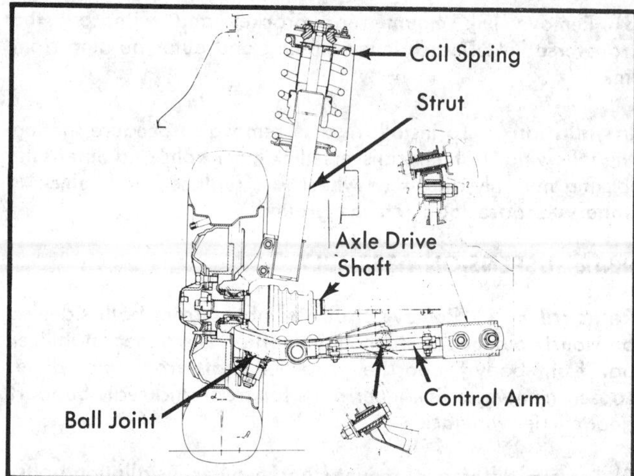

Fig. 1 Sectional View of Fiat X1/9 Rear Suspension Assembly

ADJUSTMENT

WHEEL ALIGNMENT SPECIFICATIONS & PROCEDURES

See Wheel Alignment Specifications and Procedures in WHEEL ALIGNMENT Section.

WHEEL BEARING ADJUSTMENT

See Wheel Bearing Adjustment in WHEEL ALIGNMENT Section.

REMOVAL & INSTALLATION

SUSPENSION ASSEMBLY

Removal – Raise and support vehicle; remove tire and wheel. Remove rear brake caliper and disconnect parking brake. **NOTE** – *See appropriate article in BRAKE Section.* Remove exhaust pipe. Note number and position of shims on control arm. Separate front and rear ends of lower control arm from chassis; do not lose shims. Remove hub nut and washer. Remove nuts mounting strut assembly at top. Slide suspension off axle shaft and secure axle to prevent pulling out of differential.

Installation – To install suspension assembly, reverse removal procedure. Make sure axle nut is properly torqued before lowering vehicle. Tighten all remaining bolts with weight of vehicle on all four wheels. Ensure correct amount of shims are installed.

STRUT ASSEMBLY

Removal – Raise and support vehicle; remove tire and wheel. Disconnect upper strut assembly mounts from inside engine compartment. Remove bolts mounting strut to bearing housing and carefully maneuver strut assembly from vehicle.

Disassembly – 1) Using a suitable spring compressor, collapse spring coil. With spring compressed, remove nut from center of upper mount. Release spring compressor and remove upper mount and coil spring.

2) Inspect springs for cracks or distortion. Springs are manufactured in two classes and identified by paint marks. Class A springs are marked with a yellow stripe on outside of center coils and class B springs are marked with a green stripe. If springs are replaced, use one of same class.

Reassembly – Using same spring compressor as previously implemented, reverse disassembly procedure.

Installation – To install strut assembly, reverse removal procedure. Do not tighten strut assembly lower mount until weight of vehicle is on ground.

CONTROL ARM, BUSHINGS & BALL JOINTS

Removal – Remove complete front suspension assembly as previously outlined. Remove ball joint stud nut and separate ball joint from bearing housing using suitable puller.

Disassembly – Inspect ball joint for wear or excessive play. If ball joint is defective, replace complete control arm. Inspect bushings for wear or damage. If defective bushings are found, drill out bushing metal sleeve and force rubber from control arm.

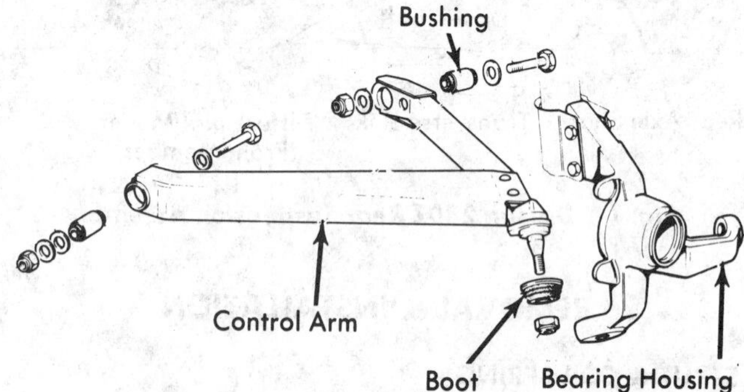

Fig. 2 Exploded View of Control Arm Assembly

Reassembly – Position outer washer, bushing and sleeve on centering pin of a suitable installer (mandrel). Place control arm over bushing and install bushing and washer for opposite side. Using suitable mandrel and necessary adaptors press in new bushing until properly seated. Repeat procedure for other side.

Installation – To install control arm, attach to bearing housing, tighten ball joint stud nut, and position suspension assembly as previously outlined.

TIGHTENING SPECIFICATIONS

Application	Ft. Lbs. (mkg)
Wheel Hub Nut	112 (15.5)
Reaction Rod-to-Control Arm	50.6 (7.0)
Ball Joint Nut	72.3 (10.0)
Control Arm Pivot Pin Nut	72.3 (10.0)
Strut-to-Bearing Housing Bolts	43.4 (6.0)
Brake Caliper-to-Bearing Housing	36.2 (5.0)
Wheel Bearing Nut	43.4 (6.0)

FIAT 124

124 Spider

DESCRIPTION

Link type rear suspension with coil springs. System uses upper and lower strut rods to attach rear axle to body. Brackets on rear axle and body support coil springs with hydraulic, double acting shock absorbers mounted inside coil spring. A stabilizer bar pivots on rear axle and body.

REMOVAL & INSTALLATION

UPPER & LOWER STRUT RODS

Removal – Raise and support vehicle. Place support under rear axle. Remove nuts and bolts attaching strut rods to axle and to body. Remove strut rods.

Installation – Before installing, inspect all parts for signs of damage or wear and replace as necessary. To install, reverse removal procedure.

SHOCK ABSORBERS

Removal – Remove shock absorber upper retaining nuts from inside luggage compartment. Remove nuts attaching shock absorber to spring seat plate and remove shock absorber.

Installation – To install, reverse removal procedure and tighten all nuts and bolts.

COIL SPRINGS

Removal – Raise rear of vehicle and support. Remove wheels and disconnect brake lines. Disconnect parking brake. Remove nuts attaching shock absorbers to body. Disconnect pressure regulator link from axle housing. Support axle with jack, disconnect upper and lower control arms and stabilizer bar. Lower suspension assembly and remove springs.

Installation – Before installing, inspect all parts for signs of excessive wear or damage and replace as necessary. To install, reverse removal procedure and tighten all nuts and bolts. Bleed and adjust brakes if necessary.

STABILIZER BAR

Removal – Remove nuts and bolts attaching stabilizer bar to rear axle and body and remove bar.

Installation – Inspect all parts for signs of distortion, wear or damage. To install, reverse removal procedure and tighten all nuts and bolts.

TIGHTENING SPECIFICATIONS

Application	Ft. Lbs. (mkg)
Stabilizer Bar	58 (8.0)
Upper Strut Rod-to-Body	25 (3.5)
Lower Strut Rod-to-Body	58 (8.0)
Upper and Lower Strut Rods-to-Axle	72 (10.0)
Shock Absorber Mountings	36 (5.0)

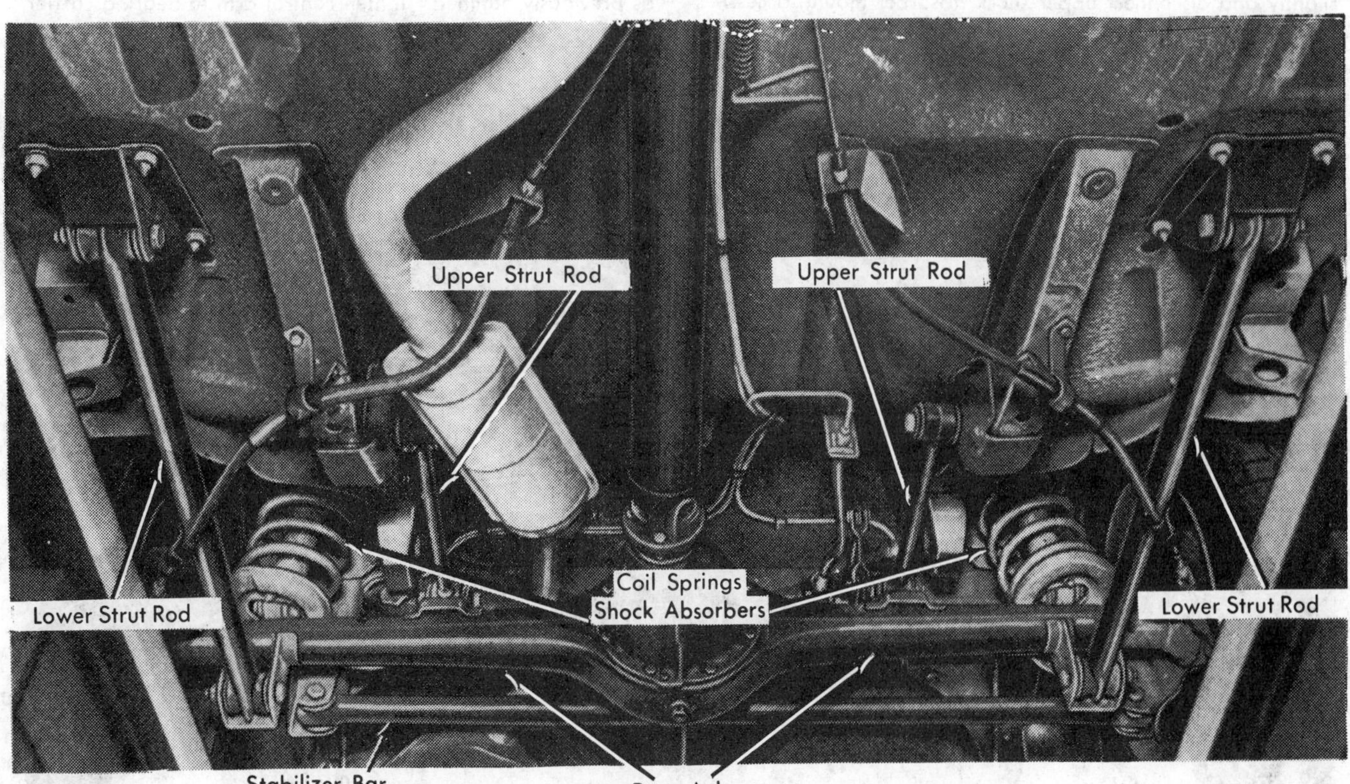

Fig. 1 Installed View of Fiat 124 Rear Suspension Assembly

FIAT 128

128
Sedan
Station Wagon
3P

DESCRIPTION

Independent type rear suspension utilizing a transverse leaf spring. Wheel bearing carriers are supported by control arms connected to chassis and by hydraulic double action shock absorbers connected at top to inner fender panel. Transverse leaf spring is connected to chassis at center and to control arms at outside.

ADJUSTMENT

WHEEL ALIGMENT SPECIFICATIONS & PROCEDURES

See Wheel Alignment Specifications & Procedures in WHEEL ALIGNMENT Section.

WHEEL BEARING ADJUSTMENT

See Wheel Bearing Adjustment in WHEEL ALIGNMENT Section.

REMOVAL & INSTALLATION

SHOCK ABSORBER & CONTROL ARM

Removal — **1)** Raise rear of vehicle, position safety stands under chassis and remove rear wheels. Disconnect and plug brake flex line. Disconnect parking brake cable from lever on back of backing plate. Position a jack under control arm, raise slightly and disconnect upper shock absorber mount, accessible from inside luggage compartment.

2) Remove outer mount pad securing spring to control arm. Remove nuts securing control arm pivot shaft to chassis. Lower jack and remove shock absorber and control arm. Note number and position of wheel alignment shims between control arm pivot shaft and body mount for installation.

Installation — To install control arm and shock absorber, reverse removal procedure. Bleed brake hydraulic system. Tighten control arm pivot shaft nuts with weight of vehicle on rear wheels.

CONTROL ARM BUSHINGS

Removal — Remove shock absorber and control arm as previously outlined. Remove pivot bolt securing control arm to bearing carrier and shock absorber mount. Remove inner pivot shaft nuts at control arm. Using a press and a suitable mandrel (A. 47057), press out on pivot shaft until bushing is partially removed. This allows for removing tool to properly center on opposite bushing. Using same procedure, remove other bushing. Remove control arm from press and extract remaining bushing. Remove bearing carrier bushings in control arm with a suitable puller (A. 47057).

Installation — **1)** Using same tools as used for removal in addition to a suitable spacer (A. 74220) installed between inner legs of control arm, press bushings into control arm onto pivot shaft. Use same tool as used for removal to reinstall bearing carrier bushings into control arm.

2) When reconnecting control arm to bearing carrier, the correct shim thickness between control arm and shock absorber mount must be determined. *See Control Arm Shim Determination.* Reinstall control arm, bearing carrier and shock absorber as previously outlined. Tighten control arm to bearing carrier pivot bolt with weight of vehicle on rear wheels.

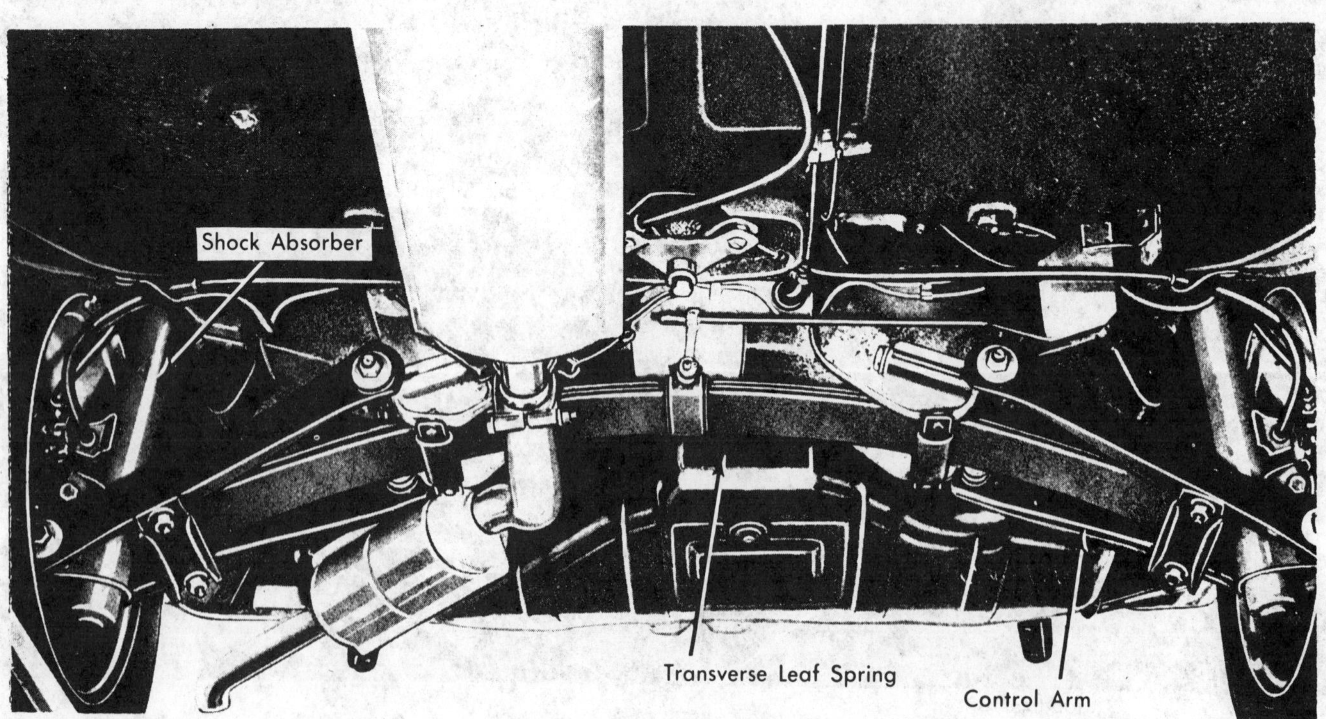

Fig. 1 Installed View of Fiat 128 Rear Suspension Assembly

FIAT 128 (Cont.)

CONTROL ARM SHIM DETERMINATION

Measure distance ("A" see illustration) between outer bushings on control arm. Measure width ("B" see illustration) of shock absorber mount. Add .118" (3 mm) to the difference of measurements "A" and "B". This will give the thickness required for both shims. Shim thickness must not vary more than .020" (.5 mm) between left and right side.

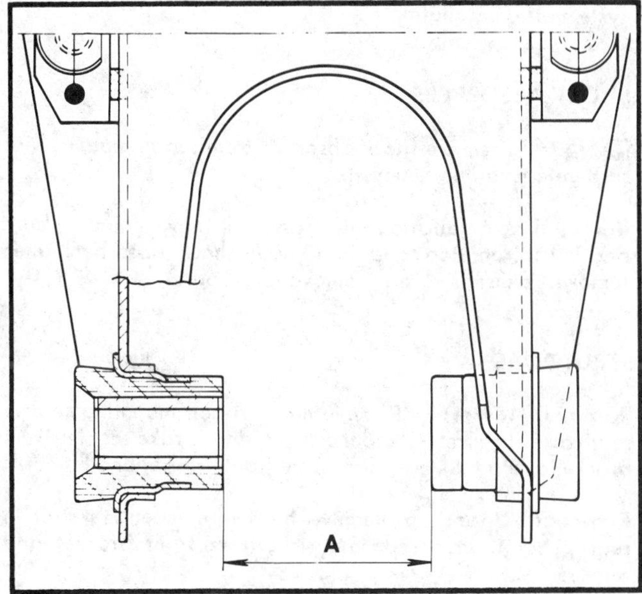

Fig. 2 Shim Thickness Measuring Dimension "A" on Control Arm

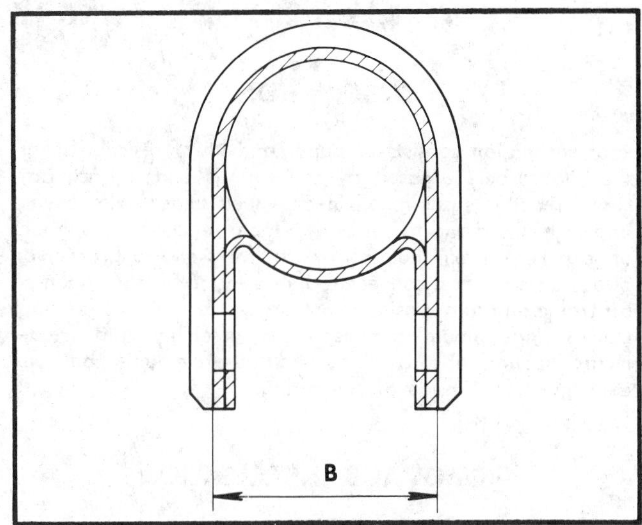

Fig. 3 Shim Thickness Measuring Dimension "B" on Control Arm

TRANSVERSE LEAF SPRING

Removal – Raise rear of vehicle, position on safety stands and remove wheels. Place a jack under left end of spring and raise enough to release spring from rubber mounting pad on control arm. Remove cotter pin and disconnect rod linking spring to brake regulator (if equipped). Remove mount for rubber pad on bottom of control arm and lower jack to release spring. Repeat same procedure for opposite side. Remove two guides securing spring to chassis and remove spring.

Installation – Inspect spring making sure there are not any cracked or broken leaves. Inspect all rubber mounts and inter leaf shims for wear or damage. To install transverse leaf spring, reverse removal procedure.

TIGHTENING SPECIFICATIONS

Application	Ft. Lbs. (mkg)
Rear Wheel Hub Nut	112 (15.5)
Leaf Spring Mounting Pad-to-Control Arm	22 (3.0)
Control Arm-to-Bearing Carrier Pivot Bolt	58 (8.0)
Control Arm-to-Chassis Pivot Bolt	36 (5.0)
Control Arm Pivot Shaft End Nuts	32 (4.4)
Upper Shock Absorber Mount	18 (2.5)
Lower Shock Absorber Mount	43 (6.0)
Brake Backing Plate Assembly-to-Bearing Carrier	18 (2.5)

FIAT 131

131

DESCRIPTION

Rear suspension consists of upper and lower reaction struts, shock absorbers encased by coil springs and a track bar. Lower reaction struts mount near wheels under axle housing and at forward end to car body. Upper reaction struts mount off bracket on axle housing and at front end to bracket on body. A track bar is connected at one end to bracket mounted off frame and at opposite end to bracket below axle housing. Coil springs mount between axle assembly and frame. Hydraulic shock absorbers are used and are mounted between axle and body, inside of coil spring.

REMOVAL & INSTALLATION

REAR SUSPENSION ASSEMBLY

Removal – Raise vehicle, support with safety stands, and remove rear wheels. Disconnect propeller shaft from rear axle.

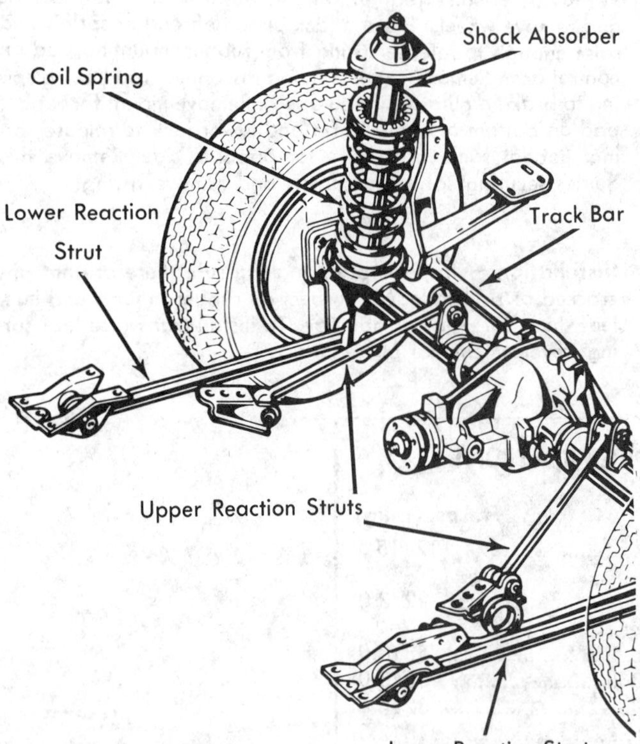

Fig. 1 Fiat 131 Rear Suspension Assembly

Disconnect parking brake cable from cable housing assembly. Disconnect track bar from frame. Position a jack under axle assembly and raise jack enough to support axle. Disconnect lower strut rods from frame bracket, then remove brake cable and brake regulator rod from bracket. Disconnect brake hose from "T" fitting on rear axle. Disconnect upper reaction struts from frame bracket. Disconnect shock absorber from upper mount and upper mount from body. Lower rear axle with suspension from vehicle.

Installation – To install rear axle, reverse removal procedure while noting the following: Tighten nuts and bolts to specifications with weight of vehicle on ground. Bleed brake system after installation.

SHOCK ABSORBERS

NOTE – *To remove shock absorber from sedan models, rear suspension must be removed.*

Removal & Installation, St. Wgn. – Remove mounting bolts and nuts from top and bottom of shock absorbers, then remove. To install, reverse removal procedure.

STRUT RODS

Removal (Lower) – Remove nut and bolt mounting strut in rear axle bracket. Disconnect parking brake cable from bracket on strut. Remove strut from front bracket and lift out.

Removal (Upper) – Remove hardware mounting strut in rear bracket, then separate strut from front bracket and remove.

Installation (Upper and Lower) – To install, reverse removal procedure.

TIGHTENING SPECIFICATIONS

Application	Ft. Lbs.(mkg)
Shock Absorber-to-Upper Mount	11(1.5)
Upper Mount-to-Body	18(2.5)
Shock Absorber Lower Mount	36(5)
Track Bar-to-Rear Axle	72(10)
Track Bar-to-Body	58(8)
Reaction Strut Rods	58(8)

HONDA

Civic
Civic CVCC
Except St. Wgn.
Accord

DESCRIPTION

Rear suspension system on all models is an independent type. Major components are: Control arm (lower), shock absorber with coil spring assembly, radius rod, and rear hub carrier. Radius rod controls rear wheel alignment.

REMOVAL & INSTALLATION

SHOCK ABSORBER

Removal – 1) Raise vehicle and suitably support on safety stands. Remove rear wheels. Disconnect brake line from bracket on shock absorber housing. Plug open ends and place lines out of way. Disconnect parking brake cable from lever on backing plate.

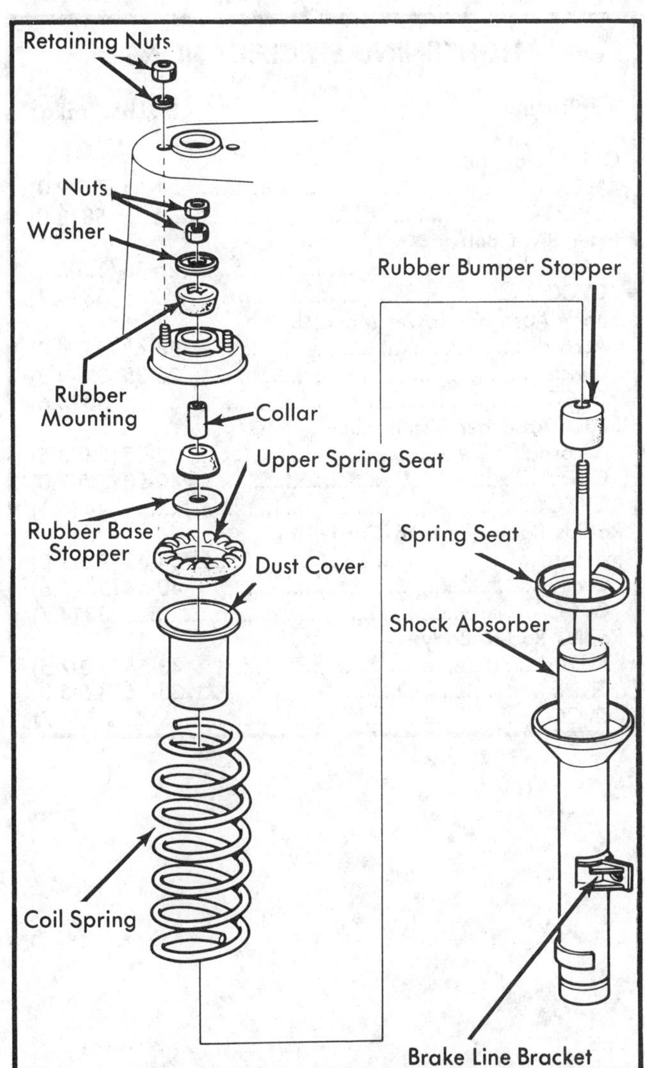

Fig. 1 Exploded View of Accord Shock Absorber Assembly – Other Models Are Similar

2) Remove bolt mounting shock absorber to knuckle. Remove cotter pin and loosen outer control arm pivot bolt. Remove two upper shock absorber retaining nuts. Lower shock absorber and coil spring from vehicle.

Disassembly – Fit spring compressor and slightly compress coils. Remove lock nut and piston rod center nut. Take off upper mounting hardware and coil spring.

Inspection – Check piston rod for smooth, even operation. Inspect for signs of oil leaks. Listen for noise or unusual binding during inspection.

Reassembly – Select new shock absorber. Fit coil spring to lower spring seat. Refit spring compressor. Collapse coil enough to insert upper mountings and tighten piston rod. Release coil spring.

Installation – To install, reverse removal procedure and note: Fit top of shock absorber first. Make sure tab on shock absorber engages slot in bearing carrier. Bleed brake system.

REAR WHEEL HUB CARRIER

Removal – Raise vehicle and place on safety stands. Remove wheel and brake drum. Disconnect and plug brake lines. Remove bolt mounting shock absorber to hub carrier. Disconnect control arm and radius rod from hub carrier. Maneuver hub carrier from vehicle.

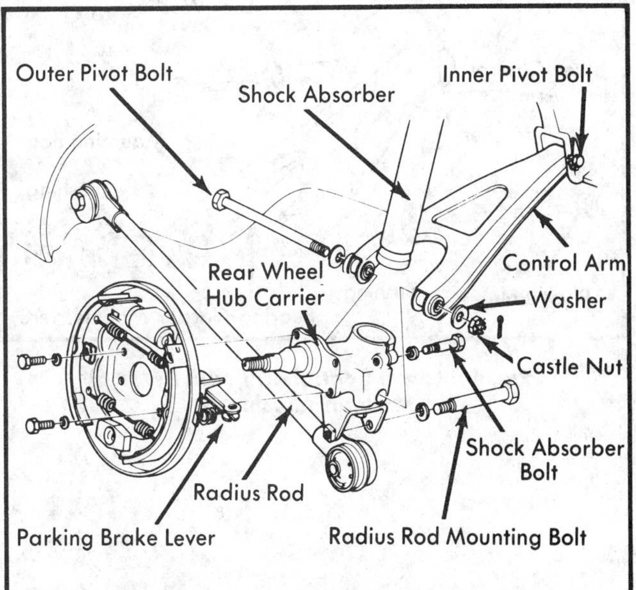

Fig. 2 Exploded View of Accord Rear Suspension Other Models Are Similar

Installation – To install hub carrier, reverse removal procedure and note following: Bleed brake system and check rear wheel alignment.

HONDA (Cont.)

RADIUS ROD

Removal – Raise and suitably support vehicle. Remove bolt mounting radius rod to hub carrier. Remove bolt mounting opposite end of radius rod to body bracket.

Inspection – Inspect all radius rod bushings and grommets for damage or excessive wear. Replace parts found defective. Make sure radius rod adjusting bolt is not damaged

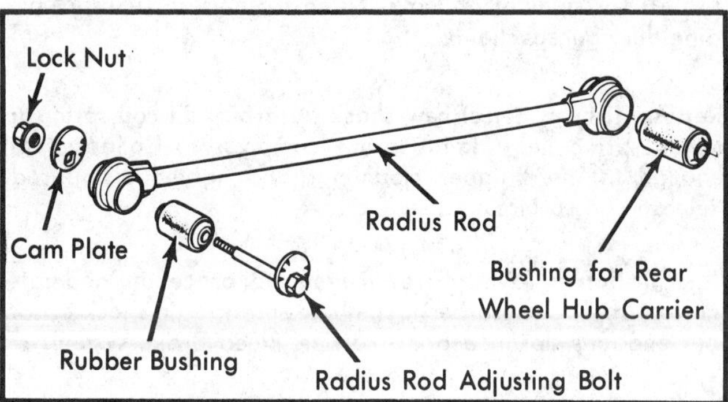

Fig. 3 Radius Control Rod with Bushings and Adjustment Bolt – Accord Shown Others Similar

Installation – To install, reverse removal procedure and note: Either lower vehicle to ground or raise rear of vehicle to simiulate normal weight before tightening radius control rod. Check and adjust wheel alignment as required.

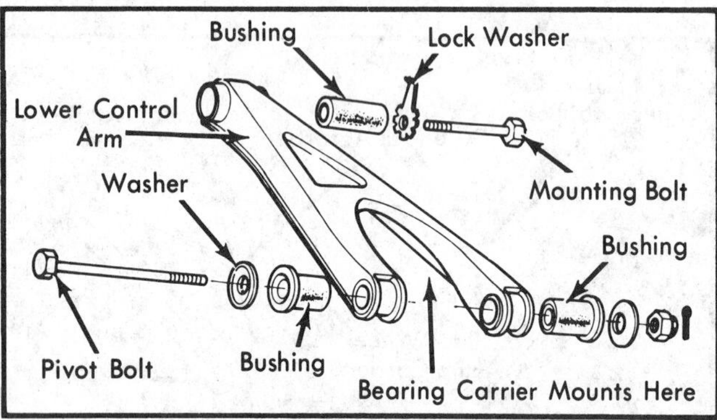

Fig. 4 Lower Control Arm with Detail of Mounting Bushings

CONTROL ARM

Removal – Raise vehicle and place on safety stands. Remove wheel and brake drum. Remove brake hoses from shock absorber mounting, then plug openings. Remove brake backing plate. Remove bolt mounting shock absorber to hub carrier. Remove both inside and outside control arm pivot bolts. Pull out control arm.

Inspection – Inspect all control arm bushings for damage or excessive wear. Replace any parts found defective. Always replace bolt lock tabs.

Installation – To install, reverse removal procedure and note following: Bleed brake system and check rear wheel alignment.

TIGHTENING SPECIFICATIONS

Application	Ft. Lbs. (mkg)
Outer Pivot Bolt	
Accord	54-65 (7.5-9.0)
CVCC	58 (8.0)
Inner Pivot Bolt	
Accord and Civic	25-36 (3.5-5.0)
CVCC	33 (4.7)
Shock Absorber Lower Mount Bolt	
Accord	36-43 (5.0-6.0)
Civic	26-35 (3.6-4.8)
CVCC	33 (4.6)
Shock Absorber Piston Nut	
Accord	22-25 (3.0-3.5)
Civic	40-50 (5.5-7.0)
CVCC	44 (6.1)
Radius Rod-to-Bearing Carrier	
Accord	54-65 (7.5-9.0)
Civic	40-54 (5.5-7.5)
CVCC	33 (4.7)
Radius Rod-to-Body	
Accord	43-54 (6.0-7.5)
Civic	25-36 (3.5-5.0)
CVCC	33 (4.7)

JAGUAR

XJ6
XJ12
XJS

DESCRIPTION

Independent, coil spring type suspension. Outer bearing carrier and hub assembly is supported by control arms at bottom and utilizes drive axles as upper support. Suspension is controlled by two coil spring/shock absorber assemblies mounted at each rear wheel. Movement of lower control arms are controlled by radius arms connected to control arms at rear and to chassis members at front.

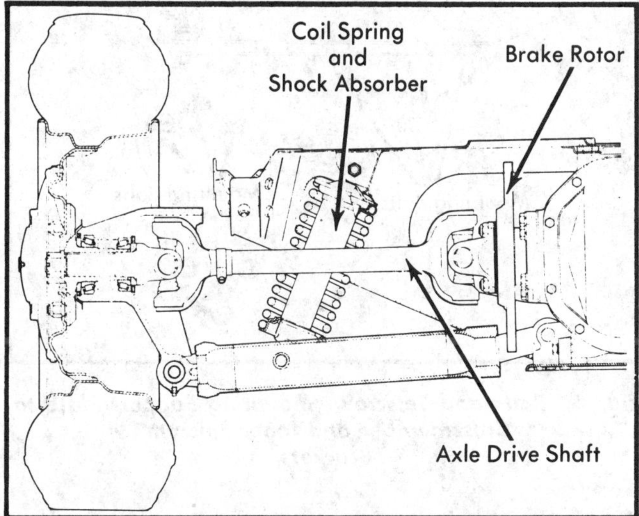

Fig. 1 Jaguar Rear Suspension Assembly

ADJUSTMENTS

WHEEL ALIGNMENT SPECIFICATIONS & PROCEDURES

See Wheel Alignment Specifications and Procedures in WHEEL ALIGNMENT Section.

REMOVAL & INSTALLATION

COIL SPRING & SHOCK ABSORBER

NOTE — *Rear springs can be removed with rear suspension installed in vehicle.*

Removal — Raise vehicle and support at lift points with jack stands. Position floor jack under control arm. Remove nut and bolt mounting top of shock absorbers to the suspension assembly crossmember. Remove washers and nuts securing shock absorbers to lower mounting. Using a drift, remove mounting piece. Withdraw shock absorber and coil spring assembly. Using a spring compressor, collapse spring until collets and spring seat can be removed. Release pressure and separate shock absorber from spring.

Installation — To install spring and shock absorber assembly, reverse removal procedure and tighten all nuts and bolts.

RADIUS ROD

Removal — 1) Raise and support vehicle on safety stands forward of radius rods. Remove tire and wheel. Remove bolt and spring washer securing safety strap to body. Remove lock wire and bolt securing radius rod to body, then remove safety strap.

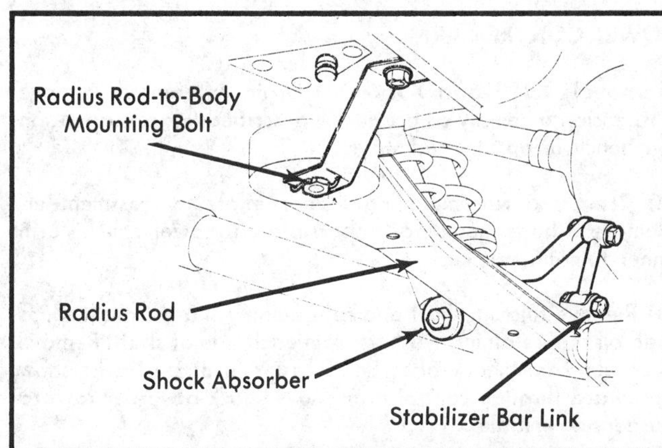

Fig. 2 Installed Position of Radius Rod

2) Remove forward lower shock absorber mounting pin. Using a punch, remove pin rearward. Bend tab washer and remove bolt mounting radius rod to control arm.

Installation — Replace any damaged radius rod bushings. When pressing bushings into radius rod, bushing should protrude from each side equal amounts. To install, reverse removal procedure.

REAR SUSPENSION ASSEMBLY

Removal — 1) Raise and support vehicle forward of radius rods. Remove tires and wheels. Place floor jack (with adaptor to hold suspension assembly) under rear suspension.

2) Disconnect intermediate exhaust pipes at both ends. On XJS models, remove rear mufflers.

3) On XJ12 and XJ6 models, remove intermediate exhaust pipe from vehicle. Block rear mufflers out of way.

4) Disconnect radius rod-to-body mounting hardware.

5) On XJS models, separate stabilizer bar from radius rods.

6) Separate brake line union from body bracket. Disconnect brake lines at flexible hoses and plug openings. Disconnect propeller shaft at differential. Lower shaft out of way.

7) Release parking brake. Separate actuating lever cable. Disconnect opposite side cable at trunnion and retain cable out of way.

8) On models equipped with overdrive units, disconnect speedometer and electrical wire.

9) On XJS models, remove bolts attaching suspension mounting rubbers to body.

JAGUAR (Cont.)

10) On XJ12 and XJ6 models, remove 8 self-locking nuts and bolts and 4 nuts keeping mounting brackets to body.

11) Lower suspension to ground and slide from vehicle. Guide intermediate exhaust pipe from suspension assembly.

Installation – Reverse removal steps and bleed brake system.

LOWER CONTROL ARM

Removal, XJ12 and XJ6 – 1) Drain differential. Remove suspension assembly as previously described. Place suspension on bench in an inverted state.

2) Remove 6 nuts mounting support plate to crossmember. Remove 8 bolts mounting support plate to lower control arm inner fulcrum brackets.

3) Remove fulcrum shaft and refit dummy shaft. Collect shims and oil seal retaining washers from each side of shaft. Remove lock nut from shock absorber fulcrum pivot and drift shaft rearward through control arm. Move shock absorber toward suspension middle.

4) Disconnect radius rod from control arm and remove shock absorber pivot assembly. Remove nut from lower control arm inner fulcrum shaft and tap shaft out. Guide control arm from vehicle.

5) Collect all thrust washers, seal retainers, seals, bearing tubes, needle bearings and spacer from each inner control arm boss.

Installation – 1) Lightly coat bearing cage with grease and press into inner fulcrum shaft boss. Stamped markings face outward. Insert bearing tube and press in other bearing. Repeat procedure for each boss.

2) Fit thrust washers to control arm. Insert control arm to inner fulcrum mounting bracket. Make sure radius rod bracket faces front of suspension.

3) Fit dummy shaft from each end to keep bearings and insert control arm with mounting bracket. Tap in fulcrum shaft.

NOTE – *Be careful not to drop thrust washers off control arm.*

4) Reverse removal procedure for installation of remaining components.

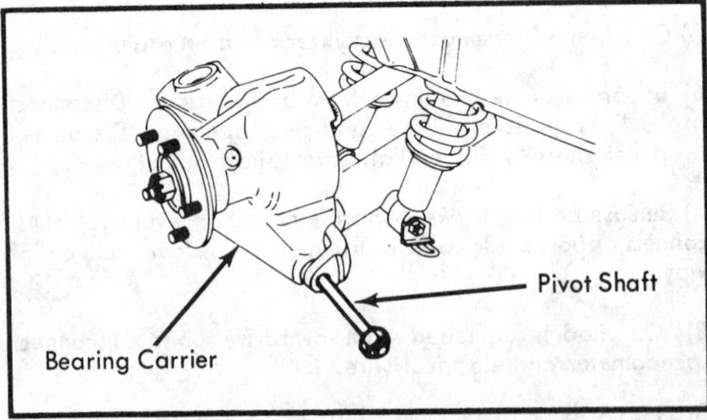

Fig. 3 Fitting Dummy Pivot Shaft

Removal, XJS – 1) Raise and support vehicle with stand placed ahead of radius rods. Remove tire and wheel.

2) Remove lock nut and drift out bearing carrier fulcrum shaft. Fit dummy shaft for support. Collect shims and oil seal retainers.

3) Lift bearing carrier up, clear of control arm. Keep in position with heavy wire attached to crossmember. Remove bolt mounting stabilizer bar link to radius rod. Move link out of way. Separate radius rod from body.

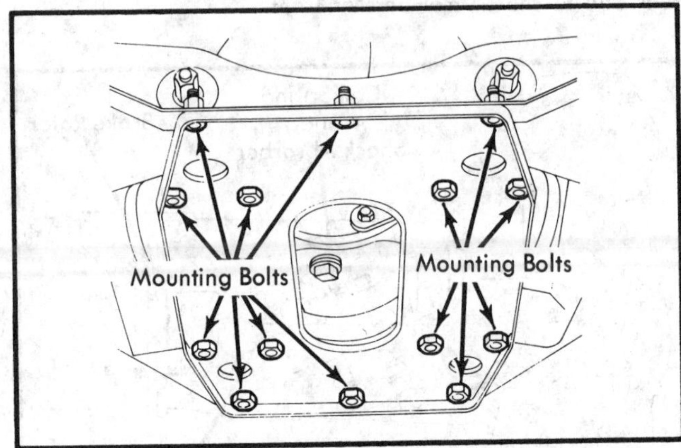

Fig. 4 Bolts and Setscrews Mounting Support Plate to Crossmember and Inner Fulcrum Brackets

4) Remove 14 bolts mounting support plate to crossmember and inner fulcrum brackets. Separate shock absorber at upper mount. Drift out pivot pin.

5) Separate inner fulcrum from control arm. Guide out control arm and radius rod.

Installation – 1) Smear bearing cage with grease and force bearing into lower control arm. Marking cast on bearing faces out. Insert bearing tube for other end and force in opposite end bearing. Repeat procedure for other boss.

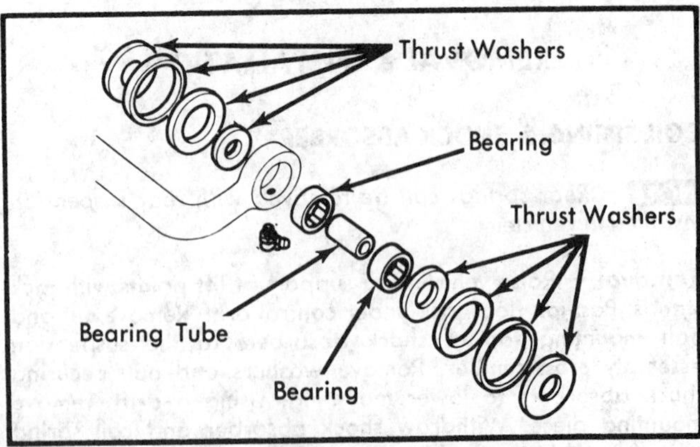

Fig. 5 Fulcrum Boss Assembly

2) Assemble radius rod to control arm. Lightly coat thrust washers, new oil seals and oil seal retainers with grease. Fit assemblies into place on control arm.

JAGUAR (Cont.)

3) Insert control arm to inner fulcrum mounting bracket. Make sure radius rod bracket faces toward front of suspension.

4) Insert dummy shaft from each end to keep bearings positioned then locate control arm in bracket. Slip in fulcrum shaft while pushing out dummy shaft. Install lock nut.

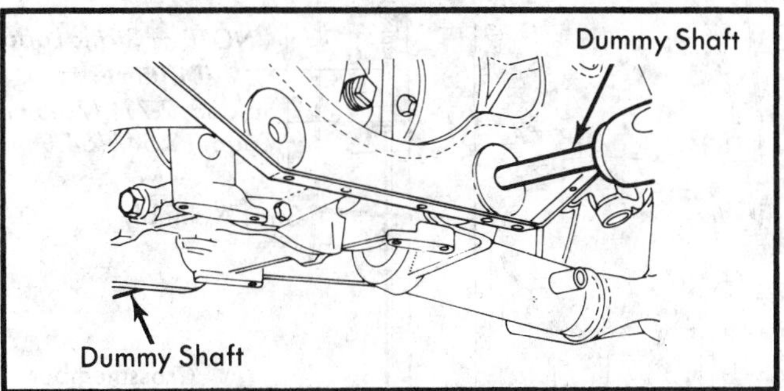

Fig. 6 Locating Control Arm in Mounting Bracket with Dummy Shafts

5) To install remaining components, reverse removal procedure.

STABILIZER BAR & LINKS

Removal, XJS – Raise vehicle and place on safety stands. Remove left rear wheel. Loosen exhaust pipe clamp nuts on right side forward of crossmember. Remove bolts mounting stabilizer bar to top of connecting links. Remove brackets mounting stabilizer bar to floorpan. Pull exhaust pipe apart. Maneuver stabilizer through left fender opening. Remove nuts and bolts mounting connecting link, then separate from radius rod.

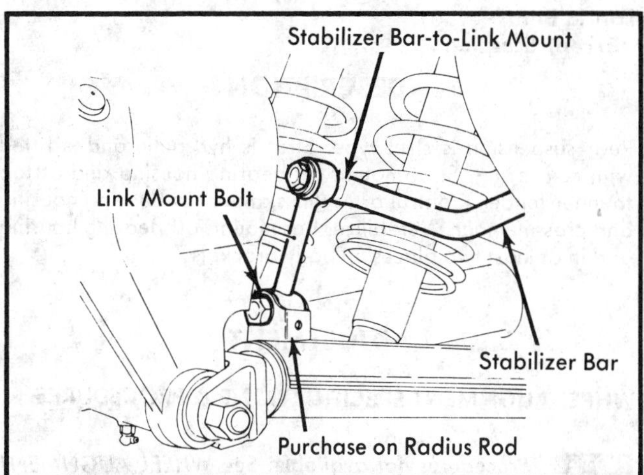

Fig. 7 Installed View of Stabilizer Bar and Connecting Link

Installation – To install stabilizer bar and connecting links, reverse removal procedure. Make sure exhaust system does not leak.

TIGHTENING SPECIFICATIONS

Application	Ft. Lbs. (mkg)
Radius Rod-to-Control Arm	60-70 (8.3-9.7)
Radius Rod-to-Body	40-45 (5.5-6.2)
Shock Absorbers	32-36 (4.4-5.0)
Support Plate-to-Crossmember and Inner Fulcrum Mounting	14-18 (1.9-2.5)
Inner Fulcrum Shaft	45-50 (6.2-6.9)
Stabilizer Bar Bracket-to-Body	14-18 (1.9-2.5)

LANCIA

Lancia Beta
Except Scorpion

DESCRIPTION

Rear suspension is strut type. Strut is hydraulic and is fitted with coil spring. Strut mounts off bearing housing and at top to inner fender. Control arms (links) mount at bearing housing and crossmember. A stabilizer bar mounts off bearing housing and in at least two places on body brackets.

ADJUSTMENT

WHEEL ALIGNMENT SPECIFICATIONS & PROCEDURES

NOTE – *Procedures not available. See WHEEL ALIGNMENT Section for Specifications.*

REMOVAL & INSTALLATION

CROSSMEMBER

Removal – Raise and support vehicle. Place a hydraulic jack under center of crossmember. Remove nuts from crossmember mounting bolts. Remove mounting crossmember from body. On models with automatic headlight aiming device, remove rear sensor and support bracket. Separate crossmember from floor pan and lower jack. Take out bolts from crossmember mounting while lowering jack. Remove spacers and washers from mounting point. Control arm links may be wedged and have to be pried against.

Installation – To install, reverse removal procedure.

STABILIZER BAR

Removal – Raise and support vehicle. Remove brake rear limiter valve control lever from stabilizer bar. Disconnect stabilizer bar ends from mountings. Attach tool 8803342 (or equivalent) and compress bar enough to remove from vehicle. Make sure bar clears muffler and hardware. If mounting grommets need replacing, use a press to force from mounting brackets.

Installation – To install, reverse removal procedure. Make sure all grommets are properly aligned with brackets.

CONTROL ARM (LINK)

Removal – Raise and support vehicle. Remove plate covering crossmember bolts. On vehicles with automatic aiming sensor, remove headlight ball pin for left side control link. Remove nuts and bolts mounting control link to crossmember and bearing carrier. Separate links from crossmember mounting. Remove wheel. Guide links from vehicle.

Installation – To install, reverse removal procedure and note: Make sure crossmember mounting bolt heads face front of vehicle. Check and reset toe-in.

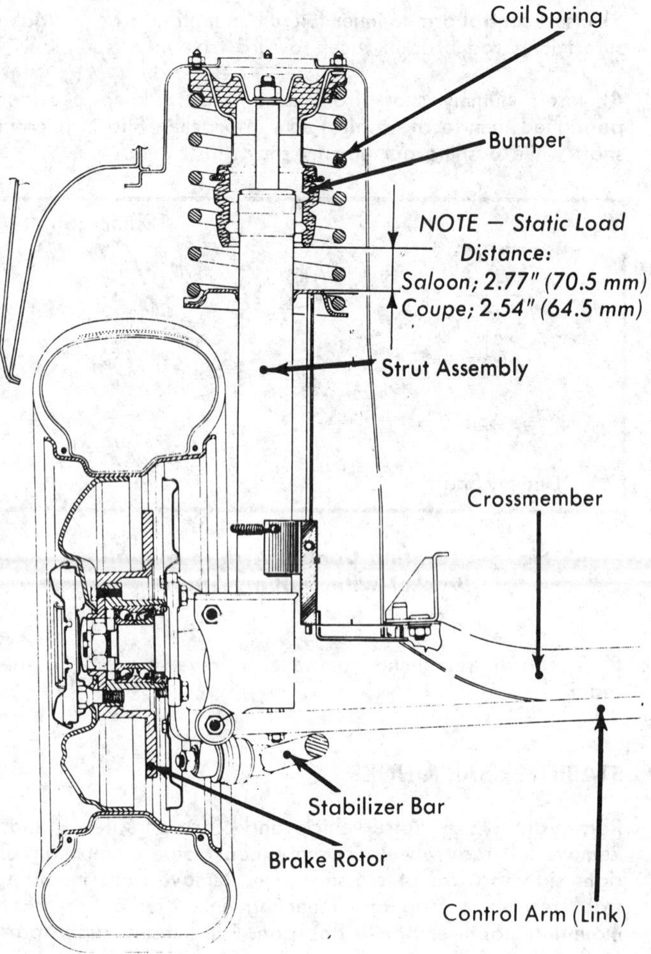

***Fig. 1* Cross Section View of Rear Suspension**

STRUT ASSEMBLY

Removal – Raise and support vehicle. Remove wheel. Fit tool 88033412 (or equivalent) to stabilizer bar and lightly tighten. Remove bolts mounting strut to bearing carrier and control links. Separate strut from mounting. Hang wheel hub and brake caliper to body. Make sure brake hose is not stretched. Work inside vehicle and remove mounting nuts from top strut plate. Draw strut out bottom of vehicle.

Installation – To install, reverse removal procedure and check static load. See *Fig. 1*.

TIGHTENING SPECIFICATIONS

Application	Ft. Lbs. (mkg)
Crossmember	18 (2.5)
Strut-to-Control Link	31 (2.3)
Stabilizer Bar Bolts	17 (2.3)

MERCEDES-BENZ

230
240D
280 Series
300D
450 Series
6.9

DESCRIPTION

Rear suspension is independent with coil springs and semi-trailing arms. Rear axle carrier is mounted to body at three points and supports rear axle assembly. Axle shafts serve as upper control arms to rear wheels. Wheel hubs are supported by semi-trailing arms which run forward to pivot points on rear axle carrier and body. Shock absorbers are mounted inside of coil springs, attached to body on top and to semi-trailing arms on bottom. Stabilizer bar is mounted to body and to wheel hubs at ends.

ADJUSTMENT

WHEEL ALIGNMENT SPECIFICATIONS & ADJUSTMENTS

See Wheel Alignment Specifications & Adjustments in WHEEL ALIGNMENT Section.

REMOVAL & INSTALLATION

SHOCK ABSORBERS

NOTE — *Shock absorbers should be removed only when vehicle is on wheels or when semi-trailing arm is supported.*

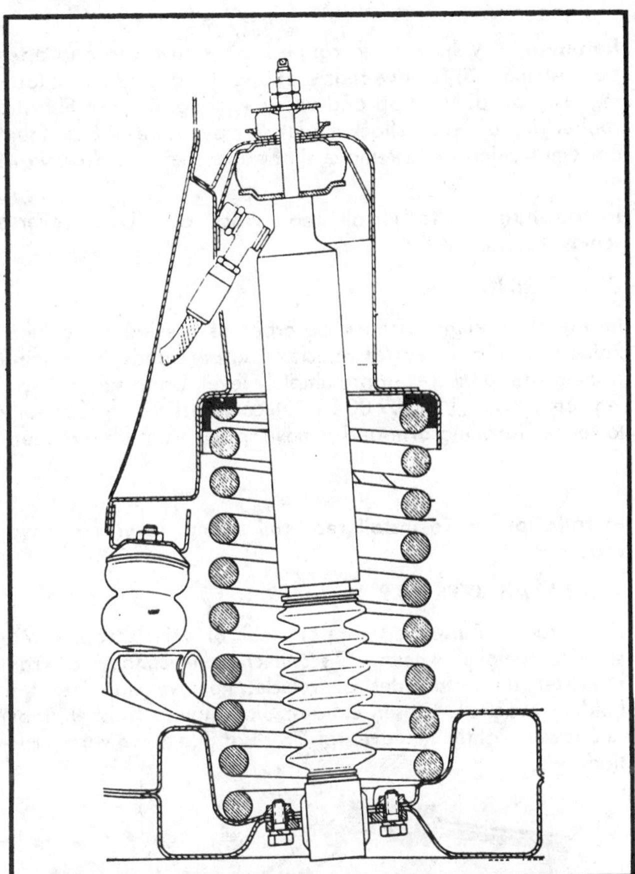

Fig. 1 Rear Spring and Shock Configuration

Fig. 2 Rear to Front View of Typical Mercedes Benz Rear Suspension

MERCEDES-BENZ (Cont.)

Removal – Vehicles with coupe top, remove top and open flap. All models, remove rear seat and backrest. Remove locking lever off of top flap and unscrew lining. Remove nut and rubber ring of upper shock mount. Remove lower shock mount on semi-trailing arm. Remove shock absorber in a downward direction.

Installation – To install rear shock absorbers, reverse removal procedure.

COIL SPRINGS

Removal – Remove shock absorber as previously outlined. Raise and support rear of vehicle on safety stands. Raise semi-trailing arm until it is approximately level. Using suitable spring compressor (115 589 00 31 00), compress spring. Carefully lower semi-trailing arm and remove spring with rubber mounting.

Installation – To install rear coil spring, reverse removal procedure.

REAR STABILIZER BAR

Removal – Raise and support rear of vehicle with safety stands, remove wheels. Disconnect connecting rod from stabilizer on both sides of vehicle. Remove stabilizer bar holding brackets. Loosen exhaust pipe mounts (rubber rings) and lower slightly. Remove stabilizer bar in a downward direction.

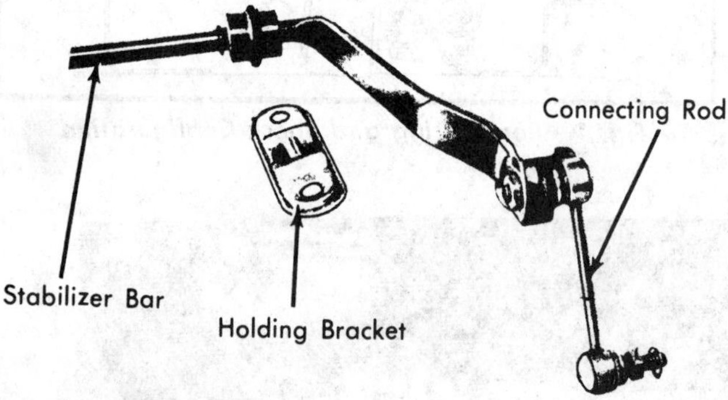

Fig. 3 Stabilizer Bar and Mounting Locations

Installation – To install rear stabilizer bar, reverse removal procedure.

NOTE – *When installing rear stabilizer bar, ensure that bend of bar arm is pointing upward.*

REAR SUSPENSION & AXLE

Removal – 1) Raise and support vehicle with safety stands, remove wheels. Disconnect and remove exhaust system. Disconnect parking brake control cables at frame and compensating lever.

2) Loosen clamp nut and disconnect drive shaft intermediate bearing from frame. Disconnect rear of drive shaft and slide forward, out of centering position.

NOTE – *On three piece drive shaft, loosen front clamp nut only.*

3) Remove shock absorber and coil spring as previously outlined. Disconnect and plug brake lines. Disconnect stabilizer bar holding clamps from frame.

4) Place jack with suitable jack top (116 589 10 61 00) under rear susupension. Disconnect supporting plates, front and rear rubber mounts from frame. Carefully lower jack and remove rear suspension from vehicle. Remove rear rubber mount from axle.

CAUTION – *When lowering and moving rear suspension, make sure cover plates of disc brakes are not damaged.*

Installation – To install rear suspension and axle, reverse removal procedure.

DIFFERENTIAL WITH AXLE SHAFTS

Removal – 1) Drain oil from differential. Disconnect brake caliper on right hand side and support to prevent damage to brake line. Remove bolt attaching rear axle shafts to rear axle shaft flanges, on both sides, and force rear axle shafts out of rear axle shaft flanges.

NOTE *If required, loosen right side rear shock absorber at upper mount and lower semi-trailing arm to deflection stop.*

2) If required, remove exhaust system. Loosen clamp nut and disconnect drive shaft intermediate bearing from frame. Disconnect drive shaft from differential and push out of centering alignment.

NOTE – *On three piece drive shaft, loosen front clamp nut only.*

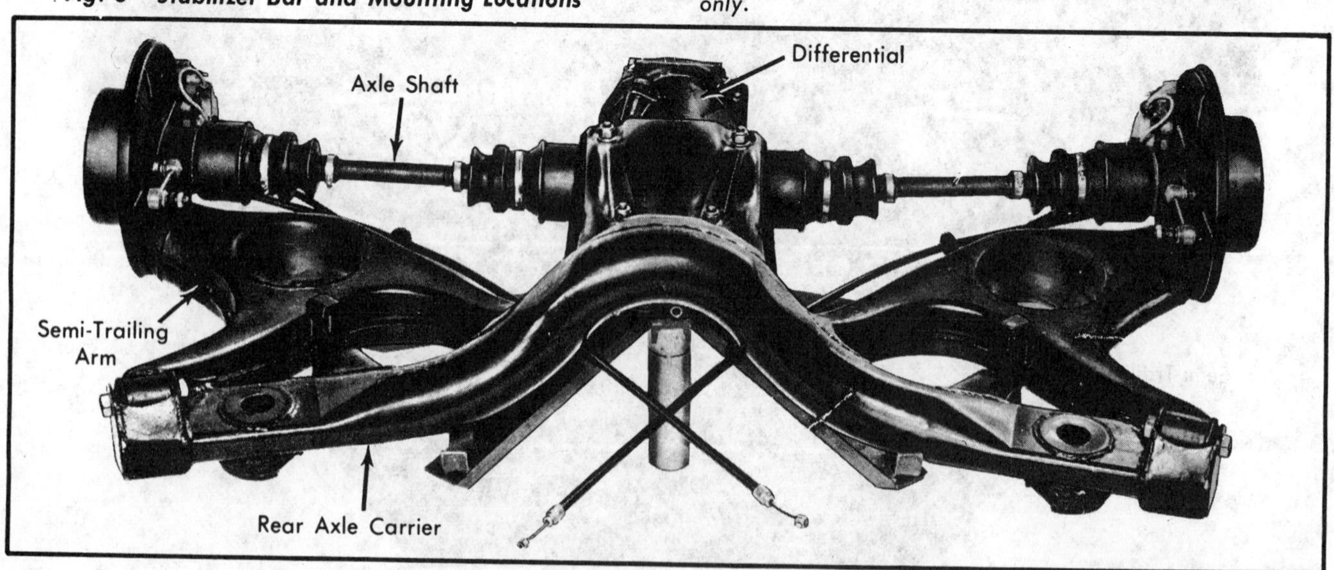

Fig. 4 Typical Mercedes Benz Rear Suspension with Components Removed

MERCEDES-BENZ (Cont.)

3) Support differential with jack and suitable support (115 589 35 63 00). Disconnect rear rubber mount from body. Disconnect differential from rear axle carrier. Lower jack and remove differential with axle shafts.

CAUTION – *When moving differential with axle shafts, make sure that axle shafts are supported and DO NOT drop down, as this might damage inner joints.*

Installation – Check all rubber parts and replace as necessary. To install differential with rear axle shafts, reverse removal procedure. Tighten down all nuts and bolts, except when connecting drive shaft to differential. These bolts must be torqued after vehicle has been rolled forward and backward to seat parts. Install exhaust system, if removed.

REAR AXLE CARRIER

Removal – Remove rear suspension, differential with rear axle shafts and semi-trailing arms as previously outlined.

Inspection – Using inspection tool *(Fig. 6)*, check rear axle carrier. When checking rear axle carriers without spot welded washers, place a .098" (2.5 mm) thick washer under receiving bolt *(Fig 5)*.

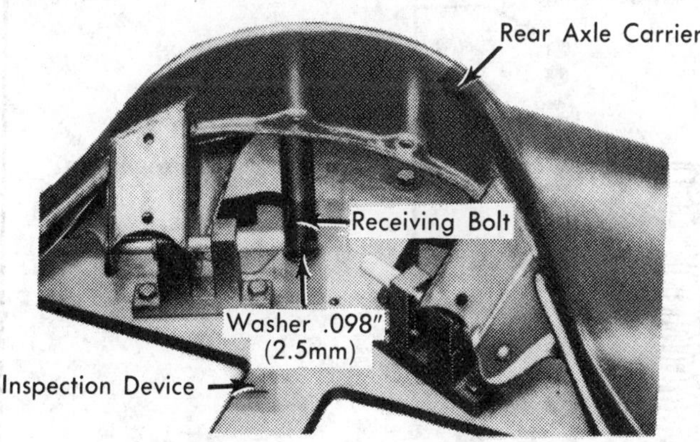

Fig. 5 Proper Washer Placement for Rear Axle Carriers without Spot Welds

Installation – To install rear axle, reverse removal procedure.

Fig. 6 Inspection Tool 115 589 04 23 00

TIGHTENING SPECIFICATIONS

Application	Ft. Lbs. (mkg)
Shock Absorber Lower Mount	33 (4.6)
Torsion Bar Bearing Bolts	47 (6.5)
Torsion Bar Connecting Rod Ball Joints	33 (4.6)
Rear Rubber Mount-to-End Cover	101 (14.0)
Rear Rubber Mount-to-Frame	18 (2.5)
Front Rubber Mounts-to-Frame	29 (4.0)
Supporting Plate-to-Frame	23-29 (3.2-4.0)
Drive Shaft Clamp Nut (Two Piece)	145 (20.0)
Drive Shaft Clamp Nut (Three Piece)	
Front	23-29 (3.2-4.0)
Rear	145 (20.0)
Semi-Trailing Arm-to-Rear Axle Carrier	87 (12.0)
Axle Shaft-to-Axle Shaft Flange	69 (9.5)
Differential-to-Rear Axle Carrier	72 (10.0)
Brake Caliper Bolts	23-29 (3.2-4.0)

OPEL

All Models

DESCRIPTION

Rear suspension system consists of: Control arm link, coil spring, track rod, and shock absorber. Track rod is connected to rear axle housing and body. Track rod helps control lateral movement of rear axle. Control arms limit the back and forth movement of rear axle.

REMOVAL & INSTALLATION

SHOCK ABSORBER

Removal & Installation – Raise vehicle and place on safety stands. Remove rear wheel. Disconnect shock absorber lower end from mounting position on rear axle housing. Working form inside trunk, remove fuel tank cover and disconnect upper end of shock absorber. To insall, reverse removal procedure.

CONTROL ARM LINK

Removal & Installation – Raise vehicle and place on safety stands. Remove rear wheel. Remove bolts mounting control arm to axle housing. Remove bolt connecting control arm link to body. Maneuver control arm link from vehicle. To install, reverse removal procedure.

COIL SPRINGS

Removal & Installation – Raise vehicle and place on safety stands. Place jack under rear axle. Disconnect lower end of shock absorber. Lower jack until coil spring can be removed. To install, reverse removal procedure and note: Spring can be compressed enough by hand to be installed.

TIGHTENING SPECIFICATIONS

Application	Ft. Lbs. (mkg)
Shock Absorber-to-Rear Axle Housing	29 (4.0)
Track Rod-to-Body Bracket	47 (6.5)
Track Rod-to-Rear Axle Housing	54 (7.5)
Control Arm Link Bolts	29 (4.0)

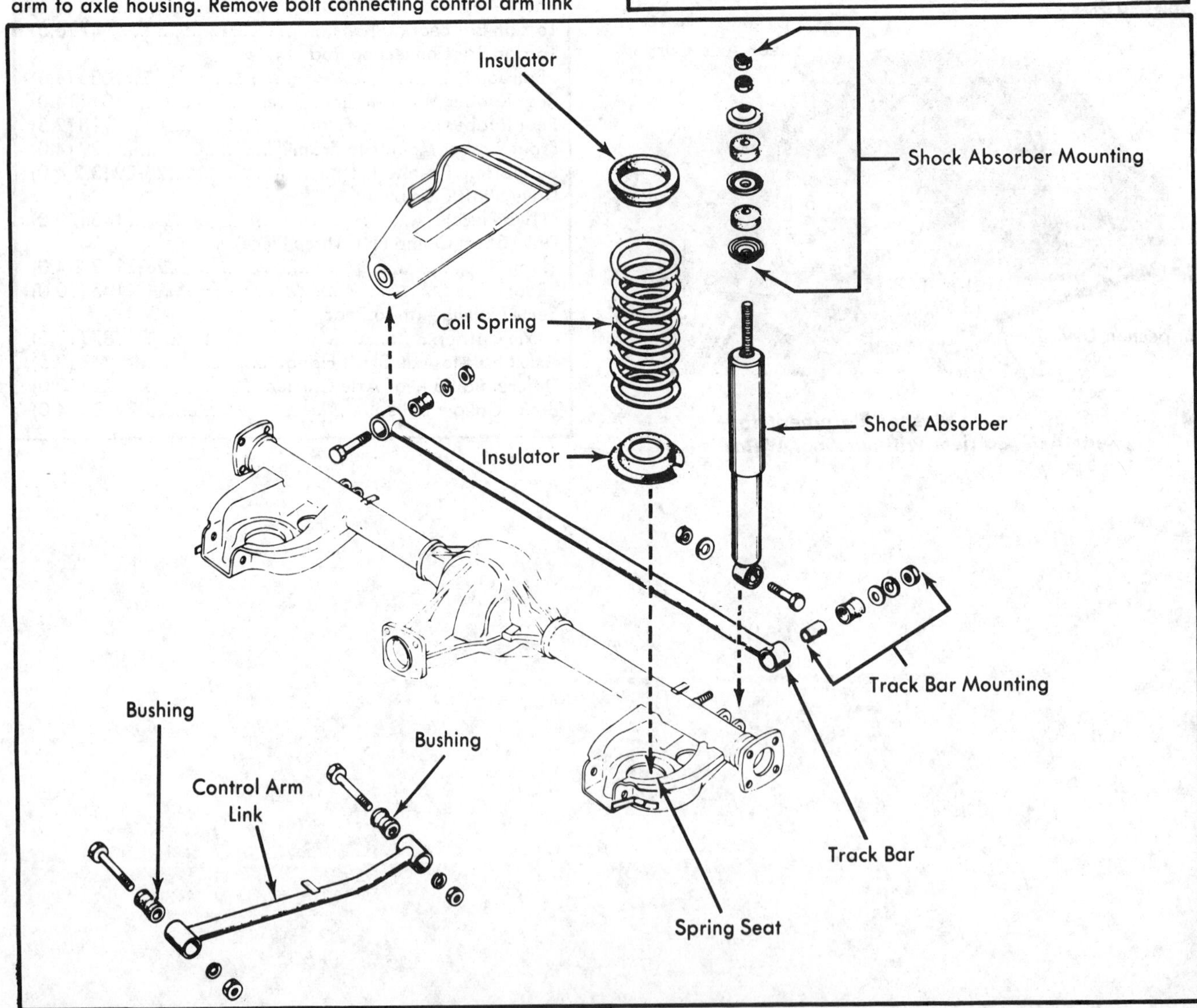

Fig. 1 Exploded View of Rear Suspension Components

PEUGEOT

504

NOTE – *Information for 604 not available.*

DESCRIPTION

504 models use independent rear suspension by means of trailing arms and coil springs. Rear hub is supported by lower trailing arms which run forward to pivot points on rear axle crossmember. Coil springs mount between suspension crossmember at top and trailing arm at bottom. Hydraulic shock absorbers also mount between suspension crossmember and trailing arm, and are located inside coil spring. A stabilizer bar is mounted to frame and connected at ends to trailing arms.

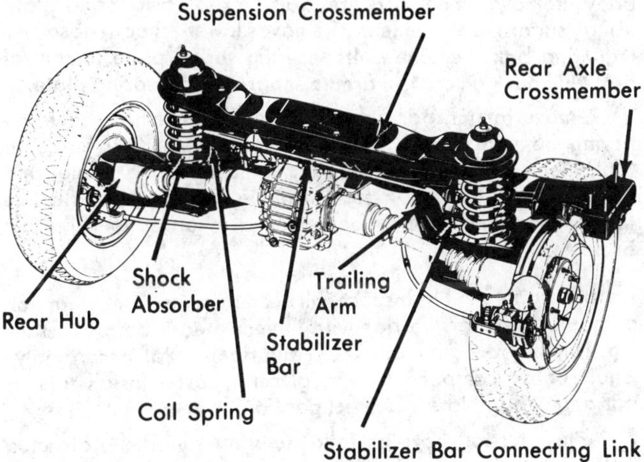

Fig. 1 Peugeot 504 Rear Suspension

REMOVAL & INSTALLATION

SHOCK ABSORBERS

Removal – From inside luggage compartment, remove lock nut at top of shock absorber while holding shock to prevent rotation. On trailing arm, remove lower pivot bolt and remove shock absorber.

Installation – To install, reverse removal procedure using new rubber washers and lock nut. Tighten upper mounting to specification, then tighten lower.

TRAILING ARMS

Removal – Raise vehicle and place safety stands under rear crossmember, remove wheel. Install suitable hub holding tool (8.0521) and loosen, but do not remove hub nut. Remove hub holding tool, unclip parking brake cable from trailing arm, and disconnect cable from rear brake. Remove stabilizer bar links from trailing arms. Remove nuts from trailing arm pivots and drive inner pivot out, installing suitable rod (8.0906) in its place. Remove trailing arm outer pivot, leave shock absorber attached, and remove rod from inner pivot. Disengage trailing arm from crossmember. Compress universal joints on drive shaft and pull assembly to disengage splined end of shaft from differential housing. **CAUTION** – *Take care not to damage differential oil seal with end of shaft.* Remove hub nut and withdraw drive shaft using suitable extractor (8.0521Z). Place jack under trailing arm, raise arm and remove shock absorber. Remove brake hose from lug on trailing arm. Remove nut securing stabilizer bar link under trailing arm, withdraw metal cup and rubber washer and refit nut immediately to prevent upper parts from falling inside arm. Unscrew rear trailing arm pivot nuts, lower jack carefully and remove coil spring. Withdraw rear arm trailing pivots and remove trailing arm.

Installation – To install, reverse removal procedure, replacing all lock nuts and lock washers. Torque all nuts and bolts to specifications, however, do not torque lower shock absorber nut and trailing arm pivot nuts until weight of vehicle, with two people in rear seat, is on suspension.

TIGHTENING SPECIFICATIONS

Application	Ft. Lbs. (mkg)
Upper Shock Absorber Nut	9 (1.2)
Lower Shock Absorber Nut	33 (4.6)
Trailing Arm Pivot Nuts	47 (6.5)
Rear Hub Nut	181 (25.0)
Stabilizer Bar Link Nuts	33 (4.6)

PORSCHE 911S & TURBO CARRERA

911S & Turbo Carrera

DESCRIPTION

Independent torsion bar type rear suspension. Torsion bars are mounted inside rear crossmember tube and anchored in center by a splined hub. Outer end of torsion bars mount into splined hubs integral with spring plates which connect at ends to control arms. Control arms pivot in mounts integral with body and also serve as rear wheel bearing carriers. Hydraulic shock absorbers mount between control arms and inner fender panel. A stabilizer bar is installed on some models.

ADJUSTMENT

WHEEL ALIGNMENT SPECIFICATIONS & PROCEDURES

See Wheel Alignment Specifications & Procedures in WHEEL ALIGNMENT Section.

REMOVAL & INSTALLATION

SHOCK ABSORBERS

Removal – 1) Raise vehicle and place safety stands in a position so weight of vehicle is still on rear wheels. Remove rubber cap from upper mount (accessible from inside engine compartment) and remove nut from shock absorber stem.

2) Remove bolt securing shock absorber to control arm and remove shock absorber. Remove rod cover and rubber buffer from shock absorber.

Installation – Inspect rubber buffer for wear or cracking and replace if necessary. Make sure that stop disc grooves face bottom of shock absorber when assembling. Install rubber buffer and cover and reverse removal procedure to install remaining components. Tighten upper and lower mounts.

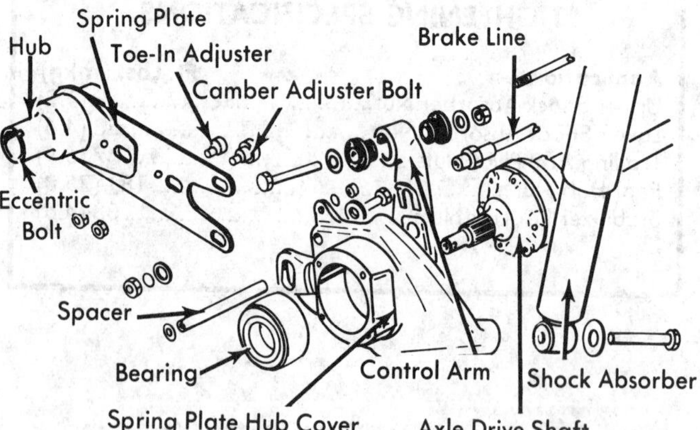

Fig. 1 Exploded View of Porsche Rear Suspension

CONTROL ARM

Removal – 1) Raise vehicle and place safety stands under body. Remove rear wheels. Detach brake system components from rear wheel hub. *See Porsche in BRAKE Section.* Remove axle hub cotter pin and nut. Remove Allen head bolts from axle shaft flanges and remove axle shaft.

2) Using a suitable driver, remove rear wheel hub from control arm. Remove cotter pin and nut from parking brake cable and pull cable out toward center of vehicle. Remove bolts securing parking brake assembly to control arm and remove assembly.

3) Raise torsion bar spring plate to take tension from shock absorber with a suitable tool. Remove lower shock absorber mount. Remove bolts securing spring plate to control arm. Disconnect brake hose from bracket on control arm. Remove nut from control arm pivot bolt and drive bolt out with a punch. Remove control arm from vehicle.

Installation – Reverse removal procedure and note the following: Use new self-locking nuts and tighten all bolts and nuts. Check wheel alignment and bleed brake system.

TORSION BAR & SPRING PLATE

Removal – 1) Raise vehicle and place safety stands under body. Remove wheel and tire. Raise torsion bar spring plate using suitable equipment. Remove lower shock absorber mounting bolt. Remove bolts securing spring plate to control arm. Pull back on control arm to separate from spring plate.

2) Remove torsion bar hub cover bolts and remove cover by prying off with a screwdriver. Remove torsion bar tensioner tool. Remove plug from body, remove spring plate and withdraw torsion bar. If torsion bar is broken, opposite side torsion bar will have to be removed in order to drive out broken piece.

Installation – 1) Inspect all components for wear or damage. Coat torsion bar with lithium grease before installing. Torsion bars are marked left and right; install accordingly. Coat rubber components with glycerin paste. Install torsion bar and spring plate in correct position.

2) Adjust torsion bars as follows: using suitable protractor (VW261), place onto lower edge of door sill. Adjust protractor so that bubble in glass tube marked "Axle Housing/Angle" is in the center.

3) Reset glass tube carrier by value specified. Place protractor onto spring plate and adjust to, on 911S models, .468±.20" (12±.5 mm), on Turbo Carrera 1.5±.20" (37±.5 mm), by turning eccentric screw on spring plate.

NOTE – *Differance between right and left measurement must not exceed .20" (.5 mm).*

4) Install hub cover and start three bolts that are accessible. Raise spring plate until remaining bolt can be installed. Reverse removal procedures for remaining components. Check rear wheel alignment.

TIGHTENING SPECIFICATIONS

Application	Ft. Lbs. (mkg)
Control Arm Pivot Bolt	87 (12.0)
Spring Plate-to-Control Arm Bolts	65 (9.0)
Camber Adjusting Bolt	43 (6.0)
Tracking Adjusting Bolt	36 (5.0)
Lower Shock Absorber Mount	54 (7.5)
Hub Nut	235 (32.5)
Axle Shaft Allen Head Bolts	
M10-8G	34 (4.7)
M8-12K	31 (4.3)
M10x55-12K	60 (8.3)
Torsion Bar Hub Cover Bolts	34 (4.7)

PORSCHE 924

924

DESCRIPTION

Independent torsion bar type rear suspension. Torsion bars mount in rear crossmember tube and anchor in center of tube by a splined hub. Outer ends of torsion bar mount into splined hubs integral with spring plates. Spring plates are bolted to control arm at a flange. Control arms pivot in mounts on crossmember tube and are integral with stub axle housing. Hydraulic shock absorbers mount on control arm and to upper body.

ADJUSTMENTS

WHEEL ALIGNMENT SPECIFICATIONS & PROCEDURES

See Wheel Alignment Specifications and Procedures in WHEEL ALIGNMENT Section.

REMOVAL & INSTALLATION

SHOCK ABSORBERS

Removal — Raise vehicle and place on safety stands. Remove wheel. Remove both bottom and top mounting nuts and bolts, then slide shock absorber from vehicle.

Installation — Inspect for hydraulic leaks and replace shock absorber if excessive leaking is apparent. Check shock absorber for smooth, even operation. To install, reverse removal procedure.

CONTROL ARM

Removal — **1)** Remove cotter pin and loosen rear hub nut. Raise vehicle and place on safety stands. Remove wheel. Remove shock absorber.

2) Remove bolts mounting axle drive shaft to stub axle. Separate axle drive shaft from stub axle and wire out of way. Use protective cap to cover exposed end of axle drive shaft.

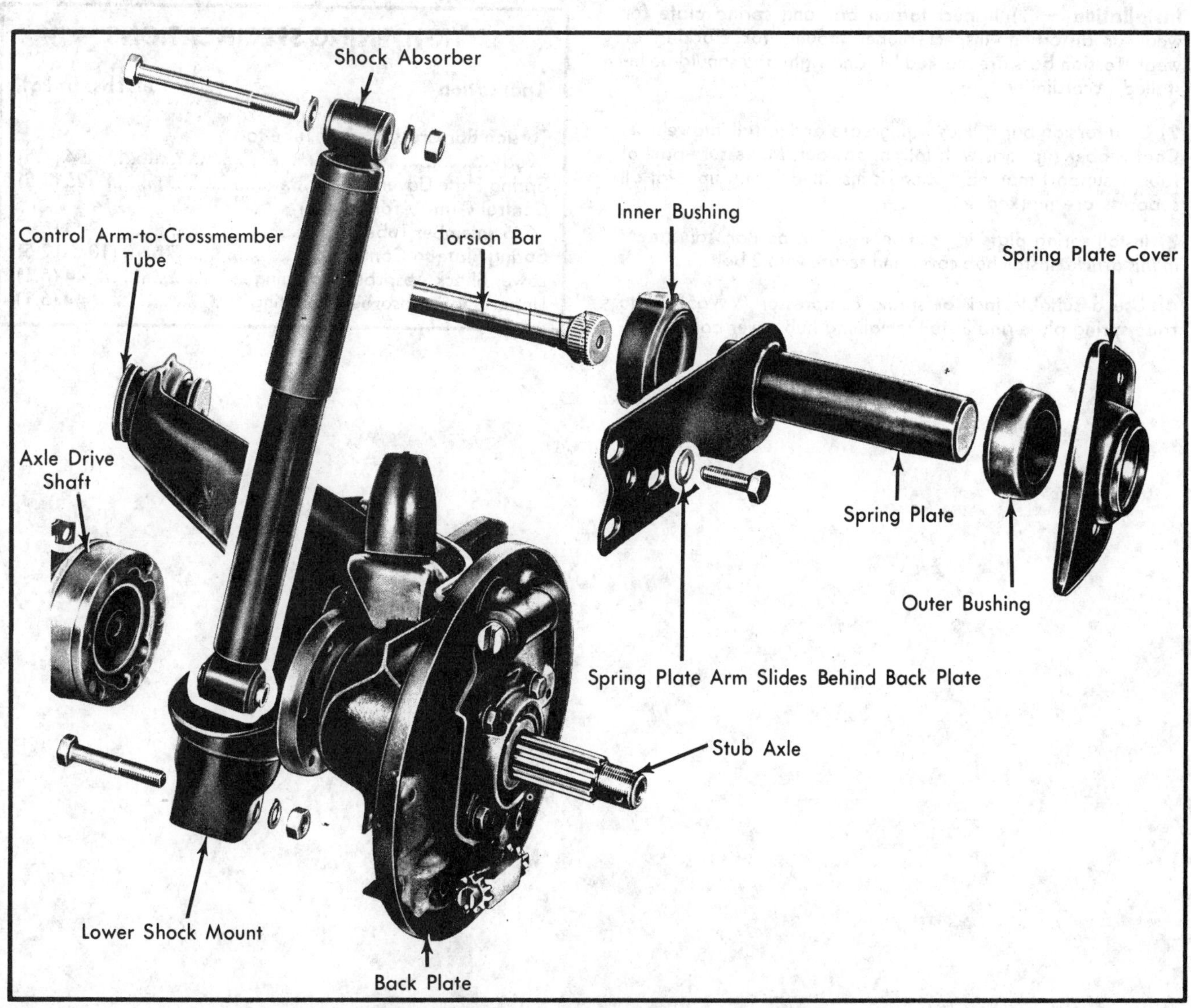

Fig. 1 Exploded View of 924 Rear Suspension

PORSCHE 924 (Cont.)

3) Remove drum and disconnect parking brake and hydraulic lines. Index mark spring plate in relation to a point on control arm. Remove control arm pivot bolt and remove arm from vehicle.

Installation – To install, reverse removal procedure. Tighten pivot bolt and lock in place by staking to edge to metal shoulder on bracket. Align spring plate marks with those on control arm. Bleed brake system.

TORSION BARS & SPRING PLATES

Removal – 1) Raise and support vehicle. Take off wheel. Scribe mark alignment position of spring plate in control arm for reassembly. Disconnect spring plate from control arm.

2) Remove bolts mounting spring plate cover. Pry off lower stop cast into torsion bar housing. Remove spring plate and withdraw torsion bar. If torsion bar is broken, opposite side torsion bar must be removed to drive out broken piece.

Installation – 1) Inspect torsion bar and spring plate for wear or distortion. Inspect rubber mounts for cracking or wear. Torsion bars are marked left and right and should be installed accordingly.

2) Coat torsion bar splines with grease and install into vehicle. Coat rubber supports with talcum powder. Make sure part of rubber support marked "Oben" is installed facing up. Not all supports are marked.

3) Install spring plate in position. *See Torsion Bar Adjustment in this article.* Install hub cover and secure with 2 bolts.

4) Use a suitable jack or spring compressor (VW655/3) to raise spring plate and install remaining hub cover bolts. To install remaining components, reverse removal procedure. Recheck rear wheel alignment.

TORSION BAR ADJUSTMENT

NOTE – *Adjust both torsion bars on vehicles with high milage.*

1) Using suitable protractor (VW261), place protractor on lower edge of door sill. Adjust protractor so bubble in glass tube marked "Axle Housing/Angle" is in center. Note reading that will indicate vehicle deviation from horizontal.

2) Rotate level carrier on protractor by specified value for spring plate angle (23°). With spring plate cover removed, place protractor on spring plate. Lift spring plate enough to remove play from splines.

3) If front of vehicle is lower, add door sill measurement to spring plate value. If rear of vehicle is lower than front, subtract door sill measurement from spring plate value. Correct spring plate angle if measured value differs from specified value by more than 5/8".

TIGHTENING SPECIFICATIONS

Application	Ft. Lbs. (mkg)
Torsion Bar Crossmember Tube-to-Body	54 (7.5)
Spring Plate Cover	25 (3.5)
Control Arm-to-Torsion Bar Crossmember Tube	44 (6.1)
Spring Plate-to-Control Arm	76-90 (10.5-12.5)
Lower Shock Absorber Moutning	44 (6.1)
Upper Shock Absorber Mounting	44 (6.1)

RENAULT R-5

R-5

DESCRIPTION

System is torsion bar type with a trailing arm. Trailing arms are mounted off chassis and have torsion bars connected to inboard edge.

ADJUSTMENT

WHEEL ALIGNMENT SPECIFICATIONS & PROCEDURES

See Wheel Alignment Specifications and Procedures in WHEEL ALIGNMENT Section.

RIDING HEIGHT ADJUSTMENT

See Riding Height Adjustment in WHEEL ALIGNMENT Section.

REMOVAL & INSTALLATION

TRAILING ARM

Removal – Raise rear of vehicle and place on safety stands. Disconnect, then carefully remove sway bar. Remove shock absorber. Disconnect brake lines and plug openings. Put torsion bar adjusting cams in zero position. Remove torsion bars from both sides. Remove mounting bolts and slide complete arm assembly from vehicle.

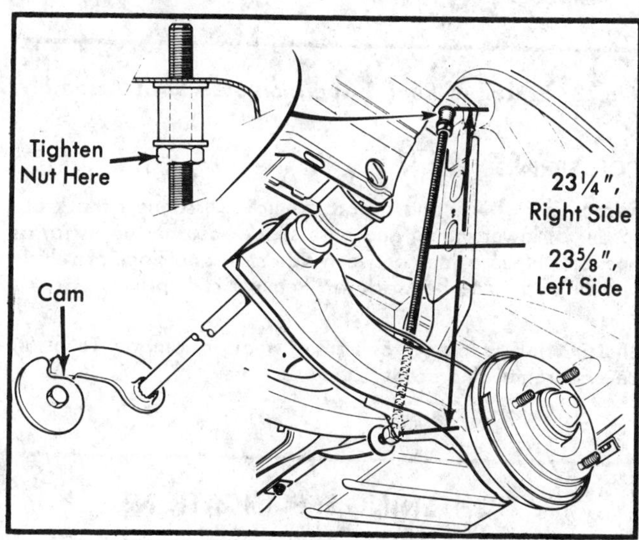

Fig. 1 Trailing Arm and Torsion Bar Assembly

Inspection – Check all bushings and spacers for obvious signs of wear or damage. Use suitable puller and/or mandrel (with press) to replace bushings.

Installation – To install, reverse removal procedure and note: Bleed brake system. Recheck brake pressure equalizer. Check rear wheel alignment.

TORSION BAR

Removal – Raise vehicle and place on safety stands. Loosen lock nut on cam and adjust until cam is zeroed. Remove shock absorber. Fit fabricated tool where shock absorber has been removed. Tighten nut until adjuster lever is raised from cam. Remove torsion bar.

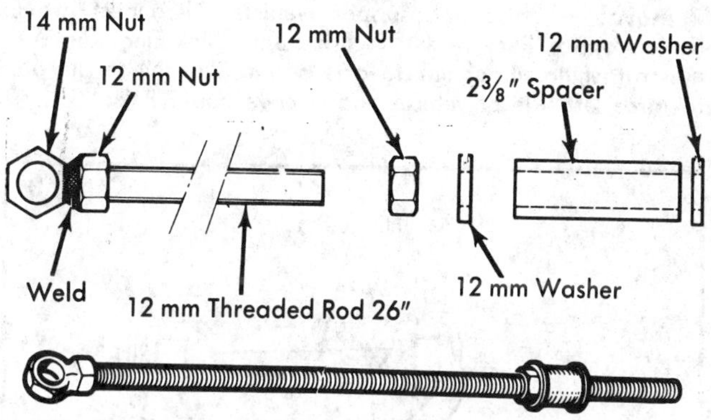

Fig. 2 Specifications for Tool Fabrication

NOTE – *Before installing torsion bar, adjust nut on tool to 23¼" (590 mm), right side and/or 23⅝" (600 mm), left side. This will allow torsion bar to be inserted.*

Installation – Put adjuster lever so it touches cam. Lightly coat torsion bar splines with grease, then insert into lever and arm. Tighten cam lock nut. Take off tool. Install shock absorber. Lower vehicle. Measure under body (riding height).

SHOCK ABSORBER

Removal – Work from inside trunk and remove upper nuts. Raise vehicle and place on safety stands. Remove lower mounting nut and take off shock absorber.

Installation – To install, reverse removal procedure. Make sure upper mounting is attached first.

RENAULT R-12 & R-17

R-12
R-17

DESCRIPTION

Link type rear suspension with coil springs. Upper link is wishbone shaped and is attached to top of axle beam and to the body. Side strut is connected to body and front of axle beam. Shock absorbers are mounted inside coil springs between axle beam and body. A stabilizer bar connects both side struts.

REMOVAL & INSTALLATION

UPPER LINK

Removal – Raise and support vehicle. Disconnect brake limiter control. Remove nuts securing upper link hinge pin and nuts attaching upper link to axle beam. Slide hinge pin out towards left side of vehicle and remove upper link.

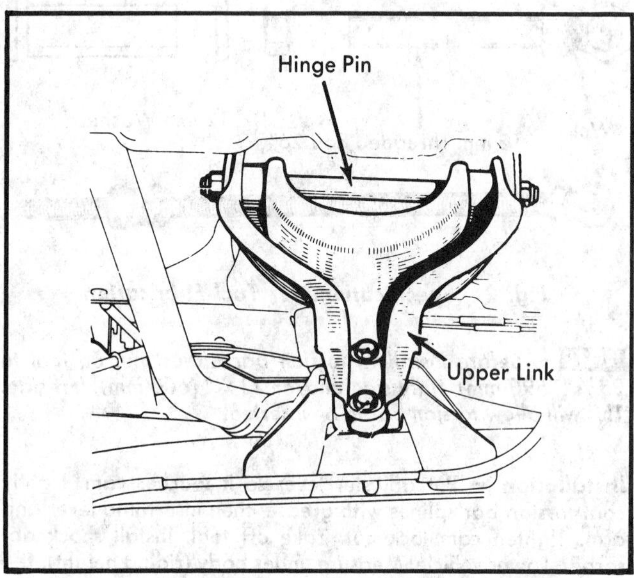

Fig. 1 Installed View of Rear Suspension Upper Link

Installation – To install, lubricate hinge pins and reverse removal procedure. Tighten all nuts and bolts to specification.

AXLE BEAM

Removal – Raise and support vehicle. Disconnect shock absorbers and push up as far as possible. Remove coil springs and remove brake drums. Disconnect parking brake cable and withdraw from backing plates. Remove nuts from side strut hinge pins and remove pins. Disconnect brake lines on rear axle beam. Place jack under axle beam and disconnect upper links. Remove axle beam.

Installation – To install, lubricate hinge pins and reverse removal procedure. Bleed and adjust rear brakes.

SIDE STRUT

Removal – Raise and support vehicle. On vehicles fitted with brake drums, remove the drum. Disconnect parking brake cable lever and remove backing plate. Free cable through side strut. Remove bolts securing stabilizer bar (if equipped) and nuts securing hinge pins. Remove side strut.

Installation – To install, lubricate hinge pins and reverse removal procedure. Tighten all nuts and bolts.

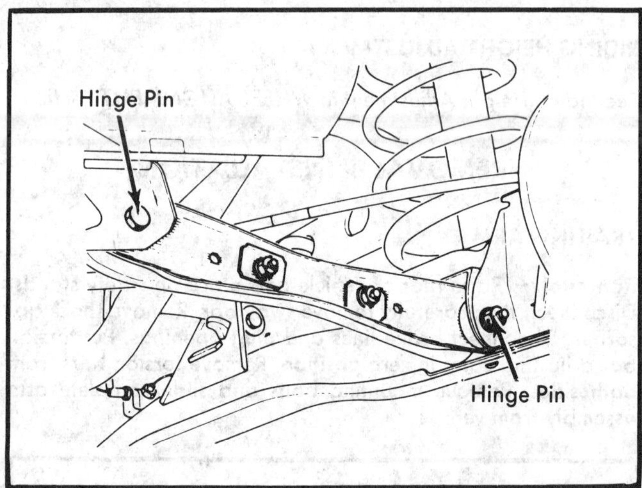

Fig. 2 Detail of Rear Suspension Side Strut Assembly

COIL SPRINGS

Removal – Raise and support vehicle. Disconnect shock absorber at lower mount and push shock absorber up as far as possible. Place a jack between side strut and floor of vehicle and tilt rear axle beam down. Remove coil spring.

Installation – Inspect for signs of wear or damage. To install, reverse removal procedure.

TIGHTENING SPECIFICATIONS

Application	Ft. Lbs. (mkg)
Side Strut Hinge Pins	20 (2.8)
Upper Link Hinge Pins	80 (11.0)
Upper Arm Center Bearing	10 (1.4)

SAAB

99

DESCRIPTION

Tube type rear axle with coil springs. Rear axle is straight tube with stub axles press fitted into the ends. Axle is mounted to body by two lower control arms, which are connected at rear to the axle tube and to the body at front. Rear links are also used which mount rearward from stub axle assembly to body. A cross bar is mounted from right side of axle and attaches to body support in center. Coil springs are mounted between lower control arms and body. Telescopic shock absorbers are used which are attached between lower control arms and body.

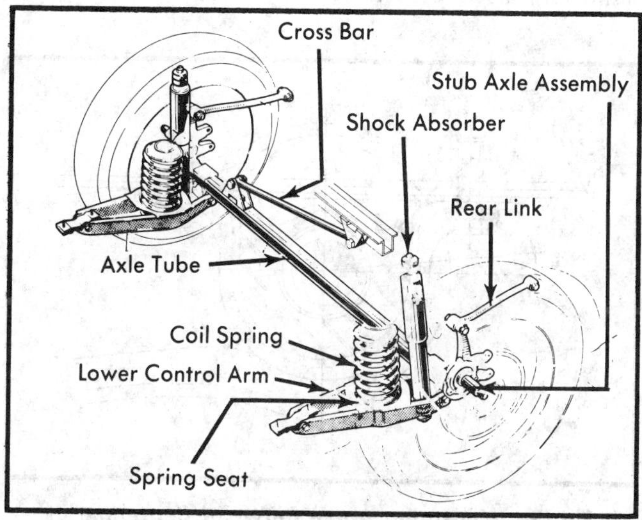

Fig. 1 Saab Rear Suspension Assembly

ADJUSTMENT

REAR WHEEL BEARINGS

See Wheel Bearing Adjustment in WHEEL ALIGNMENT Section.

REMOVAL & INSTALLATION

SHOCK ABSORBERS

Removal, Standard Type – Raise vehicle and place on safety stands. Remove tire and wheel. Disconnect shock absorbers from upper and lower mounting brackets. Remove shock absorber.

Installation – Reverse removal procedure and note: Bleed new shock absorber before installing. Place shock absorber straight up and down. Work it through full cycle several times. Make sure nuts are not overtightened. There should just be enough tension against rubber bushing to provide a solid fit.

Removal, Pneumatic Type – 1) Raise vehicle and place on safety stand at rear jacking point. Fit another safety stand under rear axle. This will stop axle from suddenly dropping.

2) Place a hydraulic jack under control arm near rear axle. Remove shock absorber mounting nuts. Remove bolts mounting control arm to rear axle. Lower control arm with jack until shock absorber can be removed.

Installation – To install, reverse removal procedure.

REAR AXLE ASSEMBLY

Removal – Raise rear of vehicle and support on safety stands. Remove wheels and tires. Disconnect rear brake hoses, lower shock absorber attachments, and cross bar. Position a jack under rear axle, lower axle and remove rear springs. Remove screws of spring link rear bushings and remove axle assembly from vehicle.

Installation – 1) To install, reverse removal procedure and note: When repositioning axle tube, DO NOT place jack in center of axle tube. Either use two jacks (one at each end) or one jack and one safety stand.

2) DO NOT tighten bearings until car weight is on suspension to ensure bushings are aligned correctly. Cross bar-to-body mounting bolt must be installed with nut facing forward. Bleed brake system.

COIL SPRING

NOTE – *DO NOT place floor jack under rear axle.*

Removal – 1) Set parking brake. Raise vehicle and place safety stands under rear axle. Remove wheel.

2) Place jack centered under control arm near coil spring. Slightly raise jack and disconnect lower end of shock absorber. Disconnect control arm from body. Let control arm down on jack until spring can be removed.

Inspection – Check spring for obvious signs of weakening or damage. Check free length of spring using table.

Coil Spring Table

Application	Free Length
Coil with GREEN Stripe	12.7" (323 mm)
Coil with YELLOW Stripe	12.9" (329 mm)
Coil with WHITE Stripe	12.4" (315 mm)
Coil with BLUE Stripe	12.8" (324 mm)

Installation – Reverse removal procedure. Make sure to use new lock nuts where control arm attaches to body.

SUBARU

1600

DESCRIPTION

Rear suspension is independent, semitrailing arm type with torsion bars. Double action hydraulic shock absorbers are also employed.

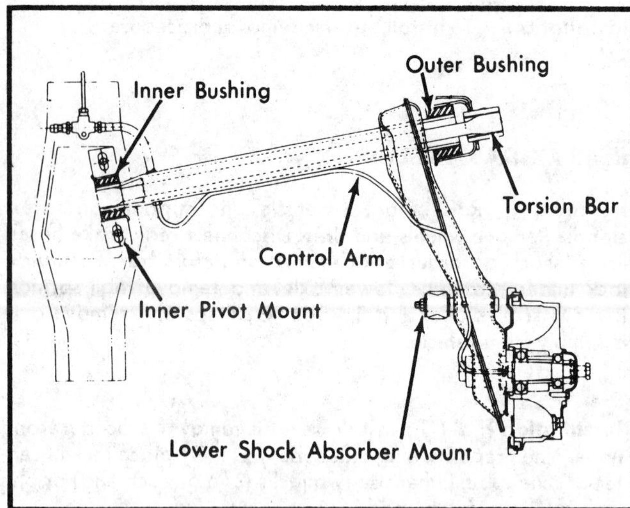

Fig. 1 Subaru Rear Suspension Components

ADJUSTMENT

WHEEL ALIGNMENT SPECIFICATIONS & PROCEDURES

See Wheel Alignment Specifications and Procedures in WHEEL ALIGNMENT Section.

REMOVAL & INSTALLATION

REAR SUSPENSION ASSEMBLY

NOTE – *To repair or replace any rear suspension components, with the exception of shock absorbers, suspension assembly, for side being repaired, must be removed.*

Removal – Raise rear of vehicle and support with safety stands. Remove rear wheels and disconnect brake line from flex line. Disconnect lower shock absorber mount. Remove bolts securing inner control arm pivot shaft mount to body. Loosen lock bolt at outer bushing. Remove outer control arm pivot shaft mount bolts and remove suspension assembly for one side. This procedure applies to both sides of rear suspension.

Disassembly – With lock bolt removed, pull outer bracket from bushing and pull torsion bar from control arm. Remove outer bushing with a suitable puller (925210000). Inner bushing can be removed in same manner.

Reassembly – Press bushing onto control arm, making sure bushings are flush with ends of control arm. Apply grease to serrations on end of torsion bar. Torsion bars are marked "R" and "L", they should be installed accordingly. The angle between center line of bushing and control arm (see illustration), should be 6°.

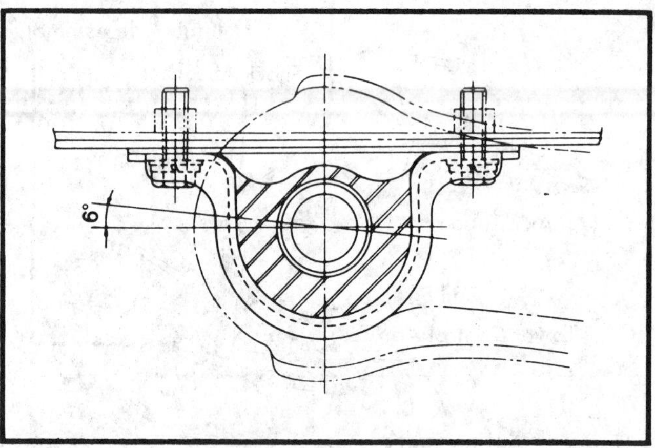

Fig. 2 Measuring Angle Between Centerline of Bushing and Control Arm

Installation – To install suspension assembly, reverse removal procedure. Tighten all bolts and nuts to specifications. Bleed hydraulic brake system and check wheel alignment.

TIGHTENING SPECIFICATIONS

Application	Ft. Lbs. (mkg)
Inner Pivot Mount Bolts	14-18 (1.9-2.5)
Outer Pivot Mount Bolts	43-65 (6.0-9.0)
Outer Pivot Bushing Lock Bolt	13-18 (1.8-2.5)

TOYOTA CELICA

Celica

DESCRIPTION

Coil spring type suspension utilizing upper and lower control arms as pivot supports. Coil springs are mounted between axle housing and chassis member. Shock absorbers are connected to axle housing at bottom and to chassis members at top. A side strut rod is mounted to rear side of axle and runs parallel with axle to mount at side of body.

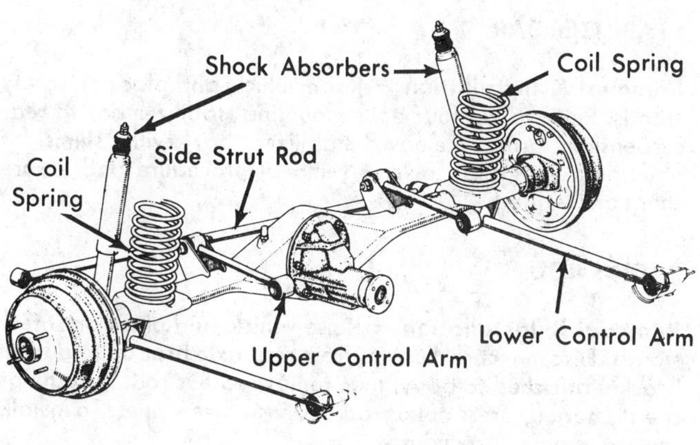

Fig. 1 Celica Rear Suspension Components

REMOVAL & INSTALLATION

SHOCK ABSORBERS

Removal – Raise vehicle and place safety stands under axle housing. Remove nut from upper shock absorber mounting stud. Remove bolt from lower mount and remove shock absorber from vehicle.

Installation – Reverse removal procedure for installation. Tighten all bolts and nuts to specifications.

COIL SPRINGS

Removal – Place a jack under center of axle housing. Raise vehicle and place safety stands under body. Disconnect shock absorber lower mount. Release jack until axle housing is at bottom of travel and remove coil springs and insulator.

Installation – Reverse removal procedure for installation.

CONTROL ARMS

Removal – Remove coil spring as previously outlined. Remove pivot bolt attaching control arm to axle housing. Raise axle housing and remove pivot bolt attaching control arm to body. Bushings in control arms are replaceable. Press out of control arm using a suitable mandrel. Use same mandrel for installing bushing.

Installation – Reverse removal procedure for installation. Tighten pivot bolts and adjust riding height.

SIDE STRUT ROD

Removal – Remove coil springs as previously outlined. Remove cotter pin and nut from axle housing mount. Raise axle housing and remove nut and washer at body mount. Bushings in side strut rod are replaceable. Press out using a suitable mandrel. Install using same mandrel.

Installation – Reverse removal procedure for installation. Tighten nuts and adjust riding height.

TIGHTENING SPECIFICATIONS

Application	Ft. Lbs. (mkg)
Shock Absorber Upper Mount	14-22 (1.9-3.0)
Shock Absorber Lower Mount	26-33 (3.6-4.5)
Control Arm Pivot Bolts	72-108 (10.0-15.0)
Side Strut Rod-to-Axle Housing Nut	25-40 (3.5-5.5)
Side Strut Rod-to-Body Mount Nut	51-65 (7.0-9.0)

Rear Suspension

TRIUMPH TR7

TR7

DESCRIPTION

Rear suspension system consists of a control arm (trailing arm), radius rod, and a stabilizer bar. A coil spring is mounted between body and control arm. Shock absorbers mount off axle housing at bottom and at top to body.

ADJUSTMENT

WHEEL ALIGNMENT SPECIFICATIONS & PROCEDURES

See Wheel Alignment Specifications in WHEEL ALIGNMENT Section.

REMOVAL & INSTALLATION

COIL SPRING & CONTROL ARM

Removal – Raise vehicle and place on safety stands. Remove wheel. Place jack under suspension control arm and compress spring ensuring vehicle does not come off stands. Remove two nuts and bolts mounting stabilizer bar to control arm. Remove nut and bolt securing rear end of suspension arm to axle bracket. Lower jack and remove spring and insulating rubbers. Detach suspension control arm front mounting and remove arm.

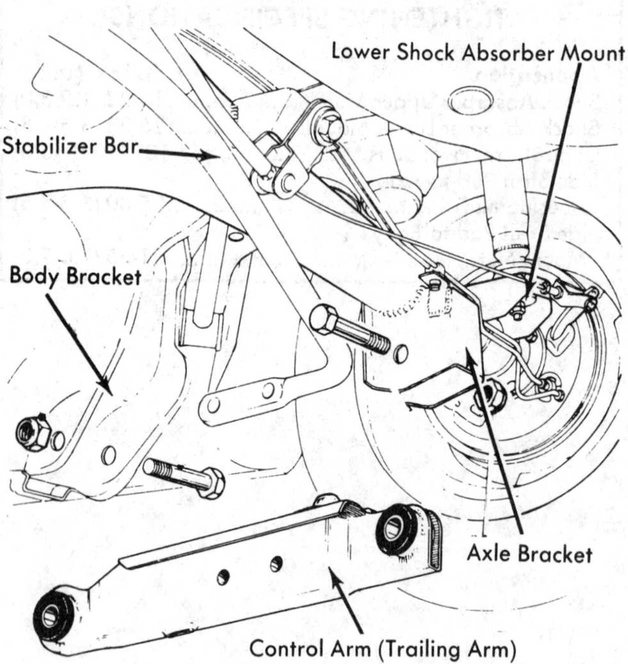

Fig. 1 Detailed View of Control Arm Removal

Installation – Insure spring insulators are in correctly, then fit spring. With jack positioned under control arm and front (body bracket end) of control arm installed, fit rear end of suspension control arm in axle bracket. Reconnect stabilizer bar to suspension arm and install wheel. Tighten suspension components with vehicle weight on ground.

SHOCK ABSORBERS

Removal – Jack up vehicle and place on safety stands; remove wheel. On right side, remove fuel filler assembly. On left side, remove upper access plate. On both sides, disconnect upper end of shock absorber and remove hardware. Disconnect and remove lower shock absorber mounting, then pull shock absorber from vehicle.

Installation – To install, reverse removal procedure and tighten nuts.

STABILIZER BAR

Removal & Installation – Raise vehicle and place on safety stands. Remove the four bolts mounting stabilizer bar to rear suspension arms. Remove stabilizer bar with shims, if equipped. To install, reverse removal procedure and ensure shims are refitted.

RADIUS ROD

Removal & Installation – Raise vehicle and place on safety stands. Disconnect radius rod from rear axle bracket and from bracket attached to body; then remove radius rod. If bushings are damaged, press out of rod and install new ones. To install, reverse removal procedure.

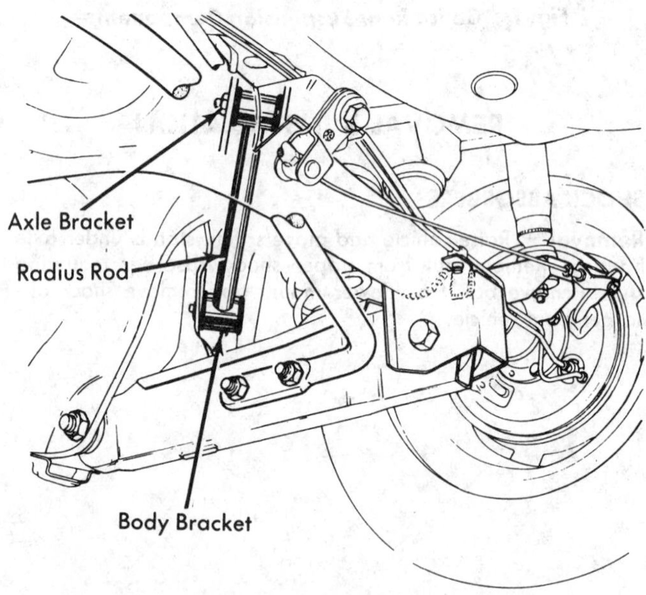

Fig. 2 Detailed View of Radius Rod Removal

TIGHTENING SPECIFICATIONS

Application	Ft. Lbs. (mg)
Stabilizer Bar-to-Control Arm	30-37 (4.2-5.1)
Shock Absorber-to-Control Arm	10-14 (1.4-1.9)
Shock Absorber-to-Body	10-14 (1.4-1.9)
Suspension Arm-to-Axle Bracket	38-48 (5.3-6.6)
Suspension Control Arm-to-Body Bracket	38-48 (5.3-6.6)

TRIUMPH SPITFIRE

Spitfire

DESCRIPTION

Semi-trailing arm, independent type with a transverse leaf spring. Strut rods are connected at front to chassis and at rear to axle bearing carrier. Transverse leaf spring is mounted in center to differential and at ends to mounts connected to bearing carrier. Hydraulic shock absorbers are mounted between bearing carrier at bottom and chassis at top.

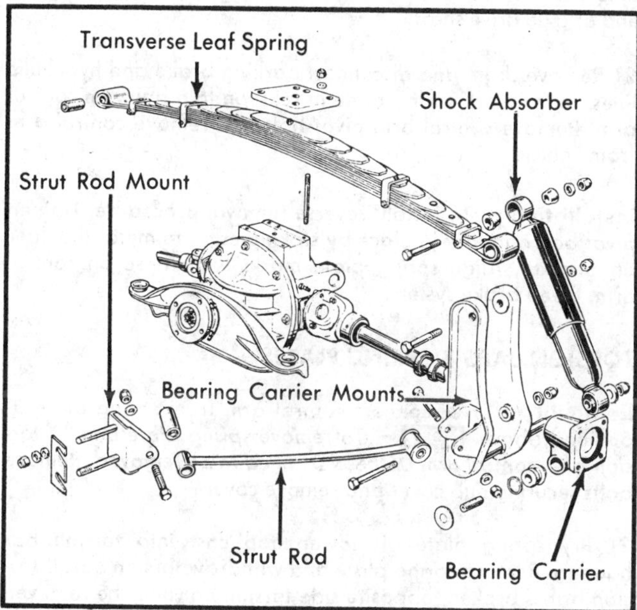

Fig. 1 Exploded View of Rear Suspension Assembly

ADJUSTMENT

WHEEL ALIGNMENT SPECIFICATIONS & PROCEDURES

See Wheel Alignment Specifications and Procedures in WHEEL ALIGNMENT Section.

REMOVAL & INSTALLATION

TRANSVERSE LEAF SPRING

Removal – Raise vehicle, position safety stands under chassis and remove both rear wheels. Remove bolts connecting transverse leaf spring to bearing carrier mount. Place a jack under lower shock absorber mount and disconnect lower shock absorber from mount on bearing carrier. From inside luggage compartment, remove plate covering spring mount on differential. Remove nuts and clamp plate from spring mount. Remove mounting studs from differential and pull spring out through side of fender well.

Installation – To install transverse leaf spring, reverse removal procedure. Spring is marked "FRONT" and must be installed correctly. Do not tighten spring to bearing carrier bolts until weight of vehicle is on rear wheels.

STRUT RODS

Removal – Raise vehicle, position safety stands under chassis and remove wheels. Place a jack under lower shock absorber mount and raise jack until strut rod bolts can be removed easily. If shims are removed from strut rod mount on chassis, make sure the same amount of shims are reinstalled.

Installation – To install strut rod, reverse removal procedure. Install same amount of shims at front mount as were removed and check rear wheel alignment.

BEARING CARRIER MOUNTS

Removal – Raise vehicle, position safety stands under chassis and remove wheel and tire. Disconnect strut rod from bearing carrier mount. Disconnect lower shock absorber mount. Remove bolt securing transverse leaf spring to bearing carrier mount. Remove pivot bolt securing mount to bearing carrier and remove mount.

Installation – To install bearing carrier mounts, reverse removal procedure.

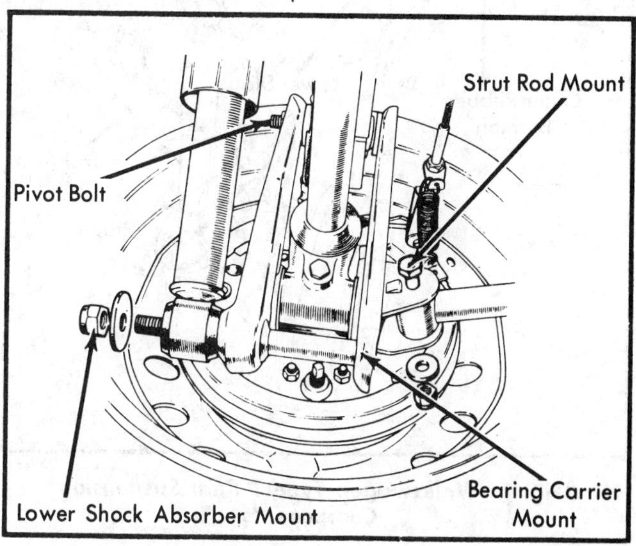

Fig. 2 Components to Remove to Take Out Bearing Carrier Mount

TIGHTENING SPECIFICATIONS

Application	Ft. Lbs. (mkg)
Lower Shock Absorber Mount	28-38 (3.9-5.3)
Upper Shock Absorber Mount	38-48 (5.3-6.6)
Strut Rod Pivot Bolts	24-32 (3.3-4.4)
Strut Rod Bracket-to-Chassis	24-32 (3.3-4.4)
Mounts-to-Bearing Carrier	38-48 (5.3-6.6)
Transverse Spring Pivot Bolts	38-48 (5.3-6.6)

VOLKSWAGEN TYPE 1

Type 1

DESCRIPTION

Independent torsion bar type rear suspension. Torsion bars are mounted inside rear crossmember tube and anchor in center by means of a splined hub. Outer ends of torsion bars mount into splined hubs integral with spring plates. Control arm and spring plate mount together. Control arms pivot in mounts connected to crossmember tube and also serve as rear wheel bearing carriers. Hydraulic shock absorbers mount off control arms.

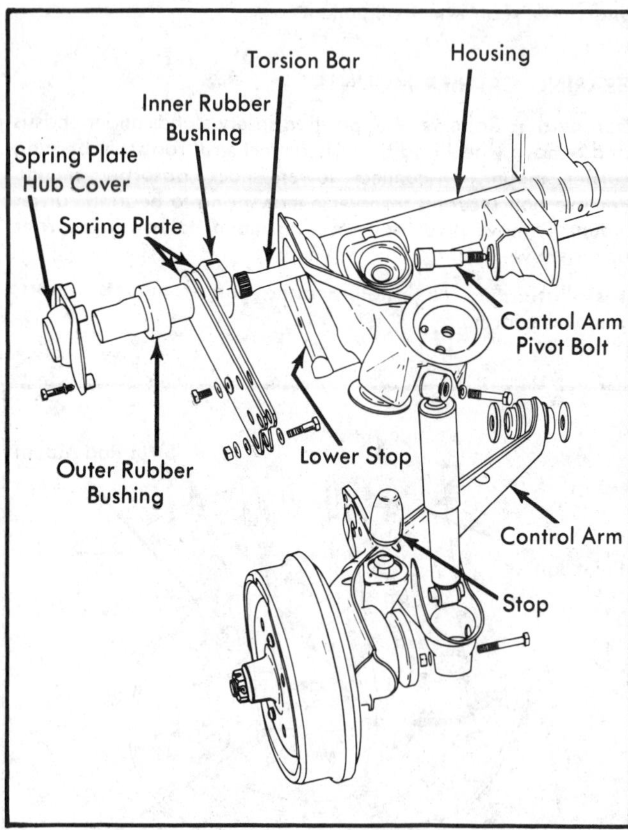

Fig. 1 Volkswagen Type 1 Rear Suspension Components

ADJUSTMENT

WHEEL ALIGNMENT SPECIFICATIONS & PROCEDURES

See Wheel Alignment Specifications and Procedures in WHEEL ALIGNMENT Section.

REMOVAL & INSTALLATION

SHOCK ABSORBERS

Removal – Raise vehicle and place on safety stands. Remove wheel. Remove both bottom and top mounting nuts and bolts, then slide shock absorber from vehicle.

Installation – Inspect for hydraulic leaks and replace shock absorber if excessive leaking is apparent. Check shock absorber for smooth, even operation. To install, reverse removal procedure.

CONTROL ARMS

Removal – 1) Remove cotter pin and loosen rear hub nut. Raise vehicle and place safety stands under body. Remove wheel. Remove shock absorber. Remove bolts mounting axle drive shaft to stub axle. Separate axle drive shaft from stub axle and wire out of way. Use protective cap to cover exposed end of axle drive shaft.

2) Remove drum and disconnect parking brake and hydraulic lines. Index mark spring plate in relation to a point on control arm. Remove control arm pivot bolt and remove control arm from vehicle.

Installation – To install, reverse removal procedure. Tighten pivot bolt and lock in place by staking edge to metal shoulder on bracket. Align spring plate marks with those on control arm. Bleed brake system.

TORSION BARS & SPRING PLATES

Removal – 1) Disconnect control arm from spring plate as outlined above. **NOTE** – *To remove spring plate and/or torsion bar, control arm DOES NOT need to be removed.* Remove bolts securing hub cover and remove cover.

2) Pry spring plate off lower stop cast into torsion bar housing. Remove spring plate and withdraw torsion bar. If torsion bar is broken, opposite side torsion bar must be removed to drive out broken piece.

Installation – 1) Inspect torsion bar and spring plate for wear or distortion. Inspect rubber mounts for cracking or wear. Torsion bars are marked left and right and should be installed accordingly. Coat torsion bar splines with grease and install in vehicle. Coat rubber supports with talcum powder. Make sure part of rubber support marked "Oben" is installed facing up.

2) Install spring plate in position. **NOTE** – *See appropriate article in WHEEL ALIGNMENT Section for torsion bar setting procedure.* Install hub cover and secure with two bolts. Raise spring plate using a spring compressor (VW655/3) and install remaining hub cover bolts. To install remaining components, reverse removal procedure. Recheck wheel alignment.

TIGHTENING SPECIFICATIONS

Application	Ft. Lbs. (mkg)
Shock Absorber Upper and Lower Mounts	43 (6.0)
Control Arm Pivot Bolt	87 (12.0)
Spring Plate-to-Control Arm	80 (11.0)
Spring Plate Hub Cover Bolts	25 (3.5)
Axle Drive Shaft-to-Stub Axle	25 (3.5)
Rear Axle Hub Nut	217 (30.0)

VOLKSWAGEN TYPE 2

Type 2

DESCRIPTION

Independent torsion bar type rear suspension. Torsion bars mount in rear crossmember tube and anchor in center of tube by means of a splined hub. Outer ends of torsion bars mount into splined hubs integral with spring plates. Control arms are connected to spring plates. Control arms pivot in mounts connected to crossmember tube and connect at ends to rear wheel bearing housing. Hydraulic shock absorbers mount between control arms and bracket integral with chassis.

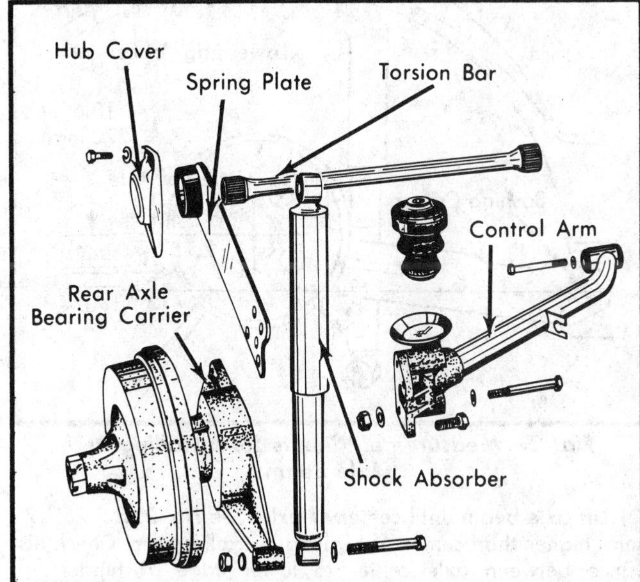

Fig. 1 Exploded View of Rear Suspension Assembly

ADJUSTMENT

WHEEL ALIGNMENT SPECIFICATIONS & PROCEDURES

See Wheel Alignment Specifications and Procedures in WHEEL ALIGNMENT Section.

REMOVAL & INSTALLATION

CONTROL ARMS

Removal — 1) Remove cotter pin and loosen rear axle hub nut. Raise vehicle and place safety stands under body. Remove wheel and tire. Remove bolts from axle drive shaft at stub axle and seperate axle drive shaft from stub axle. Disconnect shock absorbers from control arm.

2) Disconnect brake line and parking brake cable from backing plate. Mark position of spring plate in relation to control arm. Remove bolts securing spring plate to control arm. Remove control arm pivot bolt and remove control arm from vehicle.

Installation — 1) Install control arm in vehicle in an extended position, then tighten pivot bolt. Attach control arm to spring plate with index marks make during removal properly aligned; tighten bolts.

2) To install remaining components, reverse removal procedure and tighten all nuts and bolts. Check wheel alignment if new control arm has been installed.

SPRING PLATES & TORSION BARS

Removal — Disconnect spring plate from control arm as previously outlined. Remove bolts securing hub cover to crossmember and remove hub cover. Pry spring plate off lower stop (cast in housing) and pull spring plate out. Withdraw torsion bar. If broken torsion bar is being removed, opposite side torsion bar must be removed to drive out broken piece.

Installation — 1) Inspect torsion bar and spring plate for wear or distortion. Inspect rubber support bushings for wear or cracking. Grease torsion bar splines and install in vehicle. Torsion bars are marked left and right, install accordingly. Coat rubber bushings with talcum powder before installation.

2) Install spring plate on torsion bar in proper position. **NOTE** — *See appropriate article in WHEEL ALIGNMENT Section for torsion bar setting procedure.* Install rubber bushing and hub cover and secure hub cover with two bolts. Raise spring plate using spring compressor type tool (VW655/3), install remaining bolts and tighten. Reverse removal procedure for remaining components. Check wheel alignment.

TIGHTENING SPECIFICATIONS

Application	Ft. Lbs. (mkg)
Control Arm-to-Bearing Housing	94 (13.0)
Control Arm Pivot Bolt	43 (6.0)
Rear Axle Hub Nut	253 (35.0)
Shock Absorber Mounting Bolts	43 (6.0)
Torsion Bar Hub Cover	35 (4.5)
Axle Drive Shaft-to-Stub Axle	25 (3.5)

VOLKSWAGEN DASHER

Dasher

DESCRIPTION

Rear suspension is coil spring type utilizing a transverse mounted suspension rod and a trailing arm. Suspension rod is used to improve stability. Shock absorbers mount off bracket on axle beam and to upper body. Coil spring rides in spring seat welded to axle beam and wedges against damper ring at chassis/body.

ADJUSTMENTS

WHEEL ALIGNMENT SPECIFICATIONS & PROCEDURES

See Wheel Alignment Specifications and Procedures in WHEEL ALIGNMENT Section.

WHEEL BEARING ADJUSTMENT

See Wheel Bearing Adjustment in WHEEL ALIGNMENT Section

REMOVAL & INSTALLATION

REAR AXLE BEAM ASSEMBLY

Removal – 1) Raise vehicle and place safety stands under body. Take nuts off parking brake linkage equalizer bar. Force parking brake plastic cable guide bushing from clip holder. Pry down and unhook muffler from front bracket. Separate all brake cables from body mountings.

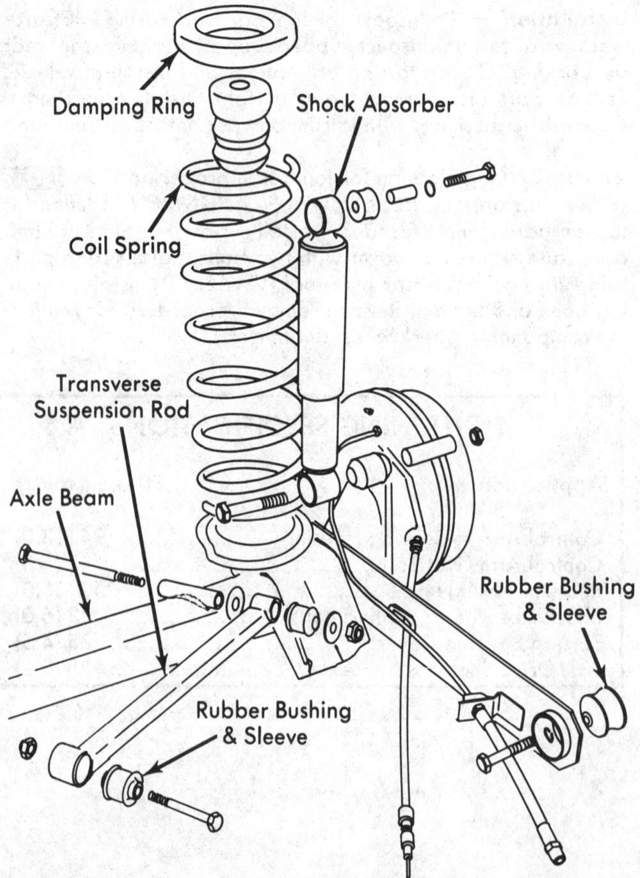

Fig. 1 Exploded View of Dasher Rear Suspension

2) Disconnect brake lines and plug open ends. Using a jack, raise axle slightly. Unhook muffler at rear. Disconnect suspension rod from mounting on axle. Disconnect and wire lower end of shock absorber out of way. Guide rear axle assembly from mounting position.

Disassembly – Place trailing arm in press and force bushing from arm. Repeat process to install new bushing. **NOTE** – *Early model bushings are not interchangeable with late model bushings.* Make sure when new bushings are installed slots in bushings are aligned horizontally in trailing arm.

Installation – 1) To install rear axle assembly, reverse removal procedure and note the following: Make sure trailing arm bushings are free of tension. Before tightening trailing arm bolts ensure arms are in middle of moving range.

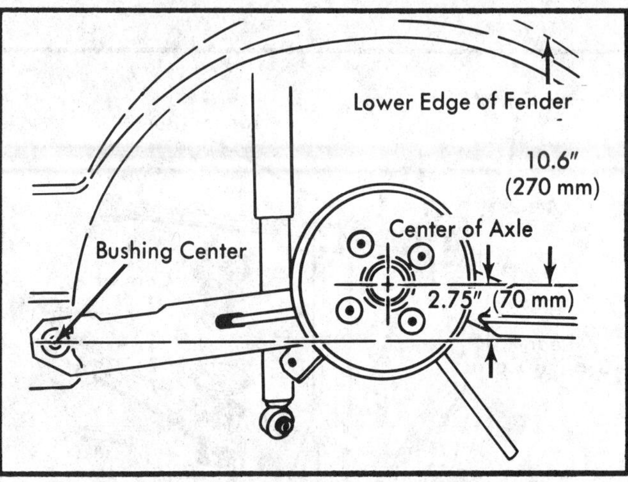

Fig. 2 Measurement Points for Installing Rear Axle Beam

2) Lift axle beam until center of axle *(See Fig. 2)* is 2.75" (70 mm) higher than center of bushing in trailing arm. Check distance between axle center to lower edge of fender lip. Distance should be 10.6" (270 mm). Tighten bolts. **NOTE** – *ONLY tighten bolts with axle located in this position.*

TRANSVERSE SUSPENSION ROD

Removal & Installation – Raise vehicle and place on safety stands. Remove suspension rod mounting bolts and tap bolts free from mounting bushings. Inspect mounting bushings and sleeves for excessive wear or damage; replace as necessary. To install, reverse removal procedure.

SHOCK ABSORBER

Removal & Installation – Raise vehicle and place on safety stands. Remove shock absorber lower mounting bolt. Remove upper mount bolt and slide shock absorber from vehicle. **NOTE** – *Lower mounting bolt must be removed first. Upper mounting bolt must be installed first.*

TIGHTENING SPECIFICATIONS

Application	Ft. Lbs. (mkg)
Shock Absorber Mounting Bolts	43 (6.0)
Suspension Rod Mounting Bolts	50 (7.0)
Trailing Arm Bolt	43 (6.0)

VOLKSWAGEN RABBIT & SCIROCCO

Rabbit
Scirocco

DESCRIPTION

Rear suspension is a link type with coil springs and using control arms and torsion beam for stabilization. Control arm and torsion beam are combined as one unit. Hydraulic shock absorbers are mounted inside coil springs and attached to control arm at the bottom and to vehicle body at the top.

REMOVAL & INSTALLATION

SUSPENSION STRUT & COIL SPRING

Removal – 1) Leave vehicle on ground. Take off plastic cap covering rear strut upper mounting nuts. Remove nuts.

2) Slowly raise vehicle until weight is off spring. Remove bolt holding lower end of strut shock absorber to axle beam mount. Raise vehicle until strut can be removed.

NOTE – *It is not necessary to use spring compressor to disassemble strut.*

Disassembly – Set strut assembly in vise. Hold piston rod and remove strut mounting nut. Take off components down to slotted nut. Remove slotted nut. Take off spacer and coil spring.

Inspection – 1) Hand check shock absorber for even resistance through entire piston stroke. Worn shock absorbers cannot be overhauled.

2) There are three spring classes used in production. Springs are identified with 1, 2, or 3 paint stripes. Replacement springs come only with 2 paint stripes and can be used inconjunction

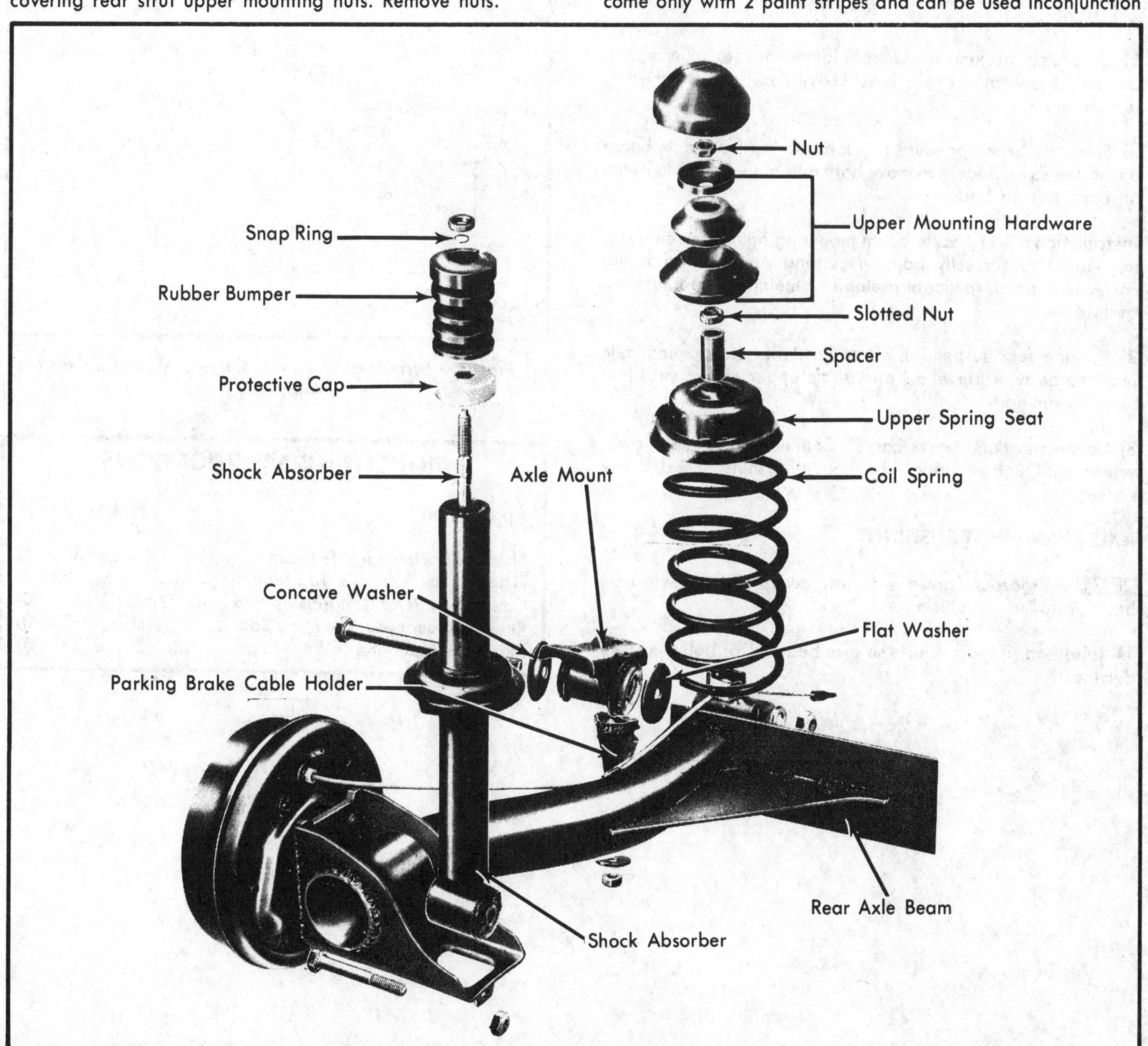

Fig. 1 Exploded View of Rabbit/Scirocco Rear Suspension Components

VOLKSWAGEN RABBIT & SCIROCCO (Cont.)

with any spring (Scirocco only). On Rabbit models only, springs must be matched sets with corresponding matched rubber bumpers.

Reassembly – 1) Fit Protective cap. Install rubber buffer with small diameter leading over piston rod. Insert snap ring and washer.

2) Place spring into lower seat. Fit upper retainer with spacer sleeve. Tighten slotted nut holding piston rod. Put on remaining upper mounting hardware and tighten piston rod.

Installation – Reverse removal procedure.

SUSPENSION ASSEMBLY

Removal – 1) Leave vehicle on ground. Disconnect upper strut mounting at body. Raise vehicle and support at rear with jack stands.

2) Disconnect parking brake at holder near rear axle mount. Disconnect and plug brake lines. Leave flex hose attached to suspension.

3) Separate brake pressure regulator spring from axle beam on models so equipped. Remove both nuts mounting axle beam on each side to body.

Installation – 1) If axle beam mounting has been removed, use *Fig. 2* to correctly adjust mounting pad. If pad is not correctly aligned, torsional preload of mounting bushings will be incorrect.

2) Position rear suspension on body. Refit nuts keeping axle beam to body. Raise wheel and guide upper end of strut into body mounting.

3) Connect parking brake cables. Connect brake lines. Lower vehicle and tighten upper strut mounting nuts. Bleed brake system.

AXLE BEAM PIVOT BUSHING

NOTE – *Procedure given is for replacing bushing with axle beam installed in vehicle.*

1) Raise and support vehicle so axle beam pivot bolt is not under load.

2) Remove 2 nuts holding axle beam to body and tap out pivot bolt.

3) Press out bushing. Select new bushing and press bushing into place. Loosely install mounting on axle beam. Concave washer and bolt head must face toward outside of vehicle. Bolt head must recess into washer.

4) Align mount as shown in *Fig. 2*. Tighten pivot bolt nut. Lower vehicle.

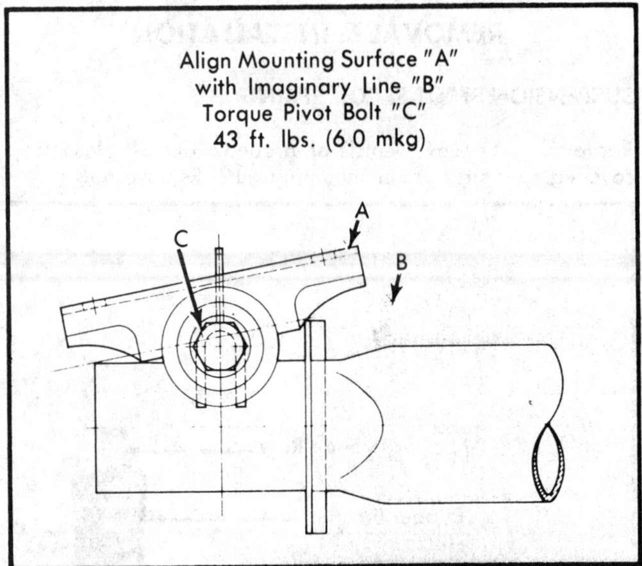

Fig. 2 Drawing Showing Correct Mounting Pad Alignment

TIGHTENING SPECIFICATIONS

Application	Ft. Lbs. (mkg)
Shock Absorber-to-Axle Beam	32 (4.5)
Piston Shock Absorber Top Mounting	25 (3.5)
Coil Spring Retainer-to-Piston Rod	14 (2.0)
Rear Axle Beam-to-Mounting Pad	43 (6.0)
Rear Axle Mounting-to-Body	32 (4.5)

VOLVO

240 Series
260 Series

DESCRIPTION

All models use a live axle with coil spring rear suspension. Control arms, running forward from axle, are used. A track bar is connected at one end to axle and on opposite side of vehicle to frame. Coil springs mount between axle assembly and frame. Hydraulic shock absorbers are used and are attached at top end to frame and at lower end to control arm. Torque rods mount to welded bracket on rear axle housing and to body above control arm. Stabilizer bar mounts off brackets on both control arms.

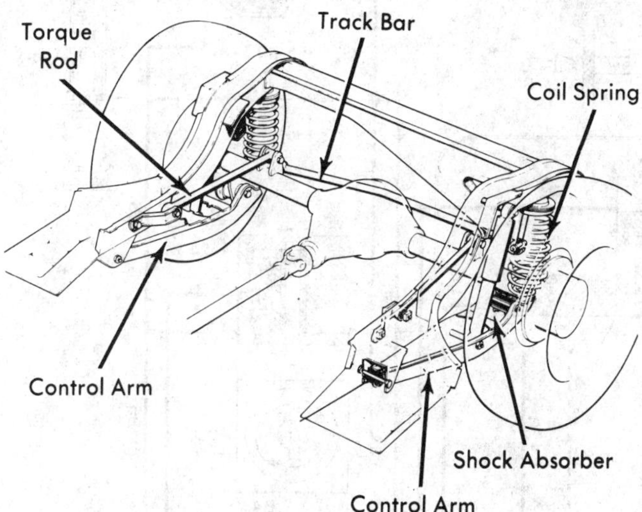

Fig. 1 Volvo Rear Suspension

REMOVAL & INSTALLATION

REAR SUSPENSION ASSEMBLY

Removal – Raise rear of vehicle and position safety stands. Remove tires and wheels. Place a jack under axle housing and raise axle until spring compresses slightly. Disconnect shock absorbers from top mount. Disconnect brake lines from rear axle, then remove brake caliper attaching bolts. Use wire to hook calipers to top shock absorber support to prevent brake lines from becoming damaged or distorted. Remove parking brake drums, and shoes, then disconnect brake cables to levers. Remove springs attaching cables to rear axle. Disconnect propeller shaft from flange on rear axle pinion. Disconnect springs from rear axle, lower rear axle and remove coil springs. Remove bolts attaching control arms and torque rod to rear axle. Pull rear axle assembly from vehicle.

Installation – To install, reverse removal procedure while noting the following: Check that all rubber spacers are properly installed. Lubricate brake lever joints with heat resistant graphite grease. Adjust rear brakes and parking brake (if necessary). Tighten all nuts and bolts.

COIL SPRINGS

Removal – Raise vehicle and place on safety stands. Remove tires and wheels. Place jack under rear axle housing and jack up axle until spring compresses. Disconnect lower shock absorber mounting, then remove spring lower retaining nut. Lower jack and remove coil spring.

Installation – To install, reverse removal procedure and tighten all nuts and bolts. Make sure rubber spring support is in correct position.

SHOCK ABSORBER

Removal – Raise rear of vehicle and support on safety stands. Remove wheel and tire. Use jack to raise rear axle. Remove upper and lower attaching nuts, then remove shock absorber.

Installation – To install, reverse removal procedure and make sure spacer sleeve is in correct position.

CONTROL ARMS

Removal – Raise rear of vehicle and position on safety stands. Position jack under rear axle housing and jack up axle until spring compresses. Disconnect shock absorber from control arm. Remove coil spring lower retaining nut, then remove spring. Remove control arm attaching bolts, and control arm.

Installation – Install attaching bolts for forward end of control arm, then install rear control arm attaching bolts. **NOTE** – *Tighten bolts finger tight only at this time.* Install coil spring and attaching nut. Raise rear axle while guiding coil spring into position, then attach shock absorber lower mount to control arm with spacer sleeve on inside. Tighten control arm attaching bolts.

STABILIZER BAR

Removal – Raise vehicle and place safety stand just in front of rear jack supports. With a jack, raise rear axle to take load off shock absorbers. Disconnect stabilizer bar mountings and guide stabilizer bar from vehicle.

Installation – Fit stabilizer bar in position on brackets. Put nuts on finger tight. Remount lower end of shock absorber. Maneuver stabilizer bar so it settles in bracket. Tighten all nuts.

TORQUE RODS & TRACK BARS

Removal – Raise rear of vehicle and place on safety stands. Disconnect track rod from mounting on body and rear axle. Inspect both bushings and sleeves for damage or excessive wear.

Installation – To install, reverse removal procedure.

MERCEDES-BENZ 6.9

DESCRIPTION

The hydropneumatic suspension is a gas pressure suspension system with hydraulic level control. The vehicle load is supported by four struts, which also serve as shock absorbers. Suspension is accomplished by the compression and decompression of the gas cushion in the pressure reservoirs. To regulate the vehicle level, the oil volume in the suspension struts is increased or reduced by means of a hydraulic system. The hydraulic system is comprised of; oil pump, pressure regulator, main pressure reservoir and oil reservoir. The pressure regulator and level selector valve are combined into one valve unit.

OPERATION

The hydraulic oil pump delivers oil from the oil reservoir to the main pressure reservoir via pressure regulator of valve unit. When the maximum oil pressure is reached, the pressure regulator revereses the oil flow. If the main oil pressure drops to the minimum, pressure regulator will reverse the flow and oil will be pumped into the main pressure reservoir until maximum pressure is again reached. If vehicle level drops due to increased load, levelling valve will open. Oil flowing into suspension struts will lift vehicle until normal level is reached. If load is reduced, levelling valve will permit oil to flow from suspension

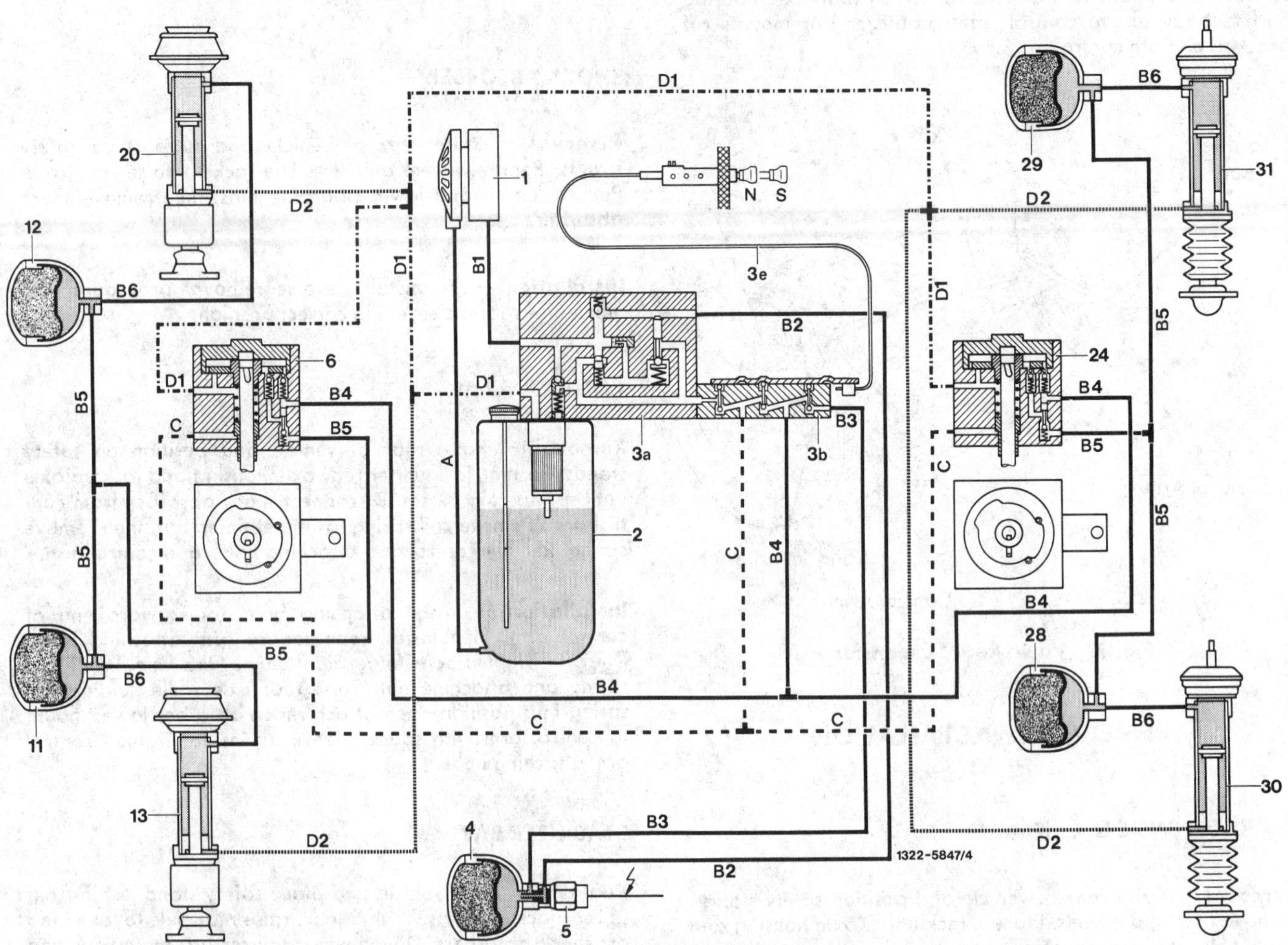

1 — Hydraulic Oil Pump
2 — Hydraulic Oil Reservoir
3 — Valve Unit
3a — Pressure Regulator of Valve Unit
3b — Level Selector Valve of Valve Unit
3e — Control Knob
4 — Main Pressure Reservoir
5 — Electir Pressure Switch
6 — Levelling Valve, Front Axle
11 — Pressure Reservoir, Left Front
12 — Pressure Reservoir, Right Front
13 — Suspension Strut, Left Front
20 — Suspension Strut, Right Front
23 — Warning Light
24 — Levelling Valve, Rear
28 — Pressure Reservoir, Left Rear
29 — Pressure Reservoir, Right Rear
30 — Suspension Strut, Left Rear
31 — Suspension Strut, Right Rear
A — Suction Line
B1 — Pressure Line
B2 — Pressure Line, Regulator Valve to Main Pressure Reservoir
B3 — Pressure Line, Main Pressure to Selector Valve
B4 — Pressure Line, Selector Valve to Levelling Valve
B5 — Pressure Line, Levelling Valve to Pressure Reservoir
B6 — Pressure Line, Pressure Reservoir to Suspension Struts
C — Control Pressure Line
D1 — Return Line, Levelling Valve to Pressure Regulator
D2 — Return Line

Fig. 1 Mercedes-Benz Hydropneumatic Suspension System

MERCEDES-BENZ 6.9 (Cont.)

struts until vehicle is back to normal level. The oil flowing from struts, is returned to oil reservoir after going through a filter.

REMOVAL & INSTALLATION

FRONT SHOCK ABSORBERS

Removal – Move switch on instrument panel to the normal position. Jack up front of vehicle and remove front wheel. Separate high-pressure hose and leak hose from lines in wheel housing. Loosen upper shock attaching bolt. Remove lower attaching bolt and remove shock.

Inspection – Check high-pressure hose, leak oil hose rubber mount and ball joint. Replace if required.

Installation – Install in reverse of removal procedure.

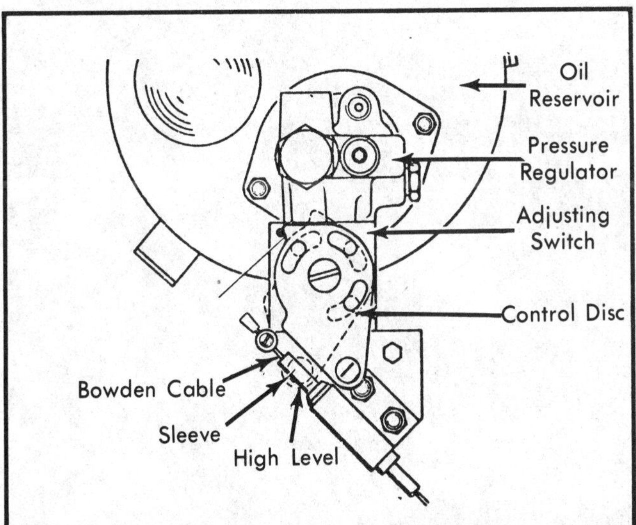

Fig. 2 Adjusting Switch for Valve Unit

REAR SHOCK ABSORBERS

Removal – Remove rear seat and back rest, remove rear trunk cover. Loosen nut on upper shock mount, remove washer and rubber ring. Jack up rear of vehicle. Remove high-pressure hose on reservoir and disconnect leak oil hose from line. Loosen lower attaching bolt and remove rear shock.

Inspection – Check high-pressure hose, leak oil hose rubber mount and ball joint. Replace if required.

Installation – 1) Insert shock into dome on frame floor. Mount lower attaching bolt, install upper attaching bolt, do not tighten. Align high-pressure hose and leak hose, by turning shock.

2) Lower vehicle, tighten upper attaching bolt and replace cover. Install rear seat and back rest. Check oil level in system and correct.

FRONT PRESSURE RESERVOIR

Removal – 1) Move switch on instrument panel to normal postion. Jack up front of vehicle. Remove left wheel, disconnect pressure lines on pressure reservoir. Loosen pressure reservoir and remove.

2) Remove battery and battery frame, from right side of vehicle. Disconnect pressure line from pressure reservoir. Remove reservoir.

Installation – Install in reverse of removal procedure.

NOTE – *When vehicle is lowered, the lever of the level controller will move into "filling postion". Since the capacity of the central reservoir is not enough for filling the suspension components, keep the engine operating.*

REAR PRESSURE RESERVOIR

Removal – With switch in normal position, jack up rear of vehicle. Disconnect pressure lines from reservoir. Remove reservoir.

Installation – Install in reverse of removal procedure.

CENTRAL RESERVOIR

Removal – 1) Disconnect puller for adjusting switch upon removal of locking ring and move disc of adjusting switch into assembly position. Jack up vehicle at front and remove left front wheel.

2) Disconnect pressure lines from central reservoir. Disconnect cable plug connection on front end. Pull cable with plug and rubber sleeve into wheel house. Loosen reservoir at front end and remove. Unscrew electrical pressure switch from central reservoir, while marking position of ring fitting.

Installation – Install in reverse of removal procedure.

OIL PUMP

Removal – Disconnect suction and pressure lines from pump. Loosen attaching bolts and remove pump.

Inspection – Check driver and clutch components replace as required.

Installation – Install in reverse of removal procedure.

VALVE UNIT

Removal – Disconnect puller for adjusting switch. Move control disc into position M (assembly). Loosen clip for puller, while applying counterhold at holder by using a hex socket wrench. Disconnect pressure lines from valve unit. Loosen attaching bolts of pressure regulator to oil reservoir and remove valve unit.

Installation – Install in reverse of removal procedure. noting the following: Install new sealing rings for sealing pressure regulator to oil reservoir.

Section 10
STEERING

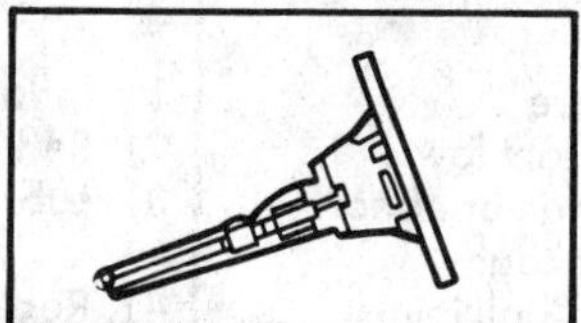

Contents

NOTE — ALSO SEE GENERAL INDEX.

Steering

MANUAL STEERING TROUBLE SHOOTING

CONDITION	POSSIBLE CAUSE	CORRECTION
▶ Hard steering	1) Incorrect tire pressure 2) Gear housing lubricant low 3) Insufficient lubrication or abnormal wear on steering linkage 4) Siezed or damaged ball joints 5) Steering shaft too tight 6) Steering column incorrectly aligned	1) Inflate tires to recommended psi 2) Refill and check for leaks 3) Lubricate or replace components 4) Replace ball joints 5) Readjust 6) Realign column
▶ Drifting	1) Incorrect tire pressure 2) Loose lug nuts 3) Mismatched tires 4) Worn or loose wheel bearings 5) Brake drag 6) Faulty shock absorbers or coil springs 7) Pitman arm binding 8) Loose steering gear 9) Vehicle uneven riding height	1) Inflate tires to correct psi 2) Tighten 3) Replace and match 4) Replace or tighten 5) Check and readjust brakes 6) Replace broken or faulty parts 7) Adjust or replace arm 8) Check for worn parts replace and adjust 9) Adjust level
▶ Excessive steering wheel play	1) Steering wheel shaft loose or worn 2) Steering linkage loose or worn 3) Worn wheel bearings 4) Worn ball joints 5) Worm shaft bearing out of adjustment 6) Loose steering gear housing	1) Adjust shaft or replace 2) Adjust or repalce 3) Replace bearings 4) Replace or adjust ball joints 5) Readjust 6) Tighten housing
▶ Steering wheel slides	1) Worm shaft or ball damaged 2) Sector shaft damaged	1) Replace components 2) Replace components
▶ Vibration or shimmy	1) Incorrect tire pressure 2) Tire out of balance 3) Worn shock absorbers or springs 4) Loose steering gear housing 5) Loose steering linkage	1) Inflate to correct psi 2) Balance tire 3) Replace defective parts 4) Tighten 5) Adjust or replace linkage
▶ Noise	1) Incorrect tire pressure 2) Wheel bearings loose or worn 3) Hub caps or rims loose	1) Inflate tires to correct psi 2) Repair or replace 3) Tighten or replace

POWER STEERING TROUBLE SHOOTING

CONDITION	POSSIBLE CAUSE	CORRECTION
▶ Hard Steering	1) Shipping spacers between column tube and shaft or in flexible couplings 2) Fluid level low 3) Control valve binding 4) Kinked or broken hoses 5) Fluid lines blocked 6) Air in system 7) Low pump pressure 8) Loose drive belt	1) Remove spacers 2) Add fluid, check for leaks 3) Replace or repair control valve 4) Straighten or replace 5) Check, clean, or replace lines 6) Bleed, refill and check for leaks 7) Check pump for worn or damaged parts 8) Adjust or replace belt
▶ Noise	1) Loose drive belt 2) Low fluid 3) Faulty valves or pump wear	1) Check, tighten, or replace belt 2) Check and add fluid 3) Repair or replace
▶ Excessive steering wheel play	1) Control valve binding	1) Repair or replace valve
▶ Sticking steering wheel	1) Binding control valve	1) Repair or replace valve

ARROW & COLT

Arrow
Colt

REMOVAL & INSTALLATION

HORN BUTTON & STEERING WHEEL

Pry off horn pad. Mark relative position of steering wheel on the shaft for reassembly reference. Remove steering wheel nut, then use a suitable puller (CT-1126 for standard wheel; DT-1001 for sports type wheel) to remove the steering wheel.

CAUTION — *Do not use excessive force to remove the steering wheel from the shaft.*

COMBINATION SWITCH (TURN SIGNAL, WIPER/WASHER, HAZARD)

To remove the combination switch assembly, tilt steering wheel to its lowest position, remove cover from switch assembly, disconnect switch wiring and withdraw switch assembly from column.

AUDI

100
Fox

REMOVAL & INSTALLATION

STEERING WHEEL & HORN CONTROL

100 — Pry off steering wheel pad toward front seat. Unscrew steering wheel nut and pull off wheel. Remove oval-head screws and washers retaining horn bar. When lifting off horn bar, note position of three springs, washers, and contact rings beneath bar.

Fox — Pull off steering wheel horn control pad by hand. Disconnect ground wire at horn button. Unscrew mounting nut and remove steering wheel.

TURN SIGNAL/DIMMER & WIPER SWITCHES

100 — With steering wheel removed, detach horn slip ring and steering column cowling. Remove horn ground contact. Pull three washers from top of steering shaft. Separate electrical connectors for switches, then remove both switch mechanisms.

Fox — When steering wheel is removed, unscrew switch base cap and disconnect electrical plugs at both lever switches, as well as horn contact ring plug. Individual switches may now be removed from base cap.

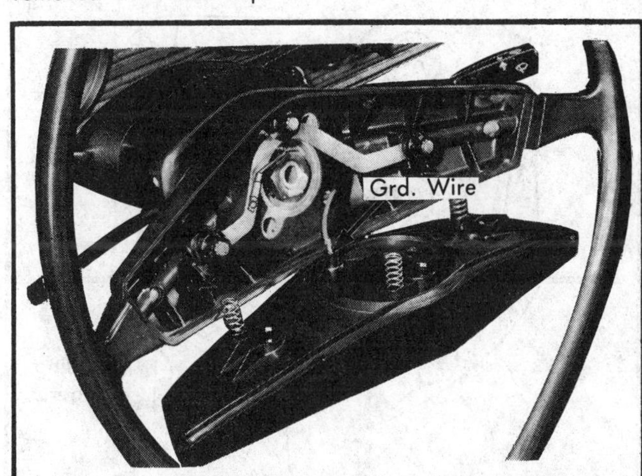

Fig. 1 Removing Horn Bar/Protective Cover from Audi Fox

BMW

320i
530i
630CSi

REMOVAL & INSTALLATION

STEERING WHEEL

Removal — Place wheels in straight-ahead position. Pry steering wheel cover off to expose wheel mounting nut. Index mark wheel and main shaft. Remove mounting nut and pull steering wheel off main shaft.

Installation — To install, reverse removal procedure and refer to reference marks made during removal.

HORN CONTROLS

Horn Button — Remove screw on back side of steering wheel spoke to free horn button.

Contact Spring — Pry off cover concealing contact spring. Replace spring if broken or if spring is unable to provide adequate contact. Make sure contact pins face inward when reinstalling existing spring or fitting new one.

Slip Ring — Disconnect electrical lead at each spoke. Remove 2 slip ring mounting screws and slide slip ring off steering wheel.

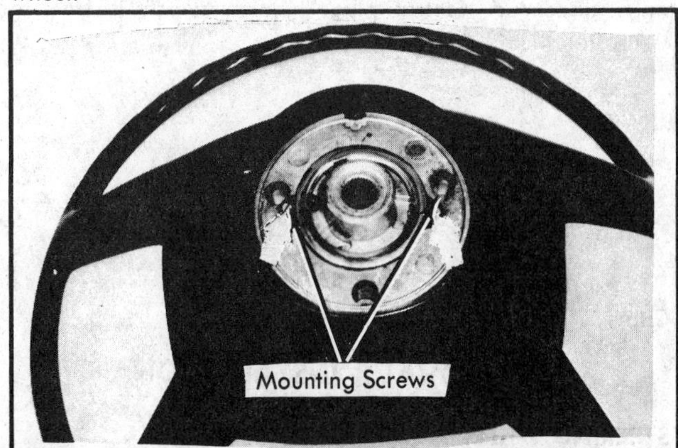

Fig. 1 Screws to Take Out for Slip Ring Removal

BMW (Cont.)

TURN SIGNAL & DIMMER SWITCH

Removal – Disconnect battery ground cable. Remove 3 mounting screws and pull down lower shroud. Remove steering wheel as previously outlined. Separate wiring from mounting straps on steering column. On 320i models, disconnect electrical plug under instrument panel. On other models, disconnect central fuse/relay plug. Remove 4 switch mounting screws and slide off switch with harness.

Installation – To install, reverse removal procedure and note: Make sure steering wheel is lined up with reference marks. Ensure turn signal assembly is centered. Finger on cancelling cam must face toward center. Distance between switch and finger should be about .118" (3 mm).

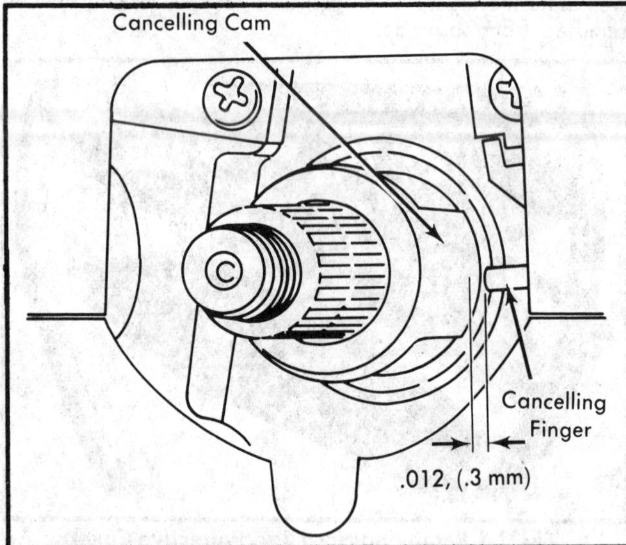

Fig. 2 Cancelling Cam and Finger with Clearance Shown

IGNITION SWITCH

Removal – Disconnect battery ground cable. Remove 3 mounting screws and pull off lower plastic shroud. Remove hollow set screw and slide out ignition switch. Disconnect horn wires on 320i models only. Disconnect steering column wire holders. On 530i and 630CSi models only, disconnect central fuse/relay plate plug and plug connector. On 320i models only, disconnect central plug. Ignition switch is free for removal.

Installation – To install, reverse removal procedure and note following: Make sure to turn ignition key all the way back before inserting. Set ignition switch at "O" position before installing. On 320i models only, marks on ignition switch must oppose each other.

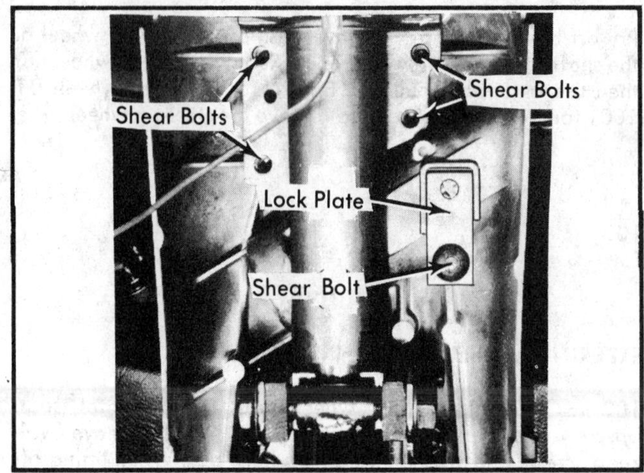

Fig. 3 Location of Shear Bolts. View Looking up from Under Steering Column. 530i and 630CSi Shown

STEERING LOCK

Removal; 530i & 630CSi – 1) Disconnect battery ground. Remove steering wheel. Remove 3 screws holding lower steering column shroud. Disconnect and remove turn signal and wiper/washer switch plate.

2) Remove shear bolts from switch plate with chisel. Remove set screw on outside of steering column tube. Pull out ignition switch. Remove steering lock plate shear bolt and pull out steering lock.

Installation – To install, reverse removal procedure.

Removal; 320i – Disconnect electrical wires from under instrument panel. Remove shroud. Remove shear bolt from lock plate and pull out steering lock.

Installation – To install, reverse removal procedure.

CAPRI

Capri

REMOVAL & INSTALLATION

STEERING WHEEL

Removal – Align wheels in straight-ahead position. Remove two screws securing steering column shroud and detach both halves. Pry out steering wheel center emblem. Unscrew steering wheel nut. Note alignment marks on wheel and shaft. Pull off steering wheel, using hand pressure only.

Installation – To install, reverse removal procedure, noting the following: Realign positioning marks of steering wheel and shaft. Ensure turn signal cancelling cam is engaged in groove on underside of steering wheel.

CAPRI (Cont.)

TURN SIGNAL & IGNITION SWITCHES

Removal — Disconnect battery. Remove steering column shroud upper and lower halves. Remove turn signal switch retaining screws, disconnect electrical plug and remove turn signal switch. Place ignition key in the "O" position, then remove screws from the lower left trim panel. Disconnect electrical plug from emergency flasher then remove trim panel. Disconnect ignition wires at connector then remove screws securing ignition switch to lock and remove ignition switch.

Installation — To install, reverse removal procedure, making sure that ignition key is in the "O" position and all wires are reconnected.

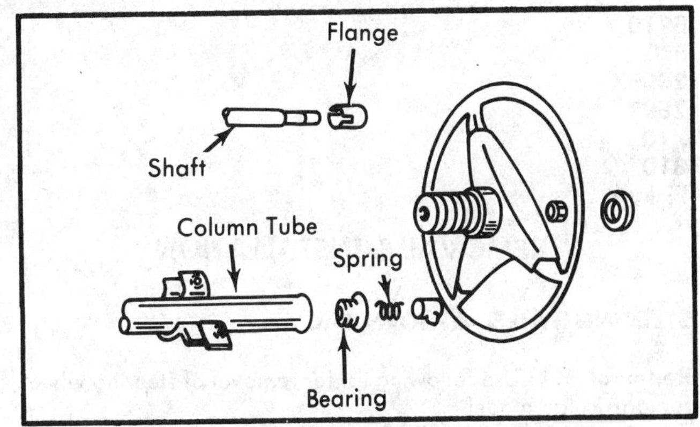

Fig. 1 Capri Steering Wheel Components

COURIER

Courier

REMOVAL & INSTALLATION

STEERING WHEEL & COMBINATION SWITCH

Removal — 1) Disconnect battery ground cable. Remove steering wheel nut cover. Index mark main shaft and steering wheel. Disconnect electrical leads. Pull steering wheel from shaft.

2) Remove plastic hazard light indicator and steering column shroud. Disconnect electrical wires at base of steering column. Remove headlight switch knob from shaft.

3) Remove snap ring retaining switch and force turn indicator cancelling cam off shaft. Take out single bolt, near bottom of switch, and pull out complete switch assembly.

Installation — 1) Fit switch assembly on steering column then, refit one retaining bolt. Place turn indicator cancelling cam into position and install snap ring. Reconnect electrical plug at column base.

2) Insert and tighten headlight knob switch. Install column shroud and plastic hazard light indicator. Refit steering wheel with index marks aligned. Connect battery ground cable.

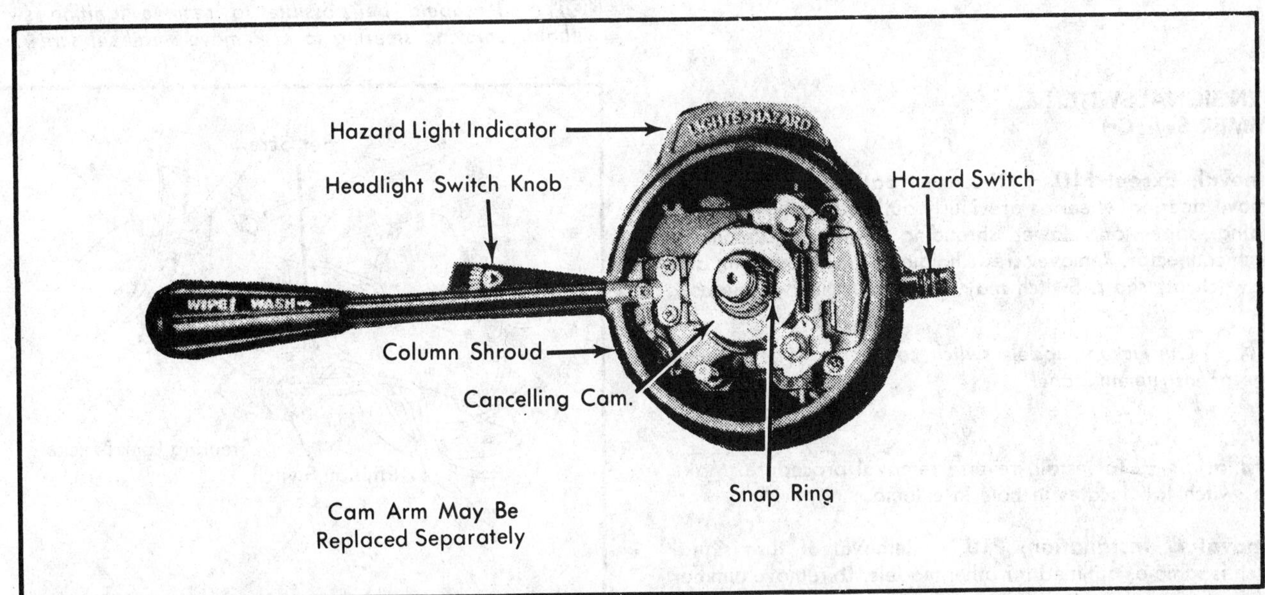

Fig. 1 Top View of Steering Column with Steering Wheel Removed to Expose Combination Switch

DATSUN

B210
F10
200SX
280Z
710
810
Pickup

REMOVAL & INSTALLATION

STEERING WHEEL & HORN PAD

Removal – **1**) Use following list for removal of steering wheel for particular model:

- On B210 models, disconnect battery ground cable. On resin model steering wheels, remove bolts on rear side of steering wheel bar. Pull out pad. Disconnect electrical wires. On 3 spoke steering wheels pad just pulls (pops) off.
- On F10 models, disconnect battery ground. On Hatchback models, remove horn pad, contact plates and spring, and contact base plate. On other models, horn pad is removed by unscrewing bolts from rear side of steering wheel.
- On 200SX and 280Z models, disconnect battery ground. Push in on horn pad and rotate counterclockwise.
- On 710 models, disconnect battery ground. Disconnect horn wire. On 2 spoke wheels, remove horn pad by pulling up and out. On 3 spoke wheels, pull straight out to remove pad.
- On 810 and Pickup models, disconnect battery ground. Remove 2 bolts on rear side of steering wheel bar and slide off horn pad.

2) Index mark top of steering column with steering wheel. Remove wheel mounting nut. Use suitable puller and extract steering wheel.

NOTE – *Do not hammer on steering wheel. Pounding may cause damage to collapsible steering column.*

Installation – On all models, reverse removal procedure. Grease any sliding components. Match index marks made during removal. Check operation.

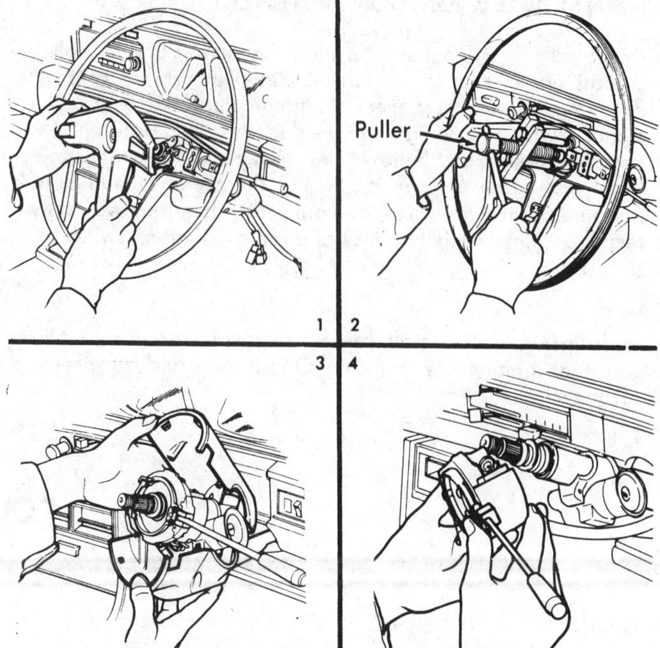

Fig. 1 Steps for Removing and Installing Steering Wheel and Combination Switch

STEERING LOCK & IGNITION SWITCH

Removal – Disconnect battery ground. Remove steering column shrouding. Drill out shear bolts. Steering lock should be free to separate from steering column. If ignition switch is to be removed from lock, separate electrical connector then remove small set screw holding switch body. Switch should now slide free.

Installation – To install, reverse removal procedure. Fit ignition switch to lock mechanism before installing lock.

NOTE – *It should be possible to remove ignition switch without removing steering lock. Remove small set screw.*

TURN SIGNAL SWITCH & DIMMER SWITCH

Removal; Except F10 – Disconnect battery ground cable. Remove steering wheel as previously outlined. Remove screws holding upper and lower shrouding together. Disconnect switch connector. Remove screws holding switch to column and lift switch off shaft. Switch may come apart in two pieces.

NOTE – *On Pickup models switch connector is near lower edge of instrument panel.*

Installation – To install, reverse removal procedure. Make sure switch tab locates in hole in column.

Removal & Installation; F10 – Removal of turn signal switch is same as outlined for other models. To remove dimmer switch, disconnect battery ground. Remove column cover. Disconnect wiring connector. Remove both retaining screws. Slide out switch. Refit by reversing removal procedure.

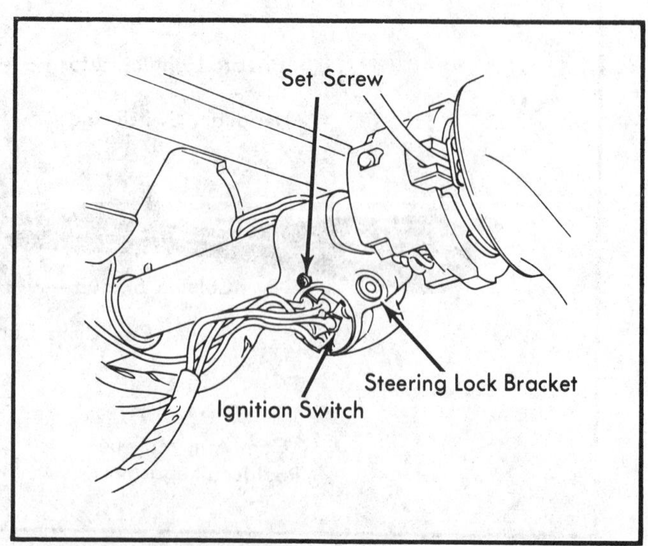

Fig. 2 Steering Lock and Ignition Switch

FIAT

124
128
131
X1/9

REMOVAL & INSTALLATION

HORN BUTTON & STEERING WHEEL

Remove battery cables. Pry off or unscrew horn button (center emblem) as necessary. Remove horn cable. On 128 and 131 models it will be necessary to remove steering column cover. On all models, unscrew steering wheel retaining nut and pull off steering wheel.

TURN SIGNAL SWITCH

After removing steering wheel as described, disconnect turn signal switch electrical wiring, loosen switch retaining nut (or screws), and remove switch from steering column.

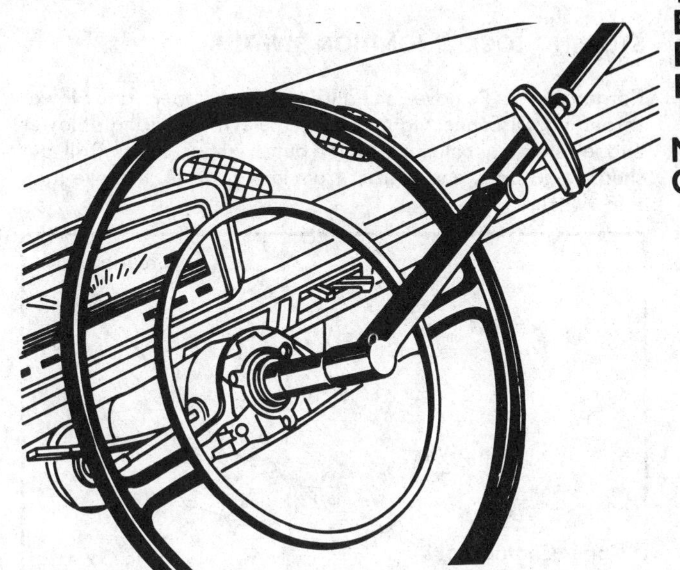

Fig. 1 Using a Torque Wrench to Tighten Steering Wheel Nut

HONDA

Civic
Civic CVCC
Accord

REMOVAL & INSTALLATION

HORN PAD & STEERING WHEEL

1) Pry off steering wheel horn pad. With front wheels in straight-ahead position, mark position of steering wheel to shaft then remove steering wheel retaining nut.

2) Steering wheel may then be pulled from shaft, using a puller tool or by hitting with hand on backside of wheel.

CAUTION – Do not apply a heavy hitting force or the shear pins within the column may be damaged.

3) Steering wheel components may then be disassembled and replaced if necessary (see *appropriate exploded view illustration*).

COMBINATION SWITCH

1) After removing steering wheel, disconnect battery (if this has not been done).

2) Remove upper and lower steering column covers. Note the bulb check switch in upper cover and illumination bulb in lower cover. These may be removed at this time if necessary. Detach all switch wiring.

CAUTION – *Never apply any impact force to steering column, as the safety collapsible shear pins will be damaged.*

3) Note position of cancelling key (for turn signal switch) and remove from switch housing (if not already removed with steering wheel).

4) The wiper/washer switch may be removed from the combination switch assembly by removing two screws. Further component disassembly or replacement may now be done as required.

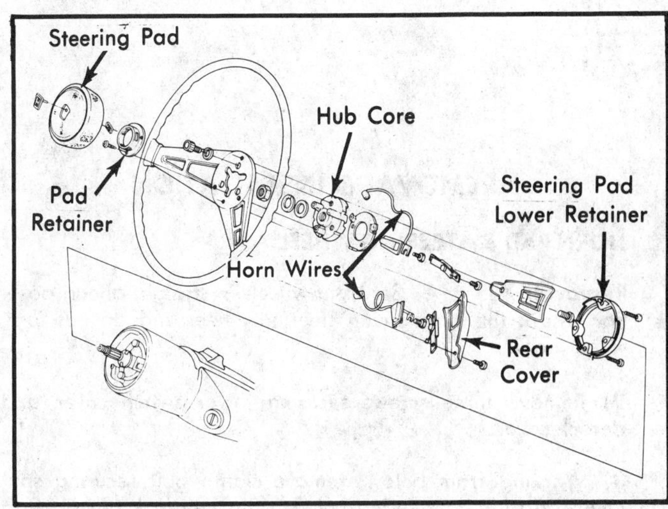

Fig. 1 Exploded View of Civic Steering Wheel and Related Components

HONDA (Cont.)

STEERING LOCK & IGNITION SWITCH

Removal – Remove steering column upper and lower shrouding. Disconnect ignition switch electrical wiring at lower end of steering column. Center punch shear bolts. Drill out shear head bolts and extract from lock bracket. Remove ignition switch.

NOTE – *On Civic CVCC models, leave ignition switch in "ACC" for disassembly.*

Installation – Insert new ignition switch. Hand tighten new shear bolts. Check switch operation at this time. Tighten shear bolts. Reconnect switch electrical leads.

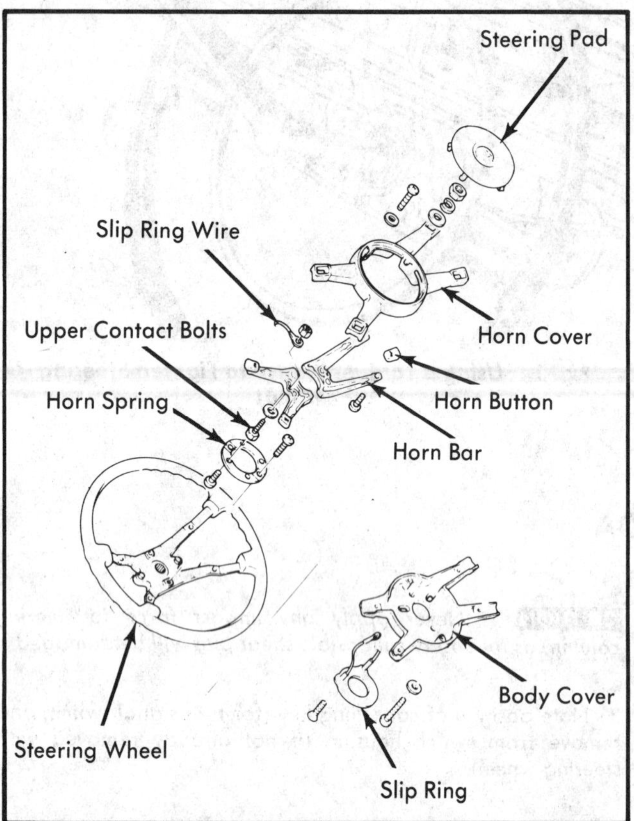

Fig. 2 Exploded View of Accord Steering Wheel and Related Components

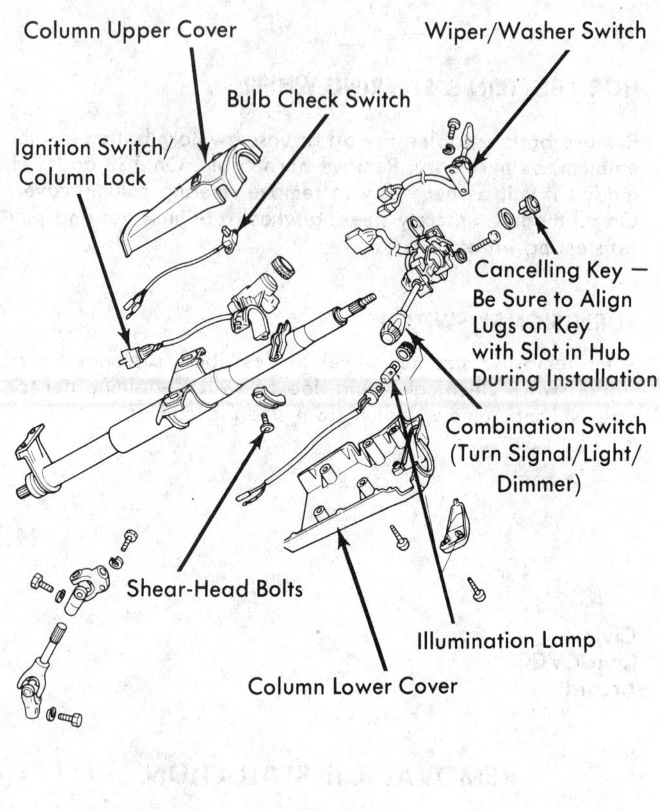

Fig. 3 Disassembled View of Upper Column Components – Accord Shown; Others Similar

JAGUAR

XJ6
XJ12
XJS

REMOVAL & INSTALLATION

HORN PAD & STEERING WHEEL

Removal; XJS – 1) Set front wheels in straight-ahead position. Mark this position on steering wheel and do not turn wheel again.

2) Remove three screws securing lower switch cover and detach cover.

3) Working from below, remove clamp bolt securing split collet adaptor to steering column. Slacken lock nut of grub screw in collet adaptor and loosen grub screw by two turns.

4) Withdraw steering wheel, complete with hand lock nut, impact rubber, collet adaptor and shaft.

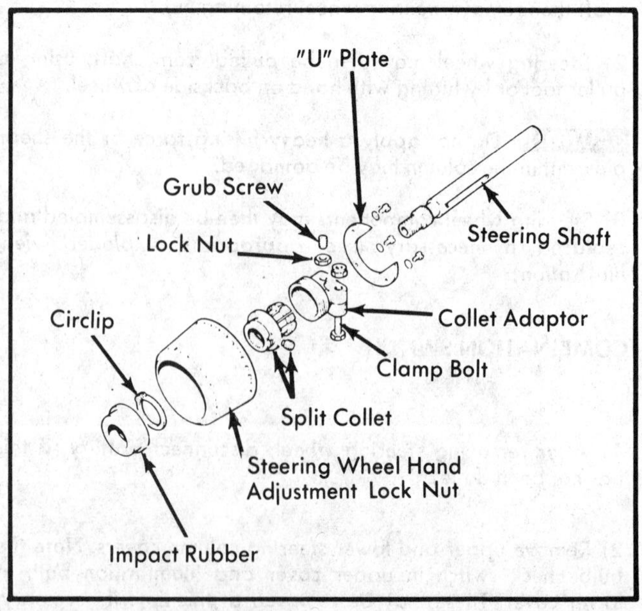

Fig. 1 Components Located Under Steering Wheel

JAGUAR (Cont.)

Dismantling – 1) Unscrew two self-tapping screws from lower face of steering wheel boss and lift off padded horn contact.

2) Unscrew nylon nut from top of steering wheel shaft and remove it carefully, taking out the horn contact tube also.

3) Remove self-locking nut and plain washer which retain steering wheel. Carefully pull steering wheel from the shaft, collecting both halves of the split cone.

Installation – To install, reverse removal procedure and note the following: Be sure that front wheels are always kept in a straight-ahead position. When tightening collet clamp, tighten grub screw finger-tight, snug down its lock nut and torque clamp bolt to 10-12 ft. lbs. (1.4-1.6 mkg).

HORN PAD & STEERING WHEEL

Removal; XJ12 & XJ6 – 1) Set front wheels in straight-ahead position. Loosen steering wheel adjustment lock nut. Pull wheel outward as far as possible. Remove both horn pad screws and take off pad.

2) Lock steering wheel. Remove horn contact plunger from upper column. Remove wheel mounting nut. Tap steering wheeloff splines and collect collets.

Installation – To install, reverse removal procedure.

STEERING LOCK

Removal – Take off upper column shrouding. Using a center punch, make several dimples in shear bolt and rotate bolt out.

Installation – Reverse removal procedure.

IGNITION SWITCH

Removal – Disconnect battery ground. Separate column shrouding from switch side. On XJS models only, disengage retaining ring holding ignition switch in housing. On XJ12 and XJ6 models, maneuver shrouding until access to ignition switch set screw is gained; loosen screw. Force switch and wiring clear of housing. On all models, disconnect ignition switch wiring at multi-pin connector. Remove switch and harness.

Installation – To install, reverse removal procedure. On XJS models only, make sure lock tab on retaining ring engages slot.

COMBINATION SWITCH

Removal; XJ12 & XJ6 – Disconnect battery ground. Take off steering column lower shroud. Remove steering wheel as previously outlined. Take off steering column upper shroud. Take cover out from below instrument panel. Loosen pinch bolt and pull combination switch assembly from steering column. Disconnect electrical wiring. Hazard flasher can now be separated by disconnecting wires, depressing tangs and pushing switch through mounting plate.

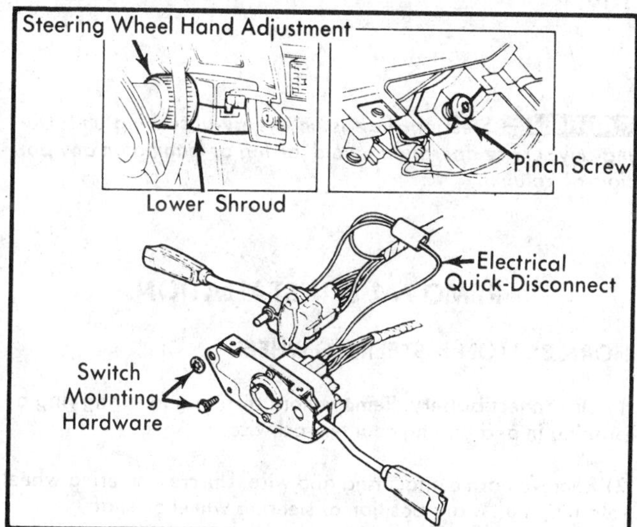

Fig. 2 Combination Switch Assembly

Installation – To install, reverse removal procedure.

LANCIA

Lancia

REMOVAL & INSTALLATION

STEERING WHEEL

Removal – Place front wheels in straight ahead position. Disconnect battery. Remove horn cover mounting screws from below steering wheel spokes. On Coupe models only, horn cover will pry off. Remove spring. Mark steering wheel and shaft. Remove mounting nut. Fit puller 88062038 (or equivalent) and remove steering wheel.

NOTE – *On some early models it will be necessary to drill and tap two holes for puller.*

Installation – To install, reverse removal procedure. Make sure index marks on steering wheel and shaft align.

STEERING COLUMN LOCK AND IGNITION SWITCH

Removal – 1) Disconnect battery. Place front wheels in straight ahead position. Remove steering shaft mounting bolt and take off lower column casing. Disconnect multi-plug from socket. Remove steering column cover nuts and lift off complete with controls and steering wheel.

2) Use a .236" (6 mm) drill and remove shear bolts mounting column lock. Punch out bolts (if necessary) and lift out lock. Remove bolt keeping ignition switch to column lock support. Fit key and turn switch to "GAR", remove key. Use a metal pointed tool, depress lock spring, and slip out lock at same time.

Installation – Reassemble ignition switch. Fit column lock into position on steering column. Tighten mounting bolts until heads shear. Refit steering shaft lower end and tighten nut. Install upper cover to steering column and tighten mounting

LANCIA (Cont.)

nuts. Reconnect multi-plug. Install steering column lower cover. Connect battery.

STEERING COLUMN ADJUSTER

Removal – **1**) Disconnect battery. Disconnect speedometer at transaxle. Remove instrument cluster bolts and knobs. Disconnect speedometer cable from under dash. Separate electrical connections and lift off cluster.

2) Remove lower column cover. Remove nuts mounting steering shaft to adjustable bracket. Place steering shaft out of way. Remove mounting nuts and take off adjuster handle. Remove nuts mounting bracket to pedal support and lift off unit.

Installation – To install, reverse removal procedure.

LUV

LUV

CAUTION – *Steering shaft is an energy-absorbing unit. During any service operation, avoid jarring or leaning on any portion of column.*

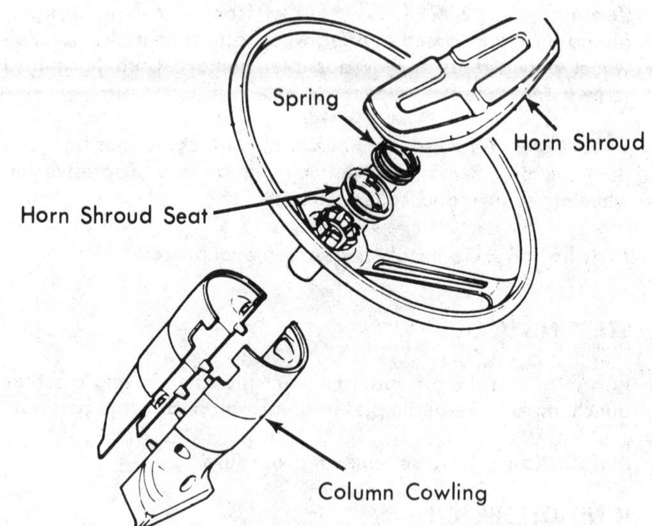

Fig. 1 LUV Steering Wheel Assembly

REMOVAL & INSTALLATION

HORN BUTTON & STEERING WHEEL

1) Disconnect battery. Remove horn shroud and spring ring by pushing in and turning counterclockwise.

2) Remove horn contact ring and wire. Unscrew steering wheel retaining nut. Mark position of steering wheel on shaft.

3) Using appropriate puller (J-24292 for standard wheel or J-2927/J-2927-10 for sport type wheel), remove steering wheel.

TURN SIGNAL/DIMMER SWITCH

Switch is a combination turn signal and headlight dimmer assembly. Disconnect battery ground and remove steering column cowling. Disconnect wires to switch harness. Remove switch by separating from clamp on mast jacket (two screws). To install, reverse removal procedures.

HAZARD WARNING SWITCH

Disconnect battery ground cable. Remove steering column cowling screws. Hazard warning switch is retained on upper half of cowling by two screws. Disconnect switch wiring harness at connector, remove mounting screws, and withdraw switch. To install, reverse removal procedure.

ADJUSTMENT

STEERING WHEEL ALIGNMENT

1) Set front wheels in straight-ahead position. Check location of spot on wormshaft which indicates gear "high point" (this should be at top center).

2) If gear is not in this position, loosen adjusting locknuts on both left and right sides of intermediate connecting rod.

3) Remove intermediate rod with inner tie rod ends attached. Turn ends an equal amount in the same direction to bring steering gear back to high point.

NOTE – *Turning ends unevenly will disturb toe-in setting; however, toe-in should be rechecked after adjustment is made and set as required.*

4) Note position of steering wheel spokes. They should be equally balanced. If they are off-center, remove steering wheel and reposition to proper alignment.

MAZDA

808 (1300 cc)
GLC (1300 cc)
808 (1600 cc)
RX3
RX4
Cosmo
Rotary Pickup

REMOVAL & INSTALLATION

STEERING WHEEL & COMBINATION SWITCH

Removal – 1) Disconnect battery ground cable. Pull off horn cap. Place front wheels in straight-ahead position. Index mark column shaft and steering wheel.

2) Remove steering column shrouding. Disconnect electrical connectors. On models so equipped, remove stop ring from steering shaft. Take out screw(s) mounting combination switch and lift assembly from vehicle.

NOTE – *Wiper switch can be removed with combination switch or separated from it.*

Installation – To install, reverse removal procedure.

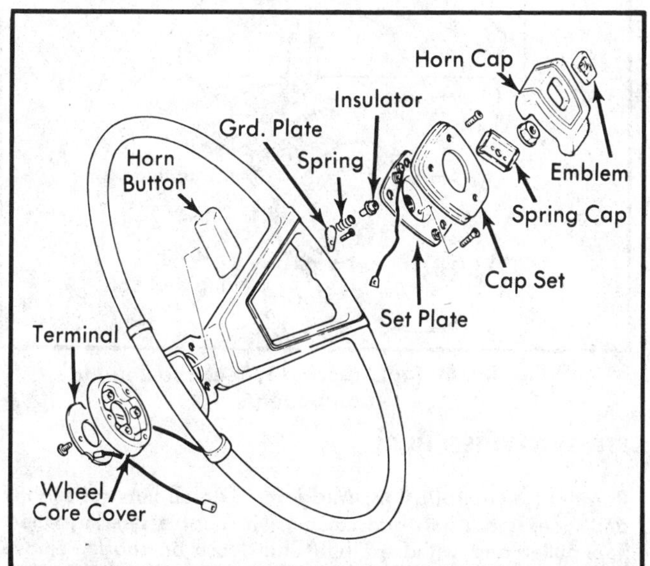

Fig. 1 Typical Mazda Steering Wheel Assembly

IGNITION SWITCH

Removal; RX4 & Cosmo – Remove steering wheel as previously outlined. Remove column shrouding. Remove combination switch. Disconnect electrical connector. Remove screw attaching switch contact *(See Fig. 2)* housing to steering lock body and slide out contact housing.

Installation – Reverse removal procedure.

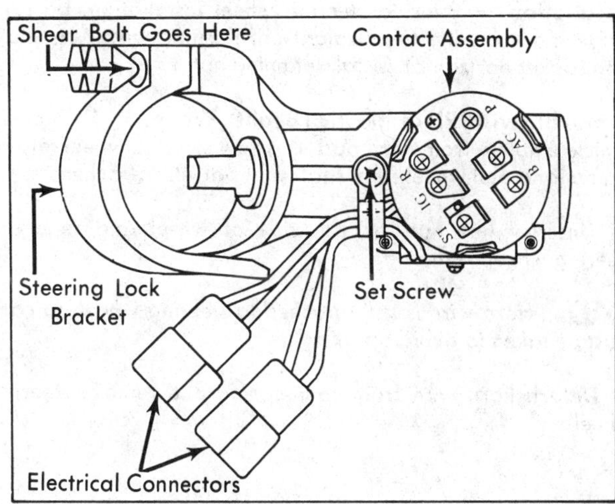

Fig. 2 RX4 and Cosmo Ignition Switch Contact Housing

KEY CYLINDER

Removal & Installation; RX4 & Cosmo – Remove steering wheel. Remove steering column shrouding. Remove set screw holding key cylinder. Insert key into cylinder and place in "ON" position. Push in on lock button and pull out key with cylinder. Reverse removal procedure to install key cylinder.

STEERING LOCK

Removal; RX4, Cosmo, 808 – Remove steering wheel, column shrouding, and combination switch. Remove 2 bolts mounting steering column bracket to instrument panel. Move shaft out from instrument panel about 1" (.039 mm). Put a groove in bolt attaching steering lock body to column shaft and remove bolt. Steering lock should be free to remove.

Installation – To install, reverse removal procedure and tighten new shear bolts until heads break.

MERCEDES-BENZ

230
240D
280, C, S
300D
450SE, SEL, SL, SLC

REMOVAL & INSTALLATION

HORN PAD & STEERING WHEEL

Removal, with Polyurethane Wheel (Soft Rubber) – 1) Grip horn pad near one corner and pull straight up until free. Pull up other corner. Remove pad from steering wheel.

2) Unscrew steering retaining nut, remove spring washer and pull steering wheel from shaft.

Installation – Prior to steering wheel installation, be sure scribe mark on shaft is straight up. Position wheel on shaft with spokes horizontal. Install retaining nut.

Removal, with Rigid Plastic (Bealit) Wheel – 1) Remove vehicle emblem from horn pad. Unscrew steering wheel retaining nut and pull wheel from shaft with pad still attached.

2) Unscrew hex nuts on backside of wheel and separate steering wheel from pad.

NOTE – *Horn wire is still attached to steering wheel, so care must be taken to avoid breaking it.*

3) Detach horn wire from contact ring and remove steering wheel.

4) Unscrew countersunk screws from steering wheel hub and remove centering pad of contact ring.

5) Remove horn ring from steering wheel. Remove locking ring from hub of pad, then remove slip ring.

Installation – To install, reverse removal procedure, noting that front wheels are always kept in a straight-ahead position and that steering wheel spokes are horizontal.

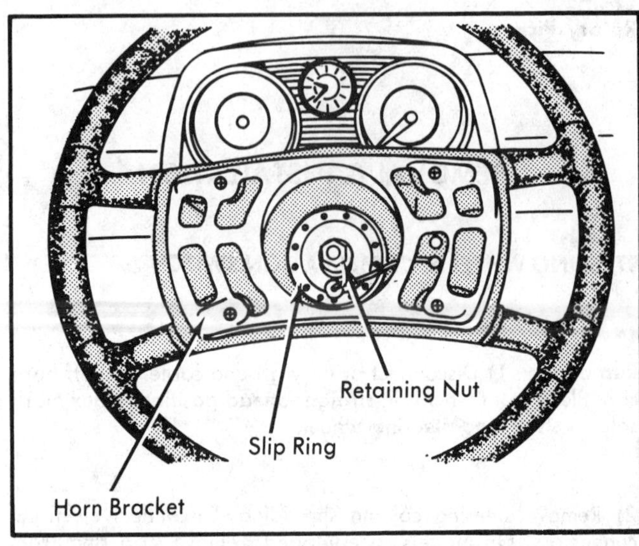

Fig. 1 Mercedes-Benz Steering Wheel with Cover Removed

MG

MGB
Midget

REMOVAL & INSTALLATION

STEERING WHEEL

Removal & Installation; Midget – Disconnect battery ground. Pry off steering pad and remove horn contact plunger from seat. Remove six bolts holding steering wheel and lock ring to hub. Lift wheel from hub and set aside. To install steering wheel, reverse removal procedure.

Removal; MGB – Remove steering wheel pad. Remove mounting nut. Index mark wheel hub and steering column. Rap steering wheel spokes with palm of hand to break loose.

Installation – Reverse removal procedure and note: Line up index marks. Hold wheel spokes horizontal when fitting steering wheel.

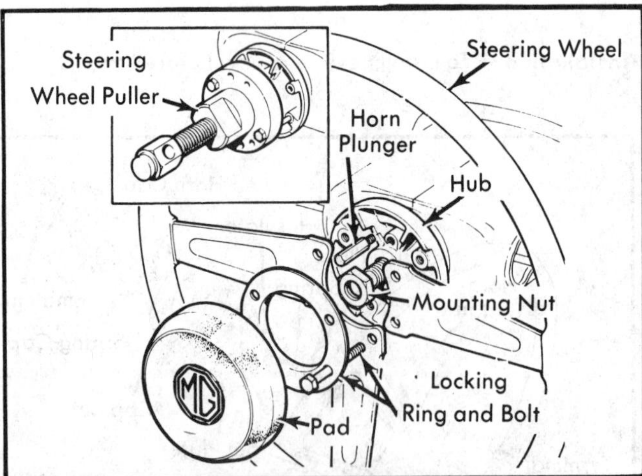

Fig. 1 Midget Steering Wheel and Related Components

STEERING WHEEL HUB

Removal & Installation; Midget – Loosen hub nut slightly and index mark hub and column. Fit suitable steering wheel hub puller and withdraw hub until loose on shaft. Remove puller tool, steering wheel nut and lift off steering hub. When installing, reverse removal procedure and note index marks made during removal.

MG (Cont.)

STEERING COLUMN LOCK & IGNITION HUB

NOTE – *Steering column must be removed before lock or switch can be removed.*

Removal – Remove necessary shrouding to gain access to lock. Make sure steering lock is disengaged. Disconnect ignition switch multi-pin connector. Drill out and remove shear bolts from lock bracket. Remove steering screw holding switch in lock and remove switch.

Installation – Center locking mechanism on column. Hand tighten new shear bolts. Reconnect multi-pin connector. Check switch and lock operation. Tighten shear bolts until heads break.

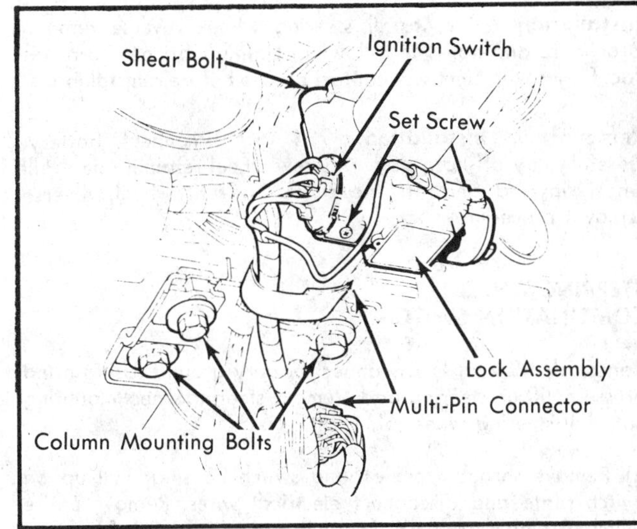

Fig. 2 Bottom View of Steering Column Showing Ignition Switch and Column Lock – MGB Shown

OPEL

All Models

REMOVAL & INSTALLATION

HORN PAD & STEERING WHEEL

Removal – 1) Disconnect battery cable. Remove two screws from backside of steering wheel which hold the horn pad in place.

2) Remove horn pad from its position and disconnect the horn contact wire from the hub connection.

3) Remove steering wheel retaining nut and washer. Position suitable puller and remove the steering wheel.

Installation – To install, reverse removal procedure after making sure that front wheels are in straight-ahead position and that steering wheel spokes are horizontal when steering wheel is installed. Make sure cancelling cam of turn signal switch engages properly.

COMBINATION SWITCH & IGNITION LOCK

Removal – 1) Remove screws holding upper and lower steering column covers in place. Remove the hazard warning button.

2) Detach the combination turn signal/lighting switch by removing the four retaining screws. Remove two retaining screws to take off the washer/wiper switch.

3) Remove the lock cylinder by removing the snap ring and three attaching bolts on the column flange. Lift off the cylinder housing, lower washer and shaft. Use a screwdriver to pry out the lower column rubber bushing.

Installation – To install, reverse removal procedure, noting that lock cylinder engages shaft properly and that cancelling cam of turn signal switch engages steering wheel properly.

PORSCHE

911 Series
924

REMOVAL & INSTALLATION

HORN PAD & STEERING WHEEL

NOTE – *On models equipped with a collapsable "can" behind the steering wheel, care must be taken in all service procedures. Do not apply excessive or striking forces to the steering wheel or steering column.*

Removal; 911 Series – 1) Align front wheels in straight-ahead position. Disconnect battery ground cable.

2) Grasp horn pad and rotate counterclockwise while pushing in. When horn pad is free, lift from steering wheel and disconnect horn contact finger.

3) Loosen steering wheel retaining nut. Mark position of steering wheel to steering shaft. Attach a suitable puller and remove the steering wheel.

PORSCHE (Cont.)

Installation – To install steering wheel, reverse removal procedure and note the following: Lightly lubricate horn contact finger with electrical contact grease before reinstalling.

Removal & Installation; 924 – Disconnect battery. Carefully pry off horn pad. Unscrew wheel retaining nut. Pull wheel upward and off the shaft. To refit wheel, reverse removal procedure.

STEERING WHEEL COMBINATION SWITCH

Removal; 924 – **1)** Disconnect battery ground. Using hand pressure, lift up steering pad. Remove steering wheel mounting nut. Pull steering wheel off shaft.

2) Remove shroud from around switch housing. Pull up on switch plate and disconnect electrical wires. Remove entire switch assembly then, separate wiper/washer switch from turn signal switch by taking out screw that mounts them together.

Installation – Refit switches together with screw. Slide switch assemblies back into place refitting spacer at same time. Make sure spacer is driven in until there is a distance of 1.6" (41 mm) from face (top edge) of spacer to top edge of shaft. This distance will ensure there is .08-.15" (2-4 mm) between steering wheel and steering column switches. Reverse removal procedure to install remaining components.

STEERING COLUMN LOCK, KEY CYLINDER & IGNITION SWITCH

Removal – **1)** Remove combination switch as previously outlined.

2) Drill out shear bolts.

3) Disconnect ignition switch wiring.

4) Disengage snap ring and slide out switch housing with bearing.

5) Use a pointed tool (scribe) and push cylinder lock retainer in to release cylinder. With key inserted and retainer depressed, pull cylinder from housing.

6) Take out ignition switch set screw and pull ignition switch back out of housing.

Installation – To install, reverse removal procedure.

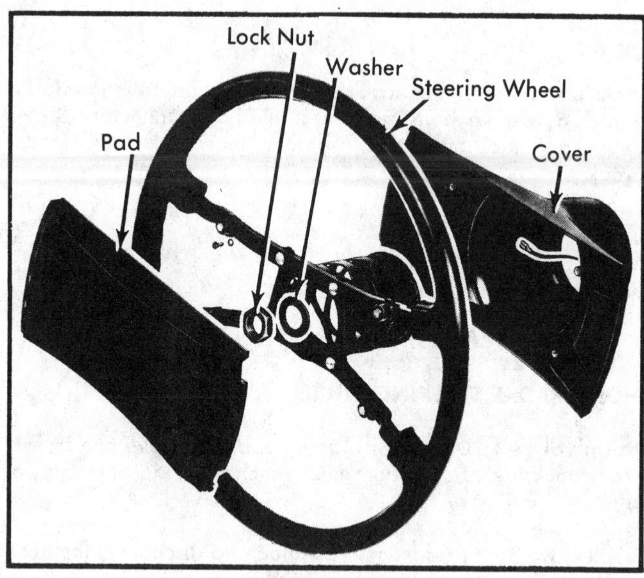

Fig. 1 Porsche 911 Steering Wheel and Related Components

RENAULT

R-5
R-15
R-17

REMOVAL & INSTALLATION

HORN PAD & STEERING WHEEL

Removal, All Models – Disconnect battery. Remove horn pad. Unscrew steering wheel retaining nut. Use a suitable puller (Dir. 21.A or equivalent) to free steering wheel from shaft.

Installation, All Models – When installing steering wheel, set front wheels in straight-ahead position and place steering wheel on shaft with spokes horizontal. Torque steering wheel nut. Replace horn pad.

TURN SIGNAL & LIGHTING SWITCH

Removal, Exc. R-5 – **1)** After removing steering wheel, remove steering column cover. Disconnect return spring on flasher switch.

2) Note location of all electrical connections to switch, then detach the wiring. Disconnect return spring for turn signal switch.

3) Remove lighting switch retaining screws and remove switch from steering column.

RENAULT (Cont.)

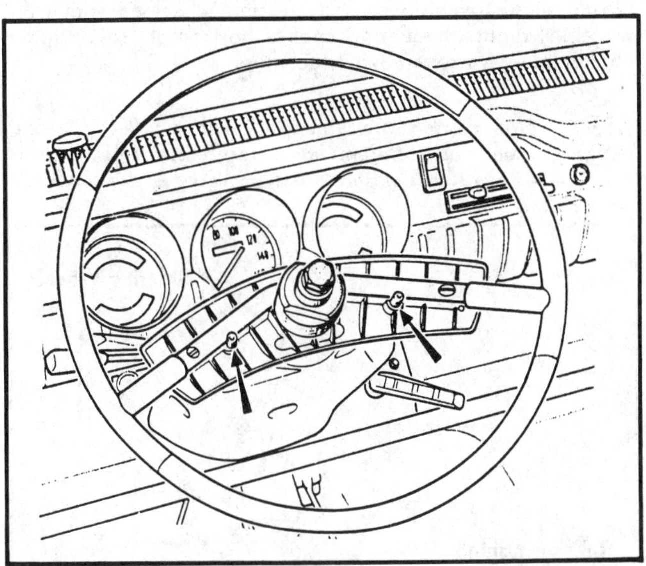

Fig. 1 Top View of Steering Wheel with Detail of Horn Pad Mounting Pins

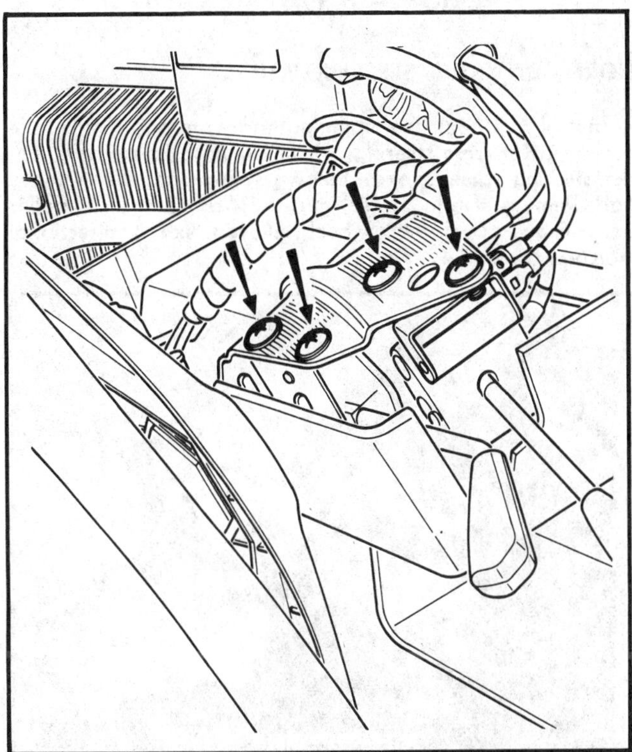

Fig. 2 Location of Switch Assembly Retaining Screws – R-5 Shown

Installation, Exc. R-5 – To install, reverse removal procedure, noting original location of all wiring connections.

NOTE – *For the following procedure, steering wheel does not have to be removed.*

Removal, R-5 – 1) Disconnect battery. Remove instrument panel housing screws. Remove screws from bottom shell of switch cover.

2) Remove screws securing turn signal/lighting switch to column. Disconnect electrical couplings and remove switch.

Installation, R-5 – To install, reverse removal procedure. Make sure electrical connections are made in their original locations.

IGNITION SWITCH/COLUMN LOCK

Removal, All Models – 1) Disconnect the battery. Remove shell cover from around switch assemblies. Disconnect electrical couplings. Turn ignition key to "G" (Garage) and remove it.

2) Unscrew the set screw and press retaining catch in with a small punch. Push switch body from backside to release it.

Installation, All Models – To install, reverse removal procedure.

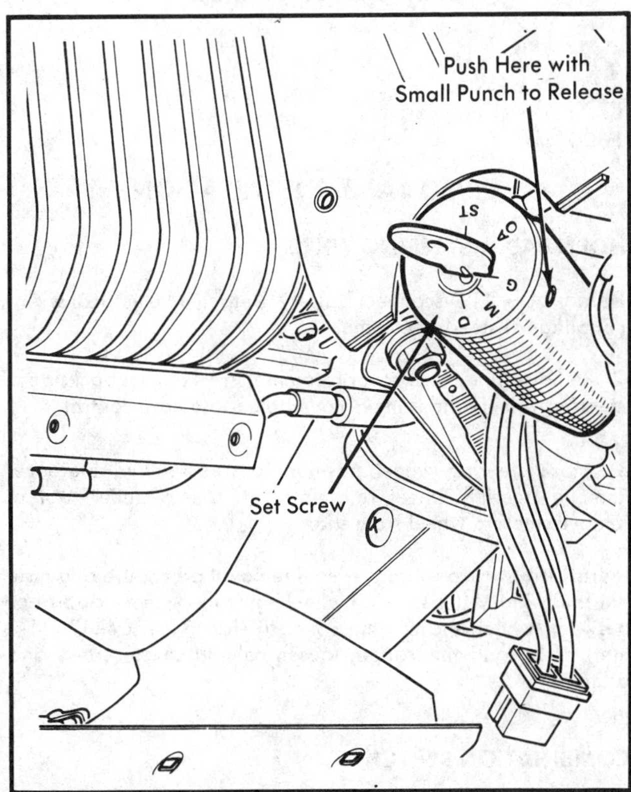

Fig. 3 Ignition Switch Removal – R-5 Shown

SAAB

99

REMOVAL & INSTALLATION

HORN CONTROL & STEERING WHEEL

Removal – Unbolt the mounting hardware and remove the bottom cover from steering column. Remove four screws, under steering wheel spokes, holding safety pad, then remove pad. Remove steering wheel nut and washer, then fit puller and remove wheel. With wheel removed, extract directional indicator assembly.

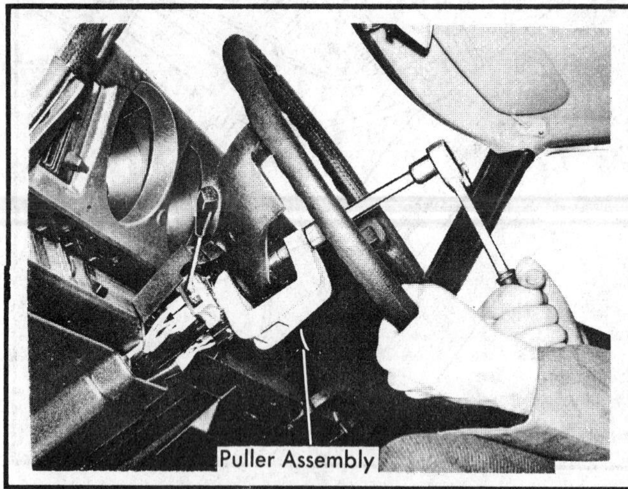

Fig. 1 Using a Universal Puller Tool to Remove Steering Assembly

Installation – Refit directional signal assembly ensuring index line coinsides with centerline of assembly housing. Install plastic sleeve over driver. Put steering wheel on with front wheels straight ahead and spokes horizontal. To complete reassembly, reverse removal procedure.

NOTE – *EMS models are equipped with smaller diameter steering wheel and different horn mechanism. Horn contact must be removed with chisel. Other procedures are similar to ones outlined here.*

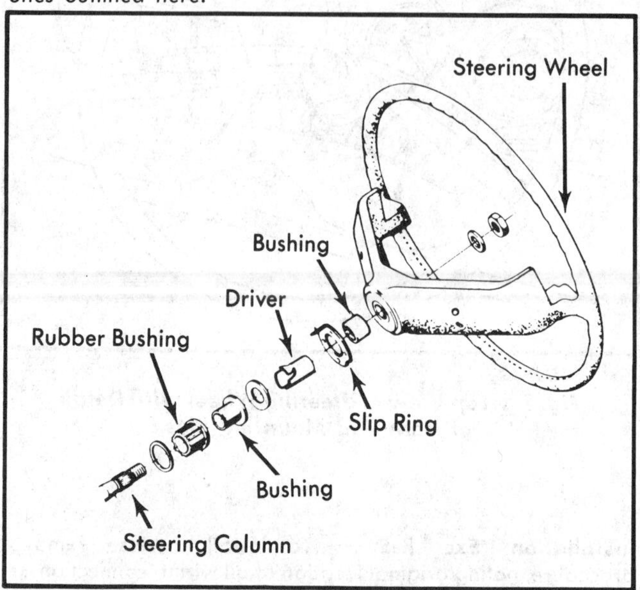

Fig.2 Exploded View of Saab Steering Wheel Except EMS Models

SUBARU

1600

REMOVAL & INSTALLATION

HORN PAD & STEERING WHEEL

Removal – 1) Disconnect battery. Detach all electrical wiring couplings at steering column.

2) Remove three horn cover retaining screws (from backside of steering wheel) and remove cover to expose horn control.

3) Mark steering wheel position for reassembly reference. Remove steering wheel retaining nut. Use a puller tool to remove steering wheel from shaft.

Installation – To install, reverse removal procedure and note the following: After steering wheel is installed, check clearance between wheel and column cover; it should be .04-.12" (1-3 mm). If beyond this range, loosen column cover screws and adjust.

COMBINATION SWITCH

Removal – Remove steering wheel as previously described. Unscrew hazard warning knob from steering column. Remove two switch retaining screws and lift assembly from steering column.

Installation – To install, reverse removal procedure.

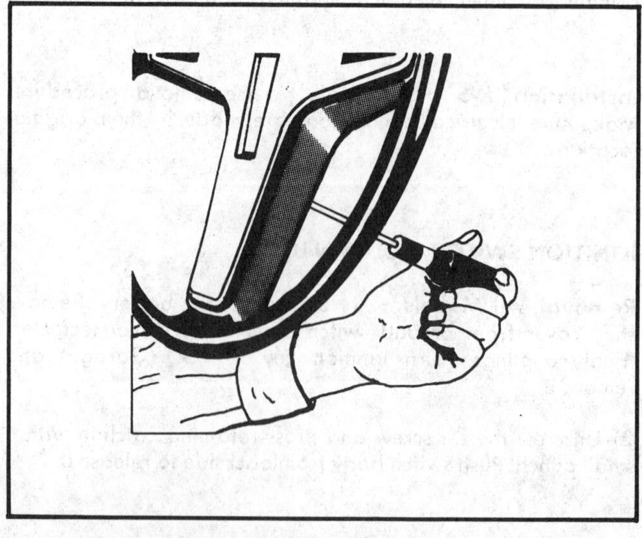

Fig. 1 Removing Horn Pad from Steering Wheel

TOYOTA

Celica
Corolla
Corona
Pickup
Land Cruiser

REMOVAL & INSTALLATION

STEERING WHEEL

NOTE — *Steering wheel removal procedure is a general one. It should be noted that all steps may not apply to every model.*

CAUTION — *Some models are equipped with collapsible type steering, DO NOT apply excessive pressure or impact to mainshaft.*

Removal — 1) Disconnect battery ground. From lower portion of steering column, disconnect any electrical wiring for indicator lights, horn or dimmer switch.

2) Remove screws holding steering wheel protective pad or plastic cover. On some models, pad will pry off.

3) Remove steering wheel mounting nut and washer (if equipped), then using suitable puller, extract steering wheel from shaft *(Fig. 1)*.

Installation — To install, reverse removal procedure.

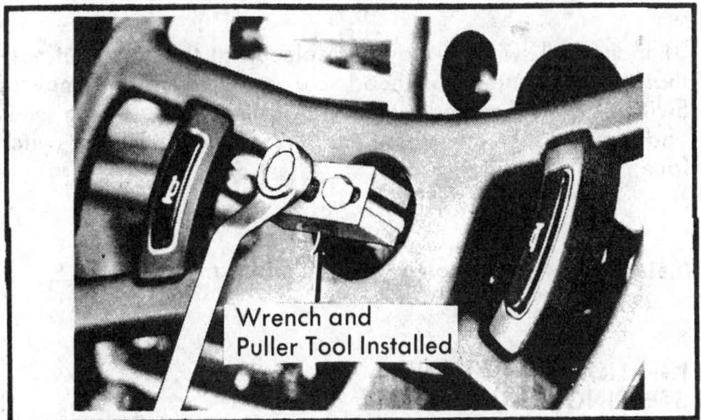

Fig. 1 Using Puller to Remove Steering Wheel

COMBINATION SWITCH

Removal — After removing steering wheel as outlined above, combination switch assembly may be removed by detaching steering column covers, and then removing retaining screws from face of switch assembly.

Installation — To install, reverse removal procedure and make sure all electrical connections are properly made. Check cancelling operation of turn signal switch.

COLUMN LOCK & IGNITION SWITCH

Removal — 1) Disconnect battery ground. Remove steering wheel as previously outlined.

NOTE — *Steering wheel removal is optional if only the ignition switch portion is being removed. Removal of wheel makes access to this operation easier.*

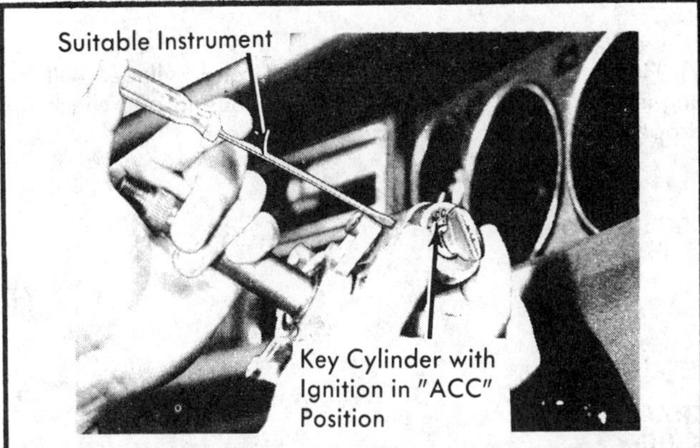

Fig. 2 Disengaging Key Cylinder from Position on Mainshaft

2) Remove screws mounting upper and lower column covers and disconnect any electrical couplings not detached during steering wheel removal.

NOTE — *On some models, access to ignition switch for its removal is gained by removing lower cover only. It is easier to perform this operation, however, by removing both cover halves.*

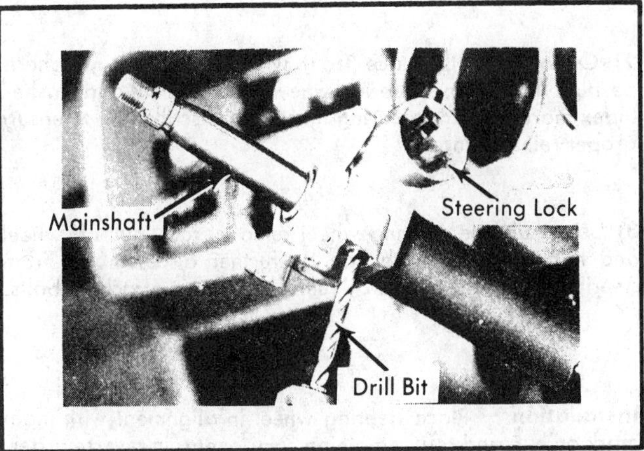

Fig. 3 Drilling Out Shear Head Bolt to Remove Steering Lock from Shaft

3) Remove turn signal switch assembly as previously described. (required only if column lock assembly is being removed).

4) Remove mainshaft bearing retainer and snap ring (if required).

5) Put ignition key in "ACC" position. Use a small pointed tool to press down stop pin on side of cylinder to free the mechanism. Pull cylinder from housing. *(Fig. 2)*

6) After removing switch cylinder, ignition lock may be removed by drilling out shear-head bolts which retain lock housing to steering column.

Installation — 1) To install column lock and switch assembly, reverse removal procedure. Tighten lock housing shear-head bolts (new) until the heads shear off.

TOYOTA (Cont.)

2) Fit key cylinder so ignition switch and cylinder will be aligned in "ACC" position. Insert into housing and check for proper locking operation and key movement.

3) Replace all other components (combination switch assembly, bearing retainer, steering wheel) as removed. Check for proper turn signal switch cancelling operation and smoothness of steering wheel movement.

TRIUMPH

TR7
Spitfire

REMOVAL & INSTALLATION

HORN CONTROL, STEERING WHEEL & HUB

Removal – 1) Disconnect battery ground. On Spitfire models, use a flat, blunt, instrument to pry off steering wheel pad. Remove horn button. On TR7 models, remove 3 screws from underside of steering wheel that secure steering wheel to pad.

2) On all models, place front wheels in a straight-ahead position and remove steering wheel attaching nut and washer. Index mark hub and steering mast with a scribe line to ensure proper reinstallation.

3) Using suitable steering wheel removal tool, pull off wheel and hub assembly. Hub can be further disassembled from steering wheel on Spitfire by removing the six attaching bolts.

Installation – Place steering wheel in alignment with index mark on hub and refit remaining components in reverse order.

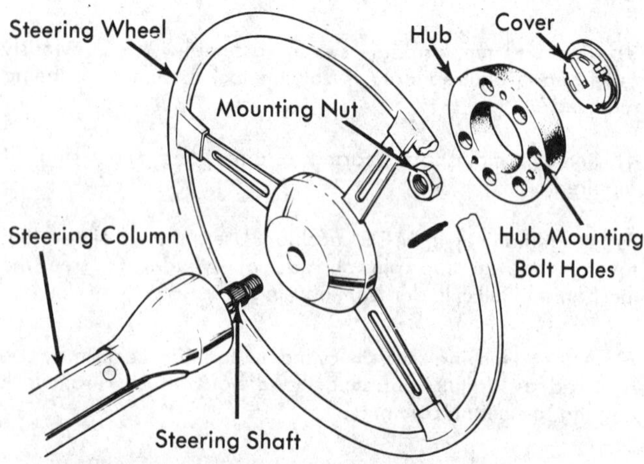

Fig. 1 Spitfire Steering Wheel Components TR7 Similar

TURN SIGNAL & WIPER SWITCHES

Removal – 1) Disconnect battery. Unscrew retaining screws for column cover halves and remove covers. Remove steering wheel as previously described.

2) Note the location of all wiring harnesses. Remove the wire harness clip securing the switch harnesses. Disconnect the two harness plugs. Loosen the switch clamp screw and remove switch assembly.

3) Individual switches may be replaced at this time, but note that the two center cross-head screws are not to be removed. Switches are separated by drilling out the two retaining rivets and removing the one cross-head screw (on right side of switch face).

Installation – To install, reverse removal procedure.

IGNITION SWITCH AND STEERING COLUMN LOCK

NOTE – *On Spitfire models, steering column must be removed. On TR7 models, plastic cover around steering shaft has to come off.*

Removal – On Spitfire only, remove nuts and washers securing steering lock shroud and withdraw shroud and column support. On all models, center punch both shear bolts mounting steering lock to column. Using a small chisel or suitable tool arrangement, remove bolts. Disconnect electrical plug and remove steering lock.

Installation – To install ignition switch and steering column lock, reverse removal procedure and note the following: Ensure dowel pin aligns in column drilling. Fit new shear head bolts and tighten evenly.

VOLKSWAGEN

Type 1
Type 2
Dasher
Rabbit
Scirocco

REMOVAL & INSTALLATION

HORN PAD & STEERING WHEEL

All Models – Disconnect battery. Carefully pry off horn pad. Unscrew steering wheel retaining nut. Pull wheel upward and off the shaft.

CAUTION – *Steering wheel or column has a collapsible section. Care must be taken when working with these components.*

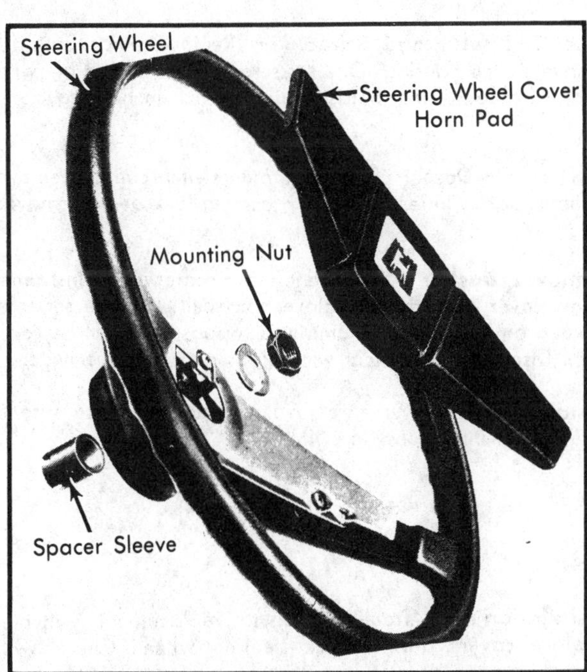

Fig. 1 Typical Volkswagen Steering Wheel Rabbit and Scirocco Shown

TURN SIGNAL & WIPER SWITCH

Removal; Type 1 – Disconnect battery ground. Place ignition key in on position. Remove steering as previously outlined. Remove circlip from groove below steering wheel splines. Disconnect electrical wiring. Remove 4 mounting screws and pull switch assembly up and out.

NOTE – *Wiper switch must be removed together then, separated. Make sure to bleed air pressure from washer reservoir before disconnecting hose of valve on switch.*

Installation – To install, reverse removal procedure and note: Make sure turn signal wires are not crushed by windshield wiper switch. Adjust distance between steering wheel hub and steering column switch to 1/16-1/8" (2-3 mm) by loosening both switch mounting screws.

Removal; Type 2, Rabbit & Scirocco – **1)** Disconnect battery ground. Using hand pressure, lift up steering pad. Remove steering wheel mounting nut. Pull steering wheel off shaft.

2) Remove screw and bolt located in bottom of switch housing and remove shroud. Push up (toward instrument panel) on switch assembly and pry off spacer sleeve. Disconnect electrical wires.

3) After removing switch assembly off steering column, remove screw holding turn signal switch to wiper/washer switch. Separate switches from each other and remove spacer sleeve from between switches.

Installation – **1)** Refit switches together with screw and spacer sleeve. Slide switch assembly onto column and hook up wires. Refer to *Fig. 2* for how far to drive on spacer sleeve.

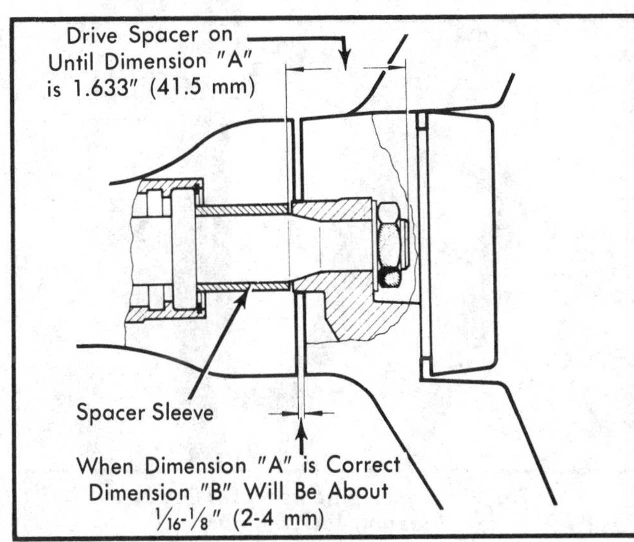

Fig. 2 Dimensions for Installing Spacer Sleeve

Removal; Dasher – Disconnect battery ground. Remove steering wheel as previously outlined. Remove 4 Phillips head screws mounting switch housing on column and lay housing forward. Remove 2 screws mounting turn signal switch to switch housing. Disconnect electrical wires. Remove switches from housing by taking out screws in mounting plate. Slide plates out of grooves and withdraw switches.

Installation – Reverse removal procedure. Make sure turn signal switch is in neutral position to avoid damage to cancel-finger when screws are tightened.

STEERING LOCK & CYLINDER

Removal; Type 1 – **1)** Remove steering wheel as previously outlined. Take off circlip and plastic bushing. Remove turn signal lever and steering lock retainer plate.

2) Feed electrical wires through while withdrawing steering lock far enough to expose cylinder release hole. Release hole is located at about 11 o'clock on housing.

3) Push a wire into opening to release spring pressure on cylinder. Take cylinder out by turning key (inserted in cylinder) counterclockwise and pulling.

4) Inspect lock guide to make sure it is still under sufficient tension. Pin should move under light finger pressure.

VOLKSWAGEN (Cont.)

Installation – To install, reverse removal procedure and note: Install cylinder by pushing (not forcing) it into place and hand tightening to left without key inserted. Forcing cylinder may bend guide pin.

Removal; Type 2, Rabbit & Scirocco – **1**) It is necessary to drill into cylinder lock to gain access to cylinder release pin. Refer to *Fig. 3* to determine where 1/8" hole must be drilled.

NOTE – *On Type 2 models, hole for cylinder removal is accessible when cover plate has been removed. Note that not all models have pre-drilled hole.*

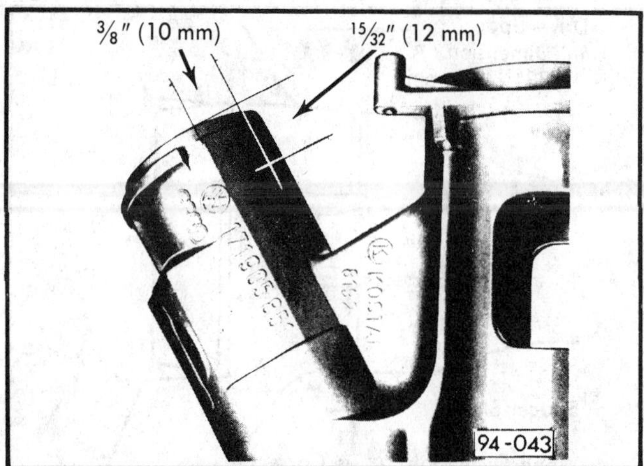

Fig. 3 Measurements for Drilling into Steering Lock Cylinder

2) Insert a pin through hole and press down spring holding lock cylinder in housing. It may be necessary to insert key to pull out cylinder.

Installation – To install, press cylinder in until it snaps into position. Reverse removal procedure for remaining components.

Removal; Dasher – **1**) Disconnect wires from ignition switch back. Fit key and place switch in "ON" position.

2) Centerpunch shear bolts mounting steering lock on column. Use a 5/16" (8.5 mm) drill to remove shear bolts. Steering lock is free for removal.

IGNITION SWITCH

Type 2, Rabbit and Scirocco – Remove shear bolt and remove switch housing. One set screw on back side of switch (near wire connector) holds ignition switch in housing.

NOTE – *On Dasher models, ignition switch can be removed without lock cylinder or steering column lock being removed.*

Removal; Dasher – Remove left and center under instrument panel cover also, remove glove box shelf. Remove set screw located on housing of column lock (opposite end of key cylinder). Disconnect electrical wire plugs and pull out switch.

Installation – Reverse removal procedure. Make sure set screw goes into recess in switch.

VOLVO

240
260

REMOVAL & INSTALLATION

HORN PAD & STEERING WHEEL

Removal – **1**) Using a screwdriver, pry up both lower corners. Do not lever screwdriver against steering wheel.

2) Grip contact plate and padding then, snap out upper corners. Disconnect electrical wire. Remove steering wheel nut. Attach suitable steering wheel puller and remove steering wheel.

Installation – To install, reverse removal procedure.

TURN SIGNAL & WIPER SWITCHES

Removal – Remove steering wheel as previously described. Remove column covers from around switches. Disconnect wiring from switch(es) to be replaced.

Installation – Attach wiring to replacement switch(es). Replace covers and replace steering wheel. Check switch operation.

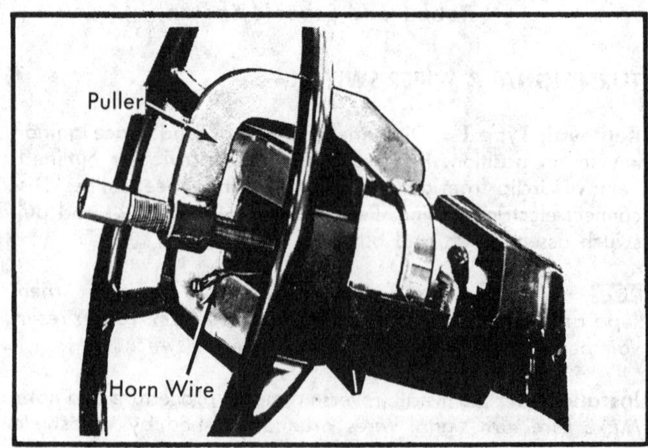

Fig. 1 Using Puller to Remove Steering Wheel

ARROW & COLT

Arrow
Colt

DESCRIPTION

Collapsible steering system is comprised of a two-piece (upper and lower) column shaft, joined by a collapsible section. This section contracts axially under impact without affecting turning motion. Upper column cover incorporates slits, allowing it to collapse under impact.

REMOVAL & INSTALLATION

STEERING COLUMN

NOTE — *During any service operations of collapsible columns or components avoid jarring or leaning on any portion of column.*

Removal — Remove air cleaner. Unbolt clamp retaining shaft to gear box. Remove horn pad, steering wheel nut and pull steering wheel. Unscrew tilt lock knob, detach column cover and remove combination switch assembly. Draw out each switch connector and detach switch. Remove floor dust cover. Loosen tilt bracket assembly retaining bolt and withdraw steering column assembly.

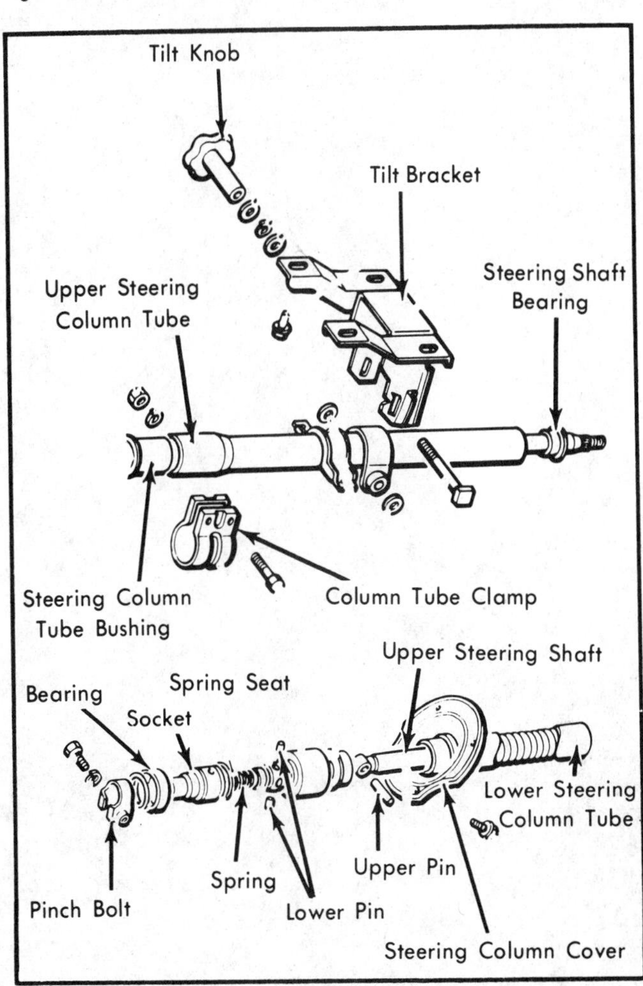

Fig. 1 Exploded View of Steering Column

Disassembly — 1) Pull lower shaft bearing out of column and remove shaft. Remove cover from the steering shaft joint socket, remove the stopper, and withdraw the retainer. With steering shaft upright, pull out joint retaining pin, using a magnet. Remove joint socket.

2) Loosen column tube clamp, draw out column tube, and remove the column bushing. When removing the tilt bracket, cut a slot in head of retaining studs, then unscrew studs, and remove steering lock. Lightly tap the tilt bracket with a wooden hammer to drive the bracket assembly from the upper end of column tube.

Inspection and Replacement — Make following checks before beginning reassembly of components:

1) Check clearance between upper coupling joint pin and bearing. Also, check clearance between upper coupling joint pin and socket. Clearance should be .0006-.002" (.016-.056 mm) for both measurements.

2) Check interference fit between lower coupling joint pin and shaft. Fit should be .001-.0013" (.003-.034 mm). Check free play of lower joint pin and bearing. Free play should be between .0006-.002" (.016-.056 mm).

3) Check steering shaft bend. Distortion must not exceed .020" (.5 mm).

4) Hold lower end of steering shaft and move upper shaft. Note any excessive movement. Replace components as necessary.

5) Check column tube bushing stop. Replace bushing if wear is excessive.

6) Inspect upper and lower steering column bearings. Replace bearing if excessively worn. Make sure clearance between steering shaft and column bearings is .0001.0045" (.015-.125 mm).

7) Check tilt bracket. Slots give and break through when driver impact hits steering wheel. Make sure slots are not damaged.

Reassembly — 1) Install bearing on steering shaft lower end with flange facing upward, then insert pin. Make sure pin does not interfere with bearing operation.

2) Grease socket, dust cover and seat. Insert spring seat and spring into socket. Place steering shaft vertically and hold other portion of steering shaft down, fit lock pin. Make sure shaft and socket rotate freely.

3) Put grease on upper and lower bearing surfaces. Fit spacer on shaft. Put steering shaft in column tube. Make sure shaft turns easily. Insert steering shaft in vehicle.

4) Fit column tube bushings onto upper and lower column tubes. Position bushings until stop touches column tube end. Tighten clamp bolt.

5) Install tilt bracket on column tube with spacers between bracket and tube. Reassemble tilt knob hardware.

ARROW & COLT (Cont.)

6) Refit steering wheel lock by aligning column tube hole with steering wheel. Lock guide dowel. Insert ignition key and check operation. If everything is operational, tighten steering wheel lock retaining bolt.

Installation – **1)** Be sure shaft can easily be turned within the column, insert column assembly, and position against instrument panel. Connect shaft to steering gear housing mainshaft with clamp bolt head upward. Position tilt bracket such that a measurement of 3.70-3.74" (84-95 mm) exists from upper end of steering shaft to upper end of column tube. Placement of shims between rear edge of bracket and instrument panel will assist in giving correct measurement.

2) Refit combination switch and attach electrical leads. Position front wheels in straight-ahead position, install steering wheel. Tighten retaining nut to specification. Make sure that free play does not exceed .04" (1.02 mm) when measured at steering wheel.

TIGHTENING SPECIFICATIONS

Application	Ft. Lbs. (mkg)
Column Tube Clamp	4-6 (.55-.83)
Steering Shaft Clamp	15-18 (2.0-2.5)
Steering Wheel Nut	25-33 (3.5-4.6)
Steering Wheel Lock	①5 (.70)

①Minimum.

AUDI

100LS
Fox

REMOVAL & INSTALLATION

Removal, 100 – 1) Remove lower instrument panel trim from around steering column. Pry off steering wheel pad. Unscrew steering wheel mounting nut and remove steering wheel. Unscrew and remove horn slip ring, column casing, and horn ground contact. Pull three washers from top of steering column. Detach electrical leads from column switches; remove switches.

2) Loosen support bolt from bracket below instrument panel. Note position of plastic slide pieces. In engine compartment, detach lower end of steering column from pinion shaft by removing pinch bolt.

3) Dislodge rubber grommet from around column in firewall. Lift column assembly out of vehicle. **CAUTION** – *This is a telescopic safety steering column and must be handled with care to prevent accidential collapsing of column.*

Installation – When installing column, ensure plastic slide pieces are in place when mounting column to instrument panel. Be sure grommet is in place on end of support tube. Replace rubber grommet in firewall after filling groove in rubber cover with transmission lubricant.

Removal, Fox – 1) Pull off steering wheel horn control by hand. Disconnect ground wire at horn button. Remove steering wheel mounting nut and pull off steering wheel. Unscrew switch base cap and disconnect plugs at both lever switches and horn contact ring.

2) Remove upper and lower instrument panel trim from around column. Unscrew bearing flange at bottom of steering column. Remove steering shaft-to-pinion pinch bolt (in engine compartment), pry off clip and drive steering column off pinion (use a brass mandrel).

3) Remove upper instrument panel trim to make shear screws accessible. **NOTE** – *These screws are also upper steering column support screws.* Drill off heads of shear screws. Remove steering lock and allow to hang by wiring. Remove steering column *(Fig. 1)*.

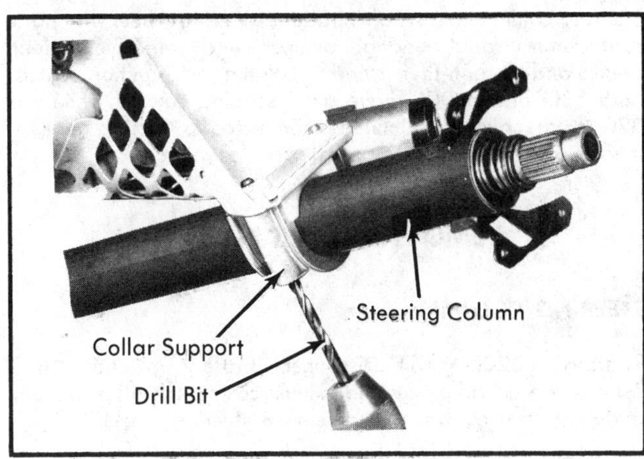

Fig. 1 Drilling Out Shear Bolts and Dropping Column Mounting Collar – Fox Models Shown

Installation – To install, reverse removal procedures, noting the following; Column has two bores for securing and locating steering lock; casting on clamp portion of lock must engage with LOWER bore in column tube. Always use self-locking nuts when installing pinch bolt at pinion. When replacing column bearing flange, longer portion of flange must be toward passenger's side.

OVERHAUL

Remove stop washer from top end of column, then remove plain washers, spring, and support. Slide column down into tube in order to gain access to column bearing. **NOTE** – *After column is reassembled and installed, check for proper operation of lock mechanism BEFORE shearing heads of lock mounting screws.*

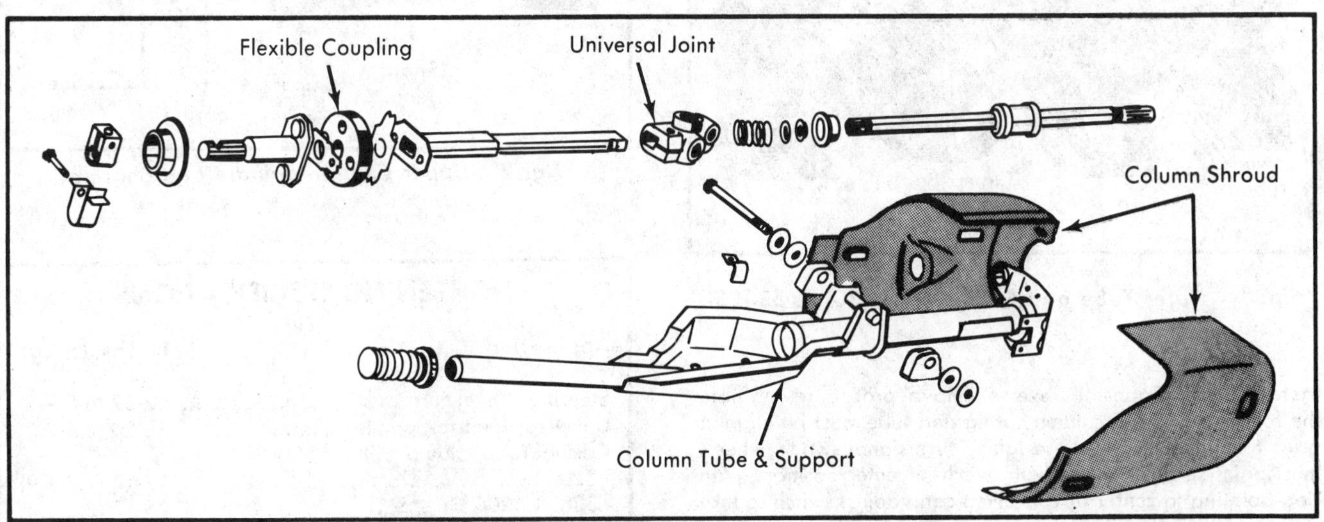

Fig. 2 Audi 100LS Steering Column Assembly

BMW

320i
530i
630CSi

DESCRIPTION

Steering column consists of a padded steering wheel with horn contact, turn signal/headlight dimmer switch, windshield wiper switch and an anti-theft steering column lock/ignition switch. Both 530i and 630CSi have a telescoping column while the 320i is not moveable. Column is connected to steering gear by means of universal joints and flexible couplings.

REMOVAL & INSTALLATION

STEERING COLUMN

Removal, 320i — 1) Disconnect battery ground cable. Remove lower half of steering column casing. Lift off pad from center of steering wheel and remove steering wheel.

2) Remove windshield wiper and turn signal switches at switch plate. Loosen set screw and pull out ignition switch.

3) Detach steering spindle at universal joint next to firewall in engine compartment. Loosen casing tube clamp at base of tube in driver's compartment. Drill or chisel off shear head bolts holding steering column to instrument panel. Remove steering column.

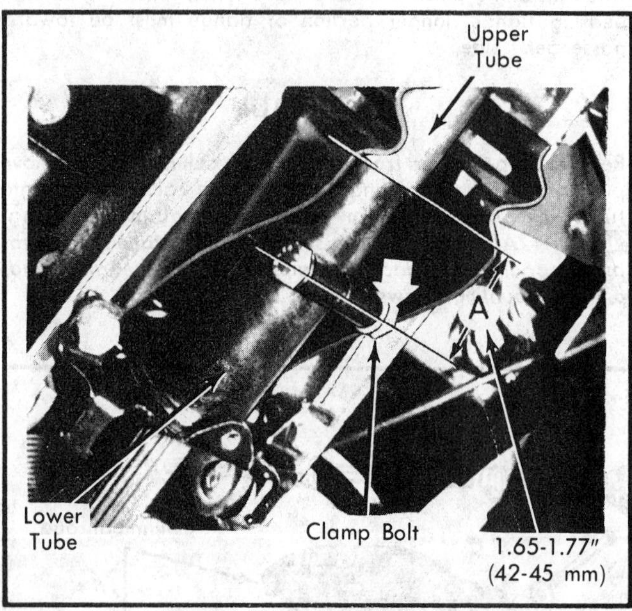

Fig. 1 Outer Tube and Clamp Bolt (530i & 630CSi)

Installation — To install, reverse removal procedure and note the following: Upper column casing and tube must be aligned prior to tightening. When installing turn signal switch, wheels must point straight ahead with switch in center position. With dog pointing to center of cancelling cam, adjust switch so that dog is about .12" (3 mm) from cancelling cam.

Removal, 530i & 630CSi — 1) Disconnect battery ground cable and remove steering wheel. Detach lower half of casing and remove turn signal and wiper switches.

2) Remove spindle shaft holder at top of column. Loosen adjusting nut and mark position of upper and lower shafts. Carefully pry spindle shaft bearing from top of column and pull shaft out from above.

3) To remove upper outer tube, disconnect horn wire at carbon brush. Drill or chisel off switch plate shear screws and disconnect wiring harnesses. Loosen clamp bolt and support screws, then slide down lower outer tube. Lift up outer casing and pull out outer tube.

Installation — To install, reverse removal procedures noting the following: Prior to tightening clamp bolt, assure that distance from centerline of clamp bolt to end of upper outer tube is between 1.65" and 1.77" (42-45 mm). Align upper and lower spindle marks and tighten adjusting nut.

SPINDLE BEARING

Remove cancelling cam and, on 530i and 630CSi only, remove bearing holder. On all models, remove collar ring, snap ring, washer, spring and split ring. Lift bearing out of tube. Press new bearing in tube until flush. Reinstall remaining parts in reverse order of disassembly.

NOTE — *On 320i only, lower bearing may be replaced by driving shaft and bearing out from top. Remove snap ring, split ring and bearing. When reinstalling, stem of split ring must face bearing and snap ring must fit in locking groove.*

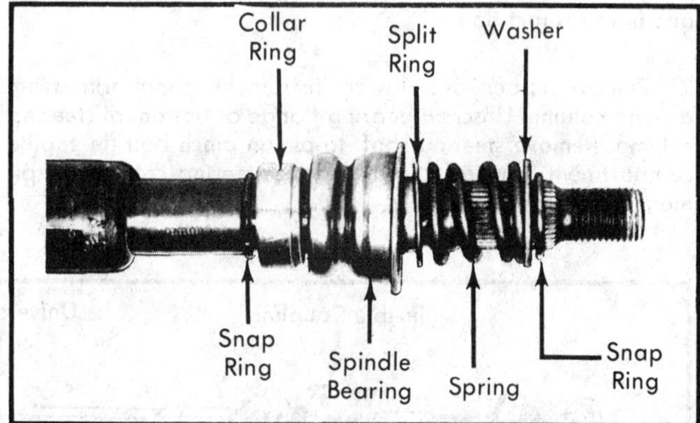

Fig. 2 Upper Column Spindle and Bearing

TIGHTENING SPECIFICATIONS

Application	Ft. Lbs. (mkg)
Steering Wheel Nut	62-69 (8.5-9.5)
Universal Joint-to-Spindle	18-20 (2.5-2.8)
Casing Tube Clamp Bolt	
320i	12-14 (1.7-1.9)
530i & 630CSi	16-17 (2.2-2.4)

CAPRI

Capri

DESCRIPTION

Steering column is a collapsible safety type. Steering wheel is mounted on a convoluted, collapsible can, which is designed to collapse used heavy impact. Cam assembly is integral with steering wheel and is removed with wheel.

REMOVAL & INSTALLATION

STEERING COLUMN

NOTE – *Steering column and steering column shaft are removed as a single unit.*

Removal – Disconnect battery. Remove upper and lower coupling clamp bolts (mark shafts for installation alignment). Tap coupling shaft down to remove from steering column. Remove steering column shroud, steering wheel and turn signal cancelling cam. Lower trim panel and remove turn signal switch. Disconnect ignition switch wires at connector. Remove steering column retaining bolts, then remove steering column with steering column shaft and grommet.

Installation – To install, reverse removal procedure and note the following: wheels should be in straight ahead position, marks on splines are aligned and couplings are not distorted.

STEERING COLUMN SHAFT

NOTE – *Steering column shaft is removed from steering column after steering column is removed from vehicle.*

Removal – Remove steering wheel and steering column as previously outlined. Remove steering lock by drilling out headless bolts. Remove clip, washer and spring from lower end of steering column shaft. Tap lower end of shaft with soft mallet to remove upper bearing, then use shaft to tap lower bearing out of steering column.

Installation – Place shaft in column and install lower bearing, spring, washers and clip. Push lower bearing in place and install upper bearing. Install steering lock with shear head bolts, then use steering lock to align shaft in column. Install steering column and steering wheel as previously outlined.

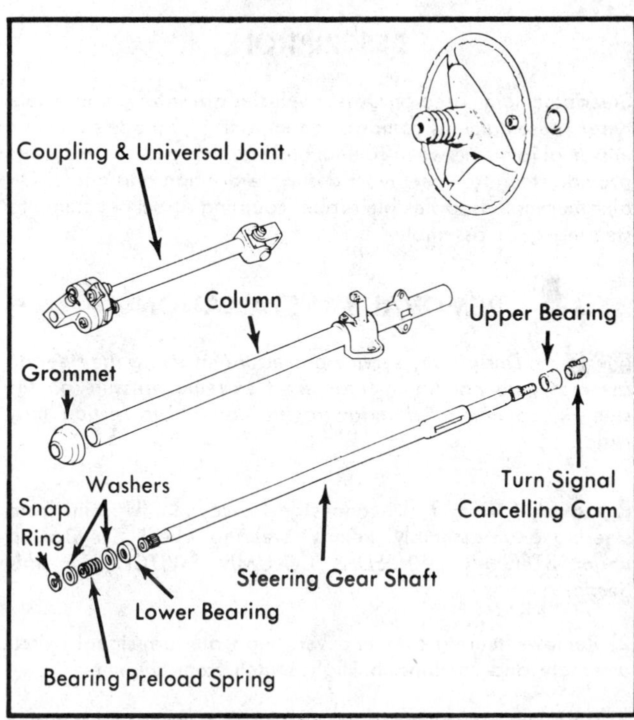

Fig. 1 Exploded View of Steering Column Assembly

TIGHTENING SPECIFICATIONS

Application	Ft. Lbs (mkg)
Steering Wheel Nut	25-30 (3.5-4.2)
Universal Joint-to-Shaft Spline	12-15 (1.7-2.1)

DATSUN F10, 200SX, B210, 710 & 810

F10
200SX
B210
710
810

DESCRIPTION

Steering column used on Datsun vehicles are safety, collapsible type. These columns compress on impact. F10 models use two universal joints between column and steering gear. These joints provide steering wheel most desirable position and angle. On all other models, a flexible rubber coupling attaches column to steering gear assembly.

REMOVAL & INSTALLATION

NOTE — *During any service procedure involving the steering assembly, do not hammer or exert extreme pressure on the steering column or damage to the collapsible section may result.*

Removal, F10 — 1) Disconnect lower column "U" joint from steering gear assembly. Remove steering wheel. *See Datsun under STEERING WHEEL & COLUMN SWITCHES in this Section.*

2) Remove steering column cover. Separate turn signal switch assembly and combination light switch from column.

3) Hold steering column upper portion by hand. Remove upper and lower steering column clamp mounting bolts. Remove screws keeping column hole cover assembly to instrument panel. Slide out steering column through passenger compartment.

NOTE — *Do not further disassemble collapsible steering column. If components are damaged and require replacement, entire assembly must be replaced.*

Inspection — 1) Check column bearings for smooth even operation. If necessary, grease bearings with suitable lubricant.

2) Check column tube for deformation or breaks. Replace components as required.

3) Check column shaft spring. Spring length should be about .512" (13 mm) under a load of about 66 lbs. (30 kg).

4) Measure distance between top end of upper column tube and top end of lower column tube. Distance should be 11.63" (295.5 mm). *See Fig. 1.*

Installation — 1) Set steering gear in straight-ahead position. Connect lower joint to steering column. Slide steering assembly through hole in floor board.

2) Tighten column tube mounting bolts. Loosen splined shaft set screw and connect shaft to joint. Connect opposite end to steering gear. Tighten pinch bolt and set screw.

3) Make sure column tube hole seal is not twisted and that lower lip makes contact with joint shaft.

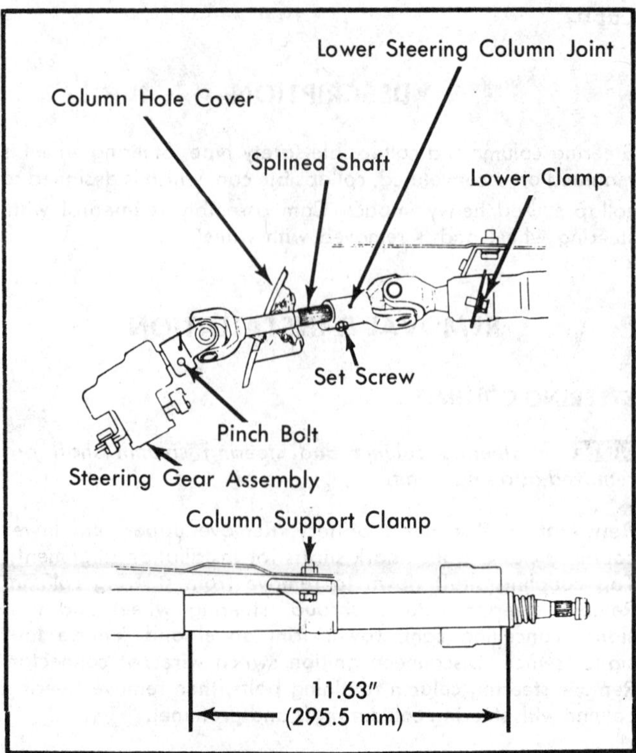

Fig. 1 Datsun F10 Steering Column Assembly

Removal, Except F10 — 1) Remove steering shaft pinch bolt. Remove steering wheel. *See Datsun under STEERING WHEEL & COLUMN SWITCHES in this Section.*

2) Remove upper and lower steering column shroud covers. Loosen screws and take off turn signal switch assembly.

3) Remove 4 bolts mounting steering column tube cover to floor board. From under instrument panel, remove bolts mounting column clamp and remove clamp. Pull steering assembly from vehicle by removing it through passanger compartment.

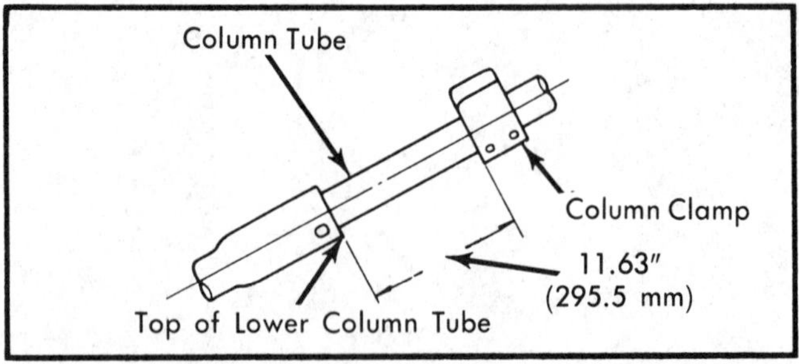

Fig. 2 Column Tube Measurement Specification

Inspection — 1) Check column bearings for smooth even operation. If necessary, grease bearings with suitable lubricant.

2) Check column tube for deformation or breaks. Replace components if necessary.

DATSUN F10, 200SX, B210, 710 & 810 (Cont.)

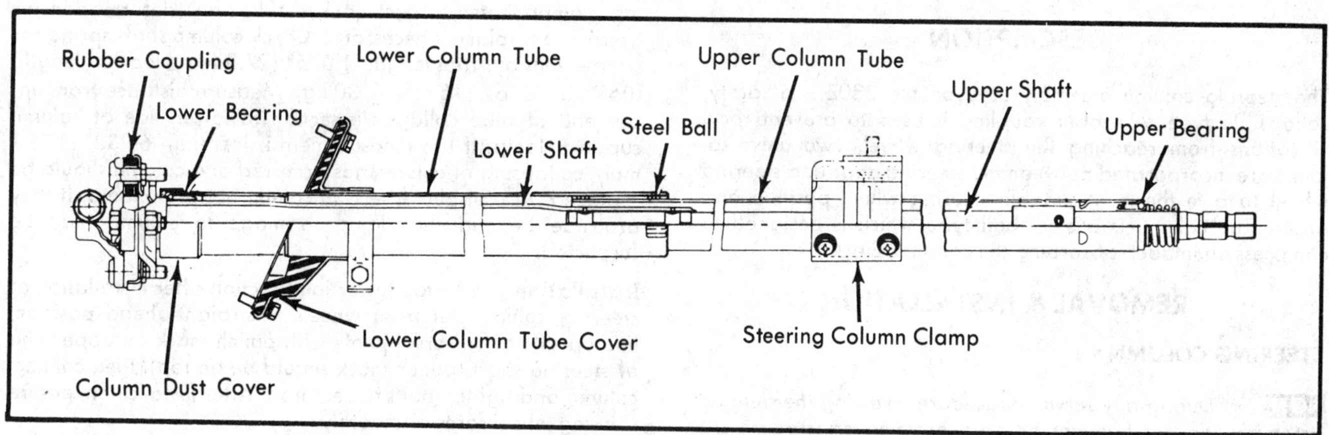

Fig. 3 Sectional View of Collapsible Steering Column – All Except F10

3) Check column shaft spring and replace spring if it seems weak.

4) On all models except 810, measure distance between column clamp and top end of lower column tube. Distance should be about 7.0" (178 mm) for 200SX and B210 models or about 7.2" (183 mm) for 710 models.

5) On 810 models, measure distance between top end of upper column tube and top end of lower column tube. Distance should be about 16.27" (413.5 mm). *See Fig. 1.*

Installation – 1) Place steering gear so wheels point straight-ahead.

2) Slide steering column in postion through passenger compartment. Guide column over worm shaft. Make sure punch mark faces up, then tighten pinch bolt.

3) Fix column under instrument panel. Refit column tube cover at floor board. Reverse removal procedure for remaining components. Make sure steering wheel rotates freely.

OVERHAUL

NOTE – *This article does not outline an overhaul procedure; it is recommended that, should damage to the column occur, it be replaced as an assembly.*

TIGHTENING SPECIFICATIONS

Application	Ft. Lbs. (mkg)
Steering Wheel Nut	
F10	14-18 (2.0-2.5)
200SX, B210	22-25 (3.0-3.5)
710	29-36 (4.0-5.0)
810	27-38 (3.7-5.3)
Steering Column Clamp Bolt	
F10	7-10 (.97-1.4)
200SX, B210	11-13 (1.5-1.8)
710, 810	9-13 (1.2-1.5)
Column Tube-to-Instrument Panel	
B210, 810	3-3.3 (.35-.45)
Rubber Coupling-to-Worm Shaft	29-36 (4.0-5.0)
Upper Joint Shaft-to-Column Bolt	
F10	14-17 (1.9-2.4)
Lower Joint-to-Steering Gear	
F10	14-17 (1.9-2.4)

DATSUN 280Z

280Z

DESCRIPTION

The steering column assembly used on the 280Z is a safety, collapsible type. A rubber coupling is used to prevent road vibrations from reaching the steering wheel. Two universal joints are incorporated between the steering gear and steering wheel to give the most suitable steering wheel position and angle. The column is a steel ball type which is designed to compress on impact, absorbing the collision shock.

REMOVAL & INSTALLATION

STEERING COLUMN

NOTE — *During any service procedure involving the steering assembly, do not hammer or exert extreme pressure on the steering column or damage to the collapsible section may result.*

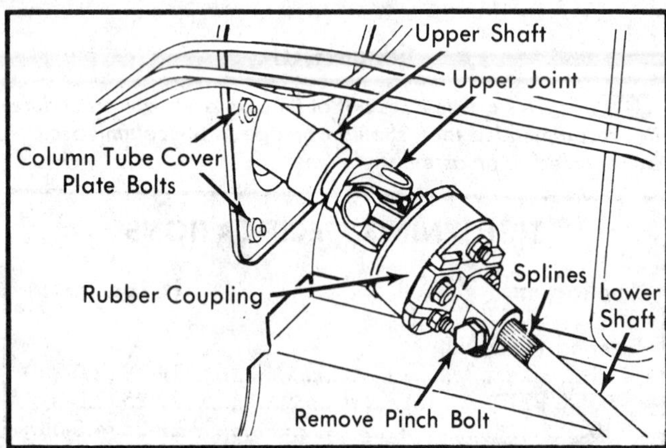

Fig. 1 Separating Upper and Lower Shafts

Removal — Disconnect column assembly from lower joint shaft at rubber coupling (remove clamp bolt). Remove steering wheel. See *Datsun under STEERING WHEEL & COLUMN SWITCHES in this section.* Detach column shroud halves and remove lighting switch assembly. Unscrew bolts retaining column tube flange plate to toeboard. Support steering column at upper end and remove column clamp bolts. Draw out steering column assembly from passenger compartment side. Loosen clamp bolt at pinion shaft and remove lower steering joint section.

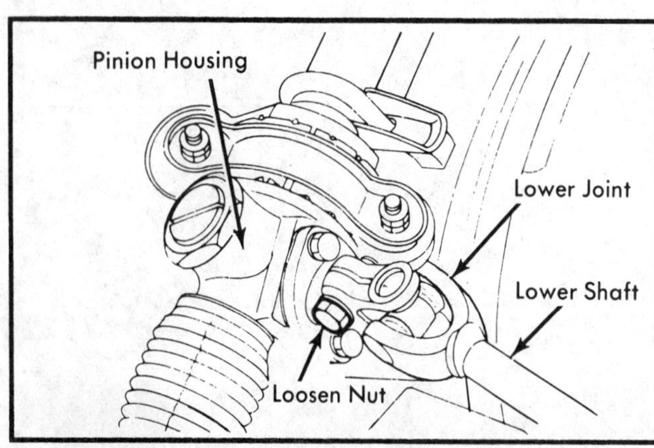

Fig. 2 Separating Lower Shaft from Pinion Gear

Inspection — Check for smoothness of rotation at all steering components. Inspect jacket tube for deformation or breakage (replace if necessary). Check column shaft spring for proper tension: free length, 1.075" (27.3 mm); loaded length, .059" @ 66 lbs. (15 mm @ 30 kg). Measure distance from upper end of tube collapsible section to lower side of column support clamp. If this measurement is less than 6.933" (176.1 mm), collapsing of column has occurred and column should be replaced. Also inspect inserts in column support clamp. If they protrude beyond the clamp, damage to column may be suspected.

Installation — Install lower joint section after installation of steering column. Set front wheels in straight-ahead position, line up slits of universal joints with punch mark on upper end of steering shaft (punch mark should be on top), then connect column and tighten bolts as required. After installation, ensure steering wheel rotates smoothly.

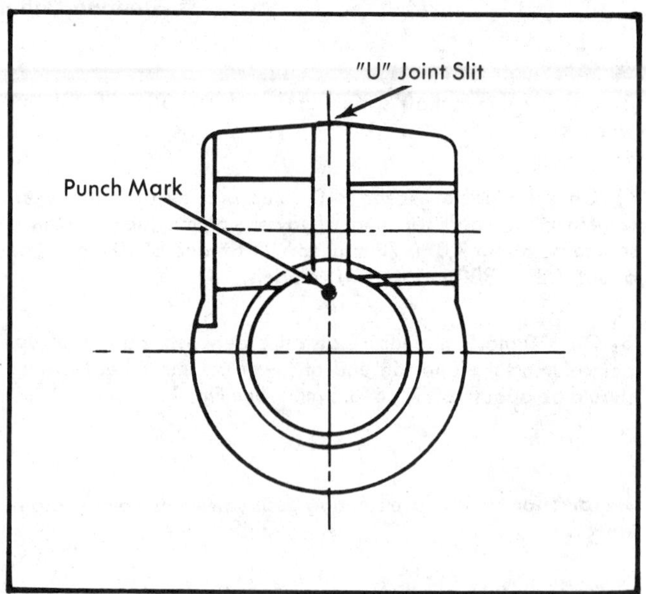

Fig. 3 Lining Up "U" Joint Slits with Steering Shaft Punch Mark

OVERHAUL

NOTE — *Refer to Inspection in this article for description of components which may be replaced; however, if damage to the collapsible section is suspected, steering column replacement is recommended.*

TIGHTENING SPECIFICATIONS

Application	Ft. Lbs. (mkg)
Steering Wheel Nut	29-36 (4.0-5.0)
Column Clamp Bolt	6-8 (0.8-1.1)
Rubber Coupling Securing Bolt	12-14 (1.7-2.0)
Lower Joint-to-Rubber Coupling	17-20 (2.3-2.7)
Lower Joint-to-Pinion Shaft	29-36 (4.0-5.0)

DATSUN PICKUP

Pickup

DESCRIPTION

The steering column is a conventional, non-collapsible type. It is supported under the instrument panel by a post clamp. The lower end of the steering column tube is bolted directly to the gear box. The worm assembly, within the gear housing, is an integral extension of the steering shaft.

REMOVAL & INSTALLATION

Since the worm gear is an integral, non-separable part of the steering shaft, the shaft must be removed as an assembly with the gear. *See appropriate article under STEERING GEARS & LINKAGE in this section.*

OVERHAUL

Replacement of bearings or bushings may be accomplished during steering gear overhaul. *See appropriate article under STEERING GEARS & LINKAGE in this section.*

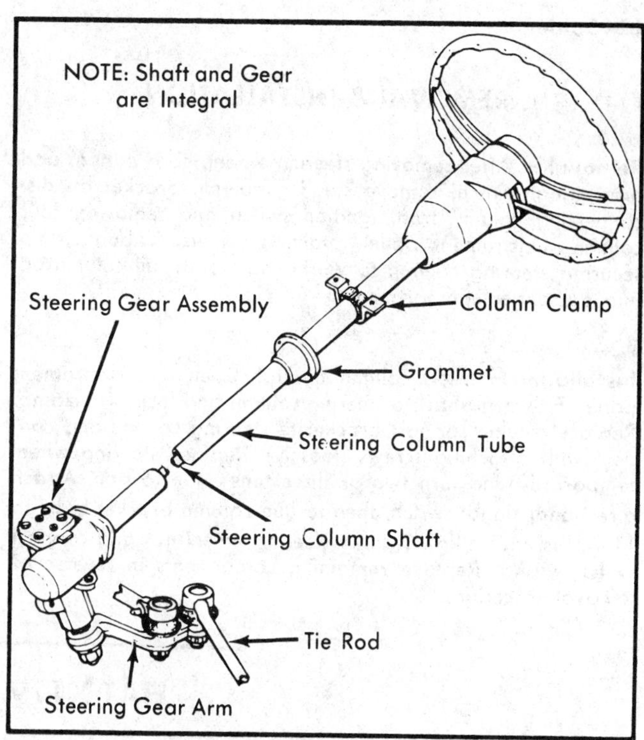

Fig. 1 Steering Column and Gear Assembly for Datsun Pickup

FIAT 124

124 Spider

REMOVAL & INSTALLATION

Removal – After removing steering wheel, horn button, and turn signal switch, remove steering column bracket by disconnecting column front ignition switch and removing four column-to-instrument panel retaining screws. Unbolt clamp securing steering column to worm shaft and pull column up into passenger compartment.

Installation – Insert column through opening in instrument panel. Fit worm shaft to steering column and lock with clamp. Replace column support bracket to steering column and connect with attaching screws (loosely). Replace steering wheel temporarily and turn two or three times side to side. Attach directional signal switch, then torque column bracket bolts to 11 ft. lbs. (1.5 mkg). Tighten steering wheel nut and connect switch wiring. Replace remaining components in reverse of removal procedure.

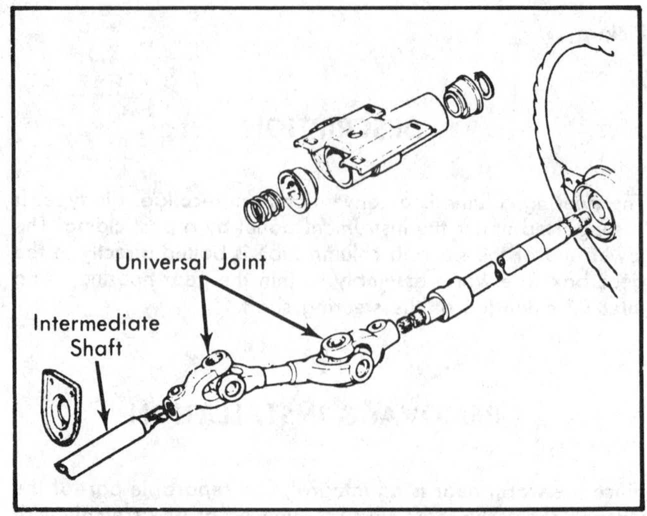

Fig. 1 Detail of Flexible Coupling Connecting Upper and Lower Portions of Steering Shaft

FIAT X1/9, 128 AND 131

X1/9
128
131

DESCRIPTION

The steering column is composed of two sections. The top section is mounted on two ball bearings, while the lower section is equipped with two universal joints.

REMOVAL & INSTALLATION

STEERING COLUMN (ALL MODELS)

Removal – Disconnect battery. Remove screws holding column cover halves. On 131 models, remove steering column adjustment knob. Detach electrical connectors at steering column. Remove nuts and washers retaining column at support bracket below instrument panel. Unscrew pinch bolt holding lower end of steering shaft to gear box. Remove column assembly from vehicle. Dismantle steering wheel and turn signal unit, if necessary.

Installation – To install, reverse removal procedure.

UPPER COLUMN BEARING REPLACEMENT (128 MODELS)

Removal – 1) Remove screws attaching horn button cover and screws attaching steering column cover. Unscrew steering wheel nut and take off wheel. Loosen turn signal switch retaining nut and disconnect electrical wiring, then remove nut and switch.

2) Withdraw retaining ring and allow spring to extend. Remove nuts attaching steering column support to instrument panel. Disconnect universal joint between upper and lower column sections. On bench, push out top end of column and remove bearing, then repeat on lower end bearing.

Installation – Replace bearings in reverse of removal procedure.

Fig. 1 Installed View of Steering Column as Viewed from Under Instrument Panel

HONDA

Accord
Civic
Civic CVCC

DESCRIPTION

Steering column is collasible type. Upper mounting bracket and base plates are attached to steering column with plastic shear pins. On impact to steering wheel pins shear. Column and mounting bracket slide downward. Base plate stays attached to body. Refer to *Fig. 1* for further detail.

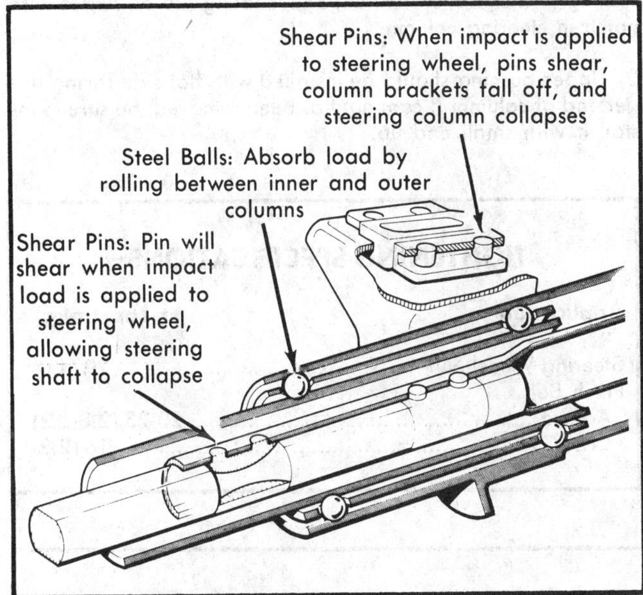

Fig. 1 Operation of Honda Collapsible Steering Column

REMOVAL & INSTALLATION

STEERING COLUMN

Removal, Except Civic – 1) Remove pinch bolt from steering shaft connector. Splined shaft will pull out with "U" joint.

2) Disconnect all electrical wires from connectors. Remove column cover halves. Remove steering wheel. *See Honda under STEERING WHEEL & COLUMN SWITCHES in this Section.*

3) Place ignition switch in locked position to prevent shaft from slipping out during column removal. Take off turn signal assembly along with combination switch. Remove upper and lower column mounting bolts, then remove steering column.

4) Disconnect pinch bolt mounting connector shaft to steering gear and remove shaft with "U" joints.

Disassembly – 1) To remove steering shaft from column take out steering column bushing, serrated bushing and horn ground ring.

2) From bottom of column, remove spacer, snap ring and bearing. Pull out steering shaft and collapsible portion. Shaft should slide out easily.

Inspection – Check steering column and steering shaft lengths.

Column & Shaft Specifications

Application	Shaft Length	Column Length
All Models	25.12 ±.02"	21.77 ±.02"
	638 ±.5 mm)............	(553 ±.5 mm)

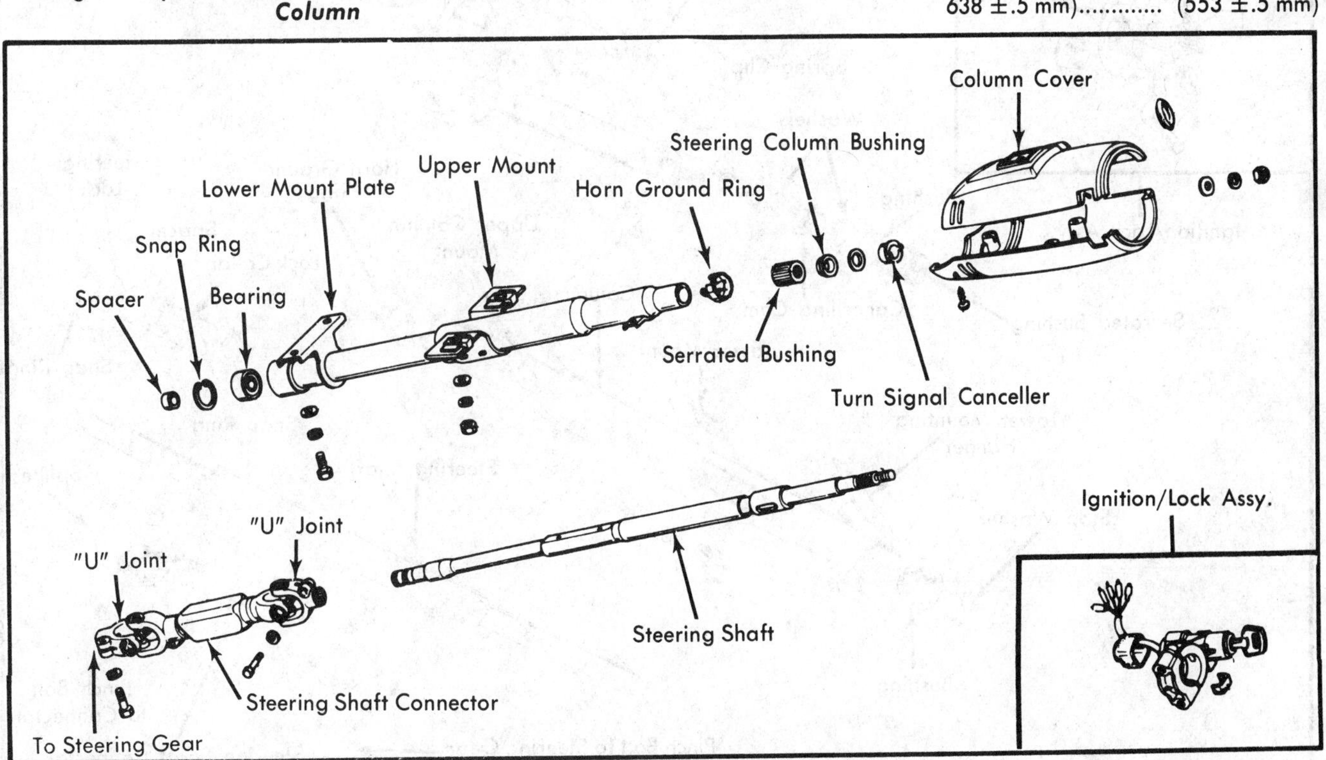

Fig. 2 Exploded View of Civic CVCC and Accord Steering Column

HONDA (Cont.)

Reassembly – 1) Install horn ring and serrated washer. Align flat sides of steering column bushing with slots in column and tap bushing into column with mallet.

2) Fit shaft to column from bottom. Fill lower end of steering column with grease.

NOTE – *Do not force or apply extreme pressure to shaft because pins may shear.*

3) Fit bushing to lower end of column, then secure with snap ring.

Installation – 1) Insert column into place in vehicle. Attach steering shaft to connector shaft.

2) Raise column and engage under instrument panel. Fit upper and lower mounting bolts. Insert turn signal mechanism over column. Make sure tabs on mechanism align with steering column notches. Fit cancelling ring.

3) Check steering column shaft clearance. Measure distance between top of column and top of shaft. Distance should be .550-.720" (16.5-17.5 mm). Refit steering wheel and column covers.

Removal, Civic – 1) Disconnect steering joint at splines by removing yoke bolts. Detach wire harness and coupler. Remove 4 attaching bolts (remove 2 upper bolts first) and take steering column out of vehicle.

2) Remove steering shaft from column by pulling out from bottom. Lower bushing will be forced out when shaft is removed. Remove upper and lower steering column covers.

3) Loosen screw on turn signal switch cam nut and lightly tap screw head to free cam nut. Remove turn signal switch. Remove upper column bushing.

Installation – 1) To assemble steering column, reverse procedure outlined above and make following notes: When installing turn signal switch, engage locating tab on switch with notch in steering column.

2) Upper bushing should be installed with flat side facing upper end of column. If cam nut has been removed, be sure to install it with small end up.

TIGHTENING SPECIFICATIONS

Application	Ft. Lbs. (mkg)
Steering Wheel Nut	29 (4.0)
Pinch Bolt	
Accord	20-23 (2.8-3.2)
Civic CVCC	16 (2.2)

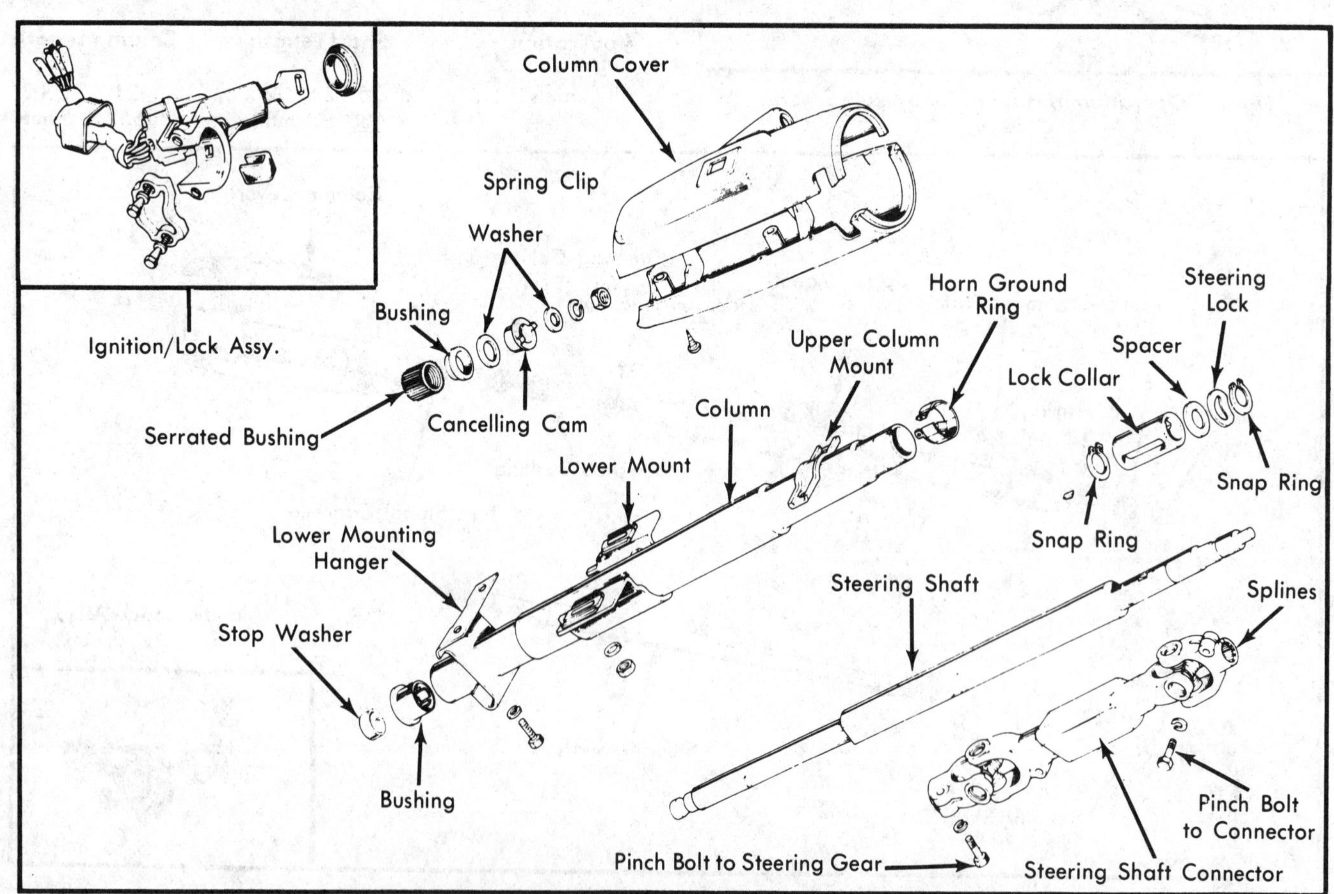

Fig. 3 Exploded View of Civic Steering Column

JAGUAR

XJ6
XJ12
XJS

DESCRIPTION

The upper and lower steering columns are the collapsible type, designed to comply with safety regulations. The collapse points are retained by nylon plugs which will shear on impact, allowing steering wheel and columns to move forward. The upper column is composed of two separate sliding shafts, with the column tube on later models being formed with an expanded metal section. The column shaft is supported on two prelubricated roller bearings. The lower column section is also comprised of two sliding portions, which are retained in a fixed length by nylon plugs.

REMOVAL & INSTALLATION

UPPER STEERING COLUMN

Removal, Except XJS – 1) Disconnect battery. Remove steering wheel, *see Jaguar under STEERING WHEEL & COLUMN SWITCHES in this Section.* Remove speedometer as follows: Remove instrument panel casing. Behind speedometer, unscrew knurled nut from right-angle bracket to gear box and disconnect speedometer drive cable. Disconnect trip record reset control cable by unscrewing knurled nut. Apply pressure to instrument panel bezel, rotate speedometer clockwise until it releases, and withdraw from panel. Withdraw headlight warning light and illuminator lights. Disconnect ground lead.

2) Remove tachometer as follows: Apply pressure to instrument bezel and rotate counterclockwise until tachometer releases. Disconnect electrical plug and socket. Remove ground lead. Withdraw illumination light holder.

3) Remove trim panel below the upper steering column. Disconnect electrical switch connections (three socket and plug connections). Detach horn contact at upper column. Unscrew self-locking nut and remove pinch bolt securing upper universal joint to lower steering column.

4) Loosen two set screws attaching lower end of upper column to its mounting strut. Working through speedometer and tachometer openings, remove two nuts securing top mounting of upper column, and support upper end of column with hand (or by other suitable means). Collect bolts, rubber washers, and any packing washers which may be at upper end of column.

5) Still supporting column, detach two set screws already loosened at lower mounting; collect packing washers. Remove upper steering column assembly from vehicle (with universal joint and switch assembly attached). **CAUTION** – *Do not use excessive force to separate upper column from lower column when removing.*

Installation – If universal joint and/or adjusting clamp have been removed, refit, then reverse removal procedure and note the following: Check that 3/8" (9.5 mm) clearance exists axially in lower universal joint; if necessary, move upper universal joint further along lower column to increase clearance. Ensure self-cancelling operation of turn signals functions properly and that steering wheel spokes are horizontal when straight-ahead position is set; if not adjust as necessary.

Removal, XJS – 1) Disconnect battery. Remove cover panel from under instrument panel. Remove trim from around instrument cluster. Remove screws mounting instrument panel to facia. Disconnect speedometer cable. Lay cluster forward and disconnect wires from behind cluster. Lift off entire cluster.

2) Remove steering column lower shroud. Lock steering wheel in straight-ahead position. Remove column adjusting mount bolt, then loosen set screw and take out adjusting assembly.

3) Disconnect ignition switch from main harness. Disconnect main harness from auxiliary controls. Remove upper "U" joint bolt. Remove bolts mounting column at lower mounting.

4) Disconnect horn. Remove upper column mounting bolts. Maneuver column free of "U" joint and vehicle. Remove other shroud half. Unscrew auxiliary switches from column, slide assemblies out of column.

5) Remove bolts securing ignition switch and lock assembly to column. Remove bolt securing horn feed and take off from column.

NOTE – *Remaining components can not be individually replaced.*

Installation – Reverse removal procedure and note: Loosely fit upper and lower mounting bolts and spacers. Adjust column so groove on inner splined shaft aligns with bolt hole in "U" joint. Make sure upper section of column fits in center of housing facia. Tighten mounting bolts. Reverse removal procedure for remaining components.

LOWER STEERING COLUMN

Removal, Except XJS – 1) Raise vehicle on hoist and remove pinch bolt securing lower "U" joint to pinion shaft. Lower vehicle. Detach lower parcel shelf. Remove both pinch bolts from upper-to-lower "U" joint.

2) Unscrew lower mounting screws of upper column. Pull lower steering column from upper "U" joint. Raise vehicle. Remove "U" joint from pinion shaft and withdraw lower steering column.

Installation – To install, reverse removal procedure and ensure gap of 3/8" (9.5 mm) exists in universal joint. **NOTE** – *Front wheels should be kept in straight-ahead position during this operation.*

Removal, XJS – 1) Place front wheels in straight-ahead position. Remove exhaust heat shields near head pipe. Remove right side heat shield near steering rack.

2) Remove nut and bolt mounting lower "U" joint to pinion shaft. Work inside passenger compartment and separate "U" joint from upper and lower column. Pull "U" joint free from upper column.

3) Remove "U" joint from lower shaft. From under vehicle, push lower column through firewall until "U" joint separates from pinion shaft. Pull "U" joint clear of pinion shaft and withdraw lower column assembly.

JAGUAR (Cont.)

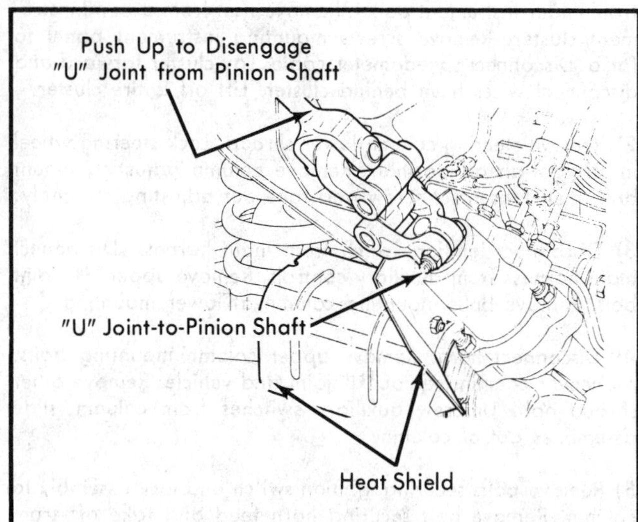

Fig. 1 Disconnecting Lower Steering Column from Pinion Shaft

Installation – Reverse removal procedure and note: Make sure steering wheel is in center position before installing lower column. Also, Do not use excessive force to fit lower column to upper column; nylon shear plug may be damaged.

STEERING COLUMN ADJUSTING CLAMP

Removal – Remove steering wheel. Pull impact rubber from steering wheel shaft. Unscrew three small cheese-head screws from beneath adjusting clamp (lock nut) and withdraw retaining plate. Unscrew collet adaptor completely and remove from shaft. Remove circlip from within upper side of adjuster. Withdraw adjuster (lock nut) collecting stop button. Slide split collet off shaft.

Installation – Clean parts thoroughly and remove any burrs with a file. Lightly lubricate all enclosed metal components. Install by reversing removal procedure.

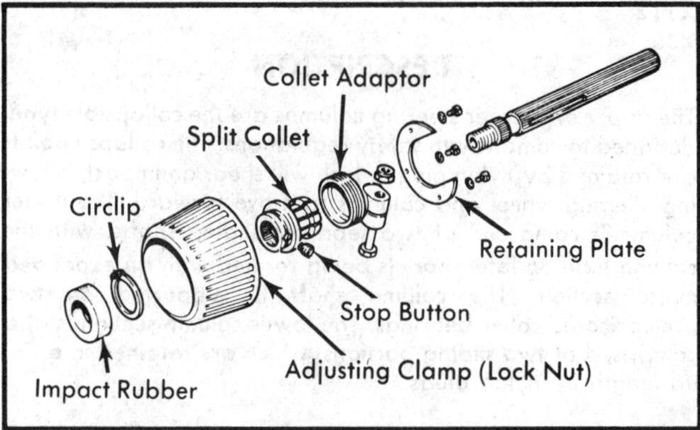

Fig. 2 Exploded View of Steering Column Adjusting Clamp

STEERING COLUMN LOWER SEAL

Removal, Except XJS – Remove upper steering column, as previously outlined. Loosen hose clip attaching upper sealing sleeve to lower column; remove clip and sleeve. Remove 3 screws securing seal retainer to instrument panel. Slide seal, retainer, and sealing sleeve up and off lower column.

Installation – Fit assembly of sealing sleeve, seal, and retainer over end of lower column carefully. Insert and tighten three retaining set screws. Carefully slide second sealing sleeve, flanged end first, over lower column as far as first sealing sleeve; position hose clip, but do not tighten. Move second sealing sleeve approximately ¼" (6 mm) toward dash, to preload it against first sealing sleeve. Secure this position with hose clip. Replace upper column assembly.

OVERHAUL

UPPER & LOWER STEERING COLUMNS

NOTE – *No repairs, adjustments, or overhaul procedures are given by the manufacturer. If damage is evident or suspected, replacement of assemblies is necessary.*

LANCIA

Lancia Beta
Except Scorpion

DESCRIPTION

All models use energy absorbing safety type steering column assemblies. Steering column is two piece. "U" joints connect upper steering column to lower shaft and lower shaft to steering gear. Upper steering column has a two inch variable adjustment. This allows column and steering wheel to be placed in most desirable position.

REMOVAL & INSTALLATION

STEERING COLUMN

Removal – 1) Disconnect battery. Place front wheels in straight ahead position. Disconnect lower steering shaft from steering gear by removing nut and bolt, then separating. Disconnect multi-plug connector from socket.

2) Remove nuts mounting steering column cover and lift off cover with steering wheel. *See Steering Wheel in this section.* Remove entire steering column assembly and place on bench.

Installation – To install steering column, reverse removal procedure and note. Make sure turn signal cancellation groove in shaft is facing right side.

OVERHAUL

Disassembly – 1) Index mark steering shaft and lower shaft. Remove bolt mounting steering column shaft with lower shaft and separate. Do not lose spring.

2) Remove mounting screw and take off turn signal light assembly and windshield wiper control. Remove snap ring, tap on steering shaft and drive out lower bearing.

3) Remove steering shaft, turn it upside down and refit in steering column. Drive upper bearing from steering column. Inspect both bearings and replace if found defective.

Reassembly – To reassemble steering column components, reverse disassembly procedure. Make sure bolt mounting steering column shaft and lower shaft faces vertically.

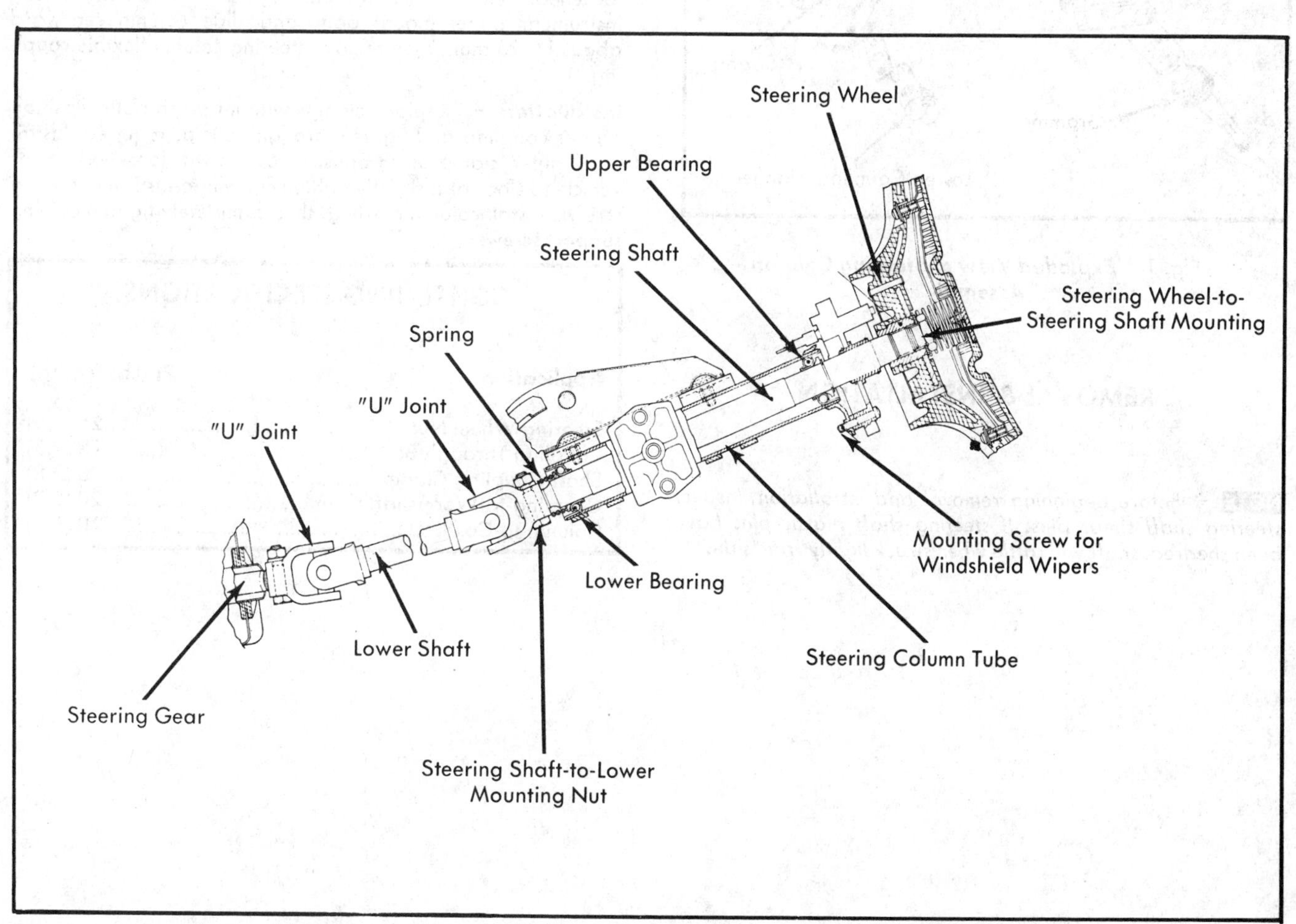

Fig. 1 Sectional View of Lancia Beta Steering Column for Component Identification

LUV

LUV

DESCRIPTION

Column is fastened to steering gear through a flexible coupling. The energy-absorbing shaft will collapse during frontal impact under predetermined loads, by shearing plastic pins.

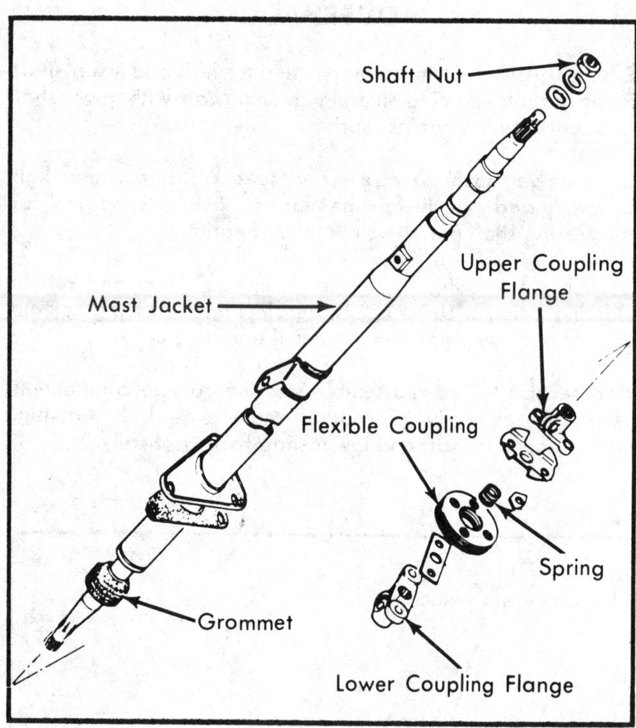

Fig. 1 ***Exploded View of Steering Column Assembly***

REMOVAL & INSTALLATION

NOTE — *Before beginning removal and installation, inspect steering shaft shear pins. If steering shaft plastic pins have been sheared, shaft will rattle when struck lightly from side.*

STEERING COLUMN

Removal — **1**) Disconnect battery ground. Remove horn cover and spring. Remove steering column shrouding and hazard warning light switch. Remove combination switch. Remove steering wheel. *See LUV under STEERING WHEEL & COLUMN SWITCHES in this Section.*

NOTE — *Avoid impact to steering wheel at all times.*

2) Raise front of vehicle and support. Remove pinch bolt holding shaft to lower coupling flange. Remove 3 mast jacket to firewall bolts. Remove 2 steering column to instrument panel bolts.

3) Separate rubber coupling from steering shaft. Carefully slide steering shaft toward inside of passenger compartment and remove from vehicle.

Installation — To install, reverse removal procedure, noting the following: Leave column-to-panel bolts slightly loose until vehicle is lowered to ground.

FLEXIBLE COUPLING

Removal — **1**) Raise front of vehicle. Remove coupling through bolts (only two can be removed). Remove coupling assembly by loosening clamp bolts.

2) If necessary to remove clamps, steering column must be loosened. Remove column mounting screws at cowl. Remove instrument panel mount bolts and slide column rearward about 1" (25 mm), then remove steering column flexible coupling.

Installation — Replace clamps without pinch bolts. Position rubber coupling and tighten through-bolts as required. Install and tighten clamp pinch bolts. If column was loosened, lower vehicle to floor and slightly tighten column-to-instrument panel screws. Install column cowling, then completely tighten column support screws.

TIGHTENING SPECIFICATIONS

Application	Ft. Lbs. (mkg)
Steering Wheel Nut	25 (3.5)
Coupling Through-Bolts	18 (2.5)
Shaft Coupling Clamp	20 (2.8)
Coupling-to-Wormshaft Clamp	20 (2.8)
Column-to-Cowl	10 (1.4)

MERCEDES-BENZ

230
240D
280E
280SE
300D
450SEL
450SL/450SLC
6.9

DESCRIPTION

Steering column consists of a padded impact absorbing steering wheel with horn control, spindle shaft, jacket tube with column mounted combination light/wiper switch and may include cruise control or gear shift control lever. Lower shaft of 230, 240D, 280E and 300D is corrugated for additional impact protection. Shafts are connected by flexible couplings to steering gear.

STEERING COLUMN

Removal – **1)** On 230, 240D, 280E and 300D, remove screws holding upper and lower cover on instrument panel and remove covers. On all models, disconnect battery and remove steering wheel. Remove instrument cluster by pulling outward as far as possible and loosening tachometer, pressure and temperature connections. On column shift vehicles, disconnect indicator plug.

2) On column shift vehicles, disconnect linkage. On all vehicles, remove steering lock. Disconnect combination switch plug and cruise control plug (if equipped). Remove Allen head screw at flexible coupling and all screws and nuts holding casing and column to instrument panel. Remove steering column housing.

Installation – To install, reverse removal procedure. On 450 and 6.9 models, hold steering shaft in place with assembly pin through hole in jacket tube. Check that lower shaft on 230, 240D, 280E and 300D is not bent or distorted. Use caution when installing jacket tube to prevent damage to this shaft.

STEERING COLUMN SHAFT

Removal, 230, 240D, 280E & 300D (Lower) – **1)** From engine compartment, remove both Allen screws holding flexible coupling to worm shaft and lower steering shaft. Slide coupling down on worm shaft and off of steering shaft.

2) From inside car, remove upper and lower cover from instrument panel/steering column. Remove Allen screws at upper coupling and slide coupling and lower shaft off of upper shaft.

Installation – To install, lubricate inner lips of bellows seal at firewall and reverse removal procedures.

NOTE – *Wheels must be in straight ahead position and notch on upper shaft must point directly upward during installation.*

Removal, 230, 240D, 280E & 300D (Upper) – **1)** With column out of car, remove combination switch. Remove jacket tube casing, then remove spacing ring from steering shaft.

2) Remove gripper ring, compression spring, supporting ring and ball bearing from steering shaft. Knock steering shaft upward out of jacket tube with plastic hammer.

Installation – Inspect and replace bearings and races if required. Reverse removal procedure and reinstall upper steering shaft.

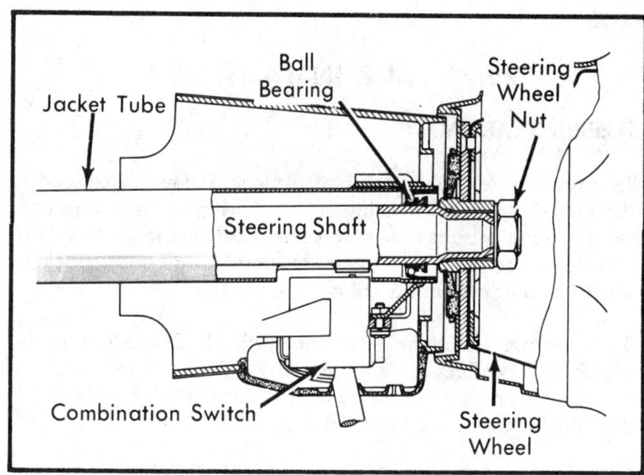

Fig. 1 Steering Wheel and Shaft (Typical)

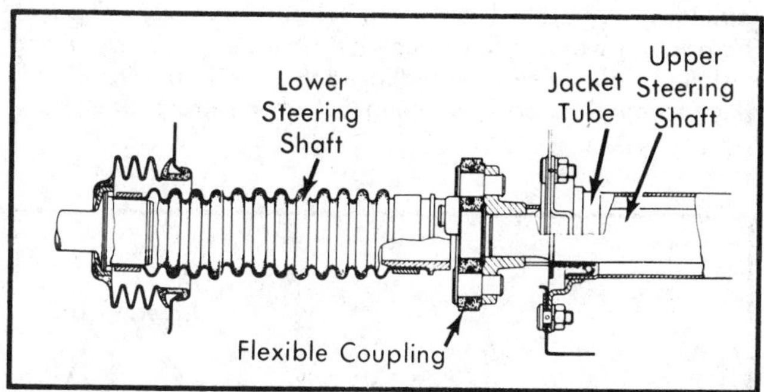

Fig. 2 Lower Steering Shaft (230, 240D, 280E, 300D)

Removal, 280SE, 450 & 6.9 – **1)** Remove steering wheel and combination switch rubber cover. Loosen switch mounting screws on bearing body and pull switch out slightly. Loosen screws holding cable of contact carbon on combination switch.

2) Remove Allen screw from upper end of steering coupling. Remove screws from jacket tube and pull steering shaft with bearing body out of jacket tube.

Installation – Replace bearings and races as required and reverse removal procedure. Check longitudinal adjustment of steering shaft by inserting assembly pin in check bore of steering column and steering shaft.

NOTE – *Late 1977 models have a steering wheel with a larger hub bore and a larger steering shaft and tube. Early version shaft should never be installed in late version tube, however late version shaft may be installed in early version tube provided the new type steering wheel is installed.*

TIGHTENING SPECIFICATIONS

Application	Ft.Lbs. (mkg)
Steering Wheel	37 (5)
Jacket Tube-to-Cross Member	7 (1.0)
Jacket Tube-to-Lower Bracket	18 (2.5)
Flexible Coupling (Allen)	18 (2.5)

MGB

MGB

REMOVAL & INSTALLATION

STEERING COLUMN

Removal – Remove pinch bolt attaching steering column to "U" joint. Disconnect steering column wiring at multi-wire connector. Remove bolts mounting column bracket to underside of instrument panel. Note quantity and position of packing washers. Guide steering column from vehicle.

Disassembly – Remove steering wheel. *See MGB under STEERING WHEEL & COLUMN SWITCHES in this Section.* Remove column covers. Remove combination switch. Take off steering lock and ignition switch.

Reassembly – Reverse disassembly procedure.

Installation – Fit column into vehicle. Refit packing washers and loosely attach column clamp bolts under instrument panel. Fit packing washers have been lost or if new column is being installed, column must be realigned. *See Column Alignment in this Section.* Connect wiring plug. Set wheels straight-ahead. Slide steering shaft into "U" joint making sure grooves align with pinch bolt holes. Fit pinch bolt and tighten.

ADJUSTMENTS

STEERING COLUMN ALIGNMENT

1) Remove "U" joint. Fit alignment gauge shown in *Fig. 2.* Make sure setscrew seats in splined groove.

2) Fit 1 packing washer between each upper column mounting bracket. Tighten bolts until washers are just pinched. Tighten column plate bolts just enough to retain column in center of hole. Make sure rack has original amount of shims. Tighten bolts.

3) To correct horizontal misalignment, move end of column, then tighten column plate bolts.

4) To correct vertical misalignment, use shims placed between rack mounting brackets and bring left and right alignment into tolerance. Do not use more than 3 shims on either bracket. Refit rack and tighten mounting bolts.

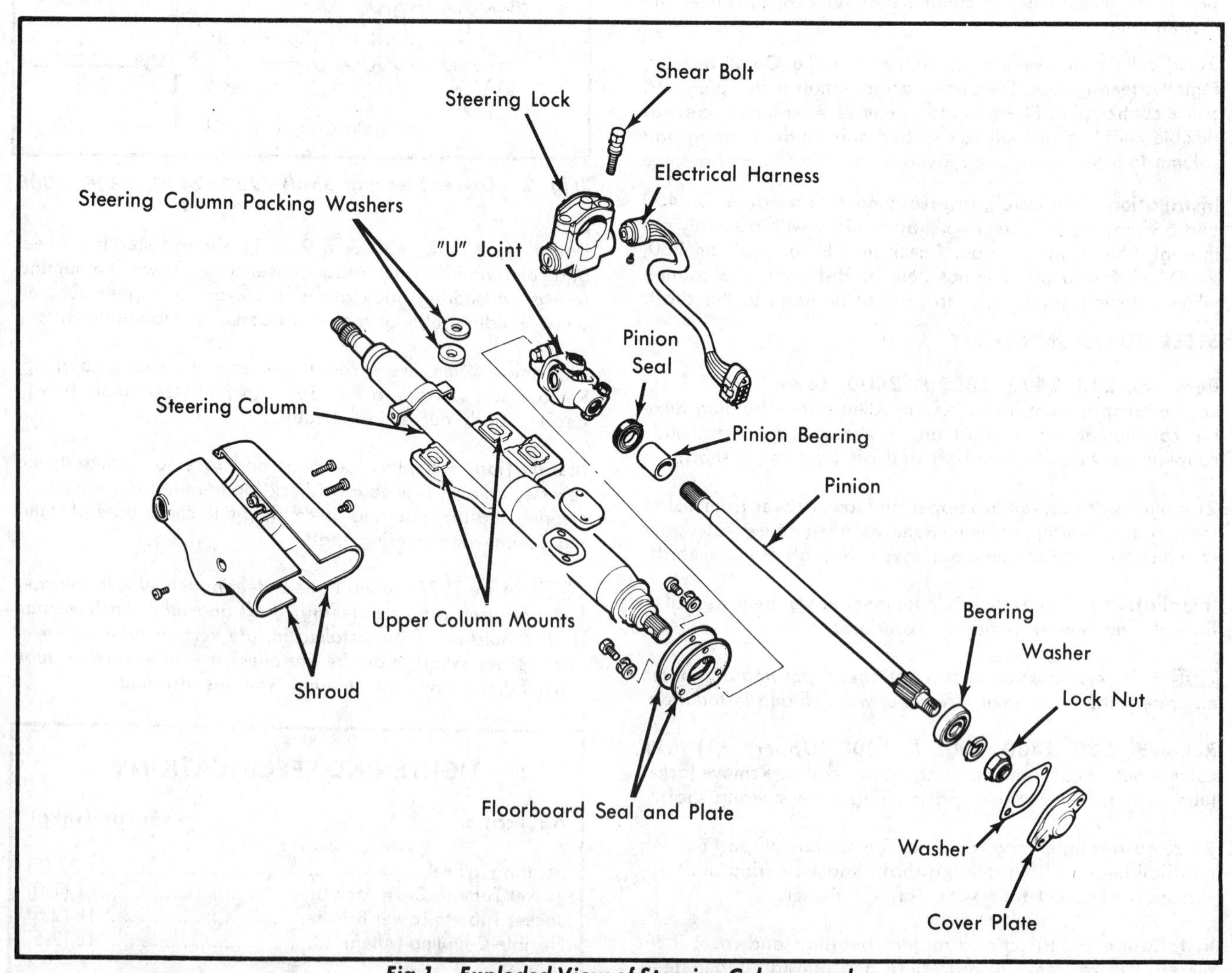

Fig.1 Exploded View of Steering Column and Related Components

MGB (Cont.)

5) Check gauge alignment. Make sure pinion has clearance. If there is interference, adjust shims. If alignment is still not adequate, readjust upper shims (packing washers). Make sure not to exceed .235" (6 mm) thickness with shims. Tighten top bolts. Take off gauge set.

6) Measure gap between column upper mounting flange and body bracket at third bolt position. Fit packing shims equal to gap. Tighten bolt. Make sure to rivet shims to rack mounting bracket before completing job.

TIGHTENING SPECIFICATIONS

Application	Ft. Lbs. (mkg)
Upper Column Mounting Bolts	12-17 (1.7-2.4)
Universal Clamp Bolts	20-22 (2.8-3.0)
Steering Wheel Nut	27-29 (3.7-4.0)

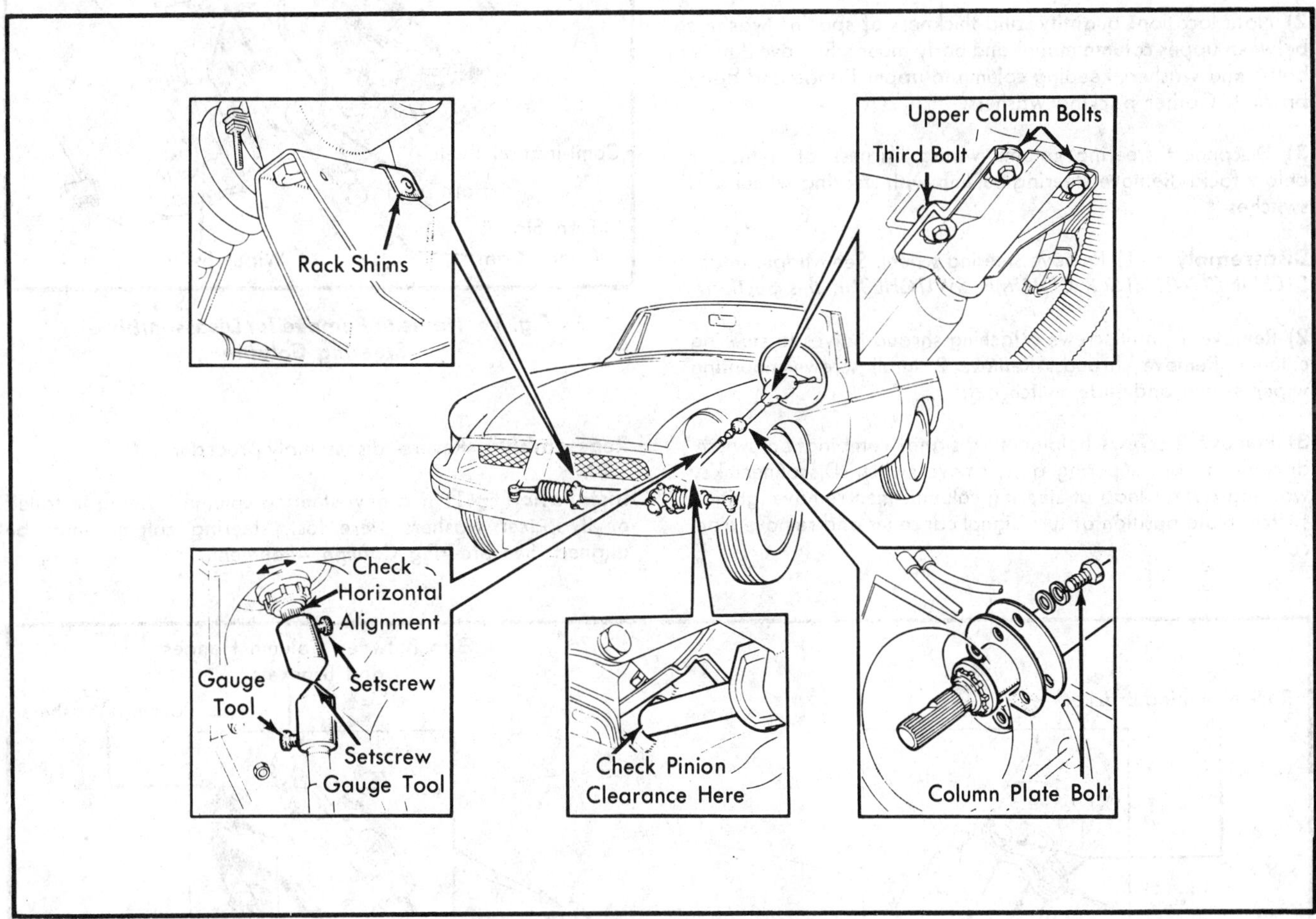

Fig. 2 Steering Column Alignment Steps

MG MIDGET

Midget

REMOVAL & INSTALLATION

STEERING COLUMN

Removal – 1) Disconnect battery cable. Remove heater air intake hose. Remove pinch bolt securing steering column clamp to steering gear pinion shaft, then remove screws securing floor board cover plate.

2) Note location, quantity, and thickness of spacing washers between upper column mount and body mount. Remove 3 nuts, bolts, and washers keeping column to upper flange and body bracket. Gather packing washers.

3) Disconnect steering column wiring harness at connector below facia. Remove steering column with steering wheel and switches.

Disassembly – 1) Remove steering wheel. See *Midget under STEERING WHEELS & COLUMN SWITCHES in this Section.*

2) Remove 4 small screws attaching shroud halves to steering column. Remove shrouds. Remove 2 small screws mounting wiper switch and slide switch out.

3) Remove 2 screws holding turn signal combination switch, disconnect horn slip ring and remove switch. Disconnect key warning buzzer lead at steering column, then remove ignition switch. Note position of turn signal canceller and remove from column.

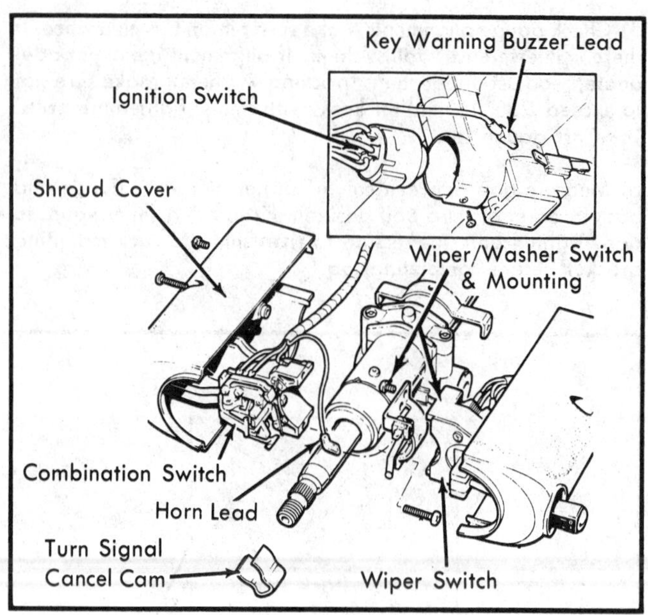

Fig. 1 Items to Remove for Disassembly of Steering Column

Reassembly – Reverse disassembly procedure.

Installation – 1) If a new steering column is being installed or if spacer washers were lost, steering column must be aligned. See *Steering Column Alignment*.

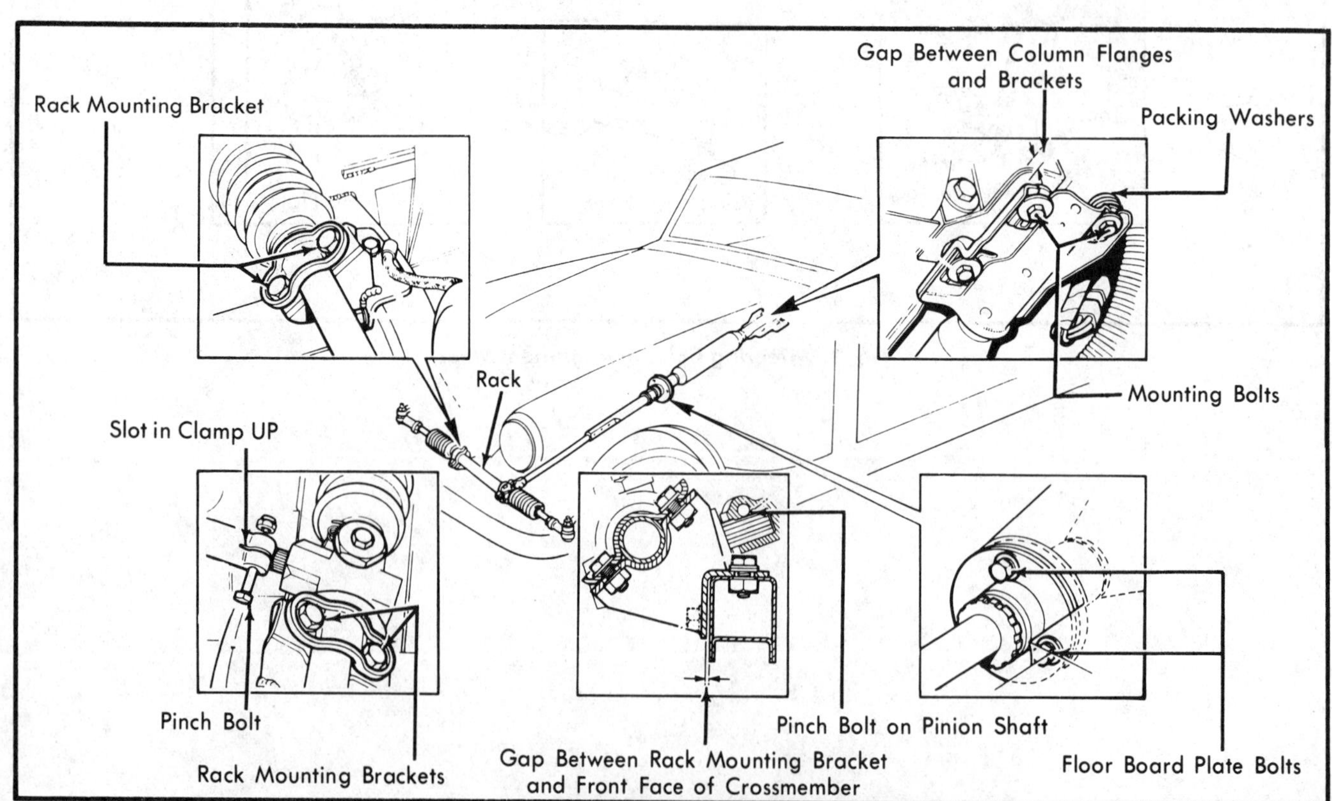

Fig. 2 Preparation and Steps for Completing Steering Rack and Column Alignment

MG MIDGET (Cont.)

2) To install old steering column, reverse removal procedure. Make sure spacer washers are installed in original position. Tighten all bolts and nuts.

STEERING COLUMN ALIGNMENT

NOTE — *Procedure given is for installing column to an existing rack assembly.*

1) Place rack in straight-ahead position with flat of pinch bolt at highest point on pinion. Slide column into position with floor board plate. Put column straight-ahead and position clamp slot up. Fit steering column over pinion shaft.

2) Fit column to upper mounting bracket and finger tighten nut. Make sure column passes through center of floor board plate. Make sure mounting bracket is straight.

3) Measure gap between upper column mounting flanges and brackets. Select correct thickness packing washers and finger tighten nuts.

4) Tighten cover plate at floor board. Tighten pinion shaft pinch bolt.

5) Rotate steering wheel from stop to stop. Note movement of rack assembly in relation to crossmember. Slowly move steering wheel in each direction until neutral position of rack is located.

6) Measure distance between rack mounting bracket at pinion end and front face of body crossmember. Install packing washers thickness of gap.

7) Remove pinion pinch bolts and floor board plate bolts. Push and pull on steering column and make sure column is free to slide. If column is too tight on pinion rack, recheck alignment. When alignment is correct tighten nuts and bolts.

TIGHTENING SPECIFICATIONS

Application	Ft. Lbs. (mkg)
Upper Column Mounting Bolts	12-17 (1.7-2.4)
Pinion Shaft Pinch Bolt	9-12 (1.2-1.7)
Steering Wheel Nut	37 (5.1)

OPEL

All Models

DESCRIPTION

Steering column is a ball type energy absorbing unit with a plastic pin type shaft. Column and shaft will collapse during a front end collision by the shearing of the injected plastic pins. The column is attached at the instrument panel and by a flexible joint at the steering gear.

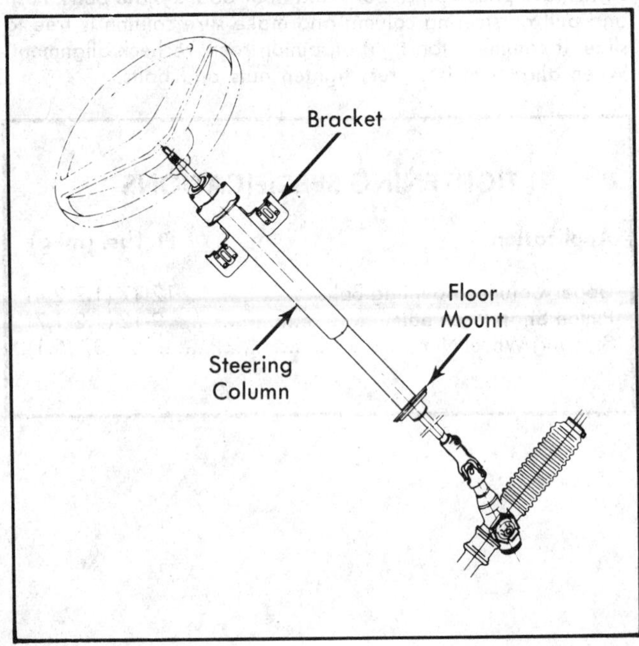

Fig. 1 Assembled View of Steering Column Assembly

REMOVAL & INSTALLATION

Removal – Disconnect battery negative cable. Remove flexible joint bolt and two lower column guide bolts. Remove two column-to-instrument panel nuts and disconnect electrical connections. Withdraw column and shaft assembly.

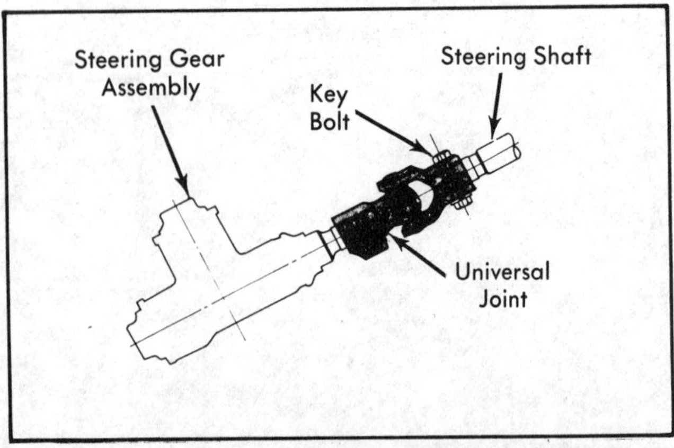

Fig. 2 Flexible Joint Connecting Steering Shaft with Steering Gear

Installation – Install steering column assembly and loosely install two upper column-to-instrument panel nuts. Insert steering shaft into flexible coupling and torque key bolt nut to specification. Slide lower column guide down and bolt to floor pan. Position front wheels straight ahead and install steering wheel, making sure the turn signal cancelling pin is in the hole in the back of steering wheel. Install steering wheel washer and nut, then torque nut to specification.

OVERHAUL

Disassembly – 1) Remove two horn button retaining screws, disconnect horn contact, then remove steering wheel nut and washer. Use suitable steering wheel puller and remove steering wheel. Remove screws from upper and lower column covers and hazard warning switch and remove switch unit.

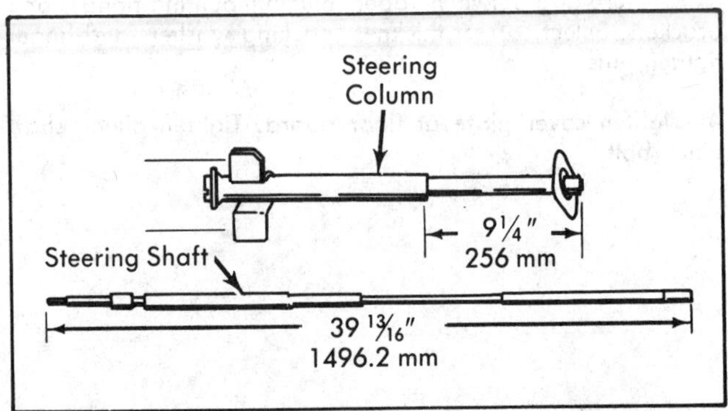

Fig. 3 Steering Column Shaft Measurement Locations

2) Remove two retaining screws and take out windshield washer and wiper switch. Remove snap ring, washer and three attaching bolts on column flange, then remove lock cylinder housing, lower washer and shaft. Pry out lower column rubber bushing with a screwdriver.

Inspection – Check measurement of lower column and steering column shaft for correct measurement *(See Fig. 3)*. If not to specifications replace component.

Assembly – 1) Assemble flat washer, lock cylinder housing, washer and snap ring on the shaft. Then install shaft assembly in the steering column and install lock cylinder retaining screws.

2) Install windshield wiper/washer switch and combination turn signal, headlight dimmer, and hazard warning flasher switch. Install upper and lower column covers and hazard warning button.

TIGHTENING SPECIFICATIONS

Application	Ft. Lbs. (mkg)
Key Bolt	18 (2.49)
Steering Wheel Nut	22 (3.04)

PEUGEOT

504

NOTE – *Procedures covering Peugeot 604 steering column not available.*

DESCRIPTION

Steering column consists of an upper and lower steering shaft connected by a universal joint. Steering shaft utilizes a rubber flexible coupling at its lower end to help absorb road shocks. Mounted on the steering column are a steering lock, gearshift control rod assembly, lighting switch, and turn signal switch.

REMOVAL & INSTALLATION

Removal – 1) Disconnect battery. Release gear change control rod and selector rod from their respective levers. Remove top pinch bolt from flexible rubber coupling.

2) Remove the lower steering column covering. Move pin retaining clip on the gearshift column upward (clip located opposite steering lock). Using a suitable drift, remove the pin.

3) Unscrew clamp bolt from lower collar of steering column universal joint (near foot pedals). Slide lower portion of steering column downward until it touches the flexible coupling.

Fig. 1 Under Instrument Panel View

4) Disconnect wiring from steering lock, and separate three wiring connectors from steering column wiring harness. Unscrew two bolts retaining handbrake lever support to instrument panel.

5) Remove four column-to-instrument panel retaining nuts. Simultaneously lower the gearshift column and steering column (move the handbrake support lever to release column wiring harness).

6) Withdraw the upper steering column assembly. Pull lower portion of steering column into vehicle interior. Remove handbrake outer cable stop clamp to enable withdrawl of handbrake return lever.

7) Remove four nuts securing steering column toeboard plate. Disengage handbrake lever support from its securing studs, to assist in removal of column plate. Extract lower gear change control assembly with toeboard plate and gasket.

Installation – 1) Replace toeboard plate gasket. Install lower gear change control assembly and handbrake return lever support. Secure the toeboard plate and support for handbrake return lever.

2) Reconnect gear selector and control rods to their respective levers. Secure handbrake outer cable stop clamp to underside of floor. Ensure free movement of handbrake lever (no free play or binding).

3) Grease lower steering column bushing, then insert lower column into place in flexible rubber coupling. Position upper steering column assembly, simultaneously connecting the steering column and gearshift column to instrument panel. Insert a new pin into the gearshift column and replace retaining clip.

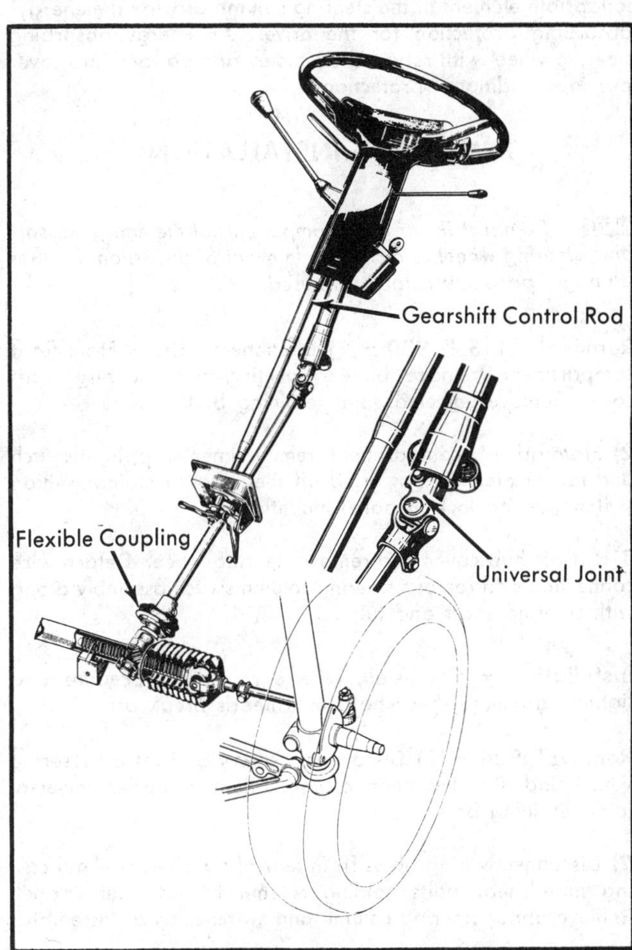

Fig. 2 Steering Column Assembly with Detail of Universal Joint Connection

4) Secure the lower part of the universal joint on steering column, using a new bolt, nut, and washer. Stake-lock the nut. Reconnect all steering column wiring and secure the harness under instrument panel.

5) Use a new bolt, nut, and washer to secure flexible coupling to the lower steering column. Stake-lock the nut. Attach handbrake lever support to instrument panel. Reconnect battery and check operations of all electrical equipment previously disconnected. Replace lower column cover.

TIGHTENING SPECIFICATIONS

Application	Ft. Lbs. (mkg)
Toeboard Plate Nuts	7.2 (1.00)
Handbrake Outer Cable Stop Clamp	3.6 (0.50)
Column-to-Instrument Panel Nuts	7.2 (1.00)
Universal Joint Nut	7.2 (1.00)
Flexible Coupling Nut	7.2 (1.00)

PORSCHE

911S
924
930 Turbo Carrera

DESCRIPTION

The steering column assemblies on all Porsche models are essentially the same, consisting of a three-piece, energy-absorbing unit, with the three pieces connected by two universal joints. The offset design of the steering shaft and the collapsible element in the steering column provide the energy-absorbing protection for the driver. An energy absorbing steering wheel with rebound chambers and padded hub cover provides additional protection.

REMOVAL & INSTALLATION

NOTE – *Do not strike or bend components of the energy absorbing steering wheel and column. In event of distortion or other damage, parts must not be re-used.*

Removal, 911S & 930 – 1) Disconnect battery. From front compartment, remove blower, ducting and steering shaft cover. Remove universal joint retaining bolt.

2) From driver's compartment, remove knee strip, light switch and tachometer. Drill or grind off shear bolts holding ignition switch/steering lock in panel mounting.

3) Lift off hub cover and remove steering wheel. Detach wire connection and remove steering column switch assembly along with steering shaft and tube.

Installation – To install, reverse removal procedure and tighten attaching shear bolts until heads break off.

Removal, 924 – 1) Disconnect battery and lift off steering wheel pad. Remove steering wheel. Remove upper universal joint retaining bolt.

2) Disconnect wiring plugs from rear of switches. Drill out casing tube shear bolts holding column to instrument panel. Remove upper steering column and switches as an assembly.

Installation – To install, reverse removal procedure noting the following: Tighten shear bolts holding column to panel until heads break off. Steering must be centered and hub lubricated when installing steering wheel. Tighten to specified torque with spokes in horizontal position.

STEERING COLUMN ASSEMBLY

Disassembly, 911S & 930 – 1) With column out of vehicle and switches removed from column, drive steering shaft out of tube. Remove lower end circlip and lower ball bearing.

2) Press Seeger ring out of top end of steering shaft tube. Remove ball bearing and contact ring.

Reassembly – 1) Install ball bearing against circlip at lower end of steering column and seat bottom circlip against bearing. Circlips must seat in recessed grooves. Place contact ring and upper bearing together on steering shaft.

2) With section of pipe, drive bearing into place on shaft. Pipe should contact inner race only. Complete assembly in reverse order of disassembly.

Disassembly, 924 – Remove turn signal and windshield wiper switches. Remove circlip and upper ball bearing from housing.

Reassembly – 1) Reverse disassembly procedures and note the following: Drive ball bearing in up to stop in housing. Switches must be in OFF position when installed.

2) Lubricate needle bearing at lower end with multi-purpose grease. Use light coat of silicone grease or talcum powder on rubber bearing.

3) Drive steering shaft spacer sleeve onto shaft so that top of sleeve is 1.614" (41 mm) below top of shaft. Cancelling tab of turn signal release ring must face to right.

TIGHTENING SPECIFICATIONS

Application	Ft. Lbs. (mkg)
Universal Joint Bolts	18-25 (2.5-3.5)
Steering Wheel Nut	
911 & 930	54 (7.5)
924	25-40 (3.5-5.5)
Steering Column Switch to Casing (Allen)	8-14 (1-2)

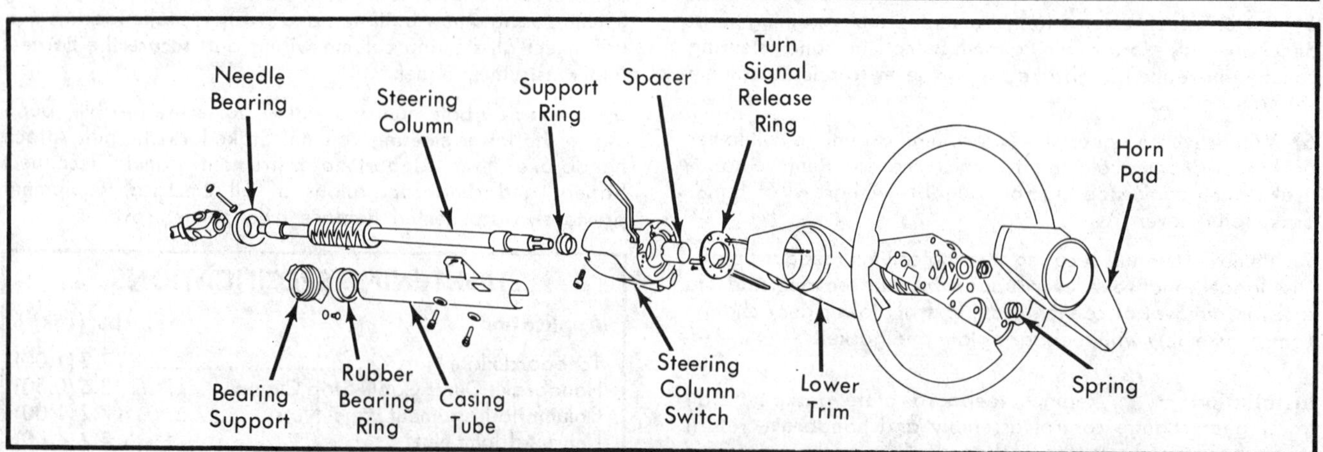

Fig. 1 **Porsche 924 Steering Column**

RENAULT

R-5
R-12
R-17

DESCRIPTION

Vehicles are equipped with an energy-absorbing collapsible column. The steering column is designed in two separate sections, which are joined by a universal joint. The upper portion of the column is designed with a sliding section which compresses on vehicle impact. At the lower end of the bottom section, the steering column is connected to the pinion flange of the steering gear through a flexible rubber coupling.

REMOVAL & INSTALLATION

STEERING COLUMN

Removal – 1) Disconnect battery cables, place steering in lock position, remove center steering wheel pad, nut, and pull steering wheel from shaft. Remove combination lighting switch housing. Remove switch retaining bolts and free switch from column. **NOTE** – *On R-5 the instrument panel and fuse box must also be removed.*

2) Mark column clamp position in relation to column tube. Remove bolt securing gear control clamp. Using suitable tool (B. Vi. 315), unscrew gear control ball joint by freeing clamp on steering column. Remove glove tray.

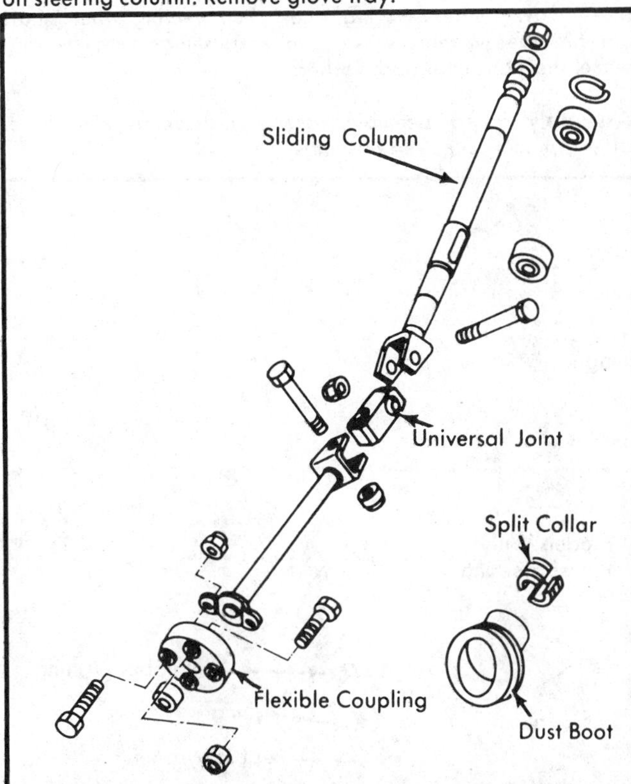

Fig. 1 Renault Steering Column with Related Components

3) Mark electrical wiring on steering lock and stop light switch (for reassembly), then disconnect from harness. Disconnect clutch and brake pedal return springs. Remove clip and take off pedals.

4) Free outer cable from its stop on pedal assembly bracket. Remove steering column universal joint pin at pedal assembly end. Remove steering column top retaining fixture (to free retaining pin, disconnect speedometer cable).

5) On vehicles without Master-Vac, remove two screws securing master cylinder and steering column. If equipped with Master-Vac, remove extra lower bolt also. Unbolt steering column from flexible coupling. Pull column assembly through firewall and into passenger compartment.

Installation, All Models – 1) To install, reverse removal procedure, noting the following: Tighten column upper securing clamp at end of installation. Set gear at center position before connecting universal joint (if separated) in the following manner:

2) Insert and tighten lower bolt, then insert upper bolt, turn steering to right lock, have an assistant hold in this position while tightening upper bolt. When wheels are in straight ahead position, upper universal joint bolt must be pointing upward. On R-5 turn steering wheel 1/4 turn right or left and tighten upper bolt.

3) Check and adjust as necessary: Clutch clearance, master cylinder clearance, brake light switch, gear shift control alignment, and operation of all disconnected electrical components.

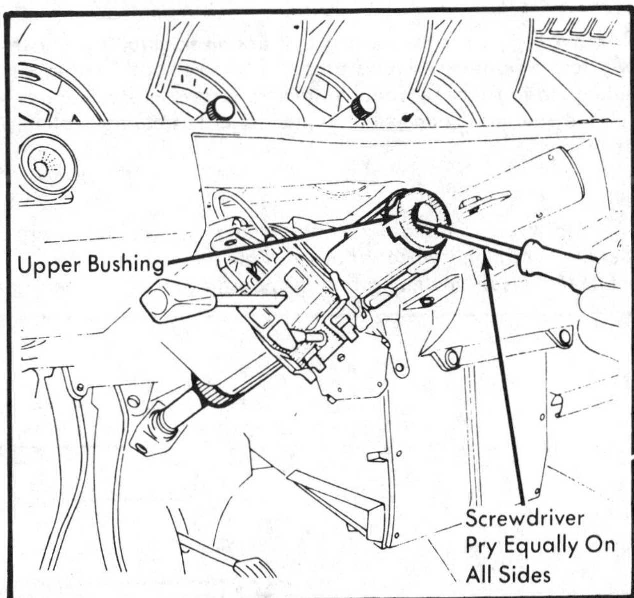

Fig. 2 Using a Screwdriver to Pry Out Upper Steering Column Bushing

OVERHAUL

REPLACING COLUMN BUSHINGS

Disassembly, All Models – Disconnect battery. Remove steering wheel, combination switch, and stoplight switch. On R-5 Remove instrument panel, directional indicator switch and fusebox. Free upper bushing snap ring. Dismantle universal joint, then tap steering shaft downward, until lower bushing is free. Pry out upper bushing with screwdriver.

Assembly – 1) Coat new bushings with suitable grease. Position lower split bushing on steering shaft and fit an old bushing below it (which has been turned down .079", 2 mm in diameter).

2) Insert lower bushing by drawing steering shaft upward, then push it back slightly to recover old bushing. Using a suitable sleeve, insert upper bushing. Then reassemble snap ring, universal joint, and components removed from top of shaft.

SAAB

99

DESCRIPTION

Steering columns used on this model is a safety, telescopic type. The lower portion of the steering shaft is designed to retract into the upper portion when frontal impact is experienced. Steering column tube is mounted at one end to pedal bracket and at other end to body. An intermediate shaft, with "U" joints at each end, transmit steering column movement to steering gear. Models with power steering units are provided with a double "U" joint.

REMOVAL & INSTALLATION

STEERING COLUMN

Removal – Unscrew locking bolt at universal joint. Remove two lower retaining screws at pedal bracket and two upper column-to-instrument panel retaining screws. Detach quick-release wiring connection and lift out steering column assembly.

Installation – Position steering column tube in place with steering shaft and wheel attached. Bolt steering shaft to "U" joint. Make sure mounting bolt is opposite groove in steering shaft. Tighten bolt. Mount steering column tube to pedal bracket and body. Connect electrical harness. Adjust steering wheel.

INTERMEDIATE SHAFT SEALING BELLOWS

Removal – Remove cover under instrument panel. Unscrew steering column-to-intermediate shaft retaining screw. Unbolt column tube from instrument panel. Pull steering column from intermediate shaft. Cut off old sealing bellows.

Installation – Lubricate suitable installation tool (899581) with vaseline or soapy water. Place tool against intermediate shaft. Ease new bellows over tool and joint. Ensure bellows are not damaged in this process. Replace steering column into intermediate shaft. Make sure that shaft is pushed in so that screw is located directly opposite the groove. Tighten retaining screw. Attach steering column to instrument panel. Check position of steering wheel and adjust if necessary. Fit bellows in dash panel. Replace cover under instrument panel.

OVERHAUL

STEERING COLUMN

Disassembly – Remove three retaining screws and remove plastic cover under steering wheel. Pull steering wheel shaft out of tube. Withdraw two rubber bushings with steering wheel shaft bushings and washers.

Assembly – To assemble, reverse disassembly procedure, after replacing required bushings.

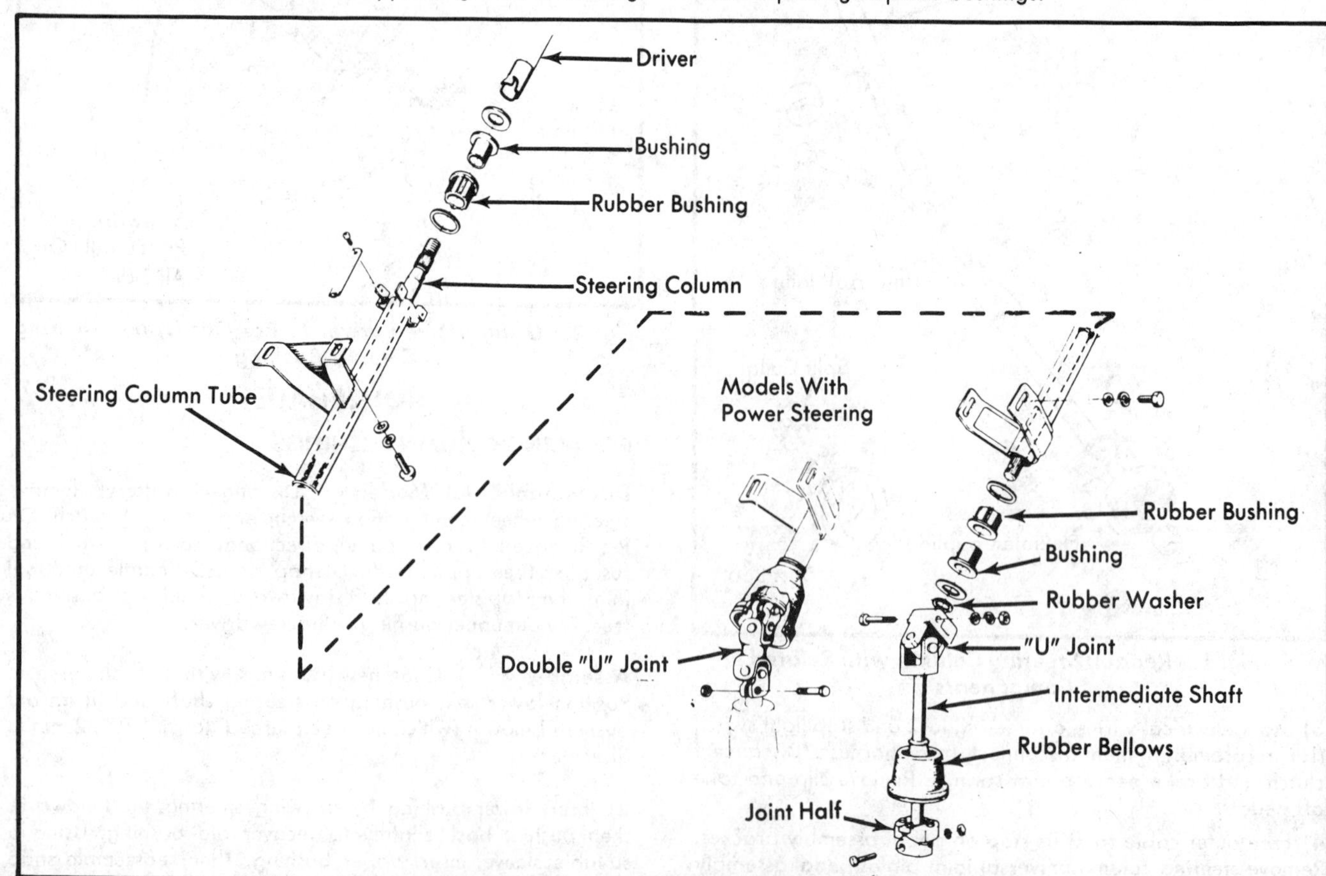

Fig. 1 Exploded View of Steering Column Assembly

SUBARU

1600

DESCRIPTION

Steering column assembly consists of a steering wheel incorporating a horn control, a combination turn signal, hazard warning, and headlight dimmer switch assembly, and an energy absorbing steering shaft. The steering column is connected to the steering gear through a universal joint coupling. The energy absorbing steering shaft is designed to collapse during a front end collision. An anti-theft locking mechanism is provided with the ignition switch. With ignition switch in "LOCK" position, and key removed, the steering shaft is locked.

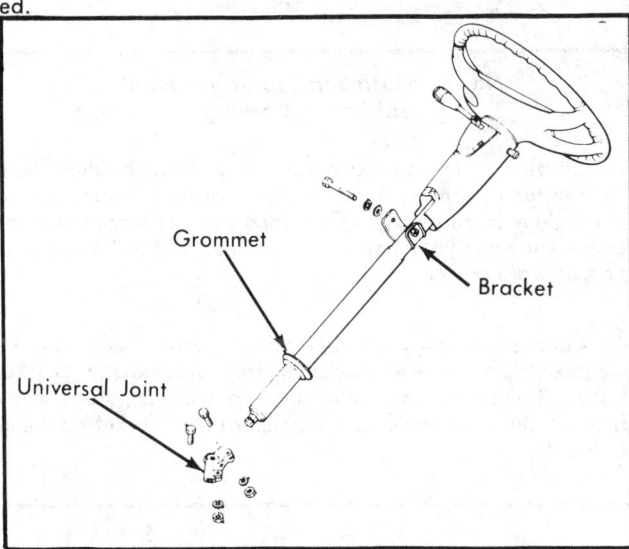

Fig. 1 Subaru Steering Column Assembly

REMOVAL & INSTALLATION

Removal – Disconnect battery, then remove steering wheel. *See Subaru under STEERING WHEEL & COLUMN SWITCHES in this section.* Disconnect lower end of steering shaft from universal joint. Remove steering column bracket bolts at instrument panel, then pull column assembly from toe board.

Installation – To install, reverse removal procedure and note the following: Temporarily tighten bracket bolts after installing column assembly to instrument panel. Tighten universal joint bolt after checking alignment of steering shaft and pinion shaft, then tighten column bracket bolts at instrument panel. After steering wheel is installed, check clearance between steering wheel and column cover. If clearance exceeds .04-.12" (1.0-3.0 mm), loosen column cover screws and adjust cover.

OVERHAUL

Disassembly – Remove screws retaining column cover to steering column, then remove hazard warning switch knob and cover. To remove steering shaft, proceed as follows: Remove snap ring, spacer, washer, and rubber washer. Remove screws retaining housing and bearing assembly to steering column, then drive assembly out of column by using a screwdriver. Remove shaft from steering column.

Inspection – 1) Universal joint should have no play in any direction. Replace if any play exists. Flex universal joint and check for binding. Replace if torque required to flex joint exceeds 0.43 ft. lbs. (0.06 mkg). Check plastic washer for damage, and serration for wear.

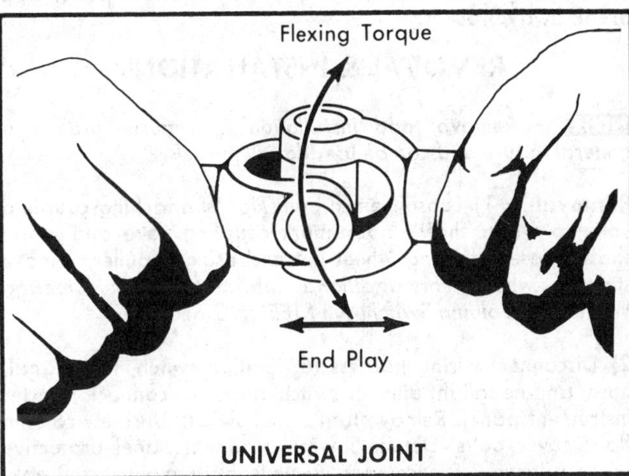

Fig. 2 Flexing "U" Joint to Check Free Play

2) Check length and run-out of steering shaft. Shaft length should be 33.12-33.20" (841.3-843.3 mm). Shaft run-out should be less than .02" (0.6 mm). Replace shaft if not within specifications, or if inspection shows any shaft damage. Check upper and lower steering column bearings for wear or damage and replace if necessary.

Reassembly – To reassemble, reverse disassembly procedure and note the following: Use a suitable locking compound on screws retaining upper bearing and housing assembly to steering column. Install steering shaft into column from lower end. After shaft, washers, spacers, and retainers have been installed, check shaft end play. If end play is more than .010" (0.3 mm), add a spacer to correct. Spacers are available in thicknesses of .012" and .020" (0.3 and 0.5 mm). With steering wheel in place, check clearance between steering wheel and column cover. If clearance exceeds .04-.12" (1.0-3.0 mm), loosen column cover screws and adjust cover.

TIGHTENING SPECIFICATIONS

Application	Ft. Lbs. (mkg)
Steering Wheel Nut	20-29 (2.77-4.01)
Column Bracket Bolt	12-14 (1.66-1.94)
Universal Joint Bolt	16-19 (2.2-2.6)

TOYOTA, EXCEPT COROLLA & LAND CRUISER FJ55

Celica
Corona
Pickup
Land Cruiser FJ40

DESCRIPTION

Vehicles incorporate energy absorbing steering columns which collapse on impact. The steering mainshaft telescopes inward while the column tube compacts around an expanded metal section. The mainshaft is connected to the gear through a flexible coupling. Column is mounted to the instrument panel on a break-away bracket.

REMOVAL & INSTALLATION

NOTE – *Removal and installation procedures are of a general nature and can be used for all models.*

Removal – 1) Loosen pinch bolt *(Fig. 1)* attaching coupling yoke to worm shaft. Index mark coupling yoke and worm shaft. Loosen steering wheel nut and using a puller, remove steering wheel. *For additional information, See Steering Wheel and Column Switches in STEERING Section.*

2) Disconnect wiring harness for ignition switch, turn signal, horn, and headlight dimmer switch at plug-in connector under instrument panel. Remove turn signal switch. Unscrew column floor cover bolts. Detach lower instrument panel protective cover (plastic), if necessary. Remove bolts mounting break-away bracket. Withdraw column assembly toward inside of passanger compartment.

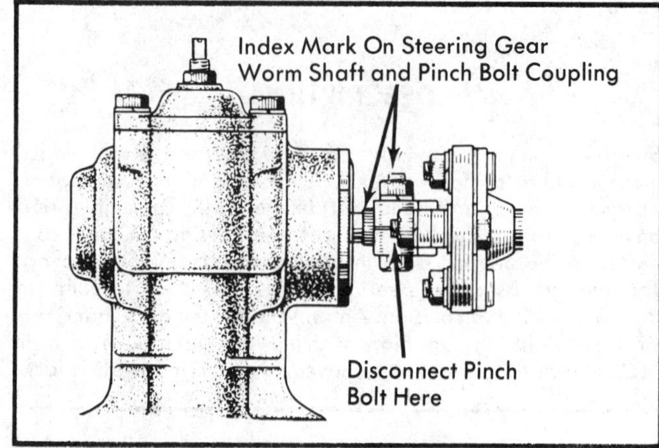

Fig. 1 Pinch Bolt Separation Point and Index Marking

Installation – 1) Insert steering column through column hole from inside of vehicle, align coupling yoke on steering worm, and tighten pinch bolt. **NOTE** – *Yoke and worm are in proper alignment when yoke bolt hole is aligned with cut-away portion of worm spline.*

2) Coat break-away bracket center portion with suitable weatherstrip adhesive. Finger tighten break-away bracket bolts. Tighten column hole cover bolts and break-away bracket nuts, then insert and tighten center bracket retaining bolt.

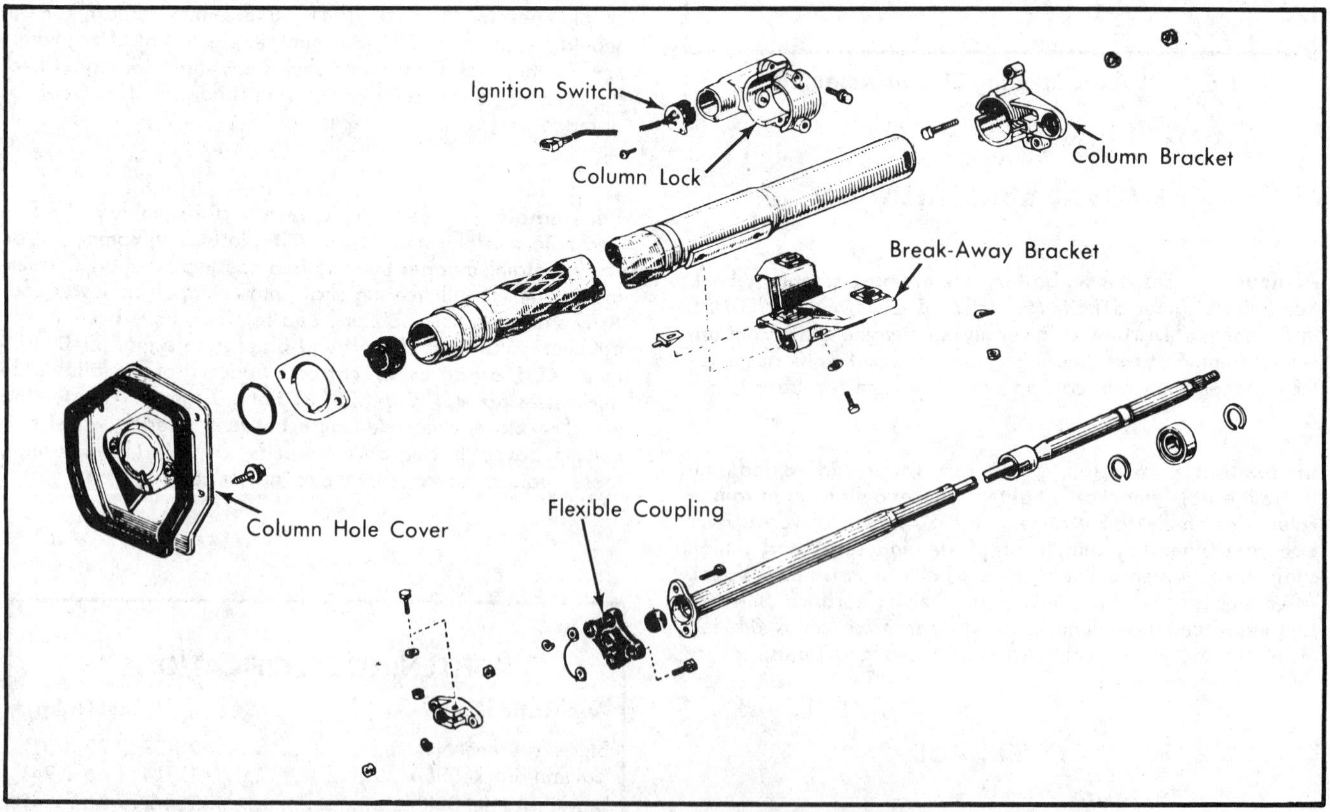

Fig. 2 Toyota Energy Absorbing Steering Column (Celica Shown; Others Similar)

TOYOTA COROLLA

Corolla

DESCRIPTION

Vehicles incorporate an energy absorbing steering column. The steering column is connected directly to the steering gear, having the steering worm as an integral part of the shaft. The column collapses on impact by shearing pin inserts. An expanded metal section of the column housing is also incorporated to assist in absorbing impact energy.

REMOVAL & INSTALLATION

STEERING COLUMN

Removal – 1) Working from inside engine compartment, remove bolt mounting steering mainshaft to steering gear box *(Fig. 1)*. Before separating units, index mark for reinstallation and place front wheels in straight-ahead position.

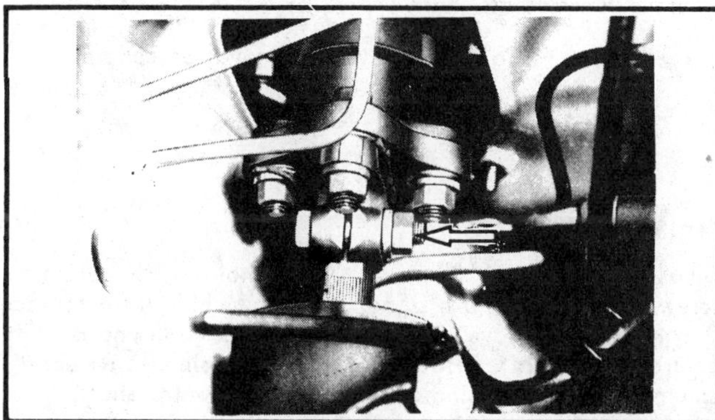

Fig. 1 Pinch Bolt Mounting Mainshaft to Steering Gear

2) Remove steering wheel and turn signal switch. *See Steering Wheel and Column Switch in STEERING Section.* From inside passenger compartment, remove bolts mounting hole cover to firewall. Remove nuts and bolts mounting the break-away bracket *(Fig. 2)* then withdraw steering column assembly into passenger compartment and free from vehicle.

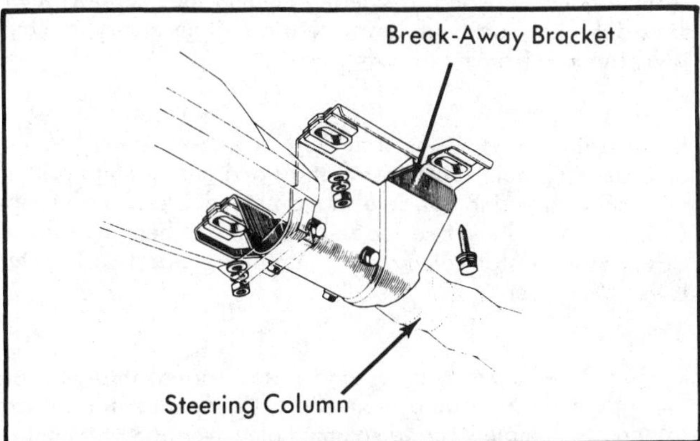

Fig. 2 Relative Position of Breakaway Bracket and Hardware

Installation – Working from inside passanger compartment, insert steering column assembly through column hole in firewall. Align index marks made during removal and tighten pinch bolt. Fit break-away bracket, but leave bolts finger tight. Position column hole cover in place with a new "O" ring seal. Push in column tube until fully seated, then tighten nuts mounting break-away bracket. Make sure hole cover locating pin contacts cover as shown in *Fig. 3.*

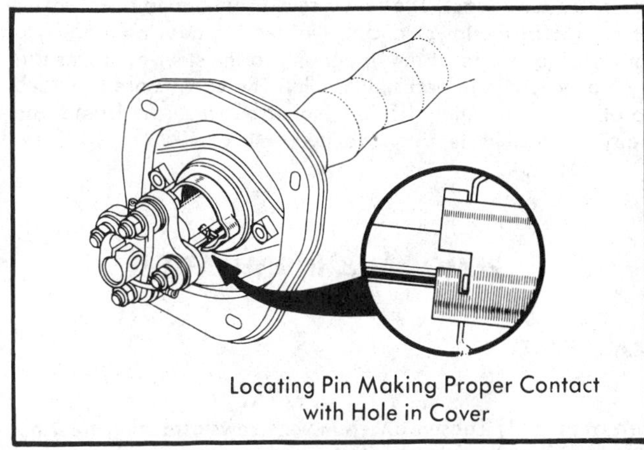

Locating Pin Making Proper Contact with Hole in Cover

Fig. 3 Proper Installation of Steering Column

OVERHAUL

STEERING COLUMN

Disassembly – Remove upper steering column bracket. From column tube, pull out mainshaft, then remove dust seal. From lower end of mainshaft, remove flexible coupling unit. Remove bolts attaching column plate, rotate column tube counterclockwise and remove it from column hole cover.

Inspection – Check mainshaft for out-of-alignment and looseness in plastic pin. Inspect column tube for deformation. Look closely at flexible coupling for deterioration, also check dust seal "O" ring for damage.

Reassembly – To reassemble components, reverse disassembly procedure and note the following: Apply a light coat of grease to both sides of "O" ring.

TIGHTENING SPECIFICATIONS

Application	Ft. Lbs. (mkg)
Steering Gear-to-Frame	25-36 (3.5-5.0)
Pitman Arm-to-Sector Shaft	72-101 (10-14)
Column Tube Clamp	22-33 (3.0-4.5)
Steering Wheel Nut	22-29 (3.0-4.0)
Pinch Bolt	14.5-22 (2.0-3.0)

TOYOTA LAND CRUISER FJ55

Land Cruiser FJ55

DESCRIPTION

The steering shaft assembly is composed of two sections. The upper section (mainshaft) is a collapsible unit, designed to compress on impact. The lower section (intermediate shaft) is connected at the lower end to the steering gear housing by a universal joint and at the upper end to the steering mainshaft by a universal joint and sliding joint. These joints are provided to allow a completely flexible mount between the frame and body, to assist in steering stability.

REMOVAL & INSTALLATION

MAIN SHAFT

Removal – 1) Loosen and remove screws attaching steering wheel pad to steering wheel. Remove steering wheel retaining nut and pull wheel from shaft.

2) Remove shift control selector shaft and bushings. Cut safety wire and remove shift fork lock bolt, then slide shift control lever out of control shaft. Remove bolt securing steering worm yoke onto steering main shaft. Disconnect electrical wiring harness and extract back-up light switch (with bracket). Detach turn signal switch.

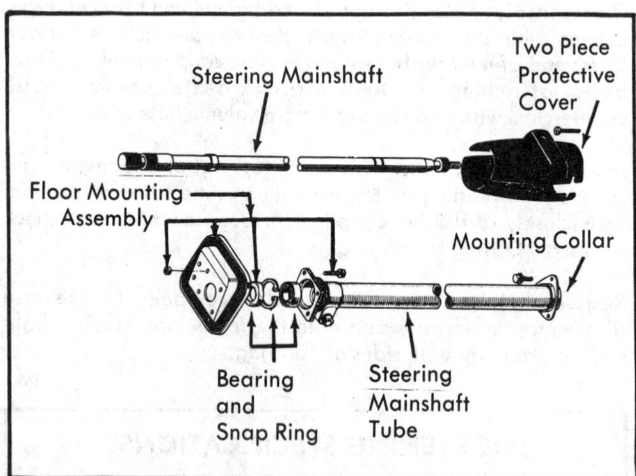

Fig. 1 ***Model FJ55 Land Cruiser Steering Mainshaft with Detail of Mounting Hardware***

3) Remove bolts attaching steering column hole cover onto floor. Remove steering column upper and lower clamps, pull out steering column tube together with steering main shaft toward passenger compartment.

Installation – To install, reverse removal procedure.

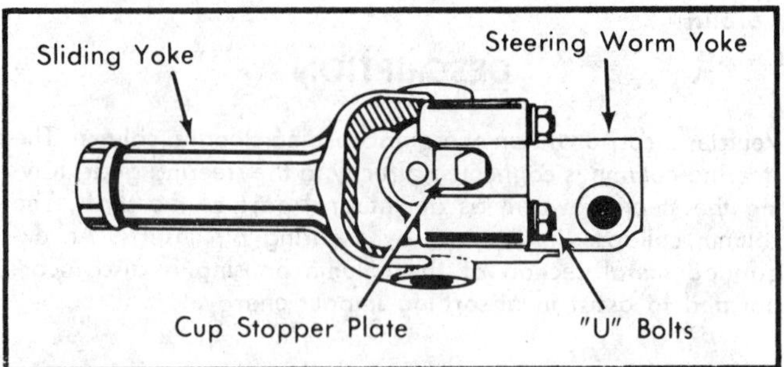

Fig. 2 ***Assembled View of Intermediate Shaft Coupling***

INTERMEDIATE SHAFT

Removal – Raise front of vehicle and support with stands. Pry off wheel cap and remove left front wheel. Remove bolts securing steering worm yokes to worm and main shaft. Remove intermediate shaft.

Installation – To install, reverse removal procedure.

OVERHAUL

MAIN SHAFT

Disassembly – 1) Remove turn signal switch retaining screws and remove turn signal switch assembly from contact ring housing. Remove "E" ring and washer from end of shift control upper shaft. Detach contact ring housing from steering column tube. Pull housing out. Remove shift control shaft.

2) Remove steering column hole cover and shift control shaft lower support bracket from steering column support. Remove steering shaft upper bearing, thrust collar, and spring. Loosen steering column lower clamp bolt and pull column tube out from support.

3) Place steering shaft in vise and straighten claw washer. Remove mainshaft bearing retaining nut and claw washer. Remove hole snap ring in steering column tube support, then drive out mainshaft (with lower bearing). If necessary, remove lower bearing from mainshaft.

Reassembly – 1) Using a suitable drift, press lower bearing onto steering main shaft. Install shaft and bearing into column tube support, using suitable mandrel and press. Install new claw washer, tighten bearing retainer nut and bend up tabs on claw washer. Install column tube onto tube support and tighten lower clamp sercurely.

2) Lubricate upper bearing and install spring, thrust collar, and upper bearing onto main shaft. Check shaft for smooth rotation. Assemble steering column hole cover and shift control shaft lower bracket.

3) Apply grease on shift control shaft lower bushing and shift control upper shaft. Install contact ring housing onto steering column tube. Secure shift control shaft upper portion to the contact ring housing with washer and "E" ring. Install turn signal switch in contact ring housing.

TOYOTA LAND CRUISER FJ55 (Cont.)

INTERMEDIATE SHAFT

Disassembly – Remove cup stopper plates *(Fig. 2)*, then remove "U" bolts securing universal joint spider bearing to steering worm yoke. Separate worm yoke from sliding yoke and shaft. Remove hole snap rings from bearing holes, then remove spider bearing.

Reassembly – 1) Pack spider bearing cups with suitable grease and assemble bearing rollers. Press bearing into one side of sliding shaft. Install bearing seal and complete the installation of spider bearing. Install suitable snap rings in one of the following sizes: .047" (1.20mm), .049" (1.25mm), .051" (1.30mm). Check joint for smooth operation.

2) Connect sliding shaft to steering worm yoke. Install cup stopper plates and "U" bolts. Assemble joint spider bearing onto sliding yoke in same manner. Pack inside hole of sliding yoke with suitable grease. Align cup stopper plates on sliding yoke side and sliding shaft side. Install dust cover and connect sliding shaft with yoke.

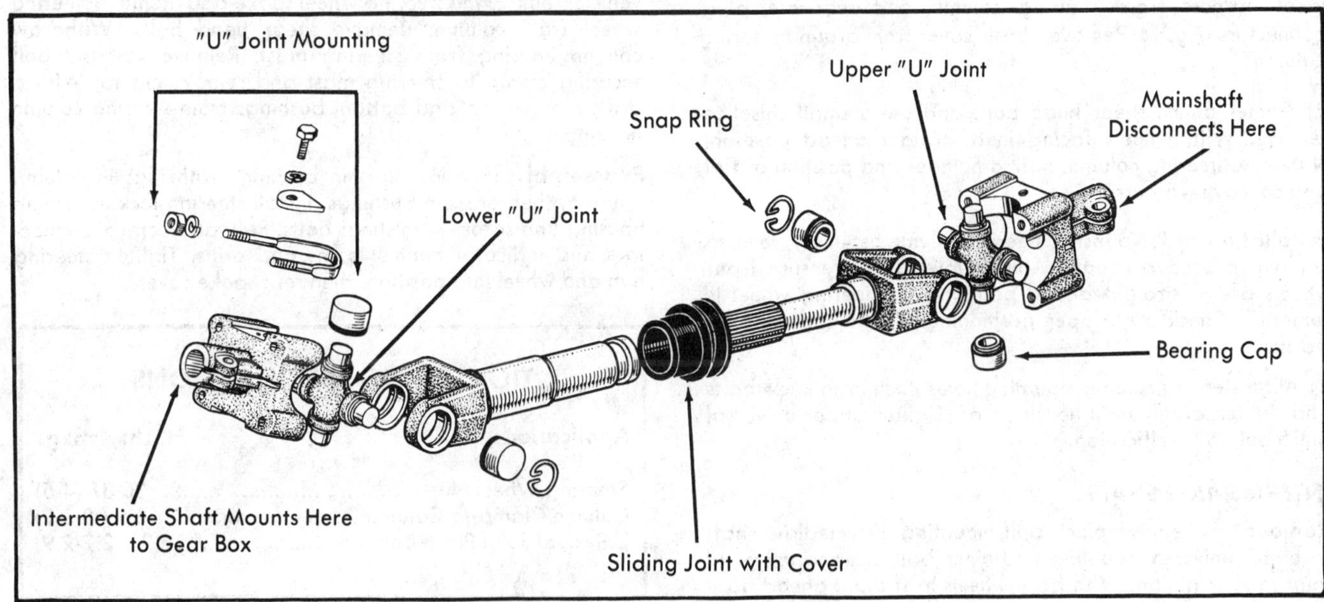

Fig. 3 Exploded View of Land Cruiser FJ55 Intermediate Steering Shaft Components

TRIUMPH TR7

TR7

DESCRIPTION

Steering coulmn houses both ignition switch and column lock device. Steering column is divided into upper and intermediate shafts. Shafts are coupled with flexible universals that attach to steering linkage.

REMOVAL AND INSTALLATION

STEERING COLUMN ASSEMBLY

Removal – 1) Disconnect battery ground. Take out pinch bolt securing upper universal to steering mast. Disconnect electrical harness from steering column and separate plug connectors *(Fig. 1)*. Remove plastic cover from around steering column.

2) Center punch shear head bolts and use a small chisel to remove. With wheels facing in a straight ahead position, withdraw steering column, noting number and position of flat and concave washers.

Installation – 1) To install steering column assembly, reverse removal procedures, noting the following: Make sure front wheels are in straight ahead position and steering wheel is centered. Check for proper positioning of flat and concave washers.

2) Align steering column mounting holes, then install new bolts and tighten evenly until heads shear. Tighten upper universal pinch bolt to specification.

INTERMEDIATE SHAFT

Removal – Remove pinch bolt mounting intermediate shaft to upper universal coupling and pinch bolt securing universal joint to rack pinion. With front wheels in straight ahead position, slide intermediate shaft upward to remove it from pinion shaft universal joint, then pull shaft downward to disengage from upper universal joint.

Installation – To install intermediate shaft, reverse removal procedure, noting the following: Make sure steering wheel is in straight ahead position and splines on intermediate shaft and rack pinion are fully engaged. Tighten pinch bolts to specification.

OVERHAUL

STEERING COLUMN ASSEMBLY

Disassembly – With steering column assembly removed from vehicle, remove the steering wheel spoke pad. Remove steering wheel from column. Remove shear head bolts. Withdraw column housing from steering mast. Remove nut and bolt securing clamp to steering mast and remove clamp. With a drift, remove top and bottom bushings from steering column housing.

Reassembly – Align slots in bushings with lugs in column housing, then press in bushings. Install steering lock in column housing and secure with shear bolts. Refit all electrical connectors and indicator control cams and arms. Tighten steering hub and wheel into position, then refit spoke cover.

TIGHTENING SPECIFICATIONS

Application	Ft. Lbs. (mkg)
Steering Wheel Nut	30-37 (4-5)
Column Clamp-to-Column	6-9 (.8-1.2)
Universal Joint Pinch Bolts	16-21 (2.2-2.9)

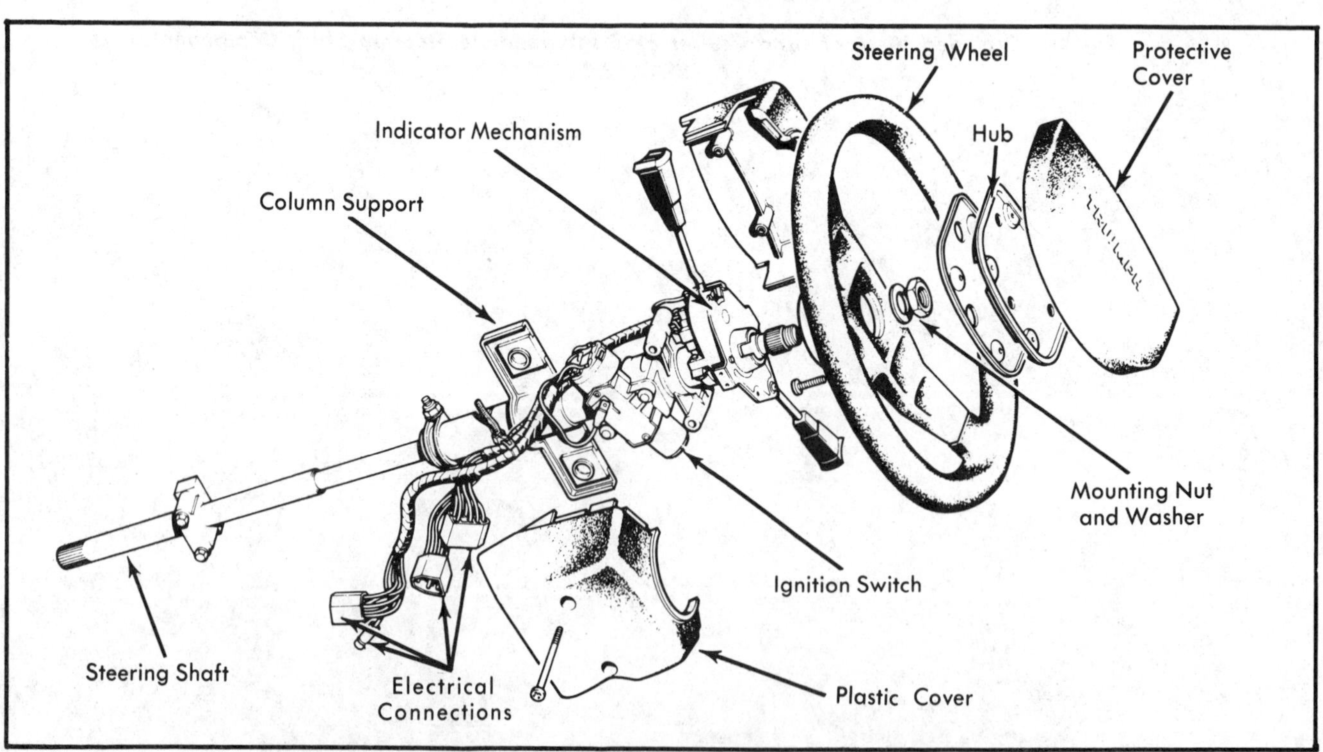

Fig. 1 Partially Disassembled View of TR7 Upper Steering Column

TRIUMPH SPITFIRE

Spitfire

DESCRIPTION

Steering column is a telescoping, safety unit which is designed to compress on impact. The lower section of column will move into the steering column, absorbing impact shock. Column is connected to pinion gear through a flexible coupling and is mounted to the instrument panel on two column supports. A grub screw is inserted through the lower support clamp and retains the lower telescoping portion in place.

REMOVAL & INSTALLATION

Removal – 1) Disconnect battery. Remove driver's parcel shelf. Unscrew pinch bolts securing steering mast to flexible coupling at gear housing. Remove nuts and washers from two bolts securing steering column forward bracket. Withdraw forward support housing and felt liner.

2) Disconnect electrical couplings for horn, turn signal switch, lights, and column lock. Remove two cap screws securing steering column rear bracket, then withdraw both clamp halves and upper plate. Remove steering column assembly with tie bar.

Installation – 1) Set front wheels in straight-ahead position. Hold steering wheel with center spoke straight down, then engage lower end of steering mast in splines of flexible coupling. Slide cardboard tube rearward and fit felt over steering mast housing, ensuring ends of felt are below mast housing.

2) Engage forward ends of tie bar in mounting bolt. Fit felt housing and engage forward mounting bolts, using spring and plain washers under nuts. Ensure spring clip is fitted on mast housing to align with rear clamp bracket. Attach upper and lower clamp halves to mast housing.

3) Place plate in bracket above clamp halves. Enter clamp bolts through tie bar, clamp halves, and mounting bracket. Tighten nuts securing forward bracket. Reconnect electrical leads for horn, turn signal switch, lights, and steering lock. Replace parcel shelf. Connect battery.

OVERHAUL

Disassembly – 1) Remove steering wheel. Detach column switches. Unlock steering column lock. Remove two set bolts and spring washers securing safety clamp, and remove safety clamp and thrust washer.

2) Withdraw lower steering mast. Pull cap from lower end of steering column tube and remove tubular cardboard spacer. Push column housing upward and withdraw turn signal cam. Pull housing toward lower end of column until it presses against column bushing. Depress rubber locating tabs on column lower bushing and withdraw steering mast and lower bushing. Pull bushing from mast. Remove upper bushing.

Assembly – To assemble, reverse disassembly procedure, noting that rubber dots on bushings are facing bottom of tube.

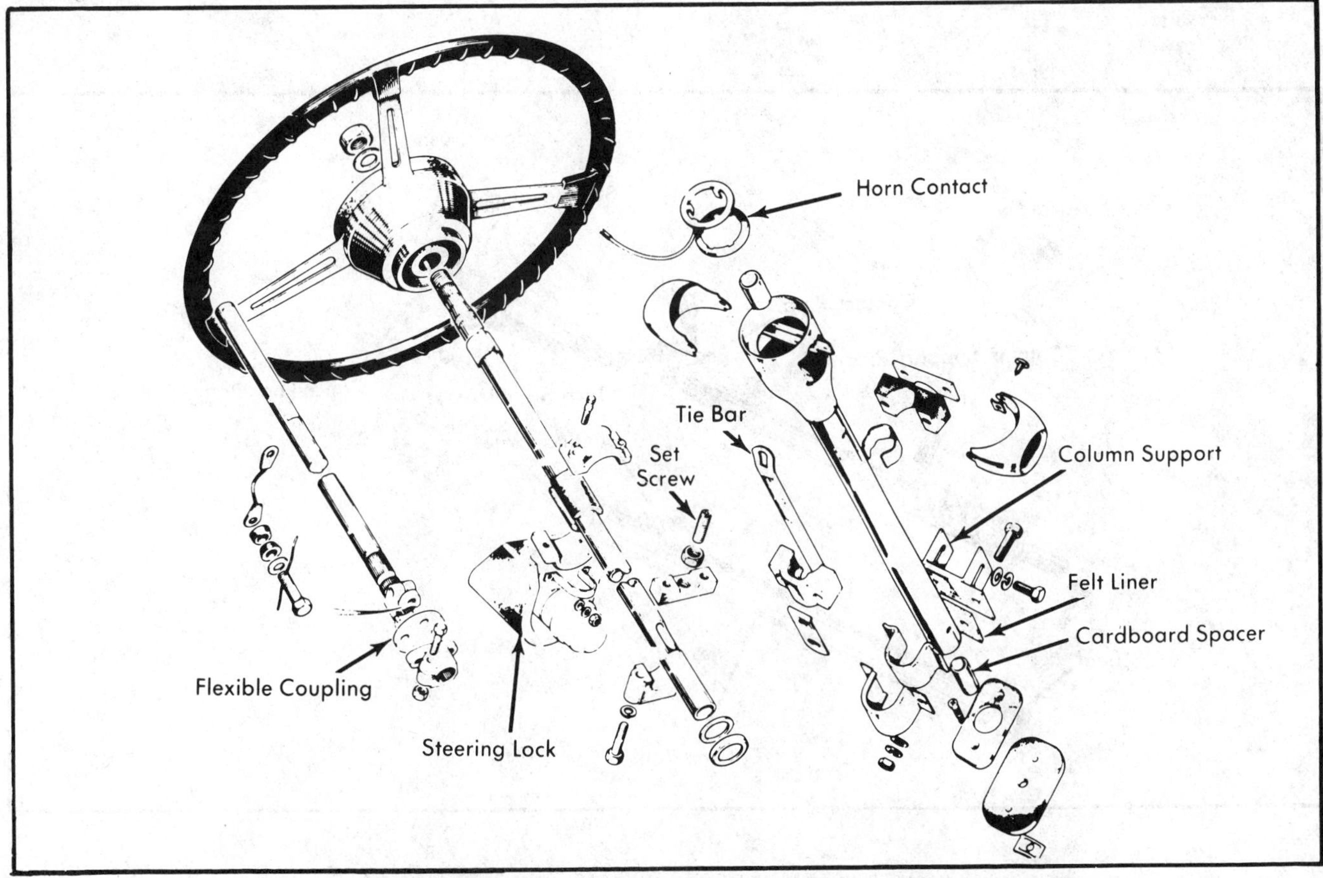

Fig. 1 Spitfire Telescoping Steering Column and Related Components

VOLKSWAGEN TYPE 1

Type 1

DESCRIPTION

The steering column has an energy-absorbing, expanded metal section at the lower end of the column which will collapse on impact. At the upper end of the steering column, the steering wheel is mounted on a collapsible hub, designed to absorb driver impact.

REMOVAL & INSTALLATION

Removal – 1) Disconnect battery ground strap. Remove fuel tank. Unscrew nut from column pinch clamp at flexible coupling. Bend up tab on support ring and remove ring (above expanded metal section, on engine side of firewall).

2) Remove steering wheel and upper column circlip. Turn ignition to "ON" position. Release air pressure from windshield washer reservoir. Disconnect all wiring and hoses from column switches. Remove the two upper column support bolts.

3) Pull column assembly up into passenger compartment. Remove bolt holding column switch to tube and remove switch. Pull tube from column shaft.

Installation – 1) Install switch assembly on column tube and align in original position. Torque socket head screw (located on underside of switch assembly, diagonally opposite to ignition switch). Install seal on lower end of column tube.

2) Position contact ring on steering column, then insert column into tube from below and secure it with circlip at top end. Install column assembly into vehicle, positioning column clamp without pinch bolt. Set front wheels in straight-ahead position and slide column onto flexible coupling. Install clamp bolt with a new self-locking nut.

3) Place support ring above energy-absorbing section and bend down the locking tab. Loosely install column support mounting bolts. Position steering wheel (ensure front wheels are still in straight-ahead position) with spokes horizontal. Install and tighten wheel nut. Adjust gap between steering wheel hub and column switch assembly to .08-.16" (2-4 mm) by moving column tube. Reconnect all wiring and hoses to column.

TIGHTENING SPECIFICATIONS

Application	Ft. Lbs. (mkg)
Steering Wheel Nut	36 (4.98)
Flexible Coupling Clamp Bolt	18 (2.49)
Socket Head Screw (Switch Assembly)	4-7 (.55-.97)
Column Support Bolts	11 (1.52)

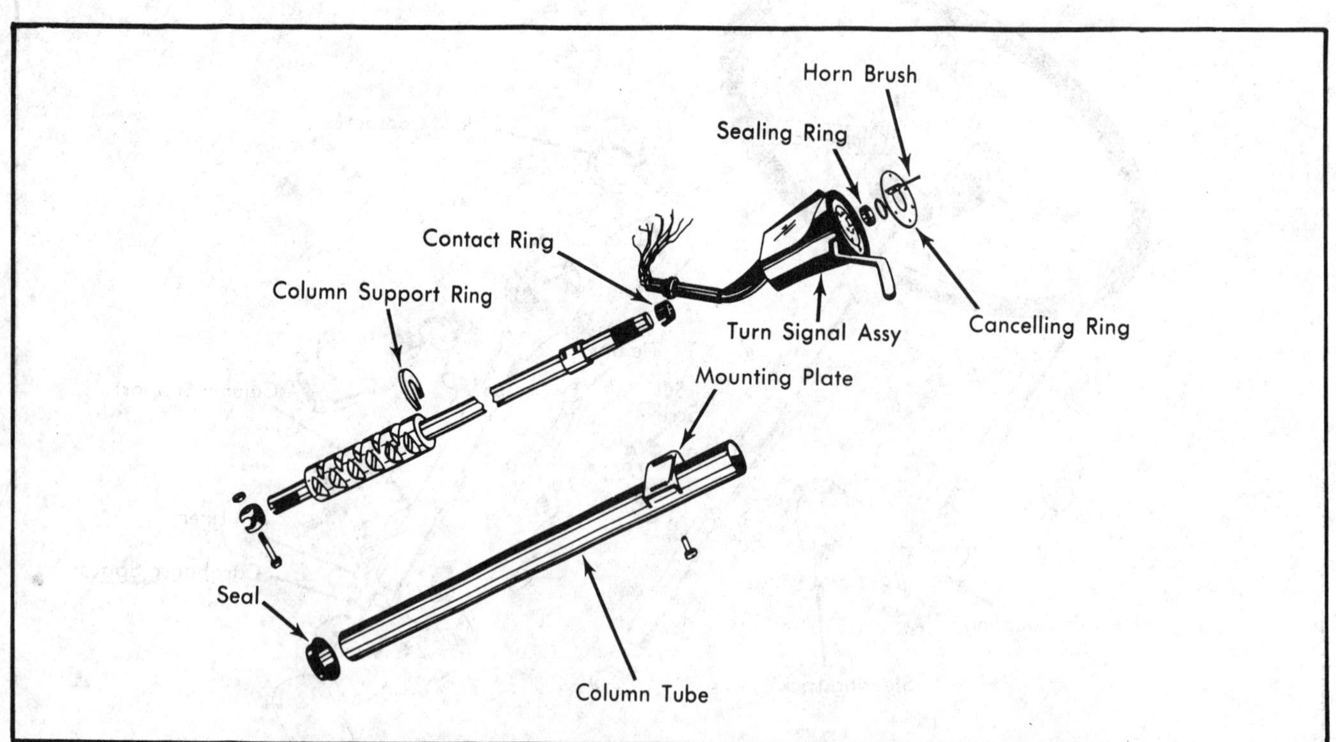

Fig. 1 Volkswagen Type 1 Steering Column and Related Components

VOLKSWAGEN TYPE 2

Type 2

DESCRIPTION

Type 2 Volkswagen models use an energy-absorbing steering column assembly. Mounting support and energy-absorbing bracket are welded to steering column. When frontal impact is encountered, column support detaches from under instrument panel. Bracket then collapses to a predetermined location and support is deflected to side. Steering shaft can be removed separately or entire steering column (with shaft) can be removed as a unit.

STEERING COLUMN ASSEMBLY

Removal – 1) Disconnect battery ground. Disconnect all electrical wires from steering column.

2) Work under vehicle and disconnect horn ground wire. Unbolt steering shaft from coupling at steering gear box pinch bolt.

3) Work between pedals and remove column cover plate. From under instrument panel, unbolt column tube support. Pull steering column assembly out of vehicle as an assembly.

NOTE – *If vehicle has been damaged, entire steering column must be replaced. Do not attempt any repairs.*

Installation – To install, reverse removal procedure and note: Make sure plastic-coated washers are replaced.

STEERING SHAFT

Removal – 1) Disconnect battery. Remove steering wheel. *See Volkswagen under STEERING WHEEL & COLUMN SWITCHES in this Section.* Put ignition/steering lock switch in "ON" position.

2) Work between pedals and remove steering column cover plate. Bend up lock plate then remove bolt keeping steering shaft coupler to steering gear.

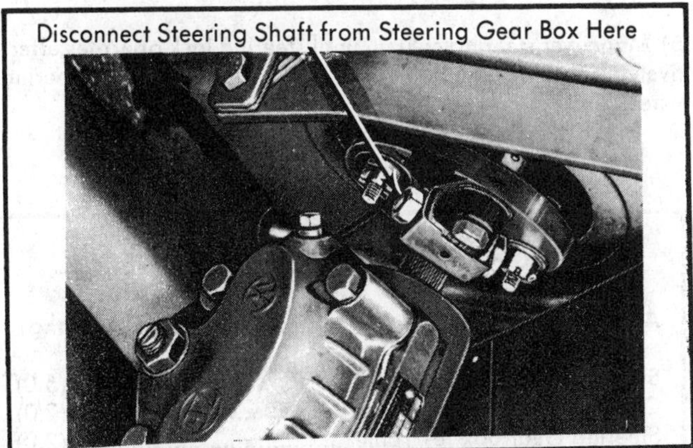

Fig. 1 Steering Shaft to Gear Box Coupling Viewed from Under Vehicle

3) Remove drag link and pitman arm. Remove 4 bolts mounting steering gear box to frame. Force steering shaft up enough so gear box can be removed.

4) Slide shaft downward and out of vehicle complete with steering coupling.

Installation – To install, reverse removal procedure and note: From chassis number 212-2038-133 there are 2 pitman arm alignment marks. Make sure the "L" (left-hand drive) mark in pitman arm aligns with index mark cast in steering gear shaft.

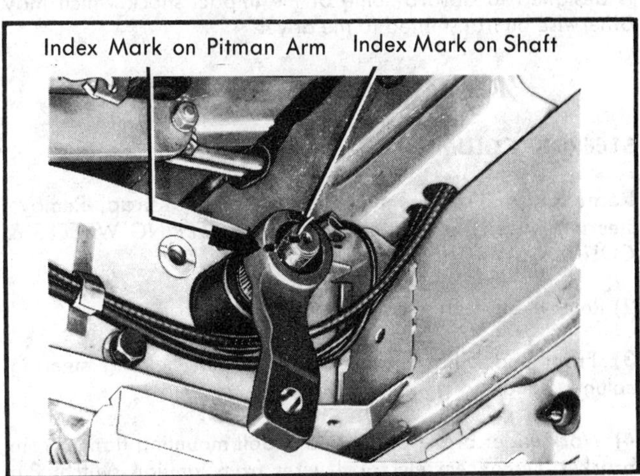

Fig. 2 Pitman Arm and Steering Gear Shaft Alignment Marks

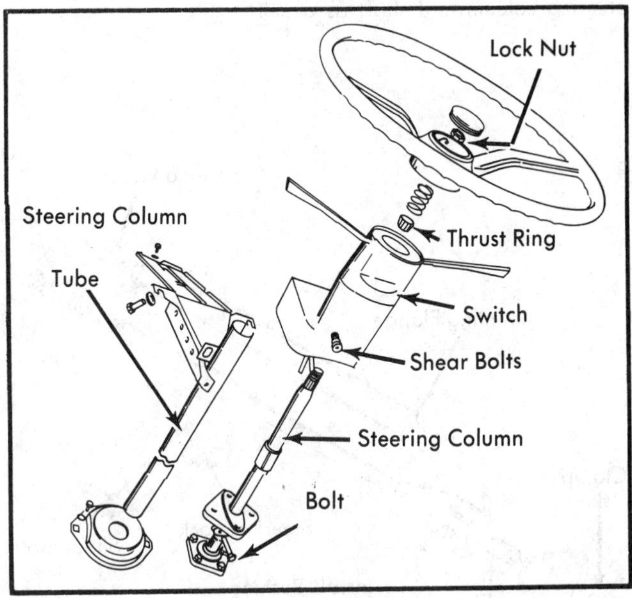

Fig. 3 Type 2 Steering Column and Bracket Assembly

TIGHTENING SPECIFICATIONS

Application	Ft. Lbs. (mkg)
Steering Wheel Nut	36 (5.0)
Flexible Coupling-to-Flange	11 (1.52)
Column Cover Plate	3.5 (.48)
Bracket Attaching Bolts	10-11 (1.38-1.52)
Coupling, Flange-to-Worm Shaft	14 (1.94)

VOLKSWAGEN DASHER

Dasher

DESCRIPTION

The Volkswagen Dasher uses a two-piece safety steering column which incorporate a flange connection. A lattice metal column support is used under the instrument panel. This device is designed to absorb some of the impact shock which may otherwise be transmitted to the driver.

REMOVAL & INSTALLATION

STEERING COLUMN

Removal – 1) Disconnect battery ground strap. Remove steering wheel. *See Volkswagen under STEERING WHEELS & COLUMN SWITCHES in this Section.*

2) Remove all steering column switches.

3) From under hood, remove pinch bolt holding steering column flange to pinion shaft.

4) Work under brake pedal and unbolt mounting flange from bracket. Disconnect electrical wires from ignition switch. Put ignition switch in "ON" position.

5) Centerpunch shear bolts holding steering lock on steering column. Drill out shear bolts. Remove steering lock. Remove steering column and shaft as a unit.

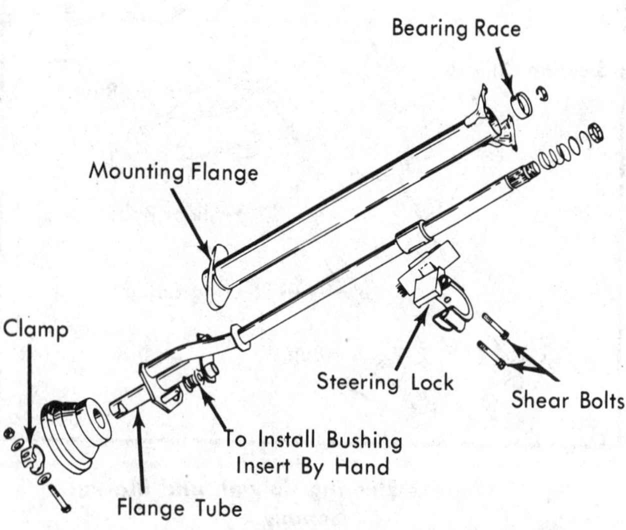

Fig. 1 Expanded View of Dasher Steering Column

Disassembly – Pull off steering wheel spacer ring and snap ring. Remove flat washer and spring. Pull steering shaft out through bottom of column. Press race out of column.

Reassembly – Examine race and replace if excessively worn. Slide steering shaft back into column then refit spring and snap ring.

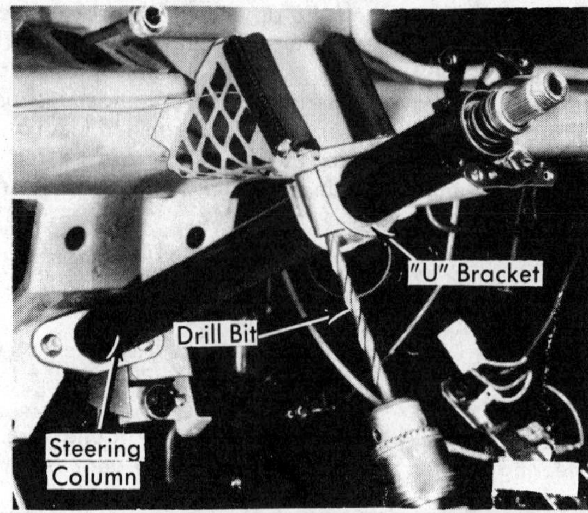

Fig. 2 Using a Drill to Remove Steering Column Shear Bolts

Installation – 1) Position column assembly back in vehicle. Install steering column lock. Make sure lock lug will snap into recess in steering column. Fit new shear bolts finger tight.

2) Bolt steering column mounting flange onto bracket so long side of flange faces right side of vehicle. Snug up flange bolts and shear bolts.

3) Connect electrical wires to ignition switch. Fit column trim. Place front wheels straight-ahead.

4) Make sure column bushings are in position on pins at lower end of steering column. Line holes in flange so flange will slide down over pins on steering column. It will be necessary to use drift to drive flange tube onto steering gear pinion shaft. Make sure flange seats to stop on pinion. Tighten pinch bolt.

5) Maneuver steering column until steering lock operates effectively. Tighten shear bolts until head snap off. Refit steering wheel.

TIGHTENING SPECIFICATIONS

Application	Ft. Lbs. (mkg)
Steering Wheel Nut	36 (5.0)
Column Mounting Flange-to-Body	14 (2.0)
Steering Gear Box-to-Frame	14 (2.0)
Gear Box Pinch Bolt	22 (3.0)

VOLKSWAGEN RABBIT & SCIROCCO

Rabbit
Scirocco

DESCRIPTION

The Volkswagen Rabbit and Scirocco use two types of steering columns. A swing-a-way type for manual transmission vehicles and a collapsible type for automatic transmission vehicles. On the swing-a-way type, the column is held in place by a clamp and leaf spring. On impact the lower angled portion of column pushes upper column against leaf spring, which disengages and allows the column to swing to the side. The collapsible type has two sheer pins. Upon impact, the pins sheer off and the lower portion of steering shaft telescopes up into upper portion of steering column.

REMOVAL & INSTALLATION

STEERING COLUMN ASSEMBLY

NOTE — Do not attepmt to remove steering shaft from column without first removing column assembly from vehicle.

Removal — **1**) Disconnect battery ground. Remove steering wheel. *See Volkswagen under STEERING WHEEL & COLUMN SWITCHES in this Section.*

2) Remove socket head bolt and Phillips head screw from switch housing recess. Tilt switch unit toward instrument panel. Pry off spacer sleeve on steering column. Pull switch unit up enough to disconnect wires. Remove switch unit from column.

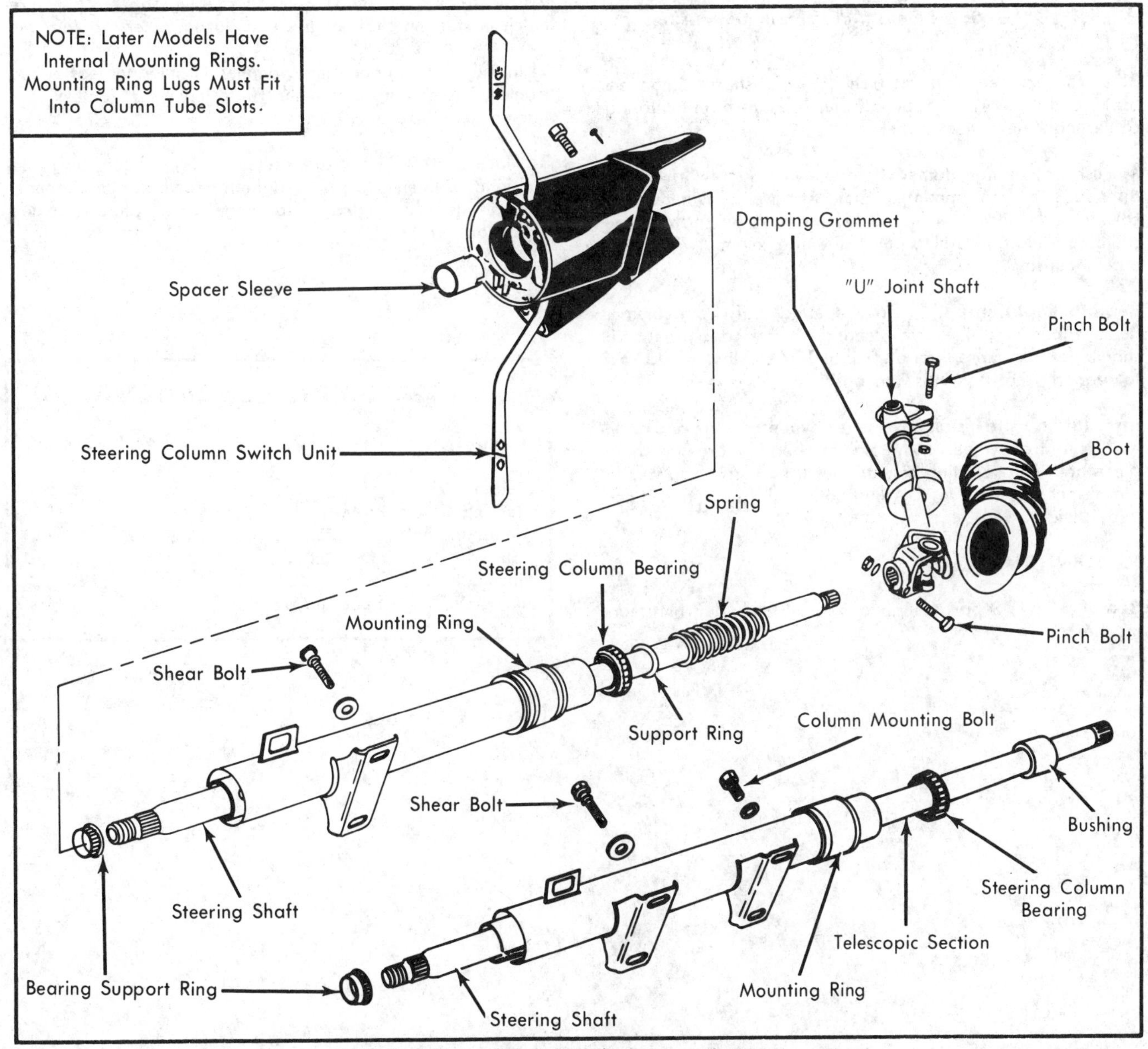

Fig. 1 Exploded View of Steering Shafts. Top Shaft is Type Used on Manual Transmission Models. Bottom Shaft Shown is Type Used on Automatic Transmission Models. Upper and Lower Portions of Each Shaft are Same.

VOLKSWAGEN RABBIT & SCIROCCO (Cont.)

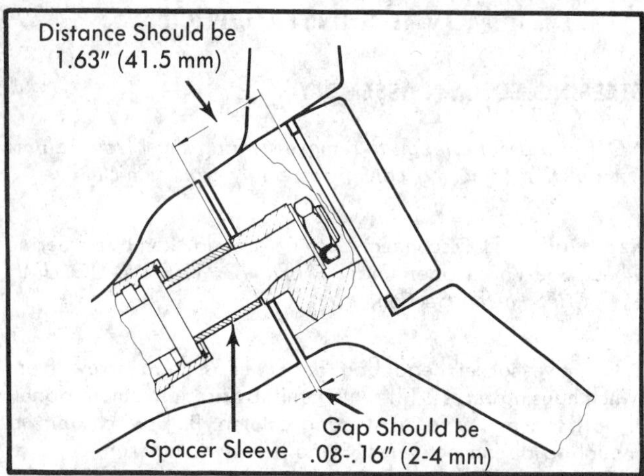

Fig. 2 Spacer Sleeve Adjustment Dimensions

3) Disconnect steering shaft from "U" joint shaft. Disconnect brake pedal push rod. Separate clutch pedal from actuating cable under instrument panel.

4) Push leaf spring retainer clip down with a screwdriver and disengage it from mounting slot. Remove bolts mounting column under instrument panel. Shear bolts will have to be centerpunched and drilled out. Pull entire column (with shaft) out of vehicle.

Bearing Replacement – Drive steering shaft from column. Remove bearings. Press in steering shaft and bearings. It should not take more than a force of 100-200 lbs. (45-90 kgs) to properly seat bearings into position.

Installation – To install, reverse removal procedure and note: Make sure front wheels point straight-ahead before tightening pinch bolt. Before fitting column switch unit, install spacer to dimensions shown in *Fig. 2*. Adjust both brake pedal and clutch pedal height.

"U" JOINT SHAFT

Removal – 1) Separate manual gearshift linkage from steering box.

2) Remove pinch bolt connecting lower end of "U" joint shaft with steering gear pinion shaft.

3) Remove nuts mounting steering gear box to frame. Pull box down to separate from lower "U" joint. Remove rubber boot from lower "U" joint.

4) Remove pinch bolt connecting upper "U" joint to steering shaft. Pull down on joint and remove shaft with "U" joints from vehicle.

NOTE – Identifications are stamped on lower end of shaft where it connects to "U" joint. Rabbit models are identified by 17L cast into shaft. Scirocco models are identified by circular knurl and 53L cast into shaft.

Installation – 1) Fit "U" joint to steering shaft. Make sure notch in steering shaft aligns with slot in lower "U" joint.

2) Install boot and damping grommet. Fit steering gear box to frame while guiding pinion shaft into lower "U" joint. Finger tighten gear box nuts.

3) Place front wheels straight-ahead. Align pinion shaft and "U" joint. Tighten pinch bolt. Tighten gear box nuts. Connect manual gearshift linkage to gear box. Check linkage operation.

TIGHTENING SPECIFICATIONS

Application	Ft. Lbs. (mkg)
Steering Wheel Nut	36 (5.0)
Steering Column-to-Instrument Panel	
Mounting Bolt	14 (2.0)
Shear Bolts	①
Pinch Bolts	22 (3.0)

① – Until bolt head snaps.

VOLVO

240 Series
260 Series

DESCRIPTION

Steering column is divided in two sections. Upper and lower sections are joined by means of a flange. A heavy frontal impact would cause flange to break from upper column. The upper portion of steering column would retain its position, eliminating possibility of its being forced toward driver. Upper part of column is carried in two ball bearings located in jacket tube. Lower end of steering column is connected to steering shaft by a flange.

REMOVAL & INSTALLATION

STEERING COLUMN

Removal – 1) Disconnect battery ground. Remove steering wheel. *See Volvo under STEERING WHEEL & COLUMN SWITCHES in this Section.*

2) Work inside engine compartment and disconnect pinch bolt mounting steering column shaft to lower shaft at universal.

3) Remove shrouding from around steering column. Remove mounting screw for turn signal and wiper switches. Slightly raise switches and disconnect electrical wires.

4) Remove switch retainer housing. Take out spring and upper bearing race. Remove steering column lock. Shear bolts will have to be drilled out and extracted with a suitable tool.

5) Slide out steering column rubber grommet at firewall. Remove steering column lower mounting bolts. Force steering column through firewall until clear of lower portion of instrument panel. Pull column toward passenger compartment and remove from vehicle.

6) Place steering column assembly in a soft jawed vise and remove steering lock mechanism.

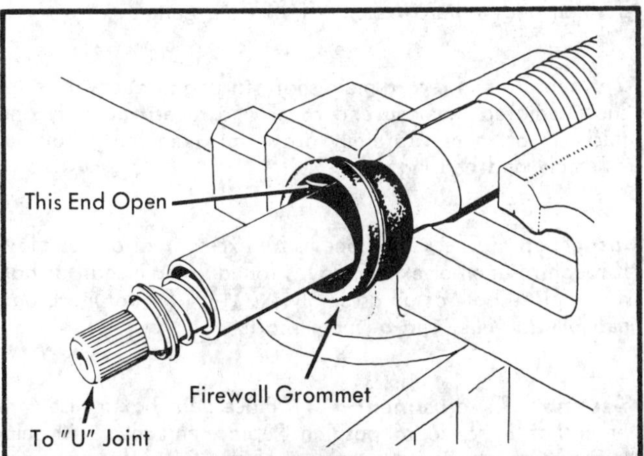

Fig. 1 New Rubber Grommet Being Installed on Steering Column

Installation – 1) Place steering column in vise and refit steering lock mechanism. Put column rubber grommet back on lower end of column. Make sure open end faces down.

2) Insert column through firewall. Adjust column into position under instrument panel. Make sure steering lock fits through hole in panel. Hook steering shaft lower end to "U" joint.

3) Finger tighten new shear bolts. Fit lower bushing to clamp and place around steering column. Finger tighten bolts. Position rubber sealing grommet in place at firewall.

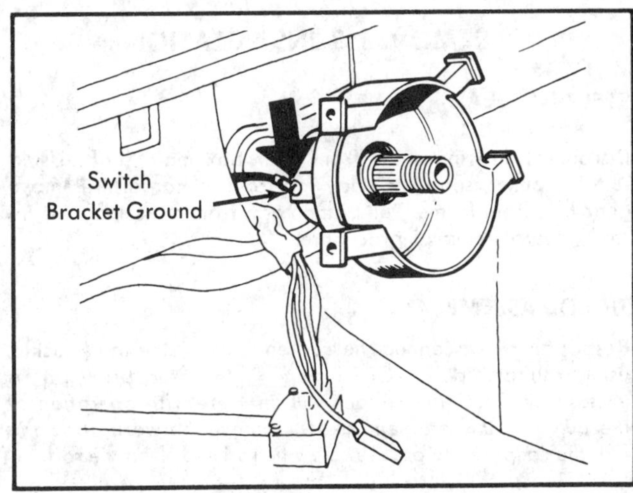

Fig. 2 Switch Bracket Ground on Steering Column

4) Install switch bracket. Make sure to use one of mounting screws as a ground. Install race and spring for upper race. Install turn signal, wiper switch and ignition switch. Connect horn wire lead.

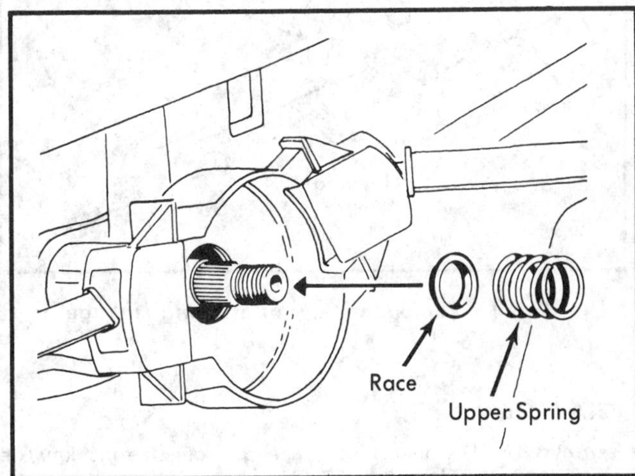

Fig. 3 Install Upper Bearing Race and Spring to Steering Column

5) Refit steering column shrouds. Install steering wheel. Check that steering wheel rotates easily. If everything is operational, tighten shear bolts until heads snap.

ARROW & COLT RECIRCULATING BALL

Arrow
Colt

DESCRIPTION

Steering system uses a recirculating ball gear of variable ratio. This type of gear minimizes gear ratio at the straight-ahead position, resulting in high stability at center; however, as the wheel is turned from center, gear ratio increases, allowing easy maneuvering.

REMOVAL & INSTALLATION

STEERING GEAR

Disconnect steering shaft from gear box main shaft. Using suitable puller, separate relay rod from pitman arm. Remove gear box from frame. Pull pitman arm from cross shaft. To install, reverse removal procedure.

TIE ROD ASSEMBLY

Removal – Disconnect tie rod ends from steering knuckle, using a suitable puller (CT-1116). **NOTE** – *If disc brake pad is excessively worn, the caliper will interfere with operation of the puller. If this problem exists, remove the worn pad, and pull the caliper outward.* Unscrew tie rod ends from tie rod.

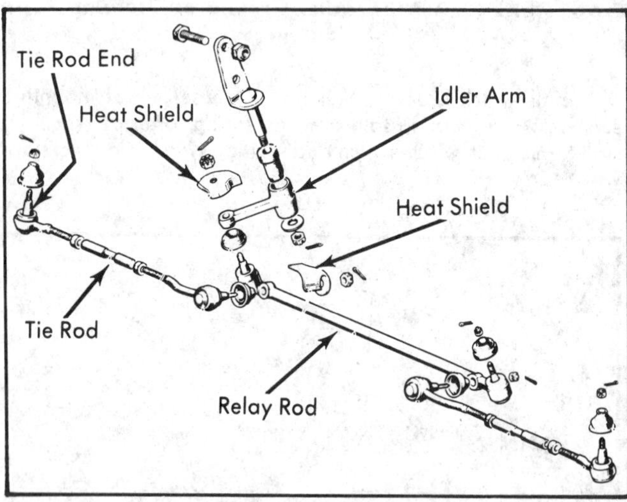

Fig. 1 Exploded View of Steering Linkage

RELAY ROD

Removal – Disconnect tie rod ends from steering knuckle arms using suitable puller (CT-1116). Detach pitman arm and idler arm, using suitable puller (C-3894-A). Remove relay rod.

Installation – Grease tie rod end dust cover and coat lower edge of cup with packing sealer before installation. Temporarily install tie rod ends to rod, so that distance from center of inner tie rod end stud to outer tie rod end stud is 12.25" (311.15 mm). Now turn tie rods until amount of threaded area showing on each side of tie rod sleeve is equal. Install assembly on vehicle and check toe-in. *See Colt in WHEEL ALIGNMENT section.*

Installation – To install, reverse removal procedure, noting the following: Ensure dust covers are well greased and that lower edge of covers are coated with packing sealer.

IDLER ARM

Removal – Disconnect idler arm from relay rod, using suitable tool (C-3894-A). Detach idler arm bracket from body frame, and remove idler arm assembly. Disassemble idler arm from bracket.

Installation – Apply soapy water to idler arm and bushing, then insert bushing as far as stepped portion will cover. Apply soapy solution to bracket shaft and, using a vise, force bracket shaft into bushing until bushing ends spread an equal amount. Tighten lock nut to specification, then further to line up cotter pin hole. Replace bracket to frame.

PITMAN ARM

Removal – After removing steering gear, disconnect pitman arm from cross shaft, using a suitable puller (CT-1106).

Installation – During installation, ensure slit on cross shaft aligns with pitman arm mark.

OVERHAUL

STEERING GEAR

Disassembly – 1) Prior to disassembly, record starting torque of main shaft (as guide during assembly). Remove adjusting screw lock nut, turn screw counterclockwise (partial turn), then remove cover. When cover is free of sector shaft, remove adjusting screw. Set gear in straight ahead (center) position and withdraw sector shaft from gear box.

2) Measure and record main shaft starting torque with sector shaft removed. Remove end cover and record quantity and thickness of shims. Carefully draw out main shaft, ball nut assembly and bearing.

Inspection – Check components for excess wear or free play. If rough rotation or excess play is found in main shaft or ball nut, replace both as an assembly. **NOTE** – *Do not move ball nut fully to either end of main shaft.*

Assembly & Adjustment – 1) Place gear box in vise with main shaft in horizontal position. Replace end cover with shim (same as removed) and torque to specifications. Measure main shaft preload. If less or greater than 3.0-4.8 INCH lbs. (.42-.66 cmkg), reduce or increase shim size to obtain proper preload.

ARROW & COLT RECIRCULATING BALL (Cont.)

2) Install adjusting screw and proper shim in groove on sector shaft. Be sure axial play of shaft is no greater than .002" (.051 mm). If greater, change shim size. Lubricate and install sector shaft in housing. Replace cover and cover bolts. Turn sector shaft several times from side to side, then turn adjusting screw in and out several times, to set proper gear mesh.

3) Loosen adjusting screw until no play is noticed at main shaft when gear in in central position. Tighten lock nut. Recheck main shaft preload; it should now be 5.7-7.4 INCH lbs. (.79-1.02 cmkg). Fill gear box with SAE 90 gear oil. Check oil level through lower right bolt hole. Proper level from hole is 0.7" (18 mm) for 1600 cc engine and .87" (22 mm) for 2000 cc engine.

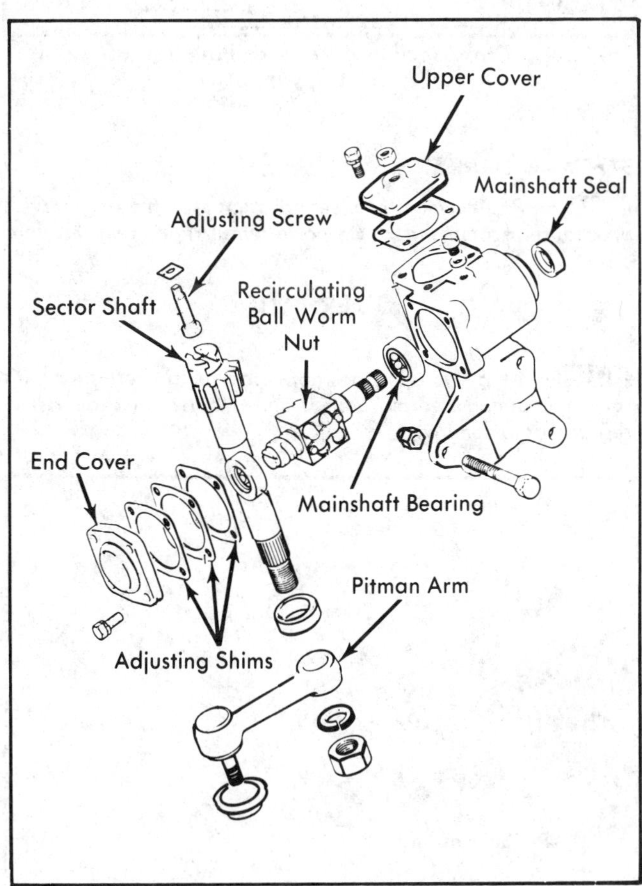

Fig. 2 Exploded View of Recirculating Ball & Nut Steering Gear – 1600 cc Engine

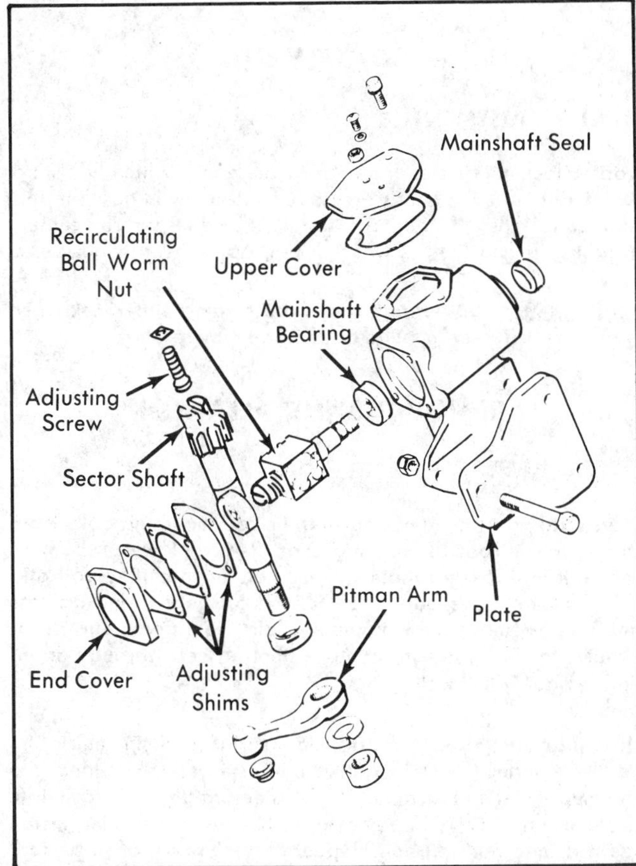

Fig. 3 Exploded View of Recirculating Ball & Nut Steering Gear – 2000 cc Engine

TIGHTENING SPECIFICATIONS

Application	Ft. Lbs. (mkg)
Gear Box-to-Frame	
1600 cc	25-29 (3.5-4.0)
2000 cc	32-36 (4.4-5.0)
Pitman Arm-to-Gear Box	94-108 (13.0-14.9)
Tie Rod Stud Nuts	29-36 (4.0-5.0)
Relay Rod-to-Pitman Arm	29-43 (4.0-6.0)
Tie Rod End Lock Nut	29-36 (4.0-5.0)
Relay Rod-to-Tie Rod	29-36 (4.0-5.0)
Turnbuckle Lock Nut	36-40 (5.0-5.5)
Idler Bracket-to-Frame	25-29 (3.5-4.0)
End Cover	11-14 (1.5-2.0)

AUDI FOX RACK & PINION

Fox

ADJUSTMENT

RACK ADJUSTMENT

Loosen lock nut on steering gear cover. Hand tighten adjusting screw until it touches thrust washer. Hold screw in position and tighten lock nut. If steering is too tight or does not self center, readjust. If gear rattles when driven, adjustment is too loose.

CAUTION — *Do not turn gear hard against either lock when vehicle is raised off ground or damage may result.*

REMOVAL & INSTALLATION

STEERING GEAR

Removal — After removing both tie rod mounting bolts from rack, pry tie rods off steering gear. Remove lower instrument panel trim. Loosen bottom steering column mounting bolt and pry off clip. Drive bottom of column off gear, using a brass mandrel. Remove gear mounting bolts from body. Turn front wheels to right lock and remove steering gear through opening in right wheel well.

Installation — Before installing steering gear in vehicle, install the slider (in which both sealing sleeves are welded into the cup — see illustration). Install steering gear. To facillitate installation of tie rods, remove one bolt from the slider, install tie rod, and reinstall bolt. Repeat procedure for other tie rod. After tightening bolts, secure with lock plate.

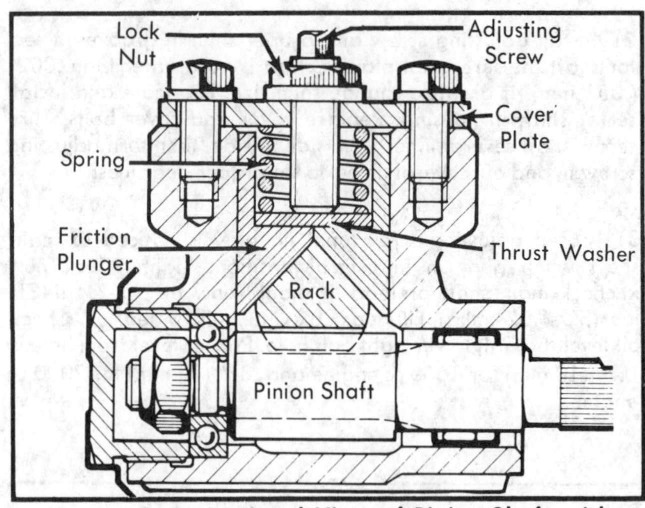

Fig. 2 Cross Sectional View of Pinion Shaft with Rack Adjustment

STEERING DAMPER

NOTE — *Replacement of steering damper is the only service procedure recommended. Do not attempt repairs on this unit.*

OVERHAUL

NOTE — *Manufacturer does not recommend overhaul of this rack and pinion steering unit. If unit is determined defective, replace as assembly.*

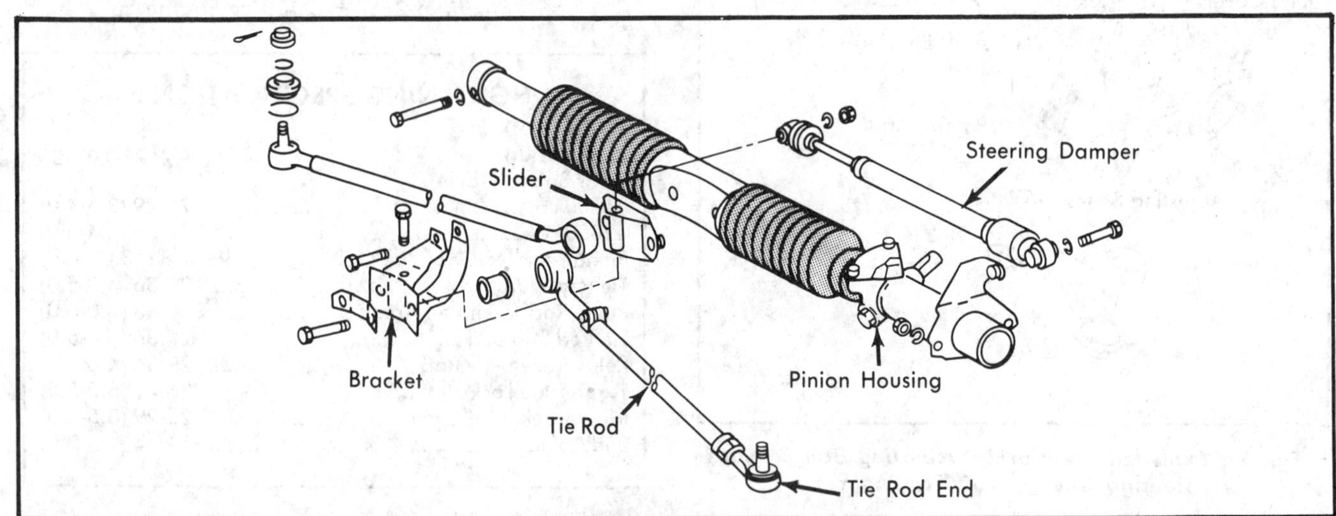

Fig. 1 Audi Fox Rack and Pinion Assembly

BMW RACK & PINION

320i

DESCRIPTION

Direct-acting manual rack and pinion gear on resilient rubber mounts is of ZF design. Steering is dampened by a single tube-type hydraulic damper. Tie rods attached at outer end of central steering rack connect to steering knuckles.

ADJUSTMENT

Steering gear assembly should be removed for proper adjustment. See *OVERHAUL procedures in this article*.

REMOVAL & INSTALLATION

STEERING GEAR

Removal and Installation – Disconnect tie rods from steering knuckles with special tool (32 2 050). Detach steering gear mounting bolts at front axle support. Remove pinch bolt from steering spindle and pull steering gear loose from universal coupling. To install, reverse removal procedure noting that wheels must point straight ahead and raised mark on dust seal must align between raised marks on steering gear box.

OVERHAUL

Disassembly – 1) Mount gear in suitable holding fixture held in a vise. Bend open right lockplate and slide rack in up to stop. Detach damper at holder.

2) Using special tool (32 2 110), detach right tie rod at rack. Loosen bellows clamp and slide bellows off housing. Move rack in far enough to apply special tool (32 2 100) to left side of rack. Loosen clamp and slide back bellows onto rack. Bend open lockplate and detach left tie rod at rack.

3) Remove cap from pinion housing, then pull out cotter pin holding set screw. Unscrew set screw with special tool (32 1 040) and remove spring retainer and spring. Lift rack to remove pressure pad and "O" ring from housing.

4) Remove pinion shaft dust cover, "V" lock ring and notched ring. Remove pinion shaft set screw with special tool (32 1 040), then pull out "O" ring and washer.

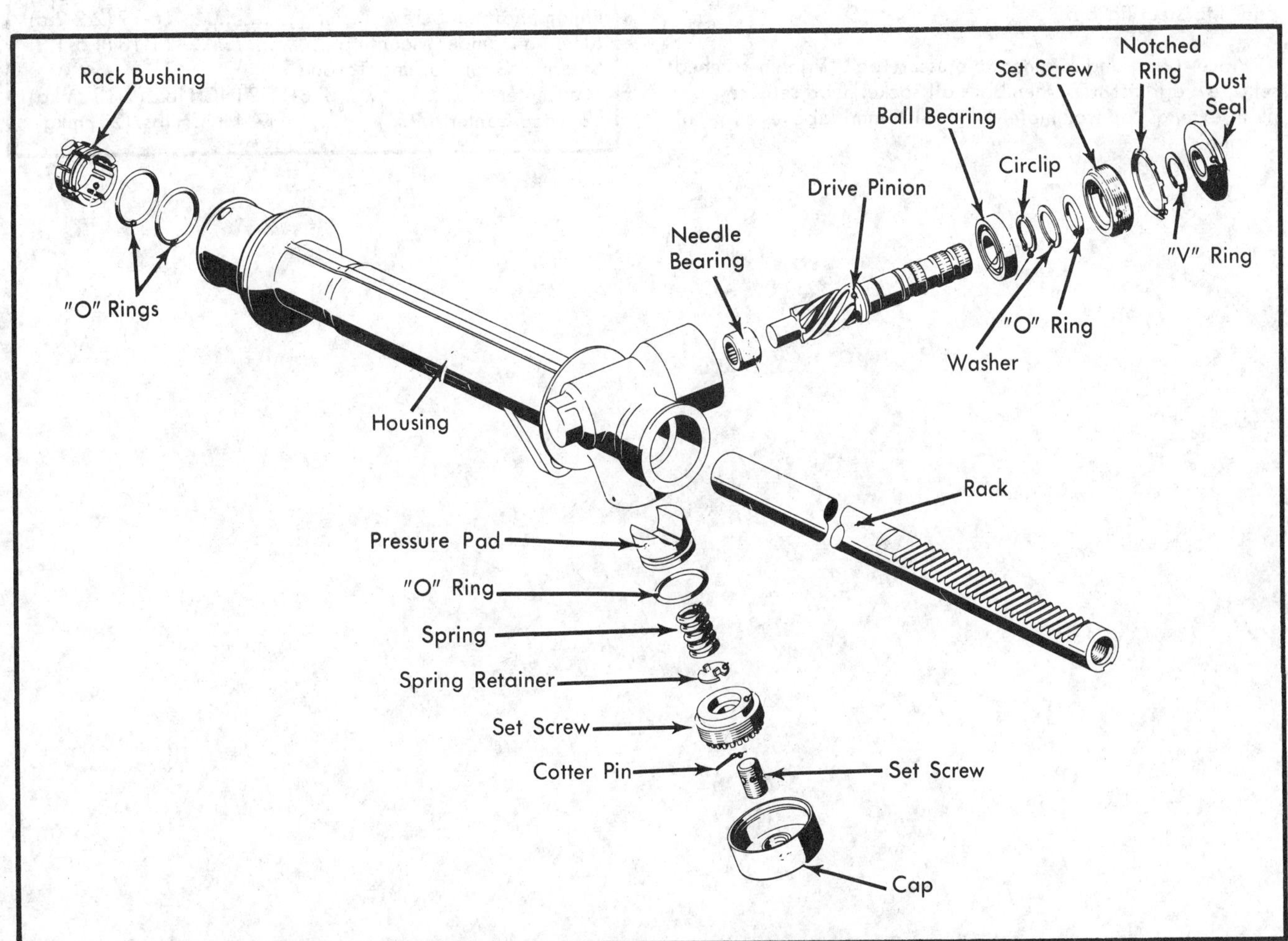

Fig. 1 Exploded View of BMW Rack & Pinion Steering Gear Assembly

BMW RACK & PINION (Cont.)

5) Clamp drive pinion spline in soft jawed vise and remove drive pinion from housing by tapping housing with plastic hammer. Remove circlip from pinion shaft and press ball bearing off of drive pinion shaft.

6) Needle bearing may be removed from housing with suitable screw type puller (Kukko 00 8 510). Remove rack bushings from housing by prying out with two screwdrivers.

Assembly – 1) Place new "O" rings on rack bushings and install bushings in steering box. Locking tabs must enage in housing lock holes. Drive needle bearing, flat side down, into box using suitable mandrel.

2) Press ball bearing onto drive pinion with closed end facing spline and install circlip. Apply thick coat of grease to spline surface of rack and thin coating to remainder of surface. Insert rack into box. Dip assembled pinion shaft in grease and install in box.

3) Tighten set screw to specifications. Insert "V" ring up to groove and press notched ring up to stop. Center rack in housing. Right end of rack should extend 3.031" (77 mm) beyond housing. Place dust seal on shaft so mark on seal is between marks on housing. Place "O" ring into pressure pad and slide pad into steering box.

4) Place spring and retainer on pressure pad. Tighten notched set screw against stop, then back off socket head set screw until it extends approximately ½" (12 mm) above edge of housing.

Adjustment – 1) Tighten notched set screw to 4 ft.lbs. (.6 mkg), then back off by one full castle slot to cotter pin hole. Install adapter (32 1 000) and torque wrench (00 2 000) on pinion shaft. Turn rack over entire length to check for sticking or binding. Set screw may be backed off no more than one notch in event of sticking or binding.

2) Move rack to center position and determine turning torque. If not within specifications, self locking set screw may be turned right to increase or to left to decrease friction.

3) Use new seals and lock plates and complete assembly procedure in reverse order of disassembly.

NOTE – *Shoulder of lock plates must engage opening of rack when installing tie rods. If replacing rubber bushing supporting steering damper, short spacers must be in place prior to tightening cover plate.*

TIGHTENING SPECIFICATIONS

Application	Ft. Lbs. (mkg)
Tie Rod to Rack	51-56 (7-8)
Tie Rod to Steering Knuckle	25-29 (3.5-4.0)
Steering Gear to Axle	35-39 (4.9-5.4)
Pinion Shaft Pinch Bolt	18-20 (2.5-2.8)
Pinion Shaft Set Screw	16-19 (2.2-2.6)
Steering Damper Mounting	11-13 (1.5-1.8)
Steering Gear Turning Torque	
At Center	7.8-11.2 INCH lbs. (9-13 cmkg)
Beyond Center (Max.)	17.4 INCH lbs. (20 cmkg)

CAPRI RACK & PINION

Capri

DESCRIPTION

Rack and pinion steering gear is mounted in rubber insulators on brackets attached to front crossmember. Movement of steering wheel is transmitted by steering shaft through universal joint and flexible coupling to helical pinion. Rotation of pinion causes rack to move laterally where connecting rods, attached to rack, transmit this movement to spindle arms, causing front wheels to change direction. Connecting rod inner ball joints are protected by convoluted rubber bellows. Design of steering gear provides for two adjustments: rack damper adjustment and pinion bearing preload adjustment. Both adjustments are obtained by varying the thickness of shim packs under cover plates.

ADJUSTMENT

NOTE – *Adjustments can be made only after steering gear assembly is removed from vehicle.* Place gear in padded vise with rack preload cover plate on top and rack in horizontal position. Remove rack preload cover plate, shim pack and gaskets. Withdraw spring and slipper. Remove pinion bearing preload cover plate, shim pack and gaskets, then make adjustments as follows:

PINION BEARING PRELOAD

Position shim pack and pinion cover plate on bearing. **NOTE** – *Shim pack must have at least three shims with one shim .093" (2.36 mm) thick against cover plate.* Tighten cover bolts then loosen until cover plate just touches shim pack. Measure distance between cover plate and steering gear housing. Distance should be .011-.013" (.28-.33 mm), if not to specifications, add or remove shims to obtain this clearance. **NOTE** – *The .093" (2.36 mm) shim must be used next to the cover plate.* When correct specification is obtained, tighten cover plate bolts.

RACK DAMPER ADJUSTMENT

Assemble slipper to rear of rack and push fully into bore. Using straightedge and feeler gauge, measure distance between top of slipper and cover plate mounting surface. Assemble a shim pack, including two gaskets, .0005-.0035" (.013-.089 mm) GREATER than measurement. Replace slipper spring, position shim pack, replace cover plate, and tighten bolts.

STARTING TORQUE CHECK

Install a suitable torque wrench to splined end of pinion shaft. Measure torque required to start pinion rotating. If this torque is not 10-18 INCH lbs. (11.5-20.7 cmkg), check for improper adjustment or gear assembly malfunction (causing friction increase).

REMOVAL & INSTALLATION

STEERING GEAR

Removal – **1)** Set steering wheel in center position. Raise and support front of vehicle (use wheel stands or hoist, not chassis stands). Unbolt flexible coupling from pinion spline. Bend back lock tabs and unscrew steering gear mounting brackets from crossmember.

2) Loosen castellated nuts securing connecting rod ends to spindle arms. Remove castellated nuts, turn wheel to either lock (to permit sideways movement), and remove gear assembly.

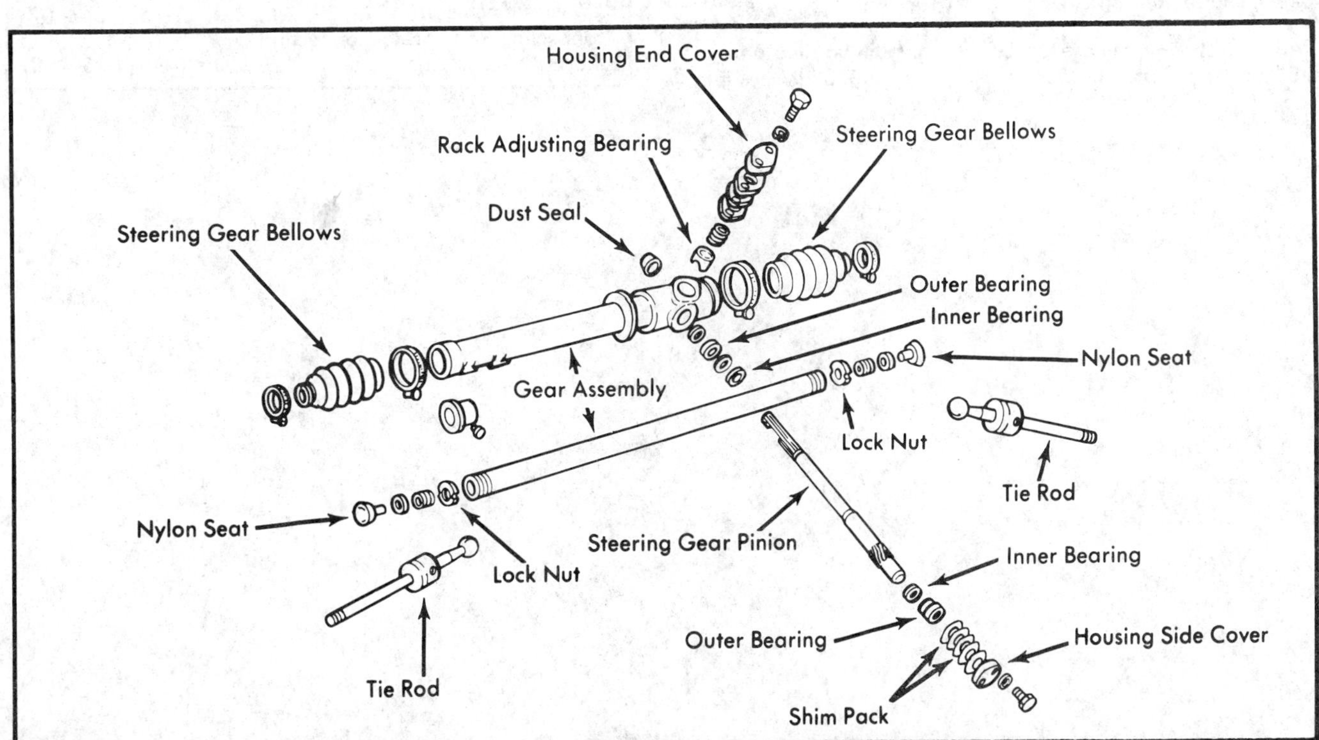

Fig. 1 Exploded View of Capri Rack & Pinion Steering Gear Assembly

CAPRI RACK & PINION (Cont.)

3) Remove connecting rod ends and lock nuts, noting number of turns required for removal.

Installation – **1)** Replace connecting rod ends and lock nuts (use same number of turns as during removal). Check steering wheel and gear in straight-ahead position. Place gear and splines on flexible coupling.

2) Secure gear assembly to crossmember (use new locking plates under screw heads). Torque screws to specification. Tighten flexible coupling-to-pinion shaft securing bolt to specification. Lower vehicle and check toe-in.

CONNECTING ROD END

Removal – Raise vehicle on hoist. Loosen lock nut on outer end of connecting rod, adjacent to ball joint. Remove nut securing connecting rod end to spindle arm, then use suitable puller (3290-C) to separate connecting rod end from spindle arm. Unscrew connecting rod end, noting number of turns required for removal.

Installation – To install, reverse removal procedure, noting the following: Note that rod end is screwed on exact same number of turns as required for removal. Torque nut on spindle arm. Recheck toe-in and wheel lock angles. Tighten lock nut on connecting rod end.

OVERHAUL

STEERING GEAR

Disassembly – **NOTE** – *Pinion bearings utilize bearing races and loose balls (28); take care not to lose bearings into gear assembly.* Remove pinion dust seal. Withdraw pinion and lower bearing assembly. Remove remainder of bearing from inside pinion housing. **NOTE** – *Preferably withdraw rack from pinion end of housing.*

Reassembly – Remove pinion oil seal from housing and install new seal. Install new upper pinion bearing. Slide rack into housing and locate it so that teeth are adjacent to pinion location. Position rack shaft in center of travel. Assemble lower bearing to pinion and install assembly into housing with alignment mark on pinion in vertical position (as installed in car).

STEERING GEAR BELLOWS

NOTE – *Removal and replacement of bellows should be done on one end at a time.*

Disassembly – Remove connecting rod end and lock nut from appropriate connecting rod, noting number of turns required for removal. Loosen bellows clamps. **NOTE** – *In production, some bellows may have been secured with wire. Replace with screw clamp.* Pull bellows off rod and housing, keeping bellows higher than gear housing to avoid spilling lubricant. Drain lubricant from assembly by traversing rack from lock to lock several times.

Reassembly – Mount steering gear in padded vise with end (from which bellows has been removed) higher than gear housing. Traverse rack to fully extend upper connecting rod. Pour 0.3 pint SAE 90 EP oil into gear housing under inner ball joint. Move rack laterally to assist oil flow. Install new bellows and securing clamps. Reinstall lock nut and connecting rod end (using same number of turns as during removal).

TIGHTENING SPECIFICATIONS

Application	Ft. Lbs. (mkg)
Pinion Cover Plate	6-8 (.83-1.11)
Rack Damper Cover Plate	6-8 (.83-1.11)
Gear-to-Crossmember	15-18 (2.07-2.49)
Connecting Rod-to-Spindle Arm	18-22 (2.49-3.04)
Coupling-to-Pinion Shaft	12-15 (1.66-2.07)
"U" Joint Pinch Bolt	12-15 (1.66-2.07)
Connecting Rod End-to-Connecting Rod	30-35 (4.15-4.84)

COURIER RECIRCULATING BALL

Courier

DESCRIPTION

Steering gear is a recirculating ball and nut type. Two tubes carry the balls through worm channels, thus transmitting the turn action of the steering shaft. Worm bearing preload and ball-nut meshload have adjustments provided, to maintain smooth steering operation.

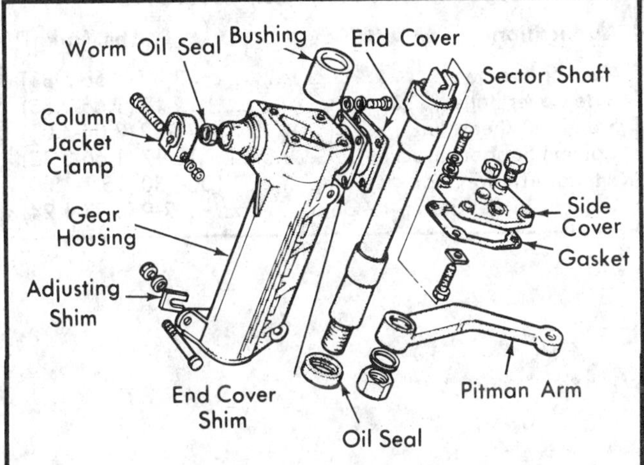

Fig. 1 Exploded View of Recirculating Ball & Nut Steering Gear

ADJUSTMENT

WORM BEARING PRELOAD

Drain gear box. Disconnect pitman arm from gear. Loosen sector adjusting screw lock nut and turn screw counterclockwise. Using torque wrench, rotate worm shaft. Preload should be 1.0-3.5 INCH lbs. (.14-.48 cmkg). If not within specification, remove end cover and shims. If preload is below minimum, reduce shim size. If above maximum increase shim size.

SECTOR SHAFT & BALL-NUT MESHLOAD

Adjusting screw in side cover sets sector shaft to provide proper mesh between sector gear teeth and ball-nut rack. Adjustment is made only after setting worm bearing preload. Disconnect pitman arm from center link. Loosen sector adjusting screw lock nut. Turn steering wheel slowly to either stop, then turn to opposite stop. Count steering wheel rotations and turn wheel to center position. Turn sector screw clockwise until worm passes high spot (center) with a torque of 5-7 INCH lbs. (.69-.97 cmkg). Hold adjusting screw in position and tighten lock nut. Recheck mesh load. Connect pitman arm to center link.

REMOVAL & INSTALLATION

STEERING GEAR

Removal – 1) Remove directional signal/dimmer switch. Unbolt steering column support bracket, then position floor covering and pad away from bottom of column. Separate toe plate and boot from dash and remove column jacket from shaft.

2) Take off air cleaner assembly. Disconnect heater hoses. Remove hydraulic lines from brake and clutch master cylinders, plug ports on both cylinders and remove from vehicle.

3) Raise vehicle on hoist. Disconnect pitman arm from sector shaft. Remove steering gear retaining bolts. Lower vehicle and remove gear and shaft assembly.

Installation – 1) Position gear to frame and install mounting bolts finger tight. Replace column jacket and dash panel boot and toe plate. Reposition floor covering. Install cancelling cam and snap ring on steering shaft, then connect directional signal/dimmer switch wires.

2) Install steering wheel (align marks made during removal). Replace spring and horn button. Install brake and clutch master cylinders and hydraulic lines. Reattach heater hoses and install air cleaner assembly.

3) Raise vehicle and tighten steering gear mounting bolts. Bleed clutch system. Attach pitman arm to sector shaft. Lower vehicle and bleed brake system.

STEERING LINKAGE

Center link can be removed from both tie rods, pitman arm, and idler arm by removing ball joint nuts and using suitable puller. After center link removal, pitman arm can be removed from sector shaft. Tie rods can also be removed with puller. Toe-in must be reset when tie rods or ball joints are replaced.

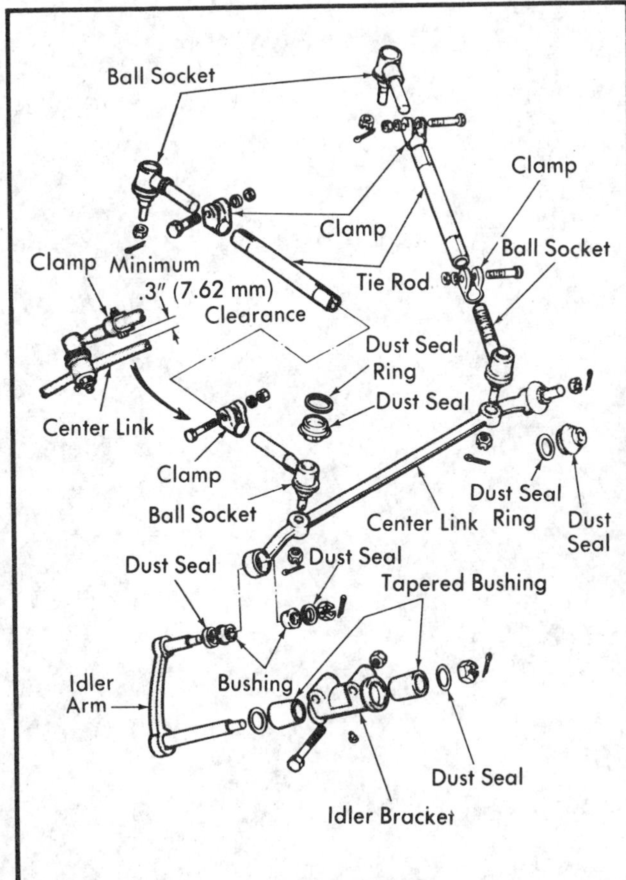

Fig. 2 Exploded View of Courier Steering Linkage

COURIER RECIRCULATING BALL (Cont.)

OVERHAUL

STEERING GEAR

Disassembly – With gear removed and drained, position gear in vise. Remove pitman arm from gear. Remove sector shaft adjusting screw lock nut. Take off side cover by removing bolts and turning adjusting screw clockwise. Remove adjusting screw and shim from sector shaft. Extract shaft from housing. Remove worm shaft and ball-nut assembly through bottom of housing after end cover and shims are removed.

Inspection – Check operation of ball-nut assembly on worm shaft. If travel is not smooth or any part is worn, replace entire assembly. Check and replace all other components as necessary.

Assembly & Adjustment – **1**) Insert worm shaft and ball-nut assembly into gear housing. Install end cover and shims. Adjust bearing preload, as previously described. Place adjusting screw in slot of sector shaft and check end clearance with feeler gauge; adjust to .001-.003" (.025-.076 mm) by adding or subtracting shims.

2) Turn worm shaft and place rack in center position of worm. Insert sector shaft and adjusting screw into gear housing, being careful not to damage bushings or seal. Align center of sector gear with center of rack. Place side cover on adjusting screw, turn screw to position cover, then install cover retaining bolts.

3) Adjust sector gear and rack backlash, as previously described. Tighten adjusting screw lock nut. Install pitman arm to sector shaft and torque to specification.

TIGHTENING SPECIFICATIONS

Application	Ft. Lbs. (mkg)
Gear-to-Frame	33-42 (4.56-5.81)
Side Cover Bolts	12-17 (1.66-2.35)
Steering Wheel Nut	22-29 (3.04-4.01)
Column Support Bracket	12-17 (1.66-2.35)
Pitman Arm-to-Gear	109-130 (15.1-18.0)
Column Jacket Clamp-to-Gear	7-9 (0.97-1.24)

DATSUN F10 RACK & PINION

F10

DESCRIPTION

Steering assembly is a direct-acting rack and pinion system with a gear ratio of 18.0: 1. This unit consists of a rack bar and toothed pinion. Backlash is held to zero by the retainer and the retainer spring.

REMOVAL & INSTALLATION

Removal – 1) Raise and support front of vehicle; remove front wheels. Remove cotter pins and nuts from tie rods, then pull tie rods from steering knuckle. Loosen bolt securing lower joint assembly to pinion, then remove bolt from lower joint assembly.

2) Remove bolts securing steering gear housing to front member, then remove steering gear and linkage by pulling them out to the side.

Installation – Install in reverse order of removal procedure noting the following: Be sure to align bracket with gear housing mount correctly and check that black clip is installed on gear housing and white clip is on rubber mount.

ADJUSTMENT

NOTE – *Adjustments are performed during gear assembly. See Overhaul as outlined.*

OVERHAUL

Disassembly – 1) Clamp rack and pinion assembly in a vise, using pads on steering gear housing to prevent damage. Remove boot clamps, then loosen tie rod lock nut and inner socket assembly. **NOTE** – *Do not disassemble inner socket assembly or tie rod assembly.* Remove tie rod assembly from rack.

2) Loosen rack adjuster lock nut (on housing), then remove adjuster, spring, and rack damper. Remove oil seal from pinion shaft, then pry snap ring from pinion housing and withdraw pinion assembly. Pull rack from gear housing.

3) Remove snap ring securing pinion bearing, then press out bearing from pinion shaft. Remove rubber mounts by striking with wood hammer. Pry snap ring from steering gear housing and remove rack bushing.

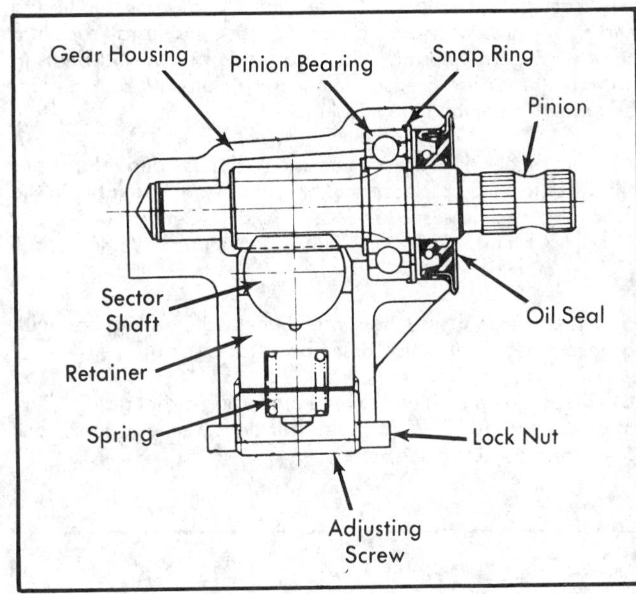

Fig. 2 Cutaway View of Steering Gear

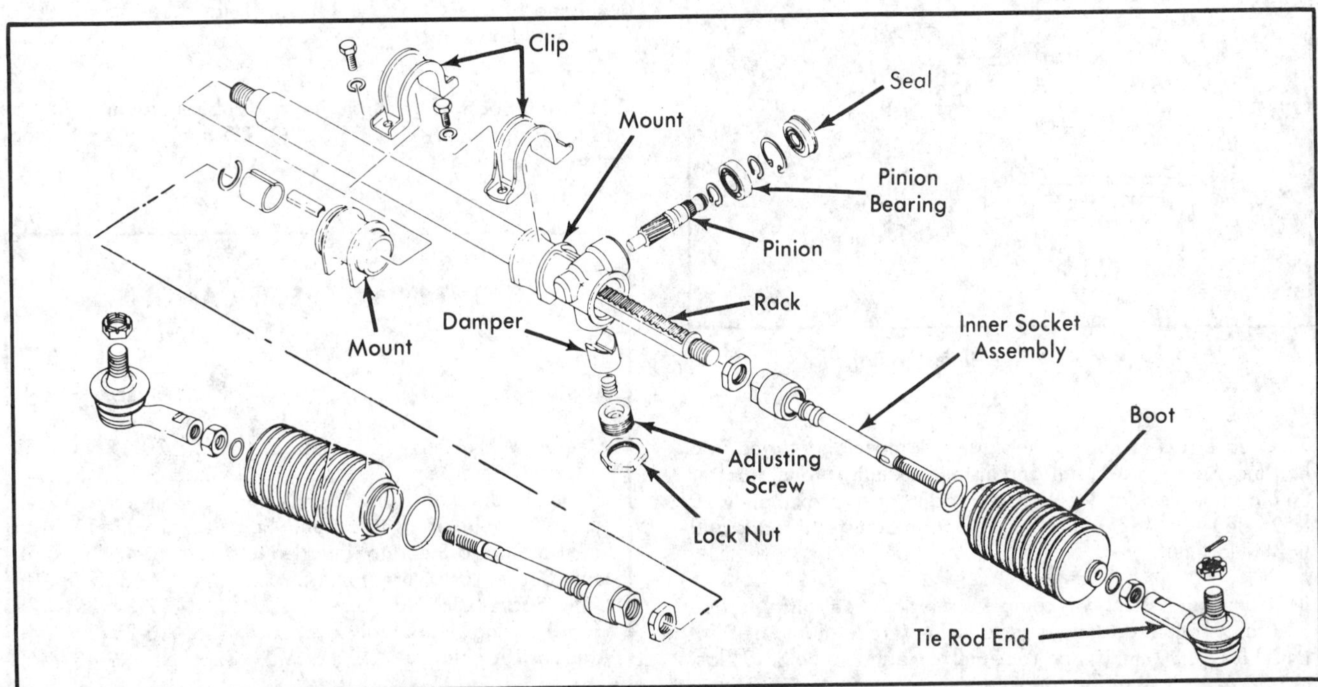

Fig. 1 Exploded View of Rack & Pinion Steering Gear Assembly

DATSUN F10 RACK & PINION (Cont.)

Assembly & Adjustment – **1**) Press bearing onto pinion gear, then install .047-.049" (1.119-1.24 mm) snap ring in shaft ring groove (inner side of bearing). Install snap ring of proper thickness in shaft ring groove (outer side of bearing), to limit bearing end play to .0039" (0.1 mm). Snap rings are available in the following thicknesses: .041-.043" (1.04-1.09 mm), .043-.045" (1.09-1.14 mm), .045-.047" (1.14-1.19 mm), .047-.049" (1.19-1.24 mm), and .049-.051" (1.24-1.29 mm).

2) Drive rack bushing into tube and secure with snap ring. Install rubber mount with plate onto tube, making sure that cut-out section in mount is aligned with hole in tube and ventilation hole is not clogged.

3) With gear clamped in vise, thinly coat rack teeth and sliding surfaces with multi-purpose grease and install rack into tube from gear housing side. Coat pinion teeth and bearing with multi-purpose grease, then mesh pinion with rack and insert pinion assembly into housing.

4) Secure bearing in housing with a snap ring of proper thickness to take up clearance. Snap rings are available in the following thicknesses: .067-.069" (1.70-1.75 mm), .065-.067" (1.65-1.70 mm), .063-.065" (1.60-1.65 mm), and .061-.063" (1.55-1.60 mm).

5) Press oil seal into housing, then pack sealing lips with grease. Check that pinion assembly rotates smoothly.

6) Check pinion for minimal end play using a dial gauge. Play must not exceed .012" (.3 mm). If it does, recheck gear, rack teeth, and adjusting snap rings.

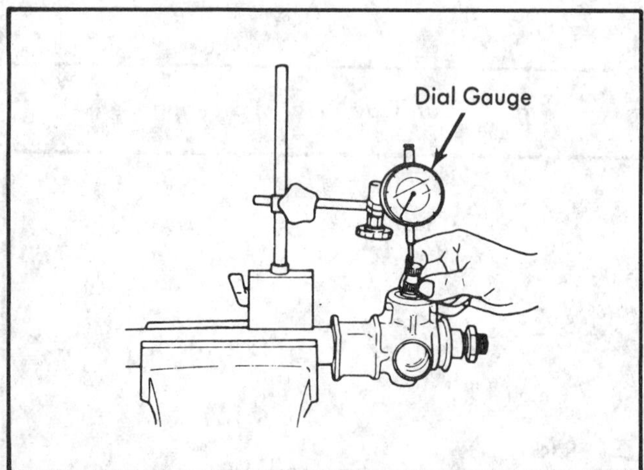

Fig. 3 Measuring Pinion Axial Play

7) Grease rack damper, then insert damper and spring into housing. Screw in adjuster and install lock nut. Turn in adjuster until damper is tight, then back off adjuster approximately 20 to 25 degrees. Apply suitable sealant on adjuster threads and tighten lock nut.

8) After gear assembly is complete, check pinion rotary torque and force required to move rack. Pinion torque should be 0-17 INCH lbs. (0-20 cmkg) and rack pull force should be 33-66 lbs. (15-30 kg). If steering gear does not meet specifications, readjust rack damper adjuster.

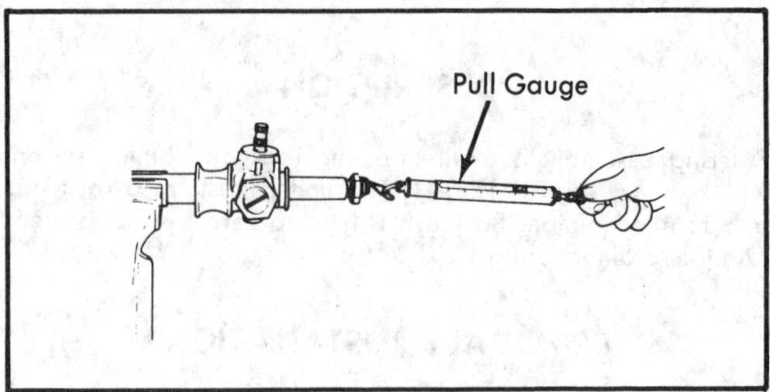

Fig. 4 Measuring Rack Pulling Force

9) Install boot to inner socket assembly, then connect socket assembly to tie rod socket and tighten lock nut temporarily. Screw in inner socket as far as it will go. Apply locking agent to threaded part of lock nut and tighten to specification.

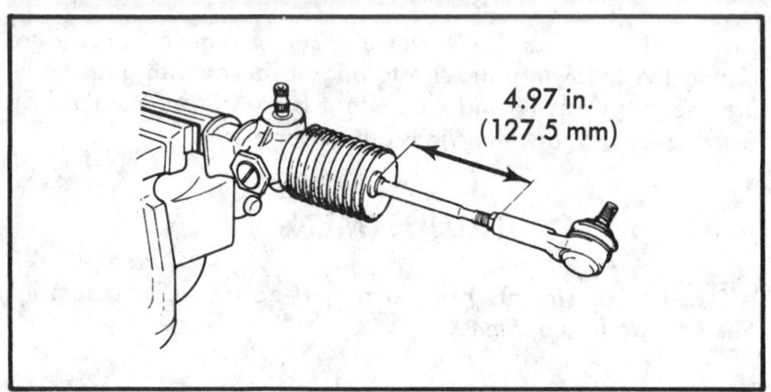

Fig. 5 Tie Rod Length Adjustment

10) Install boot and clamp on tie rod assembly, then measure swinging torque and axial play of inner socket assembly. Swinging torque should be 1.1-5.4 ft. lbs. (.15-.75 kg). Axial play should be zero.

11) Install boots to gear housing and rubber mount. Adjust tie rod length at each side to 5.02" (127.5 mm) and tighten lock nut to specifications.

TIGHTENING SPECIFICATIONS

Application	Ft. Lbs. (mkg)
Steering Wheel Nut	20-25 (3.0-3.5)
Column Clamp Bolt	6.5-10 (.9-1.4)
Upper "U" Joint Shaft-to-Column Bolt	14-17 (1.9-2.4)
Lower "U" Joint Shaft-to-Column Bolt	14-17 (1.9-2.4)
Tie Rod Stud-to-Steering Knuckle Nuts	40-47 (5.5-6.5)
Inner Socket Lock Nut	58-72 (8-10)
Outer Socket Lock Nut	27-34 (3.8-4.7)
Gear Housing Clamp Bolt	16-25 (2.2-3.4)
Adjuster Lock Nut	29-43 (4-6)

DATSUN 200SX, B210, 710 & 810 RECIRCULATING BALL

200SX
B210
710
810

DESCRIPTION

The steering gear used on these vehicles is a recirculating ball type. The worm shaft is joined to the steering shaft by a rubber shock-absorbing coupling. The steering linkage is a relay design, with the steering gear attached by a pitman arm to one end of the center link (cross shaft), while the other end of the center link moves on the idler arm.

REMOVAL & INSTALLATION

STEERING GEAR

Removal – Unbolt and remove heat shield from around steering gear (if equipped.) On 200SX, disconnect exhaust tube from manifold and remove bolt to transmission insulator. Unscrew worm shaft coupling bolt from rubber coupling. Remove pitman arm retaining nut, then use puller to extract pitman arm from steering gear. Unbolt and remove gear from vehicle.

Installation – To install, reverse removal procedure, aligning markings on pitman arm with markings on sector shaft.

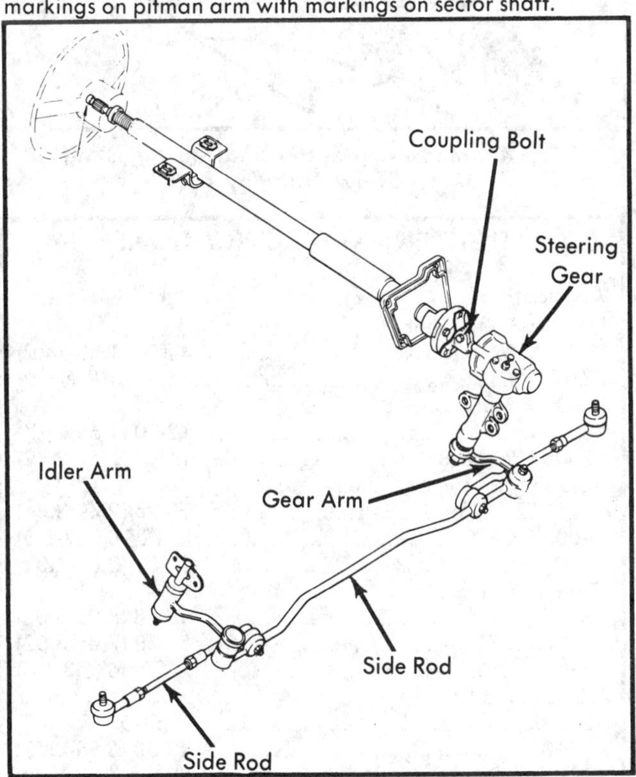

Fig. 1 Datsun Steering Gear Linkage (B210 Shown, Others Similar)

STEERING LINKAGE

Removal – Jack up front of vehicle and support with stands. Detach both outer tie rod ends from steering knuckles. Separate cross shaft from idler arm and pitman arm, then remove cross shaft and tie rods as an assembly. Idler assembly may be removed from side member, if necessary to replace bushing.

Installation – To install, reverse removal procedure, noting the following: Set tie rod end length to the prescribed setting, then check wheel alignment. See *Datsun in WHEEL ALIGNMENT section.*

Tie Rod Settings

Application	① In. (mm)
200SX, B210	12.05 (306.0)
710	12.33 (313.2)
810	
Steering Gear Arm Side	14.35 (364.5)
Idler Arm Side	14.19 (360.5)

① – As measured from center-to-center of tie rod ball studs.

ADJUSTMENT

NOTE – *Steering gear adjustments are performed during reassembly. See Overhaul as outlined below.*

OVERHAUL

STEERING GEAR

Disassembly – 1) Drain gear box of oil, then place unit in padded vise or on suitable holding fixture mounted in a vise.

2) Loosen adjusting screw lock nut and remove sector shaft cover screws. Turn adjusting screw a few turns clockwise and withdraw sector shaft. Remove rear cover. Withdraw bearing shims and worm assembly. Remove oil seal. NOTE – *Do not remove sector shaft needle bearings from housing. If defective, replace housing assembly. Do not disassemble ball nut; replace, if necessary, with worm shaft assembly.*

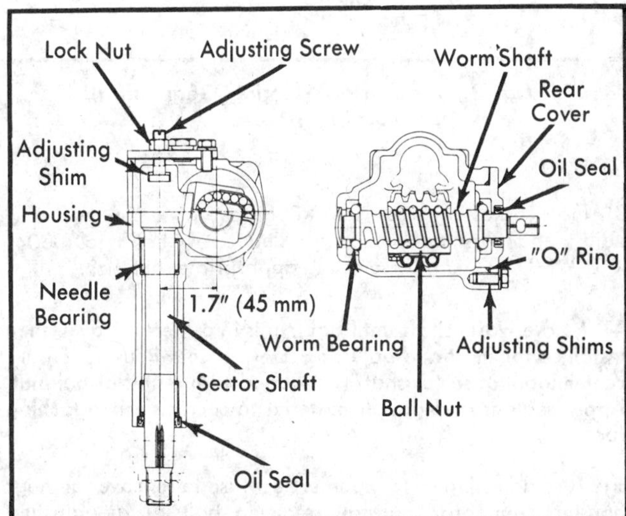

Fig. 2 Sectional View of Datsun Recirculating Ball Steering Gear

Inspection – Inspect gear teeth on sector shaft and ball nut for wear or damage; replace as necessary. Check bearings for wear or roughness during rotation. Ensure ball nut moves smoothly over its entire length of travel.

DATSUN 200SX, B210, 710 & 810 RECIRCULATING BALL (Cont.)

Assembly & Adjustment – 1) Lubricate bearings, gear, and other moving parts with gear oil. Apply suitable grease to oil seal lip and press seal into rear cover. Install "O" ring, worm shaft assembly, and worm bearing shims to gear housing. **NOTE** – *Be sure to install thicker shims to gear housing side.*

2) By selecting suitable shims, adjust worm bearing preload so that initial turning torque of worm shaft is as specified (see illustration). Rotate worm shaft a few turns to properly settle worm bearing before taking preload measurement.

Worm Bearing Preload

Application	Inch Lbs. (cmkg)
B210	3.5-5.2 (4-6)
200SX, 710 & 810	3.5-6.9 (4-8)

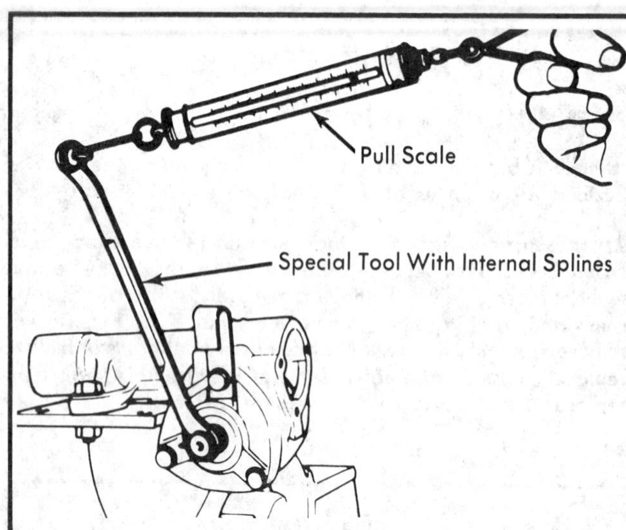

Fig. 3 Measuring Steering Gear Initial Turning Torque

3) Insert adjusting screw into "T" groove of sector shaft and adjust end play between shaft and screw head to .0004-.0012" (.01-.03 mm) by selecting appropriate shim size.

4) Rotate worm shaft until ball nut is in center of travel, then install sector shaft and adjusting screw in gear housing. Ensure center tooth of sector shaft is engaged with center of ball nut. Apply sealant and gasket material to sector shaft attaching face.

5) Turn adjusting screw counterclockwise to set cover on gear housing. Temporarily install retaining bolts. Turn adjusting screw further counterclockwise until sector shaft is drawn upward about .08-.12" (2-3 mm). Fully tighten cover bolts.

6) Push sector shaft against ball nut by gradually turning adjusting screw until sector shaft gear lightly meshes with ball nut gear, and temporarily secure adjusting screw with lock nut.

7) Install pitman arm to sector shaft and move it side-to-side several times to ensure smooth operation. Set pitman arm at center point and adjust backlash (by turning adjusting screw) such that free movement at top end of pitman arm is .004" (0.1 mm).

8) Turn adjusting screw clockwise approximately 1/8-1/6 turn and tighten lock nut securely, after moving sector shaft several times. Fill gear housing with approximately 5/8 pint (.27 litre) of suitable gear oil. Install filler plug.

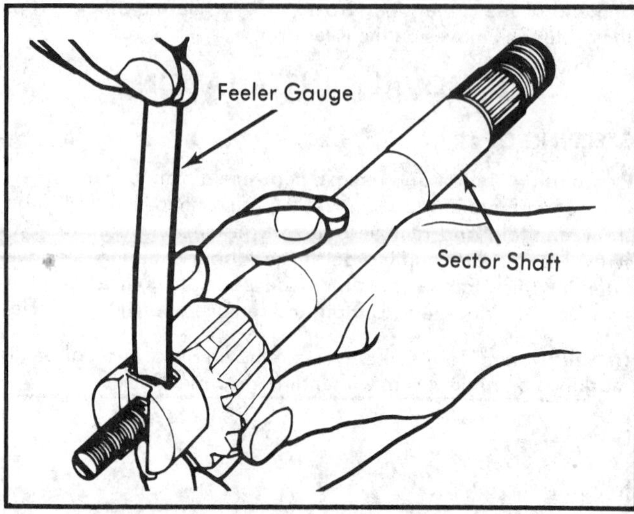

Fig. 4 Measuring Sector Shaft-to-Adjusting Screw End Play

TIGHTENING SPECIFICATIONS

Application	Ft. Lbs. (mkg)
Pitman Arm-to-Gear	
200SX, B210 & 810	94-108 (13.0-14.9)
710	101 (14.0)
Front & Rear Cover Bolts	
B210	12-20 (1.66-2.77)
200SX, 710 & 810	11-18 (1.52-2.49)
Adjusting Screw Lock Nut	
B210	18-25 (2.49-3.46)
200SX & 810	12-18 (1.7-2.5)
710	22-29 (3.04-4.01)
Gear-to-Frame	
B210	43-58 (5.95-8.02)
200SX & 710	51-58 (7.05-8.02)
810	38-46 (5.3-6.3)
Idler Arm-to-Frame	
200SX	51-58 (7.0-8.0)
B210	43-58 (5.95-8.02)
710 & 810	32-44 (4.42-6.08)
Ball Stud Nuts	
B210	40-55 (5.53-7.60)
200SX, 710 & 810	40-72 (5.53-9.95)
Tie Rod Lock Nuts	
All	58-72 (8.02-9.95)
Worm Shaft Coupling Bolt	
B210	11-16 (1.52-2.21)
200SX, 710 & 810	29-36 (4.01-4.98)

DATSUN 280Z RACK & PINION

280Z

DESCRIPTION

Steering assembly is a direct-acting rack and pinion system, with a gear ratio of 18.0:1. This unit consists of a rack bar and toothed pinion, both working in the plain bearing of the housing. Backlash is held to zero by the retainer and the retainer spring.

REMOVAL & INSTALLATION

Removal – Raise and support front of vehicle; remove front wheels. Disconnect column joint from rubber coupling (two bolts). Unbolt lower joint from gear pinion and remove lower shaft assembly. Remove splash shield, then pull tie rods from steering knuckle arms. Unbolt gear housing from front member and remove rack and pinion assembly.

Installation – Install in reverse order of removal procedure. Check wheel alignment. For wheel alignment procedures, see *Datsun in WHEEL ALIGNMENT section.*

ADJUSTMENT

NOTE – *Adjustments are performed during gear assembly process. See Overhaul as outlined.*

OVERHAUL

Disassembly – **1)** Clamp gear housing horizontally in a padded vise. Unclamp dust boot and pull boot outward to expose inner end of tie rod. Loosen tie rod retaining nut, detach tie rod socket, and remove tie rod from rack. Withdraw spring seat and tie rod spring.

2) Loosen rack adjuster lock nut (on housing), then remove adjuster, spring, and rack damper. Pry oil seal from pinion shaft, then remove pinion cover bolts, cover, and adjusting shims. Draw out pinion assembly, then rack, from housing. Pry pinion lower bearing from housing, then press pinion upper bearing from pinion gear.

Assembly & Adjustment – **1)** Press bearing onto pinion gear. With gear horizontal in padded vise, thinly coat rack teeth and sliding surfaces with suitable multi-purpose grease. Install pinion lower bearing into housing, with seal side upward, then insert pinion.

2) Set initial pinion turning torque, by selecting an adjusting shim which will give 2.6-5.2 INCH lbs. (3-6 cmkg) when pinion cover is installed and bolts are tightened (rack is not installed). Shims are available in the following sizes: .002" (.05 mm), .005" (.127 mm), .01" (.25 mm), .02" (.5 mm), and .04" (1 mm).

3) Remove pinion cover and pinion gear. Insert rack into housing, making sure rack protrudes same amount from each end. Coat pinion gear and bearing with suitable multi-purpose grease. Install pinion and properly mesh pinion gear with rack teeth. Recheck rack for equal protrusion at ends of housing. Reinstall and tighten pinion cover (with shim). Install pinion oil seal.

4) Check pinion for smooth rotation and minimal axial play. Measure axial play with a dial gauge. Play must not exceed .012" (.3 mm). If it does, recheck condition of gear and rack teeth, bearings, and adjustment shim.

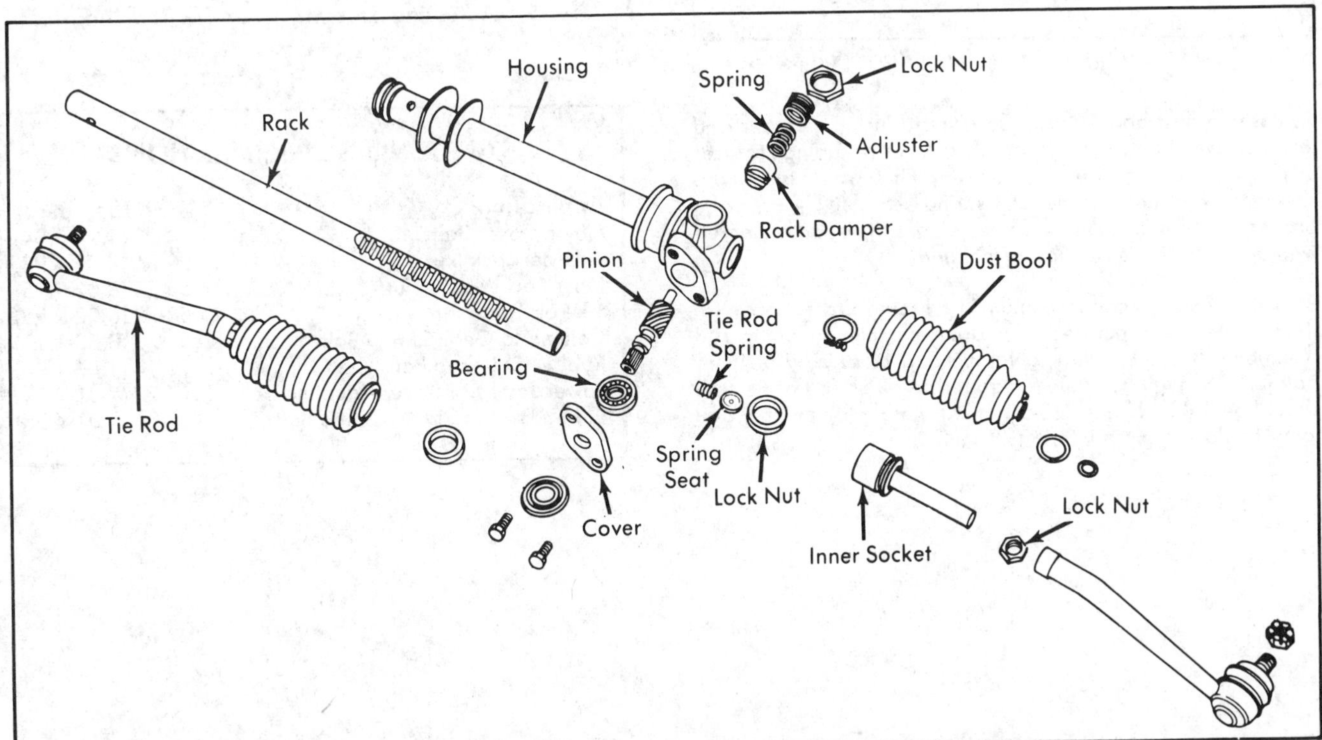

Fig. 1 Exploded View of Rack & Pinion Steering Gear Assembly

DATSUN 280Z RACK & PINION (Cont.)

5) Grease rack damper, then insert damper and spring into housing. Screw in adjuster and install lock nut. Turn in adjuster until damper is tight. Check pinion rotary torque. If beyond 0-17 INCH lbs. (0-20 cmkg), select a suitable adjuster shim for placement on top of rack damper, which will bring rotary torque within limits. Shims are available in the following sizes: .01" (.25 mm), and .04" (1 mm). Apply sealer around lock nut.

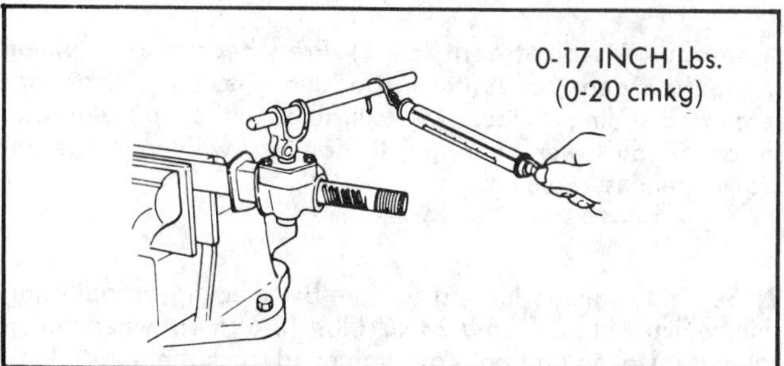

Fig. 2 Measuring Pinion Shaft Rotary Torque

6) After gear assembly is complete, recheck pinion rotary torque and force required to move rack. Pinion rotary torque should remain same as previously described, and rack pull force should be 31-37 lbs. (14-17 kg). If these torques are not within limits, readjust rack damper adjuster.

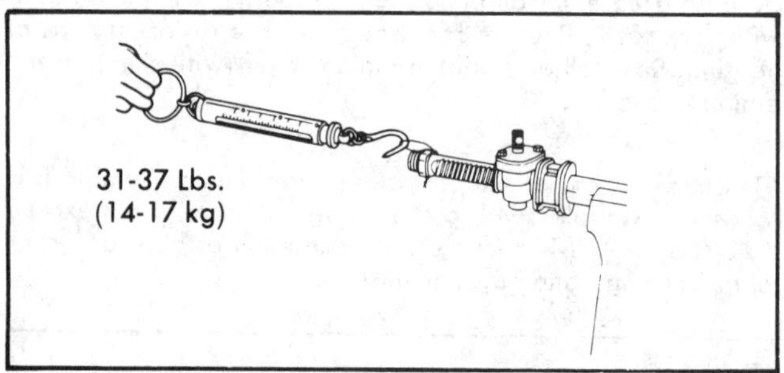

Fig. 3 Measuring Steering Gear Rack Pulling Force

7) Position dust boots on tie rod. Thread lock nut spacer and lock nut over threaded portion of rack. Coat sliding surfaces of tie rod inner socket and spring seat. Fit tie rod assembly to rack end with inner spring and spring seat. **NOTE** – *Ensure proper tie rod is installed on correct side. Left tie rod is marked with an "L", right tie rod has no marking.*

8) Screw inner socket portion until ball seat reaches rack end, then tighten lock nut securely. Upon completion of tie rod assembly, measure swinging torque and axial play of inner ball joint. Swinging torque (measured at outer end of tie rod) should be 0-43 INCH lbs. (0-50 cmkg). Axial play of inner ball joint should not exceed .002" (.05 mm).

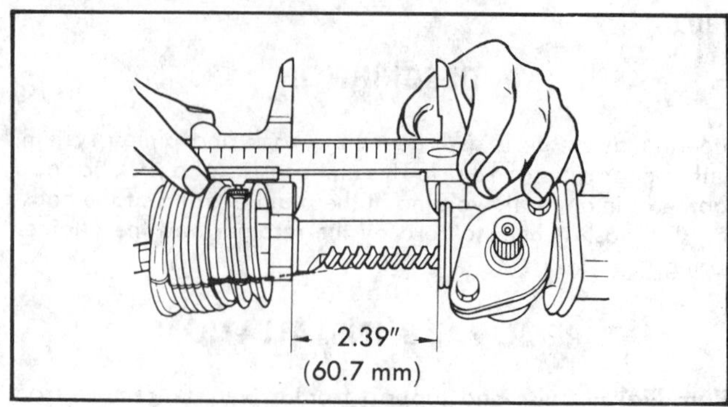

Fig. 4 Measuring Steering Gear Rack Protrusion

9) Measure rack protrusion. It should be 2.39" (60.7 mm). Attach boot and clamps, insert grease nipples at both ends of housing, and lubricate gear assembly (until a small amount of grease appears at boot outlet hole). Adjust tie rod length so that distance from outer side of lock nut to end of boot mounting groove is 1.492" (37.9 mm).

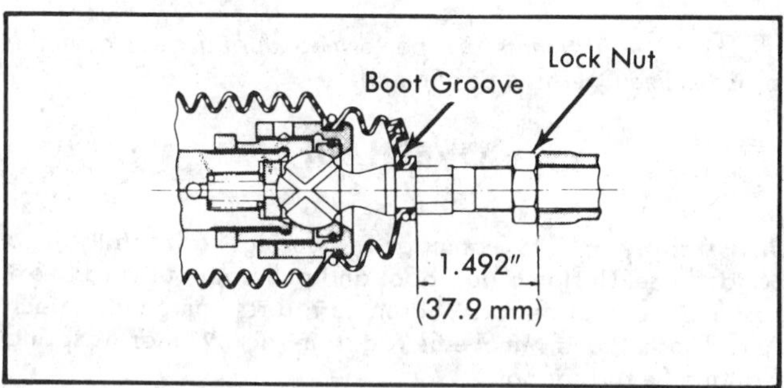

Fig. 5 Adjusting Steering Gear Tie Rod Length

TIGHTENING SPECIFICATIONS

Application	Ft. Lbs. (mkg)
Pinion Cover Bolts	14-22 (1.94-3.04)
Adjuster Lock Nut	29-36 (4.01-4.98)
Inner Socket Lock Nut	58-72 (8.02-9.95)
Tie Rod Lock Nut	58-72 (8.02-9.95)
Column-to-Gear Clamp Bolt	6-8 (0.83-1.11)
Rubber Coupling Bolt	12-14 (1.66-1.94)
Lower Joint-to-Rubber Coupling Bolt	17-20 (2.35-2.77)
Lower Joint-to-Pinion Clamp Bolt	29-36 (4.01-4.98)

DATSUN PICKUP RECIRCULATING BALL

Pickup

DESCRIPTION

The steering system is comprised of a recirculating ball type steering gear and a relay design steering linkage. The linkage connects the pitman arm to one end of an adjustable center link. The other end of the center link is connected to the idler arm assembly. Two nonadjustable tie rods connect both ends of the steering linkage to the steering knuckles.

REMOVAL & INSTALLATION

STEERING GEAR

Removal – **1)** Disconnect battery ground cable. Remove steering wheel, upper and lower column shell covers, and turn signal switch assembly. Unscrew two retaining bolts at column support clamp under instrument panel. Remove screws holding column grommet to dash panel.

2) Unscrew pitman arm retaining nut, scribe a mark for arm-to-sector shaft position and detach pitman arm. Remove three bolts securing gear housing to frame. Withdraw steering gear.

Installation – To install, reverse removal procedure, noting the following: Align pitman arm-to-sector shaft scribe marks after first setting front wheels and steering wheels in straight-ahead position.

STEERING LINKAGE

Removal – 1) Jack up front of vehicle and support on stands. Remove cotter pins and nuts retaining outer tie rod end to steering knuckles. Separate knuckles from rod ends. Detach idler arm and pitman arm from cross shaft. Remove cross shaft and tie rod assembly from vehicle.

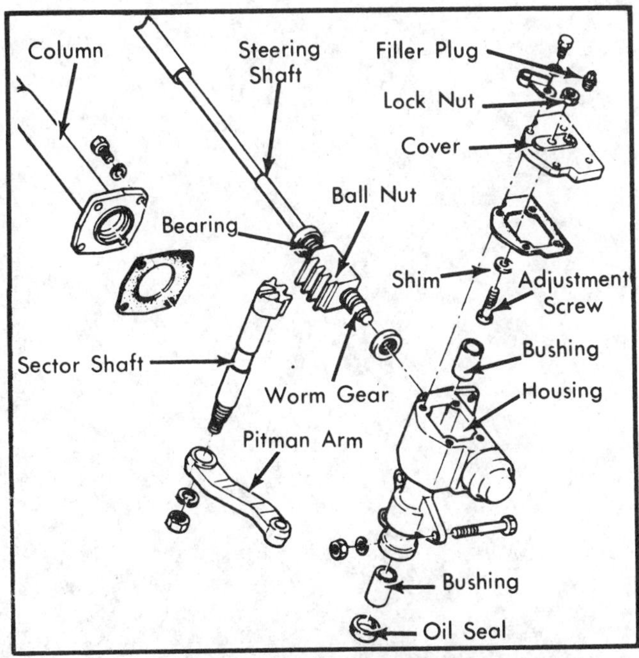

Fig. 1 Exploded View of Recirculating Ball Steering Gear Assembly

2) Unbolt idler assembly from vehicle. Disconnect both tie rods from cross shaft. Remove idler arm nut and disassemble idler unit.

Installation – Reassemble and install steering linkage in reverse of removal procedure, noting the following: Installed length of center link (as measured from center-to-center of ball studs) should be 20.7" (516 mm). Adjust toe-in and steering angle. *See Datsun in WHEEL ALIGNMENT section.*

ADJUSTMENT

NOTE – ***Adjustments are performed as part of reassembly procedure. See Overhaul as outlined below.***

OVERHAUL

STEERING GEAR

Disassembly – **1)** Drain steering gear of oil, then place assembly in padded vise. Loosen lock nut and turn sector shaft adjusting screw a few turns counterclockwise. Remove sector shaft cover bolts. Now turn adjusting screw clockwise until cover is free, then pull sector shaft and cover from gear housing. Separate sector shaft, adjusting screw, and shim from cover.

2) Unscrew column tube retaining screws and remove tube. Withdraw worm assembly from housing. Detach worm bearings and adjusting shims from assembly and column tube. **CAUTION** – *Do not allow ball nut to run freely to either end of travel on worm or ball guides may be damaged.*

3) Pry out sector shaft oil seal from housing (discard seal). Remove "O" ring from rear cover and column tube (discard "O" ring). Remove column tube bushing.

NOTE – *Do not remove sector shaft bushing from housing. If bushing is defective, replace entire worm gear assembly.*

NOTE – *Do not disassemble ball nut. If found to be defective, replace entire worm gear assembly.*

Assembly & Adjustment – **1)** Fit column tube bushing into position (coated with suitable adhesive on exterior of bushing and grease on interior). Fill space of new sector shaft oil seal lips with grease, then install seal. Place worm assembly, with bearings, into housing. Install column tube with new "O" ring and original amount of column tube shims. **NOTE** – *Be sure thicker shim is to gear housing side.*

2) Adjust worm bearing preload by selecting suitable bearing shims so that initial turning torque of steering column shaft is 2-4 INCH lbs. (2.4-4.4 cmkg) when measured at steering shaft, and 5-8 oz. (.12-.22 kg) when measured with pull scale at steering wheel circumference. **NOTE** – *Measurements given are with original bearings installed. If new bearings are used on the worm, the values should be 3.5-5 INCH lbs. (4-6 cmkg) and 6.6-11 oz. (.4-.7 kg) respectively.*

DATSUN PICKUP RECIRCULATING BALL (Cont.)

3) Install adjusting screw into "T" groove at sector shaft head. Choose suitable shim for placement beneath adjusting screw which will give an end play of .0004-.0012" (.01-.03 mm) at adjusting screw.

4) Rotate ball nut by hand until it is in center of its travel, then install sector shaft, engaging center sector tooth with center of ball nut. Coat sector cover packing faces with sealant, then install cover. Turn adjusting screw counterclockwise to bring cover into mounting position. Temporarily install cover bolts.

5) Turn adjusting screw an additional amount to bring sector shaft toward cover approximately .08-.12" (2-3 mm). Fully tighten sector cover bolts. Now gradually turn adjusting screw clockwise to push sector shaft against ball nut. When a light mesh is felt, secure lock nut.

6) Install pitman arm to sector shaft and move arm several times side to side to ensure smooth movement. Adjust backlash at neutral position of pitman arm by turning adjusting screw in or out until less than .004" (.1 mm) free play is measured at outer end of arm.

7) Turn adjusting screw approximately ⅛ - ⅙ turn clockwise and retighten lock nut. Fill gear housing with suitable oil (¾ pt.).

TIGHTENING SPECIFICATIONS

Application	Ft. Lbs. (mkg)
Column Tube-to-Gear	11-18 (1.52-2.49)
Sector Shaft Cover	11-18 (1.52-2.49)
Adjusting Screw Lock Nut	22-29 (3.04-4.01)
Gear-to-Frame	33-38 (4.56-5.25)
Steering Wheel Nut	51-54 (7.05-7.47)
Pitman Arm-to-Gear	94-108 (13.0-14.9)
Steering Linkage Connections	40-72 (5.53-9.95)

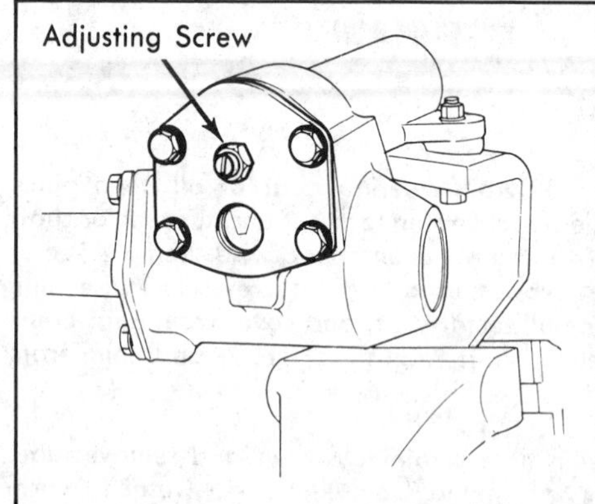

Fig. 2 Removing Sector Shaft Cover

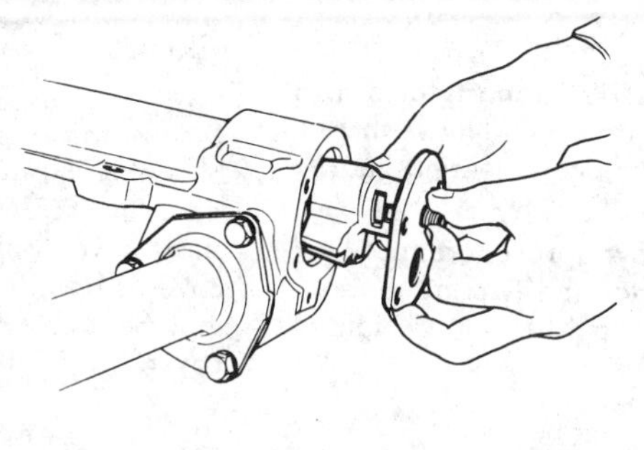

Fig. 3 Removing Sector Shaft

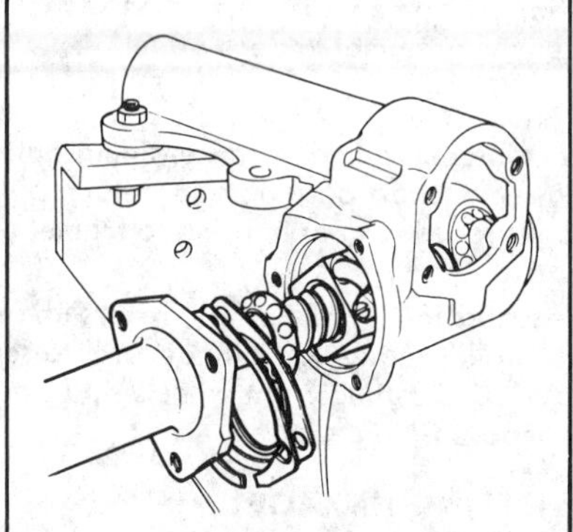

Fig. 4 Removing Steering Gear Worm

FIAT 124 WORM & ROLLER

124 Spider

DESCRIPTION

STEERING GEAR

The steering gear is a worm and roller type, having a gear ratio of 16.4-1. The steering gear box is mounted on the crossmember inside the firewall.

STEERING LINKAGE

The pitman arm, mounted to roller shaft, actuates the center cross link which is connected to the idler arm at other end. Tie rods are connected to steering knuckle on outer ends and pitman arm or idler arm on inner ends. Idler arm is supported on crossmember opposite steering box. Tie rods are adjustable, through sleeves, for setting toe-in.

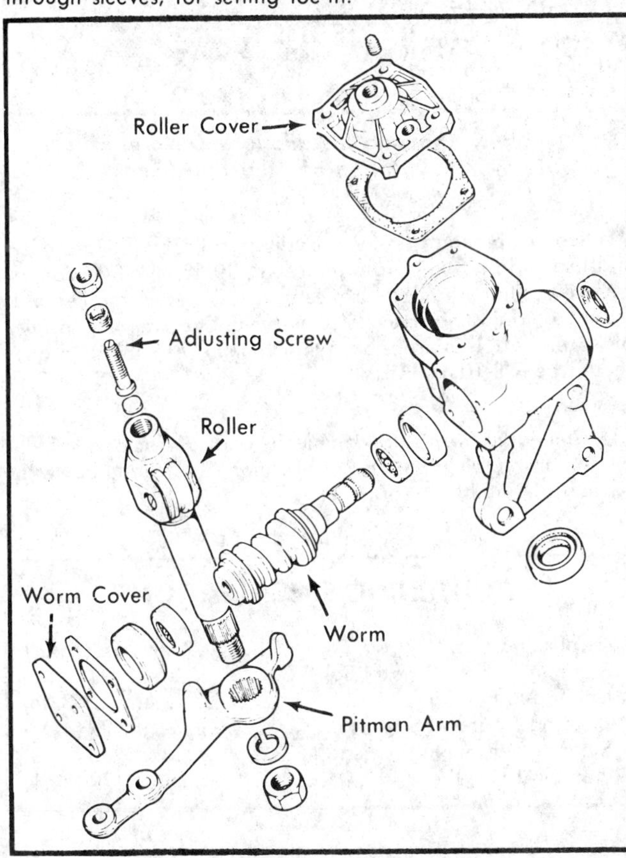

Fig. 1 Exploded View of Fiat Worm & Roller Steering Gear

ADJUSTMENT

NOTE – *Adjustments are performed as part of gear reassembly. See Overhaul as outlined below.*

REMOVAL & INSTALLATION

STEERING GEAR

Removal – 1) Disconnect battery cables, then pry off horn button, disconnect horn cable and slide horn switch out of steering column. Unscrew steering wheel nut and remove steering wheel. Remove four screws retaining turn signal switch cover. Remove turn signal switch and wiring.

2) Loosen steering column-to-instrument panel mounting bracket. Disconnect ignition switch from column bracket, then remove mounting bracket. Remove gearshift and steering column support as an assembly.

3) Using suitable puller, detach center cross link from pitman arm. Remove steering column hole cover pad from instrument panel, if necessary. If column-mounted gearshift has been removed, detach two gearshift control rod levers and pull out gearshift control main rod, after unhooking rod return spring. Unbolt steering gear box from body and withdraw from vehicle.

Installation – 1) Insert steering column from inside vehicle. Working from engine compartment, enter end of worm shaft into steering column. **NOTE** – *If vehicle has an anti-theft key switch, arrange pitman arm on steering box at half-travel (front wheels in straight-ahead position) and fit steering shaft with keyway on left side.* Lock end of steering shaft to worm shaft with clamp and washers.

2) Reconnect gearshift rods and position column support bracket (and gearshift lever, if removed), attaching loosely to instrument panel. Reconnect steering linkage to pitman arm, torquing nuts as specified. Temporarily replace steering wheel and turn two or three times from side to side, to settle shaft to steering gear. Torque steering gear retaining bolts to specification.

3) Position turn signal switch to steering column and bracket. Torque column bracket-to-instrument panel bolts to specification. Position steering wheel with spokes horizontal (ensure front wheels are straight-ahead) and torque wheel nut. **Reconnect electrical wiring for signal switch, position and attach ignition switch. Fit turn signal switch cover. Replace horn button.**

STEERING LINKAGE

Removal – Using a suitable puller (A. 47044), detach tie rod ball joints from steering knuckles. Repeat procedure on inner end ball joints and separate tie rods from center link.

Installation – Reverse removal procedure and readjust toe-in.

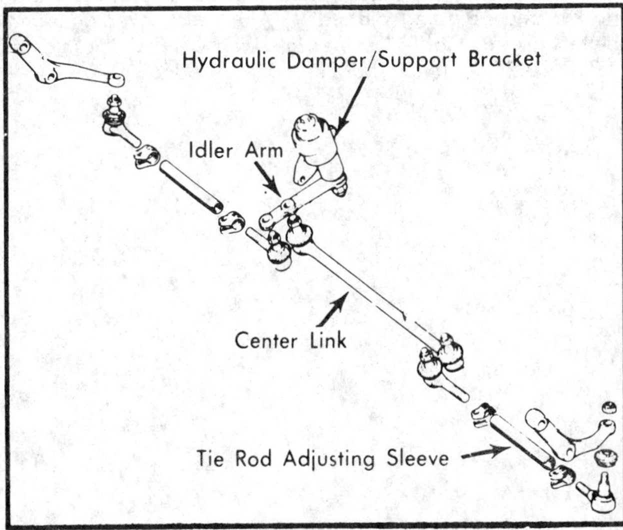

Fig. 2 Exploded View of Steering Linkage

FIAT 124 WORM & ROLLER (Cont.)

OVERHAUL

STEERING GEAR

Disassembly – **1)** Unscrew oil plug and drain gear oil, then mount assembly on suitable overhaul stand (A. 74076/1 with adaptor A. 74076/2). Detach pitman arm from roller shaft, using suitable puller (A. 47043).

2) Remove nuts and washers attaching roller shaft cover to gear box, then take off cover with roller shaft adjusting screw, adjusting disc, lock washer, and lock nut. Extract roller shaft assembly from gear housing.

3) Unbolt thrust cover from worm shaft and remove adjusting shims. Turn worm shaft and withdraw bearing. Using a suitable puller (A. 47004), extract rear bearing race from worm shaft; this releases shims under the race. **NOTE** – *Service shims are available in .0039-.0050" (.10-.15 mm) thicknesses.* Remove roller shaft oil seal. Roller shaft bushings may be removed using suitable puller (A. 74105).

Inspection – Check all contact surfaces for pitting or scoring. Also ensure contact faces of worm and roller mesh at center position. Check clearance between roller shaft and bushings. It should be .0003-.0020" (.008-.051 mm). Check for correct alignment of steering shaft to worm. Maximum allowable misalignment is .0020" (.05 mm).

Assembly & Adjustment – **1)** Remount steering box on suitable stand and adaptor (A. 74076/1/2). If installing new roller shaft bushings, drive into place with suitable drift (A. 74105), then pass a suitable reamer through bushings (A. 90336). Replace shims and bearing race for rear worm shaft bearing. **NOTE** – *Same number of shims must be installed as were removed, if proper center mesh position was found during Inspection. If not, install a different number of shims.*

2) Fit worm bearing races and install worm into gear box. Drive front ball bearing race into gear box and replace thrust cover with shims. Using a suitable dynamometer (A. 95697), check starting torque of worm shaft. It must not exceed 4.3 INCH lbs. If torque is higher than specified, shimming must be increased; if less than specified, reduce shimming.

3) Insert roller shaft oil seal, roller shaft, and cover plate with gasket and adjusting plate. **NOTE** – *Thrust cover adjusting plates are available in the following service thicknesses: .0768", .0787", .0807", .0827", .0846", .0866".*

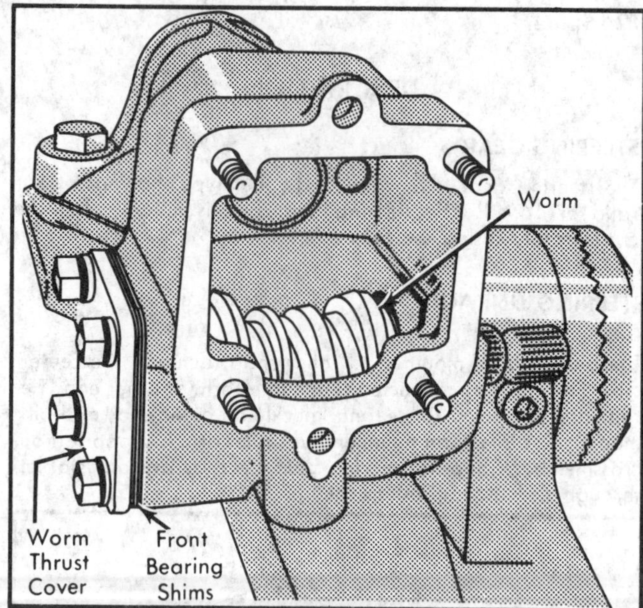

Fig. 3 View Showing Installation of Worm Thrust Cover and Location of Adjusting Shims

4) Replace pitman arm temporarily to roller shaft. The roller shaft should be free to rotate through 30.5° on either side of central position. If any clearance is noticed between roller and worm, use adjusting screw to eliminate it. Check turning torque of worm shaft, using suitable dynamometer (A. 95697): torque should be 7.8-10.4 INCH lbs.

5) When adjustments are completely and satisfactory, tighten pitman arm retaining nut to specification. Fill steering box with 7.5 oz. of suitable grease.

TIGHTENING SPECIFICATIONS

Application	Ft. Lbs. (mkg)
Steering Column Bracket Bolts	11 (1.52)
Linkage-to-Pitman Arm	22 (3.04)
Steering Gear-to-Body	29 (4.01)
Steering Wheel Nut	36 (4.98)
Pitman Arm-to-Gear	174 (24.1)

FIAT X1/9 & 128 RACK & PINION

X1/9
128

DESCRIPTION

Rack and pinion type steering gear is mounted in rubber insulators and attached to body. Gear is attached to steering shaft through universal joints. Adjustments are provided for pinion bearing play and rack yoke free play. At each end of steering rack, tie rods connect steering mechanism to front wheels.

ADJUSTMENT

NOTE – *Adjustments of the pinion bearing and rack yoke are performed during rebuilding. See Overhaul procedure.*

REMOVAL & INSTALLATION

STEERING GEAR

Removal – **1)** Disconnect battery leads. Raise and support front end of vehicle, then remove front wheels. On 128 models it may be necessary to remove the spare tire. Remove three screws holding gasket cover to steering box (at toe board).

2) Disconnect drive pinion from lower steering column section by detaching universal joint inside vehicle. Using a suitable puller (A. 47035), remove tie rods from steering knuckles.

3) Remove stone shield, then unbolt and remove steering gear assembly by sliding out from right hand side of vehicle.

OVERHAUL

Disassembly – **1)** Disconnect tie rods from ball joints (inner end of tie rods). Loosen rubber dust boot retaining clamps, then drain oil from gear. Remove dust boots, then brackets and rubber cushions attaching gear to body.

Installation – Fill gear with suitable oil before inserting into vehicle. Set front wheels in straight-ahead position, then connect drive pinion to steering column. Remount gear to body. Connect tie rods to steering knuckles and torque attaching nuts to 58 ft. lbs. Replace stone shield and front wheels.

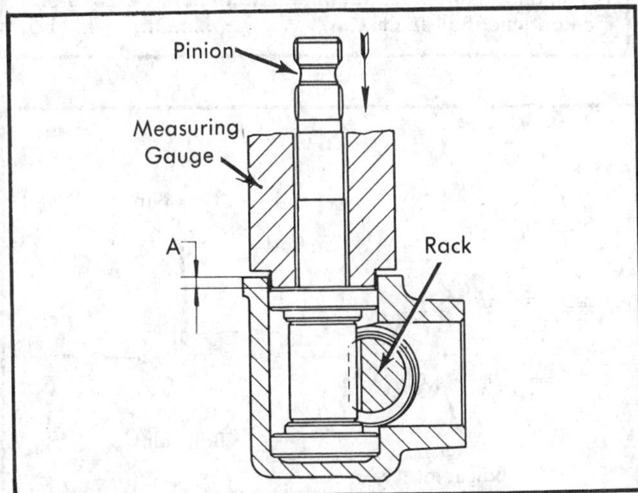

Fig. 1 View Showing Measurement "A" for Pinion Bearing Shim Thickness

2) Detach rack yoke cover plate and withdraw gasket, spring, shims, and yoke. Remove pinion cover plate and withdraw gasket, shims, and drive pinion (with upper ball bearing).

3) Mount steering gear in vise, unscrew ball joint ring nuts, then slide off joints with sockets and springs. Slide rack out of steering box, then remove lower drive pinion bearing.

Assembly & Adjustment – **1)** Set steering box in horizontal position in padded vise, with pinion flange on top. Insert lower pinion bearing, using a suitable driver (A. 74219). Replace bushing in steering box. Slide rack into position with smooth side facing pinion seating. When rack is fully in place, turn teeth to face axis of pinion seating.

2) Insert pinion, ensuring it mates properly with rack teeth, then install upper pinion bearing. Apply force to pinion to eliminate axial play, then with a suitable measuring device, measure distance "A" as shown in illustration. To this measurement, add .001-.005" (.025-.13 mm). This will give the total shim thickness to be used. Remove tool, install shim, cover plate, and oil seal. Check turning torque of pinion. It should be .3 ft. lb. (.04 mkg) or less.

3) Set rack to center position, insert rack damper yoke in its seat, install cover plate (without shims) and turn pinion 180° in both directions to settle rack and yoke. Measure gap between rack yoke cover plate and mounting surface ("B" as shown in illustration). To this measurement, add .002-.005" (.05-.13 mm). This will give total shim thickness to be used. Remove cover, insert spring, "O" ring, shim (coated with liquid adhesive), and cover. Tighten bolts as required. Ensure ground wire is in place.

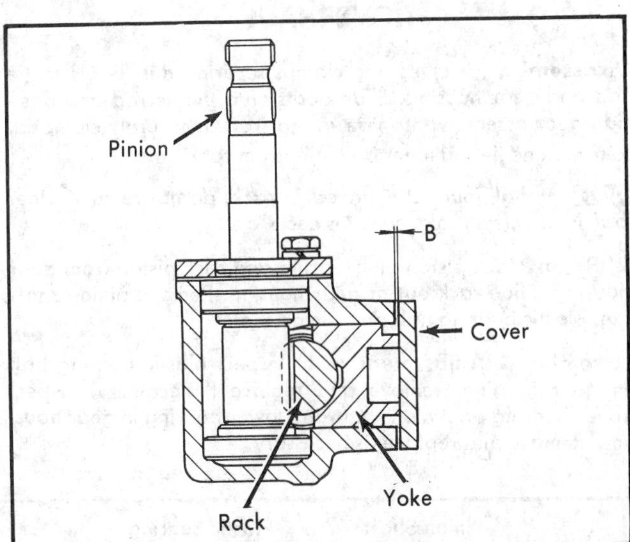

Fig. 2 View Showing Measurement "B" for Rack Yoke Shim Thickness

4) Screw ball joint ring nuts onto rack to end of threaded portion. Assemble springs and socket. Lubricate ball pins with suitable oil, and assemble to rack. Install adjustable ball joint heads and tighten until a force of 1.5-3.75 ft. lbs. (.2-.5 mkg) is required to turn the pins. Lock heads in position with nuts, then stake-lock the nut collars and ball heads. Replace rubber dust boots and clamp in place. Ensure clamp screws are positioned such that they will be accessible when gear assembly is installed in vehicle. Fill gear with 4.75 oz. (140 cc) of suitable gear oil.

NOTE – ***Lubricate dust boots with a silicone spray and be sure they are not twisted after installation.***

FIAT 131 RACK & PINION

131

DESCRIPTION

Rack and pinion type steering gear is mounted in rubber insulators and attached to frame. Gear is attached to steering shaft through universal joints. Adjustment is provided for pinion bearing preload. At each end of steering rack, tie rods connect steering mechanism to front wheels.

ADJUSTMENT

NOTE — *Adjustments of the pinion bearing preload are performed during overhaul. See Overhaul procedure.*

REMOVAL & INSTALLATION

STEERING GEAR

Removal — With wheels in straight ahead position, disconnect tie rod ball joints from steering knuckles. Disconnect steering column universal joint from pinion shaft. Remove bolts securing steering gear assembly to frame and remove steering gear from vehicle.

Installation — Make sure steering wheel is in center position, wheels are straight ahead and pinion gear is centered. Install steering gear assembly to frame. Connect steering column universal joint to pinion shaft and tie rod ball joints to steering knuckles. Check wheel alignment. *See Fiat in WHEEL ALIGNMENT section.*

OVERHAUL

Disassembly — **1)** Loosen clamps securing dust boots to tie rod and gear housing. Slide boots onto the tie rod and position gear assembly into vise so that rack is securely clamped. Remove one tie rod inner ball joint from rack.

NOTE — *Ball joints are staked to rack, do not remove other ball joint unless replacement is necessary.*

2) Remove rack piston plug, spring and rack piston from gear housing. Slide rack out of gear housing. Remove pinion shaft nut, plastic bearing half and pinion shaft.

Assembly & Adjustment — **1)** Inspect plastic bearing half in gear housing, remove and replace if necessary. Inspect roller bearing on pinion shaft and lower bearing in gear housing. Remove and replace as necessary.

2) With lower bearing in gear housing and lower plastic bearing installed, slide rack into gear housing. Install pinion shaft and upper half of plastic bearing. Install pinion shaft nut and tighten to specification. Check torque required to turn pinion shaft (with rack installed). Torque should not exceed 4 ft. lbs. (.5 mkg). With pinion torque correct, stake pinion nut in four places.

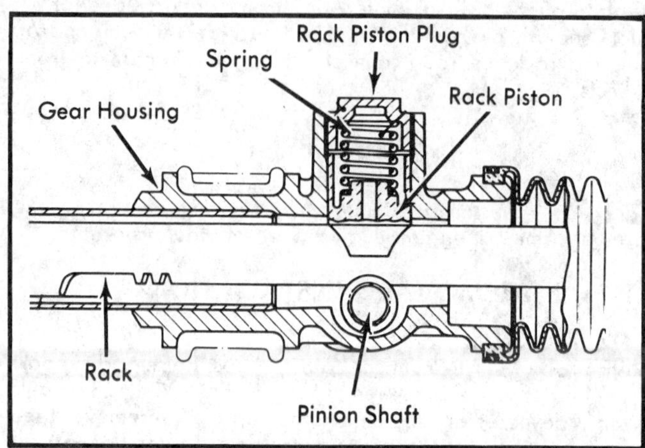

Fig. 1 Sectional View of Rack Piston Assembly

3) Center rack in gear assembly. Install rack piston, spring and rack piston plug. Stake plug in four places. With dust boots on tie rods, lubricate tie rod inner ball joint with oil and install on rack. Tighten ball joint collar to specification, then stake to rack.

4) Slide one dust boot onto gear housing and secure to gear housing and tie rod with clamps. Stand steering gear assembly on end and pour 5-5.2 oz. (145-155 cc) of oil (SAE 90 EP) into gear housing. Install other dust boot.

NOTE — *Lubricate dust boots with a silicone spray and be sure they are not twisted after installation.*

TIGHTENING SPECIFICATIONS

Application	Ft. Lbs. (mkg)
Pinion Shaft Nut	22-23 (3-3.2)
Tie Rod Inner Ball Joint	11 (1.5)

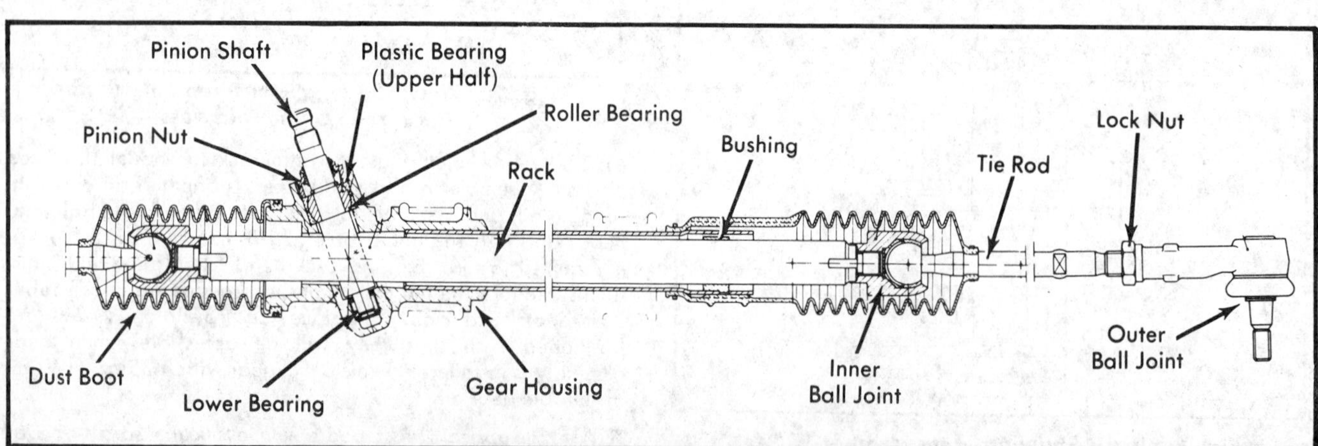

Fig. 2 Sectional View of Rack & Pinion Steering Gear Assembly

HONDA RACK & PINION

Civic
Civic CVCC
Accord

ADJUSTMENT

NOTE — *Rack piston must be adjusted whenever steering gear assembly is removed and installed.*

Make sure gear is well lubricated. Loosen rack piston adjusting screw lock nut. Tighten adjusting screw until lightly bottomed. Back off screw 45° and hold in that position while tightening lock nut. Recheck play. Move front wheels from lock-to-lock to make sure rack moves freely. Recheck steering force.

REMOVAL & INSTALLATION

STEERING GEAR

Removal — **1**) Raise front of vehicle and support with safety stands. Remove front wheels. Attach suitable engine hoist (07966-634011) to torque rod bolt and to bolt just left of distributor, and lift engine far enough to take load off engine mounts.

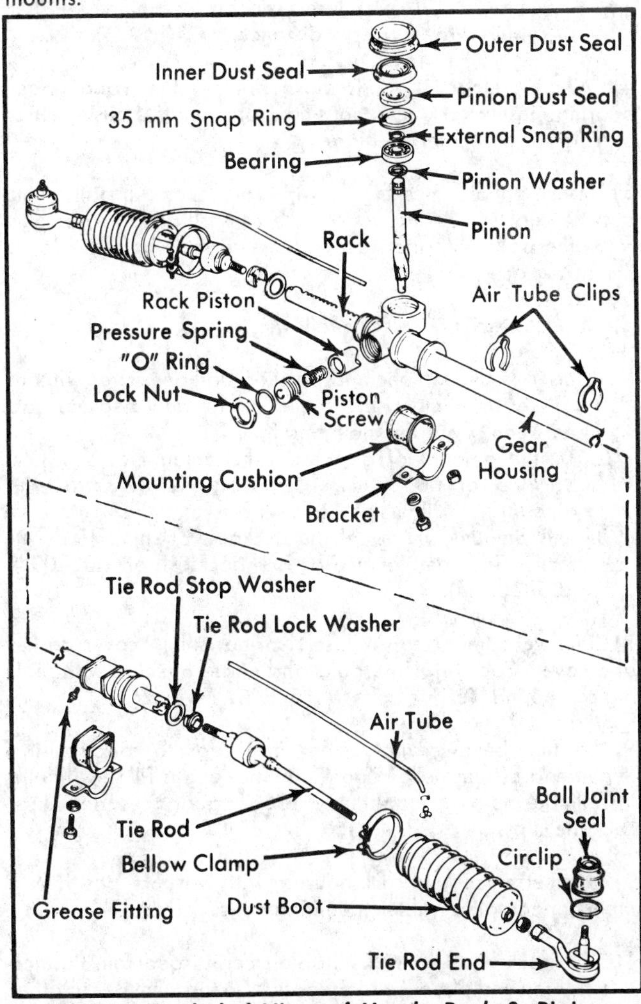

Fig. 1 Exploded View of Honda Rack & Pinion Steering Gear Assembly

2) Remove tie rod ends from steering knuckles. Disconnect linkage at engine on standard transmissions or the control cable at transmission on automatic transmissions. Disconnect exhaust pipe at manifold. Make sure engine is properly supported and remove center support member.

3) Turn steering wheel to a full lock position and remove steering shaft universal joint from pinion shaft. Unscrew steering gear retaining bolts. Bend left tie rod upward and lower rack until pinion shaft clears vehicle body. Rotate steering gear assembly until pinion shaft is facing down. Move rack toward one side until tie rod can be lowered out bottom. Remove gear assembly through bottom of subframe.

4) On Accord models, turn steering wheel to full right lock position. Remove steering shaft connector bolt and washer, then remove steering gear box mounting bracket. Move gearbox as far right as possible, disconnect left end and remove assembly from vehicle.

Installation — To install, reverse removal procedure.

OVERHAUL

STEERING GEAR

Disassembly — **1**) Disconnect air tube at tie rod dust seal clamps and move rubber boots to expose tie rod and rack joints. Straighten tie rod lock washer tabs. Remove both tie rods.

2) Remove rack screw lock nut, rack piston screw, pressure spring, and piston. Rack piston can be removed with snap ring pliers, if necessary. Remove pinion dust seal by carefully prying around pinion shaft. **CAUTION** — *Do not pry at outer edge, as housing will be damaged.*

Inspection — Check all components for wear and replace as necessary. Measure rack piston length. New spring should be 1.028" (26.1 mm) and used spring should be .945" (24 mm) for Accord and 1.087" (27.6 mm) new, .984" (25 mm) used for all others. Replace if necessary.

Assembly — Before assembling, coat each sliding component with grease, then reverse disassembly procedure, noting the following: First install steering rack to gear box. Install pinion in place and mesh it with rack. Position internal snap ring and then a new pinion dust seal. Install rack guide in proper position (note contour of guide over rack). Position pressure spring, new "O" ring on guide screw, and install screw. Adjust rack guide screw as described under Adjustment.

TIGHTENING SPECIFICATIONS

Application	Ft. Lbs. (mkg)
Center Support Member	16 (2.2)
Exhaust Manifold	40 (5.5)
Mounting Bracket (Exc. Accord)	
Pinion Shaft Side	16 (2.2)
Tube Side	22 (3)
Accord only	
Both sides	13.7-18.1 (1.9-2.5)
Rack Piston Lock Nut	33 (4.5)
Tie Rod Lock Nut	33 (4.5)
Tie Rod-to-Steering Knuckle	25 (3.5)
Universal Joint Bolt	16 (2.2)

LANCIA RACK & PINION

Lancia Beta
Coupe
Sedan
HPE

DESCRIPTION

All models use a rack and pinion steering gear. The steering wheel turning motion is transmitted by the pinion gear to the rack, causing it to move side-to-side to turn the road wheels. A steering gear damper is also attached to this rack housing. This dampens road shocks.

NOTE – *Power-assisted rack and pinion is also available on all models. See appropriate article under POWER STEERING in this section.*

ADJUSTMENT

NOTE – *Adjustments are included within the Overhaul procedure contained in this article.*

REMOVAL & INSTALLATION

Removal – **1)** Remove hub caps and loosen wheel nuts. Remove bolt from steering column coupling, located inside passenger compartment just above floor board.

2) Install suitable holding device on steering wheel to retain wheel in straight-ahead position (spokes horizontal). Raise front of vehicle and support with frame stands. Remove front wheels.

3) Separate tie rod end (steering rod) ball joints from steering knuckles. Remove steering rack housing mounting bolts and clamps, and remove rack and pinion steering assembly from vehicle.

Installation – **1)** Move rack from lock-to-lock and count number of turns on pinion as rack travels the distance. Determine the halfway point and move rack back to this position (this will set the center point).

2) Position rack and pinion assembly to its mounting and install retaining clamps and bolts. Connect tie rod end ball joints and torque retaining nuts.

3) Attach pinion shaft to steering shaft coupling. Remove the holding device from steering wheel. Replace front wheels and lower vehicle.

OVERHAUL

Disassembly – **1)** After removing rack and pinion steering gear, loosen clamp from one end of bellows and drain oil.

2) Clamp housing in soft-jawed vise. Straighten locking tabs and remove bolts holding tie rod ends to housing. Remove tie rod ends.

3) Remove rubber mounting insulators. Loosen clips and remove rubber caps and guard from housing.

4) Remove damper cover, gasket, shims, spring and damper. Remove pinion cover, gasket, shims and pinion (with upper bearing).

5) Withdraw rack and plastic bushing from housing. Remove lower pinion bearing.

6) Inspect all components for any wear. Replace as necessary.

NOTE – *It is recommended that pinion housing seal be replaced.*

Assembly & Adjustments – **1)** Insert plastic bushing into rack housing and position it in locating grooves.

2) Install lower pinion bearing, pinion and upper bearing thrust piece, upper bearing and a .09" (2.3 mm) spacing washer.

3) Set pinion bearing preload as follows:

1. Position dial gauge (set to zero) on pinion housing and measure distance between pinion cover mounting surface and top of washer.
2. To obtain a preload (turning torque) of .15-.29 ft. lbs. (.02-.04 mkg), the measured distance must be .001-.005" (.025-.130 mm). Insert shims or use thinner washer as required to set proper distance.

4) When preload is set, remove pinion, shims and upper bearing. Insert rack into housing from pinion housing end, placing rack in center position.

5) Insert pinion, meshing it with rack teeth. Install shims between upper bearing and washer. Install pinion cover and retaining bolts with lock-tab washers. Torque bolts to .15 ft. lbs. (.02 mkg).

6) Now, set rack backlash as follows:

1. Insert rack damper and position damper cover without gasket or shims. Use a feeler gauge and measure gap between cover and mounting face.
2. To the amount of gap, add the amount of specified backlash of .002-.004" (.05-.10 mm). Now subtract the amount of thickness of the cover gasket.
3. This amount will equal the thickness of shims to be installed in order to give a rack backlash of .002-.004" (.05-.10 mm).

7) Remove damper cover. Insert spring, shims, cover gasket and cover. Coat retaining bolts and edges of shims with sealing compound. Torque bolts to .15 ft. lbs. (.02 mkg).

8) Position bellows and rubber dust caps to rack housing (leave end of one bellow loose until housing is filled with oil). Install spacers before tightening rubber guard securing clips. Lock the clips.

9) Fit steering rods to rack housing with washers, positioning them horizontally. Tighten mounting bolts.

10) Fill rack housing with suitable steering gear oil. Position and tighten end of bellows left loose. Use torquemeter or other suitable device to measure and ensure a pinion turning torque of .15-.29 ft. lbs. (.02-.04 mkg).

LUV RECIRCULATING BALL

LUV

DESCRIPTION

STEERING GEARS

Steering gear is a recirculating ball and nut type. A worm gear is incorporated on lower end of steering shaft and is engaged with ball-nut through a number of recirculating balls. These balls carry the turning motion of steering shaft onto the sector shaft with minimal loss of friction. The balls circulate through the ball-nut outlet to a ball tube and back to ball-nut inlet. Adjustment is provided for backlash between sector gear and rack by a tapered sector gear in steering unit (adjustment screw is on sector shaft).

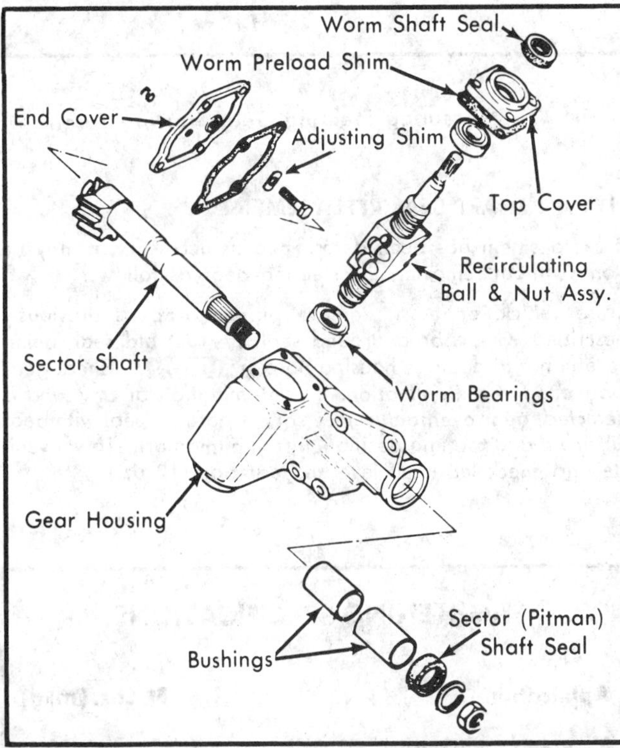

Fig. 1 Exploded View of Recirculating Ball Steering Gear Assembly

STEERING LINKAGE

Linkage consists of splined pitman arm connected to adjustable center link and a tie rod. Center link is connected to idler arm at right end, which in turn is connected to other tie rod and idler arm pivot shaft. Shaft is fastened to frame by a bracket. Tie rods are non-adjustable and connected to brake backing plates by tie rod links. All ball stud connections and idler arm have lubrication fittings. Toe-in is set by adjustable intermediate rod.

ADJUSTMENT

PRELOAD & LASH

1) Disconnect battery ground cable. Remove pitman arm nut and mark relative position of arm to shaft. Remove arm using suitable tool. Remove horn shroud and spring.

2) Turn steering wheel in one direction until stopped by gear, then turn back half way. **CAUTION** — *Do not turn wheel hard against stops, as damage to ball guides may result.* Measure and record "bearing drag" by applying torque wrench to steering wheel nut and rotate through 90° arc. **NOTE** — *Do not use torque wrench having a maximum reading of more than 50 INCH lbs.*

3) Adjust sector lash by turning steering wheel from one stop to the other, turn wheel back exactly halfway (to obtain center position), then turn sector adjusting screw clockwise to eliminate backlash between ball-nut and sector gear. Tighten lock nut.

4) Check torque at steering wheel nut, taking highest reading as steering wheel turns through center. Torque should be 3.5-8.5 INCH lbs. (4.0-9.8 cmkg). If not, loosen lock nut and readjust sector screw. Tighten lock nut and recheck torque at steering wheel.

5) If maximum specification is exceeded, turn adjusting screw counterclockwise, then turn adjuster lock nut clockwise. Reassemble pitman arm to shaft, lining up marks made during removal. Tighten pitman shaft nut to specifications. Install horn spring and shroud. Connect battery cable.

REMOVAL & INSTALLATION

STEERING GEAR

Removal — Raise vehicle on hoist. Remove Pitman arm nut and mark relative position of pitman arm to shaft. Using suitable tool, remove arm from shaft. Remove engine protection shield. Remove lower clamp-to-flexible coupling bolts. Remove gear.

Installation — Place gear in position and start (do not torque) gear mounting bolts. Install clamp-to-coupling bolts and torque. Tighten gear mounting bolts. Install pitman arm, aligning index marks and tighten nut. Install engine protection shield.

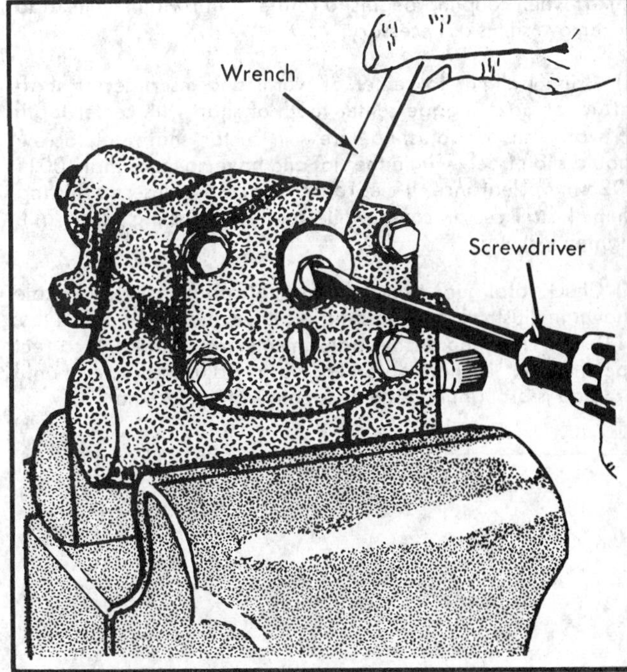

Fig. 2 Adjusting Sector Gear Lash

LUV RECIRCULATING BALL (Cont.)

OVERHAUL

STEERING GEAR

NOTE – *Recirculating ball and nut assembly parts are selectively combined. Ball tube clamp plate is sealed with paint to avoid disturbing. Any worn part, therefore, necessitates entire assembly replacement.*

Disassembly – 1) Remove steering gear as previously described. Disconnect flexible coupling from worm shaft. Drain gear box through filler plug hole (no drain hole is provided). Bring steering shaft into straight-ahead position.

2) Remove top cover bolts and adjusting screw lock nut. Separate top cover from gear box by turning adjusting screw clockwise. **NOTE** – *Hold sector shaft in straight-ahead position during removal. Do not drive shaft off gear box by impact.*

3) Remove adjusting screw and sector shaft from gear case. Remove bolts retaining end cover and shims. Remove worm and ball-nut assembly from gear box and take out lower bearing. **CAUTION** – *Keep assembly in horizontal position or ball-nut will fall onto end of worm gear, damaging ball tubes.*

Inspection – Check all parts for wear or other abnormalities; replace if conditions are noticeable. Ball-nut noise or roughness necessitates replacement of entire steering shaft assembly.

Reassembly & Adjustment – 1) Insert lower bearing into position in gear box. Install worm shaft assembly in box. Check lower end of worm shaft for proper fit in lower bearing.

2) Assemble upper bearing onto worm shaft and install adjusting shims between gear box and end cover. Install and torque bolts. **NOTE** – *Apply liquid gasket to end cover during installation.*

3) At this point, measure starting torque of pinion shaft (see illustration). Reading should be 3.0-5.6 INCH lbs. (3.5-6.4 cmkg) when coupling begins to rotate. If not within limits, add or remove shims as necessary.

4) Bring ball-nut to center of worm and insert sector shaft into gear box. Engage center tooth of shaft with center tooth of worm. Insert adjusting screw in sector shaft slot. Screw should slide freely within the slot and have no more than .001" (.025 mm) clearance. If clearance is excessive, insert adjusting shim. Install sector cover while turning adjusting screw out. Tighten lock nut.

5) Check total gear preload (starting torque) using pull scale shown in illustration. If reading is between 3.5-10.5 INCH lbs. (4.0-12.1 cmkg) no further adjustments are required. If correct specification is not obtained, turn adjusting screw until preload is brought into specification. Tighten lock nut.

6) Connect sector shaft to pitman arm (align marks made during removal) and torque Pitman arm. Install and torque pinch bolt. Fill gear box (10 ozs.). Do not overfill.

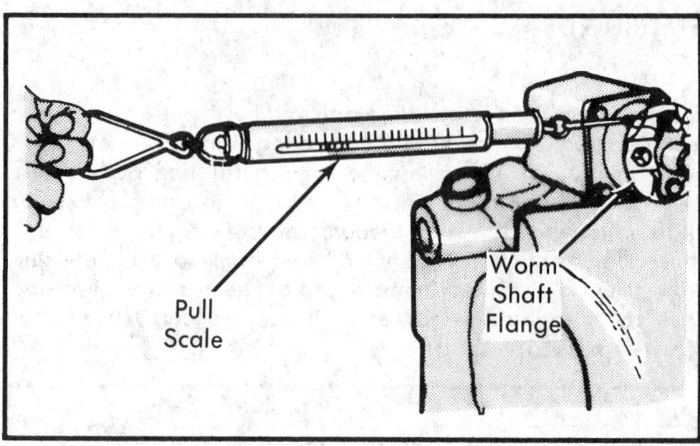

Fig. 3 Measuring Steering Gear Starting Torque

PITMAN SHAFT SEAL REPLACEMENT

If replacement has been determined as necessary, it may be done without removing the steering gear as follows:

Raise vehicle on hoist. Remove pitman arm, as previously described. Clean area around seal. Pry out old seal, being careful not to damage housing bore. **CAUTION** – *Check gear lubricant for contamination. If contamination of any kind is detected, gear overhaul is necessary.* Coat new seal with gear lubricant and tap into position. Install pitman arm. Lower vehicle and check lubricant level in gear box (10 oz.).

TIGHTENING SPECIFICATIONS

Application	Ft. Lbs. (mkg)
Pitman Arm-to-Gear	160 (22.1)
Gear & Idler Arm-to-Frame	
Large Bolts	50 (6.9)
Small Bolts	20 (2.8)
Adjusting Screw Lock Nut	20 (2.8)
Linkage Ball Joints	44 (6.1)
Center Link Lock Nuts	90 (12.4)
Coupling Pinch Bolt	20 (2.8)

MAZDA RECIRCULATING BALL

GLC
808 (1300) Mizer
808 (1600)
RX3SP
RX4
Cosmo
RE Pickup

DESCRIPTION

Steering gear is a recirculating ball type with a variable ratio, depending on turning angle of sector shaft. The pinion shaft and steering shaft are an integral (nonseparable) unit on some models, while the shaft is separable from the pinion on others. Steering linkage is basically the same for all models, having a nonadjustable center link, two adjustable tie rods, an idler arm assembly, and pitman arm.

ADJUSTMENT

NOTE — *Adjustments are performed during assembly portion of overhaul. See Overhaul procedure in this article.*

REMOVAL & INSTALLATION

STEERING GEAR

Removal (GLC, 808, RX3SP) — 1) Disconnect negative battery cable. Remove horn cap, horn contact cup and spring. Mark position of steering wheel to shaft. Unscrew steering wheel nut and remove steering wheel. Remove column covers and disconnect wiring connectors. Remove stop ring from shaft and screw from combination switch. Lift off combination switch. Remove steering lock and ignition switch assembly (except GLC).

2) Detach column support bracket. Loosen nut securing bottom of column jacket to gear housing. Pull jacket off shaft. Separate the dust cover from the dash panel.

3) Raise and support front of vehicle and remove left front wheel. Unscrew nuts and bolts securing upper control arm shaft to support bracket. Note number and placement of shims so that correct wheel alignment can be retained when reassembly is made. Remove left upper control arm.

4) Disconnect center link from pitman arm using a puller. Remove nuts and bolts holding steering gear to frame, noting any shims which may be present. Withdraw steering gear from vehicle.

Removal (RX4, Cosmo, RE Pickup) — Raise and support front of vehicle. Remove front wheel. Detach pitman arm from center link. Remove bolt securing flexible coupling to worm shaft. Detach pitman arm from gear. Remove speedometer cable from clips attached to gear housing and power brake unit. Unbolt and remove gear housing.

Installation (All Models) — To install, reverse removal procedure, ensuring any shims which were removed are installed in original positions.

NOTE — *To avoid damage to steering column components, do not apply bending or striking forces to steering shaft or column.*

STEERING LINKAGE

Steering linkage may be removed as an assembly or as individual components. Whenever tie rod setting is disturbed, toe-in must be reset. *See Mazda in WHEEL ALIGNMENT section.*

OVERHAUL

STEERING GEAR

Disassembly — Drain gear oil from housing. Remove pitman arm from sector shaft, if not done so during removal. Unscrew side cover attaching bolts and loosen adjusting screw lock nut. Turn adjusting screw in to remove side cover from housing. Take adjusting screw and shim from slot in sector shaft. Withdraw sector shaft. Unbolt end cover, then withdraw worm and ball nut assembly. On GLC, worm and ball nut assembly is held in place by an adjuster plug and lock nut instead of being bolted on end cover.

Inspection — Check ball nut rotation on worm. If movement is not smooth for full length of travel, replace worm and ball nut assembly. Ball nut is not to be serviced separately. Check worm bearings and cups, sector shaft gear surface, and oil seal. If any component is defective, replace it.

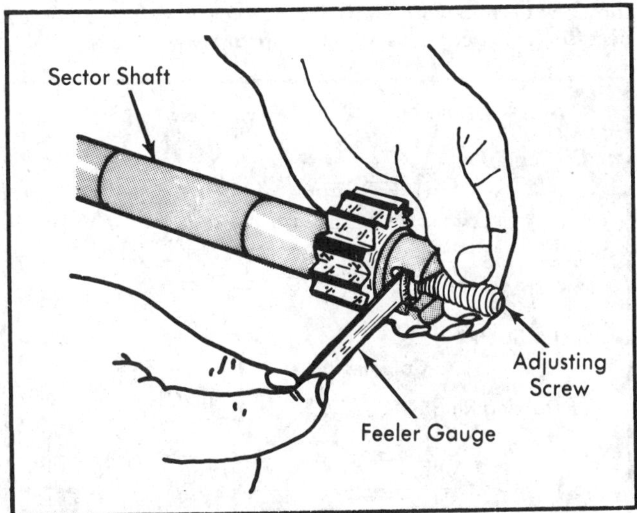

Fig. 1 Checking Adjusting Screw End Clearance

Assembly & Adjustment — 1) Replace oil seal in housing. Insert worm shaft and ball nut assembly into gear housing. Position end cover (or column jacket) with bearing preload adjusting shims and tighten cover (jacket) bolts. Attach preload checking tool (49 0180 510) to pinion splines (or top end of steering shaft) and connect a pull scale to the tool. If reading is below .22 lb. (.1 kg) reduce the shim; if above .88 lb. (.4 kg), increase the shim. On GLC only, tighten adjuster plug to give 1.7-4.3 INCH lb. (2-5 cmkg) preload.

2) Insert sector shaft into gear housing, using care not to damage oil seal. Ensure center of sector gear is aligned with center of worm gear. *See Fig. 2.* Insert adjusting screw into slot in end of sector shaft. Check end clearance as illustrated and add appropriate shim to bring clearance within 0-.004" (0-.1 mm). Place side cover and gasket over adjusting screw and turn adjusting screw until cover is in place, install attaching bolts.

MAZDA RECIRCULATING BALL (Cont.)

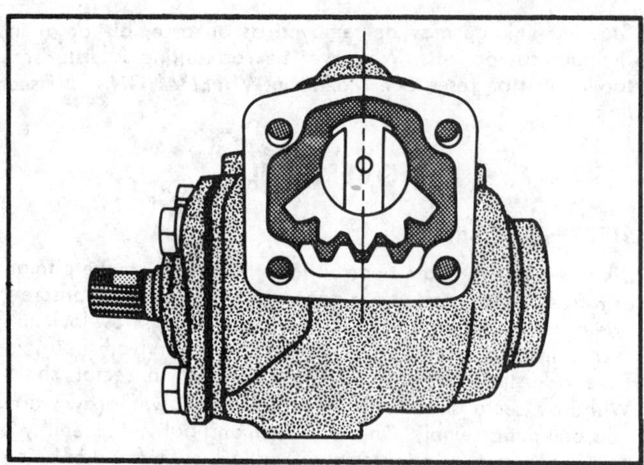

Fig. 2 Aligning Sector Gear & Rack

3) Install pitman arm onto sector shaft, aligning marks. Install and tighten retaining nut. Measure pitman arm backlash. If necessary, turn sector adjusting screw until zero backlash is obtained. Tighten adjusting screw lock nut, taking care not to disturb backlash adjustment.

4) Check worm shaft rotating torque. Attach an INCH lbs. torque wrench to worm shaft. If not to specifications, adjust as necessary. Fill gear housing with lubricant (SAE 90 EP).

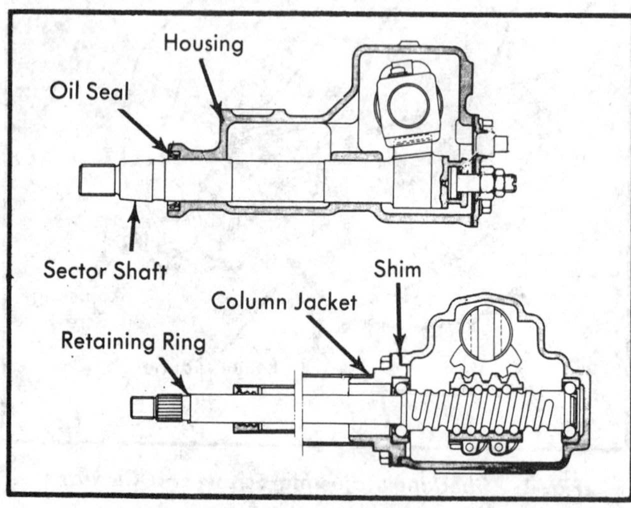

Fig. 3 Steering Gear Cutaway of RX3SP (Others Similar)

Initial Worm Bearing Preload Torque

Application	INCH lbs. (cmkg)
808, RX4 & RE Pickup	0.9-3.5 (1-4)
Cosmo	2.6-4.3 (3-5)
RX3SP & GLC	1.7-4.3 (2-5)

Final Worm Bearing Preload Torque

Application	INCH lbs. (cmkg)
808	7.8-13 (9-15)
RX3SP & GLC	5.2-10.4 (6-12)
Cosmo	5.2-11.3 (6-13)
RX4 & RE Pickup	7.9-10.4 (9-12)

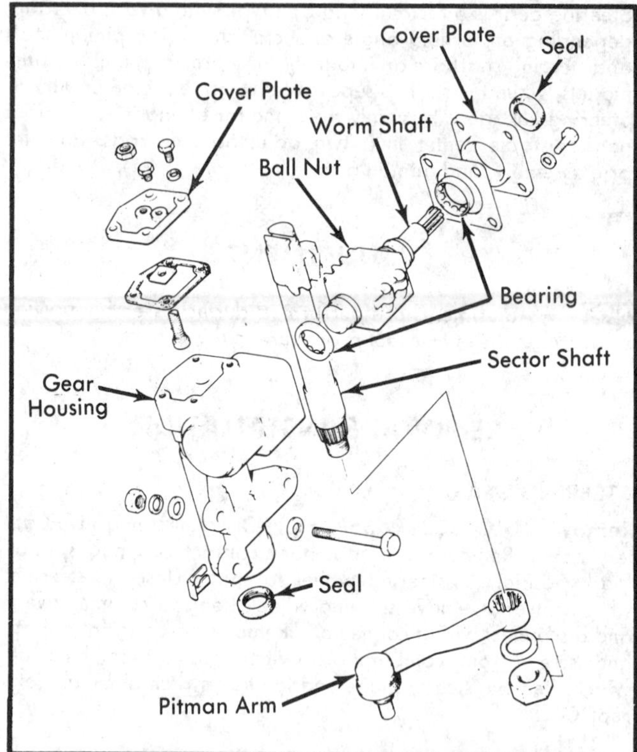

Fig. 4 Exploded View of RX4 Recirculating Ball Steering Gear (Others Similar) GLC Uses Adjuster Nut Instead of Cover Plate

TIGHTENING SPECIFICATIONS

Application	Ft. Lbs. (mkg)
Gear Box-to-Frame	
All Models	32-40 (4.4-5.5)
Pitman Arm-to-Sector Shaft	
GLC	58-87 (8-12)
808 & RX3SP	94-123 (13-17)
RX4, Cosmo & RE Pickup	108-130 (15-18)
Steering Wheel Nut	
All Models	22-29 (3-4)
Tie Rod-to-Center Link	
All Models	22-32 (3-4.5)

MGB RACK & PINION

MGB

DESCRIPTION

Steering gear is a direct-acting rack and pinion type. Gear consists of rack bar and toothed pinion mounted on front suspension crossmember. No adjustment for bearing wear in gear box is provided. Steering column is attached to pinion by "U" joint coupling.

REMOVAL & INSTALLATION

Removal – Raise and support front of vehicle and remove both front wheels. Detach tie rod ends from steering arms. Turn steering to right lock and remove "U" joint lower pinch bolt. Remove nuts and bolts securing rack assembly to crossmember, noting that front bolts are attached with self-locking nuts and that shims may be found between rack assembly and frame brackets. Withdraw rack assembly downward and remove from vehicle.

Installation – To install, reverse removal procedure after first setting steering gear and steering column in straight-ahead position. **NOTE** – *If new rack is being installed, it must be aligned. See Alignment in MGB article under Steering Columns in this section.*

OVERHAUL

Disassembly – 1) Clamp rack in padded vise. Remove pinion end cover and joint washer, placing container beneath assembly to catch oil. Remove damper cover and shims. Extract yoke, damper pad, and spring, then withdraw pinion.

2) Unlock tie rod outer lock nuts and remove tie rod ends. Unclamp and remove both rubber bellows. Release bellows seal clips and withdraw seals. Pry up tab on locking rings, slacken rings, and unscrew housing to release tie rod, ball seat, and spring.

3) Pull rack out pinion end of housing. To remove rack housing bushing, unscrew self-tapping screw and carefully drive out bushing.

Inspection – Thoroughly clean all parts and examine for wear. Particularly, note condition of rubber bellows; if they show any sign of wear, replace them. Outer ball socket assembly cannot be disassembled; if worn, it must be replaced as assembly.

Assembly – 1) Insert rack bushing and carefully drive it in until flush with housing end. Drill outer housing of bushing through screw hole with a $\frac{7}{64}$" (2.78 mm) drill to a depth of .24" (6.3 mm) so that a new retaining screw may be inserted. Coat screw head with sealing compound before tightening.

2) Replace rack from pinion end. Position seat spring, ball seat, tie rod, and ball housings. Coat ball seats liberally with SAE 90 oil. Tighten ball housings until tie rods are held firmly, without free play. This tightening is correct when a force of 32-52 Inch lbs. is required to move the tie rods. Tighten new locking rings and bend tabs.

3) Insert pinion complete with ball races and locking nut into housing. Replace pinion end cover and seal, using sealing compound on mounting edges. Peen outer edge of ball race lock nut into slot in pinion shaft, if lock nut has been removed.

4) To adjust rack damper, replace plunger in housing and tighten cover, without spring or shims, until it is just possible to rotate pinion shaft by drawing rack through housing. With a feeler gauge, measure clearance between cover and housing. To this measurement add .0005-.003" (.013-.076 mm). This figure will be the correct thickness of shims to place beneath damper cover. Remove cover and plunger, insert spring and shims with plunger and cover. Coat cover with sealing compound and tighten.

5) Replace rubber bellows; before securing bellow clip on tie rod at pinion end, stand assembly on end and pour in 1/3 pint (.2 litre) of suitable SAE 90 oil. Replace bellow clip. **NOTE** – *Oil may be pumped in through fitting on housing.*

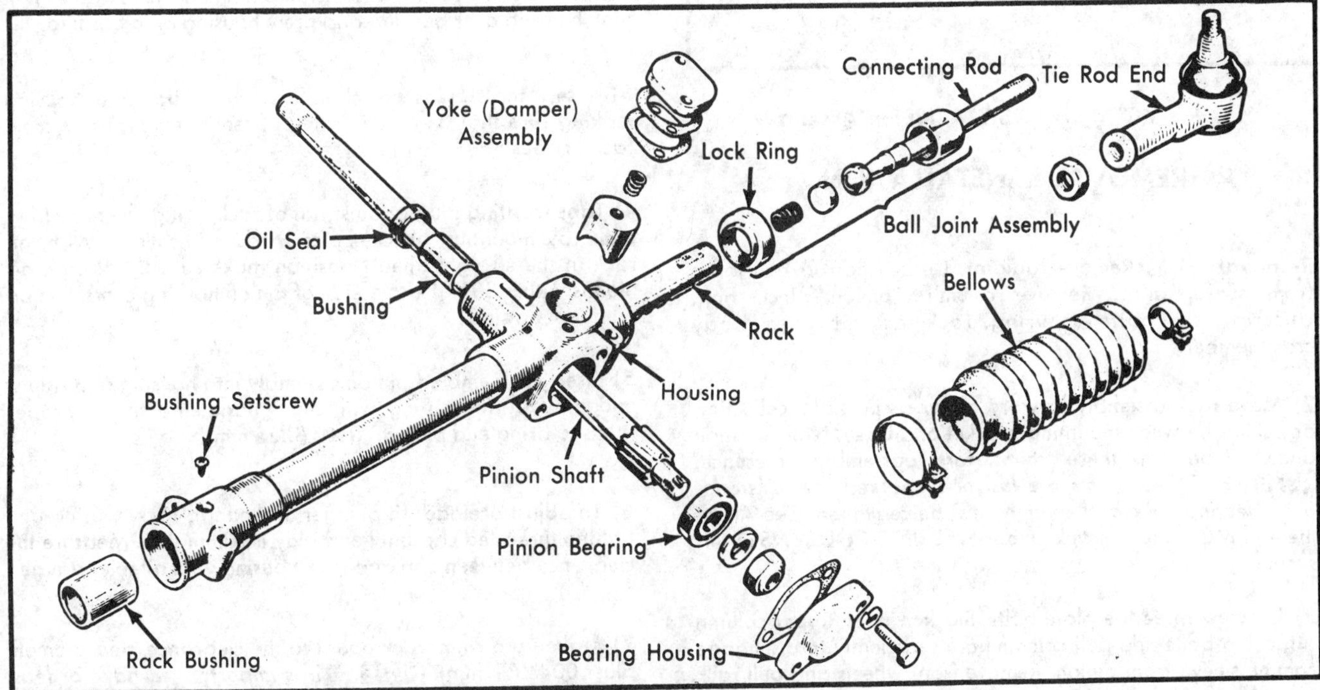

Fig. 1 Exploded View of MGB Rack and Pinion Assembly

MG MIDGET RACK & PINION

Midget

DESCRIPTION

Steering gear is a rack and pinion type and is secured above front frame crossmember, immediately behind the radiator. Tie rods, operating swivel arms, arm attached to each end of rack by ball joint enclosed in rubber bellows. Steering column engages splined end of pinion. Pinion end play is eliminated by adjustment of shims beneath pinion lower bearing. A damper pad, inserted in rack, controls backlash between pinion and rack.

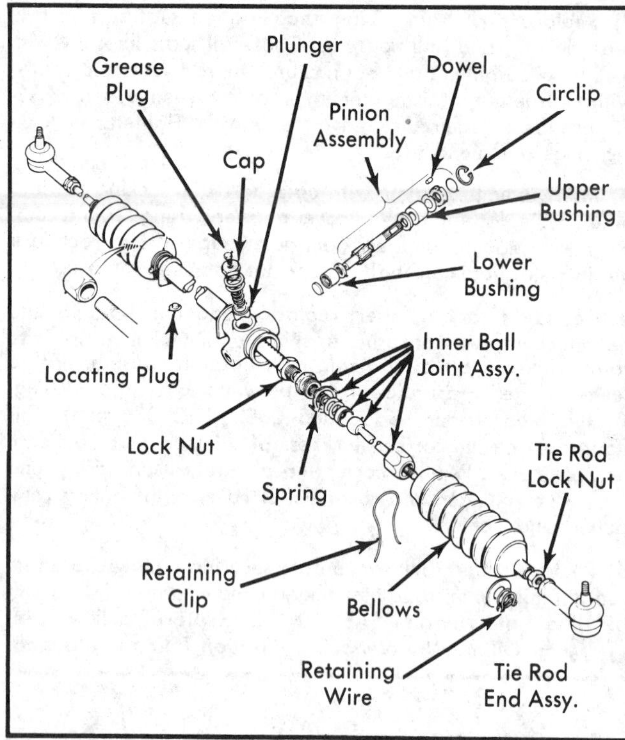

Fig. 1 MG Midget Rack & Pinion Assembly

REMOVAL & INSTALLATION

Removal – 1) Remove radiator. Detach tie rod ball joints from swivel arms. Remove column-to-pinion pinch bolt. Unscrew six bolts securing rack assembly to body crossmember.

2) Move rack assembly forward as far as possible, collecting any shims between mounting bracket and body. Note location and number of these shims for reassembly reference. **NOTE** – *If these shims are lost or unmarked for reinstallation, steering rack and column must be realigned. See Alignment in MG Midget article under STEERING COLUMNS in this section.*

3) Unscrew three toe plate bolts. Slacken three upper column attaching bolts and pull column back sufficiently to disengage column sleeve from pinion. Remove front wheels and pull rack assembly from vehicle.

Installation – To install, reverse removal procedure, noting the following: Ensure shims are returned to original positions. When joining column to pinion, check that rack and column are both in straight-ahead position. If new rack is being installed, column and rack alignment is necessary. *See Alignment in MG Midget article under STEERING COLUMNS in this section.*

OVERHAUL

Disassembly – 1) Loosen lock nuts and remove tie rod end assemblies. Release retaining clips and wires, then remove bellows and protective shields.

2) Loosen lock nuts and unscrew tie rod inner ball joint assemblies. Remove coil spring and remove lock nuts from each end of rack.

3) Disassemble inner ball joint assembly by unlocking tab washer and unscrewing sleeved nut. Remove grease plug, cap, and shims, then withdraw spring and plunger from housing. Remove circlips and withdraw pinion assembly with dowel, then press lower bushing and end plug from housing bore.

Inspection – Thoroughly clean all components and check rack and pinion for wear, cracks or damage. Examine seals and replace any faulty parts.

Reassembly – 1) Reassemble by reversing disassembly procedure, noting the following: Heat the pinion bushing and plunger in 212°F (100°C) SAE 20 engine oil for 2 hours and allow to cool to ensure pores of bushing and plunger are properly lubricated.

2) Install large bushing on pinion shaft. Place end plug into recess in lower bushing and install on pinion shaft. Position pinion housing over bushing and press housing onto bushing.

3) Insert thrust washer, chamfered bore up, into housing making sure that 3½" (88.9 mm) of teeth end protrude from face of housing.

4) Tape locating plug against flat of rack, (plug will be held in place by mounting bracket after rack is installed). With the rack in the straight-ahead position make sure the flat on pinion is within 30° of either side of pinion housing centerline on plunger cap side.

5) Insert reassembled pinion assembly into housing and adjust end play by measuring with dial guage and fitting proper shims to bring end play to .010" (0.25 mm).

6) To adjust preload, fit plunger and cap to rack housing and tighten threaded cap until end play is eliminated. Measure the clearance between cap and rack housing with a feeler gauge.

7) Make up a shim pack equal to the clearance measurement plus .004" (.1 mm). **NOTE** – *it is important to have at least one .004" (.1 mm) shim in assembly.*

MG MIDGET RACK & PINION (Cont.)

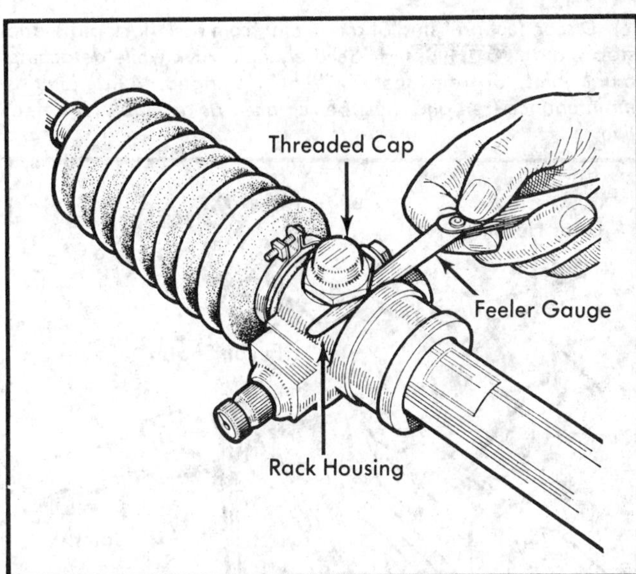

Fig. 2 Checking Rack Damper Clearance Preload Adjustment

8) Remove cap and plunger, grease plunger, then install cap, plunger and shims on the housing and tighten cap.

9) Replace grease plug with fitting and inject ½ to ¾ ounce of grease into unit. Replace grease plug, then check pinion shaft torque for 2 ft. lbs. (.91 mkg). Adjust by adding or subtracting shims.

10) Lubricate tie rod inner ball joint with graphite grease and reassemble by reversing disassembly procedures noting the following: Use a new tab washer and adjust ball end movement by measuring clearance between cap nut and tab washer.

11) Add or subtract shims to arrive at the following torque values: For steel cups 40 INCH lbs. (.46 cmkg) or for nylon cups 15-50 INCH lbs. (.17-.57 cmkg).

12) Install bellows, clips and wires and screw lock nuts on rack, making sure the distance between faces of lock nuts is 23.2" (589.3 mm).

13) Insert thrust springs into ends of rack (steel cup type only) and screw tie rod end assembly as far as possible up to the lock nut. Tighten lock nuts to 80 ft. lbs. (11.1 mkg), push bellows onto tie rods, grease ball joints, and secure bellows with clips and wires.

14) Screw tie rod end assemblies onto tie rods and check that there is 42.7" (1084.1 mm) between ball stud centers. Tighten locknuts to 30-35 ft. lbs. (4.2-4.8 mkg).

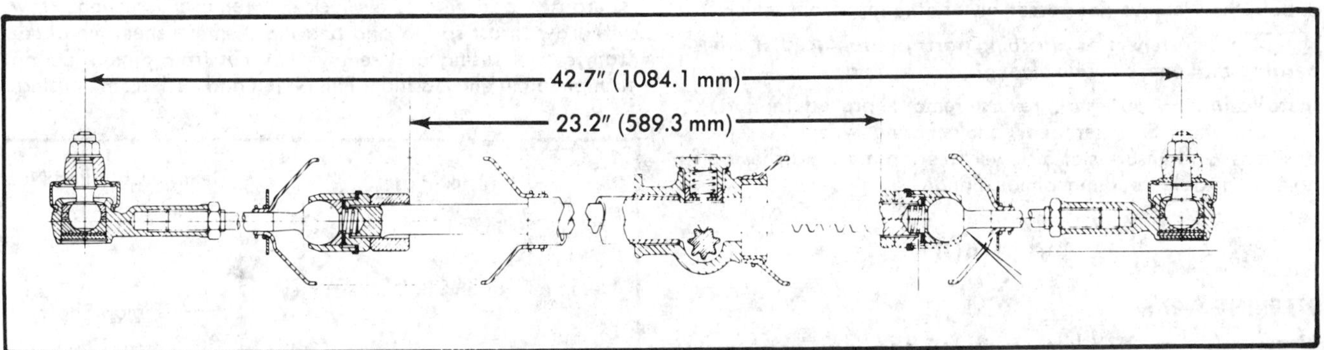

Fig. 3 MG Midget Rack Assembly Adjustments

OPEL RACK & PINION

All Models

DESCRIPTION

Steering gear is a rack and pinion type. Gear housing is held to crossmember by rubber bushing and clamps. Pinion shaft is seated in upper portion of gear housing and is supported by a needle bearing in upper housing and a bushing in lower housing. Pinion is not adjustable. Rack and pinion are held in mesh by a thrust spring and shell.

ADJUSTMENT

STEERING GEAR BACKLASH

Set gear to high point by positioning front wheels straight-ahead. Flexible coupling bolt holes will be positioned parallel to the rack. Thread adjusting screw into gear housing until a resistance is felt. Back off screw ⅛-¼ turn. Tighten lock nut. Fill area under pinion shaft rubber boot with gear lubricant and slide boot into position.

REMOVAL & INSTALLATION

STEERING GEAR

Removal – Remove splash shield from lower deflector panel and both side members. Remove clamp bolt securing flexible coupling to steering shaft. Detach tie rods from steering arms. Unbolt, then remove gear assembly and tie rods from vehicle.

NOTE – *If fasteners or attaching parts are replaced, it is imperative that ones of equivalent grade are used.*

Installation – To install, reverse removal procedure, noting the following: First set gear and steering wheel in center positions, and ensure slot of lower steering mast matches bolt hole of flexible coupling pinion flange.

OVERHAUL

STEERING GEAR

Disassembly – 1) Clamp gear assembly in padded vise. Disconnect left and right tie rod ends from axial joints (at lock nuts). **NOTE** – *Ball joint of tie rod end is maintenance-free; if defective, it must be replaced as an assembly.* Unclamp and remove both rubber bellows.

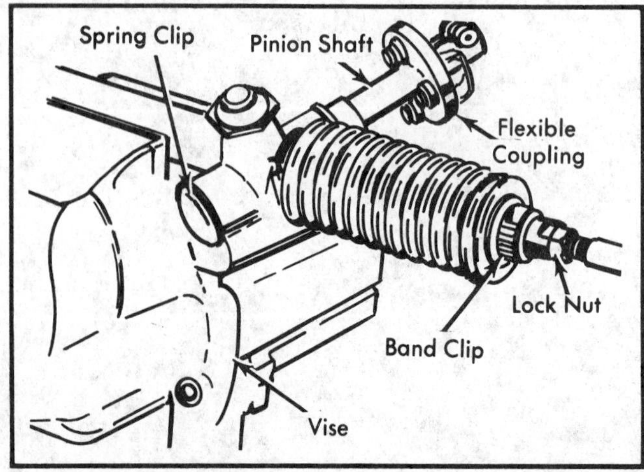

Fig. 1 Removing Tie Rod Ends from Axial Joint

2) Disconnect ball stud of axial joint from rack (lock plate and stop plate). **CAUTION** – *Securely hold rack while detaching axial joint, or rack teeth will be damaged. Axial joint is maintenance-free and must be replaced as assembly, if defective.*

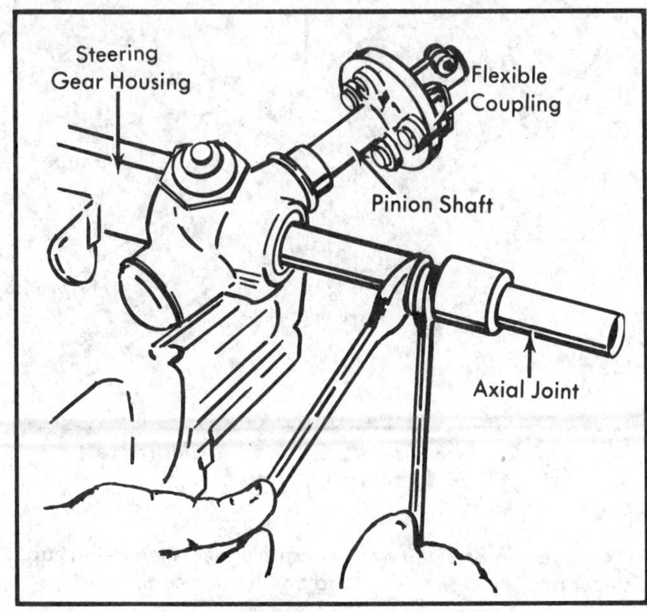

Fig. 2 Separating Axial Joint

3) Loosen adjusting screw lock nut, remove adjusting screw; withdraw thrust spring and bearing. Remove sheet metal cap from gear housing and remove hex nut from pinion. Do not turn pinion in end position. Pull pinion and rack from housing.

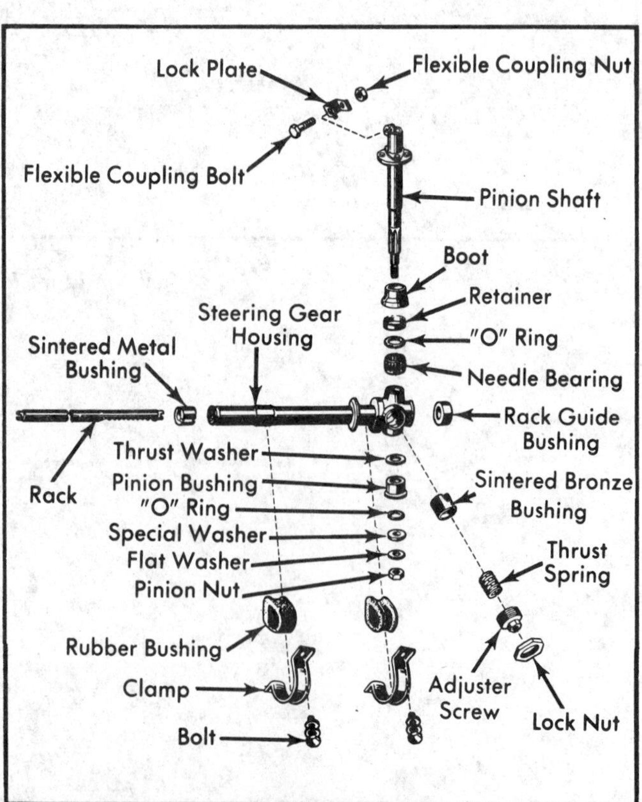

Fig. 3 Exploded View of Opel Steering Gear Assembly

OPEL RACK & PINION (Cont.)

Assembly – 1) With gear housing in padded vise, place new "O" rings onto retainer and pinion shaft bushing. Install thrust washer onto pinion bushing. Coat all moving parts with gear oil. Fill long end of housing with approximately 1¾ oz. of gear oil.

2) Insert long, smooth end of rack into short end of housing until rack ends protrude evenly from housing. Ensure that three air channels of sintered bushing are not blocked by lubricant.

3) Reassemble pinion shaft into gear assembly so that spline in pinion shaft meshes with twelfth tooth of rack. Use special pinion mounting sleeve (J-21712) during pinion installation to avoid damage to "O" ring in pinion bushing. Ensure pinion is positioned such that bolt hole in flexible coupling is on top and parallel to rack.

4) Reassemble special washer, flat washer, and new pinion nut onto pinion shaft. **CAUTION** – *Pinion nut must be tightened to 20 Ft. Lbs. (2.7 mkg). Do not exceed this specification or gear jam may result.*

5) Place sintered bronze bushing into gear housing and fill adjusting hole with gear lubricant. Reassemble thrust spring, adjuster screw, and lock nut on gear assembly.

6) Screw ball stud of axial joint together with stop plate onto both ends of rack (hold rack from turning). Slide rubber bellows into position and clamp such that clamp screws are facing same direction as adjuster screw.

TIGHTENING SPECIFICATIONS

Application	Ft. Lbs. (mkg)
Flexible Coupling Clamp	19 (2.63)
Axial Joint Ball Stud-to-Rack	65 (8.99)
Gear Housing-to-Crossmember	14 (1.94)
Adjusting Screw Lock Nut	49 (6.77)
Pinion Lock Nut	20 (2.77)
Tie Rod-to-Steering Arm	29 (4.01)

PEUGEOT RACK & PINION

504

DESCRIPTION

The steering gear is a rack and pinion assembly which is joined to the steering column by a flexible rubber coupling, and mounted to the front crossmember by flange brackets. The rack is protected by flexible rubber bellows and rides on bushings at each end of the housing. A non-adjustable tie rod is connected by a universal joint to the pinion side of the rack, and an adjustable tie rod is attached to the opposite end of the rack.

ADJUSTMENT

NOTE — *See Overhaul procedure in this article.*

REMOVAL & INSTALLATION

Removal — From under vehicle disconnect right and left tie rod ball joints. Remove the steering column clamping bolt (flexible collar). Remove the two screws attaching steering gear housing to crossmember. Using a center punch as a lever, inserted into clamping collar bolt hole, disengage steering column by rocking.

Installation — 1) Position steering wheel spokes vertically. Place right front wheel in straight ahead position and left front wheel turned inwards as far as it will go. Center steering gear rack in straight ahead position. Hook up right tie rod, rotate steering clamp 1/4 turn and align clamp with spline of steering column then install clamp on steering column.

2) Secure steering gear housing to crossmember. Replace flexible coupling bolt, nut, and lock washer. Attach left tie rod. **NOTE** — *Ensure proper alignment of the two flats on the ball joint housing with those on the connecting yoke.* Install new lock washers and tighten both ball joints. Adjust toe-in. *See Peugeot in WHEEL ALIGNMENT section.*

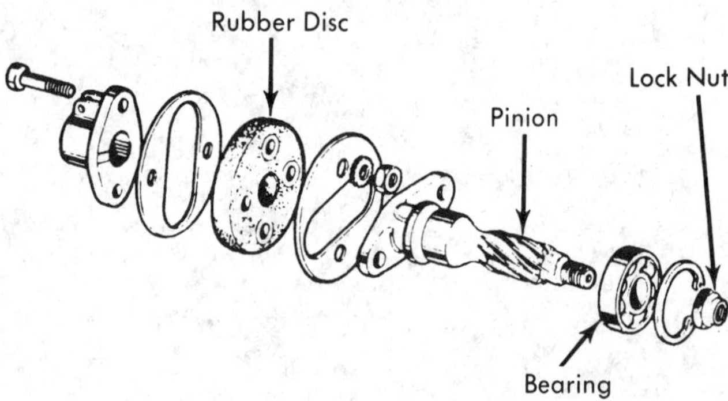

Fig. 1 Exploded View of Steering Gear Flexible Coupling and Pinion

OVERHAUL

Disassembly — 1) Place steering gear horizontally in a padded vise. Mark position of flexible coupling with gear in straight-ahead position (to assist in reassembly). Remove four rubber boot clips, and push boots away from tie rod yoke pivots. Remove both pivots and tie rods. Detach rack eye opposite pinion.

2) Remove rack plunger retaining plate, grease fitting, nylon stop, plunger spring, plunger, and sealing cup. Then, unscrew pinion nut and withdraw thrust washer and "O" ring. Extract rack from pinion side. Remove flexible bushing retaining snap rings, bushings, two steel thrust washers, and pinion bearing snap rings. Remove pinion bearing.

Inspection — Inspect all component parts for excessive wear or damage. Replace parts as necessary.

Reassembly & Adjustment — 1) Replace steering gear housing bushings. Install outer race and bearing with snap ring. Install in housing from opposite side of pinion, the inner thrust washer, flexible bushing with two rubber rings, outer thrust washer and lock ring. Lubricate with grease the bearing, rack and flexible bushing. Insert rack in housing from pinion side. Thread,temporarily, the second eye on rack with lock nut. Tighten the lock nut only slightly.

2) Push rack until lock nut touches steering gear housing. Install "O" ring and thrust washer, lubricate the pinion and install with nut locking groove, facing away from plunger housing. Starting with the pinion flange vertical, rotate it to the left through approximately 20°. *See Fig. 2.*

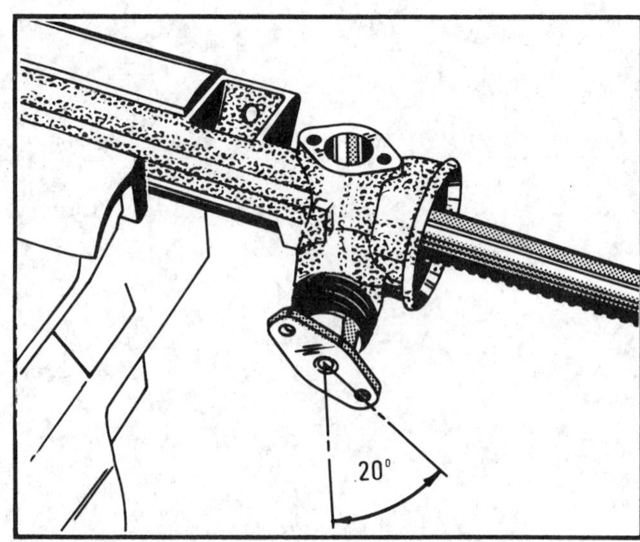

Fig. 2 View Showing Correct Alignment of Pinion Flange

3) Push in pinion until it touches the bearing. **NOTE** — *The pinion flange should now be vertical and the lock nut on the opposite end of the housing should still be in contact with the steering housing.* Clamp the pinion flange in a padded vise, then install a new lock nut on lower end of pinion. Tighten nut. Stake lock the nut collar, apply grease to the recess, and install sealing cup.

4) To measure the play in rack plunger proceed as follows: Insert plunger in its housing with spring inside plunger. Mount the thrust plate with dial indicator holder on one side. Tighten thrust plate. Install extension rod on dial indicator with extension rod in contact with plunger through the threaded hole in plate. Move the rack from side to side using the pinion. Record the highest point recorded by the dial indicator.

PEUGEOT RACK & PINION (Cont.)

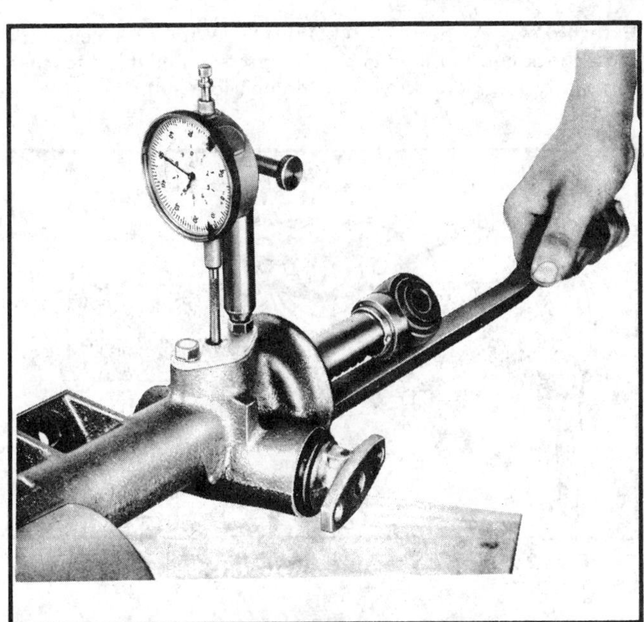

Fig. 3 Using Dial Indicator to Measure Rack Movement

5) Set the dial indicator to zero (without moving rack). Using a lever inserted below the rack, raise the rack (without force) as far as possible. Record the degree of movement registered on the dial indicator. Remove indicator and rack plunger. Place nylon stop inside the plunger. Using a straightedge and feeler gauge, note the gap between top of plunger and nylon stop. This gap must be eliminated by installing adjustment washers.

6) Plunger should now be adjusted so that there is a free play of .002-.006" (.05-.15 mm) at highest point of the rack. To obtain this free play, subtract .004" (.10 mm) from high value previously obtained (when levering rack). This will give the value of shim thickness required to bring free play within specifications. These shims should be added to those which are used to eliminate the clearance between the plunger and nylon stop.

7) Assemble (in the following order) grease nipple, shims, nylon stop, plunger, and spring into the gear housing. Secure the thrust plate. Apply grease through the nipple to lubricate the plunger.

8) Remove the eye from the far end of the housing, position the rubber bellows, then replace and adjust eye to .79-.83" (20-21 mm) between the lock nut and the shoulder of the eye. Turn both eyes so that the holes point in the same direction, then tighten the lock nuts moderately to hold this position.

9) Turn the pinion until the rack is free. Clamp rack in padded jaws of the vise and tighten the lock nut completely. Reposition the gear housing horizontally in the vise and attach yoke of tie rod with bolt head on same side as pinion flange (use a tab washer under the bolt).

10) Fit the pinion side rack boot, with its widest part perpendicular to the mounting flange faces. Position attaching clip so that its fastening part is pointing downward.

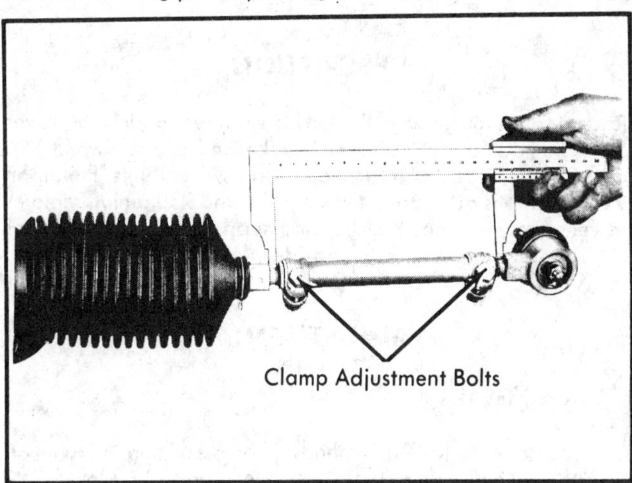

Fig. 4 Measuring Pinion Side Tie Rod for Pre-installation Adjustment

11) Now, make an initial adjustment of the pinion side tie rod as follows: Adjust the distance between the shoulders of the yoke and ball joint to 7.1" (180 mm). Make sure the distances between each end of the adjuster sleeve and the yoke and ball joint shoulders are also equal. Tighten the adjuster sleeve bolts temporarily.

12) Working on opposite end of housing, attach both ends of rubber boot, making sure boot is positioned as described above for pinion side boot. Attach the non-adjustable tie rod to the rack, holding rod in line with rack while tightening the bolt (use a new tab washer).

13) Install four new bolts and washers to attach the rubber coupling at the pinion flange (bolt heads should be toward the steering housing). Position rack in center (straight-ahead position) and attach coupling-to-column clamp, aligning reference mark made during disassembly (in this position, the clamp bolt hole should be parallel to the rack). Chisel-punch the coupling bolt threads to lock them.

TIGHTENING SPECIFICATIONS

Application	Ft. Lbs. (mkg)
Coupling-to-Column Clamp Bolt	7 (0.97)
Rubber Coupling Bolts	13 (1.75)
Tie Rod-to-Eye Bolts	33 (4.56)
Eye-to-Housing Lock Nut	25 (3.46)
Thrust Plate Bolts	7 (0.97)
Pinion Lock Nut	11 (1.52)
Gear Housing-to-Crossmember	24 (3.32)
Tie Rod Ball Joint-to-Steering Arm	31 (4.25)

PORSCHE 911S, 924 & 930 TURBO CARRERA RACK & PINION

911S
924
930 Turbo Carrera

DESCRIPTION

Rack and pinion gear is similar for all three models, however 911S tie rods attach to rack by yoke and eyebolt while 930 and 924 tie rods are attached by ball swivel joints. Pinion on 924 housing is offset to left while 911S and 930 pinion remains in center of housing. Ball bearing supported pinion engages bushing supported rack to provide play free steering action.

ADJUSTMENT

STEERING GEAR

Steering gear adjusting methods vary according to type of steering rack pressure block: (1) Steel pressure block with plastic contact surface and external housing dust boot seat; (2) Plastic pressure block with no external housing dust boot seat. (3) Adjusting screw on 924 extends through cover to take play out of steering rack.

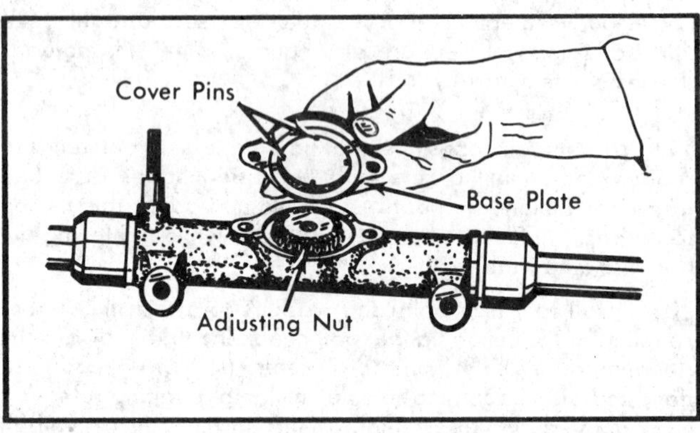

Fig. 1 Adjusting Nut with Cover

Steel Pressure Block Type – 1) With housing assembly in padded vise, detach base plate. Tighten adjusting nut seating contact. **NOTE** – *Base plate has integral pins which may be used as a wrench for this adjustment.* Back nut off contact by three teeth.

2) Check steering gear drag at pinion flange, using an INCH-lb. torque wrench. A measurement of 6.94 INCH lbs. (8 cmkg) should be obtained. If beyond this measurement, loosen adjusting nut; however, if this measurement is not less than 3.47 INCH lbs. (4 cmkg), do not retighten adjusting nut. Install base plate with gasket.

NOTE – *When installing base plate, pin in plate must fit easily between teeth of adjusting nut. If necessary, move nut slightly.*

Plastic Pressure Block Type – Remove base plate and tighten adjusting nut until 6.94 INCH lbs. (8 cmkg) torque is obtained, using method as described above. Install base plate with gasket.

External Adjustment (924 Only) – With rack centered, loosen lock nut and tighten adjusting screw until it just touches thrust washer. Hold screw and tighten lock nut.

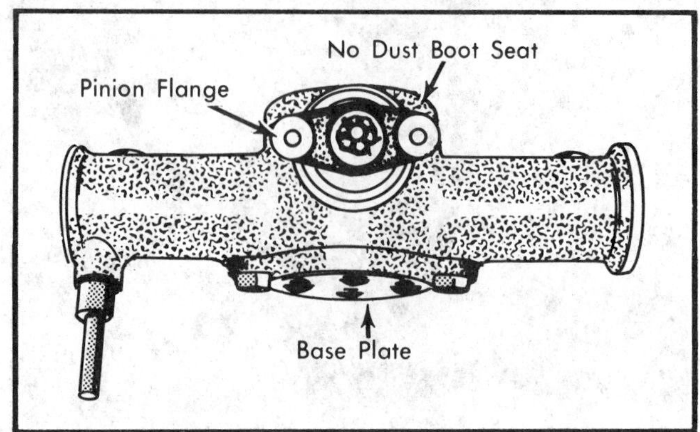

Fig. 2 Plastic Pressure Block Housing Assembly

REMOVAL & INSTALLATION

STEERING GEAR

Removal – 1) Remove bottom bolt attaching universal joint to pinion shaft. Remove nuts and detach tie rod ball joints from steering knuckles.

2) Remove steering housing retaining bolts and extract entire steering housing from right side of vehicle. Detach track rods from rack.

Installation – To install, reverse removal procedures noting that indentation in pinion shaft must line up with bolt hole in lower universal joint. On 924 only, insert special centering bolt (9116) to center gear during installation.

OVERHAUL

STEERING GEAR

Disassembly – 1) Mount steering housing in padded vise and remove base plate retaining bolts. Unscrew adjusting nut (base plate may be used as wrench). Remove pressure block and spring.

2) Move steering rack to either lock position and remove castellated nut. Using suitable puller (P 293), remove flange from pinion. Remove oil seal, lock ring and spacer. Using suitable puller (P 282), remove pinion from pinion carrier (ensure bearing does not bind against housing). Remove Woodruff key from pinion and press bearing off pinion.

3) Mark position of rack (for assembly), remove from housing, and withdraw pinion carrier. Press bearing out of pinion carrier. Remove rack bushing spring retainer from end of housing. Extract support ring and drive rack bushing out.

PORSCHE 911S, 924 & 930 TURBO CARRERA RACK & PINION (Cont.)

Reassembly – Reverse disassembly procedure, noting the following: During assembly, coat all components with suitable gear lubricant. Use shims, if necessary, to adjust axial play of pinion to zero. Fill housing with suitable gear lubricant, either before installing pinion or after, by means of bolt hole opposite base plate.

EYEBOLT (911S ONLY)

CAUTION – *Eyebolt must be installed in precise position to ensure free movement of steering components and exact guiding of track rod.*

Disassembly – Clamp gear into special tool (P 285b) without washers. Remove clamps on outer end of bellows and pull bellows off holder. Loosen bellows holder with hook spanner and unscrew eyebolt and bellows holder.

Inspection – Check eyebolt, bellows and clamps for visible wear. Replace as required.

Assembly – Mount bellows on housing. Screw bellows holder on eyebolt. Coat eyebolt threads and rack face end with sealer. Install eyebolts. Attach steering gear, without washers, to original holding tool (P 285b). Locating pins should slide easily into eyebolts, with flattened end resting against outer pin. Tighten bellows holder. Clamp bellows to gear assembly.

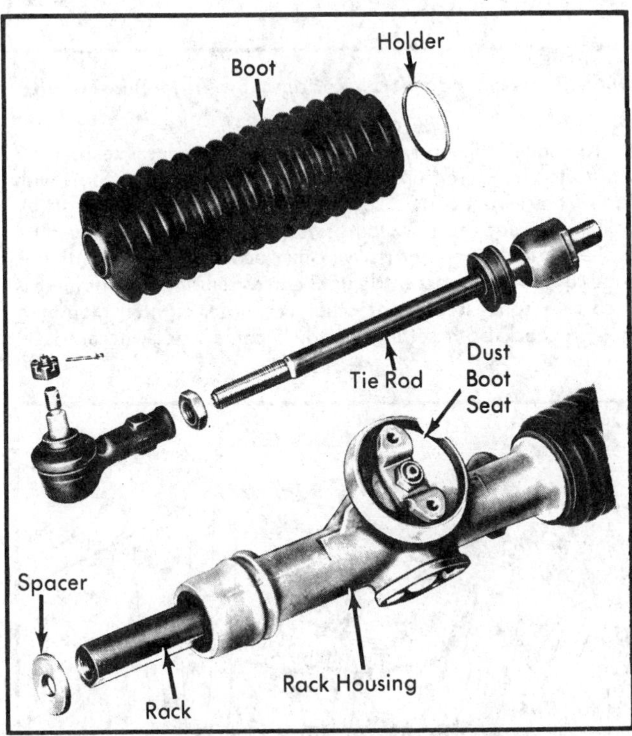

Fig. 3 Exploded View of 911S and 930 Turbo Carrera Steering Gear Assembly

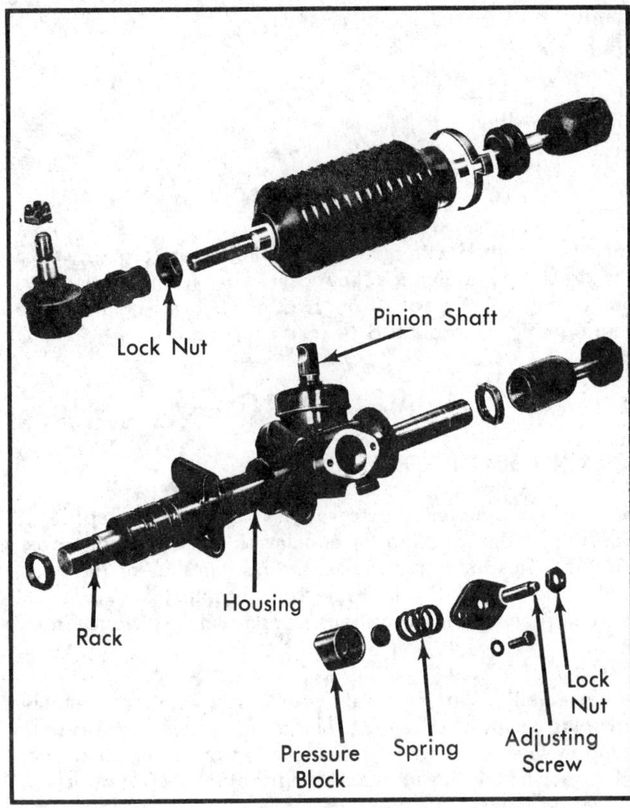

Fig. 4 Exploded View of Porsche 924 Steering Gear Assembly

TIGHTENING SPECIFICATIONS

Application	Ft.Lbs. (mkg)
Housing to Crossmember	
911S & 930	34 (4.7)
924	14-17 (2-2.4)
Tie Rod to Steering Knuckle	
911S & 930	32.5 (4.5)
924 21 (2.9) Tie Rod to Rack (Counternut)	
911S & 930	34 (4.7)
924	29 (4)
"U" Joint Coupling Bolt (All)	25 (3.5)
Bearing Cover	
911S & 930	10.8 (1.5)
924	4-6 (.6-.8)

RENAULT RACK & PINION

Renault
R-5
R-12
R-17
R-17 Gordini

DESCRIPTION

Vehicles are fitted with a rack and pinion steering gear, which has direct steering linkage (tie rods) to each front wheel. Steering housing is mounted to front crossmember and connected to steering column through a flexible coupling.

ADJUSTMENT

STEERING GEAR HEIGHT (TOE-OUT)

Steering box is mounted on eccentrics (all models except R-12 with Auto. Trans. and R-5) or on shims (R-12 with Auto. Trans. and R-5). This mounting makes the relationship of the rack ends to the ball joints adjustable, such that the track variation between high and low positions tends toward a reduction of toe-out.

1) Place vehicle on lift, or alignment rack, with front wheels on radius gauges. Attach a brake press to pedal (to prevent rolling movement of wheels). Set steering at center point and lock in position with suitable holding tool (MS. 504) attached to steering wheel.

2) Compress front axle with suitable tool (T. Av. 238-02) until top of tool is 1" (25 mm) for R-5, or 51/64" (20 mm) for all others, below underside of lower member. Attach brackets of suitable height measurement tool (T.Vv. 246-01) under vehicle so that scale boards are 51 3/16" (1.30 m) R-5, 49 3/16" (1.25 m) all others, from center of front wheels *(See Fig. 1)*.

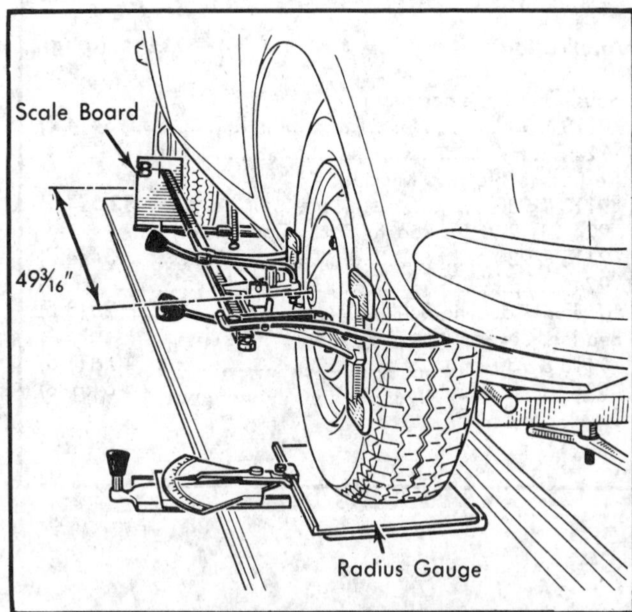

Fig. 1 Height Measurement Equipment Attached to Vehicle

3) Remove axle compression tool and raise vehicle slowly, with a jack (located in center of lower front crossmember). During this operation, the pointer of the measurement tool will have followed a curve from point "B" to one of the figures on scale "A" *(See Fig. 2)*. Read and record the nearest figure on scale boards on both sides of vehicle. Steering box height setting is correct if pointer is within 7.5-9" (190-229 mm) R-5, 6-7.75" (152-197 mm) all others, reading on scale.

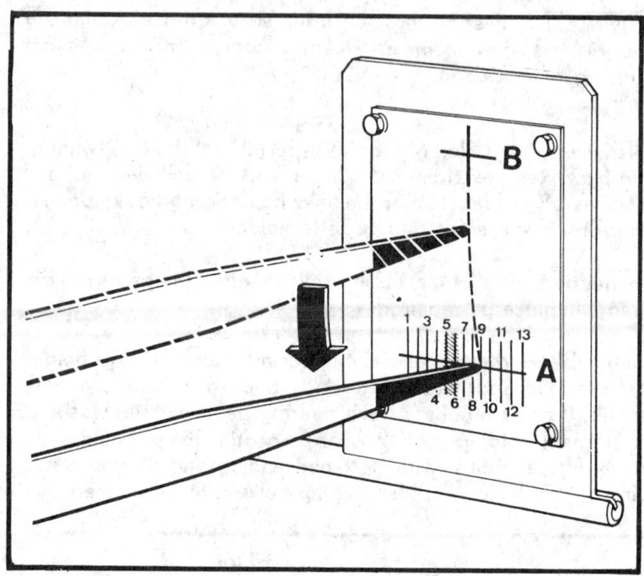

Fig. 2 Scale Board for Reading Steering Box Height

4) To make adjustment on all Renault vehicles except R-12 with Auto. Trans., ensure pointer is still on "A" scale. Start with side farthest from correct setting. Remove battery and bracket. Unlock two top bolts holding steering box. Unlock eccentric washer on crossmember (leave other eccentric locked until it is to be turned). Turn eccentric until corresponding side pointer is in correct zone. Repeat at other eccentric. Tighten mounting bolts, recheck both settings, and, if correct, lock eccentrics.

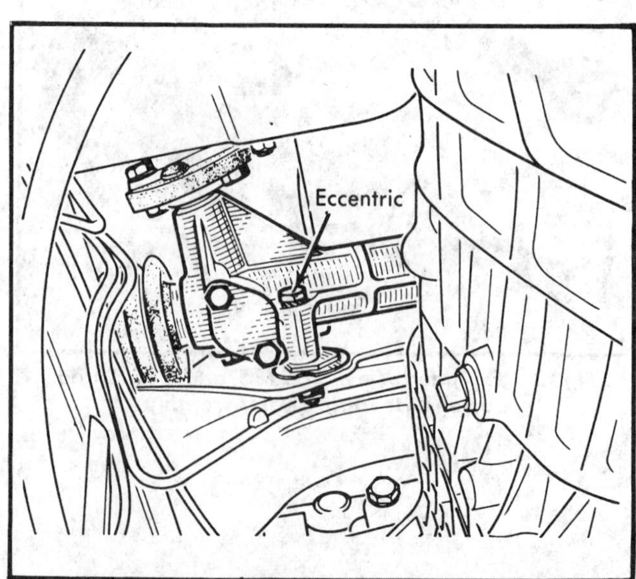

Fig. 3 Steering Box Eccentric for Adjustments

RENAULT RACK & PINION (Cont.)

5) On R-12 with Auto. Trans., an adjusting shim is inserted between each mounting boss and steering box. Lower slot of each shim varies, depending upon height setting desired. Using a shim with greatest distance between top mounting hole and lower mounting slot will give steering box its lowest setting *(See Fig. 4)*.

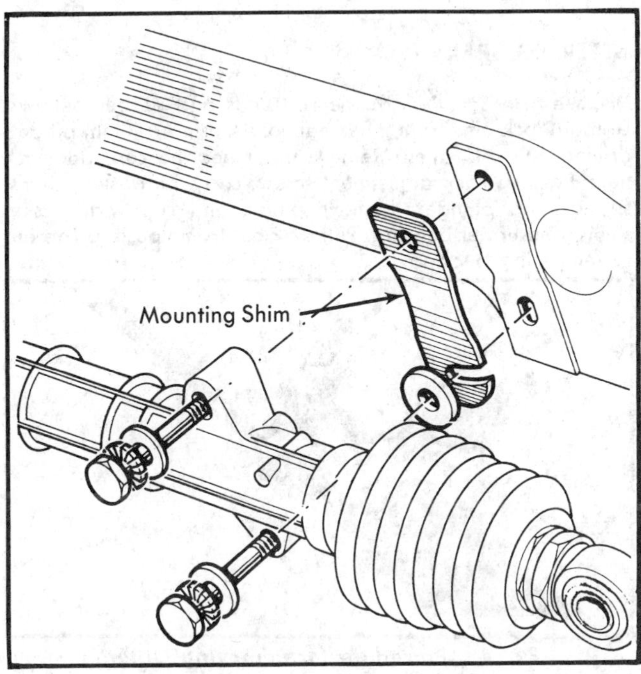

Fig. 4 Detailed Location of Mounting Shims (R-12 Shown, R-5 & R-17 Similar)

6) To replace, add, or subtract shims, remove battery and its bracket. Unlock four steering box securing bolts. **NOTE** – *Only remove top securing bolts.* Swing out shim at bottom, then remove top bolt and shim (if necessary). Determine proper new shim and position on mounting boss. Insert and tighten all mounting bolts. Recheck setting.

SETTING STEERING CENTER POINT

To find center steering point, set center of rivet head on flexible coupling in line with index mark on pinion housing. This should give a setting of 2 13/16" (71.5 mm) R-5, 2 9/16" (71.5 mm) all others, on rack *(See Fig. 5)*.

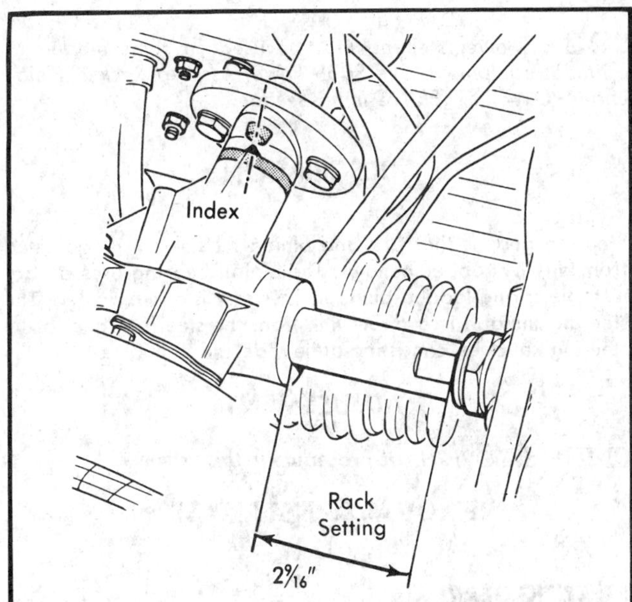

Fig. 5 Measuring Points for Setting Steering Center

REMOVAL & INSTALLATION

Removal – Remove battery and its hold-down. Unscrew bolts attaching flexible coupling. Disconnect tie rods from rack ends (at eyebolts). Unscrew four bolts securing steering box to crossmember. **NOTE** – *If steering box is not being exchanged for another, do not disturb eccentric lock tabs; this will retain original steering box height setting.*

Installation – To install, reverse removal procedure, noting the following: Coat tie rod connections with suitable grease. Check condition of rack bellows and clamps. Align tie rod connecting bolts horizontally. After steering box is installed, carry out check of steering box height setting and wheel alignment.

TIGHTENING SPECIFICATIONS

① Application	Ft. Lbs. (mkg)
Steering Box-to-Crossmember	25 (3.5)
Ball Joint Nuts	25 (3.5)
Flexible Coupling Nuts	10 (1.4)
Tie Rod Hinge-to-Rack Nuts	25 (3.5)
Steering Wheel Nut	35 (4.8)
Universal Joint Pin Nut	25 (3.5)

① – Specifications DO NOT include R-5

SAAB RACK & PINION

99

NOTE – *Power steering may be used on some models as optional equipment. See Saab Power-Assisted Rack & Pinion under POWER STEERING in this section.*

DESCRIPTION

Steering gear is the rack and pinion type. Rack is protected from dirt by rubber bellows. The pinion bearing uses an adjustable spring-loaded plunger. The gear is oil-lubricated. The steering linkage is a direct link from the steering rack to the steering knuckles, consisting of tie rods and ball joints.

ADJUSTMENT

NOTE – *See OVERHAUL procedure in this article.*

REMOVAL & INSTALLATION

STEERING GEAR

Removal – **1)** From under instrument panel, loosen the rubber bellows for steering gear intermediate shaft. Raise vehicle and remove screw mounting "U" joint to steering gear pinion. Loosen steering column tube from body, then separate steering column "U" joint from pinion.

2) Suspend steering column, with wiring harness, out of way. Remove front wheels. Using a puller, remove tie rod ends. Take off the two steering gear clamps and move rack to right stop. **NOTE** – *Insure bellows is not damaged against body.*

3) Place steering gear far enough to the right to allow tie rod to be bent down into body opening. Pull rack maximum stroke to left and lift steering gear through body opening.

Installation – To install, reverse removal procedure and check toe-in and steering wheel alignment.

OVERHAUL

STEERING GEAR

Disassembly – Remove tie rod ends and rubber bellows. Drill out lock pins from inner ball joints, using a 4 mm bit and drilling only ⅜" deep. Remove outer bearing cups and lock nuts. Remove rack adjustment screw, cap with gasket, shims, spring, and plunger. Remove pinion and cap with gasket shims, and upper bearing. Pull rack out from housing. Tap out lower pinion bearing.

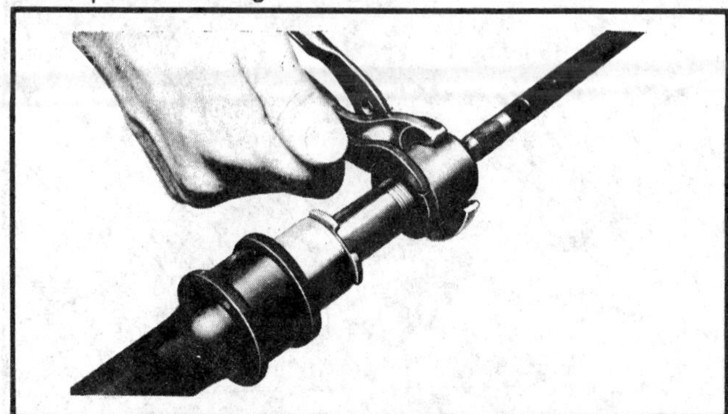

Fig. 1 Procedure for Removing Outer Bearing Cap Lock Nut

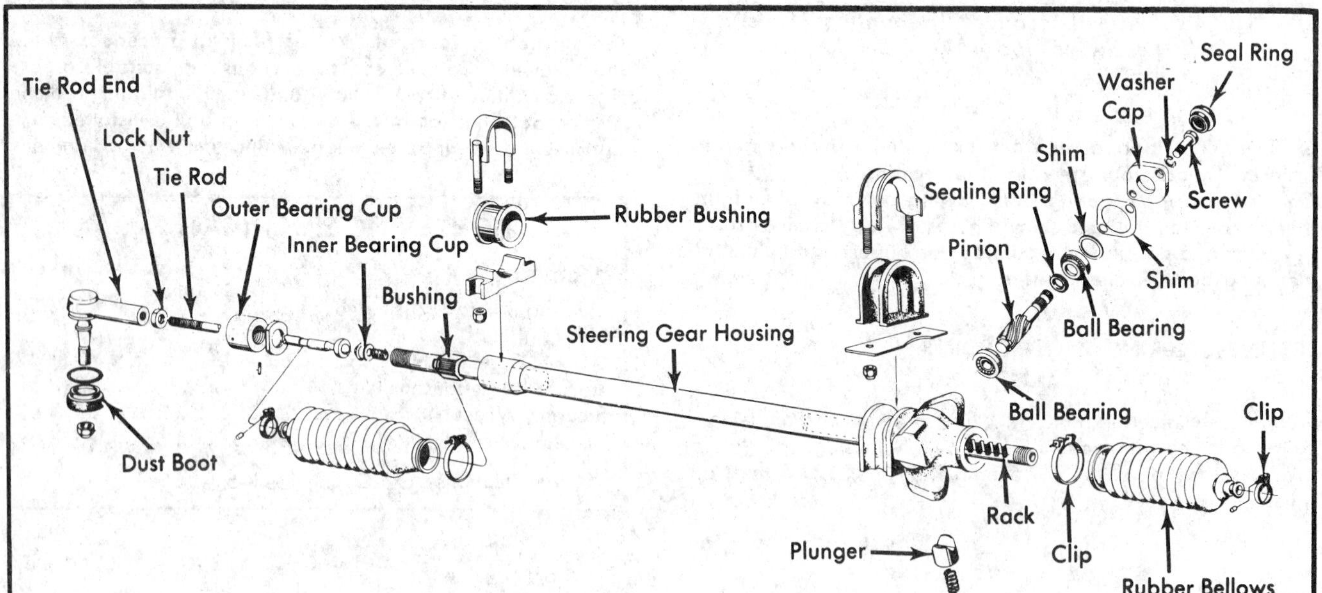

Fig. 2 Exploded View of Saab Rack & Pinion Steering Gear Assembly

SAAB RACK & PINION (Cont.)

Assembly – **1**) Ensure all parts are thoroughly cleaned before proceeding with assembly. Lubricate all parts during assembly. Seat the lower pinion bearing. **NOTE** – *Ensure extended parts of the inner bearing tracks are facing each other.*

2) Assemble inner ball joint on pinion end of rack as follows: Thread lock nut onto rack. Fit outer bearing cup on rack and fill with suitable gear oil. Insert spring and inner bearing cup. Tighten bearing cup so that there is no looseness in ball joint, but without tightness. If rack, with tie rod mounted, is held horizontally, the tie rod should be able to be placed in any position without falling under its own weight. Tighten lock nut against bearing cup and recheck ball joint tightness. Drill a new 4 mm hole ⅜" deep and insert and stake lock a new lock pin.

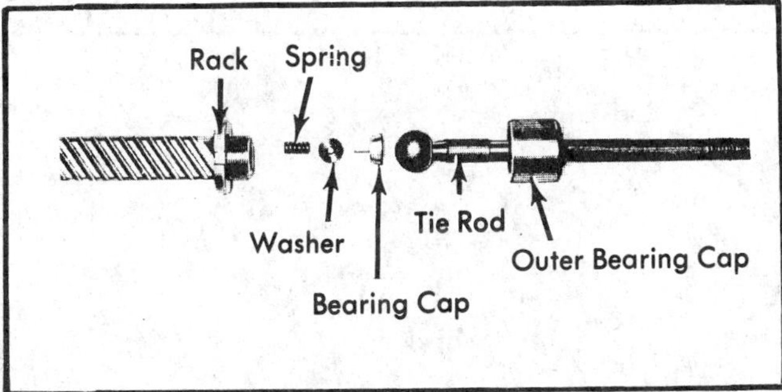

Fig.3 Exploded View of Ball Joint Assembly

3) Insert rack into housing, then fit pinion and upper bearing. Adjust pinion with shims so that there is no axial play when pinion gasket and cap are attached. Various shim sizes are available.

4) Adjust radial play of rack as follows: Insert plunger without spring and gasket, then attach cap with bolts (fingertight only). Measure clearance which exists between the cap and the housing face. To this measurement add .002-.006" (.05-.15 mm), to allow for play after completion of adjuster assembly. This total thickness will be the thickness of gasket shims required. Remove cap, install spring, shims, gasket, and cap. Check rack for free movement across entire length of its travel by rotating pinion.

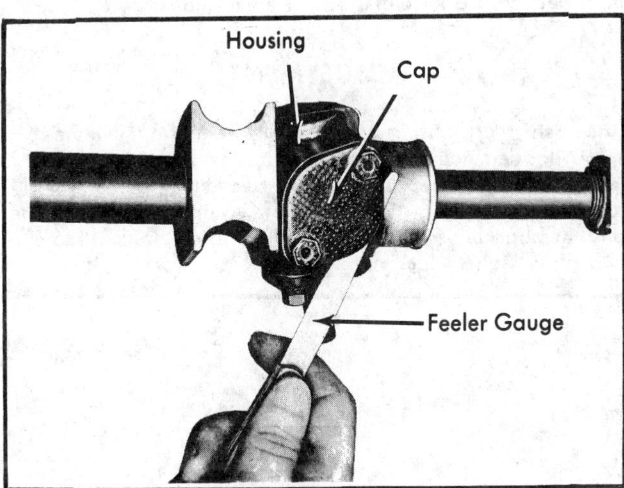

Fig. 4 Measuring Clearance Between Cap and Gear Housing

5) Assemble and adjust other ball joint in same manner as previously described. Attach bellows after lubricating contact area between bellows and tie rod (use silicone grease). Attach both inner clamps. Stand gear on end and pour 7.8 fl. ozs. of suitable EP 90 gear oil into bellows. Attach outboard bellows clamps. **NOTE** – *Outer clamps should be protected with rubber caps.* Screw on lock nuts and mount tie rod end assemblies to tie rods.

SUBARU RACK & PINION

1600

DESCRIPTION

Steering gear, mounted on crossmember, is a rack and pinion type, with backlash automatically adjusted. Pinion is connected to steering shaft by a flexible rubber coupling. Steering knuckle arms are connected to rack by tie rods which are threaded onto ball joint studs at each end of rack.

ADJUSTMENT

Backlash – Backlash is automatically held to a minimum by a spring loaded sleeve which bears against rack. Adjustment is not normally required. End play of sleeve may be corrected if necessary by turning adjusting screw in until it contacts plate, and then backing screw out 1/8 turn to obtain .006" (0.16 mm) end play. Tighten lock nut.

REMOVAL & INSTALLATION

Removal – 1) Raise vehicle and remove front wheels. Remove tie rod ends from steering knuckles. Remove parking brake cable hanger from tie rod. Disconnect pinion from steering shaft rubber coupling. Straighten lock plates and remove bolts retaining gear assembly to crossmember.

NOTE – *On 4WD vehicles, also remove fan protector and torque rod.*

2) Loosen front engine mounting bolts and raise engine about 0.2" (5 mm) to clear gear assembly. Remove gear assembly from crossmember (toward left side). Remove mounting brackets.

Installation – To install, reverse removal procedure and note the following: Tighten all bolts and nuts to specifications and secure with lock plates or cotter pins as required.

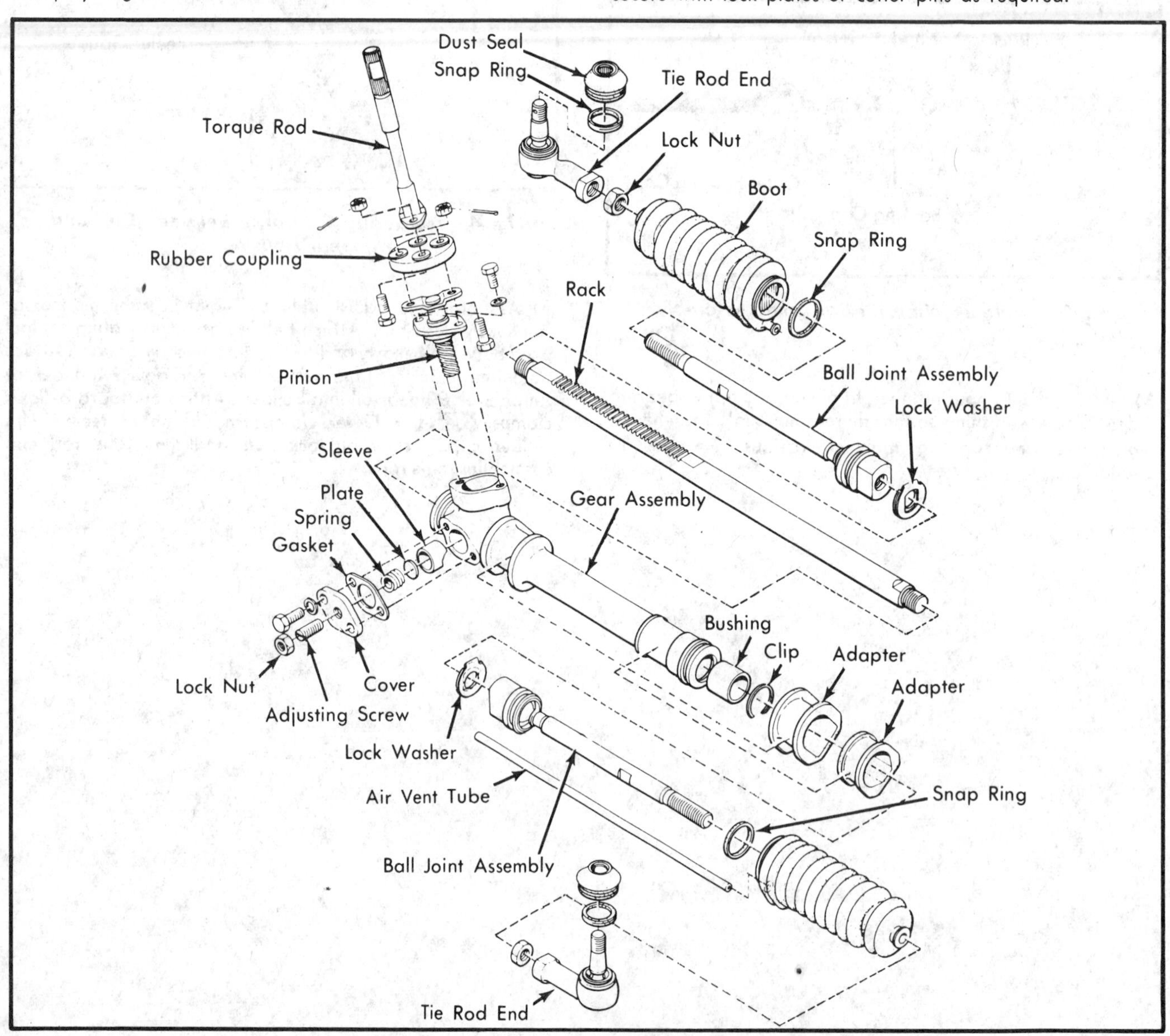

Fig. 1 Exploded View of Subaru Rack & Pinion Steering Gear Assembly

SUBARU RACK & PINION (Cont.)

OVERHAUL

Disassembly – Loosen lock nuts and remove tie rod ends. Remove air vent tube from boots. Remove snap rings from boots and pull boots from gear housing. Straighten lock washers and remove ball joints from rack ends. Loosen lock nut, completely back out adjusting screw, then remove cover, gasket, sleeve spring, sleeve plate, and sleeve. Remove pinion from rack, then remove rack from gear housing.

Inspection – Steering rack should be straight within .010" (0.3 mm). Ball joint play should not exceed .010" (0.3 mm) at 154 lbs. (70 kg). Inspect all parts and replace if worn, damaged, or not within specifications.

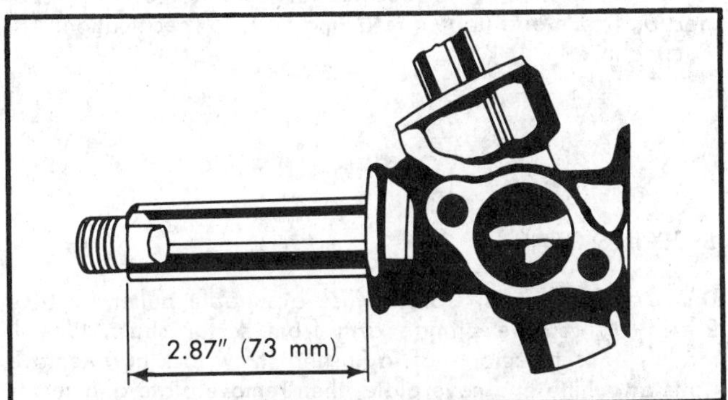

Fig. 2 View Showing Method of Centering Rack in Gear Housing

Reassembly – 1) Grease the toothed and sliding portions of rack and install rack into gear housing. Locate end of rack so that it measures 2.87" (73 mm) from end of gear housing, then grease and install pinion. Tighten pinion assembly to gear housing. In this position, rack and pinion will be centered for vehicle straight-ahead position. When center position has been established, mark the gear housing and pinion with white paint so that marks will align for center position reference.

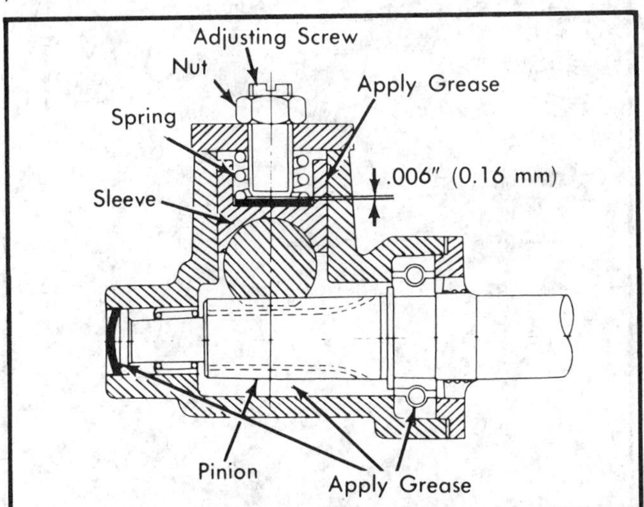

Fig. 3 View Showing Lubrication Points and Backlash Adjustment

2) Install sleeve, plate, spring, gasket, and cover to gear housing and tighten bolts. Turn adjusting screw in until it contacts plate and back off 1/8 turn to obtain .006" (0.16 mm) end play. Tighten lock nut. **NOTE** – *Use a suitable locking compound on bolt and adjusting screw threads.*

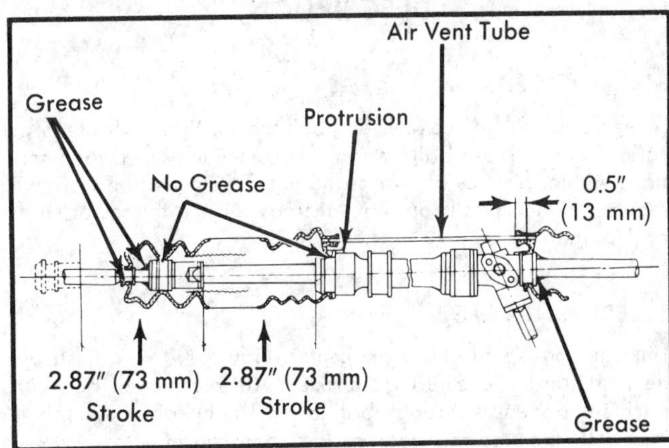

Fig. 4 View Showing Operation Checks and Lubrication of Steering Gear Assembly

3) Install lock washers and ball joints on rack ends. Tighten ball joints and bend lock washers over to secure joints. Install boots on gear housing and retain with snap rings. Install air vent tube into boots while aligning it with embossed mark on gear housing. Install tie rod ends with lock nuts, and temporarily tighten lock nuts. Rotate pinion and check operation of gear assembly. Pinion operating torque in straight ahead position should be less than 1.1 ft. lbs. (0.15 mkg) at ±1.18" (±30 mm) of rack displacement. Maximum torque should not exceed 1.59 ft. lbs. (0.22 mkg).

TIGHTENING SPECIFICATIONS

Application	Ft. Lbs. (mkg)
Pinion Flange-to-Gear Housing	6-9 (0.9-1.2)
Rack Adjuster Cover	6-9 (0.9-1.2)
Rack Adjuster Lock Nut	15-18 (2.1-2.5)
Ball Joint Ass'y-to-Rack	47-54 (6.5-7.5)
Gear-to-Crossmember	33-40 (4.5-5.5)
Rubber Coupling Self-Locking Nut	15-18 (2.1-2.5)
Tie Rod End Castellated Nut	18-22 (2.5-3.0)
Tie Rod End-to-Ball Joint Lock Nut	58-65 (8.0-9.0)

TOYOTA (EXC. LAND CRUISER) RECIRCULATING BALL

Celica
Corona
Corolla
Hi-Lux Pickup

DESCRIPTION

STEERING GEAR

Steering gear is of recirculating ball type with a variable gear ratio. Several loose ball bearings circulate in two divided sections within grooves of worm and nut. Turing motion of worm moves ball nut axially on shaft, thereby turning the sector shaft and pitman arm.

STEERING LINKAGE

Linkage consists of idler arm, center relay rod, two adjustable tie rods, and two steering knuckles. The connection between each component is through ball joints. The linkage assembly is joined to the steering gear at the pitman arm.

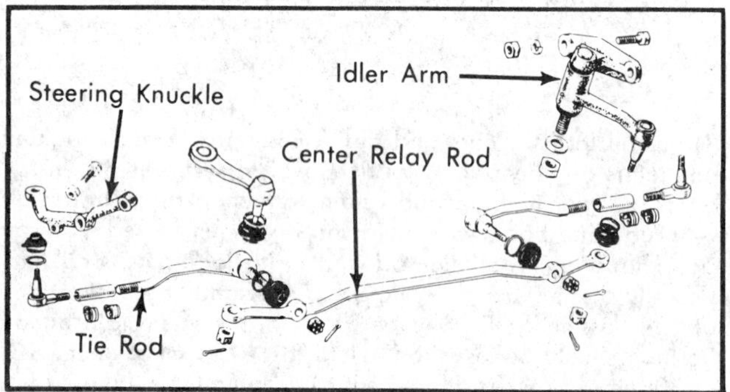

Fig. 1 Toyota Steering Linkage with Bushings and Retainers (Typical Illustration)

ADJUSTMENT

See Overhaul procedures in this article.

REMOVAL & INSTALLATION

STEERING GEAR

Removal (Exc. Corona) – Remove bolt attaching coupling yoke-to-worm shaft. Using a suitable puller (09610-20011, Celica & Corolla or 09628-62010, Hi-Lux), detach pitman arm from sector shaft. Unbolt gear housing from frame and remove from vehicle.

Removal (Corona) – Remove air cleaner for access, then remove coupling pinch bolt and two rubber disc through bolts (as viewed from pinch bolt side, the two bolts which have nuts directly against the rubber disc). Using a suitable puller (09611-20014), disconnect pitman arm from center relay rod. Unbolt gear from frame and remove from vehicle.

Installation (All Models) – Reverse removal procedure, aligning worm shaft cut portion with flexible coupling yoke.

STEERING LINKAGE

Removal – Using a suitable puller (09628-62010, Hi-Lux, or 09610-20011, Celica, Corolla & Corona), disconnect pitman arm from sector shaft. Remove idler arm support from frame. Detach tie rod ends from steering knuckles, using a suitable puller (09611-20014, Hi-Lux, Corolla & Corona, or 09611-20013, Celica). Remove steering linkage assembly from vehicle.

Installation – Connect tie ends to steering knuckles and torque retaining nuts to specification. Install pitman to sector shaft (ensure correct positioning of aligning marks as illustrated). Tighten nut to specified torque. Place idler arm support on frame and tighten retaining bolts to specification. Adjust toe-in.

OVERHAUL

STEERING GEAR

Disassembly – On Corona, use a suitable puller (09610-20011) to remove pitman arm from sector shaft. On all models, loosen sector shaft adjusting screw lock nut. Remove bolts attaching end coverplate, then remove plate and sector shaft. Drain oil from housing. Unscrew worm bearing adjusting screw lock nut, using a suitable wrench (09617-22020). Remove worm bearing adjusting screw, using a suitable tool (09616-30011, Hi-Lux, Corolla & Corona, or 09616-22010, Celica). Extract worm assembly with bearing. **NOTE** – *Do not disassemble ball nut from worm. If recirculating ball assembly has defective components, replace assembly.*

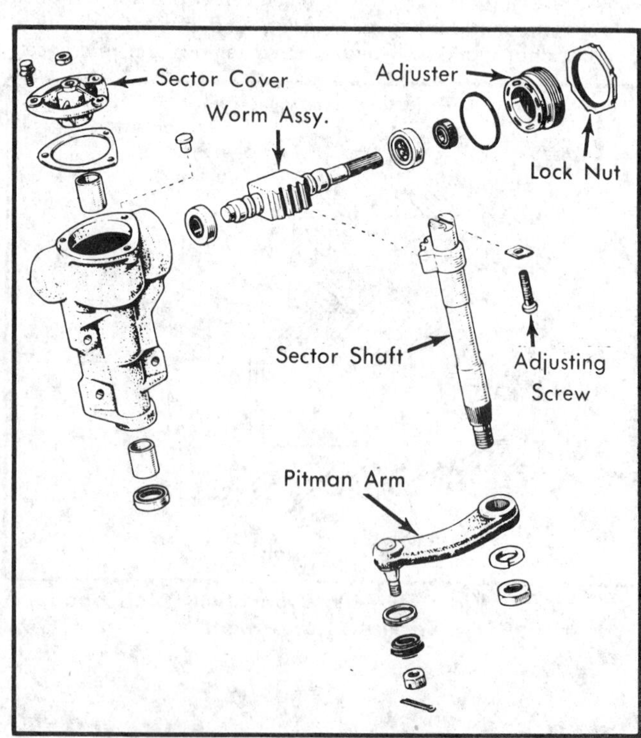

Fig. 2 Exploded View of Recirculating Ball Type Steering (Corona Shown, Others Similar)

TOYOTA (EXC. LAND CRUISER) RECIRCULATING BALL (Cont.)

Inspection – Check all components for wear or damage and replace as necessary. Check sector shaft-to-bushing clearance: it must not exceed .0020" (.05 mm). If clearance is exceeded, replace bushing or shaft.

Assembly & Adjustment – **1)** Lubricate all bearings and sliding portions of gear assembly. Install worm into gear housing, then install adjusting screw and lock nut. Check worm bearing preload: Wind a cord around worm shaft and attach a pull-scale to end of cord. Pull required to turn worm shaft should be within given specifications. Turn adjusting screw as required to bring preload within limits.

Initial Worm Bearing Preload

Celica	8.8-11.0 lbs. (4-5 kg)
Corona & Corolla	3.6-5.2 lbs. (4-6 kg)
Hi-Lux	2.6-5.2 lbs. (3-6 kg)

Fig. 3 Measuring Worm Bearing Preload

2) Install adjusting screw and thrust washer onto sector shaft and measure thrust clearance (between head of adjusting screw and bottom of "T" slot). Maximum satisfactory clearance is as specified. If clearance limit is exceeded, replace thrust washer with one of suitable size, to bring clearance into limits.

Adjusting Screw-to-Shaft Clearance

Exc. Hi-Lux	.002" (.05 mm)
Hi-Lux	.004" (.1 mm)

3) Install sector shaft to end cover and install assembly (with gasket) into gear housing. **NOTE** – *Ensure ball nut is at center travel before inserting sector shaft. Loosen adjusting screw completely, prior to shaft insertion.* After sector shaft cover is bolted into place, repeat worm bearing preload test as previously described, using sector shaft adjusting screw to obtain specified preload:

Final Worm Bearing Preload

Exc. Hi-Lux	6.9-9.5 lbs. (8-11 kg)
Hi-Lux	6.1-8.7 lbs. (7-11 kg)

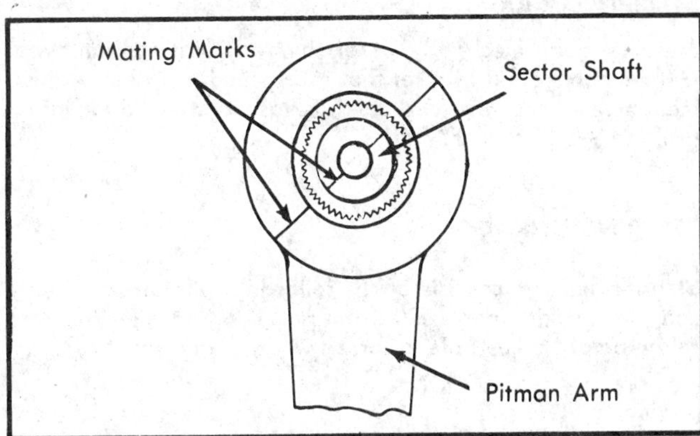

Fig. 4 Aligning Pitman Arm to Sector Shaft

4) Install pitman arm (aligning mating marks); attach a dial gauge to measure pitman arm backlash. Backlash, as measured at pitman arm outer end, should not exceed 5° from either side of center. After checking, tighten adjusting screw lock nut securely.

TIGHTENING SPECIFICATIONS

Application	Ft. Lbs. (mkg)
Steering Gear-to-Frame	
Corona	36-50 (5.0-6.9)
All Others	25-36 (3.5-5.0)
Pitman Arm-to-Sector Shaft	
Celica & Corolla	72-101 (9.9-14.0)
Corona	80-101 (11.0-14.0)
Hi-Lux	79-90 (10.9-12.4)
Worm Adjusting Screw Lock Nut	
All Exc. Celica & Corolla	58-72 (8.0-9.9)
Celica & Corolla	94-23 (13-17)
Sector Shaft End Cover	
All Models	11-16 (1.5-2.2)
Coupling Yoke-to-Worm Shaft	
Corona	14.5-36 (2-5)
All Others	14.5-22 (2-3)
Relay Rod-to-Idler Arm	
Hi-Lux	54-80 (7.5-11)
All Others	36-51 (5-7)
Tie Rod-to-Steering Knuckle	
Hi-Lux	54-80 (7.5-11)
All Others	36-51 (5-7)

TOYOTA LAND CRUISER RECIRCULATING BALL

FJ40
FJ55

DESCRIPTION

STEERING GEAR

Steering gear mechanism is of the recirculating ball type. Gear mounts off a bracket that is attached to frame. Adjustment screws are provided for backlash and preload. Initial preload is achieved with shims.

STEERING LINKAGE

Steering linkage consists of the following: pitman arm, relay rod, tie rod, damper, center arm and drag link. Tie rod and relay rod are adjustable to correct wheel alignment.

ADJUSTMENT

NOTE – *Adjustments are done during reassembly after overhaul. For adjustments, refer to Overhaul in this article.*

REMOVAL & INSTALLATION

STEERING GEAR

Removal – On FJ40 models, separate mainshaft from steering gear. On FJ55 models, disconnect flexible coupling and pull it from mounting on steering gear. On all models, separate pitman shaft linkage. Remove bolt steering gear housing to bracket/frame.

Installation – To install, reverse removal procedure and tighten all mounting bolts.

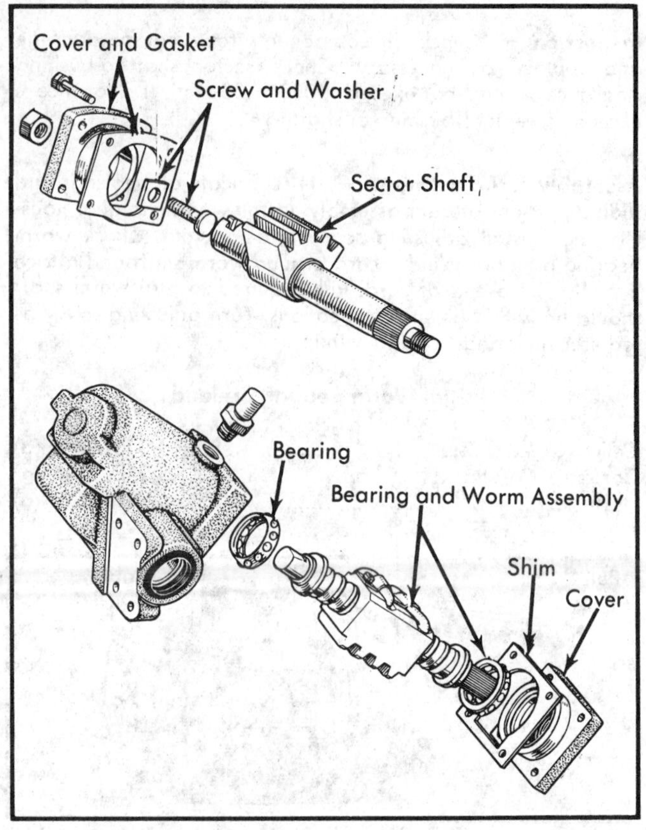

Fig. 1 Toyota Land Cruiser Steering Gear

STEERING LINKAGE

Removal – 1) – Raise and support front of vehicle, then remove front wheels. Index mark relative position of pitman arm to sector shaft and remove arm, using suitable puller. Disconnect steering drag link from steering center arm.

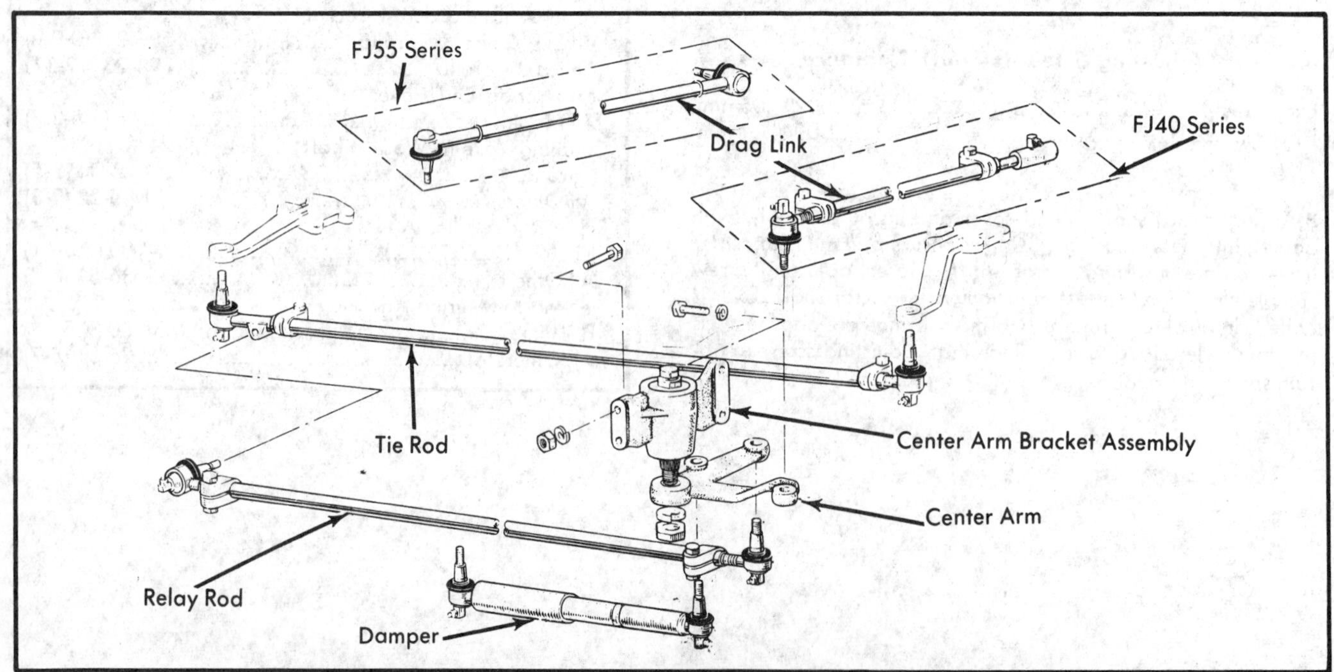

Fig. 2 Toyota Land Cruiser Front Steering Linkage with Detail of Both FJ40 and FJ55

TOYOTA LAND CRUISER RECIRCULATING BALL (Cont.)

2) Disconnect tie rod ends from both sides. Disconnect relay rod from steering center arm, then remove tie rod assembly with relay arm assembly. Disconnect end of steering damper from bracket on crossmember. Loosen and remove center arm from bracket (with steering damper). Remove steering center arm bracket from frame.

Installation – To install, reverse removal procedure and note the following: Adjust tie rod and relay rod as shown in *Fig. 3*.

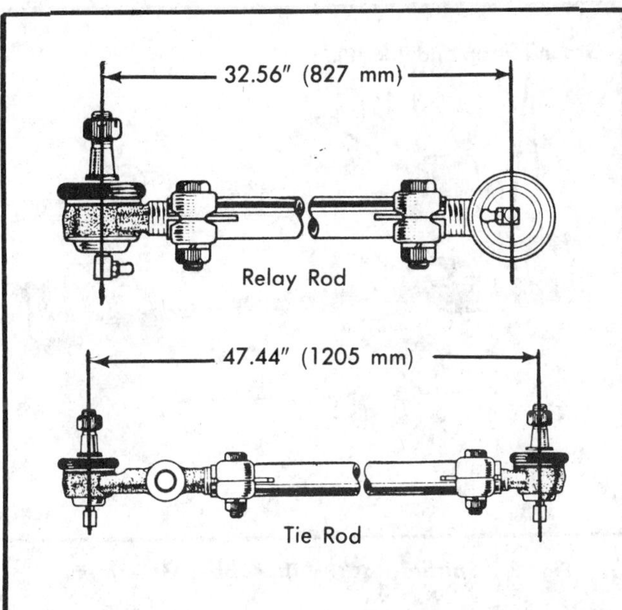

Fig. 3 Relay Rod and Tie Rod Length Adjustments for Installation

Disassembly – Drain gear lubricant, then secure housing in a vise. Remove sector shaft end cover and gasket. With sector shaft positioned at rotational center, pull assembly out of gear housing. Note number and placement of shims as they are removed. Remove gear housing end cover and gasket. Take out worm assembly, keeping bearings in sequence and don't attempt to disassemble worm assembly.

Inspection – Wash all disassembled parts and inspect for wear or damage; replace as necessary. If inner or outer races are scored or pitted, replace as required. Inspect sector shaft and bushings for wear. If replacement is necessary, use a press to remove and replace bushings. Hone bushings until clearance between bushing and sector shaft is .0004-.0024" (.009-.060 mm). Install new oil seal. Measure sector shaft thrust clearance, then select thrust washer that provides minimum clearance between sector shaft and adjustment screw: .004" (.1 mm).

Reassembly – 1) Install cover with same number of shims that were removed, then tighten bolts. **NOTE** – *When tightening cover bolts keep checking worm to see that it will turn properly.*

2) Using a pull scale, measure initial (starting) worm bearing preload for 8.8-13.2 lbs (4-6 kg). If preload is not within specifications, correct by selecting proper thickness shim(s).

3) Position worm ball nut at center, then insert sector shaft ensuring ball nut and sector mesh together at center. Loosen ball adjusting bolt all the way and install cover.

4) Set worm shaft preload to 17.6-24.2 lbs. (8-11 kg) with adjusting bolt. Make sure measurement is made with meshing positioned at center.

5) Install pitman arm and check backlash. There should be zero backlash when worm is rotated within 45° to either side. Tighten adjustment screw lock nut and recheck preload.

TIGHTENING SPECIFICATIONS

Application	Ft. Lbs. (mkg)
Sector End Cover Bolts	21.7-32.5 (3.0-4.5)
Worm Bearing Cap	21.7-32.5 (3.0-4.5)
Gear Box Bracket	28.9-39.8 (4.0-5.5)
Pitman Arm Nut	119-141 (16.5-19.5)

TRIUMPH RACK & PINION

TR7
Spitfire

DESCRIPTION

Steering gear is a rack and pinion type with direct linkage (tie rods) to steering arms. Gear housing is mounted by "U" bolts to chassis and connected to steering shaft by a flexible coupling.

ADJUSTMENTS

Rack and pinion free play are adjusted through the use of shims on the rack damper and pinion shaft. These adjustments are performed as part of overhaul procedure. *See Overhaul below.*

REMOVAL & INSTALLATION

RACK AND PINION

Removal – 1) Raise vehicle and place on safety stands. Scribe an index mark on pinion shaft and lower steering coupling for installation purposes. Disconnect tie rod ends from steering knuckle.

2) Remove pinch bolt attaching lower steering coupling to rack pinion. On TR7 models only, withdraw bolts mounting pinion end of rack to chassis. On all other models, "U" bolts mount steering rack to chassis.

3) On TR7 only, remove remaining rack mounting hardware, disconnect lower pinion shaft coupling and take rack out driver's side. On all others, slide rack forward disengaging rack pinion splines from flexible coupling. Disconnect ground strap from rack plug and withdraw steering rack.

Installation – 1) If rack has been disassembled, it must be centralized before reinstallation: Remove center plug from thrust pad and, using a piece of welding rod, locate dimple in rack shaft. When dimple in rack shaft is aligned with plug hole rack is centralized.

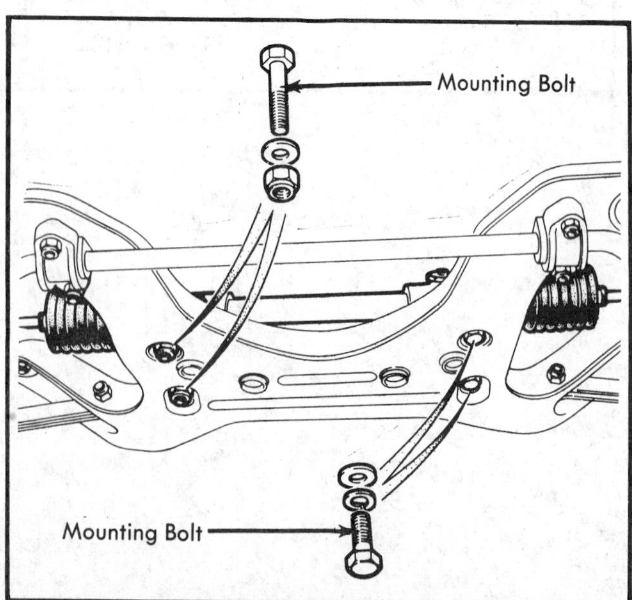

Fig. 1 Installed View of TR7 Rack Assembly

2) Carefully slide rack assembly into position but DO NOT disturb rack shaft. On TR7 models only, secure rack to chassis with mounting hardware, refit tie rod ends and tighten pinion coupling pinchbolt.

3) On all other models, hold steering wheel in straight-ahead position and engage rack pinion shaft splines in flexible coupling. Install and tighten pinch bolt. Keep rubber grommets correctly positioned on inboard side of rack flanges with lip under straight face of flange, then fit "U" bolts *(Fig. 2)*. Refit tie rod outer ends to steering arms.

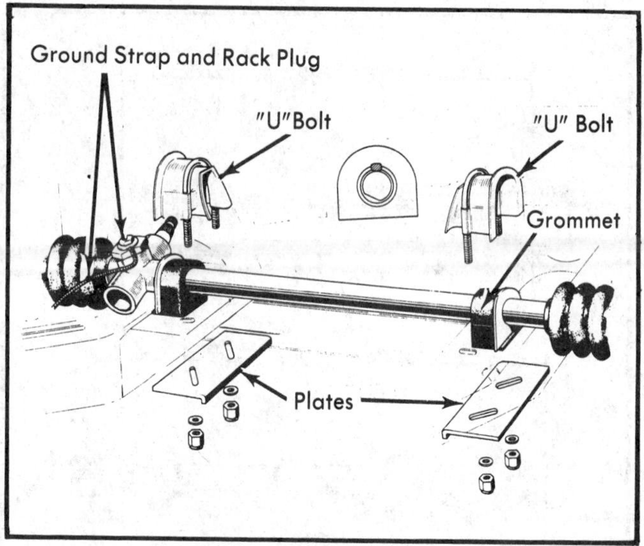

Fig. 2 Spitfire Rack with Rubber Grommets

4) Make sure all nuts and bolts are tightened and check front wheel alignment. *See Triumph in WHEEL ALIGNMENT Section.*

OVERHAUL

NOTE – *Overhaul operation is based on Spitfire models, but procedures can be generalized to include TR7.*

RACK AND PINION

Disassembly – 1) Release clip and slide bellows toward outer ball joint. Slacken inner lock nut and unscrew tie rod assembly from rack. Withdraw spring from rack end. Straighten tab washer, unscrew sleeve nut, and remove tab washer, shims, and cup.

2) Slacken outer lock nut and unscrew tie rod end from tie rod. Remove outer lock nut, bellows, and cup nut. Remove inner lock nut from rack. Repeat on other end.

3) From gear housing, remove cap of rack damper assembly. Withdraw shims, spring, and damper. Then, remove circlip from top end of pinion and pull out pinion (take care not to lose dowel pin). Remove retaining ring, shims, bushing, and thrust washer. Extract "O" ring from groove in retaining ring. Pull rack from tube and remove pinion lower thrust washer and bushing (from housing). If required, bushings may be removed from rack tube.

Reassembly – 1) Install end cover and lower bushing in pinion housing, making sure recessed end of bushing is next to end cover. Insert lower thrust washer with chamfered edge of hole facing away from bushing.

TRIUMPH RACK & PINION (Cont.)

2) Place rack shaft into housing with rack teeth toward pinion end. Install lock nuts, tie rods, springs and adaptors, then tighten lock nuts to specification.

3) Pack tie rod inner ball joints with grease and install bellows and clips.

4) Rotate rack shaft until teeth mesh with pinion, then install pinion, upper thrust washer, bushing, and shims in housing.

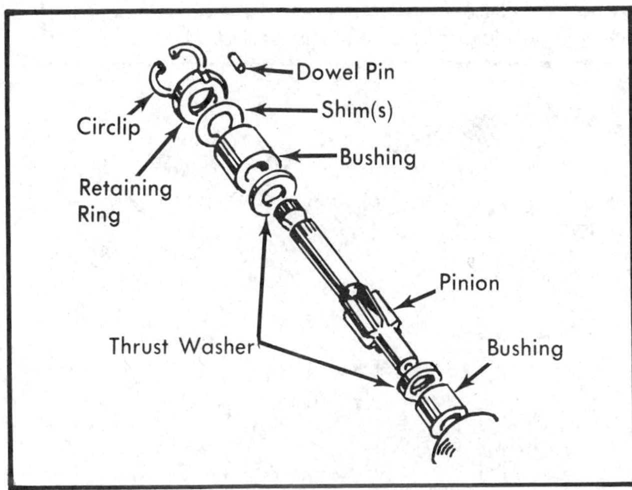

Fig. 3 Detailed View of Spitfire Pinion

5) Insert new "O" ring in retaining ring, then install retaining ring and dowel pin in housing. Install circlip and check that pinion end play does not exceed .010" (.254 mm). Adjust shim pack as necessary to meet this specification *(See Fig. 3)*.

6) Install rack damper, shims, spring and cap nut. Check rack side play (90° to shaft axis) is within .004-.008" (.1-.2 mm). Adjust as required by adding or subtracting shims *(Fig. 4)*, then reconnect ground strap (if removed).

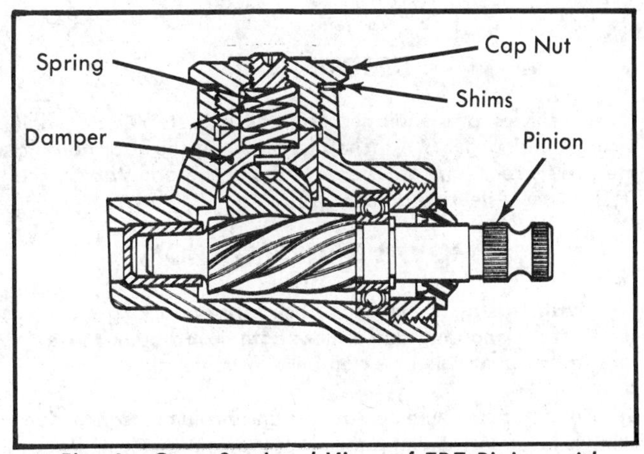

Fig. 4 Cross Sectional View of TR7 Pinion with Housing and Rack Damper (Spitfire Similar)

TIGHTENING SPECIFICATIONS

Application	Ft. Lbs. (mkg)
Steering Gear-to-Frame	
TR7	22-29 (3.0-4.0)
Spitfire	16 (2.2)
Tie Rod Lock Nuts	
TR7	30-37 (4.1-5.1)
Spitfire	38 (5.2)
Universal Joint Pinch Bolts	
TR7	16-21 (2.2-2.9)
Spitfire	14 (1.9)

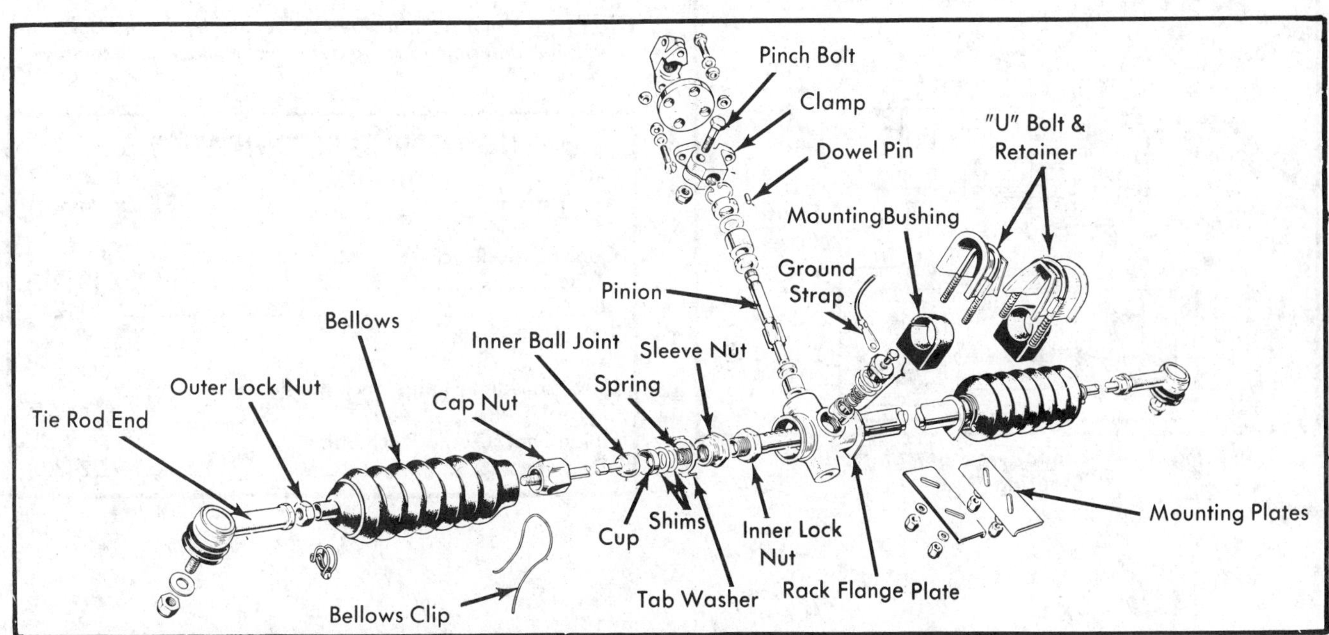

Fig. 5 Triumph Spitfire Rack and Pinion Steering

VOLKSWAGEN TYPE 1 & DASHER RACK & PINION

Type 1
Dasher

DESCRIPTION

These vehicles are equipped with an adjustable rack and pinion steering gear. Attached to center of the rack housing are two tie rods (one adjustable and one non-adjustable). The Dasher uses a steering damper.

REMOVAL & INSTALLATION

Removal, Dasher – 1) Bend back tabs on locking plate at center of rack housing and remove both tie rod bolts. Move tie rods so that gear will have clearance for removal.

2) Unbolt pinch clamp at pinion-to-column connection. Remove lower instrument panel. Loosen steering column flange at toe board. Drive steering flange tube off of steering gear.

3) Remove gear mounting screw at right end of rack housing, then unbolt rack mounting at left end. Turn front wheels to right lock, and remove steering gear through right wheel housing.

Removal, Type 1 – 1) Raise vehicle and remove front wheels. Uncover lower universal joint by moving boot, then remove universal joint clamp bolt.

2) Pry universal joint shaft off pinion. Bend up lock plate and remove bolts holding tie rod inner end to steering rack.

3) Disconnect tie rods. Remove nuts and bolts holding ends of steering rack housing to brackets, then remove rack and pinion assembly from vehicle.

NOTE – *For earlier non-adjustable models, there is a change-over kit available. When installing kit follow manufacturers instructions and DO NOT reinstall shims between housing and cover plate.*

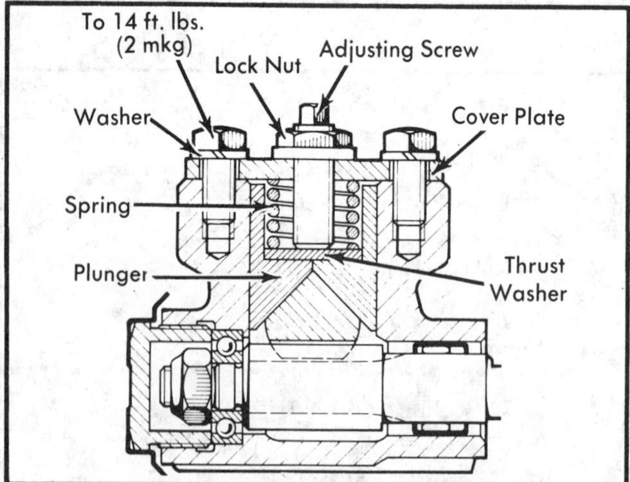

Fig. 1 Sectional View of Adjustable Steering Gear

Installation – Reverse removal procedure and torque nuts and bolts to specifications.

NOTE – *Gain access to adjusting screw on Dasher by removing cover on access hole located in spare wheel well.*

ADJUSTMENT

With components installed on vehicle, tighten adjusting screw by hand until screw just contacts thrust washer. Hold adjusting screw in position and tighten lock nut *(Fig. 1)*.

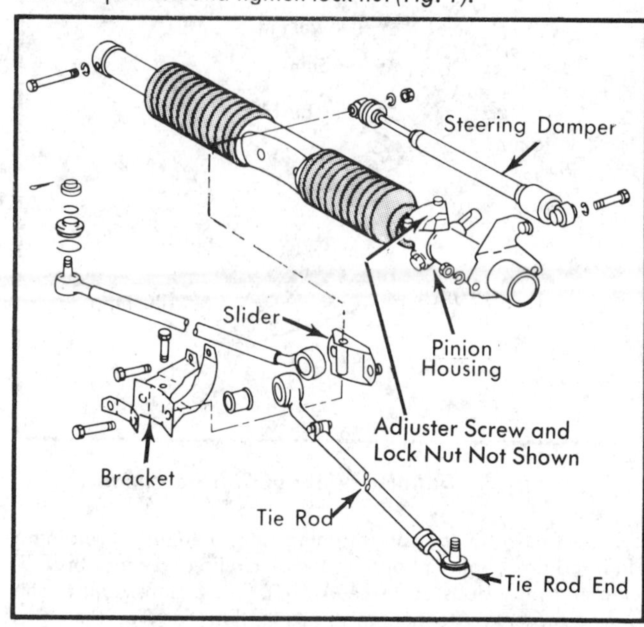

Fig. 2 Volkswagen Dasher Rack and Pinion Assembly (Type 1 Similar)

OVERHAUL

NOTE – *Manufacturer does not recommend overhaul of this unit. If it is determined to be defective, replace as assembly.*

TIGHTENING SPECIFICATIONS

Application	Ft. Lbs. (mkg)
Gear Box-to-Brackets	
Type 1	18 (2.5)
Dasher	14 (2.0)
Tie Rods-to-Rack	
All	40 (5.5)
Universal Joint Clamp Pinch Bolts	
Type 1	18 (2.5)
Pinion Shaft Clamp Pinch Bolt	
Dasher	22 (3.0)

VOLKSWAGEN TYPE 2 WORM & ROLLER

Type 2

DESCRIPTION

Beginning with 1973 models, Type 2 vehicles incorporated a worm and roller steering unit. This replaced the previously used worm and peg assembly. Steering linkage remains the same as on earlier models, consisting of an adjustable drag link, two maintenance-free tie rods (one adjustable), and a hydraulic steering damper.

ADJUSTMENT

STEERING GEAR

1) Check for excessive free play in steering by raising front of vehicle, placing wheels in straight-ahead position, and lightly turning steering wheel back and forth while holding one of the wheel spokes at outer end. Free play should not exceed ⅝" steering wheel spokes at outer end. Free play should not exceed ⅝" (15 mm) before resistance is felt in the steering wheel.

2) If free play is excessive, check for loose or worn steering linkage components, check for tight mounting of gear box, and check for proper tightness of gear box cover. If these are found to be in good condition and properly tightened, continue to next step.

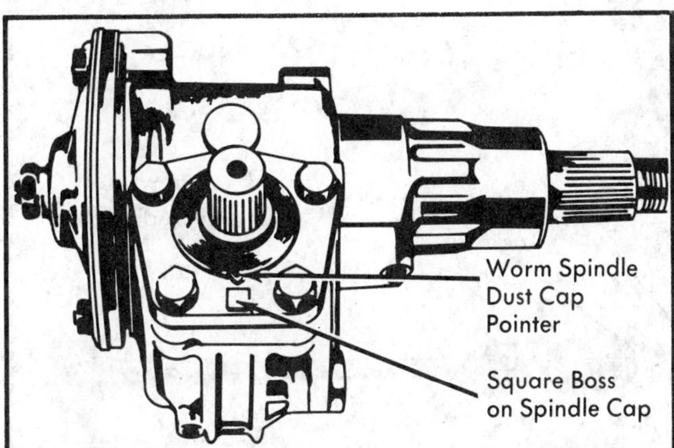

Fig. 1 Steering Gear Aligned in Central Position

3) Disconnect drag link from pitman arm. Turn steering wheel 180-200° from center, in either direction. **NOTE** — *Center position is determined when pointer on worm spindle dust cap is in line with square boss on worm cover plate.* Loosen adjusting screw lock nut and turn adjusting screw out one full turn.

4) Working under vehicle, move pitman arm back and forth while gradually tightening adjusting screw. Repeat until no play is felt at pitman arm (without stiffness). Hold adjusting screw in this position and tighten lock nut.

5) Take off horn button and disconnect horn wire. Attach a torque gauge to steering wheel nut. Turn steering wheel through centerpoint. Steering is correctly adjusted if torque gauge reads 7-11 INCH lbs. (8-12 cmkg). If necessary, repeat and recheck adjustment.

REMOVAL & INSTALLATION

STEERING GEAR

Removal — From under vehicle, remove cover plate that is below pedal cluster. Detach drag link and remove pitman arm using suitable puller. Bend back lock plate and remove clamp bolt holding coupling flange on worm spindle. Remove gear box mounting bolts and push steering column slightly upward while extracting gearbox from frame.

Installation — To install, reverse removal procedure noting that mark on drop arm is aligned with mark on shaft.

OVERHAUL

NOTE — *Manufacturer does not recommend overhaul of the worm and roller steering gear, however a defective roller shaft oil seal may be replaced without removing steering gear box from vehicle.*

OIL SEAL REPLACEMENT

To replace seal, remove pitman arm, See *Removal,* and pry out defective seal. Clean shaft and seal recess, then lubricate new seal. Center seal on shaft and drive into recess with suitable tube. Reinstall pitman arm, and using new lock plate, tighten lock nut to 101 ft. lbs. (14 mkg). Place steering gear in full right lock position and check that steering roller shaft is covered with oil.

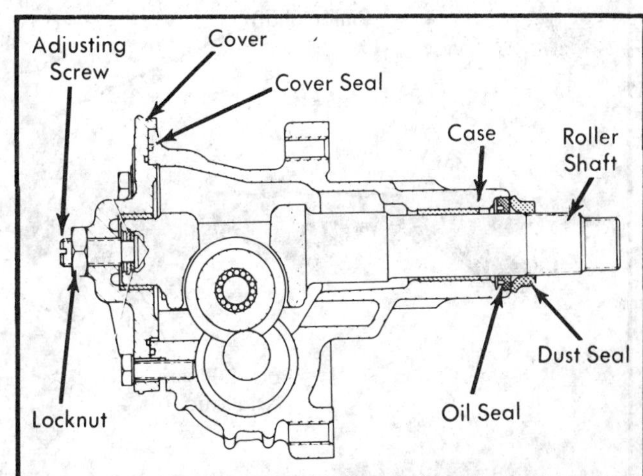

Fig. 2 Cutaway View of Worm & Roller Gearbox

TIGHTENING SPECIFICATIONS

Application	Ft. Lbs. (mkg)
Steering Gear-to-Frame	25-36 (3.5-5.0)
Pinion Shaft Nut	101 (14)
Pitman Arm-to-Drag Link	22 (3)
Adjuster Locknut	36-43 (5-6)
Flange-to-Wormshaft	14 (2)

VOLKSWAGEN RABBIT, SCIRROCO RACK & PINION

Rabbit
Scirocco

DESCRIPTION

Vehicles are equipped with a rack and pinion steering gear. Attached to rack are two tie rods, the right tie rod is adjustable and the left tie rod is non-adjustable. If left tie rod is to be replaced, replacement tie rod (part no. 171 419 804) is adjustable.

REMOVAL & INSTALLATION

Removal – Disconnect shift linkage bearing plate from rack housing. Loosen upper universal pinch bolt-to-steering column shaft. Remove lower universal pinch bolt-to-pinion shaft. Disconnect lower universal joint from pinion shaft. Disconnect tie rod outer ends from steering linkage. Disconnect steering gear housing clamp bolts and remove steering gear, with tie rods, from vehicle.

Installation – When installing steering gear assembly, correctly align and insert pinion shaft with steering shaft lower universal joint before securing steering gear housing clamp bolts. Connect tie rod outer ends to steering linkage. Tighten upper and lower universal joint pinch bolts. Connect and adjust shift linkage bearing plate to gear housing.

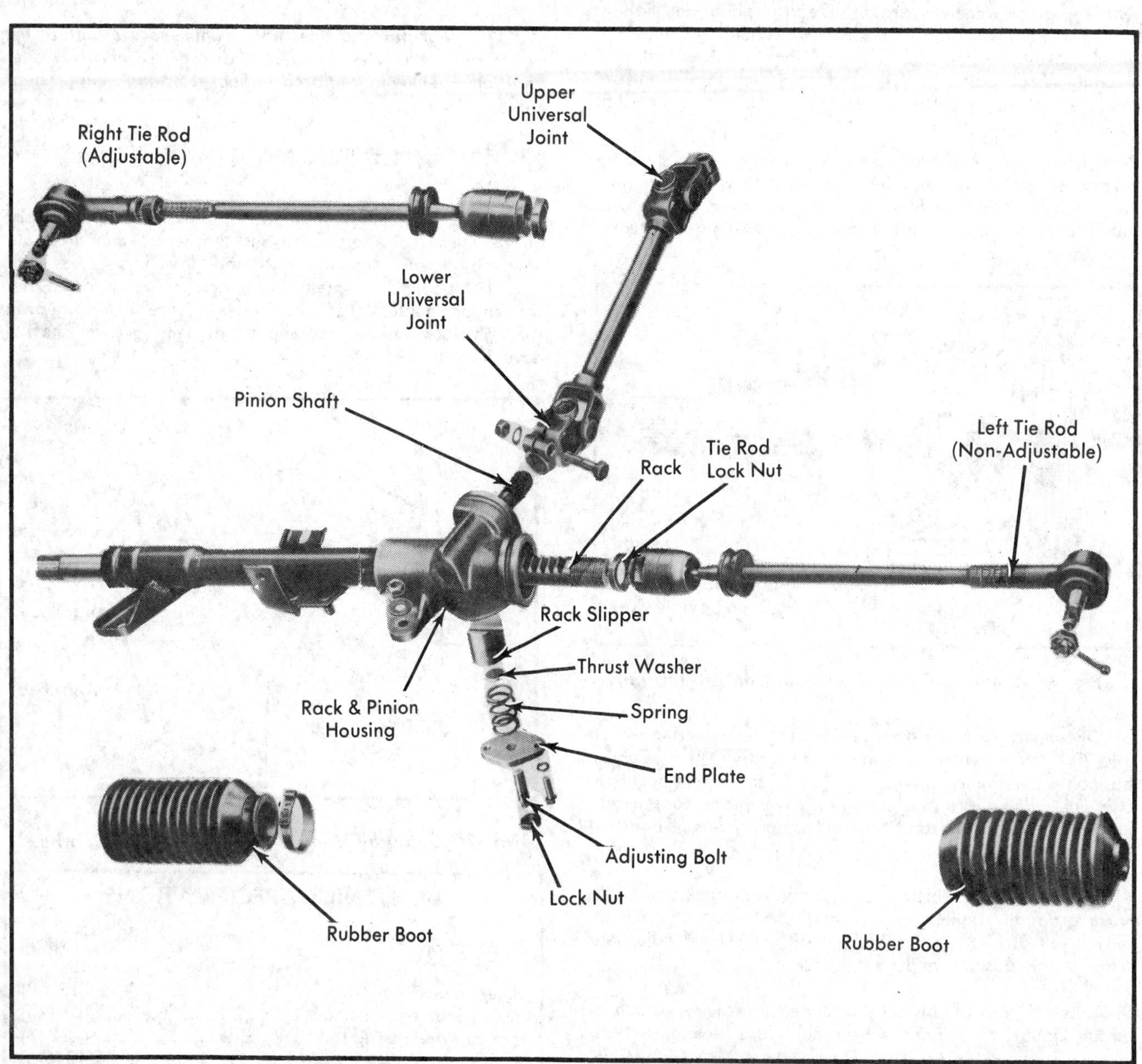

Fig. 1 Disassembled View of Rack & Pinion Steering Gear Assembly

VOLKSWAGEN RABBIT, SCIRROCO RACK & PINION (Cont.)

ADJUSTMENT

RACK & TIE RODS

1) Center rack in housing so rack protrudes an equal amount from each end of housing *(see Fig. 2)*.

2) Screw tie rods onto rack and adjust to specified dimensions *(see Fig. 3)*. **NOTE** — *Do not move rack from its centered position.* With adjustment correct, secure tie rods with lock nuts and install rubber boots.

Fig. 2 Centering Rack in Steering Gear Housing

Tie Rod Specifications

Application	Dimension "B"	Dimension "C"
Man. Trans.	2.72" (69 mm)	2.72" (69 mm)
Auto. Trans.	2.64" (67 mm)	2.72" (69 mm)

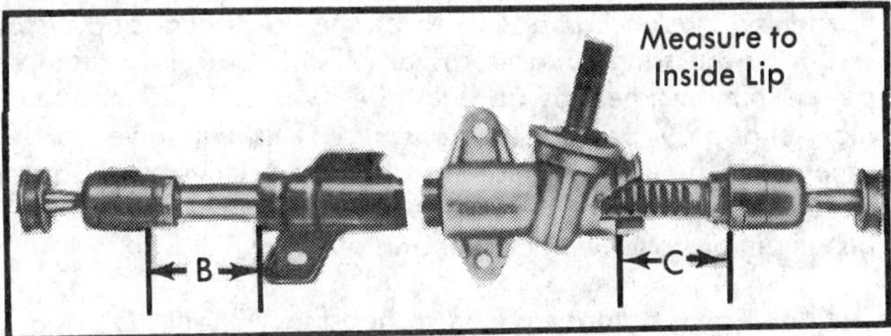

Fig. 3 Installation Adjustment of Tie Rods on Rack

3) If replacing the non-adjustable left tie rod with adjustable type, adjust tie rod length "D" to 14.92" (379 mm) *(see Fig. 4)*. Then install as described in step 1).

4) Loosen pinion shaft adjusting screw lock nut, then turn adjusting bolt until it just contacts thrust washer. Tighten lock nut.

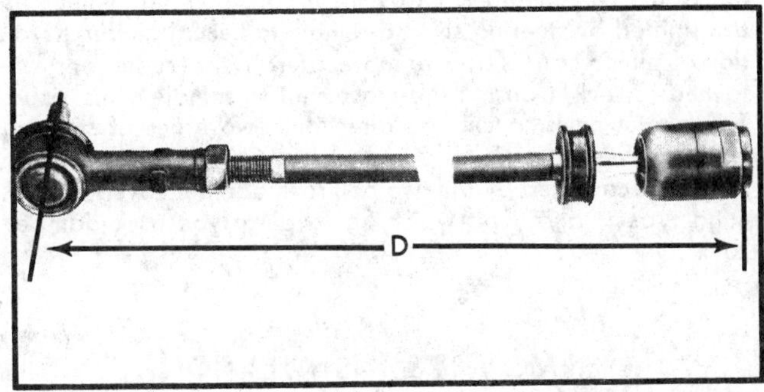

Fig. 4 Adjustment of Replacement Left Tie Rod (Part No. 171 419 804)

TIGHTENING SPECIFICATIONS

Application	Ft. Lbs. (mkg)
Tie Rod End to Steering Arm	22 (3.0)
Tie Rod End Locknut	29 (4.0)
Gear Box Mounting Bolts	14 (2.0)
Universal Joint Pinch Bolts	22 (3.0)

VOLVO RACK & PINION

240 Series
260 Series

NOTE – *For models equipped with power steering, refer to appropriate article under Power Steering in this section.*

DESCRIPTION

Rack and pinion steering gear is mounted in rubber insulators to front crossmember. Movement of steering wheel is transmitted by steering shaft assembly to helical pinion. Rotation of pinion causes rack to move laterally where tie rods, attached to rack, transmit this movement to spindle arms, causing front wheels to change direction. Two types of steering gears are used by Volvo. The first is a Cam Gear unit which may be recognized by the two bolt rack damper cover. The second type is a ZF unit which has a plug type rack damper cover.

REMOVAL & INSTALLATION

STEERING GEAR

Removal – Remove lock bolt and nut from pinion flange. Bend flange apart slightly. Raise and support front of vehicle and remove wheels. Remove tie rod nuts and disconnect ball studs from spindle using ball joint removal tool (9995043). Remove splash guard and bolts securing steering gear to crossmember. Disconnect gear from flange and remove gear.

Installation – To install, reverse removal procedure making sure that recess on pinion shaft is aligned towards lock bolt opening in flange.

TIE RODS

Removal – Raise vehicle and remove wheel(s). Remove tie rod nuts and disconnect ball studs from spindle using ball joint removal tool (5043). Remove splash guard. On cam gear units, loosen inner clamps for both rubber bellows and drain oil, then re-attach clamp on side not being removed (if applicable). Bend up tie rod lock and disconnect rod from steering gear. Clamp ball stud in vise, loosen lock nut and unscrew rod, counting number of thread turns. Remove outer clamp for rubber bellows and remove bellows.

Installation – Install rubber bellows and outer clamp. Screw on lock nut same number of turns as when removed. Install ball stud and tighten lock nut. Attach tie rod to steering gear and punch ball stud edge or lock washer tab into rack groove. On cam gear units, fill a suction gun with 6.75 oz. (200 cc) of 20W-50 engine oil and inject oil into steering gear through rubber bellows inner end. Install inner bellows clamp and tighten clamp after turning tie rod so that ball stud is up. Connect tie rod to spindle making sure that both rods are the same length within .08" (2 mm).

ADJUSTMENT

NOTE – *Adjustments are performed during gear assembly process. See Overhaul as outlined.*

OVERHAUL

CAM GEAR

Disassembly – 1) Clean steering gear exterior and check inner ball joints for wear. Loosen pinion side rubber bellows and drain oil. Remove pinion side ball stud, lock nut and rubber bellows. Bend up locked portion of ball joint and unscrew pinion side tie rod. Repeat procedure on opposite side of gear.

2) Remove rack damper cover, spring, "O" ring and piston. Remove pinion cover and lift out pinion assembly. Pull out rack from pinion side of gear housing and remove rack bushing using a puller (4078). Use a puller (5047) to remove pinion lower bearing. Clean all parts and check for wear. Replace all seals, rack bushing and worn parts.

Assembly & Adjustment – 1) Oil all parts prior to assembly with 20W-50 engine oil. Install new rack bushing so that locks align with gear housing slots, using driver tool (2993). Install pinion lower bearing using driver tool (5048). Install pinion with upper bearing, but no shims, in housing. Install pinion spacer sleeve and cover with gasket but no seal. Use a dial indicator to measure pinion end play and record for later use. Remove pinion assembly.

2) Insert rack in gear housing from pinion side using care that rack teeth do not damage rack bushing. Apply a non-hardening gasket compound to pinion cover seal and install seal in cover using suitable driver (2734). Calculate required pinion shim thickness by adding .004-.010" (.10-.25 mm) to pinion end play previously measured. This will give correct amount of pinion preload. Install pinion, shims and spacer sleeve with shims between upper bearing and spacer sleeve. Install pinion cover with gasket and seal.

3) Place rack damper piston in housing without "O" ring or spring. Using straight edge and feeler gauge, measure end play between end of piston and housing (*see Fig. 1*). Measure thickness of gasket and calculate shim thickness required to obtain a total thickness, between gasket and shim, of .001-.006" (.02-.15 mm) greater than the measured piston end play to obtain correct preload. Install spring and "O" ring in piston, install shims, gasket and cover.

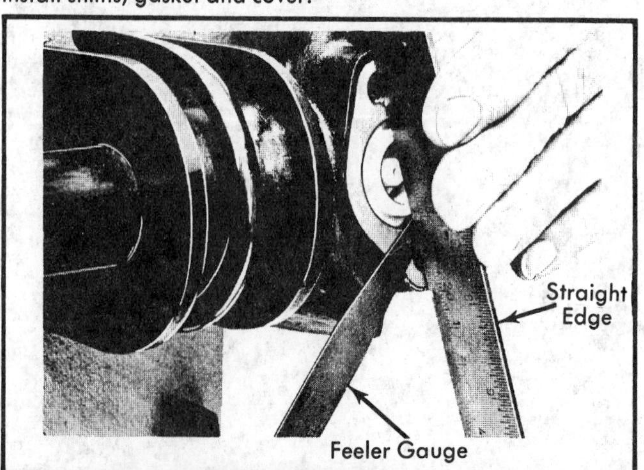

Fig. 1 Measuring Rack Damper Piston End Play (Cam Gear)

VOLVO RACK & PINION (Cont.)

4) Using suitable torque gauge (5053), crank rack back and forth from one end to the other. Torque reading should be 8-14 INCH lbs. (9-17 cmkg). Install pinion side tie rod and punch ball joint edge into rack groove.

NOTE — *When installing old tie rod, place a thin shim between ball joint and rack shoulder so unused portion of ball can be used for punch locking.*

5) Install pinion side rubber bellows with inner clamp only. Install lock nut and ball stud. Repeat procedure for other side of gear and adjust both rods to the same length within .08" (2 mm). Use a suction gun to inject 6.75 ozs. (200 cc) of 20W-50 engine oil through outer end of pinion side rubber bellows. Install outer clamps on bellows.

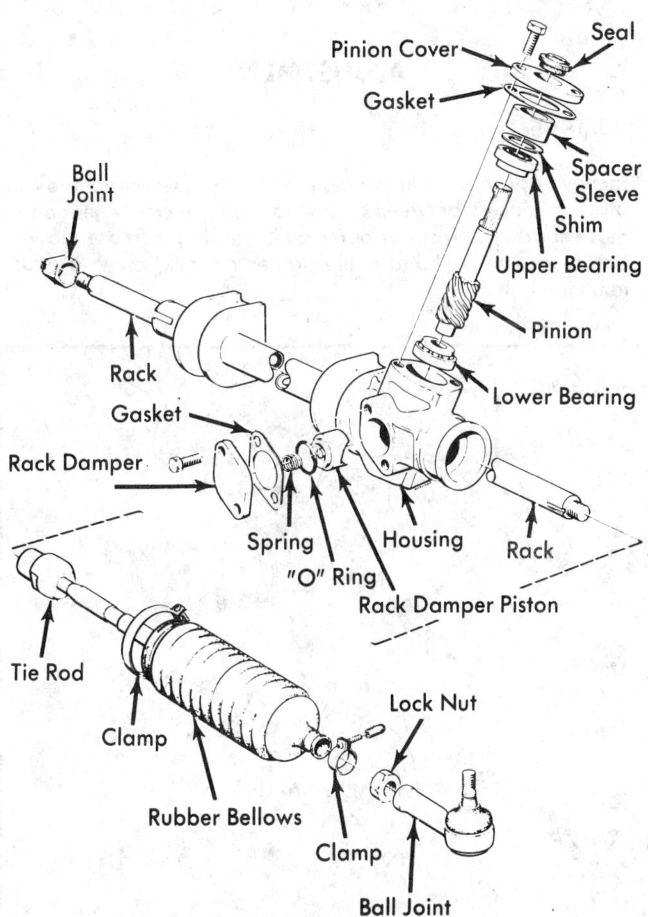

Fig. 2 Exploded View of Cam Gear Steering Gear Assembly

ZF STEERING GEAR

Disassembly — 1) Clean exterior of steering gear and check inner ball joints for wear. Remove pinion side rubber bellows. Bend up locked portion of ball joint and unscrew tie rod from rack. Remove opposite side tie rod in like manner. Remove dust seal and cotter pin for rack damper, then remove cover and spring using suitable tool (5119). Remove rack damper piston, knocking on rack with palm of hand to aid removal.

2) Remove pinion dust seal. Remove pinion nut lock ring, then remove pinion nut (tool 5119). Clamp pinion shaft in a soft jawed vise and tap lightly on housing with soft mallet to remove pinion. Remove rack from pinion side of housing and remove rack bushing by pressing in locking tabs and prying bearing out. Press pinion thrust washer and bearing from shaft. Clean all parts and check for wear. Replace all "O" rings and worn parts.

Assembly & Adjustment — 1) Press bearing onto pinion and install snap ring and thrust washer. Install new "O" rings on rack bushing and press bushing into housing making sure that tabs on bushing fit correctly into slots in housing. Grease rack with Calypsol D 4024-OK grease or equivalent. Insert rack into pinion side of housing using care not to damage rack bushing with rack teeth. Grease pinion using same grease as for rack and install pinion with bearing.

2) Install new "O" ring in pinion nut and install nut using suitable tool (5119). Torque to 18±1.5 ft.lbs. (2.5±.2 mkg). Fill cavity on top of nut with grease and install dust seal. Install new "O" ring on rack damper piston, grease piston and install piston and spring. Install, but do not tighten rack damper cover (tool 5119). Using torque gauge, crank rack back and forth between end positions. Torque should be 5-15 INCH lbs. (5.8-17.3 cm kg). To increase torque, screw in rack damper cover. Lock cover in correct position with cotter pin and install dust cover.

3) Crank out rack fully and fill rack tooth spaces with Calypsol D 4024-OK grease or equivalent. Crank rack in and then out again and repeat grease application. Approximately 1 oz. (25 g) of grease should be used. Install tie rods using new lock washers and bend washer to lock rod in place. Install rubber bellows.

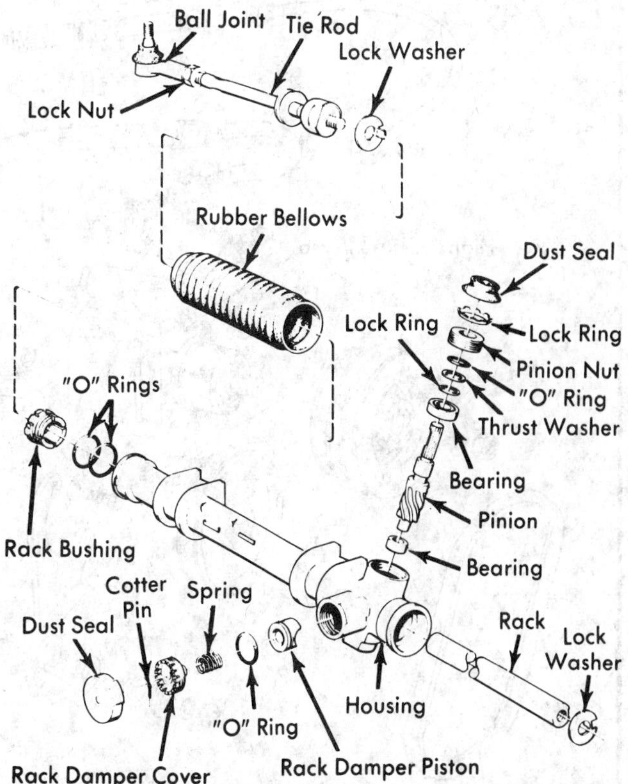

Fig. 3 Exploded View of ZF Steering Gear Assembly

AUDI 100LS POWER-ASSISTED RACK & PINION

100

DESCRIPTION

A power-assisted rack and pinion steering gear is used as standard equipment on Audi 100 models. The rack and pinion gear gains power assist from a rotary piston pinion gear assembly, a high-pressure oil pump, and an oil reservoir. The pump is mounted on the front of the engine and is belt driven. The oil reservoir is mounted near the firewall and is connected to the pump and to the gear by hydraulic fluid hoses and lines.

GENERAL SERVICE

OIL LEVEL CHECK

Remove reservoir cover, start engine, and check that oil level is at the upper mark on the reservoir. If it is necessary to add oil, be sure engine is at idle. If fluid flow is too strong, air bubbles will be created which will cause foaming and make it necessary to bleed the system.

LUBRICANT TYPE

Manufacturer recommends using Dexron type B automatic transmission fluid.

NOTE — *Do not reuse any fluid that has been drained from system.*

HYDRAULIC SYSTEM BLEEDING

Start engine and allow to idle. Make sure fluid level is at the upper reservoir mark. Turn steering wheel rapidly from right to left lock position while observing fluid. Avoid using more pressure than necessary when turning wheel. Continue until fluid level remains at upper mark and no bubbles appear in reservoir. Add oil as necessary to maintain level. Turn off engine and check that oil level does not rise more than 7/16" (11 mm) above upper mark.

ADJUSTMENT

PUMP BELT

Remove apron and disassemble pulley. Adjust belt tension by placing spacers between pulley halves to decrease tension or move spacers in front of outer pulley half to increase tension. Rotate engine by hand while tightening lock screw to avoid jamming belt.

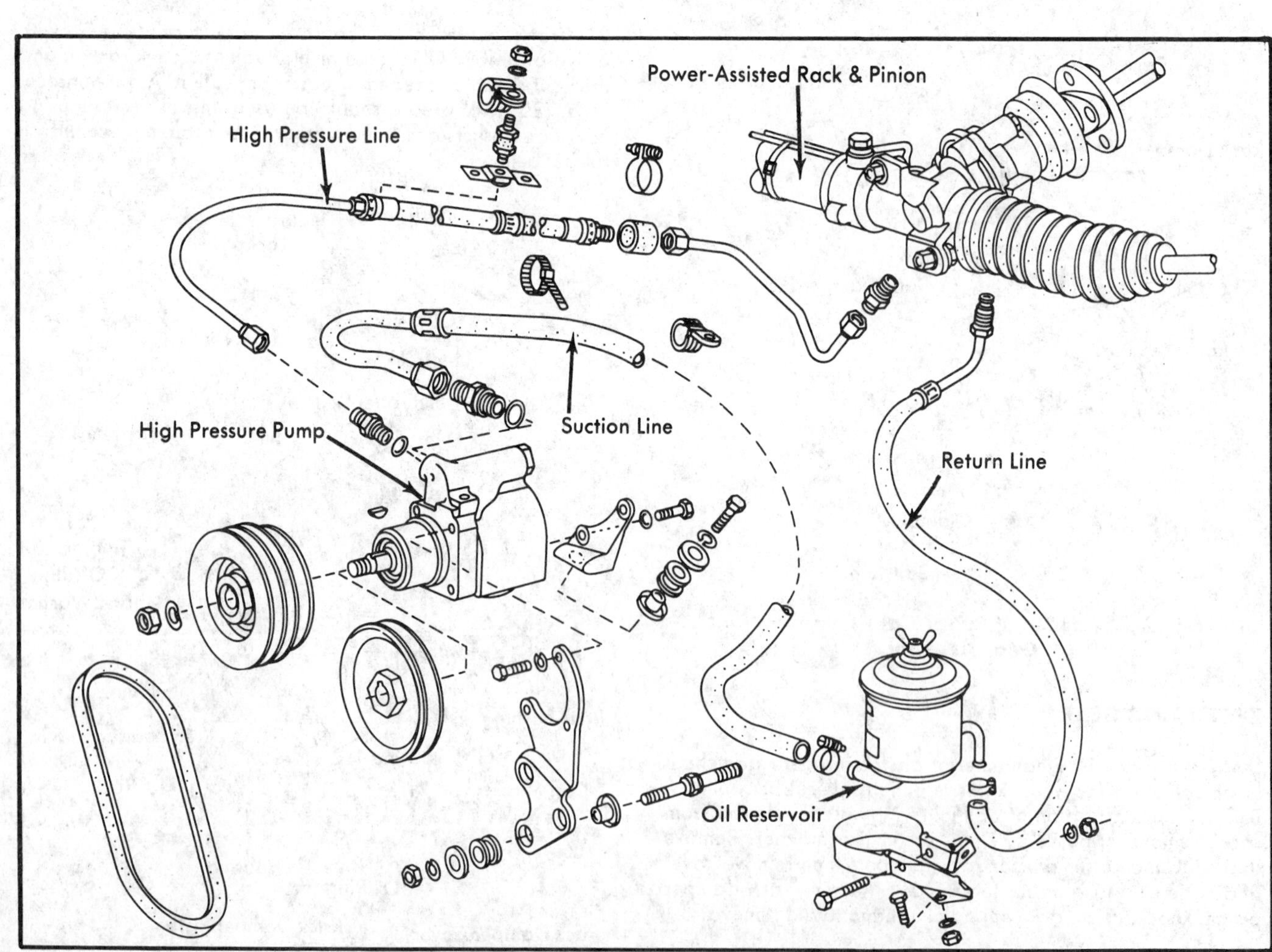

Fig. 1 Exploded View of Audi 100 Power Steering

AUDI 100LS POWER-ASSISTED RACK & PINION (Cont.)

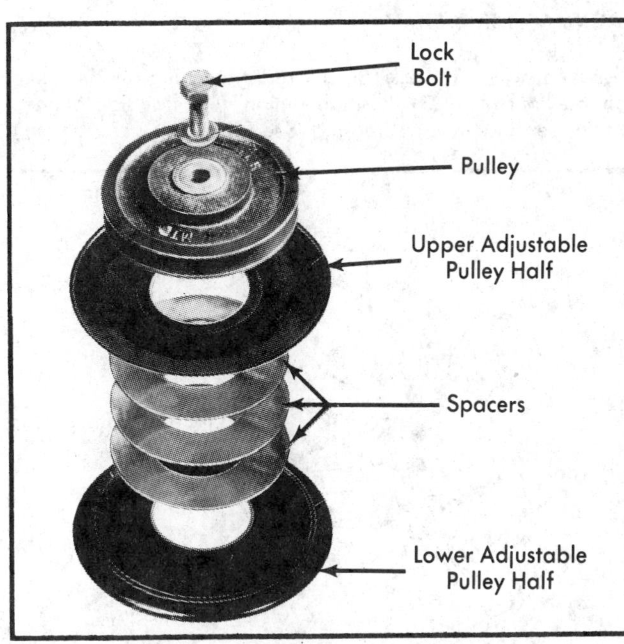

Fig. 2 Adjusting Belt Tension

TESTING

SYSTEM PRESSURE TEST

Pump Pressure Test – 1) Install a 0-1450 psi (0-102 kg/cm²) pressure gauge in line between power steering pump and piston rotary valve. Gauge must be equipped with a cutoff valve.

2) With engine running at idle, close cutoff valve and read gauge pressure. **CAUTION** – *Do not close valve for longer than five seconds or excessive heat buildup in pump will occur.* Pressure reading on gauge must be 540-1166 psi (38-82 kg/cm²). If outside range, check operation of pressure and flow control valve. Repair or replace valve as required. If pressure is still too low, replace pump.

System Pressure Test – With gauge still installed and engine at idle. Open cutoff valve, then read gauge as steering wheel is turned full right and left lock to lock. Pressure should remain 540-1166 psi (38-82 kg/cm²). If gauge reading is outside this range (to high or to low) replace entire steering gear.

Installation & Adjustment – To install, reverse removal procedure, then perform adjustment as follows: Bolt steering assembly to outer steering tube. Attach gear to crossmember, but do not tighten bolts. Loosen upper control arm mounting bolts on both sides and install special steering gauge 41-102 so that gauge rests firmly on upper control arm. Turn rack until it rests on ruler of gauge. Adjust other side in same manner and tighten mounting bolts to 18 ft. lbs. (2.5 mkg). *See Fig. 2.*

REMOVAL & INSTALLATION

STEERING GEAR

Removal – 1) If vehicle is equipped with automatic transmission, perform the following in addition to regular removal procedures described below: Drain oil, disconnect lines at steering rack, and detach steering column at gear housing. Remove power brake unit (if vehicle is equipped with brake vent jets on both sides only). Detach brake hose at adaptors on transmission. Remove rear transmission crossmember. Detach front engine support bearing and lower engine (also remove stabilizer if necessary).

2) For vehicles equipped with air conditioning, note the following additional procedures which must be performed (without disconnecting A/C hoses) before removal of gear assembly may be attempted: Disconnect activated carbon container, air cleaner, and other vacuum hoses obstructing work. Bend open or unscrew A/C hose mounting parts. Disconnect thermostat. Unscrew evaporator cover. Disconnect and remove blower motor. Pull temperature sensor out of evaporator. Remove evaporator (two screws on top, two screws inside). Place unit on carburetor. Detach accelerator linkage.

3) On vehicles without air conditioning and/or automatic transmission, or after having performed necessary operations as previously described, the following general removal procedure applies: Drain oil. Disconnect and plug pressure lines. Pry both tie rods from steering knuckles using suitable tool (VW 266 H). Detach steering from crossmember. Disconnect steering column from gear at flexible coupling. Loosen tube connection and pull off tube. Disconnect accelerator linkage connection. Slide gear assembly into right wheel housing, then up and out of vehicle.

Installation & Adjustment – To install, reverse removal procedure, then perform adjustment as follows: Bolt steering to outer steering tube. Attach gear to crossmember, but do not tighten bolts. Loosen upper control arm mounting bolts on both sides and install special steering gauge 41-102 so that gauge rests firmly on upper control arm (see Steering Gauge Installation illustration). Turn rack until it rests on ruler of gauge. Adjust other side in same manner and tighten mounting bolts to 18 ft. lbs. (2.5 mkg).

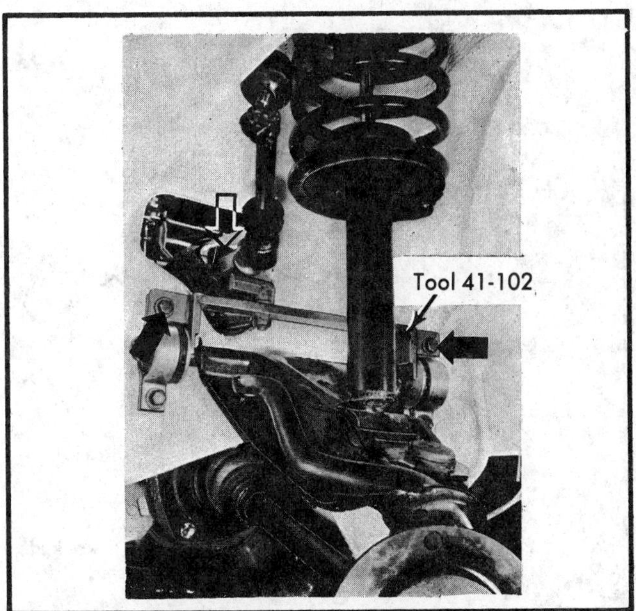

Fig. 3 Steering Gauge Installed on Upper Control Arm

AUDI 100LS POWER-ASSISTED RACK & PINION (Cont.)

OVERHAUL

Manufacturer does not recommend overhaul of the steering gear, however, leaking seals may be replaced using the following procedures.

PINION HOUSING SEALS

NOTE – *The steering gear assembly must be removed from the vehicle in order to replace any of the seals.*

Disassembly – **1**) Release pressure plate by loosening bolts, do not remove plate. Unscrew three attaching bolts and remove rotary piston valve housing.

2) Pry seal from intermediate cover and drive out seal from housing using appropriate tool.

3) Insert new seals from the inside on cover and housing and drive into seat with suitable tools (2056 and VW 295a).

Reassembly – To reassemble, reverse disassembly procedure: noting the following: Protect pinion teeth before installing intermediate cover, then tighten cover-to-housing bolts.

RACK ASSEMBLY SEALS

Disassembly – **1**) Lock rack by removing plug and inserting suitable tool (41-103). Position pinion with flat side aligned with upper bore in valve housing *(See Fig. 4)*.

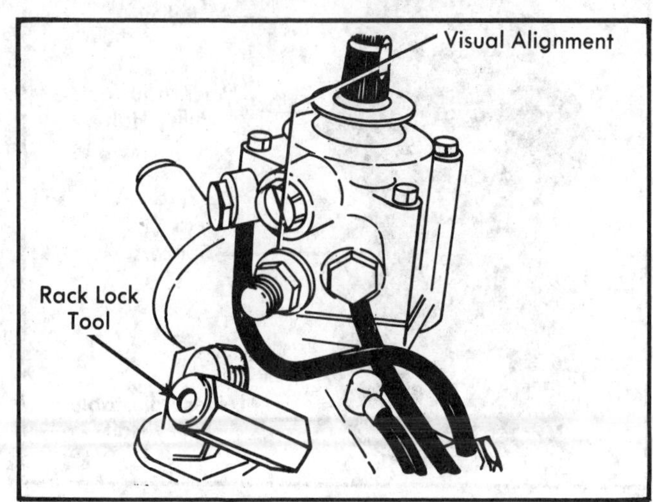

Fig. 4 Valve Housing Alignment & Rack Lock

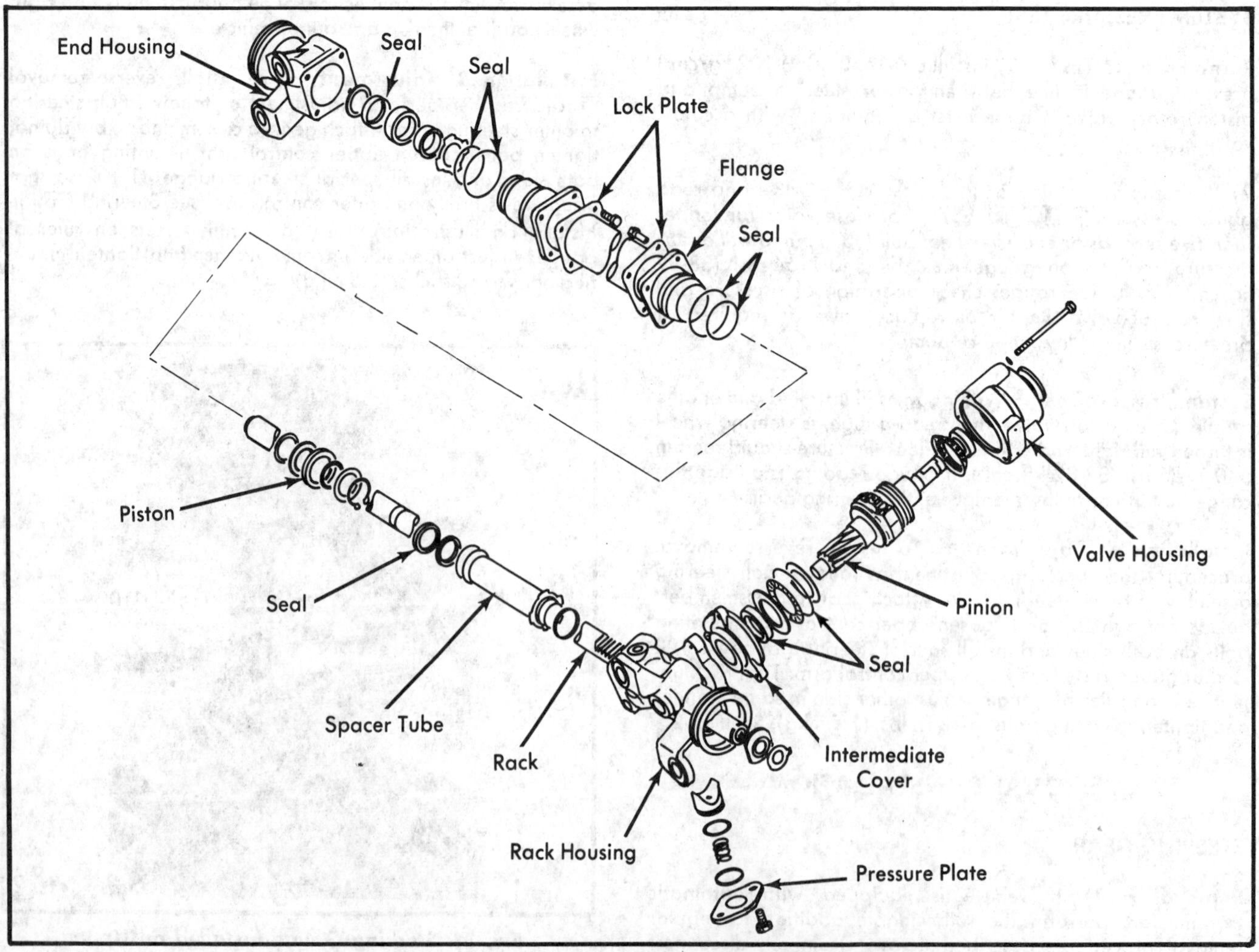

Fig. 5 Exploded View of Audi 100 Power Steering Gear

AUDI 100LS POWER-ASSISTED RACK & PINION (Cont.)

2) Remove end housing bolts and cut off lock plate, then remove lug washer, plastic sleeve, steel sleeve, seal, and washer from housing. Drive out end housing seal and replace new seal from inside housing using suitable tool (3013).

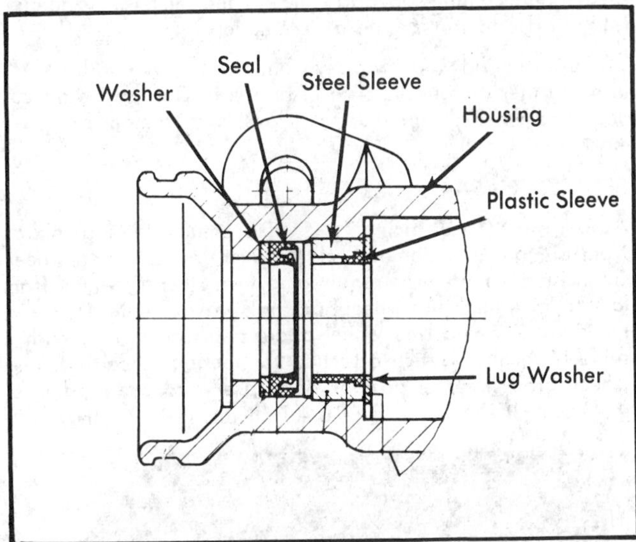

Fig. 6 Valve Housing Components

3) Remove flange bolts and cut off lock ring. Mount rack in padded vise, remove two circlips and remove piston and spacer tube from rack.

4) Drive out seal from spacer tube, then press in replacement seal with lip facing out.

Reassembly – Reverse disassembly procedures noting the following: Clean sealent from end housing flange and partially install lock bolts, then stretch "O" ring around all lock bolts to form a gasket. Tighten bolts, then fill spacer tube grooves with heavy grease and push tube into housing.

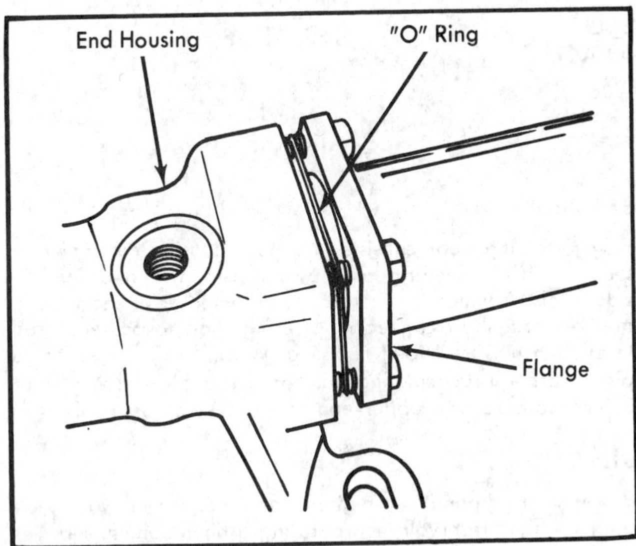

Fig. 7 End Housing Flange Seal

HIGH PRESSURE PUMP SEAL

Disassembly – **1**) Remove nut, pulley, and Woodruff key. Remove circlips and partially screw pulley nut back on pulley shaft.

2) Clamp nut (installed on shaft) in vise and strike pump housing with plastic hammer to drive out pump shaft. Install a suitable seal extractor on seal, clamp nut of extractor in vise and strike housing with plastic hammer to drive out seal.

NOTE – *Pump must be replaced if shaft or bearing is worn.*

Reassembly – Reverse disassembly procedures noting the following: Fill spaces between lips of seal with multipurpose grease. Drive seal into seat with seal lips facing impeller. Drive pump shaft onto seat, being carefull that alignment is correct.

BMW POWER-ASSISTED WORM & SECTOR

530i
630CSi

DESCRIPTION

STEERING GEAR

Power steering gear consists of a gear housing containing a sector shaft with sector gear, a power piston with gear teeth in side of piston which is in constant mesh with sector shaft teeth, and a worm shaft connecting steering shaft to power piston through a universal joint coupling. Worm shaft is geared to piston through recirculating ball contact; and a steering valve is incorporated into upper end of worm gear assembly.

STEERING PUMP

Power steering pump is a high pressure, belt driven, vane type pump. A fluid reservoir incorporating a filter element supplies hydraulic fluid to pump. Pump maintains hydraulic pressure to power steering gear assembly.

LUBRICATION

CAPACITY

System Capacity – 2.54 pints (1200 cc).

LUBRICANT TYPE

Initial or Subsequent Filling – BMW recommends Veedol Automatic Transmission Fluid ATF Special 3433.

Subsequent Filling (Max. 1/2 pint - 1/4 liter) – Veedol Automatic Transmission Fluid Type A Suffix A AQ 1407 A, or suitable equivalent.

ADJUSTMENT

PUMP BELT

Loosen adjustment bolts and shift pump to tighten belt. Adjustment is correct when it is possible to press in belt 0.2-0.4" (5-10 mm) with the thumb.

Fig. 1 Power Steering Belt Adjustment Locations

HYDRAULIC SYSTEM BLEEDING

1) Power steering must be bled whenever system is opened, or oil level falls so low that the vane type pump picks up air. Fill reservoir to upper mark with fluid. Turn engine over with starter and continue to add fluid. When oil level no longer falls, start and run engine at idle speed.

2) Turn steering wheel rapidly from lock to lock and back until no further air bubbles rise in reservoir. During this operation, and when completed, fluid level must remain at upper mark.

SECTOR SHAFT

Adjustment (In Vehicle) – **1)** Disconnect steering linkage from pitman arm. Remove center cover from steering wheel. Count number of turns required to turn steering wheel from lock to lock, then turn wheel back half way to center the steering gear. Turn steering wheel about one turn to left. With a suitable torque wrench attached to steering wheel nut, turn wheel through center position and observe torque reading at this point: It should be 8.7-10.4 Inch lbs. (10-12 cmkg).

Fig. 2 Checking Sector Shaft Adjustment with Torque Wrench

2) Before adjusting, turn steering wheel about one turn to left of straight-ahead position. Loosen lock nut and turn adjusting screw until correct torque is obtained when steering wheel passes through the straight-ahead position. Tighten lock nut and recheck adjustment.

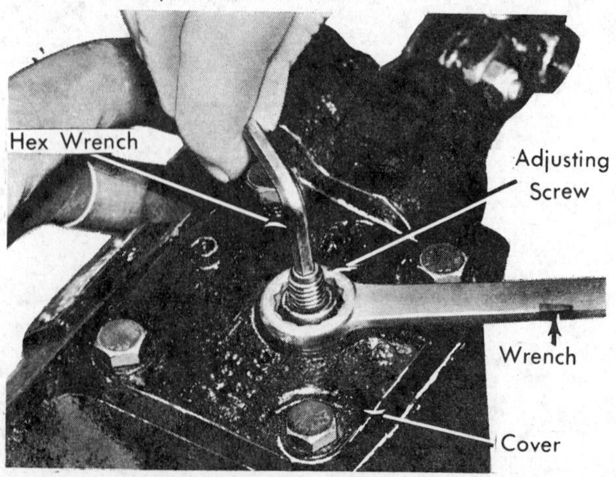

Fig. 3 Detail of Sector Shaft Adjustment

BMW POWER-ASSISTED WORM & SECTOR (Cont.)

REMOVAL & INSTALLATION

STEERING GEAR

Removal – 1) Turn steering to full left lock. This will move piston to top of its travel. Remove plug in gear housing and drain fluid. **CAUTION** – *Do not re-use fluid drained from steering.* Disconnect steering linkage from pitman arm.

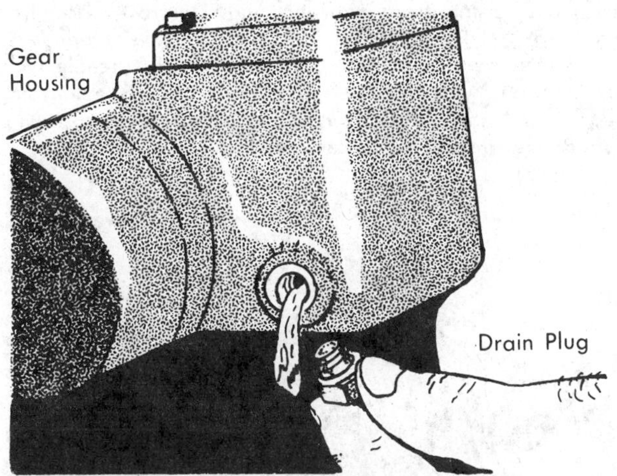

Fig. 4 Draining Steering Gear Housing

2) Mark universal joint and steering worm shaft for reassembly reference. Remove lower bolt from universal joint. Loosen upper bolt and drive universal joint upwards as far as possible on steering shaft. Disconnect hoses from steering gear. **CAUTION** – *Seal hose connections with dust caps.* Separate steering gear from front axle beam and remove downwards.

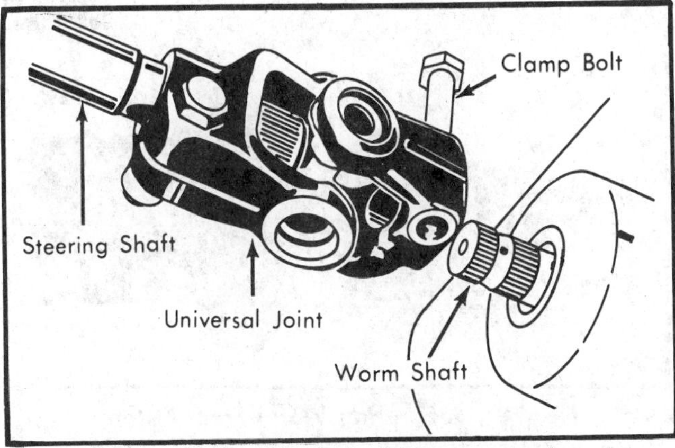

Fig. 5 Steering Shaft Disconnected from Worm Shaft

Installation – To install, reverse removal procedure and note the following: For hydraulic system bleeding, see Adjustment above.

STEERING PUMP

Removal – Disconnect hoses from steering pump. **CAUTION** – *Do not re-use fluid drained from pump and hoses.* Loosen pump mounting bolts and remove drive belt, then remove bolts and lift out pump.

Installation – To install, reverse removal procedure and note the following: For pump belt adjustment and hydraulic system bleeding, see Adjustment above.

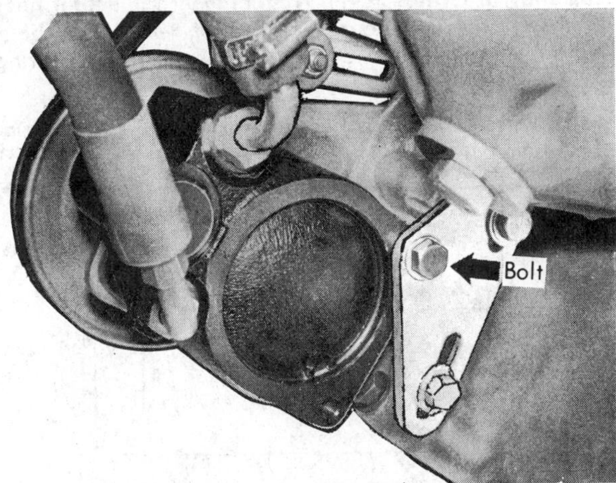

Fig. 6 Installed View of Power Steering Pump

STEERING GEAR OVERHAUL

DISASSEMBLY

Pitman Arm – 1) Mark pitman arm and sector shaft for reassembly reference then, using a suitable puller, remove pitman arm.

2) When installing: Align marks on pitman arm and sector shaft. Install lock washer with longer of two metal tabs on right of pitman arm (looking forward).

Sector Shaft Cover – 1) Remove adjusting screw lock nut and bolts from cover. Remove cover by turning adjusting screw clockwise through cover.

2) When installing: Inspect "O" ring in cover and replace if necessary. Before tightening cover bolts, turn adjusting screw until cover is firmly seated.

Sector Shaft – 1) Center sector shaft gear in housing and remove shaft.

2) Check end play of adjusting screw. Head of screw is held in sector shaft by a washer and snap ring. End play between adjusting screw and sector shaft is controlled by thickness of washer. End play should be .002" (.05 mm). Replace washer if necessary with one of correct thickness to obtain desired end play.

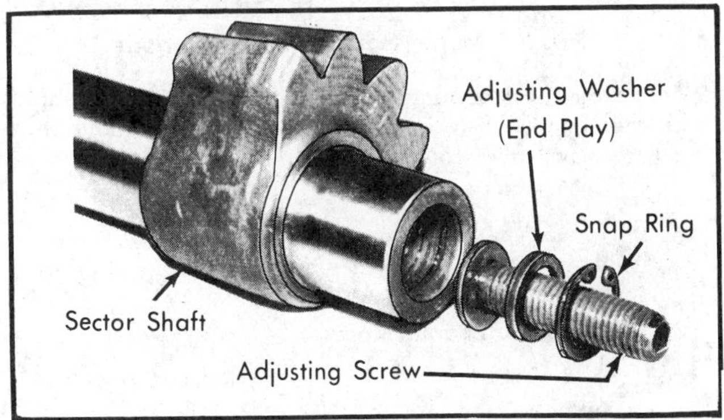

Fig. 7 Sector Shaft Adjustment Screw and Related Components

3) When installing: Pack splines of shaft with high temperature grease and insert shaft carefully to avoid damaging seals.

BMW POWER-ASSISTED WORM & SECTOR (Cont.)

Sector Shaft Bearings – 1) From pitman arm end of housing, remove snap ring and oil seal. Remove needle roller bearing with a suitable puller. Drive upper needle roller bearing, thrust washer, and oil seal out of housing.

2) When installing: Oil seal lips must face interior of steering gear housing.

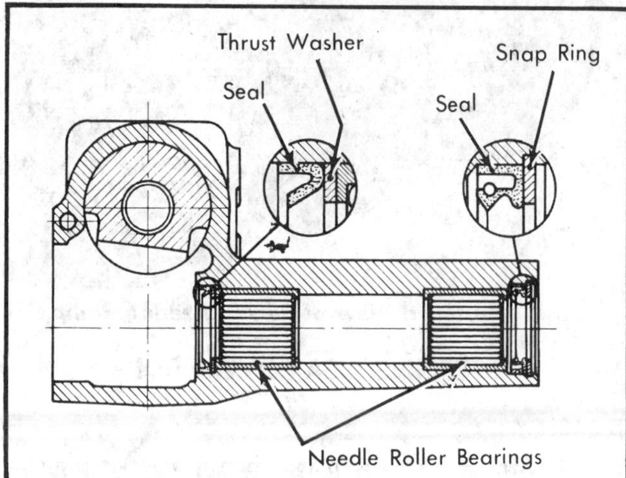

Fig. 8 Sector Shaft Bearing Positions

Valve Housing – 1) Remove protective cap from end of valve housing, then remove housing. Remove the ball bearing.

Fig. 9 Valve Housing Seal Locations

2) If needle roller bearing is to be replaced: Press off bearing race, then remove the double needle roller cage. Remove bearing race from valve housing with a suitable puller.

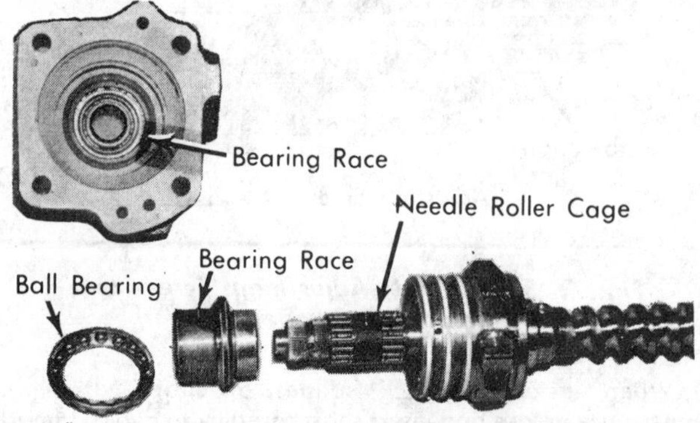

Fig. 10 Steering Gear Bearing Locations on Shaft

3) When installing: Install bearing and needle roller cage without play. To accomplish this, the needle roller cages are available in four different sizes. **CAUTION** – *Adjust torque value with bearing disc, as outlined under Intermediate Cover below.* Inspect sealing rings (four used) and replace if necessary. Cover worm shaft splines with Scotch tape to prevent damage to seal when installing housing.

Intermediate Cover – 1) Remove worm with intermediate cover and piston from gear housing. Unscrew worm from piston. **CAUTION** – *Do not lose balls.* Remove intermediate cover, then remove recirculating tube. Inspect needle roller cage, bearing washer, slotted ring, "O" ring, and sealing ring. **NOTE** – *The shim washer is required for adjusting position of slotted ring.* Inspect cover sealing rings (four used).

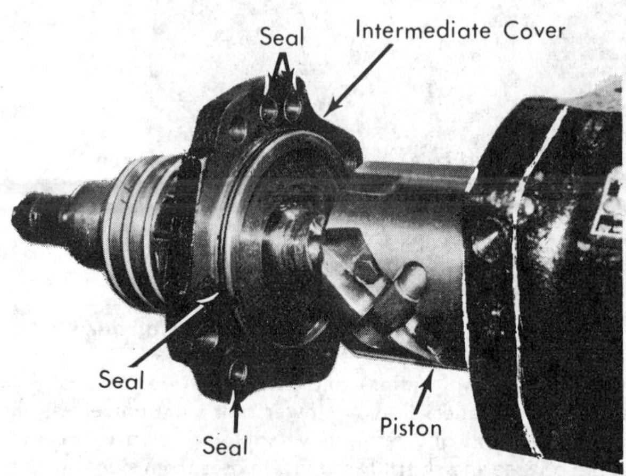

Fig. 11 Intermediate Cover Seal Locations

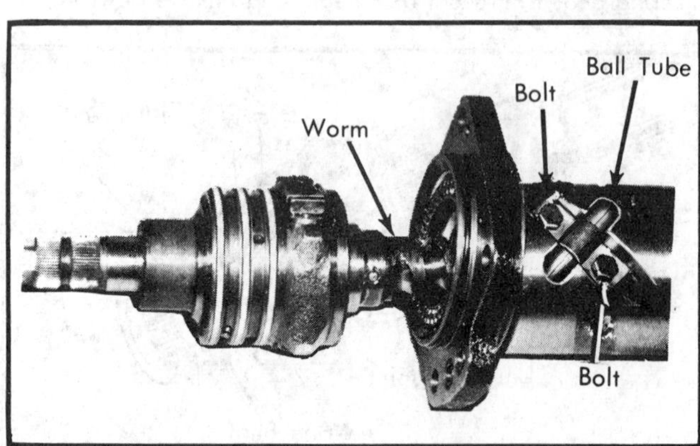

Fig. 12 Separating Worm From Piston

2) Temporarily assemble valve housing without ring seal, worm head without Teflon sealing rings, intermediate cover without "O" ring and slotted ring with ball bearing, needle roller cage and bearing washer to valve housing, and tighten screws evenly. Install torque wrench and check preload of worm bearing. Replace bearing washer if necessary with one of correct thickness to obtain torque specification shown in table at end of this article.

3) Check prestressing of Teflon ring in intermediate cap as follows: Place bearing disc and retainer ring in intermediate cap. Install "O" ring and Teflon ring (.067" (1.7 mm) thick) into groove, and install on worm shaft. Install a torque wrench and check preload with shaft in vertical position. Replace Teflon ring if necessary with one of correct thickness to obtain torque specification shown in table at end of this article.

BMW POWER-ASSISTED WORM & SECTOR (Cont.)

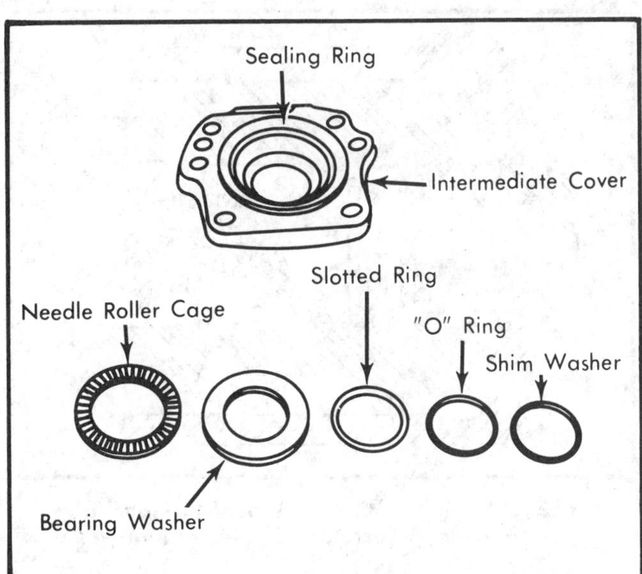

Fig. 13 Exploded View of Intermediate Cover

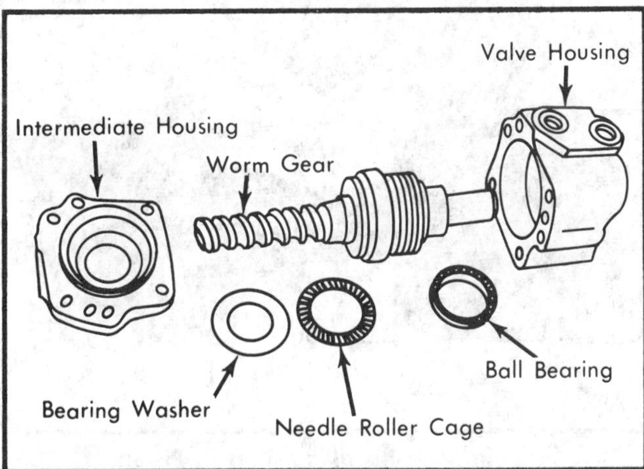

Fig. 14 Worm Bearings and Related Components

Teflon Rings (Worm Gear & Piston) – Replace Teflon rings (four rings) on worm gear and piston. Replace "O" ring (one ring) on worm gear. Use a suitable blade-type tool to push old rings out of grooves.

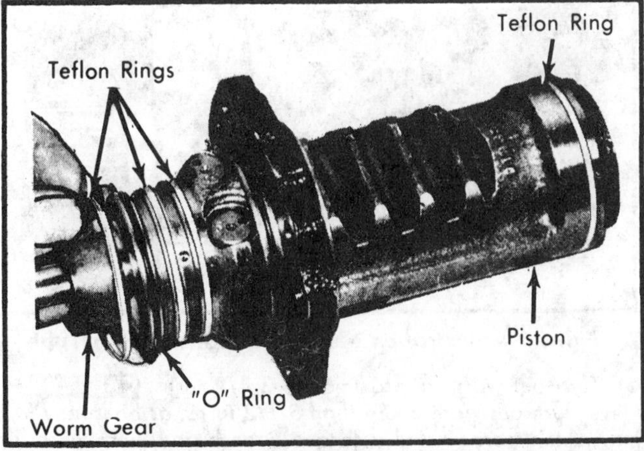

Fig. 15 Worm Gear and Piston Sealing Ring Locations

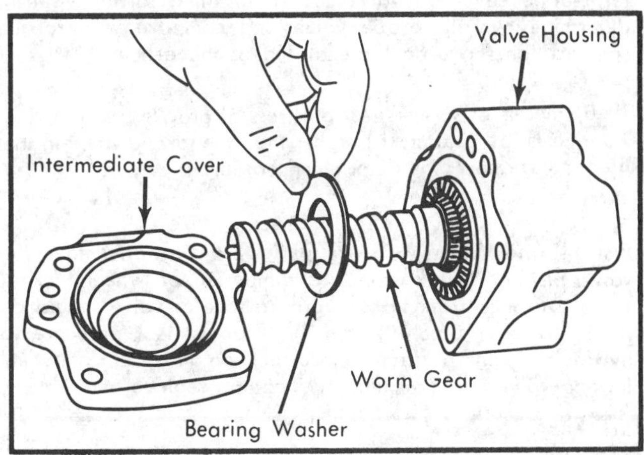

Fig. 16 Worm Adjustment Washer Installation

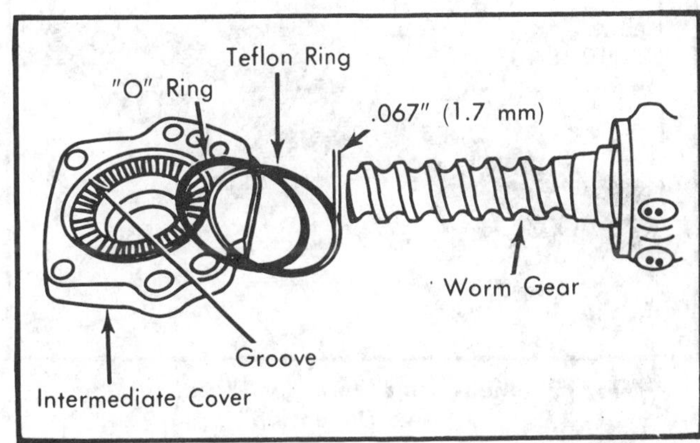

Fig. 17 Intermediate Cover with Teflon Ring

Checking and Adjusting Overall Torque Value of Worm Gear – 1) Before proceeding with check, verify the following: Teflon rings are installed in worm gear, and radial sealing ring installed in valve casing. Teflon ring is installed in intermediate cap, and frictional value of Teflon ring has been determined.

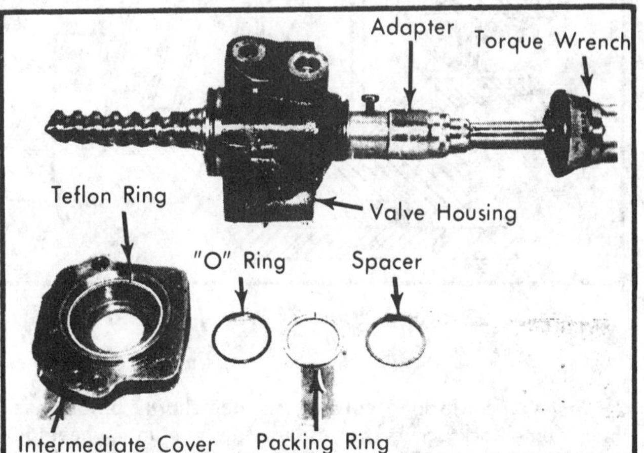

Fig. 18 Worm Gear Assembly Shown with Related Parts

2) Install "O" ring and groove packing ring, with sealing tab facing towards piston, together with spacers removed earlier. Assemble worm gear into piston casing. Install and tighten in-

BMW POWER-ASSISTED WORM & SECTOR (Cont.)

termediate cover on valve casing. Install a torque wrench; determine overall torque value and compare with torque specification shown in table at end of this article.

3) By means of spacers, set prestress of groove packing ring 0.86 INCH lbs. (1.0 cmkg) higher than the torque value in the intermediate cover as determined earlier.

Pistons and Worm – 1) **CAUTION** – *Do not remove the valve pistons.* Check standard dimension of wheel locking valve. Distance from tip of worm to face of valve should be 4.207-4.215" (106.8-107.0 mm). If adjustment of valve to hydraulic center position is incorrect, or dimension of wheel locking valve is not within specification, replace unit.

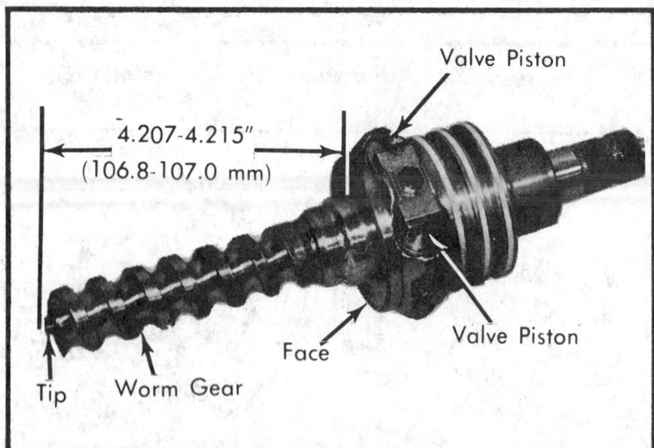

Fig. 19 Measuring Worm for Wheel Locking Valve Dimension

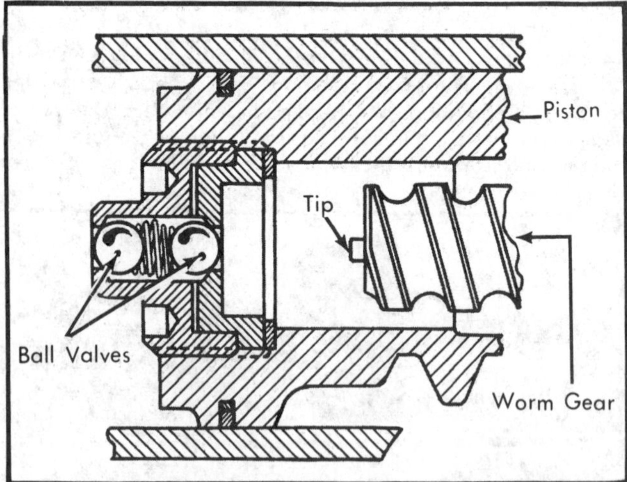

Fig. 20 Sectional View of Wheel Locking Valve

2) Since wheel locking valve must open shortly before maximum wheel lock occurs, turn adjusting screw until wheel locking valve opens .008" (2mm) before steering arm reaches its stop.

3) Install worm 1.576" (40 mm) into piston. Install 16 balls through front hole while turning worm. Place seven balls in circulation tube (retain end balls with grease). Install circulation tube on piston and lock bolts by bending over ends of clamp.

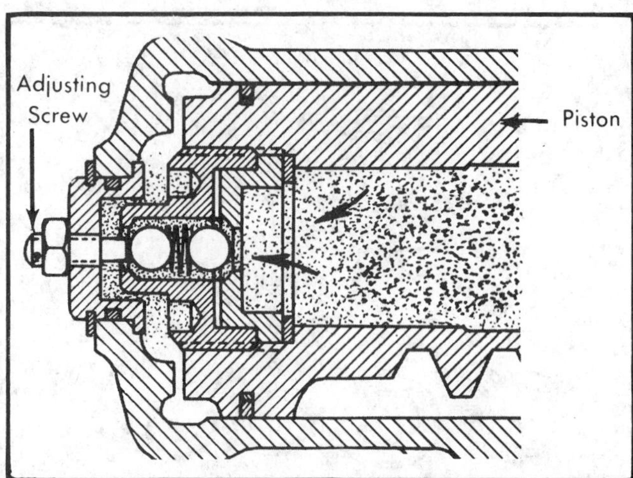

Fig. 21 Sectional View of Wheel Locking Valve Showing Adjustment Screw Location

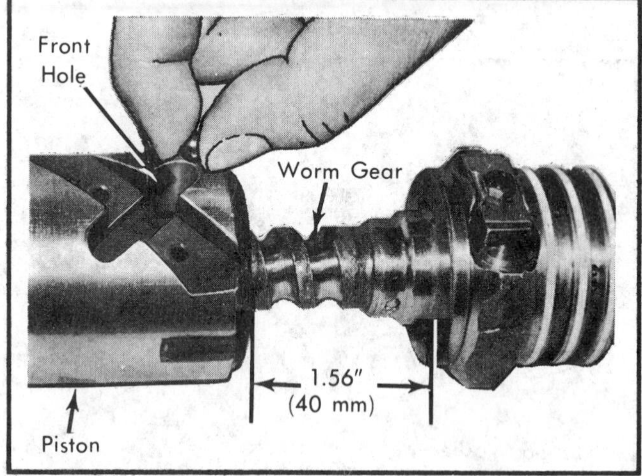

Fig. 22 Installing Balls in Piston

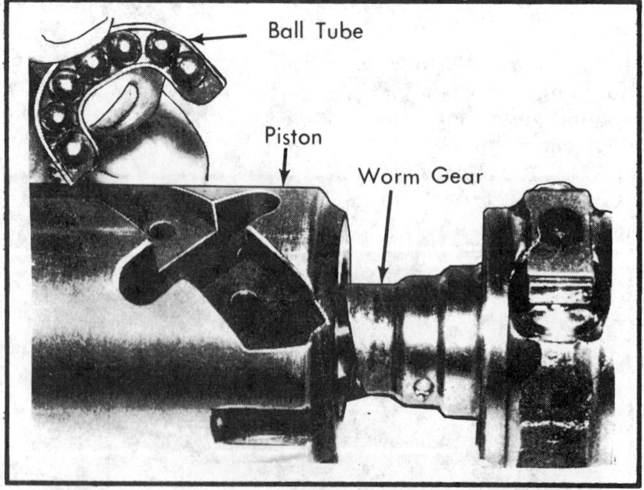

Fig. 23 Illustration Shows Ball Retained in Tube

4) Turn out worm approximately 3 1/2 turns. **CAUTION** – *Never turn out worm more than 3 1/2 turns, as balls may fall into piston bore.* Install a torque wrench and, with worm in horizontal position, measure torque value over a range of at

BMW POWER-ASSISTED WORM & SECTOR (Cont.)

least 90° and compare with torque specification shown in table at end of this article. Torque value is dependent on diameter of the balls. **CAUTION** – *Use only balls with same diameter (tolerance groups).* Remove worm after having adjusted torque value. Remove intermediate cover and connect worm to piston.

REASSEMBLY

To reassemble, reverse disassembly procedure and note the following: To adjust sector shaft, determine center of worm shaft movement by halving the total number of turns. Turn back worm shaft one complete turn to left. With a suitable torque wrench attached to worm shaft, turn shaft clockwise through the center point and observe torque reading. Torque required should be 8.7-10.4 INCH lbs. (10-12 cmkg). Loosen lock nut and turn adjusting screw until correct torque is obtained as center point is passed. Tighten lock nut and recheck adjustment.

STEERING PUMP OVERHAUL

DISASSEMBLY

1) Force down cover in a press and remove retainer ring. Remove cover, coil spring, and "O" ring. Remove end plate and "O" ring, noting location of pin in one of the small holes on end plate.

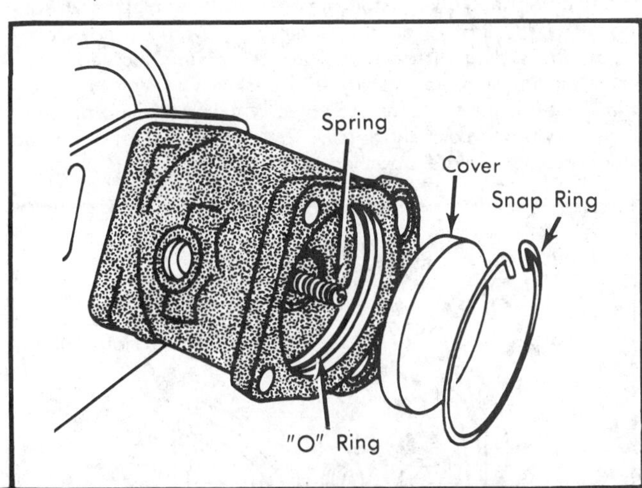

Fig. 24 Disassembled View of End Cover

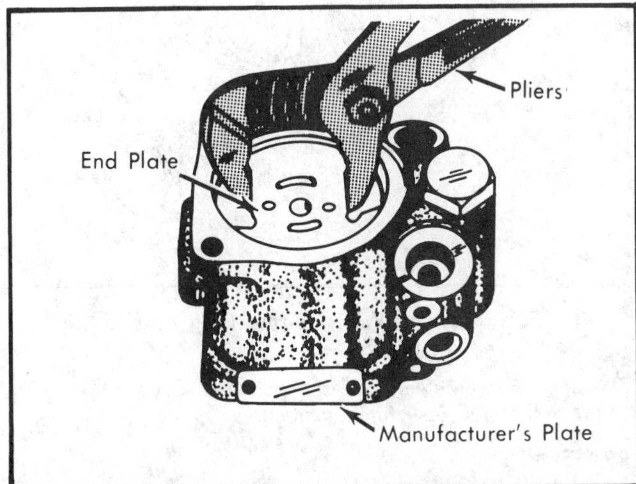

Fig. 25 Removing End Plate

2) Tilt housing and remove cam ring and rotor. Note that side of rotor with recessed hole faces drive shaft, the rounded off side of rotor faces cam ring, and the cast-in half arrow indicates direction of rotor rotation.

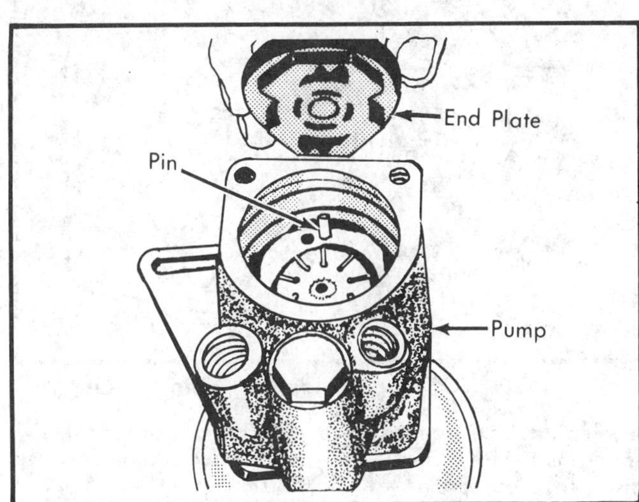

Fig. 26 Pin Location Inside of Pump Housing

3) Remove lower end plate and "O" ring. If it should be necessary to remove drive shaft, proceed as follows: Remove pulley, remove retainer ring from housing, then force out drive shaft. Inspect seal and needle roller bearing and replace if necessary. **NOTE** – *Installed depth of needle roller bearing is 1.457" +.008" (37 +0.2 mm).* Replace ball bearing on drive shaft if necessary.

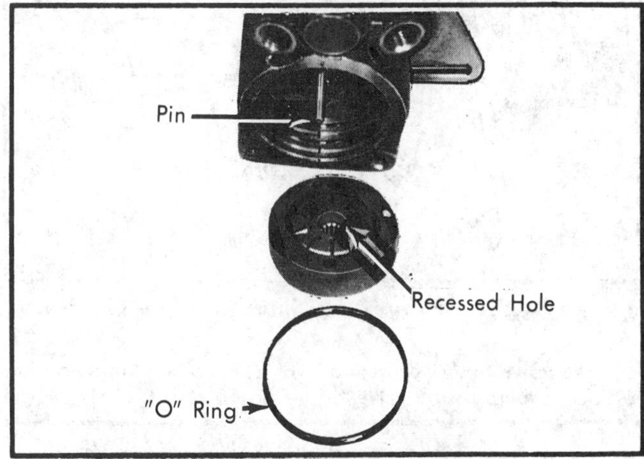

Fig. 27 View of Recessed Side of Rotor

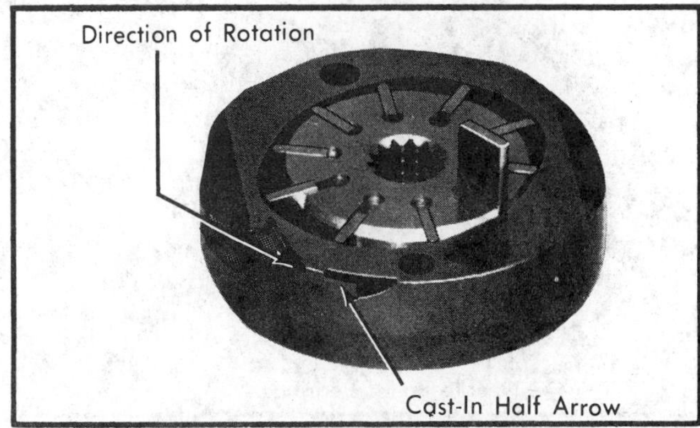

Fig. 28 Mark Showing Direction of Rotation

BMW POWER-ASSISTED WORM & SECTOR (Cont.)

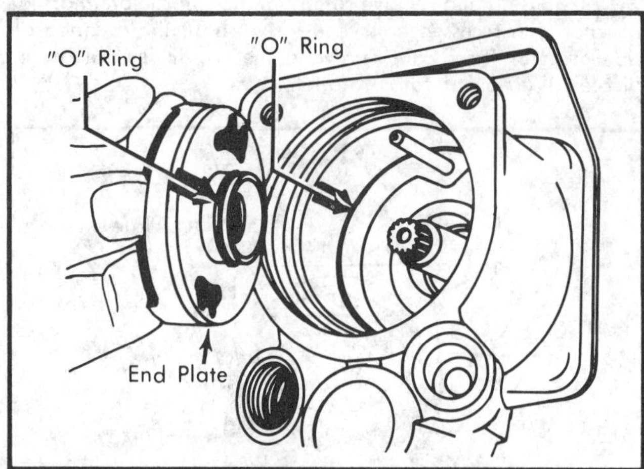

Fig. 29 "O" Ring Location in Pump Housing

4) Remove plug from pressure valve bore, then remove coil spring and valve piston. Note that threaded section on valve piston faces coil spring. **CAUTION** — *Do not alter length of coil spring or thickness of plug sealing ring.*

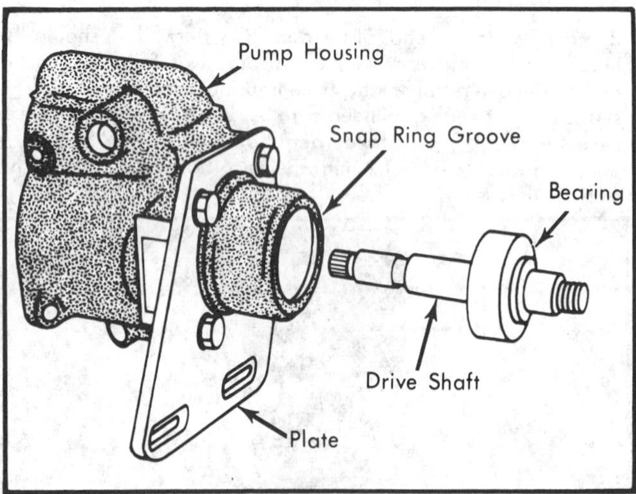

Fig. 30 Pump Drive Shaft and Housing

5) The valve tolerance group (1 or 2) is stamped into housing adjacent to pressure valve bore and valve barrel should be scribed with one or two marks (lines) agreeing with group number stamped into housing. **CAUTION** — *If valve must be replaced, install valve of same tolerance group.*

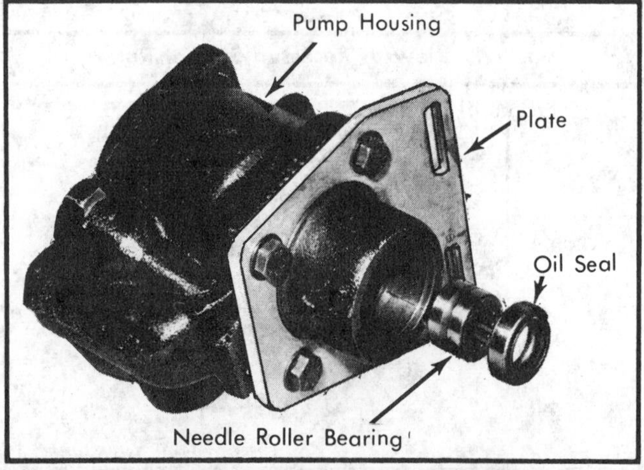

Fig. 31 Oil Seal and Needle Roller Bearing

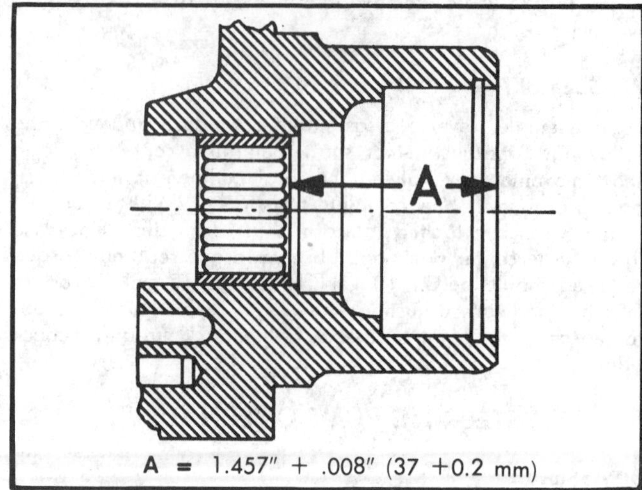

Fig. 32 Location of Needle Roller Bearing in Housing

6) Clean and inspect all parts. Clean restrictor insert in pump outlet passage. Valve piston may be disassembled for cleaning. **CAUTION** — *When disassembling piston, do not clamp across the sliding surfaces.* A pressure valve is located inside valve piston (flow limit valve), and thickness of washers determines cut-in range of pressure valve. Maximum pump pressure should not be more than 10% below the value stated on manufacturer's plate attached to pump.

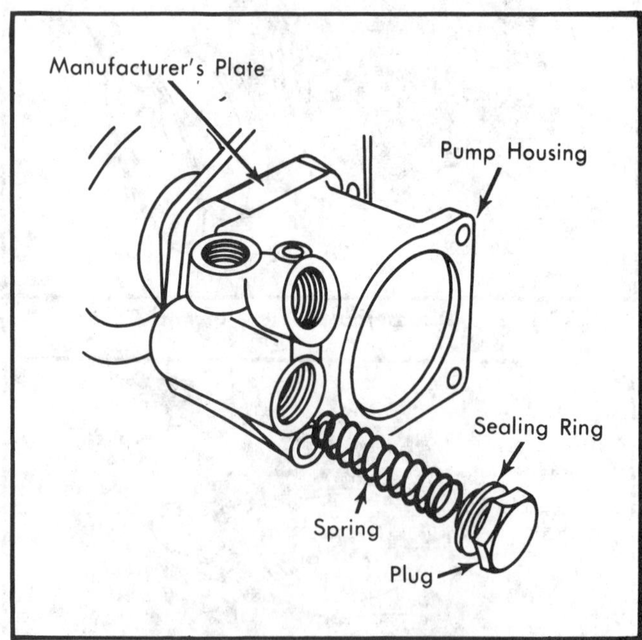

Fig. 33 Steering Pump Valve Plug and Spring

7) Clean power steering reservoir, wipe dry with lint free cloth, and install new filter element.

REASSEMBLY

To reassemble, reverse disassembly procedure.

BMW POWER-ASSISTED WORM & SECTOR (Cont.)

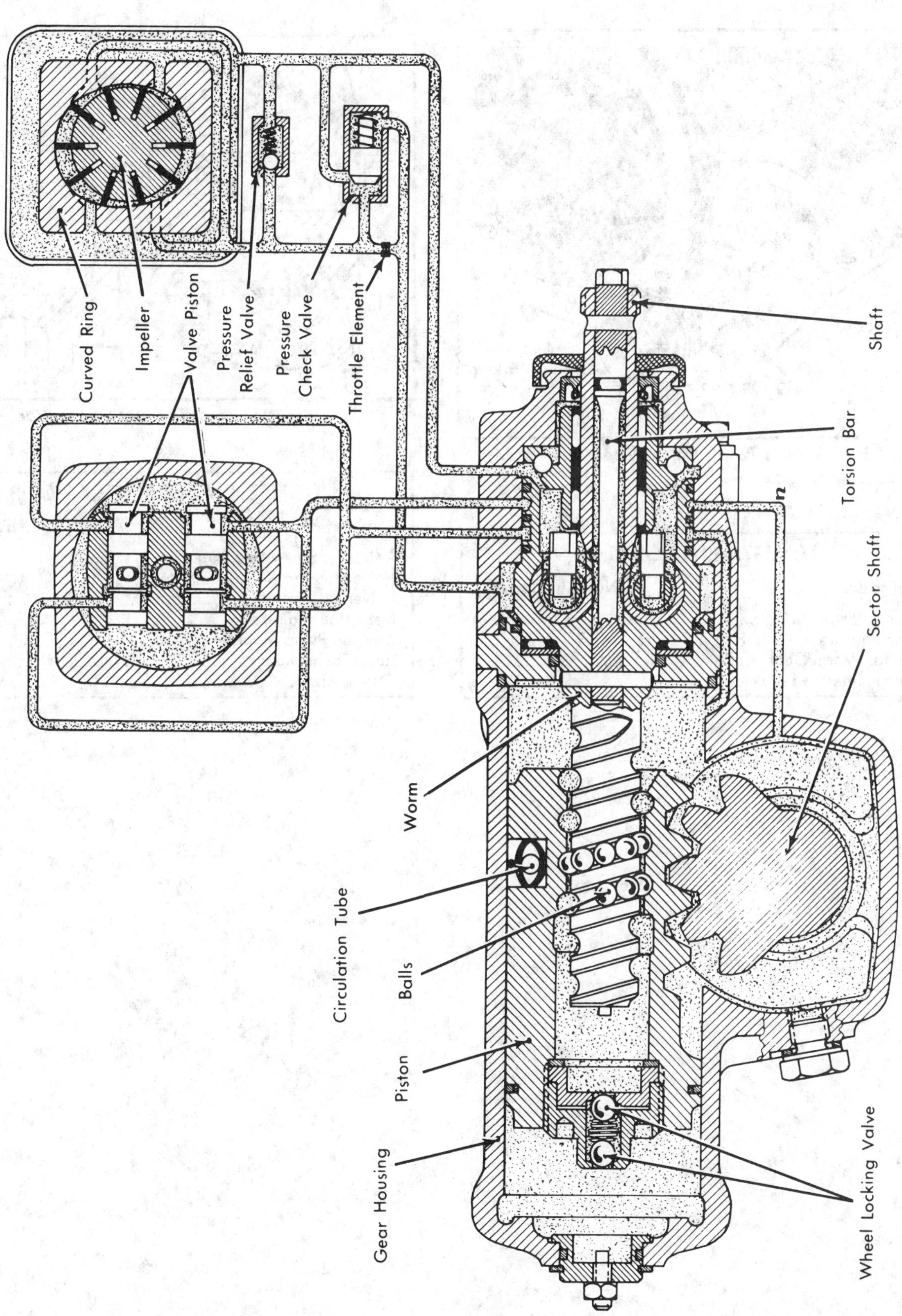

Fig. 34 Cross-Sectional View of Power Steering Gear Assembly

BMW POWER-ASSISTED WORM & SECTOR (Cont.)

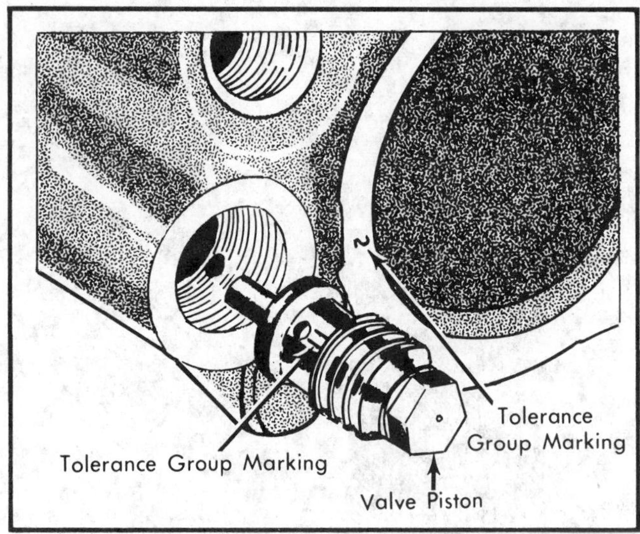

Fig. 35 Inserting Pump Valve Piston Into Position

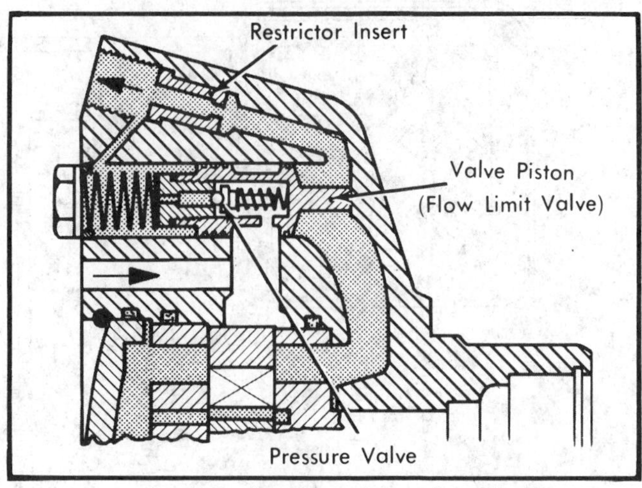

Fig. 36 Restrictor Insert Location

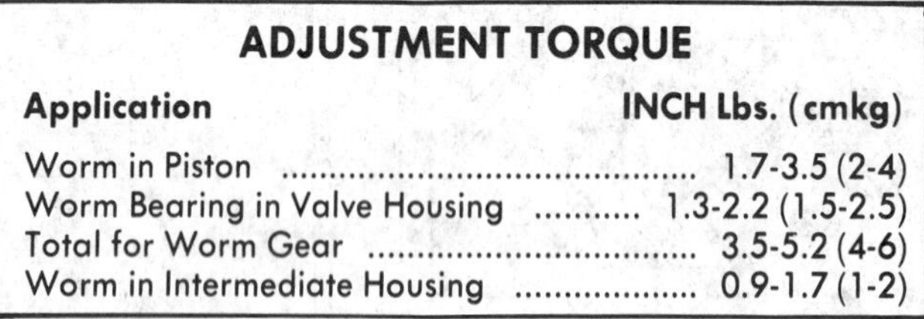

ADJUSTMENT TORQUE

Application	INCH Lbs. (cmkg)
Worm in Piston	1.7-3.5 (2-4)
Worm Bearing in Valve Housing	1.3-2.2 (1.5-2.5)
Total for Worm Gear	3.5-5.2 (4-6)
Worm in Intermediate Housing	0.9-1.7 (1-2)

TIGHTENING SPECIFICATIONS

Application	Ft. Lbs. (mkg)
Adjusting Screw Lock Nut	22 (3.0)
Valve Housing & Intermediate Cover	25 (3.5)
Universal Joint	19 (2.6)
Gear Housing	33 (4.6)
Steering Pump Mounting	17 (2.4)
Hose Connections	34 (4.7)
Pitman Arm	94 (13.0)

CAPRI POWER-ASSISTED RACK & PINION

Capri

DESCRIPTION

Power steering gear is a hydraulic-mechanical unit using an integral piston and rack design to provide power assisted steering control. Internal valving directs pump flow and controls pressure to reduce steering effort. Unit contains rotary hydraulic fluid control valve integrated to input shaft and a boost cylinder integrated with rack.

TESTING

STEERING SYSTEM TEST

1) Check belt tension, tire pressure and fluid level and adjust as necessary. Run engine at 1500 RPM and slowly turn steering wheel from lock to lock to bring power steering fluid to 158°F (70°C).

NOTE – *Do not turn wheels from lock-to-lock more than five times.*

2) Place steering wheel in straight ahead position and make sure wheels are on a clean dry surface. With a torque wrench on the steering wheel nut, measure torque required to keep steering wheel turning. Torque should be 6 ft. lbs. (.8 mkg).

PUMP PRESSURE TEST

1) Disconnect pressure line from pump and connect gauge side of a suitable power steering pressure tester to pump and pressure line to valve side of tester. Make sure valve on tester is open and fluid is at proper level. Start engine and turn steering wheel lock to lock a few times to remove any air in system. Add fluid if necessary.

2) With power steering fluid at 158°F (70°C) and engine running at 1500 RPM, turn steering wheel to lock and hold momentarily. Pressure should be 740 psi (52 kg/cm²). If pressure is below specification, hydraulic system is faulty. With engine at 1500 RPM and wheels in straight ahead position, slowly close valve on tester. If pressure drops below specification, pump is faulty. If pressure rises above specification, steering gear control valve, rack piston or piston seals are faulty.

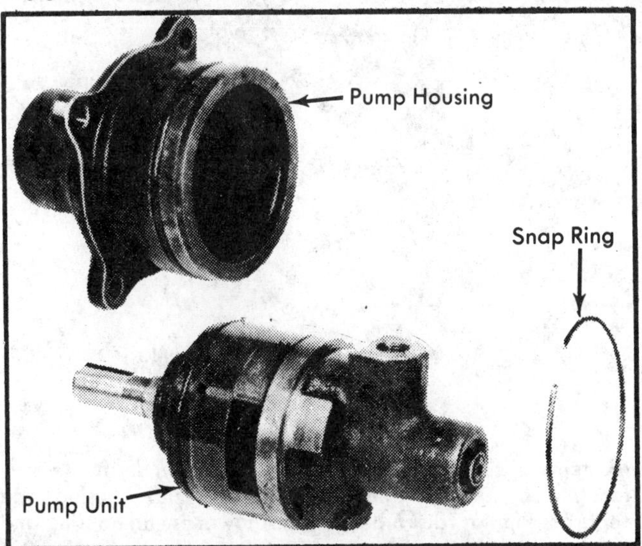

Fig. 1 Capri Power Steering Pump

REMOVAL & INSTALLATION

STEERING GEAR

Removal – Disconnect fluid lines from steering gear and allow fluid to drain. Remove steering coupler lower clamp bolt (mark splines for alignment on installation) and disconnect tie rod ends from steering arms. Remove steering gear assembly-to-frame mounting bolts and remove steering gear from vehicle. Remove the tie rod ends from tie rods (note number of turns for installation alignment).

Installation – Install tie rod ends with the same number of turns noted when removed. Position steering gear assembly in vehicle, aligning pinion shaft splines with lower coupler, and secure with bolts.

POWER STEERING PUMP

Removal – Disconnect fluid lines and allow fluid to drain. On 2300 cc engines, disconnect fuel pump and position out of way (it is not necessary to disconnect fuel lines from pump). Remove power steering pump (on 2800 cc engines, remove pump with bracket assembly) from vehicle.

Installation – To install, reverse removal procedure and fill pump or reservoir with suitable power steering fluid (D2AZ-19582-A).

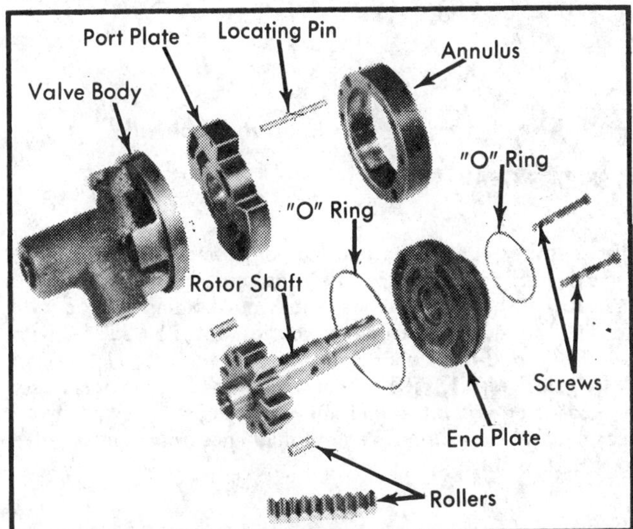

Fig. 2 Disassembled View of Capri Power Steering Pump

OVERHAUL

STEERING PUMP

Disassembly – With pump removed from vehicle, remove hub and key from pump shaft. On 2300 cc engines, remove pressure line from resevoir. Mark pump to pump housing for alignment during assembly. Remove snap ring and tap on pump shaft to remove pump unit from housing. Remove the two screws holding end plate to pump unit and remove end plate. NOTE – *Do not remove the Allen screw at rear of pump.* Remove "O" ring from end plate. Remove rotor shaft, annulus, locating pin, and port plate from valve body. Remove snap ring retaining bearing in valve body, then remove bearing and seal.

CAPRI POWER-ASSISTED RACK & PINION (Cont.)

Assembly – Install seal (with seal lip facing into body) in valve body. Lubricate port plate, locating pin, and annulus with power steering fluid and install to valve body. Install rotor shaft with rollers in annulus. Lightly grease "O" rings and position on end plate, then install end plate with screws. Install pump unit to pump housing, aligning scribe marks, and secure with snap ring.

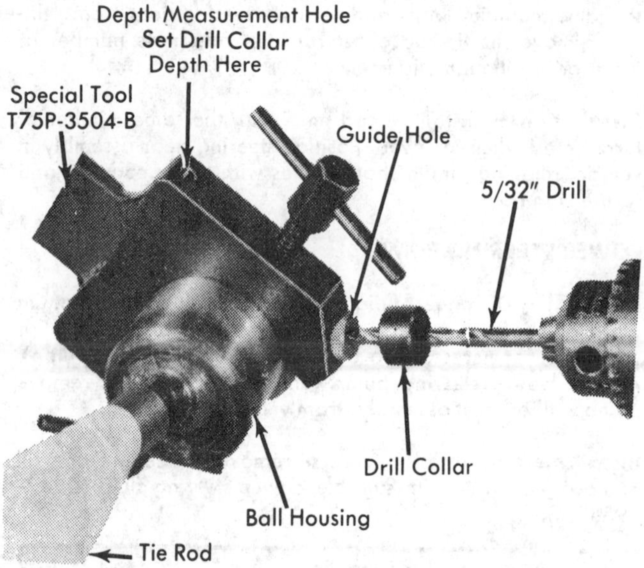

Fig. 3 Tie Rod Housing Removal

STEERING GEAR

Disassembly – **1**) With steering gear removed from vehicle, remove rubber boots from tie rods and drain fluid. Mount assembly in a vise and loosen lock nut holding tie rod ball housing. To loosen lock nut use special tool T75P-3504-B with a 5/32" drill and drill collar. Install special tool (see *Fig. 4*) and drill out lock pins. **NOTE** – *Special tool has a depth hole to set drill collar on drill bit.* Then remove housing with tie rod, nylon seat, washer and spring. Remove fluid lines from control valve to rack assembly.

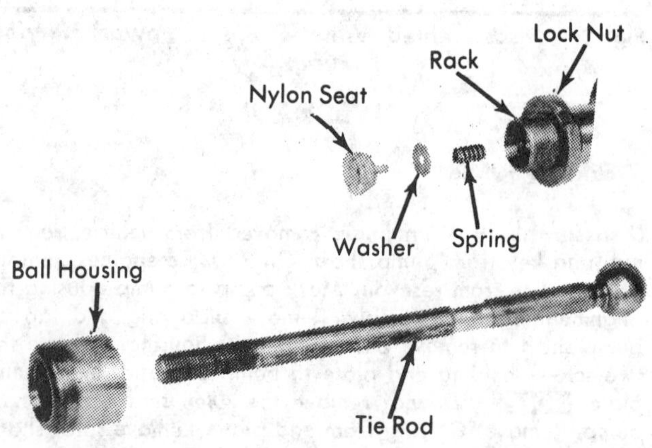

Fig. 4 Exploded View of Tie Rod Assembly

2) Remove control valve cover plate, bearing, seal, carrier assembly and spool preload spring from control valve body, then remove control valve body from pinion shaft. Remove rack adjusting bearing cover plate, shim pack, sealing ring, spring, and adjusting bearing.

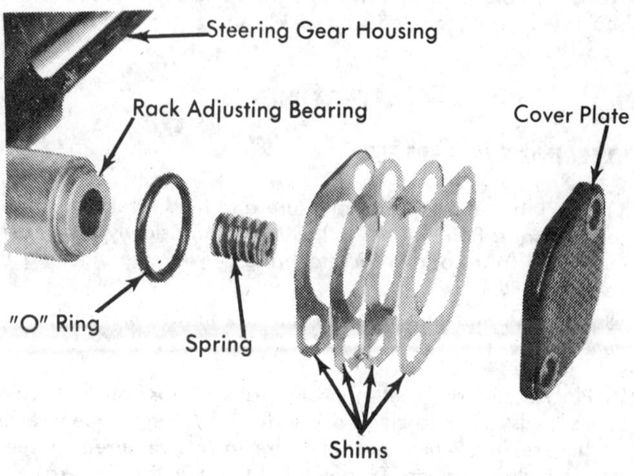

Fig. 5 Rack Adjusting Bearing Assembly

3) Position gear assembly in a vise and using a suitable tool that will lock onto splines of pinion shaft (tool T75P-3504-E), remove pinion bearing nut. Remove bearing outer race, then turn gear housing so pinion bearing is up. Remove bearing from pinion shaft and shaft from housing. Remove bearing inner race from housing.

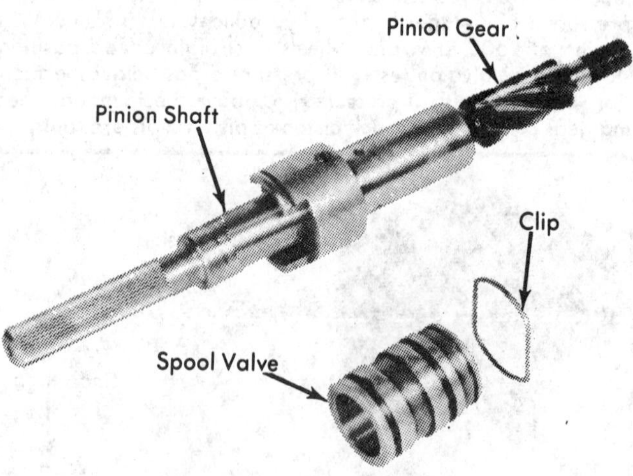

Fig. 6 Pinion Shaft Disassembled

4) Remove clip and spool valve from pinion shaft. Remove locating pegs from gear housing. Tap end housing and separate joint at rack tube. Pull rack towards end housing and remove rack and support bearing. Remove inner tube from rack tube. *Note seal, washer and snap ring order.*

CAPRI POWER-ASSISTED RACK & PINION (Cont.)

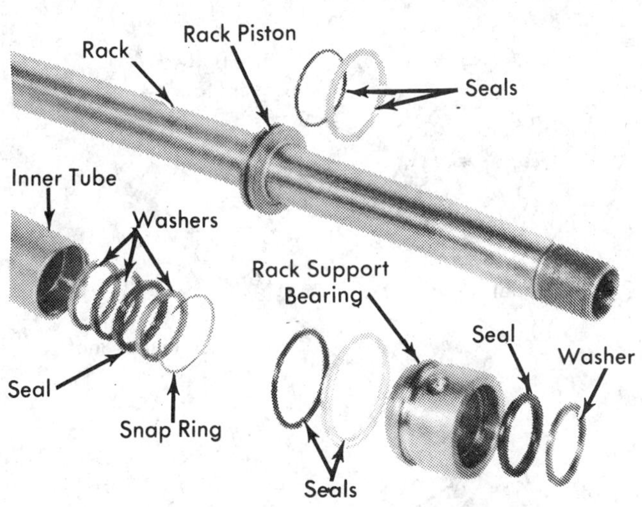

Fig. 7 Steering Rack Disassembled

5) Clean and inspect all components. Check rack and pinion teeth for damage or wear. Check bearings for wear, pitting or scoring. Replace components as necessary.

NOTE — *Use new seals when assembling power steering gear assembly.*

Assembly — **1**) Install washers, seal and snap ring onto gear end of rack. Then slide inner tube onto rack. Install seal on a suitable seal protector (T75P-3504-H) and slide protector past rack teeth to smooth part of rack, slide seal off and remove seal protector. Lubricate two seals with power steering fluid and install in gear housing. Install snap ring and washer on inner tube then push tube into gear housing.

2) Slide rack through inner tube and gear housing. Install seals on inner tube and slide washers on rack to inner tube, then install snap ring. Soak "O" ring and nylon piston ring in power steering fluid. Install "O" ring and piston ring in groove of piston on rack. Compress piston ring and slide rack outer tube over piston and into gear housing. Rack tube end with one round and one oval hole should be towards gear housing. Align locating peg holes and install pegs.

3) Install outer seals to rack support bearing and slide bearing onto rack aligning peg holes. Using seal protector, install inner seals to rack support bearing. Lubricate large washer and "O" rings with power steering fluid and install in end housing. Position seals on transfer pipe and install pipe in gear housing. Slide end housing over rack, rack tube and transfer pipe. Align locating peg holes and install peg and washer.

4) Install inner bearing race to gear housing. Install spool valve to pinion shaft and secure with clip. Install oil seal next to middle pinion shaft bearing. Position lower bearing half cup to gear housing and position rack in steering gear assembly so that equal amounts extend from each end of steering gear assembly. Slide pinion shaft into gear housing, make sure that flat on pinion shaft faces center of rack assembly.

5) Screw lower bearing seat onto pinion shaft. Adjust bearing so that when pinion shaft float is removed, there is 1.62" (41.15 mm) between gear housing flange and top of spool valve (see *Fig.* 9). Install shim and pinion shaft end cover to gear housing, torque bolts to 9-12 ft. lbs. (1.2-1.7 mkg). Recheck gear housing flange to top of spool valve. If measurement changed, measure gap between cover plate and gear housing (take measurement adjacent to bolts). Install shims .001-.002" (.025-.051 mm) thicker than measurement. If shims were needed, readjustment of gear housing flange to spool valve measurement is necessary.

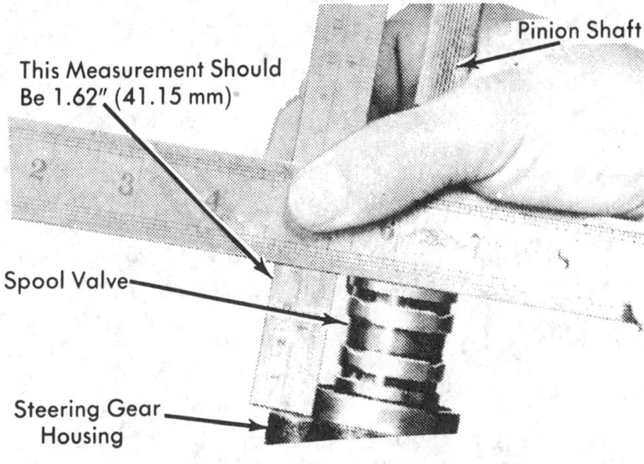

Fig. 8 Pinion Shaft Adjustment Procedure

6) Install control valve body, pinion bearing preload spring and bearing, and valve body cover plate. Tighten bolts. Attach fluid lines from control valve body to steering gear assembly.

7) Place rack adjusting bearing in gear housing, then using dial gauge and mounting block (T75P-3504-J) measure bearing deflection. Zero dial gauge and mount block on rack adjusting bearing, then turn pinion shaft so rack goes from lock to lock and record maximum gauge deflection from zero. Assemble a shim pack that is .001-.005" (.025-.27 mm) thicker than maximum deflection. With shim pack assembled, install spring, seal, shim pack and cover plate. Tighten cover plate bolts.

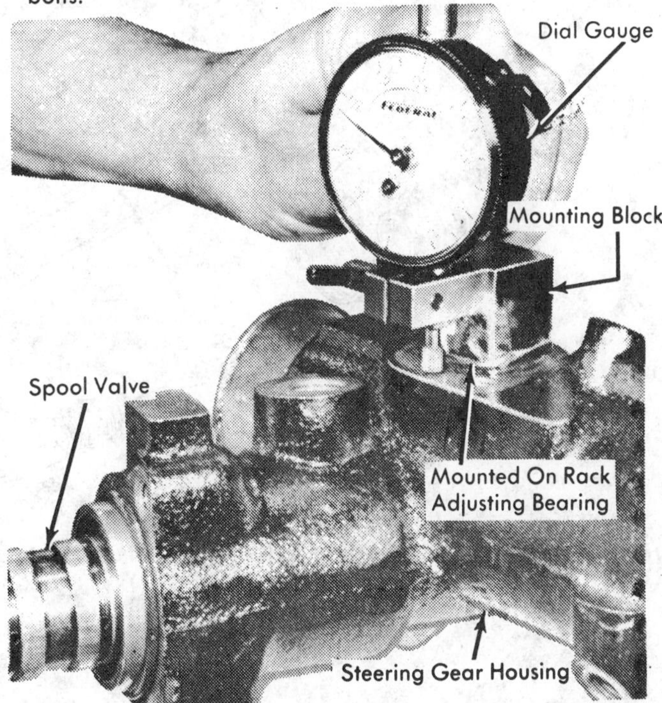

Fig. 9 Measuring Rack Adjusting Bearing Deflection

CAPRI POWER-ASSISTED RACK & PINION (Cont.)

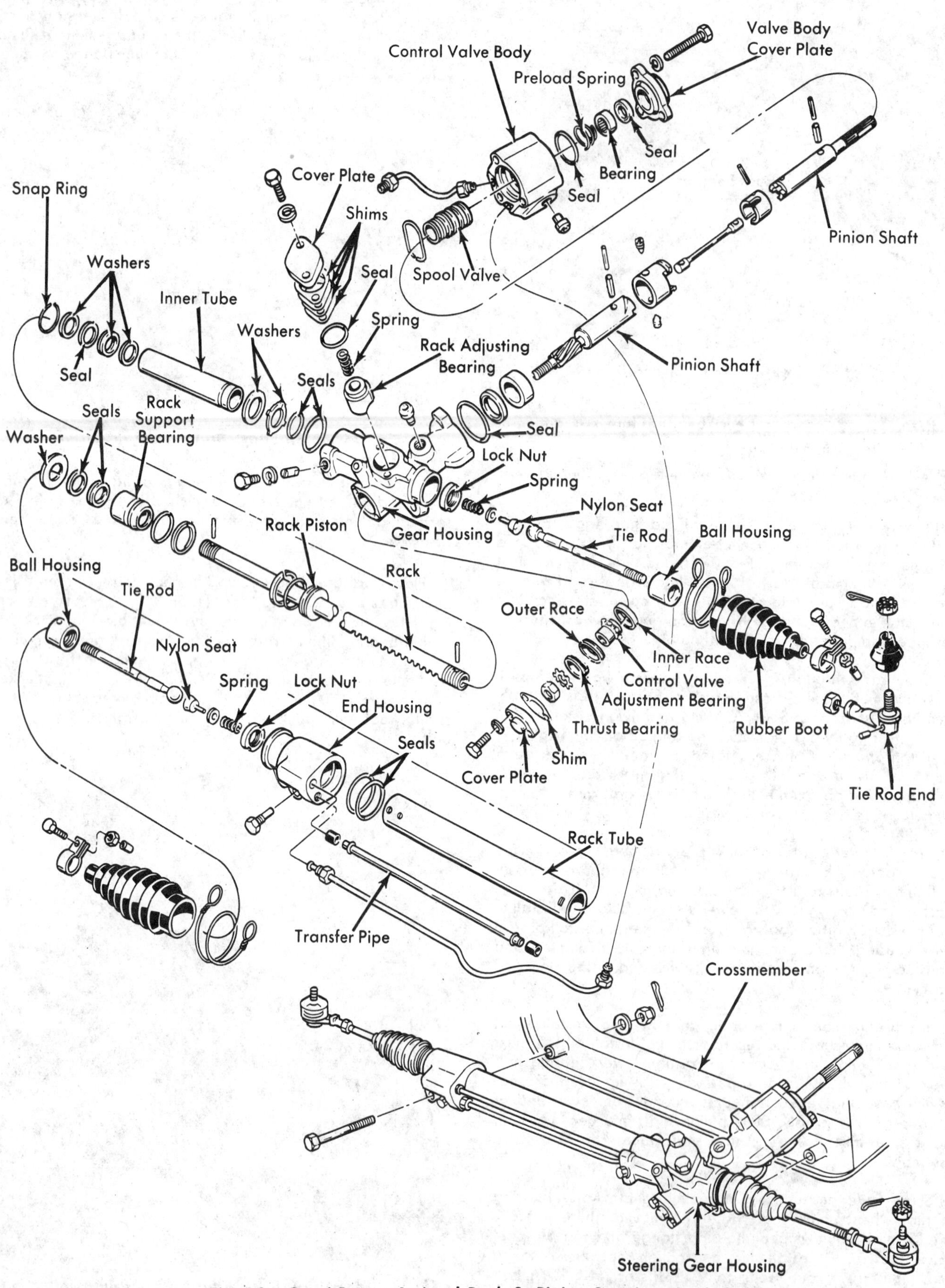

Fig. 10 Capri Power Assisted Rack & Pinion Steering (Exploded View)

CAPRI POWER-ASSISTED RACK & PINION (Cont.)

8) Lubricate and assemble tie rods then install tie rods to rack. Check turning effort of tie rods by locking two nuts to tie rod ends and turning with a torque wrench. Turning torque should be 5 ft. lbs. (.7 mkg). If torque is greater loosen ball housing and if less tighten ball housing. Recheck turning torque.

9) Hold ball housing from rotating on tie rod and tighten lock nut against ball housing to 25-35 ft. lbs. (3.5-4.8 mkg). Using special tool T75P-3504-B installed on ball housing and lock nut, drill a 5/32" hole in line of contact between lock nut and ball housing. Use the depth measurement hole on special tool for depth to drill hole. Drill hole opposite existing hole. Insert pin and stake hole to secure pin.

10) Install one rubber boot, add 1/3 pint of lubricant (SAE 40 engine oil) and install other rubber boot. Do not tighten boot clamps until gear assembly is installed in vehicle. Install gear assembly in vehicle.

11) To check control valve adjustment, connect pump pressure test gauge as described in PUMP PRESSURE TEST. Start engine and allow power steering fluid to reach normal operating temperature. With engine running, turn wheels from lock to lock. When wheels are in each lock position apply 34 INCH lbs. (39 cmkg) of torque to steering wheel nut and record pressure from gauge. Pressure should be 160 psi (11.25 kg/cm^2) in the lock position with a maximum difference of 12 psi (.8 kg/cm^2) from side to side.

12) If pressure is not within specifications, turn lower bearing to equalize pressure. Turning bearing 20° will change pressure by 25 psi (1.8 kg/cm^2). With pressure equalized at 160 psi (11.25 kg/cm^2) at each lock position, install cover plate and check fluid level.

TIGHTENING SPECIFICATIONS

Application	Ft. Lbs. (mkg)
Fluid Lines	
Pressure	19-23 (2.6-3.2)
Return	12-15 (1.7-2.1)
Pinion Bearing Cover Plate	7.5-9 (1-1.2)
Rack Slipper Cover Plate	7.5-9 (1-1.2)

DATSUN POWER STEERING

810

DESCRIPTION

Power steering is composed of power steering pump and steering gear. The pump has an integral oil reservoir and is engine driven. The steering gear incorporates a control valve and power cylinder which is pressure operated from the power steering pump by flexible lines.

GENERAL SERVICE

HYDRAULIC SYSTEM LUBRICANT

Capacity – 1½ qts.

Type – ATF Type DEXRON

BELT TENSION ADJUSTMENT

Apply thumb pressure of 22 lbs. midway between idler pulley and power steering pump pulley. Deflection should be, 0.31-0.47" (8-12 mm).

HYDRAULIC SYSTEM PRESSURE CHECK

1) Disconnect pressure line at pump and connect pressure gauge and shut off valve. Check fluid level, open shut off valve and run engine for about five seconds. Check fluid level and restart engine.

2) Turn steering wheel from lock-to-lock several times to expel air from system. Slowly close shut off valve. Pressure should be 953-1123 psi at idle.

3) If pressure is below specifications the pump is faulty. If pressure is above specifications the pressure relief valve in pump is faulty.

HYDRAULIC SYSTEM BLEEDING

Check fluid level in reservoir, raise and support front of vehicle. With engine not running, turn steering wheel from lock-to-lock several times. Check fluid level, start engine and turn steering wheel from lock-to-lock several times. If system is not bled turn steering wheel to left lock and open bleeder screw to expel remaining air.

REMOVAL & INSTALLATION

STEERING GEAR

Removal – **1)** Remove air cleaner, remove bolt from universal joint to worm shaft. Disconnect fluid lines and block off. Remove nut and washer from steering gear arm.

2) Using steering gear arm puller ST29020001, remove arm from sector shaft. Remove mounting bolts from gear housing and remove housing from vehicle.

Installation – To install reverse removal procedure and note the following: Align groove in worm shaft with bolt hole in universal joint and pass bolt through undercut section of worm shaft.

STEERING PUMP

Removal – Disconnect fluid lines at pump and block off fittings. Remove pump mounting bolts and remove drive belt from pulley. Remove pump from vehicle.

Installation – To install reverse removal procedure.

OVERHAUL

NOTE – *Manufacturer recommends replacement of power steering pump and steering gear if damaged. Do not overhaul.*

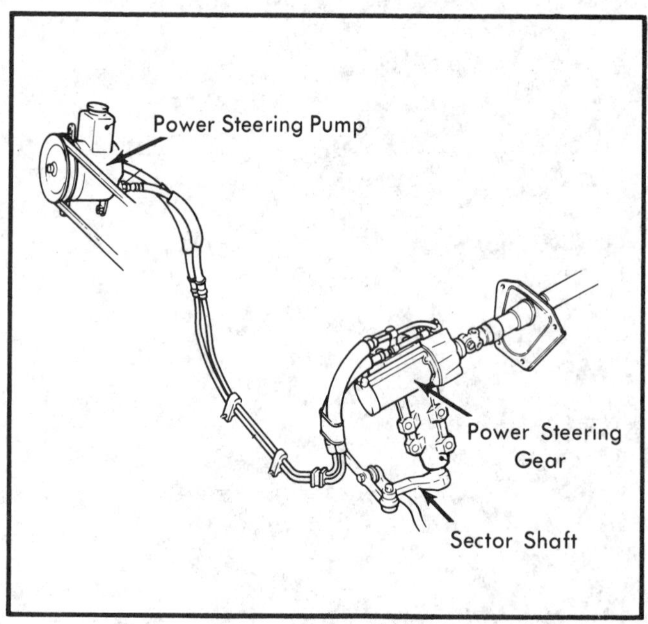

Fig. 1 Datsun Power Steering Components

TIGHTENING SPECIFICATIONS

Application	Ft. Lbs. (mkg)
Universal Joint to Worm Shaft Bolt	24-28 (3.3-3.9)
Steering Gear Arm Lock Nut	94-108 (13-15)
Pump Bleeder Screw	5-7 (0.7-0.9)
Pump Mounting Bolts	14-19 (1.9-2.6)

JAGUAR POWER-ASSISTED RACK & PINION

XJ6
XJ12
XJS

DESCRIPTION

Vehicles are equipped with a power assisted rack and pinion type steering system. The system consists of two main components: the rack and pinion steering gear and the power assist pump. The two components are connected by flexible fluid lines. The power assist pump and fluid reservoir are combined.

TESTING

Control Valve & Pinion – 1) Connect a 100 psi (7 kg/cm²) pressure gage into the pump return line, start engine and allow to idle. Pressure reading should be approximately 40 psi (2.8 kg/cm²). Turn steering gear left and right a small amount. **CAUTION** – *Gauge will be damaged if steering gear is turned excessively*. Pressure increase, as wheel is turned, should register an equal amount on either side of center.

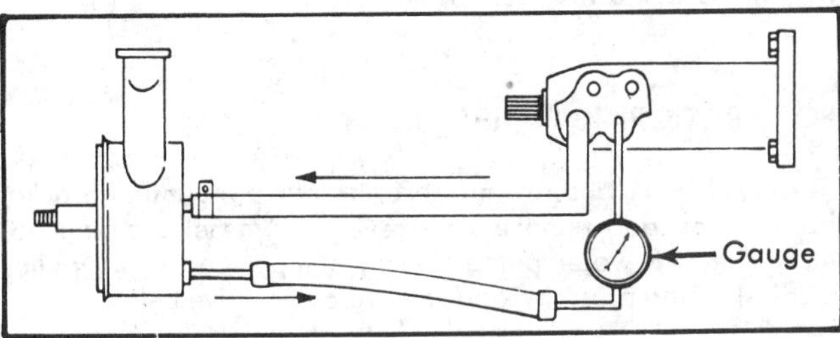

Fig. 1 Pressure Gauge Connection

2) Stop and restart engine and check that steering does not kick to one side.

Hydraulic System – 1) Connect a 1500 psi (100 kg/cm²) pressure gauge into the pump pressure line, start engine and allow to idle.

2) Turn steering to full lock and exert pressure on steering gear until gauge pressure ceases to rise. Pressure should be between 1100 psi (77.5 kg/cm²) and 1200 psi (84.4 kg/cm²).

NOTE – *If pressure is below 1100 psi (77.5 kg/cm²) at idle,* but rises with engine speed increase, the problem is either a defective pump control valve or internal leakage in rack and pinion. The following test will determine the location.

3) Connect a suitable tap (JD. 10-2) between pump and pressure gauge, isolating rack from pump *(See Fig. 2)*

4) Open tap, start engine and allow to idle. Turn steering gear to full lock and check that gauge exceeds 1100 psi (77.5 kg/cm²). If pressure is below this figure, CLOSE TAP AT ONCE, and note reading when tap reaches OFF position.

CAUTION – *Tap must not be held closed for more than 5 seconds when engine is running.*

5) If gauge reading increases to at least 1100 psi (77.5 kg/cm²) with tap off, leaks are located in steering unit, requiring overhaul. See *OVERHAUL in this article.*

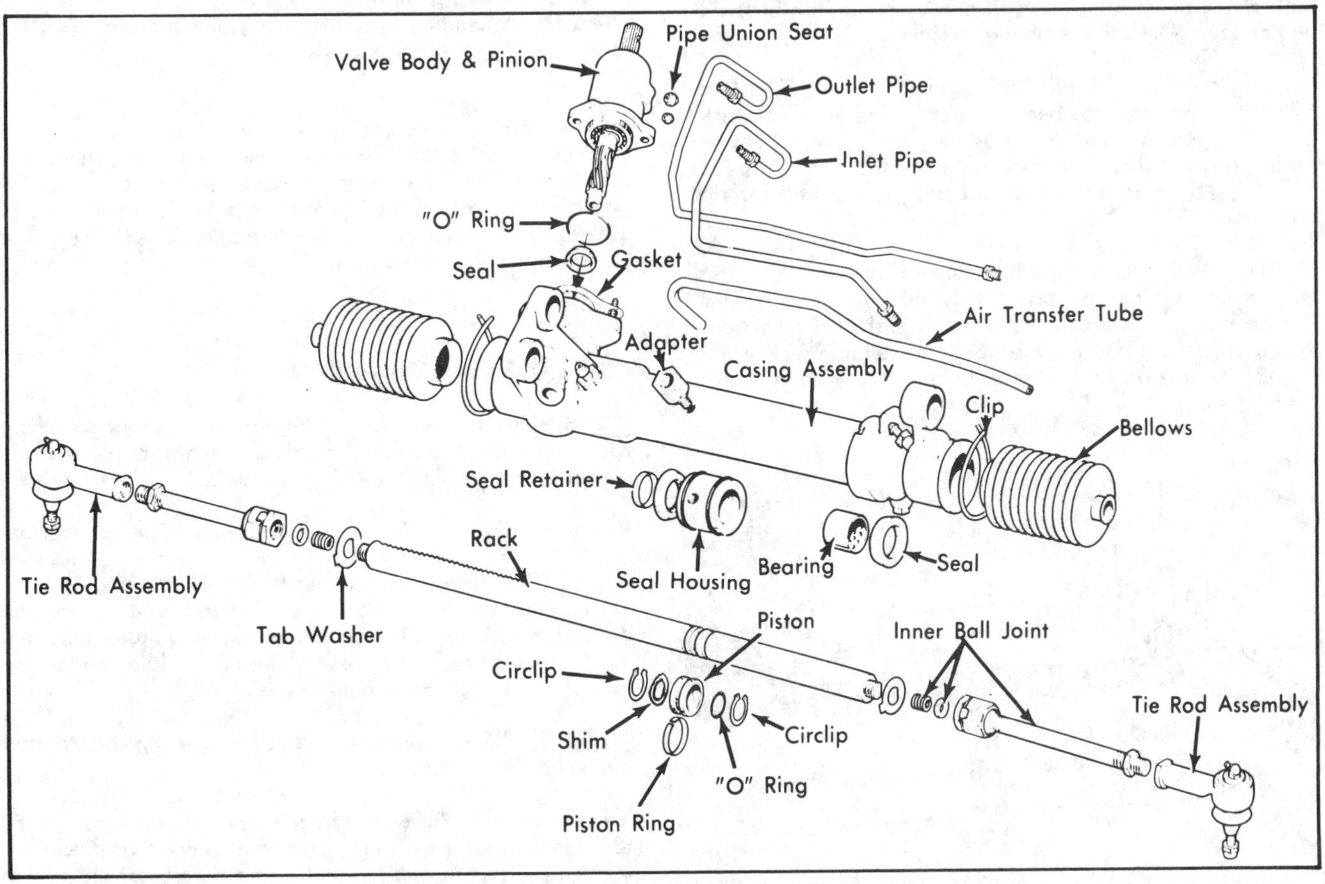

Fig. 2 Exploded View of Power Assisted Rack and Pinion

JAGUAR POWER-ASSISTED RACK & PINION (Cont.)

6) If gauge reading is above 1200 psi (84.4 kg/cm^2), problem is a blocked filter located in pump discharge port.

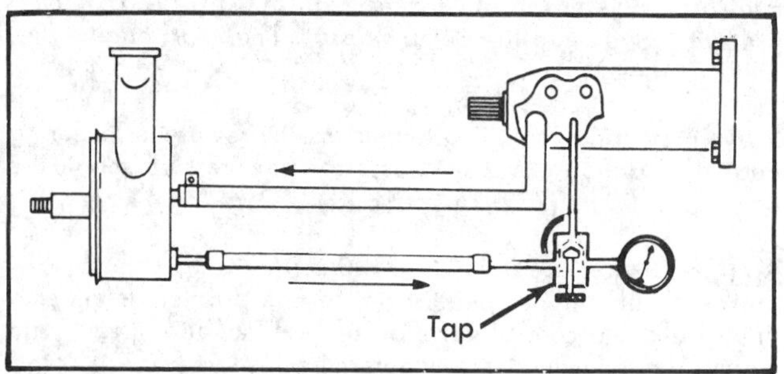

Fig. 3 Presuure Gauge and Tap Connection

SYSTEM BLEEDING

Fill reservoir to full mark on dipstick. Start engine and turn steering from lock to lock several times (to expel all air). Recheck fluid level and refill as required.

REMOVAL & INSTALLATION

STEERING GEAR

Removal – **NOTE** – *Amount and location of all washers and spacers must be noted for correct installation.* Disconnect high and low pressure lines, drain gear oil, and block off pipe connections. Remove nuts and washers and disconnect track rod ball joints from steering arms. Remove pinion pinch bolt. Unbolt and remove rack assembly from vehicle.

Installation – 1) Position rack against mounting brackets. Center lug between crossbeam brackets using proper shims to assure a gap of .10-.12" (2.54-3.05 mm) exists between rubber faces of thrust washers and inner faces of crossbeam lugs. **NOTE** – *The use of an assistant is required for this operation.*

2) Check that pinion shaft has entered universal joint and insert mounting bolts, but do not fully tighten self-locking nuts. Detach inner end of rubber bellows and push back from housing. Locate two attachment brackets of suitable service tool (JD. 36) on two large hex head bolts of lower control arms *(See Fig. 4)*.

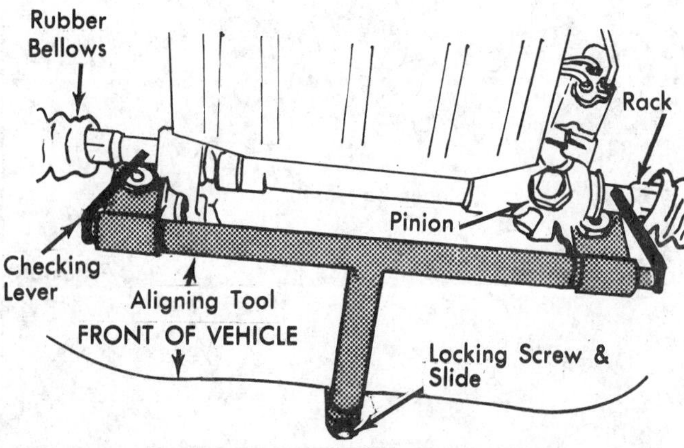

Fig. 4 Installing Rack and Pinion Gear

3) Release locking screw and adjust service tool slide until slot engages front weld flange of crossbeam, then lock slide in this position. Lift two coupled checking levers until contact is made with one or both rack shafts. Adjust position of rack assembly, if necessary, to bring both levers into contact. Tighten nuts of three securing bolts to lock in this position.

4) Remove checking tool. Replace bellows, using new clamps. Reverse remaining removal procedures. Refill system with recommended fluid and bleed. See *System Bleeding in this article*. Check wheel alignment. See *appropriate article in WHEEL ALIGNMENT Section.*

NOTE – *It is important that distance between rubber faces of thrust washers and adjacent crossbeam lugs be no less than .01" (2.54 mm). This is necessary to allow adequate rack movement. If a replacement rack is installed, it will be necessary to detach lower column from upper column to obtain correct centering of splines. See appropriate article in STEERING COLUMN Section.*

POWER STEERING PUMP

Removal – 1) Unscrew nut securing pump mounting bracket bottom bolt and remove set screw and washer securing adjusting link to water pump. Swing pump inboard, lift pulley against spring pressure, and remove pump drive belt.

2) Detach low pressure hose, drain fluid, and remove high pressure line. Block all hose connection. Unbolt and remove pump from mounting bracket, noting any spacing shims for replacement in original position.

Installation – Replace pump in reverse of removal procedure, noting the following: Make sure hose connections are clean before replacement. Fill reservoir with suitable fluid and bleed by turning pulley counterclockwise a few times to dispel any air. After pump is fully installed, bleed system. See *System Bleeding in this article.*

CONTROL VALVE AND PINION

NOTE – *Pinion assembly may be removed without detaching rack housing from vehicle. No adjustment or repair is possible except the replacement of the pinion seal.*

Removal – Remove lower steering column. See *appropriate article in STEERING COLUMN Section.* Clean pinion and rack housing, then disconnect all lines from valve housing. Remove self locking nuts securing pinion and valve housing to rack unit. Release rack adjuster lock nut and loosen adjuster threaded plug. Mark pinch bolt recess-to-housing for later reassembling. Withdraw valve and pinion housing.

CAUTION – *Do not move wheels or turn steering column after pinion has been withdrawn.*

Installation – Reverse removal procedures noting the following: Install new joint gasket and check that pinch bolt recess is correct in relation to housing before connecting universal joint.

JAGUAR POWER-ASSISTED RACK & PINION (Cont.)

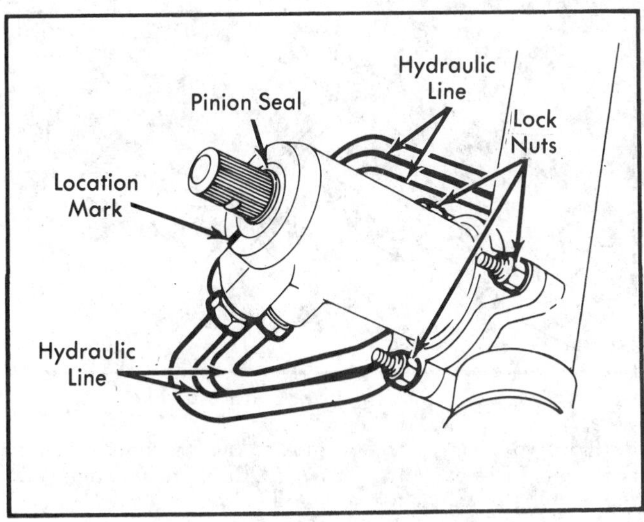

Fig. 5 Control Valve and Pinion

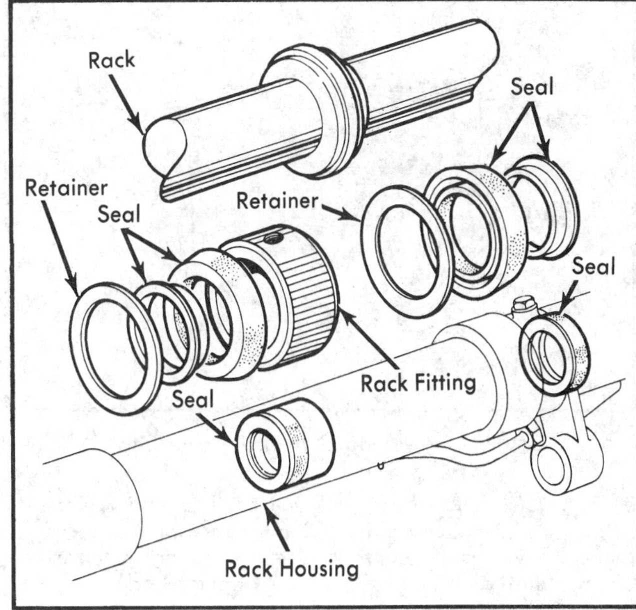

Fig. 6 Rack Seal Installation

OVERHAUL

RACK ASSEMBLY

Disassembly – 1) Thoroughly clean outside of rack assembly before attempting to dismantle. **NOTE** – *Do not disturb outer ball joints unless they are to be replaced.* Remove external lines from pinion housing. Unclamp and back off bellows to expose inner ball pins. Straighten lock tab of washer securing inner ball pin to rack shaft. Remove inner ball pin and track rod as a unit (do not diamantle ball pin assembly). Retain thrust spring and spacer.

2) Remove control valve and pinion assembly. *See Removal in this article.*

3) Remove air transfer line from end caps and unscrew ring nut from end cap. Remove end cap with bushing, seal, retaining washer and "O" ring and withdraw rack and piston.

4) Remove adaptor and seal from center of housing and withdraw pipe fitting from bore of housing, then take out seal and retainer. Discard seal. Check union insert seats and replace if necessary. Remove retainer and seal from end cap and discard seal.

Reassembly – 1) Install retainers and new seals onto rack with open side of seal facing toward center. **NOTE** – *Protect seal from rack teeth with tape.*

2) Check piston ring and housing bore for damage, replace if necessary. Install rack into housing, rack end first. Check that hole in rack fitting is aligned with hole in housing. Install adaptor and seal, then tighten securly. Install retainer and seal (open side toward washer) onto rack, then install housing onto rack and secure with ring nut.

3) Reverse disassembly procedures for the remainder of components, noting the following: Tighten lock nuts fully. Adjust threaded plug (*Fig. 6*) to give minimum of .010" (.254 mm) end play.

4) Coat both tie rod ends with grease, then install bellows. Inject 1 oz. (28 g) grease into damper grease plug. **NOTE** – *Do not overfill to the point where bellows are extended.* Refill system with a recommended fluid and bleed system. *See System Bleeding in this article.* Check wheel alignment. *See appropriate article in WHEEL ALIGNMENT Section.*

POWER STEERING PUMP

Disassembly – 1) Drain pump fluid. Detach rear mounting bracket and note size and location of all spacers. Withdraw two set screws and lock washers and detach trunnion front mounting bracket and spacers. Thoroughly clean pump exterior before proceeding.

2) Remove pulley. Detach high pressure outlet union and two mounting studs. Separate pump reservoir from body and remove "O" rings from pump body recess. Insert suitable pin punch in hole of pump body and push retaining ring away from groove. Pry ring out with screwdriver.

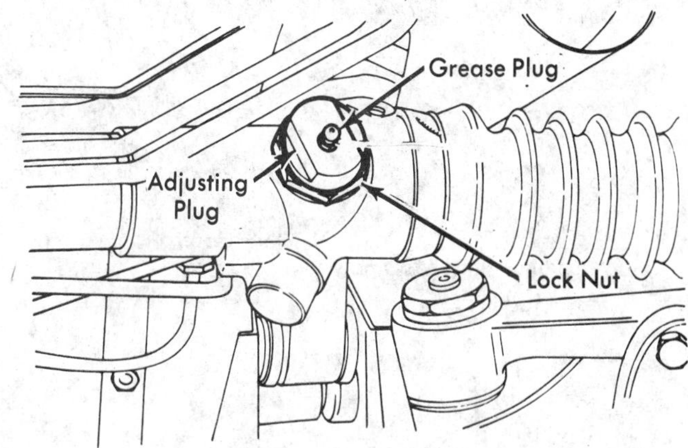

Fig. 7 Rack End Play Adjustment

JAGUAR POWER-ASSISTED RACK & PINION (Cont.)

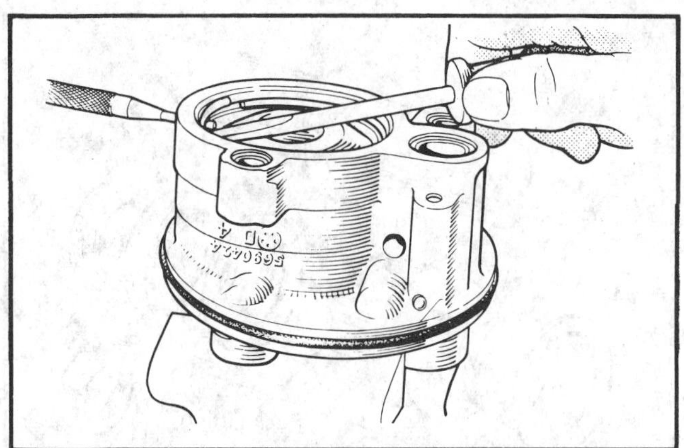

Fig. 8 Prying Out End Plate Ring

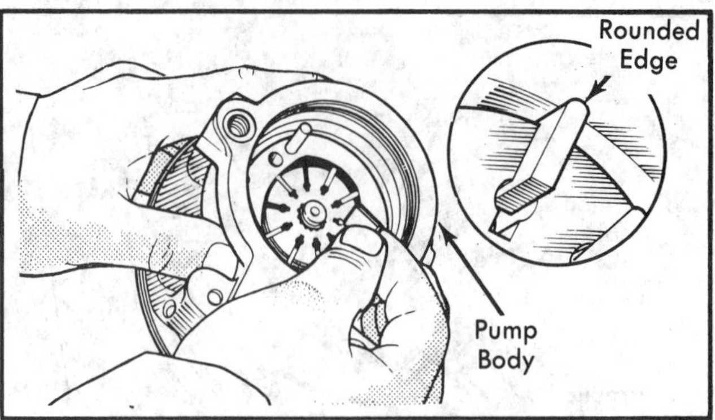

Fig. 9 Placing Vanes in Rotor Plate

3) Remove end plate (tap lightly to free, if necessary). Remove spring. Withdraw end plate "O" ring from internal recess in pump body. Remove control valve and spring. Remove key and tap shaft and rotor assembly out of pump body.

4) Separate rotor assembly components, taking care not to damage rotor vanes. Remove circlip and release rotor and thrust plate. Remove drive shaft oil seal.

Inspection – Clean all parts in solvent and replace all "O" rings and seals. **NOTE** – *Do not immerse new seals in solvent.* Check all parts for scoring or other damage. If bushing on shaft is damaged, shaft assembly must be replaced. Check flow control valve for free movement in bore.

Assembly – 1) Lubricate a new shaft seal with petroleum jelly and place seal to pump body. Insert pump shaft, splined end first (from hub end of body). Insert dowel pins with ported face up.

2) Fit rotor to splined shaft with countersunk side downward (toward thrust plate). Rotor must be free on splines. Fit retaining clip to groove in end of shaft. Position pump ring to dowel pins with rotation arrow upward.

3) Place vanes in rotor slot, making sure rounded edge of each vane faces outward *(See Fig. 9)*. Coat pressure plate "O" ring with petroleum jelly and install in lowest groove in pump body.

4) Lubricate circumference of pressure plate and install over dowel pins, with circular recess for spring, upward. **NOTE** – *Do not tap plate into position.* Coat "O" ring with petroleum jelly and install in groove in pump body. Position spring into groove in pressure plate.

5) Grease circumference of end plate with petroleum jelly to avoid damaging "O" ring. Place end plate in position with retaining ring on top. Make sure gap in clip is not opposite hole used for removal. Place assembly under a press and apply pressure until clip seats into body groove.

6) Insert valve (spring first) into pump bore. Position new "O" rings for reservoir retaining bolts and outlet union. Coat large reservoir "O" ring with petroleum jelly and fit into body groove. Install reservoir on pump body and secure with retaining studs and outlet union. Replace pulley key and pulley; secure with tab washer and nut.

7) Refill system with recommended fluid and bleed. *See System Bleeding in this article.*

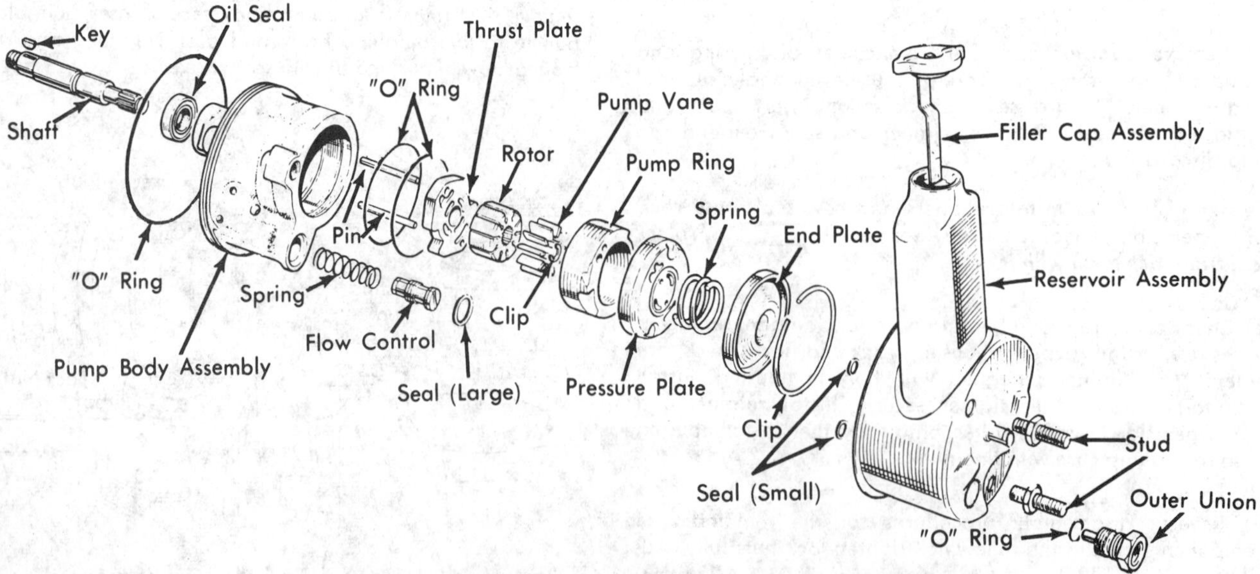

Fig. 10 Exploded View of Jaguar Power Steering Pump

LANCIA POWER-ASSISTED RACK & PINION

Lancia Beta
Coupe
Sedan
HPE

DESCRIPTION

Lancia models have an optional power-assisted rack and pinion steering system. The power assist pump is located just to the right of the engine crankshaft and is belt-driven. The non-integral fluid reservoir is situated directly above the pump.

MAINTENANCE

CHANGING & BLEEDING FLUID

1) Remove banjo bolts from power steering pump inlet and outlet ports. Take cover from reservoir. Disconnect ignition coil high tension lead.

NOTE — *On air conditioned vehicles it will be necessary to remove right front wheel and splash guard to gain access to banjo bolts.*

2) Turn steering wheel from lock-to-lock and crank engine intermittently to ensure all fluid is drained. Replace banjo bolts, using new washers.

CAUTION — *When fluid is drained, DO NOT continue to crank engine as power steering pump will be damaged.*

3) Check pump fluid reservoir filter and replace if necessary.

4) Fill reservoir with fresh fluid while intermittently cranking engine to draw fluid into pump.

5) When fluid level indicates full and remains constant, stop cranking engine and connect ignition coil lead.

6) Start engine and run at idle. Watch level of fluid in reservoir. Refill as required to maintain full level.

7) While idling engine, turn steering wheel from lock-to-lock several times until no air bubbles are seen in fluid reservoir.

8) Check all hose connections for any leakage. Stop engine and note that fluid level will rise slightly. Install reservoir cover.

REMOVAL & INSTALLATION

FLUID RESERVOIR

Removal — 1) Remove power steering pump fluid inlet banjo bolt and allow reservoir to drain. If equipped with A/C, remove right front wheel and splash gaurd to gain access to bolt.

2) Remove cover from reservoir, remove clips and detach hoses from reservoir. Remove support bracket and reservoir from vehicle.

Installation — To install, reverse removal procedure, using new washers for banjo bolts. Fill and bleed system.

POWER STEERING PUMP

Removal — 1) Raise front of vehicle and support on frame stands. Remove right front wheel and splash guard.

2) Place container under pump, remove inlet banjo bolt from pump and drain fluid.

3) In non-A/C, hold pump drive belt and remove pulley nut. Unscrew top bracket adjusting bolt and remove belt. Remove outlet banjo bolt. Slacken alternator and remove pump mounting through-bolt. Lift pump assembly and bracket from vehicle.

4) If equipped with A/C, remove air cleaner and loosen compressor mounting. Remove pump pulley nut and remove cogged drive belt. Take off pump pulley. Remove outlet banjo bolt and rear bracket. Remove pmp mounting screws and remove pump.

Installation — To install, reverse removal procedure, using new banjo bolt washers. Also, set pump belt to proper tension. Fill and bleed fluid system.

POWER-ASSISTED RACK & PINION ASSEMBLY

Removal — 1) Disconnect battery. Remove steering shaft joint bolt, located inside passenger compartment. Remove steering column lower casing, disconnect column from dash and rest on front seat.

2) Raise front of vehicle and support on frame stands. Remove front wheels.

3) Remove cooling system overflow tank. Place container under steering rack, remove fluid outlet tubing from housing and drain fluid.

4) Detach tie rod end ball joints from steering knuckles. Remove guards from tie rod housing. Remove EGR system lower piping and exhaust pipe front heat shield.

5) Remove rack and pinion steering assembly mounting bolts and lift assembly out left side of vehicle.

Installation — To install, reverse removal procedure, after setting rack in central position. Use new banjo bolt washers. Refill and bleed fluid system.

OVERHAUL

RACK ASSEMBLY

Disassembly, TRW Models — 1) Loosen clip on rubber cap at end of housing and drain oil. Install housing in vise, knock down lock plate, remove bolts and lift off steering rods from rack housing.

LANCIA POWER-ASSISTED RACK & PINION (Cont.)

2) Remove mounting clamp insulators, loosen clips and remove rubber cap and guard from housing. Remove bolts from locating support cover and withdraw shims with seal, spring, and rack locating support.

3) Straighten lock and remove pinion cover, seal, shims, and drive pinion together with upper bearing. Slide out rack and plastic bushing from housing. Remove lower bearing.

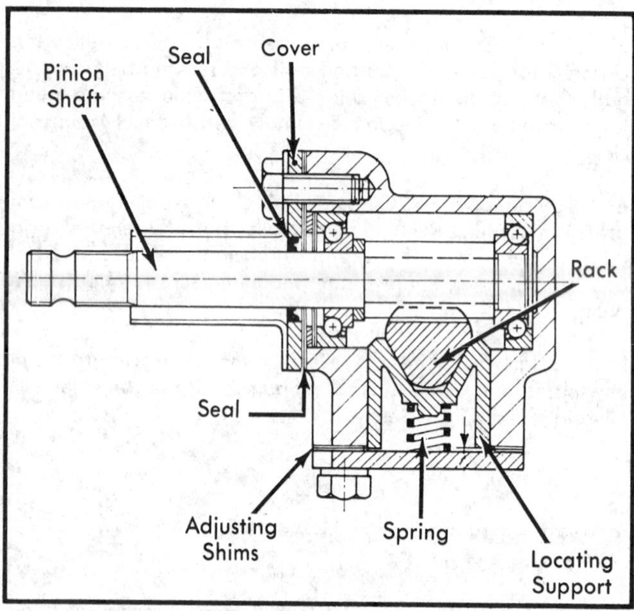

Fig. 1 Sectional View of TRW Steering Rack Housing

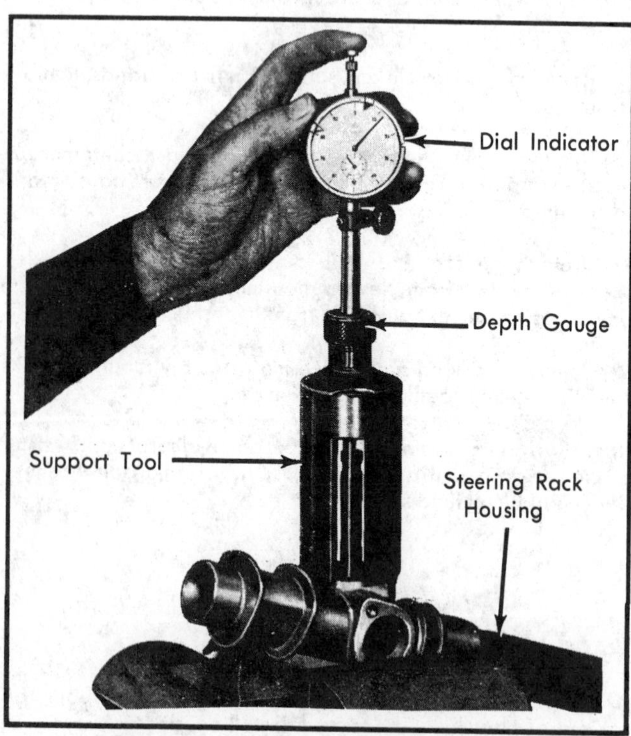

Fig. 2 Setting Bearing Pre-Load

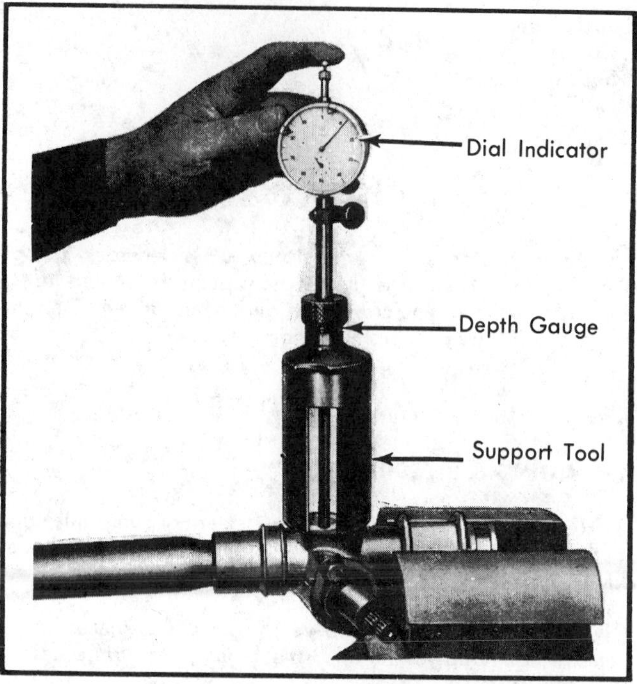

Fig. 3 Setting Backlash

Reassembly – 1) Using seal replacement tool (88062031), replace seal in pinion cover. Insert plastic bushing in rack housing and position so three locating gears engage seats in housing. Install drive pinion together with bearing and .09" (2.3 mm) washer to steering box.

2) Check bearing pre-load by installing support tool (88065001) on rack housing, then install depth gauge (88095851) with 4.7" (120 mm) long stem. Using dial indicator, set indicator on rack housing surface and measure between housing surface and washer.

3) Add value indicated to thickness of cover gasket, .010" (0.25 mm), and to value required to obtain pre-load, .001-.005" (.025-.13 mm). Install required shims, washer, cover, and mounting bolts. Torque bolts to 14.5 ft. lbs. (2 Mkg).

NOTE – *Shims are available in .005" (.13 mm), .007" (.19 mm), .010" (0.25 mm) and .09" (2.30 mm) thicknesses.*

4) Using extension and torque wrench, check turning torque for .6 ft. lbs. (.085 Mkg). To check backlash, remove cover, pinion with shims and upper bearing and insert rack. Install pinion, meshing it with rack teeth. Install shims between bearing and washer and install cover and bend lock plate.

5) Install support tool (88065001) and using dial indicator measure between housing face and top of support sticking out of housing. Add this value to backlash specifications, .002-.004" (.05-.10 mm). Then subtract thickness of cover seal, .009" (0.25 mm). This will give shim thickness required.

NOTE – *Shims are available in .002" (0.06 mm), .005" (.13 mm) and .01" (.25 mm).*

LANCIA POWER-ASSISTED RACK & PINION (Cont.)

6) Install spring to rack locating support. Install shims, cover and pinion cover mounting bolt. Torque bolt to 14.5 ft. lbs. (2 Mkg). Install rubber cover and cap to housing end. Install spacers and lock clips.

NOTE — *To ensure tightness to rack housing, coat bolts and edges of shims with sealing compound.*

Disassembly, Z.F. Models — 1) Remove damper from steering rack housing. Remove caps and install housing in vise. Knock down tabs and remove screws, disconnect steering rods. Remove buffers from housing. Remove clips, dust covers, sleeve and link from recess in housing.

2) Remove cap and cotter pin. Using spanner tool (88061024) remove adjuster and take out spring and support. Remove rack from housing, position housing with worm shaft facing upwards, remove cap and lift up retainer ring. Using spanner tool, remove adjuster.

3) Install worm shaft in vise, using rawhide or rubber mallet, hit housing lightly and remove worm shaft with bearing. Remove plastic bushing and rack "O" ring.

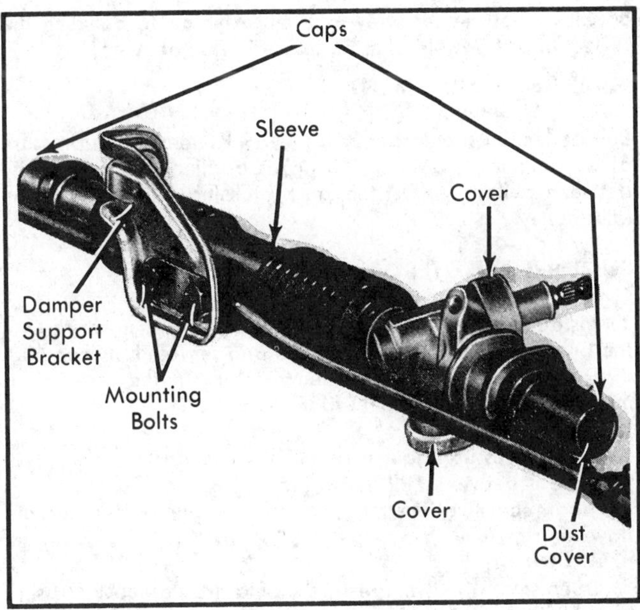

Fig. 4 Z.F. Model Steering Rack Housing

Reassembly — 1) Install new "O" ring and plastic bushing in rack housing, so that two locating gears engage with seats in housing. Using bearing installer (88022093), install worm shaft and bearing. Install and screw in adjuster.

2) Lightly grease rack and insert into housing and grease teeth of rack. Mesh rack with worm shaft and set steering rod mounting bores at center of slot. Grease and install support and spring. Tighten adjuster.

3) Install connector (88063006) to worm shaft. Using torque wrench, check turning torque, .6 ft.lbs. (.085 Mkg). Loosen adjuster as needed to install cotter pin and disconnect connector from worm shaft. Install retainer ring, fill recess in ring with grease and install caps. Install link to rack, dust covers and sleeve. Tighten mounting clips and install rubber caps.

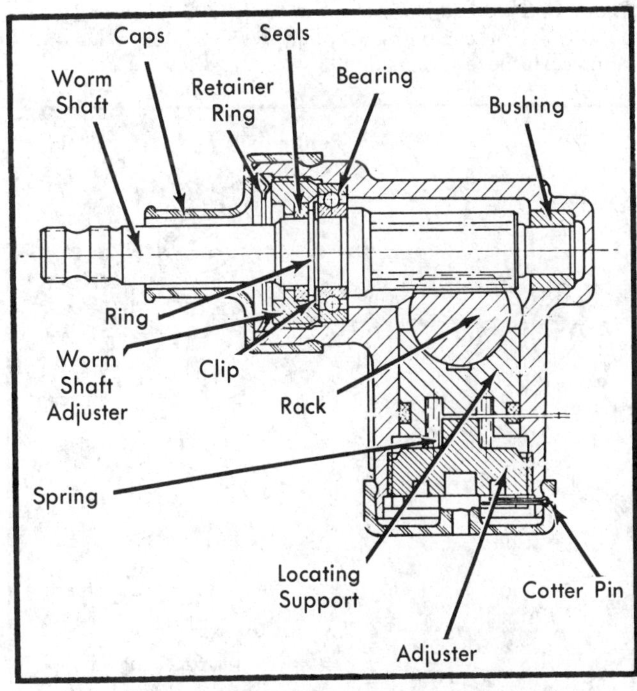

Fig. 5 Sectional View of Z.F. Model Steering Rack Housing

MAZDA POWER-ASSISTED RECIRCULATING BALL

RX4
Cosmo

DESCRIPTION

This torsion-bar type hydraulic assisted system furnishes power to reduce the amount of effort needed to turn the steering wheel. The system also reduces road shock and vibration. The power steering system includes a worm and one-piece rack piston which is meshed to the gear teeth on the steering sector shaft. The unit also incorporates a hydraulic valve, valve actuator, stub shaft and torsion bar which is mounted on the end of the worm shaft and operated by the twisting action of the torsion bar.

GENERAL SERVICE

LUBRICANT TYPE

ATF Type F (M2C33-F)

SERVICE INTERVALS

Check and add (if necessary) at first 2000 miles and every 6250 miles or 6 months. Change every 25,000 miles or 24 months whichever occurs first.

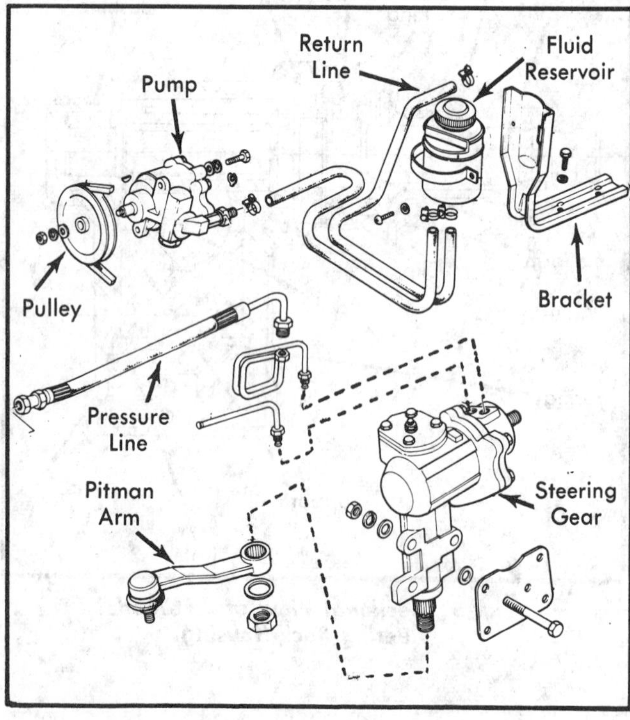

Fig. 1 Mazda Power Steering Components

HYDRAULIC SYSTEM BLEEDING

1) Fill the reservoir to the "FULL" mark and raise the front end of vehicle. To avoid foaming of the fluid during filling and testing, fabricate a stick, using the dimensions shown in *Fig. 2*.

2) Install the fabricated stick in reservoir with short end down into fluid return port on bottom of reservoir. Raise and support front of vehicle. With stick in position, turn steering wheel lock-to-lock at least ten times. Check fluid level and add if necessary.

NOTE – *Do not let the reservoir run dry.*

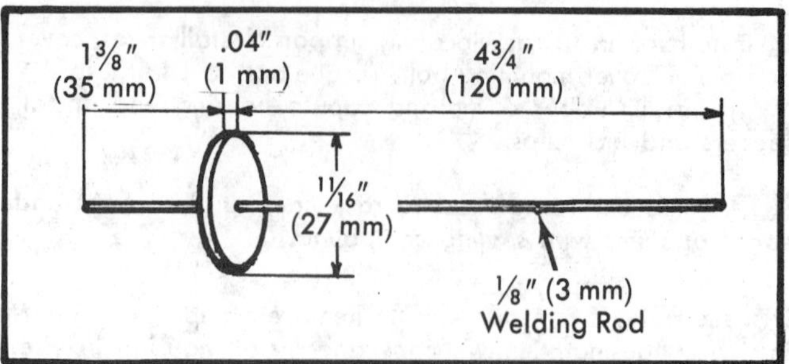

Fig. 2 Fabricated Tool

3) Attach a tube to the bleeder screw on the power steering gear. Insert open end of tube into a container partially filled with fluid.

4) Start engine and turn steering wheel to left lock position and open bleeder screw. Run engine until air bubbles cease to appear. Repeat operation with the steering wheel in the right lock position.

NOTE – *Do not let the reservoir run dry.*

5) Close the bleeder screw and fill reservoir to between the "FULL" and "LOW" level marks. *NOTE - Do not overfill*.

PUMP BELT ADJUSTMENT

Belt deflection should be .35±.04" (9±1 mm) when pressure of approximately 22 lbs. (10 kg) is applied to belt halfway between pulleys. Adjust tension by turning adjusting bolt on idler pulley.

PUMP PRESSURE TEST

1) Install a pressure gauge with shut off valve in series with the pressure hose. Start the engine and set idle between 600-700 RPM. Check that fluid temperature in the reservoir is maintained between 122°-140°F (50-60°C).

2) Close pressure gauge shut off valve and check a that pressure is between 782-896 psi (55-63 kg/cm²). If pressure is less than specifications, check for faulty pump or a sticking flow control valve.

3) Open shut off valve. Pressure should drop at least 71 psi (5 kg/cm²). If pressure drops more than this, check for bent or kinked lines or contaminated fluid.

4) With shut off valve open, turn steering wheel to full lock position, then release. If pressure drops more than 71 psi (5 kg/cm²), check for faulty valve in steering gear.

5) Turn steering wheel to full right and full left lock position. If pressure drops more than 71 psi (5 kg/cm²) with shut off valve open, look for excessive internal leakage in the power steering gear, caused by excessive valve clearances or broken seals.

REMOVAL & INSTALLATION

POWER STEERING GEAR

Removal – 1) Disconnect negative battery cable then remove engine oil filter cartridge to gain clearance for removal of the fluid lines. Disconnect and tag pressure and

MAZDA POWER-ASSISTED RECIRCULATING BALL (Cont.)

return lines for correct reassembly, then plug both lines and steering gear ports to prevent entry of dirt.

2) Raise vehicle and disconnect center link at pitman arm, then remove bolts and nuts securing steering gear housing to frame. Remove clamp bolt holding flexible coupling to steering gear, slide gear off coupling and remove steering gear from vehicle.

Installation – To install steering gear, reverse removal procedure, noting the following: Fill and bleed system, then start engine and check for leaks by turning steering wheel to left and right.

Fig. 4 Location of Identification Mark

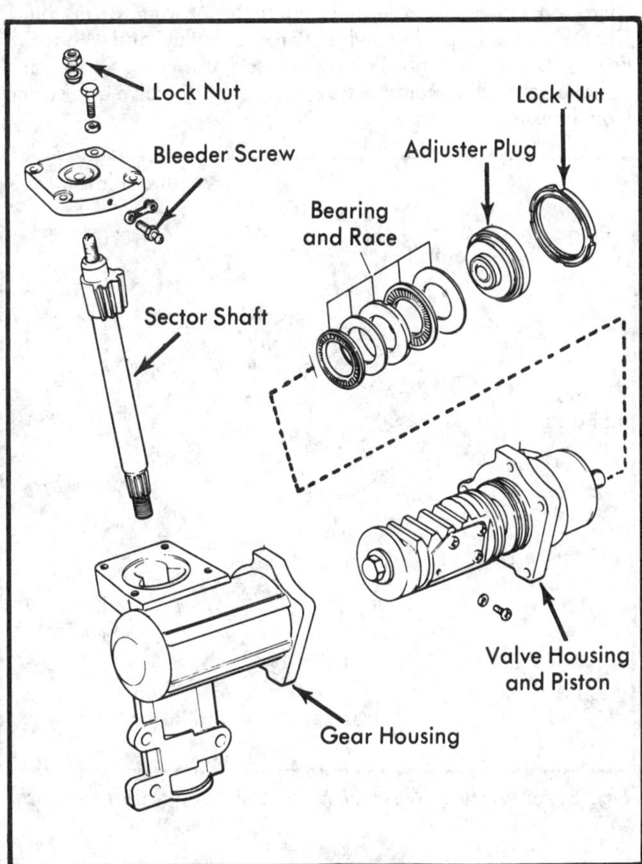

Fig. 3 Exploded View of Mazda Power Steering Gear

3) Remove side cover attaching bolts. Tap lower end of sector shaft with soft hammer to loosen, then remove cover and shaft as an assembly. Turn side cover counterclockwise to remove cover from adjusting screw.

4) Remove adjuster plug lock nut, then loosen, but do not remove the adjuster plug. Unscrew valve housing attaching bolts and remove valve housing and worm shaft as an assembly from steering gear housing.

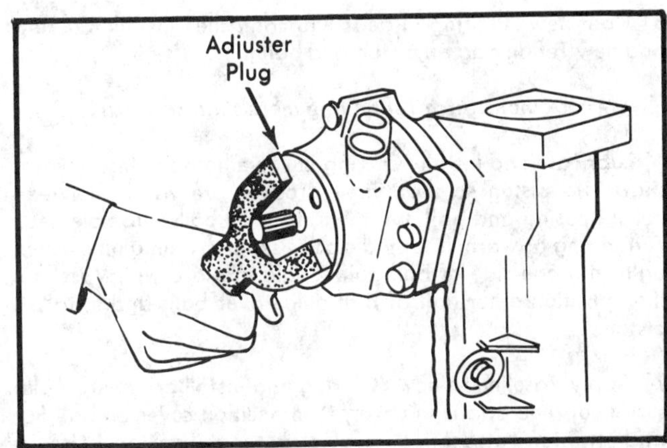

Fig. 5 Loosening Adjuster Plug

OVERHAUL

POWER STEERING GEAR

Disassembly – 1) Thoroughly clean the exterior of gear with solvent. Hold gear upside down over a drain pan and turn worm shaft back and forth several times to drain fluid, then secure gear on a work stand.

2) Remove pitman arm nut and using puller (49 0223 695D), remove pitman arm. Remove sector shaft adjusting screw lock nut. To center the gear, turn worm shaft until identification mark is in the position shown in *Fig. 4*.

5) Stand valve body and piston on end with piston end down. Rotate worm shaft counterclockwise out of the piston letting the ball bearings drop into the piston. Turn the piston upside down and catch the 26 balls in a container. Unscrew ball guide cover screws, then remove cover and ball guides.

6) Clean and inspect housing. Replace seals, if necessary, as follows: Pry lower seal from housing and remove upper seal snap ring, spacer washer, and upper seal.

7) Dip new seals in gear lubricant and coat seal bore of housing with lubricant. Place lower seal in bore with lip facing inward. Install spacer washer, then seat snap ring in groove. Insert upper seal in bore with rubber side facing out and press into place.

MAZDA POWER-ASSISTED RECIRCULATING BALL (Cont.)

8) Unscrew adjuster plug from valve housing, then remove outer bearing race, thrust bearing and inner bearing race. Remove valveand worm shaft assembly, bearing races and thrust bearing from the housing. Remove worm shaft bearing and pry oil seal and dust seal from adjuster plug. Remove Teflon ring and "O" ring from piston and ball nut.

Reassembly – **1)** Install new Teflon ring and "O" ring in valve housing. Coat new Teflon rings and "O" rings in gear lubricant and install on valve body and worm shaft. Dip bearing races and needle bearing in power steering fluid and position on worm.

2) Lubricate Teflon ring and "O" ring with power steering fluid, then carefully install worm and valve in housing. Coat new dust seal and oil seal with power steering fluid, then install dust seal with rubber side facing out and oil seal with lip facing inward on adjusting plug.

3) Drive worm shaft bearing into adjuster plug until it seats on bottom surface of bearing bore. Coat bearing races and thrust bearing with power steering fluid, then align grooves on race with pins, thrust bearing, and outer race, install on valve body.

4) Lubricate and install "O" ring in adjuster plug groove and place adjuster plug over end of stub shaft. Tighten adjuster plug enough to properly seat all parts, then tighten until initial preload is to specifications. Install, but do not tighten adjuster plug lock nut.

5) Coat new "O" ring in gear lubricant, then install "O" ring and new Teflon ring on piston and ball nut.

NOTE – *Do not stretch Teflon ring more than necessary.*

6) Lubricate and install "O" ring in valve housing. Insert worm shaft into piston so that three grooves are visible between valve housing and ball nut, then place 19 balls into hole near Teflon ring as worm is turned clockwise. Insert remaining seven balls into one side of ball guide, hold in place with Vaseline, then position other half of ball guide over balls and install in piston.

7) Apply Vaseline to new "O" ring and install on cover. Make sure neoprene pad is in cover, then position cover on ball nut and tighten attaching screws to specification. Use a straightedge to make sure guide cover head is not higher than Teflon ring. File off high spots.

NOTE – *Do not rotate piston or stub shaft after balls are inserted, as balls may fall out of circuit.*

8) Coat new "O" ring with Vaseline and install in pressure port of gear housing. Coat Teflon seal with Vaseline and install on piston, then insert piston and valve into gear housing. Align lube passages in valve housing with passages in gear housing and install, but do not tighten, attaching bolts.

9) Rotate ball nut until teeth mesh with sector teeth then tighten valve housing bolts to specification. Insert side cover "O" ring in steering gear housing, then turn stub shaft to center the piston. Screw side cover onto adjusting screw until it bottoms, then back out one and one half turns.

10) Lubricate sector shaft bearing and journal, then install sector shaft with center gear tooth meshing with center groove of rack piston. Install side cover attaching bolts and lock washers and tighten to specification.

NOTE – *Make sure cover "O" ring is in place before tightening bolts.*

11) Turn stub shaft completely to left or right, then back 90°, then using pull scale, recheck that initial preload is to specifications. Turn sector shaft adjusting screw to adjust final preload to specifications. Install new rubber seal and adjusting screw lock nut, then tighten lock nut to specifications. Align identification marks and install pitman arm on sector shaft and tighten nut to specifications.

POWER STEERING PUMP

Disassembly – **1)** Clean pump exterior and drain fluid. Clamp pump in padded vise. Remove pulley and Woodruff key. Unscrew suction line connector attaching bolts and remove connector. Remove flow control plug, valve and spring from housing.

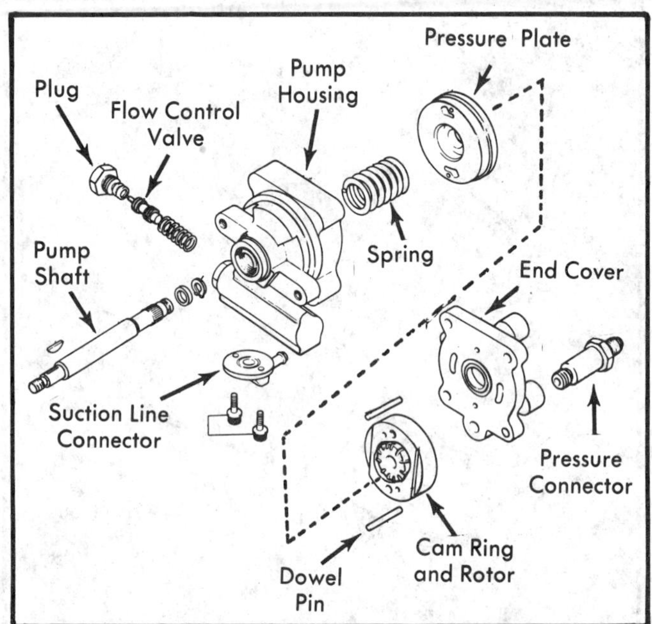

Fig. 6 Exploded View of Mazda Power Steering Pump

2) Remove end cover attaching bolts and end cover. Take off snap ring then remove collar, vanes and rotor from shaft. Remove cam ring, and tapping drive end of shaft with plastic hammer, drive out pressure plate and shaft.

3) Remove dowel pins from housing. Pry shaft seal from housing (if defective)

NOTE – *The seal will be destroyed if removed.*

Inspection - Clean parts thoroughly and check for cracks, wear or burned areas. Rotor, vanes and ring must be replaced as an assemblv if defective. Check flow control valve and plug orifices.

Reassembly – **1)** If shaft seal was removed, install new seal with metal backing facing pump end of shaft. Seat seal properly in shaft hub.

MAZDA POWER-ASSISTED RECIRCULATING BALL (Cont.)

Fig. 7 Installing Dowel Pin and Spring

2) Lubricate new "O" ring with power steering fluid and install in groove on pump body. Install both dowel pins and spring, then insert shaft in housing. Install new "O" ring on pressure plate, then coat plate and "O" ring with power steering fluid. Install pressure plate on dowel pins with recess facing out and press into place. Place cam ring on dowel pins with rotation arrow toward pressure plate.

Fig. 8 Installing Pressure Plate

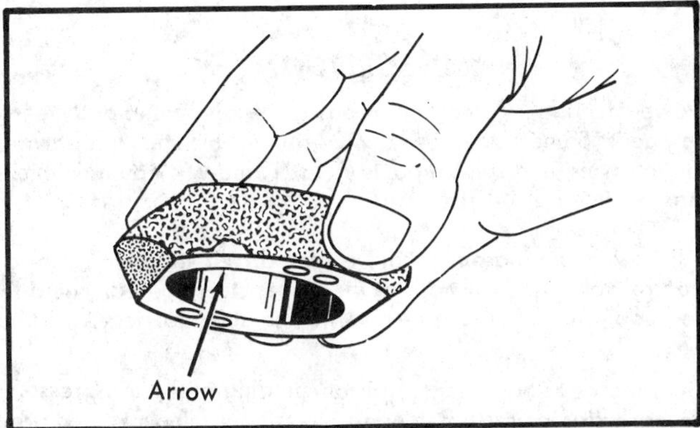

Fig. 9 Cam Ring Locating Mark

3) Coat rotor with gear lubricant and install on shaft with recessed chamfer side of bore toward pressure plate. Install vanes in rotor slots with rounded edge of vanes facing out. Make sure vanes move freely. Install collar and snap ring on splined end of shaft, sliding snap ring down until seated into ring groove.

4) Lubricate new "O" rings with power steering fluid and install on housing, then install end cover and tighten attaching bolts to specification. Place flow control valve spring and valve in hole, making sure pin end of valve is toward plug. Lubricate new "O" rings and install on plug, then install plug in housing tighten to specification.

5) Lubricate new "O" rings and install on pressure connector and suction line connector. Tighten pressure connector and suction line connector bolts to specification. Tap Woodruff key into shaft and install pulley on pump.

TIGHTENING SPECIFICATIONS

Application	Ft. Lbs. (mkg)
Valve Housing Bolts	29-36 (4.0-5.0)
Side Cover Bolts	25-30 (3.4-4.1)
Pitman Arm Nut	108-130 (15-18)
Pump End Cover Bolts	22-29 (3-4)
Pump Control Valve Plug	50-72 (7-10)
Pump Pressure Connector	50-72 (7-10)
Pump Suction Connector Bolts	5-7 (.7-1.0)
Application	**INCH Lbs. (cmkg)**
Worm Shaft Initial Preload	9-12 (10-14)
Worm Shaft Final Preload	9-14 (10-16)

MERCEDES-BENZ POWER-ASSISTED RECIRCULATING BALL

All Models

DESCRIPTION

Power steering is composed of power steering pump and steering gear. Some models use a VT27 pump which has a separate oil reservoir, and some models use a ZF and VT49 pump, which has an integral oil reservoir.

All power steering pumps are engine driven vane type with a control valve. The purpose of the power steering gear pump is to supply fluid (under pressure) to the steering gear.

Steering gear has integral piston/steering nut. Fluid pressure to each side of piston/steering nut is controlled by a control valve which is moved by a lever from steering column shaft.

LUBRICATION

Capacity – 2.6 pts. (1.5 lts.) automatic transmission fluid.

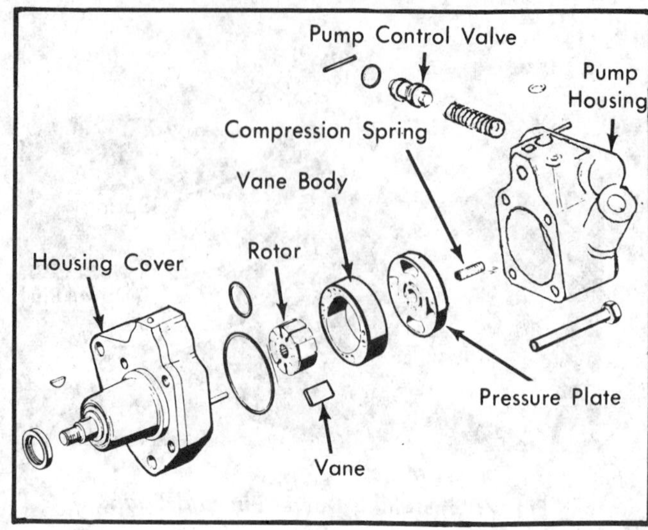

Fig. 1 Exploded View of VT27 Power Steering Pump

REMOVAL & INSTALLATION

POWER STEERING PUMP

Removal – 1) Remove power steering tank cover, spring and damping plate. Drain tank with a syringe. Disconnect and plug high pressure and return hoses.

2) Loosen fastening bolts and push pump towards engine, remove "V" belts from pulley. Remove remaining bolts and remove pressure pump with carrier.

Installation – To install power steering pump, reverse removal procedures. Fill system with recommended fluid.

POWER STEERING GEAR

Removal – 1) Drain fluid from power steering pump. Disconnect and plug pressure line and return line from steering gear. Remove bolts from steering coupling. Remove rear exhaust system and left hand exhaust pipe at manifold (all 450 models). Disconnect center link and tie rod from pitman arm. Remove bolts securing steering gear to frame, force steering gear from steering column shaft, in a downward direction.

2) Drain fluid from steering gear, remove steering coupling and pitman arm from gear (be sure to mark pitman shaft-to-pitman arm position for proper assembly).

Installation – To install steering gear, reverse removal procedure. Replace locking nuts and bolts, tighten to specifications. Fill system with recommended fluid.

OVERHAUL

POWER STEERING PUMP

Disassembly, VT27 Pump – 1) Remove knurled nut and tank cover with seal. Remove spring, damping plate and filter ring. Remove bolt and hollow screw, then remove tank with "O" rings from pump housing.

2) Remove bolts connecting pump cover to pump body. Remove compression spring from pressure plate. Mark pressure plate and vane body and then lift off pressure plate from pins on vane body.

3) Remove vane rotor with vanes and vane body. Remove all "O" rings then remove control valve from pump body. Dismantle control valve and check for worn, damaged or missing parts.

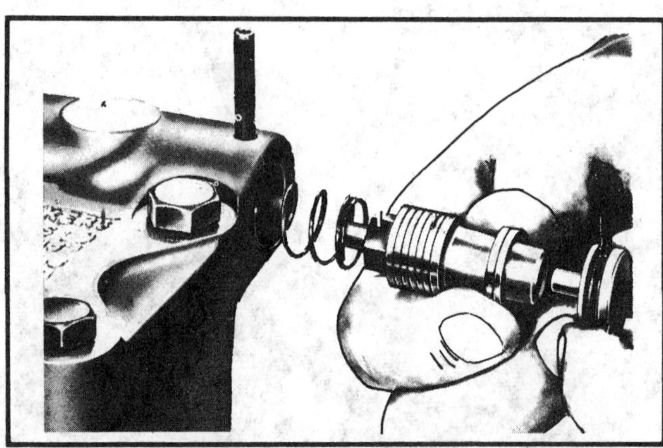

Fig. 2 Removing VT27 Pump Control Valve Assembly

Inspection, VT27 Pump – 1) Check vanes and rotor for damage or wear: vanes should slide easily in rotor. If necessary, replace vanes and rotor. Check vane body for excessive wear. If necessary to replace vane body, vanes and rotor must also be replaced.

2) Check running surfaces of housing cover. If worn, replace entire pump. Check surface of pressure plate and replace if worn. Check control valve. If worn, replace entire pump. Install shell halves on shaft and check end play. If end play exceeds specifications, replace entire pump.

MERCEDES-BENZ POWER-ASSISTED RECIRCULATING BALL (Cont.)

Assembly, VT27 Pump – To assemble steering pump, reverse disassembly procedure.

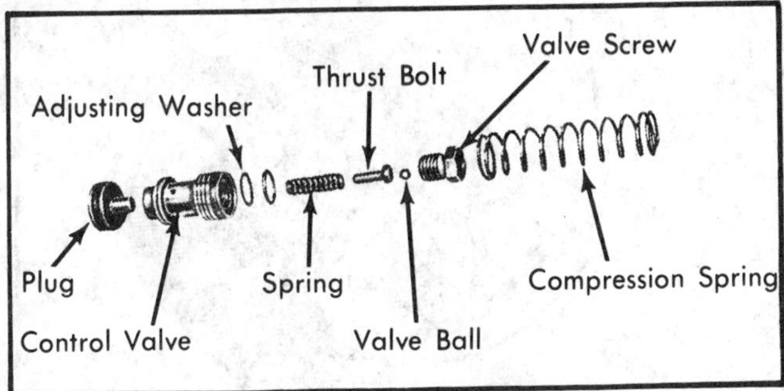

Fig. 3 Exploded View of VT27 Pump Control Valve Components

Disassembly, VT49 Pump – **1)** Remove wing nut and cover from reservoir. Remove compression spring, two damping plates and filter ring. Remove woodruff key from input shaft.

2) Install puller 1104-7251 on input shaft. Screw bolt back on puller enough to install clamping shoes 11004-6304 between puller and seal. Turn clamping cone of puller to the right up to stop and remove seal ring out of housing.

3) On rear of housing, push in cover and insert a punch through hole in housing *(See Fig. 4)*, push in on punch and remove circlip and cover. Remove spring and "O" ring from housing. Push input shaft with pressure plate at cover end, rotor, cam ring and pressure plate at input end out of housing in rearward direction.

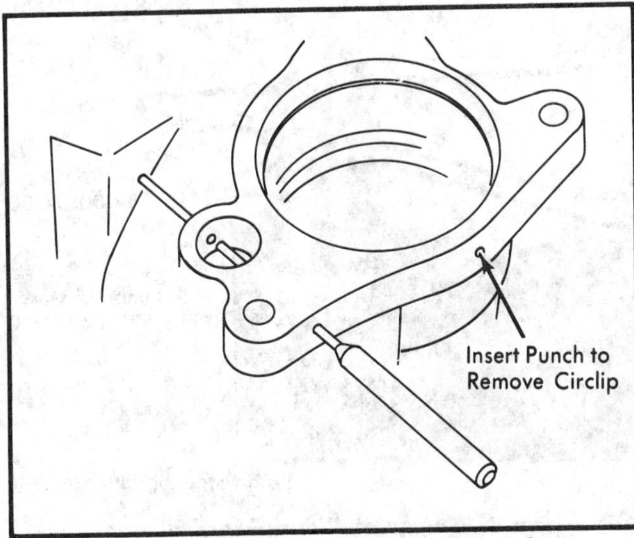

Fig. 4 Circlip Punch Hole Location & Removing Locking Pin on VT49 Pump

4) Remove locking clip from input shaft, then remove rotor and pressure plate. Remove cylinder pins from housing. Using a punch knock out locking pins in housing *(See Fig. 4)*.

5) Remove closing plug, volume control valve, and compression ring from housing. Clamp volume control valve into vise and disassemble valve and check spacer washer, valve cone and compression spring.

Inspection – Check pressure plates, input shaft, and bearing bushing for wear. Check blades for easy sliding in rotor. Check surfaces of volume control valve and bore in pump housing for wear or damage.

NOTE – *Never replace volume control valve only, replace power steering pump.*

Reassembly, VT49 Pump – To install power steering pump, reverse removal procedure. Fill system with recommended fluid.

Disassembly, ZF Pump – **1)** Remove woodruff key from input shaft. Install puller 1104-7251 on shaft. Screw bolt back on puller enough to install clamping shoes 11004-6304 between puller and seal.

2) Turn clamping core of puller to the right up to stop, remove tool, seal and washer from housing. Remove knurled nut and cover from housing. Remove retaining and compression springs. Remove upper damping plate, filter ring, and lower damping plate.

3) On rear of housing, push in cover plate and using a screwdriver remove circlip and cover. Remove "O" ring, compression spring, and pressure plate. Remove rotor with blades from input shaft and "O" ring and cam ring.

4) Remove lock ring from forward end of shaft. Press out input shaft from rear of housing. Remove circlip from shaft and remove bearing by pressing off toward rear of shaft. Remove needle bearing from housing.

5) Remove closing plug from housing Remove compression spring and volume control valve. Clamp volume control in vise, disassemble and check spacer washers, ball, and compression spring.

Inspection – Check pressure plates, input shaft, bearing housing, and bushing for wear. Check blades for easy sliding in rotor. Check surfaces of volume control valve and bore in pump housing for wear or damage.

NOTE – *Never replace volume control valve only, replace power steering pump.*

Reassembly, ZF Pump – To install power steering pump, reverse removal procedure. Fill system with recommended fluid.

POWER STEERING GEAR

Disassembly – **1)** Attach steering gear to a suitable assembly plate (116 589 01 59 00). Remove lock nut from adjusting screw and remove copper seal ring. Remove bolts attaching pitman shaft cover to steering case.

MERCEDES-BENZ POWER-ASSISTED RECIRCULATING BALL (Cont.)

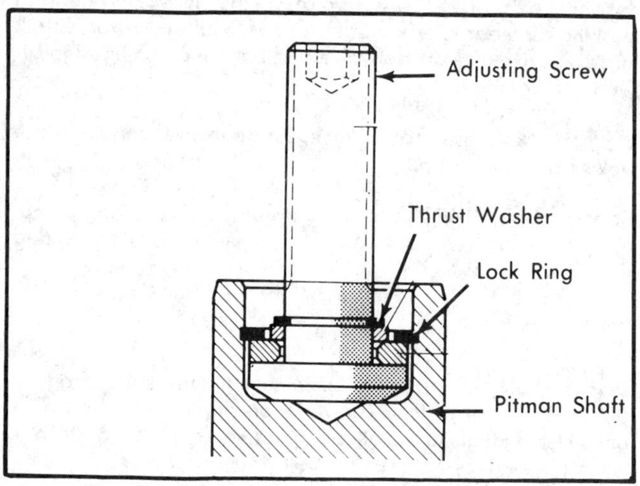

Fig. 5 Sectional View of Adjusting Screw

2) With steering in center position, turn adjusting screw counterclockwise. This forces pitman shaft, with housing, from steering gear case. Remove pitman shaft with cover. Remove "O" rings from cover. Remove lock ring and seal ring. Remove lock ring from pitman shaft and remove adjusting screw with thrust washers. See *Fig. 4*.

3) Remove bolts securing bearing cap to steering gear case. Turn worm gear counterclockwise until bearing cap is forced out of steering gear case.

NOTE – *Balls will fall out of ball guide if worm gear is turned too far.*

Fig. 6 Removing Slotted Nut with Special Hook Wrench

4) Remove bearing cap and worm gear with piston/steering nut from steering gear case.

5) Unscrew worm gear with bearing cap from piston/steering nut. **CAUTION** – *Do not lose balls.*

6) Remove "O" ring from bearing cap and attach bearing cap to a suitable assembly fixture.

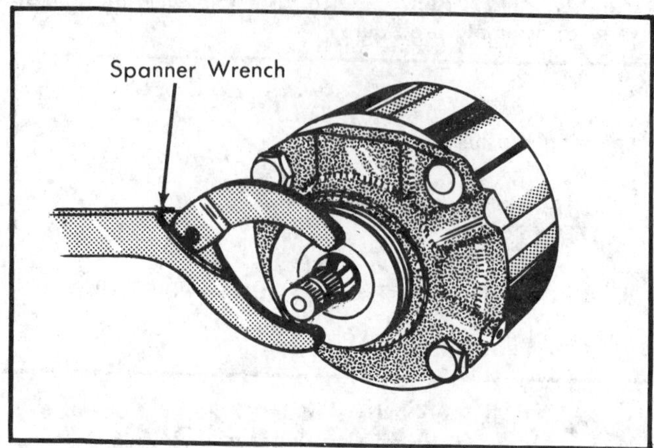

Fig. 7 Removing Bearing Insert from Bearing Cap

7) Unscrew slotted nut, using hook wrench, from bearing insert. See *Fig. 5*.

8) Remove bearing insert from bearing cap, using spanner wrench *(Fig. 6)*, then remove seal and "O" rings from worm gear.

9) Remove bearing and disc from bearing cap. Remove bolts, clamp, and both ball guide halves from piston/steering nut.

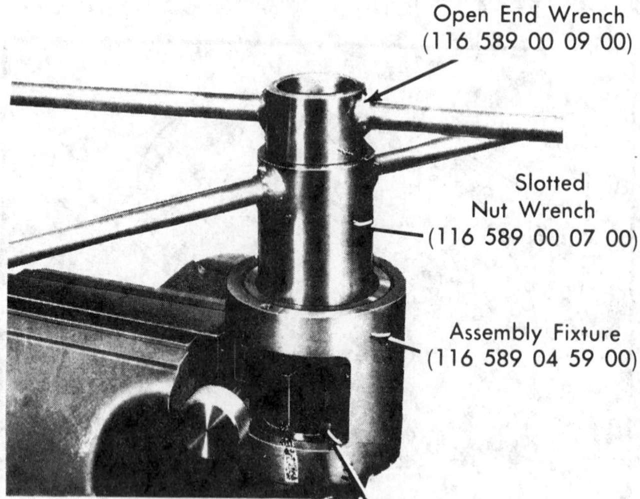

Fig. 8 Removing Worm Gear Nut from Piston/Steering Nut

10) Using suitable clamp and tools *(Fig. 7)*, remove worm gear nut from piston/steering nut. Remove seal ring and "O" ring from worm gear nut. On early models, remove axial disc from worm gear nut

11) Remove bearings from piston/steering nut. See *Fig. 8*.

12) Remove lock ring, cover and control valve from steering gear case. See *Fig. 9*.

MERCEDES-BENZ POWER-ASSISTED RECIRCULATING BALL (Cont.)

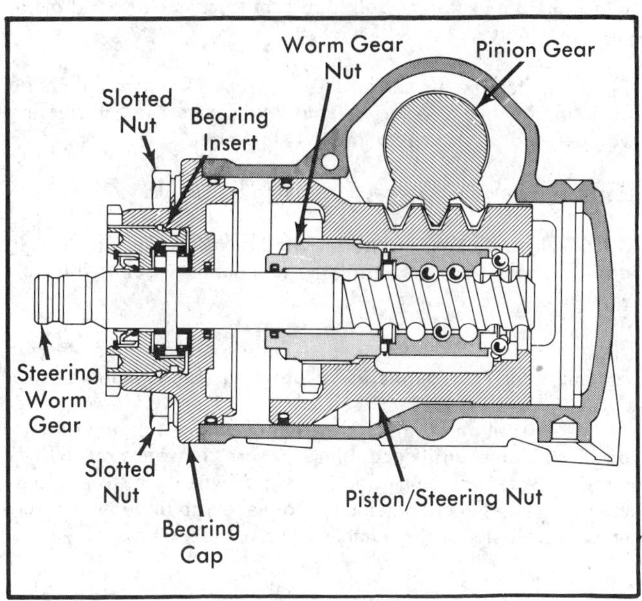

Fig. 9 Cross-Sectional View of Steering Gear

Inspection – 1) On worm gear, check ball paths and bearings surfaces for wear and damage, replace if necessary.

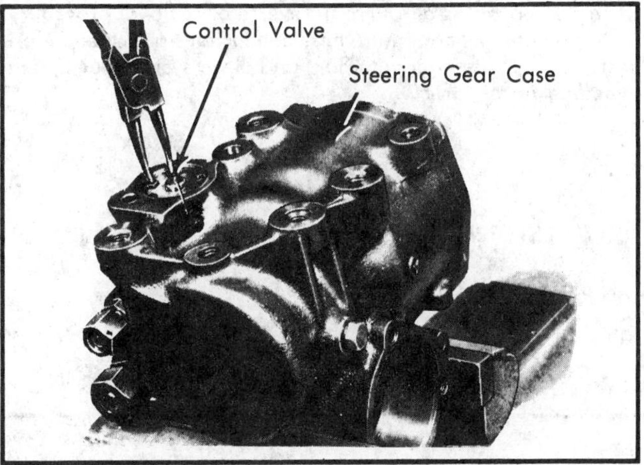

Fig. 10 Steering Gear Case with Detail of Control Valve

2) On piston/steering nut, remove seal rings, "O" rings, bearings and races, and worm gear nut. Inspect for wear or damage and replace as necessary.

3) Check pitman shaft for wear or damage on bearing surfaces, check for bent or warped shaft and replace as necessary. Check steering case, cover, and bearing insert for wear or damage and replace as necessary.

4) On control valve, check reaction piston in control valve for free movement. If necessary remove pistons from control valve by removing lock rings.

Assembly – To assemble steering gear, reverse disassembly procedure. Replace all "O" rings and sealing rings. Adjust gear to specifications.

SPECIFICATIONS

Application	Dimensions
Steering Wheel Free Play	1" Maximum
Pump Circulation Pressure	28.4-71 psi
Number of Balls in Ball Circuit	24
End Play of Pump Shaft	
New	.028" Maximum
Used	.039" Maximum

TIGHTENING SPECIFICATIONS

Application	Ft. Lbs. (mkg)
Steering Gear-to-Frame	43 (6.0)
Pitman Arm-to-Pitman Shaft	116-145 (16.0-19.0)
Linkage Ball Pin Nuts	25 (3.5)
Slotted Nut-to-Bearing Cap	87-101 (12.0-14.0)
Bearing Cap-to-Steering Gear	43-47 (6.0-6.5)
Adjusting Screw Nut	22-25 (3.0-3.5)
Idler Arm-to-Frame	87 (12.0)
Pump Shaft Nut	43 (6.0)
Pump Housing Bolts	25-29 (3.5-4.0)

PEUGEOT POWER-ASSISTED RACK & PINION

DESCRIPTION

Vehicles are equipped with a power assisted rack and pinion type steering system. The system consist of two main components: the rack and pinion steering gear and the power assist pump. The two components are connected by rigid and flexible fluid lines. The power assist pump and fluid reservoir are combined.

GENERAL SERVICE

HYDRAULIC SYSTEM LUBRICANT

Capacity – 0.7 qts.

SYSTEM BLEEDING

Fill reservoir to full mark on dipstick. Start engine and turn steering wheel from lock-to-lock several times (to expel all air). Recheck fluid level and refill as required.

REMOVAL & INSTALLATION

STEERING GEAR

Removal – **1)** Remove bolt and nut from pinch clamp on steering shaft coupling. Disconnect high and low pressure lines and drain oil, block off line connections. Using stand, support engine and remove engine mounting bolts to crossmember. Loosen rear and remove front crossmember bolts.

2) Remove clips from rack mounting bolts and remove bolts. Loosen ball joint nuts and install ball joint removing tool 8.0908, unscrew nut and remove ball joint. Remove nut from steering damper bolt. Move rack assembly towards the rear and remove from vehicle.

Installation – **1)** Adjust length of left and right tie-rods to 11.7" (298 mm). On right tie-rod, measure from center of ball joint bolt to center of steering link bolt hole. On left tie-rod, measure from center of ball joint bolt to center of bolt hole in yoke assembly.

2) Place steering wheel and front wheels in straight ahead position. Remove steering column lower cover. Install steering damper spacer and bolt into crossmember.

NOTE – *Use new nuts when installing ball joints.*

3) Install ball joints and nuts. Install new lock nut on steering damper bolt. Install steering rack mounting bolts with new washers.

NOTE – *When installing crossmember ensure that steering column is correctly aligned with power assisted steering valve.*

4) Install front and rear crossmember bolts. Install bolt and nut on pinch clamp on flex coupling. Ensure clearance of .079" (2 mm) between column and steering wheel. Install engine mounting bolts in crossmember. Connect high and low pressure lines. Install steering column cover. Torque all bolts.

POWER STEERING PUMP

Removal – Remove air cleaner and connecting hoses. Remove low and high pressure lines and drain oil. Loosen adjusting bolt, mounting bolts and remove drive belt. Using puller 8.0706, remove pulley off of pump. Remove mounting bolts and remove pump.

Installation – Install pump in reverse of removal procedure, noting the following: Ensure hose connections are clean before installing. Fill reservoir with fluid and bleed system. *See System Bleeding in this article.*

OVERHAUL

POWER STEERING PUMP

No overhaul procedures available.

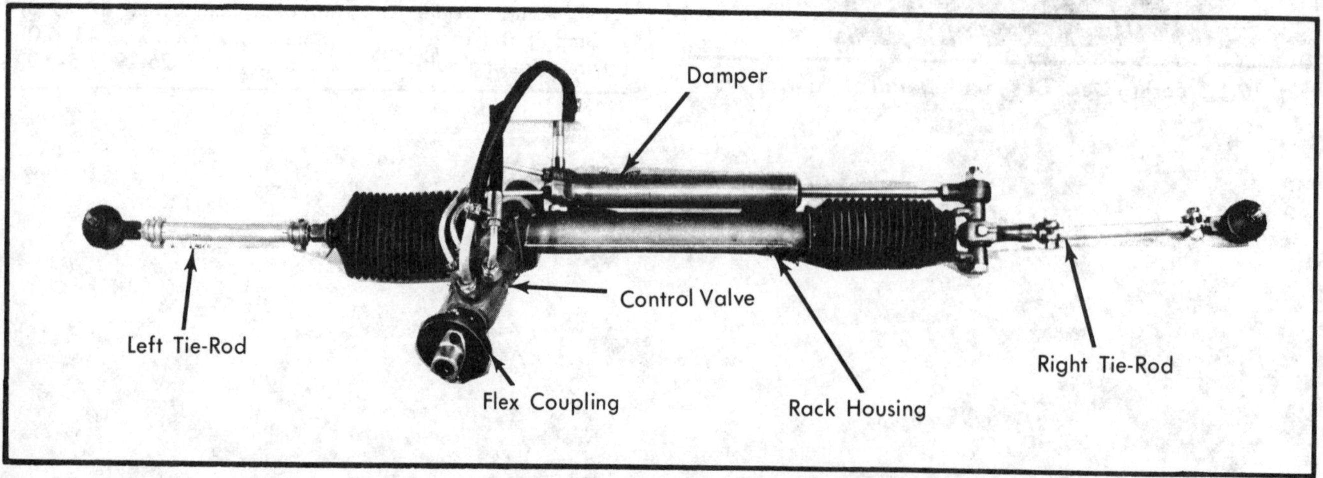

Fig. 1 Steering Rack Assembly

PEUGEOT POWER-ASSISTED RACK & PINION (Cont.)

POWER STEERING GEAR

NOTE – *Manufacture recommends using tool kit 8.0706 to aid in disassembly and reassembly of power steering rack.*

Disassembly – 1) Thoroughly clean outside of rack assembly before attempting to dismantle. Install stud tool in rack housing and clamp housing in vise by stud tool. Remove fluid lines to steering damper and block ports.

NOTE – *Do not disconnect fluid lines from control valve if valve is being reused.*

CAUTION – *Manufacture has preset piston rod on steering damper, do not loosen lock nut.*

2) Remove bolt from right steering link to damper piston rod, and bolt from damper to rack housing. Remove damper and right steering link from rack assembly. Loosen bolt in pinch clamp on left steering link and unscrew link (left hand thread).

3) Remove left ring clip, retainer ring and bellows, then remove bolt from yoke to steering link. Free retaining rings from right bellows, push bellows back, loosen yoke lock nut and remove yoke, lock nut, bellows, and retaining rings.

4) Install rack assembly vertically in vise (control valve up), remove flange (with grease fitting), spring, and plunger. Remove pinion bearing cover, hold flex coupling and using a 30 mm wrench remove pinion retaining nut.

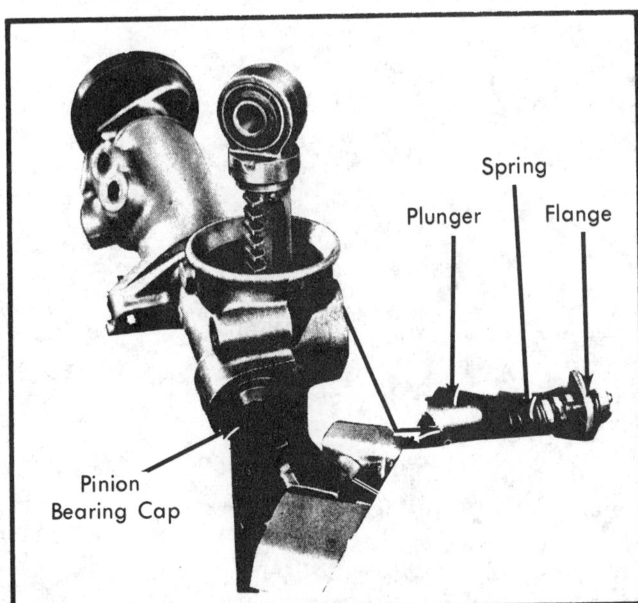

Fig. 2 Removing Flange, Spring, and Plunger

5) Remove control valve mounting bolts. Hold steering rack in housing with pin 0.0707. Remove control valve from housing. Remove pinion bearing circlip and bearing from housing.

NOTE – *If control valve is defective, replace complete valve assembly.*

Reassembly – 1) Using bearing installation tools and arbor press, install new pinion bearing in housing and circlip. Install control valve, turn valve clockwise and ensure meshing of steering rack gears and pinion gears. Install valve mounting bolts.

2) Hold flex coupling and install pinion nut, grease bearing location and install grease cap. Install guide and ring tool on lower end of steering rack (opposite end of control valve).

3) Temporarily place plunger and spring in housing. Install flange, upper bolt and dial indicator mount in lower bolt hole. Install dial indicator on mount and tighten down flange.

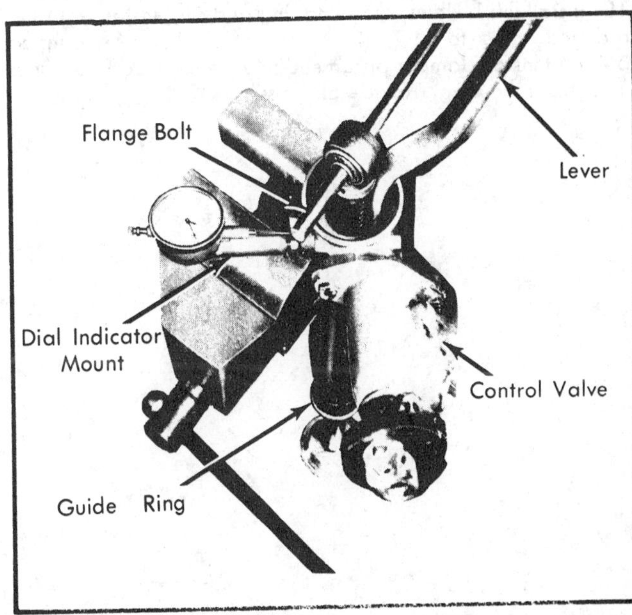

Fig. 3 Measuring Steering Rack Clearance

NOTE – *Tap rack housing lightly with a mallet, this will tend to reduce sticking effect of the grease and will stabilize dial indicator reading.*

4) Using flex coupling, turn steering rack from lock-to-lock and zero dial indicator on farthest point indicated. Using lever, push steering rack in direction of plunger and record dial indicator reading.

5) Steering rack plunger clearance should be .002" ±.004" (0.10 ± 0.05 mm) at maximum point along rack travel. To obtain required clearance subtract .004" (0.10 mm) from dial indicator reading, this measurement indicates the thickness of shim washers needed in plunger.

NOTE – *Shim washers are available in, .004" (0.10 mm), .008" (0.20 mm) and .020" (0.50 mm) thicknesses.*

6) Remove indicator, flange, spring, and plunger. Place nylon stop inside of plunger and place a straight edge on top of plunger. Space between straightedge and nylon stop is where shim washers are installed.

PEUGEOT POWER-ASSISTED RACK & PINION (Cont.)

7) Screw grease fitting in flange, install plunger, spring, flange, and mounting bolts with new washers. Remove tools from steering rack. Install right bellows and retaining rings.

8) Install right lock nut and yoke on rack, measure distance between center of yoke bolt hole and center of left steering link bolt hole for 25.55" (649 mm). Ensure both holes are in line, tighten yoke lock nut.

9) Install left yoke, bolt and lock plate on steering link. Adjust tie-rod distance to 11.7" (298 mm). Measure distance between base of yoke and tie-rod end. This measurement should be the same on both tie-rods.

10) Install left bellows, retaining ring and clip. Install right tie-rod and adjust to 11.7" (298 mm). Install damper mounting bolt and install damper piston end to yoke on rack. Insert lines in damper housing. Torque all bolts.

TIGHTENING SPECIFICATIONS

Application	Ft. Lbs. (mkg)
Ball Joint Nut	31 (4.25)
Steering Damper Nut	40 (5.5)
Steering Rack Bolts	17 (3.25)
Crossmember Bolts	31 (4.25)
Flex Coupling Bolt	11 (1.5)
Engine Mounting Bolts	25 (3.5)
Power Steering Pump Mounting Bolts	12 (1.75)
Control Valve Mounting Bolts	12 (1.75)
Pinion Shaft Nut	12 (1.75)
Plunger Flange Bolts	7 (1)
Right Yoke Lock Nut	58 (8)
Left & Right Eye Bolts	33 (4.5)

SAAB POWER-ASSISTED RACK & PINION

99

DESCRIPTION

Power steering is added to some vehicles as optional equipment. The assembly consists of a rack and pinion steering gear with a servo valve which regulates the oil flow to a servo plunger on the rack. The hydraulic pressure is generated by an oil pump which is driven by a belt attached to the crankshaft pulley. A separate oil reservoir located by the right wheel housing supplies the system with hydraulic oil. The steering gear is permanently lubricated with oil. A tube running between the two ends of the steering gear housing leads the oil past the hydraulic portion of the rack.

REMOVAL & INSTALLATION

Removal – 1) Loosen servo pump and lift away from mounting. Turn steering wheel a full turn left and remove clamping screw holding universal joint to steering gear. Remove left cover under instrument panel and remove bearing bracket mounting from body.

2) Lift steering column with universal joint and support out of way. Raise and support front of vehicle. Remove front wheels. Using tie rod remover tool (8995409), detach tie rod end assemblies from control arms. Unscrew left tie rod end assembly from tie rod.

3) Disconnect speedometer cable from transmission. Disconnect left side handbrake cable at brake yoke and vehicle housing. Remove right side handbrake cable clamp on steering gear. Remove steering gear mounting from body.

4) From left side, remove two retaining screws from steering gear, and remove intermediate piece. On right side, remove yoke and intermediate piece. Disconnect delivery and return lines from servo valve.

5) Move steering gear over to right far enough so left tie rod can be pulled down through the body opening while twisting the valve housing backward. Take steering assembly out by moving it down and to the left.

Installation – Installation, is a reversal of removal procedure; however, tie rod ends are to be connected after gear assembly has been fully installed. Adjust toe-in.

OVERHAUL

POWER STEERING GEAR

Disassembly – 1) Clean exterior of gear assembly thoroughly before beginning work. Back off lock nut and remove tie rod end assemblies. Loosen clamps and take off rubber bellows. Bend up lock plate between end piece and rack.

2) Clamp toothed end of rack in a vise. Unscrew lock nut and adjusting screw. Withdraw adjusting screw retaining plate, spring "O" ring, and plunger. Remove tubes between servo valve and servo cylinder.

3) Unscrew three lock nuts, then detach valve housing and servo valve with pinion. Keep servo valve in a clean plastic bag. Remove ring nut locking screws. Clamp gear end of housing vertically in padded vise and remove ring nut using a suitable spanner (8995961).

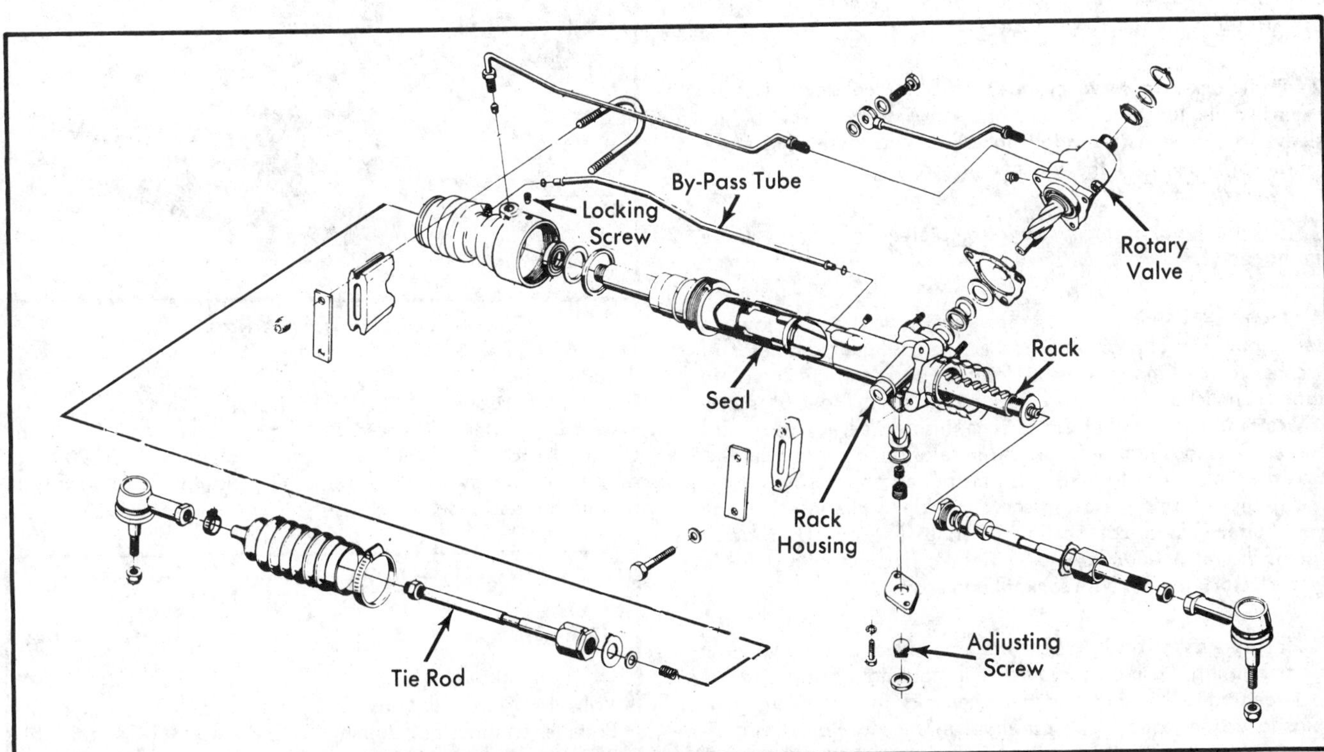

Fig. 1 Exploded View of Saab Power Steering Components

SAAB POWER-ASSISTED RACK & PINION (Cont.)

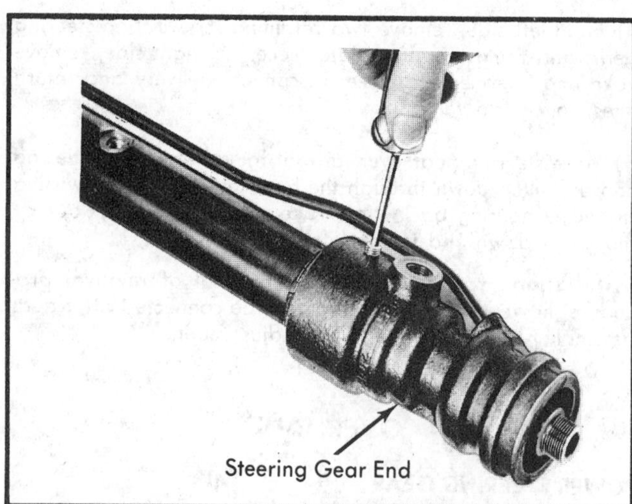

Fig. 2 Removing Ring Nut Locking Screw from Steering Gear End

4) Remove steering gear end from the cylinder and the rack while removing the bleeder tube. Set aside loose cone in hole for oil tube. Remove sealing ring, washer, and servo seal from steering gear end. Pull rack out of steering gear housing. Remove knurled sleeve, servo seal, and washer from cylinder. Remove plunger seal and snap ring.

NOTE – *Plunger cannot be detached from rack.*

Reassembly – 1) Apply Loctite to needle bearing seat and push in the needle bearing, if it has been removed. Fit snap ring and new teflon ring onto rack plunger. Slide knurled sleeve onto rack. Fit servo seal on fitting sleeve using the special cone tools (8995938 and 8995946). Slide sleeve with seal past teeth on rack. Remove tools. Turn notch in seal toward servo plunger.

2) Push rack into servo cylinder until knurled sleeve can be seen in hole for tube connection. Use a screwdriver to turn sleeve to expose its threaded hole. Screw in connecting screw temporarily to hold the washer in place.

NOTE – *Do not tighten screw completely, or rack will be damaged.*

3) Insert servo seal into its seat. Turn notch in seal toward servo plunger. Slip on the washer. Turn smaller diameter of washer toward the servo seal. Fit flat sided seal. Put cone into tube connection hole and lock cone using special screw (8995953). Cylindrical part of cone (inside steering gear end) serves to fix position of gear end in relation to servo cylinder. Screw fitting cone (8995987) onto rack end and position steering gear end onto rack and servo cylinder while inserting the vent tube. Cylindrical portion of cone fits into "U" shaped recess in end of servo cylinder. Tighten ring nut with suitable wrench. Lock the nut with socket head screw.

4) Install washer and seal between pinion and servo valve in gear housing. Position servo valve in housing. Position gasket between valve housing and gear housing. Insert sealing ring, plastic washer, and lock ring in valve housing. Place installation tool (8995979) over shaft end of valve. Attach valve housing.

5) Remove special locking screw (8995953) from connection hole in steering gear end. Install tubes between servo valve and two sides of cylinder. Position new gaskets on banjo connection of the shorter tube to the cylinder. Install rack plunger, "O" ring, spring, cover, adjusting screw, and lock nut for radial adjustment of rack.

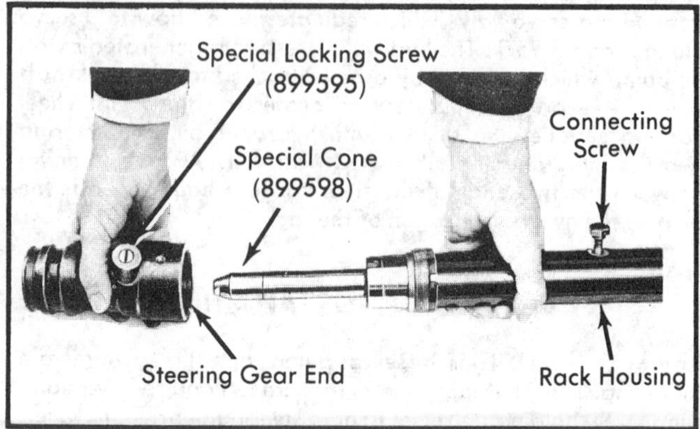

Fig. 3 Fitting Steering Gear End to Rack Housing

6) Clamp toothed end of rack in a padded vise, and install complete end pieces with thrust washer, spring, and lock washer. Lock the washer.

7) Adjust the radial play of the rack as follows: Screw in adjusting screw until resistance of the gear is felt. Back off screw $^1/_6$ turn. Check that steering gear can be turned from lock to lock without jamming. Tighten adjusting screw lock nut.

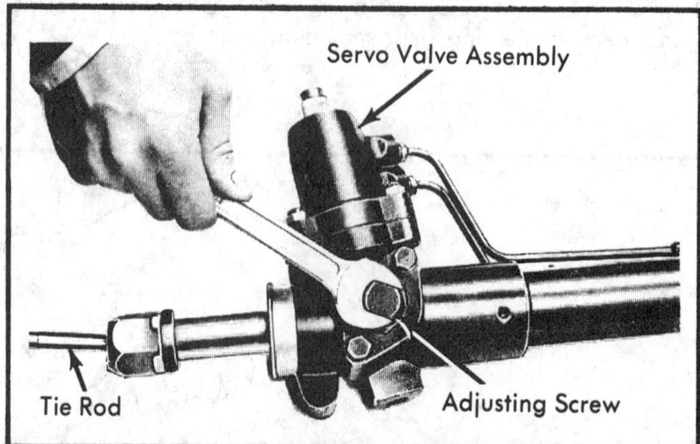

Fig. 4 Adjusting Rack Radial Play

8) Position rubber bellows and install (tighten) all clamps except one outer one. Hold steering gear vertically, with unclamped end up, and inject 6.5 fl. oz. of suitable EP 90 gear oil into the bellows. Attach remaining clamp. Install lock nuts and tie rod end assemblies.

TIGHTENING SPECIFICATIONS

Application	Ft. Lbs. (mkg)
Gear End Ring Nut	130-135 (18-19)
Valve Housing Lock Nuts	16.6 (2.3)
End Pieces (Inner Ball Joints)	47-54 (6.5-7.5)
Adjusting Screw Lock Nut	50-60 (7-8)

TOYOTA CORONA POWER-ASSISTED WORM AND SECTOR

Corona

DESCRIPTION

POWER STEERING PUMP

The power steering pump is a vane type composed of an engine driven eccentric rotor, a fixed ring (having six slotted grooves), and a flow control valve (to regulate maximum oil pressure and amount of oil flow). Slippers are fitted in each slotted groove and are pressed against rotor outside surface by pressure produced in adjoining slots and by spring tension. As rotor rotation increases or decreases, then space between the rotor and fixed ring changes accordingly, in order to control oil flow.

POWER STEERING GEAR

Power steering gear consists of a mechanism which converts steering wheel torque to cross shaft torque by means of worm and power piston nut, and of a mechanism which detects hydraulic pressure developed by vane pump and controls this pressure in proportion to the steering effort. The worm shaft is separated at the center and power is transmitted from the steering wheel to worm gear through a small diameter torsion bar.

LUBRICATION

Capacity - 1.7 pts. (800 c.c.)

Type - ATF type Dexron

ADJUSTMENTS

BELT TENSION ADJUSTMENT

With 22 lbs. (10 kg) pressure applied, belt deflection should be as shown in *Fig. 1*.

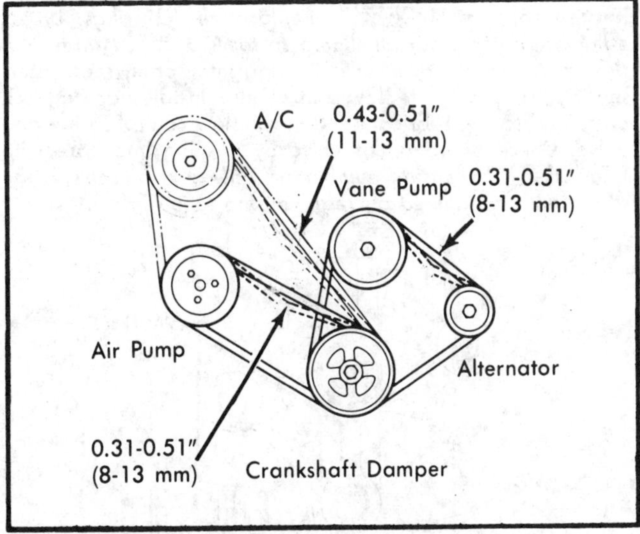

Fig. 1 Belt Deflection Measuring Points

STEERING GEAR AIR REMOVAL

1) Jack up front of vehicle and support with safety stands. Fill fluid to proper level in vane pump reservoir (turn wheels fully in both directions and recheck fluid level).

2) Turn steering wheel fully to one side and turn engine over while fluid level in reservoir is observed. **NOTE** – *Do not start engine or run starter for prolonged periods.* Repeat procedure with steering wheel turned to other side. Start engine, allow to idle, and turn wheels from side to side two or three times.

3) Remove safety stands and lower vehicle. Again allow engine to idle and turn wheels fully side to side two or three times. When steering wheel is brought to center position and engine stopped, fluid level should not show a rise. If fluid level does rise, there is air still in the system and Step **3** should be repeated.

FLUID REPLACEMENT

1) Raise and support front of vehicle. Disconnect return hose. **NOTE** – *Have container on hand as fluid will drain from disconnected hose.* Drain fluid from pump by turning engine over (do not start). Drain fluid from steering gear (turn wheel to both sides twice).

2) Refill reservoir with new fluid. Repeat draining procedure, then fill reservoir to specified level.

HYDRAULIC PRESSURE TESTING

1) Disconnect pressure line from steering gear case and mount a pressure gauge in line. Perform Steering Gear Air Removal, as previously described. After warming engine, set to idle speed. Open pressure gauge valve fully and record readings at the time steering wheel is turned completely left and completely right. Suitable pressure reading should be 1022 psi. **NOTE** – *Do not hold steering in either extreme position for any length of time as damage may result to vane pump due to rising fluid temperatures.* If pressure does not rise to specifications, pump, hoses, or steering gear is defective.

2) Gradually close pressure gauge valve and record pressure. If pressure fails to rise to same specifications as given above, pump is faulty. If less than minimum specification was recorded above during turning check, steering gear is defective. Also, if greater than maximum pressure was recorded during valve closing test, steering gear is faulty.

NOTE – *Test pressure specification is determined with fluid temperature at 176° F (80° C).*

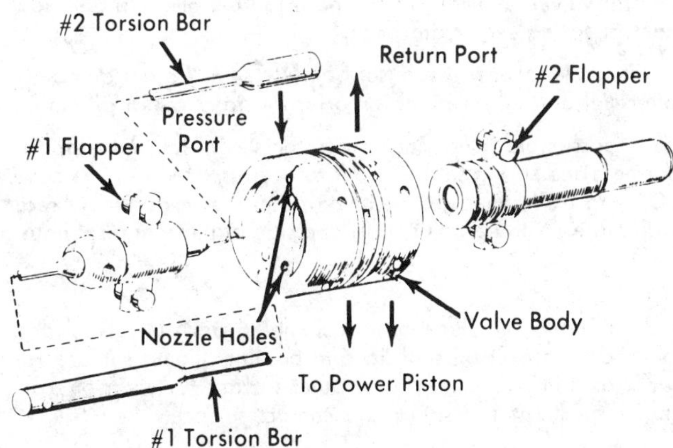

Fig. 2 Disassembled View of Valve Body and Flappers

TOYOTA CORONA POWER-ASSISTED WORM AND SECTOR (Cont.)

REMOVAL & INSTALLATION

POWER STEERING PUMP

Removal – Loosen pulley mounting nut before loosening drive belt. Disconnect pressure feed line from pump housing. **NOTE** – *Keep disconnected hose at high level to prevent fluid from draining out. Also plug pump housing hose fitting.* Disconnect inlet fluid line. Remove pump assembly from mounting bracket and adjusting strap.

Installation – Install in reverse of removal procedures, noting the following: Adjust drive belt tension as previously described, then perform Air Removal procedure.

POWER STEERING GEAR

Removal – Disconnect pressure feed hose and inlet return line from steering gear housing. Remove bolt securing the intermediate shaft to flexible coupling. Unscrew nut from cross shaft. Remove pitman arm, using suitable puller (09610-20011). Unbolt steering gear from frame, then remove gear assembly from vehicle. **NOTE** – *Do not loose shims from their mounting positions; they must be retained for replacement.*

Installation – Reverse removal procedure, noting the following: Replace mounting shims in original positions. Perform Air Removal procedure, as previously described.

OVERHAUL

POWER STEERING PUMP

Disassembly – 1) **NOTE** – *Pump disassembly will be made easier if a suitable holding tool is used (09629-22010).* Clamp holding tool in vise and mount pump assembly to tool. Remove front reservoir attaching bolt, then remove both rear reservoir bolts. Detach reservoir by tapping at pump inlet with a plastic hammer.

2) Remove pressure hose union from pump and withdraw flow control valve and compression spring. Unscrew five bolts securing pump housing halves. Remove front housing by holding rotor shaft and fixed ring, then tap front housing off with plastic hammer. Remove nut from rotor shaft. **NOTE** – *Bolt which retains front of reservoir is slightly longer than five pump housing bolts.*

3) Tap rear housing from fixed ring. **CAUTION** – *Do not tap flow control valve.* Clamp rear housing and holder in a vise. Remove screw, washer, and snap ring from in front of flow control valve. Reinstall screw and grip with pliers to pull flow control spring seat from bore.

4) Remove relief pressure set bolt. **NOTE** – *Do not disassemble relief bolt unless pump oil pressure stays low at all times.*

5) Disassemble fixed ring and rotor shaft. Pull out slippers, springs, and spring seat. Extract rotor from fixed ring. Remove "O" ring from inner groove of rear housing, then remove rear side plate. Withdraw "O" ring and side plate from front housing.

Inspection – 1) Clean all disassembled parts in solvent and blow dry. Inspect oil seal lip and bushing sliding surface for wear or damage. Check rotor outer surface for wear or scoring. Inspect rotor-to-side plate contact surface.

2) Measure overall length of rotor (between end faces) and overall length of fixed ring. If overall length of rotor is more than .0024" (.06 mm) shorter than fixed ring overall length, replace with new rotor shaft sub-assembly.

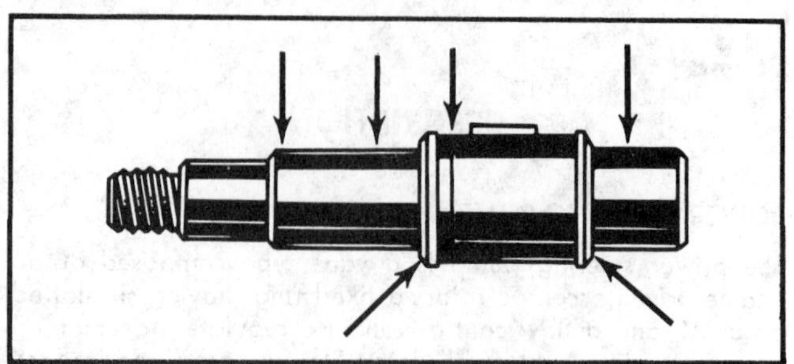

Fig. 3 Rotor Shaft Sub-Assembly Inspection Points

3) Inspect slipper for wear: Measure length and thickness. If thickness is less than .0551" (1.4 mm) or if length is less than 1.571" (39.920 mm), replace entire set.

4) Inspect front and rear housing bushings. Bushing-to-rotor shaft clearance must not exceed .0012" (.03 mm). Inspect internal surface of fixed ring. If worn, scratched, or scored, replace ring. Check front and rear side plates at sliding surfaces. Bushings cannot be replaced separately. Replace entire housing.

5) Measure free length of slipper compression springs. If less than .51" (13 mm) replace individually. If free length varies more than .02" (0.5 mm) between springs, replace entire set.

6) If flow control valve is scratched or otherwise damaged, replace it with one having the same production number. Measure compression spring for flow control valve. If free length measures less than 1.85" (47 mm), replace spring. Inspect ball and relief spring.

7) Inspect reservoir for leakage. Inspect "S" type oil seal and replace if damaged: Remove with screwdriver. Apply a suitable lubricant to lip of new seal and install using special tool 09630-30041.

Reassembly – 1) **NOTE** – *Replace all "O" rings. Unless otherwise noted, coat all sliding surfaces and "O" rings with power steering fluid.* Install "O" ring into spring seat. Insert seat and snap ring into flow control bore. Install snap ring lock plate and screw. Lubricate and install flow control spring and valve. Check operation of valve by pushing into bore with finger. **NOTE** – *Ensure number on flow control valve is the same as that stamped on rear housing (See Fig. 4).*

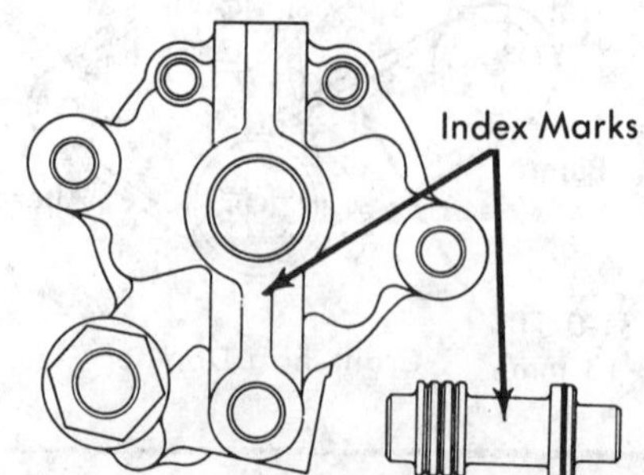

Fig. 4 Flow Control Valve and Rear Housing Index Marks

TOYOTA CORONA POWER-ASSISTED WORM AND SECTOR (Cont.)

2) Install two "O" rings on hose union and screw it into housing. Tighten to specification. Attach side plate to rear housing. Install "O" ring into groove in rear housing. Place fixed ring on rear housing. **NOTE** – *It may be helpful to install two guide bolts*. Tap fixed ring into rear housing. Remove guide bolts. **NOTE** – *Fixed ring, if replaced, must have same stamp number as on rotor shaft.*

3) Lubricate and install rotor into rear housing. Assemble the spring seat, springs, and slipper. Install slipper assembly with notched or open side facing in counterclockwise direction. **NOTE** – *Ensure all slippers face rotor.*

4) Install oil seal into front housing. Install lubricated side plate with chamfer facing front housing. Install "O" ring. Install front housing with long ear of housing facing right. Install two guide bolts and tap housing into position. Install "O" rings on five housing bolts and screw into position.

5) Place "O" ring on reservoir outlet and insert it into rear housing. Install "O" ring on long bracket bolt and insert and tighten. Tighten two rear reservoir bolts.

6) Assemble relief pressure set bolt as follows: Install relief spring with spring seat into relief valve bore, then install ball. Install two "O" rings on relief pressure set bolt. Position bolt into valve bore, with bolt extending .040" from rear housing. Do not lock bolt in place at this time.

7) Mount pulley on rotor shaft and measure shaft turning torque with pull scale. Torque should be less than 6.2 lbs. Ensure pulley turns smoothly.

NOTE – *Install assembly and make proper adjustments. See Removal & Installation procedure in this article.*

POWER STEERING GEAR

NOTE – *It is recommended that Toyota tool kit part number 09630-22010 be used in disassembling and assembling power steering gear.*

Disassembly – **1)** To aid in overhaul procedure, bolt steering gear to holding tool and clamp gear assembly and holding tool in vise. Remove cross shaft end cover retaining bolts. Tighten end cover adjusting screw until end cover "O" ring is removed.

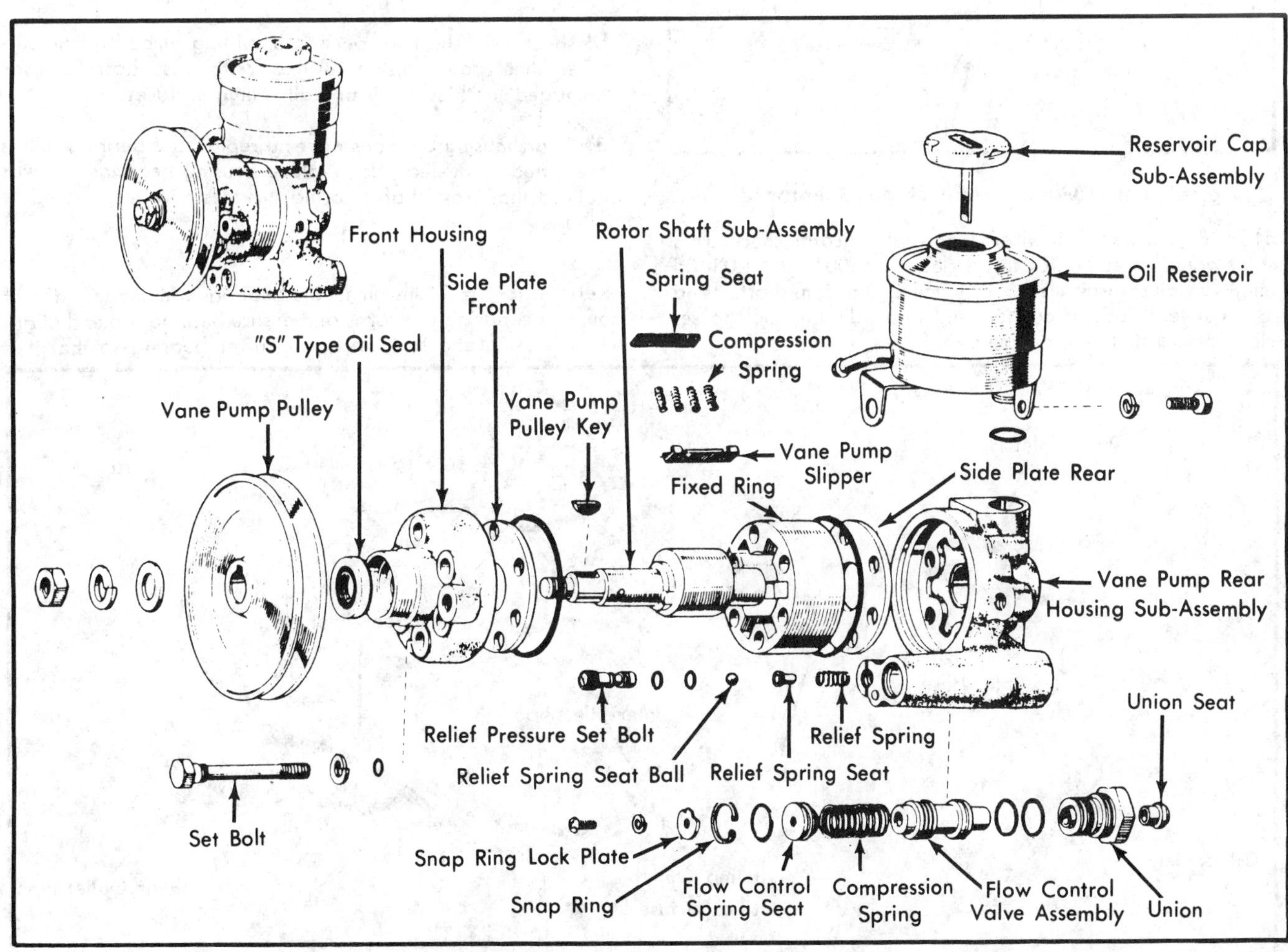

Fig. 5 Exploded View of Toyota Power Steering Pump Assembly

TOYOTA CORONA POWER-ASSISTED WORM AND SECTOR (Cont.)

2) Continue to tighten adjusting screw until end cover is released from cross shaft. Remove cross shaft by lightly tapping at bottom end with a hammer. Remove bolts attaching gear housing to valve housing.

3) Hold power piston nut with hand and turn worm shaft clockwise, then remove valve assembly and power piston.

CAUTION – *Ensure that power piston nut does not come off worm shaft. Do not disassemble valve body or remove power piston from worm shaft.*

4) Install valve assembly in vise. Using a dial indicator measure ball clearance. If clearance exceeds .006" (0.51 mm) replace valve assembly *(See Fig. 6).*

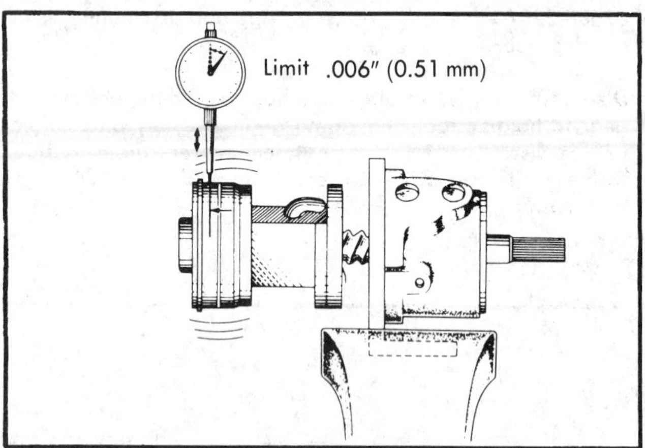

Fig. 6 Using Gauge to Check Ball Clearance

5) Install cross shaft in vise. Using dial indicator check cross shaft adjusting screw for thrust clearance .001.002" (.03-.05 mm). To adjust thrust clearance, remove seal from shaft. Using lock nut tool, loosen lock nut and turn adjusting bolt to set clearance. Install seal on cross shaft.

Fig. 7 Checking Thrust Clearance

6) Temporarily install valve assembly in gear housing and install mounting bolts. Using lock nut tool, remove lock nut and adjusting bolt from gear assembly. Remove and replace as needed, oil seal, "O" ring, and bearing assembly. Install lock nut and tighten. Remove valve assembly from gear housing

Inspection – **1**) Clean and dry all disassembled components. Unless otherwise mentioned, coat all sliding parts, "O" rings, and teflon rings with power steering fluid upon reassembly.

) Inspect cross shaft for peeling or pitting at ball rolling surface. Check power piston nut mesh with cross shaft. Look for damaged tooth surfaces or ball rolling surfaces.

3) Gear housing bearings must be replaced if bearing rollers are pitted or peeled. Also replace housing bearings if it was noticed that cross shaft bearing surfaces had been scored or pitted.

Reassembly – **1**) Install needle bearings with longer edge of outer race facing outwards and ensure bearing top end aligns with housing end surface. Install lower bearing so that it is

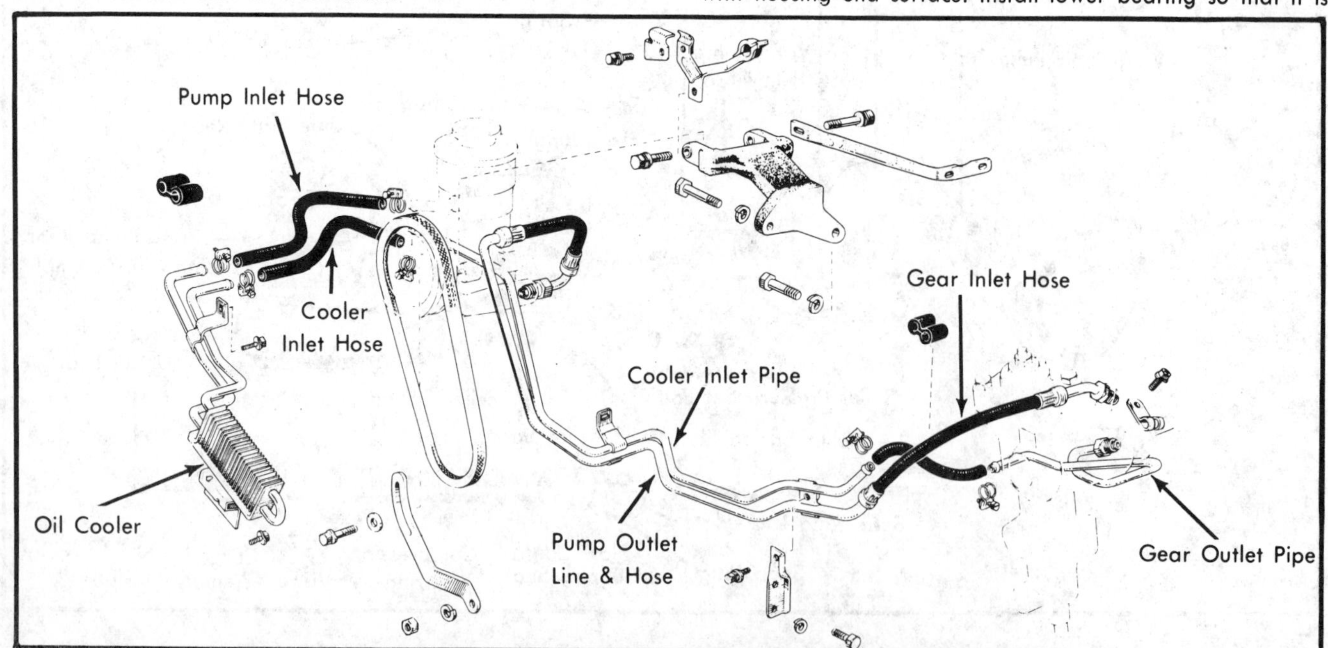

Fig. 8 Component View of Power Steering Line and Hose Placement

TOYOTA CORONA POWER-ASSISTED WORM AND SECTOR (Cont.)

positioned 0.764" (19.4 mm) away from housing inner end surface.

2) Install "O" ring, teflon ring and spacer in gear housing. Install "O" ring, valve housing, and mounting bolts. Tighten bolts to specifications. To adjust preload on worm shaft, loosen lock nut and install shaft tool and torque wrench on shaft. Preload should be 3.5-5.6 INCH lbs. (4-6.5 cmkg). Hold power piston nut to prevent it from turning.

3) Insert shaft holding tool inside of lock nut tool and tighten lock nut on worm shaft. Wrap a piece of vinyl tape around spline area of cross shaft. Align shaft gear with power piston nut gear and insert cross shaft in gear housing.

CAUTION – *Do not turn cross shaft, because of possible damage to "O" ring.*

4) Insert cross shaft (with cover attached) into housing and install mounting bolts. Tighten bolts to specifications. To adjust preload of cross shaft, set worm shaft to midpoint position. Determine total number of shaft turns and return from full lock by half that number.

5) Install shaft tool over shaft and attach a torque wrench. Using a screwdriver turn cross shaft adjusting bolt to specified preload, 2.6-3.5 INCH lbs. (3-4 cmkg). Install seal and nut on adjusting bolt, tighten nut to specifications.

6) Recheck worm gear preload to see that both right and left rotations are identical. Stake worm gear lock nut at three points.

7 Remove teflon ring and "O" ring from gear housing. Using needle bearing removing tool, remove needle bearings.

TIGHTENING SPECIFICATIONS

Application	Ft. Lbs. (mkg)
Pump Housing & Bracket Bolts	18-25 (2.5-3.5)
Hose Union-to-Pump Housing	36-50 (5.0-6.9)
Rear Reservoir Bolts	3-5 (0.4-0.7)
Worm Bearing Adj. Screw Lock Nut	72-94 (10.0-13.0)
Cross Shaft End Cover	29-40 (4.0-5.5)
Valve Housing-to-Gear Housing	29-40 (4.0-5.5)
Gear Housing-to-Frame	36-51 (5.0-7.1)
Cross Shaft-to-Pitman Arm	80-101 (11.1-14.0)
Pulley-to-Pump	25-39 (3.5-5.4)

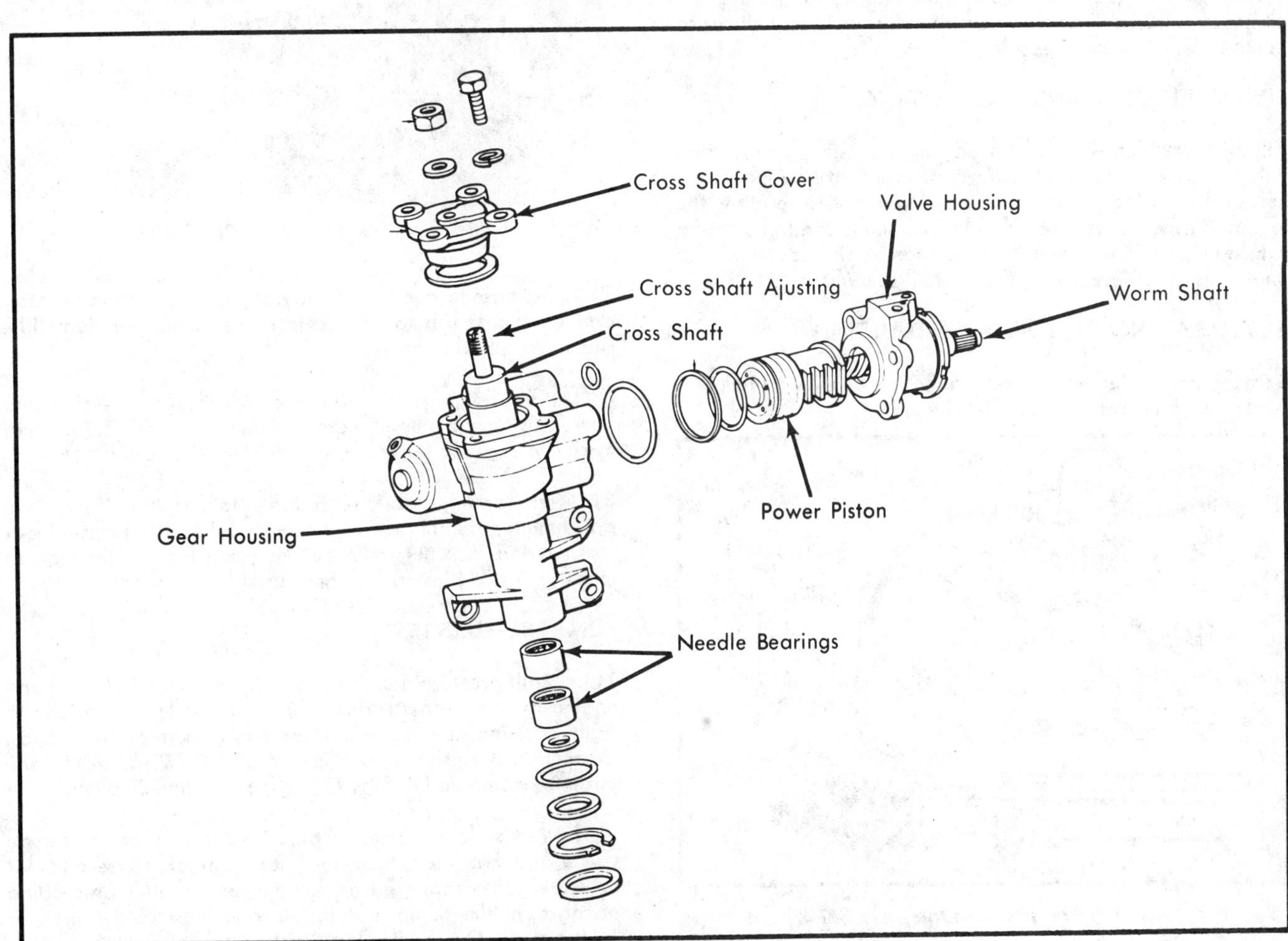

Fig. 9 Exploded View of Power Steering Gear

VOLVO POWER-ASSISTED RACK & PINION

DESCRIPTION

Rack and pinion type cam gear power steering is standard on 260 models and on 240 station wagons. This power steering unit consists of a rack and pinion steering gear and a power assist pump interconnected by flexible lines. The 240 and 260 series use a Saginaw type pump with a separate fluid reservoir. The 240 series also uses a ZF type pump with a separate fluid reservoir.

GENERAL SERVICE

STEERING GEAR LUBRICANT

Type – Engine oil SAE 20W-40 or SAE 20W-50.

Capacity – 6¾ oz.

HYDRAULIC SYSTEM LUBRICANT

Type – ATF Type A or Dexron.

Capacity – 2.3 pts.

STEERING GEAR FILLING

Remove inner clamp on right side rubber bellows, and using a suction gun, fill gear with recommended lubricant through side of bellows. Reinstall clamp, then carefully compress bellows so some oil will flow to other side.

HYDRAULIC OIL FILLING AND BLEEDING

Fill the reservoir with approved oil, then start engine and allow to idle, adding oil as level drops. Turn steering wheel left and right lock to lock in a slow even motion to allow the pump to operate at low pressure. Continue turning steering wheel until oil in reservoir is almost free of air bubbles. Check that oil is at the level mark, then install reservoir cap.

SERVO BALANCE TESTING AND ADJUSTING

Testing – 1) Connect a pressure gauge as shown in *Fig. 1)*. Make sure oil in reservoir is at level mark.

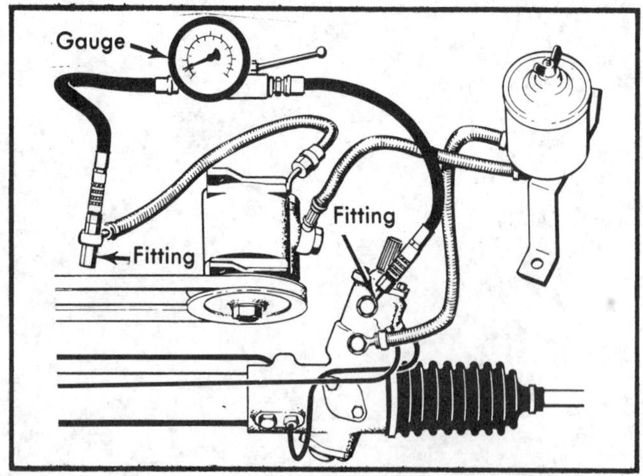

Fig. 1 Pressure Gauge Test Set Up

2) Remove steering wheel impact guard by compressing sides slightly. Install a torque wrench on steering wheel nut.

3) With engine at idle, turn steering wheel (using torque wrench) slowly to right and read torque the moment pressure reaches 170 psi (12 kg/cm²). Repeat operation turning steering wheel to left. Torque should be 30-40 INCH lbs. (35-46 cmkg) as pressure approaches 170 psi (12 kg/cm²). The difference between right and left sides may not exceed 8 INCH lbs. (9 cmkg).

4) If the difference between the sides exceeds this amount, use the following procedures for correction.

Adjusting – 1) Turn off engine and remove lock nut and lock washer from pinion lower bearing *(See Fig. 2)* Lock washer will have one tab bent down to lock adjustment nut (bearing race).

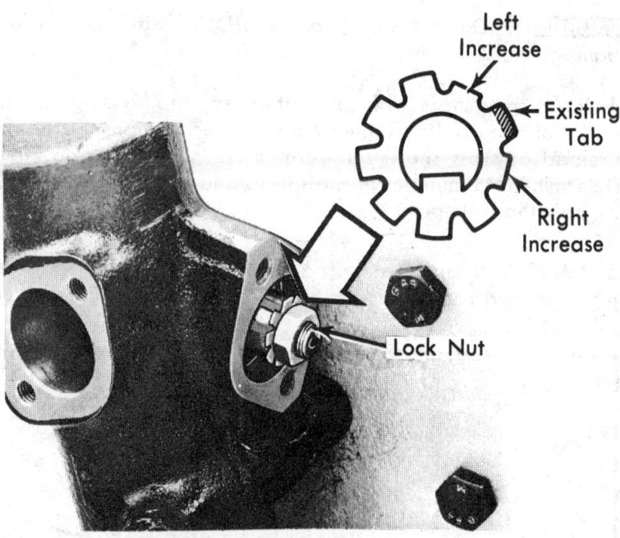

Fig. 2 Lock Washer Adjustment

2) To increase torque for left side, straighten existing bent tab and bend first tab to left. To increase torque for right side, bend first tab to right.

NOTE – *Changing tabs increases torque for one side and decreases torque an equal amount the other side. The value of torque increase or decrease is 4 INCH lbs. (4.6 cmkg).*

3) After bending tab, use suitable tool (9995049) to turn adjustment nut until groove fits lock washer tab. Reinstall lock washer and lock nut, then bend unused lock washer tab to lock nut. Install pinion cover and gasket.

PUMP PRESSURE TEST

1) – With pressure gauge connected as shown in *Fig. 1,* and engine at idle, turn steering wheel fully to left, then fully to right, pressing at end position for a maximum of 10 seconds. Correct pressure should be 895-995 psi (63-69 kg/cm²) for the Saginaw pump and 825 psi (58 kg/cm²) for the ZF pump.

2) To test system maximum pressure, close pressure gauge valve and block oil flow for maximum of 10 seconds. If pressure does not reach the values in the preceeding paragraph, the pump is defective and must be repaired or replaced, see *Overhaul in this article.*

NOTE – *The manufacturer does not recommend repair of the Saginaw pump, replace if defective.*

VOLVO POWER-ASSISTED RACK & PINION (Cont.)

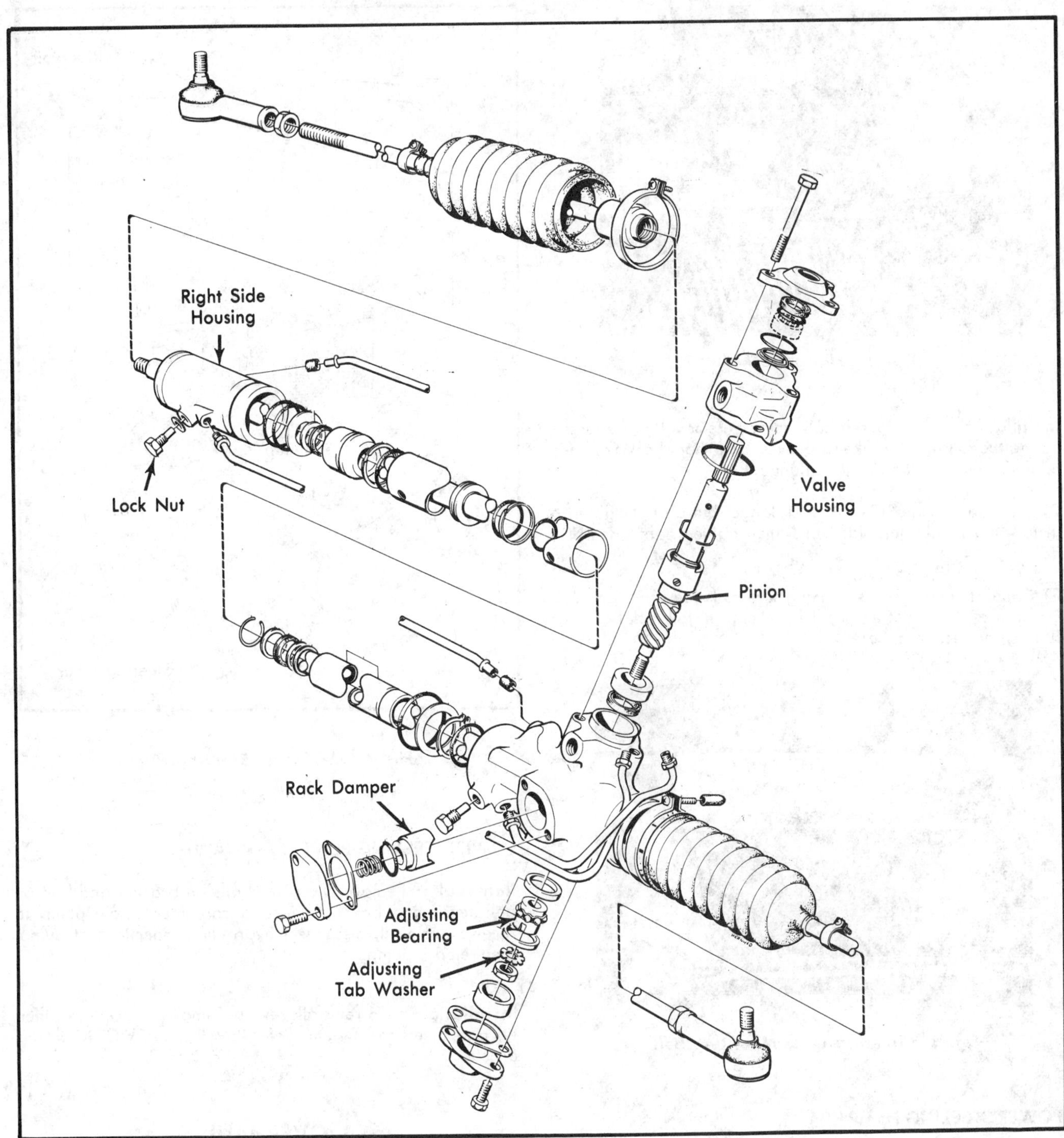

Fig. 3 Exploded View of Volvo Power Steering Components

REMOVAL & INSTALLATION

STEERING GEAR

Removal – 1) Remove lock bolt and nut from pinion flange. Bend flange apart slightly. Raise and support front of vehicle and remove wheels. Remove tie rod nuts and disconnect ball studs from spindle using suitable ball joint removal tool (5043). Remove splash guard.

2) Disconnect hoses at steering gear and install plugs in hose connections to protect against contamination. Remove bolts securing steering gear to front axle member. Pull steering gear down until free of steering shaft flange, then remove steering gear on left side of vehicle.

VOLVO POWER-ASSISTED RACK & PINION (Cont.)

Fig. 4 Flange Lock Bolt

Installation – 1) To reinstall, reverse removal procedure, noting the following: Make sure recess on pinion shaft is aligned toward lock bolt opening in flange.

2) Install right side "U" bolt and flange, but do not tighten. Install and tighten left side bolts, then tighten right side "U" bolt.

3) Connect steering rods, making sure rods are same length. Difference should not exceed 1/16" (2 mm). Install lock bolt on flange and reconnect hoses.

Fig. 5 Steering Gear Mounting Bolts

POWER STEERING PUMP (ZF)

Removal – Place a container below the pump to receive drain oil, then disconnect hydraulic connections. Remove nuts on two long bracket bolts and tensioner locking screws on both sides of pump. Remove drive belt.

2) Turn pump up and remove three screws retaining bracket to engine block, then remove pump and bracket.

Installation – 1) To reinstall, reverse removal procedures, noting the following: Use new copper washers when reconnecting pump hoses. Fill the system with new oil that meets specifications. See *GENERAL SERVICING in this article.*

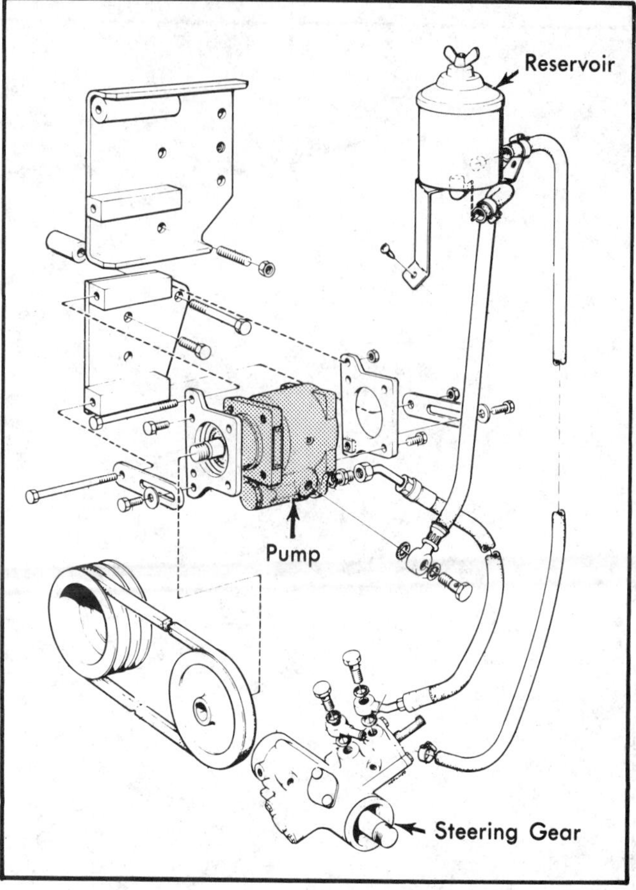

Fig. 6 ZF Power Steering Pump

POWER STEERING PUMP (SAGINAW)

Removal – Remove two pivot bolts on bracket and bolt on belt tensioning bracket. Place a container below pump to receive drain oil, disconnect hydraulic connections at pump, then remove pump.

Installation – To reinstall, reverse removal procedures, then fill and bleed the system, See *GENERAL SERVICING in this article.*

OVERHAUL

STEERING GEAR

Disassembly – 1) Clean steering gear exterior and check inner ball joints for wear. Loosen pinion side rubber bellows and drain oil. Remove steering rod using a 32 mm open end wrench, take load off of pinion with an adjustable wrench. When unscrewing steering rod, lock tab will bend up.

2) Remove oil lines, rack damper cover, piston, "O" ring, and spring. Remove pinion cover and spacer sleeve. Bend up locking tab and remove nut. Using tool (5049), unscrew inner bearing race with ball retainer and outer race from pinion.

VOLVO POWER-ASSISTED RACK & PINION (Cont.)

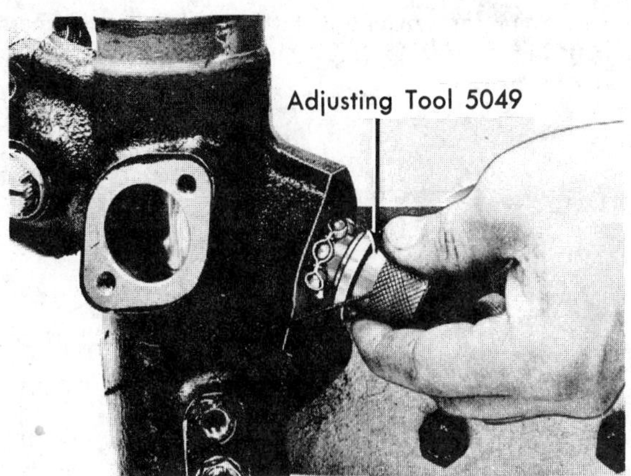

Fig. 7 Inner Bearing Race

3) Unscrew three screws from valve housing cover and remove cover and spring, then lift off valve housing and lift out pinion.

4) Unscrew right side housing lock bolt and remove housing and connecting tube from outer tube, then pull out rack and bearing sleeve. Remove bearing sleeve rack.

5) Unscrew left side housing lock bolt, then remove outer and inner tube from housing. Using suitable tool (1819) remove upper bushing from housing. Use two narrow screwdrivers and remove lower pinion bearing outer race.

CAUTION — *Do not use tool (5051) to remove upper bushing.*

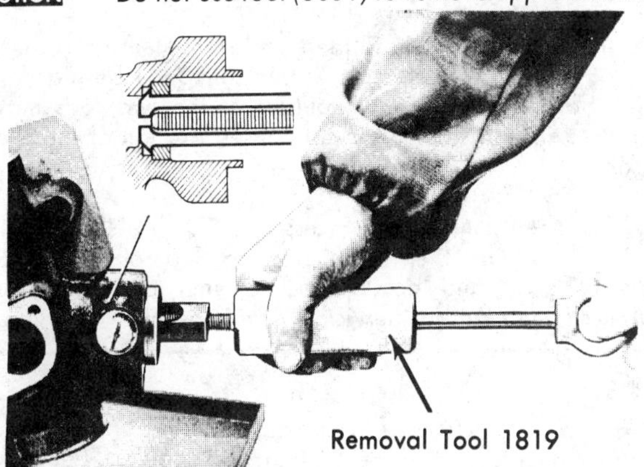

Fig. 8 Removing Upper Bushing

6) Remove "O" rings and spacer from right side housing. Use suitable tool (5051) to remove bearing and seal from valve housing cover. Remove "O" ring from cover and "O" ring, seal, and plastic rings from rack bearing sleeve.

7) Remove plastic ring and "O" ring from rack only if, damaged, worn or rack has more than 24,000 miles on vehicle. Remove oil seal from inner tube. Remove washer and snap ring from tube.

Reassembly — 1) Coat all parts with oil before reassembling. Replace all seals, "O" rings, and defective parts. Using tool (5050) install oil seal, bearing and "O" ring in valve cover. Seal should be glued into cover or cover and seal should be changed.

NOTE — *If the rack bearing is replaced, the bearing sleeve should also be replaced.*

2) Install plastic ring and "O" ring on rack bearing sleeve with "O" ring on tapered side of sleeve. Install snap ring on inner tube, then install "O" ring and plastic ring on rack piston with the "O" ring under the plastic ring.

3) Assemble spacer sleeve, oil seal, and plastic ring on rack (from tooth side). Use tape over teeth to avoid damaging oil seal, then remove tape and install spacer sleeve on rack.

4) Insert seal in left side housing with lip facing out, then press in bushing using suitable tool. Install two "O" rings in left side housing, then install the two "O" rings and spacer washer in right side housing.

5) Lubricate end of inner tube and install with spacer into left housing, then push rack (with seal and spacer rings) into inner tube. Place tool (5056) on rack and using rack and tool, press seal and spacer rings into housing. Withdraw rack approximately ¾" (20 mm) and remove tool, install lock ring.

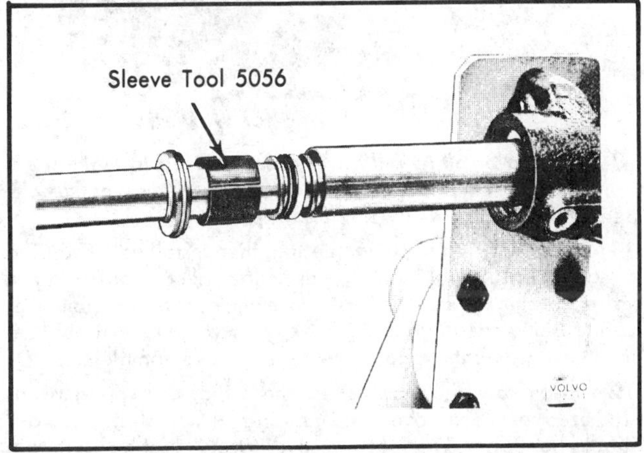

Fig. 9 Installing Seals & Spacer Rings

6) Insert outer tube in left housing, align lock bolt holes in housing and tube, lubricate tube and plastic seal on rack piston, then insert lock bolt with seal. Torque bolt to 9-12 ft. lbs. (1.24-1.66 mkg). Lubricate and insert bearing sleeve in outer tube.

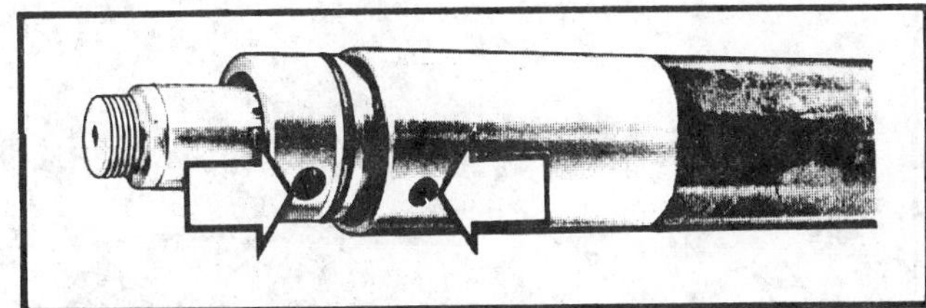

Fig. 10 Lock Bolt Hole Alignment

7) Align sleeve hole with outer tube hole, tape threaded edges and install seal. Remove tape and install plastic ring in bearing sleeve. Lubricate end of connecting tube and insert tube with rubber seal in right side of housing.

8) Install right housing with connecting tube and rubber seal. Align hole in right side of housing with hole in outer tube and install lock bolt. Torque bolt to 9-12 ft. lbs. (1.24-1.66 mkg).

9) Install upper race for pinion lower bearing and insert pinion. Screw on sleeve tool (5049) until .315" (8 mm) of the axle end comes through the retainer. Remove tool.

VOLVO POWER-ASSISTED RACK & PINION (Cont.)

10) Install outer race and spacer sleeve in housing. Press down spacer sleeve so it bottoms on bearing race, then use feeler gauge and straight edge to measure distance between spacer ring and housing. Select gasket(s) of proper thickness, then temporarily install gaskets and cover plate. Gaskets range in thickness from .008-.028" (.2-.7 mm).

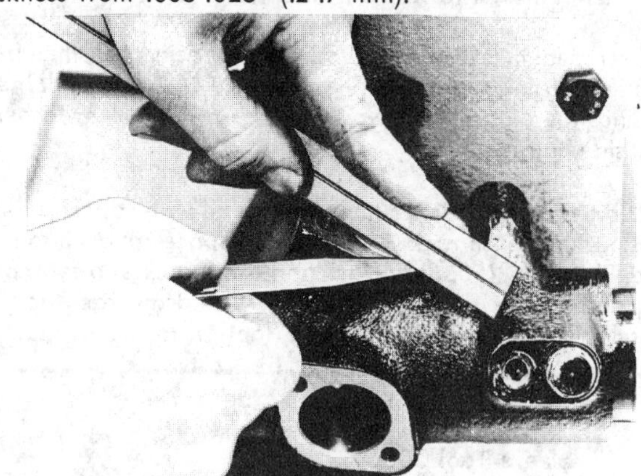

Fig. 11 Measuring for Gasket(s)

NOTE — *Cover plate will have to be removed to make servo balance adjustment after steering gear is installed on vehicle. See GENERAL SERVICING in this article.*

11) Insert "O" ring in valve housing, then install valve housing on gear. Install tool (5171) over splines. Place coil spring in valve housing, large end first. To eliminate the possibility of spring being caught in top groove of valve housing, adjust pinion upwards until spool covers the groove completely.

12) Install valve housing cover, check that coil spring is not squeezed between cover and housing. Pinion shaft shoulder should be .06" (1.5 mm) above cover face. Adjust by using tool (5049) and moving lower bearing inner race. Install lock ring and lock nut.

13) Install damper piston (without "O" ring) in housing. Press piston against rack, then use feeler gauge and straight edge to measure clearance between piston face and housing. Adjust by using shims equal to measured clearance plus .002-.006" (.05-.15 mm). Shims are available in the following thicknesses: .002" (.051 mm), .0035" (.089 mm), .005" (.127 mm), and .010" (.254 mm).

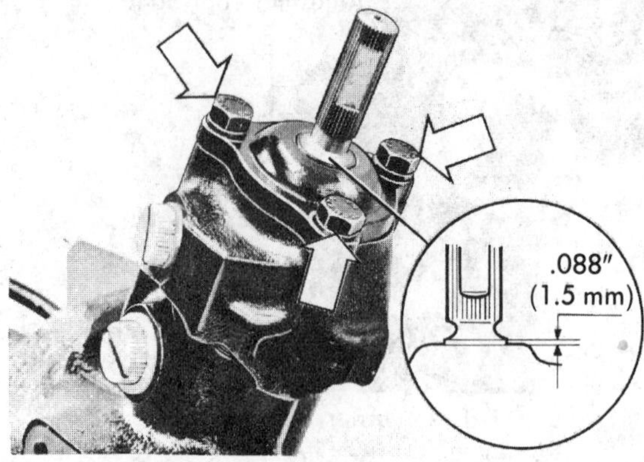

Fig. 12 Pinion Shaft Shoulder Measurement

14) Install "O" ring damper, spring, shims, and cover on housing. Use brass shims as the outer ones in stack. Connect an INCH lbs. torque wrench to pinion shaft and rotate shaft in both directions to stop. Torque should be 8-14 INCH lbs. (9-16 cmkg). If torque is excessive at any point, stop rack in that position and readjust by adding shims.

NOTE — *If rack jams with damper removed, rack is warped, and must be replaced.*

15) Install oil lines, reinstall left and right steering rods. If installing previously used rods, a thin shim may be placed between ball joint and rack shoulder or the two rods may be swapped in order to obtain an unused portion of the rod for locking.

16) Lock ball joint in rack recess and install bellows, clamps, and tie rod ends, then install steering gear on vehicle. Refill steering gear and power steering unit and check servo balance. See *General Servicing in this article.*

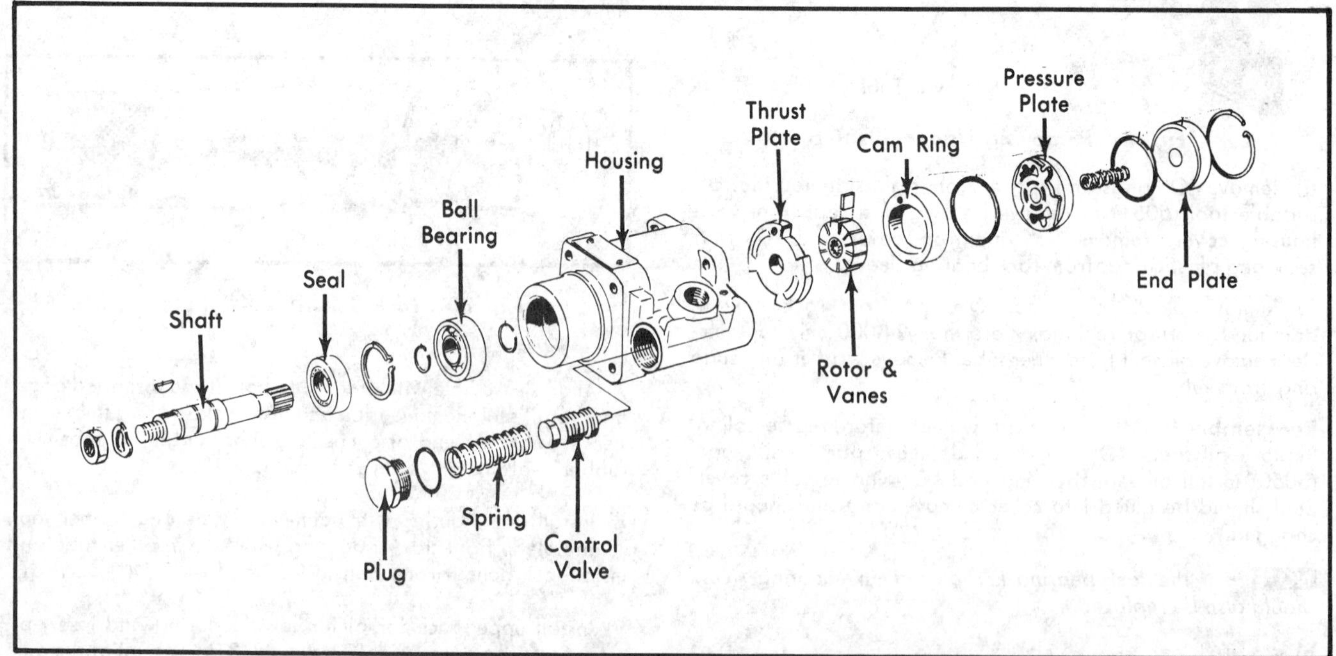

Fig. 13 Exploded View of ZF Power Steering Pump

VOLVO POWER-ASSISTED RACK & PINION (Cont.)

POWER STEERING PUMP

NOTE – *Procedures are for the ZF type pump only, manufacturer recommends replacement of the Saginaw type pump if found defective.*

Disassembly – 1) With pump removed from vehicle, pry front seal from housing. Remove rear cover snap ring and cover. Take out pressure plate and spring.

2) Turn pump over and tap on end until parts fall free. Remove ball bearing retaining ring, then push shaft out of housing. Push out thrust plate and cam ring, if still in housing.

3) Remove plug, control valve, spring and all "O" rings from housing. Check all parts for wear and scratches. Replace all worn or damaged parts and all "O" rings.

NOTE – *If pump housing bushing is defective, replace housing assembly. Rotor, vanes and cam ring are also replaced as an assembly.*

Reassembly – 1) Install bearing on shaft (if replaced). Bearing is held by rings on each side. Press bearing and shaft into housing.

2) Snap bearing retaining ring into housing. Install thrust plate in housing making sure dowel is through one of the holes in thrust plate, then place cam ring on dowel, arrow facing up.

Fig. 14 Cam Ring Installation

3) Install "O" rings in housing, small "O" ring nearest cam ring. Place rotor in housing, then insert vanes in rotor (rounded ends toward cam ring). Install pressure plate with dowel aligned in one of the holes.

4) Insert "O" ring, spring and cover, then press in cover and install retaining ring. Install control valve, spring and plug, then place shaft seal into housing and tap seal lightly until properly seated.

5) Install pump assembly on vehicle, then refill and bleed system. See *GENERAL SERVICING in this article procedure.*

English-Metric Conversion Chart

FRACTIONS TO INCHES & METRIC EQUIVALENTS

Fractions	Inches	MM	Fractions	Inches	MM
1/64	.016	.397	33/64	.516	13.097
1/32	.031	.794	17/32	.531	13.494
3/64	.047	1.191	35/64	.547	13.891
1/16	.063	1.588	9/16	.563	14.288
5/64	.078	1.984	37/64	.578	14.684
3/32	.094	2.381	19/32	.594	15.081
7/64	.109	2.778	39/64	.609	15.478
1/8	.125	3.175	5/8	.625	15.875
9/64	.141	3.572	41/64	.641	16.272
5/32	.156	3.969	21/32	.656	16.669
11/64	.172	4.366	43/64	.672	17.066
3/16	.188	4.763	11/16	.687	17.463
13/64	.203	5.159	45/64	.703	17.859
7/32	.219	5.556	23/32	.719	18.256
15/64	.234	5.953	47/64	.734	18.653
1/4	.250	6.350	3/4	.750	19.050
17/64	.266	6.747	49/64	.766	19.447
9/32	.281	7.144	25/32	.781	19.844
19/64	.297	7.541	51/64	.797	20.241
5/16	.313	7.938	13/16	.813	20.638
21/64	.328	8.334	53/64	.828	21.034
11/32	.344	8.731	27/32	.844	21.431
23/64	.359	9.128	55/64	.859	21.828
3/8	.375	9.525	7/8	.875	22.225
25/64	.391	9.922	57/64	.891	22.622
13/32	.406	10.319	29/32	.906	23.019
27/64	.422	10.716	59/64	.922	23.416
7/16	.438	11.113	15/16	.938	23.813
29/64	.453	11.509	61/64	.953	24.209
15/32	.469	11.906	31/32	.969	24.606
31/64	.484	12.303	63/64	.984	25.003
1/2	.500	12.700			

CONVERSION FACTORS

Unit	To Unit	Multiply By
LENGTH		
Millimeters	Inches	.03937
Inches	Millimeters	25.4
Meters	Feet	3.28084
Feet	Meters	.3048
Kilometers	Miles	.62137
Miles	Kilometers	1.60935
AREA		
Square Centimeters	Square Inches	.155
Square Inches	Square Centimeters	6.45159
VOLUME		
Cubic Centimeters	Cubic Inches	.06103
Cubic Inches	Cubic Centimeters	16.38703
Liters	Cubic Inches	61.025
Cubic Inches	Liters	.01639
Liters	Quarts	1.05672
Quarts	Liters	.94633
Liters	Pints	2.11344
Pints	Liters	.47317
Liters	Ounces	33.81497
Ounces	Liters	.02957
WEIGHT		
Grams	Ounces	.03527
Ounces	Grams	28.34953
Kilograms	Pounds	2.20462
Pounds	Kilograms	.45359
WORK		
Centimeter Kilograms	Inch Pounds	.8676
Inch Pounds	Centimeter Kilograms	1.15262
Meter Kilograms	Foot Pounds	7.23301
Foot Pounds	Meter Kilograms	.13826
PRESSURE		
Kilograms/ Sq. Centimeter	Pounds/Sq.Inch	14.22334
Pounds/Sq.Inch	Kilograms/Sq.Centimeter	.07031
Bar	Pounds/Sq.Inch	14.504
Pounds/Sq.Inch	Bar	.06895
Atmosphere	Pounds/Sq.Inch	14.696
Pounds/Sq.Inch	Atmosphere	.06805
TEMPERATURE		
Centigrade Degrees	Fahrenheit Degrees	$(C^\circ \times 9/5)+32$
Fahrenheit Degrees	Centigrade Degrees	$(F^\circ - 32) \times 5/9$

MILLIMETERS TO INCHES

Conversion Factor — Multiply known millimeter figure by .03937

MM	Inches	MM	Inches	MM	Inches	MM	Inches	MM	Inches
1	.039	21	.827	41	1.614	61	2.402	81	3.189
2	.079	22	.866	42	1.654	62	2.441	82	3.228
3	.118	23	.906	43	1.693	63	2.480	83	3.268
4	.157	24	.945	44	1.732	64	2.520	84	3.307
5	.197	25	.984	45	1.772	65	2.559	85	3.346
6	.236	26	1.024	46	1.811	66	2.598	86	3.386
7	.276	27	1.063	47	1.850	67	2.638	87	3.425
8	.315	28	1.102	48	1.890	68	2.677	88	3.465
9	.354	29	1.142	49	1.929	69	2.717	89	3.504
10	.394	30	1.181	50	1.969	70	2.756	90	3.543
11	.433	31	1.220	51	2.008	71	2.795	91	3.583
12	.472	32	1.260	52	2.047	72	2.835	92	3.622
13	.512	33	1.299	53	2.087	73	2.874	93	3.661
14	.551	34	1.339	54	2.126	74	2.913	94	3.701
15	.591	35	1.378	55	2.165	75	2.953	95	3.740
16	.630	36	1.417	56	2.205	76	2.992	96	3.780
17	.669	37	1.457	57	2.244	77	3.031	97	3.819
18	.709	38	1.496	58	2.283	78	3.071	98	3.858
19	.748	39	1.535	59	2.323	79	3.110	99	3.898
20	.787	40	1.575	60	2.362	80	3.150	100	3.937

INCHES TO MILLIMETERS

Conversion Factor — Multiply known inch figure by 25.40

Inches	MM	Inches	MM	Inches	MM	Inches	MM	Inches	MM
.001	.025	.040	1.016	.340	8.636	.640	16.256	.940	23.876
.002	.051	.050	1.270	.350	8.890	.650	16.510	.950	24.130
.003	.076	.060	1.524	.360	9.144	.660	16.764	.960	24.384
.004	.102	.070	1.778	.370	9.398	.670	17.018	.970	24.638
.005	.127	.080	2.032	.380	9.652	.680	17.272	.980	24.892
.006	.152	.090	2.286	.390	9.906	.690	17.526	.990	25.146
.007	.178	.100	2.540	.400	10.160	.700	17.780	1.000	25.400
.008	.203	.110	2.794	.410	10.414	.710	18.034	2.000	50.800
.009	.229	.120	3.048	.420	10.668	.720	18.288	3.000	76.200
.010	.254	.130	3.302	.430	10.922	.730	18.542	4.000	101.600
.011	.279	.140	3.556	.440	11.176	.740	18.796	5.000	127.000
.012	.305	.150	3.810	.450	11.430	.750	19.050		
.013	.330	.160	4.064	.460	11.684	.760	19.304		
.014	.356	.170	4.318	.470	11.938	.770	19.558		
.015	.381	.180	4.572	.480	12.192	.780	19.812		
.016	.406	.190	4.826	.490	12.446	.790	20.066		
.017	.432	.200	5.080	.500	12.700	.800	20.320		
.018	.457	.210	5.334	.510	12.954	.810	20.574		
.019	.483	.220	5.558	.520	13.208	.820	20.828		
.020	.508	.230	5.842	.530	13.462	.830	21.082		
.021	.533	.240	6.096	.540	13.716	.840	21.336		
.022	.559	.250	6.350	.550	13.970	.850	21.590		
.023	.584	.260	6.604	.560	14.224	.860	21.844		
.024	.610	.270	6.858	.570	14.478	.870	22.098		
.025	.635	.280	7.112	.580	14.732	.880	22.352		
.026	.652	.290	7.366	.590	14.986	.890	22.606		
.027	.686	.300	7.620	.600	15.240	.900	22.860		
.028	.711	.310	7.874	.610	15.494	.910	23.114		
.029	.737	.320	8.128	.620	15.748	.920	23.368		
.030	.762	.330	8.382	.630	16.002	.930	23.622		

Torque & Drill Conversion Chart

TORQUE CONVERSIONS
FOOT POUNDS TO METER KILOGRAMS

Ft. Lbs.	Mkg	Ft. Lbs.	Mkg	Ft. Lbs.	Mkg	Ft. Lbs.	Mkg
1	.14	26	3.60	51	7.05	76	10.51
2	.28	27	3.73	52	7.19	77	10.65
3	.41	28	3.87	53	7.33	78	10.78
4	.55	29	4.01	54	7.47	79	10.92
5	.69	30	4.15	55	7.60	80	11.06
6	.83	31	4.29	56	7.74	81	11.20
7	.97	32	4.42	57	7.88	82	11.34
8	1.11	33	4.56	58	8.02	83	11.48
9	1.24	34	4.70	59	8.16	84	11.61
10	1.38	35	4.84	60	8.30	85	11.75
11	1.52	36	4.98	61	8.43	86	11.89
12	1.66	37	5.12	62	8.57	87	12.03
13	1.80	38	5.25	63	8.71	88	12.17
14	1.94	39	5.39	64	8.85	89	12.31
15	2.07	40	5.53	65	8.99	90	12.44
16	2.21	41	5.67	66	9.13	91	12.58
17	2.35	42	5.81	67	9.26	92	12.72
18	2.49	43	5.95	68	9.40	93	12.86
19	2.63	44	6.08	69	9.54	94	13.00
20	2.77	45	6.22	70	9.68	95	13.13
21	2.90	46	6.36	71	9.82	96	13.27
22	3.04	47	6.50	72	9.95	97	13.41
23	3.18	48	6.64	73	10.09	98	13.55
24	3.32	49	6.77	74	10.23	99	13.69
25	3.46	50	6.91	75	10.37	100	13.83

DRILL SIZE & IDENTIFICATION

Drill Diam.	Drill Size	Drill Diam.	Drill Size	Drill Diam.	Drill Size	Drill Diam.	Drill Size
.413″	Z	.2280″	1	.1440″	27	.0550″	54
.404″	Y	.2210″	2	.1405″	28	.0520″	55
.397″	X	.2130″	3	.1360″	29	.0465″	56
.386″	W	.2090″	4	.1285″	30	.0430″	57
.377″	V	.2055″	5	.1200″	31	.0420″	58
.368″	U	.2040″	6	.1160″	32	.0410″	59
.358″	T	.2010″	7	.1130″	33	.0400″	60
.348″	S	.1990″	8	.1110″	34	.0390″	61
.339″	R	.1960″	9	.1100″	35	.0380″	62
.332″	Q	.1935″	10	.1065″	36	.0370″	63
.323″	P	.1910″	11	.1040″	37	.0360″	64
.316″	O	.1890″	12	.1015″	38	.0350″	65
.302″	N	.1850″	13	.0995″	39	.0330″	66
.295″	M	.1820″	14	.0980″	40	.0320″	67
.290″	L	.1800″	15	.0960″	41	.0310″	68
.281″	K	.1770″	16	.0935″	42	.0292″	69
.277″	J	.1730″	17	.0890″	43	.0280″	70
.272″	I	.1695″	18	.0860″	44	.0260″	71
.266″	H	.1660″	19	.0820″	45	.0250″	72
.261″	G	.1610″	20	.0810″	46	.0240″	73
.257″	F	.1590″	21	.0785″	47	.0225″	74
.250″	E	.1570″	22	.0760″	48	.0210″	75
.246″	D	.1540″	23	.0730″	49	.0200″	76
.242″	C	.1520″	24	.0700″	50	.0180″	77
.238″	B	.1495″	25	.0670″	51	.0160″	78
.234″	A	.1470″	26	.0635″	52	.0145″	79
				.0595″	53	.0135″	80

Notes

Notes

Latest Changes & Corrections

NOTE — *These items are late changes which arrived too late to be included in the regular data pages or are items which are not normally included but have been determined to be valuable information. These items are individually numbered to assist in relating them to the general text. To prevent overlooking these items, simply write the corresponding number of the item on the appropriate page of text.*

TUNE-UP — SECTION 1

1 ► *1976 IMPORTED CAR & TRUCK TUNE-UP/MECHANICAL SERVICE & REPAIR MANUAL* — The following list contains corrections that should be made in your manual:

1) XJ12 & XJS Valve Arrangement is: E-I-E-I-E-I-I-E-I-E-I-E.

2) XJ12 & XJS Distributor Rotation is: Counterclockwise.

3) Triumph 4 Cylinder Valve Adjustment Procedure omitted for text is:

Valve Open	Valves to Adjust
Nos. 8 & 6	Nos. 1 & 3
Nos. 4 & 7	Nos. 5 & 2
Nos. 1 & 3	Nos. 8 & 6
Nos. 5 & 2	Nos. 4 & 7

NOTE — *Valves are numbered front to rear.*

2 ► *1977 CAPRI: ENGINE DETONATION (KNOCK) CORRECTION NOTE* — Spark knock on these vehicles can be corrected by retarding the initial timing up to 6° from specification shown on Vehicle Emission Control Decal. This adjustment applies only to the Calibration Numbers shown in the chart below. Note that adjustment should be done in 2° increments until the spark knock condition is eliminated or minimized to a satisfactory level. Curb idle speed must be readjusted after timing is set. Also check and reset fast idle.

Cars Authorized for Timing Adjustment

Application	Calibration No.
2.3L "A" (1CV5)	7-21A-RO
	7-21B-RO
	7-21B-R10
	7-1X-RO
	7-1X-R10
	7-2X-R10
2.3L "B" (1CV5)	7-2A-RO
	7-2B-RO
2.8L "B" (1CV5)	7-4A-R2
	7-3A-R2

3 ► *1976 CAPRI II, IGNITION TIMING MARKS CORRECTION* — Some timing mark illustrations show engine crankshaft pulley with 3° increment markings. The markings on the crankshaft should be in 2° increments.

1975 FIAT 128 IGNITION TIMING — Inspection of timing has become more difficult with the addition of more components. More timing reference marks have been added to the transmission bell housing and flywheel, these are in addition to marks on crankshaft pulley and timing cover. If the spare tire is removed, upper side of clutch housing is visible.

4 ► *1977 AND EARLIER LANCIA: ENGINE HESITATION* — Some models may experience a slight hesitation during operation in especially cold or damp weather. Problem may be caused by air filter top cover being in the incorrect climatic setting. There are two separate air intake positions: Cold and Warm. For cold setting align reference mark I on air cleaner cover with arrow on the air cleaner duct. For warm setting make sure reference mark E on air cleaner cover aligns with arrow on duct.

5 ► *1975 MERCEDES-BENZ 280 & 280C CALIFORNIA MODELS: ADJUSTING CO VALUE AT IDLE SPEED NOTE* — Note the following procedure for adjusting the CO value on these vehicles:

1) Allow engine to idle (normal operating temperature). Disconnect the red VACUUM line at coupling hose. This will make air injection system inoperative.

2) Check CO value with an exhaust gas analyzer (or other suitable equipment). With air injection disconnected, CO value should be 6.0-8.0%. Adjust value by turning mixture adjusting screws equally.

3) Reconnect red vacuum line. Check CO value. With air injection working, CO value should be 1.5% maximum.

6 ► *1977 MERCEDES-BENZ, 230 MODELS: HIGH ALTITUDE CO% & IDLE ADJUSTMENT* — Adjustments for high altitude models differ slightly from adjustments for California and Federal models. Make note of the following differences:

Ensure high altitude adjusting disc is set to "4000" for high altitude. Adjust CO% and idle speed according to service procedure given in "Mercedes-Benz Systems & Service Procedures" under 1977 EXHAUST EMISSION SYSTEMS in this supplement or as given in appropriate carburetor article in FUEL SYSTEMS section of this supplement.

7 ► *1976 & SOME EARLIER SAAB MODELS, SPARK PLUG* **NOTE** — Manufacturer now recommends use of NGK spark plugs. These spark plugs were used to meet emission standards testing. The spark plugs provide cleaner burning in cylinders due to position of electrode when fitted in cylinder.

8 ► *1974-75 SUBARU, ALL MODELS: ICE FORMATION IN AIR CLEANER FLAME ARRESTOR* — The flame arrestor in the air cleaner housing may accumulate ice, particularly at very low temperatures. This ice formation may cause total blockage of the flame arrestor which may result in very high crankcase pressures. This could cause engine seal failure or cause engine oil to be pushed out the engine dipstick tube. Correct this situation as follows:

1) Remove air cleaner housing. Turn air cleaner upside down on a workbench. Centerpunch a mark on the "T" fitting which is in line with the vertical pipe which attaches to the air cleaner housing.

2) Drill a ¼" hole at center punch mark, being careful not to drill into the flame arrestor screen.

Latest Changes & Corrections

FOR 1977 & PREVIOUS MODELS

TUNE-UP – SECTION 1 (Cont.)

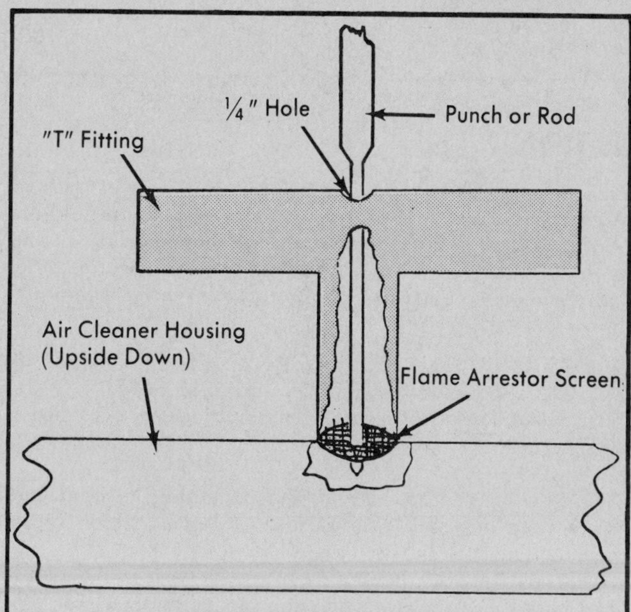

Fig. 1 Modifying Air Cleaner Flame Arrester and Screen to Prevent Ice Blockage

3) Insert a long punch or sharp rod through the hole and push the mesh of the flame arrestor screen to the side to make an opening of 3/8-1/4". Use aluminized tape or other suitable material to tape over the drilled hole in the "T" fitting.

9 ► *1976 AND LATER RABBIT AND SCIROCCO: BALLAST RESISTOR CHANGE* – Ignition coil ballast resistor has been replaced by a resistor wire. New resistor wire runs from coil terminal 15 to relay fuse plate C15. The new wire is clear with violet stripes. The resistance is approximately .9 ohms.

10 ► *1976 AND LATER RABBIT DIESEL MODELS: IDLE SPEED NOTE* – Volkswagen recently revised the engine idle speed setting for Rabbit models with diesel engines. Note that the proper setting for engine idle speed is now 770-870 RPM. All previous specifications are no longer valid.

11 ► *1977 RABBIT AND SCIROCCO: SPARK PLUG CHANGE* – When spark plugs are replaced make sure to use the ones from the revised list. Bosch, W 175 T 30; Beru, 175/14/3A; or Champion N8Y.

12 ► *1977 RABBIT DIESEL: FAN BELT CHANGE* – Rabbit models equipped with diesel engines will be fitted with a new, stronger fan belt as part of a running production change. Whenever belt replacement is required use the improved strength belt. Note that belt tension remains 3/8-5/8" (10-15 mm) thumb deflection.

13 ► *1977 AND LATER VOLKSWAGEN DASHER: REPLACEMENT SPARK PLUGS CHANGE* – When it becomes necessary to replace the spark plugs in subject vehicles with engine codes YH, YG, or YK, select one of the following types: Bosch, W 175 T 30; Beru, 175/14/3A ; Champion, N8Y.

14 ► *1977 VOLVO: VEHICLE IDENTIFICATION NOTE* – The following is an exact break-down of the Volvo vehicle identification number:

VC 242 4 5 H 1 123456

First Two Digits – Manufacturer Prefix (Volvo Car).
Third, Fourth, Fifth Digits – Model:
242, 262 – 2 Door Sedan
244, 264 – 4 Door Sedan
245, 265 – Station Wagon
Sixth Digit – Engine Type (4 = B21/6 = B27)
Seventh Digit – Engine Version (5 = "F" Version US Specs.)
Eighth Digit – Model Year (H = 1977)
Ninth Digit – Assembly Plant
Remaining Digits – Serial Number

Starting 1977 Vehicle Identification Numbers

Application	Serial Number
242	099680
244	174910
245	115350
262	002430
264	034470
265	008115

15 *1975 RABBIT AND SCIROCCO CATALYTIC CONVERTER* – It is no longer necessary to replace the converter as part of 30,-000 mile maintenance work. Disconnect the Yellow/Red wire to multi plug connector of special milage odometer so light will not come on at 30,000 miles. The light will still be activated in the case of catalytic overheating.

FUEL SYSTEMS – SECTION 2

1 ► *1977 AUDI FOX: CIS FUEL INJECTION MODIFICATIONS* – At the beginning of 1977 production, a few items in the CIS fuel injection system were modified from 1976. These include the fuel pump, having modified bracket and fuel lines and stud-and-nut electrical connections on front of pump; check valve in pump connection has 12 mm diameter connector (old was 10 mm); fuel accumulator volume was increased to 2.40 cu. in. (40 cc); throttle valve housing has 18 mm diameter; fuel distributor has check valve to avoid decrease in system pressure if control pressure regulator is defective; back pressure valve is installed in supply and return fuel lines.

2 ► *1976 & EARLIER CAPRI, VEHICLES CALIBRATED FOR NON-HIGH ALTITUDE OPERATION: RESETTING IDLE SPEED* – On vehicles calibrated for non-high altitude operation (sea level), if driving into a high altitude region, loss of engine idle speed will result and may cause rough operation or stalling. Condition may be temporarily corrected by resetting idle speed RPM specified on Emission Control Decal. Once lower altitude driving is resumed, change idle speed back to correct specification.

FOR 1977 & PREVIOUS MODELS

FUEL SYSTEMS – SECTION 2 (Cont.)

3 ▶ *1976 & EARLIER CAPRI II: STICKING OR BINDING CHOKE PLATE OR LINKAGE* – Cold ambient temperature operating conditions may, in some instances, contribute to carburetor icing and/or sticking or binding choke plates and linkage. It is good practice to make a thorough inspection of operation of choke plate and related linkage when engine performance condition requires inspection or diagnosis of the carburetor.

4 ▶ *1976 CAPRI II, FUEL TANK INACCURATE CORRECTION* – A new fuel gauge is available for 1976 and prior models. The new gauge should provide a more accurate reading at both "FULL" and "EMPTY" ends of gauge scale.

5 ▶ *1976 CAPRI II WITH 2.8L ENGINE & 2150 2-BBL. CARBURETOR: CHOKE PULLDOWN DIAPHRAGM ADJUSTMENT NOTE* – Loctite 290 has been applied to threads of the diaphragm adjusting screw on ALL applicable models shown above. DO NOT ATTEMPT to turn diaphragm adjusting screw without first softening the Loctite. This can be done by heating the area around the screw with a soldering gun or by applying fresh Loctite to the screw. Now screw should be able to turn easily without damage.

6 ▶ *1976 COLT DASHPOT CHANGE* – The carburetor dashpot used on all 1975 and 1976 Colt models with automatic transmission was eliminated in production approximately 5/75.

7 ▶ *1977 & EARLIER COURIER, VEHICLES CALIBRATED FOR NON-HIGH ALTITUDE OPERATION: RESETTING IDLE SPEED* – On vehicles calibrated for non-high altitude operation (sea level), if driving into a high altitude region, loss of engine idle speed will result and may cause rough operation or stalling.

This condition may be temporarily corrected by resetting idle speed to RPM specified on Emission Control Decal if high altitude driving is to be done for any length of time. Reset idle speed upon reaching low altitude region.

8 ▶ *1977 & EARLIER COURIER: STICKING OR BINDING CHOKE PLATE OR LINKAGE* – Cold ambient temperature operating conditions may, in some instances, contribute to carburetor icing and/or sticking or binding choke plates and linkage. It is good practice to make a thorough inspection of operation of choke plate and related linkage when engine performance condition requires inspection or diagnosis of the carburetor.

9 ▶ *1976 FIAT MODELS, FUEL SYSTEM SPILLAGE NOTE* – All models are equipped with two in-line valves. These valves are designed to interrupt gasoline spillage in the event of an accident. One valve (part no. 4362497) is located on fuel delivery line, between fuel tank and pump. The other valve (part no. 4361910) is installed near carburetor on fuel system line to fuel tank. An arrow is cast on each valve to show fuel flow direction.

10 ▶ *1976 AND EARLIER MODEL CIVIC, DAMAGED FUEL PUMP ARM NOTE* – Some models may develop a broken, cracked or bent fuel pump arm. The cause is generally improper installation technique. When replacing fuel pump, make sure pump is held squarely with head as it is put on. Also, make sure when bolts are tightened pump is held flush against head. Pump will not operate if insulator block is installed improperly. Opening in insulator must line up with opening in head.

11 ▶ *1977 PORSCHE 911S: MODIFICATIONS TO FUEL INJECTION SYSTEM* – In 1977, 911S models had some modifications made to the fuel injection system over previous years. The sensor plate lever has a riveted leaf spring, which holds the CO adjustment screw against the sensor plate lever. The sensor plate lever stop has been modified so that the rubber block is higher, limiting downward movement of the lever. The wire clip for sensor plate height adjustment has been replaced by a screw and lock nut.

12 *1975 SAAB WARM START DIFFICULTY* – Problem has been traced to a loss of fuel pressure in system after shut down; this causes a vapor lock. Fuel pressure loss may occur through fuel pump check valve. Usually the spring that seats check valve works out of its retainer and relieves spring tension from check valve.

13 ▶ *1975 SAAB, COLD START DRIVEABILITY CORRECTION* – Installation of accelerator enrichment system kit (part no. 83-28-256) should eliminate any difficulty. Kit uses existing cold start valve to provide momentary enrichment of fuel mixture each time throttle is opened during warm-up.

14 *1975 SAAB 99 ICE ACCUMULATION IN THROTTLE HOUSING* – Some 1975 models built prior to 2/76 may experience ice accumulation in throttle housing under certain conditions. To correct this problem, install crankcase ventilation kit, part number 83 31 514.

15 *1975 SAAB AIR CLEANER POSITION CHANGE* – On vehicles produced later in the model year the air cleaner snorkel has been fitted so open end is facing upward. The change reduces the possibility of water and dust entering intake system. It is recommended that all 1975 models have this change performed on them. Loosen hose clamp on snorkel and rotate snorkel until it points diagonally upward behind radiator.

16 *1975 BEETLE AND TYPE 2 AUXILIARY AIR REGULATOR REPLACEMENT* – When testing or replacing an auxiliary air regulator the following points should be taken into consideration: In trouble shooting idle problems on AFC or CIS equipped engines the difference between cold idle and warm idle is less than earlier models equipped with carburetor. Check regulator electrically as well as mechanically. The resistance between contact points of auxiliary air regulator should ber 30 ohms.

17 *1975 VOLKSWAGEN DASHER BASIC THROTTLE VALVE ADJUSTMENT* – Throttle stop screw is preset at factory and should not be changed, however if screw is turned, basic adjustment is as follows: Remove plastic cap from screw. Back out stop screw until there is a gap between screw and fast idle cam. Turn screw in until it just touches fast idle cam then screw as additional ¼ turn. Make final idle speed and CO value adjustment with engine running.

18 ▶ *1976 VOLKSWAGEN DASHER, RABBIT & SCIROCCO, CARBURETOR BOLT TORQUE NOTE* – Be sure that carburetor mounting bolts (4) are torqued to 8 ft. lbs. If correct torque is not applied, by-pass of the drainage system for choke link housing is not sealed and engine surging will result.

19 ▶ *1976 VOLKSWAGEN BEETLE & BUS: CORRECTION OF BINDING THROTTLE VALVE CONDITION* – A binding throttle

FOR 1977 & PREVIOUS MODELS

FUEL SYSTEMS — SECTION 2 (Cont.)

valve can be caused by a binding throttle valve switch, carbon deposits on throttle shaft or plate, or misaligned throttle plate. Perform the following operation to correct any or all of these conditions:

1) Check throttle valve switch for binding. Replace if necessary. Remove throttle plate and shaft. Clean, lubricate and reinstall.

NOTE — *Before removing shaft, clean burrs at threaded holes for throttle plate to prevent damage to sealing surface.*

2) After reinstalling throttle plate, loosen screws for throttle plate again. Center the throttle plate and fully tighten and peen screws.

NOTE — *Be sure to support throttle shaft when peening screws.*

3) Adjust the throttle valve switch: Loosen mounting screws for switch. Hold throttle valve in closed position. Turn throttle valve switch in direction of "open throttle" until you feel light resistance. Tighten mounting screws.

► *1976 VOLKSWAGEN BEETLE: REVISED THROTTLE LEVER* —
20 To insure accurate positioning of the throttle valve, a revised throttle valve lever having a stop screw has been released to service. This new lever is part number 043 133 131 A. Install new throttle valve lever as follows:

1) Remove return spring, connecting rod, throttle valve lever spring and lever.

2) Install connecting rod into revised throttle valve lever. Reposition new throttle valve lever into place and attach springs.

3) Turn stop screw clockwise untill it just touches throttle valve housing. From there, turn stop screw clockwise ⅛-½ turn.

4) Adjust engine idle speed with air by-pass screw. Adjust CO level.

NOTE — *Do not adjust idle speed with throttle lever stop screw.*

► *1977 AND LATER VOLKSWAGEN RABBIT DIESEL: FUEL*
21 *SYSTEM MAINTENANCE CHANGES* — Note that the following fuel maintenance procedures have recently been released by Volkswagen and supersede earlier literature:

FUEL SYSTEM BLEEDING

1) No bleeding is required.

2) Crank engine until it starts.

3) Accelerate engine several times (until engine runs smoothly).

FUEL FILTER REPLACEMENT

Removal — 1) Remove both filter support mounting nuts.

2) Rotate filter until upside down on studs.

3) Carefully loosen filter; avoid any fuel leakage.

4) Rotate filter from upside down position, unscrew filter by hand, remove and discard filter.

Installation — 1) Lightly coat new filter gasket with diesel fuel.

2) Fit filter on to support and tighten by hand.

3) Tighten filter onto mounting studs.

4) Crank engine until it starts; accelerate several times to smooth out operation.

5) Check for leaks.

FUEL FILTER WATER DRAIN

Fuel filters with primer pump and vent screw, and fuel filters with only vent screw:

- Loosen vent screw.
- Loosen drain plug and allow approximately 100 cc fuel to flow from filter.

Fuel filters without vent screw or primer pump:

- Remove fuel return line at injection pump (side with out clamp).
- Loosen drain plug on bottom of fuel filter and allow approximately 100 cc fuel to drain out.

ELECTRICAL — SECTION 3

► *1976 CAPRI II: NEUTRAL START SWITCH CHANGE* —
1 Change applies to models equipped with C-3 automatic transmission. Starting 3/75, the seat belt interlock module and wiring were deleted. This change involved the deletion of the five-pin connector for neutral start switch. The first replacement pin connector had three pins with an intergal ground. This pin connector has been replaced with a new four-pin connector with an external ground. The four pin connector can be used to any other connector, but seat belt interlock will not work.

1971-74 CAPRI WITH 1600 & 2000 cc ENGINES,
2 *ALTERNATOR CHANGE* — All of the above models were originally equipped with either Bosch or Lucas alternators. All models can now use a Motorcraft alternator as a replacement part.

1976 CAPRI II, HARD STARTING — To help improve starting
3 in cold and wet weather, fit a jumper wire to the unused terminal on starter solenoid and to the battery side of the coil.

FOR 1977 & PREVIOUS MODELS

ELECTRICAL – SECTION 3

4 ► *1976 AND EARLIER COLT MODELS: WIPER MOTOR FUSE CHANGE* — It has been discovered through testing that the 10-amp. fuse used to protect the windshield wiper motor circuit is not of high enough amperage. It is recommended that a 15-amp. fuse be used as a replacement fuse.

5 *1971-75 COLT ALTERNATOR LIGHT STAYS ON* — Some models may experience the alternator indicator light remaining on at low speeds or staying on too long. Before testing the charging circuit, see if heaterblower motor fuse has a hair line crack.

► *1976-77 COLT AND ARROW: SPEEDOMETER NOISE CORRECTION* — To stop speedometer cable noise on subject vehicles a new cable silencing bushing and packing has been released. Use following procedure to install new kit:

1) Disconnect speedometer cable from speedometer. Use a pair of needle nosed pliers and pull core (*Fig. 1*) out of housing far enough to gain access to upper cone tip.

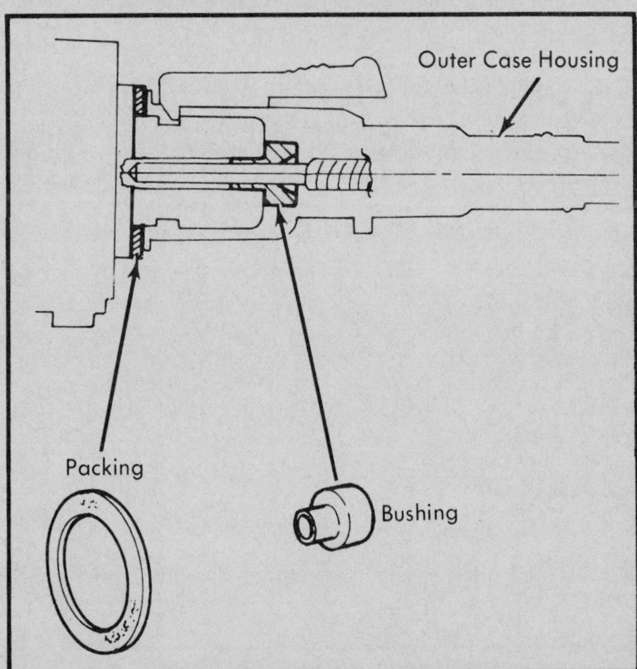

Fig. 1 Installation Position of Speedometer Cable Silencing Kit Components

CAUTION — *Do not damage core when pulling out.*

2) Install new silencing bushing on tip of core. Seat core back into housing. Make sure core is fully engaged in transmission pinion.

3) Peel protective paper from two-faced tape packing then, attach to speedometer side. Connect speedometer cable to speedometer. Check operation.

6 *1975 COLT ALTERNATOR MOUNTING* — All models use shims on pivot bolt. When mounting is loosened to adjust fan belt tension, pivot bolt must be retorqued to 18-21 ft. lbs. (2.5-2.9 mkg). If alternator is removed for overhaul, all clearance between alternator and mounting bracket must be compensated for with shims. If pivot bolt isn't retorqued, wear will result in alternator rear housing and timing case cover.

7 ► *1974 FIAT 128 AND X1/9: VACUUM HOSE ROUTING FOR DISTRIBUTOR RETARD DIAPHRAGM* — Three items control the operation of retard diaphragm: A vacuum outlet, located on carburetor below throttle butterfly; a thermovalve, located on cylinder head just above No. 3 spark plug; a vacuum delay valve, located in vacuum chamber of distributor. If vacuum hose is not routed exactly as outlined below, retard diaphragm will not function properly:

- From outlet on carburetor to one nipple on thermovalve.
- From other nipple on thermovalve to WHITE nipple on delay valve.
- From BLACK nipple on delay valve to vacuum chamber on distributor.

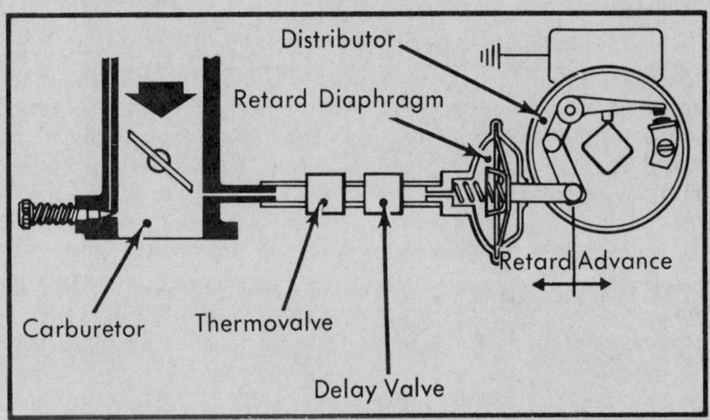

Fig. 2 Vacuum Hose Routing for Distributor Retard Diaphragm

8 ► *1974 AND LATER FIAT 124 SPECIAL AND SEDAN: SPEEDOMETER CABLE ROUTE CHANGE* — The cable routing for subject models has been changed. The change necessitates a longer cable. Refer to *Fig. 3* for correct routing angles of cable.

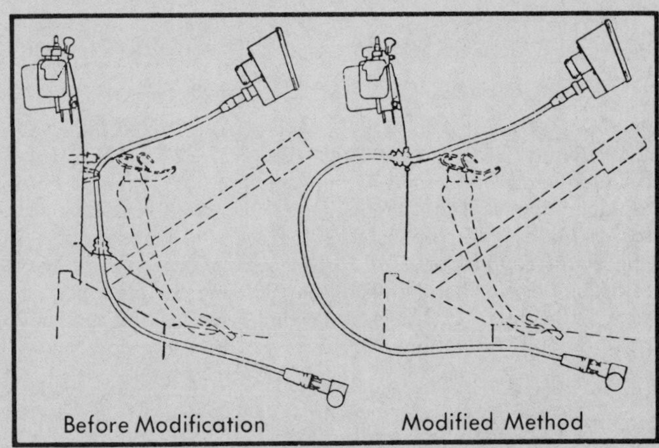

Fig. 3 Speedometer Cable Routing Modification

9 ► *1976 FIAT MODELS: IMPROPER FUSE INSTALLATION NOTE* — In some instances a low amperage fuse has been inadverently installed to protect a high amperage circuit. If problem is traced to fuse block, make sure proper amperage fuse is installed.

10 ► *1976 ALL FIAT MODELS: BATTERY BOIL OVER CORRECTION* — Charging system malfunction, as one listed above, can be remedied by reversing wiring at voltage regulator. For correct color code, refer to WIRING DIAGRAM Section.

FOR 1977 & PREVIOUS MODELS

FUEL SYSTEMS (Cont.)

11 *1974 FIAT, ALL MODELS, ERRATIC DISTRIBUTOR OPERATION — Any model can experience erratic distributor operation.* Condition is generally caused by improper ignition condenser being installed. Most independent radio manufacturer's make and provide condensers designed to lessen ignition interference. These condensers don't meet Fiat specifications and should not be used.

12 *1974-75 FIAT 128, ERRATIC CHARGING SYSTEM OR IGNITION SWITCH OPERATION* — The possible cause of this malfunction is: loose, broken or corroded wire connectors at the wire junction block. Inner fender panel holds junction block.

13 *1974-75 FIAT, ALL MODELS, STARTING AND CHARGING IMPROPER OUTPUT* — The cause of problem is possibly due to some residual paint build-up where engine or battery ground straps are attached to frame. There is also a possibility that paint coating on left engine mount is preventing full current to engine block.

14 *1974-75 FIAT WITH MARELLI 9 DIODE PLATE, ERRATIC OUTPUT* — The cause of this erratic output can possibly be one or more shorted energizing diodes. Note that in most instances alternators can be repaired and need not be replaced.

15 ▸ *1975 AND LATER MERCEDES-BENZ: STARTER MOTOR MOUNTING CHANGE* — Note that starter motors have no threaded insert in flange. Now threads are tapped directly into starter motor flange. Also, starter motor flange has been widened .12" (3 mm) in the thread bore area. Starter motors of early design can be replaced by the revised design. Make sure mounting bolts are fully tightened.

16 ▸ *1975 & EARLIER SAAB MODELS: ERRATIC INSTRUMENT OPERATION NOTE* — Temperature and fuel gauges may exhibit erratic operation below 32° F. Until vehicle interior warms up, fuel gauge may read "EMPTY" and temperature gauge may read in "HOT" range. Problem is usually caused by instrument housing retaining nuts not being tight. A related problem of fluctuating temperature gauge that might be misdiagnosed as a defective thermostat, could possibily be a loose instrument housing ground wire.

17 *1975 DASHER BALLAST RESISTOR CHANGE* — A resistor wire has been introduced to replace the ignition coil ballast resistor. Resistor wire runs from the coil terminal 15 to relay fuse plate C-15.

18 ▸ *1976 RABBIT, SCIROCCO, DASHER: ERRATIC CHARGING AT LOW ENGINE RPM NOTE* — A no charging or low charging condition of battery at low engine RPM may not be a voltage regulator or alternator problem. There may be a poor contact between alternator warning light socket and printed circuit board.

19 ▸ *1975-76 RABBIT, SCIROCCO, DASHER: FUSE CHANGE* — Fuses or windshield wiper motor/heater blower, and rear window defogger may blow when temperatures reach very low readings. Solution is to change the No. 11 fuse or No. 5 fuse (1975 Rabbit and Scirocco) to a 10 amp. (pink) fuse.

20 ▸ *1977 VOLVO WITH V6 ENGINE: DISTRIBUTOR CAP REMOVAL NOTE* — When distributor cap has to be removed for service or repair it can be inadvertently cracked when being forced by fuel distributor. To avoid cracking cap, loosen the fuel distributor mounting bolts (two Allen head, one hex head) and lift upward on fuel distributor while removing ignition distributor cap.

ENGINES – SECTION 5

1 ▸ *1977 AUDI FOX, VOLKSWAGEN RABBIT, SCIROCCO, DASHER: CYLINDERHEAD BOLT CHANGE* — New 11 mm cylinder head bolts with 12 mm polygon socket heads have replaced the earlier 10 mm head bolts that had hexagon socket heads. New bolts MUST be used in complete sets if utilized as repair parts for early models. Make sure NOT to retorque polygon head bolts at the 1000 mile maintenance service or the first 1000 miles following repair. Note that new polygon bolts do not have to be replaced during repair work.

2 ▸ *1973-74 AUDI FOX: ENGINE REMOVAL CHANGE* — Using the following procedure to supplement existing engine removal procedure:

NOTE — *Do not loosen any air conditioning hoses.*

1) Remove horn, A/C compressor, and A/C condenser.

2) Disconnect lower radiator hose and drain engine coolant. Coolant may be saved for reuse if not contaminated.

3) Disconnect coolant hoses.

4) Disconnect heater control valve cable at valve.

5) Lift out radiator with coolant fan (manual transmission only).

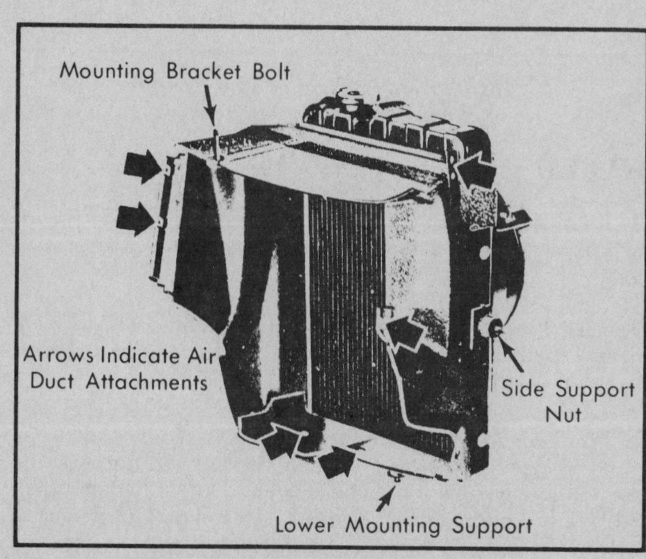

Fig. 1 Radiator Shroud Mountings

FOR 1977 & PREVIOUS MODELS

ENGINES — SECTION 5 (Cont.)

6) Remove the radiator shroud that mounts in front of radiator. Remove following to free shroud:
- Air dust attachment
- Lower mounting support
- Side support nut
- Mounting bracket bolt

7) Disconnect electrical wires from starter. Remove starter.

8) Disconnect exhaust pipe at manifold.

3 *1976 CAPRI II, OIL RESTRICTOR PIN* — On 2300 cc Brazil built engines, a pin has been installed into oil gallery behind oil pressure sender unit and must not be removed and left off. Pin restricts oil pressure to tappets during cold engine and wide open throttle operation. Without pin tappet bleed would be slowed and force valves to not completely seal. Brazil built engines are identified by 900-922 series number on white engine tag.

4 ► *1974-76 CAPRI II: PISTON "SCUFF" NOISE CORRECTION* — The scuff noise can be eliminated from the 2.3L engines with the installation of an improved connecting rod and bearing assembly. New connecting rod bearing has an oil squirt hole for increased lubrication for cylinder wall.

5 ► *1977 COLT AND ARROW WITH SILENT SHAFT 1600 cc ENGINE: TIMING BELT CAUTION* — The cogged drive belt which operates counterbalance shafts, camshaft and oil pump runs on porous (sprockets made from powered metal) metal sprockets. Make sure that when cleaning dirt etc. from the cogges of sprockets that liquid is not used. Liquid could possibably have harmful effects on operation of belt.

6 ► *1975-76 COLT: PISTON OIL RING CHANGE* — Rings have been redesigned from a one piece type to a three piece type. The new design ring has two wiper rings and one expander ring. Ring change was done to increase reliability and improve performance of oil ring.

7 ► *1976 COLT/ARROW: TIMING CHAIN CASE REMOVAL* **NOTE** — The following in vehicle procedure has only recently become available; it does not appear in either 2000 cc or 1600 cc engine article.

1) Disconnect battery. Drain radiator and remove.

2) Raise vehicle. Remove splash shield. Drain oil and remove pan. Position No. 1 piston at TDC.

3) Remove fan, water pump pulley, alternator and crankshaft pulley.

4) Remove air cleaner, distributor cap (with ignition wires), vacuum hoses, valve cover and distributor.

NOTE — *Cylinder head does not have to be removed.*

5) Take out the two front cylinder head bolts, carburetor vent tube bolt, and heater hose tube. Timing chain case can now be removed.

Installation — To install timing chain case, reverse removal procedure and note following: Make sure all mating surfaces are clean and RTV (or equivalent) sealer is applied to case cover.

8 ► *1976-77 COLT AND ARROW WITH 2000 cc ENGINE: COUNTERBALANCE SHAFT SPROCKET INSTALLATION CAUTION* — If sprockets are incorrectly installed some twisting force will be applied to chain. This force can possibably cause abnormal wear to the relative components. If service of sprockets becomes necessary, follow this caution:
- Sprocket for RIGHT side MUST be installed with chamfer on sprocket facing INWARD.
- Sprocket for LEFT side MUST be installed with chamfer facing OUTWARD.

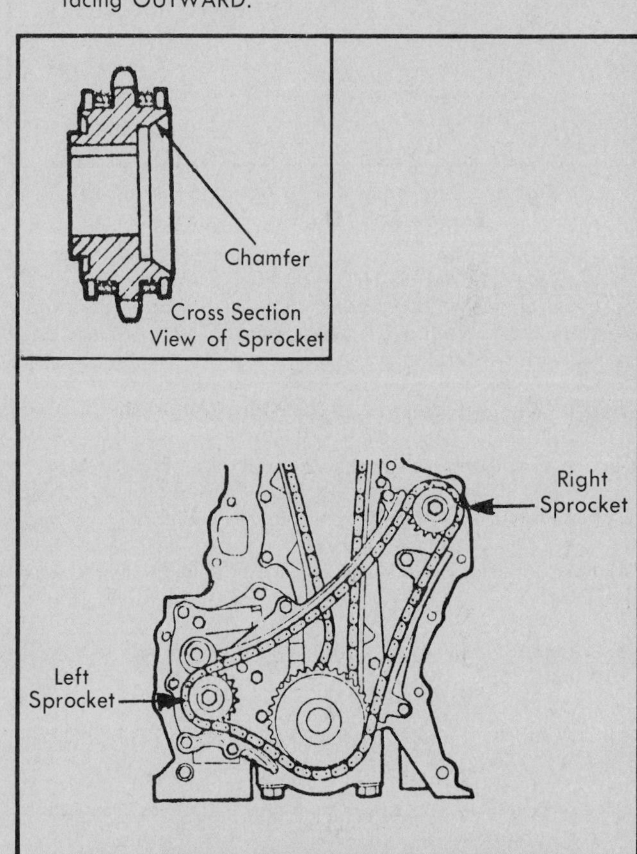

Fig. 2 Front View of Engine Showing Left and Right Counterbalance Shafts

9 ► *1975 COLT: CRANKSHAFT DESIGN CHANGE* — Since 3/75 all Colt 1600 cc engines, code "K", have been redesigned at the crankshaft pulley end. The spacer between the timing chain sprocket and front main bearing journal is now machined on the crankshaft. This change requires a new timing chain sprocket (part no. MD-002728). Short block assemblies with new design crankshaft will also need timing sprocket. With the use of spacer (part no. MD-002729) new sprocket can be used on crankshaft without machined integral spacer.

10 ► *1977 COLT AND ARROW WITH 1600 cc ENGINE: OIL SEAL CHANGE* — During the production year, as a running change, a seal retainer has been added to the rear engine oil seal. The retainer has been introduced to help prevent oil seal from dislocating from the installed position. The retainer can be installed on earlier engines released without a retainer.

FOR 1977 & PREVIOUS MODELS

ENGINES – SECTION 5 (Cont.)

Retainer is installed after oil seal has been fitted into position. Refer to *Fig. 3* for installation reference.

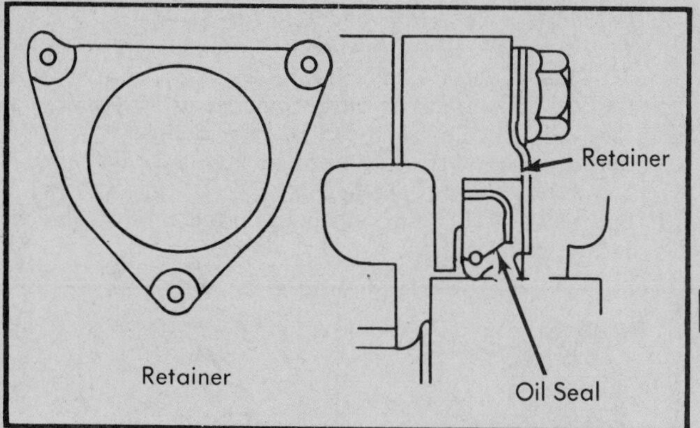

Fig. 3 Reference Illustration for Installing Engine Rear Oil Seal Retainer

► *1976 FIAT MODELS: ENGINE OIL CONSUMPTION NOTE*
11 – Some engine oil consumption is necessary and acceptable. Perform the following Oil Consumption Test to determine if repairs are needed:

NOTE – *Engine must have about 2,500-3,000 miles.*

1) Change oil and refill crankcase with necessary grade oil.

2) Run engine until normal operating temperature is reached.

3) Raise vehicle. Place No. 1 and No. 4 cylinders with pistons at TDC.

4) Immediately drain oil and allow oil to continue to drip for 15 minutes.

5) Weigh the drained engine oil. Refill crankcase with same oil.

6) Drive vehicle for approximately 100 miles through all driving conditions.

7) Repeat steps **3)**, **4)** and **5)**.

The difference in weight of oil between tests indicates consumption in ounces per 100 miles. Acceptable consumption levels are: X1/9 and 128 – 5.0-5.7 ounces per 100 miles and 124 and 131 – 7.0-7.5 ounces per 100 miles.

► *ENGINE 2869200 AND LATER 128 MODEL FIATS: OIL*
12 *PUMP CHANGE* – Beginning with engine number listed, a new design oil pump has been fitted to 128 models. The suction screen and lower cover have been changed. The inside configuration of oil pan and separator on subject vehicles has been modified to keep proper oil level around oil pump. New part numbers are: Oil Pump, 4391376; Oil Pan, 4391371.

► *1976 FIAT 131 & 124 MODELS: SHORT BLOCK NOTE* –
13 Some 132 engine short blocks are being shipped without an oil pump drive gear. Before installation, make sure drive gear is fitted to engine. If new oil pump drive gear is needed, order part no. 4274698.

► *1977 AND LATER MERCEDES-BENZ: OIL SUMP PROTEC-*
14 *TION COVER* – In instances when vehicle is being operated for sustained periods of time on rough roads, it may be necessary or desirable to install an underpan (oil sump protection cover) to reduce the possibility of damage to oil sump. Each Mercedes-Benz series of vehicles has an underpan available.

1974-75 MERCEDES BENZ M116 & M117 ENGINES,
15 *CRANKSHAFT SEALING RING CHANGE* – In production now a crankshaft sealing ring with full shoulder is being installed on front of crankshaft. Previously seal was with only a half shoulder. Additionally, face of oil seal bore on oil pan is now machined so crankshaft and oil pan will have a flat surface. Pan is mounted at front with studs for easier installation.

► *1977 MERCEDES-BENZ 220D: CYLINDER HEAD AND*
16 *GASKET CHANGE* – A new cylinder head gasket has been designed and released into production for the 615.912 engine. When new gasket is installed it is no longer necessary to retorque the head bolts after 300-600 miles. To identify the new type gasket note that there will be a protrusion beyond head contour on front left side. Only new gasket will be supplied as replacement part in future.

Also, cylinder head has been slightly modified:

- No longer any water distributors.
- Location change for water connector.
- Cylinder head cover bolt hole location change.
- Temperature sender location change.
- Fuel filter attachment change.

► *1977 AND EARLIER PEUGEOT DIESELS: COOLING*
17 *SYSTEM CHANGE* – Beginning with serial number 2350 524 the cooling system pressure for 504 diesel was increased 4 psi to 11.5 psi. The increased pressures allow for a higher boiling point. The following changes have been made to accomodate the modification:

- Cylinder head core plug covers are bolted to back of head.
- Strengthened radiator side tanks and pet cock.
- Polypropylene expansion tank.
- 11.5 psi radiator cap.
- Hose inlet union positioned higher on radiator.
- 199.5°F (93°C) thermostat.

1975 PORSCHE 911S AND CARRERA VALVE COVER
18 *INSTALLATION* – Due to the design of the exhaust system the primary muffler now complicates the valve adjustment and installation of left valve cover. To help avoid leaks and possible damage, fit gasket with some grease to hold it in place when cover is installed.

1973-74 SAAB IMPROVED EXHAUST MANIFOLD – Saab has
19 released a new type (improved design) replacement exhaust manifold for all 2 Liter engines. When installing new manifold on vehicles equipped with air conditioning some additional brackets are necessary for installation.

FOR 1977 & PREVIOUS MODELS

ENGINES – SECTION 5 (Cont.)

20 *1974 SAAB 2 LITER ENGINE VALVE CHANGE* – There have been three changes made in the valving of subject engines. Rocker arms are now equipped with two drilled holes to insure better lubrication of valve and adjuster pallet. Valve guide length has been reducedto 1.836" (46.65 mm) to insure better cooling of lower end of valve guide. New exhaust valves with larger stem diameter and a scraper edge are being used. Stem diameter has been increased to .3132-.3138" (7.955-7.970 mm), this should increase valve life and quiet operation.

21 *1975 SAAB WATER PUMP CHANGE* – A new type water pump has been released for the 1975 production year. The pump is identified by a yellow paint stripe on cover. Pump shaft is cast iron and susceptible to stress; DO NOT use hammers or drifts when removing or disassembling.

22 *1975 SAAB 99 LOOSE TIMING CHAIN* – A "rattle" may develop in the timing chain area. Noise generally is most noticeable between idle and 1500 RPM. When checking for noise, remove valve cover and check timing chain tension and chain tensioner.

23 *1973-75 SAAB WITH 2.0 LITER ENGINE, OIL LEAK*– Crankshaft oil seal on above models may develop an oil leak. There has been a new replacement oil seal released to correct problem. The new seal must be installed with spring and open lip facing toward crankcase. New part number is P/N8353732.

24 *1974 SUBARU THERMOSTAT REPLACEMENT* – It isn't necessary to replace a thermostat under the following condition: High reading on temperature gauge during initial engine warm-up. If a high reading continues after warm-up thermostat should be thoroughly checked out. The high temperature condition generally occurs when engine is run hard before reaching normal operating temperature.

25 ▸ *1976 & EARLIER SUBARU MODELS: CYLINDER HEAD GASKET NOTE* – Make sure the following steps are taken when changing cylinder head gasket on any Subaru:

1) On 1300 cc and 1400 cc engines, ensure cylinder liner protrusion is between .0025-.0036" (.063-.091 mm).

2) On all engines, coat both sides of head gasket with Permatex No. 3 (or equivalent).

3) Torque head nut on all engines to 37-43 ft. lbs. (5.2-5.8 mkg) while engine is cold and with engine oil on threads.

4) Add "LeakEnd" (or equivalent) cooling system sealant after installing new cylinder head gasket.

5) Cylinder heads must be retorqued after 1000 miles operation.

26 *1975 SUBARU VALVE CHANGE* – Intake valve location has been changed in cylinder head. Intake valves are now located in outer valve ports and exhaust valves occupy two inner valve ports. 1975 models use a single exhaust discharge port. The change has caused the need to increase the exhaust valve lash to .013-.015" (.3-.4 mm). Only adjust valves when engine is cold.

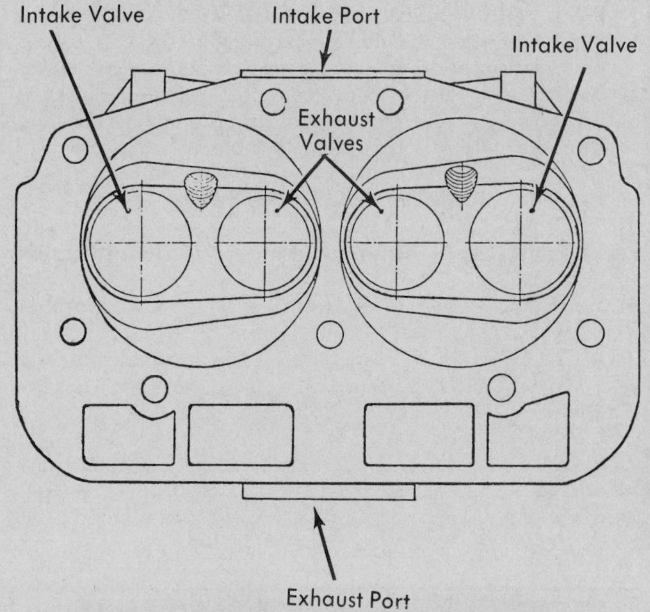

Fig. 4 New Position of Intake and Exhaust Valves

27 ▸ *1977 VOLKSWAGEN RABBIT WITH DIESEL: INJECTION PUMP SPROCKET REMOVAL ADDITION* – Loosen sprocket mounting nut a few turns. Attach puller or equipment tool shown in *Fig. 7.* Make sure puller jaws are at right angles to cross piece and that they point in direction of rotation. Tighten puller bolt being careful not to over-tension puller. Strike puller bolt head (shown by arrow) with several light taps until sprocket comes loose from shaft. Remove puller and nut.

Fig. 5 Puller Installed on Injection Pump Sprocket

28 ▸ *1977 AND LATER VOLKSWAGEN RABBIT WITH DIESEL ENGINE: POOR ENGINE PERFORMANCE* – Unsatisfactory engine performance, smoky exhaust on full throttle, inability to reach top RPM, erratic engine idle, can be caused by inadvertent switching of fuel supply bolt and return line bolt. The bolts will easily fit into either hole, however, return line bolt has a restrictor and is marked "OUT" on head of bolt.

FOR 1977 & PREVIOUS MODELS

ENGINE – SECTION 5 (Cont.)

29 ▸ *1977 VOLKSWAGEN DIESEL ENGINE: CYLINDER HEAD GASKET* — Beginning with engine number CK 024 944 a thicker cylinder head gasket has been introduced. New gasket is .008" (2 mm) thicker to compensate for piston projection above top of cylinder block. Measure piston projection and select gasket thickness according to table.

Cylinder Head Gasket Table

Piston Projection In (mm)	Gasket Thickness In. (mm)	Identification Number
.017-.025 (.43-63)	.051 (.13)	2
.025-.032 (.63-.82)	.055 (1.4)	3
.032-.036 (.82-.92)	.059 (1.5)	4
.036-.040 (.92-1.02)	.063 (1.6)	5

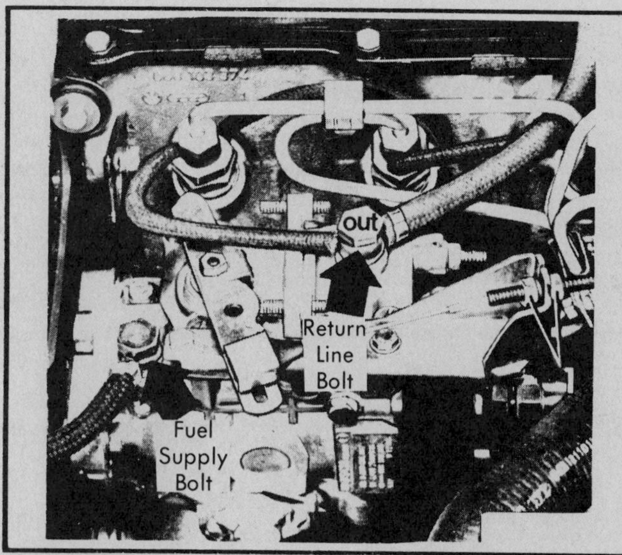

Fig. 6 Location of Fuel Supply and Fuel Return Line Bolts on Rabbit Diesel Engine

30 *1972-73 VOLKSWAGENS — PROLONGED HIGH SPEED DRIVING* — It is recommended that vehicles driven at prolonged high speeds and at temperatures above 77°F (25°C), use the following spark plugs, and that gap is set to .028" (.7 mm):

Application	VW Part No.	Bosch Part No.
Types 1, 2/1600 & 3	000 057 004	W 175 T 1
Type 2/Twin Carb.	000 057 008	W 175 T 2
Type 4	000 057 010	W 225 T 2

31 ▸ *1975 DASHER OIL PRESSURE SWITCH CHANGE* — Beginning with chassis number 326-2074-222 a new oil pressure switch has been installed during production. New switch has lower working pressure. New switch works at 2.1-6.4 psi (.15-.45 kg/cm²). Former switch worked at 4.3-8.5 psi (.3-.6 kg/cm²). New part number is 021-919-081-B.

32 ▸ *1977 AND LATER VOLKSWAGEN RABBIT WITH DIESEL ENGINE: PISTON CHANGE* — Beginning with engine number CK 024 944 a new piston with increased height was introduced. Refer to *Fig. 7* for new height measurement.

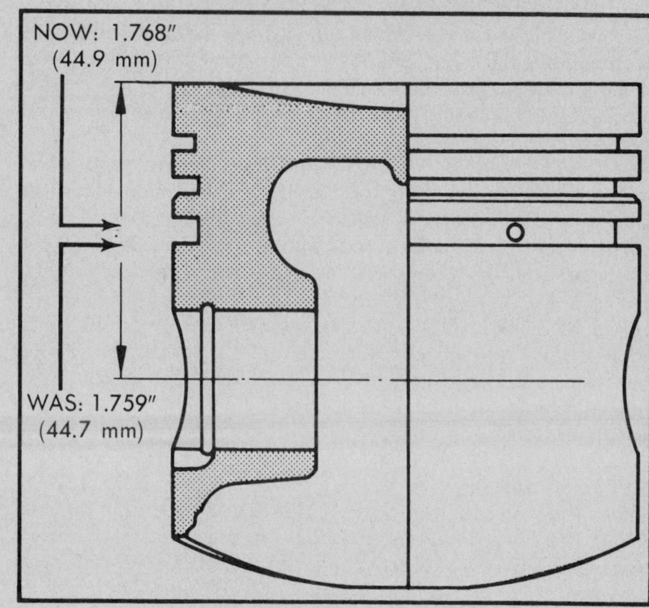

Fig. 7 Piston Height Measurement

Also, new pistons are identified by the number "9" stamped next to installation direction arrow. If new pistons are installed in early models engines, sets of four must be used.

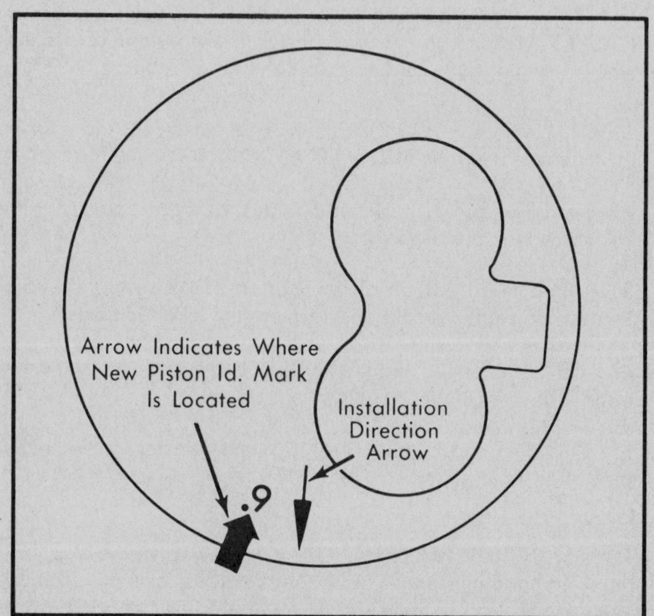

Fig. 8 Top of New Piston with Identification Mark

Latest Changes & Corrections

FOR 1977 & PREVIOUS MODELS

ENGINES — SECTION 5 (Cont.)

33 ► *1976 RABBIT, SCIROCCO, DASHER: DRIVE BELT GUIDE NOTE* — The listed models are subject to drive belt "jump" (skipping forward on pulley). In some instances rocks, ice or debris may lodge momentairly between belt and drive pulley, causing belt jump. Now available is a belt guide to prevent this occurance.

34 ► *1976 RABBIT, SCRICCO, DASHER: DRIVE BELT NOTE* — A "howling" noise, premature belt wear and/or a valve timing alteration can become apparent if drive belt is not properly adjusted. Belt correct tension is obtained when thumb and index fingers can twist belt 90°. Make twist midway on longest belt run.

35 ► *1976 RABBIT, SCIROCCO, DASHER: VALVE NOTE* — New, shorter intake and exhaust valves are available. These valves are .002" (.5 mm) shorter than standard and should be used if valve seats need excessive cutting. Short valves make it possible to use minimum thickness adjustment disc .12 (3.0 mm).

36 ► *1977 AND LATER VOLVO MODELS WITH B21 ENGINE: VALVE SPRING WASHER CHANGE* — A new valve spring washer has been released in production. The new washer can be identified by its slightly different shape. New washer will withstand greater loads. Only new washer is available as a replacement part.

CLUTCHES - SECTION 6

1 ► *1976 CAPRI II CLUTCH "SHUDDER" NOTE* — If normal checks are negative and a rubbing or "scrubby" feel at clutch pedal is evident, engine heat may be creating an interference between inner cable plastic covering and outer casing plastic lining. This problem may not be evident when engine is cold. Correct problem by repositioning clutch cable as far away from exhaust pipe as possible. If problem presists, clutch disc must be inspected.

2 ► *1976 CAPRI II: CLUTCH CABLE CHANGE* — A revised clutch cable, part number D7RY-7KB53-A, has become available. The new cable is designed to reduce pedal application effort and to be able to be fitted without any modifications.

3 *1973-75 HONDA CLUTCH-CAUSED ROLL* — Some models may suffer slow rolling forward when vehicle is in first gear and clutch pedal is fully depressed. Diagnosis should show there is a failure of clutch disc to fully disengage. To correct problem, replace clutch disc with part number 634-020 Civic and 657-030, CVCC and Wagon.

BRAKES - SECTION 7

1 ► *1976 IMPORTED CAR & TRUCK TUNE-UP/MECHANICAL SERVICE & REPAIR MANUAL* — The second brake specification table on page 7-52 has the wrong headings. Table heads should read: Column One, Application; Column Two, Drum Diameter; Column Three, Front Wheel Cylinder Diameter; Column Four, Rear Wheel Cylinder Diameter; Column Five, Master Cylinder Diameter.

Also, some of the text on page 7-54 is out of order. Refer to page 7-53 in this 1977 edition for correct text sequence.

2 ► *1976 & EARLIER AUDI 100LS MODELS: MASTER CYLINDER PRIMARY PISTON CHANGE* — Master cylinder primary cup and piston seal now have small grooves on lips. *See Fig. 1.* Piston seal identification has been changed from sliver strip around seal to chamfer "A" and groove "B". New parts can be installed in early master cylinders.

3 ► *1975 & LATER AUDI 100LS MODELS: BRAKE BOOSTER PUSH ROD CHANGE* — Rod has been shortened $\frac{5}{8}$" (16 mm). Push rod clevis has also been lengthened by that same amount. When installing new model booster in early model vehicles, enlarge clevis pin opening in brake pedal $\frac{3}{8}$" (10 mm).

4 ► *1976 FIAT MODELS: BRAKE WARNING LIGHT NOT ON CONTINUOUSLY CHANGE* Brake systems have been modified so that once the system loses hydraulic pressure, warning light will come on and remain on. Once problem has been corrected and hydraulic system properly bled, warning light will go out.

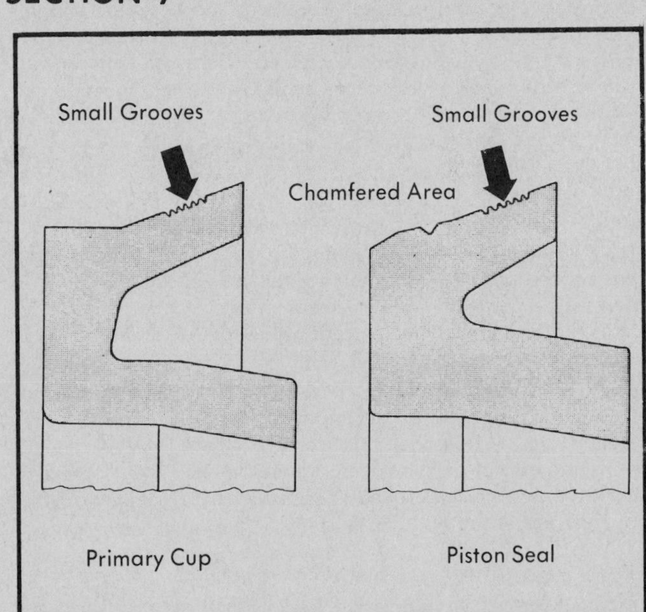

Fig. 1   Primary Cup and Piston Seal Identification

5 ► *1977 AND EARLIER HONDA MODELS: BRAKE SYSTEM MALFUNCTION CORRECTION* — Models suffering premature brake pad wear, dragging brakes or low brake pedal may be faced with improper clearance between master cylinder push rod and secondary piston. Before confirming diagnosis make following general checks:

Latest Changes & Corrections

FOR 1977 & PREVIOUS MODELS

BRAKES — SECTION 7 (Cont.)

- Rear brake adjustment
- Pad/shoe thickness
- Caliper action
- Air in hydraulic system

If everything checks out satisfactory proceed with master cylinder push rod adjustment:

1) Separate master cylinder from booster.

2) Face knurled end up. Place rod bolt adjustment gauge 6340000, Civic or 65700, CVCC (or equivalent) on master cylinder. Rotate screw until contact is just made with secondary piston.

NOTE — *CVCC adjustment gauge can be used on Civic models if retainer plate is left attached to booster when measurement is taken.*

3) Do not disturb gauge setting. Turn adjustment gauge upside down, then place it in the booster shell with master cylinder push rod fully seated. Using a feeler guage, measure distance between push rod and gauge. Gap should be .004-.024" (.1-.6 mm).

4) If required specification is not obtained, remove master cylinder push rod, loosen lock nut and reset adjustment rod. Install and recheck clearance.

1974-75 HONDA, DISC BRAKE STICKING — In areas where
6 chemicals are used to desolve ice and snow, subject models may develop a sticking caliper assembly. To correct, remove and completely disassemble caliper. Clean all components with a wire brush. Replace all seals and severly corroded or worn parts. After reassembly, apply a coat of high temperature lubricant to all sliding surfaces.

► *1977 AND LATER MERCEDES-BENZ: BRAKE DISC WEAR*
7 *LIMIT* — On vehicles equipped with calipers of 2.36" (60 mm), 1.50" (38 mm) or 1.65" (42 mm), the wear limit of brake discs has been changed. A maximum wear limit of .08" (2.0 mm) is permissible for front wheel brake discs and a maximum of .07" (1.7 mm) is permissible for rear wheel brake discs.

1974 MERCEDES BENZ IMPROVED CLUTCH PLATE — Since
8 Chassis Number 030367 an improved clutch plate has been installed on 240D models. On some of these models a slight noise may occur at idle speed; no malfunction is indicated. To correct noise, set idle speed to speed where noise disappears, but not higher than 800 RPM.

1975 MERCEDES BENZ THREE CHAMBER BRAKE FLUID
9 *RESERVOIR* — An expansion tank with three chambers has been put into production for all passenger cars. Front chamber feeds front wheels; center chamber feeds clutch circuit; rear chamber feeds rear wheels. Also, the rubber splash protection shield has been discontinued and must not be installed in the field.

1975 MERCEDES BENZ BRAKE BOOSTER MODIFICATION —
10 As of 9/75 9" brake booster (Teves or Bendix) has been modified. Unit now has six steel reaction segments instead of the earlier rubber reaction disc. Also, vacuum line from intake manifold to brake booster has been changed on 230 models. The change in brake force with the modification makes necessary slightly higher pedal pressures for initial braking.

► *1976 PORSCHE CARRERA: BRAKE LINING CHANGE* —
11 Energit 3944 FF linings are being used on front axle and Textar TP 22 HH or rear axle. These linings have not previously been used in these locations. Energit lining does have a higher friction value.

1975 SAAB DISC BRAKE SQUEAL — Noise occuring during
12 braking is caused by high frequency chatter of pads against rotors. To minimize the problem, ensure brakes are clean, in good condition, and that pad dampers are correctly in place.

► *1976 & EARLIER SAAB MODELS: PARKING BRAKE NOTE* —
13 To avoid confusion when changing parking brake cables, note that cable routing is: Left cable to right wheel; Right cable to left wheel.

► *1976 & EARLIER SAAB MODELS: BRAKE FLUID NOTE* —
14 Manufacturer does not recommend adding brake fluid to reservoir as level normally goes down. The decline in fluid level is an external indicator of disc brake pad wear. By adding fluid there will be no simple way of telling how much pad wear has occurred.

► *1976 AND EARLIER VOLVO MODELS: FRONT HUB/DISC*
15 *CHANGE* — This change has been introduced in production. New front hub has larger radius, brake disc has bigger chamfer and hexagon head mounting bolts. Note that the new brake disc can be used in conjunction with early type hub but the reverse is not true.

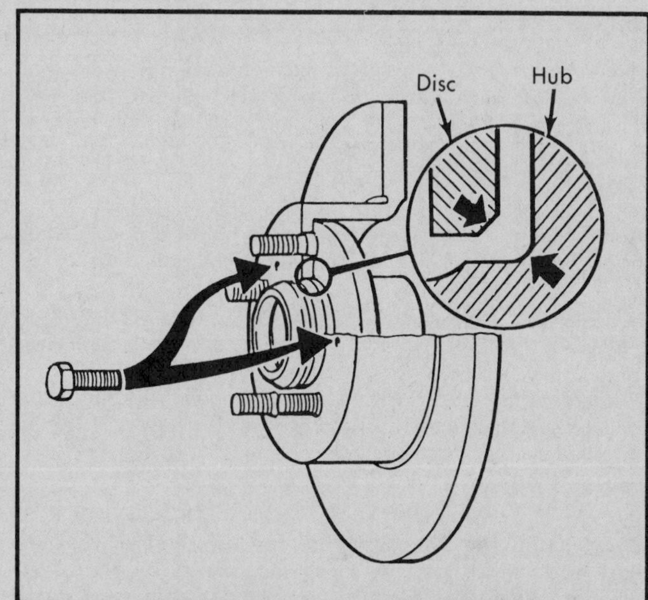

Fig. 2 Later Design Hub and Disc

► *1977 AND LATER VOLVOS: REVISED BRAKE LINE*
16 *ROUTING* — A new brake line with a different routing to right side rear brake caliper has been in production since about 4/77. The new brake line is mounted to rear axle with a protective sleeve and clamp. If brake line must be replaced on earlier model, new line must be adapted.

FOR 1977 & PREVIOUS MODELS

WHEEL ALIGNMENT – SECTION 8

17 ► *1977 AND EARLIER CAPRI II MODELS: WHEEL BEARING ADJUSTMENT CHANGE* — Procedure for adjusting front wheel bearings now requires that adjustment nut be backed off 120° after torquing. Previously it was only necessary to back off nut 90°.

18 *1976 CAPRI II WHEEL STUDS AND NUTS* - All models use metric studs and nuts. 1971-74 models used the normal 7/16"NF. Identify metric studs by the groove in the end of threaded portion. Do not interchange early and late studs and nuts.

19 ► *1976 HONDA: REAR WHEEL BEARING NOISE NOTE* — On Civic and CVCC models, a grinding noise may occur when operating on smooth road surfaces, at any speed. Raise vehicle, spin wheels and listen for evidence of bearing noise. Also, check bearing axial play by rocking wheel back and forth. If bearing is suspect, remove wheels and drums and check inner wheel bearing. Replace components as necessary.

20 ► *1976 FIAT X1/9 & 128 MODELS: PREMATURE TIRE WEAR* **NOTE** — It has been tested and shown that premature tire wear is not due to non-adjustable camber Most tire wear is attributed to toe-in. If toe-in and caster are properly adjusted and wheel properly balanced, no premature tire wear should exist.

21 ► *1972-74 SAAB: WHEEL ALIGNMENT SPECIFICATIONS CHANGE* — Recommended caster and camber angles have been changed, see following table for revised specifications:

Wheel Alignment Specifications

Application	Revised Setting	Former Setting
Caster	1°±½°	¾°±¼°
Camber	½°±½°	¾°±¼°
Toe-In	Unchanged	0°±.04"

NOTE — *On 1972 models, try to keep caster adjustment as close to lower limits as possible.*

22 ► *1972-75 VOLVO MODELS: REVISED WHEEL ALIGNMENT SPECIFICATIONS* — Listed below are the revised wheel alignment specifications for Volvo models. New specifications should be put into effect immediately.

Revised Wheel Alignment Specifications

Application	Camber	Caster
Through 1972		
140 & 164 Series		0 to +1°
1973		
140 & 164 Series		+1 to +2°
1974		
140 W/Man. Str.		+1.5 to +2.5°
140 W/Pwr. Str.		① +2 to 3°
164		+1.5 to +2.5°
1975		
164	− 1±¼°	+1±½°

① — Only use one spacer per adjustment location.

SUSPENSION – SECTION 9

1 ► *1976 CAPRI II: FRONT SUSPENSION KNOCK CORRECTION* — A knock may be noticed when operating on extremly rough roads. The noise does not indicate a suspension weakness and should disappear once normal roadway travel is regained. A new shock absorber cartridge has been released. The new shock absorber has improved dampening action and should effectively eliminate any knocking noise.

2 ► *1976 CAPRI II: ACCESSIBILITY TO REAR SHOCK ABSORBER UPPER MOUNTS CHANGE* — Rear load space trim panels have been redesigned to provide access to upper rear shock absorber mounting.

3 ► *1976 FIAT X1/9, 128 & 131 MODELS: DAMAGE TO TIE ROD BOOTS NOTE* — Before working on tie rod or before making toe-in adjustments, rotate boots by hand to ensure they are not binding. Lubricate boots with silcone after working on tie rods or as part of regular scheduled maintenance procedure.

1974 MAZDA RX-3 PULL TO THE RIGHT — Use the following procedure to correct a pull to the right after all normal correction procedures prove unsuccessful:

Install a thick bushing at rear of right control arm and a thin bushing at front of control arm. These bushings replace the existing ones where stabilizer attaches to control arm.

4 ► *1977 AND LATER MERCEDES-BENZ: SUSPENSION RATTLE CORRECTION* — On all models except 450 SL and 450 SLC a rattle may develop in the rear suspension area. Generally, the cause for the rattle is insufficient tightening of connecting linkage between sway bar and semi-trailing arm. To correct, take off connecting linkage and clean mounting surface of semi-trailing arm. Refit connecting linkage and use a lock washer between sway bar and hex nut. Tighten linkage at semi-trailing arm to 25-37 ft. lbs. (3.5-5.1 mkg) and to 24-32 ft. lbs. (3.3-4.4 mkg) at sway bar.

5 ► *1977 AND LATER MERCEDES-BENZ: UPPER CONTROL ARM BUSHING CHANGE* — As of 1/77 all models except 450 SL and 450 SLC have been fitted with a two piece upper control arm bushing. Make sure when repair is required that only one type of bushing is used (either one-piece or two-piece version). Make sure two-piece bushing is installed if vehicle has steel (not aluminum) upper control arms.

6 ► *1976 PORSCHE CARRERA: REAR BRAKE MOUNTING CHANGE* — Design is unchanged from previous years and models, except the rear suspension control arm requires two separate mounting shackles for rear brake supports.

Latest Changes & Corrections

FOR 1977 & PREVIOUS MODELS

SUSPENSION – SECTION 9 (Cont.)

7 *1975 RABBIT AND SCIROCCO COIL SPRING RATTLE AND SPRING CHANGE* – To stop a rattle coming from the coil spring (front or rear), remove coil spring and fit a damping hose: part number 321 511 123 A. On Rabbit models only, coil spring has been changed to a new style. The new coil spring can be identified by two green paint stripes on coils, old models have white stripes.

8 *1972-73 VOLKSWAGEN TYPE 3 – FRONT END NOISE* – Replacing ball joints to eliminate front end noise does not usually solve the noise problem. Manufacturer's examinations have proven that ball joints are not usually the cause of front end noise, but rather the shock absorbers, stabilizer, and their mounting parts generally are the cause of these noises. Carefully examine all front end components before replacing ball joints in an attempt to stop front end noise.

9 ► *1976 AND LATER VOLVO MODELS: COIL SPRING APPLICATION* – The following chart indicates the spring specifications since the introduction of the 240 and 260 Series vehicles:

Front Coil Springs

	B21 F	Old Spring for B27 E, F	New Spring for B27 E, F	Heavy Duty Spring
Part Number	1221636-2	1221636-2	1229137-3	1205951-5
Wire Thickness Inches mm	0.562" 14.05	0.562" 14.05	0.554" 13.85	0.592" 14.8
No.of Effective Turns	6.5	6.5	5.5	6.5
Free Length Inches mm	17.9" 453.7	17.9" 453.7	17.5" 443.6	16.2" 410.5

Rear Coil Springs

	2-and 4-door	Old spring for 5-door	New spring for 5-door	Heavy Duty
Part Number	1212426-9	1212427-7	1229052-4	1206750-0
Wire Thickness Inches mm	0.480" 12.0	0.508" 12.7	0.518" 12.95	0.552" 13.8
No. of Effective Turns	8	8	8.35	8.35

STEERING – SECTION 10

1 ► *1977 AUDI FOX: TIE ROD MODIFICATIONS* – Three changes have been made to the tie rods:

- Threaded shaft has been increased from 9/16" (14 mm) to 11/16" (17.5 mm).
- Cotter pin hole in shaft has been deleted.
- Self-locking nut has replaced castle nut and cotter pin. Nut torque is 22 ft. lbs. (3.0 mkg).

NOTE – *Make sure shaft surface is not damaged.*

3) Clean out oil seal seat. Also, clean shaft splines.

4) Use a light gauge plastic or cardboard cover to protect shaft splines when installing oil seal.

5) Smear oil seal lip with multi-purpose grease.

6) Guide oil seal into position. Using a driver, seat seal into place.

7) Refit drop arm. Torque lock nut to 101 ft. lbs. (14 mkg).

8) Place steering in full right lock position. Examine oil level. Roller shaft must be submerged in oil. Add oil as required.

2 ► *1977 AND EARLIER CAPRI II MODELS: COLLAPSIBLE STEERING WHEEL CHECK* – It is possible that the collapsible can portion of the Capri II steerting wheel will progressively deteriorate after rather severe concussion to the front suspension assembly. If subject vehicle has experienced such a blow, perform the following checks to determine extent of damage to column and collapsible can:

1) Check steering wheel condition. If any distortion is noticed, or if any earlier distortion has been repaired, replace steering wheel.

2) Check steering wheel collapsible can. *See Fig. 1.* If collapsible can is:

- Buckled
- Partially collapsed
- Fully collapsed

Install a complete new steering wheel/collapsible can assembly.

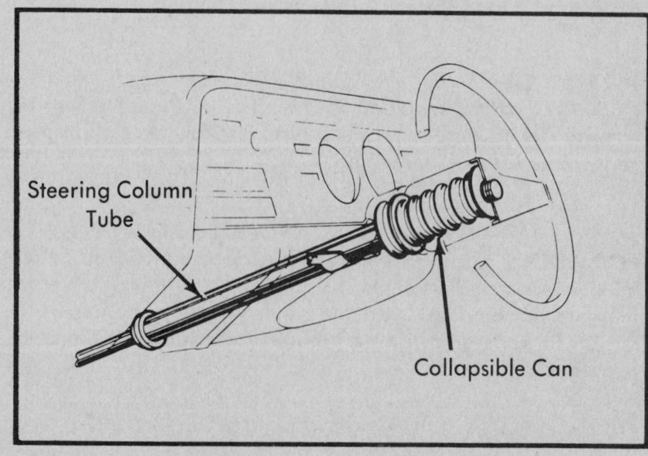

Fig. 1 Capri II Steering Wheel and Column with Detail of Steering Wheel Can Assembly

FOR 1977 & PREVIOUS MODELS

STEERING – SECTION 10 (Cont.)

3 ► *1971-76 CAPRI & CAPRI II, STIFF STEERING CORRECTION* – Occasional stiffness is generally caused by lower pinion bearings "crowding" against each other. To resolve this condition, a new design lower pinion bearing with caged ball bearings has been introduced. Before replacing bearings, check and bring into tolerances: tire psi, ball joints and front strut upper mounting bushings.

4 *1971-74 CAPRI STEERING COLUMN NOISE* – Some models may experience a "rattle" in the upper steering column. A change in the spring, to provide more preload on upper column bearing was put into production approximately 7/74. The stronger spring can be fitted to all prior models to stop steering column rattles.

5 ► *1977 AND LATER MERCEDES-BENZ: STEERING STOP CHANGE* – A new power steering unit has been installed on 230, 280E, 240D & 300D models. New unit has internal steering stops located in steering gear housing. Previously stops were on crossmember and pitman arm. New unit part number is preceeded with "A*". Note that 300CD and 280CE models are equipped with new unit from start of production. When new unit was introduced slight modifications to steering linkage were made. *See Fig. 2 and Fig. 3.* Make certain an early version system is never installed into a vehicle that does not have stops on crossmember, pitman arm, and idler arm.

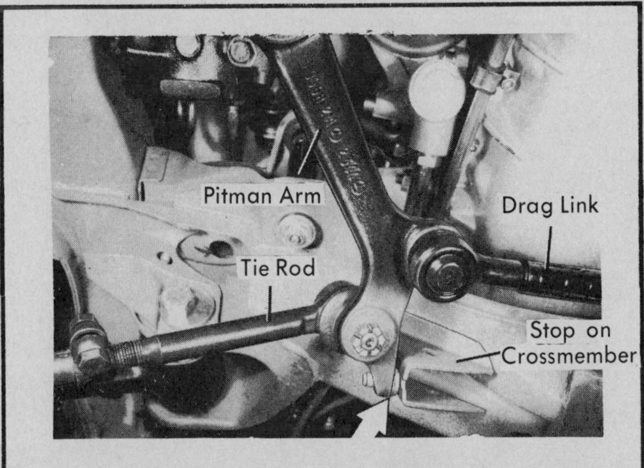

Fig. 2 Linkage Used with Early Power Steering Unit

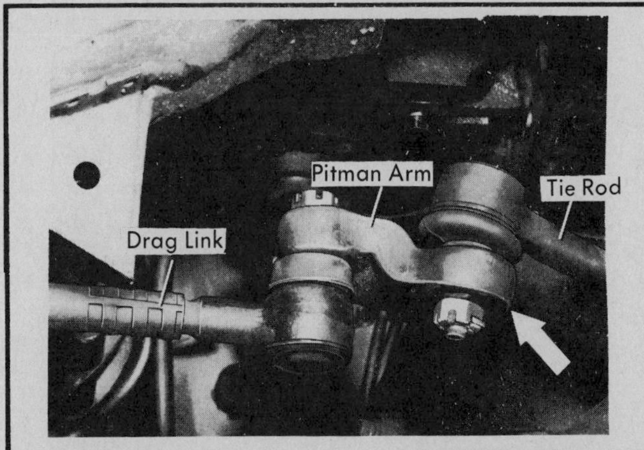

Fig. 3 Steering Linkage Used with Late Power Steering Unit

6 ► *1976 AND LATER MERCEDES-BENZ: BOLT CHANGE* – As a running production change 280 SE, 450 SEL, and 6.9 models are now fitted with self-locking bolts to hold steering knuckle arm to steering knuckle. Note new bolts are identified by the coating applied to threads. Tightening torque remains 58 ft. lbs. (8 mkg).

7 *1975 RABBIT AND SCIROCCO STEERING COLUMN TUBE CHANGE* – Steering column tube and column each have been lengthened $\frac{3}{8}$" (10 mm). Also, the column bushing has been changed. These new parts can be fitted to earlier model vehicles. Note that during installation the lug on bushing engages slot in column.

8 ► *1977 AND LATER VOLKSWAGEN TYPE 2: ROLLER SHAFT OIL SEAL REPLACEMENT* – It is now possible to replace a leaking roller shaft oil seal instead of replacing steering gear. Perform seal replacement as follows:

1) Remove steering drop arm.

2) Use a sharp tool to pry out oil seal.

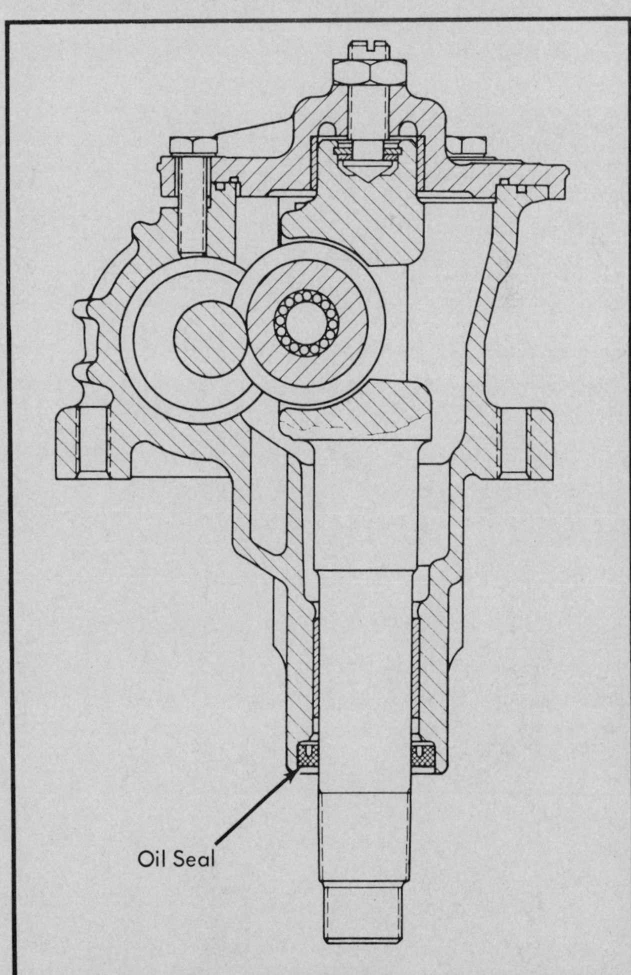

Fig. 4 Steering Gear Assembly Showing Oil Seal Location

FOR 1977 & PREVIOUS MODELS

STEERING – SECTION 10 (Cont.)

► *1977 VOLVO 240: POWER STEERING SERVO NOISE* – Some subject vehicles may encounter a vibration or audiable noise coming from the power steering servo area. Noise usually occurs between 3,100 and 4,100 RPM. The noise may even be heard when vehicle is stationary. Volvo has released a new pump mounting bracket with rubber grommets to eliminate this noise. Part number for new bracket is 1219522-8. Bracket was introduced in production at approximately the following chassis numbers: 242, 76000; 244, 120000; 245, 76000.

► *1977 AND LATER VOLVO MODELS: RACK GUIDE PIN CHANGE* – The cam gear manual steering rack put into production approximately 4/77 has been fitted with two alignment guide pins. The pins align into holes drilled into crossmember. If rack replacement is necessary, reuse old guide pins by fitting them into new rack assembly.

► *1976 AND LATER VOLVO MODELS: STEERING WHEEL NOISE* – Models equipped with the new design "off center cover pad" are suject to a "creaking" noise during maneuvers where excessive steering effort is required. Proceed as follows to eliminate noise:

- Remove steering wheel padding.
- Lubricate the four sleeves where pad attaches to steering wheel.
- Refit padding.

► *1977 AND LATER VOLVO 260 MODELS: POWER STEERING HOSE CHAFING CAUTION* – The location of the power steering reservoir has been changed. This relocating changes the fluid hose routing so it runs close to the battery purchase. To prevent premature hose failure, ensure the strip clamp mounting hose is adequately positioned.

► *1976 AND LATER VOLVO MODELS: POWER STEERING* – The only acceptable power steering fluid for subject models is: Automatic Transmission Fluid Type A, F or Dexron.

General Index

— A —

ALTERNATOR

— A —

ALTERNATOR (Cont.)

— B —

BALL JOINTS

BATTERY

NOTE — ALSO SEE INDIVIDUAL SECTION CONTENTS PAGE

– B –

– B –

General Index

– B –

BRAKES (Cont.)

Drum Brakes

Power Brake Units

– B –

BRAKES (Cont.)

– C –

CARBURETORS

NOTE — ALSO SEE INDIVIDUAL SECTION CONTENTS PAGE.

General Index

– C –

CIRCUIT BREAKERS

See *FUSES.*

CLUTCHES

COOLING SYSTEM

Capacities

– C –

COOLING SYSTEM (Cont.)

CRANKCASE

Capacities

General Index

– C –

CRANKCASE (Cont.)

– D –

DISTRIBUTORS

– D –

DISTRIBUTORS (Cont.)

NOTE — ALSO SEE INDIVIDUAL SECTION CONTENTS PAGE

— D —

DISTRIBUTORS (Cont.)

— D —

DISTRIBUTORS (Cont.)

— E —

ENGINES

NOTE — ALSO SEE INDIVIDUAL SECTION CONTENTS PAGE

General Index

— E —

ENGINES (Cont.)

— F —

FLASHERS

Hazard and Turn Signal

FUEL INJECTION

Diesel

— F —

FUEL INJECTION (Cont.)

Gasoline

FUEL PUMPS

General Index

NOTE — ALSO SEE INDIVIDUAL SECTION CONTENTS PAGE

General Index

– I –

– J –

– J –

– L –

– M –

NOTE – ALSO SEE INDIVIDUAL SECTION CONTENTS PAGE

General Index

– M –

MASTER CYLINDERS (Cont.)

– N –

NEUTRAL SAFTEY SWITCHES

– O –

OIL PAN

– R –

REGULATORS

– R –

REGULATORS (Cont.)

– S –

SPEEDOMETER

STARTERS

NOTE – ALSO SEE INDIVIDUAL SECTION CONTENTS PAGE

— S —

— S —

NOTE — ALSO SEE INDIVIDUAL SECTION CONTENTS PAGE.

General Index

— S —

NOTE — ALSO SEE INDIVIDUAL SECTION CONTENTS PAGE

– S –

NOTE — ALSO SEE INDIVIDUAL SECTION CONTENTS PAGE

General Index

– S –

SWITCHES (Cont.)

– T –

TUNE-UP

– W –

WATER PUMPS

NOTE — ALSO SEE INDIVIDUAL SECTION CONTENTS PAGE.

General Index

— W —

NOTE — ALSO SEE INDIVIDUAL SECTION CONTENTS PAGE

General Index

— W —

NOTE — ALSO SEE INDIVIDUAL SECTION CONTENTS PAGE

"WE LISTEN!"

We will greatly appreciate receiving your comments or corrections so that we may continue to publish the world's best automotive manuals. **Mail this card today. We'd like to hear from you!**

☐ Domestic ☐ Imported ☐ Trucks ☐ AC Service

☐ Tune-Up ☐ Mechanical ☐ Transmissions ☐ Emission Control

Section No.________ Page No.________ Vehicle model, year________________

Comments:________________________________

(Please print Co. name and address on the reverse side.)

"WE LISTEN!"

We will greatly appreciate receiving your comments or corrections so that we may continue to publish the world's best automotive manuals. **Mail this card today. We'd like to hear from you!**

☐ Domestic ☐ Imported ☐ Trucks ☐ AC Service

☐ Tune-Up ☐ Mechanical ☐ Transmissions ☐ Emission Control

Section No.________ Page No.________ Vehicle model, year________________

Comments:________________________________

(Please print Co. name and address on the reverse side.)

BUSINESS REPLY CARD

FIRST CLASS PERMIT NO. 3701 SAN DIEGO, CA

POSTAGE WILL BE PAID BY ADDRESSEE

MITCHELL MANUALS, INC.

P.O. BOX 80427
San Diego, California 92138

BUSINESS REPLY CARD

FIRST CLASS PERMIT NO. 3701 SAN DIEGO, CA

POSTAGE WILL BE PAID BY ADDRESSEE

MITCHELL MANUALS, INC.

P.O. BOX 80427
San Diego, California 92138

"WE LISTEN!"

We will greatly appreciate receiving your comments or corrections so that we may continue to publish the world's best automotive manuals. **Mail this card today. We'd like to hear from you!**

☐ Domestic ☐ Imported ☐ Trucks ☐ AC Service

☐ Tune-Up ☐ Mechanical ☐ Transmissions ☐ Emission Control

Section No.________ Page No.________ Vehicle model, year________________

Comments:________________________________

(Please print Co. name and address on the reverse side.)

"WE LISTEN!"

We will greatly appreciate receiving your comments or corrections so that we may continue to publish the world's best automotive manuals. **Mail this card today. We'd like to hear from you!**

☐ Domestic ☐ Imported ☐ Trucks ☐ AC Service

☐ Tune-Up ☐ Mechanical ☐ Transmissions ☐ Emission Control

Section No.________ Page No.________ Vehicle model, year________________

Comments:________________________________

(Please print Co. name and address on the reverse side.)

"WE LISTEN!"

We will greatly appreciate receiving your comments or corrections so that we may continue to publish the world's best automotive manuals. **Mail this card today. We'd like to hear from you!**

☐ Domestic ☐ Imported ☐ Trucks ☐ AC Service

☐ Tune-Up ☐ Mechanical ☐ Transmissions ☐ Emission Control

Section No.________ Page No.________ Vehicle model, year________________

Comments:________________________________

(Please print Co. name and address on the reverse side.)

NO POSTAGE
NECESSARY
IF MAILED
IN THE
UNITED STATES

BUSINESS REPLY CARD

FIRST CLASS PERMIT NO. 3701 SAN DIEGO, CA

POSTAGE WILL BE PAID BY ADDRESSEE

MITCHELL MANUALS, INC.
P.O. BOX 80427
San Diego, California 92138

NO POSTAGE
NECESSARY
IF MAILED
IN THE
UNITED STATES

BUSINESS REPLY CARD

FIRST CLASS PERMIT NO. 3701 SAN DIEGO, CA

POSTAGE WILL BE PAID BY ADDRESSEE

MITCHELL MANUALS, INC.
P.O. BOX 80427
San Diego, California 92138

NO POSTAGE
NECESSARY
IF MAILED
IN THE
UNITED STATES

BUSINESS REPLY CARD

FIRST CLASS PERMIT NO. 3701 SAN DIEGO, CA

POSTAGE WILL BE PAID BY ADDRESSEE

MITCHELL MANUALS, INC.
P.O. BOX 80427
San Diego, California 92138

BUSINESS REPLY CARD

FIRST CLASS PERMIT NO. 3701 SAN DIEGO, CA

POSTAGE WILL BE PAID BY ADDRESSEE

MITCHELL MANUALS, INC.
Attention: G. Hodes
P.O. Box 85068
San Diego, California 92138

Now . . . Save Time, Expand Your Business, ... ase Profits

with Mitchell's time-saving profit builders!

Turn Page ↗

YES! I wan… …ase my shop … 30 days. Please s… …ve checked … completely satisfied, I can return the books within 30 da…

Note: Prices apply to USA only.

- ☐ Air Conditioning & Heating.......... $50.00
- ☐ Air Cond. Basic Training.................$4.95
- ☐ Domestic Emission Control.......... $42.00
- ☐ Imported Emission Control.......... $44.00
- ☐ Imported Tune-Up........................ $65.00
- ☐ Imported Mechanical $60.00
- ☐ Imported Transmission................. $70.00
- ☐ Light Truck Tune-Up..................... $60.00
- ☐ Light Truck Mechanical $60.00
- ☐ Light Truck Transmission............. $60.00

Sub-Total	$	______
State Sales Tax*		______
Shipping & Handling	$	$4.00
If C.O.D. add $1.50		______
FINAL TOTAL	$	______

*NOTE—Your appropriate state sales tax must be included to process your order.

Please check one:

- ☐ Check or money order encl…
- ☐ Send my order C.O.D.
- ☐ Charge to Master Charge/Visa
- ☐ …
- ☐ Please send a sales representative to see me

Account # ______ Expiration Date ______

Issuing Bank ______

Your Signature ______

VISA master charge

Name ______

Company ______

Address ______

City ______

State ______ Zip ______

IMPORTANT REMINDER!

The full cost of your manuals may be taken as a business tax deduction.

Cut this form off at dashed line and mail to: **Mitchell Manuals, Inc.** *ADIT 77*

AIR CONDITIONING & HEATING SERVICE MANUAL

The manual that's used and respected by the people who KNOW the air conditioning industry. Now you can service any air conditioning or heating system—profitably! You get everything you need to make system servicing quick and easy: in-depth trouble shooting and diagnosis . . . servicing, repair and overhaul data . . . thousands of illustrations . . . hundreds of spec tables and charts . . . factory bulletins . . . labor estimating section . . . and more! Total coverage for all factory-installed systems produced in this country since 1966! Big two-volume set! **Price: only $50.00**

AIR CONDITIONING BASIC TRAINING MANUAL

Now you can have the most complete basic training manual available for air conditioning systems! This book covers all the important aspects of air conditioning service: Theory, components, operation, diagnosis, servicing, and compressor repair. A handy trouble-shooting wall chart is also included! **Price: only $4.95**

DOMESTIC EMISSION CONTROL SERVICE MANUAL

Tough new pollution laws mean big profits for you in emission control servicing! Cash in on it with Mitchell! You get the most complete and current data available . . . anywhere! Description, operation, trouble-shooting, maintenance, repair and overhaul info for all domestic car emission systems produced since 1966! PLUS—you get a complete fuel system section, engine I.D., all system wiring and vacuum diagrams. Also included: handy system application charts that give you instant access to the data you need! **Price: only $42.00**

IMPORTED EMISSION CONTROL SERVICE MANUAL

Imported cars need pollution control servicing too . . . and that means more profit opportunities for your shop! Cash in on it with this fantastic coverage—over 30 foreign manufacturers are covered in complete detail. Description, operation, trouble-shooting, maintenance, repair, and overhaul—you get it all with Mitchell. PLUS . . . you get a complete carburetion and fuel injection section, emission system wiring and vacuum diagrams, and more! Over 2,000 pages—it's the most in-depth, money-making repair tool you'll find. Start enjoying big emission control servicing profits today! **Price: only $44.00**